JOB HUNTER'S SOURCEBOOK

ISSN: 1053-1874

A THOMSON GALE CAREER INFORMATION GUIDE

JOB HUNTER'S SOURCEBOOK

Where to find employment leads and other job search resources

SIXTH EDITION   WITHDRAWN

Kristy Swartout, Project Editor

THOMSON

GALE

Detroit • New York • San Francisco • San Diego • New Haven, Conn. • Waterville, Maine • London • Munich

331,128
JOB

THOMSON

GALE

Job Hunter's Sourcebook, 6th Edition

Project Editor
Kristy Swartout

Editorial
Deborah J. Baker, Donna Batten, Grant Eldridge, Laurie J. Fundukian, Michael T. Reade, Amanda Steele, Erin Stradtner

Editorial Support Services
Scott Flaugher

Composition and Electronic Prepress
Evi Seoud

Manufacturing
Rita Wimberley

ISBN 0-7876-5934-7
ISSN 1053-1874

Printed in the United States of America
10 9 8 7 6 5 4 3 2 1

Contents

"The person who gets hired is not necessarily the one who can do that job best; but, the one who knows the most about how to get hired."

Richard Bolles

What Color Is Your Parachute?

Job hunting is often described as a campaign, a system, a strategic process. According to Joan Moore, principal of The Arbor Consulting Group, Inc. in Plymouth, Michigan, "Launching a thorough job search can be a full-time job in itself. It requires as much energy as you would put into any other major project—and it requires a creative mix of approaches to ensure its success."

Job Hunting Is Increasingly Complex

Today's competitive job market has become increasingly complex, requiring new and resourceful approaches to landing a position. The help-wanted ads are no longer the surest route to employment. In fact, most estimates indicate that only a small percentage of all jobs are found through the classified sections of local newspapers.

Although approaches vary among individual job seekers and the levels of jobs sought, a thorough job search today should involve the use of a wide variety of resources. Professional associations, library research, executive search firms, college placement offices, direct application to employers, professional journals, and networking with colleagues and friends are all approaches commonly in use. Job hotlines and resume referral services may be elements of the search as well. High-tech components might include the use of resume databases, and electronic bulletin boards that list job openings.

More than 7 Million Job Seekers

Just as the methods of job seeking have changed, so have the job hunters themselves. By choice or by chance, the U.S. Department of Labor, Bureau of Labor Statistics, Current Population Survey estimates that at any given time over 7 million Americans are seeking employment. This number includes the ranks of students pursuing their first—but probably not only—jobs. As Joyce Slayton Mitchell notes in College to Career, "Today, the average young person can look forward to six or seven different jobs, six or seven minicareers, that will make up his or her lifetime of work." Lifelong commitment to one employer is no longer the norm; professionals seeking to change companies, workers re-entering the job market after a period of absence, and people exploring new career options are also represented in significant numbers in the job seeking pool. And in a time of significant corporate change, restructuring, divestiture, and downsizing, many job seekers are in the market unexpectedly. These include a growing number of white-collar workers who find themselves competing against other professionals in a shrinking market.

Help for Job Hunters

As the job market has become more competitive and complex, job seekers have increasingly looked for job search assistance. The rapid growth in the number of outplacement firms and employment agencies during the last 24 years reflects the perceived need for comprehensive help. Similarly, the library has become an increasingly important and valuable resource in the job hunt. In fact, some librarians report that their most frequently asked reference questions pertain to job seeking. In response to this need, many libraries have developed extensive collections of career and job-hunting publications, periodicals that list job openings, and directories of employers. Some libraries have developed centralized collections of career information, complemented by such offerings as resume preparation software, career planning databases, and interviewing skills videotapes.

Valuable Guide for Job Seekers

Job Hunter's Sourcebook (JHS) was designed to assist those planning job search strategies. Any job hunter—the student looking for an internship, the recent graduate, the executive hoping to relocate—will find *JHS* an important first step in the job search process because it identifies and organizes employment leads quickly and comprehensively. Best of all, *JHS* provides all the information a job hunter needs to turn a local public library into a customized employment agency, available free-of-charge. *Library Journal* and the New York Public Library concurred, and gave the first edition of this work their annual outstanding reference awards.

Job Hunter's Sourcebook (*JHS*) is a comprehensive guide to sources of information on employment leads and other job search resources. It streamlines the job-seeking process by identifying and organizing the wide array of publications, organizations, audio-visual and electronic resources, and other job hunting tools.

JHS completes much of the research needed to begin a job search, with in-depth coverage of information sources for more than 200 specific professional and vocational occupations. Listings of resources on more than 30 essential topics of interest to job hunters complement the profiles on specific occupations, providing the job seeker with leads to all the information needed to design a complete job search strategy.

Job Hunter's Sourcebook can be used to:

Find a job. *JHS* is designed for use by job seekers at all levels—from those seeking a first job, to executives on the move, to those in transition. Each individual may select from the wide range of resources presented to develop a customized job campaign.

Use career resources more effectively. As library research becomes an increasingly important component in the job hunting process, librarians are providing more information and support to job seekers. *JHS* helps users go directly to the most appropriate library material by providing comprehensive lists of job hunting resources on high-interest professional and vocational occupations.

Build a better career resources collection. Librarians, career counselors, outplacement firms, spouse relocation services, job referral agencies, and others who advise job seekers can use *JHS* to start or expand their collections of career and job hunting materials.

Comprehensive Coverage and Convenient Arrangement

The job search resources in *JHS* are conveniently arranged into two parts, which are followed by a master index:

Part One: Sources of Job-Hunting Information by Professions and Occupations—identifies information sources on employment opportunities for 216 specific types of jobs. A "List of Profiled Professions and Occupations" lists hundreds of alternate, popular, synonymous, and related job titles and links them to the jobs profiled in *JHS*, providing quick access to information sources on specific occupations or fields of interest by all their variant names—from accountant to aircraft mechanic and sports official to stockbroker. Each profile contains complete contact information and lists a variety of sources of job-opportunity information organized into seven easy-to-use categories:

1. Sources of Help-Wanted Ads
2. Placement and Job Referral Services
3. Employer Directories and Networking Lists
4. Handbooks and Manuals
5. Employment Agencies and Search Firms
6. Online Job Sources and Services
7. Other Sources, including internships and resources such as job hotlines

Part Two: Sources of Essential Job-Hunting Information—features such employment topics as:

- Interviewing Skills
- Employment Issues for Disabled Workers
- Electronic Job Search Information
- Working at Home
- Opportunities for Freelance Workers and Independent Contractors
- Opportunities for Temporary Workers

Each category includes:

- Reference Works
- Newspapers, Magazines, and Journals
- Audio/Visual Resources
- Online and Database Services
- Software
- Other Sources, such as special associations, job-hunting kits, and organizers

The information sources listed under each topic are arranged by type of resource and include complete contact information.

Index to Information Sources—comprehensively lists all of the publications, organizations, electronic resources, and other sources of job hunting information contained in *JHS*.

Please consult the User's Guide for more information about the arrangement, content, and indexing of the information sources cited in *JHS*.

JHS Profiles High-Interest Professions and Occupations

JHS catalogs job hunting resources for more than 200 professional, technical, and trade occupations, carefully selected to provide a broad cross-section of occupations of interest to today's job seekers. The majority are profiled in the Department of Labor's *Occupational Outlook Handbook (OOH),* a leading career resource containing detailed descriptions of some 270 professional and vocational occupations. Most of the professions cited in *OOH* are also included in *JHS*, as are representative vocational occupations selected from those listed in *OOH*. To round out this list, additional occupations were included on the basis of Bureau of Labor Statistics data projecting them as high-growth positions.

Coverage of Employment Alternatives and Trends

In addition to focusing on such "how-to" topics as resume-writing and interviewing, the "Sources of Essential Job-Hunting Information" offers resources for non-traditional work options and diverse segments of the work force. Working part-time, at home, and in your own business are featured chapters, as are opportunities for minorities, older workers, women, disabled workers, and gay and lesbian job seekers. A chapter covering sources of electronic job search information is included, as well as a category titled, "Online Job Sources and Services." This category lists Internet websites related to specific job profiles.

New to this Edition

The sixth edition is a complete revision of the previous *JHS*, incorporating thousands of updates to organization and publication data. This edition also features:

- 10 new job profiles, such as event planner; forensic scientist; and tissue engineer
- New information on networking

Method of Compilation

JHS contains citations compiled from direct contact with a wide range of associations and organizations, from dozens of publisher catalogs and other secondary sources, and from selected information from other Thomson Gale databases. While many resources cited in *JHS* contain career planning information, their usefulness in the job hunting process was the primary factor in their selection. Their annotations are tailored to support that function.

Comments and Suggestions Are Welcome

Libraries, associations, employment agencies, executive search firms, referral services, publishers, database producers, and other organizations involved in helping job seekers find opportunities or companies find candidates are encouraged to submit information about their activities and products for use in future editions of *JHS*. Comments and suggestions for improving this guide are also welcome. Please contact:

Project Editor
Job Hunter's Sourcebook
Thomson Gale
27500 Drake Rd.
Farmington Hills, MI 48331-3535
Phone: (248) 699-4253
Fax: (248) 699-8075
E-mail: BusinessProducts@gale.com
URL: www.gale.com

Job Hunter's Sourcebook (*JHS*) is divided into two parts:

- Part One: Sources of Job-Hunting Information by Professions and Occupations

- Part Two: Sources of Essential Job-Hunting Information

Access to entries is facilitated by a "List of Profiled Professions and Occupations" and an "Index to Information Sources." Users should consult each section to benefit fully from the information in *JHS*.

Master List of Profiled Professions and Occupations

A "List of Profiled Professions and Occupations" alphabetically lists the job titles used to identify the professions and occupations appearing in Part One of *JHS*, as well as alternate, popular, synonymous, and related job titles and names, and occupational specialties contained within job titles. Citations include "See" references to the appropriate occupational profiles and their beginning page numbers.

JHS is designed to meet the needs of job seekers at all levels of experience in a wide range of fields. Managers as well as entry-level job hunters will find information sources that will facilitate their career-specific searches. In addition, information on professions and occupations related to those profiled will be found.

All Career Levels. The title assigned to each profile identifies its occupational field or subject area; these titles are not meant to indicate the level of positions for which information is provided. Information systems managers, for example, will find highly useful information in the "Computer Programmers" and "Computer Systems Analysts" profiles, while financial analysts will benefit from information in the "Financial Managers" profile. The "General Managers and Top Executives" profile, on the other hand, is broad in nature and useful to any management-level search; it does not focus upon a specific profession or occupation.

Other Occupations. Job seekers not finding their specific career fields listed in this guide will discover that related profiles yield valuable sources of information. For example,

legal secretaries will find relevant information about employment agencies serving the legal profession and about prospective employers in the "Legal Assistants" and "Lawyers" profiles. An individual interested in finding a position in radio advertising sales might look to the entries in the broadcasting- and sales-related profiles to find appropriate resources. Career changers, too, can use *JHS* profiles to identify new professions to which their previously acquired skills would be transferable.

Part One: Sources of Job-Hunting Information by Professions and Occupations

This section features profiles of job-hunting information for 216 specific careers. Profiles are listed alphabetically by profession or occupation. Each profile contains up to seven categories of information sources, as described below. Within each category, entries are arranged in alphabetical order by name or title. Entries are numbered sequentially, beginning with the first entry in the first profile. All resources listed are included in each relevant profile (and in Part Two chapters, as appropriate) providing a complete selection of information sources in each occupational profile.

Sources of Help-Wanted Ads. Includes professional journals, industry periodicals, association newsletters, placement bulletins, and online services. In most cases, periodicals that focus on a specific field are cited here; general periodical sources such as the *National Business Employment Weekly* are listed in Part Two under "Help-Wanted Ads." Publications specific to an industry will be found in all profiles related to that industry. Candidates in some occupational areas, such as word processing, are usually recruited from the local marketplace and therefore are not as likely to find openings through a professional publication. Profiles for these occupations may contain fewer ad sources as job hunters are better served by local newspapers and periodicals. Entries include: the source's title and the name, address, and phone number of its publisher or producer; publication frequency; subscription rate; description of contents; toll-free or additional phone numbers; and fax numbers, when applicable. Source titles appear in italics.

Placement and Job Referral Services. Various services designed to match job seekers with opportunities are included in this category. Primarily offered by professional associations, these services range from job banks to placement services to employment clearinghouses, operating on the national and local levels. Entries include: the association's or organization's name, address, and phone number; its membership, activities, and services; toll-free or additional phone numbers; and fax numbers. E-mail and website addresses are provided, when available.

Employer Directories and Networking Lists. Covers directories and rankings of companies, membership rosters from professional associations, and other lists of organizations or groups that can be used to target prospective employers and identify potential contacts for networking purposes. In some cases, Who's Who titles are included where these can provide a source of contact information in a specialized field. General directories of companies such as Standard and Poor's Register of Corporations, Directors, and Executives are cited in Part Two in the "Identifying Prospective Employers" profile. Entries include: the title and name, address, and phone number of the publisher or distributor; publication date or frequency; price; description of contents; arrangement; indexes; toll-free or additional phone numbers; and fax numbers, when available. Directory titles appear in italics.

Handbooks and Manuals. This category notes books, pamphlets, brochures, and other published materials that provide guidance and insight to the job-hunting process in a particular occupational field. Entries include: the title and name, address, and phone number of its publisher or distributor; editor's or author's name; publication date or frequency; price; number of pages; description of contents; toll-free or additional phone numbers; and fax numbers, when known. Publication titles appear in italics.

Employment Agencies and Search Firms. Features firms used by companies to recruit candidates for positions and, at times, by individuals to pursue openings. The following firms are covered:

1. Employment agencies, which are generally geared toward filling openings at entry- to mid-levels in the local job market. Candidates sometimes pay a fee for using their services. When possible, *JHS* lists agencies where the employer pays the fee.

2. Executive search firms, which are paid by the hiring organization to recruit professional and managerial candidates, usually for higher-level openings and from a regional or national market. Executive search firms are of two types: contingency, where the firm is paid only if it fills the position, and retainer, where the firm is compensated to undertake a recruiting assignment, regardless of whether or not that firm actually fills the opening. The majority of the search firms cited in *JHS* are contingency firms. Although executive search firms work for the hiring organization and contact candidates only when recruiting for a specific position, most will accept unsolicited resumes, and some may accept phone calls.

3. Temporary employment agencies, which also are included in some profiles because they can be a way to identify and obtain regular employment.

For the most part, each profile lists firms that typically service that career. Firms specializing in a particular industry are included in all profiles relevant to that industry. *JHS* covers a mix of large and small firms. Major national search firms, which are quite broad in scope, are listed only under the "General Managers and Top Executives" profile. Some occupations are not served by employment agencies or search firms (fire fighter, for example); therefore, there are no entries for this category in such profiles. Entries include: the firm's name, address, and phone number; whether it's an employment agency, executive search firm, or temporary agency; descriptive information, as appropriate; toll-free and additional phone numbers; and fax numbers, when applicable.

Online Job Sources and Services. Publicly available electronic databases, including websites that facilitate matching job hunters with openings are cited. Many are tailored to specific occupations. Entries include: the name of the product or service; the name, address, and phone number of the distributor or producer; price; special formats or arrangements; descriptive information; toll-free or additional phone numbers; and fax numbers, when applicable. For websites, URL is included along with descriptive information.

Other Sources. This category comprises a variety of resources available to the job seeker in a specific field: job hotlines providing 24-hour recordings of openings; lists of internships, fellowships, and apprenticeships; bibliographies of job-hunting materials; video and audio cassettes; and salary surveys to be used as a guide when discussing compensation. Professional associations of significance or those that provide job hunting assistance (but not full placement services) are also included here. Because of the trend toward entrepreneurship, this section offers information sources on being one's own boss in a given field as well. Resources on job and career alternatives are provided for certain professions (such as educators), as is information on working abroad.

Entries for associations and organizations include: name, address, and phone number; the membership, activities, and services of associations; toll-free or additional phone numbers; and fax numbers. E-mail and website addresses are provided, when available. Entries for other resources include: title of the publication or name of the product or service; the name, address, and phone number of its publisher, distributor, or producer; editor's or author's name; publication date or frequency; price; special formats or arrangements; descriptive information; hotline, toll-free, or additional phone numbers; and fax numbers, when available. Publication, videocassette, and audiocassette titles appear in italics.

Part Two: Sources of Essential Job-Hunting Information

This section presents 32 profiles on topics of interest to any job hunter, such as resume writing or interviewing, as well as those of specialized interest, such as working at home (see "List of Profiled Professions and Occupations" for the complete list). Profiles are arranged alphabetically by topic and contain up to six categories of information, as listed below. Within each category, citations are organized alphabetically by name or title. Entries are also numbered sequentially, continuing the number sequence from Part One. The publications, periodicals, and other sources listed are fully cited in all relevant chapters (and in Part One profiles, as appropriate), providing the reader with a complete selection of resources in a single, convenient location.

Reference Works. Includes handbooks and manuals, directories, pamphlets, and other published sources of information. Entries include: the title and name, address, and phone number of its publisher or distributor; editor's or author's name; publication date or frequency; price; number of pages; description of contents; toll-free or additional phone numbers; and fax numbers, when known. Publication titles appear in italics.

Newspapers, Magazines, and Journals. Lists items published on a serial basis. Entries include: the title and name, address, and phone number of its publisher or distributor; frequency; price; description of contents; toll-free or additional phone numbers; and fax numbers, when known. Publication titles appear in italics.

Audio/Visual Resources. Features audiocassettes, videocassettes, and filmstrips. Entries include: the title and name, address, and phone number of its distributor or producer; date; price; special formats; descriptive information; toll-free or additional phone numbers; and fax numbers, when applicable. Videocassette and audiocassette titles appear in italics.

Online and Database Services. Publicly available electronic databases, including websites that facilitate matching job hunters with openings are cited. Entries include: the name of the product or service; the name, address, and phone number of the distributor or producer; price; special formats or arrangements; descriptive information; toll-free or additional phone numbers; and fax numbers, when applicable. For websites: the online address (URL) is included along with descriptive information.

Software. This category notes software programs designed to help with various aspects of job hunting, such as resume preparation. Entries include: the name of the product or service; the name, address, and phone number of the distributor or producer; price; special formats or arrangements; hardware compatibility, if relevant; descriptive information; toll-free or additional phone numbers; and fax numbers, when applicable.

Other Sources. Varied resources such as special associations and organizations and job-hunting bibliographies, kits, and organizers are covered in this section. Citations for journal and newspaper articles are provided if a topic is relatively new. Entries include: the title of the publication or name of the organization, product, or service; the name, address, and phone number of the organization, publisher, distributor, or producer; editor's or author's name; publication date or frequency; price; special formats or arrangements; descriptive information; toll-free or additional phone numbers; and fax numbers, when applicable. Publication titles appear in italics. For article citations: the article title, publication date, and journal or newspaper title, as well as a description of the article.

Index to Information Sources

JHS provides a comprehensive Index to Information Sources that lists all publications, periodicals, associations, organizations, firms, online and database services, and other resources cited in Parts One and Two. Entries are arranged alphabetically and are referenced by their entry numbers. Titles of publications, audiocassettes, and videocassettes appear in italics.

List of Profiled Professions and Occupations

This list outlines references to occupations and professions by job titles, alternate names contained within job titles, popular names, and synonymous and related names. Beginning page numbers for each occupation's profile are provided. Titles of profiles appear in boldface.

Accountants and Auditors

SOURCES OF HELP-WANTED ADS

★1★ Accounting Horizons
American Accounting Association
5717 Bessie Dr.
Sarasota, FL 34233
Ph: (941)921-7747   Fax: (941)923-4093
Quarterly. Publication covering the banking, finance, and accounting industries.

★2★ Accounting Review
American Accounting Association
5717 Bessie Dr.
Sarasota, FL 34233
Ph: (941)921-7747   Fax: (941)923-4093
Quarterly. $160.00/year for individuals. Accounting education, research, financial reporting, and book reviews.

★3★ Assessment Journal
International Association of Assessing Officers
130 E Randolph, Ste. 850
Chicago, IL 60601-6217
Ph: (312)819-6100   Fax: (312)819-6149
Bimonthly. Subscription included in membership; $200.00/year for nonmembers. Professional journal covering taxation.

★4★ Auditwire
Institute of Internal Auditors Inc.
247 Maitland Ave.
Altamonte Springs, FL 32701-4201
Fr: 877-867-4957
Description: Six issues/year. Covers internal auditing's role in a global business environment; communicates the IIA's perspectives on current and emerging issues; and delivers news about the people, places, and events that shape the profession. Columns include: Feedback; Business & Industry; Close-Up; IS Saavy; Newsmakers; Classifieds; Affiliates; Tribute; and Calendar.

★5★ CPA Client Bulletin
American Institute of Certified Public Accountants
Harborside Financial Ctr.
201 Plz. III
Jersey City, NJ 07311
Ph: (201)938-3806

Monthly. Periodical covering accounting and personal finance.

★6★ The CPA Journal
New York State Society of CPAs
530 Fifth Ave.
New York, NY 10036-5101
Ph: (212)719-8300   Fax: (212)719-3364
E-mail: cpaj-editors@nysscpa.org
URL: http://www.cpaj.com

Monthly. $42.00/year; $5.00 for single issue. Refereed accounting journal.

★7★ Government Financial Management Topics
Association of Government Accountants
2208 Mt. Vernon Ave.
Alexandria, VA 22301-1314
Ph: (703)684-6931   Fax: (703)548-9367
Fr: 800-AGA-7211
E-mail: mforce@agacgfm.com
URL: http://www.agacgfm.org
Description: Annual. Updates the latest developments relating to government financial management, educational registration forms, and general association news. Recurring features include news of research, a calendar of events, reports of meetings, news of educational opportunities, job listings, notices of publications available, and a column titled Presidential Perspective, interviews with leading government financial managers.

★8★ Internal Auditor
Institute of Internal Auditors Inc.
247 Maitland Ave.
Altamonte Springs, FL 32701-4201
Fr: 877-867-4957
E-mail: editor@theiia.org

Bimonthly. $60.00/year for individuals;

$10.00 for single issue; $84.00/year for other countries. Internal auditing.

★9★ Journal of Accountancy
The American Institute of Certified Public Accountants
1211 Avenue of the Americas
New York, NY 10036-8775
Ph: (212)596-6200   Fax: (212)596-6213
Fr: 888-777-7077
E-mail: joaed@aicpa.org
URL: http://www.aicpa.org

Monthly. $56.00/year for individuals. Accounting journal.

★10★ Journal of Depreciation Papers
Society of Depreciation Professionals
8100-M4 Wyoming Blvd. NE, No. 228
Albuquerque, NM 87113
Ph: (505)792-4604   Fax: (505)922-1495

Annual. Professional journal covering depreciation issues for accountants.

★11★ The Journal of Taxation
RIA Group
395 Hudson St., 4th Fl.
New York, NY 10014
Ph: (212)352-2746   Fax: (212)367-6314
Fr: 800-431-9025
URL: http://checkpoint.riag.com

Monthly. $250.00/year for individuals. Journal for sophisticated tax practitioners.

★12★ Management Accounting Quarterly
Institute of Management Accountants
10 Paragon Dr.
Montvale, NJ 07645-1760
Ph: (201)573-9000   Fax: (201)474-1603
Fr: 800-638-4427

Quarterly. $60.00/year, subscription included in membership. Trade publication covering accounting theory and practices for accountants.

★13★ National Association of Black Accountants-News Plus

National Association of Black Accountants Inc.
7249-A Hanover Pkwy.
Greenbelt, MD 20770
Ph: (301)474-6222   Fax: (301)474-3114
Description: Quarterly. Addresses concerns of black business professionals, especially in the accounting profession. Reports on accounting education issues, developments affecting the profession, and the Association's activities on the behalf of minorities in the accounting profession. Recurring features include member profiles, job listings, reports of meetings, news of research, and a calendar of events.

★14★ National Public Accountant

National Society of Accountants
1010 N Fairfax St.
Alexandria, VA 22314-1504
Ph: (703)549-6400   Fax: (703)549-2984
Fr: 800-966-6679

Monthly. $20.00/year. Public accounting magazine.

★15★ NewsAccount

Colorado Society of Certified Public Accountants
7979 E Tufts Ave., Ste. 500
Denver, CO 80237-2845
Ph: (303)773-2877   Fax: (303)773-6344
Description: Six issues/year. Relays information on issues and trends affecting the Society, its members, and the accounting profession. Recurring features include letters to the editor, job listings, a calendar of events and columns titled Committees in Action, Student Corner, SEC Corner, and Technical Update.

★16★ Strategic Finance

Institute of Management Accountants
10 Paragon Dr.
Montvale, NJ 07645-1760
Ph: (201)573-9000   Fax: (201)474-1603
Fr: 800-638-4427
E-mail: sfmag@imanet.org
URL: http://www.proquest.umi.com

Monthly. $145.00/year for individuals; $73.00/year, non-profit libraries. Magazine reporting on corporate finance, accounting, cash management, and budgeting.

PLACEMENT AND JOB REFERRAL SERVICES

★17★ Association for Accounting Administration

136 S Keowee St.
Dayton, OH 45402
Ph: (937)222-0030   Fax: (937)222-5794
E-mail: aaainfo@cpaadmin.org

URL: http://www.cpaadmin.org

Description: Promotes the profession of accounting administration and office management in accounting firms and corporate accounting departments. Sponsors activities, including consulting and placement services, seminars, salary and trends surveys, and speakers' bureau. Provides a forum for representation and exchange. Offers group purchasing opportunities.

★18★ Association of Chartered Accountants in the United States (ACAUS)

341 Lafayette St., Ste. 4246
New York, NY 10012-2417
Ph: (212)334-2078   Fax: (212)431-5786
E-mail: administration@acaus.org
URL: http://www.acaus.org

Members: Chartered accountants from England, Wales, Scotland, Ireland, Canada, Australia, New Zealand, and South Africa in commerce and public practice. **Purpose:** Represents the interests of chartered accountants; promotes career development and international mobility of professionals. **Activities:** Offers educational and research programs. Maintains speakers' bureau and placement service.

★19★ Christian Management Association (CMA)

PO Box 4090
San Clemente, CA 92674-4090
Ph: (949)487-0900   Fax: (949)487-0927
Fr: 800-727-4CMA
E-mail: CMA@cmaonline.org
URL: http://www.christianity.com/cma

Description: CEO's, key leaders and managers who serve Christian organizations and churches. Provides management information, leadership training and strategic networking. management through its annual national conference, the Christian Management Institute. Holds bimonthly fellowship meeting for training and information reports. Provides job referral and professional referral service to assist Christian managment personnel.

★20★ Hospitality Financial and Technology Professionals

11709 Boulder Ln., Ste. 110
Austin, TX 78726-1832
Ph: (512)249-5333   Fax: (512)249-1533
Fr: 800-646-4387
E-mail: frank.wolfe@hftp.org
URL: http://www.hftp.org

Members: Accountants, financial officers and MIS managers in 50 countries working in hotels, resorts, casinos, restaurants, and clubs. **Purpose:** Develops uniform system of accounts. **Activities:** Conducts education, training, and certification programs; offers placement service; maintains hall of fame.

★21★ International Newspaper Financial Executives (INFE)

21525 Ridgetop Circle, Ste. 200
Sterling, VA 20166
Ph: (703)421-4060   Fax: (703)421-4068
E-mail: infehq@infe.org
URL: http://www.infesecure.org/newsite/extranet/

Members: Controllers, chief accountants, auditors, business managers, treasurers, secretaries and related newspaper executives, educators, and public accountants. **Activities:** Conducts research projects on accounting methods and procedures for newspapers. Offers placement service; maintains speakers' bureau. Produces conferences, seminars. Publishes monthly newsletter, quarterly magazine, technical manuals.

EMPLOYER DIRECTORIES AND NETWORKING LISTS

★22★ Accountants Directory

infoUSA Inc.
5711 S 86th Cir.
Omaha, NE 68127-0347
Ph: (402)930-3500   Fax: (402)331-0176
Fr: 800-555-6124
URL: http://www.abii.com

Annual. Number of listings: 119,094. Entries include: Name, address, phone (including area code), size of advertisement, year first in "Yellow Pages," name of owner or manager, number of employees. Compiled from telephone company "Yellow Pages," nationwide. Arrangement: Geographical.

★23★ American Society of Women Accountants-Membership Directory

American Society of Women Accountants
8405 Greensboro Dr., Ste. 800
McLean, VA 22102
Ph: (703)506-3265   Fr: 800-326-2163

Annual. Covers approximately 5,000 members in accounting and accounting-related fields. Entries include: Name, address, phone, fax, e-mail. Arrangement: Classified by by chapter, then alphabetical.

★24★ American Woman's Society of Certified Public Accountants-Roster

American Woman's Society of Certified Public Accountants
136 S Keowee St.
Dayton, OH 45402
Ph: (937)222-1872   Fax: (937)222-5794
Fr: 800-297-2721
URL: http://www.awscpa.org

Annual, October. Number of listings: 1,400. Entries include: Name, title; company name, address, phone; home address and phone; membership classification. Arrangement: Classified by type of membership, then geographical. Indexes: Alphabetical.

★25★ Asian American Certified Public Accountants-Membership Directory

Asian American Certified Public Accountants
225 Bush St., Ste. 780
San Francisco, CA 94104
Ph: (415)957-3000   Fax: (415)433-7919

Annual. Covers about 400 member accountants.

★26★ Bookkeeping Service Directory

infoUSA Inc.
5711 S 86th Cir.
Omaha, NE 68127-0347
Ph: (402)930-3500   Fax: (402)331-0176
Fr: 800-555-6124
URL: http://www.abii.com

Annual. Number of listings: 27,213. Entries include: Name, address, phone (including area code), size of advertisement, year first in "Yellow Pages," name of owner or manager, number of employees. Regional editions available: Eastern, Western. Compiled from telephone company "Yellow Pages," nationwide. Arrangement: Geographical.

★27★ Emerson's Directory of Leading U.S. Accounting Firms

Emerson Co.
12342 Northup Way
Bellevue, WA 98005
Ph: (425)869-0655   Fax: (425)869-0746
URL: http://www.emersoncompany.com

Biennial, March of even years. $195.00 for U.S.; $250.00 for elsewhere. Covers 500 CPA firms in the U.S. Entries include: Company name, address, phone, fax, names and titles of key personnel, number of employees, geographical area served, description of services provided and industries served. Arrangement: Geographical. Indexes: Alphabetical, by state, by size of firm, by specialty practice.

★28★ National Society of Public Accountants-Yearbook

National Society of Accountants
1010 N Fairfax St.
Alexandria, VA 22314-1504
Ph: (703)549-6400   Fax: (703)549-2984
Fr: 800-966-6679

Formerly annual; latest edition February, 1998. Covers association members and committees; also includes lists of affiliated state organizations and members of governing board. Entries include: Name, address, phone, and code indicating type of membership. Other listings include name, address, and phone. Arrangement: Geographical.

★29★ Peterson's Job Opportunities for Business Majors

Thomson Peterson's
Princeton Pke. Corporate Ctr., 2000 Lenox Dr.
PO Box 67005
Lawrenceville, NJ 08648
Ph: (609)896-1800   Fax: (609)896-4531
Fr: 800-338-3282

URL: http://www.petersons.com

Irregular, latest edition 2000 - 16th ed. $18.95. Covers the 2,000 largest U.S. employers hiring in several fields, including financial services, management consulting, consumer products, and media/ entertainment. Entries include: Organization name, address, phone, name and title of contact, number of employees, type of organization. Arrangement: Alphabetical. Indexes: Type of organization.

★30★ Tax Return Preparation & Filing Service Directory

infoUSA Inc.
5711 S 86th Cir.
Omaha, NE 68127-0347
Ph: (402)930-3500   Fax: (402)331-0176
Fr: 800-555-6124
URL: http://www.abii.com

Annual. Number of listings: 63,898. Entries include: Name, address, phone (including area code), size of advertisement, year first in "Yellow Pages," name of owner or manager, number of employees. Compiled from telephone company "Yellow Pages," nationwide. Arrangement: Geographical.

★31★ Who Audits America

Data Financial Press
PO Box 668
Menlo Park, CA 94026
Ph: (415)321-4553   Fax: (707)598-3560
E-mail: sphdfp@att.net

Reported as semiannual, June and December; latest edition June 1994. $163.00. Covers 12,000 publicly held corporations that report to the Securities and Exchange Commission, and their accounting firms. Entries include: For companies-Name, location, SIC classification, number of employees, financial data, and abbreviation indicating accounting firm used. For accounting firms-Name, address, list of clients with their annual sales, and stock trading symbols. Arrangement: Companies are alphabetical; accounting firms are geographical. There is a separate alphabetical section of "Big Eight" accounting firms, with a list of their clients having more than $1 billion in annual sales.

HANDBOOKS AND MANUALS

★32★ Accounting Trends & Techniques

American Institute of Certified Public Accountants
Harborside Financial Ctr.
201 Plaza Three
Jersey City, NJ 07311-3881
Ph: (201)938-3772   Fax: (201)938-3780
Fr: 888-777-7077

Rick Rikert. 1999. $99.00 (paper).

★33★ Best Resumes for Accountants and Financial Professionals

John Wiley & Sons Inc.
1 Wiley Dr.
Somerset, NJ 08873
Ph: (732)469-4400   Fr: 800-225-5945

Kim Marino. 1994. $19.95 (paper). Contain examples of accounting and financial resumes. Also includes details on job search techniques.

★34★ Best Websites for Financial Professionals, Business Appraisers, & Accountants

John Wiley & Sons Inc.
111 River St.
Hoboken, NJ 07030-5774
Ph: (201)748-6000   Fax: (201)748-5774

Eva M. Lang. 2001. $39.95 (paper).

★35★ Careers in Accounting

McGraw-Hill Companies
1221 Avenue of the Americas
New York, NY 10020
Ph: (212)904-2000   Fax: (847)679-2494
Fr: 800-323-4900
E-mail: ntcpub@tribune.com

Gloria L. Gaylord and Glenda E. Ried. Third edition; Revised. 1997. $17.95; $13.95 (paper). Details opportunities in public, corporate, government, and not-for-profit accounting. Topics range from choosing a specialty to finding a mentor and networking on the job.

★36★ Careers for Financial Mavens and Other Money Movers

McGraw-Hill Trade
2 Penn Plaza
New York, NY 10121
Ph: (212)904-2000   Fr: 800-722-4726
E-mail: ntcpub@tribune.com

Marjorie Eberts and Margaret Gisler. 1998. $14.95; $9.95 (paper). 232 pages.

★37★ Careers for Number Crunchers and Other Quantitative Types

McGraw-Hill Trade
2 Penn Plaza
New York, NY 10121
Ph: (212)904-2000   Fr: 800-722-4726
E-mail: ntcpub@tribune.com

Rebecca Burnett. Second edition, 2002. $15.95; $12.95 (paper). 192 pages. Provides information to math-oriented job hunters on how to become statisticians, field researchers, computer programmers, stock analysts, investment managers, bankers, engineers, accountants, underwriters, economists, market analysts, mathematicians, systems analysts, and more.

★38★ The CPA Profession: Opportunities, Responsibilities & Services

Prentice Hall PRT
200 Old Tappan Rd.
Old Tappan, NJ 07675
Fr: 800-223-1360

Harry T. Magill, Gary J. Previts and Thomas R. Robinson. 1997. $52.00 (paper).

★39★ The I Hate Selling Book: Business-Building Advice for Consultants, Attorneys, Accountants, Engineers, Architects, and Other Professionals

Allan Boress & Associates
1500 University Dr., Suite 239
Coral Springs, FL 33071
Ph: (954)345-4666　　Fax: (954)344-2453

Allan S. Boress. 2001. $29.95.

★40★ Opportunities in Accounting Careers

McGraw-Hill Contemporary Books
1221 Avenue of the Americas
New York, NY 10020
Ph: (212)904-2000　　Fr: 800-323-4900
E-mail: ntcpub@tribune.com

Martin Rosenberg. 1996. $14.95; $11.95 (paper). 205 pages. Covers job opportunities in a variety of fields and specialties and how to pursue them. Illustrated.

★41★ Opportunities in Financial Careers

McGraw-Hill Trade
2 Penn Plaza
New York, NY 10121
Ph: (212)904-2000　　Fr: 800-722-4726

Michael Sumichrast. 1997. $14.95; $11.95 (paper). 210 pages. A guide to planning for and seeking opportunities in this challenging field.

★42★ Opportunities in Insurance Careers

McGraw-Hill/Contemporary Books
1221 Avenue of the Americas
New York, NY 10020
Ph: (212)904-2000　　Fr: 800-323-4900
E-mail: ntcpub@tribune.com

Robert Schrayer. Revised, 1999. $14.95; $11.95 (paper). 148 pages. A guide to planning for and seeking opportunities in the field. Contains bibliography and illustrations.

★43★ Opportunities in International Business Careers

McGraw-Hill Trade
2 Penn Plaza
New York, NY 10121
Ph: (212)904-2000　　Fr: 800-722-4726

Jeffrey Arpan. 1994. $11.95 (paper). 200 pages. Describes what types of jobs exist in international business, where they are located, what challenges and rewards they bring, and how to prepare for and obtain jobs in international business.

★44★ Opportunities in Office Occupations

McGraw-Hill Trade
2 Penn Plaza
New York, NY 10121
Ph: (212)904-2000　　Fr: 800-722-4726

Blanche Ettinger. 1994. $14.95; $11.95 (paper). 200 pages. Covers a variety of office positions and discusses trends for the next decade. Describes the job market, opportunities, job duties, educational preparation, the work environment, and earnings.

★45★ Opportunities in State and Local Government Careers

Vgm Career Horizons
1221 Avenue of the Americas
New York, NY 10020
Ph: (212)904-2000　　Fr: 800-323-4900
E-mail: ntcpub@tribune.com

Neale J. Baxter. 1994. $14.95; $10.95 (paper). 160 pages. Points out the incentives and drawbacks of a government career. Describes hiring procedures and provides tips on filling out applications, taking physical and aptitude tests, handling interviews, and finding jobs. Describes the jobs in which 75% of all state and local government workers are employed. For each occupation, covers the nature of the work and the training required.

★46★ The Practicing CPA on Developing & Marketing Services

American Institute of Certified Public Accountants
Harborside Financial Ctr.
201 Plaza Three
Jersey City, NJ 07311-3881
Ph: (201)938-3772　　Fax: (201)938-3780
Fr: 888-777-7077

Graham c. Goddard. 1997. $34.00 (paper).

★47★ Resumes for Banking and Financial Careers

McGraw-Hill Contemporary Books
1221 Avenue of the Americas
New York, NY 10020
Ph: (212)904-2000　　Fr: 800-323-4900
E-mail: ntcpub@tribune.com

2001. $10.95 (paper). 468 pages.

★48★ Top 10 Technology Opportunities: Tips & Tools

American Institute of Certified Public Accountants
Harborside Financial Ctr.
201 Plaza Three
Jersey City, NJ 07311-3881
Ph: (201)938-3772　　Fax: (201)938-3780
Fr: 888-777-7077

Sandi Smith. 1998. $24.95 (paper). Part of the American Institute of CPAs Audit Guides Series.

★49★ Where the Jobs Are: The Hottest Careers for the 90s

The Career Press, Inc.
3 Tice Rd.
PO Box 687
Franklin Lakes, NJ 07417-1322
Ph: (201)848-0310　　Fax: (201)848-1727
Fr: 800-227-3371

Joyce Hadley. Third edition, 2000. $13.99 (paper). 400 pages. Out of print. Describes careers in fifteen general fields, from accounting to travel and hospitality.

EMPLOYMENT AGENCIES AND SEARCH FIRMS

★50★ Abel Fuller & Zedler LLC

4550 Post Oak Pl., Ste. 141
Houston, TX 77027
Ph: (713)961-3330　　Fax: (713)961-3337

Executive Search Firm.

★51★ Accu Staff Inc.

2350 W River Park Dr.
Tucson, AZ 85705
Ph: (520)690-6630

Services provided include recruiting, temporary help, retained search, outplacement, testing and consulting. Specialties include management, executive, administrative, accounting/bookkeeping, data processing, financial, sales, marketing, technical, manufacturing, industrial and secretarial/office support. Serves private industries as well as government agencies.

★52★ AD Check Associates Inc.

204 S. Franklin St.
Wilkes-Barre, PA 18701
Ph: (570)829-5066

Executive search firm.

★53★ Adams Executive Search

3416 Fairfield Trail
Clearwater, FL 33761
Ph: (727)772-1536　　Fr: (727)772-1537

Executive Search firm.

★54★ Aureus Group

11825 Q St.
Omaha, NE 68137-3503
Ph: (402)397-2980　　Fax: (402)397-1122
Fr: 800-574-9829

Executive search and recruiting consultants specializing in six areas: accounting/finance, data processing, aerospace, engineering, manufacturing, and medical professionals. Industries served: hospitals, all mainframe computer shops, and all areas of accounting.

★55★ Bishop Partners
708 3rd Ave., Ste. 2200
New York, NY 10017
Ph: (212)986-3419 Fr: (212)986-3350
Executive search firm focuses on legal and accounting fields.

★56★ Boyce Cunnane Inc.
PO Box 19064
Baltimore, MD 21284-9064
Ph: (410)583-5511
Executive search firm.

★57★ Buxbaum/Rink Consulting L.L.C.
1 Bradley Rd., Ste. 901
Woodbridge, CT 06525
Ph: (203)389-5949 Fax: (203)397-0615
Personnel consulting firms offer contingency search, recruitment and placement of accounting/finance, as well as other business management positions. In addition to serving these two major career areas, also provides similar services to operations, marketing and human resources executives. Industries served: manufacturing, financial services, and service.

★58★ Capstone Consulting Inc.
723 S. Dearborn St., Printers Row
Chicago, IL 60605
Ph: (312)922-9556 Fax: (312)922-9558
Executive search firm.

★59★ Chanko-Ward Ltd.
2 W 45th St., Ste. 1201
New York, NY 10036
Ph: (212)869-4040 Fax: (212)869-0281
Primarily engaged in executive recruiting for individuals and corporations, where disciplines of accounting, planning, mergers/acquisitions, finance, or MIS are required. In addition will function as the internal personnel department of a corporation, either to augment present staff or in a situation where there is no formal personnel department. Serves private industries as well as government agencies.

★60★ Consultants to Executive Management Company Ltd.
2 1st National Plz., Ste. 610
Chicago, IL 60603
Ph: (312)855-1500 Fax: (312)855-1510
Fr: 800-800-2362
National personnel consultancy specializes in executive search with focus on accounting and finance, management information systems, professional medical, and real estate fields.

★61★ Cornell Global
PO Box 7113
Wilton, CT 06897
Ph: (203)762-0730 Fax: (203)761-9507
Executive search firm.

★62★ DBL Associates
1334 Park View Ave., Ste. 100
Manhattan Beach, CA 90266
Ph: (310)546-8121
Executive search firm focused on the financial industry.

★63★ Dellosso and Greenberg
525 E. 82nd St., Ste. 2B
New York, NY 10028
Ph: (212)570-5350 Fax: (212)861-8050
Executive search firm.

★64★ DGL Consultants
189 S. Main St.
PO Box 450
Richford, VT 05476
Ph: (802)848-7764 Fax: (802)848-3117
Executive search firm.

★65★ Elinvar
1804 Hillsborough St.
Raleigh, NC 27605
Ph: (919)878-4454
Executive search firm.

★66★ Foster Associates
The Livery
209 Cooper Ave.
Upper Montclair, NJ 07043
Ph: (973)746-2800 Fax: (973)746-9712
Executive search firm.

★67★ Houser Martin Morris
110 110th Ave. NE, Ste. 580
PO Box 90015
Bellevue, WA 98004-9015
Ph: (425)453-2700 Fax: (425)453-8726
Focus is in the areas of retained executive search, professional and technical recruiting. Areas of specialization include software engineering, sales and marketing, information technology, legal, human resources, accounting and finance, manufacturing, factory automation, and engineering.

★68★ Penn Search Inc.
997 Old Eagle School Rd., Ste. 202
Wayne, PA 19087-1706
Ph: (610)964-8820 Fax: (610)964-8916
Offers Information Technology, Accounting and Financial executive search services.

★69★ Raines International Inc.
250 Park Ave., 17th Fl.
New York, NY 10177
Ph: (212)997-1100 Fax: (212)944-7585
International generalist firm specializing in middle to upper management executives. Concentrations include general management, finance and accounting, information technology (MIS), operations/procurement, strategic planning, investment banking, real estate/finance, human resources, insurance, and legal.

★70★ Raymond Alexander Associates
97 Lackawanna Ave., Ste. 102
Totowa, NJ 07512
Ph: (973)256-1000 Fax: (973)256-5871
Personnel consulting firm conducts executive search services in the specific areas of accounting, tax and finance. Industries served: manufacturing, financial services, and public accounting.

★71★ Rocky Mountain Recruiters, Inc.
2000 S Colorado Blvd., Ste. 200
The Annex Bldg.
Denver, CO 80222
Ph: (303)296-2000 Fax: (303)296-2223
E-mail: miket@rmrecruiters.com
URL: http://www.rmrecruiters.com
Accounting, financial, and executive search firm.

★72★ Romac International, Inc.
1001 E Palm Ave
Tampa, FL 33605
Ph: (813)552-5239 Fax: (813)552-2122
URL: http://www.romac.com
Executive search firm. More than 30 locations throughout the United States.

★73★ Spherion Corp.
2050 Spectrum Blvd.
Fort Lauderdale, FL 33309
Ph: (954)938-7600 Fax: (954)938-7666
Fr: 800-976-7678
A worldwide leader in recruiting, assessing and deploying talent. It provides the widest range of services available including consulting, managed staffing, outsourcing, search/recruitment and flexible staffing. The company has expertise in industries such as information technology, outsourcing, accounting and finance, law, manufacturing and human resources as well as clerical, administrative and light industrial.

★74★ Whitney & Associates Inc.
5001 Frontenac Ave.
Golden Valley, MN 55422-4103
Ph: (612)338-5600 Fax: (612)349-6129
Accounting and financial personnel recruiting consultants providing full-time placement and temporary staffing service with specialized expertise and emphasis in the accounting discipline. Provides direct search firm recruiting services in the five-state upper Midwest Region of Minnesota, Wisconsin, Iowa, South Dakota, and North Dakota. Provides national search services throughout its affiliation in the American Association of Finance and Accounting (AAFA).

ONLINE JOB SOURCES AND SERVICES

★75★ Accounting.com
E-mail: info@accounting.com
URL: http://www.accounting.com
Description: Job board for those seeking accounting jobs. Employers may also post positions available. Contains directory of CPA firms, discussion forum for job seekers, CPE resources, news bulletins and accounting links.

★76★ Accountingjobs.com
E-mail: jobs@atsaccountingjobs.com
URL: http://www.accountingjobs.com
Description: Site holds national employment opportunities for accounting and finance professionals. Job seekers may search over 1,000 available positions posted by employers. Employers may browse through resumes posted by the job seekers. Employer profiles are also housed on the site, as well as links to other financial/accounting resources on the web.

★77★ American Accounting Association Placement Advertising
URL: http://aaahq.org/placements/default.cfm
Description: Visitors may apply for membership to the Association at this site. **Main files include:** Placement Postings, Placement Submission Information, Faculty Development, Marketplace, more.

★78★ American Association of Finance and Accounting
E-mail: feedback@aafa.com
URL: http://www.aafa.com
Description: AAFA is the largest and oldest alliance of executive search firms specializing in the recruitment and placement of finance and accounting professionals. Contains career opportunities site with job board for both job seekers and hiring employers. One does not have to be a member to search for jobs.

★79★ Association of Certified Fraud Examiners
URL: http://www.cfenet.com
Description: Website for membership organization contains Career Center with job databank, ability to post jobs and career resources and links. **Fee:** Must be a member of organization in order to access databank; annual dues depend on level of professional and begin at $95.

★80★ California Society of Certified Public Accountants Classifieds
E-mail: tiffany.gilroy@calcpa.org
URL: http://www.calcpa.org/community/classifieds/index.html
Description: An accounting job search tool for CPAs in California. Details steps to become a CPA, provides job search posting opportunities for seekers and candidates' pages for employers looking to fill positions.

★81★ Careers in Business
E-mail: wtunstall@careerselector.com
URL: http://careers-in-business.com
Description: Job search site with concentration in business, finance, consulting, marketing and non-profit related careers. Seekers may search database or post resume, plus review resources list for further information.

★82★ Financial Job Network
E-mail: info@atsfjn.com
URL: http://www.fjn.com
Description: Contains information on international and national employment opportunities for those in the financial job market. Job listings may be submitted, as well as resumes. **Main files include:** Testimonials, Calendar, Corporate Listings, FJN Clients, more. **Fee:** Free to candidates.

★83★ Illinois Certified Public Accountant Society Career Services
URL: http://www.icpas.org/icpas/career-services/career-services.asp
Description: Offers job hunting aid to members of the Illinois CPA Society only. Opportunity for non-members to join online. **Main files include:** Overview of Services, Resume Match, Career Seminars, Career Resources, Free Job Listings, Per Diem Pool, and Career Bibliographies.

★84★ Society of Financial Examiners
URL: http://www.sofe.org
Description: Website for membership organization contains classified advertisements for financial examiner positions as well as links to resources about the profession and an opportunity to enroll in an annual career development seminar. Visitors do not have to be members of the association to view job postings.

★85★ Spherion Workforce Architects
URL: http://www.spherion.com
Description: Recruitment firm specializing in accounting and finance, sales and marketing, interim executives, technology, engineering, retail and human resources.

TRADESHOWS

★86★ Business & Technology Solutions Show
Illinois Certified Public Accounting Society
550 W. Jackson, Ste 900
Chicago, IL 60661
Ph: (312)933-0393   Fax: (312)993-9954
URL: http://www.icpas.org
Annual. **Primary Exhibits:** Computers, office equipment, software publishing and educational supplies, and financial services.

★87★ Institute of Internal Auditors - USA International Conference
Institute of Internal Auditors Inc.
247 Maitland Ave.
Altamonte Springs, FL 32701-4201
Ph: (407)830-7600   Fax: (407)831-5171
E-mail: iia@theiia.org
URL: http://www.theiia.org
Annual. **Primary Exhibits:** Internal auditing equipment, supplies, and services, software, computer related equipment. **Dates and Locations:** 2005 Jun; Chicago, IL • 2006 Jun; Houston, TX.

★88★ Institute of Management Accountants Conference
Institute of Management Accountants
10 Paragon Dr.
Montvale, NJ 07645
Fax: (201)573-1601   Fr: 800-638-4427
E-mail: info@imanet.org
URL: http://www.imanet.org
Annual. **Primary Exhibits:** Management accounting equipment, supplies, and services. Review courses, shipping companies, software companies, and risk management consultants. **Dates and Locations:** 2005 Jun; Boston, MA.

★89★ National Association of Tax Professionals Conference
National Association of Tax Professionals
720 Association Dr.
Appleton, WI 54914-1483
Ph: (920)749-1040   Fax: (920)749-1062
Fr: 800-558-3402
E-mail: natp@natptax.com
URL: http://www.natptax.com
Annual. **Primary Exhibits:** Computer hardware, tax accounting and planning software, tax research information, tax forms, one-write accounting, financial planning information, office products, business equipment, and tax business solutions.

★90★ New Jersey Accounting, Business & Technology Show & Conference
Flagg Management, Inc.
353 Lexington Ave.
New York, NY 10016
Ph: (212)286-0333   Fax: (212)286-0086
E-mail: flaggmgmt@msn.com
URL: http://www.flaggmgmt.com
Annual. **Primary Exhibits:** Information and technology, financial and business services, computer accounting systems, software, tax preparation, accounting, audit, practice management software - windows, and computer and business systems. Banking, insurance, financial and business software. Internet, online systems and middle market software and investment services.

OTHER SOURCES

★91★ Accountants and Auditors

Evon Publishing
832 N 7th Ave.
Iron River, MI 49935
Ph: (906)265-3190

Audiocassette. 1996. Part of the Careers and Vocational Guidance Series. Provides information about the nature of the work, employment outlook, educational requirements, earnings, and work conditions as well as other related information.

★92★ Accreditation Council for Accountancy and Taxation (ACAT)

1010 N. Fairfax St.
Alexandria, VA 22314-1574
Ph: (703)549-2228   Fax: (703)549-2984
Fr: 888-289-7763
URL: http://www.acatcredentials.org

Members: Participants include accounting and tax practitioners, enrolled agents, certified public accountants, students, and others interested in attaining accreditation in accounting or taxation. **Purpose:** Strives to raise professional standards and improve the practices of accountancy and taxation; to identify persons with demonstrated knowledge of the principles and practices of accountancy and taxation, to ensure the continued professional growth of accredited individuals by setting stringent continuing education requirements, to foster increased recognition for the profession in the public, private, and educational sectors. **Activities:** Conducts semiannual accreditation examination in accountancy. Tax credentials obtained through coursework and examination. Designations are: Accredited in Accountancy/Accredited Business Accountant, Accredited Tax Advisor and Accredited Tax Preparer.

★93★ Affiliated Conference of Practicing Accountants International (ACPA)

30 Massachusetts Ave.
North Andover, MA 01845-3413
Ph: (978)689-9420   Fax: (978)689-9404
E-mail: acpaintl@acpaintl.org
URL: http://www.acpaintl.org

Description: Certified public and chartered accounting firms. Encourages the interchange of professional and legislative information among members with the aim of: enhancing service and technical and professional competency; maintaining effective management administration and practice development; increasing public awareness of members' capabilities. Facilitates availability and use of specialists and industry expertise among members in areas such as manufacturing, real estate, legal and medical services, finance, wholesaling, retailing, and municipal government. Makes client referrals; compiles revenue, operating expense, and cost ratio comparisons among firms.

★94★ American Institute of Certified Public Accountants (AICPA)

1211 Avenue of the Americas
New York, NY 10036-8775
Ph: (212)596-6001   Fax: (212)596-6213
Fr: 888-777-7077
E-mail: bmelancon@aicpa.org
URL: http://www.aicpa.org

Members: Professional society of accountants certified by the states and territories. **Purpose:** Responsibilities include establishing auditing and reporting standards; influencing the development of financial accounting standards underlying the presentation of U.S. corporate financial statements; preparing and grading the national Uniform CPA Examination for the state licensing bodies. **Activities:** Conducts research and continuing education programs and oversight of practice. Maintains over 100 committees including Accounting Standards, Accounting and Review Services, AICPA Effective Legislation Political Action, Auditing Standards, Taxation, Consulting Services, Professional Ethics, Quality Review, Women and Family Issues, and Information Technology.

★95★ American Society of Tax Professionals (ASTP)

PO Box 1213
Lynnwood, WA 98046-1213
Ph: (425)774-1996   Fax: (425)672-0461
Fr: 877-674-1996
E-mail: kraemerc@juno.com
URL: http://www.taxbeacon.com/astp

Members: Tax preparers, accountants, attorneys, bookkeepers, accounting services, and public accounting firms seeking to uphold high service standards in professional tax preparation. **Purpose:** Works to enhance the image of tax professionals and make tax practice more profitable; keep members abreast of tax law and service and delivery changes; promote networking among members for mutual assistance. **Activities:** Offers continuing education and training courses and public relations and marketing planning and preparation services. Supports Certified Tax Preparer Program.

★96★ Association of Government Accountants (AGA)

2208 Mount Vernon Ave.
Alexandria, VA 22301-1314
Ph: (703)684-6931   Fax: (703)548-9367
Fr: 800-AGA-7211
E-mail: cculkin@agacgfm.org
URL: http://www.agacgfm.org/

Description: Professional society of financial managers employed by federal, state, county, and city governments in financial management and administrative positions. Conducts research; offers education and professional development programs.

★97★ Association of Healthcare Internal Auditors (AHIA)

PO Box 10
Adrian, MI 49221-0010
Ph: (517)467-7729   Fax: (517)467-6104

E-mail: ahia@ahia.org
URL: http://www.ahia.org

Members: Health care internal auditors and other interested individuals. **Purpose:** Promotes cost containment and increased productivity in health care institutions through internal auditing. Serves as a forum for the exchange of experience, ideas, and information among members; provides continuing professional education courses and informs members of developments in health care internal auditing. **Activities:** Offers employment clearinghouse services.

★98★ Association of Latino Professionals in Finance and Accounting

510 W. 6th St., No. 400
Los Angeles, CA 90014
Ph: (213)243-0004   Fax: (213)243-0006
E-mail: info@national.alpfa.org
URL: http://www.alpfa.org

Members: Hispanic certified public accountants from the private and public sectors, accounting firms, universities, and banks. **Purpose:** To maintain and promote professional and moral standards of Hispanics in the accounting field. Assists members in practice development and develops business opportunities for members. **Activities:** Sponsors continuing professional education seminars; bestows scholarships; provides employment services.

★99★ BKR International (BKR)

19 Fulton St., Ste. 306
New York, NY 10038
Ph: (212)964-2115   Fax: (212)964-2133
Fr: 800-BKR-INTL
E-mail: bkr@bkr.com
URL: http://www.bkr.com

Members: Accounting firms in the U.S. and abroad. **Purpose:** Seeks to create an international group of competent professional firms which will provide full services in major markets of the world and enable member firms to send and receive referrals. **Activities:** Helps reduce operating costs of member firms by: developing consolidated purchasing arrangements for services and supplies at the lowest possible cost; developing recruiting programs, marketing materials, and advertising to reduce the collective recruiting effort of group members; expanding the group to reduce the burden on individual member firms and increase their potential scope of services. Compiles statistics to provide member firms with data helpful to sound management decisions. Organizes clinical and administrative peer reviews to insure quality and provide management with professional counsel. Develops forms, procedures, and manuals to provide guidance and accommodate the needs of partners. Conducts 12 continuing education programs per year in all areas of expertise.

★100★ Financial Occupations

Delphi Productions
3160 4th St.
Boulder, CO 80304
Fax: (303)443-4022   Fr: 888-443-2400

URL: http://www.delphivideo.com
$95.00. 50 minutes. Part of the Careers for the 21st Century Video Library.

★101★ Information Systems Audit and Control Association and Foundation (ISACA)

3701 Algonquin Rd., Ste. 1010
Rolling Meadows, IL 60008
Ph: (847)253-1545   Fax: (847)253-1443
E-mail: membership@isaca.org
URL: http://www.isaca.org

Description: A recognized global leader in Information Technology (IT) governance, control and assurance, ISACA has assumed a role as the harmonizing source for IT control practices and standards the world over. ISACA serves its members and other constituencies by providing education, research (through its affiliated Foundation), a professional certification, conferences and publications.

★102★ Institute of Internal Auditors (IIA)

247 Maitland Ave.
Altamonte Springs, FL 32701
Ph: (407)937-1100   Fax: (407)937-1101
E-mail: iia@theiia.org
URL: http://www.theiia.org

Members: Members in internal auditing, governance, internal control, IT audit, education, and security. Leader in certification, education, research, and technological guidance for the profession.

★103★ Institute of Management Accountants (IMA)

10 Paragon Dr.
Montvale, NJ 07645
Ph: (201)474-1565   Fax: (201)474-1600
Fr: 800-638-4427
E-mail: ima@imanet.org
URL: http://www.imanet.org

Members: Management accountants in industry, public accounting, government, and academia; other persons interested in internal and management uses of accounting. **Purpose:** Conducts research on accounting methods and procedures and the management purposes served. **Activities:** Established Institute of Certified Management Accountants to implement and administer examinations for the Certified Management Accountant (CMA) program and the Certified in Financial Management (CFM) program. Annually presents chapter medals for competition, manuscripts and for the highest scores on the CMA Examination. Offers continuing education programs comprising courses, conferences, and a self-study program in management accounting areas. Offers ethics counseling services for members by telephone. Sponsors the Foundation for Applied Research.

★104★ National Association of Black Accountants (NABA)

7249A Hanover Pky.
Greenbelt, MD 20770
Ph: (301)474-6222   Fax: (301)474-3114
E-mail: nabaoffice@nabainc.org
URL: http://www.nabainc.org

Description: Minority students and professionals currently working, or interested in the fields of accounting, finance, technology, consulting or general business. Seeks, promote, develops, and represent the interests of current and future minority business professionals.

★105★ National Association of Tax Professionals (NATP)

720 Association Dr.
Appleton, WI 54914
Ph: (920)749-1040   Fax: 800-747-0001
Fr: 800-558-3402
E-mail: natp@natptax.com
URL: http://www.natptax.com

Description: Dedicated to excellence in the tax profession. Serves professionals who work in all areas of tax practice, including individual practitioners, enrolled agents, certified public accountants, accountants, attorneys, and certified financial planners.

★106★ National Society of Accountants

1010 N Fairfax St.
Alexandria, VA 22314-1574
Ph: (703)549-6400   Fax: (703)549-2984
Fr: 800-966-6679
E-mail: arichman@nsacct.org
URL: http://www.nsacct.org

Description: Professional organization and its affiliates represent 30,000 members who provide auditing, accounting, tax preparation, financial and estate planning and management services to approximately 19 million individuals and business clients. Most members are sole practitioners or partners in small to mid-size accounting firms.

★107★ *Professional Specialty Occupations*

Delphi Productions
3160 4th St.
Boulder, CO 80304
Fax: (303)443-4022   Fr: 888-443-2400
URL: http://www.delphivideo.com
$95.00. 53 minutes. Part of the Careers for the 21st Century Video Library.

Actors, Directors, and Producers

SOURCES OF HELP-WANTED ADS

★108★ ArtSEARCH
Theatre Communications Group
520 Eighth Ave., 24th Fl.
New York, NY 10018-4156
Ph: (212)609-5900   Fax: (212)609-5901
E-mail: custserv@tcg.org
URL: http://www.tcg.org

Description: Biweekly. Publishes classified listings for job opportunities in the arts, especially theatre, dance, music, and educational institutions. Listings include opportunities in administration, artistic, education, production, and career development.

★109★ AV Video & Multimedia Producer
PBI Media L.L.C.
2700 Westchester Ave.
Purchase, NY 10577-2554
Ph: (914)328-9157   Fax: (914)328-9093
Fr: 800-800-5474
E-mail: avvmmp@kipi.com
URL: http://www.kipinet.com

Monthly. $53.00/year for individuals; $65.00/year for Canada and Mexico; $85.00/year for other countries. Magazine covering audiovisual, video and multimedia production, presentation, people, technology and techniques.

★110★ Back Stage West
VNU Business Media USA
770 Broadway
New York, NY 10003
Ph: (646)654-5000
URL: http://www.vnubusinessmedia.com/

Weekly. $95.00/year. Trade publication covering the entertainment industry.

★111★ Broadcasting & Cable
Reed Business Information
360 Park Ave. S
New York, NY 10010
Ph: (646)746-6400   Fax: (646)746-6734

URL: http://www.broadcastingcable.com

Weekly. $179.00/year for U.S.; $239.00/year for Canada. News magazine covering The Fifth Estate (radio, TV, cable, and satellite), and the regulatory commissions involved.

★112★ C Magazine
C The Visual Arts Foundation
PO Box 5, Sta. B
Toronto, ON, Canada M5T 2T2
Ph: (416)539-9495   Fax: (416)539-9903
Fr: 800-745-6312

Quarterly. Periodical covering the visual and performing arts.

★113★ Daily Variety
Reed Business Information
5700 Wilshire Blvd., Ste. 120
Los Angeles, CA 90036
Ph: (323)857-6600   Fax: (323)965-2475

Daily. Global entertainment newspaper (tabloid).

★114★ Electronic Media
Crain Communications Inc.
1155 Gratiot Ave.
Detroit, MI 48207-2997
Ph: (313)446-6000
E-mail: info@crain.com
URL: http://www.crain.com/

Newspaper covering management, programming, cable and trends in the television and the media industry.

★115★ Entertainment Design Magazine
Primedia Business
9800 Metcalf Ave.
Overland Park, KS 66212
Ph: (913)341-1300   Fax: (913)967-1898
E-mail: edld@intertec.com
URL: http://www.etecnyc.net

$37.95/year for individuals; $5.95 for single issue. The business of entertainment technology and design.

★116★ Entertainment Employment Journal
Studiolot Publishing
5632 Van Nuys Blvd., Ste. 320
Van Nuys, CA 91401-4600
Ph: (818)776-2800   Fr: 800-335-4335
E-mail: info@eej.com
URL: http://www.eej.com

Semimonthly. $125.00/year. Trade magazine covering business and technical careers in broadcast, electronic media, and motion pictures.

★117★ FMedia!
FM Atlas Publishing
PO Box 336
Esko, MN 55733-0336
Ph: (218)879-7676   Fr: 800-605-2219

Description: Monthly. Lists information on the facilities and formats of FM radio, including new station grants and applications. Also provides official and unofficial news and comments, as well as FM Dxing and FM reception concerns. Recurring features include letters to the editor, news of research, job listings, and notices of publications available.

★118★ The Hollywood Reporter
The Hollywood Reporter
5055 Wilshire Blvd.
Los Angeles, CA 90036-4396
Ph: (323)525-2000   Fax: (323)525-2377
E-mail: special-issues@hollywoodreporter.com
URL: http://www.hollywoodreporter.com

Daily. Film, TV, and entertainment trade newspaper.

★119★ HOW
F & W Publications Inc.
4700 E Galbraith Rd.
Cincinnati, OH 45236-6708
Ph: (513)531-2690   Fax: (513)531-2902
Fr: 800-289-0963
E-mail: editorial@howdesign.com

Bimonthly. $49.00/year for individuals; $7.95 for single issue, Jan/Feb or May/June; $9.95 for single issue, Mar/April or July/Aug;

$11.95/year for single issue, Sept/Oct or Nov/Dec. Instructional trade magazine.

★120★ Millimeter Magazine
Primedia Business
9800 Metcalf Ave.
Overland Park, KS 66212
Ph: (913)341-1300   Fax: (913)967-1898

Monthly. $45.00/year; $7.00 for single issue. Magazine focusing on the process of motion picture and television production.

★121★ Music and Media
VNU Business Media USA
770 Broadway
New York, NY 10003
Ph: (646)654-5000
URL: http://www.vnubusinessmedia.com/box/bp/div_ent_music_musicm.

Weekly. $175.00/year. Publication covering the music and entertainment industries.

★122★ PIX
VNU Business Media USA
770 Broadway
New York, NY 10003
Ph: (646)654-5000

Monthly. Trade publication covering the arts and entertainment industries.

★123★ Post
Post Pro Publishing Inc.
25 Willowdale Ave.
Port Washington, NY 11050
Ph: (516)767-2500   Fax: (516)767-9335
URL: http://www.postmagazine.com

Monthly. Free to qualified subscribers. Magazine serving the field of television, film, video production and post-production.

★124★ Producers Masterguide
Producers Masterguide
60 E 8th St., 34th Fl.
New York, NY 10003-6514
Ph: (212)777-4002   Fax: (212)777-4101
URL: http:// www.producers.masterguide.com

Annual. $145.00/year for U.S.; $155.00/year for Canada; $175.00/year for other countries. An international film and TV production directory and guide for the professional motion picture, broadcast television, feature film, TV commercial, cable/satellite, digital and videotape industries in the U.S., Canada, the UK, the Caribbean Islands, Mexico, Australia, New Zealand, Europe, Israel, Morocco, the Far East, and South America.

★125★ Ross Reports Television and Film
VNU Business Media USA
770 Broadway
New York, NY 10003
Ph: (646)654-5000

Monthly. $59.00/year for individuals; $7.95 for single issue. Trade publication covering talent agents and casting directors in New York and Los Angeles, as well as television and film production. Special national issue every December. Sister publication to Back Stage, Back Stage West.

★126★ SHOOT
BPI Communications Inc.
575 Prospect Ave.
Lakewood, NJ 08701
Ph: (732)363-5679   Fax: (732)363-0338
Fr: 888-463-6110
E-mail: shoot@inch.com

Weekly. $79.00/year for individuals. Trade magazine covering all aspects of the commercial production industry, including creative and post-production elements.

★127★ SMPTE Journal
Society of Motion Picture and Television Engineers
595 W Hartsdale Ave.
White Plains, NY 10607
Ph: (914)761-1100   Fax: (914)761-3115
URL: http://www.smpte.org

Monthly. $90.00/year; $100.00/year for out of country. Journal containing articles pertaining to new developments in motion picture and television technology; standards and recommended practices; general news of the industry.

★128★ Variety
Reed Business Information
5700 Wilshire Blvd., Ste. 120
Los Angeles, CA 90036
Ph: (323)857-6600   Fax: (323)965-2475

Weekly. $129.00/year. Newspaper (tabloid) reporting on theatre, television, radio, music, records, and movies.

PLACEMENT AND JOB REFERRAL SERVICES

★129★ American Conservatory Theater Foundation (ACT)
30 Grant Ave., 6th Fl.
San Francisco, CA 94109
Ph: (415)834-3200   Fax: (415)834-3360
E-mail: sfjimmy@aol.com
URL: http://www.act-sf.org

Description: Provides resources for the American Conservatory Theatre which functions as a repertory theatre and accredited acting school, offering a Master of Fine Arts degree. Holds national auditions for the MFA program in Chicago, IL, New York City, and Los Angeles, CA, usually in February. Holds student matinees, school outreach programs, and in-theatre discussions between artist and audiences. Conducts professional actor-training programs, a summer training congress, and a young conservatory evening academy program for children aged 8-18. Offers children's services. Operates speakers' bureau and placement service.

★130★ Black Stuntmen's Association (BSA)
8949 W. 24th St.
Los Angeles, CA 90034
Ph: (310)202-9191   Fax: (310)842-7182

Description: Men and women (ages 18 to 50) who are members of the Screen Actors Guild and the American Federation of Television and Radio Artists. Serves as an agency for stuntpeople in motion pictures and television. Conducts stunt performances at various local schools. Plans to operate school for black stuntpeople. Offers placement service.

★131★ Health Sciences Communications Association (HESCA)
39 Wedgewood Dr., Ste. A
Jewett City, CT 06351
Ph: (860)376-5915   Fax: (860)376-6621
E-mail: hesca@hesca.org
URL: http://www.hesca.org/

Description: Media managers, graphic artists, biomedical librarians, producers, faculty members of health science and veterinary medicine schools, health professional organizations, and industry representatives. Acts as a clearinghouse for information used by professionals engaged in health science communications. Coordinates Media Festivals Program which recognizes outstanding media productions in the health sciences. Offers placement service.

★132★ National Association of Broadcasters (NAB)
1771 N St. NW
Washington, DC 20036
Ph: (202)429-5300   Fax: (202)429-4199
E-mail: nab@nab.org
URL: http://www.nab.org

Description: Representatives of radio and television stations and networks; associate members include producers of equipment and programs. Seeks to ensure the viability, strength, and success of free, over-the-air broadcasters; serves as an information resource to the industry. Monitors and reports on events regarding radio and television broadcasting. Maintains Broadcasting Hall of Fame. Offers minority placement service and employment clearinghouse.

★133★ Texas International Theatrical Arts Society (TITAS)
3101 N Fitzhugh, Ste. 301
Dallas, TX 75204
Ph: (214)528-6112   Fax: (214)528-2617

E-mail: csantos@titas.org
URL: http://www.titas.org

Description: Theatrical agencies working to book entertainers and international acts into all live music venues. Provides placement service; conducts educational seminars.

★134★ **University Film and Video Association (UFVA)**
University of Illinois Press
1325 S Oak St.
Champaign, IL 61820-6903
Ph: (914)761-1187   Fax: (914)761-3115
E-mail: journals@uicu.edu
URL: http://www.ufva.org/

Description: Professors and video/filmmakers concerned with the production and study of film and video in colleges and universities. Conducts research programs; operates placement service; presents annual grants; bestows scholarships and awards.

EMPLOYER DIRECTORIES AND NETWORKING LISTS

★135★ **Academy Players Directory**
Academy of Motion Picture Arts & Sciences
1313 N Vine St.
Los Angeles, CA 90028
Ph: (310)247-3058   Fax: (310)550-5034
E-mail: players@oscars.org
URL: http://www.playersdirectory.com

Semiannual, January and July. $75.00. Covers over 18,000 members of Screen Actors Guild (SAG), American Federation of Television and Radio Artists (AFTRA), and Actors Equity Association (AEA). All listings are paid. Entries include: Name of actor, name of agency and/or personal manager with phone; photograph, contact number. Arrangement: Classified by role type in 4 sections: Part I, Academy Award Nominee and Winners, Leading women/Ingenues; Part II, Academy Award Nominees and Winners, Leading men/Younger male leads; Part III, Characters/Comedy actors and actresses; Part IV, Children/Master index. Indexes: General, ethnic/disabled.

★136★ **Agents and Managers Directory**
IFILM Publishing
1024 N Orange Dr.
Hollywood, CA 90038
Ph: (323)308-3490   Fax: (323)308-3493

Semiannual, February and August. $59.95 per issue; $99.95 per year; $149.95 for online subscription. Covers over 1,300 agencies and management companies, and over 4,600 agents and personal managers within those companies. Majority of listings are located in Los Angeles and New York. Entries include: company name, staff names and titles, address, phone, fax, e-mail address, web site address, company type, types of clients, and guild and organization affiliations. Arrangement: Alphabetical by company. Indexes: Client category, affiliation, individual names.

★137★ **Below-the-Line Guide**
IFILM Publishing
1024 N Orange Dr.
Hollywood, CA 90038
Ph: (323)308-3490   Fax: (323)308-3493
E-mail: lrossini@ifilm.com
URL: http://www.loneeagle.com

Annual, latest edition 9th. $49.95. Covers approximately 2,500 motion picture and television cinematographers, editors, production designers, and costume designers, now includes set decorators. Entries include: Personal name; name, address, phone of agent or contact; chronological list of films or shows. Arrangement: Classified by line of business. Indexes: Film/show title, contact name, agents and managers.

★138★ **Billboard's International Talent and Touring Directory**
Billboard Books
770 Broadway
New York, NY 10003
Ph: (646)654-5000   Fax: (646)654-5487
Fr: 800-278-8477
URL: http://orderbillboard.com

Annual, October. $139.00. Covers over 12,900 artists, managers and agents from 76 countries worldwide, including the U.S.A. and Canada; tour facilities and services; venues; entertainers, booking agents, hotels, and others in the entertainment industry; international coverage. Entries include: Company name, address, phone, fax, names and titles of key personnel. Arrangement: Classified by line of business; venues are then geographical. Indexes: Product/service.

★139★ **Broadcasting & Cable Yearbook**
R.R. Bowker L.L.C.
630 Central Ave.
New Providence, NJ 07974
Ph: (908)286-1090   Fax: (908)219-0098
Fr: 888-269-5372

Annual, March, latest edition 2003-2004. $179.95. Covers over 17,000 television and radio stations in the United States, its territories, and Canada; cable MSOs and their individual systems; television and radio networks, broadcast and cable group owners, station representatives, satellite networks and services, film companies, advertising agencies, government agencies, trade associations, schools, and suppliers of professional and technical services, including books, serials, and videos; communications lawyers. Entries include: Company name, address, phone, fax, names of executives. Station listings include broadcast power, other operating details. Arrangement: Stations and systems are geographical, others are alphabetical. Indexes: Alphabetical.

★140★ **Contemporary Theatre, Film, and Television**
Thomson Gale
27500 Drake Rd.
Farmington Hills, MI 48331-3535
Ph: (248)699-4253   Fax: (248)699-8065
Fr: 800-877-GALE
URL: http://www.gale.com

Bimonthly. $175.00. Covers in 47 volumes, more than 15,000 leading and up-and-coming performers, directors, writers, producers, designers, managers, choreographers, technicians, composers, executives, and dancers in the United States, Canada, Great Britain and the world. Each volume includes updated biographies for people listed in previous volumes and in "Who's Who in the Theatre," which this series has superseded. Entries include: Name, agent and/or office addresses, personal and career data; stage, film, and television credits; writings, awards, other information. Arrangement: Alphabetical. Indexes: Cumulative name index also covers entries in "Who's Who in the Theatre" editions 1-17 and in "Who Was Who in the Theatre".

★141★ **Directors Guild of America-Directory of Members**
Directors Guild of America Inc.
7920 Sunset Blvd.
Los Angeles, CA 90046
Ph: (310)289-2000   Fax: (310)289-2029
Fr: 800-421-4173
E-mail: directory@dga.wise.net
URL: http://www.dga.org

Annual, February. $22.00. Covers over 11,000 motion picture and television directors and their assistants providing films and tapes for entertainment, commercial, industrial, and other non-entertainment fields; international coverage. Entries include: DGA member name; contact or representative address, phone; specialty; brief description of experience and credits. Arrangement: Alphabetical. Indexes: Geographical, women and minority members, agents.

★142★ **Dramatics Magazine-Summer Theatre Directory Issue**
International Thespian Society
2343 Auburn Ave.
Cincinnati, OH 45219
Ph: (513)429-3900   Fax: (513)421-7077
E-mail: lckelley@edta.org

Annual, February. $6.50. Publication includes: List of more than 200 study and performance opportunities in summer theater education programs and summer stock. Entries include: Organization, school or group name, address, phone, name of contact; description of program, dates, requirements, cost, financial aid availability, etc. Arrangement: Geographical.

★143★ The Dramatists Guild Resource Directory

The Dramatists Guild of America Inc.
1501 Broadway, Ste. 701
New York, NY 10036-3988
Ph: (212)398-9366   Fax: (212)944-0420

Annual, September. Publication includes: Lists of Broadway and off-Broadway producers; theater & producing organizations; agents; regional theaters; sources of grants, fellowships, residencies; conferences and festivals; playwriting ontests; and sources of financial assistance. Entries include: For producers-Name, address, credits, types of plays accepted for consideration. For groups-Name, address, contact name, type of material accepted for consideration, future commitment, hiring criteria, response time. For agents-Name, address. For theaters-Theater name, address, contact name, submission procedure, types of plays accepted for consideration, maximum cast, limitations, equity contract, opportunities, response time. For grants, fellowships, residencies, financial assistance, conferences, and festivals-Name, address, contact name, description, eligibility and application requirements, deadline. For play contests-Name, address, prize, deadline, description. Arrangement: Contests are by deadline; others are classified.

★144★ Fashion & Print Directory

Peter Glenn Publications
6040 NW 43rd Ter.
Boca Raton, FL 33496-4043
Ph: (561)999-8930   Fax: (561)999-8931
Fr: 888-332-6700
URL: http://www.pgdirect.com

Annual, November. $59.95. Covers advertising agencies, PR firms, marketing companies, 1000 client brand companies and related services in the U.S. and Canada. Includes photographers, marketing agency, suppliers, sources of props and rentals, fashion houses, beauty services, locations. Entries include: Company name, address, phone; paid listings numbering 5000 include description of products or services, key personnel. Arrangement: Classified by line of business.

★145★ Film Directors

Hollywood Creative Directory and Lone Eagle Publishing
1024 N. Orange Dr.
Hollywood, CA 90038
Ph: (323)308-3606   Fax: (323)308-3493
Fr: 800-815-0503
URL: http://www.loneeagle.com.

Annual. $49.95. Covers over 5,000 living and primarily active theatrical and television film directors who have made films with running times of one hour or more; over 350 deceased directors; directors of videotaped television dramas are not included. Entries include: Name, date and place of birth, address and phone (or that of agent), and chronological list of films that meet stated criteria. Over 42,000 film credits. Arrangement: Alphabetical. Indexes: Director, agent/manager, film title, foreign director name,

academy awards and nominations by year, guilds.

★146★ HOLA Pages

The Hispanic Organization of Latin Actors
107 Suffolk St., Ste. 302
New York, NY 10002
Ph: (212)253-1015   Fax: (212)253-9651
URL: http://www.hellohola.org/directory/holapage1.htm

Biennial, January of odd years. $25.00. Covers about 500 Hispanic performing artists from New York, New Jersey, and California; all listings are paid. Entries include: Name, photograph, profession(s), phone number(s). Persons listed are contacted through the publisher. Arrangement: Alphabetical.

★147★ International Dictionary of Films and Filmmakers

St. James Press
27500 Drake Rd.
Farmington Hills, MI 48331-3535
Ph: (248)699-4253   Fax: (248)699-8062
Fr: 800-877-4253

Every five years, latest edition 2000. $595.00 per set; $170.00 per volume. Covers in an illustrated multi-volume set, approximately 500 directors and filmmakers, 650 actors and actresses, and 520 writers and production artists (in volumes 2, 3, and 4 respectively). Both historical and contemporary artists are listed, chosen on the basis of international importance in film history. Entries include: Name; personal, education and career data; address, when available; filmography; bibliography of monographs and articles on and by the subject, critical essay, illustrations. Volume 1 contains entries describing approximately 680 significant films. Arrangement: Alphabetical in each volume. Indexes: Film title and nationality indexes in volumes 2, 3, and 4; geographic and personal name indexes in volume 1.

★148★ International Motion Picture Almanac

Quigley Publishing Company Inc.
64 Wintergreen Ln.
Groton, MA 01450-4219
Fr: 800-231-8239
URL: http://hometown.aol.com/quigleypub/mp.html

Annual, January. $130.00. Covers motion picture producing companies, firms serving the industry, equipment manufacturers, casting agencies, literary agencies, advertising and publicity representatives, motion picture theater circuits, buying and booking organizations, independent theaters, international film festivals, associations, theatre equipment supply companies. Entries include: Generally, company name, address, phone. For manufacturers-Products or service provided, name of contact. For producing companies-Additional details. For theaters-Name of owner, screen size. Companion volume is the "International Television and Video Almanac". Arrangement: Classified by service or activity.

★149★ International Television and Video Almanac

Quigley Publishing Company Inc.
64 Wintergreen Ln.
Groton, MA 01450-4129
Fr: 800-231-8239
URL: http://hometown.aol.com/quigleypub/mp.html

Annual, January. $130.00. Covers "Who's Who in Motion Pictures and Television and Home Video," television networks, major program producers, major group station owners, cable television companies, distributors, firms serving the television and home video industry, equipment manufacturers, casting agencies, literary agencies, advertising and publicity representatives, television stations, associations, list of feature films produced for television; statistics, industry's year in review, award winners, satellite & wireless cable provider, primtime programming, video producers, distributors, wholesalers. Entries include: Generally, company name, address, phone; manufacturer and service listings may include description of products and services and name of contact; producing, distributing, and station listings include additional detail, and contacts for cable and broadcast networks. Arrangement: Classified by service or activity. Indexes: Full.

★150★ National Directory of Arts Internships

National Network for Artist Placement
935 W. Ave. 37
Los Angeles, CA 90065
Ph: (323)222-4035   Fax: (323)225-5711
URL: http://www.artistplacement.com/intern.htm

Biennial, odd years. $85.00. Covers over 5,000 internship opportunities in dance, music, theater, art, design, film, and video & over 1,250 host organizations Entries include: Name of sponsoring organization, address, name of contact; description of positions available, eligibility requirements, stipend or salary (if any), application procedures. Arrangement: Classified by discipline, then geographical.

★151★ New England Theatre Conference-Resource Directory

New England Theatre Conference Inc.
PMB 502, 198 Tremont St.
198 Tremont St.
Boston, MA 02116-4750
Ph: (617)851-8535   Fax: (617)424-1057
URL: http://www.netconline.org/

Annual, January. Covers 800 individuals and 100 groups. Entries include: For individuals-Name, address, telephone, e-mail and fax indicating type or level of theater activity, theater and school affiliation. For groups-Name, address; telephone, box office, fax, e-mail, names and addresses of delegates. Arrangement: Alphabetical. Indexes: Members by Division.

★152★ The Official Southwest Talent
Directory

Cobb-Rendish Publishing
1920 Abrams Pkwy., Ste. 419
Dallas, TX 75214-6271
Fax: (214)855-0643

Annual, latest edition March, 1995. $25.00.
Covers over 500 adult and juvenile actors,
actresses, and models; motion picture and
audio/videotape production facilities in the
Southwest. Entries include: Name, acting or
performing specialties, and agency contact;
production services are presented in individual suppliers' ads. Arrangement: Talent classified by sex and age of performers; production sources classified by product or service.
Indexes: Personal name, ethnic group, talent
abilities.

★153★ Producers Directory

IFILM Publishing
1024 N Orange Dr.
Hollywood, CA 90038
Ph: (323)308-3490   Fax: (323)308-3493

Latest edition 46th, three times per year in
March, July, and November. $59.95 per
issue; $149.95 per year; $199.95 for online
subscription. Covers over 1,700 film and TV
production companies, studios, networks,
and TV shows, and over 7,700 creative
executives within those companies. Majority
of listings are located in Los Angeles and
New York. Entries include: Company name,
staff names and titles, address, phone, fax,
e-mail address, web site address, company
type, studio deals, and select credits. Arrangement: Alphabetical. Indexes: Company
type, studio deals, individual names.

★154★ Regional Theater Directory

American Theatre Works Inc.
PO Box 510
Dorset, VT 05251
Ph: (802)867-2223   Fax: (802)867-0144
URL: http://www.theatredirectories.com

Annual, May. $20.95. Covers regional theater companies and dinner theatres with
employment opportunities in acting, design,
production, and management. Entries include: Company name, address, phone,
name and title of contact; type of company,
activities, and size of house; whether union
affiliated, whether nonprofit or commercial;
year established; hiring procedure and number of positions hired annually, season;
description of stage; internships, description
of artistic policy and audience. Arrangement:
Geographical. Indexes: Company name,
type of plays produced.

★155★ Stage Managers Directory

Stage Managers' Association
Times Sq. Sta.
PO Box 275
New York, NY 10108-2020
Ph: (212)330-7019
URL: http://www.stagemanagers.org/
smdir.htm

Every few years. $20.00. Covers about 500
stage managers experienced in theater, bal-

let, opera, music, and other productions,
nationally. Entries include: Name, address,
phone, union affiliations, name of production
or theater company, position held, contract
or type of production (stock, opera, dance,
etc.), related skills, etc. Arrangement: Alphabetical. Indexes: Name, type of experience
(Broadway, Off-Broadway, opera, dance,
etc.), foreign language skill, geographical.

★156★ Summer Theater Directory

American Theatre Works Inc.
PO Box 510
Dorset, VT 05251
Ph: (802)867-2223   Fax: (802)867-0144
URL: http://www.theatredirectories.com

Annual, December. $20.95. Covers summer
theater companies, theme parks and cruise
lines that offer employment opportunities in
acting, design, production, and management; summer theater training programs.
Entries include: Company name, address,
phone, name and title of contact; type of
company, activities and size of house;
whether union affiliated, whether nonprofit or
commercial; year established; hiring procedure and number of positions hired annually,
season; description of stage; internships;
description of company's artistic goals and
audience. Arrangement: Geographical. Indexes: Company name.

★157★ Television Program Producers
Directory

infoUSA Inc.
5711 S 86th Cir.
Omaha, NE 68127-0347
Ph: (402)930-3500   Fax: (402)331-0176
Fr: 800-555-6124
URL: http://www.abii.com

Updated continuously; printed on request.
Number of listings: 2,062. Entries include:
Name, address, phone (including area
code), size of advertisement, year first in
"Yellow Pages," name of owner or manager,
number of employees. Compiled from telephone company "Yellow Pages," nationwide. Arrangement: Geographical.

★158★ Theatrical Agencies Directory

infoUSA Inc.
5711 S 86th Cir.
Omaha, NE 68127-0347
Ph: (402)930-3500   Fax: (402)331-0176
Fr: 800-555-6124
URL: http://www.abii.com

Updated continuously; printed on request.
Number of listings: 383. Entries include:
Name, address, phone, size of advertisement, name of owner or manager, number of
employees, year first in "Yellow Pages."
Compiled from telephone company "Yellow
Pages," nationwide. Arrangement: Geographical.

★159★ Theatrical Index

Theatrical Index Ltd.
888 8th Ave., 16th Fl.
New York, NY 10019
Ph: (212)586-6343

Weekly. $10.00 per issue; $105.00 for
monthly updates; $200.00 for bimonthly updates. Covers theatrical presentations in preproduction stage which are seeking investors; also covers producers, agents, and
theaters. Entries include: For productions-
Production name, brief details, contact. For
agents and producers-Name, address,
phone. For theaters-Name, address, box
office and backstage phone numbers.

★160★ Who's Who in the Motion
Picture Industry

Packard Publishing Co.
PO Box 2187
Beverly Hills, CA 90213
Ph: (626)791-5367

Annual, February; supplement. $24.95. Covers about 1,200 cinematographers, directors, producers, writers, and studio executives in the theatrical and television motion
picture industries. Entries include: For production companies and studios-Name, address, phone, names and titles of key personnel. For others-Name, company or agent
name, address, phone, credits. Arrangement: Classified by professional status (director, studio executive, etc.) in separate
sections for theatrical and television films.
Indexes: Alphabetical.

HANDBOOKS AND MANUALS

★161★ Acting A to Z: The Young
Person's Guide to a Stage or Screen
Career

Watson-Guptill Publications, Inc.
770 Broadway
New York, NY 10003
Ph: (646)654-5400   Fax: (646)654-5486
Fr: 800-323-9432

Katherine Mayfield. 1998. $16.95 (paper).
144 pages.

★162★ Acting in Commercials: A
Guide to Auditioning & Performing
on Camera

Watson-Guptill Publications, Inc.
770 Broadway
New York, NY 10003
Ph: (646)654-5400   Fax: (646)654-5486
Fr: 800-323-9432

Joan See. Second edition, 1998. $16.95
(paper). 192 pages.

★163★ Acting Professionally: Raw Facts about Careers in Acting
McGraw-Hill Companies
1212 Avenue of the Americas
New York, NY 10020
Ph: (212)904-2000   Fr: 800-323-4900
Robert Cohen. Fifth edition, 1997. $15.95 (paper). 177 pages. Includes bibliography.

★164★ An Actor's Guide to Getting Work
A & C Black
37 Soho Sq.
London W1D 3QZ, United Kingdom
Ph: 020 7758 0200
Simon Dunmore. Fourth edition. June 2004. $14.95 (paper). 224 pages.

★165★ The Actor's Guide to the Internet
Heinemann
88 Post Rd., W.
Westport, CT 06881-5007
Rob Kozlowski. 1999. $18.95 (paper).

★166★ Actor's Guide to Promoting Your Own Career
Smith & Kraus, Inc.
PO Box 127
Lyme, NH 03768
Ph: (603)643-6431   Fax: (603)643-1831
Fr: 800-895-4331
Glenn Alterman, editor. 1996. $11.95 (paper). Part of the Career Development and Actor's Guides Series.

★167★ The Actor's Guide Southeast: An Introductory Guide to the Southeast Regional Film & Television Market
Illustrata, Inc.
931 Monroe Dr., Ste. 102-301
Atlanta, GA 30308-1778
Ph: (404)784-7970   Fax: (404)786-4784
Fr: 800-594-3457
Nan McElroy and Melissa Ohlman-Roberge. Second edition, 2000. 128 pages.

★168★ Actors-Take Action: A Career Guide for the Competitive Actor
Heinemann
88 Post Rd. W
Westport, CT 06881-5007
Fr: 800-793-2154
Brian O'Neil. 1996. $13.95 (paper). 112 pages.

★169★ Actors Turned Directors: On Eliciting the Best Performance from an Actor and Other Secrets of Successful Directing
Silman-James Press
3624 Shannon Rd.
Los Angeles, CA 90027
Ph: (323)661-9922   Fax: (323)661-9933
Jon Stevens. 1997. $19.95. 300 pages. Guidelines for directors.

★170★ Agents on Actors: Sixty Professionals Share Their Secrets to Finding Work on the Stage and Screen
Watson-Guptill Publications, Incorporated
770 Broadway
New York, NY 10003
Ph: (646)654-5400   Fax: (646)654-5486
Fr: 800-323-9432
Hettie Lynne Hurtes. 2000. $18.95 (paper).

★171★ Back Stage Guide to Casting Directors: Who They Are, How They Work, What They Look for in Actors
Watson-Guptill Publications, Inc.
770 Broadway
New York, NY 10003
Ph: (646)654-5400   Fax: (646)654-5486
Fr: 800-323-9432
Hettie L. Hurtes. 1991. $18.95 (paper). Out of print.

★172★ Black State of the Arts: A Guide to Developing a Successful Career As a Black Performing Artist
BookWorld Services, Inc.
1933 Whitefield Park Loop
Sarasota, FL 34243
Ph: (941)758-8094   Fax: (941)753-9396
Fr: 800-444-2524
Tanya Kersey-Henley and Bruce Hawkins. Second edition, 1996. $29.95. Out of print. (paper).

★173★ Breaking into Commercials
Doubleday Direct
401 Franklin Ave.
Garden City, NY 11530
Ph: (516)873-4561   Fax: (516)873-4714
Terry Berland and Deborah Ouellette. 1997. $12.95 (paper). 272 pages.

★174★ Breaking into Film
Thomson Peterson's
202 Carnegie Ctr.
Box 67005
Princeton, NJ 08540
Fr: 800-338-3282
Kenna Mchugh. 1998. $14.95 (paper). Provides insight into jobs dealing with film and video and explains how to get a job in the film industry, with a list of key employers. Also offers advice from industry insiders and internship information.

★175★ Breaking into Television
Thomson Peterson's
202 Carnegie Ctr.
Box 67005
Princeton, NJ 08540
Fr: 800-338-3282
Weaver. 1998. $14.95 (paper). Explains how to get a job in the television industry, with a list of internship opportunities.

★176★ A Career Handbook for TV, Radio, Film, Video and Interactive Media
A & C Black
37 Soho Sq.
London W1D 3QZ, United Kingdom
Ph: 020 7758 0200
Shiona Llewellyn.

★177★ Career Information Center
Macmillan Publishing Co. Inc.
200 Old Tappan Rd.
Old Tappan, NJ 07675
Fr: 800-428-5331
Visual Education Center Staff. Seventh edition, 1999. $275.00. 2080 pages. This 13-volume set profiles over 600 occupations. Each occupational profile describes job duties, educational requirements, how to get the job, advancement possibilities, employment outlook, working conditions, earnings and benefits, and where to write for more information.

★178★ Career Opportunities in Theater and the Performing Arts
Facts on File, Inc.
132 W. 31st St., 17th Fl.
New York, NY 10001-2006
Ph: (212)967-8800   Fax: (212)967-9196
Fr: 800-322-8755
URL: http://www.factsonfile.com
Shelly Field. Second edition, 1999. $29.95; $18.95 (paper). 256 pages. Offers a complete range of information about job opportunities in the performing arts. Part of Career Opportunities Series.

★179★ Careers for Culture Lovers and Other Artsy Types
VGM Career Horizons
1221 Avenue of the Americas
New York, NY 10020
Ph: (212)904-2000   Fr: 800-323-4900
E-mail: ntcpub@tribune.com
Marjorie Eberts and Margaret Gisler. Second edition, 1999. $14.95; $9.95 (paper). 234 pages. Describes how to get work in a variety of fields related to art and culture. Opportunities include picture framer, curator, art restorer, symphony manager, disk jockey, music reviewer, dance teacher, choreographer, costume designer, theater manager, light designer, drama teacher, bookstore owner, interior decorator, antique store owner, and others.

★180★ Careers for Film Buffs and Other Hollywood Types

VGM Career Horizons
1221 Avenue of the Americas
New York, NY 10020
Ph: (212)904-2000   Fr: 800-323-4900
E-mail: ntcpub@tribune.com

Jaq Greenspon. 1994. $14.95; $9.95 (paper). 250 pages. Describes job descriptions in production, camera, sound, special effects, grips, electrical, makeup, costumes, etc.

★181★ Careers Inside the World of Sports and Entertainment

Rosen Publishing Group, Inc.
29 E. 21st St.
New York, NY 10010
Ph: (212)777-3017   Fax: 888-436-4643
Fr: 800-237-9932

Bruce McGothlin. 1995. $15.95. 64 pages. Out of print.

★182★ Careers for Night Owls and Other Insomniacs

McGraw-Hill Trade
2 Penn Plaza
New York, NY 10121
Ph: (212)904-2000   Fr: 800-722-4726
E-mail: ntcpub@tribune.com

Louise Miller. 1995. $14.95; $9.95 (paper). 160 pages.

★183★ Careers for the Stagestruck and Other Dramatic Types

McGraw-Hill Contemporary Books
1221 Avenue of the Americas
New York, NY 10020
Ph: (212)904-2000   Fr: 800-323-4900
E-mail: ntcpub@tribune.com

Lucia Mauro, 1997. $14.95; $9.95 (paper). 144 pages. Includes bibliographical references.

★184★ Commercialmania: The Successful TV Commercial Actor's Manual

Dog Gone Books
29 Yawl St., No. A
Marina del Rey, CA 90292-7159
Ph: (310)823-2704

Karl Preston. 1999. $24.95 (paper). 287 pages.

★185★ Getting into Films & Television: How to Find the Best Way In

Trans-Atlantic Publications, Inc.
311 Bainbridge St.
Philadelphia, PA 19147
Ph: (215)925-5083   Fax: (215)925-1912

Robert Angell. Sixth edition, 2000. $19.95 (paper). Part of the Jobs and Careers Series. 168 pages.

★186★ Great Jobs for Theater Majors

McGraw-Hill Companies
1221 Avenue of the Americas
New York, NY 10020
Ph: (212)904-2000   Fr: 800-323-4900
E-mail: ntcpub@tribune.com

Jan Goldberg, Stephen Lambert, Julie De-Galan. 1998. $11.95 (paper). 388 pages.

★187★ Hollywood, Here I Come!: An Insider's Guide to a Successful Acting & Modeling Career in Los Angeles

Yellow Deer Press
P.O. Box 7309A
Santa Monica, CA 90406-7309
Ph: (213)871-8755   Fr: 800-437-3267

Cynthia Hunter. 1999. $19.95.

★188★ How to Become a Working Actor

Carol Publishing Group
120 Enterprise Ave.
Secaucus, NJ 07094
Ph: (201)866-0490   Fax: (201)866-8159
Fr: 800-447-2665

Susan Wright. 1997. $10.95 (paper). 140 pages.

★189★ International Directory of Film, Photography, Video and Television

Penrose Press
PO Box 470925
San Francisco, CA 94147
Ph: (415)567-4157   Fax: (415)567-4165

Raymond Lavzzana and Denise Penrose, editors. Fifth edition, 1998. $77.00 (paper). 200 pages. Part of the International Directory of Design Series. Includes references for educational programs, professional organizations and periodical publications. The subjects covered span the range of subjects of interest to photographers, cinematographers & videographers practicing in entertainment & documentation industries, including photography, cinematography, filmaking, videography & electronic imaging. Contact information includes street addresses, telephone & fax numbers, e-mail addresses & URL links to home pages. This directory is one of ten supplemental directories that are domain-specific guides to educational programs; professional societies, trade organizations, scholarly journals, & trade magazines throughout the world.

★190★ It's Showtime: How to Perform on Television & Radio

Marketing Directions, Inc.
615 Queen St.
Southington, CT 06489
Ph: (860)276-2452   Fax: (860)276-2453
Fr: 800-562-4357

Brian Jud. 1997. $14.95 (paper). 100 pages.

★191★ Lights, Camera, Action!: Careers in Film, Television, & Video

Indiana University Press
601 N. Morton St.
Bloomington, IN 47404-3797
Ph: (812)855-4203   Fax: (812)855-7931
Fr: 800-842-6796

Josephine Langham. Second edition, 1996. $19.95 (paper).

★192★ The Los Angeles Agent Book

Sweden Press
Box 1612
Studio City, CA 91604
Ph: (818)995-4250   Fax: (818)995-4399

K. Callan. Seventh edition, 2001. $17.95 (paper). 315 pages. Describes the actor-agent relationship, provides guidance for selecting the right agent, and gives a list of agents in Los Angeles with background information on each.

★193★ The Lost Soul Companion: Comfort & Constructive Advice for Struggling Actors, Musicians, Artists, Writers & Other Free Spirits

Puckitt Press, Incorporated
P.O. Box 3248
Bloomington, IN 47402-3248
Ph: (812)331-4337

Susan M. Brackney. 2000. $10.00

★194★ The Media Jungle: A Survival Guide

Media Masters
872 Franklin Trace
Zionsville, IN 46077-1169
Ph: (317)733-9440   Fax: (317)873-4493

Carrie Van Dyke. 1996. $15.00. 92 pages.

★195★ The National Casting Guide

Peter Glenn Publications
42 Riverside Ave.
Westport, CT 06880
Ph: (203)227-4949   Fax: (203)227-6170
Fr: 888-332-6700

1998. $17.95.

★196★ 100 Best Careers in Entertainment

Macmillan Publishing Co. Inc.
200 Old Tappan Rd.
Old Tappan, NJ 07675
Fr: 800-428-5331

Shelly Field. 1995. $14.95 (paper). 352 pages.

★197★ Opportunities in Acting Careers

McGraw-Hill Contemporary Books
1221 Avenue of the Americas
New York, NY 10020
Ph: (212)904-2000   Fr: 800-323-4900
E-mail: ntcpub@tribune.com

Dick Moore. 1998. $14.95; $11.95 (paper).

198 pages. A guide to planning for and seeking opportunities in acting.

★198★ **Opportunities in Entertainment Careers**
McGraw-Hill Trade
2 Penn Plaza
New York, NY 10121
Ph: (212)904-2000   Fr: 800-722-4726
E-mail: ntcpub@tribune.com
Jan Goldberg. 1999. $14.95; $11.95 (paper). 160 pages.

★199★ **Opportunities in Film Careers**
McGraw-Hill Trade
2 Penn Plaza
New York, NY 10121
Ph: (212)904-2000   Fr: 800-722-4726
Jan Bone. 1998. $14.95; $11.95 (paper). 160 pages. Provides advice on obtaining a job in film and in corporate non-broadcast film/video production. Illustrated.

★200★ **Promoting Your Acting Career**
Allworth Press
10 E. 23rd St., Ste. 510
New York, NY 10010
Ph: (212)777-8395   Fax: (212)777-8261
Fr: 800-491-2808
Glenn Alterman. 1998. $18.95 (paper). 240 pages.

★201★ **Radio and Television Career Directory**
Thomson Gale
27500 Drake Rd.
Farmington Hills, MI 48331-3535
Ph: (248)699-GALE   Fax: 800-414-5043
Fr: 800-877-GALE
E-mail: galeord@gale.com
URL: http://www.gale.com
Bradley Morgan. Second edition, 1993. $39.00. 300 pages. Features extensive listings of contacts and entry-level job opportunities. Provides information on internships and sources of help-wanted ads.

★202★ **Resumes for Performing Arts Careers**
Vgm Career Horizons
1221 Avenue of the Americas
New York, NY 10020
Ph: (212)904-2000   Fr: 800-323-4900
E-mail: ntcpub@tribune.com
1997. $9.95 (paper). 462 pages.

★203★ **Role of a Lifetime: Four Professional Actors & How They Built Their Careers**
Watson-Guptill Publications, Inc.
770 Broadway
New York, NY 10003
Ph: (646)654-5400   Fax: (646)654-5486
Fr: 800-323-9432
Robert Simonson. 1999. $16.95 (paper). 176 pages.

★204★ **Smart Actors, Foolish Choices: A Self-Help Guide to Coping with the Emotional Stresses**
Watson-Guptill Publications, Inc.
770 Broadway
New York, NY 10003
Ph: (646)654-5400   Fax: (646)654-5486
Fr: 800-323-9432
Katherine Mayfield. 1996. $16.95 (paper). 176 pages.

★205★ **Theater Artist's Resource: The Watson-Guptill Guide to Workshops, Conferences & Artists' Colonies**
Watson-Guptill Publications, Inc.
770 Broadway
New York, NY 10003
Ph: (646)654-5400   Fax: (646)654-5486
Fr: 800-323-9432
1998. $19.95 (paper). Part of the Getting Your Act Together Series.

★206★ **Where the Jobs Are: The Hottest Careers for the 90s**
The Career Press, Inc.
3 Tice Rd.
PO Box 687
Franklin Lakes, NJ 07417-1322
Ph: (201)848-0310   Fax: (201)848-1727
Fr: 800-227-3371
Joyce Hadley. Third edition, 2000. $13.99 (paper). 400 pages. Out of print. Describes careers in fifteen general fields, from accounting to travel and hospitality.

★207★ **Working in Show Business: Behind-the-Scenes Careers in Theater, Film and Television**
Watson-Guptill Publications, Inc.
770 Broadway
New York, NY 10003
Ph: (646)654-5400   Fax: (646)654-5486
Fr: 800-323-9432
Lynne Rogers. 1997. $18.95 (paper). 400 pages.

EMPLOYMENT AGENCIES AND SEARCH FIRMS

★208★ **Century City Partners LLC**
PO Box 15747
Beverly Hills, CA 90209
Ph: (310)777-0240
Executive search firm.

★209★ **Filcro Media Staffing**
342 Madison Ave., Fl. 7
New York, NY 10017
Ph: (212)599-0909   Fax: (212)599-1023
Executive search firm for the entertainment industry.

★210★ **Howard Fischer Associates International Inc.**
1800 JFK Blvd., Fl. 7
Philadelphia, PA 19103-7401
Ph: (215)568-8363   Fax: (215)568-4815
Executive search firm. Branches in Campbell, CA and Boston, MA.

ONLINE JOB SOURCES AND SERVICES

★211★ **Mandy's International Film and TV Production Directory**
E-mail: Directory@atsmandy.com
URL: http://www.mandy.com/1/filmtvjobs.cfm
Description: Employment site intended for film and tv professionals. Employers may post free Jobs Offered listings. Job seekers may post free Jobs Wanted ads.

TRADESHOWS

★212★ **International Society for the Performing Arts Foundation Annual Conference**
International Society for the Performing Arts Foundation
17 Purdy Ave.
PO Box 909
Rye, NY 10580
Ph: (914)921-1550   Fax: (914)921-1593
E-mail: info@ispa.org
URL: http://ispa.org
Annual. **Primary Exhibits:** Information of performing artists agents and managers.

OTHER SOURCES

★213★ Academy of Television Arts and Sciences (ATAS)

5220 Lankershim Blvd.
North Hollywood, CA 91601
Ph: (818)754-2800   Fax: (818)761-2827
E-mail: todd@emmys.org
URL: http://www.emmys.org

Members: Professionals in the television and film industry. **Purpose:** To advance the arts and sciences of television through services to the industry in education, preservation of television programs, and information and community relations; to foster creative leadership in the television industry. **Activities:** Sponsors Television Academy Hall of Fame. Maintains library on television credits and historical material, the Television Academy Archives, and archives at UCLA of over 35,000 television programs. Offers internships to students. Holds luncheon and speakers series and meetings on problems of the various crafts.

★214★ Actors' Fund of America (AFA)

729 Seventh Ave., 10th FL.
New York, NY 10019
Ph: (212)221-7300   Fax: (212)764-0238
E-mail: jbeninca@actorsfund.org
URL: http://www.actorsfund.org

Description: Human service organization of the entertainment industry. Provides emergency financial assistance to those in need; makes available social services, counseling and psychotherapy, health and education services, and nursing home care and retirement housing. Conducts substance abuse programs and blood drives; sponsors survival jobs program to provide employment for those between engagements.

★215★ Alliance of Resident Theatres/ New York (ART/NY)

575 8th Ave., Ste 17 S.
New York, NY 10018
Ph: (212)244-6667   Fax: (212)714-1918
E-mail: artnewyork@aol.com
URL: http://www.offbroadwayonline.com

Description: Nonprofit professional theatres in New York City and interested theatre-related associations. Promotes recognition of the nonprofit theatre community. Provides members with administrative services and resources pertinent to their field. Facilitates discussion among the theatres; helps to solve real estate problems; serves as a public information source. Acts as advocate on behalf of members with government, corporate, and foundation funders to encourage greater support for New York's not-for-profit theatres. Sponsors seminars, roundtables, and individual consultations for members in areas such as financial management, board development and marketing. Organizes Passports to Off Broadway, an industry-wide marketing campaign.

★216★ American Association of Community Theatre (AACT)

8402 Briar Wood Cir.
Lago Vista, TX 78645
Ph: (512)267-0711   Fax: (512)267-0712
Fr: (866)687-2228
E-mail: info@aact.org
URL: http://www.aact.org

Description: Community theatre organizations; individuals involved in community theatre. Promotes excellence in community theatre through networking, workshops, publications, and festivals of community theatre productions.

★217★ American Film Marketing Association (AFMA)

10850 Wilshire Blvd., 9th Fl.
Los Angeles, CA 90024-4321
Ph: (310)446-1000   Fax: (310)446-1600
E-mail: info@afma.com
URL: http://www.afma.com

Description: Trade association for the worldwide independent film and television industry. Contributes to negotiations with foreign producer associations; developed standardized theatrical and video contracts in English, French, Italian, and Spanish. Established and maintains the AFMA International Arbitration Tribunal, a system through which prominent entertainment attorneys throughout the world assist members and consenting clients in reaching equitable and binding agreements. Facilitates the formulation of policies, standardized private and governmental contracts, and the exchange of information and experience among members. Produces the American Film Market (AFM), the largest international motion picture trade event in the World.

★218★ Association of Independent Video and Filmmakers (AIVF)

304 Hudson St., 6th Fl.
New York, NY 10013
Ph: (212)807-1400   Fax: (212)463-8519
E-mail: info@aivf.org
URL: http://www.aivf.org

Description: Represents independent media artists working at all levels across all genres. Mission is to increase the creative and professional opportunities for independent video and filmmakers and to enhance the growth of independent media by providing services, advocacy, and information. Goals are to create new opportunities for the field; to engender a strong sense of community among the very diverse constituencies of independent media artists; and to promote media arts to a broader public.

★219★ Association for Theatre in Higher Education (ATHE)

PO Box 69
Downers Grove, IL 60515
Ph: (630)964-1940   Fax: (630)964-1941
Fr: 888-284-3737
E-mail: info@athe.org
URL: http://www.athe.org

Members: Universities, colleges, and professional education programs; artists, scholars, teachers, and other individuals; students. **Purpose:** Promotes the exchange of information among individuals engaged in theatre study and research, performance, and crafts. Provides advocacy and support services. Encourages excellence in postsecondary theatre training, production, and scholarship.

★220★ Black Filmmaker Foundation (BFF)

670 Broadway, Ste. 300
New York, NY 10012
Ph: (212)253-1690   Fax: (212)253-1689
E-mail: info@dvrepublic.com
URL: http://www.dvrepublic.com

Purpose: Assists emerging filmmakers and builds audiences for their work. Produces the annual Summit: A business Caucus of People of Color in Motion Pictures and Television. Initiative dedicated to issues of human rights and social justice.

★221★ Directors Guild of America (DGA)

7920 Sunset Blvd.
Los Angeles, CA 90046
Ph: (310)289-2000   Fax: (310)289-2029
Fr: 800-420-4173
E-mail: dga@dga.org
URL: http://www.dga.org

Purpose: Independent. Negotiates agreements for members.

★222★ Media and the Arts Occupations

Delphi Productions
3160 4th St.
Boulder, CO 80304
Fax: (303)443-4022   Fr: 888-443-2400
URL: http://www.delphivideo.com

$95.00. 50 minutes. Part of the Careers for the 21st Century Video Library.

★223★ Media Communications Association International (MCA-I)

401 N Michigan Ave., No. 2200
Chicago, IL 60611
Ph: (312)321-5161   Fax: (312)673-6716
E-mail: info@mca-i.org
URL: http://www.mca-i.org

Description: Individuals engaged in multimedia communications needs analysis, scriptwriting, producing, directing, consulting, and operations management in the video, multimedia, and film fields. Seeks to advance the benefits and image of media communications professionals.

★224★ New England Theatre Conference (NETC)

Northeastern University
360 Huntington Ave.
Boston, MA 02115
Ph: (617)424-9275   Fax: (617)424-1057

E-mail: mail@netconline.org
URL: http://netconline.org/

Members: Individuals and theatre-producing groups in New England who are actively engaged in or have a particular interest in theatre activity either professionally or as an avocation. **Purpose:** Works to develop, expand, and assist theatre activity on community, educational, and professional levels in New England. **Activities:** Activities include: auditions for jobs in New England summer theatres; workshops on performance, administrative, and technical aspects of production.

★225★ **Non-Traditional Casting Project (NTCP)**
1560 Broadway, Ste. 1600
New York, NY 10036
Ph: (212)730-4750   Fax: (212)730-4820
E-mail: info@ntcp.org
URL: http://www.ntcp.org

Description: Advocates the elimination of discrimination in theatre, film, and television. Works to increase the employment of artists of color and artists with disabilities by encouraging cultural diversity throughout the artistic process and all levels of production and administration, and offering consultative services. Maintains the Artist Files containing pictures and resumes of 3,000 actors, directors, writers, designers, and stage managers of color as well as those with disabilities. Sponsors forums.

★226★ **Southeastern Theatre Conference (SETC)**
PO Box 9868
Greensboro, NC 27429-0868
Ph: (336)272-3645   Fax: (336)272-8810
E-mail: setc@mindspring.com
URL: http://www.setc.org/

Members: Individuals and theatre organizations involved in university, college, community, professional, children's, and secondary school theatres. **Purpose:** Purpose is to bring together people interested in theatre and theatre artists and craftsmen from 10 southeastern states of the U.S. in order to promote high standards and to stimulate creativity in all phases of theatrical endeavor. **Activities:** Services include: central office for business and communication; job contact service; new play project; annual auditions for summer indoor and outdoor theatres; fall auditions for professional theatres. Compiles statistics.

★227★ **Women in Film (WIF)**
8857 W. Olympic Blvd., No. 201
Beverly Hills, CA 90211-3605
Ph: (310)657-5144   Fax: (310)657-5154
E-mail: info@wif.com
URL: http://www.wif.org

Purpose: Supports women in the film and television industry and serves as a network for information on qualified women in the entertainment field. **Activities:** Sponsors screenings and discussions of pertinent issues. Provides speakers' bureau. Maintains Women in Film Foundation, which offers financial assistance to women for education, research, and/or completion of film projects.

Actuaries

SOURCES OF HELP-WANTED ADS

★228★ Actuarial Digest

Actuarial Digest
PO Box 1127
Ponte Vedra Beach, FL 32004
Ph: (904)273-1245

Description: Bimonthly. Covers issues of concern to working actuaries. Recurring features include letters to the editor, news of research, news of educational opportunities, job listings, book reviews, notices of publications available, and a column titled What's New.

★229★ ASCnet Quarterly

Applied Systems Client Network
801 Douglas Ave., Ste. 205
Altamonte Springs, FL 32714
Ph: (407)869-0404   Fax: (407)869-0418

Quarterly. Subscription included in membership. Professional magazine covering technical information, association news, and industry information for insurance professionals.

★230★ Best's Review

A.M. Best Co.
Ambest Rd.
Oldwick, NJ 08858
Fax: (908)439-2200
E-mail: best'sreview@ambest.com
URL: http://www.bestreview.com

Monthly. $21.00/year for individuals; $7.50 for single issue. Magazine covering issues and trends for the management personnel of life/health insurers, the agents, and brokers who market their products.

★231★ Business Insurance

Crain Communications Inc.
711 Third Ave.
New York, NY 10017-4036
Ph: (212)210-0100   Fax: (212)210-0244
Fr: 800-446-1420
URL: http://www.businessinsurance.com

Weekly. $97.00/year for individuals. International newsweekly reporting on corporate risk and employee benefit management news.

★232★ Contingencies

American Academy of Actuaries
1100 17th St. NW, 7th Fl.
Washington, DC 20036
Ph: (202)223-8196   Fax: (202)872-1948
E-mail: contingencies@actuary.org

Bimonthly. $24.00/year. Magazine on actuarial science and its relevance to current business problems and social issues.

★233★ The Future Actuary

Society of Actuaries
475 N Martingale, Ste. 800
Schaumburg, IL 60173-2226
Ph: (847)706-3500   Fax: (847)706-3599
URL: http://www.soa.org/publications

Description: Three issues/year. Provides actuarial students with the latest information on jobs, internships, study techniques, career development, professional conduct, and ethics. Recurring features include a calendar of events, news of educational opportunities, and job listings.

★234★ National Underwriter Property and Casualty/Risk and Benefits Management

National Underwriter Co.
5081 Olympic Blvd.
Erlanger, KY 41018
Ph: (859)692-2100   Fax: 800-874-1916
Fr: 800-543-0874
E-mail: nup&c@nuco.com

Weekly. $89.00/year. Newsweekly for agents, brokers, executives, and managers in risk and benefit insurance.

★235★ PENSION Management

Primedia Business
6151 Powers Ferry Rd.
Atlanta, GA 30339
Ph: (770)955-2500   Fax: (770)618-0348

Monthly. $68.00/year for individuals. Magazine on pension investment and fund administration.

★236★ Pensions & Investments

Crain Communications Inc.
711 Third Ave.
New York, NY 10017-4036
Ph: (212)210-0100   Fax: (212)210-0244
Fr: 800-446-1420

Biweekly. $205.00/year. Magazine containing news and features on investment management, pension management, corporate finance, and cash management.

EMPLOYER DIRECTORIES AND NETWORKING LISTS

★237★ Best's Insurance Reports

A.M. Best Co.
Ambest Rd.
Oldwick, NJ 08858
Ph: (908)439-2200   Fax: (908)439-2688
URL: http://www.ambest.com

Annual, summer. $1,495.00 for CD-ROM; $830.00 for print. Published in three editions: Life-health insurance, covering about 1,750 companies, property-casualty insurance, covering over 3,200 companies; and international, covering more than 1,200 insurers. Each edition lists state insurance commissioners and related companies and agencies (mutual funds, worker compensation funds, underwriting agencies, etc.). Entries include: For each company-Company name, address, phone; history; states in which licensed; names of officers and directors; financial data; financial analysis and Best's rating. Arrangement: Alphabetical.

★238★ Insurance Almanac

Underwriter Printing and Publishing Co.
50 E Palisade Ave.
Englewood, NJ 07631
Ph: (201)569-8808   Fax: (201)569-8817
Fr: 800-526-4700

Annual, July. $175.00. Covers over 3,000 insurance companies that write fire, casualty, accident and health, life, and Lloyd's policies; also lists mutual and reciprocal companies. Includes national, state, and local insurance associations; state insurance officials; and about 800 agents, brokers, actuaries, and adjusters. Entries include: For companies-Company name, address, phone, names of officers and directors, lines written, territory covered; for larger firms, some history and financial data. For associations-Name, address, names of staff and officers, place and date of meetings. For agents, brokers, etc.-Name, address. Arrangement: Classified by insurance lines, type of activity, etc. Indexes: Company name.

★239★ Insurance Phone Book and Directory

Douglas Publications Inc.
2807 N Parham Rd.,64 Bldg., Ste. 200
Richmond, VA 23294
Ph: (804)762-9600   Fax: (804)217-8999
Fr: 800-794-6086
URL: http://www.douglaspublications.com

Annual. $99.50. Covers about 4,000 life, accident and health, worker's compensation, auto, fire and casualty, marine, surety, and other insurance companies. Entries include: Company name, address, phone, fax, toll-free number, type of insurance provided. Arrangement: Alphabetical.

★240★ Mergent Bank and Finance Manual

Mergent Inc.
5250 77 Center Dr., Ste. 150
Charlotte, NC 28217
Ph: (704)559-7601   Fax: (704)559-6945
Fr: 800-342-5647
URL: http://www.mergent.com

Annual, July; supplements in 'Mergent Bank & Finance News Reports'. $2,095.00. Covers in four volumes, over 12,000 national, state, and private banks, savings and loans, mutual funds, unit investment trusts, and insurance and real estate companies in the United States. Entries include: Company name, headquarters and branch offices, phones, names and titles of principal executives, directors, history, Moody's rating, and extensive financial and statistical data. Arrangement: Classified by type of business. Indexes: Company name.

★241★ Who's Who in Insurance

Underwriter Printing and Publishing Co.
50 E Palisade Ave.
Englewood, NJ 07631
Ph: (201)569-8808   Fax: (201)569-8817
Fr: 800-526-4700

Annual, February. $150.00. Covers over

5,000 insurance officials, brokers, agents, and buyers. Entries include: Name, title, company name, address, home address, educational background, professional club and association memberships, personal and career data. Arrangement: Alphabetical.

HANDBOOKS AND MANUALS

★242★ Actuaries' Survival Guide: How to Succeed in One of the Most Desirable Professions

Elsevier Science & Technology Books
525 B St., Ste. 1900
San Diego, CA 92101
Ph: (781)313-4700

Fred E. Szabo. 2004. $39.95. 300 pages. Explores the function of actuaries.

★243★ Career Information Center

Macmillan Publishing Co. Inc.
200 Old Tappan Rd.
Old Tappan, NJ 07675
Fr: 800-428-5331

Visual Education Center Staff. Seventh edition, 1999. $275.00. 2080 pages. This 13-volume set profiles over 600 occupations. Each occupational profile describes job duties, educational requirements, how to get the job, advancement possibilities, employment outlook, working conditions, earnings and benefits, and where to write for more information.

★244★ Careers for Number Crunchers and Other Quantitative Types

McGraw-Hill Trade
2 Penn Plaza
New York, NY 10121
Ph: (212)904-2000   Fr: 800-722-4726
E-mail: ntcpub@tribune.com

Rebecca Burnett. Second edition, 2002. $15.95; $12.95 (paper). 192 pages. Provides information to math-oriented job hunters on how to become statisticians, field researchers, computer programmers, stock analysts, investment managers, bankers, engineers, accountants, underwriters, economists, market analysts, mathematicians, systems analysts, and more.

★245★ Opportunities in Insurance Careers

McGraw-Hill/Contemporary Books
1221 Avenue of the Americas
New York, NY 10020
Ph: (212)904-2000   Fr: 800-323-4900
E-mail: ntcpub@tribune.com

Robert Schrayer. Revised, 1999. $14.95; $11.95 (paper). 148 pages. A guide to planning for and seeking opportunities in the field. Contains bibliography and illustrations.

EMPLOYMENT AGENCIES AND SEARCH FIRMS

★246★ The Alexander Group

2700 Post Oak Blvd., Ste. 2400
Houston, TX 77056
Ph: (713)993-7900   Fax: (713)993-7979

Executive search firm. Second location in San Francisco.

★247★ Godfrey Personnel Inc.

300 W. Adams, Ste. 612
Chicago, IL 60606-5194
Ph: (312)236-4455   Fax: (312)580-6292
E-mail: jim@godfreypersonnel.com
URL: http://ww.godfreypersonnel.com

Search firm specializing in insurance industry.

★248★ International Insurance Personnel, Inc.

300 W. Wieuca Rd., Bldg. 2, Ste. 101
Atlanta, GA 30342
Ph: (404)255-9710
E-mail: info@intlinspersonnel.com
URL: http://www.intlinspersonnel.com/inter-imstafing.htm

Employment agency specializing in the area of insurance.

★249★ Questor Consultants, Inc.

2515 N. Broad St.
Colmar, PA 18915
Ph: (215)997-9262   Fax: (215)997-9226
E-mail: jobs@questorconsultants.com
URL: http://www.questorconsultants.com

Executive search firm specializing in the insurance and legal fields.

ONLINE JOB SOURCES AND SERVICES

★250★ Financial Job Network
E-mail: info@atsfjn.com
URL: http://www.fjn.com

Description: Contains information on international and national employment opportunities for those in the financial job market. Job listings may be submitted, as well as resumes. **Main files include:** Testimonials, Calendar, Corporate Listings, FJN Clients, more. **Fee:** Free to candidates.

★251★ Great Insurance Jobs
URL: http://www.greatinsurancejobs.com

Description: Contains varied insurance positions. Job seekers may browse employee profiles, post resumes, and read descriptions of hundreds of recently-posted insurance jobs.

★252★ Insurance National Search, Inc.
E-mail: stacy@atsinsurancerecruiters.com
URL: http://www.insurancerecruiters.com

Description: Contains lists of recruiters (listed by department and line of business) and available insurance positions. **Main files include:** Recruiter Resources, Recruiters Roundtable Discussion Forum, Job Listing Submission Form, Candidate Listing Submission Form. Visitors can also search by job position.

TRADESHOWS

★253★ Public Agency Risk Managers Association Convention
Public Agency Risk Managers Association
PO Box 6810
San Jose, CA 95150
Ph: (408)865-6930   Fax: 888-412-5913
Fr: 888-907-2762
E-mail: BFrancis@PARMA.com

Annual. **Primary Exhibits:** Risk management equipment, supplies, and services.

OTHER SOURCES

★254★ *Actuaries*
Evon Publishing
832 N 7th Ave.
Iron River, MI 49935
Ph: (906)265-3190

Audiocassette. 1996. $16.95. 32 minutes. Part of the Careers and Vocational Guidance Series. Provides information about the nature of the work, educational requirements, employment outlook, earnings, and work conditions as well as additional related information.

★255★ American Academy of Actuaries
1100 17th St. NW, 7th Fl.
Washington, DC 20036
Ph: (202)223-8196   Fax: (202)872-1948
E-mail: lawson@actuary.org
URL: http://www.actuary.org

Description: Ensures that the American public recognizes and benefits from the independent expertise of the actuarial profession in the formulation of public policy and the adherence of actuaries to high professional standards in discharging their responsibilities. The academy was founded in 1965 by 4 specialty actuarial associations in the U.S. to represent the entire profession: Casualty Actuarial Society; Conference of Actuaries in Public Practice (now Conference of Consulting Actuaries); Society of Actuaries;

Fraternal Actuarial Association (now defunct). Maintains speakers' bureau.

★256★ American Council of Life Insurers (ACLI)
101 Constitution Ave., NW, Ste. 700
Washington, DC 20001-2133
Ph: (202)624-2000   Fax: (202)624-2319
E-mail: acli@acli.com
URL: http://www.acli.com

Description: National trade association that represents the interests of legal reserve life insurance companies in legislative, regulatory and judicial matters at the federal, state and municipal levels of government and at the NAIC. Its member companies hold the overwhelming majority of the life insurance in force in the United States.

★257★ American Society of Pension Actuaries (ASPA)
4245 N Fairfax Dr., Ste. 750
Arlington, VA 22203
Ph: (703)516-9300   Fax: (703)516-9308
E-mail: aspa@aspa.org
URL: http://www.aspa.org

Members: Individuals involved in the consulting, administrative, and design aspects of the employee benefit business. **Purpose:** Promotes high standards in the profession; provides nine-part educational program.

★258★ Casualty Actuarial Society (CAS)
1100 N Glebe Rd., Ste. 600
Arlington, VA 22201
Ph: (703)276-3100   Fax: (703)276-3108
E-mail: office@casact.org
URL: http://www.casact.org

Description: Professional society of property/casualty actuaries. Seeks to advance the body of knowledge of actuarial science applied to property, casualty and similar risk exposures, to maintain qualification standards, promote high standards of conduct and competence, and increase awareness of actuarial science. Examinations required for membership.

★259★ Conference of Consulting Actuaries (CCA)
1110 W. Lake Cook Rd., Ste. 235
Buffalo Grove, IL 60089-1968
Ph: (847)419-9090   Fax: (847)419-9091
E-mail: cca@ccactuaries.org
URL: http://www.ccactuaries.org

Description: Full-time consulting actuaries or governmental actuaries.

★260★ Insurance Information Institute (III)
110 William St.
New York, NY 10038
Ph: (212)346-5500   Fax: (212)791-1807
Fr: 800-331-9146

E-mail: info@iii.org
URL: http://www.iii.org

Description: Property and casualty insurance companies. Provides information and educational services to mass media, educational institutions, trade associations, businesses, government agencies, and the public.

★261★ LOMA
2300 Windy Ridge Pkwy., Ste. 600
Atlanta, GA 30339-8443
Ph: (770)951-1770   Fax: (770)984-0441
E-mail: marketing@loma.org
URL: http://www.loma.org/

Description: Life and health insurance companies and financial services in the U.S. and Canada; and overseas in 45 countries; affiliate members are firms that provide professional support to member companies. Provides research, information, training, and educational activities in areas of operations and systems, human resources, financial planning and employee development. Administers FLMI Insurance Education Program, which awards FLMI (Fellow, Life Management Institute) designation to those who complete the ten-examination program.

★262★ National Association of Insurance Women International (NAIW)
1847 E 15th St.
PO Box 4410
Tulsa, OK 74104
Fax: (918)743-1968   Fr: 800-766-6249
E-mail: joinnaiw@naiw.org
URL: http://www.naiw.org

Members: Insurance industry professionals. **Purpose:** Promotes continuing education and networking for the professional advancement of its members. **Activities:** Offers education programs, meetings, services, and leadership opportunities. Provides a forum to learn about other disciplines in the insurance industry.

★263★ Society of Actuaries (SOA)
475 N Martingale Rd., Ste. 800
Schaumburg, IL 60173-2226
Ph: (847)706-3500   Fax: (847)706-3599
E-mail: ssandford@soa.org
URL: http://www.soa.org

Description: Professional organization of individuals trained in the application of mathematical probabilities to the design of insurance, pension, and employee benefit programs. Sponsors series of examinations leading to designation of fellow or associate in the society. Maintains speakers' bureau; conducts educational and research programs.

Acupuncturists

★264★ *Acupressure News*
Jin Shin Do Foundation
1084 G San Miguel Cyn. Rd.
Watsonville, CA 95076
Ph: (831)763-7702   Fax: (831)763-1551
URL: http://www.jinshindo.com

Description: Annual. Provides information on bodymind acupressure, news, and main contacts in the U.S., Canada, and Europe. Features a product catalog, a class catalog and articles.

EMPLOYER DIRECTORIES AND NETWORKING LISTS

★265★ *Acupuncture Directory*
infoUSA Inc.
5711 S 86th Cir.
Omaha, NE 68127-0347
Ph: (402)930-3500   Fax: (402)331-0176
Fr: 800-555-6124
URL: http://www.abii.com

Annual. Number of listings: 8,824. Entries include: Name, address, phone (including area code), size of advertisement, year first in "Yellow Pages," name of owner or manager, number of employees. Compiled from telephone company "Yellow Pages," nationwide. Arrangement: Geographical.

★266★ *The Gale Encyclopedia of Alternative Medicine*
Thomson Gale
27500 Drake Rd.
Farmington Hills, MI 48331-3535
Ph: (248)699-4253   Fax: (248)699-8065
Fr: 800-877-GALE
URL: http://www.gale.com

First edition Dec. 2000; new edition expected Dec. 2004. $375.00. Publication includes: Listing of organizations relevant to the alternative medicine industry. Principal content of publication is a discussion of 150 different types of modern-day therapies being practiced including reflexology, acupressure, acupuncture, biofeedback and yoga along with 275 conditions and diseases, 300 herbs and plants used, and 39 biographies of pioneers in the field.

★267★ *Health & Wellness Resource Center-Alternative Health Module*
Thomson Gale
27500 Drake Rd.
Farmington Hills, MI 48331-3535
Ph: (248)699-4253   Fax: (248)699-8065
Fr: 800-877-GALE
URL: http://www.gale.com

Database includes: Focused upon alternative medicine topics this information is located in the Health Organization Directory component: listings of agencies, schools and organizations; journals, newsletters, and publishers websites; hospitals, health care facilities, programs and special care. Data is derived from the Medical and Health Information Directory. Entries include: Contact information. Principal content of database is a medical encyclopedia, drug and herb locator, health assessment tools, medical dictionary, links to other sites, and health news and includes references to homeopathic treatments, yoga, massage therapy, etc.

HANDBOOKS AND MANUALS

★268★ *Careers in Alternative Medicine*
Rosen Publishing Group, Inc.
29 E. 21st St.
New York, NY 10010
Ph: (212)777-3017   Fax: 888-436-4643
Fr: 800-237-9932

Alan Steinfeld. 2000. $18.95. 192 pages. Presents different ways to become involved in alternative medicine.

★269★ *A Manual of Acupuncture*
Eastland Press
3257 16th Ave. W, No. 2
Seattle, WA 98119

Peter Deadman, Kevin Baker, and Mazin Al-Khafaji. 1998. $140.00. 670 pages. Describes and illustrates the channels and collaterals, the various categories of points, and methods of selection, location, and needling.

★270★ *Opportunities in Health and Medical Careers*
McGraw-Hill Trade
2 Penn Plaza
New York, NY 10121
Ph: (212)904-2000   Fr: 800-722-4726

I. Donald Snook, Jr. and Leo D'Orazio. 1997. $14.95; $11.95 (paper). 202 pages. Covers the full range of medical and health occupations. Illustrated.

★271★ *Opportunities in Holistic Health Care Careers*
McGraw-Hill/Contemporary Books
1221 Avenue of the Americas
New York, NY 10020
Ph: (212)904-2000   Fr: 800-323-4900
E-mail: ntcpub@tribune.com

Gillian Tierney. 1999. $14.95; $11.95 (paper). 160 pages.

★272★ *Planning Your Career in Alternative Medicine*
Avery Publishing Group, Inc.
120 Old Broadway
Garden City Park, NY 11040

Lyons. 2000. $22.95. $16.95 (paper). 522 pages. Provides information on getting started in a wide range of alternative medicine careers.

ONLINE JOB SOURCES AND SERVICES

★273★ Acupuncture Today

PO Box 4139
Huntington Beach, CA 92605-4139
Ph: (714)230-3150   Fax: (714)899-4273
URL: http://www.acupuncturetoday.com

Description: Provides the latest news, articles and featured items that are of interest to, and can be implemented by, the acupuncture and Oriental medicine profession.

★274★ Medhunters.com

E-mail: info@medhunters.com
URL: http://www.medhunters.com

Description: Career search site for jobs in all health care specialties; educational resources; visa and licensing information for relocation; interesting articles; relocation tools; links to professional organizations and general resources.

★275★ Medzilla

URL: http://www.medzilla.com

Description: General medical website which matches employers and job hunters to their ideal employees and jobs through search capabilities. **Main files include:** Post Jobs, Search Resumes, Post Resumes, Search Jobs, Head Hunters, Articles, Salary Survey.

★276★ ProHealthJobs

E-mail: sales@prohealthjobs.com
URL: http://www.prohealthjobs.com

Description: Career resources site for the medical and health care field. Lists professional opportunities, product information, continuing education and open positions.

OTHER SOURCES

★277★ Accreditation Commission for Acupuncture and Oriental Medicine (ACAOM)

7501 Greenway Ctr. Dr., Ste. 820
Greenbelt, MD 20770
Ph: (301)313-0855   Fax: (301)313-0912
E-mail: 73352.2467@compuserve.com
URL: http://www.acaom.org

Description: Acts as an independent body to evaluate first professional master's degree and first professional master's level certificate and diploma programs in acupuncture and first professional master's degree and first professional master's level certificate and diploma programs in Oriental medicine with concentrations in both acupuncture and herbal therapy for a level of performance, integrity and quality that entitles them to the confidence of the educational community and the public they serve. Also acts to evaluate doctoral programs in oriental medicine. Establishes accreditation criteria, arranges site visits, evaluates those programs that desire accredited status and publicly designates those programs that meet the criteria.

★278★ Acupuncture and Oriental Medicine Alliance

6405 43rd Avenue Ct., NW Ste. B
Gig Harbor, WA 98335
Ph: (253)851-6896   Fax: (253)851-6883
URL: http://AOMAlliance.org

Description: Offers free referrals from database of over 12,000 acupuncturists who are either state licensed or National Board Certified, plus information on acupuncture and oriental medicine treatment, colleges, professional issues.

★279★ American Academy of Medical Acupuncture

4929 Wilshire Blvd., Ste. 428
Los Angeles, CA 90010
Ph: (323)937-5514   Fax: (323)937-0959
E-mail: jdowden@prodigy.net
URL: http://www.medicalacupuncture.org

Members: Professional society of physicians and osteopaths who utilize acupuncture in their practices. **Purpose:** Provides ongoing training and information related to the Chinese practice of puncturing the body at specific points to cure disease or relieve pain. **Activities:** Offers educational and research programs.

★280★ California State Oriental Medical Association

2710 X St., Ste. 2A
Sacramento, CA 95818
Fax: (916)455-0356   Fr: 800-477-4564
E-mail: office@csomaonline.org
URL: http://www.csomaonline.org

Description: Offers free referrals to over 800 California-based member health professionals who practice Acupuncture and Oriental Medicine.

★281★ Council of Colleges of Acupuncture and Oriental Medicine (CCAOM)

7501 Greenway Center Dr., Ste. 820
Greenbelt, MD 20770
Ph: (301)313-0868   Fax: (301)313-0869
E-mail: ccaom@compuserve.com
URL: http://www.ccaom.org

Description: Acupuncture and oriental medicine colleges. Purposes are: to advance the status of acupuncture and oriental medicine through educational programs; to provide high-quality classroom and clinical instruction; to promote the improvement of research and teaching methods.

★282★ Health Assessment & Treating Occupations

Delphi Productions
3160 4th St.
Boulder, CO 80304
Fax: (303)443-4022   Fr: 888-443-2400
URL: http://www.delphivideo.com

$95.00. 50 minutes. Part of the Careers for the 21st Century Video Library.

★283★ Health Service Occupations

Delphi Productions
3160 4th St.
Boulder, CO 80304
Fax: (303)443-4022   Fr: 888-443-2400
URL: http://www.delphivideo.com

$95.00. 50 minutes. Part of the Careers for the 21st Century Video Library.

★284★ International Veterinary Acupuncture Society (IVAS)

PO Box 271395
Fort Collins, CO 80527-1395
Ph: (970)266-0660   Fax: (970)266-0777
E-mail: office@ivas.org
URL: http://www.ivas.org

Description: Veterinarians and veterinary students. Encourages knowledge and research of the philosophy, technique, and practice of veterinary acupuncture. Fosters high standards in the field; promotes scientific investigation. Accumulates resources for scientific research and education; collects data concerning clinical and research cases where animals have been treated with acupuncture; disseminates information to veterinary students, practitioners, other scientific groups, and the public. Offers 120 contact hour basic veterinary acupuncture course; administers certification examination; also offers advanced traditional Chinese herbal veterinary medicine.

★285★ Medicine & Related Occupations

Delphi Productions
3160 4th St.
Boulder, CO 80304
Fax: (303)443-4022   Fr: 888-443-2400
URL: http://www.delphivideo.com

$95.00. 45 minutes. Part of the Careers for the 21st Century Video Library.

★286★ National Certification Commission for Acupuncture and Oriental Medicine (NCCAOM)

11 Canal Center Plaza, Ste. 300
Alexandria, VA 22314
Ph: (703)548-9004   Fax: (703)548-9079
E-mail: info@nccaom.org
URL: http://www.nccaom.org

Description: National certification agency for practitioners of acupuncture, Chinese herbology, and Asian bodywork therapy in the United States. **Purpose:** Establishes and maintains standards of competence for the safe and effective practice of Oriental medicine; to evaluate an applicant's qualifications in relation to these established standards through the administration of national board examinations; to certify practitioners who meet these standards. Acts as consultant to state agencies in regulation, certification, and licensing of the practice of acupuncture and Oriental medicine. of acupuncture and Oriental medicine.

Administrative Assistants

SOURCES OF HELP-WANTED ADS

★287★ Journal of Staff Development

National Staff Development Council
PO Box 240
Oxford, OH 45056
Ph: (513)523-6029   Fax: (513)523-0638
Fr: 800-727-7288

Quarterly. Professional journal covering administration issues.

★288★ OfficePRO

Stratton Publishing and Marketing Inc.
5501 Backlick Rd., Ste. 240
Springfield, VA 22151
Ph: (703)914-9200   Fax: (703)914-6777
E-mail: officepromag@strattonpub.com

$25.00/year for individuals. Magazine for administrative assistants, office managers, and secretaries featuring information on trends in business, technology, career development, and management.

★289★ Personal Report for the Administrative Professional

National Institute of Business
 Management
1750 Old Meadow Rd., Ste. 302
McLean, VA 22102
Ph: (703)905-8000   Fax: (703)905-8042
Fr: 800-543-2049
E-mail: customer@nibm.net

Description: Monthly. Advises secretaries and administrative assistants concerning career, workload, supervisors, coworkers, and personal life. Recurring features include letters to the editor, interviews, and Skills Check.

★290★ Supply Chain Management Review

Reed Business Information
275 Washington St.
Newton, MA 02458-1630
Ph: (617)964-3030

Bimonthly. Publication covering business and management.

EMPLOYER DIRECTORIES AND NETWORKING LISTS

★291★ Peterson's Job Opportunities for Business Majors

Thomson Peterson's
Princeton Pke. Corporate Ctr., 2000
 Lenox Dr.
PO Box 67005
Lawrenceville, NJ 08648
Ph: (609)896-1800   Fax: (609)896-4531
Fr: 800-338-3282
URL: http://www.petersons.com

Irregular, latest edition 2000 - 16th ed. $18.95. Covers the 2,000 largest U.S. employers hiring in several fields, including financial services, management consulting, consumer products, and media/ entertainment. Entries include: Organization name, address, phone, name and title of contact, number of employees, type of organization. Arrangement: Alphabetical. Indexes: Type of organization.

HANDBOOKS AND MANUALS

★292★ Basic Administrative Law for Paralegals

Aspen Publishers Inc.
1185 Avenue of the Americas, 37th Fl.
New York, NY 10036
Ph: (212)597-0200   Fax: (212)597-0338
Fr: 800-234-1660

Anne Adams. 2002. $70.95. 358 Pages. Explore the basics of Administrative Law.

★293★ Careers Inside the World of Offices

Rosen Publishing Group, Inc.
29 E. 21st St.
New York, NY 10010
Ph: (212)777-3017   Fax: 888-436-4643
Fr: 800-237-9932

Carolyn Simpson. Revised edition, 1998. $17.95. 64 pages. Describes skills needed to work in office settings for reluctant readers.

★294★ The Complete Job-Finding Guide for Secretaries and Administrative Support Staff

AMACOM
1601 Broadway, 12th Fl.
New York, NY 10019-7420
Ph: (518)891-1500   Fax: (518)903-8168
Fr: 800-250-5308

Paul Falcone. 1995. $16.95 (paper). 256 pages. Covers several secretarial and administrative staff support positions and includes tips on resume writing, interview preparation, and other aspects of the job search.

★295★ From Secretary Track to Fast Track

AMACOM
1601 Broadway, 12th Fl.
New York, NY 10019-7420
Ph: (518)891-1500   Fax: (518)891-2372
Fr: 800-250-5308

Ken Lizotte and Barbara A. Litwak. 1996.

$15.95. 192 pages. Subtitled: *The Get Ahead Guide for Administrative Assistants, Secretaries, Office Managers, Receptionists, and Everyone Who Wants More.*

★296★ **Great Jobs for History Majors**

McGraw-Hill Trade
2 Penn Plaza
New York, NY 10121
Ph: (212)904-2000   Fr: 800-722-4726
E-mail: ntcpub@tribune.com

Julie DeGalan and Stephen Lambert. 1994. $11.95 (paper). 442 pages.

★297★ **The National Business Employment Weekly Jobs Rated Almanac**

John Wiley & Sons Inc.
1 Wiley Dr.
Somerset, NJ 08873
Ph: (732)469-4400   Fr: 800-225-5945

Les Krantz. First edition, 1995. $16.95. 340 pages. Ranks 250 jobs by environment, salary, outlook, physical demands, stress, security, travel opportunities, and geographic location.

★298★ **Opportunities in Federal Government Careers**

McGraw-Hill Trade
2 Penn Plaza
New York, NY 10121
Ph: (212)904-2000   Fr: 800-722-4726
E-mail: ntcpub@tribune.com

Neale Baxter. Second edition, 1994. $14.95; $10.95 (paper). 160 pages. Describes the spectrum of government employment, including professional, administrative, scientific, blue-collar, clerical, and technical opportunities, and how to land a job. Illustrated. Part of Opportunities in...Series.

★299★ **Opportunities in Office Occupations**

McGraw-Hill Trade
2 Penn Plaza
New York, NY 10121
Ph: (212)904-2000   Fr: 800-722-4726

Blanche Ettinger. 1994. $14.95; $11.95 (paper). 200 pages. Covers a variety of office positions and discusses trends for the next decade. Describes the job market, opportunities, job duties, educational preparation, the work environment, and earnings.

★300★ **Opportunities in Secretarial Careers**

McGraw-Hill Trade
2 Penn Plaza
New York, NY 10121
Ph: (212)904-2000   Fr: 800-722-4726
E-mail: ntcpub@tribune.com

Blanche Ettinger. 1999. 160 pages. $14.95; $11.95 (paper). Includes a chapter on finding a secretarial job with sample resumes and interview questions.

★301★ **Opportunities in State and Local Government Careers**

Vgm Career Horizons
1221 Avenue of the Americas
New York, NY 10020
Ph: (212)904-2000   Fr: 800-323-4900
E-mail: ntcpub@tribune.com

Neale J. Baxter. 1994. $14.95; $10.95 (paper). 160 pages. Points out the incentives and drawbacks of a government career. Describes hiring procedures and provides tips on filling out applications, taking physical and aptitude tests, handling interviews, and finding jobs. Describes the jobs in which 75% of all state and local government workers are employed. For each occupation, covers the nature of the work and the training required.

★302★ **Style and Sense For the Legal Profession: A Handbook for Court Reporters, Transcribers, Paralegals and Secretaries**

ETC Publications
700 E. Vereda del Sur
Palm Springs, CA 92262
Ph: (760)325-5352   Fax: (760)325-8841
Fr: 800-382-7869

Audrey Fatooh and Barbara R. Mauk. Revised, 1996. $22.95.

EMPLOYMENT AGENCIES AND SEARCH FIRMS

★303★ **Apple One Employment Services**

990 Knox St.
Torrance, CA 90504
Ph: (310)516-1572
E-mail: cduque@appleonee.com
URL: http://www.appleone.com

Employment agency. Additional offices in Anaheim, Oakland, Cerritos, San Francisco, Manhattan Beach, and Glendale.

★304★ **Career Center, Inc.**

194 Passaic St.
Hackensack, NJ 07601
Ph: (201)342-1777   Fax: (201)342-1776
Fr: 800-227-3379
E-mail: career@careercenterinc.com
URL: http://www.careercenterinc.com

Employment agency.

★305★ **Express Professional Staffing-RWJ & Associates**

7101 France Avenue South
Edina, MN 55435-4221
Ph: (952)915-2003   Fax: (952)920-9327
E-mail: bob.sannerud@rwj.com
URL: http://www.expressprofessional.com

Temporary help service. Also provides some permanent placements.

★306★ **The Linde Group, Inc.**

12158 Natural Bridge Rd., Ste 102
Bridgeton, MO 63044
Ph: (314)738-0101   Fax: (314)209-7968
E-mail: info@thelindegroup.com
URL: http://www.thelindegroup.com/lindegrouptemporaries.htm

Permanent placement and temporary help service.

★307★ **Snelling Personnel Inc.**

24301 Southland Dr., Ste 621
Hayward, CA 94545
Ph: (510)887-2423   Fax: (510)887-2399
URL: http://www.snelling.com/hayward.

Permanent employment agency and temporary help service.

★308★ **Sullivan and Cogliano**

230 2nd Ave
Waltham, MA 02451
Ph: (781)890-7890   Fr: 888-785-2641
E-mail: contact@sullivansogliano.com
URL: http://www.sullivancogliano.com

Executive search firm.

★309★ **Winters and Ross**

442 Main St.
Fort Lee, NJ 07024
Ph: (201)947-8400   Fax: (201)947-1035
E-mail: wintersandross@aol.com
URL: http://www.wintersandross.com

Permanent employment agency serving a variety of industries.

ONLINE JOB SOURCES AND SERVICES

★310★ **Admin Exchange**

E-mail: info@adminexchange.com
URL: http://www.adminexchange.com

Description: Career resources for administrative support staff. Contains resume posting and job databank. Also discussion forum and client list for recruitment purposes.

★311★ **Office Team**

URL: http://www.officeteam.com

Description: Job search site for administrative support staff. Contains resume submission and job databank, plus resources and e-mail notification of available jobs.

OTHER SOURCES

★312★ *Business and Administration*

Support Occupations
Delphi Productions
3160 4th St.
Boulder, CO 80304
Fax: (303)443-4022   Fr: 888-443-2400

URL: http://www.delphivideo.com

$95.00. 42 minutes. Part of the Careers for the 21st Century Video Library.

Adoption Agents

EMPLOYER DIRECTORIES AND NETWORKING LISTS

★313★ The Adoption Directory
Cherub Publishing Co.
110 Wessels Way
Templeton, CA 93465
Ph: (805)434-0654
URL: http://www.adopt-direct.com

Annual. $24.95. Covers adoption and surrogacy professionals, including attorneys, domestic agencies, international agencies, facilitators, counselors, consultants, service providers, vendors, organizations, and more. Entries include: Contact information, fees, number of successful adoptions and business philosophy.

★314★ Adoption Reform Organizations
Adoption Triangle Ministries
162 SW 48th St.
Cape Coral, FL 33914

Updated continuously; printed on request. Covers approximately 350 adoption search and support organizations in the U.S. Entries include: Organization name, address, phone, name and title of contact. Arrangement: Geographical.

★315★ Global Adoption Guide
International Business Publications, USA
PO Box 15343
Washington, DC 20003
Ph: (202)546-2103   Fax: (202)546-3275

3rd edition, May 2001. $99.95. Covers adoption procedures from selected countries, including China, Russia, Vietnam and others.

ONLINE JOB SOURCES AND SERVICES

★316★ Adoption Forums
URL: http://forums.adoption.com
Description: Includes job postings for adoption professionals.

TRADESHOWS

★317★ North American Council on Adoptable Children Conference
North American Council on Adoptable Children
970 Raymond Ave., Ste. 106
St. Paul, MN 55114
Ph: (651)644-3036   Fax: (651)644-9848
E-mail: info@nacac.org
URL: http://www.nacac.org

Annual. **Primary Exhibits:** Exhibits related to adoption and post-adoption.

OTHER SOURCES

★318★ Adoptee-Birthparent Support Network (ABSN)
PO Box 8273
McLean, VA 22106
Ph: (202)628-4111
E-mail: absnmail@aol.com
URL: http://www.geocities.com/Heartland/Flats/3666/ABSN.html

Members: Adoptees, adoptive parents, birthparents (biological parents), and siblings; social workers, and adoption professionals. **Purpose:** Seeks to provide support, information, and education to members and help them come to terms with the effects of adoption. **Activities:** Provides search assistance to adoptees and birthparents who wish to locate their biological relatives. Adminis-

ters public outreach and education programs; conducts legislative efforts.

★319★ Adoptees in Search (AIS)
PO Box 41016
Bethesda, MD 20824
Ph: (301)656-8555   Fax: (301)652-2106
E-mail: ais20824@aol.com

Description: Adoptees, birth and adoptive parents, adoption groups, and social service agencies. Works to increase public awareness of present adoption practice and laws, especially as they affect adopted adults. Believes that "serious moral, legal, constitutional, and human questions have been raised" by the government's policy to deny adult adoptees access to their birth records. Seeks to: help liberalize present adoption laws, particularly in regard to sealed records; foster dialogue to gain understanding of viewpoints of adoptees and birth and adoptive parents; provide search assistance. Offers professional search assistance and support groups.

★320★ American Adoption Congress (AAC)
PO Box 42730
Washington, DC 20015
Ph: (202)483-3399
E-mail: ameradoptioncong@aol.com
URL: http://www.americanadoptioncongress.org/

Description: Adopted persons, birthparents, and adoptive parents; members of related organizations devoted to leadership in adoption reform. Purposes are to: further information on adoptions and related social-psychological issues in the U.S. by study, research, teaching, and conferences; collect, publish, and disseminate information; act as a national clearinghouse and public information center. Develops alternative model plans for adoption; conducts regional educational conferences; provides research referrals to adoption-related services.

★321★ Families Adopting Children Everywhere (FACE)
PO Box 28058, Northwood Sta.
Baltimore, MD 21239
Ph: (410)488-2656
E-mail: info@faceadoption.org
URL: http://www.faceadoptioninfo.org

Description: Adoptive families; persons planning to adopt; adoption agencies and agency personnel; adoptive parent groups. Provides support to adoptive parents and families; disseminates information concerning adoption. Promotes legislation advocating children's rights; conducts research programs. Sponsors Family Building Thru Adoption, an educational course for prospective adoptive parents. Conducts independent and older child adoption seminars. Compiles statistics; maintains library.

★322★ *Human Services Occupations*
Delphi Productions
3160 4th St.
Boulder, CO 80304
Fax: (303)443-4022   Fr: 888-443-2400
URL: http://www.delphivideo.com

$95.00. 50 minutes. Part of the Careers for the 21st Century Video Library.

★323★ Independent Search Consultants (ISC)
PO Box 10192
Costa Mesa, CA 92627
E-mail: informationisc@msn.com
URL: http://www.iscsearch.org

Description: Individuals assisting in searches for birth-families separated by adoption. Seeks to: provide a means of certification for active search consultants; promote ethical standards of conduct and quality assistance; encourage public understanding of the rights of the adoptee, the adoptive parent, and the birthparent; serve as a professional association for search consultants. Offers search consultant certification on national, state, and specialized levels. Individuals qualify for certification by taking an exam, documenting 500 hours of search assistance or volunteer service, and securing personal recommendations. Sponsors panels, seminars, and workshops on adoption search. Offers speakers on all aspects of adoption education and referrals to search agencies, support groups, and certified consultants.

★324★ Liberal Education for Adoptive Families (LEAF)
1295 Omaha Ave. N.
Stillwater, MN 55082
Ph: (651)436-2215

Description: A post-adoption service organization providing legislative and agency policy reform, client counseling (including search assistance and referrals), training and technical assistance for public and private agencies, public education seminars, and media presentations. Cosponsors Minnesota Reunion Registry, which is fed into the system of the International Soundex Reunion Registry, which contains input from adoptees and birthparents throughout the U.S., Mexico, Canada, and abroad.

★325★ National Adoption Information Clearinghouse
330 C St., SW
Washington, DC 20447
Fr: 888-251-0075
URL: http://naic.acf.hhs.gov/aboutus.cfm

Description: Provides access to free information on all aspects of adoption. Includes statistics, practices, research, funding sources, and educational materials.

★326★ National Council for Adoption (NCFA)
225 N Washington St.
Alexandria, VA 22314-2561
Ph: (703)299-6633   Fax: (703)299-6004
E-mail: ncfa@ncfa-usa.org
URL: http://www.adoptioncouncil.org

Description: Represents voluntary agencies, adoptive parents, adoptees, and birthparents. Works to protect the institution of adoption and ensure the confidentiality of all involved in the adoption process. Promotes appropriate adoption practice with legislators, policymakers, human service agencies and staff, and the public. Strives for the regulation of all adoptions to ensure the protection of birthparents, children, and adoptive parents. Serves as an information clearinghouse; provides technical assistance. Conducts research programs; monitors state and national legislation affecting adoption and maternity services. Maintains hall of fame. Compiles statistics. Operates speakers' bureau; compiles statistics.

★327★ North American Council on Adoptable Children (NACAC)
970 Raymond Ave., Ste. 106
St. Paul, MN 55114
Ph: (651)644-3036   Fax: (651)644-9848
E-mail: info@nacac.org
URL: http://www.nacac.org

Members: Members of citizen adoption groups (composed primarily of adoptive parents of "special needs" children) and other individuals from judicial, child welfare, and legislative areas. **Purpose:** Advocates the right of every child to a permanent, loving home. **Activities:** Provides direct assistance to local and state advocacy efforts; acts as a clearinghouse for adoption information; liaises with other adoption organizations. Sponsors an annual national training conference. Also sponsors Adoption Awareness Month. Conducts extensive education and outreach through the media and pre- and post-adoptive support programs. Provides resources for local advocacy programs.

★328★ Stars of David International (SDI)
3175 Commercial Ave., Ste. 100
Northbrook, IL 60062-1915
Fr: 800-STAR-349
E-mail: info@starsofdavid.org
URL: http://www.starsofdavid.org/

Description: Works as a Jewish adoption information and support network. Provides a network of support, adoption information and education to prospective parents, adoptive families, adult adoptees, birth families, and the Jewish community.

★329★ World Partners Adoption (WPAdopt)
2205 Summit Oaks Ct.
Lawrenceville, GA 30043
Ph: (770)962-7860   Fax: (770)513-7767
Fr: 800-350-7338
E-mail: wpadopt@aol.com
URL: http://www.worldpartnersadoption.org/

Description: International child placement agency specializing in international adoptions from the Republic of Kazakhstan, China, Ukraine, and Russia. Children waiting for immediate adoption are age 6 months to 10 years old. Committed to providing families with comprehensive and compassionate assistance during the entire adoption process.

Adult and Vocational Education Teachers

SOURCES OF HELP-WANTED ADS

★330★ Community Colleges Journal
American Association of Community
  Colleges
1 Dupont Cir. NW, Ste. 410
Washington, DC 20036
Ph: (202)728-0200   Fax: (202)223-9390
Fr: 800-250-6557
URL: http://www.aacc.nche.edu

Educational magazine.

★331★ Lifelong Learning Today
LERN
PO Box 9
River Falls, NY 54022-0009
Fax: 888-234-8633   Fr: 800-678-5376

Description: Monthly. Provides news and
information on adult education, including
trends, issues, and events such as enrollments, postage rates, funding, legislation,
and new growth areas. Features interviews
and commentary from prominent national
educational leaders.

★332★ Tech Directions
Prakken Publications Inc.
PO Box 8623
Ann Arbor, MI 48107-8623
Ph: (734)975-2800   Fax: (734)975-2787
Fr: 800-530-WORD
E-mail: tdedit@techdirections.com
URL: http://www.techdirections.com

Free to qualified subscribers; $30.00/year for
individuals. Magazine covering issues, programs, and projects in industrial education,
technology education, trade and industry,
and vocational-technical career education.
Articles are geared for teacher and administrator use and reference from elementary
school through postsecondary levels.

PLACEMENT AND JOB REFERRAL SERVICES

**★333★ International Educator's
Institute (TIE)**
PO Box 513
Cummaquid, MA 02637
Ph: (508)362-1414   Fax: (508)362-1411
Fr: 877-375-6668
E-mail: tie@tieonline.com
URL: http://www.tieonline.com

Description: Facilitates the placement of
teachers and administrators in American,
British, and international schools. Seeks to
create a network that provides for professional development opportunities and improved financial security of members. Offers
advice and information on international
school news, recent educational developments, job placement, and investment, consumer, and professional development opportunities. Makes available insurance and travel benefits. Operates International Schools
Internship Program.

**★334★ National Association for
Industry-Education Cooperation
(NAIEC)**
235 Hendricks Blvd.
Buffalo, NY 14226-3304
Ph: (716)834-7047   Fax: (716)834-7047
E-mail: naiec@pcom.net
URL: http://www2.pcom.net/naiec/

Description: Representatives of business,
industry, education, government, labor, and
the professions. Fosters industry-education
collaboration in continuous school improvement and workforce preparation in order to
develop responsive academic and vocational programs which will more effectively serve
the needs of both the students and employers as well as further human resources and
economic development. Provides technical
assistance to schools implementing industry-
education councils, high-performance sustainable education systems and business- or
industry-sponsored programs. Promotes improved career and entrepreneurship education and supports school-based job placement. Provides staff development programs

to improve instruction and curricula and the
efficiency and effectiveness of educational
management through use of corporate and
volunteer services. Acts as national clearinghouse for information on industry involvement in education; serves as liaison between
organizations involved in industry-education
cooperation, including Council of Chief State
School Officers, National Research Center
for Career and Technical, and American
Society for Training and Development. Conducts research and policy studies.

**★335★ North American Council of
Automotive Teachers (NACAT)**
11956 Bernardo Plaza Dr., Dept. 436
San Diego, CA 92128-9713
Ph: (858)487-8126   Fax: (858)487-3617
E-mail: nacat@cts.com
URL: http://www.nacat.com

Members: Automotive teachers. **Purpose:**
Strives to cooperate with all members of the
automotive industry, and federal and state
governments to improve educational levels
and educational resources for the automotive teacher. Encourages use of uniform
curricula on specific types of car repair and
replacement. Conducts educational programs.

EMPLOYER DIRECTORIES AND NETWORKING LISTS

**★336★ American Trade Schools
Directory**
Croner Publications Inc.
10951 Sorrento Valley Rd., Ste. 1D
San Diego, CA 92121-1616
Ph: (619)546-1894   Fax: (858)546-1955
Fr: 800-441-4033
URL: http://www.sdic.net/croner

Base volume supplied upon subscription;
monthly supplements. $120.00. Covers over
12,000 private and public trade, technical,
and vocational schools. Entries include:
School name, address, phone, contact person, year school founded, private or public,

accrediting agencies, whether approved by state or Veterans Administration, home study courses offered. Arrangement: Geographical. Indexes: Occupation.

★337★ **Chronicle Two-Year College Databook**

Chronicle Guidance Publications Inc.
66 Aurora St.
Moravia, NY 13118-3576
Ph: (315)497-0330   Fax: (315)497-3359
Fr: 800-622-7284

Annual, September. $24.97. Covers over 815 associate, certificate, occupational, and transfer programs offered by more than 2,555 technical institutes, two-year colleges, and universities in the United States. Entries include: College charts section gives college name, address, phone; accreditation, enrollment, admissions, costs, financial aid; accrediting associations' names, addresses, and phone numbers. Arrangement: Part I is classified by college major; Part II is geographical. Indexes: College name.

★338★ **Chronicle Vocational School Manual**

Chronicle Guidance Publications Inc.
66 Aurora St.
Moravia, NY 13118-3576
Ph: (315)497-0330   Fax: (315)497-3359
Fr: 800-622-7284
URL: http://tnt.spidergraphics.com

Annual, September. $24.96. Covers over 945 programs of study offered by more than 2,700 vocational schools. Entries include: School name, city and ZIP code, phone, programs offered, admissions requirements, costs, enrollment, financial aid programs, year established, student services. Arrangement: Geographical. Indexes: Vocation/course.

★339★ **Directory of Public Vocational-Technical Schools, Colleges, and Institutes in the U.S.A.**

Media Marketing Group
15813 NE 18th Ct.
Vancouver, WA 98686-1474
Ph: (360)576-5864

Biennial, January of even years. $65.00. Covers over 1,400 post-secondary vocational and technical education programs in public education; private trade and technical schools are not included. Also includes state agencies responsible for vocational and technical education. Entries include: For institutions-Name, address, phone, contact person, relevant programs offered. For agencies-Name, address. Arrangement: Geographical. Indexes: Institution name, program, subject.

★340★ **Distance Learning for Higher Education: An Annotated Bibliography**

Libraries Unlimited Inc.
88 Post Rd. W.
Westport, CT 06881
Fax: (203)222-1502   Fr: 800-225-5800

$35.00. Publication includes: List of web sites that deal with accreditation, associations, organizations, discussion groups, print and online journals, and newsletters. Indexes: Alphabetical.

★341★ **Guide to Technical, Trade, & Business Schools**

Riverside Publishing/Wintergreen Orchard House
425 Springlake Dr.
Itasca, IL 60143-2079
Ph: (630)467-7000   Fax: (630)467-7192
Fr: 800-323-9540

Biennial, even years. $170.00 for national edition; $50.00 for regional edition. Covers over 3,800 accredited public and proprietary post-secondary schools offering programs in auto mechanics, aviation, business, electronics, and other technical, trade, or business fields. Available in a four-volume national edition or as four regional editions. Entries include: School name, address, phone, accrediting body, admissions contact, course offerings, placement services, and profile. Arrangement: Geographical. Indexes: Subject, special programs, sports, professional accreditations.

★342★ **National Faculty Directory**

Thomson Gale
27500 Drake Rd.
Farmington Hills, MI 48331-3535
Ph: (248)699-4253   Fax: (248)699-8065
Fr: 800-877-GALE
E-mail: businessproducts@gale.com

Annual, fall; spring supplement. $825.00 for base edition; $355.00 for supplement. Covers more than 740,000 (90,000 more in supplement) teaching faculty members at over 3,600 junior colleges, colleges, and universities in the United States and those in Canada that give instruction in English. Entries include: Name, department name, institution, address, and phone and fax numbers. Directory combines main edition and supplement. Arrangement: Alphabetical.

★343★ **National Guide to Educational Credit for Training Programs**

American Council on Education
1 Dupont Cir. NW
Washington, DC 20036-1193
Ph: (202)939-9380   Fax: (202)939-4760

$95.00. Covers courses from over 200 government and professional organizations which offer training programs for educational credit. Entries include: Organization name, address, phone, fax, Web site, and details about the organization. Arrangement: Alphabetical by sponsoring organization. Indexes: Alphabetical by organization and course.

★344★ **Online Directory of ESL Resources**

National Clearinghouse for Bilingual Education
Center for the Study of Language & Education
The George Washington University
2121 K St. NW, Ste. 260
Washington, DC 20037
Ph: (202)467-0867   Fax: 800-531-9347
Fr: 800-321-6223

Free. Covers English as a second language resources on the Internet, especially geared to teachers. Includes government resources, clearinghouses, and professional associations.

★345★ **Opportunities Abroad for Educators**

Fulbright Teacher and Administrator Exchange Program
600 Maryland Ave. SW, Ste. 320
Washington, DC 20024-2520
Ph: (202)314-3527   Fax: (202)479-6806
Fr: 800-726-0479
URL: http://www.fulbrightexchanges.org

Annual. Covers opportunities available for elementary and secondary teachers, and two year college instructors, and school administrators to attend seminars or to teach abroad under the Mutual Educational and Cultural Exchange Act of 1961. Entries include: Countries of placement, dates, eligibility requirements, teaching assignments. Arrangement: Geographical.

★346★ **Peterson's Vocational and Technical Schools and Programs**

Thomson Peterson's
Princeton Pke. Corporate Ctr., 2000 Lenox Dr.
PO Box 67005
Lawrenceville, NJ 08648
Ph: (609)896-1800   Fax: (609)896-4531
Fr: 800-338-3282

Latest edition 2001. $34.95. Covers approximately 5,800 accredited vocational and technical schools that offer training programs in over 370 career fields. Available in separate eastern and western U.S. regional editions. Entries include: Institution name, address, phone, name and title of contact, type of institution, year founded, accreditation, enrollment, faculty-to-student ratio, registration fee, student body profile, programs offered, student services, financial aid. Arrangement: Classified by program type.

★347★ **School Guide**

School Guide Publications
210 N Ave.
New Rochelle, NY 10801
Ph: (914)632-7771   Fax: (914)632-3412
Fr: 800-433-7771
URL: http://www.schoolguides.com

Annual, September. $10.00. Covers over 3,000 colleges, vocational schools, and nursing schools in the United States. Entries include: Institution name, address, phone, courses offered, degrees awarded. Arrangement: Classified by type of institution, then geographical. Indexes: Subject.

★348★ Schools-Business & Vocational Directory

infoUSA Inc.
5711 S 86th Cir.
Omaha, NE 68127-0347
Ph: (402)930-3500   Fax: (402)331-0176
Fr: 800-555-6124
URL: http://www.abii.com

Annual. Number of listings: 5,329. Entries include: Name, address, phone (including area code), size of advertisement, year first in "Yellow Pages," name of owner or manager, number of employees. Compiled from telephone company "Yellow Pages," nationwide. Arrangement: Geographical.

★349★ Schools Industrial, Technical, & Trade Directory

infoUSA Inc.
5711 S 86th Cir.
Omaha, NE 68127-0347
Ph: (402)930-3500   Fax: (402)331-0176
Fr: 800-555-6124
URL: http://www.abii.com

Annual. Number of listings: 2,932. Entries include: Name, address, phone (including area code), size of advertisement, year first in "Yellow Pages," name of owner or manager, number of employees. Compiled from telephone company "Yellow Pages," nationwide. Arrangement: Geographical.

HANDBOOKS AND MANUALS

★350★ Career Information Center

Macmillan Publishing Co. Inc.
200 Old Tappan Rd.
Old Tappan, NJ 07675
Fr: 800-428-5331

Visual Education Center Staff. Seventh edition, 1999. $275.00. 2080 pages. This 13-volume set profiles over 600 occupations. Each occupational profile describes job duties, educational requirements, how to get the job, advancement possibilities, employment outlook, working conditions, earnings and benefits, and where to write for more information.

★351★ Careers in Education

McGraw-Hill Professional
2 Penn Plaza
New York, NY 10121-2298
Ph: (212)904-2000   Fr: 800-722-4726
Roy A. Edelfelt, Alan Reiman. Fourth edition. $14.95. E-book, netLibrary.

★352★ How to Get a Job in Education

Adams Media Corp.
57 Littlefield St.
Avon, MA 02322
Ph: (508)427-7100   Fax: (508)427-6790
Fr: 800-872-5627
URL: http://www.adamsmedia.com

Joel Levin. Second edition, 1995. $15.95. 320 pages. Out of print. Prepared for recent college graduates, seasoned educators, and career-changing professionals, this publication guides the job-seeker through the necessary steps to obtaining a job in education at the elementary, secondary, and university levels. Offers advice on how to prepare for state and local examinations, how to locate teaching opportunities nationwide, and how to obtain certification. Includes a nationwide salary survey. Covers public, private, summer, and overseas opportunities.

★353★ How to Get the Teaching Position You Want: Teacher Candidate Guide

Educational Enterprises
PO Box 1836
Spring Valley, CA 91979
Ph: (619)660-7720

Phyllis Murton. Second edition, revised, 1996. $9.95 (paper). 110 pages. This book provides a comprehensive guide for the teacher candidate's job search, as the format offers information that includes: interview questions most often asked in the teaching interview (grade-level & subject-matter specific); sample forms for applications, cover letters, & resumes that will impact principals & district personnel; strategies on preparing for the teaching interview; interview follow-up techniques; inside tips from a superintendent, a principal & a counselor.

★354★ Non-Profits and Education Job Finder

Planning Communications
7215 Oak Ave.
River Forest, IL 60305-1935
Ph: (708)366-5200   Fax: (708)366-5280
Fr: 888-366-5200
URL: http://jobfindersonline.com

Daniel Lauber. 1997. $32.95; $16.95 (paper). 336 pages. Covers 1600 sources. Discusses how to use sources of non-profit sector job vacancies in a number of specialties and state-by-state, including job-matching services, job hotlines, specialty periodicals with job ads, salary surveys, and directories. Covers a variety of fields from education to religion. Includes chapters on resume and cover letter preparation and interviewing.

★355★ Opportunities in Marketing Careers

McGraw-Hill Trade
2 Penn Plaza
New York, NY 10121
Ph: (212)904-2000   Fr: 800-722-4726
Margery Steinberg. 1999. $14.95; $11.95 (paper). 202 pages. Includes guidance on

identifying and pursuing job opportunities. Illustrated.

★356★ Teaching (Career Portraits)

Vgm Career Horizons
1221 Avenue of the Americas
New York, NY 10020
Ph: (212)904-2000   Fr: 800-323-4900
E-mail: ntcpub@tribune.com

Marjorie Eberts and Margaret Gisler. 1994. $13.95. 320 pages.

★357★ Vocational Entry-Skills for Secondary and Adult Students with Learning Disabilities

Academic Therapy Publications, Incorporated
20 Commercial Blvd.
Novato, CA 94949-6191
Ph: (415)883-3314   Fax: (415)883-3720
Fr: 800-422-7249

Winifred Washburn. 1993. $12.00. Explores vocational skills for adults with learning disabilities.

EMPLOYMENT AGENCIES AND SEARCH FIRMS

★358★ Educational Placement Service

1001 Craig Rd., Ste. 170
St. Louis, MO 63146
Ph: (314)991-5855   Fax: (314)991-5295
URL: http://www.educatorjobs.com

Employment agency. Focuses on teaching, administrative, and education-related openings.

OTHER SOURCES

★359★ American Association for Adult and Continuing Education (AAACE)

4380 Forbes Blvd.
Lanham, MD 20706
Ph: (301)918-1913   Fax: (301)918-1846
E-mail: aaace10@aol.com
URL: http://www.aaace.org/

Purpose: Provides leadership in advancing adult education as a lifelong learning process. Serves as a central forum for a wide variety of adult and continuing education special interest groups. Works to stimulate local, state, and regional adult continuing education efforts; encourage mutual cooperation and support; monitor proposed legislation and offer testimony to Congress.

★360★ **American Association of Community Colleges (AACC)**

1 Dupont Cir. NW, Ste. 410
Washington, DC 20036-1176
Ph: (202)728-0200   Fax: (202)833-2467
URL: http://www.aacc.nche.edu

Members: Community colleges; individual associates interested in community college development; corporate, educational, foundation, and international associate members. **Purpose:** Office of Federal Relations monitors federal educational programming and legislation. **Activities:** Compiles statistics through data collection and policy analysis. Conducts seminars and professional training programs.

★361★ **American Association for Women in Community Colleges (AAWCC)**

1202 W Thomas Rd.
Phoenix, AZ 85013
Ph: (602)285-7449   Fax: (602)285-7832
E-mail: aawcc@pcmail.maricopa.edu
URL: http://www.pc.maricopa.edu/aawcc

Description: Women faculty members, administrators, staff members, students, and trustees of community colleges. Objectives are to: develop communication and disseminate information among women in community, junior, and technical colleges; encourage educational program development; obtain grants for educational projects for community college women. Disseminates information on women's issues and programs. Conducts regional and state professional development workshops and forums. Recognizes model programs that assist women in community colleges. A council of the American Association of Community Colleges.

★362★ **American Federation of Teachers (AFT)**

555 New Jersey Ave. NW
Washington, DC 20001
Ph: (202)879-4400   Fax: (202)879-4545
Fr: 800-238-1133
E-mail: online@aft.org
URL: http://www.aft.org

Description: Affiliated with the AFL-CIO. Works with teachers and other educational employees at the state and local level in organizing, collective bargaining, research, educational issues, and public relations. Conducts research in areas such as educational reform, teacher certification, and national assessments and standards. Represents members' concerns through legislative action; offers technical assistance. Also serves professionals with concerns similar to those of teachers, including state employees, healthcare workers, and paraprofessionals.

★363★ **Association for Career and Technical Education (ACTE)**

1410 King St.
Alexandria, VA 22314
Ph: (703)683-3111   Fax: (703)683-7424
Fr: 800-826-9972

E-mail: acte@acteonline.org
URL: http://www.acteonline.org

Description: Teachers, supervisors, administrators, and others interested in the development and improvement of vocational, technical, and practical arts education. Areas of interest include: secondary, postsecondary, and adult vocational education; education for special population groups; cooperative education. Works with such government agencies as: Bureau of Apprenticeship in Department of Labor; Office of Vocational Rehabilitation in Department of Health and Human Services; Veterans Administration; Office of Vocational and Adult Education of the Department of Education. Maintains hall of fame.

★364★ **College Reading and Learning Association (CRLA)**

PO Box 6251
Auburn, CA 95604
Ph: (530)823-1076   Fax: (530)823-6331
E-mail: debbie2@garlic.com
URL: http://www.crla.net

Description: Professionals involved in college/adult reading, learning assistance, developmental education, and tutorial services. Promotes communication for the purpose of professional growth.

★365★ *Education and Training*

Cambridge Educational
2572 Brunswick Ave.
Lawrenceville, NJ 08648-4128
Fax: 800-FAX-ON-US   Fr: 800-468-4227
URL: http://www.cambridgeeducational.com
$89.95. 2002. 18 minutes.

★366★ **International Reading Association (IRA)**

800 Barksdale Rd.
PO Box 8139
Newark, DE 19714-8139
Ph: (302)731-1600   Fax: (302)731-1057
E-mail: pubinfo@reading.org
URL: http://www.reading.org

Description: Teachers, reading specialists, consultants, administrators, supervisors, researchers, psychologists, librarians, and parents interested in promoting literacy. Seeks to improve the quality of reading instruction and promote literacy worldwide. Disseminates information pertaining to research on reading, including information on adult literacy, early childhood and literacy development, international education, literature for children and adolescents, and teacher education and professional development. Maintains over 40 special interest groups and over 70 committees.

★367★ **International Technology Education Association - Council for Supervisors (ITEA-CS)**

Virginia Department of Education
PO Box 2120, 21st Fl.
Richmond, VA 23218-2120
Ph: (804)225-2839   Fax: (804)371-2456

URL: http://www.iteawww.org

Description: Technology education supervisors from the U.S. Office of Education; local school department chairpersons; state departments of education, local school districts, territories, provinces, and foreign countries. Works to improve instruction and supervision of programs in technology education. Conducts research; compiles statistics. Sponsors competitions. Maintains speakers' bureau.

★368★ **National Association of Blind Teachers (NABT)**

1155 15th St. NW, Ste. 1004
Washington, DC 20005
Ph: (202)467-5081   Fax: (202)467-5085
Fr: 800-424-8666
E-mail: info@acb.org
URL: http://www.acb.org

Description: Public school teachers, college and university professors, and teachers in residential schools for the blind. Purpose is to promote employment and professional goals of blind persons entering the teaching profession or those established in their respective teaching fields. Serves as a vehicle for the dissemination of information and the exchange of ideas addressing special problems of members. Compiles statistics.

★369★ **National Association of Vocational Education Special Needs Personnel (NAVESNP)**

3145 Longridge Way
Grove City, OH 43123-9506
Ph: (412)675-9065   Fax: (412)675-9067
E-mail: lvb6@psu.edu

Description: Employees in programs or services related to vocational special needs education; interested individuals. To serve as a unifying association for development and operation of programs for special vocational education; to promote and maintain active leadership in vocational, career, and occupational education. Monitors submits committee reports.

★370★ **National Community Education Association (NCEA)**

3929 Old Lee Hwy., Ste. 91-A
Fairfax, VA 22030
Ph: (703)359-8973   Fax: (703)359-0972
E-mail: ncea@ncea.com
URL: http://www.ncea.com

Description: Community school directors, principals, superintendents, professors, teachers, students, and laypeople. **Purpose:** Promotes and establishes community schools as an integral part of the educational plan of every community. Emphasizes community and parent involvement in the schools, lifelong learning, and enrichment of K-12 and adult education. Serves as a clearinghouse for the exchange of ideas and information, and the sharing of efforts. **Activities:** Offers leadership training.

★371★ National Council of Teachers of Mathematics (NCTM)
1906 Association Dr.
Reston, VA 20191-1502
Ph: (703)620-9840   Fax: (703)476-2970
Fr: 800-235-7566
E-mail: orders@nctm.org
URL: http://www.nctm.org
Description: Dedicated to improving teaching and learning of mathematics. Toll-free number is for orders only.

★372★ Overseas Employment Opportunities for Educators: Department of Defense Dependents Schools
DIANE Publishing Co.
PO Box 1428
Collingdale, PA 19023-8428
Ph: (610)461-6200   Fax: (610)461-6130
Fr: 800-782-3833

Barry Leonard, editor. 1999. $20.00. 44 pages. An introduction to teachings positions in the Dept. of Defense Dependents Schools (DoDDS), a worldwide school system, operated by the DoD in 14 countries.

★373★ Teaching & Related Occupations
Delphi Productions
3160 4th St.
Boulder, CO 80304
Fax: (303)443-4022   Fr: 888-443-2400
URL: http://www.delphivideo.com

$95.00. 50 minutes. Part of the Careers for the 21st Century Video Library.

★374★ Vocational Careers Sourcebook
Thomson Gale
27500 Drake Rd.
Farmington Hills, MI 48331-3535
Ph: (248)699-GALE   Fax: (248)699-8069
Fr: 800-877-GALE
E-mail: galeord@gale.com
URL: http://www.galegroup.com

Fourth edition, 1999. $110.00. 700 pages. Directs users to career information sources related to specific occupations, such as insurance and real estate sales, corrections and police work, mechanics, armed forces options, agriculture and forestry, production work, and the trades. Contains information on general career guides, career information and services provided by trade associations, standards and certification agencies, directories of educational programs and institutions, basic reference guides and handbooks related to the occupation, trade periodicals, and more. Indexes: Alphabetical.

Aerospace Engineers

SOURCES OF HELP-WANTED ADS

★375★ Aerospace Engineering

Society of Automotive Engineers Inc.
400 Commonwealth Dr.
Warrendale, PA 15096-0001
Ph: (724)776-4841   Fax: (724)776-4026
E-mail: magazines@sae.org
URL: http://www.sae.org

$66.00/year, U.S.; $118.00/year for other countries; $15.00/year for single issue, other countries; $12.00 for single issue, U.S. Magazine for aerospace manufacturing engineers providing technical and design information.

★376★ Air Jobs Digest

World Air Data
Box 42724
Washington, DC 20015
Ph: (301)990-6800   Fax: (301)990-8484

Monthly. $96.00/year for individuals. Newspaper covering job listings in aviation and aerospace worldwide.

★377★ Aviation Maintenance

PBI Media L.L.C.
1201 Seven Locks Rd., Ste. 300
Potomac, MD 20854
Ph: (301)354-2000
URL: http://www.aviationtoday.com/cgi/catalog/info?AM

Monthly. Magazine covering aviation maintenance.

★378★ Aviation Week & Space Technology

McGraw-Hill Companies
1221 Avenue of the Americas
New York, NY 10020
Ph: (212)512-2000
URL: http://www.AviationNow.com/awst

Weekly. $95.00/year for individuals. Magazine serving the aviation and aerospace market worldwide.

★379★ Engineering Times

National Society of Professional Engineers
1420 King St.
Alexandria, VA 22314
Ph: (703)684-2875   Fax: (703)836-4875
E-mail: et@nspe.org
URL: http://http//:www.nspc.org/1et.asp

$30.00/year for individuals; $48.00/year for out of country. Magazine (tabloid) covering professional, legislative, and techology issues for an engineering audience.

★380★ ENR: Engineering News-Record

McGraw-Hill Companies
1221 Avenue of the Americas
New York, NY 10020
Ph: (212)512-2000
URL: http://www.enr.com

Weekly. $74.00/year; $5.00 for single issue. Magazine focusing on engineering and construction.

★381★ Graduating Engineer & Computer Careers

Career Recruitment Media
211 W. Wacker Dr., No. 900
Chicago, IL 60606
Ph: (312)525-3100
URL: http://www.graduatingengineer.com

$16.00/year for individuals. Magazine focusing on employment, education, and career development for entry-level engineers and computer scientists.

★382★ High Technology Careers Magazine

HTC
4701 Patrick Henry Dr., No. 1901
Santa Clara, CA 95054-1847
Ph: (408)970-8800   Fax: (408)567-0242
URL: http://www.hightechcareers.com

Bimonthly. $29.00/year; $35.00/year for Canada; $85.00/year for out of country. Magazine (tabloid) containing employment opportunity information for the engineering and technical community.

★383★ NASA Tech Briefs

Associated Business Publications Company Ltd.
317 Madison Ave.
New York, NY 10017
Ph: (212)490-3999   Fax: (212)986-7864
URL: http://www.nasatech.com

Monthly. Free to qualified subscribers. Publication covering technology for American industry and government in the fields of electronics, computers, physical sciences, materials, mechanics, machinery, fabrication technology, math and information sciences, and the life sciences.

★384★ NSBE Magazine

NSBE Publications
1454 Duke St.
Alexandria, VA 22314
Ph: (703)549-2207   Fax: (703)683-5312

$10.00/year for individuals; $2.00 for single issue. Journal providing information on engineering careers, self-development, and cultural issues for recent graduates with technical majors.

★385★ SWE

Society of Women Engineers
230 E Ohio St., No. 400
2135 Lamberton Rd.
Chicago, IL 60611-3265
Ph: (312)596-5223   Fax: (312)596-5252
E-mail: hq@swe.org
URL: http://www.swe.org

Bimonthly. $30.00/year for nonmembers. Magazine for engineering students and for women and men working in the engineering and technology fields. Covers career guidance, continuing development and topical issues.

★386★ Technology Review

Technology Review
201 Vassar St.
Cambridge, MA 02139
Ph: (617)253-8250   Fax: (617)258-5850
E-mail: trcomments@mit.edu

$30.00/year for individuals; $42.00/year for other countries; $4.95/year for single issue.

Magazine reviewing new developments in technology with an emphasis on economic, political, and social implications. Not a new product publication.

★387★ TEST Engineering & Management

The Mattingley Publishing Company Inc.
3756 Grand Ave., Ste. 205
Oakland, CA 94610-1545
Ph: (510)839-0909   Fax: (510)839-2950

Bimonthly. $40.00/year for individuals; $55.00/year for other countries; $5.00 for single issue. Trade publication that covers physical and mechanical testing and environmental simulation; edited for test engineering professionals.

★388★ WEPANEWS

Women in Engineering Programs & Advocates Network
Castle Point on the Hudson
Hoboken, NJ 07030
Ph: (201)216-5245   Fax: (201)216-5175
URL: http://www.wepan.org/newsletter.html

Description: Two issues/year. Seeks to provide greater access for women to careers in engineering. Includes news of graduate, undergraduate, freshmen, pre-college, and re-entry engineering programs for women. Recurring features include job listings, faculty, grant, and conference news, international engineering program news, action group news, notices of publications available, and a column titled Kudos.

PLACEMENT AND JOB REFERRAL SERVICES

★389★ American Indian Science and Engineering Society (AISES)

PO Box 9828
Albuquerque, NM 87119-9828
Ph: (505)765-1052   Fax: (505)765-5608
E-mail: info@aises.org
URL: http://www.aises.org

Description: American Indian and non-Indian students and professionals in science, technology, and engineering fields; corporations representing energy, mining, aerospace, electronic, and computer fields. Seeks to motivate and encourage students to pursue undergraduate and graduate studies in science, engineering, and technology. Sponsors science fairs in grade schools, teacher training workshops, summer math/science sessions for 8th-12th graders, professional chapters, and student chapters in colleges. Offers scholarships. Adult members serve as role models, advisers, and mentors for students. Operates placement service.

★390★ American Institute of Aeronautics and Astronautics (AIAA)

1801 Alexander Bell Dr., Ste. 500
Reston, VA 20191-4344
Ph: (703)264-7500   Fax: (703)264-7551
Fr: 800-NEW-AIAA
E-mail: custserv@aiaa.org
URL: http://www.aiaa.org/

Description: Scientists and engineers in the field of aeronautics and astronautics. Facilitates interchange of technological information through publications and technical meetings in order to foster overall technical progress in the field and increase the professional competence of members. Operates Public Policy program to provide federal decision-makers with the technical information and policy guidance needed to make effective policy on aerospace issues. Public Policy program activities include congressional testimony, position papers, section public policy activities, and workshops. Offers placement assistance; compiles statistics; offers educational programs. Provides abstracting services through its AIAA Access.

★391★ Engineering Society of Detroit (ESD)

26100 American Dr., Ste. 500
Southfield, MI 48034-6184
Ph: (248)355-2910   Fax: (248)355-1492
E-mail: esd@esd.org
URL: http://esd.org

Description: Engineers from all disciplines; scientists and technologists. Conducts technical programs and engineering refresher courses; sponsors conferences and expositions. Maintains speakers' bureau; offers placement services. Although based in Detroit, MI, society membership is international.

★392★ Korean Scientists and Engineers Association in America (KSEA)

1952 Gallows Rd., Ste. 300
Vienna, VA 22182
Ph: (703)748-1221   Fax: (703)748-1331
E-mail: sejong@ksea.org
URL: http://www.ksea.org

Description: Scientists and engineers holding single or advanced degrees. Goals are to: promote friendship and mutuality among Korean and American scientists and engineers; contribute to Korea's scientific, technological, industrial, and economic developments; strengthen the scientific, technological, and cultural bonds between Korea and the U.S. Sponsors symposium. Maintains speakers' bureau, placement service, and biographical archives. Compiles statistics. Maintains 100 volume library of scientific handbooks and yearbooks in Korean.

★393★ Society of Hispanic Professional Engineers (SHPE)

5400 E Olympic Blvd., Ste. 210
Los Angeles, CA 90022
Ph: (323)725-3970   Fax: (323)725-0316
E-mail: shpenational@shpe.org
URL: http://www.shpe.org

Description: Engineers, student engineers, and scientists seeking to increase the number of Hispanic engineers by providing motivation and support to students. Sponsors competitions and educational programs. Maintains placement service and speakers' bureau; compiles statistics.

EMPLOYER DIRECTORIES AND NETWORKING LISTS

★394★ American Men and Women of Science

Thomson Gale
27500 Drake Rd.
Farmington Hills, MI 48331-3535
Ph: (248)699-4253   Fax: (248)699-8065
Fr: 800-877-GALE
E-mail: amws@galegroup.com

Biennial, latest edition December 2002. $975.00. Covers over 129,700 U.S. and Canadian scientists active in the physical, biological, mathematical, computer science, and engineering fields; includes references to previous edition for deceased scientists and nonrespondents. Entries include: Name, address, education, personal and career data, memberships, honors and awards, research interest. Arrangement: Alphabetical. Indexes: Discipline (in separate volume).

★395★ Careers in Focus: Engineering

Ferguson Publishing Co.
200 W Jackson Blvd.
Chicago, IL 60606
Ph: (312)692-0109

2nd edition, 2002. $22.95. Publication includes: List of resources to consult for more information. Principal content of publication is job descriptions, advancement opportunities, educational requirements, employment outlook, salary information, and working conditions for careers in the field of engineering. Indexes: Alphabetical.

★396★ Directory of Contract Staffing Firms

C.E. Publications Inc.
PO Box 3006
Bothell, WA 98041-3006
Ph: (425)806-5200   Fax: (425)806-5585
URL: http://www.cjhunter.com/dcsf/overview.html

$15.00. Covers nearly 1,300 contract firms actively engaged in the employment of engineering, IT/IS, and technical personnel for 'temporary' contract assignments throughout the world. Entries include: Company name, address, phone, name of contact, email, web address. Arrangement: Alphabetical. Indexes: Geographical.

★397★ **Indiana Society of Professional Engineers-Directory**

Indiana Society of Professional Engineers
PO Box 20806
Indianapolis, IN 46220
Ph: (317)255-2267   Fax: (317)255-2530

Annual, fall. $55.00. Covers member registered engineers, land surveyors, engineering students, and engineers in training. Entries include: Member name, address, phone, type of membership, business information, specialty. Arrangement: Alpha by chapter area.

★398★ **International Directory of Engineering Societies and Related Organizations**

American Association of Engineering Societies
1828 L St. NW, Ste. 906
Washington, DC 20036
Ph: (202)296-2237   Fax: (202)296-1151
Fr: 888-400-AAES

Irregular, latest edition December 1998. $240.00. Covers about 1,370 national, regional, Canadian, and international organizations concerned with engineering and related fields. Entries include: Name, address, phone, fax, e-mail, key personnel, objectives, publications, activities, mailing lists, federation memberships, meeting and convention dates, and budget data. Arrangement: Alphabetical. Indexes: Acronym, geographical, area of specialization.

★399★ **Peterson's Job Opportunities in Engineering and Technology**

Thomson Peterson's
PO Box 67005
Lawrenceville, NJ 08648-6105
Fr: 800-338-3282

Compiled by the Peterson's staff. Fourth edition, 1996. $21.95 (paper). 384 pages. Profiles 2,000 high-tech companies looking primarily for technical personnel in such fields as biotechnology, telecommunications, software, computers and peripherals, defense, and aerospace. Contains job-search strategies and career options to help match education and expertise to the job market. Indexed geographically, by industry, and by hiring needs.

HANDBOOKS AND MANUALS

★400★ **The Best Resumes for Scientists and Engineers**

John Wiley & Sons Inc.
1 Wiley Dr.
Somerset, NJ 08873
Ph: (732)469-4400   Fr: 800-225-5945

Adele Lewis and David J. Moore. Second edition, 1993. $37.50; $19.95 (paper). 224 pages. Presents an extensive collection of scientific and engineering resumes, highlighting the important differences between these and resumes written for other occupations.

★401★ **Careers in High Tech**

Vgm Career Horizons
McGraw-Hill Trade
1221 Avenue of the Americas
New York, NY 10020
Ph: (212)904-2000   Fr: 800-323-4900
E-mail: ntcpub@tribune.com

Nick Basta. Second edition, 1998. $17.95; $13.95 (paper). 104 pages. Examines new career opportunities in such fields as biotechnology, computers, aerospace, telecommunications, and others.

★402★ **Engineering Your Job Search: A Job-Finding Resource for Engineering Professionals**

Professional Publications, Inc.
1250 5th Ave.
Belmont, CA 94002
Ph: (650)593-9119   Fax: (650)592-4519
Fr: 800-426-1178

Compiled by Professional Publications, editors. 1995. $24.95 (paper). 154 pages. Out of print.

★403★ **Great Jobs for Engineering Majors**

McGraw-Hill Professional
McGraw-Hill Higher Education
2 Penn Plaza
New York, NY 10121
Ph: (212)904-2000   Fr: 800-722-4726
E-mail: ntcpub@tribune.com

Geraldine O. Garner. Second edition, 2002. $14.95. 256 pages. Covers all the career options open to students majoring in engineering.

★404★ **How to Succeed as an Engineer: A Practical Guide to Enhance Your Career**

Institute of Electrical & Electronics Engineers Inc.
PO Box 87204
Vancouver, WA 98687
Ph: (360)253-9532   Fax: (360)253-4084

Todd Yuzuriha. 1999. $29.95 (paper). 367 pages.

★405★ **The I Hate Selling Book: Business-Building Advice for Consultants, Attorneys, Accountants, Engineers, Architects, and Other Professionals**

Allan Boress & Associates
1500 University Dr., Suite 239
Coral Springs, FL 33071
Ph: (954)345-4666   Fax: (954)344-2453

Allan S. Boress. 2001. $29.95.

★406★ **Keys to Engineering Success**

Prentice Hall PTR
One Lake St.
Upper Saddle River, NJ 07458
Ph: (201)236-7000

Jill S. Tietjen, Kristy A. Schloss, Carol Carter, Joyce Bishop, and Sarah Lyman. 2000. $32.00 (paper).

★407★ **Majoring in Engineering: How to Get from Your Freshman Year to Your First Job**

Farrar, Straus & Giroux, Inc.
19 Union Sq., W
New York, NY 10003
Ph: (212)741-6900   Fax: (212)633-9385
Fr: 888-330-8477

John Garcia and Carol Carter, editors. 2000. $20.00; $10.00 (paper). 134 pages.

★408★ **The New Engineer's Guide to Career Growth & Professional Awareness**

Institute of Electrical & Electronics Engineers Inc.
445 Hoes Ln.
PO Box 1331
Piscataway, NJ 08855-1331
Ph: (732)562-3967   Fax: (732)981-9334
Fr: 800-678-4333

Irving J. Gabelman, editor. 1996. $39.95 (paper). 275 pages.

★409★ **Opportunities in Aerospace Careers**

McGraw-Hill Contemporary Books
1221 Avenue of the Americas
New York, NY 10020
Ph: (212)904-2000   Fr: 800-323-4900
E-mail: ntcpub@tribune.com

Wallace R. Maples. 1995. $14.95; $11.95 (paper). Surveys jobs with the airlines, airports, the government, the military, in manufacturing, and in research and development. Includes information on job opportunities with NASA in the U.S. space program.

★410★ **Opportunities in Engineering Careers**

McGraw-Hill Contemporary Books
1221 Avenue of the Americas
New York, NY 10020
Ph: (212)904-2000   Fr: 800-323-4900
E-mail: ntcpub@tribune.com

Nicholas Basta. Revised, 1995. $14.95; $11.95 (paper). 200 pages. Outlines typical job titles, salaries, career paths, and employment prospects.

★411★ **Opportunities in High Tech Careers**

McGraw-Hill Trade
2 Penn Plaza
New York, NY 10121
Ph: (212)904-2000   Fr: 800-722-4726

Gary Colter and Deborah Yanuck. 1995. $14.95; $11.95 (paper). 160 pages. Explores high technology careers. Describes job opportunities, how to make a career decision, how to prepare for high technology jobs, job hunting techniques, and future trends.

★412★ **Opportunities in Research and Development Careers**
McGraw-Hill/Contemporary Books
1221 Avenue of the Americas
New York, NY 10020
Ph: (212)904-2000   Fr: 800-323-4900
E-mail: ntcpub@tribune.com

Jan Goldberg. 1997. $14.95; $11.95 (paper). 204 pages.

★413★ **Real People Working in Engineering**
McGraw-Hill Contemporary Books
1221 Avenue of the Americas
New York, NY 10020
Ph: (212)904-2000   Fr: 800-323-4900
E-mail: ntcpub@tribune.com

Blythe Camenson, Jan Goldberg. 1997. $14.95; $12.95 (paper). Interviews and profiles of working professionals capture a range of opportunities in this field.

★414★ **Resumes for Engineering Careers**
McGraw-Hill Trade
2 Penn Plaza
New York, NY 10121
Ph: (212)904-2000   Fr: 800-722-4726
E-mail: ntcpub@tribune.com

2000. $10.95 (paper). 456 pages. Contains sample resumes and cover letters applicable to any engineering field.

★415★ **Resumes for Scientific and Technical Careers**
McGraw-Hill Contemporary Books
1221 Avenue of the Americas
New York, NY 10020
Ph: (212)904-2000   Fr: 800-323-4900
E-mail: ntcpub@tribune.com

1999. $9.95 (paper). 450 pages. Provides resume advice for individuals interested in working in scientific and technical careers. Includes sample resumes and cover letters.

★416★ **The Standard Handbook for Aeronautical and Astronautical Engineers**
Society of Automotive Engineers, Incorporated
400 Commonwealth Dr.
Warrendale, PA 15096
Ph: (724)776-4970   Fax: (724)776-0790

Mark Davies. 2003. $175.95. 1831 pages. Educational manual for aeronautical and astronautical engineers.

★417★ **Taking Flight: Education & Training for Aviation Careers**
National Academies Press
500 5th St. NW
Washington, DC 20055
Ph: (202)334-3180   Fax: (202)334-2793
Fr: 800-624-6242

Janet S. Hansen and Clinton V. Oster, editors. 1997. $37.00 (paper). 192 pages.

★418★ **Where the Jobs Are: The Hottest Careers for the 90s**
The Career Press, Inc.
3 Tice Rd.
PO Box 687
Franklin Lakes, NJ 07417-1322
Ph: (201)848-0310   Fax: (201)848-1727
Fr: 800-227-3371

Joyce Hadley. Third edition, 2000. $13.99 (paper). 400 pages. Out of print. Describes careers in fifteen general fields, from accounting to travel and hospitality.

EMPLOYMENT AGENCIES AND SEARCH FIRMS

★419★ **Adams & Associates International**
520 Shorely Dr. 201, PO Box 129
Barrington, IL 60011-0129
Ph: (847)304-5300

Global executive search firm.

★420★ **Amtec Engineering Corp.**
2749 Saturn St.
Brea, CA 92821
Ph: (714)993-1900   Fax: (714)993-2419
E-mail: staffing@amtec-eng.com
URL: http://www.amtec-eng.com

Employment agency.

★421★ **The Arcus Group Inc.**
325 N. Saint Paul, Ste. 1340
Dallas, TX 75201
Ph: (214)871-3332   Fax: (214)871-1338

Executive search firm. Branch in Chicago.

★422★ **The Aspire Group**
52 Second Ave, 1st Fl
Waltham, MA 02451-1129
Fax: (718)890-1810   Fr: 800-546-5675
URL: http://www.bmanet.com

Employment agency.

★423★ **Brentwood International**
9841 Airport Blvd., Ste. 420
Los Angeles, CA 90045
Ph: (310)216-0033   Fax: (310)338-5484

Executive search firm with focus on information technology. Branch in Fairfield, CA.

★424★ **Cabot Consultants**
1750 Tysons Blvd., Ste. 250
McLean, VA 22102
Ph: (703)584-2310

Executive search firm.

★425★ **Christopher-Westmont & Associates Inc.**
PO Box 470188
Broadview Heights, OH 44147
Ph: (440)877-0510   Fax: (440)877-0511

Executive search firm.

★426★ **Claddagh Resources America**
3169 Holcomb Bridge Rd., Ste. 700
Norcross, GA 30071
Ph: (678)405-4400

Executive search firm.

★427★ **Colli Associates**
404 Caboose Ln.
Valrico, FL 33594
Ph: (813)681-2145   Fax: (813)661-5217
E-mail: colli@gte.net

Employment agency. Executive search firm.

★428★ **Davis & Company**
3419 Via Lido, Ste. 615
Newport Beach, CA 92663
Ph: (949)376-6995   Fax: (949)376-6995
Fr: 800-600-4417

Executive search firm. Branch in Lake Mary, FL.

★429★ **DMR Global Inc.**
10230 W. Sample Rd.
Coral Springs, FL 33065
Ph: (954)796-5043   Fax: (954)796-5044

Executive search firm.

★430★ **Eastbourne Associates Inc.**
104 Sandy Hollow Rd.
Northport, NY 11768
Ph: (631)757-1217   Fax: (631)757-1417

Executive search firm.

★431★ **Engineer One, Inc.**
PO Box 23037
Knoxville, TN 37933
Fax: (865)691-0110
E-mail: engineerone@engineerone.com
URL: http://www.engineerone.com

Employment agency.

★432★ **ESA**
141 Durham Rd., Ste. 16
Madison, CT 06443
Ph: (203)245-1983   Fax: (203)245-8428

Executive search firm.

★433★ Fisher Personnel Management Services
1862 Torrance Blvd.
PO Box 9076
Torrance, CA 90508
Ph: (310)320-6667   Fax: (310)320-1060
Executive search firm.

★434★ Focus Learning Corp.
173 Cross St.
San Luis Obispo, CA 93401
Ph: (805)543-4895   Fax: (805)773-5892
Fr: 800-458-5116

Provides professional services to corporations for the development and implementation of training programs. Assists clients with needs assessment related to training and professional development, goals definition, and development of training materials. Industries served include: government, utility, aerospace, business, and computer.

★435★ International Staffing Consultants
2901 W Coast Hwy.,Ste. 200
Newport Beach, CA 92663
Ph: (949)263-5933   Fax: (949)767-5959
E-mail: iscinc@iscworld.com
URL: http://www.iscworld.com

Employment agency. Provides placement on regular or temporary basis. Affiliate office in London.

★436★ Johnson Personnel Co.
861 N Madison St.
Rockford, IL 61107
Ph: (815)964-0840   Fax: (815)964-0855

Personnel consultants provide technical and managerial placement in industry. Industries served: aerospace, automotive, machine tool, and consumer products.

★437★ J.R. Bechtle & Company
112 Water St., Ste. 500
Boston, MA 02109
Ph: (617)722-9980   Fax: (617)722-4130
Executive search firm.

★438★ Louis Rudzinsky Associates Inc.
394 Lowell St.
PO Box 640
Lexington, MA 02420
Ph: (781)862-6727   Fax: (781)862-6868

Provides recruitment, placement, and executive search to industry (software, electronics, optics) covering positions in general management, manufacturing, engineering, and marketing. Personnel consulting activities include counsel to small and startup companies. Industries served: electronics, aerospace, optical, laser, computer, software, imaging, electro-optics, biotechnology, advanced materials, and solid-state/semiconductor.

★439★ Main Line Personnel Service, Inc.
Pagoda Blding.
100 Presidential Blvd. Ste. 200
Bala Cynwyd, PA 19004-0448
Ph: (610)667-1820   Fax: (610)668-5000
URL: http://www.mlpers.com

Employment agency.

★440★ R.J. Evans Associates Inc.
26949 Chagrin Blvd., Ste. 300
Beachwood, OH 44122
Ph: (216)464-5100   Fax: (216)464-8276
Executive search firm.

★441★ Robert Drexler Associates Inc.
PO Box 151
Saddle River, NJ 07458
Ph: (201)460-2300   Fax: (201)760-2301
Executive search firm.

★442★ Search and Recruit International
4455 South Blvd.
Virginia Beach, VA 23452
Ph: (757)490-3151   Fax: (757)497-6503
E-mail: britt@searchandrecruit.com
URL: http://www.searchandrecruit.com

Employment agency. Headquartered in Virginia Beach. Other offices in Bremerton, WA; Charleston, SC; Jacksonville, FL; Memphis, TN; Pensacola, FL; Sacramento, CA; San Bernardino, CA; San Diego, CA.

★443★ Techtronix Technical Search
PO Box 17713
Milwaukee, WI 53217-0173
Ph: (414)466-3100   Fax: (414)466-3598

Firm specializes in recruiting executives for the engineering, information systems, manufacturing, marketing, finance, and human resources industries.

★444★ Timothy D. Crowe Jr.
PO Box 6-K
Chelmsford, MA 01824-0006
Ph: (978)256-2008

Executive search firm.

★445★ Tri-Serv Inc.
22 W. Padonia Rd., Ste. C-353
Timonium, MD 21093
Ph: (410)561-1740   Fax: (410)252-7417
E-mail: info@tri-serv.coom
URL: http://www.tri-serv.com

Permanent employment agency.

★446★ Winters Technical Staffing Services
2025 Sheppard Ave. E, Ste. 4110
Willowdale, ON, Canada M2T 1V7
Ph: (416)495-7422   Fax: (416)495-8479

Technical staffing service for permanent and contract positions in all facets of engineering. Serves government agencies, consulting engineers, and all areas of manufacturing in Canada and northeast U.S.

ONLINE JOB SOURCES AND SERVICES

★447★ American Institute of Aeronautics and Astronautics Career Planning and Placement Services
URL: http://www.aiaa.org/members/index.hfm?memo=0

Description: Site for AIAA members to place recruitment advertisements, browse career opportunities listings, post resumes, and seek additional employment assistance. Non-members may become members though this site.

★448★ Spherion Workforce Architects
URL: http://www.spherion.com
Description: Recruitment firm specializing in accounting and finance, sales and marketing, interim executives, technology, engineering, retail and human resources.

TRADESHOWS

★449★ Aerospace Medical Association Annual Scientific Meeting
Aerospace Medical Association
320 S. Henry St.
Alexandria, VA 22314
Ph: (703)739-2240   Fax: (703)739-9652
URL: http://www.asma.org

Annual. **Primary Exhibits:** Products related to aerospace medicine; safety products; diagnostic and research instrumentation for the field of human factors.

★450★ SAE Aerospace Manufacturing Technology Conference and Exposition
SAE - Society of Automotive Engineers, International
400 Commonwealth Dr.
Warrendale, PA 15096-0001
Ph: (412)776-4841   Fax: (412)776-0210
E-mail: meetings@sae.org
URL: http://www.sae.org

Annual. **Primary Exhibits:** Aerospace parts, materials, components, systems, and techniques.

OTHER SOURCES

★451★ American Association of Engineering Societies (AAES)

1828 L St. NW, No. 906
Washington, DC 20036
Ph: (202)296-2237   Fax: (202)296-1151
Fr: 888-400-2237
E-mail: tprice@aaes.org
URL: http://www.aaes.org

Description: Coordinates the efforts of the member societies in the provision of reliable and objective information to the general public concerning issues which affect the engineering profession and the field of engineering as a whole; to collect, analyze, document, and disseminate data which will inform the general public of the relationship between engineering and the national welfare; to provide a forum for the engineering societies to exchange and discuss their views on matters of common interest; and to represent the U.S. engineering community aborad through representation in WFEO and UPADI.

★452★ Association for International Practical Training (AIPT)

10400 Little Patuxent Pky., Ste. 250
Columbia, MD 21044-3519
Ph: (410)997-2200   Fax: (410)992-3924
E-mail: aipt@aipt.org
URL: http://www.aipt.org

Description: Providers worldwide on-the-job training programs for students and professionals seeking international career development and life-changing experiences. Arranges workplace exchanges in hundreds of professional fields, bringing employers and trainees together from around the world. Client list ranges from small farming communities to Fortune 500 companies.

★453★ *Engineering Occupations*

Delphi Productions
3160 4th St.
Boulder, CO 80304
Fax: (303)443-4022   Fr: 888-443-2400

URL: http://www.delphivideo.com

$95.00. 50 minutes. Part of the Careers for the 21st Century Video Library.

★454★ ISA - Instrumentation, Systems, and Automation Society

67 Alexander Dr.
PO Box 12277
Research Triangle Park, NC 27709
Ph: (919)549-8411   Fax: (919)549-8288
E-mail: info@isa.org
URL: http://www.isa.org

Purpose: Fosters advancement in the theory, design, manufacture, and use of instruments, computers, and systems for measurement and control.

★455★ National Action Council for Minorities in Engineering (NACME)

Empire State Bldg., Ste. 2212
350 Fifth Ave.
New York, NY 10118-2299
Ph: (212)279-2626   Fax: (212)629-5178
E-mail: webmaster@nacme.org
URL: http://www.nacme.org/

Description: Leads the national effort to increase access to careers in engineering and other science-based disciplines. Supported by the nation's leading technology-intensive companies, NACME conducts research and public policy analysis, develops and operates national demonstration programs at precollege and university levels, and disseminates information through publications, conferences, and electronic media. NACME is also the nation's largest privately funded source of scholarships for minority students in engineering.

★456★ National Society of Professional Engineers (NSPE)

1420 King St.
Alexandria, VA 22314
Ph: (703)684-2800   Fax: (703)836-4875
Fr: 888-285-6773
E-mail: custserv@nspe.org
URL: http://www.nspe.org

Description: Professional engineers and

engineers-in-training in all fields registered in accordance with the laws of states or territories of the U.S. or provinces of Canada; qualified graduate engineers, student members, and registered land surveyors. Is concerned with social, professional, ethical, and economic considerations of engineering as a profession; encompasses programs in public relations, employment practices, ethical considerations, education, and career guidance. Monitors legislative and regulatory actions of interest to the engineering profession.

★457★ *Scientific, Engineering, and Technical Services*

Cambridge Educational
2572 Brunswick Ave.
Lawrenceville, NJ 08648-4128
Fax: 800-FAX-ON-US   Fr: 800-468-4227
URL: http://www.cambridgeeducational.com

$89.95. 2002. 18 minutes. Part of the Career Cluster Series.

★458★ Society of Women Engineers (SWE)

230 E Ohio St., No. 400
Chicago, IL 60611-3265
Ph: (312)596-5223   Fax: (312)596-5252
E-mail: hq@swe.org
URL: http://www.swe.org

Description: Educational and service organization representing both students and professional women in engineering and technical fields.

★459★ *Women in Engineering*

Her Own Words
PO Box 5264
Madison, WI 53705-0264
Ph: (608)271-7083   Fax: (608)271-0209
URL: http://www.herownwords.com/

Video. Jocelyn Riley. $95.00. 15 minutes. Resource guide also available for $45.00.

Agricultural Engineers

★470★ Great Jobs for Engineering Majors
McGraw-Hill Professional
McGraw-Hill Higher Education
2 Penn Plaza
New York, NY 10121
Ph: (212)904-2000   Fr: 800-722-4726
E-mail: ntcpub@tribune.com

Geraldine O. Garner. Second edition, 2002. $14.95. 256 pages. Covers all the career options open to students majoring in engineering.

★471★ Keys to Engineering Success
Prentice Hall PTR
One Lake St.
Upper Saddle River, NJ 07458
Ph: (201)236-7000

Jill S. Tietjen, Kristy A. Schloss, Carol Carter, Joyce Bishop, and Sarah Lyman. 2000. $32.00 (paper).

★472★ Opportunities in Agriculture Careers
McGraw-Hill Trade
2 Penn Plaza
New York, NY 10121
Ph: (212)904-2000   Fr: 800-722-4726

William C. White and Donald N. Collins. 1995. $13.95. 160 pages.

★473★ Workforce Management for Farms and Horticultural Businesses: Finding, Training and Keeping Good Employees
Natural Resource, Agricultural & Engineering Service (NRAES)
Cornell University
152 Riley Robb Hall
Ithaca, NY 14853-5170
Ph: (607)255-7654   Fax: (607)254-8770

1999. $15.00 (paper). 140 pages.

EMPLOYMENT AGENCIES AND SEARCH FIRMS

★474★ AGRI-Associates
2 Cleaver Blvd., Ste.130
Kansas City, MO 64112
Ph: (816)531-7980   Fax: (816)531-7982
E-mail: gip@agriassociates.com
URL: http://www.agriassociates.com

Executive search firm.

★475★ Agri-Business Services Inc.
20 Barron Way
Aiken, SC 29803
Ph: (803)642-4440   Fax: (803)642-5863
E-mail: info@agribusinessservices.com
URL: http://www.agribusinessservices.com

Executive search firm.

★476★ Agri-Personnel
5120 Old Bill Cook Rd.
Atlanta, GA 30349-0319
Ph: (404)768-5701   Fax: (404)768-5705

Agribusiness consultants active in executive/professional/technical recruitment and placement, and in mergers, acquisitions, and divestitures in various industries including dairy, feed, food, fertilizer, farm chemicals, poultry and egg, animal health, and pulp and paper.

★477★ Agri-Tech Personnel Inc.
4444 N Belleview, Ste. 209
Kansas City, MO 64116
Ph: (816)453-7200   Fax: (816)453-6001
E-mail: corp@agri-techpersonnel.com
URL: http://www.agri-techpersonnel.com

Executive search firm.

★478★ Boyle & Associates Retained Search Group
238 Chester St., Ste. 200
St. Paul, MN 55107
Ph: (651)223-5050   Fax: (651)297-6286

Executive search firm.

★479★ The Chase Group Inc.
7300 W 110th St., Ste. 560
Overland Park, KS 66210
Ph: (913)663-3100   Fax: (913)663-3131
E-mail: chase@chasegroup.com
URL: http://www.chasegroup.com

Executive search firm.

★480★ Emplex Associates
PO Box 2497
Southfield, MI 48037
Ph: (248)352-6362   Fr: 888-203-1010

Executive search firm.

★481★ Executive Resource Associates
1612 Bay Breeze Dr.
Virginia Beach, VA 23454
Ph: (757)481-6221   Fax: (757)481-1944
E-mail: davidr@sprintmail.com

Executive search firm.

★482★ First Search America Inc.
PO Box 85
Ardmore, TN 38449
Ph: (256)423-8800   Fax: (256)423-8801
E-mail: firstsearch@ardmore.net

Executive search firm.

★483★ Florapersonnel Inc.
1740 Lake Markham Rd.
Sanford, FL 32771
Ph: (407)320-8177   Fax: (407)320-8083

Employment agency for the horticulture industry.

★484★ High Employee Services Ltd.
525 Greenfield Rd., 2nd Fl.
Lancaster, PA 17601
Ph: (717)396-7701   Fax: (717)396-7779

Personnel consultants serving all industries including business and finance, engineering, sales and marketing, and focusing on manufacturing, industrial, and transportation operations. Conducts full time, contract staffing, and temporary (clerical and skilled) placements. Serves private industries as well as government agencies.

★485★ Miller & Associates Inc.
9036 NW 37th St.
Polk City, IA 50226
Fax: (515)965-5727   Fr: 888-965-2727
E-mail: rmiller@ag-careers.com
URL: http://www.ag-careers.com

Executive search firm.

★486★ The Montgomery Group Inc.
PO Box 30791
Knoxville, TN 37930-0791
Ph: (865)693-0325   Fax: (865)691-1900
E-mail: tmg@tmgincknox.com
URL: http://www.tmgincknox.com

Executive search firm.

★487★ MRI of Spencer
589 Hwy. 71 S
PO Box 840
Arnolds Park, IA 51331
Ph: (712)332-2011   Fax: (712)332-2051
E-mail: jayson@nationaljobs.com
URL: http://www.nationaljobs.net

Executive search firm.

★488★ MRI of Tucson
1840 E River Rd., Ste.120
Tucson, AZ 85718
Ph: (520)529-0750   Fax: (520)529-0931
E-mail: careers@mroftucson.com
URL: http://www.mroftucson.com

Executive search firm.

★489★ MRI of Williamsburg
600 Court St.
PO Box 1136
Williamsburg, IA 52361-1136
Ph: (319)668-2881   Fax: (319)668-1404
E-mail: jobs@wburgcareers.com
URL: http://www.wburgcareers.com

Executive search firm.

★490★ PERC Ltd.
PO Box 15327
Phoenix, AZ 85060-5327
Ph: (602)553-9896   Fax: (602)553-9897
Fr: 800-874-7246
E-mail: gordonstoa@qwest.net

Executive search firm.

★491★ Robert Connelly & Associates Inc.
520 Wilson Rd
Minneapolis, MN 55424
Ph: (952)925-3039   Fax: (952)922-5762
E-mail: olsen@robertconnelly.com
URL: http://www.robertconnelly.com

Executive search firm.

★492★ Robert Drexler Associates Inc.
PO Box 151
Saddle River, NJ 07458
Ph: (201)460-2300   Fax: (201)760-2301

Executive search firm.

★493★ RSM McGladrey Search Group
400 Locust St., Ste. 675
Des Moines, IA 50309
Ph: (515)281-9280
E-mail: iowaexecutivesearch@asrsmi.com
URL: http://www.mcgladrey.com

Executive search firm.

★494★ Sherwood Lehman Massucco Inc.
3455 W Shaw Ave., Ste. 110
Fresno, CA 93711-3201
Ph: (559)276-8572   Fax: (559)276-2351
E-mail: slinc@employmentexpert.com
URL: http://www.employmentexpert.com

Executive search firm.

★495★ Smith, Brown & Jones
7415 W 130th St., Ste. 100
Overland Park, KS 66213
Ph: (913)814-7770   Fax: (913)814-8440
E-mail: dlsmith@smithbrownjones.com
URL: http://www.smithbrownjones.com

Executive search firm.

★496★ Smith & Laue Search
4370 NE Halsey St.
Portland, OR 97213
Ph: (503)460-9181   Fax: (503)460-9182
E-mail: chuck@smithlaue.com

Executive search firm.

★497★ Spencer Stuart
401 N Michigan Ave., Ste. 3400
Chicago, IL 60611
Ph: (312)822-0080   Fax: (312)822-0116
URL: http://www.spencerstuart.com

Executive search firm.

★498★ Steven Douglas Associates Retainer Division
3040 Universal Blvd., Ste. 180
Weston, FL 33331
Ph: (954)385-8595   Fax: (954)453-8575

Executive search firm.

★499★ Techtronix Technical Search
PO Box 17713
Milwaukee, WI 53217-0173
Ph: (414)466-3100   Fax: (414)466-3598

Firm specializes in recruiting executives for the engineering, information systems, manufacturing, marketing, finance, and human resources industries.

★500★ Tom Allison Associates
625 Stagecoach Rd. SE
Albuquerque, NM 87123
Ph: (505)275-7771   Fax: (505)275-7771
E-mail: tallison@spinn.net

Executive search firm.

★501★ Trambley the Recruiter
5353 Wyoming Blvd. NE, Ste. 8
Albuquerque, NM 87109-3132
Ph: (505)821-5440   Fax: (505)821-8509

Personnel consultant recruits and places engineering professionals in specific areas of off-road equipment design, and manufacturing. Industries served: construction, agricultural, lawn and garden, oil exploration, and mining equipment manufacturing.

OTHER SOURCES

★502★ Agriculture Industry
Evon Publishing
832 N 7th Ave.
Iron River, MI 49935
Ph: (906)265-3190

Audiocassette. 1996. $16.95. 32 minutes. Part of the Careers and Vocational Guidance Series. Provides information about the nature of the work, educational requirements, employment outlook, earnings, and work

conditions as well as additional related information.

★503★ Council for Agricultural Science and Technology (CAST)
4420 West Lincoln Way
Ames, IA 50014-3447
Ph: (515)292-2125   Fax: (515)292-4512
E-mail: cast@cast-science.org
URL: http://www.cast-science.org

Members: Scientific societies, associate societies, individuals, corporations, foundations, and trade associations. **Purpose:** Promotes science-based information on food, fiber, agricultural, natural resource, and related societal and environmental issues.

★504★ Engineering Occupations
Delphi Productions
3160 4th St.
Boulder, CO 80304
Fax: (303)443-4022   Fr: 888-443-2400
URL: http://www.delphivideo.com

$95.00. 50 minutes. Part of the Careers for the 21st Century Video Library.

★505★ Scientific, Engineering, and Technical Services
Cambridge Educational
2572 Brunswick Ave.
Lawrenceville, NJ 08648-4128
Fax: 800-FAX-ON-US   Fr: 800-468-4227
URL: http://www.cambridgeeducational.com

$89.95. 2002. 18 minutes. Part of the Career Cluster Series.

★506★ Women in Engineering
Her Own Words
PO Box 5264
Madison, WI 53705-0264
Ph: (608)271-7083   Fax: (608)271-0209
URL: http://www.herownwords.com/

Video. Jocelyn Riley. $95.00. 15 minutes. Resource guide also available for $45.00.

Agricultural Scientists

SOURCES OF HELP-WANTED ADS

★507★ American Journal of Alternative Agriculture

Henry A. Wallace Institute for Alternative
  Agriculture
9200 Edmonston Rd., Ste. 117
Greenbelt, MD 20770-1551
Ph: (301)441-8777   Fax: (301)220-0164

Quarterly. $24.00/year. Journal covering agricultural science.

★508★ BioWorld Magazine

American Health Consultants Inc.
3525 Piedmont Rd., Bldg. 6, Ste. 400
Atlanta, GA 30305
Ph: (404)262-7436   Fax: (404)262-7837
Fr: 800-688-2421
E-mail: customerservice@ahcpub.com

Free to qualified subscribers; $75.00/year for others. Magazine covering the biotechnology industry.

★509★ Cell

Cell Press
1100 Massachusetts Ave.
Cambridge, MA 02138
Ph: (617)661-7057   Fax: (617)661-7061
E-mail: advertising@cell.com
URL: http://www.cell.com

Biweekly. $125.00/year for individuals, U.S.; $242.00/year for other countries; $210.00/year for Canada; $799.00/year for institutions; $899.00/year for institutions, other countries. Journal on molecular and cell biology.

★510★ Crop Science-Soil Science-Agronomy News

American Society of Agronomy
677 S Segoe Rd.
Madison, WI 53711-1086
Ph: (608)273-8080   Fax: (608)273-2021
E-mail: news@agronomy.org

Description: Monthly. Publishes information on agronomy, crop science, soil science, and related topics. Provides news of the societies and members; reports of annual meetings; listings of publications; announcements of awards, retirements, and deaths; job listings; and a calendar of events.

★511★ Farmland News

Farmland News
104 Depot St.
PO Box 240
Archbold, OH 43502-0240
Ph: (419)445-9456   Fax: (419)445-4444

Weekly. $27.00/year for individuals; $48.00 for two years. Rural human-interest newspaper (tabloid).

★512★ Feedstuffs

Miller Publishing Co.
12400 Whitewater Dr., Ste. 160
Minnetonka, MN 55343
Ph: (952)930-1832   Fax: (952)938-4390
URL: http://www.feedstuffs.com

Weekly. $135.00/year. Magazine serving the grain and feed industries and animal agriculture.

★513★ Nature International Weekly Journal of Science

Nature Publishing Group
345 Park Ave. S
New York, NY 10010-1707
Ph: (212)726-9200   Fax: (212)689-9711
Fr: 888-331-6288
E-mail: nature@natureny.com
URL: http://www.nature.com

Weekly. $145.00/year for individuals; $495.00/year for institutions. Magazine covering science and technology, including the fields of biology, biochemistry, genetics, medicine, earth sciences, physics, pharmacology, and behavioral sciences.

★514★ Resource

American Society of Agricultural
  Engineers
2950 Niles Rd.
St. Joseph, MI 49085-9659
Ph: (269)429-0300   Fax: (269)429-3852
Fr: 800-371-2723
URL: http://www.asae.org

Monthly. $69.12/year. Magazine covering technology for food and agriculture.

★515★ The Scientist

The Scientist Inc.
3535 Market St., Ste. 200
Philadelphia, PA 19104-2645
Ph: (215)386-9601   Fax: (215)386-7542
Fr: 800-258-6008
E-mail: info@the-scientist.com
URL: http://www.the-scientist.com

Biweekly. $49.00/year for individuals; $149.00/year for institutions; $24.00/year for students; $82.00/year for other countries; $49.00/year for students, other countries; $174.00/year for institutions, other countries. News journal (tabloid) for life scientists featuring news, opinions, research, and professional section.

★516★ The Soilless Grower

Hydroponic Society of America
PO Box 1183
El Cerrito, CA 94530
Fax: (510)232-2384
URL: http://hsa.hydroponics.org

Description: Bimonthly. Covers issues and research in hydroponics. Recurring features include letters to the editor, a calendar of events, reports of meetings, news of educational opportunities, job listings, book reviews, and notices of publications available.

PLACEMENT AND JOB REFERRAL SERVICES

★517★ American Society of Agronomy (ASA)
677 S. Segoe Rd.
Madison, WI 53711
Ph: (608)273-8080   Fax: (608)273-2021
E-mail: headquarters@agronomy.org
URL: http://www.agronomy.org

Description: Professional society of agronomists, plant breeders, physiologists, soil scientists, chemists, educators, technicians, and others concerned with crop production and soil management, and conditions affecting them. Sponsors fellowship program and student essay and speech contests. Provides placement service.

★518★ Association of Applied IPM Ecologists (AAIE)
PO Box 10880
Napa, CA 94581
Ph: (707)265-9349   Fax: (707)265-9349
E-mail: director@aaie.net
URL: http://www.aaie.net

Description: Professional agricultural pest management consultants, entomologists, and field personnel. Promotes the implementation of integrated pest management in agricultural and urban environments. Provides a forum for the exchange of technical information on pest control. Offers placement service.

★519★ Federation of American Societies for Experimental Biology (FASEB)
9650 Rockville Pike
Bethesda, MD 20814-3998
Ph: (301)634-7000   Fax: (301)634-7001
E-mail: admin@faseb.org
URL: http://www.faseb.org

Description: Federation of scientific societies with a total of 40,000 members: The American Physiological Society; American Society for Biochemistry and Molecular Biology; American Society for Pharmacology and Experimental Therapeutics; American Society for Investigative Pathology; American Society for Nutritional Sciences; the American Association of Immunologists; the American Society for Bone and Mineral Research; American Society for Clinical Investigation; the Indocrine Society; the American Society of Human Genetics; Society for Developmental Biology; Biophysical Society; American Association of Anatomists; and the Protein Society. **Activities:** Maintains placement service.

★520★ Korean Scientists and Engineers Association in America (KSEA)
1952 Gallows Rd., Ste. 300
Vienna, VA 22182
Ph: (703)748-1221   Fax: (703)748-1331
E-mail: sejong@ksea.org

URL: http://www.ksea.org
Description: Scientists and engineers holding single or advanced degrees. Goals are to: promote friendship and mutuality among Korean and American scientists and engineers; contribute to Korea's scientific, technological, industrial, and economic developments; strengthen the scientific, technological, and cultural bonds between Korea and the U.S. Sponsors symposium. Maintains speakers' bureau, placement service, and biographical archives. Compiles statistics. Maintains 100 volume library of scientific handbooks and yearbooks in Korean.

★521★ Women in Agribusiness (WIA)
PO Box 986
Kearney, MO 64060
Description: Women in agribusiness. Provides a forum for the discussion of ideas and information related to agribusiness. Offers placement, networking, and peer/mentor support services.

EMPLOYER DIRECTORIES AND NETWORKING LISTS

★522★ Agricultural & Industrial Manufacturers Representatives Association-Membership Directory
Agricultural & Industrial Manufacturers Representatives Association
7500 Flying Cloud Dr., Ste. 900
Eden Prairie, MN 55344-3756
Fax: (952)835-4774   Fr: 800-759-2467

Annual, October. $50.00. Covers 120 members; coverage includes Canada. Entries include: Company name, address, phone, name of principal executive, territory covered. Arrangement: Alphabetical.

★523★ Agricultural Research Institute-Membership Directory
Agricultural Research Institute
505 Capito Ct.
Washington, DC 20002
Ph: (202)675-8333   Fax: (202)675-8334

Annual. $50.00. Covers 125 member institutions; also lists study panels and committees interested in environmental issues, pest control, agricultural meteorology, biotechnology, food irradiation, agricultural policy, research and development, food safety, technology transfer, and remote sensing. Entries include: Name, title of primary contact, address, phone, fax. Arrangement: Alphabetical.

★524★ American Men and Women of Science
Thomson Gale
27500 Drake Rd.
Farmington Hills, MI 48331-3535
Ph: (248)699-4253   Fax: (248)699-8065
Fr: 800-877-GALE

E-mail: amws@galegroup.com
Biennial, latest edition December 2002. $975.00. Covers over 129,700 U.S. and Canadian scientists active in the physical, biological, mathematical, computer science, and engineering fields; includes references to previous edition for deceased scientists and nonrespondents. Entries include: Name, address, education, personal and career data, memberships, honors and awards, research interest. Arrangement: Alphabetical. Indexes: Discipline (in separate volume).

★525★ Colorado Agricultural Outlook Forum Directory
Colorado Department of Agriculture
700 Kipling St., Ste. 4000
Lakewood, CO 80215-8000
Ph: (303)239-4100   Fax: (303)239-4125

Latest edition 2003. Covers groups involved with agriculture in Colorado including agricultural associations in Colorado and nationally, Colorado land trusts, state government agencies, federal government agencies, congressional offices of Colorado senators and representatives, farm/ranch management assistance groups, Colorado State University (CSU) research centers and cooperative extension offices by county, and Future Farmers of America (FFA) high school chapters. Entries include: Name, address, phone, fax, and URL. For CSU and FFA information–Name, phone number. Arrangement: By category, then alphabetical.

★526★ Directory of State Departments of Agriculture
U.S. Department of Agriculture
14 Independence Ave. SW, Rm. 3977-S. Bldg.
Washington, DC 20250
Ph: (202)720-6920   Fax: (202)690-3794

Biennial, late summer of odd years. Covers state departments of agriculture and their officials. Entries include: Department name, address, phone, names and titles of key personnel, department branches. Arrangement: Geographical.

★527★ Peterson's Job Opportunities in Engineering and Technology
Thomson Peterson's
PO Box 67005
Lawrenceville, NJ 08648-6105
Fr: 800-338-3282

Compiled by the Peterson's staff. Fourth edition, 1996. $21.95 (paper). 384 pages. Profiles 2,000 high-tech companies looking primarily for technical personnel in such fields as biotechnology, telecommunications, software, computers and peripherals, defense, and aerospace. Contains job-search strategies and career options to help match education and expertise to the job market. Indexed geographically, by industry, and by hiring needs.

HANDBOOKS AND MANUALS

★528★ The Best Resumes for Scientists and Engineers

John Wiley & Sons Inc.
1 Wiley Dr.
Somerset, NJ 08873
Ph: (732)469-4400   Fr: 800-225-5945

Adele Lewis and David J. Moore. Second edition, 1993. $37.50; $19.95 (paper). 224 pages. Presents an extensive collection of scientific and engineering resumes, highlighting the important differences between these and resumes written for other occupations.

★529★ Career Information Center

Macmillan Publishing Co. Inc.
200 Old Tappan Rd.
Old Tappan, NJ 07675
Fr: 800-428-5331

Visual Education Center Staff. Seventh edition, 1999. $275.00. 2080 pages. This 13-volume set profiles over 600 occupations. Each occupational profile describes job duties, educational requirements, how to get the job, advancement possibilities, employment outlook, working conditions, earnings and benefits, and where to write for more information.

★530★ Careers in Health Care

McGraw-Hill Trade
2 Penn Plaza
New York, NY 10121
Ph: (212)904-2000   Fr: 800-722-4726
E-mail: ntcpub@tribune.com

Barbara M. Swanson. Fourth edition, 2000. $17.95; $13.95 (paper). 320 pages. Describes job duties, work settings, salaries, licensing and certification requirements, educational preparation, and future outlook. Gives ideas on how to secure a job.

★531★ Farmers, Scientists and Plant Breeding: Integrating Knowledge and Practice

Oxford University Press, Incorporated
198 Madison Ave.
New York, NY 10016-4314
Ph: (212)726-6000   Fax: (212)726-6440

David Arthur Cleveland, Daniela Soleri. 2002. $100.00. Illustrated. 360 pages.

★532★ Guide to Nontraditional Careers in Science

Hemisphere Publishing Corp.
325 Chestnut St., 8th Fl.
Philadelphia, PA 19106
Ph: (215)785-5800   Fax: (215)269-0363
Fr: 800-821-8312

Karen Young Kreeger. 1998. $38.95 (paper). 263 pages.

★533★ Opportunities in Agriculture Careers

McGraw-Hill Trade
2 Penn Plaza
New York, NY 10121
Ph: (212)904-2000   Fr: 800-722-4726

William C. White and Donald N. Collins. 1995. $13.95. 160 pages.

★534★ Opportunities in Environmental Careers

McGraw-Hill Trade
2 Penn Plaza
New York, NY 10121
Ph: (212)904-2000   Fr: 800-722-4726
E-mail: ntcpub@tribune.com

Odom Fanning. Revised, 2002. $12.95 (paper). 160 pages. Describes a broad range of opportunities in fields such as environmental health, recreation, physics, and hygiene, and provides job search advice. Part of Opportunities in...Series.

★535★ Opportunities in Farming and Agriculture Careers

McGraw-Hill Trade
2 Penn Plaza
New York, NY 10121
Ph: (212)904-2000   Fr: 800-722-4726

William C. White and Donald N. Collins. Revised, 1995. $14.95; $11.95 (paper). 205 pages. Covers opportunities in such fields as agricultural engineering, management, experimental farming, agricultural sales, teaching, and others, and provides job-hunting advice. Illustrated. Out of print.

★536★ Opportunities in Research and Development Careers

McGraw-Hill/Contemporary Books
1221 Avenue of the Americas
New York, NY 10020
Ph: (212)904-2000   Fr: 800-323-4900
E-mail: ntcpub@tribune.com

Jan Goldberg. 1997. $14.95; $11.95 (paper). 204 pages.

★537★ Resumes for Scientific and Technical Careers

McGraw-Hill Contemporary Books
1221 Avenue of the Americas
New York, NY 10020
Ph: (212)904-2000   Fr: 800-323-4900
E-mail: ntcpub@tribune.com

1999. $9.95 (paper). 450 pages. Provides resume advice for individuals interested in working in scientific and technical careers. Includes sample resumes and cover letters.

★538★ To Boldly Go: A Practical Career Guide for Scientists

American Geophysical Union
2000 Florida Ave., NW
Washington, DC 20009
Ph: (202)462-6900   Fax: (202)328-0566
Fr: 800-966-2481

Peter S. Fiske. 1996. $19.00 (paper).

★539★ Where the Jobs Are: The Hottest Careers for the 90s

The Career Press, Inc.
3 Tice Rd.
PO Box 687
Franklin Lakes, NJ 07417-1322
Ph: (201)848-0310   Fax: (201)848-1727
Fr: 800-227-3371

Joyce Hadley. Third edition, 2000. $13.99 (paper). 400 pages. Out of print. Describes careers in fifteen general fields, from accounting to travel and hospitality.

EMPLOYMENT AGENCIES AND SEARCH FIRMS

★540★ Agra Placements, Ltd.

8187 University Blvd.
Clive, IA 50325
Ph: (515)225-6562   Fax: (515)225-7733
E-mail: iowa@agraplacements.com
URL: http://www.agraplacements.com

Executive search firm. Branch offices in Peru, IN, Lincoln, IL, and New Ulm, MN.

★541★ Agri-Personnel

5120 Old Bill Cook Rd.
Atlanta, GA 30349-0319
Ph: (404)768-5701   Fax: (404)768-5705

Agribusiness consultants active in executive/professional/technical recruitment and placement, and in mergers, acquisitions, and divestitures in various industries including dairy, feed, food, fertilizer, farm chemicals, poultry and egg, animal health, and pulp and paper.

★542★ Management Search, Inc.

3013 NW 59th St.,Ste.A-1
Oklahoma City, OK 73112
Ph: (405)842-3173   Fax: (405)842-8360
E-mail: dorwig@mgmtsearch.com
URL: http://www.mgmtsearch.com

Executive search firm specializing in the field of agri-business.

★543★ Winters Technical Staffing Services

2025 Sheppard Ave. E, Ste. 4110
Willowdale, ON, Canada M2T 1V7
Ph: (416)495-7422   Fax: (416)495-8479

Technical staffing service for permanent and contract positions in all facets of engineering. Serves government agencies, consulting engineers, and all areas of manufacturing in Canada and northeast U.S.

TRADESHOWS

★544★ **Agri News Farm Show**

Agri News Farm Show
PO Box 6118
18 1st Ave. SE
Rochester, MN 55903-6118
Ph: (507)285-7600   Fax: (507)281-7436
Fr: 800-533-1727
URL: http://www.agrinews.com

Annual. **Primary Exhibits:** Agricultural equipment, supplies, and services. **Dates and Locations:** 2005 Mar 23-24; Rochester, MN; Graham Arena.

★545★ **American Feed Industry Association Feed Industries Show**

American Feed Industry Association
1501 Wilson Blvd., Ste. 1100
Arlington, VA 22209
Ph: (703)524-0810   Fax: (703)524-1921
E-mail: afia@afia.org

Biennial. **Primary Exhibits:** Feed equipment, services, and ingredients. **Dates and Locations:** 2005 May 02-04; Kansas City, MO; Kansas City Center • 2007 May 07-09; Minneapolis, MN; Minneapolis Convention Center.

★546★ **Empire Farm Days**

Empire State Potato Growers, Inc.
PO Box 566
Stanley, NY 14561
Ph: (585)526-5326   Fax: (585)526-6576
Fr: 877-697-7837
E-mail: mwickham@empirepotatogrowers.com
URL: http://www.empirepotatogrowers.com

Annual. **Primary Exhibits:** Agricultural equipment, supplies, and services.

★547★ **Farm Progress Show**

Farm Progress Companies, Inc.
191 S Gary Ave.
Carol Stream, IL 60188-2089
Ph: (630)462-2870   Fax: (630)588-2081
E-mail: mrandal@farmprogress.com
URL: http://www.agrilandexpo.com

Annual. **Primary Exhibits:** Farm machinery and equipment, trucks, livestock equipment, buildings, seed, chemicals, computers, and other agricultural products and services.

★548★ **Mid-America Farm Show**

Salina Area Chamber of Commerce
120 West Ash
Salina, KS 67401
Ph: (785)827-9301   Fax: (785)827-9758
E-mail: chamber@informatics.net

Annual. **Primary Exhibits:** Agricultural equipment, supplies, and services, including irrigation equipment, fertilizer, farm implements, hybrid seed, agricultural chemicals, tractors, feed, farrowing crates and equipment, silos and bins, storage equipment, and farm buildings.

★549★ **Mid-South Farm and Gin Supply Exhibit**

Southern Cotton Ginners Association
874 Cotton Gin Pl.
Memphis, TN 38106
Ph: (901)947-3104   Fax: (901)947-3103
E-mail: scga@netten.net

Annual. **Primary Exhibits:** Agricultural equipment, supplies and services. **Dates and Locations:** 2005 Feb 25-26; Memphis, TN.

★550★ **Midwest Farm Show**

North Country Enterprises LLC
PO Box 832
Chippewa Falls, WI 54729
Ph: (715)723-2775   Fax: (715)723-2775
E-mail: North_Country25@aol.com

Annual. **Primary Exhibits:** Farm materials handling equipment, supplies, and services. **Dates and Locations:** 2005 Jan 19-20; La Crosse, WI.

★551★ **National Western Stock Show and Rodeo**

The Western Stock Show Association
4655 Humboldt St.
Denver, CO 80216
Ph: (303)297-1166   Fax: (303)292-1708
Fr: 800-336-6977
URL: http://www.nationalwestern.com

Annual. **Primary Exhibits:** Jewelry, apparel, household goods, agricultural products, and service groups. A great blend of agriculture, western and urban products including agriculture equipment, supplies and services, horse items, household products, apparel, jewelry, buildings, childrens' items, art, food and tools.

★552★ **North American Farm and Power Show**

Tradexpos, Inc.
811 Oakland Ave. W.
PO Box 1067
Austin, MN 55912
Ph: (507)437-1378   Fax: (507)437-8917
Fr: 800-347-5225
E-mail: tradexpo@smig.net
URL: http://www.tradexpos.com

Annual. **Primary Exhibits:** Farm equipment, supplies, and services; lawn and garden equipment; industrial equipment.

★553★ **Northwest Agricultural Show**

Northwest Horticultural Congress
4672 Drift Creek Rd., SE
Sublimity, OR 97385
Ph: (503)769-7120   Fax: (503)769-3549

Annual. **Primary Exhibits:** Agricultural equipment and services.

★554★ **Southern Farm Show**

Southern Shows, Inc.
PO Box 36859
Charlotte, NC 28236
Ph: (704)376-6594   Fax: (704)376-6345
Fr: 800-849-0248
E-mail: sabernethy@southernshows.com
URL: http://www.southernshows.com

Annual. **Primary Exhibits:** Agriculture equipment, supplies, and chemicals.

★555★ **Triumph of Agriculture Exposition - Farm and Ranch Machinery Show**

Mid-America Expositions, Inc.
7015 Spring St.
Omaha, NE 68106-3518
Ph: (402)346-8003   Fax: (402)346-5412
Fr: 800-475-SHOW
E-mail: showoffice@aol.com
URL: http://www.showofficeonline.com

Annual. **Primary Exhibits:** Farm equipment and supplies. **Dates and Locations:** 2004 Mar 9-10; Omaha, NE; Civic Auditorium.

★556★ **Western Farm Show**

Western Retail Implement and Hardware Association
638 W. 39th St.
Kansas City, MO 64111
Ph: (816)561-5323   Fax: (816)561-1249
URL: http://www.westernfarmshow.com

Annual. **Primary Exhibits:** equipment, supplies, and services relating to the agricultural industry.

OTHER SOURCES

★557★ *Agriculture Industry*

Evon Publishing
832 N 7th Ave.
Iron River, MI 49935
Ph: (906)265-3190

Audiocassette. 1996. $16.95. 32 minutes. Part of the Careers and Vocational Guidance Series. Provides information about the nature of the work, educational requirements, employment outlook, earnings, and work conditions as well as additional related information.

★558★ **American Institute of Biological Sciences (AIBS)**

1444 I St. NW, Ste. 200
Washington, DC 20005-2210
Ph: (202)628-1500   Fax: (202)628-1509
Fr: 800-992-2427
E-mail: rogrady@aibs.org
URL: http://www.aibs.org

Members: Professional member organization and federation of biological associations, laboratories, and museums whose members have an interest in the life sciences. **Purpose:** Promotes unity and effectiveness of effort among persons engaged in biological research, education, and application of biological sciences, including agriculture, environment, and medicine. Seeks to further the relationships of biological sciences to other sciences and industries. Conducts roundtable series; provides names of prominent biologists who are willing to serve as speakers and curriculum consultants; provides advisory committees and other services to the Department of Energy, Environmental Protection Agency, National Science Foundation, Department of Defense, and National Aeronautics and Space Administration. Maintains educational consultant panel.

★559★ American Society for
Horticultural Science (ASHS)
113 S West St., Ste. 200
Alexandria, VA 22314-2851
Ph: (703)836-4606   Fax: (703)836-2024
E-mail: ashs@ashs.org
URL: http://www.ashs.org

Description: Promotes and encourages scientific research and education in horticulture throughout the world. Members represent all areas of horticulture science.

★560★ Association for International
Practical Training (AIPT)
10400 Little Patuxent Pky., Ste. 250
Columbia, MD 21044-3519
Ph: (410)997-2200   Fax: (410)992-3924
E-mail: aipt@aipt.org
URL: http://www.aipt.org

Description: Providers worldwide on-the-job training programs for students and professionals seeking international career development and life-changing experiences. Arranges workplace exchanges in hundreds of professional fields, bringing employers and trainees together from around the world. Client list ranges from small farming communities to Fortune 500 companies.

★561★ Council for Agricultural
Science and Technology (CAST)
4420 West Lincoln Way
Ames, IA 50014-3447
Ph: (515)292-2125   Fax: (515)292-4512
E-mail: cast@cast-science.org
URL: http://www.cast-science.org

Members: Scientific societies, associate societies, individuals, corporations, foundations, and trade associations. **Purpose:** Promotes science-based information on food, fiber, agricultural, natural resource, and related societal and environmental issues.

★562★ Minority Women In Science
(MWIS)
Directorate for Education and Human
Resources Programs
1200 New York Ave. NW
Washington, DC 20005
Ph: (202)326-7019   Fax: (202)371-9849
E-mail: sassefa@aaas.org

Description: A national network group of the American association for the Advancement of Science (AAAS), Education and Human Resources Directorate. The objectives of this group are: to identify and share information on resources and programs that could help in mentoring young women and minorities interested in science and engineering careers, and to strengthen communication among women and minorities in science and education.

★563★ National Postsecondary
Agricultural Student Organization
(PAS)
6060 FFA Dr.
PO Box 68960
Indianapolis, IN 46268-0960
Ph: (317)802-4220   Fax: (317)802-5220
E-mail: pas@teamaged.org
URL: http://www.nationalpas.org

Description: Agriculturally-related student organization; provides opportunity for individual growth, leadership and career preparation. Promotes development of leadership abilities through employment programs, course work, and organization activities.

★564★ Scientific, Engineering, and
Technical Services
Cambridge Educational
2572 Brunswick Ave.
Lawrenceville, NJ 08648-4128
Fax: 800-FAX-ON-US   Fr: 800-468-4227
URL: http://www.cambridgeeducational.com

$89.95. 2002. 18 minutes. Part of the Career Cluster Series.

★565★ Scientific Occupations
Delphi Productions
3160 4th St.
Boulder, CO 80304
Fax: (303)443-4022   Fr: 888-443-2400
URL: http://www.delphivideo.com

$95.00. 60 minutes. Part of the Careers for the 21st Century Video Library.

★566★ Soil Science Society of
America (SSSA)
677 S Segoe Rd.
Madison, WI 53711
Ph: (608)273-8080   Fax: (608)273-2021
E-mail: headquarters@agronomy.org
URL: http://www.soils.org

Description: Professional soil scientists, including soil physicists, soil classifiers, land use and management specialists, chemists, microbiologists, soil fertility specialists, soil cartographers, conservationists, mineralogists, engineers, and others interested in fundamental and applied soil science.

AI Programmers

★567★ **AI Magazine**

American Association for Artificial
Intelligence
445 Burgess Dr.
Menlo Park, CA 94025-3496
Ph: (650)328-3123   Fax: (650)321-4457
URL: http://www.aaai.org/organization/contact.html

Quarterly. $50.00/year for U.S.; $75.00/year
for other countries. Magazine about artificial
intelligence.

★568★ **Applied Artificial Intelligence**

Taylor & Francis
325 Chestnut St., Ste. 800
Philadelphia, PA 19106
Ph: (215)625-8900   Fax: (215)625-2940
Fr: 800-354-1420
URL: http://www.tandf.co.uk/journals/tf/
08839514.html

$415.00/year. Journal covering applied artifi-
cial intelligence.

★569★ **Computational & Mathematical
Organization Theory**

Kluwer Academic/Plenum Publishing Corp.
233 Spring St., 7th Fl.
New York, NY 10013-1578
Ph: (212)620-8000   Fax: (212)463-0742
Fr: 800-221-9369
URL: http://www.wkap.nl/journalhome.htm/
1381-298X

Quarterly. $350.00/year for institutions, print
or online edition only; $420.00/year for insti-
tutions, print and online editions; $125.00/
year for individuals. Journal covering organizational research using computer simulation,
logic and artificial intelligence.

★570★ **Computer Speech & Language**

Academic Press
525 B St., Ste. 1900
San Diego, CA 92101-4495
Ph: (619)231-6616   Fax: (619)699-6715
Fr: 800-321-5068
E-mail: usjcs@elsevier.com
URL: http://www.elsevier.com/locate/issn/
0885-2308

$335.00/year for institutions; $138.00/year
for individuals. Scholarly journal covering
speech by humans and machines.

★571★ **Computists' Weekly**

Computists International
4064 Sutherland Dr.
Palo Alto, CA 94303
Ph: (650)493-4176   Fr: 888-625-5385
E-mail: editor@computists.com
URL: http://www.computists.com

Description: Forty issues/year. Features
news and opportunities in artificial intelligence, information science, and computer
science. Available online only.

★572★ **Cybernetics and Systems**

Taylor & Francis
325 Chestnut St., Ste. 800
Philadelphia, PA 19106
Ph: (215)625-8900   Fax: (215)625-2940
Fr: 800-354-1420
URL: http://www.tandf.co.uk/journals/tf/
01969722.html

$351.00/year for individuals. International
forum for developments in cybernetics with
applications spanning artificial intelligence to
economics.

★573★ **Dr. Dobb's Journal**

CMP Media LLC (San Francisco)
2800 Campus Dr.
San Mateo, CA 94403
Ph: (650)513-4300   Fax: (650)513-4618
E-mail: webmaster@ercb.com
URL: http://www.ddj.com

Monthly. Magazine covering computer programming.

★574★ **International Journal on
Artificial Intelligence Tools**

World Scientific Publishing Co. Inc.
1060 Main St., Ste. 202
River Edge, NJ 07661
Ph: (201)487-9655   Fax: (201)487-9656
Fr: 800-227-7562

Quarterly. $210.00/year. Journal covering
design, development, and testing of AI tools.

★575★ **Journal of Artificial Intelligence
Research (JAIR)**

Morgan Kaufmann Publishers
500 Sansome Street, Ste. 400
San Francisco, CA 94111
Ph: 888-864-7547   Fax: (415)982-2665
E-mail: mkp@mkp.com
URL: http://www.cs.washington.edu/re-
search/jair/home.html

Covers all areas of artificial intelligence.

★576★ **Journal of Intelligent
Information Systems**

Kluwer Academic/Plenum Publishing Corp.
233 Spring St., 7th Fl.
New York, NY 10013-1578
Ph: (212)620-8000   Fax: (212)463-0742
Fr: 800-221-9369
URL: http://www.wkap.nl/jouralhome.htm/
0925-9902

Bimonthly. $527.00/year for institutions, print
or online edition only; $632.40/year for insti-
tutions, print and online editions; $210.00/
year for individuals. Journal integrating artificial intelligence and database technologies.

★577★ **Journal of Intelligent and
Robotic Systems**

Kluwer Academic/Plenum Publishing Corp.
233 Spring St., 7th Fl.
New York, NY 10013-1578
Ph: (212)620-8000   Fax: (212)463-0742
Fr: 800-221-9369
URL: http://www.wkap.nl/jouralhome.htm/
0921-0296

Monthly. $900.00/year for institutions, print
or online edition only; $570.00/year for indi-
viduals. Journal covering systems and con-

trol science with artificial intelligence and computer science concepts.

★578★ *PC AI*

Knowledge Technology Inc.
PO Box 30130
Phoenix, AZ 85046
Ph: (602)971-1869
E-mail: info@pcai.com
URL: http://www.pcai.com/pcai/

Bimonthly. $25.00/year for individuals. Geared toward practical application of intelligent technology; covers developments in expert systems, neural networks, fuzzy logic, object-oriented development, languages and all other areas of artificial intelligence.

★579★ *Presence*

The MIT Press
5 Cambridge Ctr.
Cambridge, MA 02142-1493
Ph: (617)253-5646   Fax: (617)258-6779
Fr: 800-405-1619
E-mail: presence@mit.edu
URL: http://mitpress.mit.edu/catalog/item

Bimonthly. $80.00/year for individuals. Scholarly journal on teleoperators and virtual environments.

★580★ *Robotica*

Cambridge University Press
40 W 20th St.
New York, NY 10011-4211
Ph: (212)924-3900   Fax: (212)691-3239
Fr: 800-221-4512
E-mail: journals_advertising@cup.org
URL: http://titles.cambridge.org/journals/journal_catalogue.asp?m

Bimonthly. $176.00/year for individuals; $498.00/year for institutions. Journal of robotics studies.

★581★ *Robotics World*

Douglas Publications Inc.
2807 N Parham Rd.,64 Bldg., Ste. 200
Richmond, VA 23294
Ph: (804)762-9600   Fax: (804)217-8999
Fr: 800-794-6086
E-mail: robs111@aol.com
URL: http://www.douglaspublications.com/robotics.html

$42.00/year for individuals; $67.00 for two years; $57.00/year for Canada; $82.00/year for elsewhere. Professional magazine covering flexible automation and intelligent machines.

★582★ *Software Development*

CMP Media L.L.C.
600 Community Dr.
Manhasset, NY 11030
Ph: (516)562-5000
E-mail: aweber@cmp.com
URL: http://www.sdmagazine.com

Monthly. $39.00/year for individuals within USA; $45.00/year within Canada; $54.00/

year for elsewhere. Magazine for the computer programming industry.

EMPLOYER DIRECTORIES AND NETWORKING LISTS

★583★ *Advanced Manufacturing Technology*

Technical Insights/John Wiley & Sons Inc.
111 River St.
Hoboken, NJ 07030-5774
Ph: (201)748-6000   Fax: (201)748-6088
Fr: 800-245-6217
E-mail: amtinfo@insights.com
URL: http://www.insights.com

Monthly. $630.00 for U.S.; $690.00 for elsewhere. Publication includes: List of companies involved in developing advanced manufacturing technologies such as robotics, artificial intelligence in computers, ultrasonics, lasers, and waterjet cutters; also lists sources of information and education on high-technology. Entries include: Company or organization name, address, phone, name of contact; description of process, product, or service. Principal content is articles and analysis of advanced manufacturing technology. Arrangement: Classified by subject.

★584★ *Robot Builder's Sourcebook*

Electronic Privacy Information Center
1718 Connecticut Ave. NW, Ste. 200
Washington, DC 20009

$24.95. Covers over 2,500 mail-order suppliers and other sources for amateur robotics materials. Entries include: Name, address, phone, e-mail address, URL, and information about the resource. Arrangement: By category, then alphabetical.

HANDBOOKS AND MANUALS

★585★ *AI Application Programming*

Charles River Media
10 Downer Avenue
Hingham, MA 02043
Fax: (703)996-1010   Fr: 800-382-8505
E-mail: info@charlesriver.com
URL: http://www.charlesriver.com/word.html

M. Tim Jones. 2003. $54.95. 363 pages. Software engineer Jones demystifies techniques associated with artificial intelligence and shows how they can be useful in everyday applications.

★586★ *Artificial Intelligence: A Modern Approach*

Prentice Hall PRT
One Lake Street
Upper Saddle River, NJ 07458
Ph: (201)236-7616   Fax: (201)236-7696

Stuart J. Russell and Peter Norvig. Second edition. 2002. $89.00. 1132 pages. Provides an introduction to the theory and practice of artificial intelligence.

★587★ *Career Opportunities in Computers and Cyberspace*

Facts on File
132 W. 31st St., 17th Fl.
New York, NY 10001-2006
Ph: (212)967-8800   Fax: (212)967-8107
Fr: 800-322-8755

Harry Henderson. 1999. $26.95 (paper). Part of the Career Opportunities Series. 224 pages.

★588★ *Choosing a Career in Computers*

Rosen Publishing Group, Inc.
29 E. 21st St.
New York, NY 10010
Ph: (212)777-3017   Fax: (212)777-0277
Fr: 800-237-9932

Weigant, Chris. 2000. $17.95.

★589★ *Computer Job Survival Guide*

Technion Books
PO Box 171
Leverett, MA 01054
URL: http://www.realrates.com/order.htm

Janet Ruhl. 2002. $24.95. 211 pages. Learn from seasoned professionals the secrets of how to break into the computer field and create a long-term, high-earning computer career.

★590★ *Encyclopedia of Artificial Intelligence*

John Wiley & Sons Inc.
111 River St.
Hoboken, NJ 07030-5774
Ph: (201)748-6000   Fax: (201)748-6088
Fr: 800-225-5945

Stuart C. Shapiro. Second edition. 1992. $342.72. 1792 pages. Written by 350 experts in industry, government and academia, this book covers all fields encompassed by Artificial Intelligence.

★591★ *Expert Resumes for Computer and Web Jobs*

JIST Publishing
8902 Otis Ave.
Indianapolis, IN 46216-1033
Ph: (317)613-4200   Fax: (317)613-4307
Fr: 800-648-5478

Wendy Enelow and Louis Kursmark. 2001. $16.95 (paper).

★592★ Mathematical Methods in Artificial Intelligence

John Wiley & Sons Inc.
111 River St.
Hoboken, NJ 07030-5774
Ph: (201)748-6000   Fax: (201)748-6088
Fr: 800-225-5945

Edward A. Bender. 1996. $44.95. Hardcover. 656 pages. Introduces the important mathematical foundations and tools in AI and describes their applications to the design of AI algorithms.

★593★ Preparing for an Outstanding Career in Computers: Questions and Answers for Professionals and Students

Rafi Systems, Incorporated
750 N. Diamond Bar Blvd., Suite 224
Diamond Bar, CA 91765
Ph: (909)593-8124   Fax: (909)629-1034
Fr: 800-584-6706

Mohamed Rafiquzzaman. 2001. $19.95.

★594★ Unlocking the Clubhouse: Women in Computing

MIT Press
5 Cambridge Ctr., Suite 4
Cambridge, MA 02142-1493
Ph: (617)253-5646   Fax: (617)253-6779
Fr: 800-356-0343

Jane Margolis and Allan Fisher. 2001. $24.95.

ONLINE JOB SOURCES AND SERVICES

★595★ Computer Jobs

URL: http://www.computerjobs.com
Description: Provides listings of computer-related job opportunities.

★596★ Guru

URL: http://www.guru.com
Description: Job board specializing in contract jobs for creative and information technology professionals. Also provides online incorporation and educational opportunities for independent contractors along with articles and advice.

★597★ ZDNet Tech Jobs

URL: http://www.zdnet.com/special/filters/techjobs/
Description: Site houses a listing of national employment opportunities for professionals in high tech fields. Also contains resume building tips and relocation resources. Powered by Dice.com

OTHER SOURCES

★598★ American Association for Artificial Intelligence (AAAI)

445 Burgess Dr.
Menlo Park, CA 94025-3442
Ph: (650)328-3123   Fax: (650)321-4457
URL: http://www.aaai.org

Members: Artificial intelligence researchers; students, libraries, corporations, and others interested in the subject. **Purpose:** Seeks to unite researchers and developers of artificial intelligence in order to provide an element of cohesion in the field; serves as focal point and organizer for conferences. Areas of interest include interpretation of visual data, robotics, expert systems, natural language processing, knowledge representation, and artificial intelligence programming technologies. **Activities:** Holds tutorials.

★599★ Artificial Intelligence Center-SRI International

333 Ravenswood Avenue
Menlo Park, CA 94025-3493
Ph: (650)859-2641   Fax: (650)859-3735

Description: SRI International's Artificial Center (AIC) is one of the world's major centers of research in artificial intelligence.

★600★ Cognitive Science Society (CSS)

Department of Psychology
University Texas
Austin, TX 78712
Ph: (512)232-4645   Fax: (512)471-3053
E-mail: cogsci@psy.utexas.edu
URL: http://www.cognitivesciencesociety.org

Description: Published Ph.D.s (500); students and Ph.D.s not actively publishing (300) in the fields of psychology, artificial intelligence, and cognitive science. Promotes the dissemination of research in cognitive science and allied sciences. (Cognitive science is a branch of artificial intelligence that seeks to simulate human reasoning and associative powers on a computer, using specialized software.)

★601★ Computer Occupations

Delphi Productions
3160 4th St.
Boulder, CO 80304
Fax: (303)443-4022   Fr: 888-443-2400
URL: http://www.delphivideo.com

$95.00. 50 minutes. Part of the Careers for the 21st Century Video Library.

★602★ Computing Research Association (CRA)

1100 Seventeenth Street NW, Ste. 507
Washington, DC 20036-4632
Ph: (202)234-2111   Fax: (202)667-1066
E-mail: info@cra.org
URL: http://cra.org/

Description: An association of more than 200 North American academic departments of computer science, computer engineering, and related fields; laboratories and centers in industry government, and academia engaging in basic computing research; and affiliated professional societies.

★603★ IEEE Computer Society (CS)

1730 Massachusetts Ave. NW
Washington, DC 20036-1992
Ph: (202)371-0101   Fax: (202)728-9614
E-mail: csinfo@computer.org
URL: http://www.computer.org

Description: Computer professionals. Promotes the development of computer and information sciences and fosters communication within the information processing community. Sponsors conferences, symposia, workshops, tutorials, technical meetings, and seminars. Operates Computer Society Press. Presents scholarships; bestows technical achievement and service awards and certificates.

★604★ IEEE Systems, Man, and Cybernetics Society (SMCS)

3 Park Ave. 17th Fl.
New York, NY 10016-5997
Ph: (212)419-7900   Fax: (212)752-4929
Fr: 800-678-4333
URL: http://www.ieeesmc.org

Description: A society of the Institute of Electrical and Electronics Engineers. Serves as a forum on the theoretical and practical considerations of systems engineering, human machine systems, and cybernetics with a particular focus on synthetic and natural systems involving humans and machines.

★605★ IMAGE Society

PO Box 6221
Chandler, AZ 85246-6221
Ph: (602)839-8709
E-mail: image@asu.edu
URL: http://www.public.asu.edu/~image

Description: Individuals and organizations interested in the technological advancement and application of real-time visual simulation (medical, virtual reality, telepresence, aeronautical, and automotive) and other related virtual reality technologies.

★606★ Information Technology Services

Cambridge Educational
2572 Brunswick Ave.
Lawrenceville, NJ 08648-4128
Fax: 800-FAX-ON-US   Fr: 800-468-4227
URL: http://www.cambridgeeducational.com

$89.95. 2002. 18 minutes. Part of the Career Cluster Series.

★607★ International Association for Artificial Intelligence and Law (IAAIL)
College of Computer Science
360 Huntingtonn Ave.
161 Cullinane Hall
Boston, MA 02115
Ph: (617)373-5116   Fax: (617)373-5121
E-mail: hafner@ccs.neu.edu
URL: http://www.iaail.org

Members: Computer science and law academics and professionals. **Purpose:** Promotes research and development in the field of artificial intelligence and law.

★608★ International Society of Applied Intelligence (ISAI)
Southwest Texas State University
Department of Computer Science
601 University Dr.
San Marcos, TX 78666-4616
Ph: (512)245-3409   Fax: (512)245-8750
E-mail: ma04@swt.edu
URL: http://isai.cs.swt.edu

Members: Researchers, academics, computer scientists, and others with an interest in artificial intelligence and expert systems. **Purpose:** Promotes increased knowledge of intelligent systems and improved scientific literacy in the field. **Activities:** Conducts research and educational programs; gathers and disseminates information on intelligent systems research; facilitates communication and cooperation among members.

★609★ MIT Computer Science and Artificial Intelligence Laboratory
32 Vassar Street
Cambridge, MA 02139
Ph: (617)253-5851   Fax: (617)258-8682
E-mail: webmaster@csail.mit.udu

Description: Active since 1959. Interdisciplinary laboratory of over 200 people that spans several academic departments and has active projects ongoing with members of every academic school at MIT. Offers research, current job listings, and educational outreach.

★610★ Society for Computer Simulation International (SCSI)
PO Box 17900
San Diego, CA 92177-7900
Ph: (858)277-3888   Fax: (858)277-3930
E-mail: info@scs.org
URL: http://www.scs.org

Members: Persons professionally engaged in simulation, particularly through the use of computers and similar devices that employ mathematical or physical analogies. **Activities:** Maintains speakers' bureau.

★611★ Special Interest Group on Artificial Intelligence (SIGART)
Association of Computing Machinery
1515 Broadway, 17th Fl.
New York, NY 10036
Ph: (212)626-0605   Fax: (212)302-5826
Fr: 800-342-6626

E-mail: frawley@acm.org
URL: http://www.acm.org/sigart/

Description: A special interest group of the Association for Computing Machinery. Individuals interested in the application of computers to tasks normally requiring human intelligence. Purpose is to enhance the capabilities of computers in this area.

★612★ Special Interest Group on Simulation (SIGSIM)
1515 Broadway
New York, NY 10036
Fr: 800-342-6626
URL: http://www.acm.org/sigsim/main/frame.html

Description: A special interest group of Association for Computing Machinery. Researchers and practitioners in computer simulation including professionals in business and industry. Holds technical meetings at annual conference of ACM. Promotes research and conducts surveys on topics such as the type of computer simulation courses being offered at colleges and universities. Is currently researching the application of simulation principles and theory to subdisciplines of computer science.

Aircraft Mechanics and Engine Specialists

SOURCES OF HELP-WANTED ADS

★613★ Aerospace Engineering
Society of Automotive Engineers Inc.
400 Commonwealth Dr.
Warrendale, PA 15096-0001
Ph: (724)776-4841   Fax: (724)776-4026
E-mail: magazines@sae.org
URL: http://www.sae.org

$66.00/year, U.S.; $118.00/year for other countries; $15.00/year for single issue, other countries; $12.00 for single issue, U.S. Magazine for aerospace manufacturing engineers providing technical and design information.

★614★ Air Jobs Digest
World Air Data
Box 42724
Washington, DC 20015
Ph: (301)990-6800   Fax: (301)990-8484

Monthly. $96.00/year for individuals. Newspaper covering job listings in aviation and aerospace worldwide.

★615★ Aviation Maintenance
PBI Media L.L.C.
1201 Seven Locks Rd., Ste. 300
Potomac, MD 20854
Ph: (301)354-2000
URL: http://www.aviationtoday.com/cgi/catalog/info?AM

Monthly. Magazine covering aviation maintenance.

★616★ Aviation Week & Space Technology
McGraw-Hill Companies
1221 Avenue of the Americas
New York, NY 10020
Ph: (212)512-2000
URL: http://www.AviationNow.com/awst

Weekly. $95.00/year for individuals. Magazine serving the aviation and aerospace market worldwide.

★617★ Commuter Air International
Commuter Air International
6151 Powers Ferry Rd. NW
Atlanta, GA 30339-2941
Fax: (404)618-0343

Monthly. Free to qualified subscribers; $45.00/year for institutions.

★618★ Flying
Hachette Filipacchi Media U.S. Inc.
1633 Broadway
New York, NY 10019
Ph: (212)767-6000

Monthly. $26.00/year; $3.95 for single issue. General aviation magazine.

★619★ General Aviation News
Flyer Media Inc.
PO Box 39099
Lakewood, WA 98439-0099
Ph: (253)471-9888   Fax: (253)471-9911
Fr: 800-426-8538
E-mail: comments@generalaviationnews.com
URL: http://www.flyer-online.com

Biweekly. $35.00/year; $55.00 for two years; $70.00/year. General aviation newspaper (tabloid) for aircraft pilots and owners.

★620★ Rotor & Wing
PBI Media L.L.C.
1201 Seven Locks Rd., Ste. 300
Potomac, MD 20854
Ph: (301)354-2000
URL: http://www.aviationtoday.com/index.html

Monthly. Magazine covering helicopters.

PLACEMENT AND JOB REFERRAL SERVICES

★621★ Aviation Maintenance Foundation International (AMFI)
900 Ogden Ave., Ste. 222
Downers Grove, IL 60515
Ph: (630)725-9287   Fax: (630)725-9814
E-mail: amfic@ix.netcom.com

Members: Trade association consisting of licensed aircraft mechanics, students, and schools as well as companies involved in the aviation maintenance industry. **Purpose:** To promote and improve the industry through education and research. Conducts surveys and market studies. **Activities:** Appoints professional aviation maintenance delegates to foreign countries. Sponsors competitions. Conducts seminars; maintains speakers' bureau and placement service; compiles statistics. Operates charitable program; compiles statistics.

EMPLOYER DIRECTORIES AND NETWORKING LISTS

★622★ Aircraft Servicing & Maintenance Directory
infoUSA Inc.
5711 S 86th Cir.
Omaha, NE 68127-0347
Ph: (402)930-3500   Fax: (402)331-0176
Fr: 800-555-6124
URL: http://www.abii.com

Annual. Number of listings: 4,418. Entries include: Name, address, phone, size of advertisement, name of owner or manager, number of employees, year first in "Yellow Pages." Compiled from telephone company "Yellow Pages," nationwide. Arrangement: Geographical.

★623★ Airline Companies Directory

infoUSA Inc.
5711 S 86th Cir.
Omaha, NE 68127-0347
Ph: (402)930-3500   Fax: (402)331-0176
Fr: 800-555-6124
URL: http://www.abii.com

Annual. Number of listings: 2,335 (U.S. edition); 684 (Canadian edition). Entries include: Name, address, phone (including area code), size of advertisement, year first in "Yellow Pages," name of owner or manager, number of employees. Compiled from telephone company "Yellow Pages," nationwide. Arrangement: Geographical.

★624★ AOPA's Airport Directory

Aircraft Owners and Pilots Association
421 Aviation Way
Frederick, MD 21701
Ph: (301)695-2000   Fax: (301)695-2375
Fr: 800-872-2672
E-mail: airportdirectory@aopa.org
URL: http://www.aopa.org

Biennial, January. $39.95. Covers 5,300 U.S. public-use landing facilities, including airports, heliports, seaplane bases, and approximately 1,800 private-use landing facilities; 5,000 aviation service companies. Entries include: For landing facilities-Airport type and name, city, phone, runway dimensions, types of instrument approaches, hours operated, communications frequencies, runway light system, local attractions, ground transportation, restaurants, hotels. For aviation service companies-Company name, phone, airport affiliation, operating hours, fuel type, unicom frequency. Arrangement: Geographical. Indexes: Cross-Reference index of U.S. landing facilities.

★625★ National Air Transportation Association-Official Membership Directory

National Air Transportation Association
4226 King St.
Alexandria, VA 22302
Ph: (703)845-9000   Fax: (703)845-8176
Fr: 800-808-6282

Annual, October. $95.00. Covers more than 1,000 regular, associate, and affiliate members; regular members include airport service organizations, air taxi operators, and commuter airlines. Entries include: Company name, address, phone, fax number, name and title of contact. Arrangement: Regular members are classified by service; associate and affiliate members are alphabetical in separate sections. Indexes: Geographical.

★626★ World Aviation Directory & Aerospace Database

Aviation Week
1200 G St. NW, Ste. 200
Washington, DC 20005
Ph: (202)383-2484   Fax: (202)383-2478
Fr: 800-551-2015
E-mail: wad@mcgraw-hill.com
URL: http://www.wadaviation.com

Semiannual, March and September.

$245.00 for print; $995.00 for online version. Key statistics on the database include 19,000 airlines, manufacturers, MRO stations, airports military/government and distributors/suppliers; 6,000 product/service categories and 150,000 listings; 60,000 aviation/aerospace professionals; 500,000 users across all 3 platforms/formats and, Commercial, Military & Business Aviation Fleet Data Arrangement: Classified by major activity (manufacturers, airlines, etc.). Indexes: Company and organization, personnel, product, trade name.

HANDBOOKS AND MANUALS

★627★ The Air Crafters: Airplane Mechanics

Xlibris Corporation
436 Walnut St., 11th Fl.
Philadelphia, PA 19106
Ph: (215)923-4686   Fax: (215)923-4685
Fr: 888-795-4274

Reginaldo L. Ortiz. 2002. $20.99. 155 pages.

★628★ Career Information Center

Macmillan Publishing Co. Inc.
200 Old Tappan Rd.
Old Tappan, NJ 07675
Fr: 800-428-5331

Visual Education Center Staff. Seventh edition, 1999. $275.00. 2080 pages. This 13-volume set profiles over 600 occupations. Each occupational profile describes job duties, educational requirements, how to get the job, advancement possibilities, employment outlook, working conditions, earnings and benefits, and where to write for more information.

★629★ Careers in Travel, Tourism, and Hospitality

McGraw-Hill Contemporary Books
1221 Avenue of the Americas
New York, NY 10020
Ph: (212)904-2000   Fr: 800-323-4900
E-mail: ntcpub@tribune.com

Marjorie Eberts, Linda Brothers, and Ann Gisler. 1997. $17.95; 13.95 (paper). 192 pages.

★630★ Introduction to Aircraft Flight Mechanics

American Institute of Aeronautics & Astronautics
1801 Alexander Bell Dr., Ste. 500
Reston, VA 02191-4344
Ph: (301)645-3651   Fax: (301)843-0159
Fr: 800-682-2422

Thomas R. Yechout. 2003. $109.95. Illustrated. 700 pages. Beginner's education on flight mechanics.

★631★ Opportunities in Aerospace Careers

McGraw-Hill Contemporary Books
1221 Avenue of the Americas
New York, NY 10020
Ph: (212)904-2000   Fr: 800-323-4900
E-mail: ntcpub@tribune.com

Wallace R. Maples. 1995. $14.95; $11.95 (paper). Surveys jobs with the airlines, airports, the government, the military, in manufacturing, and in research and development. Includes information on job opportunities with NASA in the U.S. space program.

★632★ Opportunities in Airline Careers

McGraw-Hill Contemporary Books
1221 Avenue of the Americas
New York, NY 10020
Ph: (212)904-2000   Fr: 800-323-4900
E-mail: ntcpub@tribune.com

Adrian A. Paradis. 1997. $14.95; $11.95 (paper). 205 pages.

★633★ Opportunities in Travel Careers

McGraw-Hill Contemporary Books
1221 Avenue of the Americas
New York, NY 10020
Ph: (212)904-2000   Fr: 800-323-4900
E-mail: ntcpub@tribune.com

Robert Scott Milne. 1996. $14.95; $11.95 (paper). 198 pages. Discusses what the jobs are and where to find them in airlines, shipping lines, and railroads. Discusses related opportunities in hotels, motels, resorts, travel agencies, public relation firms, and recreation departments. Illustrated.

★634★ Taking Flight: Education & Training for Aviation Careers

National Academies Press
500 5th St. NW
Washington, DC 20055
Ph: (202)334-3180   Fax: (202)334-2793
Fr: 800-624-6242

Janet S. Hansen and Clinton V. Oster, editors. 1997. $37.00 (paper). 192 pages.

EMPLOYMENT AGENCIES AND SEARCH FIRMS

★635★ Amtec Engineering Corp.

2749 Saturn St.
Brea, CA 92821
Ph: (714)993-1900   Fax: (714)993-2419
E-mail: staffing@amtec-eng.com
URL: http://www.amtec-eng.com

Employment agency.

TRADESHOWS

★636★ Professional Aviation Maintenance Symposium and Trade Show

Professional Aviation Maintenance Association
636 Eye St. NW, Ste. 300
Washington, DC 20036-3736
Ph: (202)216-9220   Fax: (202)216-9224
E-mail: hq@pama.org
URL: http://www.pama.org

Annual. **Primary Exhibits:** Aviation and aerospace products for the aviation maintenance industry.

OTHER SOURCES

★637★ Aircraft Electronics Association (AEA)

4217 S. Hocker
Independence, MO 64055-0963
Ph: (816)373-6565   Fax: (816)478-3100
E-mail: info@aea.net
URL: http://www.aea.net

Members: Companies engaged in the sales, engineering, installation, and service of electronic aviation equipment and systems. **Purpose:** Seeks to advance the science of aircraft electronics; promote uniform and stable regulations and uniform standards of performance; establish and maintain a code of ethics; gather and disseminate technical data; advance the education of members and the public in the science of aircraft electronics. **Activities:** Is active in the areas of supplement type certificates, test equipment licensing, temporary FCC licensing for new installations, spare parts availability and pricing, audiovisual technician training, equipment and spare parts loan, profitable installation, and service facility operation. Provides employment information, equipment exchange information and service assistance on member installations anywhere in the world.

★638★ Aircraft Mechanics and Engine Specialists

Evon Publishing
832 N 7th Ave.
Iron River, MI 49935
Ph: (906)265-3190

Audiocassette. 1996. $16.95. 32 minutes. Part of the Careers and Vocational Guidance Series. Provides information about the nature of the work, educational requirements, employment outlook, earnings, and work conditions as well as additional related information.

★639★ Math at Work: Women in Nontraditional Careers

Her Own Words
PO Box 5264
Madison, WI 53705-0264
Ph: (608)271-7083   Fax: (608)271-0209
URL: http://www.herownwords.com/
Video. Jocelyn Riley. $95.00. 15 minutes. Resource guide also available for $45.00.

★640★ Mechanics & Repairers

Delphi Productions
3160 4th St.
Boulder, CO 80304
Fax: (303)443-4022   Fr: 888-443-2400
URL: http://www.delphivideo.com

$95.00. 50 minutes. Part of the Careers for the 21st Century Video Library.

★641★ Professional Aviation Maintenance Association (PAMA)

Ronald Reagan Washington National Airport
Washington, DC 20001
Ph: (703)417-8800   Fax: (703)417-8801
E-mail: hq@pama.org
URL: http://www.pama.org

Members: Airframe and powerplant (A & P) technicians and aviation industry-related companies. **Purpose:** Strives to increase the professionalism of the individual aviation technician through greater technical knowledge and better understanding of safety requirements. Establishes communication among technicians throughout the country. Fosters and improves methods, skills, learning, and achievement in the aviation maintenance field.

Aircraft Pilots and Flight Engineers

PLACEMENT AND JOB REFERRAL SERVICES

★654★ Organization of Black Airline Pilots (OBAP)

8630 Fenton St., Ste. 126
Silver Spring, MD 20910
Fr: 800-JET-OBAP
URL: http://www.obap.org

Description: Cockpit crew members of commercial air carriers, corporate pilots, and other interested individuals. Seeks to enhance minority participation in the aerospace industry. Maintains liaison with airline presidents and minority and pilot associations. Conducts lobbying efforts, including congressional examinations into airline recruitment practices. Provides scholarships; co-sponsors Summer Flight Academy for Youth. Offers job placement service and charitable program; operates speakers' bureau; compiles statistics on airline hiring practices.

★655★ Pilots International Association (PIA)

PO Box 907
Minneapolis, MN 55440
Fax: (612)520-6760
E-mail: webmaster@airsport.com
URL: http://www.airsport.com/clpilint.htm

Members: Private, commercial, airline, military, and student pilots in 49 countries; associate members are persons other than pilots who are interested in flying. **Purpose:** Promotes airplane use and cooperates with government agencies and private and public flying organizations to increase the general safety of flying. Encourages the development of convenient landing and service facilities and the use of aircraft fuel taxes for aviation development. Fosters international understanding of common aircraft problems. **Activities:** Services include job placement and group life and health insurance. Maintains film-lending library and collection of general flying periodicals.

EMPLOYER DIRECTORIES AND NETWORKING LISTS

★656★ Airline Companies Directory

infoUSA Inc.
5711 S 86th Cir.
Omaha, NE 68127-0347
Ph: (402)930-3500   Fax: (402)331-0176
Fr: 800-555-6124
URL: http://www.abii.com

Annual. Number of listings: 2,335 (U.S. edition). 684 (Canadian edition). Entries include: Name, address, phone (including area code), size of advertisement, year first in "Yellow Pages," name of owner or manager, number of employees. Compiled from telephone company "Yellow Pages," nationwide. Arrangement: Geographical.

★657★ AOPA's Airport Directory

Aircraft Owners and Pilots Association
421 Aviation Way
Frederick, MD 21701
Ph: (301)695-2000   Fax: (301)695-2375
Fr: 800-872-2672
E-mail: airportdirectory@aopa.org
URL: http://www.aopa.org

Biennial, January. $39.95. Covers 5,300 U.S. public-use landing facilities, including airports, heliports, seaplane bases, and approximately 1,800 private-use landing facilities; 5,000 aviation service companies. Entries include: For landing facilities-Airport type and name, city, phone, runway dimensions, types of instrument approaches, hours operated, communications frequencies, runway light system, local attractions, ground transportation, restaurants, hotels. For aviation service companies-Company name, phone, airport affiliation, operating hours, fuel type, unicom frequency. Arrangement: Geographical. Indexes: Cross-Reference index of U.S. landing facilities.

★658★ National Air Transportation Association-Official Membership Directory

National Air Transportation Association
4226 King St.
Alexandria, VA 22302
Ph: (703)845-9000   Fax: (703)845-8176
Fr: 800-808-6282

Annual, October. $95.00. Covers more than 1,000 regular, associate, and affiliate members; regular members include airport service organizations, air taxi operators, and commuter airlines. Entries include: Company name, address, phone, fax number, name and title of contact. Arrangement: Regular members are classified by service; associate and affiliate members are alphabetical in separate sections. Indexes: Geographical.

★659★ World Aviation Directory & Aerospace Database

Aviation Week
1200 G St. NW, Ste. 200
Washington, DC 20005
Ph: (202)383-2484   Fax: (202)383-2478
Fr: 800-551-2015
E-mail: wad@mcgraw-hill.com
URL: http://www.wadaviation.com

Semiannual, March and September. $245.00 for print; $995.00 for online version. Key statistics on the database include 19,000 airlines, manufacturers, MRO stations, airports military/government and distributors/suppliers; 6,000 product/service categories and 150,000 listings; 60,000 aviation/aerospace professionals; 500,000 users across all 3 platforms/formats and, Commercial, Military & Business Aviation Fleet Data Arrangement: Classified by major activity (manufacturers, airlines, etc.). Indexes: Company and organization, personnel, product, trade name.

HANDBOOKS AND MANUALS

★660★ Ace the Technical Pilot Interview

McGraw-Hill Professional
2 Penn Plaza
New York, NY 10121
Ph: (212)904-2000

Gary Bristow. 2002. $29.95 (paper).

★661★ Career Information Center

Macmillan Publishing Co. Inc.
200 Old Tappan Rd.
Old Tappan, NJ 07675
Fr: 800-428-5331

Visual Education Center Staff. Seventh edition, 1999. $275.00. 2080 pages. This 13-volume set profiles over 600 occupations. Each occupational profile describes job duties, educational requirements, how to get the job, advancement possibilities, employment outlook, working conditions, earnings and benefits, and where to write for more information.

★662★ Careers for Night Owls and Other Insomniacs

McGraw-Hill Trade
2 Penn Plaza
New York, NY 10121
Ph: (212)904-2000   Fr: 800-722-4726
E-mail: ntcpub@tribune.com

Louise Miller. 1995. $14.95; $9.95 (paper). 160 pages.

★663★ Careers in Travel, Tourism, and Hospitality

McGraw-Hill Contemporary Books
1221 Avenue of the Americas
New York, NY 10020
Ph: (212)904-2000   Fr: 800-323-4900
E-mail: ntcpub@tribune.com

Marjorie Eberts, Linda Brothers, and Ann Gisler. 1997. $17.95; 13.95 (paper). 192 pages.

★664★ Flight Engineer FAA Written Exam

Gleim Publications
P.O. Box 12848, University Sta.
Gainesville, FL 32604
Ph: (352)375-0772   Fax: (352)375-6940
Fr: 800-874-5346

Irvin N. Gleim. 2000. $26.95.

★665★ Flight Plan to the Flight Deck: Strategies for a Pilot Career

Cage Consulting, Inc.
3333 Quebec, Ste. 1022
Denver, CO 80207
Ph: (303)329-0656   Fax: (303)329-5426
Fr: 888-899-2243

Judy A. Tarver. 1997. $16.95 (paper). 120 pages.

★666★ Opportunities in Aerospace Careers

McGraw-Hill Contemporary Books
1221 Avenue of the Americas
New York, NY 10020
Ph: (212)904-2000   Fr: 800-323-4900
E-mail: ntcpub@tribune.com

Wallace R. Maples. 1995. $14.95; $11.95 (paper). Surveys jobs with the airlines, airports, the government, the military, in manufacturing, and in research and development. Includes information on job opportunities with NASA in the U.S. space program.

★667★ Opportunities in Airline Careers

McGraw-Hill Contemporary Books
1221 Avenue of the Americas
New York, NY 10020
Ph: (212)904-2000   Fr: 800-323-4900
E-mail: ntcpub@tribune.com

Adrian A. Paradis. 1997. $14.95; $11.95 (paper). 205 pages.

★668★ Opportunities in Travel Careers

McGraw-Hill Contemporary Books
1221 Avenue of the Americas
New York, NY 10020
Ph: (212)904-2000   Fr: 800-323-4900
E-mail: ntcpub@tribune.com

Robert Scott Milne. 1996. $14.95; $11.95 (paper). 198 pages. Discusses what the jobs are and where to find them in airlines, shipping lines, and railroads. Discusses related opportunities in hotels, motels, resorts, travel agencies, public relation firms, and recreation departments. Illustrated.

★669★ The Proficient Pilot Series

Aviation Supplies & Academics, Incorporated
7005 132nd Pl., SE
Newcastle, WA 98059-3153
Ph: (425)235-1500   Fax: (425)235-0128
Fr: 800-272-2359

Barry Schiff. 2002.

★670★ Taking Flight: Education & Training for Aviation Careers

National Academies Press
500 5th St. NW
Washington, DC 20055
Ph: (202)334-3180   Fax: (202)334-2793
Fr: 800-624-6242

Janet S. Hansen and Clinton V. Oster, editors. 1997. $37.00 (paper). 192 pages.

TRADESHOWS

★671★ AOPA Expo - Aircraft Owners and Pilots Association

Aircraft Owners and Pilots Association
421 Aviation Way
Frederick, MD 21701
Ph: (301)695-2000   Fax: (301)695-2375
Fr: 800-USA-AOPA
URL: http://www.aopa.org

Annual. **Primary Exhibits:** Single-engine and multi-engine aircraft, avionics, airframes, powerplant and equipment, financing information, and related equipment, supplies, and services.

★672★ National Business Aviation Association Annual Meeting & Convention

National Business Aviation Association
1200 18th St. NW, Ste. 400
Washington, DC 20036
Ph: (202)783-9000   Fax: (202)862-5552
Fr: 800-FLY-NBAA
E-mail: Lpeters@NBAA.org
URL: http://www.nbaa.org

Annual. **Primary Exhibits:** Products and services limited to the design, operation, or servicing or business aircraft.

OTHER SOURCES

★673★ American Almanac of Jobs and Salaries

Morrow Avon
1350 Avenue of the Americas
New York, NY 10019
Ph: (212)261-6788   Fr: 800-242-7737

John W. Wright. Revised edition, 2000. $20.00 (paper). 672 pages. This is a comprehensive guide to the wages of hundreds of occupations in a wide variety of industries and organizations.

★674★ Math at Work: Women in Nontraditional Careers

Her Own Words
PO Box 5264
Madison, WI 53705-0264
Ph: (608)271-7083   Fax: (608)271-0209
URL: http://www.herownwords.com/

Video. Jocelyn Riley. $95.00. 15 minutes. Resource guide also available for $45.00.

★675★ National Black Coalition of Federal Aviation Employees (NBCFAE)

PO Box 23779
Washington, DC 20026-3779
Ph: (843)245-3104   Fax: (301)780-9454
E-mail: mamie.mallory@faa.gov
URL: http://www.nbcfae.com

Description: Federal Aviation Administration employees. Purposes are to: promote professionalism and equal opportunity in the workplace; locate and train qualified minorities for FAA positions; help the FAA meet its affirmative action goals; monitor black, female, and minority trainees; educate members and the public about their rights and FAA personnel and promotion qualifications; develop a voice for black, female, and minority FAA employees. Recruits minorities from community and schools who qualify for employment; sponsors seminars for members and for those who wish to be employed by the FAA. Awards scholarships; maintains speakers' bureau; sponsors competitions.

★676★ Ninety-Nines, International Organization of Women Pilots

4300 Amelia Earhart Rd.
Oklahoma City, OK 73159
Ph: (405)685-7969   Fax: (405)685-7985
Fr: 800-994-1929
E-mail: jody99prez@cs.com
URL: http://www.ninety-nines.org

Members: Women pilots united to foster a better understanding of aviation. **Activities:** Encourages cross-country flying; provides consulting service and gives indoctrination flights; flies missions for charitable assistance programs; endorses air races. Develops programs and courses for schools and youth organizations and teaches ground school subjects. Participates in flying competitions. Maintains resource center and women's aviation museum. Conducts lecture on personal aviation experience, and charitable event. Compiles statistics.

★677★ Professional Specialty Occupations

Delphi Productions
3160 4th St.
Boulder, CO 80304
Fax: (303)443-4022   Fr: 888-443-2400
URL: http://www.delphivideo.com

$95.00. 53 minutes. Part of the Careers for the 21st Century Video Library.

★678★ Women in Engineering

Her Own Words
PO Box 5264
Madison, WI 53705-0264
Ph: (608)271-7083   Fax: (608)271-0209
URL: http://www.herownwords.com/

Video. Jocelyn Riley. $95.00. 15 minutes. Resource guide also available for $45.00.

★679★ Women in Nontraditional Careers: An Introduction

Her Own Words
PO Box 5264
Madison, WI 53705
Ph: (608)271-7083   Fax: (608)271-0209
URL: http://www.herownwords.com/

Video. Jocelyn Riley. $95.00. 15 minutes. Resource guide also available for $45.00.

Air Traffic Controllers

SOURCES OF HELP-WANTED ADS

★680★ Air Jobs Digest
World Air Data
Box 42724
Washington, DC 20015
Ph: (301)990-6800   Fax: (301)990-8484
Monthly. $96.00/year for individuals. Newspaper covering job listings in aviation and aerospace worldwide.

★681★ Airport Highlights
Airports Council International/North
  America
1775 K St. NW, No. 500
Washington, DC 20006-1502
Ph: (202)293-8500   Fax: (202)887-5365
E-mail: publicaffairs@aci-na.org
Description: Monthly. Spotlights airport news, regulatory and Congressional developments, domestic and international aviation news, industry issues, and employment and business opportunities.

**★682★ Aviation Week & Space
Technology**
McGraw-Hill Companies
1221 Avenue of the Americas
New York, NY 10020
Ph: (212)512-2000
URL: http://www.AviationNow.com/awst
Weekly. $95.00/year for individuals. Magazine serving the aviation and aerospace market worldwide.

★683★ Commuter Air International
Commuter Air International
6151 Powers Ferry Rd. NW
Atlanta, GA 30339-2941
Fax: (404)618-0343
Monthly. Free to qualified subscribers; $45.00/year for institutions.

**★684★ Commuter/Regional Airline
News**
PBI Media L.L.C.
1201 Seven Locks Rd., Ste. 300
Potomac, MD 20854
Ph: (301)354-2000   Fax: (301)309-3847
Fr: 800-777-5006
URL: http://www.phillips.com
Description: Weekly. Covers the commuter/regional airline industry, including airline management, marketing, labor, personnel changes, aircraft acquisitions, new products, and the financial and operational environment. Recurring features include interviews, news of research, a calendar of events, reports of meetings, job listings, and notices of publications available.

★685★ Flying
Hachette Filipacchi Media U.S. Inc.
1633 Broadway
New York, NY 10019
Ph: (212)767-6000
Monthly. $26.00/year; $3.95 for single issue. General aviation magazine.

★686★ General Aviation News
Flyer Media Inc.
PO Box 39099
Lakewood, WA 98439-0099
Ph: (253)471-9888   Fax: (253)471-9911
Fr: 800-426-8538
E-mail: comments@generalaviationnews.com
URL: http://www.flyer-online.com
Biweekly. $35.00/year; $55.00 for two years; $70.00/year. General aviation newspaper (tabloid) for aircraft pilots and owners.

EMPLOYER DIRECTORIES AND NETWORKING LISTS

★687★ Airline Companies Directory
infoUSA Inc.
5711 S 86th Cir.
Omaha, NE 68127-0347
Ph: (402)930-3500   Fax: (402)331-0176
Fr: 800-555-6124
URL: http://www.abii.com
Annual. Number of listings: 2,335 (U.S. edition); 684 (Canadian edition). Entries include: Name, address, phone (including area code), size of advertisement, year first in "Yellow Pages," name of owner or manager, number of employees. Compiled from telephone company "Yellow Pages," nationwide. Arrangement: Geographical.

★688★ AOPA's Airport Directory
Aircraft Owners and Pilots Association
421 Aviation Way
Frederick, MD 21701
Ph: (301)695-2000   Fax: (301)695-2375
Fr: 800-872-2672
E-mail: airportdirectory@aopa.org
URL: http://www.aopa.org
Biennial, January. $39.95. Covers 5,300 U.S. public-use landing facilities, including airports, heliports, seaplane bases, and approximately 1,800 private-use landing facilities; 5,000 aviation service companies. Entries include: For landing facilities-Airport type and name, city, phone, runway dimensions, types of instrument approaches, hours operated, communications frequencies, runway light system, local attractions, ground transportation, restaurants, hotels. For aviation service companies-Company name, phone, airport affiliation, operating hours, fuel type, unicom frequency. Arrangement: Geographical. Indexes: Cross-Reference index of U.S. landing facilities.

★689★ Federal Career Opportunities

Federal Research Service Inc.
7360 McWhorter Pl., Ste. 201
PO Box 1708
Annandale, VA 22003
Ph: (703)281-0200   Fax: (703)281-7639
Fr: 800-822-5627
URL: http://www.fedjobs.com/index.html

Biweekly. $7.95 per copy. Covers more than 3,000 current federal job vacancies in the United States and overseas; includes permanent, part-time, and temporary positions. Entries include: Position title, location, series and grade, job requirements, special forms, announcement number, closing date, application address. Arrangement: Classified by occupation.

★690★ Federal Jobs Digest

Federal Jobs Digest
325 Pennsylvania Ave. SE
Washington, DC 20003
Ph: (914)366-0333   Fax: (914)366-0059
Fr: 800-824-5000
URL: http://www.jobsfed.com

Biweekly. $5.50 per issue; $34.00 for three months; $125.00 for year. Covers over 10,000 specific job openings in the federal government in each issue. Vacancies from over 300 Federal Agencies are covered. Entries include: Position name, title, General Schedule (GS) grade, and Wage Grade (WG), closing date for applications, announcement number, application address, phone, and name of contact. Arrangement: By federal department or agency, then geographical.

★691★ National Air Transportation Association-Official Membership Directory

National Air Transportation Association
4226 King St.
Alexandria, VA 22302
Ph: (703)845-9000   Fax: (703)845-8176
Fr: 800-808-6282

Annual, October. $95.00. Covers more than 1,000 regular, associate, and affiliate members; regular members include airport service organizations, air taxi operators, and commuter airlines. Entries include: Company name, address, phone, fax number, name and title of contact. Arrangement: Regular members are classified by service; associate and affiliate members are alphabetical in separate sections. Indexes: Geographical.

★692★ World Aviation Directory & Aerospace Database

Aviation Week
1200 G St. NW, Ste. 200
Washington, DC 20005
Ph: (202)383-2484   Fax: (202)383-2478
Fr: 800-551-2015
E-mail: wad@mcgraw-hill.com
URL: http://www.wadaviation.com

Semiannual, March and September. $245.00 for print; $995.00 for online version. Key statistics on the database include 19,000 airlines, manufacturers, MRO sta-

tions, airports military/government and distributors/suppliers; 6,000 product/service categories and 150,000 listings; 60,000 aviation/aerospace professionals; 500,000 users across all 3 platforms/formats and, Commercial, Military & Business Aviation Fleet Data Arrangement: Classified by major activity (manufacturers, airlines, etc.). Indexes: Company and organization, personnel, product, trade name.

HANDBOOKS AND MANUALS

★693★ Career Information Center

Macmillan Publishing Co. Inc.
200 Old Tappan Rd.
Old Tappan, NJ 07675
Fr: 800-428-5331

Visual Education Center Staff. Seventh edition, 1999. $275.00. 2080 pages. This 13-volume set profiles over 600 occupations. Each occupational profile describes job duties, educational requirements, how to get the job, advancement possibilities, employment outlook, working conditions, earnings and benefits, and where to write for more information.

★694★ Careers for Night Owls and Other Insomniacs

McGraw-Hill Trade
2 Penn Plaza
New York, NY 10121
Ph: (212)904-2000   Fr: 800-722-4726
E-mail: ntcpub@tribune.com

Louise Miller. 1995. $14.95; $9.95 (paper). 160 pages.

★695★ The National Business Employment Weekly Jobs Rated Almanac

John Wiley & Sons Inc.
1 Wiley Dr.
Somerset, NJ 08873
Ph: (732)469-4400   Fr: 800-225-5945

Les Krantz. First edition, 1995. $16.95. 340 pages. Ranks 250 jobs by environment, salary, outlook, physical demands, stress, security, travel opportunities, and geographic location.

★696★ Opportunities in Aerospace Careers

McGraw-Hill Contemporary Books
1221 Avenue of the Americas
New York, NY 10020
Ph: (212)904-2000   Fr: 800-323-4900
E-mail: ntcpub@tribune.com

Wallace R. Maples. 1995. $14.95; $11.95 (paper). Surveys jobs with the airlines, airports, the government, the military, in manufacturing, and in research and development. Includes information on job opportunities with NASA in the U.S. space program.

★697★ Staffing the ATM System: The Selection of Air Traffic Controllers

Ashgate Publishing, Limited
Gower House, Croft Rd.
Aldershot
Hampshire GU11 3HR, United Kingdom

Mike Heil. 2002. $79.95. Illustrated. 214 pages.

★698★ Taking Flight: Education & Training for Aviation Careers

National Academies Press
500 5th St. NW
Washington, DC 20055
Ph: (202)334-3180   Fax: (202)334-2793
Fr: 800-624-6242

Janet S. Hansen and Clinton V. Oster, editors. 1997. $37.00 (paper). 192 pages.

TRADESHOWS

★699★ Air Traffic Control Association Convention

Air Traffic Control Association
2300 Clarendon Blvd., Ste. 711
Arlington, VA 22201-3367
Ph: (703)522-5717   Fax: (703)527-7251
E-mail: info@atca.org
URL: http://www.atca.org

Annual. **Primary Exhibits:** ATC/aviation equipment, supplies, and services.

★700★ Airports Council International/ North America Convention

Airports Council International - North America
1775 K St. NW, Ste. 500
Washington, DC 20006
Ph: (202)293-8500   Fax: (202)331-1362
E-mail: tbernard@aci-na.org
URL: http://www.aci-na.org

Annual. **Primary Exhibits:** Air Aviation industry equipment, products and services. **Dates and Locations:** 2004 Sep 19-22; Houston, TX; Houston Convention and Visitors Bureau.

OTHER SOURCES

★701★ Air Traffic Control Association (ATCA)

1101 King St., Ste. 300
Alexandria, VA 22314
Ph: (703)299-2430   Fax: (703)299-2437
E-mail: info@atca.org
URL: http://www.atca.org

Members: Air traffic controllers; private, commercial, and military pilots; private and business aircraft owners and operators; aircraft and electronics engineers; airlines, aircraft manufacturers, and electronic and human engineering firms. **Purpose:** Promotes the establishment and maintenance of a safe and efficient air traffic control system. **Activities:** Conducts special surveys and studies on air traffic control problems. Participates in aviation community conferences.

★702★ *Air Traffic Controllers*
Evon Publishing
832 N 7th Ave.
Iron River, MI 49935
Ph: (906)265-3190

Audiocassette. 1996. $16.95. 32 minutes. Part of the Careers and Vocational Guidance Series. Provides information about the nature of the work, educational requirements, employment outlook, earnings, and work conditions as well as additional related information.

★703★ *Math at Work: Women in Nontraditional Careers*
Her Own Words
PO Box 5264
Madison, WI 53705-0264
Ph: (608)271-7083   Fax: (608)271-0209
URL: http://www.herownwords.com/

Video. Jocelyn Riley. $95.00. 15 minutes. Resource guide also available for $45.00.

★704★ **National Black Coalition of Federal Aviation Employees (NBCFAE)**
PO Box 23779
Washington, DC 20026-3779
Ph: (843)245-3104   Fax: (301)780-9454
E-mail: mamie.mallory@faa.gov
URL: http://www.nbcfae.com

Description: Federal Aviation Administration employees. Purposes are to: promote professionalism and equal opportunity in the workplace; locate and train qualified minorities for FAA positions; help the FAA meet its affirmative action goals; monitor black, female, and minority trainees; educate members and the public about their rights and FAA personnel and promotion qualifications; develop a voice for black, female, and minority FAA employees. Recruits minorities from community and schools who qualify for employment; sponsors seminars for members and for those who wish to be employed by the FAA. Awards scholarships; maintains speakers' bureau; sponsors competitions.

★705★ *Technical & Related Occupations*
Delphi Productions
3160 4th St.
Boulder, CO 80304
Fax: (303)443-4022   Fr: 888-443-2400
URL: http://www.delphivideo.com

$95.00. 49 minutes. Part of the Careers for the 21st Century Video Library.

Alcohol and Drug Abuse Counselors

SOURCES OF HELP-WANTED ADS

★706★ Alcoholism: Clinical and Experimental Research

Lippincott Williams & Wilkins
530 Walnut St.
Philadelphia, PA 19106
Ph: (215)521-8300   Fax: (215)521-8902
Fr: 800-638-3030
E-mail: jewers@lww.com
URL: http://www.alcoholism-cer.com/

Monthly. $337.00/year for individuals; $645.00/year for institutions; $411.00/year for other countries; $736.00/year for institutions, other countries. Publishing original clinical and research studies on alcoholism and alcohol-induced organ damage.

★707★ The American Journal of Drug and Alcohol Abuse

Marcel Dekker Inc.
270 Madison Ave.
New York, NY 10016
Ph: (212)696-9000   Fax: (212)685-4540
Fr: 800-228-1160
E-mail: custserv@dekker.com
URL: http://www.dekker.com/servlet/product/productid/ADA

Quarterly. $95.00/year for individuals, print and electronic rate; $895.00/year for institutions; $825.00/year for institutions, print or electronic combination rate. Medical journal focusing on the preclinical, clinical, pharmacological, administrative, and social aspects of substance misuse.

★708★ AMHCA Advocate

American Mental Health Counselors Association (AMHCA)
801 N Fairfax St., Ste. 304
Alexandria, VA 22314
Ph: (703)548-6002   Fax: (703)548-4775
Fr: 800-326-2642
URL: http://www.amhca.org

Description: Six issues/year. Publishes news of the programs, members, and activities of AMHCA. Provides updates regarding credentialing of counselors, mental health-related legislation, and insurance coverage of the expenses of mental health counseling. Recurring features include news of meetings and conferences and articles on topics of interest to clinical mental health counselors.

★709★ APA Monitor

American Psychological Association
750 1st St. NE
Washington, DC 20002-4242
Ph: (202)336-5500   Fax: (202)336-5620
Fr: 800-374-2721
E-mail: journals@apa.org
URL: http://www.apa.org/monitor/

Monthly. Free to qualified subscribers; $46.00/year for nonmembers; $87.00/year for institutions. Official newspaper of the APA. Reports on the science, profession, and social responsibility of psychology, including latest legislative developments affecting mental health, education, and research support.

★710★ Counseling Today

American Counseling Association
5999 Stevenson Ave.
Alexandria, VA 22304-3300
Ph: (703)823-9800   Fax: (703)823-0252
Fr: 800-347-6647
E-mail: ct@counseling.org
URL: http://www.counseling.org/ctonline

Description: Monthly. Covers news and issues relevant to the counseling profession.

★711★ Counselor Education and Supervision

American Counseling Association
5999 Stevenson Ave.
Alexandria, VA 22304-3300
Ph: (703)823-9800   Fax: (703)823-0252
Fr: 800-347-6647

Quarterly. $50.00/year for individuals; $70.00/year for institutions. Journal covering counseling theories, techniques, skills, teaching, training, and trends.

★712★ Journal of Child and Adolescent Substance Abuse

The Haworth Press Inc.
10 Alice St.
Binghamton, NY 13904-1580
Ph: (607)722-5857   Fax: (607)722-1424
Fr: 800-429-6784
URL: http://www.haworthpress.com

Quarterly. $36.00/year for individuals; $75.00/year for institutions; $145.00/year for libraries. Journal covering strategies for chemically dependent adolescents and their families.

★713★ Journal of Counseling and Development

American Counseling Association
5999 Stevenson Ave.
Alexandria, VA 22304-3300
Ph: (703)823-9800   Fax: (703)823-0252
Fr: 800-347-6647
URL: http://www.counseling.org

Quarterly. $40.00/year for individuals; $175.00/year for institutions. Journal for counseling and human development professionals concerning research, empirical data on current issues, and emerging counseling trends.

★714★ Journal of Counseling Psychology

American Psychological Association
750 1st St. NE
Washington, DC 20002-4242
Ph: (202)336-5500   Fax: (202)336-5620
Fr: 800-374-2721
E-mail: journals@apa.org
URL: http://www.apa.org/journals/cou.html

Quarterly. $41.00/year for members; $23.00/year for students; $81.00/year for nonmembers; $199.00/year for institutions. Journal presenting empirical studies about counseling processes and interventions, theoretical articles about counseling, and studies dealing with evaluation of counseling applications and programs.

★715★ Journal of Studies on Alcohol

Rutgers University
607 Allison Rd.
Piscataway, NJ 08854-8001
Ph: (732)445-3510   Fax: (732)445-5944
E-mail: patc@rci.rutgers.edu

Bimonthly. $140.00/year for individuals; $29.00 for single issue. Journal containing original research reports about alcohol and other drugs, their use and misuse, and their biomedical, behavioral, and sociocultural effects.

★716★ Spectrum

Association for Counselor Education and
  Supervision (ACES)
5999 Stevenson Ave.
Alexandria, VA 22304
Ph: (703)823-9800

Description: Quarterly. Focuses on "the need for quality education and supervision of counselors in all work settings," the accreditation process, and professional development activities for counselors. Recurring features include news of the activities, programs, and members of ACES and related organizations.

★717★ Substance Use & Misuse

Marcel Dekker Inc.
270 Madison Ave.
New York, NY 10016
Ph: (212)696-9000   Fax: (212)685-4540
Fr: 800-228-1160
E-mail: custserv@dekker.com
URL: http://www.dekker.com/servlet/product/productid/JA

$275.00/year for individuals, print and electronic rate; $2,295.00/year for institutions. Medical journal reporting individual and community problems brought on by drug, alcohol, and tobacco use, abuse, and dependency. Also considers legal and social aspects of addiction.

PLACEMENT AND JOB REFERRAL SERVICES

★718★ National Association on Drug Abuse Problems (NADAP)

355 Lexington Ave.
New York, NY 10017
Ph: (212)986-1170   Fax: (212)697-2939
E-mail: info@nadap.com
URL: http://www.nadap.org

Description: Sponsored by business and labor organizations. Serves as an information clearinghouse and referral bureau for corporations and local communities interested in prevention of substance abuse and treatment of substance abusers. Provides: resources to local communities seeking to combat drug and alcohol abuse; corporate services for employers interested in creating a drug-free workplace. Community education and development services include: de-

velopment of drug and alcohol awareness presentations for community organizations; identification of local substance abuse treatment resources; consultation on development of local prevention, treatment, and vocational programs. Corporate services include: provision of drug and alcohol information seminars in the workplace and through union organizations; assistance in formulation of company drug and alcohol policies; aid in the development and implementation of employee assistance programs; training of supervisors; assistance for companies and labor unions wishing to make full use of local treatment agency networks. Makes available vocational education services including training in job hunting, job interview workshops, training programs for substance abuse treatment professionals, and individual consultations for recovering substance abusers seeking to return to the job market. Provides placement services; has conducted surveys on the employability of rehabilitated drug users and found that former addicts perform comparably with others hired for similar jobs. Operates Neighborhood Prevention Network, through which local communities develop parent support groups and youth peer leadership groups dedicated to combatting drug and alcohol abuse. NPN provides substance abuse prevention and early intervention services for children and youth and ongoing training and materials dealing with specific issues in urban substance abuse. Maintains speakers' bureau.

EMPLOYER DIRECTORIES AND NETWORKING LISTS

★719★ Alcoholism Information & Treatment Directory

infoUSA Inc.
5711 S 86th Cir.
Omaha, NE 68127-0347
Ph: (402)930-3500   Fax: (402)331-0176
Fr: 800-555-6124
URL: http://www.abii.com

Annual. Number of listings: 13,834. Entries include: Name, address, phone (including area code), size of advertisement, year first in "Yellow Pages," name of owner or manager, number of employees. Compiled from telephone company "Yellow Pages," nationwide. Arrangement: Geographical.

★720★ Directory of Alcoholism Resources and Services

Alcoholism Council of New York
352 Park Ave. S., 8 Fl.
New York, NY 10010
Ph: (212)252-7001   Fax: (212)252-7021
Fr: 800-56-SOBER

Biennial. $25.00. Covers over 100 detoxification facilities, sobering-up stations, inpatient rehabilitation agencies, residences, halfway houses, outpatient alcohol abuse services, and related agencies and organizations in New York City. Entries include: Organization

or facility name, address, phone, services offered, and other data. Arrangement: Classified by type of treatment or service offered.

★721★ Drug Abuse and Addiction Info/Treatment Directory

infoUSA Inc.
5711 S 86th Cir.
Omaha, NE 68127-0347
Ph: (402)930-3500   Fax: (402)331-0176
Fr: 800-555-6124
URL: http://www.abii.com

Annual. Number of listings: 9,484. Entries include: Name, address, phone (including area code), size of advertisement, year first in "Yellow Pages," name of owner or manager, number of employees. Compiled from telephone company "Yellow Pages," nationwide. Arrangement: Geographical.

★722★ Drug Information for Teens: Health Tips About the Physical and Mental Effects of Substance Abuse

Omnigraphics Inc.
615 Griswold St., Ste. 1400
Detroit, MI 48226
Ph: (313)961-1340   Fax: (313)961-1383
Fr: 800-234-1340

$58.00. Publication includes: List of state and national organizations with additional information and assistance regarding substance abuse. Principal content of publication is information about various aspects of drug and alcohol abuse. Indexes: Alphabetical.

★723★ Drugs, Alcohol, and Tobacco: Learning About Addictive Behavior

Macmillan Reference USA
300 Park Ave. S, 9th Fl.
New York, NY 10010-5354
Ph: (212)654-8493   Fax: (212)654-4746
Fr: 800-877-GALE

$275.00. Publication includes: List of organizations of interest regarding addictions. Entries include: Name, address, phone, and URL. Principal content of publication is information focusing on drugs, alcohol, and tobacco addictions and their relation to society. Indexes: Alphabetical.

★724★ Drugs and Controlled Substances: Information for Students

Thomson Gale
27500 Drake Rd.
Farmington Hills, MI 48331-3535
Ph: (248)699-4253   Fax: (248)699-8065
Fr: 800-877-GALE

$99.00. Publication includes: List of web sites for each entry. Principal content of publication is information about legal addictive drugs, illegal drugs, other controlled substances, and often-abused prescription and over-the-counter drugs. Indexes: Alphabetical.

★725★ Iowa Substance Abuse & Gambling Service Directory

Substance Abuse Information Center
500 First St. SE
Cedar Rapids, IA 52401
Ph: (319)398-5133   Fax: (319)398-0476
URL: http://www.drugfreeinfo.org

Annual, fall. Covers about 190 alcohol and drug abuse treatment and prevention programs. Entries include: For treatment and prevention programs-Name, organization name, address, phone, services; names, addresses, and phone numbers of branch offices, counties covered; code indicates whether a recipient of state or federal substance abuse funds. For others-Name, name and title of contact, address, phone. Arrangement: Classified by activity; treatment programs, gambling treatment programs and prevention programs are geographical. Indexes: Program name, program county.

★726★ National Directory of Drug and Alcohol Abuse Treatment Programs

Substance Abuse and Mental Health
  Services Administration
5600 Fishers Ln., Rm. 12-105,Parklawn
  Bldg.
Rockville, MD 20857
Ph: (301)443-4795   Fax: (301)443-0284
E-mail: directory@smdi.com
URL: http://www.findtreatment.samhsa.gov

Annual. Covers about 11,000 federal, state, local, and privately funded facilities providing drug abuse and alcoholism treatment services. Entries include: Facility name, address, phone, and selected services provided; based on the National Survey of Substance Abuse Treatment Services. Arrangement: State, city, alphabetical by facility.

★727★ Roster: Substance Abuse Treatment Centers

Nebraska Health and Human Services-
  Regulations and Licensure
301 Centennial Mall S
Lincoln, NE 68509
Ph: (402)471-3324   Fax: (402)471-4970
URL: http://www.hhs.state.ne.us/lis/lis.asp

Annual, October. Covers approximately 50 licensed substance abuse treatment centers in Nebraska. Entries include: Facility name, address, phone, name and title of contact, number of beds, type of operation, license number. Arrangement: Geographical.

HANDBOOKS AND MANUALS

★728★ Careers in Counseling & Human Services

Taylor and Francis
325 Chestnut St., 8t Fl.
Philadelphia, PA 19106
Ph: (215)625-2919   Fax: (215)269-0363
Fr: 800-821-8312

Brooke B. Collison and Nancy J. Garfield,

editors. Second edition, 1995. $19.95 (paper). 153 pages.

★729★ Careers in Social and Rehabilitation Services

McGraw-Hill Trade
2 Penn Plaza
New York, NY 10121
Ph: (212)904-2000   Fr: 800-722-4726
E-mail: ntcpub@tribune.com

Geraldine O. Garner. Second edition, 2001. $19.95; 14.95 (paper). 128 pages.

★730★ Clinical Supervision in Alcohol and Drug Abuse Counseling: Principles, Models, Methods

John Wiley & Sons, Incorporated
111 River St.
Hoboken, NJ 07030
Ph: (201)748-6000   Fax: (201)748-6088

David J. Powell, Archie Brodsky. 2004. $40.00. 448 pages.

★731★ Essentials of Chemical Dependency Counseling

PRO-ED, Inc.
8700 Shoal Creek Blvd.
Austin, TX 78757-6897
Ph: (512)451-3246   Fax: (512)451-8542
Fr: 800-897-3202

Gary W. Lawson, Ellis and P. Clayton Rivers. Third edition, 2000. $49.00.

★732★ Global Criteria: The 12 Core Functions of the Substance Abuse Counselor

Learning Publications, Inc.
PO Box 1338
Holmes Beach, FL 34218-1338
Fr: 800-222-1525

John Herdman. Second edition, 1997. $20.95 (paper). 96 pages.

★733★ Great Jobs for Liberal Arts Majors

McGraw-Hill Professional
2 Penn Plaza
New York, NY 10121
Ph: (212)904-2000   Fr: 800-722-4726
E-mail: ntcpub@tribune.com

Blythe Camenson. Second edition, 2001. $14.95 (paper). 256 pages.

★734★ Great Jobs for Psychology Majors

McGraw-Hill Trade
2 Penn Plaza
New York, NY 10121
Ph: (212)904-2000   Fr: 800-722-4726
E-mail: ntcpub@tribune.com

Julie DeGalan and Stephen Lambert. 1995. $11.95 (paper). 468 pages. Out of print.

★735★ Introduction to Alcoholism Counseling: A Bio-Psycho-Social Approach

Taylor and Francis, Inc.
325 Chestnut St.
Philadelphia, PA 19106
Ph: (215)625-8900   Fax: (215)625-2940
Fr: 800-821-8312

Jerome D. Levin. Second edition, 1995. $79.95 (paper). 225 pages.

★736★ Opportunities in Counseling and Development Careers

McGraw-Hill Contemporary Books
1221 Avenue of the Americas
New York, NY 10020
Ph: (212)904-2000   Fr: 800-323-4900
E-mail: ntcpub@tribune.com

Neale Baxter, Mark U. Toch, and Philip A. Perry. 1997. $14.95; $11.95 (paper). 160 pages. A guide to planning for and seeking opportunities in this challenging field. Illustrated.

★737★ Opportunities in Mental Health Careers

McGraw-Hill Trade
2 Penn Plaza
New York, NY 10121
Ph: (212)904-2000   Fr: 800-722-4726

Philip A. Perry and George Blake. 1996. $14.95; $11.95 (paper). 160 pages.

★738★ Professional Alcohol and Drug Counselor Supervisor's Handbook

Learning Publications, Inc.
PO Box 1338
Holmes Beach, FL 34218-1338
Fr: 800-222-1525

Lawrence Clayton and Randy Van Nostrand. 1999. $18.95 (paper). 96 pages.

★739★ The Treatment of Drinking Problems: A Guide for Helping Professions

Cambridge University Press
110 Midland Ave.
Port Chester, NY 10573-4930
Ph: (914)937-9600   Fax: (914)937-4712
Fr: 800-872-7423

Griffith Edwards, Christopher C. Cook and Jane Marshall. 1997. $110.00.

TRADESHOWS

★740★ American Counseling Association World Conference

American Counseling Association
5999 Stevenson Ave.
Alexandria, VA 22304-3300
Ph: (703)823-9800   Fax: (703)823-0252
Fr: 800-347-6647

E-mail: meetings@counseling.org
URL: http://www.counseling.org

Annual. **Primary Exhibits:** Books, career development information, college selection, student financial aid, testing and measurement techniques, practice management companies, software, rehabilitation aids, and community agencies and private clinics specializing in substance abuse and mental health.

★741★ **Association for Counselor Education and Supervision National Conference**

Association for Counselor Education and Supervision
c/o American Counseling Association
5999 Stevenson Ave.
Alexandria, VA 22304
Ph: (703)823-9800   Fax: (703)823-0252
Fr: 800-347-6647

Quadrennial. **Primary Exhibits:** Exhibits relating to the professional preparation of counselors.

OTHER SOURCES

★742★ **Alcoholics Anonymous World Services (AA)**

Box 459
Grand Central Sta.
475 Riverside Dr., 11th Fl.
New York, NY 10163
Ph: (212)870-3400   Fax: (212)870-3003
URL: http://www.aa.org

Description: Individuals recovering from alcoholism. AA maintains that members can solve their common problem and help others achieve sobriety through a twelve step program that includes sharing their experience, strength, and hope with each other. Self-supported through members' contributions, AA is not allied with any sect, denomination, political organization, or institution and does not endorse nor oppose any cause.

★743★ **American Academy of Addiction Psychiatry (AAAP)**

7301 Mission Rd., Ste. 252
Prairie Village, KS 66208
Ph: (913)262-6161   Fax: (913)262-4311
E-mail: info@aaap.org
URL: http://www.aaap.org

Members: Psychiatrists and other health care and mental health professionals treating people with addictive behaviors. **Purpose:** Promotes accessibility to highest quality treatment for all who need it; promotes excellence in clinical practice in addiction psychiatry; educates the public to influence public policy regarding addictive illness; provides continuing education for addiction professionals; disseminates new information in the field of addiction psychiatry; and encourages research on the etiology,

prevention, identification, and treatment of the addictions.

★744★ **American Council on Alcoholism (ACA)**

PO Box 25126
Arlington, VA 22202
Ph: (703)248-9005   Fax: (703)248-9007
Fr: 800-527-5344
E-mail: aca2@earthlink.net
URL: http://www.aca-usa.org

Description: Works to educate the public about the effects of alcohol, alcoholism, alcohol abuse, and the need for prompt, effective, affordable, and available treatment. Provides a toll-free Helpline for alcoholism treatment and recovery referral and assistance.

★745★ **American Society of Addiction Medicine (ASAM)**

4601 N. Park Ave., Arcade Ste. 101
Chevy Chase, MD 20815
Ph: (301)656-3920   Fax: (301)656-3815
E-mail: email@asam.org
URL: http://www.asam.org

Description: Physicians with special interest and experience in the field of alcoholism and other drug dependencies and who wish to share this experience with other professionals in order to extend their knowledge of addictive diseases; promote dissemination of that knowledge; enlighten the public regarding these problems; advance education and research in the field of addiction. Holds annual Ruth Fox Course for Physicians, annual Medical-Scientific Conference and five other conferences/courses.

★746★ **Christian Addiction Rehabilitation Association (CARA)**

Whosoever Gospel Mission and Rescue Home
101 E. Chelten Ave
Philadelphia, PA 19144
Ph: (215)438-3094
URL: http://www.iugm.org/cara.html

Description: Provides support and serves as a clearinghouse of information for individuals involved in ministry to addicts. Conducts two conferences per year.

★747★ **Do It Now Foundation (DINF)**

PO Box 27568
Tempe, AZ 85285
Ph: (480)736-0599   Fax: (480)736-0771
Fr: 877-515-9411
E-mail: info@doitnow.org
URL: http://www.doitnow.org

Description: Works to provide factual information to students and adults about prescription drugs, over-the-counter drugs, street drugs, alcohol, eating disorders, AIDS, and related health issues. Assists organizations engaged in alcohol and drug abuse education.

★748★ **Hazelden Foundation (HF)**

15245 Pleasant Valley Rd.
PO Box 11-C03
Center City, MN 55012-0011
Ph: (651)213-4000   Fax: (651)213-4590
Fr: 800-257-7810
E-mail: info@hazelden.org
URL: http://www.hazelden.org

Description: Provides treatment, recovery, education, and professional services for chemical dependency and other addictive behaviors. Operates: Hazelden Foundation Center, a treatment center; Fellowship Club in New York, St. Paul and West Palm Beach, Florida, an intermediate care facility; Hazelden Center for Youth and Families for adolescents and young adults; Hazelden Renewal Center for individuals recovering from addictive behaviors and their families; Hanley-Hazelden Center in West Palm Beach, Florida, for inpatient and outpatient treatment; Also provides: aftercare therapy; counselor training; 5-7 day, live-in family program that acquaints relatives and other associates of chemically-dependent individuals with problems of chemical dependency; continuing education programs for professionals; and communities.

★749★ *Health Assessment & Treating Occupations*

Delphi Productions
3160 4th St.
Boulder, CO 80304
Fax: (303)443-4022   Fr: 888-443-2400
URL: http://www.delphivideo.com

$95.00. 50 minutes. Part of the Careers for the 21st Century Video Library.

★750★ **Institute for Integral Development (IID)**

PO Box 2172
Colorado Springs, CO 80901
Ph: (719)634-7943   Fax: (719)630-7025
Fr: 800-544-9562
E-mail: iidevo@aol.com
URL: http://www.institutefortraining.com

Description: Provides a forum for discussion of issues pertaining to alcoholism and other addictions; seeks to train educators, medical professionals, and mental health practitioners in understanding and assisting addicted individuals. Sponsors seminars and workshops; provides educational audiotapes; offers consulting services. Maintains speakers' bureau; operates small library.

★751★ **International Commission for the Prevention of Alcoholism and Drug Dependency (ICPA)**

12501 Old Columbia Pike
Silver Spring, MD 20904
Ph: (301)680-6719   Fax: (301)680-6707
E-mail: the_icpa@hotmail.com

Members: Representatives of national public health committees and other individuals interested in the physical and social effects of alcoholism and drug dependency. **Purpose:** Fosters the scientific study of alcohol and drugs, their effects on the physical, mental, and moral powers of the individual, and their effects on social, economic, political, and religious life. **Activities:** Encourages preventive education; disseminates information on drug and alcohol abuse. Serves as a liaison with similar groups around the world. Sponsors exchange and research programs. Conducts film shows, forums, and radio and television events.

★752★ NAADAC The Association for Addiction Professionals (NAADAC)

901 N Washington St., Ste. 600
Alexandria, VA 22314
Ph: (703)741-7686   Fax: 800-377-1136
Fr: 800-548-0497
E-mail: naadac@naadac.org
URL: http://www.naadac.org

Description: Counselors providing addiction treatment. Objective is to provide national representation for counselors as well as for their training and education. Works to gain public recognition of alcoholism as a disease. Seeks legislation establishing accreditation standards for counselors. Informs the public about chemical dependency and the availability of assistance.

★753★ Narcotic Educational Foundation of America (NEFA)

28245 Ave. Crocker, Ste. 230
Santa Clarita, CA 91355-1201
Ph: (661)775-6968   Fax: (661)775-1648
Fr: 877-775-6272
E-mail: lwhite@cnoa.org
URL: http://www.cnoa.org/NEFA.htm

Description: Conducts an education program revealing the dangers that result from the illicit and abusive use of narcotics and dangerous drugs, so that youth and adults will be protected from both mental and physical drug dependency and harm.

★754★ National Association of Substance Abuse Trainers and Educators (NASATE)

6400 Press Dr.
Southern University at New Orleans
New Orleans, LA 70126
Ph: (504)286-5234
E-mail: eharrell@suno.edu

Members: Accredited colleges and universities offering 12 or more course credit hours in the field of substance abuse. **Purpose:** Goal is to provide a network for exchange on courses, student population, degreed and nondegreed programs, and graduate study in chemical dependency training. Acts as a clearinghouse for students interested in substance abuse training programs; assists universities with the development of such programs. Provides for the exchange of information among universities concerning certificates, continuing education units, degrees, and opportunities for transfer and enrollment in undergraduate, graduate, and professional schools. Examines the educational and training needs of students and their career mobility as substance abuse practitioners.

Animal Caretakers, Technicians, and Trainers

SOURCES OF HELP-WANTED ADS

★755★ American Bee Journal
Dadant & Sons Inc.
51 S 2nd St.
Hamilton, IL 62341
Ph: (217)847-3324   Fax: (217)847-3660
Fr: 800-637-7468
E-mail: abj@dadant.com

Monthly. $22.95/year for individuals; $3.00 for single issue. Magazine for hobbyist and professional beekeepers. Covers hive management, honey handling, disease control, honey markets, foreign beekeeping, beekeeping history, bee laws, honey plants, marketing, and government beekeeping research.

★756★ American Journal of Veterinary Research
American Veterinary Medical Association
1931 N Meacham Rd., Ste. 100
Schaumburg, IL 60173-4360
Ph: (847)925-8070   Fax: (847)925-1329

Monthly. $150.00/year for individuals. Veterinary research journal reporting on nutrition and diseases of domestic, wild, and furbearing animals.

★757★ American Mustang and Burro Association Journal
American Mustang and Burro Association
PO Box 788
Lincoln, CA 95648-0788
Ph: (530)633-9271   Fax: (916)632-1855
Fr: 800-US-4-WILD

Quarterly. Journal covering horses and burros.

★758★ Animal Keepers' Forum
American Association of Zoo Keepers Inc.
3601 SW 29th St., Ste. 133
Topeka, KS 66614-2054
Ph: (785)273-9149   Fax: (785)273-1980
Fr: 800-242-4519

E-mail: akfeditor@kscoxmail.com
URL: http://aazk.org

Monthly. $40.00/year for individuals; $125.00/year for institutions; $4.00 for single issue. Professional journal of the American Association of Zoo Keepers, Inc.

★759★ ASA Bulletin
Avicultural Society of America
c/o Joe Krader
2910 Alps Rd.
Corona, CA 92881-3996

Monthly. Subscription included in membership. Covers the care, feeding, and breeding of birds in captivity. Contains membership roster and listings of bird specialty organizations and new members.

★760★ California Thoroughbred
California Thoroughbred Breeders
  Association
201 Colorado Pl.
PO Box 60018
Arcadia, CA 91066-6018
Ph: (626)445-7800   Fax: (626)574-0852

Monthly. $45.00/year for nonmembers. Magazine about horse breeding and racing.

★761★ The Chronicle of the Horse
The Chronicle of the Horse Inc.
PO Box 46
Middleburg, VA 20118
Ph: (540)687-6341   Fax: (540)687-3937
E-mail: staff@chronofhorse.com

Weekly. $49.00/year; $2.95 for single issue. Magazine covering English riding and horse sports.

★762★ Dog World
Fancy Publications
PO Box 57900
Los Angeles, CA 90057
Ph: (213)385-2222   Fax: (213)385-8565
E-mail: dogworld3@aol.com
URL: http://www.dogworldmag.com

Monthly. $28.00/year for individuals; $3.99 for single issue. Magazine serving breeders,

exhibitors, hobbyists and professionals in kennel operations, groomers, veterinarians, animal hospitals/clinics and pet suppliers.

★763★ DVM Newsmagazine
Advanstar Communications Inc.
7500 Old Oak Blvd.
Cleveland, OH 44130-3369
Ph: (440)243-8100   Fax: (440)891-2777
E-mail: dvmnewsmagazine@advanstar.com
URL: http://www.dvmnewsmagazine.com

Monthly. $39.00/year; $4.00 for single issue. Magazine for veterinarians in private practices in the United States.

★764★ Equus
Primedia Equine Group
656 Quince Orchard Rd., Ste. 600
Gaithersburg, MD 20878
Ph: (301)977-3900   Fax: (301)990-9015
E-mail: equuslts@aol.com

Monthly. $24.00/year for individuals; $3.99 for single issue. Magazine featuring health, care, and understanding of horses.

★765★ Journal of Animal Science
American Society of Animal Science
1111 N Dunlap Ave.
Savoy, IL 61874
Ph: (217)356-3182   Fax: (217)398-4119

Monthly. Professional journal covering animal science.

★766★ The Morgan Horse
American Morgan Horse Association
PO Box 960
Shelburne, VT 05482-0960
Ph: (802)985-4944   Fax: (802)985-8897

Monthly. $27.50/year for individuals; $4.00 for single issue. Magazine for Morgan horse enthusiasts.

★767★ New Methods

Ronald S. Lippert, A.H.T.
PO Box 22605
San Francisco, CA 94122-0605
Ph: (707)459-4535

Description: Monthly. Examines common problems and concerns in the field of animal health technology. "Provides professionals with the best in network sources" as well as items on animal care and protection and medical breakthroughs. Recurring features include letters to the editor, interviews, notices of publications available, job listings, news of educational opportunities, and news of research.

★768★ Newsletter-Animal Behavior Society

Animal Behavior Society
Animal Behavior Office
Indiana University
2611 E 10th St., Office 170
Bloomington, IN 47408-2603
Ph: (812)856-5541   Fax: (812)856-5542
URL: http://www.animalbehavior.org

Description: Quarterly. Informs members of the Society of activities, events, meetings, announcements and opportunities in the field of animal behavior. Recurring features include a news of educational opportunities, job listings, and notices of publications available.

★769★ Saddle Horse Report

Saddle Horse Report
PO Box 1007
Shelbyville, TN 37162-1007
Ph: (615)684-8123   Fax: (615)684-8196
E-mail: shr@horseworld.net

Weekly. $50.00/year for individuals. Newspaper containing national coverage of horse shows and sales.

★770★ TRENDS Magazine

American Animal Hospital Association
PO Box 150899
Denver, CO 80215-0899
Ph: (303)986-2800   Fax: (303)986-1700
Fr: 800-252-2242
E-mail: trendsmagazine@aahanet.org

Bimonthly. $60.00/year for U.S. and Canada; $70.00/year for other countries. Professional magazine covering the management of small animal veterinary practices.

★771★ Western Horseman

Western Horseman
PO Box 7980
Colorado Springs, CO 80933
Ph: (719)633-5524   Fax: (719)633-1392
Fr: 800-874-6774

Monthly. $20.00/year for individuals; $27.00/year for other countries; $2.95 for single issue. Magazine covering forms of horsemanship and all breeds of horses; emphasizing western stock horses and western lifestyle.

PLACEMENT AND JOB REFERRAL SERVICES

★772★ American Veterinary Medical Association (AVMA)

1931 N Meacham Rd., Ste. 100
Schaumburg, IL 60173-4360
Ph: (847)925-8070   Fax: (847)925-1329
Fr: 800-248-2862
E-mail: awhitsett@avma.org
URL: http://www.avma.org

Description: Professional society of veterinarians. Conducts educational and research programs. Provides placement service. Sponsors American Veterinary Medical Association Foundation (also known as AVMF Foundation) and Educational Commission for Foreign Veterinary Graduates. Compiles statistics. Accredits veterinary medical education programs and veterinary technician education programs.

★773★ National Animal Control Association (NACA)

PO Box 480851
Kansas City, MO 64148-0851
Ph: (913)768-1319   Fax: (913)768-1378
E-mail: naca@interserv.com
URL: http://www.nacanet.org

Description: Animal control agencies, humane societies, public health and safety agencies, corporations, and individuals. Works to educate and train personnel in the animal care and control professions. Seeks to teach the public responsible pet ownership; operates the NACA Network to provide animal control information; evaluates animal control programs. Provides training guides for animal control officers; makes available audiovisual materials. Conducts research. Operates placement service and speakers' bureau.

EMPLOYER DIRECTORIES AND NETWORKING LISTS

★774★ American Association of Bovine Practitioners-Directory

American Association of Bovine
  Practitioners
Box 1755
Rome, GA 30162-1755
Ph: (706)232-2220   Fax: (706)232-2232

Triennial, latest edition June 1996; annual supplements. Covers 5,000 member veterinarians who have a special interest in treatment of dairy and beef cattle. Entries include: Name, office address and phone. Arrangement: Alphabetical. Indexes: Alphabetical.

★775★ Animal Hospitals Directory

infoUSA Inc.
5711 S 86th Cir.
Omaha, NE 68127-0347
Ph: (402)930-3500   Fax: (402)331-0176
Fr: 800-555-6124
URL: http://www.abii.com

Annual. Number of listings: 15,285. Entries include: Name, address, phone (including area code), size of advertisement, year first in "Yellow Pages," name of owner or manager, number of employees. Compiled from telephone company "Yellow Pages" nationwide. Arrangement: Geographical.

★776★ Directory of Animal Care and Control Agencies

American Humane Association
63 Inverness Dr. E
Englewood, CO 80112-5117
Ph: (303)792-9900   Fax: (303)792-5333
Fr: 800-227-4645

Updated continuously; printed on request. $125.00 base edition to nonprofits; $800.00 base edition to others; $3.00 state edition to nonprofits; $15.00 state edition to others. Covers over 6,000 animal protection agencies; Canadian and some other foreign agencies are available; national and individual state editions are available. Entries include: Agency name, address, phone, contact. Arrangement: Geographical.

★777★ Kennels Boarding & Breeding Directory

infoUSA Inc.
5711 S 86th Cir.
Omaha, NE 68127-0347
Ph: (402)930-3500   Fax: (402)331-0176
Fr: 800-555-6124
URL: http://www.abii.com

Annual. Number of listings: 2,738. Entries include: Name, address, phone (including area code), size of advertisement, year first in "Yellow Pages," name of owner or manager, number of employees. Compiled from telephone company "Yellow Pages," nationwide. Arrangement: Geographical.

★778★ Pet Washing & Grooming Directory

infoUSA Inc.
5711 S 86th Cir.
Omaha, NE 68127-0347
Ph: (402)930-3500   Fax: (402)331-0176
Fr: 800-555-6124
URL: http://www.abii.com

Annual. Number of listings: 21,803. Entries include: Name, address, phone (including area code) size of advertisement, year first in "Yellow Pages," name of owner or manager, number of employees. Compiled from telephone company "Yellow Pages," nationwide. Arrangement: Geographical.

HANDBOOKS AND MANUALS

★779★ Career Information Center

Macmillan Publishing Co. Inc.
200 Old Tappan Rd.
Old Tappan, NJ 07675
Fr: 800-428-5331

Visual Education Center Staff. Seventh edition, 1999. $275.00. 2080 pages. This 13-volume set profiles over 600 occupations. Each occupational profile describes job duties, educational requirements, how to get the job, advancement possibilities, employment outlook, working conditions, earnings and benefits, and where to write for more information.

★780★ Careers with Animals

Barron's Educational Series, Incorporated
250 Wireless Blvd.
Hauppauge, NY 11788-3917
Ph: (631)434-3311   Fax: (631)434-3723
Fr: 800-645-3476

Audrey Pavia. 2001. $10.95. 160 pages. Explores careers within the animal industry.

★781★ Careers with Dogs

Barron's Educational Series, Inc.
250 Wireless Blvd.
Hauppauge, NY 11788-3917
Ph: (631)434-3311   Fax: (631)434-3723
Fr: 800-645-3476

Audrey Pavia. 1998. $8.95 (paper). 112 pages. Covers various types of work available for animal lovers. Includes information on salaries, qualifications, and job-hunting.

★782★ Careers in Veterinary Medicine

Rosen Publishing Group, Inc.
29 E. 21st St.
New York, NY 10010
Ph: (212)777-3017   Fax: 888-436-4643
Fr: 800-237-9932

Jane Caryl Duncan. Revised edition, 1994. $16.95; $9.95 (paper). Contains advice from a real veterinarian and a description of her work.

★783★ Opportunities in Animal and Pet Care Careers

McGraw-Hill Trade
2 Penn Plaza
New York, NY 10121
Ph: (212)904-2000   Fax: (212)755-5645
Fr: 800-722-4726

Mary Price Lee and Richard S. Lee. 2001. $12.95. 160 pages. Covers the field from small animal medicine to large animal medicine, and provides job-hunting advice. Illustrated.

★784★ Opportunities in Zoo Careers

McGraw-Hill Trade
2 Penn Plaza
New York, NY 10121
Ph: (212)904-2000   Fr: 800-722-4726
E-mail: ntcpub@tribune.com

Blythe Camenson. 1997. $14.95; $11.95 (paper).

★785★ Wild Careers!: Working with Animals

SeaWorld, Incorporated
500 SeaWorld Dr.
San Diego, CA 92109
Ph: (619)225-4275   Fax: (619)226-3634
Fr: 800-237-4268

Loran Wlodarski. 2002. $7.99. Illustrated. 88 pages. Exploring a career in the animal industry.

★786★ Working with Animals: The UK, Europe and Worldwide

Vacation Work Publications
9 Park End St.
Oxford OX1 1HJ, United Kingdom

Victoria Pybus. Second edition. 2003. $19.95. Illustrated. 288 pages. Educating on a career as a vetinarian.

TRADESHOWS

★787★ American Animal Hospital Association Annual Meeting

American Animal Hospital Association
PO Box 150899
Denver, CO 80215-0899
Ph: (303)986-2800   Fax: (303)986-1700
Fr: 800-252-2242

Annual. **Primary Exhibits:** Scientific displays related to small-animal veterinary care, computer software, marketing consulting services, pet care products, and pet foods.

★788★ American Humane Association Annual Meeting and Training Conference/Animal Protection

American Humane Association
63 Inverness Dr., E.
Englewood, CO 80112-5117
Ph: (303)792-9900   Fax: (303)792-5333

Annual. **Primary Exhibits:** Animal welfare equipment, including pet food, cages, trucks, ID programs, and health and veterinary products.

OTHER SOURCES

★789★ American Association for Laboratory Animal Science (AALAS)

9190 Crestwyn Hills Dr.
Memphis, TN 38125-8538
Ph: (901)754-8620   Fax: (901)753-0046
E-mail: info@aalas.org
URL: http://www.aalas.org

Members: Persons and institutions professionally concerned with the production, use, care, and study of laboratory animals. **Purpose:** Serves as clearinghouse for collection and exchange of information on all phases of laboratory animal care and management and on the care, use, and procurement of laboratory animals used in biomedical research. **Activities:** Conducts examinations and certification through its Animal Technician Certification Program.

★790★ American Boarding Kennels Association (ABKA)

1702 E Pikes Peak Ave.
Colorado Springs, CO 80909-5717
Ph: (719)667-1600   Fax: (719)667-0116
E-mail: info@abka.com
URL: http://www.abka.com

Members: Persons or firms that board pets; kennel suppliers; others interested in the boarding kennel industry. **Purpose:** Seeks to upgrade the industry through educational programs, seminars and conventions. **Activities:** Provides insurance plans for members and supplies pet care information to the public. Promotes code of ethics and accreditation program for recognition and training of superior kennel operators. Compiles statistics.

★791★ American Border Leicester Association (ABLA)

PO Box 947
Canby, OR 97013-0947
Ph: (503)266-7156   Fax: (503)245-8570
E-mail: momfarm@canby.com
URL: http://www.ablasheep.org/

Members: Owners and admirers of Border Leicester sheep. **Purpose:** Promotes Border Leicesters as a source of wool and meat. **Activities:** Sets breed standards and confers certification; maintains breed registry. Sponsors competitions; conducts educational programs.

★792★ American Water Spaniel Club

629 Westhill Ave.
Idaho Falls, ID 83402
Fr: 800-555-AWSC
URL: http://
www.americanwaterspanielclub.org

Members: Owners, breeders, and admirers of water spaniels. **Purpose:** Promotes quality breeding and acceptance of breed standards as approved by the American Kennel Club. **Activities:** Represents the interests of breeders; provides shelter and care to abandoned and abused water spaniels; conducts educational programs; sponsors competitions; compiles statistics.

★793★ National Dog Groomers
Association of America (NDGAA)
Box 101
Clark, PA 16113
Ph: (724)962-2711   Fax: (724)962-1919
E-mail: ndga@nauticom.net
URL: http://www.nauticom.net/www/ndga/

ndgaainc_001.htm

Description: Dog groomers and supply distributors organized to upgrade the profession. Conducts state and local workshops; sponsors competitions and certification testing. Makes groomer referrals.

Anthropologists

SOURCES OF HELP-WANTED ADS

★794★ AWIS Magazine
Association for Women in Science
1200 New York Ave. NW, Ste. 650
Washington, DC 20005
Ph: (202)326-8940   Fax: (202)326-8960
Fr: 800-886-AWIS

Description: Bimonthly. Covers issues, legislation, and trends related to science education for girls, women, and minorities. Includes information on grants and fellowships, job openings, educational programs, events, and notices of publications available.

★795★ Classical Antiquity
University of California Press/Journals
2120 Berkeley Way
Berkeley, CA 94720
Ph: (510)642-4247   Fax: (510)643-7127
URL: http://www.ucpress.edu/journals/ca/index.htm

Semiannual. $36.00/year for individuals; $95.00/year for institutions; $21.00/year for students. Scholarly journal covering interdisciplinary research and issues in Classics-Greek and Roman literature, history, art, philosophy, archaeology, and philology.

★796★ Human Nature
Aldine de Gruyter
200 Saw Mill River Rd.
Hawthorne, NY 10532
Ph: (914)747-0110   Fax: (914)747-1326
URL: http://www.archaeoworld.com/journals/humannature/

$165.00/year for institutions; $85.00/year for individuals; $50.00/year for members of HBES and ISHE. Interdisciplinary journal covering the biological, social and environmental factors behind human behavior.

★797★ Journal of Folklore Research
Indiana University Press
601 N Morton St.
Bloomington, IN 47404-3797
Ph: (812)855-8817   Fax: (812)855-8507
Fr: 800-842-6796

Quarterly. $27.50/year for individuals; $50.00/year for institutions; $37.50/year for individuals, other countries; $60.00/year for institutions, other countries. Journal covering anthropology and folklore.

★798★ Oral History Review
University of California Press/Journals
2120 Berkeley Way
Berkeley, CA 94720
Ph: (510)642-4247   Fax: (510)643-7127
URL: http://www.ucpress.edu/journals/ohr/

Semiannual. $60.00/year for individuals; $35.00/year for students; $80.00/year for contributing individuals; $92.00/year for member institutions; $120.00/year for sponsoring institutions. Scholarly journal of the Oral History Association covering oral history of people who have participated in important political, cultural, and economic social developments in modern times.

PLACEMENT AND JOB REFERRAL SERVICES

★799★ African Studies Association (ASA)
Rutgers the State University of New Jersey
132 George St.- Douglass Campus
New Brunswick, NJ 08901-1400
Ph: (732)932-8173
E-mail: callasa@rci.rutgers.edu

Members: Persons specializing in teaching, writing, or research on Africa including political scientists, historians, geographers, anthropologists, economists, librarians, linguists, and government officials; persons who are studying African subjects; institutional members are universities, libraries, government agencies, and others interested in receiving information about Africa. **Purpose:** Seeks to foster communication and to stimulate research among scholars on Africa. **Activities:** Sponsors placement service; conducts panels and discussion groups; presents exhibits and films.

EMPLOYER DIRECTORIES AND NETWORKING LISTS

★800★ American Journal of Physical Anthropology-American Association of Physical Anthropologists Membership Directory Issue
American Association of Physical Anthropologists
State University of New York/Buffalo
380 MFAC
Buffalo, NY 14261
Ph: (716)636-2414

Annual, December. Publication includes: 1,500 physical anthropologists and scientists in closely related fields interested in the advancement of the science of physical anthropology through research and teaching of human variation, primate paleoanthropology, and primate evolution. Entries include: Name, affiliation, address. Arrangement: Alphabetical.

★801★ Newsletter-Society for Historical Archaeology Membership Directory Issue
Society for Historical Archaeology
19 Mantua Rd.
Mount Royal, NJ 08061
Ph: (856)224-0995   Fax: (856)423-3420

Annual, June. Publication includes: List of about 2,100 member archaeologists, historians, anthropologists, and ethnohistorians, and other individuals and institutions having an interest in historical archeology or allied fields. Entries include: Name, address. Arrangement: Alphabetical.

HANDBOOKS AND MANUALS

★802★ Careers in Anthropology
Mayfield Publishing Co.
1280 Villa St.
Mountain View, CA 94041-1176
Ph: (650)960-3222   Fax: (650)960-0328
Fr: 800-433-1279

John T. Omohundro. Second edition, 2000.

★803★ Doing Fieldwork in Japan
University of Hawaii Press
2840 Kolowalu St.
Honolulu, HI 96822-1888
Ph: (808)956-8255   Fax: (808)988-6052

Victoria Lyon-Bestor. January 2003. $55.00.
Illustrated. 424 pages. Exploring social sciences in Japan.

★804★ A Guide to Careers in Physical Anthropology
Greenwood Publishing Group Inc.
88 Post Rd. W
Westport, CT 06881
Fax: (203)222-1502   Fr: 800-225-5800

Alan S. Ryan. 2001. $67.95.

★805★ Opportunities in Social Science Careers
McGraw-Hill Companies
860 Taylor Station Rd.
Blacklick, OH 43004-0545
Fax: (614)755-5645   Fr: 800-722-4726

Rosanne J. Marek. March 2004. $22.95. 160 Pages. VGM Opportunities Series.

★806★ Visions of Culture: An Introduction to Anthropological Theories and Theorists
AltaMira Press
1630 N. Main St., No. 367
Walnut Creek, CA 94596
Ph: (925)938-7243   Fax: (925)933-9720

Jerry D. Moore. Second edition. May 2004. $29.95. 352 pages. Focused on college students interested in Anthropology.

TRADESHOWS

★807★ American Association of Physical Anthropologists Scientific/ Professional Meeting
American Association of Physical Anthropologists
c/o Mark Weiss
Dept. of Anthropology
Wayne State University
Detroit, MI 48202
Ph: (313)577-2552   Fax: (313)577-5958
E-mail: mweiss@sun.science.wayne.edu

URL: http://www.physanth.org
Annual. **Primary Exhibits:** Exhibits for the advancement of the science of physical anthropology through research and teaching of human variation, primate paleoanthropology, and primate evolution.

★808★ American Society for Ethnohistory Conference
American Society for Ethnohistory
c/o R. David Edmunds, Pres.
University of Texas at Dallas
2601 N Floyd Rd.
Richardson, TX 75080
Annual. **Primary Exhibits:** Exhibits relating to the cultural history of ethnic groups worldwide. **Dates and Locations:** 2004 Dates not set; Chicago, IL • 2005 Dates not set; Santa Fe, NM.

★809★ Congress of the International Society for Human Ethology
International Society for Human Ethology
c/o Dr. Peter Lafrenieve
362 Little Hall
Department of Psychology
University of Maine
Orono, ME 04469
Ph: (207)581-2044   Fax: (207)581-6128
E-mail: peterlaf@maine.edu
URL: http://evolution.humb.univie.ac.at

Biennial. **Primary Exhibits:** Books, journals, and equipment for observational research.

★810★ Organization of American Historians Annual Meeting
Organization of American Historians
112 N. Bryan St.
Bloomington, IN 47408-4199
Ph: (812)855-7311   Fax: (812)855-0696
E-mail: oah@oah.org
URL: http://www.oah.org

Annual. **Primary Exhibits:** Equipment, supplies, and services of interest to historians, including textbooks and computer software.

OTHER SOURCES

★811★ American Academy of Forensic Sciences (AAFS)
410 N 21st St.
PO Box 669
Colorado Springs, CO 80904-2798
Ph: (719)636-1100   Fax: (719)636-1993
E-mail: awarren@aafs.org
URL: http://www.aafs.org

Description: Professional society of criminalists, scientists, members of the bench and bar, pathologists, biologists, psychiatrists, examiners of questioned documents, toxicologists, odontologists, anthropologists, and engineers. Works to encourage the study, improve the practice, elevate the standards, and advance the cause of the forensic sciences; improve the quality of

scientific techniques, tests, and criteria; plan, organize, and administer meetings, reports, and other projects for the stimulation and advancement of these and related purposes. Maintains Forensic Sciences Job Listing; conducts selected research for the government; offers forensic expert referral service.

★812★ American Association of Physical Anthropologists (AAPA)
Office of the Dean
College of Arts & Sciences
6525 Sheridan Rd.
Chicago, IL 60626
Ph: (773)899-3703   Fax: (773)508-3514
E-mail: fsmith3@luc.edu
URL: http://www.physanth.org

Description: Professional society of physical anthropologists and scientists in closely related fields interested in the advancement of the science of physical anthropology through research and teaching of human variation, paleoanthropology, and primatology.

★813★ American Society for Eighteenth-Century Studies (ASECS)
Wake Forest University
PO Box 7867
Winston-Salem, NC 27109
Ph: (336)727-4694   Fax: (336)727-4697
E-mail: asecs@wfu.edu
URL: http://asecs.press.jhu.edu/

Description: Scholars and others interested in the cultural history of the 18th century. Encourages and advances study and research in this area; promotes the interchange of information and ideas among scholars from different disciplines (such as librarianship and bibliography) who are interested in the 18th century. Cosponsors seven fellowship programs; sponsors Graduate Student Caucus.

★814★ American Society of Primatologists (ASP)
Loyola University
6303 St. Charles Ave.
New Orleans, LA 70118
Ph: (504)865-3255   Fax: (504)865-3970
E-mail: zucker@loyno.edu
URL: http://www.asp.org

Description: Promotes the discovery and exchange of information regarding nonhuman primates, including all aspects of their anatomy, behavior, development, ecology, evolution, genetics, nutrition, physiology, reproduction, systematics, conservation, husbandry, and use in biomedical research.

★815★ Amerind Foundation (AF)
PO Box 400
2100 N Amerind Rd.
Dragoon, AZ 85609
Ph: (520)586-3666   Fax: (520)586-4679
E-mail: amerind@amerind.org
URL: http://www.amerind.org

Purpose: Conducts research in anthropology and archaeology of the greater American southwest and northern Mexico and ethnology in the Western Hemisphere. **Activities:** Offers artist shows; volunteer opportunities, internship program, and visiting scholar program. Operates museum.

★816★ Anthropology Film Center

HC70 Box 3209
Glorieta, NM 87535
Ph: (505)757-2219
E-mail: info@anthrofilm.org
URL: http://www.anthrofilm.org

Description: General anthropologists, visual anthropologists, culture and communication specialists, applied anthropologists, musicologists, linguists, and educators. Seeks to further scholarship, research, and practice in visual anthropology by using consultation and research services, seminars, publications, teaching, equipment outfitting, and specialized facilities. The Anthropology Film Center develops, reviews, and administers research projects in the following areas: generation and analysis of anthropology film (design, collection, and investigation of naturally occurring human behavior in context through visual technologies and methodologies); film as visual communication; sociovidistics (investigation of the social organization surrounding the production, use, and display of photographs and film materials in their cultural contexts); culture and human perception; visual/aural arts and media. Other activities include: generation and publication of research films and reports; consultation with universities and institutions; resident fellow program. Offers Ethnographic and Documentary Film Program which provides introductory basics in photography, film making and ethnology, and hands on training with story boarding, camera, sound, editing and lighting exercises.

★817★ Association of Black Anthropologists (ABA)

10300 Jollyville Rd., No. 532
Austin, TX 78756
Ph: (512)471-4380   Fax: (512)471-1798
E-mail: jsa35@columbia.edu
URL: http://www.aaanet.org/assembly.htm

Description: A section of the American Anthropological Association. Anthropologists and others interested in the study of blacks and other peoples subjected to exploitation and oppression. Works to: formulate conceptual and methodological frameworks to advance understanding of all forms of human diversity and commonality; advance theoretical efforts to explain the conditions that produce social inequalities based on race, ethnicity, class, or gender; develop research methods that involve the peoples studied and local scholars in all stages of investigation and dissemination of findings.

★818★ Institute for the Study of Man (ISM)

1133 13th St. NW, No. C-2
Washington, DC 20005
Ph: (202)371-2700   Fax: (202)371-1523
E-mail: iejournal@aol.com
URL: http://www.jies.org

Description: Purpose is to publish books and journals in areas related to anthropology, historical linguistics, and the human sciences.

★819★ International Studies Association (ISA)

324 Social Sciences Bldg.
University of Arizona
Tucson, AZ 85721
Ph: (520)621-7715   Fax: (520)621-5780
E-mail: isa@u.arizona.edu
URL: http://www.isanet.org

Members: Social scientists and other scholars from a wide variety of disciplines who are specialists in international affairs and cross-cultural studies; academicians; government officials; officials in international organizations; business executives; students. **Purpose:** Promotes research, improved teaching, and the orderly growth of knowledge in the field of international studies; emphasizes a multidisciplinary approach to problems. **Activities:** Conducts conventions, workshops and discussion groups.

★820★ International Women's Anthropology Conference (IWAC)

Anthropology Department
25 Waverly Pl.
New York University
New York, NY 10003
Ph: (212)998-8550   Fax: (212)995-4014
E-mail: constance.sutton@nyu.edu

Members: Women anthropologists and sociologists who are researching and teaching topics such as women's role in development, feminism, and the international women's movement. **Purpose:** Encourages the exchange of information on research, projects, and funding; addresses policies concerning women from an anthropological perspective. Conducts periodic educational meetings with panel discussions.

★821★ *Professional Specialty Occupations*

Delphi Productions
3160 4th St.
Boulder, CO 80304
Fax: (303)443-4022   Fr: 888-443-2400
URL: http://www.delphivideo.com

$95.00. 53 minutes. Part of the Careers for the 21st Century Video Library.

★822★ Program on the Analysis and Resolution of Conflicts (CSP)

Syracuse University
Anthropology Department
410 Maxwell Hall
Syracuse, NY 13244-1090
Ph: (315)443-2367   Fax: (315)443-3818
E-mail: rar@mailbox.syr.edu

Members: Anthropologists. **Purpose:** Fosters research on the social and cultural dynamics of peace and war. **Activities:** Provides curricular services; operates speakers' bureau and placement service; compiles statistics. Sponsors seminars and professional workshops.

★823★ *Scientific, Engineering, and Technical Services*

Cambridge Educational
2572 Brunswick Ave.
Lawrenceville, NJ 08648-4128
Fax: 800-FAX-ON-US   Fr: 800-468-4227
URL: http://www.cambridgeeducational.com

$89.95. 2002. 18 minutes. Part of the Career Cluster Series.

★824★ *Scientific Occupations*

Delphi Productions
3160 4th St.
Boulder, CO 80304
Fax: (303)443-4022   Fr: 888-443-2400
URL: http://www.delphivideo.com

$95.00. 60 minutes. Part of the Careers for the 21st Century Video Library.

★825★ Society for Applied Anthropology (SFAA)

PO Box 2436
Oklahoma City, OK 73101-2436
Ph: (405)843-5113   Fax: (405)843-8553
E-mail: info@sfaa.net
URL: http://www.sfaa.net

Description: Professional society of anthropologists, sociologists, psychologists, health professionals, industrial researchers, and educators. **Purpose:** Promotes scientific investigation of the principles controlling relations between human beings, and to encourage wide application of these principles to practical problems.

Archaeologists

★826★ **American Archaeology**

Archaeological Conservancy
5301 Central Ave. NE, Ste. 402
Albuquerque, NM 87108
Ph: (505)266-1540   Fax: (505)266-0311

Quarterly. Subscription included in membership. Magazine covering archaeology in the Americas.

★827★ **Artifax**

Institute for Biblical Archeology
5606 Medical Cir.
Madison, WI 53719
Ph: (608)271-1025   Fax: (608)271-1150
Fr: 800-373-9692
E-mail: scribe@broadcast.net
URL: http://www.fullfeed.com/~scribe/artifax.htm

Description: Quarterly. Contains the latest information on developments in the field of Biblical Archeology, as well as thoughtful background articles for the layman interested in Biblical Archeology. Recurring features include letters to the editor, interviews, news of research, reports of meetings, news of educational opportunities, job listings, and book reviews. Also contains a column titled Archeology News Digest.

★828★ **ASOR Newsletter**

American Schools of Oriental Research (ASOR)
825 Houston Mill Rd., Ste. 330
Atlanta, GA 30329
Ph: (404)727-0807   Fax: (404)727-4719
E-mail: asorpubs@asor.org
URL: http://www.bu.edu/asor

Description: Quarterly. Carries news and reports from archaeological institutes in Amman, Jerusalem, and Cyprus. Recurring features include news of research, a calendar of events, reports of meetings, news of educational opportunities, job listings, and notices of publications available.

★829★ **AWIS Magazine**

Association for Women in Science
1200 New York Ave. NW, Ste. 650
Washington, DC 20005
Ph: (202)326-8940   Fax: (202)326-8960
Fr: 800-886-AWIS

Description: Bimonthly. Covers issues, legislation, and trends related to science education for girls, women, and minorities. Includes information on grants and fellowships, job openings, educational programs, events, and notices of publications available.

★830★ **Classical Antiquity**

University of California Press/Journals
2120 Berkeley Way
Berkeley, CA 94720
Ph: (510)642-4247   Fax: (510)643-7127
URL: http://www.ucpress.edu/journals/ca/index.htm

Semiannual. $36.00/year for individuals; $95.00/year for institutions; $21.00/year for students. Scholarly journal covering interdisciplinary research and issues in Classics-Greek and Roman literature, history, art, philosophy, archaeology, and philology.

★831★ **East Asian Art & Archaeology Newsletter**

Department of the History of Art
Tappan Hall, Rm. 50
Ann Arbor, MI 48109-1357
Ph: (313)936-2539   Fax: (313)647-4121
URL: http://www.umich.edu/~hartspc/NEAAA.html

Description: Three issues/year. Functions as an information guide to Asian exhibitions, museums, symposia, cultural research, and lectures. Recurring features include news of research, a calendar of events, reports of meetings, news of educational opportunities, job listings, book reviews, and notices of publications available.

★832★ **Midcontinental Journal of Archaeology**

Office of the State Archaeologist
700 Clinton St. Bldg.
Iowa City, IA 52242-1030

Semiannual. Journal covering archaeology.

★833★ **PE & RS Photogrammetric Engineering & Remote Sensing**

The Imaging and Geospatial Information Society
5410 Grosvenor Ln., Ste. 210
Bethesda, MD 20814
Ph: (301)493-0290   Fax: (301)493-0208
E-mail: asprs@asprs.org

Monthly. $130.00/year. Journal covering photogrammetry, remote sensing, geographic information systems, cartography, and surveying, global positioning systems, digital photogrammetry.

★834★ **PRISCUM**

Paleontological Society
118 Ozark Hall
Department of Geology
University of Arkansas
Fayetteville, AR 72701
Ph: (501)575-3370   Fax: (501)575-3846

Description: Semiannual. Carries news of membership activities and announcements of events, publications, employment opportunities, and activities pertaining to geology and paleontology. Recurring features include notices of awards, available sources of research funding, notices of new journals and books available, and book reviews.

★835★ **Sea History Gazette**

National Maritime Historical Society
5 John Walsh Blvd.
PO Box 68
Peekskill, NY 10566
Ph: (914)737-7878   Fax: (914)737-7816
E-mail: editorial@seahistory.org

Description: Six issues/year. Carries news from the fields of maritime history and preservation, including items on ship preservation, marine archaeology, sail training, and museum and exhibit openings. Designed for the layman and professional involved with the maritime heritage community. Recurring features include a calendar of events, reports of meetings, job listings, and book reviews.

PLACEMENT AND JOB REFERRAL SERVICES

★836★ American Philological Association (APA)

Johns Hopkins University Press, Journals Division
PO Box 19966
Baltimore, MD 21211-0966
Ph: (410)516-6987　　Fax: (410)516-6968
Fr: 800-548-1784
URL: http://www.apaclassics.org

Members: Teachers of Latin and Greek, classical archaeologists with literary interests, and comparative linguists. **Purpose:** For the advancement and diffusion of philological information. **Activities:** Sponsors placement service and campus advisory service to provide advice on instructional programs in classical studies.

★837★ Archaeological Institute of America (AIA)

656 Beacon St., 4th Fl.
Boston, MA 02215-2006
Ph: (617)353-9361　　Fax: (617)353-6550
E-mail: aia@aia.bu.edu
URL: http://www.archaeological.org

Purpose: Educational and scientific society of archaeologists and others interested in archaeological study and research. Founded five schools of archaeology: American School of Classical Studies (Athens, 1881); School of Classical Studies of the American Academy (Rome, 1895); American Schools of Oriental Research (Jerusalem, 1900 and Baghdad, 1921); School of American Research (1907, with headquarters at Santa Fe, NM). Is allied with three research institutes: American Research Institute in Turkey; American Institute of Iranian Studies; American Research Center in Egypt. **Activities:** Maintains annual lecture program for all branch societies. Operates placement service for archeology educators. Sponsors educational programs for middle school children.

★838★ Society for American Archaeology (SAA)

900 2nd St. NE, No. 12
Washington, DC 20002-3557
Ph: (202)789-8200　　Fax: (202)789-0284
E-mail: headquarters@saa.org
URL: http://www.saa.org

Members: Professionals, avocationals, students, and others interested in American archaeology. **Purpose:** Stimulates scientific research in the archaeology of the New World by creating closer professional rela-

tions among archaeologists, and between them and others interested in American archaeology; advocating the conservation of archaeological data and furthering the control or elimination of commercialization of archaeological objects; promoting a more rational public appreciation of the aims and limitations of archaeological research. **Activities:** Maintains placement service and educational programs.

EMPLOYER DIRECTORIES AND NETWORKING LISTS

★839★ Newsletter-Society for Historical Archaeology Membership Directory Issue

Society for Historical Archaeology
19 Mantua Rd.
Mount Royal, NJ 08061
Ph: (856)224-0995　　Fax: (856)423-3420

Annual, June. Publication includes: List of about 2,100 member archaeologists, historians, anthropologists, and ethnohistorians, and other individuals and institutions having an interest in historical archeology or allied fields. Entries include: Name, address. Arrangement: Alphabetical.

HANDBOOKS AND MANUALS

★840★ Careers for Mystery Buffs and Other Snoops and Sleuths

McGraw-Hill Trade
2 Penn Plaza
New York, NY 10121
Ph: (212)904-2000　　Fr: 800-722-4726
E-mail: ntcpub@tribune.com

Blythe Camenson. 1996. $14.95; $9.95 (paper). 210 pages.

★841★ Opportunities in Social Science Careers

McGraw-Hill Companies
860 Taylor Station Rd.
Blacklick, OH 43004-0545
Fax: (614)755-5645　　Fr: 800-722-4726

Rosanne J. Marek. March 2004. $22.95. 160 Pages. VGM Opportunities Series.

TRADESHOWS

★842★ American Society for Ethnohistory Conference

American Society for Ethnohistory
c/o R. David Edmunds, Pres.
University of Texas at Dallas
2601 N Floyd Rd.
Richardson, TX 75080

Annual. **Primary Exhibits:** Exhibits relating to the cultural history of ethnic groups worldwide. **Dates and Locations:** 2004 Dates not set; Chicago, IL • 2005 Dates not set; Santa Fe, NM.

★843★ Society for American Archaeology Conference

Society for American Archaeology
900 2nd St. NE, No. 12
Washington, DC 20002
Ph: (202)789-8200　　Fax: (202)789-0284
E-mail: headquarters@saa.org
URL: http://www.saa.org

Annual. **Primary Exhibits:** Archaeological equipment, supplies, and services academic books, GPS, GIS, software.

OTHER SOURCES

★844★ Amerind Foundation (AF)

PO Box 400
2100 N Amerind Rd.
Dragoon, AZ 85609
Ph: (520)586-3666　　Fax: (520)586-4679
E-mail: amerind@amerind.org
URL: http://www.amerind.org

Purpose: Conducts research in anthropology and archaeology of the greater American southwest and northern Mexico and ethnology in the Western Hemisphere. **Activities:** Offers artist shows; volunteer opportunities, internship program, and visiting scholar program. Operates museum.

★845★ Archaeological Conservancy (AC)

5301 Central Ave. NE, Ste. 902
Albuquerque, NM 87108-1530
Ph: (505)266-1540　　Fax: (505)266-0311
E-mail: tacinfo@nm.net
URL: http://www.americanarchaeology.com

Members: People interested in preserving prehistoric and historic sites for interpretive or research purposes (most members are not professional archaeologists). **Purpose:** Seeks to acquire for permanent preservation, through donation or purchase, the ruins of past American cultures, primarily those of American Indians. Works throughout the U.S. to preserve cultural resources presently on private lands and protect them from the destruction of looters, modern agricultural practices, and urban sprawl. **Activities:** Operates with government agencies, universities, and museums to permanently preserve acquired sites.

★846★ ASPRS - The Imaging and Geospatial Information Society

5410 Grosvenor Ln., Ste. 210
Bethesda, MD 20814-2160
Ph: (301)493-0290   Fax: (301)493-0208
E-mail: asprs@asprs.org
URL: http://www.asprs.org

Members: Firms, individuals, government employees, and academicians engaged in photogrammetry, photointerpretation, remote sensing, and geographic information systems and their application to such fields as archaeology, geographic information systems, military reconnaissance, urban planning, engineering, traffic surveys, meteorological observations, medicine, geology, forestry, agriculture, construction, and topographic mapping. Mission is to advance knowledge and improve understanding of these sciences and to promote responsible applications. **Activities:** Offers voluntary certification program open to persons associated with one or more functional area of photogrammetry, remote sensing, and GIS. Surveys the profession of private firms in photogrammetry and remote sensing in the areas of productsand services

★847★ Center for American Archeology (CAA)

PO Box 366
Kampsville, IL 62053
Ph: (618)653-4316   Fax: (618)653-4232
E-mail: caa@caa-archeology.org
URL: http://www.caa-archeology.org

Description: Philanthropic organizations, foundations, corporations, professional and amateur archaeologists, students, and others interested in archaeology in the U.S. Conducts archaeological research and disseminates the results. Excavates, analyzes, and conserves archaeological sites and artifacts. Sponsors tours, lectures, and educational and outreach programs, including university, middle school and junior high, and high school field schools; offers professional training at levels of detail ranging from secondary to postgraduate. Maintains speakers' bureau. Operates Center for American Archeology Visitors Center.

★848★ Epigraphic Society (ES)

97 Village Post Rd.
Danvers, MA 01923
Ph: (978)774-1275   Fax: (978)750-9043
E-mail: donalb@aol.com
URL: http://www.epigraphy.org

Description: Individuals interested in deciphering ancient inscriptions, including professional and amateur epigraphers (specialists in engraved inscriptions) and linguists. Members launch expeditions to North America and overseas. Reports discoveries and decipherments and assesses their historical implications. Participates in group lecture and teaching programs with other archaeological societies and university departments of archaeology and history. Conducts specialized education and research programs. Operates museum. Maintains numerous committees.

★849★ Register of Professional Archaeologists (RPA)

5024-R Campbell Blvd.
Baltimore, MD 21236
Ph: (410)933-3486   Fax: (410)931-8111
E-mail: glasow@anth.ucsb.edu
URL: http://www.rpanet.org

Description: Professional archaeologists satisfying basic requirements in training and experience, including private consultants, individuals working with large firms, and academic personnel. Objectives are to define professionalism in archaeology; provide a measure against which to evaluate archaeological actions and research; establish certification standards; provide for grievance procedures; demonstrate to other archaeologists and the public the nature of professional archaeology. Monitors related legislative activities; maintains register archives. Is developing educational programs and drafting standards and guidelines for field schools.

★850★ *Scientific, Engineering, and Technical Services*

Cambridge Educational
2572 Brunswick Ave.
Lawrenceville, NJ 08648-4128
Fax: 800-FAX-ON-US   Fr: 800-468-4227
URL: http://www.cambridgeeducational.com

$89.95. 2002. 18 minutes. Part of the Career Cluster Series.

★851★ Society for Historical Archaeology (SHA)

PO Box 30446
Tucson, AZ 85751-0446
Ph: (914)762-0773   Fax: (914)762-4058
E-mail: saramascia@aol.com
URL: http://www.sha.org

Description: Archaeologists, historians, anthropologists, and ethnohistorians; other individuals and institutions with an interest in historical archaeology or allied fields. Aim is to bring together persons interested in studying specific historic sites, manuscripts, and published sources, and to develop generalizations concerning historical periods and cultural dynamics as these emerge through the techniques of archaeological excavation and analysis. Main focus is the era beginning with the exploration of the non-European world by Europeans, and geographical areas in the Western Hemisphere, but also considers Oceanian, African, and Asian archaeology during the relatively late periods.

Architects

SOURCES OF HELP-WANTED ADS

★852★ AIA Louisiana News Briefs

AIA Louisiana
521 America St.
Baton Rouge, LA 70802
Ph: (225)387-5579   Fax: (225)387-2743
E-mail: hq@aiala.com
URL: http://www.aiala.com

Description: Bimonthly. Covers Association activities as well as those of the American Institute of Architects. Reports on professional standards and legislation, workshops and conventions, and other issues concerning building design and construction. Contains job listings.

★853★ Architectural Record

McGraw-Hill Companies
1221 Avenue of the Americas
New York, NY 10020
Ph: (212)512-2000
URL: http://www.mcgraw-hill.com

$59.00/year for individuals; $7.00 for single issue. Magazine focusing on architecture.

★854★ Architectural West

Dodson Publications Inc.
546 Court St.
Reno, NV 89501
Ph: (775)333-1080   Fax: (775)333-1081
URL: http://www.architecturalwest.com

Bimonthly. $12.00/year for individuals. Trade magazine covering issues for architects and specifiers of exterior building materials in the western United States.

★855★ Builder

Hanley-Wood L.L.C.
1 Thomas Cir., Ste. 600
Washington, DC 20005
Ph: (202)452-0800   Fax: (202)785-1974
URL: http://www.builderonline.com

Monthly. $29.95/year for individuals. Magazine covering housing and construction industry.

★856★ Civil Engineering-ASCE

American Society of Civil Engineers
1801 Alexander Bell Dr.
Reston, VA 20191
Ph: (703)295-6300   Fax: (703)295-6222
Fr: 800-548-2723
E-mail: ztrem@ce.udel.edu
URL: http://www.pubs.asce.org/ceonline/newce.html

Monthly. $30.00/year for members; $160.00/year for individuals; $160.00/year for institutions, nonmembers; $205.00/year for out of country; $50.00/year for foreign members; $205.00/year for institutions, other countries. Professional magazine.

★857★ Custom Home

Hanley-Wood L.L.C.
1 Thomas Cir., Ste. 600
Washington, DC 20005
Ph: (202)452-0800   Fax: (202)785-1974

Bimonthly. $24.00/year for individuals; $10.00 for single issue; $36.00/year for other countries. Trade publication.

★858★ Design Cost Data

DC & D Technologies Inc.
8602 N 40th St.
Tampa, FL 33604
Ph: (813)989-9300   Fax: (813)980-3982
Fr: 800-533-5680
E-mail: webmaster@dcd.com
URL: http://www.dcd.com

Bimonthly. $84.40/year for individuals. Publication providing real cost data case studies of various types completed around the country for design and building professionals.

★859★ Fabric Architecture

Industrial Fabrics Association International
1801 County Rd. B W
Roseville, MN 55113-4061
Ph: (651)222-2508   Fax: (651)225-6966
Fr: 800-225-4324
URL: http://www.ifai.com

Bimonthly. $39.00/year; $43.00/year for Canada and Mexico; $55.00/year for out of country. Magazine specializing in interior and exterior design ideas and technical information for architectural fabric applications in architecture and the landscape.

★860★ INTERIORS

VNU Business Media USA
770 Broadway
New York, NY 10003
Ph: (646)654-5000

Monthly. $40.00/year for individuals. Magazine for interior designers and architects.

★861★ Kitchen and Bath Design News

Cygnus Business Media Inc.
445 Broad Hollow Rd.
Melville, NY 11747
Ph: (631)845-2700   Fax: (631)845-2798
Fr: 800-308-6397
E-mail: kbdneditor@aol.com
URL: http://www.kitchen-bath-design.com/

Monthly. Trade journal.

★862★ Metal Architecture

Modern Trade Communications Inc.
7450 N Skokie Blvd.
Skokie, IL 60077
Ph: (847)674-2200   Fax: (847)674-3676
E-mail: ma@moderntrade.com

Monthly. Trade journal serving architectural, engineering, and construction firms.

★863★ The Military Engineer

The Society of American Military Engineers
607 Prince St.
Alexandria, VA 22314-3117
Ph: (703)549-3800   Fax: (703)684-0231
URL: http://www.same.org

$56.00/year; $7.00 for single issue. Journal on military and civil engineering.

★864★ PM Network

Project Management Institute
4 Campus Blvd.
Newtown Square, PA 19073-3299
Ph: (610)356-4600   Fax: (610)356-4647

Monthly. $42.00/year for members. Professional journal covering industry applications and practical issues in managing projects.

★865★ Professional Builder

Reed Business Information
360 Park Ave. S
New York, NY 10014
Ph: (646)746-7764
URL: http://www.probuilder.com

Monthly. $10.00 for single issue; $139.95/year for by mail.

★866★ Texas Architect

Texas Society of Architects
816 Congress Ave., Ste. 970
Austin, TX 78701-2443
Ph: (512)478-7386   Fax: (512)478-0528
Fr: 877-286-4144
E-mail: txarch@txarch.com
URL: http://www.texasarchitect.org

Bimonthly. $21.00/year; $4.00 for single issue. Magazine for design professionals and their clients.

PLACEMENT AND JOB REFERRAL SERVICES

★867★ American Institute of Architects (AIA)

1735 New York Ave. NW
Washington, DC 20006-5292
Ph: (202)626-7300   Fax: (202)626-7547
Fr: 800-AIA-3837
E-mail: infocentral@aia.org
URL: http://www.aia.org

Description: Professional society of architects. Regular members are professional, licensed architects; associate members are graduate architects, not yet licensed; emeritus members are retired architects. Fosters professionalism and accountability among members through continuing education and training; promotes design excellence by influencing change in the industry. Sponsors educational programs with schools of architecture, graduate students, and elementary and secondary schools; conducts professional development programs. Advises on professional competitions; supplies construction documents. Established the American Architectural Foundation. Sponsors Octagon Museum; operates bookstore; stages exhibitions; compiles statistics. Provides monthly news service on design and construction. Operates speakers' bureau, placement services, conducts research programs, charitable activities, and children's services.

★868★ Council of Educational Facility Planners, International (CEFPI)

9180 E Desert Cove Dr., No. 104
Scottsdale, AZ 85260-6231
Ph: (480)391-0840   Fax: (480)391-0940
E-mail: contact@cefpi.org
URL: http://www.cefpi.com

Members: Individuals and firms who are responsible for planning, designing, creating, maintaining, and equipping the physical environment of education. **Purpose:** Sponsors an exchange of information, professional experiences, best practices research results, and other investigative techniques concerning educational facility planning. **Activities:** Include publication and review of current and emerging practices in educational facility planning; identification and execution of needed research; development of professional training programs; strengthening of planning services on various levels of government and in institutions of higher learning; leadership in the development of higher standards for facility design and the physical environment of education. Operates speakers' bureau; sponsors placement service; compiles statistics.

★869★ Professional Women in Construction (PWC)

315 E. 56th St.
New York, NY 10022-3730
Ph: (212)486-7745   Fax: (212)486-0228
E-mail: pwcusa1@aol.com
URL: http://www.pwcusa.org

Description: Management-level women and men in construction and allied industries; owners, suppliers, architects, engineers, field personnel, office personnel, and bonding/surety personnel. Provides a forum for exchange of ideas and promotion of political and legislative action, education, and job opportunities for women in construction and related fields; forms liaisons with other trade and professional groups; develops research programs. Strives to reform abuses and to assure justice and equity within the construction industry. Sponsors mini-workshops. Maintains Action Line which provides members with current information on pertinent legislation and on the association's activities and job referrals.

★870★ Society of American Registered Architects (SARA)

305 E 46th St.
New York, NY 10017
Ph: (218)728-4293   Fax: (218)728-5361
E-mail: rickhja@hotmail.com
URL: http://www.sara-national.org

Description: Architects registered or licensed under the laws of states and territories of the U.S. Sponsors seminars and professional and student design competitions. Offers placement service.

EMPLOYER DIRECTORIES AND NETWORKING LISTS

★871★ Almanac of Architecture and Design

Greenway Consulting
30 Technology Pkwy. S, Ste. 200
Norcross, GA 30092
Ph: (770)209-3770   Fax: (770)209-3778

Annual. $37.50. Publication includes: Lists of professional organizations, degree programs, and leading firms in architecture and design. Principal content of publication is a collection of information regarding architecture and design.

★872★ Architects Directory

infoUSA Inc.
5711 S 86th Cir.
Omaha, NE 68127-0347
Ph: (402)930-3500   Fax: (402)331-0176
Fr: 800-555-6124
URL: http://www.abii.com

Annual. Number of listings: 38,839 (U.S. edition); 3,125 (Canadian edition). Entries include: Name, address, phone (including area code), size of advertisement, year first in "Yellow Pages," name of owner or manager, number of employees. Regional editions available: Eastern, $725; Western, $645.00. Compiled from telephone company "Yellow Pages," nationwide. Arrangement: Geographical.

★873★ Architecture Sourcebook: A Guide to Resources on the Practice of Architecture

Omnigraphics Inc.
615 Griswold St., Ste. 1400
Detroit, MI 48226
Ph: (313)961-1340   Fax: (313)961-1383
Fr: 800-234-1340

$22.50. Publication includes: List of associations for each of 14 building types; list of architecture collections in the United States; and list of architectural book clubs, sources for recently published architectural books, and out-of-print dealers. Entries include: For architecture collections–Name, address, phone, and brief description of special collections. Indexes: Author/title; Subject.

★874★ Association of University Interior Designers-Membership Chairperson

Association of University Interior Designers
c/o Terri Smith-Wright
Purdue University
The Office of Purchasing
West Lafayette, IN 47907
Ph: (765)494-9603   Fax: (765)496-1579

Twice yearly, June and October. Covers nearly 100 in-house interior designers, landscape designers, architects, and purchasing agents associated with universities. Entries include: Name, title, affiliation, address, phone. Arrangement: Alphabetical.

★875★ Athletic Business-Professional Directory Section

Athletic Business Publications Inc.
4130 Lien Rd.
Madison, WI 53704
Ph: (608)249-0186   Fax: (608)249-1153
Fr: 800-722-8764

Monthly. $8.00. Publication includes: List of architects, engineers, contractors, and consultants in athletic facility planning and construction; all listings are paid. Entries include: Company name, address, phone, fax and short description of company. Arrangement: Alphabetical.

★876★ Contemporary Designers

St. James Press
27500 Drake Rd.
Farmington Hills, MI 48331-3535
Ph: (248)699-4253   Fax: (248)699-8062
Fr: 800-877-4253

Irregular, 3rd edition 1996. $190.00. Covers 685 living designers and outstanding deceased designers from the recent past in the fields of art, architecture, industry, environment, textile, fashion, furniture, theater, film, graphic arts, and interior design; international coverage. Entries include: Name, date and place of birth, address, spouse's and children's names, educational background, area of specialization, projects completed, exhibitions, memberships; bibliography of materials by or about the entrant; signed critical essay. Arrangement: Alphabetical. Indexes: Nationality, designer type.

★877★ ENR-Top 500 Design Firms Issue

McGraw-Hill Companies
1221 Ave. of the Americas
New York, NY 10020
Ph: (212)512-2000   Fax: (212)512-3840

Annual, April. $10.00. Publication includes: List of 500 leading architectural, engineering, and specialty design firms selected on basis of annual billings. Entries include: Company name, headquarters location, type of firm, current and prior year rank in billings, types of services, countries in which operated in preceding year. Arrangement: Ranked by billings.

★878★ ENR-Top International Design Firms Issue

McGraw-Hill Companies
1221 Ave. of the Americas
New York, NY 10020
Ph: (212)512-2000   Fax: (212)512-3840

Annual, July issue of "Engineering News Record". $10.00. Publication includes: List of 200 design firms (including United States firms) competing outside their own national borders who received largest dollar volume of foreign contracts in preceding calendar year. Entries include: Company name, headquarters location, type of firm, current and previous year rankings in total billings, types of services, countries in which operated in preceding year. Arrangement: By amount billed to international clients in previous year.

★879★ Illinois Architecture Reference Directory

Metropolitan Press Publications
190 S Roselle Rd.
Schaumburg, IL 60193
Ph: (847)895-3950   Fax: (847)895-3951

Annual, December. $20.00. Publication includes: List of architects who reside in Illinois, and a directory of architectural, engineering, preservationist, allied professional, educational, art, historical, and construction organizations throughout the United States. Entries include: For Illinois architects-Name, address, phone, whether a member of the American Institute of Architects (AIA). For organizations-Name of firm or association, address, phone, director. Arrangement: Illinois architects list is alphabetical; organizations are classified by type (professional, governmental, etc.). Indexes: AIA members.

★880★ International Architecture Centres

John Wiley & Sons Inc.
111 River St.
Hoboken, NJ 07030-5774
Ph: (201)748-6000   Fr: 800-255-5945

Published May 2003. $60.00. Publication includes: A directory of international architecture centers. Principal content of publication is articles about issues that mold the work of architecture centers in the United Kingdom, Europe and North America, such as regeneration, sustainability, government policy, culture, housing and others.

★881★ The Military Engineer-Directory

The Society of American Military Engineers (SAME)
607 Prince St.
Alexandria, VA 22314-3117
Ph: (703)549-3800   Fax: (703)684-0231
E-mail: dir@same.org
URL: http://www.same.org

Updated daily. Database covers: Approximately 2,800 member architect, engineer, engineering-related firms and government agencies and equipment manufacturers, suppliers and contractors who provide products and services to government and private sector entities; also lists firms with experience and equipment useable in event of disasters/emergencies. Database includes: Firm name, address, phone, E-mail, home page, names of principals, business class, type of ownership, number of employees, and the engineering specialities of the firm. Arrangement: Alphabetical. Indexes: Alphabetical by state and country; alphabetical by business class.

★882★ ProFile: The Architects Sourcebook

Reed Construction Data
30 Technology Pkwy. S
Norcross, GA 30092
Ph: (770)209-3664   Fax: 800-444-1059
Fr: 800-949-0276
E-mail: profile@reedbusiness.com
URL: http://www.firstsourceonl.com

Annual. $225.00. Covers more than 27,000 architectural firms. Entries include: For firms-Firm name, address, phone, fax, year established, key staff and their primary responsibilities (for design, specification, etc.), number of staff personnel by discipline, types of work, geographical area served, projects. "ProFile" is an expanded version of, and replaces, the "Firm Directory." Arrangement: Firms are geographical. Indexes: Firm name, key individuals, specialization by category, consultants.

★883★ Society of American Registered Architects-National Directory

Society of American Registered Architects
23 Nepperhan Ave.
Elmsford, NY 10523-2506
Ph: (914)631-3600   Fax: (914)631-1319
URL: http://www.sara-national.org

Annual, January. Covers 1,000 architects registered or licensed under the laws of states and territories of the United States. Entries include: Name, affiliation, address, phone, office size, specialties, and dollar volume of work. Arrangement: Alphabetical. Indexes: Cross-referenced by state registration.

HANDBOOKS AND MANUALS

★884★ Architect?: A Candid Guide to the Profession

MIT Press
5 Cambridge Ctr., Ste. 4
Cambridge, MA 02142-1493
Ph: (617)253-5646   Fax: (617)253-6779
Fr: 800-356-0343

Roger K. Lewis. 1998. $22.95 (paper). 304 pages.

★885★ Architect's Handbook of Professional Practice, Student Edition

John Wiley & Sons Inc.
111 River Rd.
Hoboken, NJ 07030-5774
Ph: (201)748-6000   Fax: (201)748-6088

The American Institute of Architects. Thirteenth edition, 2001. $90.00. 624 pages.

★886★ The Architect's Handbook of Professional Practice Update 2004
John Wiley & Sons, Incorporated
111 River St.
Hoboken, NJ 07030
Ph: (201)748-6000   Fax: (201)748-6088
March 2004. $85.00. CD-ROM & paper. 176 pages.

★887★ Architectural Knowledge: The Idea of a Profession
Routledge
29 W. 35th St.
New York, NY 10001-2299
Ph: (212)216-7800   Fax: (212)564-7854
Francis Duffy and Les Hutton. 1998. $48.95 (paper). 224 pages.

★888★ Career Information Center
Macmillan Publishing Co. Inc.
200 Old Tappan Rd.
Old Tappan, NJ 07675
Fr: 800-428-5331
Visual Education Center Staff. Seventh edition, 1999. $275.00. 2080 pages. This 13-volume set profiles over 600 occupations. Each occupational profile describes job duties, educational requirements, how to get the job, advancement possibilities, employment outlook, working conditions, earnings and benefits, and where to write for more information.

★889★ How to Start and Operate Your Own Design Firm
McGraw-Hill Companies
2 Penn Plaza
New York, NY 10121-2298
Ph: (212)904-4509   Fr: 800-338-3987
Albert W. Rubeling, Jr. 1994. $33.00. 192 pages.

★890★ The I Hate Selling Book: Business-Building Advice for Consultants, Attorneys, Accountants, Engineers, Architects, and Other Professionals
Allan Boress & Associates
1500 University Dr., Suite 239
Coral Springs, FL 33071
Ph: (954)345-4666   Fax: (954)344-2453
Allan S. Boress. 2001. $29.95.

★891★ Opportunities in Architecture Careers
McGraw-Hill Trade
2 Penn Plaza
New York, NY 10121
Ph: (212)904-2000   Fax: (212)755-5645
Fr: 800-722-4726
Robert J. Piper and Richard D. Rush. 1994. $14.95; $11.95 (paper). 160 pages. Guide to planning for and seeking opportunities in the field. Illustrated.

★892★ Opportunities in Computer-Aided Design and Computer-Aided Manufacturing
McGraw-Hill Trade
2 Penn Plaza
New York, NY 10121
Ph: (212)904-2000   Fr: 800-722-4726
Jan Bone. 1994. $14.95; $11.95 (paper). 160 pages. Defines CAD (computer-aided design), CAM (computer-aided manufacturing), and MAP (manufacturing automation protocol). Explains career opportunities in the CAD/CAM field, and education and training needed. Gives job-hunting tips.

★893★ Opportunities in Environmental Careers
McGraw-Hill Trade
2 Penn Plaza
New York, NY 10121
Ph: (212)904-2000   Fr: 800-722-4726
E-mail: ntcpub@tribune.com
Odom Fanning. Revised, 2002. $12.95 (paper). 160 pages. Describes a broad range of opportunities in fields such as environmental health, recreation, physics, and hygiene, and provides job search advice. Part of Opportunities in...Series.

★894★ Opportunities in Real Estate Careers
McGraw-Hill Professional
2 Penn Plaza
New York, NY 10121
Ph: (212)904-2000   Fr: 800-722-4726
E-mail: ntcpub@tribune.com
Mariwyn Evans. 2002. $15.95; $11.95 (paper). 160 pages.

★895★ Resumes for Architecture and Related Careers
McGraw-Hill Trade
2 Penn Plaza
New York, NY 10121
Ph: (212)904-2000   Fr: 800-722-4726
VGM Career Horizons Editors. 1996. $9.95 (paper). 160 pages.

EMPLOYMENT AGENCIES AND SEARCH FIRMS

★896★ Agra Placements, Ltd.
8187 University Blvd.
Clive, IA 50325
Ph: (515)225-6562   Fax: (515)225-7733
E-mail: iowa@agraplacements.com
URL: http://www.agraplacements.com
Executive search firm. Branch offices in Peru, IN, Lincoln, IL, and New Ulm, MN.

★897★ Claremont-Branan, Inc.
1298 Rockbridge Rd., Ste. B
Stone Mountain, GA 30087
Ph: (770)925-2915   Fax: (770)925-2601
Employment agency. Executive search firm.

★898★ The Coxe Group Inc.
1218 3rd Ave., Ste. 1700
Seattle, WA 98101-3021
Ph: (206)467-4040   Fax: (206)467-4038
Executive search firm.

★899★ RitaSue Siegel Resources, Inc.
20 E. 46th St.
New York, NY 10017-2417
Ph: (212)682-2100   Fax: (212)682-2946
E-mail: ritasues@ritasue.com
URL: http://www.ritasuesiegelresources.com
Executive search firm specializing in industrial and product design.

★900★ Specialized Search Associates
15200 Jog Rd., Ste. 201
Delray Beach, FL 33446
Ph: (561)499-3711   Fax: (561)499-3770
Fr: 888-405-2650
E-mail: lm7880@aol.com
Executive search firm that specializes in construction, engineering, and sales.

TRADESHOWS

★901★ American Institute of Architects, Minnesota Annual Convention and Exhibition
American Institute of Architects, Minnesota Chapter
275 Market St., Ste. 54
Minneapolis, MN 55405
Ph: (612)338-6763   Fax: (612)338-7981
URL: http://www.aia-mn.org
Annual. **Primary Exhibits:** Windows, concrete, roofing, millwork, tile, construction management companies, and other construction products.

★902★ Cincinnati Construction Expo
Industry Week
Penton Media, Inc.
1300 9th St. Ste. 316
Cleveland, OH 44114-1503
Ph: (513)528-1550   Fax: (513)528-1131
E-mail: exposource1@aol.com
URL: http://www.exposupersite.com
Annual. **Primary Exhibits:** Building products and services for architects, contractors, and builders.

OTHER SOURCES

★903★ Asian American Architects and Engineers

1670 Pine St.
San Francisco, CA 94109
Ph: (415)928-5910   Fax: (415)921-0182
E-mail: info@asianinc.org
URL: http://www.asianinc.org

Members: Minorities. **Purpose:** Provides contracts and job opportunities for minorities in the architectural and eningeering fields. **Activities:** Serves as a network for the promotion in professional fields.

★904★ Association for International Practical Training (AIPT)

10400 Little Patuxent Pky., Ste. 250
Columbia, MD 21044-3519
Ph: (410)997-2200   Fax: (410)992-3924
E-mail: aipt@aipt.org
URL: http://www.aipt.org

Description: Providers worldwide on-the-job training programs for students and professionals seeking international career development and life-changing experiences. Arranges workplace exchanges in hundreds of professional fields, bringing employers and trainees together from around the world. Client list ranges from small farming communities to Fortune 500 companies.

★905★ CoreNet Global

260 Peachtree St. NW
Atlanta, GA 30303-1237
Ph: (404)589-3200   Fax: (404)589-3201
Fr: 800-726-8111
E-mail: corenet@corenetglobal.org
URL: http://www.corenetglobal.org

Description: Executives, attorneys, real estate department heads, architects, engineers, analysts, researchers, and anyone responsible for the management, administration, and operation of national and regional real estate departments of national and international corporations. Provides a meeting ground for the exchange of ideas, experience, and problems among members; encourages professionalism within corporate real estate through education and communication; protects the interests of corporate realty in dealing with adversaries, public or private; maintains contact with other real estate organizations; publicizes the availability of fully qualified members to the job market. Maintains Institute for Corporate Real Estate as educational arm. Conducts seminars, including concentrated workshops on the corporate real estate field. Compiles statistics; sponsors competitions; maintains biographical archives and placement service.

★906★ Math at Work: Women in Nontraditional Careers

Her Own Words
PO Box 5264
Madison, WI 53705-0264
Ph: (608)271-7083   Fax: (608)271-0209
URL: http://www.herownwords.com/

Video. Jocelyn Riley. $95.00. 15 minutes. Resource guide also available for $45.00.

★907★ National Center for Construction Education and Research

3600 NW 43rd St., Bldg. G
PO Box 141104
Gainesville, FL 32606-1104
Ph: (352)334-0911   Fax: (352)334-0932
Fr: 888-NCCER-20
E-mail: info@nccer.org
URL: http://www.nccer.org

Description: Education foundation committed to the development and publication of Contren(TM) Learning Series, the source of craft training, management education and safety resources for the construction industry.

★908★ National Council of Architectural Registration Boards (NCARB)

1801 K St. NW, Ste. 1100K
Washington, DC 20006-1310
Ph: (202)783-6500   Fax: (202)783-0290
E-mail: customerservice@ncarb.org
URL: http://www.ncarb.org

Members: Federation of state boards for the registration of architects in the United States, District of Columbia, Puerto Rico, Virgin Islands, Guam, and the Northern Mariana Islands.

★909★ Professional Specialty Occupations

Delphi Productions
3160 4th St.
Boulder, CO 80304
Fax: (303)443-4022   Fr: 888-443-2400
URL: http://www.delphivideo.com

$95.00. 53 minutes. Part of the Careers for the 21st Century Video Library.

★910★ Women in Building Construction

Her Own Words
PO Box 5264
Madison, WI 53705-0264
Ph: (608)271-7083   Fax: (608)271-0209
URL: http://www.herownwords.com/

Video. Jocelyn Riley. $95.00. 15 minutes. Resource guide also available for $45.00.

Archivists and Curators

SOURCES OF HELP-WANTED ADS

★911★ The Abbey Newsletter

Abbey Publications Inc.
7105 Geneva Dr.
Austin, TX 78723-1510
Ph: (512)929-3992   Fax: (512)929-3995
URL: http://palimpsest.stanford.edu/byorg/abbey/

Description: Six issues/year. Encourages the development of library and archival conservation, particularly technical advances and cross-disciplinary research in the field. Covers book repair and the conservation of books, papers, photographs, and non-paper materials. Recurring features include book reviews, news of research, job listings, convention reports, a calendar of events, and an occasional column about equipment and supplies.

★912★ ACDA Bulletin

Association of Catholic Diocesan Archivists (ACDA)
711 W Monroe St.
Chicago, IL 60661-3515
Ph: (773)736-5150
E-mail: archives@diopitt.org

Description: Three issues/year. Recurring features include reports of meetings, news of educational opportunities, job listings, book reviews, and notices of publications available.

★913★ AMIA Newsletter

Association of Moving Image Archivists (AMIA)
8949 Wilshire Blvd.
Beverly Hills, CA 90211
Ph: (310)550-1300   Fax: (310)550-1363

Description: Quarterly. Presents information on the preservation of film and video materials, and the moving image archival profession. REC news of research, a calendar of events, reports of meetings, job listings, book reviews, and notices of publications available.

★914★ Archival Outlook

Society of American Archivists
527 S Wells St., 5th Fl.
Chicago, IL 60607-3922
Ph: (312)922-0140   Fax: (312)347-1452

Description: Bimonthly. Publishes news of relevance to the professional archival community. Recurring features include a calendar of events, news from constituent groups, news of educational opportunities, professional resources available, and job listings.

★915★ C Magazine

C The Visual Arts Foundation
PO Box 5, Sta. B
Toronto, ON, Canada M5T 2T2
Ph: (416)539-9495   Fax: (416)539-9903
Fr: 800-745-6312

Quarterly. Periodical covering the visual and performing arts.

★916★ Dusty Shelf

Kansas City Area Archivists
NARA
2312 E Bannister Rd.
Kansas City, MO 64131-3011
Fax: (816)926-6982
URL: http://www.umkc.edu/kcaa/dustyshelf/dusty.htm

Description: Three issues/year. Contains essays and editorials on local and national archives. Recurring features include a calendar of events, reports of meetings, news of educational opportunities, job listings, notices of publications available, and a column titled Conservation Notes.

★917★ History News

American Association for State & Local History
1717 Church St.
Nashville, TN 37203-2991
Ph: (615)320-3203   Fax: (615)327-9013
URL: http://www.aaslh.org

Quarterly. $50.00/year, includes membership; $75.00/year for institutions, includes membership. Magazine for employees of historic sites, museums, and public history agencies. Coverage includes museum edu-cation programs and techniques for working with volunteers.

★918★ Mid-Atlantic Archivist

Mid-Atlantic Regional Archives Conference
c/o George Washington University
The Gelman Library
2130 H St. NW
Washington, DC 20052
Ph: (202)994-7283   Fax: (202)463-6205

Description: Quarterly. Contains news and information for and about members of the Conference. Seeks exchange of information between colleagues, improvement of competence among archivists, and encourages professional involvement of persons actively engaged in the preservation and use of historical research materials. Recurring features include letters to the editor, news of members, book reviews, a calendar of events, and columns titled Preservation News, Reference Shelf, Session Abstracts, Software News, and Employment Opportunities.

★919★ New England Archivists Newsletter

New England Archivists
Massachusetts Archives
220 Morrissey Blvd.
Boston, MA 02125
Ph: (617)727-2816

Description: Quarterly. Contains regional archival news and announcements. Recurring features include a calendar of events, reports of meetings, job listings, book reviews, workshops, reports on repositories, and feature articles on archival subjects. 20-year accumulative index available.

★920★ Preservation

National Trust for Historic Preservation
1785 Massachusetts Ave. NW
Washington, DC 20036-2117
Ph: (202)588-6296   Fax: (202)588-6223
Fr: 800-944-6847
URL: http://www.nthp.org

Bimonthly. $20.00/year. Magazine featuring historic preservation.

★921★ *Sky & Telescope*

Sky Publishing Corp.
49 Bay State Rd.
Cambridge, MA 02138
Ph: (617)864-7360   Fax: (617)864-6117
Fr: 800-253-0245
URL: http://www.skypub.com

Monthly. $39.95/year for individuals; $29.95/year for students; $4.99/year for single issue. Magazine on astronomy and space science.

★922★ *Technology & Conservation of Art, Architecture & Antiquities*

The Technology Organization Inc.
76 Highland Ave.
Somerville, MA 02143
Ph: (617)623-2253

Quarterly. Magazine on art, architecture, and archeology.

PLACEMENT AND JOB REFERRAL SERVICES

★923★ **American Association of Museums (AAM)**

1575 Eye St. NW, Ste. 400
Washington, DC 20005
Ph: (202)289-1818   Fax: (202)289-6578
E-mail: membership@aam-us.org
URL: http://www.aam-us.org

Description: Directors, curators, registrars, educators, exhibit designers, public relations officers, development officers, security managers, trustees, and volunteers in museums. Represents all museums, including art, history, science, military and maritime, and youth, as well as aquariums, zoos, botanical gardens, arboretums, historic sites, and science and technology centers. Dedicated to promoting excellence within the museum community. Assists museum staff, boards, and volunteers through advocacy, professional education, information exchange, accreditation, and guidance.

★924★ **American Society for Information Science and Technology (ASIST)**

1320 Fenwick Ln., No. 510
Silver Spring, MD 20910
Ph: (301)495-0900   Fax: (301)495-0810
E-mail: asis@asis.org
URL: http://www.asis.org

Members: Information specialists, scientists, librarians, administrators, social scientists, and others interested in the use, organization, storage, retrieval, evaluation, and dissemination of recorded specialized information. **Purpose:** Seeks to improve the information transfer process through research, development, application, and education. **Activities:** Provides a forum for the discussion, publication, and critical analysis of work dealing with the theory, practice, research, and development of elements involved in communication

of information. Members are engaged in a variety of activities and specialties including classification and coding systems, automatic and associative indexing, machine translation of languages, special librarianship and library systems analysis, and copyright issues. Sponsors National Auxiliary Publications Service, which provides reproduction services and a central depository for all types of information (operated for ASIS by Microfiche Publications). Maintains placement service. Sponsors numerous special interest groups. Conducts continuing education programs and professional development workshops.

★925★ **Natural Science for Youth Foundation (NSYF)**

130 Azalea Dr.
Roswell, GA 30075
Ph: (770)594-9367   Fax: (770)594-7738
E-mail: info@slpt.org

Description: Sponsors natural science centers, junior nature museums, native animal parks, and trailside museums. Provides information service. Conducts training courses in museum and nature center management. Maintains museum and placement service.

★926★ **Print Council of America (PCA)**

Carl A. Weyerhaeuser Curator of Prints
Fogg Art Museum
Harvard University Art Museums
32 Quincy St.
Cambridge, MA 02138
E-mail: cohn@fas.harvard.edu
URL: http://www.printcouncil.org

Description: Museum professionals. Fosters the study and appreciation of new and old prints, drawings, and photographs; stimulates discussion. Sponsors educational programs and research publications; offers placement services.

★927★ **Special Libraries Association (SLA)**

1700 18th St. NW
Washington, DC 20009-2514
Ph: (202)234-4700   Fax: (202)265-9317
E-mail: sla@sla.org
URL: http://www.sla.org/

Description: International association of information professionals who work in special libraries serving business, research, government, universities, newspapers, museums, and institutions that use or produce specialized information. Seeks to advance the leadership role of special librarians. Offers consulting services to organizations that wish to establish or expand a library or information services. Conducts strategic learning and development courses, public relations, and government relations programs. Provides employment services. Operates knowledge exchange on topics pertaining to the development and management of special libraries. Maintains Hall of Fame.

EMPLOYER DIRECTORIES AND NETWORKING LISTS

★928★ *American Art Directory*

LexisNexis Group
121 Chanlon Rd.
New Providence, NJ 07974
Ph: (908)464-6800   Fax: (908)771-7704
Fr: 800-526-4902
URL: http://nationalregisterpub.com

Biennial. $299.00. Covers over 7,000 museums, art libraries, and art organizations, and 1,700 art schools; also includes lists of state directors and supervisors of art education in schools, traveling exhibition booking agencies, corporations having art holdings for public viewing, newspapers that carry art notes, art scholarships and fellowships; and 190 national, regional, and state open art exhibitions. Entries include: For museums-Name, address, phone, fax, electronic mail address, name of curator; days and hours of operation, collection, budget, publications. For exhibits-Name, address, phone, fax, electronic mail address, name of contact; date, deadline. For schools-Name, address, phone, name of director, names of faculty members, majors or degrees offered, tuition fees; summer school or adult hobby class information. For newspapers-Name, address, phone, name of art editor. Arrangement: Geographical. Indexes: Geographical, collection/subject/name, personal name, institution name.

★929★ *Directory of Special Libraries and Information Centers*

Thomson Gale
27500 Drake Rd.
Farmington Hills, MI 48331-3535
Ph: (248)699-4253   Fax: (248)699-8065
Fr: 800-877-GALE
E-mail: businessproducts@gale.com
URL: http://www.galegroup.com

Annual. $975.00 for set; $740.00 for set without supplement; $560.00 for indexes. Covers over 34,000 special libraries, information centers, documentation centers, etc.; about 500 networks and consortia; major special libraries abroad also included. Volume 1 part 3 contains 6 other appendices (besides networks and consortia): Regional and Subregional Libraries for the Blind & Physically Handicapped, Patent & Trademark Depository Libraries, Regional Government Depository Libraries, United Nations Depository Libraries, World Bank Depository Libraries, and European Community Depository Libraries. Entries include: Library name, address, phone, fax, e-mail address; contact; year founded; sponsoring organization; special collections; subject interests; names and titles of staff; services (copying, online searches); size of collection; subscriptions; computerized services and automated operations; Internet home page address; publications; special catalogs; special indexes. For consortia and networks-Name, address, phone, contact. Other appendices have varying amounts of directory information. Contents of Volume 1 are available in "Subject

Directory of Special Libraries and Information Centers". Arrangement: Libraries are alphabetical by name of sponsoring organization or institution; consortia and networks are geographical. Indexes: Subject. Geographic and personnel indexes constitute volume 2.

★930★ Guide to Employment Sources in the Library & Information Professions

Office for Human Resource Development and Recruitment
50 E Huron St.
Chicago, IL 60611
Ph: (312)280-4282   Fax: (312)280-3256
URL: http://www.ala.org/hrdr/employment_guide.html

Annual, spring. Free. Covers library job sources, such as specialized and state and regional library associations, state library agencies, federal library agencies, and overseas exchange programs. Entries include: Library, company, or organization name, address, phone; contact name, description of services, publications, etc. This is a reprint of a segment of the "Bowker Annual of Library and Book Trade Information," described separately. Arrangement: Classified by type of source.

★931★ International Directory of Corporate Art Collections

ARTnews
PO Box 1608
Largo, FL 33779
Ph: (813)581-7328   Fax: (813)585-6398

Biennial, March of even years. $109.95. Covers about 1,300 art collections maintained or sponsored by businesses and corporations in the United States, Canada, Europe, and Japan. Entries include: Collection name; company name, name of contact, address, phone; line of business, description of collection; size and location of collection; publications, exhibitions, loan and viewing policies, other corporate arts activities. Arrangement: Alphabetical. Indexes: Geographical, personal name, media and type of art, type of business, collection status.

★932★ Membership Directory and Roster of State and National Archives and Records Officials

National Association of Government Archives and Records Administrators (NAGARA)
48 Howard St.
Albany, NY 12207
Ph: (518)463-8644   Fax: (518)463-8656

Annual, latest edition 1995-96. $10.00. Covers state government records management and archival programs in the fifty states, the District of Columbia, American Samoa, Guam, Northern Mariana Islands, Puerto Rico, the Virgin Islands, and Canadian provinces; individual archivists and records managers, National Archives and Records Administration staff. Entries include: Name, address, phone, fax, e-mail address, names and titles of key personnel. Arrangement:

Separate geographical sections for state programs, individuals, Canadian provinces, and NARA staff.

★933★ Midwest Archives Conference-Membership Directory

Midwest Archives Conference
c/o Menzi Behrnd-Klodt
7422 Longmeadow Rd.
Madison, WI 53717
Ph: (608)827-5727
URL: http://www.midwestarchives.org

Annual. Covers more than 1,000 individual and institutional members, largely librarians, archivists, records managers, manuscripts curators, historians, and historical society personnel; about 25 archival associations in the Midwest. Entries include: For institutions-Name of archives, parent organization, address, phone. For individuals-Name, title, business address, phone. Arrangement: Separate alphabetical sections for individuals and institutions.

★934★ Museums Directory

infoUSA Inc.
5711 S 86th Cir.
Omaha, NE 68127-0347
Ph: (402)930-3500   Fax: (402)331-0176
Fr: 800-555-6124
URL: http://www.abii.com

Annual. Number of listings: 8,916. Entries include: Name, address, phone (including area code), size of advertisement, year first in "Yellow Pages," name of owner or manager, number of employees. Compiled from telephone company "Yellow Pages," nationwide. Arrangement: Geographical.

★935★ Official Museum Directory

LexisNexis Group
121 Chanlon Rd.
New Providence, NJ 07974
Ph: (908)464-6800   Fax: (908)771-7704
Fr: 800-526-4902

Annual, December. $245.00. Covers approximately 7,850 institutions of art, history, and science in the United States, including general museums, college and university museums, children's and junior museums, company museums, national park and nature center displays, and highly specialized museums. Also includes a separate volume of 2,000 suppliers of services and products to museums. Entries include: For museums-Name, address, phone, date established, personnel, governing authority, brief description of museum and type of collections, facilities, activities, publications, hours of operation, admission prices, membership fees, attendance figures. For suppliers-Company name, address, phone, name and title of contact. Arrangement: Museums are geographical; suppliers are by specialty. Indexes: Museum personnel (with name, title, affiliation, city, and state); type of museum (with name, city, and state); alphabetical; special collection.

★936★ Society of American Archivists Directory of Individual and Institutional Members

Society of American Archivists
527 S Wells St., 5th Fl.
Chicago, IL 60607-3922
Ph: (312)922-0140   Fax: (312)347-1452

Biennial, latest edition 1998-99. $50.00. Covers 4,600 individual and institutional members concerned with management and custody of current and historical records, and with archival administration. Entries include: Member name, company or institution where member works, address, phone, fax, computer network names and identification. Arrangement: Alphabetical. Indexes: Institution/company name, section membership, geographic listing of individual members.

★937★ Who's Who in American Art

Marquis Who's Who
121 Chanlon Rd.
New Providence, NJ 07974
Ph: (908)673-1101   Fax: (908)673-1189
Fr: 800-473-7020
E-mail: art@renp.com
URL: http://www.marquiswhoswho.com

Biennial, Spring of odd years. $265.00. Covers about 11,800 people active in visual arts, including sculptors, painters, illustrators, printmakers, collectors, curators, writers, educators, dealers, critics, patrons, and museum executives. Also includes cumulative necrology from 1953. Entries include: Name, professional classification, address; artists' listings include dealer's name and address, preferred media, works in public collections, awards, publications, teaching positions, etc.; other listings may include same information plus statement of research interests, etc. Arrangement: Alphabetical. Indexes: Geographical, professional classification.

HANDBOOKS AND MANUALS

★938★ Advocating Archives: An Introduction to Public Relations for Archivists

Scarecrow Press, Incorporated
4501 Forbes Blvd., Ste. 200
Lanham, MD 20706-4310
Ph: (301)459-3366   Fax: (301)429-5747

Elsie Freeman Finch. March 2003. $34.95. Illustrated. 186 pages. Study on archiving public relations.

★939★ Careers for Culture Lovers and Other Artsy Types

VGM Career Horizons
1221 Avenue of the Americas
New York, NY 10020
Ph: (212)904-2000   Fr: 800-323-4900
E-mail: ntcpub@tribune.com

Marjorie Eberts and Margaret Gisler. Second edition, 1999. $14.95; $9.95 (paper). 234

pages. Describes how to get work in a variety of fields related to art and culture. Opportunities include picture framer, curator, art restorer, symphony manager, disk jockey, music reviewer, dance teacher, choreographer, costume designer, theater manager, light designer, drama teacher, bookstore owner, interior decorator, antique store owner, and others.

★940★ *Careers in the Visual Arts: A Guide to Jobs, Money, Opportunities, and an Artistic Life*

Watson-Guptill Publications, Inc.
BPI Communications, Inc.
770 Broadway
New York, NY 10003
Ph: (646)654-5400   Fax: (646)654-5486
Fr: 800-323-9432

Dee Ito. 1993. $14.95 (paper). 320 pages. Out of print. Gives a broad overview of each field included, with educational requirements and employment opportunities. Includes ideas on how to get started.

★941★ *Designing a Career in Public History: Becoming a Professional Historian*

Krieger Publishing Co.
PO Box 9542
Melbourne, FL 32902-9542
Ph: (407)724-9542   Fax: (407)951-3671
Fr: 800-724-0025

Donna M. Neary.

★942★ *Ethics and the Archival Profession: Introduction and Case Studies*

Society of American Archivists
527 S. Wells St., 5th Fl.
Chicago, IL 60607-3992
Ph: (312)922-0140   Fax: (312)347-1452

Karen M. Benedict. November 2003. $34.95.

★943★ *Great Jobs for History Majors*

McGraw-Hill Trade
2 Penn Plaza
New York, NY 10121
Ph: (212)904-2000   Fr: 800-722-4726
E-mail: ntcpub@tribune.com

Julie DeGalan and Stephen Lambert. 1994. $11.95 (paper). 442 pages.

★944★ *Great Jobs for Liberal Arts Majors*

McGraw-Hill Professional
2 Penn Plaza
New York, NY 10121
Ph: (212)904-2000   Fr: 800-722-4726
E-mail: ntcpub@tribune.com

Blythe Camenson. Second edition, 2001. $14.95 (paper). 256 pages.

★945★ *Museum Archives: An Introduction*

Society of American Archivists
527 S. Wells St., 5th Fl.
Chicago, IL 60607-3992
Ph: (312)922-0140   Fax: (312)347-1452

Deborah Wythe. January 2004.

★946★ *Museum Careers & Training: A Professional Guide*

Greenwood Publishing Group, Inc.
88 Post Rd., W.
Westport, CT 06881-5007
Ph: (203)226-3571   Fax: (203)222-1502
Fr: 800-225-5800

Victor J. Danilov. 1994. $95.00. 560 pages. Describes various museum positions and training programs available.

★947★ *Museum Jobs from A-Z: What They Are, How to Prepare, and Where to Find Them*

Batax Museum Publishing
2051 Wheeler Ln.
Switzerland, FL 32259
Ph: (904)287-2464

G.W. Bates. 1994. $9.95 (paper). Provides information, including descriptions and training needs, for 62 museum occupations.

★948★ *Opportunities in Crafts Careers*

McGraw-Hill Trade
2 Penn Plaza
New York, NY 10121
Ph: (212)904-2000   Fr: 800-722-4726

Marianne Munday. 1994. $14.95; $11.95 (paper). 160 pages. Provides information about careers and job opportunities in such areas as fine and applied arts, antiques and collectibles, ceramics, woodworking, sewing and needlecraft, and more. Illustrated. Out of stock.

★949★ *Opportunities in Museum Careers*

McGraw-Hill/Contemporary Books
1221 Avenue of the Americas
New York, NY 10020
Ph: (212)904-2000   Fr: 800-323-4900

Blythe Camenson. 1996. $14.95; $11.95 (paper). 160 pages.

★950★ *Opportunities in Zoo Careers*

McGraw-Hill Trade
2 Penn Plaza
New York, NY 10121
Ph: (212)904-2000   Fr: 800-722-4726
E-mail: ntcpub@tribune.com

Blythe Camenson. 1997. $14.95; $11.95 (paper).

EMPLOYMENT AGENCIES AND SEARCH FIRMS

★951★ **Gossage Sager Associates LLC**
25 W. 43rd St., Ste. 812
New York, NY 10036
Ph: (212)417-9468   Fax: (212)997-1127
E-mail: dsager@g=ossagesager.com
URL: http://www.gossagesager.com

Executive search firm. Concentrates in placement of library and information professionals on permanent basis nationwide.

OTHER SOURCES

★952★ **American Institute for Conservation of Historic and Artistic Works (AIC)**
1717 K St. NW, Ste. 200
Washington, DC 20006
Ph: (202)452-9545   Fax: (202)452-9328
E-mail: info@aic-faic.org
URL: http://aic.stanford.edu

Members: Professionals, scientists, administrators, and educators in the field of art conservation; interested individuals. **Purpose:** Advances the practice and promotes the importance of the preservation of cultural property. **Activities:** Coordinates the exchange of knowledge, research, and publications. Establishes and upholds professional standards. Publishes conservation literature. Compiles statistics. Represents membership to allied professional associations and advocates on conservation-related issues. Solicits and dispenses money exclusively for charitable, scientific, and educational objectives.

★953★ *Archivists and Curators*
Evon Publishing
832 N 7th Ave.
Iron River, MI 49935
Ph: (906)265-3190

Audiocassette. 1996. $16.95. 32 minutes. Part of the Careers and Vocational Guidance Series. Provides information about the nature of the work, educational requirements, employment outlook, earnings, and work conditions as well as additional related information.

★954★ *College Art Association (CAA)*
275 7th Ave.
New York, NY 10001
Ph: (212)691-1051   Fax: (212)627-2381
E-mail: nyoffice@collegeart.org
URL: http://www.collegeart.org

Description: Professional organization of artists, art historians and fine art educators, museum directors, and curators. Seeks to raise the standards of scholarship and of the teaching of art and art history throughout the country.

★955★ Society of American Archivists (SAA)
527 S Wells, 5th Fl.
Chicago, IL 60607
Ph: (312)922-0140   Fax: (312)347-1452
E-mail: info@archivists.org
URL: http://www.archivists.org

Description: Individuals and institutions concerned with the identification, preservation, and use of records of historical value.

★956★ Women's Caucus for Art (WCA)
Canal Street Sta.
PO Box 1498
New York, NY 10013
Ph: (212)634-0007
E-mail: info@nationalwca.com
URL: http://www.nationalwca.com

Members: Professional women in visual art fields including artists, critics, art historians, museum and gallery professionals, arts administrators, educators and students, and collectors of art. **Purpose:** Objectives are to increase recognition for contemporary and historical achievements of women in art; ensure equal opportunity for employment, art commissions, and research grants; encourage professionalism and shared information among women in art; stimulate and publicize research and publications on women in the visual arts. **Activities:** Conducts workshops, periodic affirmative action research, and statistical surveys. Presents annual honor awards to senior women in the visual arts.

Art Therapists

★968★ Great Jobs for Psychology Majors

McGraw-Hill Trade
2 Penn Plaza
New York, NY 10121
Ph: (212)904-2000   Fr: 800-722-4726
E-mail: ntcpub@tribune.com

Julie DeGalan and Stephen Lambert. 1995. $11.95 (paper). 468 pages. Out of print.

★969★ Handbook of Art Therapy

Guildford Press
72 Spring Street
New York, NY 10012

Cathy A. Malchiodi. 2002. $48.00. 461 pages. Provides complete and practical overview of art therapy.

★970★ A Therapist's Guide to Art Therapy Assessments: Tools of the Trade

Charles C Thomas Publisher, Ltd.
2600 S. 1st.
PO Box 19265
Springfield, IL 62794-9265
Ph: (217)789-8980   Fax: (217)789-9130
Fr: 800-258-9980

Stephanie L. Brooke. 1996. $25.95. 164 pages.

★971★ Working with Images: The Art of Art Therapist

Charles C. Thomas Publisher, Ltd.
2600 S. First St.
Springfield, IL 62794-9265
Ph: (217)789-8980   Fax: (217)789-9130
Fr: 800-258-8980

Bruce L. Moon. January 2002. $43.95 (paper) $67.95 (trade cloth). 270 pages. Explores art therapy.

OTHER SOURCES

★972★ American Art Therapy Association (AATA)

1202 Allanson Rd.
Mundelein, IL 60060-3808
Ph: (847)949-6064   Fax: (847)566-4580
Fr: 888-290-0878
E-mail: info@arttherapy.org
URL: http://www.arttherapy.org

Description: Art therapists, students, and individuals in related fields. Supports the progressive development of therapeutic uses of art, the advancement of research, and improvements in the standards of practice. Has established specific professional criteria for training art therapists. Facilitates the exchange of information and experience. Compiles statistics.

★973★ American Society of Psychopathology of Expression (ASPE)

74 Lawton St.
Brookline, MA 02446
Ph: (617)738-9821   Fax: (617)975-0411

Description: Psychiatrists, psychologists, art therapists, sociologists, art critics, artists, social workers, linguists, educators, criminologists, writers, and historians. At least two-thirds of the members must be physicians. Fosters collaboration among specialists in the United States who are interested in the problems of expression and in the artistic activities connected with psychiatric, sociological, and psychological research. Disseminates information about research and clinical applications in the field of psychopathology of expression. Sponsors consultations, seminars, and lectures on art therapy.

★974★ International Expressive Arts Therapy Association (IEATA)

PO Box 332399
San Francisco, CA 94132
Ph: (415)522-8939

URL: http://www.ieata.org/

Description: Provides resources about the expressive arts and how they may relate to other discipline, such as psychology, education and business.

★975★ National Art Education Association (NAEA)

1916 Association Dr.
Reston, VA 20191-1590
Ph: (703)860-8000   Fax: (703)860-2960
E-mail: naea@dgs.dgsys.com
URL: http://www.naea-reston.org

Members: Teachers of art at elementary, middle, secondary, and college levels; colleges, libraries, museums, and other educational institutions. **Purpose:** Studies problems of teaching art; encourages research and experimentation. **Activities:** Serves as clearinghouse for information on art education programs, materials, and methods of instruction. Sponsors special institutes. Cooperates with other national organizations for the furtherance of creative art experiences for youth.

★976★ National Coalition of Creative Arts Therapy Associations (NCCATA)

8455 Colesville Rd., Ste. 1000
Silver Spring, MD 20910
Ph: (201)224-9146   Fax: (201)224-9146
E-mail: miriam.berger@nyu.edu
URL: http://www.nccata.org

Description: Creative arts therapists. Promotes therapeutic and rehabilitative uses of the arts in medicine, mental health, special education, and forensic and social services; coordinates member associations' activities and efforts in meeting common objectives while supporting and advancing each group's discipline. Works to: represent members' interests in legislative activities; define joint positions on public policy issues; facilitate communication among members; initiate educational and research programs. Compiles statistics.

Auto and Diesel Mechanics

SOURCES OF HELP-WANTED ADS

★977★ *Automotive Body Repair News*

Reed Business Information
360 Park Ave. S
New York, NY 10014
Ph: (646)746-7764
URL: http://www.abrn.com/abrn/

Monthly. Magazine reporting automotive repair industry news.

★978★ *Automotive Cooling Journal*

NARSA
PO Box 97
East Greenville, PA 18041
Ph: (215)541-4500   Fax: (215)679-4977
Fr: 800-551-3232
E-mail: acj@narsa.org
URL: http://www.narsa.org

Monthly. $30.00/year. Automotive trade magazine.

★979★ *Automotive Fleet*

Bobit Publishing
21061 S Western Ave.
Torrance, CA 90501
Ph: (310)533-2400   Fax: (310)533-2500

Monthly. $35.00/year for individuals; $42.00/year for Canada; $53.00/year for other countries. Automotive magazine covering the car and light truck fleet market.

★980★ *Automotive News*

Crain Communications Inc.
1155 Gratiot Ave.
Detroit, MI 48207-2997
Ph: (313)446-6000   Fax: (313)446-0347
Fr: 800-678-9595
E-mail: autonews@crain.com
URL: http://www.automotivenews.com

Weekly. $139.00/year for individuals; $5.00 for single issue; $215.00/year for Canada; $355.00/year for other countries. Tabloid reporting on all facets of the automotive and truck industry, as well as related businesses.

★981★ *BodyShop Business*

Babcox
3550 Embassy Pkwy.
Akron, OH 44333-8318
Ph: (330)670-1234   Fax: (330)670-0874
E-mail: dlloyd@babcox.com
URL: http://www.bodyshopbusiness.com

Monthly. Free to qualified subscribers; $64.00/year for U.S.; $109.00 for two years, U.S.; $84.00/year for Canada and Mexico; $143.00 for two years, Canada and Mexico; $124.00/year for other countries; $211.00/year for two years, other countries; $10.00 for single issue, U.S.; $15.00/year for single issue, elsewhere. Magazine providing management and technical information that can be applied to running an efficient and profitable collision repair shop.

★982★ *Bus Ride*

Power Trade Media L.L.C.
1550 E Missouri, Ste. 202
Phoenix, AZ 85014-2456
Ph: (602)265-7600   Fax: (602)227-7588
Fr: 800-541-2670
URL: http://www.busride.com/frend/

Free to qualified subscribers; $35.00/year for individuals; $4.50/year for single issue. Magazine for managers of bus, motorcoach and transit operations.

★983★ *Engine Builder*

Babcox
3550 Embassy Pkwy.
Akron, OH 44333-8318
Ph: (330)670-1234   Fax: (330)670-0874
E-mail: dwooldridge@babcox.com
URL: http://www.engine-builder.com

Monthly. Free to qualified subscribers; $64.00/year for U.S.; $84.00/year for Canada and Mexico; $124.00/year for elsewhere; $109.00 for two years, U.S.; $143.00 for two years, Canada and Mexico; $211.00 for two years, other countries; $10.00 for single issue, U.S.; $15.00/year for single issue, other countries. Magazine covering management topics, technical information, and new product news for owners and managers of leading volume rebuilding businesses.

★984★ *The Good Guys*

Automatic Transmission Rebuilders
  Association
2400 Latigo Abve.
Oxnard, CA 93030
Ph: (805)604-2000   Fax: (805)654-0970
E-mail: atra@atra-gears.com

Description: Monthly. Contains news of the Association, its chapters, and Association programs. Lists service contract and insurance information, job listings, and personnel changes in the Association. Recurring features include news of research, notices of publications available, reports of meetings, news of educational opportunities, and a calendar of events.

★985★ *Import Automotive Parts & Accessories*

Meyers Publishing
6211 Van Nuys Blvd.
Van Nuys, CA 91401
Ph: (818)785-3900   Fax: (818)785-4397
E-mail: iapa@meyerspublishing.com

$75.00/year for Canada; $105.00/year for other countries; $55.00/year for U.S. $10.00 for single issue. Trade magazine for the automotive aftermarket.

★986★ *Import Car*

Babcox
3550 Embassy Pkwy.
Akron, OH 44333-8318
Ph: (330)670-1234   Fax: (330)670-0874
E-mail: jstankard@babcox.com
URL: http://www.import-car.com

Monthly. Free to qualified subscribers; $64.00/year for U.S.; $109.00 for two years, U.S.; $84.00/year for Canada and Mexico; $143.00 for two years, Canada and Mexico; $124.00/year for other countries; $211.00 for two years, other countries; $10.00 for single issue, U.S.; $15.00/year for single issue, other countries. Magazine serves import specialist repair shops that derive more than 50% of revenue from servicing import nameplates.

★987★   *The Motion Systems Distributor*
Penton Media Inc.
1300 E 9th St.
Cleveland, OH 44114-1503
Ph: (216)696-7000   Fax: (216)931-9799
URL: http://www.penton.com/cgi-bin/super-directory/details.pl?id=3

Bimonthly. $36.00/year for individuals; $40.50/year for Canada; $49.50/year for other countries. Completely separate from PT Design, this bi-monthly publication is tailored to the informational needs of the motion systems distributor. Published six times, this sales and management magazine goes to sales and branch management personnel, owners/operators of distributor companies in the U.S. and their technical personnel, and selected suppliers.

★988★   *Motor Service*
Adams Business Media
250 S Wacker Dr., Ste. 1150
Chicago, IL 60606
Ph: (312)977-0999   Fax: (312)980-3135
E-mail: autonet@mail.aip.com
URL: http://www.autotruck.net

Monthly. $38.00/year for individuals. Magazine for auto repair shops.

★989★   *Popular Mechanics*
Hearst Magazines
1790 Broadway
New York, NY 10019
E-mail: popularmechanics@hearst.com
URL: http://www.popularmechanics.com/

Monthly. $5.75 for single issue; $8.50 for single issue-other countries. Magazine focusing on autos, the home, and leisure. Prints Latin American Edition.

★990★   *ServiceInsights*
Heather Publishing Company Inc.
PO Box 201427
Arlington, TX 76006
Ph: (817)860-2375   Fax: (817)548-0004
Fr: 800-860-2375
E-mail: bill@serviceinsights.com

Monthly. $40.00/year; $90.00/year for other countries; $5.00/year for single issue. Automotive magazine.

★991★   *Transmission Digest*
MD Publications Inc.
3057 E Cairo
PO Box 2210
Springfield, MO 65801-2210
Ph: (417)866-3917   Fax: (417)866-2781
Fr: 800-274-7890

Monthly. $39.00/year for individuals; $4.75 for single issue.

★992★   *Transport Topics*
American Trucking Associations Inc.
2200 Mill Rd.
Alexandria, VA 22314-4677
Ph: (703)838-1700   Fax: (703)683-2292
Fr: 800-517-7370

E-mail: ttnews@ttnews.com
URL: http://www.ttnews.com

Weekly. $99.00/year for individuals. Newspaper (tabloid) covering the trucking industry, for executives and managers of large and small fleets at for-hire and private carriers.

★993★   *Undercar Digest*
M D Publications Inc.
PO Box 2210
Springfield, MO 65801-2210
Ph: (417)866-3917   Fax: (417)866-2781
Fr: 800-274-7890

Monthly. $39.00/year; $4.75 for single issue. Magazine for the undercar service and supply industry.

★994★   *Underhood Service*
Babcox
3550 Embassy Pkwy.
Akron, OH 44333-8318
Ph: (330)670-1234   Fax: (330)670-0874
E-mail: jstankard@babcox.com
URL: http://www.underhoodservice.com

Monthly. Free to qualified subscribers; $64.00/year for U.S.; $84.00/year for Canada and Mexico; $124.00/year for elsewhere; $109.00 for two years, U.S.; $143.00 for two years, Canada and Mexico; $211.00 for two years, other countries; $10.00 for single issue, U.S.; $15.00/year for single issue, other countries. Magazine covering service and repair shops doing 50% or more of service underhood.

PLACEMENT AND JOB REFERRAL SERVICES

★995★   **Automation Technology Services**
3790 Industrial Dr.
Rochester Hills, MI 48309
Fax: (248)853-1796
E-mail: robert.martins@ats.com

Description: Technicians working in the automotive service industry. Seeks to create an industry-wide communications program to enhance the public and professional image of the automotive technician. Represents members before federal regulatory agencies, domestic and foreign manufacturers, trade groups, and the public; offers professional recognition program for technicians who have superior diagnostic skills and a high customer satisfaction rating. Maintains placement services; compiles statistics.

HANDBOOKS AND MANUALS

★996★   *Career Information Center*
Macmillan Publishing Co. Inc.
200 Old Tappan Rd.
Old Tappan, NJ 07675
Fr: 800-428-5331

Visual Education Center Staff. Seventh edition, 1999. $275.00. 2080 pages. This 13-volume set profiles over 600 occupations. Each occupational profile describes job duties, educational requirements, how to get the job, advancement possibilities, employment outlook, working conditions, earnings and benefits, and where to write for more information.

★997★   *Careers in Trucking*
Rosen Publishing Group, Inc.
29 E. 21st St.
New York, NY 10010
Ph: (212)777-3017   Fax: 888-436-4643
Fr: 800-237-9932

Donald D. Schauer. Revised edition, 2000. $18.95. 144 pages. Describes employment in the trucking industry including driving, operations, maintenance, sales, and administration. Covers qualifications, training, future outlook, and salaries. Offers career planning and job hunting advice.

TRADESHOWS

★998★   **AERA Expo**
AERA - Engine Rebuilders Association
330 Lexington Dr.
Buffalo Grove, IL 60089
Ph: (847)541-6550   Fax: (847)541-5808
URL: http://www.aera.org

Annual. **Primary Exhibits:** Automotive services equipment, parts, tools, supplies, and services.

★999★   **International Autobody Congress and Exposition - NACE**
VNU Expositions, Inc. - Bill Communications, Inc.
1199 S. Belt Line Rd., Ste. 100
Coppell, TX 75019
Ph: (972)906-6500   Fax: (972)906-6501
E-mail: jjames@vnuexpo.com
URL: http://www.vnuexpo.com

Annual. **Primary Exhibits:** Autobody repair equipment, supplies, and services.

★1000★   **National Automotive Radiator Service Association Annual Trade Show and Convention**
National Automotive Radiator Service Association
PO Box 97
East Greenville, PA 18041
Ph: (215)541-4500   Fax: (215)679-4977

E-mail: narsa@aol.com

Annual. **Primary Exhibits:** Manufacturers in the automotive cooling industry.

OTHER SOURCES

★1001★ *Auto Mechanic*

Cambridge Educational
2572 Brunswick Ave.
Lawrenceville, NJ 08648-4128
Fax: 800-FAX-ON-US   Fr: 800-468-4227
URL: http://www.cambridgeeducational.com

$39.95. 15 minutes. Part of the Vocational Visions Career series.

★1002★ Automotive Service Association (ASA)

1901 Airport Fwy.
PO Box 929
Bedford, TX 76095-0929
Ph: (817)283-6205   Fax: (817)685-0225
Fr: 800-ASA-SHOP
E-mail: asainfo@asashop.org
URL: http://www.asashop.org

Members: Automotive service businesses including body, paint, and trim shops, engine rebuilders, radiator shops, brake and wheel alignment services, transmission shops, tune-up services, and air conditioning services; associate members are manufacturers and wholesalers of automotive parts, and the trade press. **Purpose:** Represents independent business owners and managers before private agencies and national and state legislative bodies. Promotes confidence between consumer and the automotive service industry, safety inspection of motor vehicles, and better highways.

★1003★ COIN Career Guidance System

COIN Educational Products
3361 Executive Pky., Ste. 302
Toledo, OH 43606
Ph: (419)536-5353   Fax: (419)536-7056
Fr: 800-274-8515
URL: http://www.coin3.com/highschool/

guidance.asp

CD-ROM. Provides career information through seven cross-referenced files covering postsecondary schools, college majors, vocational programs, military service, apprenticeship programs, financial aid, and scholarships. Apprenticeship file describes national apprenticeship training programs, including information on how to apply, contact agencies, and program content. Military file describes more than 200 military occupations and training opportunities related to civilian employment.

★1004★ Gasoline and Automotive Service Dealers Association (GASDA)

9520 Seaview Ave.
Brooklyn, NY 11236
Ph: (718)241-1111   Fax: (718)763-6589
E-mail: gasdal@cs.com

Members: Owners/operators or dealers of service stations or automotive repair facilities (900); interested individuals (100). **Purpose:** Aim is to educate, inform, and help increase professionalism of members and of the industry. **Activities:** Offers periodic technical training clinics, and other educational programs including advanced automotive technical training, prepaid group legal services plan and group health insurance, and liaison with government agencies. Informs members of political and legislative action or changes affecting their industry.

★1005★ *Mechanics & Repairers*

Delphi Productions
3160 4th St.
Boulder, CO 80304
Fax: (303)443-4022   Fr: 888-443-2400
URL: http://www.delphivideo.com

$95.00. 50 minutes. Part of the Careers for the 21st Century Video Library.

★1006★ National Institute for Automotive Service Excellence (ASE)

101 Blue Seal Dr. SE
Leesburg, VA 20175
Ph: (703)669-6600   Fax: (703)669-6127
Fr: 877-273-8324
E-mail: webmaster@asecert.org
URL: http://www.asecert.org

Members: Governed by a 40-member board of directors selected from all sectors of the automotive service industry and from education, government, and consumer groups. **Purpose:** Encourages and promotes the highest standards of automotive service in the public interest. **Activities:** Conducts continuing research to determine the best methods for training automotive technicians; encourages the development of effective training programs. Tests and certifies the competence of automobile, medium/heavy truck, collision repair, school bus and engine machinist technicians as well as parts specialists.

★1007★ Truck-Frame and Axle Repair Association (TARA)

3741 Enterprise Dr., SW
Rochester, MN 55902
Ph: 800-232-8272   Fax: (507)529-0380
E-mail: w.g.reich@att.net
URL: http://www.taraassoc.com

Members: Owners and operators of heavy-duty truck repair facilities and their mechanics; allied and associate members are manufacturers of heavy-duty trucks and repair equipment, engineers, trade press, and insurance firms. **Purpose:** Seeks to help members share skills and technical knowledge and keep abreast of new developments and technology to better serve customers in areas of minimum downtime, cost, and maximum efficiency. **Activities:** Conducts studies and surveys regarding safety, fuel conservation, and heavy-duty truck maintenance and repairs. Has formed TARA's Young Executives to help make young people at TARA members' repair facilities more proficient in normal business functions and to ensure the future of TARA.

★1008★ *Women in Nontraditional Careers: An Introduction*

Her Own Words
PO Box 5264
Madison, WI 53705
Ph: (608)271-7083   Fax: (608)271-0209
URL: http://www.herownwords.com/

Video. Jocelyn Riley. $95.00. 15 minutes. Resource guide also available for $45.00.

Bakers

SOURCES OF HELP-WANTED ADS

★1009★ *Milling & Baking News*
Sosland Publishing Co.
4800 Main St., Ste. 100
Kansas City, MO 64112-2513
Ph: (816)756-1000   Fax: (816)756-0494
Fr: 800-338-6201
E-mail: mbn@sosland.com

Weekly. $104.00/year for individuals. Trade magazine covering the grain-based food industries.

HANDBOOKS AND MANUALS

★1010★ *Career Opportunities in the Food and Beverage Industry*
Facts on File, Inc.
132 W. 31st St., 17th Fl.
New York, NY 10001-2006
Ph: (212)967-8800   Fax: (212)967-8107
Fr: 800-322-8755
URL: http://www.factsonfile.com

Barbara Sims-Bell. Second edition, 2001. $18.95 (paper). Provides the job seeker with information about locating and landing 80 skilled and unskilled jobs in the industry. Includes detailed job descriptions for many specific positions and lists trade associations, recruiting organizations, and major agencies. Contains index and bibliography.

★1011★ *Careers for Gourmets and Others Who Relish Food*
McGraw-Hill Trade
2 Penn Plaza
New York, NY 10121
Ph: (212)904-2000   Fr: 800-722-4726
E-mail: ntcpub@tribune.com

Mary Donovan. Second edition, 2002. $15.95; $12.95 (paper). 192 pages. Discusses such job prospects as foods columnist, cookbook writer, test kitchen worker, pastry chef, recipe developer, food festival organizer, restaurant manager, and food stylist.

★1012★ *Choosing a Career in the Restaurant Industry*
Rosen Publishing Group, Inc.
29 E. 21st St.
New York, NY 10010
Ph: (212)777-3017   Fax: 888-436-4643
Fr: 800-237-9932

Eileen Beal. 1996. $17.95. 64 pages. Explores various jobs in the restaurant industry. Describes job duties, salaries, educational preparation, and job hunting. Contains information about fast food, catering, and small businesses.

★1013★ *Culinary Arts Career Starter*
LearningExpress, LLC
900 Broadway, Ste. 604
New York, NY 10003
Ph: (212)995-2566   Fax: (212)995-5512
Fr: 800-295-9556

Mary Masi. 1999. $14.95 (paper). 229 pages.

★1014★ *How to Open a Financially Successful Bakery*
Atlanta Publishing Company
1210 SW 23rd Pl.
Ocala, FL 34474-7014
Fr: 800-555-4037

Sharon L. Fullen. March 2004. $39.95 (CD-ROM, paper). Success in business for bakers.

★1015★ *Opportunities in Culinary Careers*
McGraw-Hill Contemporary Books
1221 Avenue of the Americas
New York, NY 10020
Ph: (212)904-2000   Fr: 800-323-4900
E-mail: ntcpub@tribune.com

Mary Deirdre Donovan. 1998. $14.95; $11.95 (paper). 160 pages. Describes the educational preparation and training of chefs and cooks and explores a variety of food service jobs in restaurants, institutions, and research and development. Lists major culinary professional associations and schools. Offers guidance on landing a first job in cooking and related fields.

★1016★ *Opportunities in Restaurant Careers*
Vgm Career Horizons
1221 Avenue of the Americas
New York, NY 10020
Ph: (212)904-2000   Fr: 800-323-4900
E-mail: ntcpub@tribune.com

Carol Caprione Chmelynski. 1998. $14.95; $11.95 (paper). 160 pages. Covers opportunities in the food service industry and details salaries, benefits, training opportunities, and professional associations. Special emphasis is put on becoming a successful restaurant manager by working up through the ranks. Illustrated.

TRADESHOWS

★1017★ **American School Food Service Association Annual National Conference**
American School Food Service Association
700 S. Washington St., Ste. 300
Alexandria, VA 22314-4287
Ph: (703)739-3900   Fax: (703)739-3915
Fr: 800-877-8822

Annual. **Primary Exhibits:** Food service supplies and equipment, including educational services and computers.

★1018★ **Institute of Food Technologists Annual Meeting and Food Expo**
Institute of Food Technologists
525 W. Van Buren St., Ste. 1000
Chicago, IL 60607-3814
Ph: (312)782-8424   Fax: (312)782-8348
E-mail: info@ift.org

URL: http://www.ift.org

Annual. **Primary Exhibits:** Food ingredients, equipment, laboratory equipment and supplies, and other services rendered to the food processing industry. **Dates and Locations:** 2005 Jul 16-20; New Orleans, LA • 2006 Jul 22-26; Orlando, FL.

★1019★ **International Baking Industry Exposition**

IBIE Exhibition Management
401 N. Michigan Ave.
Chicago, IL 60611
Ph: (312)644-6610   Fax: (312)644-0575
E-mail: info@bakingexpo.org

Primary Exhibits: Baking equipment, supplies, and services.

★1020★ **National Restaurant Association Restaurant and Hotel-Motel Show**

National Restaurant Association
150 N. Michigan Ave., Ste. 2000
Chicago, IL 60601
Ph: (312)853-2525   Fax: (312)853-2548

Annual. **Primary Exhibits:** Food service equipment, supplies, and services and food and beverage products for the hospitality industry.

OTHER SOURCES

★1021★ **American Culinary Federation (ACF)**

10 San Bartola Dr.
St. Augustine, FL 32086
Ph: (904)824-4468   Fax: (904)825-4758
Fr: 800-624-9458
E-mail: acf@acfchefs.net
URL: http://www.acfchefs.org

Description: Oldest and largest organization of chefs and cooks in the U.S. Primary objectives are to promote the culinary profession and provide on-going educational training and networking for members. Provides opportunities for competition, professional recognition, and access to educational forums with other culinarians at local, regional, national, and international events. Maintains the Educational Institute of the ACF which operates the National Apprenticeship Program for Cooks and pastry cooks. Has programs that address certification of the individual chef's skills, accreditation of culinary programs, apprenticeship of cooks and pastry cooks, professional development, and the fight against childhood hunger.

★1022★ *Food and Beverage Service Occupations*

Evon Publishing
832 N 7th Ave.
Iron River, MI 49935
Ph: (906)265-3190

Audiocassette. 1996. $16.95. 32 minutes. Part of the Careers and Vocational Guidance Series. Provides information about the nature of the work, educational requirements, employment outlook, earnings, and work conditions as well as additional related information.

★1023★ **Independent Bakers Association (IBA)**

PO Box 3731
Washington, DC 20027
Ph: (202)333-8190   Fax: (202)337-3809
E-mail: independentbaker@yahoo.com
URL: http://www.independentbaker.org

Members: Trade association representing small-medium wholesale bakers and allied trade members. **Purpose:** Represents independent wholesale bakers on federal legislative and regulatory issues. **Activities:** Offers annual Smith-Schaus-Smith internships.

★1024★ **International Association of Culinary Professionals (IACP)**

304 W Liberty St., Ste. 201
Louisville, KY 40202
Ph: (502)581-9786   Fax: (502)589-3602
Fr: 800-928-4227
E-mail: iacp@hqtrs.com
URL: http://www.iacp.com

Description: Cooking school owners, food writers, chefs, caterers, culinary specialists, directors, teachers, cookbook authors, food stylists, food photographers, student/apprentices, and individuals in related industries in 20 countries. Objectives are to: promote the interests of cooking schools, teachers, and culinary professionals; encourage the exchange of information and education; promote professional standards and accreditation procedures. Maintains IACP Foundation to award culinary scholarships and grants.

★1025★ **International Council on Hotel, Restaurant, and Institutional Education (CHRIE)**

2613 N Parham Rd., 2nd Fl.
Richmond, VA 23294
Ph: (804)346-4800   Fax: (804)346-5009
E-mail: info@chrie.org
URL: http://www.chrie.org

Description: Schools and colleges offering specialized education and training in hospitals, recreation, tourism and hotel, restaurant, and institutional administration; individuals, executives, and students. Provides networking opportunities and professional development.

★1026★ **Les Amis d'Escoffier**

1230 Main St., Rte. 9
Leicester, MA 01524
Ph: (508)892-9090   Fax: (508)892-3620
E-mail: info@castlerestaurant.com
URL: http://www.castlerestaurant.com/default.htm

Members: An educational organization of professionals in the food and wine industries. **Activities:** Maintains museum, speakers' bureau, hall of fame, and placement service. Sponsors charitable programs.

Bill and Account Collectors

SOURCES OF HELP-WANTED ADS

★1027★ *Accounting Horizons*
American Accounting Association
5717 Bessie Dr.
Sarasota, FL 34233
Ph: (941)921-7747   Fax: (941)923-4093
Quarterly. Publication covering the banking, finance, and accounting industries.

★1028★ *Brookings Papers on Economic Activity*
Brookings Institution Press
1775 Massachusetts Ave. NW
Washington, DC 20036
Ph: (202)797-6000   Fax: (202)797-6195
Fr: 800-275-1447
Semiannual. Publication covering economics and business.

★1029★ *Business Credit*
National Association of Credit Management
8840 Columbia 100 Pkwy.
Columbia, MD 21045
Ph: (410)740-5560   Fax: (410)740-5574
Fr: 800-955-8815
E-mail: bcm@nacm.org
Monthly. $54.00/year, US businesses; $48.00/year for libraries; $7.00/year for single issue. Magazine covering finance, business credit management, providing information for the extension of credit, maintenance of accounts receivable, and cash asset management.

★1030★ *Commercial Lending Review*
Aspen Publishers Inc.
1185 Avenue of the Americas, 37th Fl.
New York, NY 10036
Ph: (212)597-0200   Fax: (212)597-0390
Fr: 800-447-1717
E-mail: cgreene@world.std.com
URL: http://www.aspenpublishers.com
$325.00/year for individuals. Journal covering all aspects of lending for commercial banks, community and regional banks and other financial institutions.

★1031★ *CPA Client Bulletin*
American Institute of Certified Public Accountants
Harborside Financial Ctr.
201 Plz. III
Jersey City, NJ 07311
Ph: (201)938-3806
Monthly. Periodical covering accounting and personal finance.

★1032★ *U.S. Banker*
Thomson Financial
195 Broadway
New York, NY 10007
Ph: (646)822-2000
URL: http://www.electronicbanker.com
Monthly. $59.00/year for individuals. Magazine serving the financial services industry.

EMPLOYER DIRECTORIES AND NETWORKING LISTS

★1033★ *Career Opportunities in Banking, Finance, and Insurance*
Facts on File Inc.
132 W 31st St., 17th Fl.
New York, NY 10001
Ph: (212)967-8800   Fax: 800-678-3633
Fr: 800-322-8755
$49.50. Publication includes: Lists of colleges with programs supporting banking, finance, and industry; professional associations; professional certifications; regulatory agencies; and Internet resources for career planning. Principal content of publication is job descriptions for professions in the banking, finance, and insurance industries. Indexes: Alphabetical.

HANDBOOKS AND MANUALS

★1034★ *Careers in Banking and Finance*
Rosen Publishing Group, Inc.
29 E. 21st St.
New York, NY 10010
Ph: (212)777-3017   Fax: 888-436-4643
Fr: 800-237-9932
Patricia Haddock. 2001. $16.95 139 pages. Offers advice on job hunting. Describes jobs at all levels in banking and finance. Contains information about the types of financial organizations where the jobs are found, educational requirements, job duties, and salaries.

★1035★ *The 1999 Managing Credit, Receivables and Collections Yearbook*
IOMA Institute of Management & Administration
29 W. 35th St.
New York, NY 10001
Ph: (212)244-0360   Fax: (212)564-0465
Schaeffer, Mary L. 1999. $199.00 (paper). 200 pages.

EMPLOYMENT AGENCIES AND SEARCH FIRMS

★1036★ *Allard Associates Inc.*
425 Market St., Ste. 2200
San Francisco, CA 94105
Ph: (530)661-7562   Fax: 800-526-7791
Fr: 800-291-5279
Executive search firm. Focuses on financial placement surrounding the credit card industry.

★1037★ American Human Resources Associates Ltd. (AHRA)
PO Box 18269
Cleveland, OH 44118-0269
Ph: (440)995-7120   Fr: 877-342-5833

Executive search firm. Focused on real estate, banking and credit & collection.

★1038★ Barkstone Group LLC
113 South St.
PO Box 218
Litchfield, CT 06759-0218
Ph: (860)567-2400   Fax: (860)567-1466

Executive search firm focused on the banking industry.

★1039★ J Nicolas Arthur
77 Franklin St., Fl. 3
Boston, MA 02110
Ph: (617)204-9000   Fax: (617)303-8934

Executive search firm specializing in the finance industry.

OTHER SOURCES

★1040★ Account Management Systems
3225 South MacDill Ave., Ste.306
Tampa, FL 33629
URL: http://www.amscollects.com

Description: National and international commercial debt collection agency. Specializes in business-to-business debt collection.

★1041★ Allied Finance Adjusters
PO Box 20708
Chicago, IL 60620
Fr: 800-621-3016
URL: http://www.alliedfinanceadjusters.com

Description: Association of professional repossessors, investigators, and recovery agents.

★1042★ American Bankers Association (ABA)
1120 Connecticut Ave. NW
Washington, DC 20036
Ph: (202)663-5000   Fax: (202)663-7543
Fr: 800-BAN-KERS
E-mail: mwhitake@aba.com
URL: http://www.aba.com

Members: Principally commercial banks and trust companies; combined assets of members represent approximately 90% of the U.S. banking industry; approximately 94% of members are community banks with less than $500 million in assets. **Purpose:** Seeks to enhance the role of commerical bankers as preeminent providers of financial services through communications, research, legal action, lobbying of federal legislative and regulatory bodies, and education and training programs. Serves as spokesperson for the banking industry; facilitates exchange of information among members. Maintains the American Institute of Banking, an industry-sponsored adult education program. **Activities:** Conducts educational and training programs for bank employees and officers through a wide range of banking schools and national conferences. Maintains liaison with federal bank regulators; lobbies Congress on issues affecting commercial banks; testifies before congressional committees; represents members in U.S. postal rate proceedings. Serves as secretariat of the International Monetary Conference and the Financial Institutions Committee for the American National Standards Institute. Files briefs and lawsuits in major court cases affecting the industry. Conducts teleconferences with state banking associations on such issues as regulatory compliance; works to build consensus and coordinate activities of leading bank and financial service trade groups. Provides services to members including: public advocacy; news media contact; insurance program providing directors and officers with liability coverage, financial institution bond, and trust errors and omissions coverage; research service operated through ABA Center for Banking Information; fingerprint set processing in conjunction with the Federal Bureau of Investigation; discounts on operational and income-producing projects through the Corporation for American Banking. Conducts conferences, forums, and workshops covering subjects such as small business, consumer credit, agricultural and community banking, trust management, bank operations, and automation. Sponsors ABA Educational Foundation and the Personal Economics Program, which educates schoolchildren and the community on banking, economics, and personal finance.

★1043★ American Financial Services Association (AFSA)
919 18th St. NW
Washington, DC 20006
Ph: (202)296-5544   Fax: (202)223-0321
E-mail: afsa@afsamail.com
URL: http://www.americanfinsvcs.org

Description: Companies whose business is primarily direct credit lending to consumers and/or the purchase of sales finance paper on consumer goods. Some members have insurance and retail subsidiaries; some are themselves subsidiaries of highly diversified parent corporations. Encourages the business of financing individuals and families for necessary and useful purposes, at reasonable charges, including interest; promotes consumer understanding of basic money management principles as well as constructive uses of consumer credit. Educational services include films, textbooks, and study units for the classroom and budgeting guides for individuals and families. Compiles statistical reports; offers seminars.

★1044★ Association of Credit and Collection Professionals
PO Box 390106
Minneapolis, MN 55439
Ph: (952)926-6547

URL: http://www.acainternational.org

Description: Organization of credit and collection professionals that provides accounts receivable management services.

★1045★ Association for Financial Professionals (AFP)
7315 Wisconsin Ave., Ste. 600W
Bethesda, MD 20814-3211
Ph: (301)907-2862   Fax: (301)907-2864
E-mail: jkaitz@afponline.org
URL: http://www.afponline.org

Purpose: Seeks to establish a national forum for the exchange of concepts and techniques related to improving the management of treasury and the careers of professionals through research, education, publications, and recognition of the treasury management profession through a certification program. **Activities:** Conducts educational programs. Operates career center.

★1046★ Commercial Finance Association (CFA)
225 W 34th St., Ste. 1815
New York, NY 10122
Ph: (212)594-3490   Fax: (212)564-6053
E-mail: postmaster@cfa.com
URL: http://www.cfa.com

Members: Organizations engaged in asset-based financial services including commercial financing and factoring and lending money on a secured basis to small- and medium-sized business firms. **Purpose:** Acts as a forum for information and consideration about ideas, opportunities, and legislation concerning asset-based financial services. Seeks to improve the industry's legal and operational procedures. **Activities:** Offers job placement and reference services for members. Sponsors School for Field Examiners and other educational programs. Compiles statistics; conducts seminars and surveys; maintains speakers' bureau and 21 committees.

★1047★ Consumer Data Industry Association
1090 Vermont Ave. NW, Ste. 200
Washington, DC 20005-4905
Ph: (202)408-7401   Fax: (202)371-0134
URL: http://www.cdiaonline.org

Description: International association of credit reporting and collection service offices. Maintains hall of fame and biographical archives; conducts specialized educational programs. Offers computerized services and compiles statistics.

★1048★ Credit Professionals International (CPI)
525 B N Laclede Station Rd.
St. Louis, MO 63119
Ph: (314)961-0031   Fax: (314)961-0040
E-mail: creditpro@creditprofessionals.org
URL: http://www.creditprofessionals.org

Description: Individuals employed in credit or collection departments of business firms or professional offices. Conducts educational program in credit work. Sponsors Career Club composed of members who have been involved in credit work at least 25 years.

★1049★ National Association of Credit Management (NACM)

8815 Centre Park Drive
Columbia, MD 21045
Ph: (410)740-5560
URL: http://www.nacm.org/

Description: Provides information, products and services for effective business credit and accounts receivable management.

★1050★ National Association of Credit Union Services Organizations (NACUSO)

PMB 3419 Via Lido, No.135
Newport Beach, CA 92663
Ph: (949)645-5296   Fax: (949)645-5297
Fr: 888-462-2870
E-mail: bdorsa@nacuso.org
URL: http://www.nacuso.org

Members: Credit union service organizations and their employees. **Purpose:** Promotes professional advancement of credit union service organization staff; seeks to insure adherence to high standards of ethics and practice among members. **Activities:** Conducts research and educational programs; formulates and enforces standards of conduct and practice; maintains speakers' bureau; compiles statistics.

★1051★ Society of Certified Credit Executives (SCCE)

PO Box 390106
Minneapolis, MN 55439-0106
Ph: (952)926-6547   Fax: (952)926-1624
E-mail: scce@collector.com
URL: http://www.acainternational.org

Description: A division of the International Credit Association. Credit executives who have been certified through SCCE's professional certification programs. Seeks to improve industry operations while expanding the knowledge of its members. Maintains placement service.

Biological Scientists

SOURCES OF HELP-WANTED ADS

★1052★ AAPG Explorer
American Association of Petroleum
Geologists
1444 S Boulder
PO Box 979
Tulsa, OK 74101-0979
Ph: (918)584-2555   Fax: (918)560-2636
Fr: 800-364-AAPG
E-mail: postmaster@aapg.org
URL: http://www.aapg.org

Monthly. $63.00/year for individuals; $7.00
for single issue. Magazine containing articles
about energy issues with an emphasis on
exploration for hydrocarbons and energy
minerals.

**★1053★ The American Biology
Teacher**
National Association of Biology Teachers
12030 Sunrise Valley Dr., Ste. 110
Reston, VA 20191
Ph: (703)264-9696   Fax: (703)264-7778
Fr: 800-406-0775
E-mail: publication@nabt.org
URL: http://www.nabt.org

$125.00/year; $135.00/year for other countries; $10.00 for single issue. Journal featur-
ing articles on biology, science, and education for elementary, high school and college
level biology teachers. Includes audio-visual,
book, computer, and research reviews.

**★1054★ American Biotechnology
Laboratory**
International Scientific Communications
Inc.
30 Controls Dr.
PO Box 870
Shelton, CT 06484-0870
Ph: (203)926-9300   Fax: (203)926-9310

$160.00/year for individuals. Biotechnology
magazine.

★1055★ American Laboratory News
International Scientific Communications
Inc.
30 Controls Dr.
PO Box 870
Shelton, CT 06484-0870
Ph: (203)926-9300   Fax: (203)926-9310
E-mail: maureenj@iscpubs.com
URL: http://www.iscpubs.com

Monthly. $235.00/year. Trade magazine for
scientists.

★1056★ Annual Review of Genetics
Annual Reviews Inc.
PO Box 10139
Palo Alto, CA 94303-0139
Ph: (650)493-4400   Fax: (650)855-9815
Fr: 800-523-8635

Annual. Periodical covering issues in genetics and the biological sciences.

**★1057★ Annual Review of
Microbiology**
Annual Reviews Inc.
PO Box 10139
Palo Alto, CA 94303-0139
Ph: (650)493-4400   Fax: (650)855-9815
Fr: 800-523-8635

Annual. Periodical covering microbiology
and the biological sciences.

★1058★ ASC Newsletter
Natural Science Collections Alliance
1725 K St. NW, Ste. 601
Washington, DC 20006-1401
Ph: (202)835-9050   Fax: (202)835-7334

Description: Bimonthly. Discusses care,
maintenance, management, and preservation of systematic biological collections. Carries news of wildlife permit regulations, and
information on the Association and other
museums and professional societies. Recurring features include book reviews, notices
of employment opportunities, and a calendar
of events.

★1059★ ASPB News
American Society of Plant Biologists
15501 Monona Dr.
Rockville, MD 20855-2768
Ph: (301)251-0560   Fax: (301)279-2996

Description: Bimonthly. Offers news of interest to plant physiologists, biochemists,
horticulturists, and plant molecular and cell
biologists engaged in research and teaching.
Alerts members to public policy issues,
educational opportunities, meetings, seminars, and conventions pertinent to the field.
Recurring features include letters to the
editor, reports of meetings, job listings, a
calendar of events, news from regional sections, and teaching ideas.

★1060★ AWIS Magazine
Association for Women in Science
1200 New York Ave. NW, Ste. 650
Washington, DC 20005
Ph: (202)326-8940   Fax: (202)326-8960
Fr: 800-886-AWIS

Description: Bimonthly. Covers issues, legislation, and trends related to science education for girls, women, and minorities. Includes information on grants and fellowships, job openings, educational programs,
events, and notices of publications available.

★1061★ BioWorld Magazine
American Health Consultants Inc.
3525 Piedmont Rd., Bldg. 6, Ste. 400
Atlanta, GA 30305
Ph: (404)262-7436   Fax: (404)262-7837
Fr: 800-688-2421
E-mail: customerservice@ahcpub.com

Free to qualified subscribers; $75.00/year for
others. Magazine covering the biotechnology
industry.

★1062★ Cell
Cell Press
1100 Massachusetts Ave.
Cambridge, MA 02138
Ph: (617)661-7057   Fax: (617)661-7061
E-mail: advertising@cell.com
URL: http://www.cell.com

Biweekly. $125.00/year for individuals, U.S.;

$242.00/year for other countries; $210.00/year for Canada; $799.00/year for institutions; $899.00/year for institutions, other countries. Journal on molecular and cell biology.

★1063★ **Earth Work**
Student Conservation Association
PO Box 550
Charlestown, NH 03603
Ph: (603)543-1700   Fax: (603)543-1828
E-mail: earthwork@sca-inc.org
URL: http://www.sca-inc.org

Description: Eleven issues/year. Contains listings of environmental positions, ranging from internships and administrative assistants for environmental groups to camp directors, state natural resource managers, and biologists.

★1064★ **The Electrochemical Society Interface**
Electrochemical Society Inc.
65 S Main St.
Pennington, NJ 08534-2839
Ph: (609)737-1902   Fax: (609)737-2743
E-mail: interface@electrochem.org
URL: http://www.electrochem.org

Quarterly. $40.00/year; $10.00 for single issue. Publication featuring news and articles of interest to members of the Electrochemical Society.

★1065★ **Flora of North America Newsletter**
Flora of North America Association (FNA)
PO Box 299
St. Louis, MO 63166
Ph: (314)577-9515   Fax: (314)577-0830
URL: http://www.mobot.org

Description: Quarterly. Communicates news of FNA projects and other topics of interest to floristic researchers. Recurring features include news of research, reports of meetings, job listings, and notices of publications available.

★1066★ **Invertebrate Biology**
Allen Press
810 E 10th
Lawrence, KS 66044
Ph: (785)843-1234   Fax: (785)843-1244
Fr: 800-627-0326
URL: http://www.invertebrate biology.org/ibgenl.htm

Quarterly. $38.00/year for individuals, includes membership; $19.00/year for students, includes membership; $48.00/year for Canada and Mexico; $52.00/year for elsewhere; $85.00/year for libraries in U.S., Canada and Mexico; $110.00/year for libraries elsewhere. Scientific journal covering the biology of invertebrate animals and research in the fields of cell and molecular biology, ecology, physiology, systematics, genetics, biogeography and behavior.

★1067★ **Journal of Bacteriology**
ASM Journals
1752 N St. NW
Washington, DC 20036-2904
Ph: (202)942-9207   Fax: (202)942-9333
URL: http://www.journals.asm.org

Semimonthly. $89.00/year for U.S. members; $771.00/year for nonmembers and U.S. institutions. Journal publishing articles about bacteria and other microorganisms, including fungi and other unicellular, eucaryotic organisms.

★1068★ **Lab Animal**
Nature Publishing Group
345 Park Ave. S
New York, NY 10010-1707
Ph: (212)726-9200   Fax: (212)689-9711
Fr: 888-331-6288
E-mail: labanimal@natureny.com
URL: http://www.labanimal.com

Free. Life science magazine.

★1069★ **Lepidoptera Research Foundation Newsletter**
Lepidoptera Research Foundation
9620 Heather Rd.
Beverly Hills, CA 90210
Ph: (310)274-1052   Fax: (310)275-3290

Description: Irregular. Functions as a supplement to the technical publication The Journal of Research on the Lepidoptera. Reports on the Foundation's activities and carries calls for papers, notices of publications available, job listings, and announcements.

★1070★ **Nature Biotechnology**
Nature Publishing Group
345 Park Ave. S
New York, NY 10010-1707
Ph: (212)726-9200   Fax: (212)689-9711
Fr: 888-331-6288
E-mail: biotech@natureny.com
URL: http://www.biotechnology.nature.com

Monthly. $75.00/year for individuals; $545.00/year for institutions. Scientific research journal.

★1071★ **Nature International Weekly Journal of Science**
Nature Publishing Group
345 Park Ave. S
New York, NY 10010-1707
Ph: (212)726-9200   Fax: (212)689-9711
Fr: 888-331-6288
E-mail: nature@natureny.com
URL: http://www.nature.com

Weekly. $145.00/year for individuals; $495.00/year for institutions. Magazine covering science and technology, including the fields of biology, biochemistry, genetics, medicine, earth sciences, physics, pharmacology, and behavioral sciences.

★1072★ **Ornithological Newsletter**
Dr. Cheryl L. Trine
3889 E Valley View
Berrien Springs, MI 49103
Ph: (616)471-7886
URL: http://birds.cornell.edu/OSNA/orn-newsl.htm

Description: Bimonthly. Provides information of interest to ornithologists. Recurring features include listings of available grants and awards, news of members, a calendar of events, activities of sponsoring societies, and notices of publications available. Notices of employment opportunities are also available on the Web version.

★1073★ **Plant Science Bulletin**
Dept. of Biology
3507 Laclede Ave.
St. Louis, MO 63103-2010
Ph: (314)977-3903   Fax: (314)977-3658

Description: Quarterly. Carries news of this Association of plant scientists, with some issues including brief articles of more general interest in the field. Recurring features include notices of awards, meetings, courses, and study and professional opportunities; annotated lists of botanical books; and book reviews.

★1074★ **Popular Science**
Time4 Media Inc.
2 Park Ave., 10th Fl.
New York, NY 10016
Ph: (212)779-5493   Fax: (212)779-5118

Monthly. $13.94/year; $2.00 for single issue. General interest science magazine.

★1075★ **Science**
American Association for the Advancement of Science
1200 New York Ave. NW
Washington, DC 20005
Ph: (202)326-6400   Fax: (202)371-9849
URL: http://htpp://www.sciencemag.org

Weekly. $105.00/year for individuals; $7.00 for single issue. Magazine devoted to science, scientific research, and public policy.

★1076★ **The Scientist**
The Scientist Inc.
3535 Market St., Ste. 200
Philadelphia, PA 19104-2645
Ph: (215)386-9601   Fax: (215)386-7542
Fr: 800-258-6008
E-mail: info@the-scientist.com
URL: http://www.the-scientist.com

Biweekly. $49.00/year for individuals; $149.00/year for institutions; $24.00/year for students; $82.00/year for other countries; $49.00/year for students, other countries; $174.00/year for institutions, other countries. News journal (tabloid) for life scientists featuring news, opinions, research, and professional section.

★1077★ Seed Technologist News

Association of Official Seed Analysts Inc.
PMB 411
1763 E University Blvd., Ste. A
Las Cruces, NM 88001
Ph: (505)522-1437   Fax: (505)522-1437

Description: Three issues/year. Relates activities of the Society, with reports from various chapters across the U.S. and Canada. Publishes technical information about testing seeds and ensuring seed quality. Recurring features include news of research, a calendar of events, reports of meetings, news of educational opportunities, job listings, book reviews, and notices of publications available.

PLACEMENT AND JOB REFERRAL SERVICES

★1078★ American Society for Biochemistry and Molecular Biology (ASBMB)

9650 Rockville Pike
Bethesda, MD 20814
Ph: (301)530-7145   Fax: (301)571-1824
URL: http://www.faseb.org/asbmb

Members: Biochemists and molecular biologists who have conducted and published original investigations in biological chemistry and/or molecular biology. **Activities:** Operates placement service.

★1079★ American Society for Cell Biology (ASCB)

8120 Woodmont Ave., Ste. 750
Bethesda, MD 20814-2762
Ph: (301)347-9300   Fax: (301)347-9310
E-mail: ascbinfo@ascb.org
URL: http://www.ascb.org

Description: Scientists with educational or research experience in cell biology or an allied field. Offers placement service.

★1080★ American Society for Histocompatibility and Immunogenetics (ASHI)

17000 Commerce Pky., Ste. C
Mount Laurel, NJ 08054
Ph: (856)638-0428   Fax: (856)439-0525
E-mail: info@ashi-hla.org
URL: http://www.ashi-hla.org

Members: Scientists, physicians, and technologists involved in research and clinical activities related to histocompatibility testing (a state of mutual tolerance that allows some tissues to be grafted effectively to others). **Activities:** Conducts proficiency testing and educational programs. Maintains liaison with regulatory agencies; offers placement services and laboratory accreditation. Has co-sponsored development of histocompatability specialist and laboratory certification program.

★1081★ American Society for Microbiology (ASM)

1752 N St. NW
Washington, DC 20036
Ph: (202)737-3600   Fax: (202)942-8341
E-mail: oed@asmusa.org
URL: http://www.asm.org

Description: Scientific society of microbiologists. Promotes the advancement of scientific knowledge in order to improve education in microbiology. Encourages the highest professional and ethical standards, and the adoption of sound legislative and regulatory policies affecting the discipline of microbiology at all levels. Communicates microbiological scientific achievements to the public. Maintains numerous committees and 23 divisions, and placement services; compiles statistics.

★1082★ American Society of Plant Biologists (ASPB)

15501 Monona Dr.
Rockville, MD 20855-2768
Ph: (301)251-0560   Fax: (301)279-2996
E-mail: info@aspb.org
URL: http://www.aspb.org

Members: Professional society of plant biologists, plant biochemists, and other plant scientists engaged in research and teaching. **Activities:** Offers placement service for members; conducts educational and public affairs programs.

★1083★ American Water Works Association (AWWA)

6666 W Quincy Ave.
Denver, CO 80235
Ph: (303)794-7711   Fax: (303)347-0804
Fr: 800-926-7337
E-mail: rrenner@awwa.org
URL: http://www.awwa.org

Members: Water utility managers, superintendents, engineers, chemists, bacteriologists, and other individuals interested in public water supply; municipal- and investor-owned water departments; boards of health; manufacturers of waterworks equipment; government officials and consultants interested in water supply. **Purpose:** Develops standards and supports research programs in waterworks design, construction, operation, and management. **Activities:** Conducts in-service training schools and prepares manuals for waterworks personnel. Maintains hall of fame. Offers placement service via member newsletter; compiles statistics. Offers training; children's services; and information center on the water utilities industry, potable water, and water reuse.

★1084★ Association of Applied IPM Ecologists (AAIE)

PO Box 10880
Napa, CA 94581
Ph: (707)265-9349   Fax: (707)265-9349
E-mail: director@aaie.net
URL: http://www.aaie.net

Description: Professional agricultural pest management consultants, entomologists, and field personnel. Promotes the implementation of integrated pest management in agricultural and urban environments. Provides a forum for the exchange of technical information on pest control. Offers placement service.

★1085★ Biophysical Society (BPS)

9650 Rockville Pike
Bethesda, MD 20814
Ph: (301)530-7114   Fax: (301)530-7133
E-mail: society@biophysics.org
URL: http://www.biophysics.org

Description: Biophysicists, physical biochemists, and physical and biological scientists interested in the application of physical laws and techniques to the analysis of biological or living phenomena. Maintains placement service.

★1086★ Engineering Society of Detroit (ESD)

26100 American Dr., Ste. 500
Southfield, MI 48034-6184
Ph: (248)355-2910   Fax: (248)355-1492
E-mail: esd@esd.org
URL: http://esd.org

Description: Engineers from all disciplines; scientists and technologists. Conducts technical programs and engineering refresher courses; sponsors conferences and expositions. Maintains speakers' bureau; offers placement services. Although based in Detroit, MI, society membership is international.

★1087★ Environmental Mutagen Society (EMS)

1821 Michael Faraday Dr., Ste. 300
Reston, VA 20190
Ph: (703)438-8220   Fax: (703)438-3113
E-mail: emshq@aim-hq.com
URL: http://www.ems-us.org

Members: Bioscientists in universities, governmental agencies, and industry. **Purpose:** Promotes basic and applied studies of mutagenesis (the area of genetics dealing with mutation and molecular biology); disseminates information relating to environmental mutagenesis. **Activities:** Offers placement service.

★1088★ Federation of American Societies for Experimental Biology (FASEB)

9650 Rockville Pike
Bethesda, MD 20814-3998
Ph: (301)634-7000   Fax: (301)634-7001
E-mail: admin@faseb.org
URL: http://www.faseb.org

Description: Federation of scientific societies with a total of 40,000 members: The American Physiological Society; American Society for Biochemistry and Molecular Biology; American Society for Pharmacology and Experimental Therapeutics; American Society for Investigative Pathology; American Society for Nutritional Sciences; the American Association of Immunologists; the American Society for Bone and Mineral

Research; American Society for Clinical Investigation; the Indocrine Society; the American Society of Human Genetics; Society for Developmental Biology; Biophysical Society; American Association of Anatomists; and the Protein Society. **Activities:** Maintains placement service.

★1089★ Korean Scientists and Engineers Association in America (KSEA)

1952 Gallows Rd., Ste. 300
Vienna, VA 22182
Ph: (703)748-1221   Fax: (703)748-1331
E-mail: sejong@ksea.org
URL: http://www.ksea.org

Description: Scientists and engineers holding single or advanced degrees. Goals are to: promote friendship and mutuality among Korean and American scientists and engineers; contribute to Korea's scientific, technological, industrial, and economic developments; strengthen the scientific, technological, and cultural bonds between Korea and the U.S. Sponsors symposium. Maintains speakers' bureau, placement service, and biographical archives. Compiles statistics. Maintains 100 volume library of scientific handbooks and yearbooks in Korean.

★1090★ Society for Cryobiology (SC)

Harvard Medical School
Shriners Hospital for Children
51 Blossom St.
Boston, MA 02114
Ph: (617)371-4883   Fax: (617)371-4950
E-mail: mtoner@sbi.org
URL: http://www.societyforcryobiology.org

Description: Basic and applied research in the field of low temperature biology and medicine. Promotes interdisciplinary approach to freezing, freeze-drying, hypothermia, hibernation, physiological effects of low environmental temperature on animals and plants, medical applications of reduced temperatures, cryosurgery, hypothermic perfusion and cryopreservation of organs, cryoprotective agents and their pharmacological action, and pertinent methodologies. Operates charitable program and placement service.

★1091★ Society for In Vitro Biology (SIVB)

9315 Largo Dr., Ste. 255
Largo, MD 20774
Ph: (301)324-5054   Fax: (301)324-5057
Fr: 800-741-7476
E-mail: sivb@sivb.org
URL: http://www.sivb.org

Description: Professional society of individuals using mammalian, invertebrate, plant cell tissue, and organ cultures as research tools in chemistry, physics, radiation, medicine, physiology, nutrition, and cytogenetics. Aims are to foster collection and dissemination of information concerning the maintenance and experimental use of tissue cells in vitro and to establish evaluation and development procedures. Operates placement service.

★1092★ Society for Industrial Microbiology (SIM)

3929 Old Lee Hwy., Ste. 92A
Fairfax, VA 22030-2421
Ph: (703)691-3357   Fax: (703)691-7991
E-mail: info@simhq.org
URL: http://www.simhq.org

Description: Mycologists, bacteriologists, biologists, chemists, engineers, zoologists, and others interested in biological processes as applied to industrial materials and processes concerning microorganisms. Serves as liaison between the specialized fields of microbiology. Maintains placement service; conducts surveys and scientific workshops in industrial microbiology.

EMPLOYER DIRECTORIES AND NETWORKING LISTS

★1093★ American Men and Women of Science

Thomson Gale
27500 Drake Rd.
Farmington Hills, MI 48331-3535
Ph: (248)699-4253   Fax: (248)699-8065
Fr: 800-877-GALE
E-mail: amws@galegroup.com

Biennial, latest edition December 2002. $975.00. Covers over 129,700 U.S. and Canadian scientists active in the physical, biological, mathematical, computer science, and engineering fields; includes references to previous edition for deceased scientists and nonrespondents. Entries include: Name, address, education, personal and career data, memberships, honors and awards, research interest. Arrangement: Alphabetical. Indexes: Discipline (in separate volume).

★1094★ Biotechnology Directory

Nature Publishing Group
345 Park Ave. S
New York, NY 10010-1707
Ph: (212)726-9200   Fax: (212)689-9711
Fr: 888-331-6288
URL: http://guide.nature.com

Annual, December, latest edition 2002. $315.00; $195.00 for elsewhere. Covers more than 11,000 companies, universities, research centers, and government agencies, and suppliers of products and services to the field. Entries include: Organization name, address, phone, telex, fax, contact; description of products, services, or research. Arrangement: Geographical. Indexes: Product, organization.

★1095★ Federation of American Societies for Experimental Biology-Directory of Members

Federation of American Societies for Experimental Biology
9650 Rockville Pke.
Bethesda, MD 20814-3998
Ph: (301)634-7100   Fax: (301)634-7809
Fr: 800-43F-ASEB

URL: http://www.faseb.org/

Annual, Fall. $68.00 for nonmembers; $34.00 for members. Covers about 61,000 members of The American Physiological Society, American Society for Biochemistry and Molecular Biology, American Society for Pharmacology and Experimental Therapeutics, American Society for Investigative Pathology, American Society for Nutritional Sciences, The American Association of Immunologists, Biophysical Society, American Association of Anatomists, The Protein Society, The American Society for Bone and Mineral Research, American Society for Clinical Investigation, The Endocrine Society, The American Society of Human Genetics, Society for Developmental Biology, American Peptide Society, Society for the Study of Reproduction and Radiation Research Society. Entries include: Name, address, title, affiliation, memberships in federation societies, highest degree, year elected to membership, phone, fax and email address. Membership directories of the Biophysical Society, The Protein Society, The American Society for Bone and Mineral Research, and American Society for Clinical Investigation are also available separately. Arrangement: Alphabetical. Indexes: Geographical.

★1096★ Peterson's Job Opportunities in Engineering and Technology

Thomson Peterson's
PO Box 67005
Lawrenceville, NJ 08648-6105
Fr: 800-338-3282

Compiled by the Peterson's staff. Fourth edition, 1996. $21.95 (paper). 384 pages. Profiles 2,000 high-tech companies looking primarily for technical personnel in such fields as biotechnology, telecommunications, software, computers and peripherals, defense, and aerospace. Contains job-search strategies and career options to help match education and expertise to the job market. Indexed geographically, by industry, and by hiring needs.

HANDBOOKS AND MANUALS

★1097★ The Best Resumes for Scientists and Engineers

John Wiley & Sons Inc.
1 Wiley Dr.
Somerset, NJ 08873
Ph: (732)469-4400   Fr: 800-225-5945

Adele Lewis and David J. Moore. Second edition, 1993. $37.50; $19.95 (paper). 224 pages. Presents an extensive collection of scientific and engineering resumes, highlighting the important differences between these and resumes written for other occupations.

★1098★ Business and Careers in Marine Sciences

Hydrodryne Marine, Inc.
595 Arrowhead Tr.
Knoxville, TN 37919
Ph: (423)523-1198   Fax: (423)588-6922

James S. McNutt, Jr. 1993. $24.00 (paper). 332 pages.

★1099★ Careers in Horticulture and Botany

McGraw-Hill Trade
2 Penn Plaza
New York, NY 10121
Ph: (212)904-2000   Fr: 800-722-4726
E-mail: ntcpub@tribune.com

Jerry Garner. 1996. $17.95; 13.95 (paper). 255 pages. Includes bibliographical references

★1100★ Conducting Meaningful Experiments: 40 Steps to Becoming a Scientist

Sage Publications, Inc.
2455 Teller Rd.
Thousand Oaks, CA 91320-2218
Ph: (805)499-0721   Fax: (805)499-0871

R. Barker Bausell. 1994. $48.00; $41.95 (paper). 149 pages.

★1101★ Great Jobs for Biology Majors

McGraw-Hill Trade
2 Penn Plaza
New York, NY 10121
Ph: (212)904-2000   Fr: 800-722-4726
E-mail: ntcpub@tribune.com

Blythe Camenson. 1999. $11.95 (paper). 438 pages. Written for students entering the workforce. Describes jobs and career paths, as well as the process of writing resumes, networking, interviewing, and evaluating job offers.

★1102★ Guide to Nontraditional Careers in Science

Hemisphere Publishing Corp.
325 Chestnut St., 8th Fl.
Philadelphia, PA 19106
Ph: (215)785-5800   Fax: (215)269-0363
Fr: 800-821-8312

Karen Young Kreeger. 1998. $38.95 (paper). 263 pages.

★1103★ Meeting the Nation's Needs for Biomedical and Behavioral Scientists

National Academies Press
500 5th St. NW
Washington, DC 20055
Ph: (202)334-3180   Fax: (202)334-2793
Fr: 800-624-6242

Ira J. Hirsh and John D. Stobo, editors. 1994. $27.00 (paper). 162 pages.

★1104★ Opportunities in Biological Science Careers

McGraw-Hill Trade
2 Penn Plaza
New York, NY 10121
Ph: (212)904-2000   Fr: 800-722-4726
E-mail: ntcpub@tribune.com

Charles A. Winter. 1998. $14.95; $11.95 (paper). 200 pages. Identifies employers and outlines opportunities in plant and animal biology, biological specialties, biomedical sciences, applied biology, and other areas. Illustrated.

★1105★ Opportunities in Environmental Careers

McGraw-Hill Trade
2 Penn Plaza
New York, NY 10121
Ph: (212)904-2000   Fr: 800-722-4726
E-mail: ntcpub@tribune.com

Odom Fanning. Revised, 2002. $12.95 (paper). 160 pages. Describes a broad range of opportunities in fields such as environmental health, recreation, physics, and hygiene, and provides job search advice. Part of Opportunities in...Series.

★1106★ Opportunities in High Tech Careers

McGraw-Hill Trade
2 Penn Plaza
New York, NY 10121
Ph: (212)904-2000   Fr: 800-722-4726

Gary Colter and Deborah Yanuck. 1995. $14.95; $11.95 (paper). 160 pages. Explores high technology careers. Describes job opportunities, how to make a career decision, how to prepare for high technology jobs, job hunting techniques, and future trends.

★1107★ Opportunities in Research and Development Careers

McGraw-Hill/Contemporary Books
1221 Avenue of the Americas
New York, NY 10020
Ph: (212)904-2000   Fr: 800-323-4900
E-mail: ntcpub@tribune.com

Jan Goldberg. 1997. $14.95; $11.95 (paper). 204 pages.

★1108★ Resumes for Environmental Careers

McGraw-Hill Trade
2 Penn Plaza
New York, NY 10121
Ph: (212)904-2000   Fr: 800-722-4726
E-mail: ntcpub@tribune.com

2002. $9.95 (paper). 160 pages. Provides resume advice tailored to people pursuing careers focusing on the environment. Includes sample resumes and cover letters.

★1109★ Resumes for Scientific and Technical Careers

McGraw-Hill Contemporary Books
1221 Avenue of the Americas
New York, NY 10020
Ph: (212)904-2000   Fr: 800-323-4900
E-mail: ntcpub@tribune.com

1999. $9.95 (paper). 450 pages. Provides resume advice for individuals interested in working in scientific and technical careers. Includes sample resumes and cover letters.

★1110★ To Boldly Go: A Practical Career Guide for Scientists

American Geophysical Union
2000 Florida Ave., NW
Washington, DC 20009
Ph: (202)462-6900   Fax: (202)328-0566
Fr: 800-966-2481

Peter S. Fiske. 1996. $19.00 (paper).

★1111★ Where the Jobs Are: The Hottest Careers for the 90s

The Career Press, Inc.
3 Tice Rd.
PO Box 687
Franklin Lakes, NJ 07417-1322
Ph: (201)848-0310   Fax: (201)848-1727
Fr: 800-227-3371

Joyce Hadley. Third edition, 2000. $13.99 (paper). 400 pages. Out of print. Describes careers in fifteen general fields, from accounting to travel and hospitality.

EMPLOYMENT AGENCIES AND SEARCH FIRMS

★1112★ Ambler Associates

14881 Quorum Dr., Ste. 450
Dallas, TX 75254-7018
Ph: (972)404-8712   Fax: (972)404-8761
Fr: 800-728-8712

Executive search firm.

★1113★ Amtec Engineering Corp.

2749 Saturn St.
Brea, CA 92821
Ph: (714)993-1900   Fax: (714)993-2419
E-mail: staffing@amtec-eng.com
URL: http://www.amtec-eng.com

Employment agency.

★1114★ Artemis Search

642 Buzzie Center
Lafayette, CA 94549
Ph: (510)388-4191   Fax: (510)339-4195

Executive search firm focused on Biotech and life sciences.

★1115★ Behavioral Science Associates Inc.
2135 E. University Dr., Ste. 121
Mesa, AZ 85213
Ph: (480)833-2629   Fax: (480)833-1029
Fr: 800-233-4318

Executive search firm.

★1116★ Biomedical Search Consultants
PO Box 721
Hawleyville, CT 06440-0721
Ph: (203)426-1445
E-mail: ta4nabio@cs.com

Employment agency.

★1117★ Caliber Associates
5090 Shoreham Pl., Ste. 201
San Diego, CA 92122
Ph: (858)551-7880   Fax: (858)551-7887

Executive search firm.

★1118★ CEO Resources Inc.
200 E. State St., Ste. 101
Media, PA 19063
Ph: (610)565-9767

Executive search firm.

★1119★ Clark Executive Search Inc.
135 N. Ferry Rd.
PO Box 560
Shelter Island, NY 11964
Ph: (631)749-3540

Executive search firm.

★1120★ Corporate Search International
980 Hammond St., Ste. 650
Atlanta, GA 30328
Ph: (770)399-8489   Fax: (770)740-0939

Executive search firm.

★1121★ CTR
581 Bellwood Dr., Ste. 100
Santa Clara, CA 95054
Ph: (408)980-8082

Executive search firm.

★1122★ The Custer Group
6005 Tattersall Ct.
Brentwood, TN 37027
Ph: (615)309-0577   Fr: (509)847-7762

Executive search firm.

★1123★ Daly & Company Inc.
175 Federal St.
Boston, MA 02110-2210
Ph: (617)262-2800   Fax: (617)728-4477

Executive search firm.

★1124★ Diversified Health Search
2005 Market St., Ste. 3300
1 Commerce Square
Philadelphia, PA 19103
Ph: (215)732-6666   Fax: (215)568-8399

Executive search firm. Branches in Burlington, MA and New York.

★1125★ The Domann Organization Inc.
1 Market St.
San Francisco, CA 94105
Fr: 800-923-6626

Executive search firm.

★1126★ Dynamic Synergy Corp.
600 Entrada Dr., Fl. 2
Santa Monica, CA 90402
Ph: (310)573-7300

Executive search firm.

★1127★ Empire International
1147 Lancaster Ave.
Berwyn, PA 19312
Ph: (610)647-7976   Fax: (610)647-8488

Executive search firm.

★1128★ Erspamer Associates
4010 W. 65th St., Ste. 100
Edina, MN 55435
Ph: (952)925-3747   Fax: (952)925-4022
E-mail: hdhuntrel@aol.com

Executive search firm specializing in technical management.

★1129★ Eton Technology Partners
1 Baltimore Pl., Ste. 130
Atlanta, GA 30308
Ph: (404)872-6413   Fax: (404)685-9208

Executive search firm.

★1130★ The Fawcett Group
39 Ross Rd.
Swampscott, MA 01907
Ph: (781)592-9555   Fax: (661)457-2083

Executive search firm.

★1131★ Intech Summit Group, Inc.
5075 Shoreham Pl., Ste. 280
San Diego, CA 92122
Ph: (858)452-2100   Fax: (858)452-8500
E-mail: isg@isgsearch.com
URL: http://www.isgsearch.com

Employment agency and executive recruiter with a branch in Carlsbad, CA.

★1132★ JPM International
26060 Acero
Mission Viejo, CA 92691
Ph: (949)699-4300   Fax: (949)699-4333
Fr: 800-685-7856

E-mail: leslieo@jpmintl.com
URL: http://www.jpmintl.com

Executive search firm and employment agency.

★1133★ K.S. Frary & Associates
16 Schooner Ridge, Ste. 301
Marblehead, MA 01945
Ph: (781)631-2464   Fax: (781)631-2465

Executive search firm.

★1134★ Lybrook Associates, Inc.
PO Box 741
Bristol, RI 02809
Ph: (401)254-5840   Fax: (401)254-5088
E-mail: chemistry@lybrook.com
URL: http://www.lybrook.com

Executive search firm specializing in the field of chemistry.

★1135★ Professional Placement Associates, Inc.
287 Bowman Ave., Ste. 309
Purchase, NY 10577
Ph: (914)251-1000   Fax: (914)251-1055
E-mail: lschachter@ppasearch.com
URL: http://www.ppasearch.com

Executive search firm specializing in the health and medical field.

★1136★ Team Placement Service, Inc.
5113 Leesburg Pike, Ste. 510
Falls Church, VA 22041-3242
Ph: (703)820-8618   Fax: (703)820-3368
Fr: 800-495-6767
E-mail: 4jobs@teamplace.com
URL: http://www.teamplace.com

Temporary agency that also handles some permanent placements.

ONLINE JOB SOURCES AND SERVICES

★1137★ American Institute of Biological Sciences Classifieds
URL: http://spars.aibs.org/aibsclassifieds/txtintro.html

Description: Section of the American Institute of Biological Sciences website used for posting available positions, research awards and fellowships, and other classified ads.

★1138★ American Society of Plant Biologists Job Bank
E-mail: dgordon@aspb.org
URL: http://www.aspb.org/jobbank/

Description: A service of the American Society of Plant Biologists, intended to aid its members in locating jobs and job resources. Site lists new jobs weekly in its job bank.
Fee: A fee of $150 is charged for all

academic/government/industry permanent positions and for all positions, regardless of rank, posted by private companies. Postdoctoral Positions; Research/Technical Positions (non-Ph.D.); and Assistantships, Fellowships, and Internships at universities and not-for-profit agencies are published at no charge.

★1139★ **Bio.com Career Center**
URL: http://career.bio.com/pages/index.cfm
Description: Contains a job index searchable by employer name, discipline, or location. Suitable for job hunters tracking down specific medical, biological, biochemical, or pharmaceutical companies and positions. Also references at Career Guide and Career Forum sections.

★1140★ **BioView.com**
URL: http://www.bioview.com
Description: Provides information on bio-pharmaceutical jobs, news, and resources. Job hunters may search jobs by keyword, state, and job title or discipline. **Main files include:** Submit Company Summary, CareerView, CompanyView, NewsView, InvestorView, MarketView. **Fee:** Single Job Posting - $225/60 days Unlimited Job Postings $2,000/month. Posting packages also available.

★1141★ **Bioview.com Career Opportunities**
URL: http://www.biolinks.com/career
Description: An internet search engine designed by scientists for scientists. Offers searchable career and candidate listings and options to post jobs or resumes. **Main files include:** BioBoard, Medline, Databases and Research Tools, Journals, Medical Sites, Scientific Companies, and more.

★1142★ **FASEB Career Resources**
9650 Rockville Pike
Bethesda, MD 20814
Ph: (301)530-7020   Fax: (301)571-0699
E-mail: jroberts@atsfaseb.org
URL: http://ns2.faseb.org/careerweb
Description: A career opportunity site combined with a development service that attempts to pair applicants at all career levels with employers who hire biomedical scientists and technicians. Biomedical career development is highlighted through career resource tools. **Main files include:** Careers OnLine DataNet, Career OnLine Classified.

★1143★ **GrantsNet**
E-mail: grantsnet@atsaaas.org
URL: http://www.grantsnet.org
Description: Grant-locating site intended for scientists in training who may become vulnerable in an era of competitive funding. Includes a directory of over 600 programs with contact information within a searchable database.

★1144★ **The SciWeb Biotechnology Career Home Page**
URL: http://www.biocareer.com
Description: Career resource center resulting from the collaboration of the Biotechnology Industry Organization (BIO) and *SciWeb*. Aims to connect job seekers with recruiters in the biotechnology industry. **Main files include:** Post Resume, Search Resume, Post Job, Search Job, Career Resources. **Fee:** Normal Listing Fees: $150.00 for the first two months, $75.00 per additional monthly renewal. Academic PostDoctoral Listings are posted for free.

TRADESHOWS

★1145★ **American Institute of Biological Sciences Annual Meeting**
American Institute of Biological Sciences
1444 I St. NW, Ste. 200
Washington, DC 20005
Ph: (202)628-1500   Fax: (202)628-1509
Fr: 800-992-2427

Annual. **Primary Exhibits:** Publishers, scientific equipment companies.

★1146★ **American Society for Biochemistry and Molecular Biology Annual Meeting**
American Society for Biochemistry and Molecular Biology
9650 Rockville Pike
Bethesda, MD 20814-3998
Ph: (301)634-7145   Fax: (301)634-7126
E-mail: asbmb@asbmb.faseb.org
URL: http://www.faseb.org/asbmb/asbmb

Annual. **Primary Exhibits:** Biological chemistry and molecular biology equipment, supplies, and services.

★1147★ **American Society for Cell Biology Annual Meeting**
American Society for Cell Biology (ASCB)
9650 Rockville Pike
Bethesda, MD 20814
Ph: (301)530-7153   Fax: (301)530-7139
URL: http://www.ascb.org/ascb

Annual. **Primary Exhibits:** Equipment, supplies, and services related to doing research in cell and molecular biology. **Dates and Locations:** 2004 Dec 04-08; Washington, DC; Washington D.C. Convention Center • 2005 Dec 10-14; San Francisco, CA; Moscone Center.

★1148★ **American Society of Cytopathology Annual Scientific Meeting**
American Society of Cytopathology
400 W. 9th St., Ste. 201
Wilmington, DE 19801
Ph: (302)429-8802   Fax: (302)429-8807
E-mail: asc@cytopathology.org
URL: http://www.cytopathology.org

Annual. **Primary Exhibits:** Cytopathology microscopes, analysis equipment and supplies, publishers. **Dates and Locations:** 2004 Nov 13-17; Chicago, IL; Sheraton Chicago Hotel & Towers • 2005 Nov 5-9; San Diego, CA; Town & Country Resort & Convention Center • 2006 Nov 4-8; Toronto, ON, Canada; Sheraton Centre Toronto.

★1149★ **Biophysical Society Annual Meeting**
Biophysical Society
9650 Rockville Pike
Bethesda, MD 20814
Ph: (301)530-7114   Fax: (301)530-7133
E-mail: society@biophysics.org
URL: http://www.biophysics.org

Annual. **Primary Exhibits:** Biomedical research equipment, supplies, and services, including instruments and publications. **Dates and Locations:** 2005 Feb 11-15; Long Beach, CA; Convention Center • 2006 Feb 15-22; Salt Lake City, UT • 2007 Mar 02-06; Baltimore, MD • 2008 Feb 22-26; Long Beach, CA.

★1150★ **International Society for Analytical Cytology Conference**
International Society for Analytical Cytology
PO Box 7849
Breckenridge, CO 80424
Ph: (970)453-2058   Fax: (970)453-2636

Biennial. **Primary Exhibits:** Exhibits relating to the use of high power technical equipment on cytology, the branch of biology dealing with the study of the structure, function, multiplication, pathology, and life history of cells.

★1151★ **Society for Developmental Biology Annual Meeting**
Society for Developmental Biology
9650 Rockville Pike
Bethesda, MD 20814-3998
Ph: (301)571-0647   Fax: (301)571-5704
URL: http://www.sdb.bio.purdue.edu/

Annual. **Primary Exhibits:** Exhibits related to problems of development and growth of organisms, scientific journals & scientific tools & post-doc.

★1152★ **The Wildlife Society Annual Conference**
The Wildlife Society
5410 Grosvenor Ln., Ste. 200
Bethesda, MD 20814-2144
Ph: (301)897-9770   Fax: (301)530-2471
E-mail: tws@wildlife.org
URL: http://www.wildlife.org

Annual. **Primary Exhibits:** Exhibits relating to wildlife conservation, including field equipment, instruments, software, books, outdoor clothing and gear, wildlife artists, environmental consultants, conservation groups, scientific associations, natural resource companies and industry groups and government agencies. **Dates and Locations:** 2005

Sep 24-28; Madison, WI; Mononce Terrace Convention Center • 2006 Sep 23-27; Anchorage, AK; Egan Convention Center.

OTHER SOURCES

★1153★ American Academy of Clinical Toxicology (AACT)

777 E Park Dr.
PO Box 8820
Harrisburg, PA 17105-8820
Ph: (717)558-7847   Fax: (717)558-7845
Fr: 888-633-5784
E-mail: jreisinger@pamedsoc.org
URL: http://www.clintox.org

Members: Physicians, veterinarians, pharmacists, nurses research scientists, and analytical chemists. **Purpose:** Works to unite medical scientists and facilitate the exchange of information; encourage the development of therapeutic methods and technology. **Activities:** Conducts professional training in poison information and emergency service personnel.

★1154★ American Academy of Forensic Sciences (AAFS)

410 N 21st St.
PO Box 669
Colorado Springs, CO 80904-2798
Ph: (719)636-1100   Fax: (719)636-1993
E-mail: awarren@aafs.org
URL: http://www.aafs.org

Description: Professional society of criminalists, scientists, members of the bench and bar, pathologists, biologists, psychiatrists, examiners of questioned documents, toxicologists, odontologists, anthropologists, and engineers. Works to encourage the study, improve the practice, elevate the standards, and advance the cause of the forensic sciences; improve the quality of scientific techniques, tests, and criteria; plan, organize, and administer meetings, reports, and other projects for the stimulation and advancement of these and related purposes. Maintains Forensic Sciences Job Listing; conducts selected research for the government; offers forensic expert referral service.

★1155★ American Association of Anatomists (AAA)

9650 Rockville Pike
Bethesda, MD 20814-3998
Ph: (301)634-7910   Fax: (301)634-7965
E-mail: exec@anatomy.org
URL: http://www.anatomy.org

Description: Professional society of anatomists and scientists in related fields.

★1156★ American Institute of Biological Sciences (AIBS)

1444 I St. NW, Ste. 200
Washington, DC 20005-2210
Ph: (202)628-1500   Fax: (202)628-1509
Fr: 800-992-2427

E-mail: rogrady@aibs.org
URL: http://www.aibs.org

Members: Professional member organization and federation of biological associations, laboratories, and museums whose members have an interest in the life sciences. **Purpose:** Promotes unity and effectiveness of effort among persons engaged in biological research, education, and application of biological sciences, including agriculture, environment, and medicine. Seeks to further the relationships of biological sciences to other sciences and industries. Conducts roundtable series; provides names of prominent biologists who are willing to serve as speakers and curriculum consultants; provides advisory committees and other services to the Department of Energy, Environmental Protection Agency, National Science Foundation, Department of Defense, and National Aeronautics and Space Administration. Maintains educational consultant panel.

★1157★ Association for International Practical Training (AIPT)

10400 Little Patuxent Pky., Ste. 250
Columbia, MD 21044-3519
Ph: (410)997-2200   Fax: (410)992-3924
E-mail: aipt@aipt.org
URL: http://www.aipt.org

Description: Providers worldwide on-the-job training programs for students and professionals seeking international career development and life-changing experiences. Arranges workplace exchanges in hundreds of professional fields, bringing employers and trainees together from around the world. Client list ranges from small farming communities to Fortune 500 companies.

★1158★ Biotechnology Occupations

Delphi Productions
3160 4th St.
Boulder, CO 80304
Fax: (303)443-4022   Fr: 888-443-2400
URL: http://www.delphivideo.com

$95.00. 49 minutes. Part of the Emerging Careers Video Library.

★1159★ Forensic Sciences Foundation (FSF)

410 N 21st St., Ste. 203
Colorado Springs, CO 80904
Ph: (719)636-1100   Fax: (719)636-1993
URL: http://www.aafs.org

Purpose: Works to conduct research in the procedures and standards utilized in the practice of forensic sciences; develop and implement useful educational and training programs and methods of benefit to forensic sciences; conduct programs of public education concerning issues of importance to the forensic sciences; engage in activities which will promote, encourage, and assist the development of the forensic sciences. **Activities:** Provides referral service for forensic scientists. Compiles statistics. Operates the Forensic Sciences Foundation Press.

★1160★ Minority Women In Science (MWIS)

Directorate for Education and Human Resources Programs
1200 New York Ave. NW
Washington, DC 20005
Ph: (202)326-7019   Fax: (202)371-9849
E-mail: sassefa@aaas.org

Description: A national network group of the American association for the Advancement of Science (AAAS), Education and Human Resources Directorate. The objectives of this group are: to identify and share information on resources and programs that could help in mentoring young women and minorities interested in science and engineering careers, and to strengthen communication among women and minorities in science and education.

★1161★ Radiation Research Society (RRS)

10105 Cottesmore Ct.
Great Falls, VA 22066-3540
Ph: (703)757-4585   Fax: (703)757-0454
E-mail: info@radres.org
URL: http://www.radres.org

Description: Professional society of biologists, physicists, chemists, and physicians contributing to knowledge of radiation and its effects. Promotes original research in the natural sciences relating to radiation; facilitates integration of different disciplines in the study of radiation effects.

★1162★ Scientific, Engineering, and Technical Services

Cambridge Educational
2572 Brunswick Ave.
Lawrenceville, NJ 08648-4128
Fax: 800-FAX-ON-US   Fr: 800-468-4227
URL: http://www.cambridgeeducational.com

$89.95. 2002. 18 minutes. Part of the Career Cluster Series.

★1163★ Scientific Occupations

Delphi Productions
3160 4th St.
Boulder, CO 80304
Fax: (303)443-4022   Fr: 888-443-2400
URL: http://www.delphivideo.com

$95.00. 60 minutes. Part of the Careers for the 21st Century Video Library.

★1164★ Soil Science Society of America (SSSA)

677 S Segoe Rd.
Madison, WI 53711
Ph: (608)273-8080   Fax: (608)273-2021
E-mail: headquarters@agronomy.org
URL: http://www.soils.org

Description: Professional soil scientists, including soil physicists, soil classifiers, land use and management specialists, chemists, microbiologists, soil fertility specialists, soil cartographers, conservationists, mineralogists, engineers, and others interested in fundamental and applied soil science.

★1165★ Teratology Society (TS)
1821 Michael Faraday Dr., Ste. 300
Reston, VA 20190-5348
Ph: (703)438-3104   Fax: (703)438-3113
E-mail: tshq@teratology.org
URL: http://www.teratology.org

Description: Individuals from academia, government, private industry, and the professions. Objective is to stimulate scientific interest in, and promote the exchange of ideas and information about, problems of abnormal biological development and malformations at the fundamental or clinical level. Sponsors annual education course, and presentations. Is establishing archives of society documents and history.

Biomedical Engineers

★1166★ American Biotechnology Laboratory

International Scientific Communications Inc.
30 Controls Dr.
PO Box 870
Shelton, CT 06484-0870
Ph: (203)926-9300   Fax: (203)926-9310

$160.00/year for individuals. Biotechnology magazine.

★1167★ Annual Review of Genetics

Annual Reviews Inc.
PO Box 10139
Palo Alto, CA 94303-0139
Ph: (650)493-4400   Fax: (650)855-9815
Fr: 800-523-8635

Annual. Periodical covering issues in genetics and the biological sciences.

★1168★ Annual Review of Microbiology

Annual Reviews Inc.
PO Box 10139
Palo Alto, CA 94303-0139
Ph: (650)493-4400   Fax: (650)855-9815
Fr: 800-523-8635

Annual. Periodical covering microbiology and the biological sciences.

★1169★ AWIS Magazine

Association for Women in Science
1200 New York Ave. NW, Ste. 650
Washington, DC 20005
Ph: (202)326-8940   Fax: (202)326-8960
Fr: 800-886-AWIS

Description: Bimonthly. Covers issues, legislation, and trends related to science education for girls, women, and minorities. Includes information on grants and fellowships, job openings, educational programs, events, and notices of publications available.

★1170★ BMES Bulletin

Biomedical Engineering Society
8401 Corporate Dr., Ste. 110
Landover, MD 20785-2224
Ph: (301)459-1999   Fax: (301)459-2444
URL: http://www.bmes.org

Description: Quarterly. Provides news and information on the Society; presents articles on bioengineering science. Recurring features include letters to the editor, news of research, a calendar of events, reports of meetings, news of educational opportunities, job listings, and columns titled Public Affairs, Student Chapter News, and Society News.

★1171★ Cell

Cell Press
1100 Massachusetts Ave.
Cambridge, MA 02138
Ph: (617)661-7057   Fax: (617)661-7061
E-mail: advertising@cell.com
URL: http://www.cell.com

Biweekly. $125.00/year for individuals, U.S.; $242.00/year for other countries; $210.00/year for Canada; $799.00/year for institutions; $899.00/year for institutions, other countries. Journal on molecular and cell biology.

★1172★ Graduating Engineer & Computer Careers

Career Recruitment Media
211 W. Wacker Dr., No. 900
Chicago, IL 60606
Ph: (312)525-3100
URL: http://www.graduatingengineer.com

$16.00/year for individuals. Magazine focusing on employment, education, and career development for entry-level engineers and computer scientists.

★1173★ High Technology Careers Magazine

HTC
4701 Patrick Henry Dr., No. 1901
Santa Clara, CA 95054-1847
Ph: (408)970-8800   Fax: (408)567-0242
URL: http://www.hightechcareers.com

Bimonthly. $29.00/year; $35.00/year for Canada; $85.00/year for out of country. Magazine (tabloid) containing employment opportunity information for the engineering and technical community.

★1174★ Invertebrate Biology

Allen Press
810 E 10th
Lawrence, KS 66044
Ph: (785)843-1234   Fax: (785)843-1244
Fr: 800-627-0326
URL: http://www.invertebrate biology.org/ibgenl.htm

Quarterly. $38.00/year for individuals, includes membership; $19.00/year for students, includes membership; $48.00/year for Canada and Mexico; $52.00/year for elsewhere; $85.00/year for libraries in U.S., Canada and Mexico; $110.00/year for libraries elsewhere. Scientific journal covering the biology of invertebrate animals and research in the fields of cell and molecular biology, ecology, physiology, systematics, genetics, biogeography and behavior.

★1175★ NSBE Magazine

NSBE Publications
1454 Duke St.
Alexandria, VA 22314
Ph: (703)549-2207   Fax: (703)683-5312

$10.00/year for individuals; $2.00 for single issue. Journal providing information on engineering careers, self-development, and cultural issues for recent graduates with technical majors.

★1176★ SWE

Society of Women Engineers
230 E Ohio St., No. 400
2135 Lamberton Rd.
Chicago, IL 60611-3265
Ph: (312)596-5223   Fax: (312)596-5252
E-mail: hq@swe.org
URL: http://www.swe.org

Bimonthly. $30.00/year for nonmembers. Magazine for engineering students and for women and men working in the engineering and technology fields. Covers career guidance, continuing development and topical issues.

★1177★ Technology Review

Technology Review
201 Vassar St.
Cambridge, MA 02139
Ph: (617)253-8250   Fax: (617)258-5850
E-mail: trcomments@mit.edu

$30.00/year for individuals; $42.00/year for other countries; $4.95/year for single issue. Magazine reviewing new developments in technology with an emphasis on economic, political, and social implications. Not a new product publication.

★1178★ WEPANEWS

Women in Engineering Programs &
  Advocates Network
Castle Point on the Hudson
Hoboken, NJ 07030
Ph: (201)216-5245   Fax: (201)216-5175
URL: http://www.wepan.org/newsletter.html

Description: Two issues/year. Seeks to provide greater access for women to careers in engineering. Includes news of graduate, undergraduate, freshmen, pre-college, and re-entry engineering programs for women. Recurring features include job listings, faculty, grant, and conference news, international engineering program news, action group news, notices of publications available, and a column titled Kudos.

PLACEMENT AND JOB REFERRAL SERVICES

★1179★ American Indian Science and Engineering Society (AISES)

PO Box 9828
Albuquerque, NM 87119-9828
Ph: (505)765-1052   Fax: (505)765-5608
E-mail: info@aises.org
URL: http://www.aises.org

Description: American Indian and non-Indian students and professionals in science, technology, and engineering fields; corporations representing energy, mining, aerospace, electronic, and computer fields. Seeks to motivate and encourage students to pursue undergraduate and graduate studies in science, engineering, and technology. Sponsors science fairs in grade schools, teacher training workshops, summer math/science sessions for 8th-12th graders, professional chapters, and student chapters in colleges. Offers scholarships. Adult members serve as role models, advisers, and mentors for students. Operates placement service.

★1180★ Engineering Society of Detroit (ESD)

26100 American Dr., Ste. 500
Southfield, MI 48034-6184
Ph: (248)355-2910   Fax: (248)355-1492

E-mail: esd@esd.org
URL: http://esd.org

Description: Engineers from all disciplines; scientists and technologists. Conducts technical programs and engineering refresher courses; sponsors conferences and expositions. Maintains speakers' bureau; offers placement services. Although based in Detroit, MI, society membership is international.

★1181★ Korean Scientists and Engineers Association in America (KSEA)

1952 Gallows Rd., Ste. 300
Vienna, VA 22182
Ph: (703)748-1221   Fax: (703)748-1331
E-mail: sejong@ksea.org
URL: http://www.ksea.org

Description: Scientists and engineers holding single or advanced degrees. Goals are to: promote friendship and mutuality among Korean and American scientists and engineers; contribute to Korea's scientific, technological, industrial, and economic developments; strengthen the scientific, technological, and cultural bonds between Korea and the U.S. Sponsors symposium. Maintains speakers' bureau, placement service, and biographical archives. Compiles statistics. Maintains 100 volume library of scientific handbooks and yearbooks in Korean.

★1182★ Society of Hispanic Professional Engineers (SHPE)

5400 E Olympic Blvd., Ste. 210
Los Angeles, CA 90022
Ph: (323)725-3970   Fax: (323)725-0316
E-mail: shpenational@shpe.org
URL: http://www.shpe.org

Description: Engineers, student engineers, and scientists seeking to increase the number of Hispanic engineers by providing motivation and support to students. Sponsors competitions and educational programs. Maintains placement service and speakers' bureau; compiles statistics.

★1183★ Society for Industrial Microbiology (SIM)

3929 Old Lee Hwy., Ste. 92A
Fairfax, VA 22030-2421
Ph: (703)691-3357   Fax: (703)691-7991
E-mail: info@simhq.org
URL: http://www.simhq.org

Description: Mycologists, bacteriologists, biologists, chemists, engineers, zoologists, and others interested in biological processes as applied to industrial materials and processes concerning microorganisms. Serves as liaison between the specialized fields of microbiology. Maintains placement service; conducts surveys and scientific workshops in industrial microbiology.

EMPLOYER DIRECTORIES AND NETWORKING LISTS

★1184★ AGT International Membership Directory

Association of Genetic Technologists
AGT Executive Office
P.O. Box 15945-288
Lenexa, KS 66285-5945
Ph: (913)541-0497   Fax: (913)599-5340
URL: http://www.agt-info.org/Publication.html

Annual, fall/winter. $50.00 for members; $100.00 for nonmembers. Covers about 520 laboratories studying heritable and acquired chromosomal disorders using cytogenetic, genetics, and cellular biology techniques. Entries include: Laboratory name, address, phone, areas of specialization, techniques, numbers and types of laboratory tests performed, and names of director and cytogenetic technologists. Arrangement: Geographical. Indexes: Director name, ACT member name.

★1185★ American Men and Women of Science

Thomson Gale
27500 Drake Rd.
Farmington Hills, MI 48331-3535
Ph: (248)699-4253   Fax: (248)699-8065
Fr: 800-877-GALE
E-mail: amws@galegroup.com

Biennial, latest edition December 2002. $975.00. Covers over 129,700 U.S. and Canadian scientists active in the physical, biological, mathematical, computer science, and engineering fields; includes references to previous edition for deceased scientists and nonrespondents. Entries include: Name, address, education, personal and career data, memberships, honors and awards, research interest. Arrangement: Alphabetical. Indexes: Discipline (in separate volume).

★1186★ Biotechnology Directory

Nature Publishing Group
345 Park Ave. S
New York, NY 10010-1707
Ph: (212)726-9200   Fax: (212)689-9711
Fr: 888-331-6288
URL: http://guide.nature.com

Annual, December, latest edition 2002. $315.00; $195.00 for elsewhere. Covers more than 11,000 companies, universities, research centers, and government agencies, and suppliers of products and services to the field. Entries include: Organization name, address, phone, telex, fax, contact; description of products, services, or research. Arrangement: Geographical. Indexes: Product, organization.

HANDBOOKS AND MANUALS

★1187★ The Best Resumes for Scientists and Engineers

John Wiley & Sons Inc.
1 Wiley Dr.
Somerset, NJ 08873
Ph: (732)469-4400   Fr: 800-225-5945

Adele Lewis and David J. Moore. Second edition, 1993. $37.50; $19.95 (paper). 224 pages. Presents an extensive collection of scientific and engineering resumes, highlighting the important differences between these and resumes written for other occupations.

★1188★ The Biomedical Engineering Handbook

CRC Press LLC
2000 NW Corporate Blvd.
Boca Raton, FL 33431
Ph: (561)994-0555   Fax: (561)989-8732
Fr: 800-272-7737

Joseph D. Bronzino, editor. Second edition, 1999. $139.95. 3168 pages.

★1189★ Careers in High Tech

Vgm Career Horizons
McGraw-Hill Trade
1221 Avenue of the Americas
New York, NY 10020
Ph: (212)904-2000   Fr: 800-323-4900
E-mail: ntcpub@tribune.com

Nick Basta. Second edition, 1998. $17.95; $13.95 (paper). 104 pages. Examines new career opportunities in such fields as biotechnology, computers, aerospace, telecommunications, and others.

★1190★ Careers in Science and Engineering

National Academies Press
500 5th St. NW
Washington, DC 20055
Ph: (202)334-3180   Fax: (202)334-2793
Fr: 800-624-6242

1996. $11.95. 160 pages. Covers planning for graduate school and beyond.

★1191★ Engineering Your Job Search: A Job-Finding Resource for Engineering Professionals

Professional Publications, Inc.
1250 5th Ave.
Belmont, CA 94002
Ph: (650)593-9119   Fax: (650)592-4519
Fr: 800-426-1178

Compiled by Professional Publications, editors. 1995. $24.95 (paper). 154 pages. Out of print.

★1192★ Hidden Job Market

Thomson Peterson's
PO Box 67005
Lawrenceville, NJ 08648-6105
Fr: 800-338-3282

Ninth edition, 1999. $18.95 (paper). 319 pages. Guide to 2,000 fast-growing companies that are hiring now. Focuses on high technology companies in such fields as environmental consulting, genetic engineering, home health care, telecommunications, alternative energy systems, and others. Part of Peterson's Hidden Job Market series.

★1193★ The I Hate Selling Book: Business-Building Advice for Consultants, Attorneys, Accountants, Engineers, Architects, and Other Professionals

Allan Boress & Associates
1500 University Dr., Suite 239
Coral Springs, FL 33071
Ph: (954)345-4666   Fax: (954)344-2453

Allan S. Boress. 2001. $29.95.

★1194★ Introduction to Biomedical Engineering

Harcourt College Publishers
6277 Sea Harbor Dr.
Orlando, FL 32887
Fr: 800-782-4479

Susan M. Blanchard, Joseph D. Bronzino and John Denis Enderle, editors. 1999. $69.95. 656 pages.

★1195★ Majoring in Engineering: How to Get from Your Freshman Year to Your First Job

Farrar, Straus & Giroux, Inc.
19 Union Sq., W
New York, NY 10003
Ph: (212)741-6900   Fax: (212)633-9385
Fr: 888-330-8477

John Garcia and Carol Carter, editors. 2000. $20.00; $10.00 (paper). 134 pages.

★1196★ Meeting the Nation's Needs for Biomedical and Behavioral Scientists

National Academies Press
500 5th St. NW
Washington, DC 20055
Ph: (202)334-3180   Fax: (202)334-2793
Fr: 800-624-6242

Ira J. Hirsh and John D. Stobo, editors. 1994. $27.00 (paper). 162 pages.

★1197★ Opportunities in Biological Science Careers

McGraw-Hill Trade
2 Penn Plaza
New York, NY 10121
Ph: (212)904-2000   Fr: 800-722-4726
E-mail: ntcpub@tribune.com

Charles A. Winter. 1998. $14.95; $11.95 (paper). 200 pages. Identifies employers and outlines opportunities in plant and animal biology, biological specialties, biomedical sciences, applied biology, and other areas. Illustrated.

★1198★ Opportunities in Engineering Careers

McGraw-Hill Contemporary Books
1221 Avenue of the Americas
New York, NY 10020
Ph: (212)904-2000   Fr: 800-323-4900
E-mail: ntcpub@tribune.com

Nicholas Basta. Revised, 1995. $14.95; $11.95 (paper). 200 pages. Outlines typical job titles, salaries, career paths, and employment prospects.

★1199★ Opportunities in High Tech Careers

McGraw-Hill Trade
2 Penn Plaza
New York, NY 10121
Ph: (212)904-2000   Fr: 800-722-4726

Gary Colter and Deborah Yanuck. 1995. $14.95; $11.95 (paper). 160 pages. Explores high technology careers. Describes job opportunities, how to make a career decision, how to prepare for high technology jobs, job hunting techniques, and future trends.

★1200★ Opportunities in Research and Development Careers

McGraw-Hill/Contemporary Books
1221 Avenue of the Americas
New York, NY 10020
Ph: (212)904-2000   Fr: 800-323-4900
E-mail: ntcpub@tribune.com

Jan Goldberg. 1997. $14.95; $11.95 (paper). 204 pages.

★1201★ Peterson's Job Opportunities in Engineering and Technology

Thomson Peterson's
PO Box 67005
Lawrenceville, NJ 08648-6105
Fr: 800-338-3282

Compiled by the Peterson's staff. Fourth edition, 1996. $21.95 (paper). 384 pages. Profiles 2,000 high-tech companies looking primarily for technical personnel in such fields as biotechnology, telecommunications, software, computers and peripherals, defense, and aerospace. Contains job-search strategies and career options to help match education and expertise to the job market. Indexed geographically, by industry, and by hiring needs.

★1202★ Real People Working in Engineering

McGraw-Hill Contemporary Books
1221 Avenue of the Americas
New York, NY 10020
Ph: (212)904-2000   Fr: 800-323-4900
E-mail: ntcpub@tribune.com

Blythe Camenson, Jan Goldberg. 1997. $14.95; $12.95 (paper). Interviews and profiles of working professionals capture a range of opportunities in this field.

★1203★ *Resumes for Engineering Careers*
McGraw-Hill Trade
2 Penn Plaza
New York, NY 10121
Ph: (212)904-2000   Fr: 800-722-4726
E-mail: ntcpub@tribune.com
2000. $10.95 (paper). 456 pages. Contains sample resumes and cover letters applicable to any engineering field.

★1204★ *Resumes for Scientific and Technical Careers*
McGraw-Hill Contemporary Books
1221 Avenue of the Americas
New York, NY 10020
Ph: (212)904-2000   Fr: 800-323-4900
E-mail: ntcpub@tribune.com
1999. $9.95 (paper). 450 pages. Provides resume advice for individuals interested in working in scientific and technical careers. Includes sample resumes and cover letters.

★1205★ *Where the Jobs Are: The Hottest Careers for the 90s*
The Career Press, Inc.
3 Tice Rd.
PO Box 687
Franklin Lakes, NJ 07417-1322
Ph: (201)848-0310   Fax: (201)848-1727
Fr: 800-227-3371
Joyce Hadley. Third edition, 2000. $13.99 (paper). 400 pages. Out of print. Describes careers in fifteen general fields, from accounting to travel and hospitality.

EMPLOYMENT AGENCIES AND SEARCH FIRMS

★1206★ **Abbott Associates**
20880 Fish Rd.
Wilder, ID 83676
Ph: (208)482-4303
Executive search firm with focus on senior level.

★1207★ **Ames & Ames LLC**
PO Box 4704
Menlo Park, CA 94026
Ph: (650)218-7404
Executive search firm.

★1208★ **Amtec Engineering Corp.**
2749 Saturn St.
Brea, CA 92821
Ph: (714)993-1900   Fax: (714)993-2419
E-mail: staffing@amtec-eng.com

URL: http://www.amtec-eng.com
Employment agency.

★1209★ **Battalia Winston International**
555 Madison Ave.
New York, NY 10022
Ph: (212)308-8080   Fax: (212)308-1309
Executive search firm. Branches in Los Angeles, Chicago, Wellesley Hills MA, Edison NJ.

★1210★ **Biomedical Search Consultants**
PO Box 721
Hawleyville, CT 06440-0721
Ph: (203)426-1445
E-mail: ta4nabio@cs.com
Employment agency.

★1211★ **BioPharmMed**
550 North Reo St., Ste. 300
Tampa, FL 33609
Ph: (813)261-5117
Executive search firm.

★1212★ **BioQuest**
100 Spear St., Ste. 1125
San Francisco, CA 94105
Ph: (415)777-2422
Executive search firm focused in healthcare and life sciences.

★1213★ **Cameron Consulting Group**
1245 Q St.
Sacramento, CA 95814
Ph: (916)447-9015
Executive search firm.

★1214★ **The Caplan Taylor Group**
897 Oak Park Blvd.
PMB 308
Pismo Beach, CA 93449-3287
Ph: (805)481-3000
Executive search firm.

★1215★ **Carlyn International Inc.**
155 Monterrey Rd.
Montgomery, TX 77356
Ph: (936)597-9494   Fax: (936)597-5901
Executive search firm.

★1216★ **The Cassie-Shipherd Group**
26 Main St.
Toms River, NJ 08753
Ph: (732)473-1779   Fax: (732)473-1023
Executive search firm. Branches in San Diego; Bridgewater, NJ; New Bern, NC; and Salt Lake City.

★1217★ **The Coelyn Group**
1 Park Plaza, Fl. 6
Irvine, CA 92614
Ph: (949)553-8855   Fax: (949)363-0837
Executive search firm.

★1218★ **D'Antoni Partners Inc.**
1825 Walnut Hill Ln., Ste. 120
Irving, TX 75038
Ph: (972)331-2585   Fax: (972)252-7913
Executive search firm.

★1219★ **Day & Associates**
577 Airport Blvd., Ste. 130
Burlingame, CA 94010
Executive search firm.

★1220★ **Elwell & Associates Inc.**
31920 Nottingwood
Farmington Hills, MI 48334
Ph: (248)488-9750   Fax: (248)488-9751
Executive search firm.

★1221★ **Emerging Medical Technologies Inc.**
7784 S. Addison Way
Aurora, CO 80016
Ph: (303)699-1990
Executive search firm focused on the medical devices industry.

★1222★ **Erspamer Associates**
4010 W. 65th St., Ste. 100
Edina, MN 55435
Ph: (952)925-3747   Fax: (952)925-4022
E-mail: hdhuntrel@aol.com
Executive search firm specializing in technical management.

★1223★ **Evenium**
520 Marquette Ave., Ste. 800
Minneapolis, MN 55402
Ph: (612)436-3200   Fax: (612)436-3157
Executive search firm.

★1224★ **J. Blakeslee International Inc.**
645 E. Blithedale Ave.
Mill Valley, CA 94941
Ph: (415)389-7300   Fax: (415)389-7302
Executive search firm.

★1225★ **JPM International**
26060 Acero
Mission Viejo, CA 92691
Ph: (949)699-4300   Fax: (949)699-4333
Fr: 800-685-7856
E-mail: leslieo@jpmintl.com
URL: http://www.jpmintl.com
Executive search firm and employment agency.

★1226★ Lloyd Staffing
445 Broad Hollow Rd., Ste.119
Melville, NY 11747
Ph: (631)777-7600 Fax: (631)777-7626
Fr: 888-292-6678
E-mail: info@lloydstaffing.com
URL: http://www.lloydstaffing.com

Personnel agency and search firm.

★1227★ O'Keefe and Associates
PO Box 1092
Southport, CT 06890-2092
Ph: (203)254-2544 Fax: (203)254-2126
E-mail: jokeefe@okeefeinc.com
URL: http://www.okeefeinc.com

Executive search firm.

★1228★ 1 Exec Street
201 Post St., Ste. 401
San Francisco, CA 94108
Ph: (415)982-0555 Fax: (415)982-0550

Executive search firm.

★1229★ Rosemary Cass Ltd.
175 Post Rd. W
Westport, CT 06880
Ph: (203)454-2920 Fax: (203)454-4643

Executive search firm.

★1230★ Techtronix Technical Search
PO Box 17713
Milwaukee, WI 53217-0173
Ph: (414)466-3100 Fax: (414)466-3598

Firm specializes in recruiting executives for the engineering, information systems, manufacturing, marketing, finance, and human resources industries.

ONLINE JOB SOURCES AND SERVICES

★1231★ Bio.com Career Center
URL: http://career.bio.com/pages/index.cfm
Description: Contains a job index searchable by employer name, discipline, or location. Suitable for job hunters tracking down specific medical, biological, biochemical, or pharmaceutical companies and positions. Also references at Career Guide and Career Forum sections.

★1232★ BioView.com
URL: http://www.bioview.com
Description: Provides information on bio-pharmaceutical jobs, news, and resources. Job hunters may search jobs by keyword, state, and job title or discipline. **Main files include:** Submit Company Summary, CareerView, CompanyView, NewsView, InvestorView, MarketView. **Fee:** Single Job Posting - $225/60 days Unlimited Job Postings

$2,000/month. Posting packages also available.

★1233★ Bioview.com Career Opportunities
URL: http://www.biolinks.com/career
Description: An internet search engine designed by scientists for scientists. Offers searchable career and candidate listings and options to post jobs or resumes. **Main files include:** BioBoard, Medline, Databases and Research Tools, Journals, Medical Sites, Scientific Companies, and more.

★1234★ FASEB Career Resources
9650 Rockville Pike
Bethesda, MD 20814
Ph: (301)530-7020 Fax: (301)571-0699
E-mail: jroberts@atsfaseb.org
URL: http://ns2.faseb.org/careerweb
Description: A career opportunity site combined with a development service that attempts to pair applicants at all career levels with employers who hire biomedical scientists and technicians. Biomedical career development is highlighted through career resource tools. **Main files include:** Careers OnLine DataNet, Career OnLine Classified.

★1235★ Genetics Society of America:Positions Open
E-mail: dprice@atsgenetics.faseb.org.
URL: http://www.faseb.org/genetics/g-gsa/open_positions.shtml
Description: Listing of position announcements formerly published in @it1Genetics@it2. Members may e-mail job listings to the site to be posted.

★1236★ GrantsNet
E-mail: grantsnet@atsaaas.org
URL: http://www.grantsnet.org
Description: Grant-locating site intended for scientists in training who may become vulnerable in an era of competitive funding. Includes a directory of over 600 programs with contact information within a searchable database.

★1237★ The SciWeb Biotechnology Career Home Page
URL: http://www.biocareer.com
Description: Career resource center resulting from the collaboration of the Biotechnology Industry Organization (BIO) and *SciWeb*. Aims to connect job seekers with recruiters in the biotechnology industry. **Main files include:** Post Resume, Search Resume, Post Job, Search Job, Career Resources. **Fee:** Normal Listing Fees: $150.00 for the first two months, $75.00 per additional monthly renewal. Academic PostDoctoral Listings are posted for free.

★1238★ Spherion Workforce Architects
URL: http://www.spherion.com

Description: Recruitment firm specializing in accounting and finance, sales and marketing, interim executives, technology, engineering, retail and human resources.

TRADESHOWS

★1239★ American Society for Engineering Education Annual Conference and Exposition
American Society for Engineering Education
1818 N St., Ste. 600
Washington, DC 20036
Ph: (202)331-3500 Fax: (202)265-8504
URL: http://www.asee.org

Annual. **Primary Exhibits:** Publications, engineering supplies and equipment, computers, software, and research companies all products and services related to engineering education. **Dates and Locations:** 2005 Jun 12-15; Portland, OR • 2006 Jun 18-21; Chicago, IL • 2007 Jun 24-27; Honolulu, HI.

OTHER SOURCES

★1240★ American Association of Engineering Societies (AAES)
1828 L St. NW, No. 906
Washington, DC 20036
Ph: (202)296-2237 Fax: (202)296-1151
Fr: 888-400-2237
E-mail: tprice@aaes.org
URL: http://www.aaes.org

Description: Coordinates the efforts of the member societies in the provision of reliable and objective information to the general public concerning issues which affect the engineering profession and the field of engineering as a whole; to collect, analyze, document, and disseminate data which will inform the general public of the relationship between engineering and the national welfare; to provide a forum for the engineering societies to exchange and discuss their views on matters of common interest; and to represent the U.S. engineering community aborad through representation in WFEO and UPADI.

★1241★ *Biotechnology Occupations*
Delphi Productions
3160 4th St.
Boulder, CO 80304
Fax: (303)443-4022 Fr: 888-443-2400
URL: http://www.delphivideo.com

$95.00. 49 minutes. Part of the Emerging Careers Video Library.

★1242★ Engineering Occupations
Delphi Productions
3160 4th St.
Boulder, CO 80304
Fax: (303)443-4022   Fr: 888-443-2400
URL: http://www.delphivideo.com

$95.00. 50 minutes. Part of the Careers for the 21st Century Video Library.

★1243★ National Action Council for Minorities in Engineering (NACME)
Empire State Bldg., Ste. 2212
350 Fifth Ave.
New York, NY 10118-2299
Ph: (212)279-2626   Fax: (212)629-5178
E-mail: webmaster@nacme.org
URL: http://www.nacme.org/

Description: Leads the national effort to increase access to careers in engineering and other science-based disciplines. Supported by the nation's leading technology-intensive companies, NACME conducts research and public policy analysis, develops and operates national demonstration programs at precollege and university levels, and disseminates information through publications, conferences, and electronic media. NACME is also the nation's largest privately funded source of scholarships for minority students in engineering.

★1244★ National Society of Professional Engineers (NSPE)
1420 King St.
Alexandria, VA 22314
Ph: (703)684-2800   Fax: (703)836-4875
Fr: 888-285-6773
E-mail: custserv@nspe.org
URL: http://www.nspe.org

Description: Professional engineers and engineers-in-training in all fields registered in accordance with the laws of states or territories of the U.S. or provinces of Canada; qualified graduate engineers, student members, and registered land surveyors. Is concerned with social, professional, ethical, and economic considerations of engineering as a profession; encompasses programs in public relations, employment practices, ethical considerations, education, and career guidance. Monitors legislative and regulatory actions of interest to the engineering profession.

★1245★ Resumes for High Tech Careers
Vgm Career Horizons
1221 Avenue of the Americas
New York, NY 10020
Ph: (212)904-2000   Fr: 800-323-4900
E-mail: ntcpub@tribune.com

Second edition, 1997. $9.95 (paper). 462 pages. Demonstrates how to tailor a resume that catches a high tech employer's attention. Part of Resumes for... series.

★1246★ Scientific, Engineering, and Technical Services
Cambridge Educational
2572 Brunswick Ave.
Lawrenceville, NJ 08648-4128
Fax: 800-FAX-ON-US   Fr: 800-468-4227
URL: http://www.cambridgeeducational.com

$89.95. 2002. 18 minutes. Part of the Career Cluster Series.

★1247★ Society of Women Engineers (SWE)
230 E Ohio St., No. 400
Chicago, IL 60611-3265
Ph: (312)596-5223   Fax: (312)596-5252
E-mail: hq@swe.org
URL: http://www.swe.org

Description: Educational and service organization representing both students and professional women in engineering and technical fields.

★1248★ Women in Engineering
Her Own Words
PO Box 5264
Madison, WI 53705-0264
Ph: (608)271-7083   Fax: (608)271-0209
URL: http://www.herownwords.com/

Video. Jocelyn Riley. $95.00. 15 minutes. Resource guide also available for $45.00.

Bricklayers and Cement Masons

SOURCES OF HELP-WANTED ADS

★1249★ **Architectural West**
Dodson Publications Inc.
546 Court St.
Reno, NV 89501
Ph: (775)333-1080   Fax: (775)333-1081
URL: http://www.architecturalwest.com
Bimonthly. $12.00/year for individuals. Trade magazine covering issues for architects and specifiers of exterior building materials in the western United States.

★1250★ **BIA News**
Brick Industry Association
11490 Commerce Park Dr., Ste. 300
Reston, VA 20191
Ph: (703)620-0010   Fax: (703)620-3928
Monthly. $30.00/year. Trade publication covering issues for the brick industry.

★1251★ **Builder**
Hanley-Wood L.L.C.
1 Thomas Cir., Ste. 600
Washington, DC 20005
Ph: (202)452-0800   Fax: (202)785-1974
URL: http://www.builderonline.com
Monthly. $29.95/year for individuals. Magazine covering housing and construction industry.

★1252★ **Concrete Products**
Primedia Business
9800 Metcalf Ave.
Overland Park, KS 66212
Ph: (913)341-1300   Fax: (913)967-1898
E-mail: concreteproducts@intertec.com
URL: http://www.concreteproducts.com
Monthly. $54.00/year for U.S.; $74.00/year for other countries. Magazine on concrete products and ready-mixed concrete.

★1253★ **Construction Digest**
Construction Digest
5804 W 74th St.
Indianapolis, IN 46278
Ph: (317)293-6860   Fax: (317)293-7840
Fr: 888-893-6860
Semimonthly. $3.00 for single issue. Magazine for the public works and construction engineering industries.

★1254★ **CONSTRUCTOR**
Associated General Contractors
  Information
333 John Carlyle St., Ste. 200
Alexandria, VA 22314
Ph: (703)837-5355   Fax: (703)837-5402
URL: http://www.agc.org
Monthly. $15.00/year for members; $250.00/year for nonmembers; $4.00/year for single issue except July, November, and December; $25.00/year for single issue-November, December; $325.00 for single issue-July. Management magazine for the Construction Industry.

★1255★ **Professional Builder**
Reed Business Information
360 Park Ave. S
New York, NY 10014
Ph: (646)746-7764
URL: http://www.probuilder.com
Monthly. $10.00 for single issue; $139.95/year for by mail.

★1256★ **WIT**
Northern New England Tradeswomen
189 N Main St., Ste. 9
Barre, VT 05641-4173
Ph: (802)476-4040   Fax: (802)476-3346
Description: Three issues/year. Provides a network of support, information, and skill sharing for women in skilled trades professions.

EMPLOYER DIRECTORIES AND NETWORKING LISTS

★1257★ **ABC Today-Associated Builders and Contractors National Membership Directory Issue**
Associated Builders & Contractors Inc.
4250 N Fairfax Dr., 9th Fl.
Arlington, VA 22203
Ph: (703)812-2000   Fax: (703)812-8203
Annual, December. $150.00. Publication includes: List of approximately 19,000 member construction contractors and suppliers. Entries include: Company name, address, phone, name of principal executive, code to volume of business, business specialty. Arrangement: Classified by chapter, then by work specialty.

★1258★ **Constructor-AGC Directory of Membership and Services Issue**
AGC Information Inc.
333 John Carlyle St., Ste. 200
Alexandria, VA 22314
Ph: (703)548-3118   Fax: (703)548-3119
URL: http://www.agc.org
Annual, July. $250.00 for nonmembers; $15.00 for members; $250.00 for other countries. Publication includes: List of over 8,500 member firms and 24,000 national associate member firms engaged in building, highway, heavy, industrial, municipal utilities, and railroad construction (SIC 1541, 1542, 1611, 1622, 1623, 1629); listing of state and local chapter officers. Entries include: For firms-Company name, address, phone, fax, names of principal executives, and code indicating type of construction undertaken. For officers-Name, title, address. Arrangement: Geographical, Alphabetical. Indexes: Company name.

★1259★ **ENR-Top 400 Construction Contractors Issue**

McGraw-Hill Companies
1221 Ave. of the Americas
New York, NY 10020
Ph: (212)512-2000   Fax: (212)512-3840

Annual, May issue of "Engineering News Record". $10.00. Publication includes: List of 400 United States contractors receiving largest dollar volumes of contracts in preceding calendar year. Separate lists of 50 largest design/construct management firms; 50 largest program and construction managers; 25 building contractors; 25 heavy contractors. Entries include: Company name, headquarters location, total value of contracts received in preceding year, value of foreign contracts, countries in which operated, construction specialities. Arrangement: By total value of contracts received.

★1260★ **Masonry Contractors Directory**

infoUSA Inc.
5711 S 86th Cir.
Omaha, NE 68127-0347
Ph: (402)930-3500   Fax: (402)331-0176
Fr: 800-555-6124
URL: http://www.abii.com

Annual. Number of listings: 13,770. Entries include: Name, address, phone (including area code), size of advertisement, year first in "Yellow Pages," name of owner or manager, number of employees. Compiled from telephone company "Yellow Pages," nationwide. Arrangement: Geographical.

HANDBOOKS AND MANUALS

★1261★ **Exploring Careers in Construction**

Prentice Hall PTR
200 Old Tappan Rd.
Old Tappan, NJ 07675
Ph: (201)236-7000   Fr: 800-223-1360

1998. $12.00. 94 pages.

★1262★ **Exploring Careers in the Construction Industry**

Rosen Publishing Group Inc.
29 E. 21st St.
New York, NY 10010
Ph: (212)777-3017   Fax: 888-436-4643
Fr: 800-237-9932

Elizabeth Stewart Lytle. Revised edition, 1994. $16.95; $9.95 (paper). Out of print.

★1263★ **Getting Started As a Contractor**

Summertree Books
811 Moundridge Dr.
Lawrence, KS 66049
Ph: (913)841-7643   Fax: (913)843-1816

J.L. McCabe. 1994. $10.95 (paper). 65 pages. Out of print.

★1264★ **Opportunities in Building Construction Trades**

McGraw-Hill Trade
2 Penn Plaza
New York, NY 10121
Ph: (212)904-2000   Fr: 800-722-4726

Michael Sumichrast. Second edition, 1998. $14.95; $11.95 (paper). 202 pages. From custom builder to rehabber, the many kinds of companies that employ craftspeople and contractors are explored. Includes job descriptions, requirements, and salaries for dozens of specialties within the construction industry. Contains a complete list of Bureau of Apprenticeship and Training state and area offices. Illustrated.

★1265★ **Opportunities in Masonry Careers**

McGraw-Hill Trade
2 Penn Plaza
New York, NY 10121
Ph: (212)904-2000   Fr: 800-722-4726

Chris Santilli. 1994. $14.95; $11.95 (paper). 160 pages.

★1266★ **Your Opportunities in the Trades**

Energeia Publishing, Inc.
1307 Fairmount Ave., S
Salem, OR 97302-4313
Ph: (503)362-1480   Fax: (503)362-2123
Fr: 800-639-6048

Ramel Waltman. 1995. $2.50 (paper). 8 pages. Covers the construction and building industries.

TRADESHOWS

★1267★ **Brick Show**

Brick Industry Association
11490 Commerce Park Dr., Ste. 300
Reston, VA 20191
Ph: (703)620-0010   Fax: (703)620-3928
E-mail: stephens@bia.org
URL: http://www.bia.org

Annual. **Primary Exhibits:** Displays related to the brick industry.

★1268★ **ICCON - International Commercial Construction Exposition**

National Association of Home Builders of the United States
1201 15th St. NW
Washington, DC 20005-2800
Ph: (202)266-8109   Fax: (202)266-8223
Fr: 800-368-5242
E-mail: exposales@nahb.com
URL: http://www.buildersshow.com

Primary Exhibits: Equipment, supplies, and services for the construction industries.

★1269★ **World of Concrete**

Hanley-Wood L.L.C.
426 S. Westgate
Addison, IL 60101
Ph: (630)543-0870   Fax: (630)543-3112
Fr: 800-837-0870
E-mail: woc@wocnet.com
URL: http://www.worldofconcrete.com

Annual. **Primary Exhibits:** Equipment and services for the construction industry. **Dates and Locations:** 2005 Jan; Las Vegas, NV; Convention Center.

OTHER SOURCES

★1270★ **Associated Builders and Contractors (ABC)**

1300 N. 17th St., Ste. 800
Rosslyn, VA 22209
Ph: (703)812-2000   Fax: (703)812-8201
E-mail: info@abc.org
URL: http://www.abc.org

Description: Construction contractors, subcontractors, suppliers, and associates. Aim is to foster and perpetuate the principles of rewarding construction workers and management on the basis of merit. Sponsors management education programs and craft training; also sponsors apprenticeship and skill training programs. Disseminates technological and labor relations information.

★1271★ **Associated General Contractors of America (AGC)**

333 John Carlyle St., Ste. 200
Alexandria, VA 22314
Ph: (703)548-3118   Fax: (703)548-3119
E-mail: sandhers@agc.org
URL: http://www.agc.org

Description: General construction contractors; subcontractors; industry suppliers; service firms. Provides market services through its divisions. Conducts special conferences and seminars designed specifically for construction firms. Compiles statistics on job accidents reported by member firms. ors. Maintains 65 committees, including joint cooperative committees with other associations and liaison committees with federal agencies.

★1272★ **Associated Specialty Contractors (ASC)**

3 Bethesda Metro Ctr., Ste. 1100
Bethesda, MD 20814
Ph: (301)657-3110   Fax: (301)215-4500
E-mail: dgw@necanet.org
URL: http://www.assoc-spec-con.org

Description: Subcontractor associations with a total of 25,000 members representing electrical, heating, piping, mechanical, air conditioning, sheet metal, plumbing, ventilating, painting and decorating, and roofing and insulation contractors. Promotes liaison with general contractors, architects, and engineers on inter-industry matters, codes, bidding, and contracting procedures. Coordinates governmental affairs, research, and educational matters.

★1273★ Building Trades
Delphi Productions
3160 4th St.
Boulder, CO 80304
Fax: (303)443-4022   Fr: 888-443-2400
URL: http://www.delphivideo.com

$95.00. 46 minutes. Part of the Careers for the 21st Century Video Library.

**★1274★ COIN Career Guidance
System**
COIN Educational Products
3361 Executive Pky., Ste. 302
Toledo, OH 43606
Ph: (419)536-5353   Fax: (419)536-7056
Fr: 800-274-8515
URL: http://www.coin3.com/highschool/
guidance.asp

CD-ROM. Provides career information through seven cross-referenced files covering postsecondary schools, college majors, vocational programs, military service, apprenticeship programs, financial aid, and scholarships. Apprenticeship file describes national apprenticeship training programs, including information on how to apply, contact agencies, and program content. Military file describes more than 200 military occupations and training opportunities related to civilian employment.

★1275★ Construction Trade Helpers
Evon Publishing
832 N 7th Ave.
Iron River, MI 49935
Ph: (906)265-3190

Audiocassette. 1996. $16.95. 32 minutes. Part of the Careers and Vocational Guidance Series. Provides information about the na-

ture of the work, educational requirements, employment outlook, earnings, and work conditions as well as additional related information.

**★1276★ Mason Contractors
Association of America (MCAA)**
33 S Rosell Rd.
Schaumburg, IL 60193
Ph: (847)301-0001   Fax: (847)301-1110
Fr: 800-536-2225
E-mail: madelizzi@masoncontractors.org
URL: http://www.masoncontractors.com

Description: Masonry construction firms. Conducts specialized education and research programs. Compiles statistics.

★1277★ The Masonry Society (TMS)
3970 Broadway, Ste. 201-D
Boulder, CO 80304-1135
Ph: (303)939-9700   Fax: (303)541-9215
E-mail: info@masonrysociety.org
URL: http://www.masonrysociety.org

Description: Individuals interested in the art and science of masonry. Professional, technical and educational association dedicated to the advancement and knowledge of masonry. Gathers and disseminates technical information.

**★1278★ National Association of Home
Builders (NAHB)**
1201 15th St. NW
Washington, DC 20005
Ph: (202)266-8200   Fax: (202)822-0586
Fr: 800-368-5242
E-mail: info@nahb.com
URL: http://www.nahb.org

Description: Single and multifamily home builders, commercial builders, and others associated with the building industry. Lobbies on behalf of the housing industry and conducts public affairs activities to increase

public understanding of housing and the economy. Collects and disseminates data on current developments in home building and home builders' plans through its Economics Department and nationwide Metropolitan Housing Forecast. Maintains NAHB Research Center, which functions as the research arm of the home building industry. Sponsors seminars and workshops on construction, mortgage credit, labor relations, cost reduction, land use, remodeling, and business management. Compiles statistics; offers charitable program, spokesman training, and placement service; maintains speakers' bureau, and Hall of Fame. Subsidiaries include the National Council of the Housing Industry. Maintains over 50 committees in many areas of construction; operates National Commercial Builders Council, National Council of the Multifamily Housing Industry, National Remodelers Council, and National Sales and Marketing Council.

**★1279★ National Association of
Women in Construction (NAWIC)**
327 S Adams St.
Fort Worth, TX 76104
Ph: (817)877-5551   Fax: (817)877-0324
Fr: 800-552-3506
E-mail: nawic@nawic.org
URL: http://www.nawic.org

Description: Seeks to enhance the success of women in the construction industry.

**★1280★ Women in Nontraditional
Careers: An Introduction**
Her Own Words
PO Box 5264
Madison, WI 53705
Ph: (608)271-7083   Fax: (608)271-0209
URL: http://www.herownwords.com/

Video. Jocelyn Riley. $95.00. 15 minutes. Resource guide also available for $45.00.

Broadcast Technicians

★1281★ Advanced Imaging

Cygnus Business Media Inc.
445 Broad Hollow Rd.
Melville, NY 11747
Ph: (631)845-2700   Fax: (631)845-2798
Fr: 800-308-6397
E-mail: Len.Yencharis@cygnuspub.com
URL: http://www.advancedimagingmag.com

Monthly. Free to qualified subscribers. Magazine covering the full range of electronic imaging technology and its uses.

★1282★ AV Video & Multimedia Producer

PBI Media L.L.C.
2700 Westchester Ave.
Purchase, NY 10577-2554
Ph: (914)328-9157   Fax: (914)328-9093
Fr: 800-800-5474
E-mail: avvmmp@kipi.com
URL: http://www.kipinet.com

Monthly. $53.00/year for individuals; $65.00/year for Canada and Mexico; $85.00/year for other countries. Magazine covering audio-visual, video and multimedia production, presentation, people, technology and techniques.

★1283★ Broadcasting & Cable

Reed Business Information
360 Park Ave. S
New York, NY 10010
Ph: (646)746-6400   Fax: (646)746-6734
URL: http://www.broadcastingcable.com

Weekly. $179.00/year for U.S.; $239.00/year for Canada. News magazine covering The Fifth Estate (radio, TV, cable, and satellite), and the regulatory commissions involved.

★1284★ CED (Communications Engineering & Design)

Communications Engineering & Design
PO Box 266006
Highlands Ranch, CO 80163-6006
Ph: (303)470-4800   Fax: (303)470-4890
URL: http://www.cedmagazine.com

Monthly. $54.00/year for individuals. Technical/business publication serving the engineering/management community within broadband/cable TV networks, telecommunications carriers, data and interactive networks.

★1285★ Communications

PBI Media L.L.C.
1201 Seven Locks Rd., Ste. 300
Potomac, MD 20854
Ph: (301)354-2000
E-mail: ctmagazine@aol.com

Monthly. Free to qualified subscribers. Magazine catering to cable TV industry's technical community; written by industry engineers, technicians, managers, and professionals.

★1286★ Community Radio News

National Federation of Community
  Broadcasters (NFCB)
Fort Mason Ctr., Bldg. D
San Francisco, CA 94123
Ph: (415)771-1160   Fax: (415)771-1160

Description: Monthly. Serves as a medium of communication for independent, community-licensed radio stations. Contains brief articles and news items on such topics as public broadcasting and programming, legislative developments, activities of the Federal Communications Commission, and local stations. Recurring features include notices of grants and awards, job openings, and a calendar of events/conferences for noncommercial broadcasters.

★1287★ db, The Sound Engineering Magazine

db, The Sound Engineering Magazine
203 Commack Rd., No. 1010
Commack, NY 11725

Bimonthly. $15.00/year. Technical magazine for recording, broadcast, and sound reinforcement audio engineers.

★1288★ Electronic Media

Crain Communications Inc.
1155 Gratiot Ave.
Detroit, MI 48207-2997
Ph: (313)446-6000
E-mail: info@crain.com
URL: http://www.crain.com/

Newspaper covering management, programming, cable and trends in the television and the media industry.

★1289★ Entertainment Employment Journal

Studiolot Publishing
5632 Van Nuys Blvd., Ste. 320
Van Nuys, CA 91401-4600
Ph: (818)776-2800   Fr: 800-335-4335
E-mail: info@eej.com
URL: http://www.eej.com

Semimonthly. $125.00/year. Trade magazine covering business and technical careers in broadcast, electronic media, and motion pictures.

★1290★ FMedia!

FM Atlas Publishing
PO Box 336
Esko, MN 55733-0336
Ph: (218)879-7676   Fr: 800-605-2219

Description: Monthly. Lists information on the facilities and formats of FM radio, including new station grants and applications. Also provides official and unofficial news and comments, as well as FM Dxing and FM reception concerns. Recurring features include letters to the editor, news of research, job listings, and notices of publications available.

★1291★ The Hollywood Reporter

The Hollywood Reporter
5055 Wilshire Blvd.
Los Angeles, CA 90036-4396
Ph: (323)525-2000   Fax: (323)525-2377
E-mail: special-issues@hollywoodreporter.com
URL: http://www.hollywoodreporter.com

Daily. Film, TV, and entertainment trade newspaper.

★1292★ Journal of the Audio Engineering Society

Audio Engineering Society
60 E 42nd St., Rm. 2520
New York, NY 10165-2520
Ph: (212)661-8528   Fax: (212)682-0477
URL: http://www.aes.org/journal

$180.00/year for individuals, surface mail; $225.00/year for individuals, airmail. Journal reporting engineering developments and scientific progress in audio engineering for audio professionals, educators, executives, consumers, and students.

★1293★ Millimeter Magazine

Primedia Business
9800 Metcalf Ave.
Overland Park, KS 66212
Ph: (913)341-1300   Fax: (913)967-1898

Monthly. $45.00/year; $7.00 for single issue. Magazine focusing on the process of motion picture and television production.

★1294★ Mix

Primedia Business
6400 Hollis St., Ste. 12
Emeryville, CA 94608
Ph: (510)653-3307   Fax: (510)653-5142
Fr: 800-541-7706
E-mail: mixeditorial@intertec.com
URL: http://http//www.mixonline.com

Monthly. $37.95/year for individuals. Magazine focusing on audio and video music production in the recording industry.

★1295★ Post

Post Pro Publishing Inc.
25 Willowdale Ave.
Port Washington, NY 11050
Ph: (516)767-2500   Fax: (516)767-9335
URL: http://www.postmagazine.com

Monthly. Free to qualified subscribers. Magazine serving the field of television, film, video production and post-production.

★1296★ Producers Masterguide

Producers Masterguide
60 E 8th St., 34th Fl.
New York, NY 10003-6514
Ph: (212)777-4002   Fax: (212)777-4101
URL: http://
www.producers.masterguide.com

Annual. $145.00/year for U.S.; $155.00/year for Canada; $175.00/year for other countries. An international film and TV production directory and guide for the professional motion picture, broadcast television, feature film, TV commercial, cable/satellite, digital and videotape industries in the U.S., Canada, the UK, the Caribbean Islands, Mexico, Australia, New Zealand, Europe, Israel, Morocco, the Far East, and South America.

★1297★ QST

American Radio Relay League Inc.
225 Main St.
Newington, CT 06111
Ph: (860)594-0200   Fax: (860)594-0303
Fr: 888-277-5289
E-mail: qst@arrl.org

Monthly. $34.00/year for individuals. Amateur radio magazine.

★1298★ R&B Airplay Monitor

VNU Business Media USA
770 Broadway
New York, NY 10003
Ph: (646)654-5000
URL: http://www.vnubusinessmedia.com/box/bp/div_ent_music_airm.ht

Weekly. $295.00/year for individuals. Trade publication covering the radio and telecommunications industries.

★1299★ SCRIBE

Scribe Media
5606 Medical Cir.
Madison, WI 53719
Ph: (608)271-1025   Fax: (608)271-1150
Fr: 800-373-9692
URL: http://www.msn.fullfeed.com/~scribe/

Description: Quarterly. Concerned about informational programming in religious broadcasting and broadcast journalism. Recurring features include letters to the editor, interviews, news of research, reports of meetings, news of educational opportunities, job listings, and book reviews.

★1300★ SMPTE Journal

Society of Motion Picture and Television Engineers
595 W Hartsdale Ave.
White Plains, NY 10607
Ph: (914)761-1100   Fax: (914)761-3115
URL: http://www.smpte.org

Monthly. $90.00/year; $100.00/year for out of country. Journal containing articles pertaining to new developments in motion picture and television technology; standards and recommended practices; general news of the industry.

PLACEMENT AND JOB REFERRAL SERVICES

★1301★ Broadcast Foundation of College/University Students (BROADCAST)

89 Longview Rd.
Port Washington, NY 11050
Ph: (516)883-2897   Fax: (516)883-0159
E-mail: rstarleton@aol.com

Members: College students interested in broadcasting and professional broadcasters interested in encouraging practical broadcasting experience in colleges and universities. **Activities:** Conducts annual survey of all professional broadcasting stations for part-time and summer employment for college students. Sponsors job advisory and placement service.

★1302★ Health Sciences Communications Association (HESCA)

39 Wedgewood Dr., Ste. A
Jewett City, CT 06351
Ph: (860)376-5915   Fax: (860)376-6621
E-mail: hesca@hesca.org
URL: http://www.hesca.org/

Description: Media managers, graphic artists, biomedical librarians, producers, faculty members of health science and veterinary medicine schools, health professional organizations, and industry representatives. Acts as a clearinghouse for information used by professionals engaged in health science communications. Coordinates Media Festivals Program which recognizes outstanding media productions in the health sciences. Offers placement service.

★1303★ National Association of Broadcasters (NAB)

1771 N St. NW
Washington, DC 20036
Ph: (202)429-5300   Fax: (202)429-4199
E-mail: nab@nab.org
URL: http://www.nab.org

Description: Representatives of radio and television stations and networks; associate members include producers of equipment and programs. Seeks to ensure the viability, strength, and success of free, over-the-air broadcasters; serves as an information resource to the industry. Monitors and reports on events regarding radio and television broadcasting. Maintains Broadcasting Hall of Fame. Offers minority placement service and employment clearinghouse.

EMPLOYER DIRECTORIES AND NETWORKING LISTS

★1304★ Bacon's Metro California Media

Bacon's Information Inc.
332 S Michigan Ave., Ste. 900
Chicago, IL 60604
Ph: (312)922-2400   Fax: (312)987-9773
Fr: 800-621-0561
URL: http://www.bacons.com

Annual, November. $250.00. Covers consumer media in the state of California including newspapers, radio television & cable stations, magazines, broadcast programs, ethnic media, news services & syndicates. Entries include: Name, address, phone, names of editors and creative staff, with titles or indication of assignments. Arrangement: Geographical, classified by type of outlet. Indexes: Alphabetical.

★1305★ Bacon's Radio/TV/Cable Directory, Volume 1

Bacon's Information Inc.
332 S Michigan Ave., Ste. 900
Chicago, IL 60604
Ph: (312)922-2400   Fax: (312)987-9773
Fr: 800-621-0561
URL: http://www.bacons.com/research/radiotvcable.htm

Annual, November. $375.00. Covers over 13,500 radio and television stations, including college radio and public television stations, and cable companies. Entries include: For radio and television stations-Call letters, address, phone, names and titles of key personnel, programs, times broadcast, name of contact, network affiliation, frequency or channel number, target audience data. For cable companies-Name, address, phone, description of activities. Arrangement: Geographical.

★1306★ BIA's Television Yearbook

BIA Financial Network Inc.
15120 Enterprise Ct.
Chantilly, VA 20151
Ph: (703)818-2425   Fax: (703)803-3299
Fr: 800-331-5086
URL: http://www.bia.com

Annual, March. $99.00. Covers U.S. television markets and their inclusive stations, television equipment manufacturers, and related service providers and trade associations. Entries include: For stations-Call letters, address; name and phone of general manager, owner, and other key personnel; technical attributes, rep firm, network affiliation, last acquistion date and price and ratings for total day and prime time. For others-Company or organization name, address, phone, description. Arrangement: Classified by market. Indexes: Numerical by market rank; call letters.

★1307★ Broadcasting & Cable Yearbook

R.R. Bowker L.L.C.
630 Central Ave.
New Providence, NJ 07974
Ph: (908)286-1090   Fax: (908)219-0098
Fr: 888-269-5372

Annual, March, latest edition 2003-2004. $179.95. Covers over 17,000 television and radio stations in the United States, its territories, and Canada; cable MSOs and their individual systems; television and radio networks, broadcast and cable group owners, station representatives, satellite networks and services, film companies, advertising agencies, government agencies, trade associations, schools, and suppliers of professional and technical services, including books, serials, and videos; communications lawyers. Entries include: Company name, address, phone, fax, names of executives. Station listings include broadcast power, other operating details. Arrangement: Stations and systems are geographical, others are alphabetical. Indexes: Alphabetical.

★1308★ Burrelle's New York Media Directory

Burrelle's Information Services
75 E. Northfield Rd.
Livingston, NJ 07039
Ph: (973)992-6600   Fax: (973)992-7675
Fr: 800-631-1160
URL: http://www.burrellesluce.com/mediadata/regional.html

Annual. $200.00. Covers Print and electronic media in New York. Entries include: Name, address, phone, fax, names and titles of key personnel, geographical area served, subsidiary and branch names and locations, description. Arrangement: Geographical; magazines are arranged by subject. Indexes: Name, subject, geographical.

★1309★ CPB Public Broadcasting Directory

Corporation for Public Broadcasting
901 E St. NW
Washington, DC 20004-2037
Ph: (202)879-9600   Fax: (202)783-9700
URL: http://www.cpb.org/directory/home.html

Annual. $15.00. Covers public television and radio stations, national and regional public broadcasting organizations and networks, state government agencies and commissions, and other related organizations. Entries include: For radio and television stations-Station call letters, frequency or channel, address, phone, licensee name, licensee type, date on air, antenna height, area covered, names and titles of key personnel. For organizations-Name, address, phone, name and title of key personnel. Arrangement: National and regional listings are alphabetical; state groups and the public radio and television stations are each geographical; other organizations and agencies are alphabetical. Indexes: Geographical, personnel, call letter, licensee type (all in separate indexes for radio and television).

★1310★ FM Atlas

FM Atlas Publishing
PO Box 336
Esko, MN 55733-0336
Ph: (218)879-7676   Fr: 800-605-2219
URL: http://members.aol.com/fmatlas/home.html

Irregular, latest edition 2003; Previous edition 1999. $21.00; $19.00 each for two books. Covers approximately 10,500 FM stations located in North America. Entries include: Call letters, location, musical format, transmitting radius in kilometers, whether stereo or monaural, FM subcarriers, etc. Arrangement: Geographical, then by frequency.

★1311★ International Motion Picture Almanac

Quigley Publishing Company Inc.
64 Wintergreen Ln.
Groton, MA 01450-4219
Fr: 800-231-8239
URL: http://hometown.aol.com/quigleypub/mp.html

Annual, January. $130.00. Covers motion picture producing companies, firms serving the industry, equipment manufacturers, casting agencies, literary agencies, advertising and publicity representatives, motion picture theater circuits, buying and booking organizations, independent theaters, international film festivals, associations, theatre equipment supply companies. Entries include: Generally, company name, address, phone. For manufacturers-Products or service provided, name of contact. For producing companies-Additional details. For theaters-Name of owner, screen size. Companion volume is the "International Television and Video Almanac". Arrangement: Classified by service or activity.

★1312★ International Television and Video Almanac

Quigley Publishing Company Inc.
64 Wintergreen Ln.
Groton, MA 01450-4129
Fr: 800-231-8239
URL: http://hometown.aol.com/quigleypub/mp.html

Annual, January. $130.00. Covers "Who's Who in Motion Pictures and Television and Home Video," television networks, major program producers, major group station owners, cable television companies, distributors, firms serving the television and home video industry, equipment manufacturers, casting agencies, literary agencies, advertising and publicity representatives, television stations, associations, list of feature films produced for television; statistics, industry's year in review, award winners, satellite & wireless cable provider, primtime programming, video producers, distributors, wholesalers. Entries include: Generally, company name, address, phone; manufacturer and service listings may include description of products and services and name of contact; producing, distributing, and station listings include additional detail, and contacts for cable and broadcast networks. Arrangement: Classified by service or activity. Indexes: Full.

★1313★ North Carolina News Media Directory

Brian Highberger Publisher
PO Box 316
Mount Dora, FL 32756
Fax: (866)586-7020   Fr: 800-749-6399

Annual, April. $60.00. Covers about 730 newspapers, periodicals, radio and television broadcasting stations, and press services operating in North Carolina. Entries include: Publisher or company name, address, phone, names and titles of key personnel, publication title, call letters, hours of operation, and frequency. Arrangement: Classified by type of media. Indexes: Title, call letters, county index.

★1314★ Producers Directory

IFILM Publishing
1024 N Orange Dr.
Hollywood, CA 90038
Ph: (323)308-3490   Fax: (323)308-3493

Latest edition 46th, three times per year in March, July, and November. $59.95 per issue; $149.95 per year; $199.95 for online subscription. Covers over 1,700 film and TV production companies, studios, networks, and TV shows, and over 7,700 creative executives within those companies. Majority of listings are located in Los Angeles and New York. Entries include: Company name, staff names and titles, address, phone, fax, e-mail address, web site address, company type, studio deals, and select credits. Arrangement: Alphabetical. Indexes: Company type, studio deals, individual names.

★1315★ The R & R Directory

Radio and Records Inc.
10100 Santa Monica Blvd., 3rd Fl.
Los Angeles, CA 90067-4004
Ph: (310)553-4330   Fax: (310)203-8727
E-mail: moreinfo@rronline.com
URL: http://www.radioandrecords.com

Semiannual, Spring and Fall. $75.00. Covers more than 3,000 radio group owners, equipment manufacturers, jingle producers, TV production houses and spot producers, record companies, representative firms, research companies, consulting firms, media brokers, networks, program suppliers, trade associations, and other organizations involved in the radio and record industry. Entries include: Organization name, address, phone, fax, E-mail, name and title of contacts, branch offices or subsidiary names and locations. Arrangement: Alphabetical; classified by subject. Indexes: Company.

★1316★ Radio Advertising Source

SRDS
1700 .E Higgins Rd.
Des Plaines, IL 60018-5605
Ph: (847)375-5000   Fax: (847)375-5001
Fr: 800-851-7737
URL: http://www.srds.com

Quarterly. $534.00. Covers over 10,500 AM and FM stations, networks, syndicators, group owners, and representative firms. Entries include: Call letters, name of owning company, address, phone; names of representatives and station personnel; demostration detail, station format, signal strength, programming opportunities, special features. Arrangement: Geographical by state, then Arbitron metro and nonmetro area.

★1317★ Radio Programming Profile

BF/Communication Services Inc.
311 Martling Ave.
Tarrytown, NY 10591-4709
Ph: (516)364-2593

Three times yearly. $250.00. Covers about 3,000 AM and FM radio stations in top 200 markets, with hour-by-hour format information (type of music, news, etc.) for each. Entries include: Station call letters, address, phone, names of executives, hour-by-hour format information. Arrangement: Alphabetical by market and call letters. Volume 1 has top 70 ranking markets; Volume 2 has markets 71-200.

★1318★ Radio Stations and Broadcasting Companies Directory

infoUSA Inc.
5711 S 86th Cir.
Omaha, NE 68127-0347
Ph: (402)930-3500   Fax: (402)331-0176
Fr: 800-555-6124
URL: http://www.abii.com

Annual. Number of listings: 13,087. Entries include: Name, address, phone (including area code), size of advertisement, year first in "Yellow Pages," name of owner or manager, number of employees. Available by sinal type. Compiled from telephone company "Yellow Pages," nationwide. Arrangement: Geographical.

★1319★ RTNDA Communicator-Directory Issues

Radio-Television News Directors
 Association
1600 K St. NW, No. 700
Washington, DC 20006
Ph: (202)659-6510   Fax: (202)223-4007
Fr: 800-807-8632

Semiannual, January and July. Number of listings: 3,000; membership includes Canada and some foreign countries. Entries include: Member name, address, phone; and name of radio or television station, network, or other news organization with which affiliated. Arrangement: Same information given in alphabetical and geographical arrangements.

★1320★ Television & Cable Factbook

Warren Communications News
2115 Ward Ct. NW
Washington, DC 20037
Ph: (202)872-9202   Fax: (202)293-3435
Fr: 800-771-9202
URL: http://www.warren-news.com/fact-

book.htm

Annual, March. Weekly updates available. $795.00. Covers commercial and noncommercial television stations and networks, including educational, low-power and instructional TV stations, and translators; United States cable television systems; cable and television group owners; program and service suppliers; and brokerage and financing companies. Entries include: For stations- Call letters, licensee name and address, studio address and phone; identification of owners, sales and legal representatives and chief station personnel; rates, technical data, map of service area, and Nielsen circulation data. For cable systems-Name, address, basic and pay subscribers, programming and fees, physical plant; names of personnel and ownership. ownership. Arrangement: Geographical by state, province, city, county, or country. Indexes: Call letters, product/service, name, general subject.

★1321★ Television Stations & Broadcasting Companies Directory

infoUSA Inc.
5711 S 86th Cir.
Omaha, NE 68127-0347
Ph: (402)930-3500   Fax: (402)331-0176
Fr: 800-555-6124
URL: http://www.abii.com

Updated continuously; printed on request. Number of listings: 4,158. Entries include: Name, address, phone (including area code), size of advertisement, year first in "Yellow Pages," name of owner or manager, number of employees. Compiled from telephone company "Yellow Pages," nationwide. Arrangement: Geographical.

★1322★ The Top National TV News, Talk and Magazine Shows

Todd Publications
PO Box 635
Nyack, NY 10960
Ph: (845)358-6213   Fax: (845)358-6213
Fr: (866)896-0916

Biennial, latest edition 2000. $50.00. Covers the most popular information shows on U.S. television. Entries include: Name, address, phone of company, name and title of contact and description of format. Arrangement: By rank.

★1323★ TV and Cable Source

SRDS
1700 .E Higgins Rd.
Des Plaines, IL 60018-5605
Ph: (847)375-5000   Fax: (847)375-5001
Fr: 800-851-7737
URL: http://www.srds.com

Quarterly. $520.00. Covers all domestic & international commercial television stations and networks; public television stations, cable networks, systems, interconnects, rep firms, and group owners. Includes separate section showing production specifications of stations and systems. Entries include: Call letters, parent company, address, phone, representative, personnel, facilities, special features, programming. Production specifications section shows call letters or system name, address, and preferred specifications for ad copy. Arrangement: Classified by DMA ranking, then by call letters.

★1324★ **Working Press of the Nation**

R.R. Bowker L.L.C.
630 Central Ave.
New Providence, NJ 07974
Ph: (908)286-1090   Fax: (908)219-0098
Fr: 888-269-5372
E-mail: wpn@bowker.com

Annual, September. $530.00 for set; $295.00 each volume. Covers in three separate volumes, syndicates and over 8,500 daily and weekly newspapers; 1,750 newsletters; over 16,800 radio and television stations; 5,500 magazines; 1,000 internal publications. Entries include: Name of publication or station, address, phone, fax, e-mail and URL, names of executives, editors, writers, etc., as appropriate. Broadcasting and magazine volumes include data on kinds of material accepted. Technical and mechanical requirements for publications are given. Arrangement: Magazines are classified by subject; newspapers and broadcasting stations are geographical. Indexes: Newspaper department/editor by interest, metro area, feature syndicate subject; magazine subject, publication title; television director/personnel by subject, radio personnel and director by subject.

HANDBOOKS AND MANUALS

★1325★ **Breaking into Television**

Thomson Peterson's
202 Carnegie Ctr.
Box 67005
Princeton, NJ 08540
Fr: 800-338-3282

Weaver. 1998. $14.95 (paper). Explains how to get a job in the television industry, with a list of internship opportunities.

★1326★ **Career Information Center**

Macmillan Publishing Co. Inc.
200 Old Tappan Rd.
Old Tappan, NJ 07675
Fr: 800-428-5331

Visual Education Center Staff. Seventh edition, 1999. $275.00. 2080 pages. This 13-volume set profiles over 600 occupations. Each occupational profile describes job duties, educational requirements, how to get the job, advancement possibilities, employment outlook, working conditions, earnings and benefits, and where to write for more information.

★1327★ **Careers in Communications**

VGM Career Horizons
4255 W. Touhy Ave.
Lincolnwood, IL 60646-1975
Ph: (847)679-5500   Fax: (847)679-2494
Fr: 800-323-4900
E-mail: ntcpub@tribune.com

Shonan Noronha. Third edition, 1998. $17.95; $13.95 (paper). 418 pages. Examines the fields of journalism, photography, radio, television, film, public relations, and advertising. Gives concrete details on job locations and how to secure a job. Suggests many resources for job hunting.

★1328★ **Great Jobs for Music Majors**

McGraw-Hill Companies
1221 Avenue of the Americas
New York, NY 10020
Ph: (212)904-2000   Fr: 800-323-4900
E-mail: ntcpub@tribune.com

Jan Goldberg, Stephen Lambert, Julie De-Galan. 1997. $11.95 (paper). 365 pages.

★1329★ **Inside Broadcasting**

Routledge
7625 Empire Dr.
Florence, KY 41042
Fr: 800-634-7064

1997. $24.99. 232 pages. Part of the Career Builders Guide Series.

★1330★ **Lights, Camera, Action!: Careers in Film, Television, & Video**

Indiana University Press
601 N. Morton St.
Bloomington, IN 47404-3797
Ph: (812)855-4203   Fax: (812)855-7931
Fr: 800-842-6796

Josephine Langham. Second edition, 1996. $19.95 (paper).

★1331★ **On-the-Air Anywhere: A Beginner's Guide to Broadcasting**

Dorrance Publishing Co., Inc.
643 Smithfield St.
Pittsburgh, PA 15222
Ph: (412)288-4543   Fax: (412)288-1786
Fr: 800-788-7654

Charlie Pullen. 1996. $8.00 (paper). 80 pages.

★1332★ **Opportunities in Broadcasting Careers**

McGraw-Hill Trade
2 Penn Plaza
New York, NY 10121
Ph: (212)904-2000   Fr: 800-722-4726

Elmo I. Ellis. 1998. $14.95; $11.95 (paper). Discusses opportunities and job search techniques in broadcasting, television, and radio. Illustrated.

★1333★ **Opportunities in Cable Television Careers**

McGraw-Hill Trade
2 Penn Plaza
New York, NY 10121
Ph: (212)904-2000   Fr: 800-722-4726

Jan Bone. 1994. $14.95; $11.95 (paper). 160 pages. Focuses on what the jobs are, where they are, and how to get them. Illustrated.

★1334★ **Opportunities in Television and Video Careers**

McGraw-Hill Trade
2 Penn Plaza
New York, NY 10121
Ph: (212)904-2000   Fr: 800-722-4726
E-mail: ntcpub@tribune.com

Shonan Noronha. 1998. $14.95; $11.95 (paper). 206 pages. Details the employment opportunities open in television, cable, corporate video, institutional and government media, including independent production, and discusses how to land a job. Illustrated.

★1335★ **Radio and Television Career Directory**

Thomson Gale
27500 Drake Rd.
Farmington Hills, MI 48331-3535
Ph: (248)699-GALE   Fax: 800-414-5043
Fr: 800-877-GALE
E-mail: galeord@gale.com
URL: http://www.gale.com

Bradley Morgan. Second edition, 1993. $39.00. 300 pages. Features extensive listings of contacts and entry-level job opportunities. Provides information on internships and sources of help-wanted ads.

★1336★ **Working in Show Business: Behind-the-Scenes Careers in Theater, Film and Television**

Watson-Guptill Publications, Inc.
770 Broadway
New York, NY 10003
Ph: (646)654-5400   Fax: (646)654-5486
Fr: 800-323-9432

Lynne Rogers. 1997. $18.95 (paper). 400 pages.

EMPLOYMENT AGENCIES AND SEARCH FIRMS

★1337★ **The Cheyenne Group**

60 E. 42nd St., Ste. 2821
New York, NY 10165
Ph: (212)471-5000   Fax: (212)471-5050

Executive search firm.

★1338★ Fitzgibbon & Associates
PO Box 1108
Media, PA 19063
Ph: (610)565-7566

Executive search firm focused on the communications industry.

★1339★ Jim Young & Associates Inc.
Holland Creek
1424 Clear Lake Rd.
Weatherford, TX 76086
Ph: (817)599-7623   Fax: (817)599-4483
Fr: 800-433-2160

Specializes in the placement of cable television, telecommunications, cellular telephone, RF engineering and satellite communications personnel. Industries served: cable television, telecommunications, and cellular.

ONLINE JOB SOURCES AND SERVICES

★1340★ Society of Broadcast Engineers Job Line
URL: http://www.sbe.org/jobline.html

Description: Job Line is one benefit of membership in the Society of Broadcast Engineers. Includes a resume service to distribute resumes to employers, job contact information, and descriptions of job openings. Also accessible via telephone.

TRADESHOWS

★1341★ CES - Spring
CEMA - Consumer Electronics Manufacturers Association
2500 Wilson Blvd.
Arlington, VA 22201-3834
Ph: (866)233-7968   Fax: (703)907-7601
E-mail: CESinfo@CE.org
URL: http://www.cesweb.org/about_ces/fact_sheet.asp

Annual. **Primary Exhibits:** Audio hardware, computer and multimedia hardware, cellular and wireless communications, home office equipment, video hardware, home theater products, and digital photography equipment.

★1342★ DSP World Spring Design Conference
CMP Media LLC (San Francisco)
2800 Campus Dr.
San Mateo, CA 94403
Ph: (650)513-4400   Fax: (650)513-4646
URL: http://www.cmp.com

Annual. **Primary Exhibits:** Digital signal processing and communication.

★1343★ Eastern Cable Television Trade Show and Convention
Convention and Show Management Co.
6175 Barfield Rd., Ste. 220
Atlanta, GA 30328
Ph: (404)252-2454   Fax: (404)252-0215

Annual. **Primary Exhibits:** Cable television industry equipment, supplies, and services.

★1344★ Expo Comm Miami
Keith Reed Media Events
303 Vintage Park Dr.
Foster City, CA 94404
Ph: (650)578-6897   Fax: (650)525-0193
Fr: 800-488-2883
E-mail: mtrask@zdcf.com

Primary Exhibits: Provides a platform for the latest telecommunications, telephony, broadband and wireless communications, products and services.

★1345★ Great Lakes Cable Expo
Great Lakes Cable Expo
6910 N. Shadeland Ave., Ste. 206
Indianapolis, IN 46220
Ph: (317)845-8100   Fax: (317)578-0621

Annual. **Primary Exhibits:** Cable industry-related equipment, supplies, and services.

★1346★ National Association of State Telecommunications Directors Conference
National Association of State Telecommunications Directors
2760 Research Park Dr.
PO Box 11910
Lexington, KY 40578-1910
Ph: (606)244-8187   Fax: (606)244-8001
E-mail: nastd@csg.org
URL: http://www.csg.org/nastd

Annual. **Primary Exhibits:** Exhibits for state telecommunications systems.

★1347★ SMPTE Technical Conference Exhibition
Society of Motion Picture and Television Engineers
595 W. Hartsdale Ave.
White Plains, NY 10607
Ph: (914)761-1100   Fax: (914)761-3115
E-mail: smpte@smpte.org
URL: http://www.smpte.org

Annual. **Primary Exhibits:** Equipment, lights, cameras, film, tape, and lenses.

★1348★ Society of Broadcast Engineers Engineering Conference
Society of Broadcast Engineers
9247 N. Meridian St., No. 305
Indianapolis, IN 46260-1946
Ph: (317)846-9000   Fax: (317)846-9120
URL: http://www.sbe.org

Annual. **Primary Exhibits:** Equipment, supplies, and services for the broadcast industry.

★1349★ Southern States Communication Association Convention
Southern States Communication Association
College of Communication and Fine Arts
151 Bibb Graves Hall
Troy State University
Troy, AL 36082
Ph: (912)681-5138   Fax: (912)681-0822
E-mail: director@sca.net
URL: http://www.ssca.net/

Annual. **Primary Exhibits:** Communications equipment; textbooks.

★1350★ TeleCon East
Applied Business Telecommunications
201 Sandpointe Ave. Ste. 600
Santa Ana, CA 92707-8700
Ph: (925)513-4242   Fr: 800-829-3400

Primary Exhibits: Telecommunications equipment, supplies, and services.

★1351★ Utilities Telecommunications Council Annual Conference and Exhibition
Utilities Telecommunications Council
1901 Pennsylvania Ave. NW Ste. 500
Washington, DC 20006-3400
Ph: (202)872-0030   Fax: (202)872-1331

Annual. **Primary Exhibits:** Telecommunications equipment and services.

OTHER SOURCES

★1352★ Association for Educational Communications and Technology (AECT)
1800 N Stonelake Dr., Ste. 2
Bloomington, IN 47408
Ph: (812)335-7675   Fax: (812)335-7678
Fr: 877-677-AECT
E-mail: aect@aect.org
URL: http://www.aect.org

Description: Instructional technology professionals. Provides leadership in educational communications and technology by linking professionals holding a common interest in the use of educational technology and its application of the learning process.

★1353★ Broadcast Technicians
Evon Publishing
832 N 7th Ave.
Iron River, MI 49935
Ph: (906)265-3190

Audiocassette. 1996. $16.95. 32 minutes. Part of the Careers and Vocational Guidance Series. Provides information about the nature of the work, educational requirements, employment outlook, earnings, and work conditions as well as additional related information.

★1354★ **Corporation for Public Broadcasting (CPB)**
401 9th St. NW
Washington, DC 20004-2129
Ph: (202)879-9600   Fax: (202)879-9700
Fr: 800-272-2190
E-mail: comments@cpb.org
URL: http://www.cpb.org

Description: A private, nonprofit corporation authorized under Public Broadcasting Act of 1967. Funded by U.S. government. Works to promote and finance the growth and development of noncommercial radio and television. Makes grants to local public television and radio stations, program producers, and regional networks; studies emerging technologies; works to provide adequate long-range financing from the U.S. government and other sources for public broadcasting. Supports children's services; compiles statistics; sponsors training programs. Presents awards annually for outstanding local television and radio programs.

★1355★ **Country Radio Broadcasters (CRB)**
819 18th Ave. South
Nashville, TN 37203
Ph: (615)327-4487   Fax: (615)329-4492
E-mail: ed_salamon@crb.org
URL: http://www.crb.org/

Description: Seeks to advance and promote the study of the science of broadcasting through the mutual exchange of ideas by conducting seminars and workshops, as well as providing scholarships to broadcasting students.

★1356★ **Media Alliance (MA)**
814 Mission St., Ste. 205
San Francisco, CA 94103
Ph: (415)546-6334   Fax: (415)546-6218
E-mail: info@media-alliance.org
URL: http://www.media-alliance.org

Description: Writers, photographers, editors, broadcast workers, public relations practicioners, videographers, filmmakers, commercial artists and other media workers and aspiring media workers. Supports free press and independent, alternative journalism that services progressive politics and social justice.

★1357★ *Media and the Arts Occupations*
Delphi Productions
3160 4th St.
Boulder, CO 80304
Fax: (303)443-4022   Fr: 888-443-2400
URL: http://www.delphivideo.com

$95.00. 50 minutes. Part of the Careers for the 21st Century Video Library.

★1358★ **National Association of Black Owned Broadcasters (NABOB)**
1155 Connecticut Ave. NW, 6th Fl.
Washington, DC 20036
Ph: (202)463-8970   Fax: (202)429-0657
E-mail: info@nabob.org
URL: http://www.nabob.org

Description: Black broadcast station owners; black formatted stations not owned or controlled by blacks; organizations having an interest in the black consumer market or black broadcast industry; individuals interested in becoming owners; and communications schools, departments, and professional groups and associations. Represents the interests of existing and potential black radio and television stations. Is currently working with the Office of Federal Procurement Policy to determine which government contracting major advertisers and advertising agencies are complying with government initiatives to increase the amount of advertising dollars received by minority-owned firms. Conducts lobbying activities; provides legal representation for the protection of minority ownership policies. Sponsors annual Communications Awards Dinner each March. Conducts workshops; compiles statistics.

★1359★ **National Cable and Telecommunications Association (NCTA)**
1724 Massachusetts Ave. NW
Washington, DC 20036
Ph: (202)775-3550   Fax: (202)775-3675
E-mail: webmaster@ncta.com
URL: http://www.ncta.com

Description: Franchised cable operators, programmers, and cable networks; associate members are cable hardware suppliers and distributors; affiliate members are brokerage and law firms and financial institutions; state and regional cable television associations cooperate, but are not affiliated, with NCTA. Serves as national medium for exchange of experiences and opinions through research, study, discussion, and publications. Represents the cable industry before Congress, the Federal Communications Commission, and various courts on issues of primary importance. Conducts research program in conjunction with National Academy of Cable Programming. Sponsors, in conjunction with Motion Picture Association of America, the Coalition Opposing Signal Theft, an organization designed to deter cable signal theft and to develop antipiracy materials. Provides promotional aids and information on legal, legislative, and regulatory matters. Compiles statistics.

★1360★ **National Religious Broadcasters (NRB)**
9510 Technology Dr.
Manassas, VA 20110
Ph: (703)330-7000   Fax: (703)330-7100

E-mail: adunlap@nrb.org
URL: http://www.nrb.org

Description: Christian communicators. Fosters electronic media access for the Gospel; promotes standards of excellence; integrity and accountability; and provides networking and fellowship opportunities for its members.

★1361★ *Radio and Television Broadcasting*
Evon Publishing
832 N 7th Ave.
Iron River, MI 49935
Ph: (906)265-3190

Audiocassette. 1996. $16.95. 32 minutes. Part of the Careers and Vocational Guidance Series. Provides information about the nature of the work, educational requirements, employment outlook, earnings, and work conditions as well as additional related information.

★1362★ **Society of Broadcast Engineers**
9247 N Meridian St., Ste. 305
Indianapolis, IN 46260
Ph: (317)846-9000   Fax: (317)846-9120
E-mail: jporay@sbe.org
URL: http://www.sbe.org

Description: Broadcast engineers, students, and broadcast professionals in closely allied fields. Promotes professional abilities of members and provides information exchange. Provides support to local chapters. Maintains certification program; represents members' interests before the Federal Communications Commission and other governmental and industrial groups. Offers educational workshops and seminars. Provides volunteer frequency coordination service for the nation's broadcasters.

★1363★ *Technical & Related Occupations*
Delphi Productions
3160 4th St.
Boulder, CO 80304
Fax: (303)443-4022   Fr: 888-443-2400
URL: http://www.delphivideo.com

$95.00. 49 minutes. Part of the Careers for the 21st Century Video Library.

★1364★ **Women in Cable and Telecommunications (WIT)**
14555 Avion Pkwy., Ste. 250
Chantilly, VA 20151
Ph: (703)234-9810   Fax: (703)817-1595
URL: http://www.wict.org

Description: Empowers and educate women to achieve their professional goals by providing opportunities for leadership, networking and advocacy.

Budget Analysts

★1365★ *Accounting Horizons*
American Accounting Association
5717 Bessie Dr.
Sarasota, FL 34233
Ph: (941)921-7747   Fax: (941)923-4093

Quarterly. Publication covering the banking, finance, and accounting industries.

★1366★ *Brookings Papers on Economic Activity*
Brookings Institution Press
1775 Massachusetts Ave. NW
Washington, DC 20036
Ph: (202)797-6000   Fax: (202)797-6195
Fr: 800-275-1447

Semiannual. Publication covering economics and business.

★1367★ *Budget and Management Analyst*
Vocational Biographies, Inc.
PO Box 31
Sauk Centre, MN 56378-0031
Ph: (612)352-6516   Fax: (612)352-5546
Fr: 800-255-0752

1992. $5.00. Four-page pamphlet containing a personal narrative about a worker's job, work likes and dislikes, career path from high school to the present. Education and training, the rewards and frustrations, and the effects of the job on the rest of the worker's life. The data file portion of this pamphlet gives a concise occupational summary, including work descriptions, working conditions, places of employment, personal characteristics, education and training, job outlook, and salary range.

★1368★ *Commercial Lending Review*
Aspen Publishers Inc.
1185 Avenue of the Americas, 37th Fl.
New York, NY 10036
Ph: (212)597-0200   Fax: (212)597-0390
Fr: 800-447-1717

E-mail: cgreene@world.std.com
URL: http://www.aspenpublishers.com

$325.00/year for individuals. Journal covering all aspects of lending for commercial banks, community and regional banks and other financial institutions.

★1369★ *CPA Client Bulletin*
American Institute of Certified Public Accountants
Harborside Financial Ctr.
201 Plz. III
Jersey City, NJ 07311
Ph: (201)938-3806

Monthly. Periodical covering accounting and personal finance.

EMPLOYER DIRECTORIES AND NETWORKING LISTS

★1370★ *Career Opportunities in Banking, Finance, and Insurance*
Facts on File Inc.
132 W 31st St., 17th Fl.
New York, NY 10001
Ph: (212)967-8800   Fax: 800-678-3633
Fr: 800-322-8755

$49.50. Publication includes: Lists of colleges with programs supporting banking, finance, and industry; professional associations; professional certifications; regulatory agencies; and Internet resources for career planning. Principal content of publication is job descriptions for professions in the banking, finance, and insurance industries. Indexes: Alphabetical.

★1371★ *Internet Guide to Personal Finance and Investment*
Greenwood Publishing Group Inc.
88 Post Rd. W.
PO Box 5007
Westport, CT 06881-5007
Ph: (203)226-3571   Fax: (203)226-6009
Fr: 800-225-5800

$55.00. Covers over 1,400 web sites regarding personal finance and investment. Entries include: Name of web site, URL, sponsor of site, and description of contents. Indexes: Web site title; Sponsor; Subject.

HANDBOOKS AND MANUALS

★1372★ *The Basics of Budgeting*
AMACOM
1601 Broadway, 12th Fl.
New York, NY 10019
Ph: (212)903-8315   Fax: (212)903-8083

Robert G. Finney. 1993. $19.95.

★1373★ *Budget Analyst*
National Learning Corp.
212 Michael Dr.
Syosset, NY 11791
Ph: (516)921-8888   Fax: (516)921-8743
Fr: 800-645-6337

Jack Rudman. 1994. $34.95. Test guide including questions and answers for students or professionals in the field who seek advancement through examination. Also included in the series: Senior Budget Analyst, Principal Budget Analyst, Associate Budget Analyst, and Assistant Budget Analyst.

★1374★ *Careers in Finance*
McGraw-Hill Trade
2 Penn Plaza
New York, NY 10121
Ph: (212)904-2000   Fr: 800-323-4900
E-mail: ntcpub2@aol.com

Trudy Ring, editor. 1994. $13.95 and $17.95. Covers financial careers in such areas as higher education, corporate and public finance, and commercial and investment banking.

★1375★ *Cost and Statistical Analyst*
National Learning Corp.
212 Michael Dr.
Syosset, NY 11791
Ph: (516)921-8888   Fax: (516)921-8743
Fr: 800-645-6337

Jack Rudman. 1994. $39.95. Test guide including questions and answers for students or professionals in the field who seek advancement through examination.

★1376★ *Handbook of Budgeting*
John Wiley & Sons Inc.
1 Wiley Dr.
Somerset, NJ 08873
Ph: (732)469-4400   Fr: 800-526-5368

Robert Rachlin, editor. Fourth edition, 1998. $190.00. Discusses budgeting preparation, presentation, and analysis. Contains examples of forms, techniques, and reports.

★1377★ *Opportunities in Federal Government Careers*
McGraw-Hill Trade
2 Penn Plaza
New York, NY 10121
Ph: (212)904-2000   Fr: 800-722-4726
E-mail: ntcpub@tribune.com

Neale Baxter. Second edition, 1994. $14.95; $10.95 (paper). 160 pages. Describes the spectrum of government employment, including professional, administrative, scientific, blue-collar, clerical, and technical opportunities, and how to land a job. Illustrated. Part of Opportunities in...Series.

★1378★ *The Portable MBA in Finance and Accounting*
John Wiley & Sons Inc.
1 Wiley Dr.
Somerset, NJ 08873
Ph: (732)469-4400   Fr: 800-526-5368

John Leslie Livingstone. 1997. $34.95. Offers advice to businesses. Includes prepar-

ing budgets, implementing business plans, and evaluating acquisition targets.

EMPLOYMENT AGENCIES AND SEARCH FIRMS

★1379★ **Chrisman & Company Inc.**
350 S. Figueroa St., Ste. 550
Los Angeles, CA 90071
Ph: (213)620-1192

Executive search firm.

★1380★ **Conspectus Inc.**
222 Purchase St., Ste. 318
Rye, NY 10580
Ph: (914)925-0600

Executive search firm concentrated on the financial industry.

★1381★ **David M. Ellner Associates**
13 Central Dr.
Port Washington, NY 11050
Ph: (212)279-0665

Executive search firm.

ONLINE JOB SOURCES AND SERVICES

★1382★ **American Association of Finance and Accounting**
E-mail: feedback@aafa.com
URL: http://www.aafa.com

Description: AAFA is the largest and oldest alliance of executive search firms specializing in the recruitment and placement of finance and accounting professionals. Contains career opportunities site with job board for both job seekers and hiring employers.

One does not have to be a member to search for jobs.

TRADESHOWS

★1383★ *FIM-National - Financial Investment Management Exposition and Conference*
Flagg Management, Inc.
353 Lexington Ave.
New York, NY 10016
Ph: (212)286-0333   Fax: (212)286-0086
E-mail: flaggmgmt@msn.com
URL: http://www.flaggmgmt.com

Annual. **Primary Exhibits:** Online investment systems internet information series, portfolio management systems, online trading and execution systems. Investment industry professionals and information and technology systems management.

OTHER SOURCES

★1384★ *Financial Occupations*
Delphi Productions
3160 4th St.
Boulder, CO 80304
Fax: (303)443-4022   Fr: 888-443-2400
URL: http://www.delphivideo.com

$95.00. 50 minutes. Part of the Careers for the 21st Century Video Library.

Carpenters

SOURCES OF HELP-WANTED ADS

★1385★ Builder
Hanley-Wood L.L.C.
1 Thomas Cir., Ste. 600
Washington, DC 20005
Ph: (202)452-0800   Fax: (202)785-1974
URL: http://www.builderonline.com

Monthly. $29.95/year for individuals. Magazine covering housing and construction industry.

★1386★ Construction Digest
Construction Digest
5804 W 74th St.
Indianapolis, IN 46278
Ph: (317)293-6860   Fax: (317)293-7840
Fr: 888-893-6860

Semimonthly. $3.00 for single issue. Magazine for the public works and construction engineering industries.

★1387★ CONSTRUCTOR
Associated General Contractors
  Information
333 John Carlyle St., Ste. 200
Alexandria, VA 22314
Ph: (703)837-5355   Fax: (703)837-5402
URL: http://www.agc.org

Monthly. $15.00/year for members; $250.00/year for nonmembers; $4.00/year for single issue except July, November, and December; $25.00/year for single issue-November, December; $325.00 for single issue-July. Management magazine for the Construction Industry.

★1388★ Kitchen and Bath Design News
Cygnus Business Media Inc.
445 Broad Hollow Rd.
Melville, NY 11747
Ph: (631)845-2700   Fax: (631)845-2798
Fr: 800-308-6397
E-mail: kbdneditor@aol.com

URL: http://www.kitchen-bath-design.com/
Monthly. Trade journal.

★1389★ Panel World
Hatton-Brown Publishers
PO Box 2268
Montgomery, AL 36102
Ph: (334)834-1170   Fax: (334)834-4525
Fr: 800-669-5613
URL: http://www.panelworldmag.com

Bimonthly. $28.00/year; free to qualified subscribers. Business magazine serving the worldwide veneer, plywood, and panel board industry.

★1390★ Professional Builder
Reed Business Information
360 Park Ave. S
New York, NY 10014
Ph: (646)746-7764
URL: http://www.probuilder.com

Monthly. $10.00 for single issue; $139.95/year for by mail.

★1391★ WIT
Northern New England Tradeswomen
189 N Main St., Ste. 9
Barre, VT 05641-4173
Ph: (802)476-4040   Fax: (802)476-3346

Description: Three issues/year. Provides a network of support, information, and skill sharing for women in skilled trades professions.

★1392★ Wood & Wood Products
Vance Publishing Corp.
400 Knightsbridge Pkwy.
Lincolnshire, IL 60069
Ph: (847)634-2600   Fax: (847)634-4343
Fr: 800-621-2845

Monthly. $30.00/year for individuals; $50.00/year for other countries; $3.00 for single issue. Magazine for furniture, cabinet, and woodworking industry.

EMPLOYER DIRECTORIES AND NETWORKING LISTS

★1393★ ABC Today-Associated Builders and Contractors National Membership Directory Issue
Associated Builders & Contractors Inc.
4250 N Fairfax Dr., 9th Fl.
Arlington, VA 22203
Ph: (703)812-2000   Fax: (703)812-8203

Annual, December. $150.00. Publication includes: List of approximately 19,000 member construction contractors and suppliers. Entries include: Company name, address, phone, name of principal executive, code to volume of business, business specialty. Arrangement: Classified by chapter, then by work specialty.

★1394★ Cabinet Makers Directory
infoUSA Inc.
5711 S 86th Cir.
Omaha, NE 68127-0347
Ph: (402)930-3500   Fax: (402)331-0176
Fr: 800-555-6124
URL: http://www.abii.com

Annual. Number of listings: 17,633. Entries include: Name, address, phone (including area code), size of advertisement, year first in "Yellow Pages," name of owner or manager, number of employees. Compiled from telephone company "Yellow Pages," nationwide. Arrangement: Geographical.

★1395★ Carpenters Directory
infoUSA Inc.
5711 S 86th Cir.
Omaha, NE 68127-0347
Ph: (402)930-3500   Fax: (402)331-0176
Fr: 800-555-6124
URL: http://www.abii.com

Annual. Number of listings: 7,890. Entries include: Name, address, phone (including area code), size of advertisement, year first in "Yellow Pages," name of owner or manager, number of employees. Compiled from telephone company "Yellow Pages," nationwide. Arrangement: Geographical.

★1396★ *Constructor-AGC Directory of Membership and Services Issue*

AGC Information Inc.
333 John Carlyle St., Ste. 200
Alexandria, VA 22314
Ph: (703)548-3118   Fax: (703)548-3119
URL: http://www.agc.org

Annual, July. $250.00 for nonmembers; $15.00 for members; $250.00 for other countries. Publication includes: List of over 8,500 member firms and 24,000 national associate member firms engaged in building, highway, heavy, industrial, municipal utilities, and railroad construction (SIC 1541, 1542, 1611, 1622, 1623, 1629); listing of state and local chapter officers. Entries include: For firms-Company name, address, phone, fax, names of principal executives, and code indicating type of construction undertaken. For officers-Name, title, address. Arrangement: Geographical, Alphabetical. Indexes: Company name.

★1397★ *ENR-Top 400 Construction Contractors Issue*

McGraw-Hill Companies
1221 Ave. of the Americas
New York, NY 10020
Ph: (212)512-2000   Fax: (212)512-3840

Annual, May issue of "Engineering News Record". $10.00. Publication includes: List of 400 United States contractors receiving largest dollar volumes of contracts in preceding calendar year. Separate lists of 50 largest design/construct management firms; 50 largest program and construction managers; 25 building contractors; 25 heavy contractors. Entries include: Company name, headquarters location, total value of contracts received in preceding year, value of foreign contracts, countries in which operated, construction specialities. Arrangement: By total value of contracts received.

★1398★ *Woodworkers Directory*

infoUSA Inc.
5711 S 86th Cir.
Omaha, NE 68127-0347
Ph: (402)930-3500   Fax: (402)331-0176
Fr: 800-555-6124
URL: http://www.abii.com

Annual. Number of listings: 9,163. Entries include: Name, address, phone (including area code), size of advertisement, year first in "Yellow Pages," name of owner or manager, number of employees. Compiled from telephone company "Yellow Pages," nationwide. Arrangement: Geographical.

HANDBOOKS AND MANUALS

★1399★ *Exploring Careers in the Construction Industry*

Rosen Publishing Group Inc.
29 E. 21st St.
New York, NY 10010
Ph: (212)777-3017   Fax: 888-436-4643
Fr: 800-237-9932

Elizabeth Stewart Lytle. Revised edition, 1994. $16.95; $9.95 (paper). Out of print.

★1400★ *Opportunities in Building Construction Trades*

McGraw-Hill Trade
2 Penn Plaza
New York, NY 10121
Ph: (212)904-2000   Fr: 800-722-4726

Michael Sumichrast. Second edition, 1998. $14.95; $11.95 (paper). 202 pages. From custom builder to rehabber, the many kinds of companies that employ craftspeople and contractors are explored. Includes job descriptions, requirements, and salaries for dozens of specialties within the construction industry. Contains a complete list of Bureau of Apprenticeship and Training state and area offices. Illustrated.

★1401★ *Opportunities in Carpentry Careers*

McGraw-Hill/Contemporary Books
1221 Avenue of the Americas
New York, NY 10020
Ph: (212)904-2000   Fr: 800-323-4900
E-mail: ntcpub@tribune.com

Roger Sheldon. 1999. $14.95; $11.95 (paper). 202 pages. Discusses how to get started and covers the job market. Illustrated.

★1402★ *Opportunities in Crafts Careers*

McGraw-Hill Trade
2 Penn Plaza
New York, NY 10121
Ph: (212)904-2000   Fr: 800-722-4726

Marianne Munday. 1994. $14.95; $11.95 (paper). 160 pages. Provides information about careers and job opportunities in such areas as fine and applied arts, antiques and collectibles, ceramics, woodworking, sewing and needlecraft, and more. Illustrated. Out of stock.

★1403★ *Working Alone: Tips and Techniques for Solo Building*

Taunton Press, Incorporated
63 S. Main St., Box 5506
Newtown, CT 06470-5506
Ph: (203)426-8171   Fax: (203)426-7184
Fr: 800-477-8727

John Carroll. 1999. $17.95.

TRADESHOWS

★1404★ **Florida Industrial Woodworking Expo**

Trade Shows, Inc.
PO Box 2000
Claremont, NC 28610-2000
Ph: (828)459-9894   Fax: (828)459-1312
E-mail: tsisales@tsiexpos.com
URL: http://www.tsiexpos.com

Biennial. **Primary Exhibits:** Machinery, tooling, supplies, and services for the furniture, cabinet, casegoods, millwork, and industrial wood products industries.

★1405★ **ICCON - International Commercial Construction Exposition**

National Association of Home Builders of the United States
1201 15th St. NW
Washington, DC 20005-2800
Ph: (202)266-8109   Fax: (202)266-8223
Fr: 800-368-5242
E-mail: exposales@nahb.com
URL: http://www.buildersshow.com

Primary Exhibits: Equipment, supplies, and services for the construction industries.

★1406★ **International Woodworking Machinery and Furniture Supply Fair - USA**

Marketing/Association Services Inc.
4342 Redwood Ave., No. C309
Marina del Rey, CA 90292-6480
Ph: (310)302-1077   Fax: (310)306-5288
E-mail: eschwa1511@aol.com

Biennial. **Primary Exhibits:** Woodworking machinery and supplies for furniture, woodworking, kitchen cabinets, architectural woodwork, and specialty wood products.

★1407★ **Mid-Atlantic Industrial Woodworking Expo**

Trade Shows, Inc.
PO Box 2000
Claremont, NC 28610-2000
Ph: (828)459-9894   Fax: (828)459-1312
E-mail: tsisales@tsiexpos.com
URL: http://www.tsiexpos.com

Annual. **Primary Exhibits:** Woodworking and furniture industry equipment, supplies, and services. **Dates and Locations:** 2005 Apr 15-16; Fort Washington, PA; Fort Washington Expo Center.

★1408★ **WMS - Woodworking Machinery and Supply Expo**

Reed Exhibitions (North American Headquarters)
383 Main Ave.
PO Box 6059
Norwalk, CT 06851
Ph: (203)840-5402   Fax: (203)840-9402
E-mail: inquiry@reedexpo.com
URL: http://www.reedexpo.com

Biennial. **Primary Exhibits:** Woodworking

and furniture manufacturing equipment, supplies, and services, including sanding, finishing, machinery and supplies, gluing and laminating machinery and supplies, hardware and fasteners, upholstery machinery and material, portable tools, packaging and shipping equipment and supplies, plant, material, handling and safety equipment, material-lumber, plywood, veneers, particle board and laminates.

★1409★ **Wood Technology Clinic and Show**

CMP Media LLC (San Francisco)
2800 Campus Dr.
San Mateo, CA 94403
Ph: (650)513-4400   Fax: (650)513-4646
URL: http://www.cmp.com

Annual. **Primary Exhibits:** Equipment, supplies, and services related to the wood products industry, including sawmilling panel production and woodworking.

OTHER SOURCES

★1410★ **Associated Builders and Contractors (ABC)**

1300 N. 17th St., Ste. 800
Rosslyn, VA 22209
Ph: (703)812-2000   Fax: (703)812-8201
E-mail: info@abc.org
URL: http://www.abc.org

Description: Construction contractors, subcontractors, suppliers, and associates. Aim is to foster and perpetuate the principles of rewarding construction workers and management on the basis of merit. Sponsors management education programs and craft training; also sponsors apprenticeship and skill training programs. Disseminates technological and labor relations information.

★1411★ **Associated General Contractors of America (AGC)**

333 John Carlyle St., Ste. 200
Alexandria, VA 22314
Ph: (703)548-3118   Fax: (703)548-3119
E-mail: sandhers@agc.org
URL: http://www.agc.org

Description: General construction contractors; subcontractors; industry suppliers; service firms. Provides market services through its divisions. Conducts special conferences and seminars designed specifically for construction firms. Compiles statistics on job accidents reported by member firms. ors. Maintains 65 committees, including joint

cooperative committees with other associations and liaison committees with federal agencies.

★1412★ **Associated Specialty Contractors (ASC)**

3 Bethesda Metro Ctr., Ste. 1100
Bethesda, MD 20814
Ph: (301)657-3110   Fax: (301)215-4500
E-mail: dgw@necanet.org
URL: http://www.assoc-spec-con.org

Description: Subcontractor associations with a total of 25,000 members representing electrical, heating, piping, mechanical, air conditioning, sheet metal, plumbing, ventilating, painting and decorating, and roofing and insulation contractors. Promotes liaison with general contractors, architects, and engineers on inter-industry matters, codes, bidding, and contracting procedures. Coordinates governmental affairs, research, and educational matters.

★1413★ *Building Trades*

Delphi Productions
3160 4th St.
Boulder, CO 80304
Fax: (303)443-4022   Fr: 888-443-2400
URL: http://www.delphivideo.com

$95.00. 46 minutes. Part of the Careers for the 21st Century Video Library.

★1414★ **COIN Career Guidance System**

COIN Educational Products
3361 Executive Pky., Ste. 302
Toledo, OH 43606
Ph: (419)536-5353   Fax: (419)536-7056
Fr: 800-274-8515
URL: http://www.coin3.com/highschool/guidance.asp

CD-ROM. Provides career information through seven cross-referenced files covering postsecondary schools, college majors, vocational programs, military service, apprenticeship programs, financial aid, and scholarships. Apprenticeship file describes national apprenticeship training programs, including information on how to apply, contact agencies, and program content. Military file describes more than 200 military occupations and training opportunities related to civilian employment.

★1415★ **National Association of Home Builders (NAHB)**

1201 15th St. NW
Washington, DC 20005
Ph: (202)266-8200   Fax: (202)822-0586
Fr: 800-368-5242

E-mail: info@nahb.com
URL: http://www.nahb.org

Description: Single and multifamily home builders, commercial builders, and others associated with the building industry. Lobbies on behalf of the housing industry and conducts public affairs activities to increase public understanding of housing and the economy. Collects and disseminates data on current developments in home building and home builders' plans through its Economics Department and nationwide Metropolitan Housing Forecast. Maintains NAHB Research Center, which functions as the research arm of the home building industry. Sponsors seminars and workshops on construction, mortgage credit, labor relations, cost reduction, land use, remodeling, and business management. Compiles statistics; offers charitable program, spokesman training, and placement service; maintains speakers' bureau, and Hall of Fame. Subsidiaries include the National Council of the Housing Industry. Maintains over 50 committees in many areas of construction; operates National Commercial Builders Council, National Council of the Multifamily Housing Industry, National Remodelers Council, and National Sales and Marketing Council.

★1416★ **National Association of Women in Construction (NAWIC)**

327 S Adams St.
Fort Worth, TX 76104
Ph: (817)877-5551   Fax: (817)877-0324
Fr: 800-552-3506
E-mail: nawic@nawic.org
URL: http://www.nawic.org

Description: Seeks to enhance the success of women in the construction industry.

★1417★ *Women in Building Construction*

Her Own Words
PO Box 5264
Madison, WI 53705-0264
Ph: (608)271-7083   Fax: (608)271-0209
URL: http://www.herownwords.com/

Video. Jocelyn Riley. $95.00. 15 minutes. Resource guide also available for $45.00.

★1418★ *Women in Nontraditional Careers: An Introduction*

Her Own Words
PO Box 5264
Madison, WI 53705
Ph: (608)271-7083   Fax: (608)271-0209
URL: http://www.herownwords.com/

Video. Jocelyn Riley. $95.00. 15 minutes. Resource guide also available for $45.00.

Caterers

SOURCES OF HELP-WANTED ADS

★1419★ Foodservice East
The Newbury Street Group Inc.
165 New Boston St., No. 236
Woburn, MA 01801
Ph: (781)376-9080   Fax: (781)376-0010
Fr: 800-852-5212
E-mail: fdsvceast@.aol.com

$30.00/year for individuals. Compact Tabloid covering trends and analysis of the foodservice industry in the Northeast. A business-to-business publication featuring news, analysis and trends for the Northeast food service professional.

★1420★ Midwest Foodservice News
Pinnacle Publishing Group
2736 Sawbury Blvd.
Columbus, OH 43235
Ph: (614)336-0710   Fax: (614)336-0713

Bimonthly. Free to qualified subscribers; $24.00/year for others. Food service trade magazine featuring new products and suppliers and other industry news including food news, restaurant association updates, news of chefs, restaurant concepts, earnings, and openings and closings.

★1421★ The National Culinary Review
American Culinary Federation Inc.
10 San Bartola Dr.
St. Augustine, FL 32086
Ph: (904)824-4468   Fax: (904)825-4758
Fr: 800-624-9458
E-mail: acf@acfchefs.net

Monthly. $50.00/year for individuals; $3.00 for single issue. Trade magazine covering food and cooking.

★1422★ Restaurant Business
VNU Business Publications
770 Broadway
New York, NY 10003
Ph: (646)654-5000   Fax: (646)654-4977

E-mail: 200-4782@mcimail.com
URL: http://http:/www.foodservicetoday.com

$105.00/year for individuals; $10.00 for single issue. Trade magazine for restaurants and commercial food service.

★1423★ Restaurant Hospitality
Penton Media Inc.
1300 E 9th St.
Cleveland, OH 44114-1503
Ph: (216)696-7000   Fax: (216)931-9799
E-mail: rheditors@aol.com

Monthly. Free to qualified subscribers; $60.00/year for individuals; $5.95 for single issue. Magazine for managers and other executives of restaurant chains, independent restaurants, and hotels - foodservice operations.

PLACEMENT AND JOB REFERRAL SERVICES

★1424★ Les Amis d'Escoffier
1230 Main St., Rte. 9
Leicester, MA 01524
Ph: (508)892-9090   Fax: (508)892-3620
E-mail: info@castlerestaurant.com
URL: http://www.castlerestaurant.com/default.htm

Members: An educational organization of professionals in the food and wine industries. **Activities:** Maintains museum, speakers' bureau, hall of fame, and placement service. Sponsors charitable programs.

EMPLOYER DIRECTORIES AND NETWORKING LISTS

★1425★ Caterers Directory
infoUSA Inc.
5711 S 86th Cir.
Omaha, NE 68127-0347
Ph: (402)930-3500   Fax: (402)331-0176
Fr: 800-555-6124
URL: http://www.abii.com

Annual. Number of listings: 47,196. Entries include: Company name, address, and phone (including area code), size of advertisement, year first in "Yellow Pages," name of owner or manager, number of employees. Regional editions also available. Compiled from telephone company "Yellow Pages," nationwide. Arrangement: Geographical.

★1426★ Directory of Chain Restaurant Operators
Chain Store Guide
3922 Coconut Palm Dr.
Tampa, FL 33619
Ph: (813)627-6800   Fax: (813)627-6882
Fr: 800-927-9292
URL: http://www.csgis.com

Annual, April. $775.00 for CD-ROM; $975.00 for CD-ROM and directory. Covers chain restaurant operators, chain hotel operators, nontraditional foodservice operators and food service management operators who operate 2 or more food service locations. Entries include: For chain restaurant operators-company name, address, phone and fax numbers; e-mail and web addresses; type of business; listing type; total annual sales; food service sales; system wide sales; percent of sales of alcohol; percent of sales from Internet; alcohol types served; total units; company owned units; units franchised to and from; trade names; co-branded names and numbers; food service management location types; trading areas; foreign trading areas; units by primary menu types and type of foodservice; self distributing and catering services indicators; franchise affiliations names and locations; primary distributors names and locations; parent and subsidiary company names and locations; regional; divisional; and branch office locations; distribution centers locations; year founded; public company indicator; key personnel with titles. For chain hotel operators-includes number of restaurants in hotels. For food service management operators-includes number of food service management accounts and total number of locations served. Arrangement: Geographical. Indexes: Alphabetical, type of food service, menu type, franchisee, food service management, state, exclusions.

★1427★ Party Planning Service Directory

infoUSA Inc.
5711 S 86th Cir.
Omaha, NE 68127-0347
Ph: (402)930-3500   Fax: (402)331-0176
Fr: 800-555-6124
URL: http://www.abii.com

Annual. Number of listings: 8,789. Entries include: Name, address, phone (including area code), size of advertisement, year first in "Yellow Pages," name of owner or manager, number of employees. Compiled from telephone company "Yellow Pages," nationwide. Arrangement: Geographical.

HANDBOOKS AND MANUALS

★1428★ The Best Home-Based Businesses for the 90s

Putnam Publishing Group
375 Hudson St.
New York, NY 10014
Ph: (212)366-2000   Fax: (212)366-2643
Fr: 800-331-4624

Paul Edwards and Sarah Edwards. Second edition, 1991. $11.95 (paper). 272 pages. Profiles 95 businesses and careers that can be conducted from one's home. Lists sources of additional information. Out of print.

★1429★ Breaking into the Catering Business

Carol Publishing Group
120 Enterprise Ave.
Secaucus, NJ 07094
Ph: (201)866-0490   Fax: (201)866-8159
Fr: 800-447-2665

Kara Levine and Erika Temko. 1994. $8.95. 128 pages. Out of print.

★1430★ Career Opportunities in the Food and Beverage Industry

Facts on File, Inc.
132 W. 31st St., 17th Fl.
New York, NY 10001-2006
Ph: (212)967-8800   Fax: (212)967-8107
Fr: 800-322-8755
URL: http://www.factsonfile.com

Barbara Sims-Bell. Second edition, 2001. $18.95 (paper). Provides the job seeker with

information about locating and landing 80 skilled and unskilled jobs in the industry. Includes detailed job descriptions for many specific positions and lists trade associations, recruiting organizations, and major agencies. Contains index and bibliography.

★1431★ Careers in Catering, Hotel Administration and Management

Kogan Page, Ltd.
22 Broad St., Ste. 34
Milford, CT 06460

Russell Joseph. Fifth edition, 1997. $14.95 (paper). Part of the Kogan Page Careers Series. Out of print.

★1432★ Careers for Gourmets and Others Who Relish Food

McGraw-Hill Trade
2 Penn Plaza
New York, NY 10121
Ph: (212)904-2000   Fr: 800-722-4726
E-mail: ntcpub@tribune.com

Mary Donovan. Second edition, 2002. $15.95; $12.95 (paper). 192 pages. Discusses such job prospects as foods columnist, cookbook writer, test kitchen worker, pastry chef, recipe developer, food festival organizer, restaurant manager, and food stylist.

★1433★ Catering Service Business Possibility Encyclopedia

Frieda Carrol Communications
Prosperity & Profits Unlimited Distribution
  Services
PO Box 416
Denver, CO 80201-0416
Ph: (303)575-5676   Fax: (970)292-2136

1997. $59.95 (ringbound).

★1434★ Choosing a Career in the Restaurant Industry

Rosen Publishing Group, Inc.
29 E. 21st St.
New York, NY 10010
Ph: (212)777-3017   Fax: 888-436-4643
Fr: 800-237-9932

Eileen Beal. 1996. $17.95. 64 pages. Explores various jobs in the restaurant industry. Describes job duties, salaries, educational preparation, and job hunting. Contains information about fast food, catering, and small businesses.

★1435★ Culinary Arts Career Starter

LearningExpress, LLC
900 Broadway, Ste. 604
New York, NY 10003
Ph: (212)995-2566   Fax: (212)995-5512
Fr: 800-295-9556

Mary Masi. 1999. $14.95 (paper). 229 pages.

★1436★ How to Open and Operate a Home-Based Catering Business

Globe Pequot Press
PO Box 480
Guilford, CT 06437-0480
Ph: (203)458-4500   Fax: (203)458-4604
Fr: 800-243-0495

Denise Vivaldo. 1993. $15.95 (paper). 224 pages. Out of print. Written by a successful homebased caterer.

★1437★ How to Start a Home-Based Catering Business

The Globe Pequot Press
246 Goose Ln.
Guilford, CT 06437
Ph: (203)458-4500   Fax: (203)458-4604

Denise Vivaldo. Fourth edition. December 2002. $17.95. 256 pages. Part of the Home-Based Business Series.

★1438★ Opportunities in Culinary Careers

McGraw-Hill Contemporary Books
1221 Avenue of the Americas
New York, NY 10020
Ph: (212)904-2000   Fr: 800-323-4900
E-mail: ntcpub@tribune.com

Mary Deirdre Donovan. 1998. $14.95; $11.95 (paper). 160 pages. Describes the educational preparation and training of chefs and cooks and explores a variety of food service jobs in restaurants, institutions, and research and development. Lists major culinary professional associations and schools. Offers guidance on landing a first job in cooking and related fields.

★1439★ Opportunities in Restaurant Careers

Vgm Career Horizons
1221 Avenue of the Americas
New York, NY 10020
Ph: (212)904-2000   Fr: 800-323-4900
E-mail: ntcpub@tribune.com

Carol Caprione Chmelynski. 1998. $14.95; $11.95 (paper). 160 pages. Covers opportunities in the food service industry and details salaries, benefits, training opportunities, and professional associations. Special emphasis is put on becoming a successful restaurant manager by working up through the ranks. Illustrated.

★1440★ Start and Run a Profitable Catering Business

Self-Counsel Press, Inc.
1704 N. State St.
Bellingham, WA 98225
Ph: (360)676-4530   Fax: (360)676-4549
Fr: 877-877-6490

George Erdosh. 1994. $14.95 (paper). 184 pages. Out of print.

★1441★ *Successful Catering: Managing the Catering Operation for Maximum Profit*

Atlantic Publishing Company
1210 SW 3rd Pl.
Ocala, FL 34474-7014
Fr: 800-555-4037

Sony Bode. January 2003. $19.95. 144 Pages. Illustrated.

★1442★ *Working in Hotels and Catering*

Thomson Learning
7625 Empire Dr.
Florence, KY 41042
Ph: (859)525-6620   Fax: (859)525-0978
Fr: 800-347-7707

Roy Woods. Second edition, 1997. $35.95 (paper). 252 pages.

★1443★ *Working in Hotels and Catering: How to Find Great Employment Opportunities Worldwide*

Trans-Atlantic Publications, Inc.
311 Bainbridge St.
Philadelphia, PA 19147
Ph: (215)925-5083   Fax: (215)925-1912

Mark Hempshell. 1997. $19.95 (paper). Part of the Jobs and Careers Series. 174 pages.

ONLINE JOB SOURCES AND SERVICES

★1444★ **Pioneer College Caterers Online**

E-mail: careers@pcconline.com
URL: http://www.foodindustryjobs.com

Description: Job databank and resume submission service for food industry workers in Christian college cafeterias.

TRADESHOWS

★1445★ **American School Food Service Association Annual National Conference**

American School Food Service Association
700 S. Washington St., Ste. 300
Alexandria, VA 22314-4287
Ph: (703)739-3900   Fax: (703)739-3915
Fr: 800-877-8822

Annual. **Primary Exhibits:** Food service supplies and equipment, including educational services and computers.

★1446★ **Annual Hotel, Motel, and Restaurant Supply Show of the Southeast**

Leisure Time Unlimited, Inc.
708 Main St.
PO Box 332
Myrtle Beach, SC 29578
Ph: (843)448-9483   Fax: (843)626-1513
Fr: 800-261-5591
E-mail: ltushows@aol.com
URL: http://www.dickenschristmashow.com

Annual. **Primary Exhibits:** Carpeting, furniture, coffee makers, produce companies, wine and beer and food companies, and services to motels, hotels, and restaurants. **Dates and Locations:** 2005 Jan 25-27; Myrtle Beach, SC.

★1447★ **Heart of America Hospitality Expo**

Missouri Restaurant Association
1810 Craig Rd. Ste. 225
St. Louis, MO 65101

Annual. **Primary Exhibits:** Food service and hospitality industries equipment, supplies, and services.

★1448★ **Institute of Food Technologists Annual Meeting and Food Expo**

Institute of Food Technologists
525 W. Van Buren St., Ste. 1000
Chicago, IL 60607-3814
Ph: (312)782-8424   Fax: (312)782-8348
E-mail: info@ift.org
URL: http://www.ift.org

Annual. **Primary Exhibits:** Food ingredients, equipment, laboratory equipment and supplies, and other services rendered to the food processing industry. **Dates and Locations:** 2005 Jul 16-20; New Orleans, LA • 2006 Jul 22-26; Orlando, FL.

★1449★ **International Baking Industry Exposition**

IBIE Exhibition Management
401 N. Michigan Ave.
Chicago, IL 60611
Ph: (312)644-6610   Fax: (312)644-0575
E-mail: info@bakingexpo.org

Primary Exhibits: Baking equipment, supplies, and services.

★1450★ **Louisiana Foodservice Expo**

Louisiana Restaurant Association
2700 N. Arnoult Rd.
Metairie, LA 70002-5916
Ph: (504)454-2277   Fax: (504)454-2663
Fr: 800-256-4572
E-mail: sandyr@lra.org

Annual. **Primary Exhibits:** Food service equipment, supplies, and services, food products.

★1451★ **Midsouthwest Foodservice Convention and Exposition**

Oklahoma Restaurant Association
3800 N. Portland
Oklahoma City, OK 73112
Ph: (405)942-8181   Fax: (405)942-0541
Fr: 800-375-8181

Annual. **Primary Exhibits:** Providers of foodservice and hospitality products, services and equipment.

★1452★ **National Restaurant Association Restaurant and Hotel-Motel Show**

National Restaurant Association
150 N. Michigan Ave., Ste. 2000
Chicago, IL 60601
Ph: (312)853-2525   Fax: (312)853-2548

Annual. **Primary Exhibits:** Food service equipment, supplies, and services and food and beverage products for the hospitality industry.

★1453★ **Northeast Food Service and Lodging Exposition and Conference**

Reed Exhibitions (North American Headquarters)
383 Main Ave.
PO Box 6059
Norwalk, CT 06851
Ph: (203)840-5402   Fax: (203)840-9402
E-mail: inquiry@reedexpo.com
URL: http://www.reedexpo.com

Annual. **Primary Exhibits:** Food services, operating equipment, and services for the hospitality and institutional foodservice industry.

★1454★ **Ozark Food and Equipment Show**

Missouri Restaurant Association
1810 Craig Rd. Ste. 225
St. Louis, MO 65101

Annual. **Primary Exhibits:** Foodservice supplies, services, and equipment.

★1455★ **South Carolina Foodservice Expo**

South Carolina Foodservice Expo
111 Shannon Dr.
Spartanburg, SC 29301
Ph: (864)574-9323   Fax: (864)574-0784
E-mail: scsfsa@aol.com

Annual. **Primary Exhibits:** Food and foodservice equipment, supplies, and services.

★1456★ **Southeastern Restaurant, Hospitality & Foodservice Show**

Reed Exhibitions (North American Headquarters)
383 Main Ave.
PO Box 6059
Norwalk, CT 06851
Ph: (203)840-5402   Fax: (203)840-9402
E-mail: inquiry@reedexpo.com
URL: http://www.reedexpo.com

Annual. **Primary Exhibits:** Equipment, supplies, and services for hotels, restaurants, and travel-related businesses.

★1457★ Upper Midwest Hospitality, Restaurant, and Lodging Show - UP Show

Hospitality Minnesota - Minnesota's Restaurant, Hotel, and Resort Associations
305 E. Roselawn Ave.
St. Paul, MN 55117
Ph: (651)778-2400   Fax: (651)778-2424
E-mail: info@hospitalitymn.com
URL: http://www.hospitalitymn.com

Annual. **Primary Exhibits:** Food, beverages, hospitality business services, lodging supplies, and foodservice equipment.

OTHER SOURCES

★1458★ *Food and Beverage Service Occupations*

Evon Publishing
832 N 7th Ave.
Iron River, MI 49935
Ph: (906)265-3190

Audiocassette. 1996. $16.95. 32 minutes. Part of the Careers and Vocational Guidance Series. Provides information about the nature of the work, educational requirements, employment outlook, earnings, and work conditions as well as additional related information.

★1459★ International Association of Culinary Professionals (IACP)

304 W Liberty St., Ste. 201
Louisville, KY 40202
Ph: (502)581-9786   Fax: (502)589-3602
Fr: 800-928-4227
E-mail: iacp@hqtrs.com
URL: http://www.iacp.com

Description: Cooking school owners, food writers, chefs, caterers, culinary specialists, directors, teachers, cookbook authors, food stylists, food photographers, student/apprentices, and individuals in related industries in 20 countries. Objectives are to: promote the interests of cooking schools, teachers, and culinary professionals; encourage the exchange of information and education; promote professional standards and accreditation procedures. Maintains IACP Foundation to award culinary scholarships and grants.

★1460★ International Council on Hotel, Restaurant, and Institutional Education (CHRIE)

2613 N Parham Rd., 2nd Fl.
Richmond, VA 23294
Ph: (804)346-4800   Fax: (804)346-5009
E-mail: info@chrie.org
URL: http://www.chrie.org

Description: Schools and colleges offering specialized education and training in hospitals, recreation, tourism and hotel, restaurant, and institutional administration; individuals, executives, and students. Provides networking opportunities and professional development.

★1461★ International Inflight Food Service Association (IFSA)

5775 Peachtree-Dunwoody Rd., Bldg. G, No. 500
Atlanta, GA 30342
Ph: (404)252-3663   Fax: (404)252-0774
E-mail: ifsa@kellencompany.com
URL: http://www.ifsanet.com

Members: Global professional association created to serve the needs and interests of the airline and railway personnel, inflight and railway caterers and suppliers responsible for providing passenger foodservice on regularly scheduled travel routes.

★1462★ National Restaurant Association (NRA)

1200 17th St., NW
Washington, DC 20036
Ph: (202)331-5900   Fax: (202)331-2429
Fr: 800-424-5156
E-mail: info@dineout.org
URL: http://www.restaurant.org

Description: Restaurants, cafeterias, clubs, contract foodservice management, drive-ins, caterers, institutional food services, and other members of the foodservice industry; also represents establishments belonging to nonaffiliated state and local restaurant associations in governmental affairs. Supports foodservice education and research in several educational institutions. Affiliated with the Educational Foundation of the National Restaurant Association to provide training and education for operators, food and equipment manufacturers, distributors, and educators. Has 300,000 member locations.

Chefs and Cooks

SOURCES OF HELP-WANTED ADS

★1463★ Chef

Talcott Communications Corp.
2B W Kinzie, 12th Fl.
Chicago, IL 60610
Ph: (312)849-2220   Fax: (312)849-2174
Fr: 800-229-1967
E-mail: chef@talcott.com

$32.00/year for individuals; $2.95/year. Food information for chefs.

★1464★ Foodservice East

The Newbury Street Group Inc.
165 New Boston St., No. 236
Woburn, MA 01801
Ph: (781)376-9080   Fax: (781)376-0010
Fr: 800-852-5212
E-mail: fdsvceast@.aol.com

$30.00/year for individuals. Compact Tabloid covering trends and analysis of the foodservice industry in the Northeast. A business-to-business publication featuring news, analysis and trends for the Northeast food service professional.

★1465★ Hotel & Motel Management

Advanstar Communications Inc.
7500 Old Oak Blvd.
Cleveland, OH 44130-3369
Ph: (440)243-8100   Fax: (440)891-2777
URL: http://https://www.advanstar.com/index_allpubs.html

Magazine (tabloid) covering the global lodging industry.

★1466★ Midwest Foodservice News

Pinnacle Publishing Group
2736 Sawbury Blvd.
Columbus, OH 43235
Ph: (614)336-0710   Fax: (614)336-0713

Bimonthly. Free to qualified subscribers; $24.00/year for others. Food service trade magazine featuring new products and suppliers and other industry news including food

news, restaurant association updates, news of chefs, restaurant concepts, earnings, and openings and closings.

★1467★ The National Culinary Review

American Culinary Federation Inc.
10 San Bartola Dr.
St. Augustine, FL 32086
Ph: (904)824-4468   Fax: (904)825-4758
Fr: 800-624-9458
E-mail: acf@acfchefs.net

Monthly. $50.00/year for individuals; $3.00 for single issue. Trade magazine covering food and cooking.

★1468★ Restaurant Business

VNU Business Publications
770 Broadway
New York, NY 10003
Ph: (646)654-5000   Fax: (646)654-4977
E-mail: 200-4782@mcimail.com
URL: http://http://www.foodservicetoday.com

$105.00/year for individuals; $10.00 for single issue. Trade magazine for restaurants and commercial food service.

★1469★ Restaurant Hospitality

Penton Media Inc.
1300 E 9th St.
Cleveland, OH 44114-1503
Ph: (216)696-7000   Fax: (216)931-9799
E-mail: rheditors@aol.com

Monthly. Free to qualified subscribers; $60.00/year for individuals; $5.95 for single issue. Magazine for managers and other executives of restaurant chains, independent restaurants, and hotels - foodservice operations.

★1470★ Restaurants & Institutions

Reed Business Information
360 Park Ave. S
New York, NY 10014
Ph: (646)746-7764
E-mail: gdrummond@reedbusiness.com
URL: http://www.rimag.com

Magazine focusing on foodservice and lodging management.

★1471★ Western Itasca Review & Deerpath Shopper

Lebhar-Friedman Inc.
425 Park Ave.
New York, NY 10022-3556
Ph: (212)756-5088   Fax: (212)756-5120
Fr: 800-453-2427

Weekly. $34.50/year for individuals. Local newspaper and shopper.

PLACEMENT AND JOB REFERRAL SERVICES

★1472★ Chefs de Cuisine Association of America (CCAA)

301 E 45th St.
New York, NY 10017
Ph: (212)599-2717   Fax: (212)599-2717

Description: Professional executive chefs; chefs who own restaurants; pastry chefs for hotels, clubs, and restaurants. Maintains 350 volume library and placement service for members.

★1473★ Les Amis d'Escoffier

1230 Main St., Rte. 9
Leicester, MA 01524
Ph: (508)892-9090   Fax: (508)892-3620
E-mail: info@castlerestaurant.com
URL: http://www.castlerestaurant.com/default.htm

Members: An educational organization of professionals in the food and wine industries. **Activities:** Maintains museum, speakers' bureau, hall of fame, and placement service. Sponsors charitable programs.

EMPLOYER DIRECTORIES AND NETWORKING LISTS

★1474★ College/University Foodservice Who's Who

Information Central Inc.
Box 3900
Prescott, AZ 86302
Ph: (520)778-1513   Fax: (520)778-1513

Triennial. $345.00. Covers over 2,700 food service programs in colleges and universities. Entries include: Institution name, address, phone, enrollment, total annual food purchases, number of meals served per day; name of management company, principal food service executive(s), services, fast food chains on campus. Arrangement: Geographical. Indexes: Alphabetical.

★1475★ School Foodservice Who's Who

Information Central Inc.
Box 3900
Prescott, AZ 86302
Ph: (520)778-1513   Fax: (520)778-1513

Triennial, latest edition January 1999. $650.00. Covers about 5,800 food service programs in public and Catholic school systems with enrollments in excess of 1,500 students. Separate listings of the biggest buyers (school districts reporting over $1.5 million/year in foodservice purchases), state school foodservice officials, and co-op buying groups and food management companies involved in food service. Entries include: School district name, address, phone, fax; food service budget, key food service executive, number of meals served daily, types of food and services, food management company, fast food brands. Arrangement: Geographical. Indexes: School districts.

HANDBOOKS AND MANUALS

★1476★ Becoming a Chef

John Wiley & Sons Inc.
111 River St.
Hoboken, NJ 07030-5774
Ph: (201)748-6000   Fax: (201)748-6880
Fr: 800-225-5945

A. Dornenburg. 1997. $46.95. Part of Culinary Arts series.

★1477★ Career Opportunities in the Food and Beverage Industry

Facts on File, Inc.
132 W. 31st St., 17th Fl.
New York, NY 10001-2006
Ph: (212)967-8800   Fax: (212)967-8107
Fr: 800-322-8755
URL: http://www.factsonfile.com

Barbara Sims-Bell. Second edition, 2001. $18.95 (paper). Provides the job seeker with

information about locating and landing 80 skilled and unskilled jobs in the industry. Includes detailed job descriptions for many specific positions and lists trade associations, recruiting organizations, and major agencies. Contains index and bibliography.

★1478★ Careers for Gourmets and Others Who Relish Food

McGraw-Hill Trade
2 Penn Plaza
New York, NY 10121
Ph: (212)904-2000   Fr: 800-722-4726
E-mail: ntcpub@tribune.com

Mary Donovan. Second edition, 2002. $15.95; $12.95 (paper). 192 pages. Discusses such job prospects as foods columnist, cookbook writer, test kitchen worker, pastry chef, recipe developer, food festival organizer, restaurant manager, and food stylist.

★1479★ Careers in Travel, Tourism, and Hospitality

McGraw-Hill Contemporary Books
1221 Avenue of the Americas
New York, NY 10020
Ph: (212)904-2000   Fr: 800-323-4900
E-mail: ntcpub@tribune.com

Marjorie Eberts, Linda Brothers, and Ann Gisler. 1997. $17.95; 13.95 (paper). 192 pages.

★1480★ Choosing a Career in the Restaurant Industry

Rosen Publishing Group, Inc.
29 E. 21st St.
New York, NY 10010
Ph: (212)777-3017   Fax: 888-436-4643
Fr: 800-237-9932

Eileen Beal. 1996. $17.95. 64 pages. Explores various jobs in the restaurant industry. Describes job duties, salaries, educational preparation, and job hunting. Contains information about fast food, catering, and small businesses.

★1481★ Culinary Arts Career Starter

LearningExpress, LLC
900 Broadway, Ste. 604
New York, NY 10003
Ph: (212)995-2566   Fax: (212)995-5512
Fr: 800-295-9556

Mary Masi. 1999. $14.95 (paper). 229 pages.

★1482★ How to Get a Job with a Cruise Line

Ticket to Adventure, Inc.
PO Box 41005
St. Petersburg, FL 33743-1005
Ph: (727)822-5029   Fax: (727)821-3409
Fr: 800-929-7447

Mary Fallon Miller. Fifth edition, 2001. $16.95 (paper). 336 pages. Explores jobs with cruise ships, describing duties, responsibilities, benefits, and training. Lists cruise

ship lines and schools offering cruise line training. Offers job hunting advice.

★1483★ Opportunities in Culinary Careers

McGraw-Hill Contemporary Books
1221 Avenue of the Americas
New York, NY 10020
Ph: (212)904-2000   Fr: 800-323-4900
E-mail: ntcpub@tribune.com

Mary Deirdre Donovan. 1998. $14.95; $11.95 (paper). 160 pages. Describes the educational preparation and training of chefs and cooks and explores a variety of food service jobs in restaurants, institutions, and research and development. Lists major culinary professional associations and schools. Offers guidance on landing a first job in cooking and related fields.

★1484★ Opportunities in Restaurant Careers

Vgm Career Horizons
1221 Avenue of the Americas
New York, NY 10020
Ph: (212)904-2000   Fr: 800-323-4900
E-mail: ntcpub@tribune.com

Carol Caprione Chmelynski. 1998. $14.95; $11.95 (paper). 160 pages. Covers opportunities in the food service industry and details salaries, benefits, training opportunities, and professional associations. Special emphasis is put on becoming a successful restaurant manager by working up through the ranks. Illustrated.

ONLINE JOB SOURCES AND SERVICES

★1485★ Pioneer College Caterers Online

E-mail: careers@pcconline.com
URL: http://www.foodindustryjobs.com

Description: Job databank and resume submission service for food industry workers in Christian college cafeterias.

★1486★ StarChefs.com

URL: http://www.starchefs.com

Description: StarChefs.com Jobfinder contains job board, resume writing service and career advice for job seekers in the culinary arts. Seekers can sign up for free e-mail account and receive job notifications through this service.

TRADESHOWS

★1487★ American School Food Service Association Annual National Conference

American School Food Service
Association
700 S. Washington St., Ste. 300
Alexandria, VA 22314-4287
Ph: (703)739-3900   Fax: (703)739-3915
Fr: 800-877-8822

Annual. **Primary Exhibits:** Food service supplies and equipment, including educational services and computers.

★1488★ Institute of Food Technologists Annual Meeting and Food Expo

Institute of Food Technologists
525 W. Van Buren St., Ste. 1000
Chicago, IL 60607-3814
Ph: (312)782-8424   Fax: (312)782-8348
E-mail: info@ift.org
URL: http://www.ift.org

Annual. **Primary Exhibits:** Food ingredients, equipment, laboratory equipment and supplies, and other services rendered to the food processing industry. **Dates and Locations:** 2005 Jul 16-20; New Orleans, LA • 2006 Jul 22-26; Orlando, FL.

★1489★ International Baking Industry Exposition

IBIE Exhibition Management
401 N. Michigan Ave.
Chicago, IL 60611
Ph: (312)644-6610   Fax: (312)644-0575
E-mail: info@bakingexpo.org

Primary Exhibits: Baking equipment, supplies, and services.

★1490★ National Restaurant Association Restaurant and Hotel-Motel Show

National Restaurant Association
150 N. Michigan Ave., Ste. 2000
Chicago, IL 60601
Ph: (312)853-2525   Fax: (312)853-2548

Annual. **Primary Exhibits:** Food service equipment, supplies, and services and food and beverage products for the hospitality industry.

OTHER SOURCES

★1491★ American Culinary Federation (ACF)

10 San Bartola Dr.
St. Augustine, FL 32086
Ph: (904)824-4468   Fax: (904)825-4758
Fr: 800-624-9458

E-mail: acf@acfchefs.net
URL: http://www.acfchefs.org

Description: Oldest and largest organization of chefs and cooks in the U.S. Primary objectives are to promote the culinary profession and provide on-going educational training and networking for members. Provides opportunities for competition, professional recognition, and access to educational forums with other culinarians at local, regional, national, and international events. Maintains the Educational Institute of the ACF which operates the National Apprenticeship Program for Cooks and pastry cooks. Has programs that address certification of the individual chef's skills, accreditation of culinary programs, apprenticeship of cooks and pastry cooks, professional development, and the fight against childhood hunger.

★1492★ Association for International Practical Training (AIPT)

10400 Little Patuxent Pky., Ste. 250
Columbia, MD 21044-3519
Ph: (410)997-2200   Fax: (410)992-3924
E-mail: aipt@aipt.org
URL: http://www.aipt.org

Description: Providers worldwide on-the-job training programs for students and professionals seeking international career development and life-changing experiences. Arranges workplace exchanges in hundreds of professional fields, bringing employers and trainees together from around the world. Client list ranges from small farming communities to Fortune 500 companies.

★1493★ *Chef*

Cambridge Educational
2572 Brunswick Ave.
Lawrenceville, NJ 08648-4128
Fax: 800-FAX-ON-US   Fr: 800-468-4227
URL: http://www.cambridgeeducational.com

$39.95. 15 minutes. Part of the Vocational Visions Career series.

★1494★ *Food and Beverage Service Occupations*

Evon Publishing
832 N 7th Ave.
Iron River, MI 49935
Ph: (906)265-3190

Audiocassette. 1996. $16.95. 32 minutes. Part of the Careers and Vocational Guidance Series. Provides information about the nature of the work, educational requirements, employment outlook, earnings, and work conditions as well as additional related information.

★1495★ International Association of Culinary Professionals (IACP)

304 W Liberty St., Ste. 201
Louisville, KY 40202
Ph: (502)581-9786   Fax: (502)589-3602
Fr: 800-928-4227
E-mail: iacp@hqtrs.com

URL: http://www.iacp.com

Description: Cooking school owners, food writers, chefs, caterers, culinary specialists, directors, teachers, cookbook authors, food stylists, food photographers, student/apprentices, and individuals in related industries in 20 countries. Objectives are to: promote the interests of cooking schools, teachers, and culinary professionals; encourage the exchange of information and education; promote professional standards and accreditation procedures. Maintains IACP Foundation to award culinary scholarships and grants.

★1496★ International Council on Hotel, Restaurant, and Institutional Education (CHRIE)

2613 N Parham Rd., 2nd Fl.
Richmond, VA 23294
Ph: (804)346-4800   Fax: (804)346-5009
E-mail: info@chrie.org
URL: http://www.chrie.org

Description: Schools and colleges offering specialized education and training in hospitals, recreation, tourism and hotel, restaurant, and institutional administration; individuals, executives, and students. Provides networking opportunities and professional development.

★1497★ National Restaurant Association (NRA)

1200 17th St., NW
Washington, DC 20036
Ph: (202)331-5900   Fax: (202)331-2429
Fr: 800-424-5156
E-mail: info@dineout.org
URL: http://www.restaurant.org

Description: Restaurants, cafeterias, clubs, contract foodservice management, drive-ins, caterers, institutional food services, and other members of the foodservice industry; also represents establishments belonging to non-affiliated state and local restaurant associations in governmental affairs. Supports foodservice education and research in several educational institutions. Affiliated with the Educational Foundation of the National Restaurant Association to provide training and education for operators, food and equipment manufacturers, distributors, and educators. Has 300,000 member locations.

★1498★ United States Personal Chef Association

481 Rio Rancho Boulevard NE
Rio Rancho, NM 87124
Fr: 800-995-2138
URL: http://www.uspca.com

Description: The largest organization dedicated to the personal service industry.

Chemical Engineers

★1499★ *Adhesives Age*
Primedia Business
9800 Metcalf Ave.
Overland Park, KS 66212
Ph: (913)341-1300   Fax: (913)967-1898
Monthly. $60.00/year for individuals. Magazine containing news and technology for those engaged in the manufacturing, application, research, and marketing of adhesives, sealants, and related products.

★1500★ *Chemical Engineering*
Chemical Week Associates
110 Williams St., 11th Fl.
New York, NY 10038
Ph: (212)621-4900   Fax: (212)621-4949
URL: http://www.che.com
Monthly. $29.50/year for individuals; $46.00/year for other countries. Chemical process industries magazine.

★1501★ *Chemical Engineering Progress*
American Institute of Chemical Engineers
3 Park Ave.
New York, NY 10016-5991
Ph: (212)591-7845   Fax: (212)591-8883
Fr: 800-242-4363
E-mail: davec@aiche.org
URL: http://www.cepmagazine.org
Monthly. Free for members; $95.00/year for nonmembers, North America; $155.00/year for nonmembers, international. Chemical process industries magazine.

★1502★ *Chemical Equipment*
Reed Business Information
301 Gibraltar Dr.
Morris Plains, NJ 07950
Ph: (973)292-5100   Fax: (973)539-3476
Tabloid on the chemical process industry.

★1503★ *Chemical Market Reporter*
Schnell Publishing Company Inc.
2 Rector St., 26th Fl.
New York, NY 10006-1819
Ph: (212)791-4200   Fax: (212)791-4313
Weekly. $109.00/year for individuals. International tabloid newspaper for the chemical process industries. Includes analytical reports on developments in the chemical marketplace, plant expansions, new technology, corporate mergers, finance, current chemical prices, and regulatory matters.

★1504★ *The Chemist*
American Institute of Chemists Inc.
315 Chestnut St.
Philadelphia, PA 19106
Ph: (215)873-8224   Fax: (215)925-1954
E-mail: publications@theaic.org
Description: Six issues/year. Covers news items relating to the chemical profession and membership in the Institute. Reports on legislation, licensure, earnings, awards, and professional education. Recurring features include news of employment opportunities and news of members. Published alternate months as a magazine.

★1505★ *Code News*
West Group
6111 Oak Tree Blvd.
Independence, OH 44131
Ph: (216)520-5600   Fax: (216)520-5655
Fr: 800-362-4500
Description: Bimonthly. Covers Ohio state law and legislation and other issues as they affect the building industries. Recurring features include a calendar of events, reports of meetings, news of educational opportunities, job listings, book reviews, notices of publications available, and a column titled Contractor's Corner.

★1506★ *The Electrochemical Society Interface*
Electrochemical Society Inc.
65 S Main St.
Pennington, NJ 08534-2839
Ph: (609)737-1902   Fax: (609)737-2743

E-mail: interface@electrochem.org
URL: http://www.electrochem.org
Quarterly. $40.00/year; $10.00 for single issue. Publication featuring news and articles of interest to members of the Electrochemical Society.

★1507★ *Engineering Times*
National Society of Professional Engineers
1420 King St.
Alexandria, VA 22314
Ph: (703)684-2875   Fax: (703)836-4875
E-mail: et@nspe.org
URL: http://http//:www.nspc.org/1et.asp
$30.00/year for individuals; $48.00/year for out of country. Magazine (tabloid) covering professional, legislative, and techology issues for an engineering audience.

★1508★ *ENR: Engineering News-Record*
McGraw-Hill Companies
1221 Avenue of the Americas
New York, NY 10020
Ph: (212)512-2000
URL: http://www.enr.com
Weekly. $74.00/year; $5.00 for single issue. Magazine focusing on engineering and construction.

★1509★ *Graduating Engineer & Computer Careers*
Career Recruitment Media
211 W. Wacker Dr., No. 900
Chicago, IL 60606
Ph: (312)525-3100
URL: http://www.graduatingengineer.com
$16.00/year for individuals. Magazine focusing on employment, education, and career development for entry-level engineers and computer scientists.

★1510★ High Technology Careers Magazine

HTC
4701 Patrick Henry Dr., No. 1901
Santa Clara, CA 95054-1847
Ph: (408)970-8800   Fax: (408)567-0242
URL: http://www.hightechcareers.com

Bimonthly. $29.00/year; $35.00/year for Canada; $85.00/year for out of country. Magazine (tabloid) containing employment opportunity information for the engineering and technical community.

★1511★ Modern Plastics

Chemical Week Associates
110 Williams St., 11th Fl.
New York, NY 10038
Ph: (212)621-4900   Fax: (212)621-4949
URL: http://www.modplas.com

Monthly. $59.00/year. Magazine for the plastics industry.

★1512★ Nanoparticle News

Business Communications Company Inc.
25 Van Zant St.
Norwalk, CT 06855-1781
Ph: (203)853-4266   Fax: (203)853-0348

Bimonthly. Publication covering issues in the chemical industry.

★1513★ NSBE Magazine

NSBE Publications
1454 Duke St.
Alexandria, VA 22314
Ph: (703)549-2207   Fax: (703)683-5312

$10.00/year for individuals; $2.00 for single issue. Journal providing information on engineering careers, self-development, and cultural issues for recent graduates with technical majors.

★1514★ Plastics Engineering

Society of Plastics Engineers
14 Fairfield Dr.
PO Box 0403
Brookfield, CT 06804-0403
Ph: (203)775-0471   Fax: (203)775-8490
URL: http://www.4spe.org

Monthly. $110.00/year for individuals; $190.00 for two years. Plastics trade magazine.

★1515★ Plastics News

Crain Communications Inc.
1725 Merriman Rd.
Akron, OH 44313-5283
Ph: (330)836-9180   Fax: (330)836-2365
E-mail: info@plasticsnews.com
URL: http://www.plasticsnews.com

Weekly. $69.00/year for individuals. Magazine (tabloid) for the plastics industry providing business news.

★1516★ Powder and Bulk Engineering

CSC Publishing Inc.
1155 Northland Dr.
St. Paul, MN 55120-1288
Ph: (651)282-5600   Fax: (651)282-5650

Monthly. Journal serving chemical, food, plastics, pulp and paper, and electronic industries.

★1517★ Power

McGraw-Hill Companies
1221 Avenue of the Americas
New York, NY 10020
Ph: (212)512-2000

Monthly. $19.00/year; $5.00 for single issue. Magazine for engineers in electric utilities, process and manufacturing plants, commercial and service establishments, and consulting, design, and construction engineering firms working in the power technology field.

★1518★ Rubber World

Rubber World
1867 W Market St.
PO Box 5451
Akron, OH 44313
Ph: (216)864-2122   Fax: (216)864-5298
URL: http://rubberworld.com

Monthly. $29.00/year. Rubber manufacturing magazine.

★1519★ SWE

Society of Women Engineers
230 E Ohio St., No. 400
2135 Lamberton Rd.
Chicago, IL 60611-3265
Ph: (312)596-5223   Fax: (312)596-5252
E-mail: hq@swe.org
URL: http://www.swe.org

Bimonthly. $30.00/year for nonmembers. Magazine for engineering students and for women and men working in the engineering and technology fields. Covers career guidance, continuing development and topical issues.

★1520★ Technology Review

Technology Review
201 Vassar St.
Cambridge, MA 02139
Ph: (617)253-8250   Fax: (617)258-5850
E-mail: trcomments@mit.edu

$30.00/year for individuals; $42.00/year for other countries; $4.95/year for single issue. Magazine reviewing new developments in technology with an emphasis on economic, political, and social implications. Not a new product publication.

★1521★ WEPANEWS

Women in Engineering Programs & Advocates Network
Castle Point on the Hudson
Hoboken, NJ 07030
Ph: (201)216-5245   Fax: (201)216-5175
URL: http://www.wepan.org/newsletter.html

Description: Two issues/year. Seeks to provide greater access for women to careers in engineering. Includes news of graduate, undergraduate, freshmen, pre-college, and re-entry engineering programs for women. Recurring features include job listings, faculty, grant, and conference news, international engineering program news, action group news, notices of publications available, and a column titled Kudos.

PLACEMENT AND JOB REFERRAL SERVICES

★1522★ American Indian Science and Engineering Society (AISES)

PO Box 9828
Albuquerque, NM 87119-9828
Ph: (505)765-1052   Fax: (505)765-5608
E-mail: info@aises.org
URL: http://www.aises.org

Description: American Indian and non-Indian students and professionals in science, technology, and engineering fields; corporations representing energy, mining, aerospace, electronic, and computer fields. Seeks to motivate and encourage students to pursue undergraduate and graduate studies in science, engineering, and technology. Sponsors science fairs in grade schools, teacher training workshops, summer math/science sessions for 8th-12th graders, professional chapters, and student chapters in colleges. Offers scholarships. Adult members serve as role models, advisers, and mentors for students. Operates placement service.

★1523★ American Institute of Chemical Engineers (AICHE)

3 Park Avenue
New York, NY 10016-5991
Ph: (212)591-7338   Fax: (212)591-8897
Fr: 800-242-4363
E-mail: xpress@aiche.org
URL: http://www.aiche.org

Description: Professional society of chemical engineers. Establishes standards for chemical engineering curricula; offers employment services. Presents technical conferences, petrochemical and refining exposition, and continuing education programs. Sponsors competitions. Offers speakers' bureau; complies statistics.

★1524★ American Oil Chemists' Society (AOCS)

2211 W Bradley Ave.
PO Box 3489
Champaign, IL 61821-1827
Ph: (217)359-2344   Fax: (217)351-8091
E-mail: general@aocs.org
URL: http://www.aocs.org

Members: Chemists, biochemists, chemical engineers, research directors, plant personnel, and others in laboratories and chemical process industries concerned with animal, marine, and vegetable oils and fats, and their extraction, refining, safety, packaging, quality control, and use in consumer and industrial products such as foods, drugs, paints, waxes, lubricants, soaps, and cosmetics. **Activities:** Sponsors short courses; certifies referee chemists; distributes cooperative check samples; sells official reagents. Maintains 100 committees. Operates job placement service for members only.

★1525★ **Engineering Society of Detroit (ESD)**
26100 American Dr., Ste. 500
Southfield, MI 48034-6184
Ph: (248)355-2910   Fax: (248)355-1492
E-mail: esd@esd.org
URL: http://esd.org

Description: Engineers from all disciplines; scientists and technologists. Conducts technical programs and engineering refresher courses; sponsors conferences and expositions. Maintains speakers' bureau; offers placement services. Although based in Detroit, MI, society membership is international.

★1526★ **Korean Scientists and Engineers Association in America (KSEA)**
1952 Gallows Rd., Ste. 300
Vienna, VA 22182
Ph: (703)748-1221   Fax: (703)748-1331
E-mail: sejong@ksea.org
URL: http://www.ksea.org

Description: Scientists and engineers holding single or advanced degrees. Goals are to: promote friendship and mutuality among Korean and American scientists and engineers; contribute to Korea's scientific, technological, industrial, and economic developments; strengthen the scientific, technological, and cultural bonds between Korea and the U.S. Sponsors symposium. Maintains speakers' bureau, placement service, and biographical archives. Compiles statistics. Maintains 100 volume library of scientific handbooks and yearbooks in Korean.

★1527★ **National Organization for the Professional Advancement of Black Chemists and Chemical Engineers (NOBCChE)**
PO Box 77040
Washington, DC 20013
Ph: (202)667-1699   Fax: (202)667-1705
Fr: 800-776-1419
E-mail: president@nobcche.org
URL: http://www.nobcche.org

Description: Black professionals in science and chemistry. Seeks to aid black scientists and chemists in reaching their full professional potential; encourages black students to pursue scientific studies and employment; promotes participation of blacks in scientific research. Provides volunteers to teach science courses in selected elementary schools; sponsors scientific field trips for students; maintains speakers' bureau for schools. Conducts technical seminars in Africa. Sponsors competitions; presents

awards for significant achievements to individuals in the field. Maintains library of materials pertaining to chemistry, science, and black history; keeps archive of organization's books and records. Maintains placement service; compiles statistics.

★1528★ **Society of Hispanic Professional Engineers (SHPE)**
5400 E Olympic Blvd., Ste. 210
Los Angeles, CA 90022
Ph: (323)725-3970   Fax: (323)725-0316
E-mail: shpenational@shpe.org
URL: http://www.shpe.org

Description: Engineers, student engineers, and scientists seeking to increase the number of Hispanic engineers by providing motivation and support to students. Sponsors competitions and educational programs. Maintains placement service and speakers' bureau; compiles statistics.

EMPLOYER DIRECTORIES AND NETWORKING LISTS

★1529★ *American Institute of Chemists-Professional Directory*
American Institute of Chemists Inc.
315 Chestnut St.
Philadelphia, PA 19106
Ph: (215)873-8224   Fax: (215)925-1954
URL: http://www.theaic.org

Annual, spring. $75.00. Covers more than 3,500 member chemists. Entries include: Individual name and title, address, phone, name of employer, position title, principal job responsibility, principal field of chemistry, highest academic degree, certification, year elected to membership, membership category, local affiliation. Commercial use requires special permission. Arrangement: Alphabetical. Indexes: Geographical.

★1530★ *American Men and Women of Science*
Thomson Gale
27500 Drake Rd.
Farmington Hills, MI 48331-3535
Ph: (248)699-4253   Fax: (248)699-8065
Fr: 800-877-GALE
E-mail: amws@galegroup.com

Biennial, latest edition December 2002. $975.00. Covers over 129,700 U.S. and Canadian scientists active in the physical, biological, mathematical, computer science, and engineering fields; includes references to previous edition for deceased scientists and nonrespondents. Entries include: Name, address, education, personal and career data, memberships, honors and awards, research interest. Arrangement: Alphabetical. Indexes: Discipline (in separate volume).

★1531★ *Careers in Focus: Engineering*
Ferguson Publishing Co.
200 W Jackson Blvd.
Chicago, IL 60606
Ph: (312)692-0109

2nd edition, 2002. $22.95. Publication includes: List of resources to consult for more information. Principal content of publication is job descriptions, advancement opportunities, educational requirements, employment outlook, salary information, and working conditions for careers in the field of engineering. Indexes: Alphabetical.

★1532★ *Chemical Week-Buyers Guide Issue*
Chemical Week Associates
110 Williams St., 11th Fl.
New York, NY 10038
Ph: (212)621-4900   Fax: (212)621-4949
Fr: 800-774-5733
URL: http://www.chemweek.com/cwbg.html

Annual, October. $115.00. Publication includes: About 4,200 manufacturers and suppliers of chemical raw materials to the chemical process industries; 400 manufacturers of packaging materials; and suppliers of products and services to the chemical process industries, including hazardous waste/environmental services, computer services, plant design, contruction, consulting, shipping, and transportation. Entries include: Over 17,000 product/service listings, Company name, address, phone; local addresses and phone numbers for up to 25 sales locations. Arrangement: Separate alphabetical sections for chemical, packaging, and hazardous waste/environmental services. Indexes: Product (all sections); trade name (chemical and packaging sections only).

★1533★ *Consulting Services*
Association of Consulting Chemists and Chemical Engineers Inc.
PO Box 297
Sparta, NJ 07871-0297
Ph: (973)729-6671   Fax: (973)729-7088
URL: http://www.wwwprovider.com/chem/

Biennial, even years. $30.00. Covers about 160 member consultants in chemistry, chemical engineering, metallurgy, etc. Entries include: Individual name, address, certificate number, qualifications, affiliation, experience, facilities, staff. Arrangement: Classified by area of expertise. Indexes: Personal name, geographical.

★1534★ *Directory of Chemical Producers-United States*
SRI Consulting
333 Ravenswood Ave.
Menlo Park, CA 94025-3477
Ph: (650)859-3900   Fax: (650)859-2182
E-mail: dcp@sric.sri.com
URL: http://www.sri-chem.com

Annual. $2,210.00 for print; $2,760.00 for CD-ROM. Covers over 1,200 United States basic chemical producers manufacturing 7,900 chemicals in commercial quantities at more than 3,500 plant locations. Entries include: For companies-Company name, division or subsidiary names, corporate address, phone, fax, telex, location of each subsidiary, division, and manufacturing plant, and the products made at each plant location. For products-Producer name and plant locations, alternate product names (if any). Subscription price includes bound volume, plus access to the directory staff for inquiries. Arrangement: Companies are alphabetical; products are alphabetical and by group (dyes, pesticides, etc.); manufacturing plants are geographical. Indexes: Geographical, product.

★1535★ **Directory of Contract Staffing Firms**
C.E. Publications Inc.
PO Box 3006
Bothell, WA 98041-3006
Ph: (425)806-5200   Fax: (425)806-5585
URL: http://www.cjhunter.com/dcsf/overview.html

$15.00. Covers nearly 1,300 contract firms actively engaged in the employment of engineering, IT/IS, and technical personnel for 'temporary' contract assignments throughout the world. Entries include: Company name, address, phone, name of contact, email, web address. Arrangement: Alphabetical. Indexes: Geographical.

★1536★ **Directory of Custom Chemical Manufacturers**
Delphi Marketing Services Inc.
400 E 89th St., Ste. 2J
New York, NY 10128
Fax: (212)369-6390

Annual, late spring. $295.00. Covers over 280 custom chemical manufacturers. Entries include: Company name, address, phone, name and title of contact, unit processes and reactions carried out, areas of expertise, equipment available. Arrangement: Alphabetical. Indexes: Product/service, subject, and geographical.

★1537★ **Directory of World Chemical Producers**
Chemical Information Services Inc.
PO Box 743512
Dallas, TX 75374
Ph: (214)349-6200   Fax: (214)349-6286
URL: http://www.chemicalinfo.com

Annual. $1,050.00 for book; $2,470.00 for CD-ROM or Internet subscription. Covers over 20,000 producers of all classes of chemicals worldwide; including bulk pharmaceuticals, fire chemicals, agrochemicals, dyes, pigments, cosmetic, food ingredients, intermediates, etc. Entries include: Company name, address, phone, fax, telex, email address, websites, contact information. Arrangement: Product, CAS#, geographical.

★1538★ **Indiana Society of Professional Engineers-Directory**
Indiana Society of Professional Engineers
PO Box 20806
Indianapolis, IN 46220
Ph: (317)255-2267   Fax: (317)255-2530

Annual, fall. $55.00. Covers member registered engineers, land surveyors, engineering students, and engineers in training. Entries include: Member name, address, phone, type of membership, business information, specialty. Arrangement: Alpha by chapter area.

★1539★ **International Directory of Engineering Societies and Related Organizations**
American Association of Engineering Societies
1828 L St. NW, Ste. 906
Washington, DC 20036
Ph: (202)296-2237   Fax: (202)296-1151
Fr: 888-400-AAES

Irregular, latest edition December 1998. $240.00. Covers about 1,370 national, regional, Canadian, and international organizations concerned with engineering and related fields. Entries include: Name, address, phone, fax, e-mail, key personnel, objectives, publications, activities, mailing lists, federation memberships, meeting and convention dates, and budget data. Arrangement: Alphabetical. Indexes: Acronym, geographical, area of specialization.

★1540★ **LabGuide**
American Chemical Society
1155 16th St. NW
Washington, DC 20036
Ph: (202)872-4600   Fax: (202)776-8258
Fr: 800-227-5558
E-mail: labguide@acs.org
URL: http://pubs.acs.org/

Annual, September. $50.00. Publication includes: List of about 2,200 manufacturers of scientific instruments, equipment, chemicals, and other supplies for scientific research and chemical laboratories; laboratory supply houses; analytical and research services. Entries include: Company name, address, phone, fax, e-mail, URL, products, and services. Arrangement: Alphabetical. Indexes: Product, chemical, service, instrument, company name.

★1541★ **Peterson's Job Opportunities in Engineering and Technology**
Thomson Peterson's
PO Box 67005
Lawrenceville, NJ 08648-6105
Fr: 800-338-3282

Compiled by the Peterson's staff. Fourth edition, 1996. $21.95 (paper). 384 pages. Profiles 2,000 high-tech companies looking primarily for technical personnel in such fields as biotechnology, telecommunications, software, computers and peripherals, defense, and aerospace. Contains job-search strategies and career options to help match education and expertise to the job market.

Indexed geographically, by industry, and by hiring needs.

★1542★ **Purchasing/CPI Edition-Chemicals Yellow Pages**
Cahners Publishing Co.
275 Washington St.
Newton, MA 02458
Ph: (617)641-2100   Fax: (617)558-4700
URL: http://www.purchasing.com

Annual, September. $88.00. Covers manufacturers and distributors of 10,000 chemicals and raw materials; manufacturers and distributors of containers and packaging; transportation services and storage facilities; environmental/hazardous waste services and eqpt. Entries include: Company name, address, branch and district office names and locations, phone. Arrangement: Separate alphabetical sections for suppliers, chemicals, and trade names; distributors are geographical.

★1543★ **U.S. National Committee for the International Union of Pure and Applied Chemistry-Directory**
U.S. National Committee for the International Union of Pure and Applied Chemistry
National Academy of Sciences
2101 Constitution Ave. NW
Washington, DC 20418
Ph: (202)334-2243   Fax: (202)334-2231

Annual, July. Covers 29 member chemists and chemical engineers in the United States.

HANDBOOKS AND MANUALS

★1544★ **The Best Resumes for Scientists and Engineers**
John Wiley & Sons Inc.
1 Wiley Dr.
Somerset, NJ 08873
Ph: (732)469-4400   Fr: 800-225-5945

Adele Lewis and David J. Moore. Second edition, 1993. $37.50; $19.95 (paper). 224 pages. Presents an extensive collection of scientific and engineering resumes, highlighting the important differences between these and resumes written for other occupations.

★1545★ **Career Management for Scientists and Engineers**
American Chemical Society
1155 16th St., NW
Washington, DC 20036
Ph: (202)872-4600   Fr: 800-227-5558

John K. Borchardt. May 2000. $20.00. Illustrated. 272 pages. College level studies.

★1546★ **Careers for Chemists: A World Outside the Lab**

American Chemical Society
1155 16th St., NW
Washington, DC 20036
Ph: (202)872-4600   Fr: 800-227-5558

Fred Owens, Roger Uhler and Corrine A. Marasco. 1997. 211 pages.

★1547★ **Engineering Your Job Search: A Job-Finding Resource for Engineering Professionals**

Professional Publications, Inc.
1250 5th Ave.
Belmont, CA 94002
Ph: (650)593-9119   Fax: (650)592-4519
Fr: 800-426-1178

Compiled by Professional Publications, editors. 1995. $24.95 (paper). 154 pages. Out of print.

★1548★ **Great Jobs for Chemistry Majors**

McGraw-Hill Trade
2 Penn Plaza
New York, NY 10121
Ph: (212)904-2000   Fr: 800-722-4726
E-mail: ntcpub@tribune.com

Mark Rowh. 1999. $11.95 (paper). 340 pages.

★1549★ **Great Jobs for Engineering Majors**

McGraw-Hill Professional
McGraw-Hill Higher Education
2 Penn Plaza
New York, NY 10121
Ph: (212)904-2000   Fr: 800-722-4726
E-mail: ntcpub@tribune.com

Geraldine O. Garner. Second edition, 2002. $14.95. 256 pages. Covers all the career options open to students majoring in engineering.

★1550★ **How to Succeed as an Engineer: A Practical Guide to Enhance Your Career**

Institute of Electrical & Electronics
  Engineers Inc.
PO Box 87204
Vancouver, WA 98687
Ph: (360)253-9532   Fax: (360)253-4084

Todd Yuzuriha. 1999. $29.95 (paper). 367 pages.

★1551★ **The I Hate Selling Book: Business-Building Advice for Consultants, Attorneys, Accountants, Engineers, Architects, and Other Professionals**

Allan Boress & Associates
1500 University Dr., Suite 239
Coral Springs, FL 33071
Ph: (954)345-4666   Fax: (954)344-2453

Allan S. Boress. 2001. $29.95.

★1552★ **Is There a Chemical Engineer Inside You?: A Student's Guide to Exploring Chemical Engineering**

Bonamy Publishing
PO Box 70362
Eugene, OR 97401
Ph: (541)988-1005   Fax: (541)988-1008
Fr: 877-644-6337

Celeste Baine. $5.95 (paper). 32 pages. Explores Chemical Engineering as a career.

★1553★ **Majoring in Engineering: How to Get from Your Freshman Year to Your First Job**

Farrar, Straus & Giroux, Inc.
19 Union Sq., W
New York, NY 10003
Ph: (212)741-6900   Fax: (212)633-9385
Fr: 888-330-8477

John Garcia and Carol Carter, editors. 2000. $20.00; $10.00 (paper). 134 pages.

★1554★ **The New Engineer's Guide to Career Growth & Professional Awareness**

Institute of Electrical & Electronics
  Engineers Inc.
445 Hoes Ln.
PO Box 1331
Piscataway, NJ 08855-1331
Ph: (732)562-3967   Fax: (732)981-9334
Fr: 800-678-4333

Irving J. Gabelman, editor. 1996. $39.95 (paper). 275 pages.

★1555★ **Opportunities in Chemistry Careers**

McGraw-Hill/Contemporary Books
1221 Avenue of the Americas
New York, NY 10020
Ph: (212)904-2000   Fr: 800-323-4900

John H. Woodburn. Second edition, 2002. $12.95 (paper). 160 pages. Part of the VGM Opportunities Series.

★1556★ **Opportunities in Engineering Careers**

McGraw-Hill Contemporary Books
1221 Avenue of the Americas
New York, NY 10020
Ph: (212)904-2000   Fr: 800-323-4900
E-mail: ntcpub@tribune.com

Nicholas Basta. Revised, 1995. $14.95; $11.95 (paper). 200 pages. Outlines typical job titles, salaries, career paths, and employment prospects.

★1557★ **Opportunities in High Tech Careers**

McGraw-Hill Trade
2 Penn Plaza
New York, NY 10121
Ph: (212)904-2000   Fr: 800-722-4726

Gary Colter and Deborah Yanuck. 1995. $14.95; $11.95 (paper). 160 pages. Explores high technology careers. Describes job op-portunities, how to make a career decision, how to prepare for high technology jobs, job hunting techniques, and future trends.

★1558★ **Opportunities in Research and Development Careers**

McGraw-Hill/Contemporary Books
1221 Avenue of the Americas
New York, NY 10020
Ph: (212)904-2000   Fr: 800-323-4900
E-mail: ntcpub@tribune.com

Jan Goldberg. 1997. $14.95; $11.95 (paper). 204 pages.

★1559★ **Real People Working in Engineering**

McGraw-Hill Contemporary Books
1221 Avenue of the Americas
New York, NY 10020
Ph: (212)904-2000   Fr: 800-323-4900
E-mail: ntcpub@tribune.com

Blythe Camenson, Jan Goldberg. 1997. $14.95; $12.95 (paper). Interviews and pro-files of working professionals capture a range of opportunities in this field.

★1560★ **Resumes for Engineering Careers**

McGraw-Hill Trade
2 Penn Plaza
New York, NY 10121
Ph: (212)904-2000   Fr: 800-722-4726
E-mail: ntcpub@tribune.com

2000. $10.95 (paper). 456 pages. Contains sample resumes and cover letters applicable to any engineering field.

★1561★ **Resumes for Scientific and Technical Careers**

McGraw-Hill Contemporary Books
1221 Avenue of the Americas
New York, NY 10020
Ph: (212)904-2000   Fr: 800-323-4900
E-mail: ntcpub@tribune.com

1999. $9.95 (paper). 450 pages. Provides resume advice for individuals interested in working in scientific and technical careers. Includes sample resumes and cover letters.

EMPLOYMENT AGENCIES AND SEARCH FIRMS

★1562★ **ARI Inernational**

1501 Ocean Ave.
Seal Beach, CA 90740
Ph: (562)795-5111   Fax: (562)596-9794

International executive search firm.

★1563★ **Asset Group Inc.**
PO Box 211
Verona, NJ 07044
Ph: (973)571-1367   Fax: (973)571-1387
International executive search firm.

★1564★ **The Baer Group**
3161 Coleridge Rd., Ste. 300
Cleveland, OH 44118
Ph: (216)371-9982
Executive search firm.

★1565★ **The Beam Group**
11 Penn Ctr., Ste. 502
Philadelphia, PA 19103
Ph: (215)988-2100   Fax: (215)988-1558
Executive search firm.

★1566★ **The Bonner Group**
59 E. Mill Rd.
PO Box 15
Long Valley, NJ 07853
Ph: (908)876-5200   Fax: (908)876-9275
Executive search firm.

★1567★ **Bosland Gray Associates**
Waterview Plaza
2001 Rte. 46, Ste. 310
Parsippany, NJ 07054
Ph: (973)402-4964
Executive search firm.

★1568★ **Brooke Chase Associates Inc.**
1443 Tallevast Rd.
Sarasota, FL 34243
Ph: (941)358-3111   Fax: (941)358-3311
Executive search firm. Branches in San Rafael, CA; Chicago; and Charlotte, NC.

★1569★ **Cadillac Engineering and Manufacturing Inc.**
7909 Latchington Ct.
Charlotte, NC 28227
Ph: (704)568-6825   Fax: (704)568-6825
Provides engineering consulting services and engineering personnel to the manufacturing, plastics, and chemical industries.

★1570★ **Capstone Inc.**
971 Albany Shaker Rd.
Latham, NY 12110
Ph: (518)783-9300   Fax: (518)783-9328
Executive search firm.

★1571★ **Carlyn International Inc.**
155 Monterrey Rd.
Montgomery, TX 77356
Ph: (936)597-9494   Fax: (936)597-5901
Executive search firm.

★1572★ **Catalyx Group**
303 W. 42nd St., Ste. 607
New York, NY 10036
Ph: (212)956-3525
Executive search firm.

★1573★ **Cochran, Cochran & Yale LLC**
955 E. Henrietta Rd.
Rochester, NY 14623
Ph: (585)424-6060   Fax: (585)424-6069
Executive search firm. Branches in Denver, CO; Williamsville, NY.

★1574★ **Colli Associates**
404 Caboose Ln.
Valrico, FL 33594
Ph: (813)681-2145   Fax: (813)661-5217
E-mail: colli@gte.net
Employment agency. Executive search firm.

★1575★ **Conboy, Sur & Associates Inc.**
545 5th Ave., Ste. 630
New York, NY 10017
Ph: (212)687-4460   Fax: (212)687-4584
Executive search firm.

★1576★ **Corporate Search International**
980 Hammond St., Ste. 650
Atlanta, GA 30328
Ph: (770)399-8489   Fax: (770)740-0939
Executive search firm.

★1577★ **Crowder & Company**
40950 Woodward Ave., Ste. 335
Bloomfield Hills, MI 48304
Ph: (248)645-0909   Fax: (248)645-2366
Executive search firm.

★1578★ **Ellington & Associates**
1755 Park St., Ste. 200
Naperville, IL 60563
Ph: (630)305-0088   Fax: (630)305-0839
Firm specializes in recruiting for the chemical, food, and pulp and paper industries.

★1579★ **ETI Search International**
980 Hammond Dr., Ste. 650
Atlanta, GA 30328
Ph: (770)399-8492   Fax: (770)399-8487
Executive search firm.

★1580★ **ExecuTech**
500 S. Depeyster St.
PO Box 707
Kent, OH 44240-0013
Ph: (330)677-0010   Fax: (330)677-0148
Executive search firm. Second location in Nathalie, VA.

★1581★ **Executive Directions**
9701 Cleveland Ave. NW
PO Box 3006
North Canton, OH 44720
Ph: (330)499-1001   Fax: (330)499-2579
Executive search firm.

★1582★ **Executive Recruiters Agency**
14 Office Park Dr., Ste. 100
PO Box 21810
Little Rock, AR 72221-1810
Ph: (501)224-7000   Fax: (501)224-8534
E-mail: grogers@execrecruit.com
URL: http://www.execrecruit.com
Personnel service firm.

★1583★ **JW Barleycorn & Associates Inc.**
1614 Lancaster Ave.
Reynoldsburg, OH 43068
Ph: (614)861-4400   Fax: (614)861-5558
Executive search firm.

★1584★ **Ken Clark International**
2000 Lenox Dr., Ste. 200
Lawrenceville, NJ 08648
Ph: (609)308-5200   Fax: (609)308-5250
Executive search firm. Branches in Newport Beach, CA; Deerfield, IL; Waltham, MA; and Wayne, PA.

★1585★ **Main Line Personnel Service, Inc.**
Pagoda Blding.
100 Presidential Blvd. Ste. 200
Bala Cynwyd, PA 19004-0448
Ph: (610)667-1820   Fax: (610)668-5000
URL: http://www.mlpers.com
Employment agency.

★1586★ **Polly Brown Associates Inc.**
230 Park Ave., Ste. 1152
New York, NY 10169
Ph: (212)661-7575   Fax: (212)808-4126
Executive search firm.

★1587★ **Rand Personnel**
1200 Truxtun, Ste. 130
Bakersfield, CA 93301
Ph: (805)325-0751   Fax: (805)325-4120
Personnel service firm serving a variety of fields.

★1588★ **Search and Recruit International**
4455 South Blvd.
Virginia Beach, VA 23452
Ph: (757)490-3151   Fax: (757)497-6503
E-mail: britt@searchandrecruit.com
URL: http://www.searchandrecruit.com
Employment agency. Headquartered in Virginia Beach. Other offices in Bremerton, WA;

Charleston, SC; Jacksonville, FL; Memphis, TN; Pensacola, FL; Sacramento, CA; San Bernardino, CA; San Diego, CA.

★1589★ Techtronix Technical Search

PO Box 17713
Milwaukee, WI 53217-0173
Ph: (414)466-3100   Fax: (414)466-3598

Firm specializes in recruiting executives for the engineering, information systems, manufacturing, marketing, finance, and human resources industries.

★1590★ TRC Staffing Services Inc.

2110 15 Mile Rd., Ste. B
Sterling Heights, MI 48310
Ph: (586)939-3210   Fax: (586)978-0572

A full-service executive search company with permanent placements encompassing engineering, industrial sales, financial and computer science positions. Screen, interview, and verify past employment for all candidates prior to referral. Also assist personnel staffs in the attainment of their EEO/AAP goals with the placement of talented individuals in positions which are underutilized with minorities and/or women. In addition, firm has a clerical temporary service division, TRC Temporary Service; and an employment agency, TRC Staffing Services.

★1591★ Tri-Serv Inc.

22 W. Padonia Rd., Ste. C-353
Timonium, MD 21093
Ph: (410)561-1740   Fax: (410)252-7417
E-mail: info@tri-serv.coom
URL: http://www.tri-serv.com

Permanent employment agency.

★1592★ Winters Technical Staffing Services

2025 Sheppard Ave. E, Ste. 4110
Willowdale, ON, Canada M2T 1V7
Ph: (416)495-7422   Fax: (416)495-8479

Technical staffing service for permanent and contract positions in all facets of engineering. Serves government agencies, consulting engineers, and all areas of manufacturing in Canada and northeast U.S.

ONLINE JOB SOURCES AND SERVICES

★1593★ American Chemical Society: JobSpectrum.org

E-mail: jobmaster@jobspectrum.org
URL: http://www.jobspectrum.org

Description: JobSpectrum is a joint venture of the ACS Publications Division and the ACS Membership. Division. Offers online interviewing between employers and potential employees, postings for positions available and situations wanted, and regularly

updated career advice and information for American Chemical Society members only.

★1594★ Spherion Workforce Architects

URL: http://www.spherion.com

Description: Recruitment firm specializing in accounting and finance, sales and marketing, interim executives, technology, engineering, retail and human resources.

TRADESHOWS

★1595★ American Society for Engineering Education Annual Conference and Exposition

American Society for Engineering
  Education
1818 N St., Ste. 600
Washington, DC 20036
Ph: (202)331-3500   Fax: (202)265-8504
URL: http://www.asee.org

Annual. **Primary Exhibits:** Publications, engineering supplies and equipment, computers, software, and research companies all products and services related to engineering education. **Dates and Locations:** 2005 Jun 12-15; Portland, OR • 2006 Jun 18-21; Chicago, IL • 2007 Jun 24-27; Honolulu, HI.

★1596★ AOCS Annual Meeting & Expo

American Oil Chemist Society
PO Box 3489
Champaign, IL 61826-3489
Ph: (217)359-2344   Fax: (217)351-8091
E-mail: meetings@aocs.org
URL: http://www.aocs.org

Annual. **Primary Exhibits:** Fat and oil processing plant equipment, supplies, and services; laboratory instrumentation; chemical ingredients for foods, detergents, and personal care products; and publications.

★1597★ Federation of Analytical Chemistry and Applied Spectroscopy Societies Convention

Federation of Analytical Chemistry and
  Spectroscopy Societies
13 N. Cliffe Dr.
Wilmington, DE 19809
Ph: (302)798-5161   Fax: (302)944-8837

Annual. **Primary Exhibits:** Spectroscopy, chromatography, and analytical chemistry equipment.

★1598★ National Industrial Automation Show & Conference

Reed Exhibitions (North American
  Headquarters)
383 Main Ave.
PO Box 6059
Norwalk, CT 06851
Ph: (203)840-5402   Fax: (203)840-9402
E-mail: inquiry@reedexpo.com
URL: http://www.reedexpo.com

Annual. **Primary Exhibits:** Chemical engineering & processing, electronics, machinery equipment, supplies, and services.

OTHER SOURCES

★1599★ American Academy of Environmental Engineers (AAEE)

130 Holiday Ct., No. 100
Annapolis, MD 21401
Ph: (410)266-3311   Fax: (410)266-7653
E-mail: academy@aaee.net
URL: http://www.aaee.net

Members: Environmentally oriented registered professional engineers certified by examination as Diplomates of the Academy. **Purpose:** Works to improve the standards of environmental engineering; to certify those with special knowledge of environmental engineering; to furnish lists of those certified to the public. **Activities:** Maintains speakers' bureau. Recognizes areas of specialization: Air Pollution Control; General Environmental; Hazardous Waste Management; Industrial Hygiene; Radiation Protection; Solid Waste Management; Water Supply and Wastewater. Requires written and oral examinations for certification. Works with other professional organizations on environmentally oriented activities. Identifies potential employment candidates through Talent Search Service.

★1600★ American Association of Engineering Societies (AAES)

1828 L St. NW, No. 906
Washington, DC 20036
Ph: (202)296-2237   Fax: (202)296-1151
Fr: 888-400-2237
E-mail: tprice@aaes.org
URL: http://www.aaes.org

Description: Coordinates the efforts of the member societies in the provision of reliable and objective information to the general public concerning issues which affect the engineering profession and the field of engineering as a whole; to collect, analyze, document, and disseminate data which will inform the general public of the relationship between engineering and the national welfare; to provide a forum for the engineering societies to exchange and discuss their views on matters of common interest; and to represent the U.S. engineering community aborad through representation in WFEO and UPADI.

★1601★ American Chemical Society (ACS)

1155 16th St. NW
Washington, DC 20036
Ph: (202)872-4600   Fax: (202)776-8258
Fr: 800-227-5558
E-mail: webmaster@acs.org
URL: http://www.acs.org

Members: Scientific and educational society

of chemists and chemical engineers. **Activities:** Conducts studies and surveys; special programs for disadvantaged persons; legislation monitoring, analysis, and reporting; courses for graduate chemists and chemical engineers; radio and television programming. Offers career guidance counseling; administers the Petroleum Research Fund and other grants and fellowship programs. Operates Employment Clearing Houses. Compiles statistics. Maintains speakers' bureau. Maintains 33 divisions.

★1602★ **American Institute of Chemists (AIC)**
315 Chestnut St.
Philadelphia, PA 19106-2702
Ph: (215)873-8224   Fax: (215)925-1954
E-mail: info@theaic.org
URL: http://www.theaic.org

Description: Chemists and chemical engineers. Promotes advancement of chemical professions in the U.S.; protects public welfare by establishing and enforcing high practice standards; represents professional interests of chemists and chemical engineers. Sponsors National Certification Commission in Chemistry and Chemical Engineering and AIC Foundation.

★1603★ **Association for International Practical Training (AIPT)**
10400 Little Patuxent Pky., Ste. 250
Columbia, MD 21044-3519
Ph: (410)997-2200   Fax: (410)992-3924
E-mail: aipt@aipt.org
URL: http://www.aipt.org

Description: Providers worldwide on-the-job training programs for students and professionals seeking international career development and life-changing experiences. Arranges workplace exchanges in hundreds of professional fields, bringing employers and trainees together from around the world. Client list ranges from small farming communities to Fortune 500 companies.

★1604★ *Chemical Engineers*
Evon Publishing
832 N 7th Ave.
Iron River, MI 49935
Ph: (906)265-3190

Audiocassette. 1996. $16.95. 32 minutes. Part of the Careers and Vocational Guidance Series. Provides information about the nature of the work, educational requirements, employment outlook, earnings, and work conditions as well as additional related information.

★1605★ *Chemistry*
Evon Publishing
832 N 7th Ave.
Iron River, MI 49935
Ph: (906)265-3190

Audiocassette. 1996. $16.95. 32 minutes. Part of the Careers and Vocational Guidance Series. Provides information about the nature of the work, educational requirements, employment outlook, earnings, and work conditions as well as additional related information.

★1606★ *Engineering Occupations*
Delphi Productions
3160 4th St.
Boulder, CO 80304
Fax: (303)443-4022   Fr: 888-443-2400
URL: http://www.delphivideo.com

$95.00. 50 minutes. Part of the Careers for the 21st Century Video Library.

★1607★ **International Society of India Chemists and Chemical Engineers (ISICCE)**
Advanced Research Chemicals
1110 W. Keystone Ave.
Catoosa, OK 74015
Ph: (918)266-6789   Fax: (918)266-6796
E-mail: sales@fluoridearc.com

Description: Chemists and chemical engineers from India. Goal is to bring together Indians in the chemical profession who live in the U.S. Aids members in securing jobs in their fields. Provides consultation to industries in India and helps individuals to start their own chemical companies in the U.S. Provides a forum for the exchange of social and technical issues. Plans to organize symposia, short courses, and exchange program. Compiles statistics.

★1608★ **ISA - Instrumentation, Systems, and Automation Society**
67 Alexander Dr.
PO Box 12277
Research Triangle Park, NC 27709
Ph: (919)549-8411   Fax: (919)549-8288
E-mail: info@isa.org
URL: http://www.isa.org

Purpose: Fosters advancement in the theory, design, manufacture, and use of instruments, computers, and systems for measurement and control.

★1609★ **National Action Council for Minorities in Engineering (NACME)**
Empire State Bldg., Ste. 2212
350 Fifth Ave.
New York, NY 10118-2299
Ph: (212)279-2626   Fax: (212)629-5178
E-mail: webmaster@nacme.org
URL: http://www.nacme.org/

Description: Leads the national effort to increase access to careers in engineering

and other science-based disciplines. Supported by the nation's leading technology-intensive companies, NACME conducts research and public policy analysis, develops and operates national demonstration programs at precollege and university levels, and disseminates information through publications, conferences, and electronic media. NACME is also the nation's largest privately funded source of scholarships for minority students in engineering.

★1610★ **National Society of Professional Engineers (NSPE)**
1420 King St.
Alexandria, VA 22314
Ph: (703)684-2800   Fax: (703)836-4875
Fr: 888-285-6773
E-mail: custserv@nspe.org
URL: http://www.nspe.org

Description: Professional engineers and engineers-in-training in all fields registered in accordance with the laws of states or territories of the U.S. or provinces of Canada; qualified graduate engineers, student members, and registered land surveyors. Is concerned with social, professional, ethical, and economic considerations of engineering as a profession; encompasses programs in public relations, employment practices, ethical considerations, education, and career guidance. Monitors legislative and regulatory actions of interest to the engineering profession.

★1611★ *Scientific, Engineering, and Technical Services*
Cambridge Educational
2572 Brunswick Ave.
Lawrenceville, NJ 08648-4128
Fax: 800-FAX-ON-US   Fr: 800-468-4227
URL: http://www.cambridgeeducational.com

$89.95. 2002. 18 minutes. Part of the Career Cluster Series.

★1612★ **Society of Women Engineers (SWE)**
230 E Ohio St., No. 400
Chicago, IL 60611-3265
Ph: (312)596-5223   Fax: (312)596-5252
E-mail: hq@swe.org
URL: http://www.swe.org

Description: Educational and service organization representing both students and professional women in engineering and technical fields.

★1613★ *Women in Engineering*
Her Own Words
PO Box 5264
Madison, WI 53705-0264
Ph: (608)271-7083   Fax: (608)271-0209
URL: http://www.herownwords.com/

Video. Jocelyn Riley. $95.00. 15 minutes. Resource guide also available for $45.00.

Chemists

★1614★ AATCC Review

American Association of Textile Chemists
 and Colorists
PO Box 12215
Research Triangle Park, NC 27709
Ph: (919)549-8141   Fax: (919)549-8933
URL: http://www.aatcc.org

Monthly. $180.00/year for U.S. and Canada;
$210.00/year for other countries. Magazine
focusing on dyeing, finishing of fibers and
fabrics.

★1615★ Adhesives Age

Primedia Business
9800 Metcalf Ave.
Overland Park, KS 66212
Ph: (913)341-1300   Fax: (913)967-1898

Monthly. $60.00/year for individuals. Maga-
zine containing news and technology for
those engaged in the manufacturing, application, research, and marketing of adhesives, sealants, and related products.

**★1616★ American Biotechnology
 Laboratory**

International Scientific Communications
 Inc.
30 Controls Dr.
PO Box 870
Shelton, CT 06484-0870
Ph: (203)926-9300   Fax: (203)926-9310

$160.00/year for individuals. Biotechnology
magazine.

**★1617★ American Paint and Coatings
 Journal**

Douglas Publications Inc.
2807 N Parham Rd., 64 Bldg., Ste. 200
Richmond, VA 23294
Ph: (804)762-4455   Fax: (804)935-0271
Fr: 800-223-1797

Semimonthly. $35.00/year. Magazine serv-
ing paint, varnish and lacquer manufacturers.

**★1618★ Applied Occupational &
 Environmental Hygiene**

Applied Industrial Hygiene Inc.
1330 Kemper Meadow Dr., Ste. 600
Cincinnati, OH 45240
Ph: (513)742-2020   Fax: (513)742-3355
E-mail: comm@acgih.org

Monthly. $159.00/year for individuals;
$269.00/year for institutions. Peer-reviewed
journal presenting applied solutions for the
prevention of occupational and environmental disease and injury.

★1619★ AWIS Magazine

Association for Women in Science
1200 New York Ave. NW, Ste. 650
Washington, DC 20005
Ph: (202)326-8940   Fax: (202)326-8960
Fr: 800-886-AWIS

Description: Bimonthly. Covers issues, legislation, and trends related to science education for girls, women, and minorities. Includes information on grants and fellowships, job openings, educational programs,
events, and notices of publications available.

★1620★ Chemical Equipment

Reed Business Information
301 Gibraltar Dr.
Morris Plains, NJ 07950
Ph: (973)292-5100   Fax: (973)539-3476

Tabloid on the chemical process industry.

★1621★ Chemical Processing

Putman Media
555 W Pierce Rd., Ste. 301
Itasca, IL 60143
Ph: (630)467-0052   Fax: (630)467-1109
URL: http://www.chemicalprocessing.com

Monthly. $68.00/year for individuals;
$115.00/year for other countries; $14.00 for
single issue. Magazine for the chemical
process industry.

★1622★ The Chemist

American Institute of Chemists Inc.
315 Chestnut St.
Philadelphia, PA 19106
Ph: (215)873-8224   Fax: (215)925-1954
E-mail: publications@theaic.org

Description: Six issues/year. Covers news
items relating to the chemical profession and
membership in the Institute. Reports on
legislation, licensure, earnings, awards, and
professional education. Recurring features
include news of employment opportunities
and news of members. Published alternate
months as a magazine.

**★1623★ The Electrochemical Society
 Interface**

Electrochemical Society Inc.
65 S Main St.
Pennington, NJ 08534-2839
Ph: (609)737-1902   Fax: (609)737-2743
E-mail: interface@electrochem.org
URL: http://www.electrochem.org

Quarterly. $40.00/year; $10.00 for single
issue. Publication featuring news and articles of interest to members of the Electrochemical Society.

★1624★ Modern Plastics

Chemical Week Associates
110 Williams St., 11th Fl.
New York, NY 10038
Ph: (212)621-4900   Fax: (212)621-4949
URL: http://www.modplas.com

Monthly. $59.00/year. Magazine for the plas-
tics industry.

★1625★ Nanoparticle News

Business Communications Company Inc.
25 Van Zant St.
Norwalk, CT 06855-1781
Ph: (203)853-4266   Fax: (203)853-0348

Bimonthly. Publication covering issues in the
chemical industry.

★1626★ Nature Biotechnology

Nature Publishing Group
345 Park Ave. S
New York, NY 10010-1707
Ph: (212)726-9200 Fax: (212)689-9711
Fr: 888-331-6288
E-mail: biotech@natureny.com
URL: http://www.biotechnology.nature.com

Monthly. $75.00/year for individuals; $545.00/year for institutions. Scientific research journal.

★1627★ Nature International Weekly Journal of Science

Nature Publishing Group
345 Park Ave. S
New York, NY 10010-1707
Ph: (212)726-9200 Fax: (212)689-9711
Fr: 888-331-6288
E-mail: nature@natureny.com
URL: http://www.nature.com

Weekly. $145.00/year for individuals; $495.00/year for institutions. Magazine covering science and technology, including the fields of biology, biochemistry, genetics, medicine, earth sciences, physics, pharmacology, and behavioral sciences.

★1628★ Paper, Film & Foil Converter

Primedia Business
29 N Wacker Dr.
Chicago, IL 60606
Ph: (312)726-2802 Fax: (312)726-2574
Fr: 800-621-9907
E-mail: pffceditor@primediabusiness.com
URL: http://www.pffc-online.com

Monthly. $83.00/year for individuals. Magazine focusing on flexible packaging, paperboard, and film.

★1629★ Plastics Engineering

Society of Plastics Engineers
14 Fairfield Dr.
PO Box 0403
Brookfield, CT 06804-0403
Ph: (203)775-0471 Fax: (203)775-8490
URL: http://www.4spe.org

Monthly. $110.00/year for individuals; $190.00 for two years. Plastics trade magazine.

★1630★ Plastics World

Cygnus Business Media Inc.
445 Broad Hollow Rd.
Melville, NY 11747
Ph: (631)845-2700 Fax: (631)845-2798
Fr: 800-308-6397

Monthly. $20.00/year for individuals. Plastics magazine.

★1631★ Powder and Bulk Engineering

CSC Publishing Inc.
1155 Northland Dr.
St. Paul, MN 55120-1288
Ph: (651)282-5600 Fax: (651)282-5650

Monthly. Journal serving chemical, food, plastics, pulp and paper, and electronic industries.

★1632★ Science

American Association for the Advancement of Science
1200 New York Ave. NW
Washington, DC 20005
Ph: (202)326-6400 Fax: (202)371-9849
URL: http://htpp://www.sciencemag.org

Weekly. $105.00/year for individuals; $7.00 for single issue. Magazine devoted to science, scientific research, and public policy.

★1633★ The Scientist

The Scientist Inc.
3535 Market St., Ste. 200
Philadelphia, PA 19104-2645
Ph: (215)386-9601 Fax: (215)386-7542
Fr: 800-258-6008
E-mail: info@the-scientist.com
URL: http://www.the-scientist.com

Biweekly. $49.00/year for individuals; $149.00/year for institutions; $24.00/year for students; $82.00/year for other countries; $49.00/year for students, other countries; $174.00/year for institutions, other countries. News journal (tabloid) for life scientists featuring news, opinions, research, and professional section.

★1634★ Soap/Cosmetics/Chemical Specialties

Cygnus Business Media Inc.
445 Broad Hollow Rd.
Melville, NY 11747
Ph: (631)845-2700 Fax: (631)845-2798
Fr: 800-308-6397

Monthly. Free to qualified subscribers; $60.00/year for individuals. Trade magazine for household and personal care products.

PLACEMENT AND JOB REFERRAL SERVICES

★1635★ American Association of Cereal Chemists (AACC)

3340 Pilot Knob Rd.
St. Paul, MN 55121-2097
Ph: (651)454-7250 Fax: (651)454-0766
E-mail: aacc@scisoc.org
URL: http://www.aaccnet.org/

Description: Professional society of scientists and other individuals in the grain processing industry (milling, baking, convenience foods, and feeds). Encourages research on cereal grains, oil seeds, pulses, and related materials, and studies their processing, utilization, and products. Seeks to develop and standardize analytical methods used in cereal and seed chemistry and to disseminate scientific and technical information through workshops and publications. Offers honors for outstanding research. Maintains over 20 technical subcommittees. Conducts short courses for continuing education and annual sanitation certification program.

★1636★ American Association of Textile Chemists and Colorists (AATCC)

PO Box 12215
Research Triangle Park, NC 27709-2215
Ph: (919)549-8141 Fax: (919)549-8933
E-mail: pattyb@aatcc.org
URL: http://www.aatcc.org

Description: Professional association for textile design, processing and testing. Works as an authority for industry standard test methods and evaluation procedures.

★1637★ American Oil Chemists' Society (AOCS)

2211 W Bradley Ave.
PO Box 3489
Champaign, IL 61821-1827
Ph: (217)359-2344 Fax: (217)351-8091
E-mail: general@aocs.org
URL: http://www.aocs.org

Members: Chemists, biochemists, chemical engineers, research directors, plant personnel, and others in laboratories and chemical process industries concerned with animal, marine, and vegetable oils and fats, and their extraction, refining, safety, packaging, quality control, and use in consumer and industrial products such as foods, drugs, paints, waxes, lubricants, soaps, and cosmetics. **Activities:** Sponsors short courses; certifies referee chemists; distributes cooperative check samples; sells official reagents. Maintains 100 committees. Operates job placement service for members only.

★1638★ American Society for Neurochemistry (ASN)

9037 Ron Den Ln.
Windermere, FL 34786
Ph: (407)876-0750
E-mail: amazing@iag.net
URL: http://www.ASNeurochem.org

Description: Members are investigators in the field of neurochemistry and scientists who are qualified specialists in other disciplines and are interested in the activities of the society. Purposes are to advance and promote the science of neurochemistry and related neurosciences and to increase and enhance neurochemical knowledge; to facilitate the dissemination of information concerning neurochemical research; to encourage the research of individual neurochemists. Conducts roundtables; distributes research communications. Maintains placement service.

★1639★ American Society of Plant Biologists (ASPB)
15501 Monona Dr.
Rockville, MD 20855-2768
Ph: (301)251-0560   Fax: (301)279-2996
E-mail: info@aspb.org
URL: http://www.aspb.org

Members: Professional society of plant biologists, plant biochemists, and other plant scientists engaged in research and teaching. **Activities:** Offers placement service for members; conducts educational and public affairs programs.

★1640★ American Water Works Association (AWWA)
6666 W Quincy Ave.
Denver, CO 80235
Ph: (303)794-7711   Fax: (303)347-0804
Fr: 800-926-7337
E-mail: rrenner@awwa.org
URL: http://www.awwa.org

Members: Water utility managers, superintendents, engineers, chemists, bacteriologists, and other individuals interested in public water supply; municipal- and investor-owned water departments; boards of health; manufacturers of waterworks equipment; government officials and consultants interested in water supply. **Purpose:** Develops standards and supports research programs in waterworks design, construction, operation, and management. **Activities:** Conducts in-service training schools and prepares manuals for waterworks personnel. Maintains hall of fame. Offers placement service via member newsletter; compiles statistics. Offers training; children's services; and information center on the water utilities industry, potable water, and water reuse.

★1641★ Engineering Society of Detroit (ESD)
26100 American Dr., Ste. 500
Southfield, MI 48034-6184
Ph: (248)355-2910   Fax: (248)355-1492
E-mail: esd@esd.org
URL: http://esd.org

Description: Engineers from all disciplines; scientists and technologists. Conducts technical programs and engineering refresher courses; sponsors conferences and expositions. Maintains speakers' bureau; offers placement services. Although based in Detroit, MI, society membership is international.

★1642★ Federation of Analytical Chemistry and Spectroscopy Societies (FACSS)
2019 Galisteo St., Bldg. I
PO Box 24379
Santa Fe, NM 87502
Ph: (505)820-1648   Fax: (505)989-1073
E-mail: facss@facss.org
URL: http://www.facss.org

Members: Professional societies representing 9000 analytical chemists and spectroscopists. Members are Analysis Instrumentation Division of the Instrument Society of America; Association of Analytical Chemists; Coblentz Society; Division of Analytical Chemistry of the American Chemical Society; Division of Analytical Chemistry of the Royal Society of Chemistry; Society for Applied Spectroscopy. **Purpose:** Objective is to provide a forum to address the challenges of analytical chemistry, chromatography, and spectroscopy. **Activities:** Reviews technical papers; maintains placement service.

★1643★ Korean Scientists and Engineers Association in America (KSEA)
1952 Gallows Rd., Ste. 300
Vienna, VA 22182
Ph: (703)748-1221   Fax: (703)748-1331
E-mail: sejong@ksea.org
URL: http://www.ksea.org

Description: Scientists and engineers holding single or advanced degrees. Goals are to: promote friendship and mutuality among Korean and American scientists and engineers; contribute to Korea's scientific, technological, industrial, and economic developments; strengthen the scientific, technological, and cultural bonds between Korea and the U.S. Sponsors symposium. Maintains speakers' bureau, placement service, and biographical archives. Compiles statistics. Maintains 100 volume library of scientific handbooks and yearbooks in Korean.

★1644★ National Organization for the Professional Advancement of Black Chemists and Chemical Engineers (NOBCChE)
PO Box 77040
Washington, DC 20013
Ph: (202)667-1699   Fax: (202)667-1705
Fr: 800-776-1419
E-mail: president@nobcche.org
URL: http://www.nobcche.org

Description: Black professionals in science and chemistry. Seeks to aid black scientists and chemists in reaching their full professional potential; encourages black students to pursue scientific studies and employment; promotes participation of blacks in scientific research. Provides volunteers to teach science courses in selected elementary schools; sponsors scientific field trips for students; maintains speakers' bureau for schools. Conducts technical seminars in Africa. Sponsors competitions; presents awards for significant achievements to individuals in the field. Maintains library of materials pertaining to chemistry, science, and black history; keeps archive of organization's books and records. Maintains placement service; compiles statistics.

★1645★ Society of Cosmetic Chemists (SCC)
120 Wall St., Ste. 2400
New York, NY 10005
Ph: (212)668-1500   Fax: (212)668-1504
E-mail: scc@scconline.org
URL: http://www.scconline.org

Description: Professional society of scientists involved in the cosmetic industry. Sponsors educational institution support programs to stimulate growth of cosmetic science-related programs. Maintains placement service.

★1646★ Society for In Vitro Biology (SIVB)
9315 Largo Dr., Ste. 255
Largo, MD 20774
Ph: (301)324-5054   Fax: (301)324-5057
Fr: 800-741-7476
E-mail: sivb@sivb.org
URL: http://www.sivb.org

Description: Professional society of individuals using mammalian, invertebrate, plant cell tissue, and organ cultures as research tools in chemistry, physics, radiation, medicine, physiology, nutrition, and cytogenetics. Aims are to foster collection and dissemination of information concerning the maintenance and experimental use of tissue cells in vitro and to establish evaluation and development procedures. Operates placement service.

EMPLOYER DIRECTORIES AND NETWORKING LISTS

★1647★ American Board of Clinical Chemistry-Directory of Diplomates
American Board of Clinical Chemistry
c/o Thomas C. Stewart Ph.D., DABCC
Louisiana Reference Laboratories
6746 Goya Ave.
Baton Rouge, LA 70806
Ph: (504)926-9173   Fax: (504)926-2521
Fr: 800-888-4758

Annual, winter. Covers about 800 chemists trained in clinical and toxicological chemistry and certified by the board. Entries include: Name, office address. Arrangement: Alphabetical.

★1648★ American Institute of Chemists-Professional Directory
American Institute of Chemists Inc.
315 Chestnut St.
Philadelphia, PA 19106
Ph: (215)873-8224   Fax: (215)925-1954
URL: http://www.theaic.org

Annual, spring. $75.00. Covers more than 3,500 member chemists. Entries include: Individual name and title, address, phone, name of employer, position title, principal job responsibility, principal field of chemistry, highest academic degree, certification, year elected to membership, membership category, local affiliation. Commercial use requires special permission. Arrangement: Alphabetical. Indexes: Geographical.

★1649★ *American Men and Women of Science*

Thomson Gale
27500 Drake Rd.
Farmington Hills, MI 48331-3535
Ph: (248)699-4253   Fax: (248)699-8065
Fr: 800-877-GALE
E-mail: amws@galegroup.com

Biennial, latest edition December 2002. $975.00. Covers over 129,700 U.S. and Canadian scientists active in the physical, biological, mathematical, computer science, and engineering fields; includes references to previous edition for deceased scientists and nonrespondents. Entries include: Name, address, education, personal and career data, memberships, honors and awards, research interest. Arrangement: Alphabetical. Indexes: Discipline (in separate volume).

★1650★ *Chemical Week-Buyers Guide Issue*

Chemical Week Associates
110 Williams St., 11th Fl.
New York, NY 10038
Ph: (212)621-4900   Fax: (212)621-4949
Fr: 800-774-5733
URL: http://www.chemweek.com/cwbg.html

Annual, October. $115.00. Publication includes: About 4,200 manufacturers and suppliers of chemical raw materials to the chemical process industries; 400 manufacturers of packaging materials; and suppliers of products and services to the chemical process industries, including hazardous waste/environmental services, computer services, plant design, contruction, consulting, shipping, and transportation. Entries include: Over 17,000 product/service listings, Company name, address, phone; local addresses and phone numbers for up to 25 sales locations. Arrangement: Separate alphabetical sections for chemical, packaging, and hazardous waste/environmental services. Indexes: Product (all sections); trade name (chemical and packaging sections only).

★1651★ *Consulting Services*

Association of Consulting Chemists and Chemical Engineers Inc.
PO Box 297
Sparta, NJ 07871-0297
Ph: (973)729-6671   Fax: (973)729-7088
URL: http://www.wwwprovider.com/chem/

Biennial, even years. $30.00. Covers about 160 member consultants in chemistry, chemical engineering, metallurgy, etc. Entries include: Individual name, address, certificate number, qualifications, affiliation, experience, facilities, staff. Arrangement: Classified by area of expertise. Indexes: Personal name, geographical.

★1652★ *Directory of Chemical Producers-United States*

SRI Consulting
333 Ravenswood Ave.
Menlo Park, CA 94025-3477
Ph: (650)859-3900   Fax: (650)859-2182
E-mail: dcp@sric.sri.com

URL: http://www.sri-chem.com

Annual. $2,210.00 for print; $2,760.00 for CD-ROM. Covers over 1,200 United States basic chemical producers manufacturing 7,900 chemicals in commercial quantities at more than 3,500 plant locations. Entries include: For companies-Company name, division or subsidiary names, corporate address, phone, fax, telex, location of each subsidiary, division, and manufacturing plant, and the products made at each plant location. For products-Producer name and plant locations, alternate product names (if any). Subscription price includes bound volume, plus access to the directory staff for inquiries. Arrangement: Companies are alphabetical; products are alphabetical and by group (dyes, pesticides, etc.); manufacturing plants are geographical. Indexes: Geographical, product.

★1653★ *Directory of Custom Chemical Manufacturers*

Delphi Marketing Services Inc.
400 E 89th St., Ste. 2J
New York, NY 10128
Fax: (212)369-6390

Annual, late spring. $295.00. Covers over 280 custom chemical manufacturers. Entries include: Company name, address, phone, name and title of contact, unit processes and reactions carried out, areas of expertise, equipment available. Arrangement: Alphabetical. Indexes: Product/service, subject, and geographical.

★1654★ *Directory of World Chemical Producers*

Chemical Information Services Inc.
PO Box 743512
Dallas, TX 75374
Ph: (214)349-6200   Fax: (214)349-6286
URL: http://www.chemicalinfo.com

Annual. $1,050.00 for book; $2,470.00 for CD-ROM or Internet subscription. Covers over 20,000 producers of all classes of chemicals worldwide; including bulk pharmaceuticals, fire chemicals, agrochemicals, dyes, pigments, cosmetic, food ingredients, intermediates, etc. Entries include: Company name, address, phone, fax, telex, email address, websites, contact information. Arrangement: Product, CAS#, geographical.

★1655★ *LabGuide*

American Chemical Society
1155 16th St. NW
Washington, DC 20036
Ph: (202)872-4600   Fax: (202)776-8258
Fr: 800-227-5558
E-mail: labguide@acs.org
URL: http://pubs.acs.org/

Annual, September. $50.00. Publication includes: List of about 2,200 manufacturers of scientific instruments, equipment, chemicals, and other supplies for scientific research and chemical laboratories; laboratory supply houses; analytical and research services. Entries include: Company name, address, phone, fax, e-mail, URL, products, and ser-

vices. Arrangement: Alphabetical. Indexes: Product, chemical, service, instrument, company name.

★1656★ *Peterson's Job Opportunities in Engineering and Technology*

Thomson Peterson's
PO Box 67005
Lawrenceville, NJ 08648-6105
Fr: 800-338-3282

Compiled by the Peterson's staff. Fourth edition, 1996. $21.95 (paper). 384 pages. Profiles 2,000 high-tech companies looking primarily for technical personnel in such fields as biotechnology, telecommunications, software, computers and peripherals, defense, and aerospace. Contains job-search strategies and career options to help match education and expertise to the job market. Indexed geographically, by industry, and by hiring needs.

★1657★ *Purchasing/CPI Edition-Chemicals Yellow Pages*

Cahners Publishing Co.
275 Washington St.
Newton, MA 02458
Ph: (617)641-2100   Fax: (617)558-4700
URL: http://www.purchasing.com

Annual, September. $88.00. Covers manufacturers and distributors of 10,000 chemicals and raw materials; manufacturers and distributors of containers and packaging; transportation services and storage facilities; environmental/hazardous waste services and eqpt. Entries include: Company name, address, branch and district office names and locations, phone. Arrangement: Separate alphabetical sections for suppliers, chemicals, and trade names; distributors are geographical.

★1658★ *U.S. National Committee for the International Union of Pure and Applied Chemistry-Directory*

U.S. National Committee for the International Union of Pure and Applied Chemistry
National Academy of Sciences
2101 Constitution Ave. NW
Washington, DC 20418
Ph: (202)334-2243   Fax: (202)334-2231

Annual, July. Covers 29 member chemists and chemical engineers in the United States.

HANDBOOKS AND MANUALS

★1659★ *The Best Resumes for Scientists and Engineers*

John Wiley & Sons Inc.
1 Wiley Dr.
Somerset, NJ 08873
Ph: (732)469-4400   Fr: 800-225-5945

Adele Lewis and David J. Moore. Second edition, 1993. $37.50; $19.95 (paper). 224

pages. Presents an extensive collection of scientific and engineering resumes, highlighting the important differences between these and resumes written for other occupations.

★1660★ Career Management for Chemists

Springer-Verlag New York, Inc.
175 Fifth Ave.
New York, NY 10010
Ph: (212)460-1500   Fax: (212)473-6272

John Fetzer. July 2004. $39.95. Illustrated. 257 pages. Vocational guide for Chemists.

★1661★ Careers for Chemists: A World Outside the Lab

American Chemical Society
1155 16th St., NW
Washington, DC 20036
Ph: (202)872-4600   Fr: 800-227-5558

Fred Owens, Roger Uhler and Corrine A. Marasco. 1997. 211 pages.

★1662★ Great Jobs for Chemistry Majors

McGraw-Hill Trade
2 Penn Plaza
New York, NY 10121
Ph: (212)904-2000   Fr: 800-722-4726
E-mail: ntcpub@tribune.com

Mark Rowh. 1999. $11.95 (paper). 340 pages.

★1663★ Guide to Nontraditional Careers in Science

Hemisphere Publishing Corp.
325 Chestnut St., 8th Fl.
Philadelphia, PA 19106
Ph: (215)785-5800   Fax: (215)269-0363
Fr: 800-821-8312

Karen Young Kreeger. 1998. $38.95 (paper). 263 pages.

★1664★ Opportunities in Chemistry Careers

McGraw-Hill/Contemporary Books
1221 Avenue of the Americas
New York, NY 10020
Ph: (212)904-2000   Fr: 800-323-4900

John H. Woodburn. Second edition, 2002. $12.95 (paper). 160 pages. Part of the VGM Opportunities Series.

★1665★ Opportunities in Environmental Careers

McGraw-Hill Trade
2 Penn Plaza
New York, NY 10121
Ph: (212)904-2000   Fr: 800-722-4726
E-mail: ntcpub@tribune.com

Odom Fanning. Revised, 2002. $12.95 (paper). 160 pages. Describes a broad range of opportunities in fields such as environmental health, recreation, physics, and hygiene, and

provides job search advice. Part of Opportunities in...Series.

★1666★ Opportunities in High Tech Careers

McGraw-Hill Trade
2 Penn Plaza
New York, NY 10121
Ph: (212)904-2000   Fr: 800-722-4726

Gary Colter and Deborah Yanuck. 1995. $14.95; $11.95 (paper). 160 pages. Explores high technology careers. Describes job opportunities, how to make a career decision, how to prepare for high technology jobs, job hunting techniques, and future trends.

★1667★ Opportunities in Research and Development Careers

McGraw-Hill/Contemporary Books
1221 Avenue of the Americas
New York, NY 10020
Ph: (212)904-2000   Fr: 800-323-4900
E-mail: ntcpub@tribune.com

Jan Goldberg. 1997. $14.95; $11.95 (paper). 204 pages.

★1668★ Resumes for Scientific and Technical Careers

McGraw-Hill Contemporary Books
1221 Avenue of the Americas
New York, NY 10020
Ph: (212)904-2000   Fr: 800-323-4900
E-mail: ntcpub@tribune.com

1999. $9.95 (paper). 450 pages. Provides resume advice for individuals interested in working in scientific and technical careers. Includes sample resumes and cover letters.

★1669★ To Boldly Go: A Practical Career Guide for Scientists

American Geophysical Union
2000 Florida Ave., NW
Washington, DC 20009
Ph: (202)462-6900   Fax: (202)328-0566
Fr: 800-966-2481

Peter S. Fiske. 1996. $19.00 (paper).

★1670★ What's Cooking in Chemistry?: How Leading Chemists Succeed in the Kitchen

John Wiley & Sons, Inc.
111 River St.
Hoboken, NJ 07030
Ph: (201)748-6000   Fax: (201)748-6088

Hubertus Bell. $40.00. Illustrated. 243 pages.

★1671★ Where the Jobs Are: The Hottest Careers for the 90s

The Career Press, Inc.
3 Tice Rd.
PO Box 687
Franklin Lakes, NJ 07417-1322
Ph: (201)848-0310   Fax: (201)848-1727
Fr: 800-227-3371

Joyce Hadley. Third edition, 2000. $13.99 (paper). 400 pages. Out of print. Describes careers in fifteen general fields, from accounting to travel and hospitality.

EMPLOYMENT AGENCIES AND SEARCH FIRMS

★1672★ Amtec Engineering Corp.

2749 Saturn St.
Brea, CA 92821
Ph: (714)993-1900   Fax: (714)993-2419
E-mail: staffing@amtec-eng.com
URL: http://www.amtec-eng.com

Employment agency.

★1673★ Biomedical Search Consultants

PO Box 721
Hawleyville, CT 06440-0721
Ph: (203)426-1445
E-mail: ta4nabio@cs.com

Employment agency.

★1674★ The Brentwood Group Inc.

170 Kinnelon Rd., Ste. 7
Kinnelon, NJ 07405
Ph: (973)283-1000   Fax: (973)283-1220

Executive search firm.

★1675★ Briant Associates Inc.

18 E. Dundee Rd. Bldg 2, Ste. 202
Barrington, IL 60010
Ph: (847)382-5725   Fax: (847)382-7265

Executive search firm.

★1676★ Ellington & Associates

1755 Park St., Ste. 200
Naperville, IL 60563
Ph: (630)305-0088   Fax: (630)305-0839

Firm specializes in recruiting for the chemical, food, and pulp and paper industries.

★1677★ Erspamer Associates

4010 W. 65th St., Ste. 100
Edina, MN 55435
Ph: (952)925-3747   Fax: (952)925-4022
E-mail: hdhuntrel@aol.com

Executive search firm specializing in technical management.

★1678★ Intech Summit Group, Inc.

5075 Shoreham Pl., Ste. 280
San Diego, CA 92122
Ph: (858)452-2100   Fax: (858)452-8500
E-mail: isg@isgsearch.com
URL: http://www.isgsearch.com

Employment agency and executive recruiter with a branch in Carlsbad, CA.

★1679★ Lybrook Associates, Inc.

PO Box 741
Bristol, RI 02809
Ph: (401)254-5840   Fax: (401)254-5088
E-mail: chemistry@lybrook.com
URL: http://www.lybrook.com

Executive search firm specializing in the field of chemistry.

★1680★ Professional Placement Associates, Inc.

287 Bowman Ave., Ste. 309
Purchase, NY 10577
Ph: (914)251-1000   Fax: (914)251-1055
E-mail: lschachter@ppasearch.com
URL: http://www.ppasearch.com

Executive search firm specializing in the health and medical field.

★1681★ Team Placement Service, Inc.

5113 Leesburg Pike, Ste. 510
Falls Church, VA 22041-3242
Ph: (703)820-8618   Fax: (703)820-3368
Fr: 800-495-6767
E-mail: 4jobs@teamplace.com
URL: http://www.teamplace.com

Temporary agency that also handles some permanent placements.

★1682★ Tri-Serv Inc.

22 W. Padonia Rd., Ste. C-353
Timonium, MD 21093
Ph: (410)561-1740   Fax: (410)252-7417
E-mail: info@tri-serv.coom
URL: http://www.tri-serv.com

Permanent employment agency.

ONLINE JOB SOURCES AND SERVICES

★1683★ American Chemical Society: JobSpectrum.org

E-mail: jobmaster@jobspectrum.org
URL: http://www.jobspectrum.org

Description: JobSpectrum is a joint venture of the ACS Publications Division and the ACS Membership. Division. Offers online interviewing between employers and potential employees, postings for positions available and situations wanted, and regularly updated career advice and information for American Chemical Society members only.

★1684★ American Oil Chemists Society Career Opportunities

E-mail: kathya@aocs.org
URL: http://www.aocs.org/member/jobcent/

Description: Section of the AOCS homepage intended to aid members in finding jobs in the oil chemistry field. Job areas include analytical, health and nutrition, processing, surfactants and detergents, general fats and oils/chemistry, and others. Jobs may be posted and searched.

TRADESHOWS

★1685★ AOAC International Annual Meeting and Exposition

AOAC International
481 North Frederick Ave., Ste. 500
Gaithersburg, MD 20877-2417
Ph: (301)924-7077   Fax: (301)924-7089
Fr: 800-379-2622
E-mail: aoac@aoac.org
URL: http://www.aoac.org

Annual. **Primary Exhibits:** Scientific and laboratory supplies and publications exhibits and posters. **Dates and Locations:** 2004 Sep 19-23; St. Louis, MO • 2005 Sep 11-15; Orlando, FL.

★1686★ Federation of Analytical Chemistry and Applied Spectroscopy Societies Convention

Federation of Analytical Chemistry and Spectroscopy Societies
13 N. Cliffe Dr.
Wilmington, DE 19809
Ph: (302)798-5161   Fax: (302)944-8837

Annual. **Primary Exhibits:** Spectroscopy, chromatography, and analytical chemistry equipment.

OTHER SOURCES

★1687★ American Academy of Clinical Toxicology (AACT)

777 E Park Dr.
PO Box 8820
Harrisburg, PA 17105-8820
Ph: (717)558-7847   Fax: (717)558-7845
Fr: 888-633-5784
E-mail: jreisinger@pamedsoc.org
URL: http://www.clintox.org

Members: Physicians, veterinarians, pharmacists, nurses research scientists, and analytical chemists. **Purpose:** Works to unite medical scientists and facilitate the exchange of information; encourage the development of therapeutic methods and technology. **Activities:** Conducts professional training in poison information and emergency service personnel.

★1688★ American Chemical Society (ACS)

1155 16th St. NW
Washington, DC 20036
Ph: (202)872-4600   Fax: (202)776-8258
Fr: 800-227-5558
E-mail: webmaster@acs.org
URL: http://www.acs.org

Members: Scientific and educational society of chemists and chemical engineers. **Activities:** Conducts studies and surveys; special programs for disadvantaged persons; legislation monitoring, analysis, and reporting; courses for graduate chemists and chemical engineers; radio and television programming. Offers career guidance counseling; administers the Petroleum Research Fund and other grants and fellowship programs. Operates Employment Clearing Houses. Compiles statistics. Maintains speakers' bureau. Maintains 33 divisions.

★1689★ American Crystallographic Association (ACA)

PO Box 96, Ellicott Sta.
Buffalo, NY 14205-0096
Ph: (716)856-9600   Fax: (716)852-4846
E-mail: aca@hwi.buffalo.edu
URL: http://www.hwi.buffalo.edu/aca/

Members: Chemists, biochemists, physicists, mineralogists, and metallurgists interested in crystallography and in the application of X-ray, electron, and neutron diffraction. **Purpose:** Promotes the study of the arrangement of atoms in matter, its causes, its nature, and its consequences, and of the tools and methods used in such studies. **Activities:** Maintains employment clearinghouse for members and employers.

★1690★ American Institute of Chemists (AIC)

315 Chestnut St.
Philadelphia, PA 19106-2702
Ph: (215)873-8224   Fax: (215)925-1954
E-mail: info@theaic.org
URL: http://www.theaic.org

Description: Chemists and chemical engineers. Promotes advancement of chemical professions in the U.S.; protects public welfare by establishing and enforcing high practice standards; represents professional interests of chemists and chemical engineers. Sponsors National Certification Commission in Chemistry and Chemical Engineering and AIC Foundation.

★1691★ American Microchemical Society (AMS)

2 June Way
Middlesex, NJ 08846
Fax: (609)951-2809
E-mail: hek.felder@worldnet.att.net
URL: http://www.microchem.org

Purpose: Promotes interest in the practice and teaching of microchemistry. **Activities:** Participates in exhibits and symposia. Maintains placement service.

★1692★ Association for International Practical Training (AIPT)
10400 Little Patuxent Pky., Ste. 250
Columbia, MD 21044-3519
Ph: (410)997-2200   Fax: (410)992-3924
E-mail: aipt@aipt.org
URL: http://www.aipt.org

Description: Providers worldwide on-the-job training programs for students and professionals seeking international career development and life-changing experiences. Arranges workplace exchanges in hundreds of professional fields, bringing employers and trainees together from around the world. Client list ranges from small farming communities to Fortune 500 companies.

★1693★ *Chemistry*
Evon Publishing
832 N 7th Ave.
Iron River, MI 49935
Ph: (906)265-3190

Audiocassette. 1996. $16.95. 32 minutes. Part of the Careers and Vocational Guidance Series. Provides information about the nature of the work, educational requirements, employment outlook, earnings, and work conditions as well as additional related information.

★1694★ International Society of Chemical Ecology (ISCE)
Dept. of Biology
State University of New York ESF
1 Forestry Dr.
Syracuse, NY 13210-2726
E-mail: stephen.foster@ndsu.nodak.edu
URL: http://www.chemecol.org

Description: Chemists, ecologists, biologists, and others with an interest in chemical ecology. Purpose is to promote understanding of the origin, function, and importance of natural chemicals that mediate communication and interactions within and among organisms. Seeks to broaden the scope of chemical ecology and to stimulate cooperation and exchange of information among members of diverse scientific fields. Conducts educational programs designed to foster knowledge in the area of chemical ecology.

★1695★ International Society of India Chemists and Chemical Engineers (ISICCE)
Advanced Research Chemicals
1110 W. Keystone Ave.
Catoosa, OK 74015
Ph: (918)266-6789   Fax: (918)266-6796

E-mail: sales@fluoridearc.com

Description: Chemists and chemical engineers from India. Goal is to bring together Indians in the chemical profession who live in the U.S. Aids members in securing jobs in their fields. Provides consultation to industries in India and helps individuals to start their own chemical companies in the U.S. Provides a forum for the exchange of social and technical issues. Plans to organize symposia, short courses, and exchange program. Compiles statistics.

★1696★ Minority Women In Science (MWIS)
Directorate for Education and Human Resources Programs
1200 New York Ave. NW
Washington, DC 20005
Ph: (202)326-7019   Fax: (202)371-9849
E-mail: sassefa@aaas.org

Description: A national network group of the American association for the Advancement of Science (AAAS), Education and Human Resources Directorate. The objectives of this group are: to identify and share information on resources and programs that could help in mentoring young women and minorities interested in science and engineering careers, and to strengthen communication among women and minorities in science and education.

★1697★ Radiation Research Society (RRS)
10105 Cottesmore Ct.
Great Falls, VA 22066-3540
Ph: (703)757-4585   Fax: (703)757-0454
E-mail: info@radres.org
URL: http://www.radres.org

Description: Professional society of biologists, physicists, chemists, and physicians contributing to knowledge of radiation and its effects. Promotes original research in the natural sciences relating to radiation; facilitates integration of different disciplines in the study of radiation effects.

★1698★ *Scientific, Engineering, and Technical Services*
Cambridge Educational
2572 Brunswick Ave.
Lawrenceville, NJ 08648-4128
Fax: 800-FAX-ON-US   Fr: 800-468-4227
URL: http://www.cambridgeeducational.com

$89.95. 2002. 18 minutes. Part of the Career Cluster Series.

★1699★ *Scientific Occupations*
Delphi Productions
3160 4th St.
Boulder, CO 80304
Fax: (303)443-4022   Fr: 888-443-2400
URL: http://www.delphivideo.com

$95.00. 60 minutes. Part of the Careers for the 21st Century Video Library.

★1700★ Soil Science Society of America (SSSA)
677 S Segoe Rd.
Madison, WI 53711
Ph: (608)273-8080   Fax: (608)273-2021
E-mail: headquarters@agronomy.org
URL: http://www.soils.org

Description: Professional soil scientists, including soil physicists, soil classifiers, land use and management specialists, chemists, microbiologists, soil fertility specialists, soil cartographers, conservationists, mineralogists, engineers, and others interested in fundamental and applied soil science.

★1701★ Water Environment Federation (WEF)
601 Wythe St.
Alexandria, VA 22314-1994
Ph: (703)684-2452   Fax: (703)684-2492
Fr: 800-666-0206
E-mail: csc@wef.org
URL: http://www.wef.org

Description: Technical societies representing chemists, biologists, ecologists, geologists, operators, educational and research personnel, industrial wastewater engineers, consultant engineers, municipal officials, equipment manufacturers, and university professors and students dedicated to the enhancement and preservation of water quality and resources. Seeks to advance fundamental and practical knowledge concerning the nature, collection, treatment, and disposal of domestic and industrial wastewaters, and the design, construction, operation, and management of facilities for these purposes. Disseminates technical information; promotes good public relations and regulations that improve water quality and the status of individuals working in this field. Conducts educational and research programs.

Child Care Workers and Nannies

PLACEMENT AND JOB REFERRAL SERVICES

★1702★ International Nanny Association (INA)
191 Clarksville Rd.
Princeton Junction, NJ 08550-3111
Ph: (609)799-7527   Fax: (856)858-2519
Fr: 888-878-1477
E-mail: ina@nanny.org
URL: http://www.nanny.org

Description: An educational association for nannies and those who educate, place, employ, and support professional in-home child care. Membership is open to those who are directly involved with the in-home child care profession, including nannies, nanny employers, nanny placement agency owners (and staff), nanny educators, and providers of special services related to the nanny profession.

EMPLOYER DIRECTORIES AND NETWORKING LISTS

★1703★ Child Care Service Directory
infoUSA Inc.
5711 S 86th Cir.
Omaha, NE 68127-0347
Ph: (402)930-3500   Fax: (402)331-0176
Fr: 800-555-6124
URL: http://www.abii.com

Annual. Number of listings: 73,270. Entries include: Name, address, phone (including area code), size of advertisement, year first in "Yellow Pages," name of owner or manager, number of employees. Regional editions available. Compiled from telephone company "Yellow Pages," nationwide. Arrangement: Geographical.

★1704★ Directory of Family Child Care Associations, Support Groups, & Support Agencies
Children's Foundation
725 15th St. NW, Ste. 505
Washington, DC 20005-2109
Ph: (202)347-3300   Fax: (202)347-3382

Annual, February. $25.00. Covers over 2,500 organizations and support groups for child care providers in the U.S. Entries include: Organization name, address, phone, subsidiary and branch names and locations. Arrangement: Geographical.

★1705★ Directory of Federal Programs Helping Child Care
ERIC Document Reproduction Service
7420 Fullerton Rd., Ste. 110
Springfield, VA 22153-2852
Ph: (703)440-1400   Fax: (703)440-1408
Fr: 800-443-ERIC

Covers Federal programs that assist child care professionals. Entries include: Name, address, phone of program name and title of contact, description of program and financial information.

★1706★ Sitting Services Directory
infoUSA Inc.
5711 S 86th Cir.
Omaha, NE 68127-0347
Ph: (402)930-3500   Fax: (402)331-0176
Fr: 800-555-6124
URL: http://www.abii.com

Updated continuously; printed on request. Number of listings: 913. Entries include: Name, address, phone, size of advertisement, name of owner or manager, number of employees, year first in "Yellow Pages." Compiled from telephone company "Yellow Pages," nationwide. Arrangement: Geographical.

★1707★ So You Want to Open a Profitable Day Care Center...A Basic How to Do It Guide
Mosby Inc.
11830 Westline Industrial Dr.
St. Louis, MO 63146
Ph: (314)872-8370   Fax: (314)432-1380
Fr: 800-325-4177

Irregular, previous edition 1992; latest edition 1994. $19.95. Publication includes: Lists of government bureaus, business administration offices, small business information, and early childhood education resources which issue licenses necessary for the legal operation of child care centers; organizations and associations that provide assistance to child care operators; child care related publications that provide practical easy to follow instructions that will assist entrepreneurs who are considering the operation of day care centers. Includes professionals to contact, assessment of day care needs, education curriculum guidance, child safety, and business considerations. Entries include: For government bureaus-Name, address. For organizations and associations-Name, address, phone. For publications-Title, publisher name, address, phone, price, brief description of publication. Principal content of publication is a step-by-step guide to opening day care centers. Arrangement: Separate sections for government bureaus, organizations and associations, and publications. Indexes: Subject.

HANDBOOKS AND MANUALS

★1708★ The Au Pair and Nanny's Guide to Working Abroad
Vacation Work Publications
9 Park End St.
Oxford OX1 1HJ, United Kingdom
Susan Griffith, Sharon Legg. Fourth edition. December 2002. $17.95. Illustrated. 320 pages.

★1709★ Careers for Caring People and Other Sensitive Types
VGM Career Horizons
1221 Avenue of the Americas
New York, NY 10020
Ph: (212)904-2000   Fr: 800-323-4900
E-mail: ntcpub@tribune.com

Adrian Paradis. 1995. $14.95; $9.95 (paper). 205 pages.

★1710★ Careers in Child Care
McGraw-Hill/Contemporary Books
1221 Avenue of the Americas
New York, NY 10020
Ph: (212)904-2000   Fr: 800-323-4900
E-mail: ntcpub@tribune.com

Marjorie Eberts. Second edition, 2000. $19.95. 175 pages.

★1711★ Careers for Kids at Heart and Others Who Adore Children
McGraw-Hill Contemporary Books
1221 Avenue of the Americas
New York, NY 10020
Ph: (212)904-2000   Fr: 800-323-4900
E-mail: ntcpub@tribune.com

Marjorie Eberts and Margaret Gisler. Second edition, 1999. $14.95; $9.95 (paper). 192 pages.

★1712★ Child and Adult Care Professionals
Glencoe/McGraw-Hill
8787 Orion Pl.
Columbus, OH 43240-4027
Fr: 800-334-7344

Karen Stephens. Third edition. $61.32. Illustrated. 688 pages.

★1713★ Household Careers: Nannies, Butlers, Maids and More: The Complete Guide for Finding Household Employment or 'If the Dog Likes You, You're Hired!'
Five Star Publications, Inc.
PO Box 6698
Chandler, AZ 85246-6698
Ph: (602)940-8182   Fax: (602)940-8787
Fr: 800-545-7827

Linda F. Radke. 2001. 102 pages.

★1714★ Nanny Essentials: A Necessary Tool for the Childcare Professional
Nanny Essentials LLC
235 S. Hustis St.
Hustisford, WI 53034

December 2003. $26.95. A reference book for childcare professionals.

★1715★ Opportunities in Child Care Careers
McGraw-Hill Trade
2 Penn Plaza
New York, NY 10121
Ph: (212)904-2000   Fr: 800-722-4726

Renee Wittenberg. 1998. $14.95; $11.95 (paper). 210 pages. Discusses various job opportunities and how to secure a position. Illustrated.

★1716★ Opportunities in Homecare Services Careers
McGraw-Hill Trade
2 Penn Plaza
New York, NY 10121
Ph: (212)904-2000   Fr: 800-722-4726

Anna deSola Cardoza. 1994. $14.95; $11.95 (paper). 160 pages. Professional child care careers, including various types of therapy and post-intensive surgery assistance.

★1717★ Opportunities in Mental Health Careers
McGraw-Hill Trade
2 Penn Plaza
New York, NY 10121
Ph: (212)904-2000   Fr: 800-722-4726

Philip A. Perry and George Blake. 1996. $14.95; $11.95 (paper). 160 pages.

★1718★ Profitable Child Care: How to Start and Run a Successful Business
Facts on File, Inc.
132 W. 31st St., 17th Fl.
New York, NY 10001-2006
Ph: (212)967-8800   Fax: (212)967-8107
Fr: 800-322-8755
URL: http://www.factsonfile.com

Nan L. Howkins and Heidi K. Rosenholtz. 1993. $33.95. 288 pages. Out of print.

★1719★ Start and Run a Profitable Home Daycare: Your Step-by-Step Business Plan
Self-Counsel Press, Inc.
1704 N. State St.
Bellingham, WA 98225
Ph: (360)676-4530   Fax: (360)676-4549
Fr: 877-877-6490

Catherine Pruissen. 1993. $14.95 (paper). 216 pages. Out of print.

★1720★ Starting and Operating A Child Care Center: A Guide
Readers Press
523 Burning Embers Ln.
Jacksonville, FL 32225-5146
Lillie M. Robinson. 1994. $29.95. The guide focuses on making the decision to direct a center; finding a suitable location; equipping the center; attracting, hiring, using incentives, evaluating & separating the staff; enrolling & caring for the children; establishing relationships with parents, substitutes, & volunteers; managing & accounting for in-

come, expenses & inventory. It deals with health, safety & nutritional needs of the children & ways of using objective evaluation procedures to assess the program, staff & children.

★1721★ Working with Children: How to Find the Right Qualifications, Training and Job Opportunities
Trans-Atlantic Publications, Inc.
311 Bainbridge St.
Philadelphia, PA 19147
Ph: (215)925-5083   Fax: (215)925-1912

Meg Jones. 1997. 142 pages. Part of the Jobs and Careers Series.

★1722★ Working with Young Children: Teacher's Resource
Goodheart Willcox Publisher
18604 W. Creek Dr.
Tinley Park, IL 60477-6243
Ph: (708)687-5000   Fax: 888-409-3900
Fr: 800-323-0440

Judy Herr. September 2002. $191.20 (Compact Disc). Illustrated. Educational format.

EMPLOYMENT AGENCIES AND SEARCH FIRMS

★1723★ Capitol Search
215 E. Ridgewood Ave., Ste. 205
Ridgewood, NJ 07450
Ph: (201)444-6666

Employment agency.

TRADESHOWS

★1724★ Association for Childhood Education International Annual International Conference & Exhibition
Association for Childhood Education International
17904 Georgia Ave., Ste. 215
Olney, MD 20832
Ph: (301)570-2111   Fax: (301)570-2212
Fr: 800-423-3563
E-mail: aceimc@aol.com
URL: http://www.acei.org

Annual. **Primary Exhibits:** Commercial and educational exhibits of interest to teachers, teacher educators, college students, day care personnel and other care givers.

★1725★ National Association for the Education of Young Children Annual Conference

National Association for the Education of
Young Children
1509 16th St., NW
Washington, DC 20036
Ph: (202)232-8777   Fax: (202)328-1846
Fr: 800-424-2460
E-mail: conference@naevc.org
URL: http://www.naevc.org

Annual. **Primary Exhibits:** Educational materials and equipment designed for children ages birth through eight years old. **Dates and Locations:** 2004 Nov 10-13; Anaheim, CA; Anaheim Convention Center.

★1726★ Southern Early Childhood Association Annual Meeting

Southern Early Childhood Association
7107 W. 12th., No. 102
Box 55930
Little Rock, AR 72215-5930
Ph: (501)663-0353   Fax: (501)663-2114
Fr: 800-305-7322

Annual. **Primary Exhibits:** Publications, school supplies, playground equipment, and toys.

OTHER SOURCES

★1727★ Center for the Child Care Workforce, A Project of the American Federation of Teachers Educational Foundation (CCW/AFTEF)

555 New Jersey Ave. NW
Washington, DC 20001
Ph: (202)662-8005   Fax: (202)662-8006

E-mail: ccw@aft.org
URL: http://www.ccw.org

Purpose: Works to develop innovative solutions to the child care crisis to improve salaries, working conditions, and status of child care workers; to increase public awareness about the importance of child care work and the training and skill it demands; to develop resources and create an information sharing network for child care workers nationwide. **Activities:** Gathers current information on salaries and benefits; offers consultation services. Sponsors research projects; compiles statistics; operates speakers' bureau. Maintains extensive file of materials on working conditions and research on child care workers.

★1728★ Education and Training

Cambridge Educational
2572 Brunswick Ave.
Lawrenceville, NJ 08648-4128
Fax: 800-FAX-ON-US   Fr: 800-468-4227
URL: http://www.cambridgeeducational.com

$89.95. 2002. 18 minutes.

★1729★ National Association for the Education of Young Children (NAEYC)

1509 16th St. NW
Washington, DC 20036
Ph: (202)232-8777   Fax: (202)328-1846
Fr: 800-424-2460
E-mail: naeyc@naeyc.org
URL: http://www.naeyc.org

Description: Teachers and directors of preschool and primary schools, kindergartens, child care centers, and early other learning programs for young childhood; early childhood education and child development educators, trainers, and researchers and other professionals dedicated to young children's healthy development.

★1730★ National Association of Nannies

PMB 2004, 25 Rte. 31 S., Ste. C
Pennington, NJ 08534
Fr: 800-344-6266
URL: http://www.nannyassociation.com

Description: Promotes the nanny as a legitimate career choice.

★1731★ Personal & Building Service Occupations

Delphi Productions
3160 4th St.
Boulder, CO 80304
Fax: (303)443-4022   Fr: 888-443-2400
URL: http://www.delphivideo.com

$95.00. 48 minutes. Part of the Careers for the 21st Century Video Library.

★1732★ Working with Children

Cambridge Educational
2572 Brunswick Ave.
Lawrenceville, NJ 08648-4128
Fax: 800-FAX-ON-US   Fr: 800-468-4227
URL: http://www.cambridgeeducational.com

$89.95. 2000. 23 minutes. This program examines alternative positions offering the opportunity to work with children of different ages and the qualifications necessary for those jobs. A nanny, social worker, nonfaculty school worker, and retail salesperson describe their job responsibilities and explain why they find their work so enjoyable.

Chiropractors

SOURCES OF HELP-WANTED ADS

★1733★ Journal of the American Chiropractic Association
American Chiropractic Association
1701 Clarendon Blvd.
Arlington, VA 22209
Ph: (703)276-8800   Fax: (703)243-2593
Fr: 800-986-4636

Monthly. Subscription included in membership; $80.00/year for nonmembers. Professional journal covering chiropractic procedures and research, and developments in other fields of interest to chiropractors.

PLACEMENT AND JOB REFERRAL SERVICES

★1734★ Christian Chiropractors Association (CCA)
2550 Stover, No. B-102
PO Box 9715
Fort Collins, CO 80525
Ph: (970)482-1404   Fax: (970)482-1538
Fr: 800-999-1970
E-mail: carlas@frii.com
URL: http://www.christianchiropractors.org

Description: Works to spread the Gospel of Christ throughout the U.S. and abroad. Offers Christian fellowship and works to unify Christian chiropractors around the essentials of the fail, "leaving minor points of doctrine to the conscience of the individual believer." Focus is on world missions; seeks to expand the variety of mission fields; aids in placement of Christian chiropractors as missionaries.

EMPLOYER DIRECTORIES AND NETWORKING LISTS

★1735★ Chiropractors DC Directory
infoUSA Inc.
5711 S 86th Cir.
Omaha, NE 68127-0347
Ph: (402)930-3500   Fax: (402)331-0176
Fr: 800-555-6124
URL: http://www.abii.com

Annual. Number of listings: 58,584. Entries include: Name, address, phone (including area code), size of advertisement, year first in "Yellow Pages," name of owner or manager, number of employees. Regional editions available; please inquire. Compiled from telephone company "Yellow Pages" nationwide. Arrangement: Geographical.

★1736★ Women's Auxiliary of the International Chiropractors Association-Membership Roster
Women's Auxiliary of the International Chiropractors Association (ICA)
1110 N Glebe Rd., Ste. 1000
Arlington, VA 22201
Ph: (703)528-5000   Fax: (703)528-5023

Biennial. Covers about 500 women who are chiropractic assistants, chiropractors, or related to members of the ICA.

HANDBOOKS AND MANUALS

★1737★ The Business of Chiropractic: How to Prosper after Startup
Do Write Publishing
1227 Cedar Hill Rd.
Dandridge, TN 37725
Ph: (865)397-4358   Fax: (423)397-4358
1999. $29.95 (paper).

★1738★ Careers in Medicine
McGraw-Hill Contemporary Books
1221 Avenue of the Americas
New York, NY 10020
Ph: (212)904-2000   Fr: 800-323-4900
E-mail: ntcpub@tribune.com

Terence J. Sacks. Second edition, 1996. $17.95; $13.95 (paper). 144 pages. Examines the many paths open to M.D.s, D.O.s, and M.D./Ph.D.s, including clinical private or group practice, hospitals, public health organizations, the armed forces, emergency rooms, research institutions, medical schools, pharmaceutical companies and private industry, and research/advocacy groups like the World Health Organization. A special chapter on osteopathy and chiropractic explores this branch of medicine.

★1739★ Opportunities in Chiropractic Careers
McGraw-Hill Trade
2 Penn Plaza
New York, NY 10121
Ph: (212)904-2000   Fr: 800-722-4726
R.C. Shafer. 1994. $14.95; $10.95 (paper). 160 pages. A guide to planning for and building a career in the field. Illustrated.

★1740★ Opportunities in Sports and Athletics Careers
McGraw-Hill Trade
2 Penn Plaza
New York, NY 10121
Ph: (212)904-2000   Fr: 800-722-4726
E-mail: ntcpub@tribune.com

William Ray Heitzmann. 1994. 160 pages. $14.95; $11.95 (paper). A guide to planning for and seeking opportunities in this growing field. Illustrated.

★1741★ Opportunities in Sports Medicine Careers
McGraw-Hill Trade
2 Penn Plaza
New York, NY 10121
Ph: (212)904-2000   Fr: 800-722-4726
E-mail: ntcpub@tribune.com

William Ray Heitzmann. 1995. $14.95;

$11.95 (paper). 160 pages. Discusses a variety of opportunities in this field and how to pursue them. Contains bibliography and illustrations.

★1742★ *Resumes for Health and Medical Careers*
McGraw-Hill Trade
2 Penn Plaza
New York, NY 10121
Ph: (212)904-2000   Fr: 800-722-4726
E-mail: ntcpub@tribune.com
1997. $9.95 (paper). 455 pages.

ONLINE JOB SOURCES AND SERVICES

★1743★ **Medhunters.com**
E-mail: info@medhunters.com
URL: http://www.medhunters.com
Description: Career search site for jobs in all health care specialties; educational resources; visa and licensing information for relocation; interesting articles; relocation tools; links to professional organizations and general resources.

★1744★ **ProHealthJobs**
E-mail: sales@prohealthjobs.com
URL: http://www.prohealthjobs.com
Description: Career resources site for the medical and health care field. Lists professional opportunities, product information, continuing education and open positions.

TRADESHOWS

★1745★ **American Chiropractic Association Annual Convention and Exhibition**
American Chiropractic Association
1701 Clarendon Blvd.
Arlington, VA 22209
Ph: (703)276-8800   Fax: (703)243-2593
Fr: 800-986-4636
Annual. **Primary Exhibits:** Chiropractic ta-

bles and products, nutritional supplements, computer services and equipment, mattress companies, and publishers.

OTHER SOURCES

★1746★ **American Chiropractic Association (ACA)**
1701 Clarendon Blvd.
Arlington, VA 22209
Ph: (703)276-8800   Fax: (703)243-2593
Fr: 800-986-4636
E-mail: memberinfo@amerchiro.org
URL: http://www.amerchiro.org
Description: Enhances the philosophy, science, and art of chiropractic, and the professional welfare of individuals in the field. Promotes legislation defining chiropractic health care and improves the public's awareness and utilization of chiropractic. Conducts chiropractic survey and statistical study; maintains library. Sponsors Correct Posture Week in May and Spinal Health Month in October. Chiropractic colleges have student ACA groups.

★1747★ **Council on Chiropractic Education (CCE)**
8049 N 85th Way
Scottsdale, AZ 85258-4321
Ph: (480)443-8877   Fax: (480)483-7333
E-mail: cce@cce-usa.org
URL: http://www.cce-usa.org
Description: Advocates high standards in chiropractic education; establishes criteria of institutional excellence for educating chiropractic physicians; acts as national accrediting agency for chiropractic colleges. Conducts workshops for college teams, consultants, and chiropractic college staffs.

★1748★ *Exploring Health Occupations*
Cambridge Educational
2572 Brunswick Ave.
Lawrenceville, NJ 08648-4128
Fax: 800-FAX-ON-US   Fr: 800-468-4227
URL: http://www.cambridgeeducational.com
Two videos. $139.95. 1999.

★1749★ *Health Service Occupations*
Delphi Productions
3160 4th St.
Boulder, CO 80304
Fax: (303)443-4022   Fr: 888-443-2400
URL: http://www.delphivideo.com
$95.00. 50 minutes. Part of the Careers for the 21st Century Video Library.

★1750★ **Holistic Dental Association (HDA)**
PO Box 5007
Durango, CO 81301
Ph: (970)259-1091   Fax: (970)259-1091
E-mail: info@holisticdental.org
URL: http://www.holisticdental.org
Description: Dentists, chiropractors, dental hygienists, physical therapists, and medical doctors. Goals are: to provide a holistic approach to better dental care for patients; to expand techniques, medications, and philosophies that pertain to extractions, anesthetics, fillings, crowns, and orthodontics. Encourages use of homeopathic medications, acupuncture, cranial osteopathy, nutritional techniques, and physical therapy in treating patients in addition to conventional treatments. Sponsors training and educational seminars.

★1751★ **International Chiropractors Association (ICA)**
1110 N. Glebe Rd., Ste. 1000
Arlington, VA 22201
Ph: (703)528-5000   Fax: (703)528-5023
Fr: 800-423-4690
E-mail: chiro@chiropractic.org
URL: http://www.chiropractic.org/
Description: Professional society of chiropractors, chiropractic educators, students, and laypersons. Sponsors professional development programs and practice management seminars.

★1752★ *Medicine & Related Occupations*
Delphi Productions
3160 4th St.
Boulder, CO 80304
Fax: (303)443-4022   Fr: 888-443-2400
URL: http://www.delphivideo.com
$95.00. 45 minutes. Part of the Careers for the 21st Century Video Library.

Civil Engineers

SOURCES OF HELP-WANTED ADS

★1753★ American City and County
Primedia Business
6151 Powers Ferry Rd.
Atlanta, GA 30339
Ph: (770)955-2500   Fax: (770)618-0348
Monthly. $67.00/year for individuals. Municipal and county administration magazine.

★1754★ AWIS Magazine
Association for Women in Science
1200 New York Ave. NW, Ste. 650
Washington, DC 20005
Ph: (202)326-8940   Fax: (202)326-8960
Fr: 800-886-AWIS

Description: Bimonthly. Covers issues, legislation, and trends related to science education for girls, women, and minorities. Includes information on grants and fellowships, job openings, educational programs, events, and notices of publications available.

★1755★ Better Roads
James Informational Media Inc.
2720 S River Rd., Ste. 126
Des Plaines, IL 60018
Ph: (847)298-8446   Fax: (847)391-9058
Fr: 800-957-9305

Monthly. $20.00/year . Free to qualified subscribers; $20.00/year for individuals; $90.00/year for other countries. Magazine serving federal, state, county, city, and township officials involved in road, street, bridge, and airport construction, maintenance and safety.

★1756★ Civil Engineering-ASCE
American Society of Civil Engineers
1801 Alexander Bell Dr.
Reston, VA 20191
Ph: (703)295-6300   Fax: (703)295-6222
Fr: 800-548-2723
E-mail: ztrem@ce.udel.edu
URL: http://www.pubs.asce.org/ceonline/

newce.html
Monthly. $30.00/year for members; $160.00/year for individuals; $160.00/year for institutions, nonmembers; $205.00/year for out of country; $50.00/year for foreign members; $205.00/year for institutions, other countries. Professional magazine.

★1757★ Consulting-Specifying Engineer
Reed Business Information
360 Park Ave. S
New York, NY 10014
Ph: (646)746-7764
URL: http://www.csemag.com/index.asp?webzine=cse&publication=cse

The integrated engineering magazine of the building construction industry.

★1758★ Engineering Times
National Society of Professional
  Engineers
1420 King St.
Alexandria, VA 22314
Ph: (703)684-2875   Fax: (703)836-4875
E-mail: et@nspe.org
URL: http://http//:www.nspc.org/1et.asp

$30.00/year for individuals; $48.00/year for out of country. Magazine (tabloid) covering professional, legislative, and techology issues for an engineering audience.

★1759★ ENR: Engineering News-Record
McGraw-Hill Companies
1221 Avenue of the Americas
New York, NY 10020
Ph: (212)512-2000
URL: http://www.enr.com

Weekly. $74.00/year; $5.00 for single issue. Magazine focusing on engineering and construction.

★1760★ Graduating Engineer & Computer Careers
Career Recruitment Media
211 W. Wacker Dr., No. 900
Chicago, IL 60606
Ph: (312)525-3100
URL: http://www.graduatingengineer.com

$16.00/year for individuals. Magazine focusing on employment, education, and career development for entry-level engineers and computer scientists.

★1761★ High Technology Careers Magazine
HTC
4701 Patrick Henry Dr., No. 1901
Santa Clara, CA 95054-1847
Ph: (408)970-8800   Fax: (408)567-0242
URL: http://www.hightechcareers.com

Bimonthly. $29.00/year; $35.00/year for Canada; $85.00/year for out of country. Magazine (tabloid) containing employment opportunity information for the engineering and technical community.

★1762★ ITE Journal
Institute of Transportation Engineers
1099 14th St. NW, Ste. 300 W
Washington, DC 20005-3438
Ph: (202)289-0222   Fax: (202)289-7722
URL: http://www.ite.org

Monthly. $65.00/year for U.S. and Canada; $85.00/year for other countries. Technical magazine focusing on the plan, design, and operation of surface transportation systems.

★1763★ MainStream
American Water Works Association
  (AWWA)
6666 W Quincy Ave.
Denver, CO 80235
Ph: (303)347-6272   Fax: (303)794-7310
URL: http://www.awwa.org/mainstream

Description: Biweekly, online; print issue is quarterly. Carries news of the Association and features about the drinking water industry, including regulations, legislation, conservation, treatment, quality, distribution, management, and utility operations. Recurring features include letters to the editor, a calendar of events, reports of meetings, news of educational opportunities, notices of publications available, education and job opportunities in the industry and legislative news.

★1764★ The Military Engineer
The Society of American Military
  Engineers
607 Prince St.
Alexandria, VA 22314-3117
Ph: (703)549-3800   Fax: (703)684-0231
URL: http://www.same.org

$56.00/year; $7.00 for single issue. Journal on military and civil engineering.

★1765★ The Municipality
League of Wisconsin Municipalities
202 State St., Ste. 300
Madison, WI 53703-2215
Ph: (608)267-2380   Fax: (608)267-0645
Fr: 800-991-5502

Monthly. $12.00/year. Magazine for officials of Wisconsin's local municipal governments.

★1766★ NSBE Magazine
NSBE Publications
1454 Duke St.
Alexandria, VA 22314
Ph: (703)549-2207   Fax: (703)683-5312

$10.00/year for individuals; $2.00 for single issue. Journal providing information on engineering careers, self-development, and cultural issues for recent graduates with technical majors.

★1767★ PM Network
Project Management Institute
4 Campus Blvd.
Newtown Square, PA 19073-3299
Ph: (610)356-4600   Fax: (610)356-4647

Monthly. $42.00/year for members. Professional journal covering industry applications and practical issues in managing projects.

★1768★ Public Works
Public Works Journal Corp.
PO Box 688
200 S Broad St.
Ridgewood, NJ 07451
Ph: (201)445-5800   Fax: (201)445-5170
Fr: 800-524-2364
URL: http://www.pwmag.com

Monthly. Free to qualified subscribers; $60.00/year for others. Trade magazine covering the public works industry nationwide for city, county, and state.

★1769★ SWE
Society of Women Engineers
230 E Ohio St., No. 400
2135 Lamberton Rd.
Chicago, IL 60611-3265
Ph: (312)596-5223   Fax: (312)596-5252
E-mail: hq@swe.org

URL: http://www.swe.org

Bimonthly. $30.00/year for nonmembers. Magazine for engineering students and for women and men working in the engineering and technology fields. Covers career guidance, continuing development and topical issues.

★1770★ Technology Review
Technology Review
201 Vassar St.
Cambridge, MA 02139
Ph: (617)253-8250   Fax: (617)258-5850
E-mail: trcomments@mit.edu

$30.00/year for individuals; $42.00/year for other countries; $4.95/year for single issue. Magazine reviewing new developments in technology with an emphasis on economic, political, and social implications. Not a new product publication.

★1771★ Water Engineering & Management
Scranton Gillette Communications Inc.
380 E NW Hwy., Ste. 200
Des Plaines, IL 60016-2282
Ph: (847)298-6622   Fax: (847)390-0408
E-mail: wemeditor@gcmail.com
URL: http://www.waterinfocenter.com

Monthly. $40.00/year for individuals; $6.00 for single issue; $64.00 for two years; $150.00 for two years, other countries. Trade magazine dedicated to the advancement of the state of the art and the transfer of technology in the field of municipal, county and regional water supply and water pollution control. Serves consulting sanitary engineers and managers of water/wastewater facilities who specify/buy products and services.

★1772★ WEPANEWS
Women in Engineering Programs &
  Advocates Network
Castle Point on the Hudson
Hoboken, NJ 07030
Ph: (201)216-5245   Fax: (201)216-5175
URL: http://www.wepan.org/newsletter.html

Description: Two issues/year. Seeks to provide greater access for women to careers in engineering. Includes news of graduate, undergraduate, freshmen, pre-college, and re-entry engineering programs for women. Recurring features include job listings, faculty, grant, and conference news, international engineering program news, action group news, notices of publications available, and a column titled Kudos.

★1773★ Western City
League of California Cities
1400 K St., 4th Fl.
Sacramento, CA 95814
Ph: (916)658-8223   Fax: (916)658-8289
Fr: 800-262-1801
URL: http://www.westerncity.com

Monthly. $39.00/year for individuals; $63.00 for two years. Municipal interest magazine.

PLACEMENT AND JOB REFERRAL SERVICES

★1774★ American Indian Science and Engineering Society (AISES)
PO Box 9828
Albuquerque, NM 87119-9828
Ph: (505)765-1052   Fax: (505)765-5608
E-mail: info@aises.org
URL: http://www.aises.org

Description: American Indian and non-Indian students and professionals in science, technology, and engineering fields; corporations representing energy, mining, aerospace, electronic, and computer fields. Seeks to motivate and encourage students to pursue undergraduate and graduate studies in science, engineering, and technology. Sponsors science fairs in grade schools, teacher training workshops, summer math/science sessions for 8th-12th graders, professional chapters, and student chapters in colleges. Offers scholarships. Adult members serve as role models, advisers, and mentors for students. Operates placement service.

★1775★ American Water Works Association (AWWA)
6666 W Quincy Ave.
Denver, CO 80235
Ph: (303)794-7711   Fax: (303)347-0804
Fr: 800-926-7337
E-mail: rrenner@awwa.org
URL: http://www.awwa.org

Members: Water utility managers, superintendents, engineers, chemists, bacteriologists, and other individuals interested in public water supply; municipal- and investor-owned water departments; boards of health; manufacturers of waterworks equipment; government officials and consultants interested in water supply. Purpose: Develops standards and supports research programs in waterworks design, construction, operation, and management. Activities: Conducts in-service training schools and prepares manuals for waterworks personnel. Maintains hall of fame. Offers placement service via member newsletter; compiles statistics. Offers training; children's services; and information center on the water utilities industry, potable water, and water reuse.

★1776★ Engineering Society of Detroit (ESD)
26100 American Dr., Ste. 500
Southfield, MI 48034-6184
Ph: (248)355-2910   Fax: (248)355-1492
E-mail: esd@esd.org
URL: http://esd.org

Description: Engineers from all disciplines; scientists and technologists. Conducts technical programs and engineering refresher courses; sponsors conferences and expositions. Maintains speakers' bureau; offers placement services. Although based in Detroit, MI, society membership is international.

★1777★ Korean Scientists and Engineers Association in America (KSEA)

1952 Gallows Rd., Ste. 300
Vienna, VA 22182
Ph: (703)748-1221   Fax: (703)748-1331
E-mail: sejong@ksea.org
URL: http://www.ksea.org

Description: Scientists and engineers holding single or advanced degrees. Goals are to: promote friendship and mutuality among Korean and American scientists and engineers; contribute to Korea's scientific, technological, industrial, and economic developments; strengthen the scientific, technological, and cultural bonds between Korea and the U.S. Sponsors symposium. Maintains speakers' bureau, placement service, and biographical archives. Compiles statistics. Maintains 100 volume library of scientific handbooks and yearbooks in Korean.

★1778★ Society of Hispanic Professional Engineers (SHPE)

5400 E Olympic Blvd., Ste. 210
Los Angeles, CA 90022
Ph: (323)725-3970   Fax: (323)725-0316
E-mail: shpenational@shpe.org
URL: http://www.shpe.org

Description: Engineers, student engineers, and scientists seeking to increase the number of Hispanic engineers by providing motivation and support to students. Sponsors competitions and educational programs. Maintains placement service and speakers' bureau; compiles statistics.

EMPLOYER DIRECTORIES AND NETWORKING LISTS

★1779★ American Men and Women of Science

Thomson Gale
27500 Drake Rd.
Farmington Hills, MI 48331-3535
Ph: (248)699-4253   Fax: (248)699-8065
Fr: 800-877-GALE
E-mail: amws@galegroup.com

Biennial, latest edition December 2002. $975.00. Covers over 129,700 U.S. and Canadian scientists active in the physical, biological, mathematical, computer science, and engineering fields; includes references to previous edition for deceased scientists and nonrespondents. Entries include: Name, address, education, personal and career data, memberships, honors and awards, research interest. Arrangement: Alphabetical. Indexes: Discipline (in separate volume).

★1780★ American Society of Civil Engineers-Official Register

American Society of Civil Engineers
1801 Alexander Bell Dr.
Reston, VA 20191
Ph: (703)295-6300   Fax: (703)295-6222
Fr: 800-548-2723

URL: http://www.asce.org

Annual, December. $24.00 for members; $28.80 international. Publication includes: Rosters of technical, professional, educational, and research committees, national officers, regional councils, sections and branches, award recipients. Principal content of publication is coverage of society data and statistics. Indexes: Alphabetical.

★1781★ Careers in Focus: Engineering

Ferguson Publishing Co.
200 W Jackson Blvd.
Chicago, IL 60606
Ph: (312)692-0109

2nd edition, 2002. $22.95. Publication includes: List of resources to consult for more information. Principal content of publication is job descriptions, advancement opportunities, educational requirements, employment outlook, salary information, and working conditions for careers in the field of engineering. Indexes: Alphabetical.

★1782★ Directory of Contract Staffing Firms

C.E. Publications Inc.
PO Box 3006
Bothell, WA 98041-3006
Ph: (425)806-5200   Fax: (425)806-5585
URL: http://www.cjhunter.com/dcsf/overview.html

$15.00. Covers nearly 1,300 contract firms actively engaged in the employment of engineering, IT/IS, and technical personnel for 'temporary' contract assignments throughout the world. Entries include: Company name, address, phone, name of contact, email, web address. Arrangement: Alphabetical. Indexes: Geographical.

★1783★ Engineers-Civil Directory

infoUSA Inc.
5711 S 86th Cir.
Omaha, NE 68127-0347
Ph: (402)930-3500   Fax: (402)331-0176
Fr: 800-555-6124
URL: http://www.abii.com

Annual. Number of listings: 10,081. Entries include: Name, address, phone (including area code), size of advertisement, year first in "Yellow Pages," name of owner or manager, number of employees. Compiled from telephone company "Yellow Pages," nationwide. Arrangement: Geographical.

★1784★ Engineers-Structural Directory

infoUSA Inc.
5711 S 86th Cir.
Omaha, NE 68127-0347
Ph: (402)930-3500   Fax: (402)331-0176
Fr: 800-555-6124
URL: http://www.abii.com

Annual. Number of listings: 5,023. Entries include: Name, address, phone (including area code), size of advertisement, year first in "Yellow Pages," name of owner or manager, number of employees. Compiled from

telephone company "Yellow Pages," nationwide. Arrangement: Geographical.

★1785★ ENR-Top 500 Design Firms Issue

McGraw-Hill Companies
1221 Ave. of the Americas
New York, NY 10020
Ph: (212)512-2000   Fax: (212)512-3840

Annual, April. $10.00. Publication includes: List of 500 leading architectural, engineering, and specialty design firms selected on basis of annual billings. Entries include: Company name, headquarters location, type of firm, current and prior year rank in billings, types of services, countries in which operated in preceding year. Arrangement: Ranked by billings.

★1786★ ENR-Top International Design Firms Issue

McGraw-Hill Companies
1221 Ave. of the Americas
New York, NY 10020
Ph: (212)512-2000   Fax: (212)512-3840

Annual, July issue of "Engineering News Record". $10.00. Publication includes: List of 200 design firms (including United States firms) competing outside their own national borders who received largest dollar volume of foreign contracts in preceding calendar year. Entries include: Company name, headquarters location, type of firm, current and previous year rankings in total billings, types of services, countries in which operated in preceding year. Arrangement: By amount billed to international clients in previous year.

★1787★ Indiana Society of Professional Engineers-Directory

Indiana Society of Professional Engineers
PO Box 20806
Indianapolis, IN 46220
Ph: (317)255-2267   Fax: (317)255-2530

Annual, fall. $55.00. Covers member registered engineers, land surveyors, engineering students, and engineers in training. Entries include: Member name, address, phone, type of membership, business information, specialty. Arrangement: Alpha by chapter area.

★1788★ International Directory of Engineering Societies and Related Organizations

American Association of Engineering Societies
1828 L St. NW, Ste. 906
Washington, DC 20036
Ph: (202)296-2237   Fax: (202)296-1151
Fr: 888-400-AAES

Irregular, latest edition December 1998. $240.00. Covers about 1,370 national, regional, Canadian, and international organizations concerned with engineering and related fields. Entries include: Name, address, phone, fax, e-mail, key personnel, objectives, publications, activities, mailing lists, federation memberships, meeting and convention dates, and budget data. Arrangement: Alphabetical. Indexes: Acronym, geographical, area of specialization.

★1789★ **Peterson's Job Opportunities in Engineering and Technology**

Thomson Peterson's
PO Box 67005
Lawrenceville, NJ 08648-6105
Fr: 800-338-3282

Compiled by the Peterson's staff. Fourth edition, 1996. $21.95 (paper). 384 pages. Profiles 2,000 high-tech companies looking primarily for technical personnel in such fields as biotechnology, telecommunications, software, computers and peripherals, defense, and aerospace. Contains job-search strategies and career options to help match education and expertise to the job market. Indexed geographically, by industry, and by hiring needs.

HANDBOOKS AND MANUALS

★1790★ **The Best Resumes for Scientists and Engineers**

John Wiley & Sons Inc.
1 Wiley Dr.
Somerset, NJ 08873
Ph: (732)469-4400   Fr: 800-225-5945

Adele Lewis and David J. Moore. Second edition, 1993. $37.50; $19.95 (paper). 224 pages. Presents an extensive collection of scientific and engineering resumes, highlighting the important differences between these and resumes written for other occupations.

★1791★ **Career Development: A Special Issue of the Journal of Management in Engineering**

American Society of Civil Engineers
1801 Alexander Bell Dr.
Reston, VA 20191-4400
Ph: (703)295-6300   Fax: (703)295-6211
Fr: 800-548-2723

Stuart G. Walesh, editor. 1998. $15.00 (paper). 68 pages.

★1792★ **Engineering Your Job Search: A Job-Finding Resource for Engineering Professionals**

Professional Publications, Inc.
1250 5th Ave.
Belmont, CA 94002
Ph: (650)593-9119   Fax: (650)592-4519
Fr: 800-426-1178

Compiled by Professional Publications, editors. 1995. $24.95 (paper). 154 pages. Out of print.

★1793★ **Great Jobs for Engineering Majors**

McGraw-Hill Professional
McGraw-Hill Higher Education
2 Penn Plaza
New York, NY 10121
Ph: (212)904-2000   Fr: 800-722-4726
E-mail: ntcpub@tribune.com

Geraldine O. Garner. Second edition, 2002. $14.95. 256 pages. Covers all the career options open to students majoring in engineering.

★1794★ **How to Succeed as an Engineer: A Practical Guide to Enhance Your Career**

Institute of Electrical & Electronics
  Engineers Inc.
PO Box 87204
Vancouver, WA 98687
Ph: (360)253-9532   Fax: (360)253-4084

Todd Yuzuriha. 1999. $29.95 (paper). 367 pages.

★1795★ **The I Hate Selling Book: Business-Building Advice for Consultants, Attorneys, Accountants, Engineers, Architects, and Other Professionals**

Allan Boress & Associates
1500 University Dr., Suite 239
Coral Springs, FL 33071
Ph: (954)345-4666   Fax: (954)344-2453

Allan S. Boress. 2001. $29.95.

★1796★ **Keys to Engineering Success**

Prentice Hall PTR
One Lake St.
Upper Saddle River, NJ 07458
Ph: (201)236-7000

Jill S. Tietjen, Kristy A. Schloss, Carol Carter, Joyce Bishop, and Sarah Lyman. 2000. $32.00 (paper).

★1797★ **Majoring in Engineering: How to Get from Your Freshman Year to Your First Job**

Farrar, Straus & Giroux, Inc.
19 Union Sq., W
New York, NY 10003
Ph: (212)741-6900   Fax: (212)633-9385
Fr: 888-330-8477

John Garcia and Carol Carter, editors. 2000. $20.00; $10.00 (paper). 134 pages.

★1798★ **The New Engineer's Guide to Career Growth & Professional Awareness**

Institute of Electrical & Electronics
  Engineers Inc.
445 Hoes Ln.
PO Box 1331
Piscataway, NJ 08855-1331
Ph: (732)562-3967   Fax: (732)981-9334
Fr: 800-678-4333

Irving J. Gabelman, editor. 1996. $39.95 (paper). 275 pages.

★1799★ **Opportunities in Civil Engineering Careers**

VGM Career Horizons
N T C Contemporary Publishing
  Company
1221 Avenue of the Americas
New York, NY 10020
Ph: (212)904-2000   Fr: 800-323-4900
E-mail: ntcpub@tribune.com

Joseph Hagerty, Louis F. Cohn, Philip Pessy, and Tom Cosgrove. 1996. $14.95; $11.95 (paper). 205 pages. Describes career opportunities in the different fields of civil engineering and tells how to prepare for and launch such a career.

★1800★ **Opportunities in Engineering Careers**

McGraw-Hill Contemporary Books
1221 Avenue of the Americas
New York, NY 10020
Ph: (212)904-2000   Fr: 800-323-4900
E-mail: ntcpub@tribune.com

Nicholas Basta. Revised, 1995. $14.95; $11.95 (paper). 200 pages. Outlines typical job titles, salaries, career paths, and employment prospects.

★1801★ **Opportunities in High Tech Careers**

McGraw-Hill Trade
2 Penn Plaza
New York, NY 10121
Ph: (212)904-2000   Fr: 800-722-4726

Gary Colter and Deborah Yanuck. 1995. $14.95; $11.95 (paper). 160 pages. Explores high technology careers. Describes job opportunities, how to make a career decision, how to prepare for high technology jobs, job hunting techniques, and future trends.

★1802★ **Opportunities in Research and Development Careers**

McGraw-Hill/Contemporary Books
1221 Avenue of the Americas
New York, NY 10020
Ph: (212)904-2000   Fr: 800-323-4900
E-mail: ntcpub@tribune.com

Jan Goldberg. 1997. $14.95; $11.95 (paper). 204 pages.

★1803★ **Opportunities in State and Local Government Careers**

Vgm Career Horizons
1221 Avenue of the Americas
New York, NY 10020
Ph: (212)904-2000   Fr: 800-323-4900
E-mail: ntcpub@tribune.com

Neale J. Baxter. 1994. $14.95; $10.95 (paper). 160 pages. Points out the incentives and drawbacks of a government career. Describes hiring procedures and provides tips on filling out applications, taking physical and aptitude tests, handling interviews, and finding jobs. Describes the jobs in which 75% of all state and local government workers are employed. For each occupation, covers the nature of the work and the training required.

★1804★ Real People Working in Engineering

McGraw-Hill Contemporary Books
1221 Avenue of the Americas
New York, NY 10020
Ph: (212)904-2000   Fr: 800-323-4900
E-mail: ntcpub@tribune.com

Blythe Camenson, Jan Goldberg. 1997. $14.95; $12.95 (paper). Interviews and profiles of working professionals capture a range of opportunities in this field.

★1805★ Resumes for Engineering Careers

McGraw-Hill Trade
2 Penn Plaza
New York, NY 10121
Ph: (212)904-2000   Fr: 800-722-4726
E-mail: ntcpub@tribune.com

2000. $10.95 (paper). 456 pages. Contains sample resumes and cover letters applicable to any engineering field.

★1806★ Resumes for Scientific and Technical Careers

McGraw-Hill Contemporary Books
1221 Avenue of the Americas
New York, NY 10020
Ph: (212)904-2000   Fr: 800-323-4900
E-mail: ntcpub@tribune.com

1999. $9.95 (paper). 450 pages. Provides resume advice for individuals interested in working in scientific and technical careers. Includes sample resumes and cover letters.

★1807★ Where the Jobs Are: The Hottest Careers for the 90s

The Career Press, Inc.
3 Tice Rd.
PO Box 687
Franklin Lakes, NJ 07417-1322
Ph: (201)848-0310   Fax: (201)848-1727
Fr: 800-227-3371

Joyce Hadley. Third edition, 2000. $13.99 (paper). 400 pages. Out of print. Describes careers in fifteen general fields, from accounting to travel and hospitality.

EMPLOYMENT AGENCIES AND SEARCH FIRMS

★1808★ Claremont-Branan, Inc.

1298 Rockbridge Rd., Ste. B
Stone Mountain, GA 30087
Ph: (770)925-2915   Fax: (770)925-2601

Employment agency. Executive search firm.

★1809★ Engineer One, Inc.

PO Box 23037
Knoxville, TN 37933
Fax: (865)691-0110
E-mail: engineerone@engineerone.com
URL: http://www.engineerone.com

Employment agency.

★1810★ High Employee Services Ltd.

525 Greenfield Rd., 2nd Fl.
Lancaster, PA 17601
Ph: (717)396-7701   Fax: (717)396-7779

Personnel consultants serving all industries including business and finance, engineering, sales and marketing, and focusing on manufacturing, industrial, and transportation operations. Conducts full time, contract staffing, and temporary (clerical and skilled) placements. Serves private industries as well as government agencies.

★1811★ International Staffing Consultants

2901 W Coast Hwy.,Ste. 200
Newport Beach, CA 92663
Ph: (949)263-5933   Fax: (949)767-5959
E-mail: iscinc@iscworld.com
URL: http://www.iscworld.com

Employment agency. Provides placement on regular or temporary basis. Affiliate office in London.

★1812★ Main Line Personnel Service, Inc.

Pagoda Blding.
100 Presidential Blvd. Ste. 200
Bala Cynwyd, PA 19004-0448
Ph: (610)667-1820   Fax: (610)668-5000
URL: http://www.mlpers.com

Employment agency.

★1813★ R J Dishaw & Associates

PO Box 671262
Dallas, TX 75367-1262
Ph: (972)924-5000   Fax: (972)924-5003

Executive search firm.

★1814★ Search and Recruit International

4455 South Blvd.
Virginia Beach, VA 23452
Ph: (757)490-3151   Fax: (757)497-6503
E-mail: britt@searchandrecruit.com
URL: http://www.searchandrecruit.com

Employment agency. Headquartered in Virginia Beach. Other offices in Bremerton, WA; Charleston, SC; Jacksonville, FL; Memphis, TN; Pensacola, FL; Sacramento, CA; San Bernardino, CA; San Diego, CA.

★1815★ TRC Staffing Services Inc.

2110 15 Mile Rd., Ste. B
Sterling Heights, MI 48310
Ph: (586)939-3210   Fax: (586)978-057?

A full-service executive search company with permanent placements encompassing engineering, industrial sales, financial and computer science positions. Screen, interview and verify past employment for all candidates prior to referral. Also assist personnel staffs in the attainment of their EEO/AAP goals with the placement of talented individuals in positions which are underutilized with minorities and/or women. In addition, firm has a clerical temporary service division, TRC Temporary Service; and an employment agency, TRC Staffing Services.

★1816★ Tri-Serv Inc.

22 W. Padonia Rd., Ste. C-353
Timonium, MD 21093
Ph: (410)561-1740   Fax: (410)252-7417
E-mail: info@tri-serv.coom
URL: http://www.tri-serv.com

Permanent employment agency.

★1817★ Winters Technical Staffing Services

2025 Sheppard Ave. E, Ste. 4110
Willowdale, ON, Canada M2T 1V7
Ph: (416)495-7422   Fax: (416)495-8479

Technical staffing service for permanent and contract positions in all facets of engineering. Serves government agencies, consulting engineers, and all areas of manufacturing in Canada and northeast U.S.

ONLINE JOB SOURCES AND SERVICES

★1818★ Spherion Workforce Architects

URL: http://www.spherion.com

Description: Recruitment firm specializing in accounting and finance, sales and marketing, interim executives, technology, engineering, retail and human resources.

OTHER SOURCES

★1819★ American Academy of Environmental Engineers (AAEE)

130 Holiday Ct., No. 100
Annapolis, MD 21401
Ph: (410)266-3311   Fax: (410)266-7653
E-mail: academy@aaee.net
URL: http://www.aaee.net

Members: Environmentally oriented registered professional engineers certified by examination as Diplomates of the Academy. **Purpose:** Works to improve the standards of environmental engineering; to certify those with special knowledge of environmental engineering; to furnish lists of those certified to the public. **Activities:** Maintains speakers' bureau. Recognizes areas of specialization: Air Pollution Control; General Environmental; Hazardous Waste Management; Industrial Hygiene; Radiation Protection; Solid Waste Management; Water Supply and Wastewater. Requires written and oral examinations for certification. Works with other professional organizations on environmentally oriented activities. Identifies potential employment candidates through Talent Search Service.

★1820★ American Association of Blacks in Energy (AABE)

927 15th St. NW, Ste. 200
Washington, DC 20005
Ph: (202)371-9530   Fax: (202)371-9218
Fr: 800-466-0204
E-mail: aabe@aabe.org
URL: http://www.aabe.org

Description: Blacks in energy-related professions, including engineers, scientists, consultants, academicians, and entrepreneurs; government officials and public policymakers; interested students. Represents blacks and other minorities in matters involving energy use and research, the formulation of energy policy, the ownership of energy resources, and the development of energy technologies. Seeks to increase the knowledge, understanding, and awareness of the minority community in energy issues by serving as an energy information source for policymakers, recommending blacks and other minorities to appropriate energy officials and executives, encouraging students to pursue professional careers in the energy industry, and advocating the participation of blacks and other minorities in energy programsand policymaking activities. Updates members on key legislation and regulations being developed by the Department of Energy, the Department of Interior, the Department of Commerce, the Small Business Administration, and other federal and state agencies. Offers information on current job openings

★1821★ American Association of Engineering Societies (AAES)

1828 L St. NW, No. 906
Washington, DC 20036
Ph: (202)296-2237   Fax: (202)296-1151
Fr: 888-400-2237
E-mail: tprice@aaes.org
URL: http://www.aaes.org

Description: Coordinates the efforts of the member societies in the provision of reliable and objective information to the general public concerning issues which affect the engineering profession and the field of engineering as a whole; to collect, analyze, document, and disseminate data which will inform the general public of the relationship between engineering and the national welfare; to provide a forum for the engineering societies to exchange and discuss their views on matters of common interest; and to represent the U.S. engineering community

aborad through representation in WFEO and UPADI.

★1822★ American Society of Civil Engineers (ASCE)

1801 Alexander Bell Dr.
Reston, VA 20191-4400
Ph: (703)295-6300   Fax: (703)295-6222
Fr: 800-548-2723
URL: http://www.asce.org

Description: Professional society of civil engineers. Enhances the welfare of humanity by advancing the science and profession of engineering. Offers continuing education courses and technical specialty conferences. Develops technical codes and standards; publishes technical and professional journals, manuals and a variety of books. Works closely with Congress, the White House and federal agencies to build sound national policy on engineering issues. Supports research of new civil engineering technology and material. Informs the public about various engineering-related topics.

★1823★ Asian American Architects and Engineers

1670 Pine St.
San Francisco, CA 94109
Ph: (415)928-5910   Fax: (415)921-0182
E-mail: info@asianinc.org
URL: http://www.asianinc.org

Members: Minorities. **Purpose:** Provides contracts and job opportunities for minorities in the architectural and eningeering fields. **Activities:** Serves as a network for the promotion in professional fields.

★1824★ Association for International Practical Training (AIPT)

10400 Little Patuxent Pky., Ste. 250
Columbia, MD 21044-3519
Ph: (410)997-2200   Fax: (410)992-3924
E-mail: aipt@aipt.org
URL: http://www.aipt.org

Description: Providers worldwide on-the-job training programs for students and professionals seeking international career development and life-changing experiences. Arranges workplace exchanges in hundreds of professional fields, bringing employers and trainees together from around the world. Client list ranges from small farming communities to Fortune 500 companies.

★1825★ *Civil Engineers*

Evon Publishing
832 N 7th Ave.
Iron River, MI 49935
Ph: (906)265-3190

Audiocassette. 1996. $16.95. 32 minutes. Part of the Careers and Vocational Guidance Series. Provides information about the nature of the work, educational requirements, employment outlook, earnings, and work conditions as well as additional related information.

★1826★ *Engineering Occupations*

Delphi Productions
3160 4th St.
Boulder, CO 80304
Fax: (303)443-4022   Fr: 888-443-2400
URL: http://www.delphivideo.com

$95.00. 50 minutes. Part of the Careers for the 21st Century Video Library.

★1827★ National Action Council for Minorities in Engineering (NACME)

Empire State Bldg., Ste. 2212
350 Fifth Ave.
New York, NY 10118-2299
Ph: (212)279-2626   Fax: (212)629-5178
E-mail: webmaster@nacme.org
URL: http://www.nacme.org/

Description: Leads the national effort to increase access to careers in engineering and other science-based disciplines. Supported by the nation's leading technology-intensive companies, NACME conducts research and public policy analysis, develops and operates national demonstration programs at precollege and university levels, and disseminates information through publications, conferences, and electronic media. NACME is also the nation's largest privately funded source of scholarships for minority students in engineering.

★1828★ National Association of Traffic Accident Reconstructionists and Investigators (NATARI)

PO Box 398
Chadds Ford, PA 19317
Ph: (610)558-5176   Fax: (610)558-5176
E-mail: lizgurn@aol.com
URL: http://www.actar.org/natari.htm

Description: Engineers, attorneys, police officers, private investigators, medical examiners, and other individuals involved in the analysis of motor vehicle traffic accidents. Gathers and disseminates information on techniques and equipment of potential use to members; reviews literature in the field. Participating Organization of the Accreditation Commission for Traffic Accident Reconstruction.

★1829★ *Scientific, Engineering, and Technical Services*

Cambridge Educational
2572 Brunswick Ave.
Lawrenceville, NJ 08648-4128
Fax: 800-FAX-ON-US   Fr: 800-468-4227
URL: http://www.cambrigeeducational.com

$89.95. 2002. 18 minutes. Part of the Career Cluster Series.

★1830★ Society of Women Engineers (SWE)

230 E Ohio St., No. 400
Chicago, IL 60611-3265
Ph: (312)596-5223   Fax: (312)596-5252
E-mail: hq@swe.org
URL: http://www.swe.org

Description: Educational and service organization representing both students and professional women in engineering and technical fields.

★1831★ Water Environment Federation (WEF)

601 Wythe St.
Alexandria, VA 22314-1994
Ph: (703)684-2452   Fax: (703)684-2492
Fr: 800-666-0206
E-mail: csc@wef.org
URL: http://www.wef.org

Description: Technical societies representing chemists, biologists, ecologists, geologists, operators, educational and research personnel, industrial wastewater engineers, consultant engineers, municipal officials, equipment manufacturers, and university professors and students dedicated to the enhancement and preservation of water quality and resources. Seeks to advance fundamental and practical knowledge concerning the nature, collection, treatment, and disposal of domestic and industrial wastewaters, and the design, construction, operation, and management of facilities for these purposes. Disseminates technical information; promotes good public relations and regulations that improve water quality and the status of individuals working in this field. Conducts educational and research programs.

★1832★ Women in Engineering

Her Own Words
PO Box 5264
Madison, WI 53705-0264
Ph: (608)271-7083   Fax: (608)271-0209
URL: http://www.herownwords.com/

Video. Jocelyn Riley. $95.00. 15 minutes. Resource guide also available for $45.00.

★1833★ Women in Highway Construction

Her Own Words
PO Box 5264
Madison, WI 53705-0264
Ph: (608)271-7083   Fax: (608)271-0209
URL: http://www.herownwords.com/

Video. Jocelyn Riley. $95.00. 15 minutes. Resource guide also available for $45.00.

Claims Examiners

SOURCES OF HELP-WANTED ADS

★1834★ *Best's Review*
A.M. Best Co.
Ambest Rd.
Oldwick, NJ 08858
Fax: (908)439-2200
E-mail: best'sreview@ambest.com
URL: http://www.bestreview.com

Monthly. $21.00/year for individuals; $7.50 for single issue. Magazine covering issues and trends for the management personnel of life/health insurers, the agents, and brokers who market their products.

★1835★ *Business Insurance*
Crain Communications Inc.
711 Third Ave.
New York, NY 10017-4036
Ph: (212)210-0100   Fax: (212)210-0244
Fr: 800-446-1420
URL: http://www.businessinsurance.com

Weekly. $97.00/year for individuals. International newsweekly reporting on corporate risk and employee benefit management news.

★1836★ *CLAIMS*
Claims
15112 64th Ave. W
Edmonds, WA 98026
Ph: (425)745-6394
E-mail: editor@claimsmag.com
URL: http://www.claimsmag.com

Monthly. $42.00/year for individuals; $8.00 for single issue. Magazine for the property-casualty insurance claims industry.

★1837★ *National Underwriter Property and Casualty/Risk and Benefits Management*
National Underwriter Co.
5081 Olympic Blvd.
Erlanger, KY 41018
Ph: (859)692-2100   Fax: 800-874-1916
Fr: 800-543-0874

E-mail: nup&c@nuco.com

Weekly. $89.00/year. Newsweekly for agents, brokers, executives, and managers in risk and benefit insurance.

EMPLOYER DIRECTORIES AND NETWORKING LISTS

★1838★ *Best's Insurance Reports*
A.M. Best Co.
Ambest Rd.
Oldwick, NJ 08858
Ph: (908)439-2200   Fax: (908)439-2688
URL: http://www.ambest.com

Annual, summer. $1,495.00 for CD-ROM; $830.00 for print. Published in three editions: Life-health insurance, covering about 1,750 companies, property-casualty insurance, covering over 3,200 companies; and international, covering more than 1,200 insurers. Each edition lists state insurance commissioners and related companies and agencies (mutual funds, worker compensation funds, underwriting agencies, etc.). Entries include: For each company-Company name, address, phone; history; states in which licensed; names of officers and directors; financial data; financial analysis and Best's rating. Arrangement: Alphabetical.

★1839★ *Business Insurance-Third-Party Claims Administrators Issue*
Business Insurance
360 N Michigan Ave.
Chicago, IL 60601-3806
Ph: (312)649-5319   Fax: (312)280-3174
Fr: 800-678-2724
URL: http://businessinsurance.365media.com/

Annual, February. $15.00. Publication includes: List of approximately 150 third-party claims administration, adjusting, and auditing firms that process claims for self-insured clients, including employee benefit-and property/casualty claims. Entries include: Company name, address, phone, fax, number of employees, number of claims processing

staff, number of clients, method of compensation, prior year's revenues (when available), along with percent attributed to claims administration, adjusting and auditing for self-insured clients; claims volume by number of projects conducted; specialty or area of expertise. Arrangement: Alphabetical, by company.

★1840★ *Insurance Almanac*
Underwriter Printing and Publishing Co.
50 E Palisade Ave.
Englewood, NJ 07631
Ph: (201)569-8808   Fax: (201)569-8817
Fr: 800-526-4700

Annual, July. $175.00. Covers over 3,000 insurance companies that write fire, casualty, accident and health, life, and Lloyd's policies; also lists mutual and reciprocal companies. Includes national, state, and local insurance associations; state insurance officials; and about 800 agents, brokers, actuaries, and adjusters. Entries include: For companies-Company name, address, phone, names of officers and directors, lines written, territory covered; for larger firms, some history and financial data. For associations-Name, address, names of staff and officers, place and date of meetings. For agents, brokers, etc.-Name, address. Arrangement: Classified by insurance lines, type of activity, etc. Indexes: Company name.

★1841★ *Insurance Consultants & Advisors Directory*
infoUSA Inc.
5711 S 86th Cir.
Omaha, NE 68127-0347
Ph: (402)930-3500   Fax: (402)331-0176
Fr: 800-555-6124
URL: http://www.abii.com

Annual. Number of listings: 11,032. Entries include: Name, address, phone (including area code), size of advertisement, year first in "Yellow Pages," name of owner or manager, number of employees. Compiled from telephone company "Yellow Pages," nationwide. Arrangement: Geographical.

★1842★ Insurance Phone Book and Directory

Douglas Publications Inc.
2807 N Parham Rd.,64 Bldg., Ste. 200
Richmond, VA 23294
Ph: (804)762-9600　　Fax: (804)217-8999
Fr: 800-794-6086
URL: http://www.douglaspublications.com

Annual. $99.50. Covers about 4,000 life, accident and health, worker's compensation, auto, fire and casualty, marine, surety, and other insurance companies. Entries include: Company name, address, phone, fax, toll-free number, type of insurance provided. Arrangement: Alphabetical.

★1843★ Kirshner's Insurance Directories

National Underwriter Co.
5081 Olympic Blvd.
Erlanger, KY 41018
Ph: (859)692-2100　　Fax: 800-874-1916
Fr: 800-543-0874
URL: http://www.nationalunderwriter.com/kirschners/

Annual, all editions except California and Pacific Northwest (semiannual). $19.95. Covers Insurance agents and agencies in all 50 states and the District of Columbia. Published in 24 separate editions for Southern California, Northern California, Pacific Northwest (AK, ID, HI, OR, WA, MT), Michigan, Illinois, New England states (CT, ME, MA, NH, RI, VT), Ohio, Rocky Mountain states (AZ, CO, NV, NM, UT, WY), South Central states (GA, AL, MS), Indiana, Texas, Kentucky/Tennessee, East Central states (VA, WV, NC, SC), South Central West states (AR, OK, LA), Wisconsin, Central states (KS, MO, NE), North Central states (IA, MN, ND, SD), Mid-Atlantic states (DE, MD, NJ, DC), Pennsylvania, Florida. Entries include: For companies-Name, address, key personnel (with addresses abd phone numbers). Arrangement: Separate alphabetical sections for insurance companies, wholesalers, field agents, and agencies. Indexes: Type of insurance.

★1844★ Mergent Bank and Finance Manual

Mergent Inc.
5250 77 Center Dr., Ste. 150
Charlotte, NC 28217
Ph: (704)559-7601　　Fax: (704)559-6945
Fr: 800-342-5647
URL: http://www.mergent.com

Annual, July; supplements in 'Mergent Bank & Finance News Reports'. $2,095.00. Covers in four volumes, over 12,000 national, state, and private banks, savings and loans, mutual funds, unit investment trusts, and insurance and real estate companies in the United States. Entries include: Company name, headquarters and branch offices, phones, names and titles of principal executives, directors, history, Moody's rating, and extensive financial and statistical data. Arrangement: Classified by type of business. Indexes: Company name.

★1845★ National Association of Catastrophe Adjusters-Membership Roster

National Association of Catastrophe Adjusters Inc.
PO Box 821864
North Richland Hills, TX 76182
Ph: (817)498-3466　　Fax: (817)498-0480
URL: http://www.nacatadj.org

Annual, March. Covers about 400 insurance catastrophe claims adjusters and adjusting firms; about 150 related insurance firms (associate members). Entries include: Name, address, phone, spouse's name. Arrangement: Separate geographical sections for regular associate and business associate members. Indexes: Alphabetical; geographical.

★1846★ National Insurance Association-Member Roster

National Insurance Association
411 Chapel Hill St.
Durham, NC 27701

Annual, June. Covers about 13 insurance companies owned or controlled by African-Americans. Entries include: Company name, address, phone, date founded, states in which licensed, officers. Arrangement: Alphabetical.

★1847★ Who's Who in Insurance

Underwriter Printing and Publishing Co.
50 E Palisade Ave.
Englewood, NJ 07631
Ph: (201)569-8808　　Fax: (201)569-8817
Fr: 800-526-4700

Annual, February. $150.00. Covers over 5,000 insurance officials, brokers, agents, and buyers. Entries include: Name, title, company name, address, home address, educational background, professional club and association memberships, personal and career data. Arrangement: Alphabetical.

★1848★ Yearbook

American Association of Managing
　General Agents
PO Box 26547
Overland Park, KS 66225-6547
URL: http://www.iix.com/aamga

Annual, spring. Covers 250 managing general agents of insurance companies and their more than 500 branch offices; coverage includes Canada. Entries include: Name, address, names and titles of principal and contact, insurance companies represented. Arrangement: Geographical.

HANDBOOKS AND MANUALS

★1849★ Best Websites for Financial Professionals, Business Appraisers, & Accountants

John Wiley & Sons Inc.
111 River St.
Hoboken, NJ 07030-5774
Ph: (201)748-6000　　Fax: (201)748-5774
Eva M. Lang. 2001. $39.95 (paper).

★1850★ Opportunities in Insurance Careers

McGraw-Hill/Contemporary Books
1221 Avenue of the Americas
New York, NY 10020
Ph: (212)904-2000　　Fr: 800-323-4900
E-mail: ntcpub@tribune.com

Robert Schrayer. Revised, 1999. $14.95; $11.95 (paper). 148 pages. A guide to planning for and seeking opportunities in the field. Contains bibliography and illustrations.

EMPLOYMENT AGENCIES AND SEARCH FIRMS

★1851★ Employment Advisors

815 Nicollet Mall Ste 200
Minneapolis, MN 55402
Ph: (612)339-3944
E-mail: info@collegegraduateregistry.com
URL: http://www.collegegraduateregistry.com

Employment agency. Places candidates in variety of fields.

★1852★ Godfrey Personnel Inc.

300 W. Adams, Ste. 612
Chicago, IL 60606-5194
Ph: (312)236-4455　　Fax: (312)580-6292
E-mail: jim@godfreypersonnel.com
URL: http://ww.godfreypersonnel.com

Search firm specializing in insurance industry.

★1853★ International Insurance Personnel, Inc.

300 W. Wieuca Rd., Bldg. 2, Ste. 101
Atlanta, GA 30342
Ph: (404)255-9710
E-mail: info@intlinspersonnel.com
URL: http://www.intlinspersonnel.com/interimstafing.htm

Employment agency specializing in the area of insurance.

★1854★ Questor Consultants, Inc.

2515 N. Broad St.
Colmar, PA 18915
Ph: (215)997-9262　　Fax: (215)997-9226

E-mail: jobs@questorconsultants.com
URL: http://www.questorconsultants.com

Executive search firm specializing in the insurance and legal fields.

OTHER SOURCES

★1855★ Business and Administration Support Occupations
Delphi Productions
3160 4th St.
Boulder, CO 80304
Fax: (303)443-4022   Fr: 888-443-2400
URL: http://www.delphivideo.com

$95.00. 42 minutes. Part of the Careers for the 21st Century Video Library.

★1856★ Insurance Agent
Cambridge Educational
2572 Brunswick Ave.
Lawrenceville, NJ 08648-4128
Fax: 800-FAX-ON-US   Fr: 800-468-4227
URL: http://www.cambridgeeducational.com

$39.95. 15 minutes. Part of the Vocational Visions Career Series.

★1857★ Insurance Claims and Policy Processing Occupations
Evon Publishing
832 N 7th Ave.
Iron River, MI 49935
Ph: (906)265-3190

Audiocassette. 1996. $16.95. 32 minutes. Part of the Careers and Vocational Guidance Series. Provides information about the nature of the work, educational requirements, employment outlook, earnings, and work conditions as well as additional related information.

★1858★ Insurance Information Institute (III)
110 William St.
New York, NY 10038
Ph: (212)346-5500   Fax: (212)791-1807
Fr: 800-331-9146
E-mail: info@iii.org
URL: http://www.iii.org

Description: Property and casualty insurance companies. Provides information and educational services to mass media, educational institutions, trade associations, businesses, government agencies, and the public.

★1859★ LOMA
2300 Windy Ridge Pkwy., Ste. 600
Atlanta, GA 30339-8443
Ph: (770)951-1770   Fax: (770)984-0441
E-mail: marketing@loma.org
URL: http://www.loma.org/

Description: Life and health insurance companies and financial services in the U.S. and Canada; and overseas in 45 countries; affiliate members are firms that provide professional support to member companies. Provides research, information, training, and educational activities in areas of operations and systems, human resources, financial planning and employee development. Administers FLMI Insurance Education Program, which awards FLMI (Fellow, Life Management Institute) designation to those who complete the ten-examination program.

★1860★ National Association of Insurance Women International (NAIW)
1847 E 15th St.
PO Box 4410
Tulsa, OK 74104
Fax: (918)743-1968   Fr: 800-766-6249
E-mail: joinnaiw@naiw.org
URL: http://www.naiw.org

Members: Insurance industry professionals. **Purpose:** Promotes continuing education and networking for the professional advancement of its members. **Activities:** Offers education programs, meetings, services, and leadership opportunities. Provides a forum to learn about other disciplines in the insurance industry.

★1861★ National Association of Public Insurance Adjusters (NAPIA)
21165 Whitfield Pl., No. 105
Potomac Falls, VA 20165
Ph: (703)433-9217   Fax: (703)433-0369
E-mail: info@napia.com
URL: http://www.napia.com

Members: Professional society of public insurance adjusters. **Activities:** Sponsors certification and professional education programs.

Clinical Laboratory Technologists and Technicians

SOURCES OF HELP-WANTED ADS

★1862★ **ACTA Cytologica**
Science Printers and Publishers Inc.
PO Drawer 12425
8342 Olive Blvd.
St. Louis, MO 63132-2814
Ph: (314)991-4440   Fax: (314)991-4654
E-mail: editor@acta-cytol.com
URL: http://www.acta-cytol.com

Bimonthly. $185.00/year for individuals; $259.00/year for institutions; $45.00 for single issue. Journal publishing scientific articles offering significant contributions to the advancement of clinical cytology.

★1863★ **ADVANCE for Medical Laboratory Professionals**
Merion Publications Inc.
2900 Horizon Dr.
PO Box 61556
King of Prussia, PA 19406-0956
Ph: (610)278-1400
E-mail: advance@merion.com
URL: http://www.advanceweb.com

Biweekly. Free. Magazine reaches technologists and laboratory managers with professional news and employment opportunities.

★1864★ **American Clinical Laboratory**
International Scientific Communications Inc.
30 Controls Dr.
PO Box 870
Shelton, CT 06484-0870
Ph: (203)926-9300   Fax: (203)926-9310
URL: http://www.iscpubs.com

$237.00/year for individuals. Technical magazine on clinical laboratory techniques.

★1865★ **American Laboratory News**
International Scientific Communications Inc.
30 Controls Dr.
PO Box 870
Shelton, CT 06484-0870
Ph: (203)926-9300   Fax: (203)926-9310
E-mail: maureenj@iscpubs.com
URL: http://www.iscpubs.com

Monthly. $235.00/year. Trade magazine for scientists.

★1866★ **ASPB News**
American Society of Plant Biologists
15501 Monona Dr.
Rockville, MD 20855-2768
Ph: (301)251-0560   Fax: (301)279-2996
Description: Bimonthly. Offers news of interest to plant physiologists, biochemists, horticulturists, and plant molecular and cell biologists engaged in research and teaching. Alerts members to public policy issues, educational opportunities, meetings, seminars, and conventions pertinent to the field. Recurring features include letters to the editor, reports of meetings, job listings, a calendar of events, news from regional sections, and teaching ideas.

★1867★ **CAP Today**
College of American Pathologists
325 Waukegan Rd.
Northfield, IL 60093-2750
Ph: (847)832-7000   Fax: (847)832-8150
Fr: 800-323-4040
URL: http://www.cap.org

Monthly. $60.00/year for individuals, U.S.; $75.00/year, Canada; $130.00/year, foreign. Magazine covering advances in pathology tests and equipment, clinical lab management and operations trends, and related regulatory and legislative changes.

★1868★ **Cell**
Cell Press
1100 Massachusetts Ave.
Cambridge, MA 02138
Ph: (617)661-7057   Fax: (617)661-7061
E-mail: advertising@cell.com

URL: http://www.cell.com

Biweekly. $125.00/year for individuals, U.S.; $242.00/year for other countries; $210.00/year for Canada; $799.00/year for institutions; $899.00/year for institutions, other countries. Journal on molecular and cell biology.

★1869★ **Clinical Laboratory News**
American Association for Clinical Chemistry
2101 L St. NW, Ste. 202
Washington, DC 20037-1526
Ph: (202)857-0717   Fax: (202)887-5093
Fr: 800-892-1400
E-mail: cln@aacc.org
URL: http://www.aacc.org

Monthly. $30.00/year; $4.00 for single issue; $65.00/year for out of country. Scholarly magazine providing current news in the field of clinical laboratory science.

★1870★ **Cytometry**
John Wiley and Sons Inc.
111 River St.
Hoboken, NJ 07030
Ph: (201)748-8866   Fax: (201)748-8824

$1,016.00/year for U.S.; $1,196.00/year for Canada and Mexico; $1,349.00/year for other countries. International journal covering all aspects of analytical cytology.

★1871★ **Laboratory Medicine**
American Society of Clinical Pathologists
2100 W Harrison St.
Chicago, IL 60612
Ph: (312)738-1336   Fax: (312)738-0101
URL: http://www.asep.org

Monthly. $50.00/year for individuals; $8.00 for single issue. Professional journal covering medical technology and pathology.

★1872★ **Medical Laboratory Observer (MLO)**
Thomson Medical Economics
5 Paragon Dr.
Montvale, NJ 07645-1742
Ph: (201)358-7200   Fax: (201)722-2680

E-mail: mlosales@nelsonpub.com
URL: http://www.mlo-online.com/
Monthly. $70.00/year. Free. Trade journal.

★1873★ **MEEN Imaging Technology News**

Reilly Communications Group
16 E Schaumburg Rd.
Schaumburg, IL 60194
Ph: (847)882-6336   Fax: (847)519-0166
URL: http://www.ITNonline.net

Bimonthly. $50.00/year for individuals; $80.00/year for Canada; $110.00/year for other countries, air mail; $10.00 for single issue. Trade magazine (tabloid) serving users and buyers of medical imaging technologies and services.

★1874★ **Nature International Weekly Journal of Science**

Nature Publishing Group
345 Park Ave. S
New York, NY 10010-1707
Ph: (212)726-9200   Fax: (212)689-9711
Fr: 888-331-6288
E-mail: nature@natureny.com
URL: http://www.nature.com

Weekly. $145.00/year for individuals; $495.00/year for institutions. Magazine covering science and technology, including the fields of biology, biochemistry, genetics, medicine, earth sciences, physics, pharmacology, and behavioral sciences.

★1875★ **Vantage Point**

Clinical Laboratory Management Association
989 Old Eagle School Rd., Ste. 815
Wayne, PA 19087
Ph: (610)995-9580   Fax: (610)995-9568
E-mail: publications@clma.org
URL: http://www.clma.org

Description: Semimonthly. Features general, health care, and laboratory management tips, trends, and legislative news. Recurring features include news of educational opportunities, job listings, and columns titled Manager's Workshop, Healthcare Management Briefs, Career Corner, Online Update and Legislative Update.

PLACEMENT AND JOB REFERRAL SERVICES

★1876★ **American Association for Clinical Chemistry (AACC)**

2101 L St. NW, Ste. 202
Washington, DC 20037-1558
Ph: (202)857-0717   Fax: (202)887-5093
Fr: 800-892-1400
E-mail: info@aacc.org
URL: http://www.aacc.org

Members: Clinical laboratory scientists and others engaged in the practice of clinical

laboratory science in independent laboratories, hospitals, and allied institutions. Sponsors education programs; publishes books.

★1877★ **Clinical Ligand Assay Society (CLAS)**

3139 S Wayne Rd.
Wayne, MI 48184
Ph: (734)722-6290   Fax: (734)722-7006
E-mail: clas@clas.org
URL: http://www.clas.org

Description: Seeks to establish and promote high standards in the science and application of ligand assay technology by encouraging research, education practitioners, and fostering communication and cooperation among individuals in laboratories in medicine, academia, and industry. Sponsors job placement service.

★1878★ **Endocrine Society (ES)**

8401 Connecticut Ave., Ste. 900
Chevy Chase, MD 20815-5817
Ph: (301)941-0200   Fax: (301)941-0259
E-mail: endostaff@endo-society.org
URL: http://www.endo-society.org

Purpose: Promotes excellence in research, education, and clinical practice in endocrinology and related disciplines. **Activities:** Maintains placement service.

EMPLOYER DIRECTORIES AND NETWORKING LISTS

★1879★ **AGT International Membership Directory**

Association of Genetic Technologists
AGT Executive Office
P.O. Box 15945-288
Lenexa, KS 66285-5945
Ph: (913)541-0497   Fax: (913)599-5340
URL: http://www.agt-info.org/Publication.html

Annual, fall/winter. $50.00 for members; $100.00 for nonmembers. Covers about 520 laboratories studying heritable and acquired chromosomal disorders using cytogenetic, genetics, and cellular biology techniques. Entries include: Laboratory name, address, phone, areas of specialization, techniques, numbers and types of laboratory tests performed, and names of director and cytogenetic technologists. Arrangement: Geographical. Indexes: Director name, ACT member name.

★1880★ **AHA Guide to the Health Care Field**

American Hospital Association (AHA)
1 N. Franklin St., 27th Fl.
Chicago, IL 60606
Ph: (312)422-2050   Fax: (312)422-4700
Fr: 800-424-4301

Annual, August. $295.00. Covers hospitals,

networks, multi-health care systems, free-standing ambulatory surgery centers, psychiatric facilities, long-term care facilities, substance abuse programs, and other health-related organizations. Entries include: For hospitals-Facility name, address, phone, administrator's name, number of beds, facilities and services, number of employees, expenses, other statistics. For other organizations-Name, address, phone, fax, name and title of contact. Arrangement: Geographical. Indexes: Hospital name.

★1881★ **Directory of Accredited Laboratories**

American Association for Laboratory Accreditation
5301 Buckeystown Pke., Ste. 350
Frederick, MD 21704-8307
Ph: (301)644-3202   Fax: (301)662-2974
URL: http://www.a2la.org

Weekly, on web site. Free. Covers over 1,600 testing and calibration laboratories and inspection agencies accredited for technical competence as measured against national and international standards in the following fields of testing: metrology, acoustics and vibration, construction materials, biology, chemistry, electricity, environmental, geotechnical, mechanical, thermal, and nondestructive. Entries include: Name of laboratory, address, phone, contact, certificate number, current period of accreditation, fields of accreditation technologies and methodologies. Arrangement: Alphabetical. Indexes: Fields of accreditation.

★1882★ **Directory of Hospital Personnel**

Thomson Medical Economics
5 Paragon Dr.
Montvale, NJ 07645-1742
Ph: (201)358-7200   Fax: (201)722-2680

Annual, November. $325.00. Covers 200,000 executives at 7,000 U.S. hospitals. Entries include: Name of hospital, address, phone, number of beds, type and JCAHO status of hospital, names and titles of key department heads and staff, medical and nursing school affiliations; number of residents, interns, and nursing students. Arrangement: Geographical. Indexes: Hospital name, personnel, hospital size.

★1883★ **Guide to Careers in the Health Professions**

The Princeton Review
1745 Broadway
New York, NY 10019
Ph: (212)829-6928   Fax: (212)940-7400
Fr: 800-733-3000

Published January, 2001. $24.95. Presents advice and information for those searching for satisfying careers in the health professions. Publication includes: Directory of schools and academic programs. Entries include: Name, address, phone, tuition, program details, employment profiles.

★1884★ Hospital Blue Book

Billian/Transworld Publishing Inc.
2100 Powers Ferry Rd.
Ste. 300
Atlanta, GA 30339
Ph: (770)955-8484   Fax: (770)955-8485
Fr: 800-533-8484
E-mail: blu-book@billian.com

Annual, January. $285.00 for national edition; $160.00 for southern edition. Covers more than 6,687 hospitals; some listings also appear in a separate southern edition of this publication. Entries include: Name of hospital, accreditation, mailing address, phone, fax, number of beds, type of facility (nonprofit, general, state, etc.); list of administrative personnel and chiefs of medical services, with specific titles. Arrangement: Geographical.

★1885★ Laboratories Medical Directory

infoUSA Inc.
5711 S 86th Cir.
Omaha, NE 68127-0347
Ph: (402)930-3500   Fax: (402)331-0176
Fr: 800-555-6124
URL: http://www.abii.com

Annual. Number of listings: 9,073. Entries include: Name, address, phone (including area code), size of advertisement, year first in "Yellow Pages," name of owner or manager, number of employees. Compiled from telephone company "Yellow Pages," nationwide. Arrangement: Geographical.

★1886★ Medical and Health Information Directory

Thomson Gale
27500 Drake Rd.
Farmington Hills, MI 48331-3535
Ph: (248)699-4253   Fax: (248)699-8065
Fr: 800-877-GALE
E-mail: businessproducts@gale.com

Annual. $285.00 per volume; $675.00 per set. Covers in Volume 1, more than 26,500 medical and health oriented associations, organizations, institutions, and government agencies, including health maintenance organizations (HMOs), preferred provider organizations (PPOs), insurance companies, pharmaceutical companies, research centers, and medical and allied health schools. In Volume 2, over 12,000 medical book publishers; medical periodicals, directories, audiovisual producers and services, medical libraries and information centers, electronic resources, and health-related internet search engines. In Volume 3, more than 35,500 clinics, treatment centers, care programs, and counseling/diagnostic services for 34 subject areas. Entries include: Institution, service, or firm name, address, phone, fax, email and URL; many include names of key personnel and, when pertinent, descriptive annotation. Volume 3 was formerly listed separately as Health Services Directory. Arrangement: Classified by organization activity, service, etc. Indexes: Each volume has a complete alphabetical name and keyword index.

Handbooks and Manuals

★1887★ Careers in Health Care

McGraw-Hill Trade
2 Penn Plaza
New York, NY 10121
Ph: (212)904-2000   Fr: 800-722-4726
E-mail: ntcpub@tribune.com

Barbara M. Swanson. Fourth edition, 2000. $17.95; $13.95 (paper). 320 pages. Describes job duties, work settings, salaries, licensing and certification requirements, educational preparation, and future outlook. Gives ideas on how to secure a job.

★1888★ Clinical Lab Technician

R & E Publishers, Inc.
2132 O'Toole Ave.
San Jose, CA 95131-1302
Ronald R. Smith. 1993. $2.50 (paper). 24 pages.

★1889★ Opportunities in Clinical Laboratory Science Careers

McGraw-Hill Professional
2 Penn Plaza
New York, NY 10121-2298
Ph: (212)904-2000   Fr: 800-722-4726

Karen R. Karni. $15.95 (netLibrary). Explores clinical laboratory science careers.

★1890★ Opportunities in Health and Medical Careers

McGraw-Hill Trade
2 Penn Plaza
New York, NY 10121
Ph: (212)904-2000   Fr: 800-722-4726

I. Donald Snook, Jr. and Leo D'Orazio. 1997. $14.95; $11.95 (paper). 202 pages. Covers the full range of medical and health occupations. Illustrated.

★1891★ Opportunities in Medical Imaging Careers

McGraw-Hill/Contemporary Books
1221 Ave Of The Americas
New York, NY 10020
Ph: (212)904-2000   Fax: (973)302-2300
Fr: 800-225-5945

Clifford J. Sherry. 1993. $14.95. 160 pages.

★1892★ Opportunities in Medical Technology Careers

McGraw-Hill/Contemporary Books
1221 Avenue of the Americas
New York, NY 10020
Ph: (212)904-2000   Fr: 800-323-4900
E-mail: ntcpub@tribune.com

Karen R. Karni. Revised, 1996. $14.95; $11.95 (paper). 205 pages. Details opportunities for various technical medical personnel and supplies up-to-date information on salary levels and employment outlook. Append-

ices list associations and unions in each field. Illustrated.

★1893★ Resumes for the Health Care Professional

John Wiley & Sons Inc.
111 River Rd.
Hoboken, NJ 07030-5774
Ph: (201)748-6000   Fax: (201)748-6088
Fr: 800-225-5945

Kim Marino. Second edition, 2000. $14.95 (paper). 224 pages.

★1894★ Resumes for Health and Medical Careers

McGraw-Hill Trade
2 Penn Plaza
New York, NY 10121
Ph: (212)904-2000   Fr: 800-722-4726
E-mail: ntcpub@tribune.com

1997. $9.95 (paper). 455 pages.

★1895★ Resumes for Science Careers

McGraw-Hill Professional
1221 Avenue of the Americas
New York, NY 10020
Ph: (212)904-2000   Fr: 800-323-4900
E-mail: ntcpub@tribune.com

1997. $9.95 (paper). 466 pages.

★1896★ VGM's Handbook of Health Care Careers

McGraw-Hill Trade
2 Penn Plaza
New York, NY 10121
Ph: (212)904-2000   Fr: 800-722-4726
E-mail: ntcpub@tribune.com

VGM Career Horizons Staff. Second edition, revised, 1997. $12.95 (paper). 112 pages.

Employment Agencies and Search Firms

★1897★ CA Durakis Associates, Inc.

4 Padonia Woods Ct.
Baltimore, MD 21030
Ph: (410)252-2055

Executive search firm.

★1898★ The Coelyn Group

1 Park Plaza, Fl. 6
Irvine, CA 92614
Ph: (949)553-8855   Fax: (949)363-0837

Executive search firm.

★1899★ The Domann Organization Inc.
1 Market St.
San Francisco, CA 94105
Fr: 800-923-6626
Executive search firm.

★1900★ ENI
3705 S. Long Beach Blvd.
Holgate, NJ 08008
Ph: (609)207-1376
Executive search firm.

★1901★ Fitzgerald Associates
21 Muzzey St.
Lexington, MA 02421
Ph: (781)863-1945   Fax: (781)863-8872
Executive search firm specifically for the healthcare industry.

★1902★ Flannery, Sarna & Associates LLC
N14 W23777 Stone Ridge Dr., Ste. 120
Waukesha, WI 53188
Ph: (262)523-1206   Fax: (262)523-1873
Executive search firm.

ONLINE JOB SOURCES AND SERVICES

★1903★ Medhunters.com
E-mail: info@medhunters.com
URL: http://www.medhunters.com
Description: Career search site for jobs in all health care specialties; educational resources; visa and licensing information for relocation; interesting articles; relocation tools; links to professional organizations and general resources.

★1904★ ProHealthJobs
E-mail: sales@prohealthjobs.com
URL: http://www.prohealthjobs.com
Description: Career resources site for the medical and health care field. Lists professional opportunities, product information, continuing education and open positions.

TRADESHOWS

★1905★ American Association of Blood Banks Annual Meeting and TXPO
American Association of Blood Banks
8101 Glenbrook Rd.
Bethesda, MD 20814-2749
Ph: (301)907-6977   Fax: (301)907-6895
E-mail: aabb@aabb.org

URL: http://www.aabb.org
Annual. **Primary Exhibits:** Products related to blood banking and transfusion medicine: gloves, donor coaches, chairs, recruitment articles. **Dates and Locations:** 2005 Oct 15-18; Seattle, WA • 2006 Oct 21-24; Miami Beach, FL.

★1906★ APIC Annual Meeting and Educational Conference
Hachero Hill, Inc.
6220 Montrose Rd.
Rockville, MD 20852
Ph: (301)984-9450   Fax: (301)984-6338
Annual. **Primary Exhibits:** Pharmaceuticals, disinfectants, soaps, data processing software, sterilization devices, chemicals, housekeeping equipment and supplies, and related products.

★1907★ College of American Pathologists and American Society of Clinical Pathologists Fall Meeting
American Society of Clinical Pathologists
2100 W. Harrison
Chicago, IL 60612
Ph: (312)738-1336   Fax: (312)738-1619
Annual. **Primary Exhibits:** Technical, scientific, and laboratory equipment.

OTHER SOURCES

★1908★ Accrediting Bureau of Health Education Schools (ABHES)
7777 Leesburg Pke., Ste. 730
Falls Church, VA 22043-2403
Ph: (703)917-9503
E-mail: ijacobson@abhes.org
URL: http://www.abhes.org
Description: Serves as a nationally recognized accrediting agency of health education institutions and schools conducting medical laboratory technician and medical assistant education programs. Establishes criteria and standards for the administration and operation of health education institutions. Seeks to enhance the profession through the improvement of schools, courses, and the competence of graduates. Schools must apply voluntarily for accreditation; once accredited, they must report to the bureau annually and be reexamined at least every 6 years. Has accredited 15 programs for medical laboratory technicians, 124 medical assistants, and 80 institutions of allied health.

★1909★ American Medical Technologists (AMT)
710 Higgins Rd.
Park Ridge, IL 60068-5765
Ph: (847)823-5169   Fax: (847)823-0458
Fr: 800-275-1268
E-mail: mail@amt1.com
URL: http://www.amt1.com

Description: National professional association and certifying body for medical laboratory technologists, technicians, medical assistants, dental assistants, and phlebotomists. Maintains job information service. Sponsors AMT Institute for Education, evaluates and recommends continuing education programs.

★1910★ American Society for Clinical Laboratory Science (ASCLS)
6701 Democracy Blvd., Ste. 300
Bethesda, MD 20817
Ph: (301)657-2768   Fax: (301)657-2909
E-mail: ascls@ascls.org
URL: http://www.ascls.org
Members: Primarily clinical laboratory personnel who have an associate or baccalaureate degree and clinical training and specialists who hold at least a master's degree in one of the major fields of clinical laboratory science such as bacteriology, mycology, or biochemistry; also includes technicians, specialists, and educators with limited certificates and students enrolled in approved programs of clinical laboratory studies and military medical technology schools. **Purpose:** Promotes and maintains high standards in clinical laboratory methods and research and advances standards of education and training of personnel. **Activities:** Conducts educational program of seminars and workshops. Sponsors award competition to encourage the writing of scientific papers. Approves programs of continuing education and maintains records on participation in continuing education programs for members.

★1911★ American Society of Cytopathology (ASC)
400 W 9th St., Ste. 201
Wilmington, DE 19801
Ph: (302)429-8802   Fax: (302)429-8807
E-mail: jjenkins@cytopathology.org
URL: http://www.cytopathology.org
Description: Physicians, Cytotechnologists and scientists dedicated to the cytologic method of diagnostic pathology.

★1912★ Clinical Laboratory Technologists and Technicians
Evon Publishing
832 N 7th Ave.
Iron River, MI 49935
Ph: (906)265-3190
Audiocassette. 1996. $16.95. 32 minutes. Part of the Careers and Vocational Guidance Series. Provides information about the nature of the work, educational requirements, employment outlook, earnings, and work conditions as well as additional related information.

★1913★ Commission on Accreditation of Allied Health Education Programs (CAAHEP)

35 E. Wacker Dr., Ste. 1970
Chicago, IL 60601-2208
Ph: (312)553-9355   Fax: (312)553-9616
E-mail: caahep@caahep.org
URL: http://www.caahep.org

Description: Serves as a nationally recognized accrediting agency for allied health programs in 18 occupational areas.

★1914★ Exploring Health Occupations

Cambridge Educational
2572 Brunswick Ave.
Lawrenceville, NJ 08648-4128
Fax: 800-FAX-ON-US   Fr: 800-468-4227
URL: http://www.cambridgeeducational.com

Two videos. $139.95. 1999.

★1915★ Health Service Occupations

Delphi Productions
3160 4th St.
Boulder, CO 80304
Fax: (303)443-4022   Fr: 888-443-2400
URL: http://www.delphivideo.com

$95.00. 50 minutes. Part of the Careers for the 21st Century Video Library.

★1916★ Health Technologists & Technicians

Delphi Productions
3160 4th St.
Boulder, CO 80304
Fax: (303)443-4022   Fr: 888-443-2400
URL: http://www.delphivideo.com

$95.00. 50 minutes. Part of the Careers for the 21st Century Video Library.

★1917★ Medical Technicians and Technologists

Cambridge Educational
2572 Brunswick Ave.
Lawrenceville, NJ 08648-4128
Fax: 800-FAX-ON-US   Fr: 800-468-4227
URL: http://www.cambridgeeducational.com

$79.95. 15 minutes. Part of the Exploring Health Occupations Series.

★1918★ Medicine & Related Occupations

Delphi Productions
3160 4th St.
Boulder, CO 80304
Fax: (303)443-4022   Fr: 888-443-2400
URL: http://www.delphivideo.com

$95.00. 45 minutes. Part of the Careers for the 21st Century Video Library.

★1919★ National Credentialing Agency for Laboratory Personnel (NCA)

PO Box 15945-289
Lenexa, KS 66285
Ph: (913)438-5110   Fax: (913)599-5340
E-mail: nca-info@goamp.com
URL: http://www.nca-info.org

Description: Persons who direct, educate, supervise, or practice in clinical laboratory science. To assure the public and employers of the competence of clinical laboratory personnel; to provide a mechanism for individuals demonstrating competency in the field to achieve career mobility. Develops and administers competency-based examinations for certification of clinical laboratory personnel; provides for periodic recertification by examination or through documentation of continuing education. Compiles statistics.

College and University Faculty

★1920★ AAEE Connections

American Association for Employment in Education
3040 Riverside Dr., Ste. 125
Columbus, OH 43221
Ph: (614)485-1111   Fax: (614)485-9609

Description: Quarterly. Publishes news of the Association, whose aim is "to enhance and promote the concept of career planning and placement as an integral part of the educational process and to undertake activities designed to help schools, colleges, and universities meet their educational staffing needs." Also concerned with teacher education and the supply of/demand for teachers. Recurring features include news of members, state and regional news, and announcements of upcoming conferences and meetings.

★1921★ AAHE Bulletin

American Association for Higher Education (AAHE)
1 Dupont Cir., Ste. 360
Washington, DC 20036
Ph: (202)293-6440   Fax: (202)293-0073
E-mail: bulletin@aahe.org

Description: Ten issues/year. Discusses effectiveness in higher education. Focuses on academic affairs, employment, public policy, teaching methods, technology, and assessment. Recurring features include interviews, news of research, and practical articles.

★1922★ AATSEEL Newsletter

American Association of Teachers of Slavic and East European Languages (AATSEEL)
University of Iowa
Department of Russian
Iowa City, IA 52242
Ph: (319)335-0170   Fax: (319)335-0640
Description: Four issues/academic year (Feb, Apr, Oct, Dec). Carries articles of interest to teachers of Slavic languages. Reports on study programs, teaching innovations, and Association news. Recurring features include news of members, notices of employment opportunities, a calendar of events, reviews of materials, and columns titled Chapter Minutes, Computer Information, Communicative Corner, and Russian Language Features.

★1923★ Academic Exchange Quarterly

Rapid Intellect Group Inc.
PO Box 131
Stuyvesant Falls, NY 12174
Ph: (518)372-1347
E-mail: AEQ@rapidintellect.com
URL: http://rapidintellect.com/AEQweb/

Quarterly. $156.00/year for individuals; $116.00/year, professional rate; $39.00 for single issue. Periodical covering issues in education.

★1924★ Accounting Review

American Accounting Association
5717 Bessie Dr.
Sarasota, FL 34233
Ph: (941)921-7747   Fax: (941)923-4093

Quarterly. $160.00/year for individuals. Accounting education, research, financial reporting, and book reviews.

★1925★ The American Biology Teacher

National Association of Biology Teachers
12030 Sunrise Valley Dr., Ste. 110
Reston, VA 20191
Ph: (703)264-9696   Fax: (703)264-7778
Fr: 800-406-0775
E-mail: publication@nabt.org
URL: http://www.nabt.org

$125.00/year; $135.00/year for other countries; $10.00 for single issue. Journal featuring articles on biology, science, and education for elementary, high school and college level biology teachers. Includes audio-visual, book, computer, and research reviews.

★1926★ American School & University

Primedia Business
9800 Metcalf Ave.
Overland Park, KS 66212
Ph: (913)341-1300   Fax: (913)967-1901
Fr: (866)505-7173
E-mail: asu@primediabusiness.com
URL: http://www.primediabusiness.com

Monthly. $50.00/year for individuals. Trade magazine.

★1927★ Change

Heldref Publications
1319 18th St. NW
Washington, DC 20036-1802
Ph: (202)296-6267   Fax: (202)296-5149
Fr: 800-365-9753
URL: http://www.heldref.org/html/chg.html

Bimonthly. $51.00/year for individuals; $103.00/year for institutions. Magazine dealing with contemporary issues in higher learning.

★1928★ The Chronicle of Higher Education

The Chronicle of Higher Education
1255 23rd St. NW, Ste. 700
Washington, DC 20037-1125
Ph: (202)466-1000   Fax: (202)452-1033
URL: http://chronicle.com

Weekly. $82.50/year for individuals; $3.75 for single issue. Higher education magazine (tabloid).

★1929★ Columbia Journalism Review

Columbia Journalism Review
2950 Broadway, Journalism Bldg.
Columbia University
New York, NY 10027
Ph: (212)854-1881   Fax: (212)854-8580
E-mail: cjr@columbia.edu
URL: http://www.cjr.org

Bimonthly. $18.00/year; $4.95 for single issue. Magazine focusing on journalism.

★1930★ Community Colleges Journal
American Association of Community
  Colleges
1 Dupont Cir. NW, Ste. 410
Washington, DC 20036
Ph: (202)728-0200   Fax: (202)223-9390
Fr: 800-250-6557
URL: http://www.aacc.nche.edu

Educational magazine.

★1931★ Connections
Association of Jesuit Colleges and
  Universities
1 Dupont Cir., Ste. 405
Washington, DC 20036
Ph: (202)862-9893   Fax: (202)862-8523
E-mail: publications@ajcunet.edu

Description: Monthly, except July and August. Furnishes information on legislative
action affecting higher education and on
Jesuit colleges and universities in the U.S.
Recurring features include news of research,
calendar of events, reports of meetings,
notices of publications available, and columns titled Federal Relations, New Programs, and News from the Campuses.

★1932★ Educational Researcher
American Educational Research
  Association
1230 17th St. NW
Washington, DC 20036-3078
Ph: (202)223-9485   Fax: (202)775-1824
URL: http://www.aera.net

$41.00/year for individuals; $8.00 for single
issue; $56.00/year for institutions; $50.00/
year for out of country; free to members of
AERA. Educational research journal.

★1933★ Electronic Learning
Scholastic Library Publishing Inc.
90 Old Sherman Tpke.
Danbury, CT 06816
Ph: (203)797-3500   Fax: (203)797-3657
Fr: 800-621-1115

$19.00/year. Magazine focusing on electron-
ic education.

★1934★ Financial Management
Financial Management Association
School of Business
University of S Florida
Tampa, FL 33620-5500
Ph: (813)974-2084   Fax: (813)974-3318
E-mail: kporto@coba.usf.edu

Quarterly. $95.00/year for individuals;
$20.00 for single issue. Journal covering
business, economics, finance and management.

**★1935★ Journal of College Teaching
& Learning**
Western Academic Press
PO Box 620760
Littleton, CO 80162
Ph: (303)904-4750   Fax: (303)978-0413

Monthly. $495.00/year for institutions. Refer-
eed academic journal covering all areas of
college level teaching, learning and administration.

**★1936★ The Journal of Continuing
Education in Nursing**
SLACK Inc.
6900 Grove Rd.
Thorofare, NJ 08086-9447
Ph: (856)848-1000   Fax: (856)853-5991
Fr: 800-257-8290
E-mail: jcen@slackinc.com

Bimonthly. $69.00/year for individuals;
$139.00/year for institutions, add 7% Cana-
da; $40.00/year for other countries. Journal
for nurses involved in planning and implementing educational programs for the practitioner and others in patient care.

**★1937★ Journal of Higher Education
Outreach and Engagement (JHEOE)**
Institute of Higher Education (IHE)
Meigs Hall
Athens, GA 30602-6772
Ph: (706)542-0579   Fax: (706)583-0281
E-mail: jheoe@uga.edu
URL: http://www.uga.edu/jheoe/

$35.00/year for individuals; $45.00/year for
Canada; $60.00/year for elsewhere, surface
mail; $70.00/year for elsewhere, airmail;
$95.00/year for institutions; $105.00/year for
institutions, Canada; $110.00/year for institu-
tions elsewhere, surface mail; $120.00/year
for institutions elsewhere, airmail. Journal
covering higher education outreach and engagement for scholars, practitioners, and
professionals.

**★1938★ Journal of Language, Identity,
and Education**
Lawrence Erlbaum Associates Inc.
10 Industrial Ave.
Mahwah, NJ 07430-2262
Ph: (201)236-9500   Fax: (201)236-0072
Fr: 800-9-BOOKS-9
E-mail: journals@erlbaum.com
URL: http://www.erlbaum.com/shop/
tek9.asp?pg=products&specific=1

Quarterly. $40.00/year for individuals;
$70.00/year for out of country; $225.00/year
for institutions; $255.00/year for institutions,
other countries. Scholarly, interdisciplinary
journal covering issues in language, identity
and education worldwide for academics,
educators and policy specialists in a variety
of disciplines, and others.

**★1939★ Journal of Latinos and
Education**
Lawrence Erlbaum Associates Inc.
10 Industrial Ave.
Mahwah, NJ 07430-2262
Ph: (201)236-9500   Fax: (201)236-0072
Fr: 800-9-BOOKS-9
E-mail: journals@erlbaum.com
URL: http://www.erlbaum.com/shop/
tek9.asp?pg=products&specific=1

Quarterly. $40.00/year for individuals;
$70.00/year for out of country; $195.00/year
for institutions; $225.00/year for institutions,
other countries. Scholarly, multidisciplinary
journal covering educational issues that impact Latinos for researchers, teaching professionals, academics, scholars, institutions,
and others.

**★1940★ Matrix: The Magazine for
Leaders in Higher Education**
Professional Media Group L.L.C.
36 Clipper Ct., Ste. B
Mystic, CT 06355-2138

Bimonthly. Trade publication covering issues
for higher education professionals.

★1941★ NAIA News
National Association of Intercollegiate
  Athletics
23500 W 105th St.
PO Box 1325
Olathe, KS 66051-1325
Ph: (913)791-0044   Fax: (913)791-9555
E-mail: naianews@naia.org
URL: http://www.naia.org

Description: Daily. Provides news and information on the Association, which strives to
"develop intercollegiate athletic programs as
an integral part of the total educational
program of the college rather than as a
separate commercial or promotional adjunct." Aims toward uniformity and equity in
policies and practices. Recurring features
include news of members and events, notices of awards, and job listings. America
Online, Inc.

**★1942★ NewsNet, the Newsletter of
the AAASS**
American Association for the
  Advancement of Slavic Studies (AAASS)
8 Story St.
Cambridge, MA 02138
Ph: (617)495-0677   Fax: (617)495-0680
E-mail: newsnet@fas.harvard.edu

Description: Bimonthly, during the academic year. Reports on Association activities and
on Slavic study research in institutions
throughout the world. Alerts readers to research grants, internships, and fellowship
opportunities as well as to employment
opportunities in universities across the country. Announces awards, upcoming conferences, courses, new scholarly publications,
and annual research.

★1943★ *Notices of the American Mathematical Society*

American Mathematical Society
201 Charles St.
Providence, RI 02904-2294
Ph: (401)455-4000   Fax: (401)331-3842
Fr: 800-321-4267
URL: http://www.ams.org/notices

$401.00/year, individual members; $321.00/year, institutional members. AMS journal publishing programs, meeting reports, new publications announcements, upcoming mathematical meetings, scientific development trends, computer software reviews, and federal funding reports.

★1944★ *Nurse Educator*

Lippincott Williams & Wilkins
530 Walnut St.
Philadelphia, PA 19106
Ph: (215)521-8300   Fax: (215)521-8902
Fr: 800-638-3030
URL: http://www.nurseeducatoronline.com/

Bimonthly. $87.95/year for individuals; $201.95/year for institutions; $151.95/year for other countries; $261.95/year for institutions, other countries. Journal for nursing educators.

★1945★ *OECD Observer*

Organization for Economic Cooperation and Development
2001 L St. NW, Ste. 650
Washington, DC 20036-4922
Ph: (202)785-6323   Fax: (202)785-0350
Fr: 800-456-6323
URL: http://www.oecdobserver.org

Bimonthly. $50.00/year for individuals. Magazine on economic affairs, science, and technology.

★1946★ *Perspective Atlas*

Association of Teachers of Latin American Studies
PO Box 754
Flushing, NY 11362
Ph: (718)428-1237   Fax: (718)428-1237
URL: http://atlas0754.com

Description: Quarterly. Presents news of the Association, women's studies and teaching abroad programs, and conferences. Recurring features include notices of publications available, grant opportunities, and employment.

★1947★ *The Physics Teacher*

American Association of Physics Teachers
One Physics Ellipse
College Park, MD 20740-3845
Ph: (301)209-3350   Fax: (301)209-0845
E-mail: tpt@appstate.edu
URL: http:///www.aapt.org/tpt

$94.00/year for individuals; $47.00/year. Scientific education magazine.

★1948★ *The Science Teacher*

National Science Teachers Association
1840 Wilson Blvd.
Arlington, VA 22201-3000
Ph: (703)243-7100   Fax: (703)243-7177
Fr: 800-722-6782
E-mail: thescienceteacher@nsta.org
URL: http://www.nsta.org

$65.00/year for individuals. Journal on science education.

★1949★ *The Technology Teacher*

International Technology Education Association
1914 Association Dr., Ste. 201
Reston, VA 20191
Ph: (703)620-4146   Fax: (703)860-0353
E-mail: iteapubs@iris.com

$70.00/year. Magazine on technology education.

★1950★ *Today's OEA*

Oregon Education Association
6900 SW Atlanta St.
Portland, OR 97223-2513
Ph: (503)684-3300   Fax: (503)684-8063

Bimonthly. Free to qualified subscribers; $10.00/year for nonmembers. Membership magazine covering educational issues statewide and nationally.

★1951★ *University Aviation Association Newsletter*

University Aviation Association
3410 Skyway Dr.
Auburn, AL 36830-6444
Ph: (334)844-2434   Fax: (334)844-2432
E-mail: deweech@auburn.edu

Description: Bimonthly. Provides information on Association activities and projects, events of other aviation organizations that bear on higher education, and the future impact of collegiate aviation education. Recurring features include feature articles on outstanding individual and institutional members, statistics, a calendar of events, news of members, news of research, an editorial, letters to the editor, book reviews, employment information, and the president's report.

★1952★ *Weatherwise*

Heldref Publications
1319 18th St. NW
Washington, DC 20036-1802
Ph: (202)296-6267   Fax: (202)296-5149
Fr: 800-365-9753
URL: http://www.heldref.org/html/body_ww.html

Bimonthly. $35.00/year for individuals; $74.00/year for institutions, other countries. Popular weather magazine for students, teachers, and professionals.

★1953★ *Wisconsin Lawyer*

State Bar of Wisconsin
5302 Eastpark Blvd.
PO Box 7158
Madison, WI 53707-7158
Ph: (608)257-3838   Fax: (608)257-5502
Fr: 800-444-9404
E-mail: wislawyer@wisbar.org
URL: http://www.wisbar.org/wislawmag/

Monthly. $42.00/year for individuals; $24.00/year for law libraries, educational groups, law students. Magazine for Wisconsin legal professionals.

PLACEMENT AND JOB REFERRAL SERVICES

★1954★ **Academy of International Business (AIB)**

University of Hawaii at Manoa - CBA
2404 Maile Way
Honolulu, HI 96822
Ph: (808)956-3665   Fax: (808)956-3261
E-mail: aib@cba.hawaii.edu
URL: http://www.aibworld.net

Description: University professors, researchers, writers, managers, executives, and attorneys in the international business education field. Facilitates information exchange among people in academia, business, and government and encourages research activities that advance the knowledge of international business operations and increase the available body of teaching materials. Has compiled an inventory of collegiate courses in international business, a survey of research projects, and statistics. Maintains placement service.

★1955★ **Academy of Management (AM)**

PO Box 3020
Briarcliff Manor, NY 10510-8020
Ph: (914)923-2607   Fax: (914)923-2615
E-mail: aom@pace.edu
URL: http://www.aomonline.org

Description: Professors in accredited universities and colleges who teach management; selected business executives who have made significant written contributions to the literature in the field of management and organization. Offers placement service.

★1956★ **American Academy of Religion (AAR)**

825 Houston Mill Rd. NE, No. 300
Atlanta, GA 30329
Ph: (404)727-3049   Fax: (404)727-7959
E-mail: aar@aarweb.org
URL: http://www.aarweb.org

Members: Professional society of scholars and teachers in the field of religion. **Purpose:** Encourages scholarship, research, and publications in the study of religion, and stimulates effective teaching. **Activities:** Conducts research programs; offers research grants and placement services; compiles statistics.

★1957★ American Association for Employment in Education (AAEE)
3040 Riverside Dr., Ste. 125
Columbus, OH 43221-2550
Ph: (614)485-1111   Fax: (614)485-9609
E-mail: aaee@osu.edu
URL: http://www.aaee.org

Description: Colleges, universities, and other post-secondary educational institutions which are not-for-profit and prepare teachers and other educational personnel for service in public and private educational institutions, organizations and agencies; elementary, middle and secondary educational institutions which are not-for-profit organizations and which employ teachers and other educational personnel; not for profit organizations (including government agencies) whose primary activities consists of providing information or services relating to career planning, placement, and recruitment activities in education.

★1958★ American Association of Teachers of French (A.A.T.F.)
Mail Code 4510
Southern Illinois University
Carbondale, IL 62901-4510
Ph: (618)453-5731   Fax: (618)453-5733
E-mail: abrate@siu.edu
URL: http://www.frenchteachers.org

Members: Teachers of French in public and private elementary and secondary schools, colleges, and universities. **Activities:** Sponsors National French Week each November to take French out of the classroom and into the schools and community. Conducts National French Contest in elementary and secondary schools and awards prizes at all levels. Maintains Materials Center with promotional and pedagogical materials; National French Honor Society (high school), Placement Bureau, Pen Pal Bureau, summer scholarships.

★1959★ American Association of Teachers of Spanish and Portuguese (AATSP)
423 Exton Commons
Exton, PA 19341-2951
Ph: (610)363-7005   Fax: (610)363-7116
E-mail: corporate@aatsp.org
URL: http://www.aatsp.org

Description: Teachers of Spanish and Portuguese languages and literatures and others interested in Hispanic culture. Operates placement bureau and maintains pen pal registry. Sponsors honor society, Sociedad Honoraria Hispanica and National Spanish Examinations for secondary school students.

★1960★ American Classical League (ACL)
Miami University
Oxford, OH 45056
Ph: (513)529-7741   Fax: (513)529-7742

E-mail: info@aclclassics.org
URL: http://www.aclclassics.org

Members: Teachers of classical languages in high schools and colleges. **Purpose:** To promote the teaching of Latin and other classical languages. Presents scholarship. **Activities:** Maintains placement service, teaching materials, and resource center at Miami University in Oxford, OH to sell teaching aids to Latin and Greek teachers.

★1961★ American Philosophical Association (APA)
University of Delaware
31 Amstel Ave.
Newark, DE 19716
Ph: (302)831-1112   Fax: (302)831-8690
E-mail: apaonline@udel.edu
URL: http://www.udel.edu/apa

Members: College and university teachers of philosophy and others with an interest in philosophy. **Purpose:** Facilitates exchange of ideas in philosophy, encourages creative and scholarly activity in philosophy, and fosters the professional work of teachers of philosophy. **Activities:** Participates in international congresses of philosophy and maintains affiliations with national and international philosophical organizations. Maintains placement service; sponsors competitions. Oversees selection of Romanell, Schutz and Carus lecturers and other prizes and awards.

★1962★ American Political Science Association (APSA)
1527 New Hampshire Ave. NW
Washington, DC 20036-1206
Ph: (202)483-2512   Fax: (202)483-2657
E-mail: apsa@apsanet.org
URL: http://www.apsanet.org

Description: College and university teachers of political science, public officials, research workers, and businessmen. "Encourages the impartial study and promotes the development of the art and science of government." Develops research projects of public interest and educational programs for political scientists and journalists; seeks to improve the knowledge of and increase citizen participation in political and governmental affairs. Serves as clearinghouse for teaching and research positions in colleges, universities, and research bureaus in the U.S. and abroad and for positions open to political scientists in government and private business; conducts Congressional Fellowship Program, which enables political scientists and journalists to spend a year working with members of Congress and congressional committees; conducts the Committee on Professional Ethic, Rights and Freedom which is concerned with the professional ethics, human rights, and academic freedom of political scientists. Gives cash awards and citations for best books and theses of the year in various phases of political science at annual convention. Offers placement service.

★1963★ Association of American Law Schools (AALS)
1201 Connecticut Ave. NW, Ste. 800
Washington, DC 20036-2605
Ph: (202)296-8851   Fax: (202)296-8869
E-mail: aals@aals.org
URL: http://www.aals.org

Description: Law schools association. Seeks to improve the legal profession through legal education. Interacts for law professors with state and federal government, other legal education and professional associations, and other national higher education and learned society organizations. Compiles statistics; sponsors teacher placement service. Presents professional development programs.

★1964★ Association for Direct Instruction (ADI)
PO Box 10252
Eugene, OR 97440
Ph: (541)485-1293   Fax: (541)683-7543
Fr: 800-995-2464
E-mail: info@adihome.org
URL: http://www.adihome.org

Members: Public school regular and special education teachers and university instructors. **Purpose:** Encourages, promotes, and engages in research aimed at improving educational methods. Promotes dissemination of developmental information and skills that facilitate the education of adults and children. **Activities:** Administers a preschool for developmentally delayed children. Offers educational training workshops for instructors. Maintains speakers' bureau, and placement service.

★1965★ Association of Southern Baptist Colleges and Schools (ASBCS)
PO Box 11655
Jackson, TN 38308-0127
Ph: (731)660-3497   Fax: (731)664-6459
E-mail: bob_agee@baptistschools.org
URL: http://www.baptistschools.org

Members: Southern Baptist senior colleges, universities, junior colleges, academies, and Bible schools. **Purpose:** Promotes Christian education through literature, faculty workshops, student recruitment, teacher placement, trustee orientation, statistical information, and other assistance to members.

★1966★ Association of University Professors of Ophthalmology (AUPO)
PO Box 420369
San Francisco, CA 94142-0369
Ph: (415)561-8548   Fax: (415)561-8531
E-mail: aupo@aao.org

Members: Heads of departments or divisions of ophthalmology in accredited medical schools throughout the U.S. and Canada; directors of ophthalmology residency programs in institutions not connected to medical schools. **Purpose:** Promotes medical education, research, and patient care relating to ophthalmology. **Activities:** Operates Ophthalmology Matching Program and faculty placement service, which aids ophthalmologists interested in being associated with university ophthalmology programs to locate such programs.

★1967★ College Language Association (CLA)

Howard University
Modern Languages & Literatures
  Department
Washington, DC 20059
Ph: (202)806-6762   Fax: (202)806-4514
E-mail: jdavis@fac.howard.edu
URL: http://www.clascholars.org

Description: Teachers of English and modern foreign languages, primarily in historically black colleges and universities. Maintains placement service.

★1968★ College Media Advisers (CMA)

University of Memphis
MJ-300
Memphis, TN 38152-6661
Ph: (901)678-2403   Fax: (901)678-4798
E-mail: rsplbrgn@memphis.edu
URL: http://www.collegemedia.org

Members: Professional association serving advisers, directors, and chairmen of boards of college student media (newspapers, yearbooks, magazines, handbooks, directories, and radio and television stations); heads of schools and departments of journalism; and others interested in junior college, college, and university student media. **Purpose:** Serves as clearinghouse for student media; acts as consultant on student theses and dissertations on publications. Encourages high school journalism and examines its relationships to college and professional journalism. **Activities:** Conducts national survey of student media in rotation each year by type: newspapers, magazines, and yearbooks; radio and television stations. Compiles statistics. Maintains placement service and speakers' bureau.

★1969★ Council for Jewish Education (CJE)

11 Olympia Ln.
Monsey, NY 10952
Ph: (845)368-8657   Fax: (845)369-6538
E-mail: mjscje@aol.com

Description: Teachers of Hebrew in universities; heads of Bureaus of Jewish Education and their administrative departments; faculty members of Jewish teacher training schools. Seeks to: further the cause of Jewish education in America; raise professional standards and practices; promote the welfare and growth of Jewish educational workers; improve and strengthen Jewish life. Conducts educational programs; cosponsors a Personnel Placement Committee with Jewish Education Service of North America.

★1970★ Decision Sciences Institute (DSI)

University Plz.
35 Broad St.
Atlanta, GA 30303
Ph: (404)651-4073   Fax: (404)651-2804
E-mail: dsi@gsu.edu
URL: http://www.decisionsciences.org/

Members: Businesspersons and members of business school faculties. **Activities:** Maintains placement service.

★1971★ Financial Management Association International (FMA)

College of Business Administration, Ste. 3331
University of South Florida
Tampa, FL 33620-5500
Ph: (813)974-2084   Fax: (813)974-3318
E-mail: fma@coba.usf.edu
URL: http://www.fma.org

Members: Professors of financial management; corporate financial officers. **Purpose:** Facilitates exchange of ideas among persons involved in financial management or the study thereof. **Activities:** Conducts workshops for comparison of current research projects and development of cooperative ventures in writing and research. Sponsors honorary society for superior students at 300 colleges and universities. Offers placement services.

★1972★ International Educator's Institute (TIE)

PO Box 513
Cummaquid, MA 02637
Ph: (508)362-1414   Fax: (508)362-1411
Fr: 877-375-6668
E-mail: tie@tieonline.com
URL: http://www.tieonline.com

Description: Facilitates the placement of teachers and administrators in American, British, and international schools. Seeks to create a network that provides for professional development opportunities and improved financial security of members. Offers advice and information on international school news, recent educational developments, job placement, and investment, consumer, and professional development opportunities. Makes available insurance and travel benefits. Operates International Schools Internship Program.

★1973★ National Association for Sport and Physical Education (NASPE)

1900 Association Dr.
Reston, VA 20191
Ph: (703)476-3410   Fax: (703)476-8316
Fr: 800-213-7193
E-mail: naspe@aahperd.org
URL: http://www.aahperd.org

Description: Men and women professionally involved with physical activity and sports. Seeks to improve the total sport and physical activity experience in America. Conducts research and education programs in such areas as sport psychology, curriculum development, kinesiology, history, philosophy,

sport sociology, and the biological and behavioral basis of human activity. Develops and distributes public information materials which explain the value of physical education programs. Supports councils involved in organizing and supporting elementary, secondary, and college physical education and sport programs; administers the National Council of Athletic Training in conjunction with the National Association for Girls and Women in Sport; serves the professional interests of coaches, trainers, and officials. Maintains hall of fame, placement service, and media resource center for public information and professional preparation. Member benefits include group insurance and discounts.

★1974★ National Association of Teachers' Agencies (NATA)

797 Kings Hwy.
Fairfield, CT 06432
Ph: (203)333-0611   Fax: (203)334-7224
E-mail: info@jobsforteachers.com
URL: http://www.jobsforteachers.com

Description: Private employment agencies engaged primarily in the placement of teaching and administration personnel. Works to standardize records and promote a strong ethical sense in the placement field. Maintains speakers' bureau.

★1975★ National Communication Association (NCA)

1765 N St. NW
Washington, DC 20036
Ph: (202)464-4622   Fax: (202)464-4600
E-mail: smorreale@natcom.org
URL: http://www.natcom.org

Members: Elementary, secondary, college, and university teachers, speech clinicians, media specialists, communication consultants, students, theater directors, and other interested persons; libraries and other institutions. **Purpose:** To promote study, criticism, research, teaching, and application of the artistic, humanistic, and scientific principles of communication, particularly speech communication. Sponsors the publication of scholarly volumes in speech. **Activities:** Conducts international debate tours in the U.S. and abroad. Maintains placement service.

★1976★ U.S.-China Education Foundation (USCEF)

4140 Oceanside Blvd.
PMB 112, No. 159
Oceanside, CA 92056-6005
Ph: (760)644-0977
E-mail: SAGE.Kennedypres@cex.net
URL: http://www.sage-usa.net

Members: A project of the Society for the Advancement of Global Education. **Purpose:** Purposes are to promote the learning of the Chinese languages (including Mandarin, Cantonese, and minority languages such as Mongolian) by Americans, and the learning of English by Chinese. **Activities:** Conducts short-term travel-study program to prepare Americans and Chinese for stays of four, six, or eight months or one to four years in China or the U.S., respectively. Operates teacher placement service and speakers' bureau. A project of S.A.G.E. the Society for the Development of Global Education.

★1977★ **University Photographers Association of America (UPAA)**
SUNY Brockport
350 New Campus Dr.
Brockport, NY 14420-2931
Ph: (585)395-2133   Fax: (585)395-2733
E-mail: jdusen@brockport.edu
URL: http://www.upaa.org/

Description: College and university personnel engaged professionally in photography, audiovisual work, or journalism for universities. Seeks to advance applied photography and the profession through the exchange of thoughts and opinions among its members. Awards fellowship for exceptional work in the advancement of photography. Provides a medium for exchange of ideas and technical information on photography, especially university photographic work. Sponsors exhibits. Provides placement service for members.

EMPLOYER DIRECTORIES AND NETWORKING LISTS

★1978★ *Accredited Institutions of Postsecondary Education*
Oryx Press
1434 E San Miguel Ave.
Phoenix, AZ 85014-2422
Fr: 800-225-5800

Annual, May. $59.95. Covers more than 5,500 accredited institutions and programs of postsecondary education in the United States and U.S.-chartered schools in 14 countries. Entries include: Institution name, address, phone, whether public or private, any religious affiliation, type of institution and student body, branch campuses or affiliated institutions, date of first accreditation and latest reaffirmation of accrediting body, accredited programs in professional fields, level of degrees offered, name of chief executive officer, size and composition of enrollment, type of academic calendar. Arrangement: Geographical. Indexes: Institution.

★1979★ *American Art Directory*
LexisNexis Group
121 Chanlon Rd.
New Providence, NJ 07974
Ph: (908)464-6800   Fax: (908)771-7704
Fr: 800-526-4902
URL: http://nationalregisterpub.com

Biennial. $299.00. Covers over 7,000 museums, art libraries, and art organizations, and 1,700 art schools; also includes lists of state directors and supervisors of art education in schools, traveling exhibition booking agencies, corporations having art holdings for public viewing, newspapers that carry art notes, art scholarships and fellowships; and 190 national, regional, and state open art exhibitions. Entries include: For museums-Name, address, phone, fax, electronic mail address, name of curator; days and hours of operation, collection, budget, publications. For exhibits-Name, address, phone, fax, electronic mail address, name of contact; date, deadline. For schools-Name, address, phone, name of director, names of faculty members, majors or degrees offered, tuition fees; summer school or adult hobby class information. For newspapers-Name, address, phone, name of art editor. Arrangement: Geographical. Indexes: Geographical, collection/subject/name, personal name, institution name.

★1980★ *American Universities and Colleges*
Walter de Gruyter Inc.
200 Saw Mill River Rd.
Hawthorne, NY 10532
Ph: (914)747-0110   Fax: (914)747-1326
URL: http://www.degruyter.com/rs/

Quadrennial, latest edition 16, 2001. $298.00. Covers over 1,900 accredited four-year and graduate colleges and universities. Includes a list of statewide coordinating boards of higher education. Entries include: For schools-Name, address, history, governing board, calendar, freshmen and general student body characteristics, distinctive programs, student life, whether it has a reserve officers training corps (ROTC), graduate work, degrees conferred, fees, student financial aid, departments and teaching staff, enrollment, foreign students, publications, library, finances, buildings and grounds, administration; separate descriptions of each major division within a university. For boards-Name, address, name of director. Arrangement: Geographical. Indexes: Institution name, general.

★1981★ *Association of American University Presses-Directory*
Association of American University Presses
71 W 23rd St., Ste. 901
New York, NY 10010-4102
Ph: (212)989-1010   Fax: (212)989-0275

Annual, November. $18.00; $23.00 postpaid. Covers 124 presses and affiliates worldwide. Entries include: Press name, address, phone, e-mail, URL; titles and names of complete editorial and managerial staffs; editorial program; mailing, warehouse, printing, and/or customer service addresses; other details. Arrangement: Classified by press affiliation, alphabetical by press name. Indexes: Personal name.

★1982★ *Association for University Business and Economic Research-Membership Directory*
Association for University Business and Economic Research/AUBER
801 W Michigan St.
Indianapolis, IN 46202-5151
Ph: (317)274-2204   Fax: (317)274-3312

Annual, January. $10.00. Covers member institutions in the United States and abroad with centers, bureaus, departments, etc., concerned with business and economic research. Entries include: Name of bureau, center, etc., sponsoring institution name, address, phone, names and titles of director and staff, publications and frequency. Arrangement: Geographical. Indexes: Director name, institution name.

★1983★ *Chronicle Four-Year College Databook*
Chronicle Guidance Publications Inc.
66 Aurora St.
Moravia, NY 13118-3576
Ph: (315)497-0330   Fax: (315)497-3359
Fr: 800-622-7284

Annual, September. $24.99. Covers more than 825 baccalaureate, master's, doctoral, and first professional programs offered by more than 2,450 colleges and universities in the United States. Entries include: College charts section gives college name, address, phone; accreditation, enrollment, admissions, costs, financial aid; accreditation associations' names, addresses, and phone numbers. Appendices gives details on admissions and other information special to each college. Arrangement: Part I, classified by college major; Part II, geographical. Indexes: College name.

★1984★ *Chronicle Two-Year College Databook*
Chronicle Guidance Publications Inc.
66 Aurora St.
Moravia, NY 13118-3576
Ph: (315)497-0330   Fax: (315)497-3359
Fr: 800-622-7284

Annual, September. $24.97. Covers over 815 associate, certificate, occupational, and transfer programs offered by more than 2,555 technical institutes, two-year colleges, and universities in the United States. Entries include: College charts section gives college name, address, phone; accreditation, enrollment, admissions, costs, financial aid; accrediting associations' names, addresses, and phone numbers. Arrangement: Part I is classified by college major; Part II is geographical. Indexes: College name.

★1985★ *Directory of Interior Design Programs Accredited by FIDER*
Foundation for Interior Design Education Research
146 Monroe Center NW, Ste. 1318
Grand Rapids, MI 49503-2822
Ph: (616)458-0400   Fax: (616)458-0460
URL: http://www.fider.org

Semiannual, June and November. Covers

128 interior design programs in the United States and Canada in conformance with the accreditation standards of the foundation. Entries include: Type of program, name of institution, name of department chair or program head, phone, dates of last and next accreditation review, degrees offered, e-mail and web address. Arrangement: Geographical, degree level offered, then alphabetical by institution name.

★1986★ Employment Information in the Mathematical Sciences

American Mathematical Society
201 Charles St.
Providence, RI 02904-2294
Ph: (401)455-4000   Fax: (401)331-3842
Fr: 800-321-4AMS
E-mail: eims-info@ams.org
URL: http://www.ams.org/eims/

Five times a year. $180.00 for institutions; $108.00 for individuals; $45.00 for students. Covers colleges and universities with departments in the mathematical sciences, and non-academic and foreign organizations with employment openings. Entries include: For departments-Name, address, name and title of contact; job title, job description, salary (if applicable). Arrangement: Classified as academic or nonacademic, then geographical.

★1987★ Fifty State Educational Directories

Career Guidance Foundation
8090 Engineer Rd., Ste. B
San Diego, CA 92111
Ph: (858)560-8051   Fax: (858)278-8960
Fr: 800-854-2670
URL: http://www.cgf.org

Annual, latest edition June 1996. $89.00. Microfiche. Collection consists of reproductions of the state educational directories published by the departments of education of individual 50 states. Directory contents vary, but the majority contain listings of elementary and secondary schools, colleges and universities, and state education officials. Amount of detail in each also varies. Entries include: Usually, institution name, address, and name of one executive.

★1988★ Fulbright Scholar Program Grants for U.S. Faculty and Professionals

Council for International Exchange of Scholars
3007 Tilden St. NW, Ste. 5L
Washington, DC 20008-3009
Ph: (202)686-4000   Fax: (202)362-3442
E-mail: apprequest@cies.iie.org
URL: http://www.cies.org/

Annual, March. Covers about 800 grants available for postdoctoral university lecturing and advanced research by American citizens in more than 140 countries. Entries include: Periods in which grants are tenable; number of grants available for the country; language or other requirement; fields in which lectures and research are desired; stipend, housing; additional income for dependents, applications and reference forms. Arrangement:

Geographical. Indexes: Professional, discipline.

★1989★ Grants, Fellowships, and Prizes of Interest to Historians

American Historical Association
400 A St., S.E.
Washington, DC 20003-3889
Ph: (202)544-2422   Fax: (202)544-8307
E-mail: grantguide@theaha.org
URL: http://www.theaha.org/members/grants/index.cfm

Annual, September. Covers over 450 sources of funding (scholarships, fellowships, internships, awards, and book and essay prizes) in the United States and abroad for graduate students, postdoctoral researchers, and institutions in the humanities. Entries include: Name of source, institution name or contact, address, phone, eligibility and proposal requirements, award or stipend amount, location requirements for research, application deadlines. Arrangement: Alphabetical in three categories: support for individual research and teaching; grants for groups and organizations for research and education; and book, article, essay, and manuscript prizes.

★1990★ Higher Education Directory

Higher Education Publications Inc.
6400 Arlington Blvd., Ste. 648
Falls Church, VA 22042
Ph: (703)532-2300   Fax: (703)532-2305
Fr: 888-349-7715
URL: http://www.hepinc.com

Annual, October. $70.00. Covers over 4,100 degree granting colleges and universities accredited by approved agencies recognized by the U.S. Secretary of Education and by the Council of Higher Education Accreditation (CHEA); 103 systems offices; over 550 related associations and state government agencies; recognized accrediting agencies. Entries include: For institutions-Name, address, congressional district, phone, fax, year established; Carnegie classification; enrollment; type of student body; religious or other affiliation; undergraduate tuition and fees; type of academic calendar; highest degree offered; accreditations; IRS status; names, titles and job classification codes for academic and administrative officers. For associations and state agencies-Name, address, phone, name of chief executive officer. Same content and coverage as the base volume of the Department of Education's publication "Directory of Postsecondary Institutions". Arrangement: Geographical, alphabetical by state. Indexes: Administrator name (with phone and e-mail addresses), accreditation, FICE numbers, college or university name.

★1991★ Mathematical Sciences Professional Directory

American Mathematical Society
201 Charles St.
Providence, RI 02904-2294
Ph: (401)455-4000   Fax: (401)331-3842
Fr: 800-321-4AMS

URL: http://www.ams.org

Annual. $55.00 for nonmembers; $44.00 for members. Covers 37 professional organizations concerned with mathematics, government agencies, academic institutions with department in the mathematical sciences, nonacademic organizations, and individuals. Entries include: For professional organizations and government agencies-Name, address, names and titles of key personnel. For institutions-Name, address; name, title, and address of department chair. Arrangement: Classified by type of organization; institutions are then geographical; others, alphabetical. Indexes: University or college name.

★1992★ Modern Language Association of America-Job Information List

Modern Language Association of America
26 Broadway, 3rd Fl.
New York, NY 10004-1789
Ph: (646)576-5000   Fax: (646)458-0030
URL: http://www.mla.org

Quarterly, February, April, October, December. $45.00. Covers available positions for college teachers of English and foreign languages in four-year colleges and universities; February issue includes separate section of openings in two-year institutions. Separate editions for English and American language and literature and for foreign language openings. Entries include: Department chair statement, including institution name; contact name, address, phone; definite or possible openings; related information for job seekers (change in deadline date, or job description, notice of a vacancy filled, etc.). Arrangement: First section-Statements of department chairmen. Second section (in October and February only)-List of departments reporting no vacancies.

★1993★ National Directory of Alternative Schools

National Coalition of Alternative Community Schools
1289 Jewett St.
Ann Arbor, MI 48104-6201
Ph: (734)668-9171   Fax: (734)769-9629
Fr: 888-771-9171

Biennial, odd years. $18.00. Covers over 500 alternative education programs, including home schools, and state and regional coalitions of alternative schools and colleges; also lists organizations and networks offering services and resources to those working with children; international coverage. Entries include: Name, address, phone, name of contact; many also include descriptions of programs. Arrangement: Schools are geographical. Indexes: Complete index of entries.

★1994★ National Directory of College Athletics

Collegiate Directories Inc.
PO Box 450640
Cleveland, OH 44145
Ph: (440)835-1172   Fax: (440)835-8835
Fr: 800-426-2232
URL: http://www.collegiatedirectories.com

Annual, August. $39.95. Covers men's athletic departments of 2,100 senior and junior colleges in the United States and Canada. Entries include: School name, address, enrollment, colors, team nicknames, stadium and/or gym capacity; names of president, men's athletic director, athletic administrative staff, physical education director and coaches for each sport; athletic department phones, faxes, etc.; association affiliations. Arrangement: Alphabetical. Indexes: Schools by program and division; Alphabetical by advertisers and products.

★1995★ **National Faculty Directory**

Thomson Gale
27500 Drake Rd.
Farmington Hills, MI 48331-3535
Ph: (248)699-4253   Fax: (248)699-8065
Fr: 800-877-GALE
E-mail: businessproducts@gale.com

Annual, fall; spring supplement. $825.00 for base edition; $355.00 for supplement. Covers more than 740,000 (90,000 more in supplement) teaching faculty members at over 3,600 junior colleges, colleges, and universities in the United States and those in Canada that give instruction in English. Entries include: Name, department name, institution, address, and phone and fax numbers. Directory combines main edition and supplement. Arrangement: Alphabetical.

★1996★ **Opportunities Abroad for Educators**

Fulbright Teacher and Administrator
  Exchange Program
600 Maryland Ave. SW, Ste. 320
Washington, DC 20024-2520
Ph: (202)314-3527   Fax: (202)479-6806
Fr: 800-726-0479
URL: http://www.fulbrightexchanges.org

Annual. Covers opportunities available for elementary and secondary teachers, and two year college instructors, and school administrators to attend seminars or to teach abroad under the Mutual Educational and Cultural Exchange Act of 1961. Entries include: Countries of placement, dates, eligibility requirements, teaching assignments. Arrangement: Geographical.

★1997★ **Patterson's Schools Classified**

Educational Directories Inc.
PO Box 68097
Schaumburg, IL 60168-0097
Ph: (847)891-1250   Fax: (847)891-0945
Fr: 800-357-6183
URL: http://www.ediusa.com

Annual, April. $15.00. Covers over 7,000 accredited colleges, universities, community colleges, junior colleges, career schools and teaching hospitals. Entries include: School name, address, phone, URL, e-mail, name of administrator or admissions officer, description, professional accreditation (where applicable). Updated from previous year's edition of 'Patterson's American Education'. Arrangement: Classified by area of study, then geographical by state. Indexes: Alphabetical by name.

★1998★ **School Guide**

School Guide Publications
210 N Ave.
New Rochelle, NY 10801
Ph: (914)632-7771   Fax: (914)632-3412
Fr: 800-433-7771
URL: http://www.schoolguides.com

Annual, September. $10.00. Covers over 3,000 colleges, vocational schools, and nursing schools in the United States. Entries include: Institution name, address, phone, courses offered, degrees awarded. Arrangement: Classified by type of institution, then geographical. Indexes: Subject.

★1999★ **Who's Who in American Art**

Marquis Who's Who
121 Chanlon Rd.
New Providence, NJ 07974
Ph: (908)673-1101   Fax: (908)673-1189
Fr: 800-473-7020
E-mail: art@renp.com
URL: http://www.marquiswhoswho.com

Biennial, Spring of odd years. $265.00. Covers about 11,800 people active in visual arts, including sculptors, painters, illustrators, printmakers, collectors, curators, writers, educators, dealers, critics, patrons, and museum executives. Also includes cumulative necrology from 1953. Entries include: Name, professional classification, address; artists' listings include dealer's name and address, preferred media, works in public collections, awards, publications, teaching positions, etc.; other listings may include same information plus statement of research interests, etc. Arrangement: Alphabetical. Indexes: Geographical, professional classification.

★2000★ **Who's Who in American Law**

Marquis Who's Who
121 Chanlon Rd.
New Providence, NJ 07974
Ph: (908)673-1101   Fax: (908)673-1189
Fr: 800-473-7020
E-mail: law@renp.com
URL: http://www.marquiswhoswho.com

Biennial, Winter of odd years. $310.50. Covers over 23,000 lawyers, judges, law school deans and professors, and other legal professionals. Entries include: Name, home and office addresses, place and date of birth, educational background, career history, civic positions, professional memberships, publications, awards, special achievements. Arrangement: Alphabetical. Indexes: Fields of practice, professional area.

HANDBOOKS AND MANUALS

★2001★ **Career Information Center**

Macmillan Publishing Co. Inc.
200 Old Tappan Rd.
Old Tappan, NJ 07675
Fr: 800-428-5331

Visual Education Center Staff. Seventh edition, 1999. $275.00. 2080 pages. This 13-volume set profiles over 600 occupations. Each occupational profile describes job duties, educational requirements, how to get the job, advancement possibilities, employment outlook, working conditions, earnings and benefits, and where to write for more information.

★2002★ **Career Opportunities for Writers**

Checkmark Books
132 W. 31st St., 17th Fl.
New York, NY 10001-2006
Ph: (212)967-8800   Fax: (212)967-9196
Fr: 800-322-8755
URL: http://www.factsonfile.com

Rosemary Ellen Guiley and Janet Frick. Fourth edition, 2000. $45.00. Part of the Career Opportunities Series. Describes more than 100 jobs in eight major fields, offering such details as duties, salaries, perquisites, employment and advancement opportunities, organizations to join, and opportunities for women and minorities.

★2003★ **Careers in Horticulture and Botany**

McGraw-Hill Trade
2 Penn Plaza
New York, NY 10121
Ph: (212)904-2000   Fr: 800-722-4726
E-mail: ntcpub@tribune.com

Jerry Garner. 1996. $17.95; 13.95 (paper). 255 pages. Includes bibliographical references

★2004★ **Careers in Journalism**

Kogan Page
1221 Avenue of the Americas
New York, NY 10020
Ph: (212)904-2000   Fr: 800-323-4900
E-mail: ntcpub@tribune.com

Jan Goldberg. Second edition, 1999. $17.95; 13.95 (paper). 192 pages.

★2005★ **Clinician to Academician: A Handbook for Those who Aspire to Become Faculty Members**

American Occupational Therapy
  Association, Inc.
4720 Montgomery Ln.
PO Box 31220
Bethesda, MD 20824-1220
Ph: (301)652-2682   Fax: (301)652-7711
Fr: 800-729-2682

Caroline R. Brayley. 1996. $20.00 (paper). 65 pages.

★2006★ Cracking the Academia Nut: A Guide to Preparing for Your Academic Career

Harvard University, Office of Career Services
54 Dunster St.
Cambridge, MA 02138
Ph: (617)495-2595   Fax: (617)495-3584

Margaret L. Newhouse. 1997. $13.00 (paper). 173 pages.

★2007★ Customizing Your Resume for Teaching Positions

Rowman and Littlefield
4720 Boston Way
Lanham, MD 20706
Ph: (301)459-3366   Fax: (301)459-2118
Fr: 800-462-6420

Edward G. Pultorak. 1993. 52 pages.

★2008★ Educator's Job Search: The Ultimate Guide to Finding Positions in Education

National Education Association
PO Box 2035
Annapolis Junction, MD 20701
Fr: 800-229-4200

Martin Kimeldorf. 1993. $15.95 (paper). 88 pages.

★2009★ Great Jobs for English Majors

McGraw-Hill Trade
2 Penn Plaza
New York, NY 10121
Ph: (212)904-2000   Fr: 800-722-4726
E-mail: ntcpub@tribune.com

Julie DeGalan. Second edition, 2000. $12.95 (paper). 462 pages.

★2010★ Great Jobs for History Majors

McGraw-Hill Trade
2 Penn Plaza
New York, NY 10121
Ph: (212)904-2000   Fr: 800-722-4726
E-mail: ntcpub@tribune.com

Julie DeGalan and Stephen Lambert. 1994. $11.95 (paper). 442 pages.

★2011★ Great Jobs for Liberal Arts Majors

McGraw-Hill Professional
2 Penn Plaza
New York, NY 10121
Ph: (212)904-2000   Fr: 800-722-4726
E-mail: ntcpub@tribune.com

Blythe Camenson. Second edition, 2001. $14.95 (paper). 256 pages.

★2012★ Great Jobs for Music Majors

McGraw-Hill Companies
1221 Avenue of the Americas
New York, NY 10020
Ph: (212)904-2000   Fr: 800-323-4900
E-mail: ntcpub@tribune.com

Jan Goldberg, Stephen Lambert, Julie De-Galan. 1997. $11.95 (paper). 365 pages.

★2013★ Great Jobs for Psychology Majors

McGraw-Hill Trade
2 Penn Plaza
New York, NY 10121
Ph: (212)904-2000   Fr: 800-722-4726
E-mail: ntcpub@tribune.com

Julie DeGalan and Stephen Lambert. 1995. $11.95 (paper). 468 pages. Out of print.

★2014★ Great Jobs for Sociology Majors

McGraw-Hill Trade
2 Penn Plaza
New York, NY 10121
Ph: (212)904-2000   Fr: 800-722-4726
E-mail: ntcpub@tribune.com

Stephen Lambert. 1996. $11.95 (paper). 514 pages.

★2015★ Great Jobs for Theater Majors

McGraw-Hill Companies
1221 Avenue of the Americas
New York, NY 10020
Ph: (212)904-2000   Fr: 800-323-4900
E-mail: ntcpub@tribune.com

Jan Goldberg, Stephen Lambert, Julie De-Galan. 1998. $11.95 (paper). 388 pages.

★2016★ How to Get a Job in Education

Adams Media Corp.
57 Littlefield St.
Avon, MA 02322
Ph: (508)427-7100   Fax: (508)427-6790
Fr: 800-872-5627
URL: http://www.adamsmedia.com

Joel Levin. Second edition, 1995. $15.95. 320 pages. Out of print. Prepared for recent college graduates, seasoned educators, and career-changing professionals, this publication guides the job-seeker through the necessary steps to obtaining a job in education at the elementary, secondary, and university levels. Offers advice on how to prepare for state and local examinations, how to locate teaching opportunities nationwide, and how to obtain certification. Includes a nationwide salary survey. Covers public, private, summer, and overseas opportunities.

★2017★ How to Get the Teaching Position You Want: Teacher Candidate Guide

Educational Enterprises
PO Box 1836
Spring Valley, CA 91979
Ph: (619)660-7720

Phyllis Murton. Second edition, revised, 1996. $9.95 (paper). 110 pages. This book provides a comprehensive guide for the teacher candidate's job search, as the format offers information that includes: interview questions most often asked in the teaching interview (grade-level & subject-matter specific); sample forms for applications, cover letters, & resumes that will impact principals & district personnel; strategies on preparing for the teaching interview; interview follow-up techniques; inside tips from a superintendent, a principal & a counselor.

★2018★ Increasing Faculty Diversity: The Occupational Choices of High-Achieving Minority Students

Harvard University Press
79 Garden St
Cambridge, MA 02138
Ph: (617)495-2600   Fax: (617)495-5898

Stephen Cole, Elinor Barber. January 2003. $45.00. Illustrated. 384 pages. Education teachers about minority opportunities.

★2019★ Job Search in Academe: Strategic Rhetorics for Faculty Job Candidates

Stylus Publishing, LLC
PO Box 605
Herndon, VA 20172-0605
Ph: (703)661-1581   Fax: (703)661-1501

Dawn M. Formo and Cheryl Reed. 1998. Identifies opportunities for job seekers in the humanities and social sciences, and advises on the preparation of effective CV's and portfolios.

★2020★ On the Market: Surviving the Academic Job Search

Berkley Publishing Group
375 Hudson St.
New York, NY 10014
Ph: (212)366-2000   Fax: (212)366-2385

Christina Boufis and Victoria C. Olsen, editors. 1997. $12.95 (paper). 368 pages. A guide for Ph.D.'s seeking an academic position.

★2021★ Opportunities in Overseas Careers

McGraw-Hill Trade
2 Penn Plaza
New York, NY 10121
Ph: (212)904-2000   Fr: 800-722-4726

Blythe Camenson. 1998. $14.95; $11.95 (paper). 106 pages.

★2022★ Opportunities in Teaching Careers

McGraw-Hill/Contemporary Books
1221 Avenue of the Americas
New York, NY 10020
Ph: (212)904-2000   Fr: 800-323-4900
E-mail: ntcpub@tribune.com

Janet Fine. 2000. $14.95; $11.95 (paper). 200 pages. Discusses licensing and accreditation programs, sources of placement information, job-seeking correspondence, selection procedures, and paths to advancement. Also covers professional associations, nontraditional teaching opportunities, and jobs abroad.

★2023★ Opportunities in Technical Education Careers
McGraw-Hill/Contemporary Books
1221 Avenue of the Americas
New York, NY 10020
Ph: (212)904-2000   Fr: 800-323-4900
E-mail: ntcpub@tribune.com
Robert Connelly. 1998. 200 pages. $14.95; $11.95 (paper).

★2024★ Real People Working in Education
McGraw-Hill Contemporary Books
1221 Avenue of the Americas
New York, NY 10020
Ph: (212)904-2000   Fr: 800-323-4900
E-mail: ntcpub@tribune.com
Blythe Camenson, Jan Goldberg. 1997. $17.95; $12.95 (paper). Interviews and profiles of working professionals capture a range of opportunities in this field.

★2025★ Teaching (Career Portraits)
Vgm Career Horizons
1221 Avenue of the Americas
New York, NY 10020
Ph: (212)904-2000   Fr: 800-323-4900
E-mail: ntcpub@tribune.com
Marjorie Eberts and Margaret Gisler. 1994. $13.95. 320 pages.

★2026★ Tomorrow's Professor: Preparing for Academic Careers in Science and Engineering
John Wiley & Sons, Inc.
111 River St.
Hoboken, NJ 07030-5774
Ph: (201)748-6000   Fax: (201)748-6088
Fr: 800-225-5945
Rick Reis. 2001. $49.95 (paper). 436 pages. Contains advice for graduate students, post-doctorate fellows and workers, nontenured professors, and future PhD's.

EMPLOYMENT AGENCIES AND SEARCH FIRMS

★2027★ Berardi & Associates
1140 Avenue of the Americas, Fl. 8
New York, NY 10036
Ph: (212)403-6180   Fax: (212)764-9690
Executive search firm.

★2028★ Boston Search Group Inc.
224 Clarendon St., Ste. 41
Boston, MA 02116-3729
Ph: (617)266-4333   Fax: (781)735-0562
Executive search firm.

★2029★ Brigham Hill Consultancy
2909 Cole Ave., Ste. 220
Dallas, TX 75204
Ph: (214)871-8700   Fax: (214)871-6004
Executive search firm.

★2030★ CHM Partners International LLC
466 Southern Blvd.
Chatham, NJ 07928-1462
Ph: (973)966-1600   Fax: (973)966-6933
Executive search firm.

★2031★ Compass Group Ltd.
Birmingham Place Bldg.
401 S. Old Woodward, Ste. 460
Birmingham, MI 48009-6613
Ph: (248)540-9110   Fax: (248)647-8288
Executive search firm. Second location in Oak Brook, IL.

★2032★ The Dalley Hewitt Company
1401 Peachtree St. NE, Ste. 500
Atlanta, GA 30309
Ph: (404)885-6642   Fax: (404)355-6136
Executive search firm.

★2033★ Deerfield Associates
572 Washington St., Ste. 15
Wellesley, MA 02482
Fax: (781)237-5600
Executive search firm.

★2034★ Development Resource Group Inc (DRG)
104 E. 40th St., Ste. 304
New York, NY 10016
Ph: (212)983-1600   Fax: (212)983-1687
Executive search firm.

★2035★ Dunn Associates
229 Limberline Dr.
Greensburg, PA 15601
Ph: (724)832-9822   Fax: (724)832-9836
Fr: 877-586-2538
Executive search firm.

★2036★ Educational Management Network
2015 Spring Rd., Ste. 510
Oak Brook, IL 60523
Ph: (630)990-1370
Executive search firm with five locations throughout the United States.

★2037★ EFL Associates
7101 College Blvd., Ste. 550
Overland Park, KS 66210-1891
Ph: (913)451-8866   Fax: (913)451-3219
Executive search firm. Locations in Englewood, CO and Lake Forest, IL.

★2038★ Ford Webb Associates Inc.
27 Main St.
Concord, MA 01742
Ph: (978)371-4900
Executive search firm.

★2039★ PN French Associates Inc.
126 Noell Farm Rd.
Carlisle, MA 01741
Ph: (978)369-4569
Executive search firm.

★2040★ Sunny Bates Associates
345 7th Ave., Fl. 8
New York, NY 10001
Ph: (212)691-5252   Fax: (212)691-3133
Executive search firm.

ONLINE JOB SOURCES AND SERVICES

★2041★ Academic360.com
E-mail: webmaster@atsacademic360.com
URL: http://www.academic360.com/
Description: Site is a collection of internet resources gathered for the academic job hunter. Contains links to over 1,400 colleges and universities that advertise job openings online. Positions listed are not limited to teaching positions.

TRADESHOWS

★2042★ American Association of Physics Teachers Winter Meeting
American Association of Physics Teachers (AAPT)
One Physics Ellipse
College Park, MD 20740-3845
Ph: (301)209-3311   Fax: (301)345-1857
E-mail: aapt@www.aapt.org
URL: http://www.aapt.org
Annual. **Primary Exhibits:** Physics textbooks, apparatus, and software.

★2043★ American Society for Engineering Education Annual Conference and Exposition
American Society for Engineering Education
1818 N St., Ste. 600
Washington, DC 20036
Ph: (202)331-3500   Fax: (202)265-8504
URL: http://www.asee.org
Annual. **Primary Exhibits:** Publications, engineering supplies and equipment, computers, software, and research companies all products and services related to engineering

education. **Dates and Locations:** 2005 Jun 12-15; Portland, OR • 2006 Jun 18-21; Chicago, IL • 2007 Jun 24-27; Honolulu, HI.

★2044★ American Technical Education Association National Conference on Technical Education

American Technical Education Association
c/o North Dakota State College of
  Science
800 N. 6th St.
Wahpeton, ND 58076
Ph: (701)671-2240   Fax: (701)671-2260
URL: http://www.ndscs.nodak.edu/atea/

Annual. **Primary Exhibits:** Supplies and services related to post secondary technical education. **Dates and Locations:** 2005 March; New Orleans, LA.

★2045★ Association for Education in Journalism and Mass Communication Annual Convention

Association for Education in Journalism
  and Mass Communication
234 Outlet Point Blvd., Ste. A
Columbia, SC 29210-5667
Ph: (803)798-0274   Fax: (803)772-3509
E-mail: aejmc@aejmc.org
URL: http://www.aejmc.org

Annual. **Primary Exhibits:** Publications, information retrieval services, and special programs.

★2046★ Council of Graduate Schools Annual Meeting

Council of Graduate Schools
1 Dupont Cir. NW, Ste. 430
Washington, DC 20036
Ph: (202)223-3791   Fax: (202)331-7157
E-mail: ngaffney@cgs.nche.edu
URL: http://www.cgsnet.org

Annual. **Primary Exhibits:** Exhibits related to the improvement and advancement of graduate education.

★2047★ Northwest Association of Schools and Colleges Meeting

Northwest Association of Schools and
  Colleges
c/o Boise State University
1910 University Dr.
Boise, ID 83725
Ph: (208)334-3226   Fax: (208)334-3228
E-mail: sclemens@bsumail.idbsu.edu
URL: http://www.idbsu.edu/nasc

Semiannual. **Primary Exhibits:** Educational equipment, supplies, and services.

★2048★ Southwestern Federation of Administrative Disciplines Convention

Southwestern Federation of Administrative
  Disciplines
2700 Bay Area Blvd.
Houston, TX 77058
Ph: (713)283-3122   Fax: (713)283-3951
URL: http://www.swfao.swt.edu

Annual. **Primary Exhibits:** Educational materials and services.

★2049★ UCEA Annual Conference

National University Continuing Education
  Association
1 Dupont Cir., Ste. 615
Washington, DC 20036
Ph: (202)659-3130   Fax: (202)785-0374

Annual. **Primary Exhibits:** Exhibits related to continuing education and online learning at institutions of higher learning.

OTHER SOURCES

★2050★ Academy of Legal Studies in Business (ALSB)

Department of Finance
120 Upham Hall
Miami University
Oxford, OH 45056
Ph: (513)529-2945   Fax: (513)523-8180
Fr: 800-831-2903
E-mail: herrondj@muohio.edu
URL: http://www.alsb.org

Description: Teachers of business law and legal environment in colleges and universities. Promotes and encourages business law scholarship and teaching outside of the law school environment. Sponsors annual conference each August.

★2051★ Academy of Marketing Science (AMS)

University of Miami
School of Bus. Admin.
PO Box 248012
Coral Gables, FL 33124
Ph: (305)284-6673   Fax: (305)284-3762
E-mail: ams.sba@miami.edu
URL: http://www.ams-web.org

Description: Marketing academicians and practitioners; individuals interested in fostering education in marketing science. Purpose is to promote the advancement of knowledge and the furthering of professional standards in the field of marketing. Explores the special application areas of marketing science and its responsibilities as an economic, ethical, and social force; promotes research and the widespread dissemination of findings. Facilitates exchange of information and experience among members, and the transfer of marketing knowledge and technology to developing countries; promotes marketing science on an international level. Provides a forum for discussion and refinement of concepts, methods and applications, and the opportunity to publish papers in the field. Assists member educators in the development of improved teaching methods, devices, directions, and materials. Offers guidance and direction in marketing practice and reviewer assistance on scholarly works. Contributes to the solution of marketing problems encountered by individual firms,

industries, and society as a whole. Encourages members to utilize their marketing talents to the fullest through redirection, reassignment, and relocation. Sponsors competitions.

★2052★ American Almanac of Jobs and Salaries

Morrow Avon
1350 Avenue of the Americas
New York, NY 10019
Ph: (212)261-6788   Fr: 800-242-7737

John W. Wright. Revised edition, 2000. $20.00 (paper). 672 pages. This is a comprehensive guide to the wages of hundreds of occupations in a wide variety of industries and organizations.

★2053★ American Association of Community Colleges (AACC)

1 Dupont Cir. NW, Ste. 410
Washington, DC 20036-1176
Ph: (202)728-0200   Fax: (202)833-2467
URL: http://www.aacc.nche.edu

Members: Community colleges; individual associates interested in community college development; corporate, educational, foundation, and international associate members. **Purpose:** Office of Federal Relations monitors federal educational programming and legislation. **Activities:** Compiles statistics through data collection and policy analysis. Conducts seminars and professional training programs.

★2054★ American Association for Health Education (AAHE)

1900 Association Dr.
Reston, VA 20191
Ph: (703)476-3437   Fax: (703)476-6638
Fr: 800-213-7193
E-mail: aahe@aahperd.org
URL: http://www.aahperd.org/aahe

Members: Professionals who have responsibility for health education in schools, colleges, communities, hospitals and clinics, and industries. **Purpose:** Works for the advancement of health education through program activities and federal legislation; encouragement of close working relationships between all health education and health service organizations; achievement of good health and well-being for all Americans automatically, without conscious thought and endeavor. Member of the American Alliance for Health, Physical Education, Recreation and Dance.

★2055★ American Association of Teachers of German (AATG)

112 Haddontowne Ct., No. 104
Cherry Hill, NJ 08034-3668
Ph: (856)795-5553   Fax: (856)795-9398
E-mail: headquarters@aatg.org
URL: http://www.aatg.org

Description: Teachers of German at all levels; individuals interested in German language and culture. Offers in-service teacher-training workshops, materials, student honor society, national German examination, and stipends/scholarships.

★2056★ American Association for Women in Community Colleges (AAWCC)

1202 W Thomas Rd.
Phoenix, AZ 85013
Ph: (602)285-7449   Fax: (602)285-7832
E-mail: aawcc@pcmail.maricopa.edu
URL: http://www.pc.maricopa.edu/aawcc

Description: Women faculty members, administrators, staff members, students, and trustees of community colleges. Objectives are to: develop communication and disseminate information among women in community, junior, and technical colleges; encourage educational program development; obtain grants for educational projects for community college women. Disseminates information on women's issues and programs. Conducts regional and state professional development workshops and forums. Recognizes model programs that assist women in community colleges. A council of the American Association of Community Colleges.

★2057★ American Catholic Philosophical Association (ACPA)

Fordham University
Administration Bldg.
Bronx, NY 10458
Ph: (718)817-4081   Fax: (718)817-5709
E-mail: acpa@fordham.edu
URL: http://www.acpa-main.org

Description: College and university teachers of philosophy; students engaged in research; writers and others interested in philosophical knowledge.

★2058★ American Mathematical Society (AMS)

201 Charles St.
Providence, RI 02904-2294
Ph: (401)455-4000   Fax: (401)331-3842
Fr: 800-321-4AMS
E-mail: ams@ams.org
URL: http://www.ams.org/

Description: Professional society of mathematicians and educators. Promotes the interests of mathematical scholarship and research. Holds institutes, seminars, short courses, and symposia to further mathematical research; awards prizes. Offers placement services; compiles statistics.

★2059★ American Society of Psychopathology of Expression (ASPE)

74 Lawton St.
Brookline, MA 02446
Ph: (617)738-9821   Fax: (617)975-0411

Description: Psychiatrists, psychologists, art therapists, sociologists, art critics, artists, social workers, linguists, educators, criminologists, writers, and historians. At least two-thirds of the members must be physicians. Fosters collaboration among specialists in the United States who are interested in the

problems of expression and in the artistic activities connected with psychiatric, sociological, and psychological research. Disseminates information about research and clinical applications in the field of psychopathology of expression. Sponsors consultations, seminars, and lectures on art therapy.

★2060★ Art Directors Club (ADC)

106 W 29th St.
New York, NY 10001
Ph: (212)643-1440   Fax: (212)643-4266
E-mail: info@adcny.org
URL: http://www.adcny.org

Members: Art directors of advertising magazines and agencies, visual information specialists, and graphic designers; associate members are artists, cinematographers, photographers, copywriters, educators, journalists, and critics. Purpose: Promotes and stimulates interest in the practice of art direction. Activities: Sponsors Annual Exhibition of Advertising, Editorial and Television Art and Design; International Traveling Exhibition; Hall of Fame. Provides educational, professional, and entertainment programs; on-premise art exhibitions; portfolio review program. Conducts panels for students and faculty.

★2061★ Association of Departments of English (ADE)

26 Broadway, 3rd Fl.
New York, NY 10004-1789
Ph: (646)576-5130   Fax: (646)834-4045
E-mail: dlaurence@mla.org
URL: http://www.ade.org

Description: Administrators of college and university departments of English, humanities, rhetoric, and communications. To improve the teaching of English and the administration of English departments. Conducts studies and surveys of literature and writing courses. Sponsors sessions at major English conventions and conferences nationwide. Sponsored by Modern Language Association of America.

★2062★ Association for Education in Journalism and Mass Communication (AEJMC)

234 Outlet Pointe Blvd., Ste. A
Columbia, SC 29210-5667
Ph: (803)798-0271   Fax: (803)772-3509
E-mail: aejmc@aejmc.org
URL: http://www.aejmc.org/

Description: Professional organization of college and university journalism and communication teachers. Works to improve methods and standards of teaching and stimulate research. Compiles statistics on enrollments and current developments in journalism education. Maintains a listing of journalism and communication teaching positions available and teaching positions wanted, revised bimonthly.

★2063★ Association for Library and Information Science Education (ALISE)

1009 Commerce Park Dr., Ste. 150
Oak Ridge, TN 37830
Ph: (865)425-0155   Fax: (865)481-0390
E-mail: contact@alise.org
URL: http://www.alise.org

Description: Graduate schools offering degree programs in library science and their faculties. Seeks to: promote excellence in education for library and information science as a means of increasing the effectiveness of library and information services; provide a forum for the active interchange of ideas and information among library educators; promote research related to teaching and to library and information science; formulate and promulgate positions on matters related to library education. Offers employment program at annual conference.

★2064★ Association for the Study of Higher Education (ASHE)

202 Hill Hall
Columbia, MO 65211-2190
Ph: (573)882-9645   Fax: (573)884-2197
E-mail: ashe@coe.missouri.edu
URL: http://www.ashe.missouri.edu

Description: Professors, researchers, administrators, policy analysts, graduate students, and others concerned with the study of higher education. Purposes are to advance the study of higher education and facilitate and encourage discussion of priority issues for research in the study of higher education.

★2065★ College Reading and Learning Association (CRLA)

PO Box 6251
Auburn, CA 95604
Ph: (530)823-1076   Fax: (530)823-6331
E-mail: debbie2@garlic.com
URL: http://www.crla.net

Description: Professionals involved in college/adult reading, learning assistance, developmental education, and tutorial services. Promotes communication for the purpose of professional growth.

★2066★ Conference on College Composition and Communication (CCCC)

1111 W. Kenyon Rd.
Urbana, IL 61801-1096
Ph: (217)328-3870   Fax: (217)328-0977
Fr: 800-369-6283
E-mail: public_info@ncte.org
URL: http://www.ncte.org/groups/cccc

Description: Members are college and university educators involved in teaching composition and communica tion.

★2067★ Convention of American Instructors of the Deaf (CAID)

PO Box 377
Bedford, TX 76095-0377
Ph: (817)354-8414

E-mail: caid@swbell.net
URL: http://www.caid.org/

Members: Professional organization of teachers, administrators, and professionals in allied fields related to education of the deaf and hard-of-hearing. **Purpose:** Objectives are to provide opportunities for a free interchange of views concerning methods and means of educating the deaf and hard-of-hearing; to promote such education by the publication of reports, essays, and other information; to develop more effective methods of teaching deaf and hard-of-hearing children.

★2068★ **Eastern Finance Association**

Department of Finance
University of Mississippi
PO Box 1848
University, MS 38677
Ph: (662)915-7721
E-mail: mwalker@bus.olemiss.edu
URL: http://www.easternfinance.org

Description: College and university professors and financial officers (1200); libraries (450). Provides a meeting place for persons interested in any aspect of finance, including financial management, investments, and banking. Sponsors research competitions.

★2069★ *Education and Training*

Cambridge Educational
2572 Brunswick Ave.
Lawrenceville, NJ 08648-4128
Fax: 800-FAX-ON-US   Fr: 800-468-4227
URL: http://www.cambridgeeducational.com
$89.95. 2002. 18 minutes.

★2070★ **Friends Council on Education (FCE)**

1507 Cherry St.
Philadelphia, PA 19102
Ph: (215)241-7245   Fax: (215)241-7299
E-mail: quakered@aol.com
URL: http://www.friendscouncil.org

Members: Representatives appointed by Friends Yearly Meetings; heads of Quaker secondary and elementary schools and colleges; members-at-large. **Purpose:** Acts as a clearinghouse for information on Quaker schools and colleges. **Activities:** Holds meetings and conferences on education and provides in-service training for teachers, administrators, and trustees in Friends schools.

★2071★ *How to Prepare Your Curriculum Vitae*

McGraw-Hill Trade
2 Penn Plaza
New York, NY 10121
Ph: (212)904-2000   Fr: 800-722-4726
E-mail: ntcpub@tribune.com

Acy L. Jackson. Second edition, 1996. $14.95 (paper). 550 pages. Dozens of examples from academics in all disciplines and at all career levels illustrate the principles of writing an effective C.V. Worksheets guide the reader through a step-by-step process that begins with describing, in draft form, all pertinent experiences, and then helps shape, organize, and edit experiences and credentials into a professional curriculum vitae. Includes sample cover letters tailored to academic institutions.

★2072★ **Modern Language Association of America (MLA)**

26 Broadway, 3rd Fl.
New York, NY 10004-1789
Ph: (646)576-5000   Fax: (646)458-0300
E-mail: info@mla.org
URL: http://www.mla.org

Members: College and university teachers of English and of modern foreign languages. **Purpose:** Seeks to advance all aspects of literary and linguistic study. Under its Foreign Language Program, researches foreign language teaching primarily at the postsecondary level of U.S. education. Under its English Program, acts as a clearinghouse for information of interest to teachers of English literature and composition. **Activities:** Conducts Job Information Service. Operates 84 divisions.

★2073★ **NAFSA/Association of International Educators (NAFSA)**

1307 New York Ave. NW, 8th Fl.
Washington, DC 20005
Ph: (202)737-3699   Fax: (202)737-3657
E-mail: inbox@nafsa.org
URL: http://www.nafsa.org

Description: Individuals, organizations, and institutions dealing with international educational exchange, including foreign student advisers, overseas educational advisers, credentials and admissions officers, administrators and teachers of English as a second language, community support personnel, study-abroad administrators, and embassy cultural or educational personnel. Promotes self-regulation standards and responsibilities in international educational exchange; offers professional development opportunities primarily through publications, workshops, grants, and regional and national conferences. Advocates for increased awareness and support of international education and exchange on campuses, in government, and in communities. Offers services including: a job registry for employers and professionals involved with international education; a consultant referral service. Sponsors joint liaison activities with a variety of other educational and government organizations to conduct a census of foreign student enrollment in the U.S.; conducts workshops about specific subjects and countries.

★2074★ **National Alliance of Black School Educators (NABSE)**

310 Pennsylvania Ave. SE
Washington, DC 20003
Ph: (202)608-6310   Fax: (202)608-6319
Fr: 800-221-2654
E-mail: nabse@nabse.org
URL: http://www.nabse.org

Description: Black educators from all levels; others indirectly involved in the education of black youth. Purpose is to promote awareness, professional expertise, and commitment among black educators. Goals are to: eliminate and rectify the results of racism in education; work with state, local, and national leaders to raise the academic achievement level of all black students; increase members' involvement in legislative activities; facilitate the introduction of a curriculum that more completely embraces black America; improve the ability of black educators to promote problem resolution; create a meaningful and effective network of strength, talent, and professional support. Sponsors workshops, commission meetings, and special projects. Encourages research, especially as it relates to blacks, and the presentation of papers during national conferences. Plans to establish a National Black Educators Data Bank and offer placement service.

★2075★ **National Art Education Association (NAEA)**

1916 Association Dr.
Reston, VA 20191-1590
Ph: (703)860-8000   Fax: (703)860-2960
E-mail: naea@dgs.dgsys.com
URL: http://www.naea-reston.org

Members: Teachers of art at elementary, middle, secondary, and college levels; colleges, libraries, museums, and other educational institutions. **Purpose:** Studies problems of teaching art; encourages research and experimentation. **Activities:** Serves as clearinghouse for information on art education programs, materials, and methods of instruction. Sponsors special institutes. Cooperates with other national organizations for the furtherance of creative art experiences for youth.

★2076★ **National Association of Blind Teachers (NABT)**

1155 15th St. NW, Ste. 1004
Washington, DC 20005
Ph: (202)467-5081   Fax: (202)467-5085
Fr: 800-424-8666
E-mail: info@acb.org
URL: http://www.acb.org

Description: Public school teachers, college and university professors, and teachers in residential schools for the blind. Purpose is to promote employment and professional goals of blind persons entering the teaching profession or those established in their respective teaching fields. Serves as a vehicle for the dissemination of information and the exchange of ideas addressing special problems of members. Compiles statistics.

★2077★ **National Association of College and University Business Officers (NACUBO)**

2501 M St., NW, Ste. 400
Washington, DC 20037-1308
Ph: (202)861-2500   Fax: (202)861-2583
URL: http://www.nacubo.org

Members: Colleges, universities, and companies that are members of a regional association. **Purpose:** Develops and maintains national interest in improving the principles and practices of business and financial administration in higher education. **Activities:** Sponsors workshops in fields such as cash management, grant and contract maintenance, accounting, investment, student loan administration, and costing. Conducts research and information exchange programs between college and university personnel; compiles statistics.

★2078★ National Council for Geographic Education (NCGE)
206A Martin Hall
Jacksonville State University
Jacksonville, AL 36265-1602
Ph: (256)782-5293   Fax: (256)782-5336
E-mail: ncge@jsucc.jsu.edu
URL: http://www.ncge.org

Description: Teachers of geography and social studies in elementary and secondary schools, colleges, and universities; geographers in governmental agencies and private businesses. Encourages the training of teachers in geographic concepts, practices, teaching methods, and techniques; works to develop effective geographic educational programs in schools and colleges and with adult groups; stimulates the production and use of accurate and understandable geographic teaching aids and materials.

★2079★ National Council of Teachers of Mathematics (NCTM)
1906 Association Dr.
Reston, VA 20191-1502
Ph: (703)620-9840   Fax: (703)476-2970
Fr: 800-235-7566
E-mail: orders@nctm.org
URL: http://www.nctm.org

Description: Dedicated to improving teaching and learning of mathematics. Toll-free number is for orders only.

★2080★ Organization of American Historians (OAH)
112 N. Bryan Ave.
Bloomington, IN 47408-4199
Ph: (812)855-7311   Fax: (812)855-0696
E-mail: oah@oah.org
URL: http://www.oah.org

Description: Professional historians, including college faculty members, secondary school teachers, graduate students, and other individuals in related fields; institutional subscribers are college, university, high school and public libraries, and historical agencies. Promotes historical research and study. Sponsors 12 prize programs for historical writing; maintains speakers' bureau. Conducts educational programs.

★2081★ *Overseas Employment Opportunities for Educators: Department of Defense Dependents Schools*
DIANE Publishing Co.
PO Box 1428
Collingdale, PA 19023-8428
Ph: (610)461-6200   Fax: (610)461-6130
Fr: 800-782-3833

Barry Leonard, editor. 1999. $20.00. 44 pages. An introduction to teachings positions in the Dept. of Defense Dependents Schools (DoDDS), a worldwide school system, operated by the DoD in 14 countries.

★2082★ *Teaching & Related Occupations*
Delphi Productions
3160 4th St.
Boulder, CO 80304
Fax: (303)443-4022   Fr: 888-443-2400
URL: http://www.delphivideo.com

$95.00. 50 minutes. Part of the Careers for the 21st Century Video Library.

Computer and Information Systems Managers

★2083★ **AS/400 Systems Management**
Adams Business Media
250 S Wacker Dr., Ste. 1150
Chicago, IL 60606
Ph: (312)977-0999   Fax: (312)980-3135
E-mail: 73222.3344@compuserve.com
URL: http://www.hotlink400.com

Monthly. $42.00/year for individuals. Management-oriented magazine for DP/MIS managers with an IBM AS/400 on site.

★2084★ **Communications of the ACM**
Association for Computing Machinery
1515 Broadway
New York, NY 10036
Ph: (212)626-0500   Fax: (212)944-1318
Fr: 800-342-6626
URL: http://www.acm.org/about_acm/ov_pubs.html

Monthly. Computing news magazine.

★2085★ **Component Development Strategies**
Paul Harman
2040 Polk St.
Box 334
San Francisco, CA 94109-2520
Ph: (415)669-1860
URL: http://www.cutter.com/cds

Description: Monthly. Contains product reviews, industry news and trends, and market forecasts. Recurring features include a calendar of events, reports of meetings, and notices of publications available.

★2086★ **Computer Economics Networking Strategies Report**
Computer Economics Inc.
5841 Edison Pl.
Carlsbad, CA 92008
Ph: (619)438-8100
URL: http://www.computereconomics.com

Description: Monthly. Provides an execu-

tive overview for Management Information Systems (MIS) and network professionals who are involved in network strategic planning and implementation. Covers such topics as comparative analyses of hardware and software systems, costs of ownership studies, analyses of emerging protocols and standards, and cost-saving opportunities.

★2087★ **Computer Economics Report**
Computer Economics Inc.
5841 Edison Pl.
Carlsbad, CA 92008
Ph: (619)438-8100
URL: http://www.computereconomics.com

Description: Monthly. Provides analyses of new IBM technologies and acquisition and financial management strategies from an end-user perspective. Recurring features include cost comparisons, price/performance analyses, new product forecasts, and evaluations of acquisition techniques for medium and large computer systems. Also available in international edition.

★2088★ **Cutter IT Journal**
Cutter Information Corp.
37 Broadway, Ste. 1
Arlington, MA 02474-5552
Ph: (781)641-5118   Fax: (781)648-1950
Fr: 800-964-5118
E-mail: itjournal@cutter.com
URL: http://www.cutter.com/itjournal

Description: Monthly. Provides IT managers with practical and objective views on the latest technology and management trends.

★2089★ **E-Business Application Delivery**
Cutter Information Corp.
37 Broadway, Ste. 1
Arlington, MA 02474-5552
Ph: (781)641-5118   Fax: (781)648-1950
Fr: 800-964-5118
E-mail: ead@cutter.com
URL: http://www.cutter.com/ead

Description: Monthly. Contains hands-on tool reviews, industry news and trends,

product developments, and application case studies.

★2090★ **HIMSS News**
Healthcare Information and Management
  Systems Society
230 E Ohio St., Ste. 500
Chicago, IL 60611
Ph: (312)664-4467   Fax: (312)664-6143

Description: Monthly. Reports the news of the Healthcare Information and Management Systems Society (HIMSS), which provides leadership in healthcare for the management of technology, information, and change through publications, educational opportunities, and member services.

★2091★ **I/S Analyzer**
The 400 Group
990 Washington St., Ste. 308
Dedham, MA 02026
Ph: (781)320-8909   Fax: (781)320-9466
Fr: 877-440-0477

Description: Monthly. Focuses on management issues of concern to information systems and data processing executives. Focuses in-depth on one topic per issue, with commentary, relevant case studies, and a concluding summary.

★2092★ **Information Executive**
Association of Information Technology
  Professionals
315 S NW Hwy., Ste. 200
Park Ridge, IL 60068
Ph: (847)825-8124   Fax: (847)825-1693
Fr: 800-224-9371
E-mail: 70430.35@compuserve.com

Description: Ten issues/year. Provides up-to-date information on the changes and developments of the information systems industry.

★2093★ Information Technology Adviser

Progressive Business Publications
370 Technology Dr.
Malvern, PA 19355
Ph: (610)695-8600   Fax: (610)647-8089
Fr: 800-220-5000
URL: http://www.pbp.com

Description: Semimonthly. Presents information to keep IT/IS managers up to date on how technology cuts costs, boosts productivity, and makes companies more successful. Recurring features include interviews, news of research, a calendar of events, news of educational opportunities, and a column titled Sharpen Your Judgment.

★2094★ InfoWorld

InfoWorld
155 Bovet Rd.
San Mateo, CA 94402
Ph: (650)572-7341   Fax: (415)312-0580
Fr: 800-227-8365

Weekly. Free to qualified subscribers; $180.00/year for individuals. Weekly IS publication.

★2095★ The National Report on Computers & Health

United Communications Group
11300 Rockville Pke., Ste. 1100
Rockville, MD 20852
Ph: (301)816-8950   Fax: (301)816-8945
Fr: 800-929-4824

Description: Biweekly. Reports on data processing and clinical hospital information systems.

★2096★ PC Computing

Ziff-Davis Media Inc.
28 E 28th St.
New York, NY 10016-7930
Ph: (212)503-3500

Monthly. Magazine on personal computers.

★2097★ PC Magazine

Ziff-Davis Media Inc.
28 E 28th St.
New York, NY 10016-7930
Ph: (212)503-3500

Semimonthly. Consumer magazine focusing on the personal computer industry.

★2098★ PC Week

Ziff-Davis Media Inc.
28 E 28th St.
New York, NY 10016-7930
Ph: (212)503-3500
URL: http://www.pcweek.com

Weekly. Free to qualified subscribers; $195.00/year for individuals; $250.00/year for Canada and Mexico; $395.00/year for other countries; $6.00 for single issue. Tabloid featuring microcomputer products and developments.

★2099★ PC WORLD

101 Communications
9121 Oakdale Ave.
Chatsworth, CA 91311
Ph: (818)734-1520   Fax: (818)734-1522
URL: http://www.pcworld.com

Monthly. $29.90/year for individuals; $5.95 for single issue.

★2100★ Performance Computing

CMP Media L.L.C.
600 Community Dr.
Manhasset, NY 11030
Ph: (516)562-5000
URL: http://www.performance-computing.com

Monthly. Free to qualified subscribers; $55.00/year, nonqualified. Magazine for professional users of UNIX and UNIX-like systems, and Windows NT.

★2101★ Report on IBM

DataTrends Publications Inc.
614 Jacob Ct. SW
Leesburg, VA 20177
Ph: (703)779-0574

Description: Weekly. Involved with International Business Machines Corporation (IBM) activities and lines of business, with emphasis on information systems in businesses, factories and homes. Contains news and articles on new IBM introductions, new markets and market strategies, and industry trends.

★2102★ SIGMIS Management Information Systems

Association for Computing Machinery
1515 Broadway, 17th Fl.
New York, NY 10036-5701
Ph: (212)869-7440   Fax: (212)944-1318
Fr: 800-342-6626
URL: http://www.acm.org/sigmis

Description: Quarterly. Covers information systems and technologies for management.

★2103★ Technology Trends

Enterprise Technology Corp.
305 Madison Ave.
New York, NY 10165
Ph: (212)972-1860   Fax: (212)687-6126

Description: Six issues/year. Discusses news on computer software technology and its perceived value to the business community.

EMPLOYER DIRECTORIES AND NETWORKING LISTS

★2104★ 4 Data Base

Hunt-Scanlon Publishing
20 Signal Rd.
Stamford, CT 06902-7907
Ph: (203)352-2920   Fax: (203)352-2930

Annual. $1,350.00 for individuals. Database covers more than 100,000 top and middle management professionals in human resources, finance, sales and marketing, and information technology at over 10,000 companies in the U.S. Entries include: Company name, address, phone, number of employees, SIC codes, revenues, individual name, title, phone number, industry specialization.

HANDBOOKS AND MANUALS

★2105★ America's Top 101 Computer and Technical Jobs

JIST Publishing
8902 Otis Ave.
Indianapolis, IN 46216-1033
Ph: (317)613-4200   Fax: 800-547-8329

Michael J. Farr. 2004. $15.95. 368 pages. Job hunting in computer and technical industries.

★2106★ Career Opportunities in Computers and Cyberspace

Facts on File
132 W. 31st St., 17th Fl.
New York, NY 10001-2006
Ph: (212)967-8800   Fax: (212)967-8107
Fr: 800-322-8755

Harry Henderson. 1999. $26.95 (paper). Part of the Career Opportunities Series. 224 pages.

★2107★ Careers Inside the World of Technology

Rosen Publishing Group, Inc.
29 E. 21st St.
New York, NY 10010
Ph: (212)777-3017   Fax: 888-436-4643
Fr: 800-237-9932

Jean W. Spencer. Revised edition, 1998. $16.95. 64 pages. Describes computer-related careers for reluctant readers.

★2108★ Choosing a Career in Computers

Rosen Publishing Group, Inc.
29 E. 21st St.
New York, NY 10010
Ph: (212)777-3017   Fax: (212)777-0277
Fr: 800-237-9932

Weigant, Chris. 2000. $17.95.

★2109★ **The Digital Frontier Job & Opportunity Finder**
Moon Lake Media
PO Box 251466
Los Angeles, CA 90025
Ph: (310)535-2453

Don B. Altman. 1996. $19.95 (paper). 256 pages.

★2110★ **The e-learning Question and Answer Book: A Survival Guide for Trainers and Business Managers**
AMACOM
1601 Broadway, 12th Fl.
New York, NY 10019-7420
Ph: (212)586-8100   Fax: (212)903-8168

Allan Henderson. October 2002. $19.95. Illustrated. 176 pages. Education for the internet.

★2111★ **Get Your IT Career in Gear!**
McGraw-Hill Professional
2 Penn Plaza
New York, NY 10121
Ph: (212)904-2000   Fr: 800-722-4726

Goff, Leslie. 2001. $24.99 (Trade paper). 401 pages.

★2112★ **Hiring and Retaining Top IT Professionals: The Guide for Savvy Hiring Managers and Job Hunters Alike**
McGraw-Hill Companies
1221 Avenue of the Americas
New York, NY 10020
Ph: (212)904-2000   Fr: 800-323-4900

Adamsky, Howard. 2001. $24.99 (Trade paper). 256 pages.

★2113★ **How to Be a Successful Computer Consultant**
McGraw-Hill Companies
860 Taylor Station Rd.
Blacklick, OH 43004-0545
Fax: (614)755-5645   Fr: 800-722-4726

Walid Mougayar and Alan R. Simon. Fourth edition, revised, 1998. $29.95 (paper). Out of print.

★2114★ **MIS Manager's Appraisal Guide: Practical Guidelines and Forms for Evaluating and Appraising Your MIS Staff**
McGraw-Hill Companies
Two Penn Plaza
New York, NY 10121-2298
Fr: 800-338-3987

Lyon, Lockwood. 1994. $39.95 (Cloth). 290 pages.

★2115★ **The New High-Tech Manager: Six Rules for Success in Changing Times**
Artech House, Inc.
685 Canton St.
Norwood, MA 02062
Ph: (781)769-9750   Fax: (781)769-6334
Fr: 800-225-9977

Durham, Kenneth and Bruce Kennedy. 1997. $66.00 (Trade cloth). 201 pages.

★2116★ **Opportunities in Computer Systems Careers**
McGraw-Hill Contemporary Books
1221 Avenue of the Americas
New York, NY 10020
Ph: (212)904-2000   Fr: 800-323-4900
E-mail: ntcpub@tribune.com

Julie King Burns. 1996. $14.95; $11.95 (paper). 160 pages.

★2117★ **Preparing for an Outstanding Career in Computers: Questions and Answers for Professionals and Students**
Rafi Systems, Inc.
750 N. Diamond Bar Blvd., Suite 224
Diamond Bar, CA 91765
Ph: (909)593-8124   Fax: (909)629-1034
Fr: 800-584-6706

Rafiquzzaman, Mohamed. 2001. $19.95 (Trade cloth). 145 pages.

★2118★ **Winning Resumes for Computer Personnel**
Barron's Educational Series, Inc.
250 Wireless Blvd.
Hauppauge, NY 11788-3917
Ph: (631)434-3311   Fax: (631)434-3723
Fr: 800-645-3476

Anne Hart. Second edition, 1998. $12.95 (paper). 320 pages.

★2119★ **Your Opportunities in Computers**
Energeia Publishing, Inc.
1307 Fairmount Ave., S
Salem, OR 97302-4313
Ph: (503)362-1480   Fax: (503)362-2123
Fr: 800-639-6048

John Tribbett. 1994. $2.50 (paper). 8 pages.

EMPLOYMENT AGENCIES AND SEARCH FIRMS

★2120★ **Abbott Associates**
20880 Fish Rd.
Wilder, ID 83676
Ph: (208)482-4303

Executive search firm with focus on senior level.

★2121★ **AmiTech Group**
6405 Metcalf Ave., Ste. 107
Overland Park, KS 66202
Ph: (913)384-9150

Executive search firm. Focuses on technology and engineering.

★2122★ **Ashton Computer Professionals Inc.**
15 Chesterfield, Pl. C
North Vancouver, BC, Canada V7M 3K3
Ph: (604)904-0304   Fax: (604)904-0305

Provides personnel recruitment and temporary contract services, specializing in advanced computer technology based fields, i.e., management information services, software engineering, product manufacturing, telecommunications, management personnel in all technology based disciplines. Serves private industries as well as government agencies.

★2123★ **Austin Group Inernational**
117 Laura Lane, Ste. 200
Austin, TX 78746
Ph: (512)329-8077

Executive search firm.

★2124★ **Baldwin Associates LLC**
3 Goose Cove Rd.
Bath, ME 04530-4017
Ph: (207)442-7070   Fax: (207)442-8995

Executive search firm focused on the high-technology industry.

★2125★ **Berkana International Ltd.**
20021 Ballinger Way NE, Ste. C
Seattle, WA 98155
Ph: (206)363-6970   Fax: (206)547-3843

Executive search firm.

★2126★ **Bethesda Pharmaceuticals Ltd.**
PO Box 30557
Bethesda, MD 20824
Ph: (301)907-8838

Executive search firm.

★2127★ **BioPharmMed**
550 North Reo St., Ste. 300
Tampa, FL 33609
Ph: (813)261-5117

Executive search firm.

★2128★ **Brenner Executive Resources Inc.**
1230 Avenue of the Americas, Fl. 3
New York, NY 10036
Ph: (917)639-4035

Executive search firm focused on information technology.

★2129★ The Brentwood Group Ltd.
4949 SW Meadows Rd., Ste. 140
Lake Oswego, OR 97035
Ph: (503)697-8136   Fax: (503)697-8161
Executive search firm focused on the high technology industry.

★2130★ Busch International
5150 El Camino Real, Ste. A-30
Los Altos, CA 94022
Ph: (650)623-0990
Executive search firm focused solely on high-technology electronics.

★2131★ CA Durakis Associates, Inc.
4 Padonia Woods Ct.
Baltimore, MD 21030
Ph: (410)252-2055
Executive search firm.

★2132★ Carol Maden Group
2019 Cunningham Dr., Ste. 218
Hampton, VA 23666
Ph: (757)827-9010   Fax: (757)827-9081
Personnel consultants offering placement service in computer technology and engineering, servicing manufacturing and private industries nationwide. Temporary placement servicing clerical and light industrial.

★2133★ Caywood Partners Ltd.
6484 Washington St., Ste. B
Yountville, CA 94599
Ph: (707)945-1340
Executive search firm. Focuses on networking industries.

★2134★ cFour Partners
100 Wilshire Blvd., Ste. 1840
Santa Monica, CA 90401
Ph: (310)394-2639   Fax: (310)394-2669
Executive search firm.

★2135★ Chaves & Associates
1698 Post Rd. E
Westport, CT 06880
Ph: (203)222-2222   Fax: (203)259-5200
E-mail: gen@chaves.com
URL: http://www.in-sitesearch.com
Executive search firm.

★2136★ CJA Executive Search
17852 17th St., Ste. 209
Tustin, CA 92780
Ph: (714)573-1820   Fax: (714)731-3952
Fr: 800-559-2559
Executive search firm. Second location in Los Angeles.

★2137★ CNR Search
4535 Saddlehorn Dr.
Reno, NV 89511
Ph: (775)851-2829   Fax: (775)851-4514
Provides staffing services of permanent and temporary employees. Works primarily on a retained basis. Contingency on a limited basis. Active in providing human resources consulting services. Also active in mergers and acquisitions in high technology firms. Industries served: computer; information services; insurance, pharmaceutical and health care.

★2138★ Dahl-Morrow International
608 S. King, Ste. 103
Leesburg, VA 20175
Ph: (703)779-5600   Fax: (703)779-5678
Executive search firm specializes in high technology.

★2139★ Dean Associates
PO Box 1079
Santa Cruz, CA 95061
Ph: (831)423-2931
Executive search firm focused on the high technology industry.

★2140★ Deborah Bishop & Associates
883 Island Dr., Ste. 212
Alameda, CA 94502
Ph: (510)523-2305
Executive search firm. Concentrates on the high-tech industry only.

★2141★ DillonGray
2333 San Ramon Valley Blvd., Ste. 125
San Ramon, CA 94583
Ph: (925)743-4444   Fax: (925)743-1144
Executive search firm focused on technology related companies.

★2142★ Executive Directions Inc.
PO Box 223
Foxboro, MA 02035
Ph: (508)698-3030   Fax: (508)543-6047
Executive search firm.

★2143★ Faircastle Technology Group LLC
27 Wells Rd., Ste. 1117
Monroe, CT 06468-1266
Ph: (203)459-0631
Executive search firm focused on high technology.

★2144★ The Finnegan Partnerships
PO Box 1183
Palos Verdes Estates, CA 90274-1938
Ph: (310)377-4762
Executive search firm.

★2145★ Fisher & Associates
1063 Lenor Way
San Jose, CA 95128
Ph: (408)554-0156   Fax: (408)246-7807
Executive search firm focused on the high technology industry.

★2146★ George Houchens Associates
2222 Rivenoak Ct.
Ann Arbor, MI 48103
Ph: (734)665-0305   Fax: (734)665-4961
Specializes in recruiting top quality executive, technical, and sales/marketing professionals for permanent positions in the computer, electronics, biomedical, and other high technology industries. Positions handled include: computer product engineering, (software and hardware), management information systems, office automation and related systems, computer networking and communications, Wireless/RF/Mobile, computer aided engineering, expert systems, quality assurance, CIM/CAM, industrial control, robotics, image processing, motion control, automated inspection, material handling, and other related specialties.

★2147★ Howard Fischer Associates International Inc.
1800 JFK Blvd., Fl. 7
Philadelphia, PA 19103-7401
Ph: (215)568-8363   Fax: (215)568-4815
Executive search firm. Branches in Campbell, CA and Boston, MA.

★2148★ James Bangert & Associates Inc.
15500 Wayzata Blvd., Ste. 1030 F
Wayzata, MN 55391
Ph: (952)475-3454   Fax: (952)473-4306
Executive search firm.

★2149★ Jim Ward Associates
35 Browning Ave.
Toronto, ON, Canada M4K 1V8
Ph: (416)463-1661   Fax: (416)463-1688
Placement service provides careers and contract positions and professionals specifically related to the computing field. Industries served: various industries from government to small business; including banking, service, retail, distribution, manufacturing that use central, distributed or network computing facilities.

★2150★ LW Foote Company
110-110th Ave. NE, Ste. 603
Bellevue, WA 98004-5840
Ph: (425)451-1660   Fax: (425)451-1535
Executive search firm.

★2151★ Michael Anthony Associates Inc.

42 Washington St., Ste. 301
Wellesley, MA 02481-1803
Ph: (781)237-4950   Fax: (781)237-6811
Fr: 800-337-4950

Applications development, systems programming, communications, and database specialists servicing the IBM mainframe, midrange, and PC marketplace. Provides technical expertise of conversions, system software installation and upgrades, performance and tuning, capacity planning, and data communications. In addition to contract services also provides retained search and contingency placement of computer professionals ranging from senior staff to senior management. Also act as brokers for independent consultants and small consulting firms requiring the services of marketing specialists. Industries served: banking, financial services, hospitals, HMO's, manufacturers, software development, universities, defense, and consulting firms.

★2152★ Neil Fink Associates

Ghirardelli Square
900 N. Point St., Ste. 210
San Francisco, CA 94109-1192
Ph: (415)441-3777   Fax: (415)775-4925
Executive search firm.

★2153★ 1 Exec Street

201 Post St., Ste. 401
San Francisco, CA 94108
Ph: (415)982-0555   Fax: (415)982-0550
Executive search firm.

★2154★ R.J. Evans Associates Inc.

26949 Chagrin Blvd., Ste. 300
Beachwood, OH 44122
Ph: (216)464-5100   Fax: (216)464-8276
Executive search firm.

★2155★ Timothy D. Crowe Jr.

PO Box 6-K
Chelmsford, MA 01824-0006
Ph: (978)256-2008
Executive search firm.

ONLINE JOB SOURCES AND SERVICES

★2156★ ComputerJobs.com

URL: http://www.computerjobs.com
Description: The site is an employment tool for technology professionals. Information on positions is updated hourly for seekers. Jobs may be searched by skill, or by location nationally or in a specific state or city job market. Contains thousands of job postings.

National jobs may be posted for free. Also career resources for IT professionals.

★2157★ Computerwork.com

E-mail: candidate_support@computerwork.com
URL: http://computerwork.com/
Description: Job search and resume submission service for professionals in information technology.

★2158★ Computerworld Careers

URL: http://www.computerworld.com/cwi/careers/
Description: Offers career opportunities for IT (information technology) professionals. Job seekers may search the jobs database, register at the site, and read about job surveys and employment trends. Employers may post jobs.

★2159★ Computing Research Association Job Announcements

URL: http://www.cra.org/main/cra.jobs.html
Description: Contains dated links to national college and university computer technology positions.

★2160★ Dice.com

URL: http://www.dice.com
Description: Job search database for computer consultants and high-tech professionals, listing thousands of high tech permanent contract and consulting jobs for programmers, software engineers, systems administrators, web developers, and hardware engineers. Also free career advice e-mail newsletter and job posting e-alerts.

★2161★ Guru

URL: http://www.guru.com
Description: Job board specializing in contract jobs for creative and information technology professionals. Also provides online incorporation and educational opportunities for independent contractors along with articles and advice.

★2162★ Ittalent.com

E-mail: ewsmith@ITtalent.com
URL: http://www.ittalent.com
Description: Job search and resume submission service for professionals in information technology.

★2163★ Spherion Workforce Architects

URL: http://www.spherion.com
Description: Recruitment firm specializing in accounting and finance, sales and marketing, interim executives, technology, engineering, retail and human resources.

★2164★ ZDNet Tech Jobs

URL: http://www.zdnet.com/special/filters/techjobs/
Description: Site houses a listing of national employment opportunities for professionals in high tech fields. Also contains resume building tips and relocation resources. Powered by Dice.com

TRADESHOWS

★2165★ CommUnity

Keith Reed Media Events
303 Vintage Park Dr.
Foster City, CA 94404
Ph: (650)578-6897   Fax: (650)525-0193
Fr: 800-488-2883
E-mail: mtrask@zdcf.com

Primary Exhibits: Integrated data, voice and video; presents integrated solutions to the IT professional.

★2166★ EC World - Electronic Commerce World Conference and Exhibition

EC Media Group
div. of Thomson Financial Publishing
2021 Coolidge St.
Hollywood, FL 33020-2400
Ph: (954)925-5900   Fax: (954)925-7533
Fr: 800-336-4887
E-mail: amy.fleming@tfn.com
URL: http://www.ecmediagroup.com

Annual. **Primary Exhibits:** Equipment, supplies, and services for the electronic commerce industry.

★2167★ SoftWorld Presents: Extended Enterprise Solutions and Strategies

Imark Communications, Inc.
PO Box 8249
Natick, MA 01760
Ph: (508)647-8600   Fax: (508)647-0241
Fr: 800-955-1226
URL: http://imark-com.com

Primary Exhibits: Software and services that focus on the customer, vendor, and partner-facing ebusiness capabilities that are needed to achieve a competitive advantage.

★2168★ XPLOR Conference

XPLOR International
24238 Hawthorne Blvd.
Torrance, CA 90505-6505
Ph: (310)791-9521   Fax: (310)375-4240
Fr: 800-669-7567
E-mail: info@xplor.org
URL: http://www.xplor.org

Annual. **Primary Exhibits:** Equipment, supplies, and services for users and manufacturers of advanced electronic document systems.

OTHER SOURCES

★2169★ AFCOM

742 E. Chapman Ave.
Orange, CA 92866
Ph: (714)997-7966   Fax: (714)997-9743
E-mail: afcom@afcom.com
URL: http://www.afcom.com

Members: Data center, networking and enterprise systems management professionals from medium and large scale main frame, midrange and client/server data centers worldwide. **Purpose:** Dedicated to meeting the professional needs of the enterprise system management community. **Activities:** Provides information and support through educational events, research and assistance hotlines, and surveys.

★2170★ Association of Computer Professionals (ACP)

9 Forest Dr.
Plainview, NY 11803
Ph: (516)938-8223   Fax: (516)938-3073
E-mail: sybosworth@aol.com

Members: Authors, consultants, programmers, publishers, and teachers in the computer field who provide products or services to users or to other professionals. **Purpose:** Works to advance the art and science of computer professionals through educational means. Encourages education and instruction of the public regarding what the association views as the beneficial use of computers and computer technology. **Activities:** Provides members with information on accounting, business management, creative marketing techniques, law, microcomputer advances, tax matters, technical developments, and special earning opportunities. Addresses issues of software protection, contract law, tax benefits, potential tax problems, and financial subjects such as sources of capital for new ventures and expanding businesses.

★2171★ Association of Information Technology Professionals

401 N Michigan Ave., Ste. 2400
PO Box 809189
Chicago, IL 60611-4267
Ph: (312)245-1070   Fax: (312)527-6636
Fr: 800-224-9371
E-mail: aitp_hq@aitp.org
URL: http://www.aitp.org

Members: Managerial personnel, staff, educators, and individuals interested in the management of information resources. Founder of the Certificate in Data Processing examination program, now administered by an intersociety organization. **Purpose:** Maintains Legislative Communications Network. Professional education programs include EDP-oriented business and management principles self-study courses and a series of videotaped management development seminars. Sponsors student organizations around the country interested in information technology and encourages members to serve as counselors for the Scout computer merit badge. Conducts research projects, including a business information systems curriculum for two- and four-year colleges.

★2172★ Association for Women in Computing (AWC)

41 Sutter St., Ste. 1006
San Francisco, CA 94104
Ph: (415)905-4663
E-mail: info@awc-hq.org
URL: http://www.awc-hq.org

Members: Individuals interested in promoting the education, professional development, and advancement of women in computing.

★2173★ *Computer Occupations*

Delphi Productions
3160 4th St.
Boulder, CO 80304
Fax: (303)443-4022   Fr: 888-443-2400
URL: http://www.delphivideo.com

$95.00. 50 minutes. Part of the Careers for the 21st Century Video Library.

★2174★ Computing Technology Industry Association (CompTIA)

1815 S Meyers Rd., Ste. 300
Oakbrook Terrace, IL 60181
Ph: (630)678-8300   Fax: (630)627-2930
E-mail: info@comptia.org
URL: http://www.comptia.org

Description: Trade association of more than 19,000 companies and professional IT members in the rapidly converging computing and communications market. Has members in more than 89 countries and provides a unified voice for the industry in the areas of e-commerce standards, vendor-neutral certification, service metrics, public policy and workforce development. Serves as information clearinghouse and resource for the industry; sponsors educational programs.

★2175★ *Information Technology Occupations*

Delphi Productions
3160 4th St.
Boulder, CO 80304
Fax: (303)443-4022   Fr: 888-443-2400
URL: http://www.delphivideo.com

$95.00. 52 minutes. Part of the Emerging Careers Video Library.

★2176★ *Information Technology Services*

Cambridge Educational
2572 Brunswick Ave.
Lawrenceville, NJ 08648-4128
Fax: 800-FAX-ON-US   Fr: 800-468-4227
URL: http://www.cambridgeeducational.com

$89.95. 2002. 18 minutes. Part of the Career Cluster Series.

Computer Operators

SOURCES OF HELP-WANTED ADS

★2177★ Communications of the ACM
Association for Computing Machinery
1515 Broadway
New York, NY 10036
Ph: (212)626-0500   Fax: (212)944-1318
Fr: 800-342-6626
URL: http://www.acm.org/about_acm/ov_
pubs.html

Monthly. Computing news magazine.

★2178★ Computerworld
101 Communications
9121 Oakdale Ave.
Chatsworth, CA 91311
Ph: (818)734-1520   Fax: (818)734-1522
URL: http://www.computerworld.com

Weekly. $48.00/year for individuals. News-
paper for information systems executives.

★2179★ Datamation
Reed Business Information
275 Washington St.
Newton, MA 02458
Ph: (617)558-4900   Fax: (617)630-3830
Fr: 800-357-4745
E-mail: bsemich@cahners.com
URL: http://www.datamation.com

Semimonthly. $69.00/year; $10.00 for single
issue. Magazine on computers and information processing.

★2180★ IEEE Software Magazine
IEEE Computer Society
PO Box 3014
Los Alamitos, CA 90720-1264
Ph: (714)821-8380   Fax: (714)821-4010
Fr: 800-272-6657
URL: http://computer.org

Bimonthly. Magazine covering the computer
software industry for the community of leading software practitioners.

★2181★ NEWS/400
iSeries Network
221 E 29th St.
Loveland, CO 80538
Ph: (970)663-4700   Fax: (970)667-2321
Fr: 800-621-1544
E-mail: letters@iseriesnetwork.com
URL: http://www.iseriesnetwork.com

Monthly. Trade magazine for programmers
and data processing managers who use IBM
iSeries.

★2182★ PC Computing
Ziff-Davis Media Inc.
28 E 28th St.
New York, NY 10016-7930
Ph: (212)503-3500

Monthly. Magazine on personal computers.

★2183★ PC Magazine
Ziff-Davis Media Inc.
28 E 28th St.
New York, NY 10016-7930
Ph: (212)503-3500

Semimonthly. Consumer magazine focusing
on the personal computer industry.

★2184★ PC Week
Ziff-Davis Media Inc.
28 E 28th St.
New York, NY 10016-7930
Ph: (212)503-3500
URL: http://www.pcweek.com

Weekly. Free to qualified subscribers;
$195.00/year for individuals; $250.00/year
for Canada and Mexico; $395.00/year for
other countries; $6.00 for single issue. Tab-
loid featuring microcomputer products and
developments.

EMPLOYER DIRECTORIES AND NETWORKING LISTS

★2185★ Computer Directory
Computer Directories Inc.
23815 Nichols Sawmill Rd.
Hockley, TX 77447
Ph: (281)259-5959   Fax: (281)356-7980
Fr: 800-234-4353
URL: http://www.compdirinc.com

Annual, fall. Covers approximately 130,000
computer installations; 19 separate volumes
for Alaska/Hawaii, Connecticut/New Jersey,
Dallas/Ft. Worth, Eastern Seaboard, Far
Midwest, Houston, Illinois, Midatlantic, Midcentral, Mideast, Minnesota/Wisconsin,
North Central, New England, New York
Metro, Northwest, Ohio, Pennsylvania/West
Virginia, Southeast, and Southwest Texas.
Entries include: Company name, address,
phone, fax, email, name and title of contact,
hardware used, software application, operating system, programming language, computer graphics, networking system. Arrangement: Geographical. Indexes: Alphabetical,
industry, hardware.

**★2186★ Directory of Top Computer
Executives**
Applied Computer Research
PO Box 82266
Phoenix, AZ 85071-2266
Ph: (602)216-9100   Fax: (602)216-9200
Fr: 800-234-2227
URL: http://www.itmarketintelligence.com

Semiannual, June and December. $245.00
for single volume; $420.00 for two-volume
set; $625.00 for three-volume set. Covers in
three volumes, over 55,000 U.S. and Canadian executives with major information technology or communications responsibilities in
over 30,000 U.S. and Canadian companies.
Entries include: Company name, address,
phone, subsidiary and/or division names,
major systems installed, names and titles of
top information system executives, number
of IT employees, nuimber of PCs, and web
address. Arrangement: Geographical within
separate eastern, western, and Canadian

volumes. Indexes: Industry; alphabetical by company name.

★2187★ Northwest High Tech

Resolution Business Press Inc.
12307 NE 149th Ct.
Kirkland, WA 98034
Ph: (425)487-6248   Fax: (425)649-1897
E-mail: info@respress.com
URL: http://www.respress.com

Annual. $34.95. Covers over 2,000 computer-related companies in Washington, Oregon, and Idaho, and British Columbia and Alberta, Canada. Entries include: Company; name, address, phone, fax; toll-free number; names and titles of key personnel; product/service, programming languages, financial data, number of employees, operating systems, expansion plans (including hiring and site expansion plans), company market information, Standard Industrial Classification (SIC) code., internet addresses. Arrangement: Geographical. Indexes: Company name, SIC.

HANDBOOKS AND MANUALS

★2188★ America's Fastest Growing Jobs

JIST Works, Inc.
8902 Otis Ave.
Indianapolis, IN 46216-1033
Ph: (317)613-4200   Fax: (317)613-4307
Fr: 800-648-5478
E-mail: jistworks@aol.com
URL: http://www.jist.com

Seventh edition, 2002. $16.95 (paper). 438 pages. Each job profile explains the nature of the work, skills and abilities required, employment outlook, average earnings, related occupations, education and training requirements, and employment opportunities. Also contains career planning information and job search tips.

★2189★ America's Top 101 Computer and Technical Jobs

JIST Publishing
8902 Otis Ave.
Indianapolis, IN 46216-1033
Ph: (317)613-4200   Fax: 800-547-8329

Michael J. Farr. 2004. $15.95. 368 pages. Job hunting in computer and technical industries.

★2190★ Career Opportunities in Computers and Cyberspace

Facts on File
132 W. 31st St., 17th Fl.
New York, NY 10001-2006
Ph: (212)967-8800   Fax: (212)967-8107
Fr: 800-322-8755

Harry Henderson. 1999. $26.95 (paper). Part of the Career Opportunities Series. 224 pages.

★2191★ Careers for Computer Buffs and Other Technological Types

VGM Career Horizons
1221 Avenue of the Americas
New York, NY 10020
Ph: (212)904-2000   Fr: 800-323-4900
E-mail: ntcpub@tribune.com

Marjorie Eberts, Margaret Gisler and Maria Olsen. Second edition, 1999. $14.95; $9.95 (paper).

★2192★ Careers in Computers

VGM Career Horizons
1221 Avenue of the Americas
New York, NY 10020
Ph: (212)904-2000   Fr: 800-323-4900
E-mail: ntcpub@tribune.com

Lila B. Stair and Leslie Stair. Third edition, 2002. $19.95; $14.95 (paper). Describes trends affecting computer careers and explores a wide range of job opportunities from programming to consulting. Provides job qualifications, salary data, job market information, personal and educational requirements, career paths, and the place of the job in the organizational structure. Offers advice on education, certification, and job search.

★2193★ Careers Inside the World of Technology

Rosen Publishing Group, Inc.
29 E. 21st St.
New York, NY 10010
Ph: (212)777-3017   Fax: 888-436-4643
Fr: 800-237-9932

Jean W. Spencer. Revised edition, 1998. $16.95. 64 pages. Describes computer-related careers for reluctant readers.

★2194★ The Digital Frontier Job & Opportunity Finder

Moon Lake Media
PO Box 251466
Los Angeles, CA 90025
Ph: (310)535-2453

Don B. Altman. 1996. $19.95 (paper). 256 pages.

★2195★ Expert Resumes for Computer and Web Jobs

JIST Publishing
8902 Otis Ave.
Indianapolis, IN 46216-1033
Ph: (317)613-4200   Fax: (317)613-4307
Fr: 800-648-5478

Wendy Enelow and Louis Kursmark. 2001. $16.95 (paper).

★2196★ Exploring Careers in the Computer Field

Rosen Publishing Group, Inc.
29 E 21st St.
New York, NY 10010
Ph: (212)777-3017   Fax: 888-436-4643
Fr: 800-237-9932

Joseph Weintraub. Revised edition, 1993.

$14.95; $9.95 (paper). Discusses entry into the field, salaries, future trends, and offers job search advice. Surveys the newest growth areas in the computer industry including artificial intelligence, desktop publishing, and personal computers. Out of stock.

★2197★ Exploring High-Tech Careers

Rosen Publishing Group, Inc.
29 E. 21st St.
New York, NY 10010
Ph: (212)777-3017   Fax: (212)777-0277
Fr: 800-237-9932

Scott Southworth. Revised edition, 1993. $14.95; $9.95 (paper). 118 pages. Out of print. Gives an orientation to the field of high technology and high-tech jobs. Describes educational preparation and job hunting. Includes a glossary and bibliography.

★2198★ Get Your IT Career in Gear!

McGraw-Hill Professional
2 Penn Plaza
New York, NY 10121
Ph: (212)904-2000

Leslie Goff. 2001. $24.99 (paper).

★2199★ Great Jobs for Computer Science Majors

McGraw-Hill Companies
1221 Avenue of the Americas
New York, NY 10020
Ph: (212)904-2000   Fr: 800-323-4900
E-mail: ntcpub@tribune.com

Jan Goldberg, Stephen Lambert, Julie De-Galan. 1997. $11.95 (paper). 365 pages.

★2200★ The JobBank Guide to Computer and High-Tech Companies

Adams Media Corp.
57 Littlefield St.
Avon, MA 02322
Ph: (508)427-7100   Fax: (508)427-6790
Fr: 800-872-5627
URL: http://www.adamsmedia.com

Second edition, 1999. $17.95 (paper). 704 pages. Contains profiles of more than 4,500 high-tech employers.

★2201★ Opportunities in Computer Careers

McGraw-Hill Professional
2 Penn Plaza
New York, NY 10121-2298
Ph: (212)904-2000   Fr: 800-722-4726

Julie Kling Burns. $12.95 (netLibrary). Computer vocational guidance and counseling.

★2202★ **Opportunities in Office Occupations**

McGraw-Hill Trade
2 Penn Plaza
New York, NY 10121
Ph: (212)904-2000   Fr: 800-722-4726

Blanche Ettinger. 1994. $14.95; $11.95 (paper). 200 pages. Covers a variety of office positions and discusses trends for the next decade. Describes the job market, opportunities, job duties, educational preparation, the work environment, and earnings.

★2203★ **Preparing for an Outstanding Career in Computers: Questions and Answers for Professionals and Students**

Rafi Systems, Incorporated
750 N. Diamond Bar Blvd., Suite 224
Diamond Bar, CA 91765
Ph: (909)593-8124   Fax: (909)629-1034
Fr: 800-584-6706

Mohamed Rafiquzzaman. 2001. $19.95.

★2204★ **Unlocking the Clubhouse: Women in Computing**

MIT Press
5 Cambridge Ctr., Suite 4
Cambridge, MA 02142-1493
Ph: (617)253-5646   Fax: (617)253-6779
Fr: 800-356-0343

Jane Margolis and Allan Fisher. 2001. $24.95.

★2205★ **The Unofficial Guide to Getting a Job at Microsoft**

McGraw-Hill Education Group
800 Taylor Staion Rd.
Blacklick, OH 43004-0545
Fax: (614)755-5645   Fr: 800-722-4726

Rebecca Smith. 2000. $16.95 (paper).

★2206★ **Winning Resumes for Computer Personnel**

Barron's Educational Series, Inc.
250 Wireless Blvd.
Hauppauge, NY 11788-3917
Ph: (631)434-3311   Fax: (631)434-3723
Fr: 800-645-3476

Anne Hart. Second edition, 1998. $12.95 (paper). 320 pages.

★2207★ **Your Opportunities in Computers**

Energeia Publishing, Inc.
1307 Fairmount Ave., S
Salem, OR 97302-4313
Ph: (503)362-1480   Fax: (503)362-2123
Fr: 800-639-6048

John Tribbett. 1994. $2.50 (paper). 8 pages.

EMPLOYMENT AGENCIES AND SEARCH FIRMS

★2208★ **The Aspire Group**

52 Second Ave, 1st Fl
Waltham, MA 02451-1129
Fax: (718)890-1810   Fr: 800-546-5675
URL: http://www.bmanet.com

Employment agency.

★2209★ **Carol Maden Group**

2019 Cunningham Dr., Ste. 218
Hampton, VA 23666
Ph: (757)827-9010   Fax: (757)827-9081

Personnel consultants offering placement service in computer technology and engineering, servicing manufacturing and private industries nationwide. Temporary placement servicing clerical and light industrial.

★2210★ **Data Systems Search Consultants**

1615 Bonanza St., Ste.205
Walnut Creek, CA 94596
Ph: (925)256-0635   Fax: (925)256-9099
E-mail: dsscinfo@dssc.com
URL: http://www.dssc.com

Employment agency. Executive search firm.

★2211★ **Dean Associates**

PO Box 1079
Santa Cruz, CA 95061
Ph: (831)423-2931

Executive search firm focused on the high technology industry.

★2212★ **Jim Ward Associates**

35 Browning Ave.
Toronto, ON, Canada M4K 1V8
Ph: (416)463-1661   Fax: (416)463-1688

Placement service provides careers and contract positions and professionals specifically related to the computing field. Industries served: various industries from government to small business; including banking, service, retail, distribution, manufacturing that use central, distributed or network computing facilities.

★2213★ **The Murphy Group**

245 W Roosevelt Rd., Bldg.15 Ste.101
Chicago, IL 60185
Ph: (630)639-5110   Fax: (630)639-5113
E-mail: info@murphygroup.com
URL: http://www.murphygroup.com

Employment agency. Places personnel in a variety of positions. Additional offices located in Napierville, Park Ridge, and OakBrook.

★2214★ **Romac International, Inc.**

1001 E Palm Ave
Tampa, FL 33605
Ph: (813)552-5239   Fax: (813)552-2122
URL: http://www.romac.com

Executive search firm. More than 30 locations throughout the United States.

★2215★ **Tri-Serv Inc.**

22 W. Padonia Rd., Ste. C-353
Timonium, MD 21093
Ph: (410)561-1740   Fax: (410)252-7417
E-mail: info@tri-serv.coom
URL: http://www.tri-serv.com

Permanent employment agency.

★2216★ **Worlco Computer Resources, Inc.**

997 Old Eagle School Rd., Ste. 219
Wayne, PA 19087-1706
Ph: (610)293-9070   Fax: (610)293-1027
E-mail: parisi@worlco.com
URL: http://www.worlco.com

Employment agency and executive search firm. Second location in Cherry Hill, New Jersey.

ONLINE JOB SOURCES AND SERVICES

★2217★ **ComputerJobs.com**
URL: http://www.computerjobs.com

Description: The site is an employment tool for technology professionals. Information on positions is updated hourly for seekers. Jobs may be searched by skill, or by location nationally or in a specific state or city job market. Contains thousands of job postings. National jobs may be posted for free. Also career resources for IT professionals.

★2218★ **Computerwork.com**
E-mail: candidate_support@computerwork.com
URL: http://computerwork.com/

Description: Job search and resume submission service for professionals in information technology.

★2219★ **Computerworld Careers**
URL: http://www.computerworld.com/cwi/careers/

Description: Offers career opportunities for IT (information technology) professionals. Job seekers may search the jobs database, register at the site, and read about job surveys and employment trends. Employers may post jobs.

★2220★ **Computing Research Association Job Announcements**
URL: http://www.cra.org/main/cra.jobs.html

Description: Contains dated links to national college and university computer technology positions.

★2221★ Guru
URL: http://www.guru.com

Description: Job board specializing in contract jobs for creative and information technology professionals. Also provides online incorporation and educational opportunities for independent contractors along with articles and advice.

★2222★ Ittalent.com
E-mail: ewsmith@ITtalent.com
URL: http://www.ittalent.com

Description: Job search and resume submission service for professionals in information technology.

★2223★ ZDNet Tech Jobs
URL: http://www.zdnet.com/special/filters/techjobs/

Description: Site houses a listing of national employment opportunities for professionals in high tech fields. Also contains resume building tips and relocation resources. Powered by Dice.com

---

TRADESHOWS

★2224★ XPLOR Conference
XPLOR International
24238 Hawthorne Blvd.
Torrance, CA 90505-6505
Ph: (310)791-9521   Fax: (310)375-4240
Fr: 800-669-7567
E-mail: info@xplor.org
URL: http://www.xplor.org

Annual. **Primary Exhibits:** Equipment, supplies, and services for users and manufacturers of advanced electronic document systems.

OTHER SOURCES

★2225★ AFCOM
742 E. Chapman Ave.
Orange, CA 92866
Ph: (714)997-7966   Fax: (714)997-9743
E-mail: afcom@afcom.com
URL: http://www.afcom.com

Members: Data center, networking and enterprise systems management professionals from medium and large scale main frame, midrange and client/server data centers worldwide. **Purpose:** Dedicated to meeting the professional needs of the enterprise system management community. **Activities:** Provides information and support through educational events, research and assistance hotlines, and surveys.

★2226★ Association of Computer Professionals (ACP)
9 Forest Dr.
Plainview, NY 11803
Ph: (516)938-8223   Fax: (516)938-3073
E-mail: sybosworth@aol.com

Members: Authors, consultants, programmers, publishers, and teachers in the computer field who provide products or services to users or to other professionals. **Purpose:** Works to advance the art and science of computer professionals through educational means. Encourages education and instruction of the public regarding what the association views as the beneficial use of computers and computer technology. **Activities:** Provides members with information on accounting, business management, creative marketing techniques, law, microcomputer advances, tax matters, technical developments, and special earning opportunities. Addresses issues of software protection, contract law, tax benefits, potential tax problems, and financial subjects such as sources of capital for new ventures and expanding businesses.

★2227★ Association of Information Technology Professionals
401 N Michigan Ave., Ste. 2400
PO Box 809189
Chicago, IL 60611-4267
Ph: (312)245-1070   Fax: (312)527-6636
Fr: 800-224-9371
E-mail: aitp_hq@aitp.org
URL: http://www.aitp.org

Members: Managerial personnel, staff, educators, and individuals interested in the management of information resources. Founder of the Certificate in Data Processing examination program, now administered by an intersociety organization. **Purpose:** Maintains Legislative Communications Network. Professional education programs include EDP-oriented business and management principles self-study courses and a series of videotaped management development seminars. Sponsors student organizations around the country interested in information technology and encourages members to serve as counselors for the Scout computer merit badge. Conducts research projects, including a business information systems curriculum for two- and four-year colleges.

★2228★ Association for Women in Computing (AWC)
41 Sutter St., Ste. 1006
San Francisco, CA 94104
Ph: (415)905-4663
E-mail: info@awc-hq.org
URL: http://www.awc-hq.org

Members: Individuals interested in promoting the education, professional development, and advancement of women in computing.

★2229★ Black Data Processing Associates (BDPA)
6301 Ivy Ln., Ste. 700
Greenbelt, MD 20770
Ph: (301)220-2180   Fax: (301)220-2185
Fr: 800-727-BDPA
E-mail: president@bdpa.org
URL: http://www.bdpa.org

Description: Persons employed in the information processing industry, including electronic data processing, electronic word processing, and data communications; others interested in information processing. Seeks to accumulate and share information processing knowledge and business expertise in order to increase the career and business potential of minorities in the information processing field. Conducts professional seminars, workshops, tutoring services, and community introductions to data processing. Makes annual donation to the United Negro College Fund.

★2230★ *Computer Occupations*
Delphi Productions
3160 4th St.
Boulder, CO 80304
Fax: (303)443-4022   Fr: 888-443-2400
URL: http://www.delphivideo.com

$95.00. 50 minutes. Part of the Careers for the 21st Century Video Library.

★2231★ *Computer and Peripheral Equipment Operators*
Evon Publishing
832 N 7th Ave.
Iron River, MI 49935
Ph: (906)265-3190

Audiocassette. 1996. $16.95. 32 minutes. Part of the Careers and Vocational Guidance Series. Provides information about the nature of the work, educational requirements, employment outlook, earnings, and work conditions as well as additional related information.

★2232★ *Information Technology Occupations*
Delphi Productions
3160 4th St.
Boulder, CO 80304
Fax: (303)443-4022   Fr: 888-443-2400
URL: http://www.delphivideo.com

$95.00. 52 minutes. Part of the Emerging Careers Video Library.

★2233★ *Information Technology Services*
Cambridge Educational
2572 Brunswick Ave.
Lawrenceville, NJ 08648-4128
Fax: 800-FAX-ON-US   Fr: 800-468-4227
URL: http://www.cambridgeeducational.com

$89.95. 2002. 18 minutes. Part of the Career Cluster Series.

★2234★ Institute for Certification of Computing Professionals (ICCP)

2350 E Devon Ave., Ste. 115
Des Plaines, IL 60018-4610
Ph: (847)299-4227   Fax: (847)299-4280
Fr: 800-U-GET-CCP
E-mail: office@iccp.org
URL: http://www.iccp.org

Members: Professional societies united to promote the development of computer examinations which are of high quality, directed toward information technology professionals, and designed to encourage competence and professionalism. Individuals passing the exams automatically become members of the Institute for Certification of Computing Professionals. Individuals passing exams become certified as CCP or ACP. **Activities:** Has developed code of ethics and good practice to which those taking the exams promise to adhere. Maintains speakers' bureau; compiles statistics.

★2235★ Special Interest Group for Computers and the Physically Handicapped (SIGCAPH)

Church St. Sta.
PO Box 12115
New York, NY 10249
Ph: (212)626-0500   Fax: (212)944-1318
E-mail: chair_sigcaph@acm.org
URL: http://www.acm.org/sigcaph

Description: Promotes the professional interests of computing personnel with physical disabilities and the application of computing & information technology in solving relevant disability problems. Studies to educate the public to support careers for the disabled.

Computer Programmers

SOURCES OF HELP-WANTED ADS

★2236★ ACM Computing Surveys
Association for Computing Machinery
1515 Broadway
New York, NY 10036
Ph: (212)626-0500   Fax: (212)944-1318
Fr: 800-342-6626
URL: http://www.acm.org

Quarterly. $30.00/year for members; $160.00/year for nonmembers; $25.00/year for students. Journal presenting surveys and tutorials in computer science.

★2237★ ACM Transactions on Graphics
Association for Computing Machinery
1515 Broadway
New York, NY 10036
Ph: (212)626-0500   Fax: (212)944-1318
Fr: 800-342-6626
URL: http://www.acm.org/

Quarterly. $45.00/year for members; $170.00/year for nonmembers; $40.00/year for students. Computer graphics journal.

★2238★ AS/400 Systems Management
Adams Business Media
250 S Wacker Dr., Ste. 1150
Chicago, IL 60606
Ph: (312)977-0999   Fax: (312)980-3135
E-mail: 73222.3344@compuserve.com
URL: http://www.hotlink400.com

Monthly. $42.00/year for individuals. Management-oriented magazine for DP/MIS managers with an IBM AS/400 on site.

★2239★ Communications of the ACM
Association for Computing Machinery
1515 Broadway
New York, NY 10036
Ph: (212)626-0500   Fax: (212)944-1318
Fr: 800-342-6626
URL: http://www.acm.org/about_acm/ov_

pubs.html
Monthly. Computing news magazine.

★2240★ Computerworld
101 Communications
9121 Oakdale Ave.
Chatsworth, CA 91311
Ph: (818)734-1520   Fax: (818)734-1522
URL: http://www.computerworld.com

Weekly. $48.00/year for individuals. Newspaper for information systems executives.

★2241★ Computists' Weekly
Computists International
4064 Sutherland Dr.
Palo Alto, CA 94303
Ph: (650)493-4176   Fr: 888-625-5385
E-mail: editor@computists.com
URL: http://www.computists.com

Description: Forty issues/year. Features news and opportunities in artificial intelligence, information science, and computer science. Available online only.

★2242★ Database Programming & Design
CMP Media L.L.C.
600 Community Dr.
Manhasset, NY 11030
Ph: (516)562-5000
E-mail: tgibb@cmp.com
URL: http://www.intelligententerprise.com/dbpdsearch.shtml

Monthly. Computer magazine.

★2243★ Datamation
Reed Business Information
275 Washington St.
Newton, MA 02458
Ph: (617)558-4900   Fax: (617)630-3830
Fr: 800-357-4745
E-mail: bsemich@cahners.com
URL: http://www.datamation.com

Semimonthly. $69.00/year; $10.00 for single issue. Magazine on computers and information processing.

★2244★ Digital News & Review
Reed Business Information
275 Washington St.
Newton, MA 02458
Ph: (617)558-4900   Fax: (617)630-3830
Fr: 800-357-4745

Semimonthly. Free to qualified subscribers.

★2245★ e-Business Advisor
e-Business Advisor
PO Box 429002
San Diego, CA 92142-9002
Ph: (858)278-5600   Fax: (858)278-0300
Fr: 800-336-6060
E-mail: CustomerService@Advisor.com
URL: http://www.advisor.com/

Magazine for developing strategies, practices, and innovations for e-business applications.

★2246★ Enterprise Systems
101 Communications L.L.C.
1300 Virginia Dr., Ste. 401
Fort Washington, PA 19034-3221
Ph: (215)643-8000   Fax: (215)643-3901
URL: http://www.esj.com

Monthly. Free to qualified subscribers. Journal providing authoritative, in-depth information for all IS professionals in multi-platform large-scale enterpreise.

★2247★ IEEE Computer Graphics and Applications
IEEE Computer Society
PO Box 3014
Los Alamitos, CA 90720-1264
Ph: (714)821-8380   Fax: (714)821-4010
Fr: 800-272-6657
E-mail: rbaldwin@computer.org
URL: http://www.computer.org/cga/

Bimonthly. $32.00/year for members; $320.00/year for institutions. Magazine addressing the interests and needs of professional designers and users of computer graphics hardware, software, and systems.

★2248★ IEEE Software Magazine
IEEE Computer Society
PO Box 3014
Los Alamitos, CA 90720-1264
Ph: (714)821-8380   Fax: (714)821-4010
Fr: 800-272-6657
URL: http://computer.org

Bimonthly. Magazine covering the computer software industry for the community of leading software practitioners.

★2249★ InformationWEEK
CMP Media L.L.C.
600 Community Dr.
Manhasset, NY 11030
Ph: (516)562-5000
E-mail: llally@cmp.com
URL: http://www.mfi.com

Weekly. Free to qualified subscribers. Magazine focusing on data and information processing news and strategies.

★2250★ InfoWorld
InfoWorld
155 Bovet Rd.
San Mateo, CA 94402
Ph: (650)572-7341   Fax: (415)312-0580
Fr: 800-227-8365

Weekly. Free to qualified subscribers; $180.00/year for individuals. Weekly IS publication.

★2251★ Job Express
FVI & Wendy Vandamme
111 Lookout Rd.
Mountain Lakes, NJ 07046
Ph: (973)299-1535   Fax: (973)335-4866

Description: Biweekly except August. Contains surveys of billing rates for contract computer services, listings of open assignments and contracts, and situations wanted. Covers tradeshows and seminars.

★2252★ NEWS/400
iSeries Network
221 E 29th St.
Loveland, CO 80538
Ph: (970)663-4700   Fax: (970)667-2321
Fr: 800-621-1544
E-mail: letters@iseriesnetwork.com
URL: http://www.iseriesnetwork.com

Monthly. Trade magazine for programmers and data processing managers who use IBM iSeries.

★2253★ PC Computing
Ziff-Davis Media Inc.
28 E 28th St.
New York, NY 10016-7930
Ph: (212)503-3500

Monthly. Magazine on personal computers.

★2254★ PC Magazine
Ziff-Davis Media Inc.
28 E 28th St.
New York, NY 10016-7930
Ph: (212)503-3500

Semimonthly. Consumer magazine focusing on the personal computer industry.

★2255★ PC Today
Sandhills Publishing
120 W Harvest Dr.
PO Box 85310
Lincoln, NE 68501-5310
Ph: (402)479-2141   Fax: (402)479-2120
Fr: 800-247-4880

Monthly. $24.00/year; $32.00/year for other countries; $2.95/year for single issue; $3.50/year. Magazine for personal computer users.

★2256★ PC Week
Ziff-Davis Media Inc.
28 E 28th St.
New York, NY 10016-7930
Ph: (212)503-3500
URL: http://www.pcweek.com

Weekly. Free to qualified subscribers; $195.00/year for individuals; $250.00/year for Canada and Mexico; $395.00/year for other countries; $6.00 for single issue. Tabloid featuring microcomputer products and developments.

★2257★ PC WORLD
101 Communications
9121 Oakdale Ave.
Chatsworth, CA 91311
Ph: (818)734-1520   Fax: (818)734-1522
URL: http://www.pcworld.com

Monthly. $29.90/year for individuals; $5.95 for single issue.

★2258★ Performance Computing
CMP Media L.L.C.
600 Community Dr.
Manhasset, NY 11030
Ph: (516)562-5000
URL: http://www.performance-computing.com

Monthly. Free to qualified subscribers; $55.00/year, nonqualified. Magazine for professional users of UNIX and UNIX-like systems, and Windows NT.

PLACEMENT AND JOB REFERRAL SERVICES

★2259★ American Indian Science and Engineering Society (AISES)
PO Box 9828
Albuquerque, NM 87119-9828
Ph: (505)765-1052   Fax: (505)765-5608
E-mail: info@aises.org

URL: http://www.aises.org

Description: American Indian and non-Indian students and professionals in science, technology, and engineering fields; corporations representing energy, mining, aerospace, electronic, and computer fields. Seeks to motivate and encourage students to pursue undergraduate and graduate studies in science, engineering, and technology. Sponsors science fairs in grade schools, teacher training workshops, summer math/science sessions for 8th-12th graders, professional chapters, and student chapters in colleges. Offers scholarships. Adult members serve as role models, advisers, and mentors for students. Operates placement service.

EMPLOYER DIRECTORIES AND NETWORKING LISTS

★2260★ Computer Directory
Computer Directories Inc.
23815 Nichols Sawmill Rd.
Hockley, TX 77447
Ph: (281)259-5959   Fax: (281)356-7980
Fr: 800-234-4353
URL: http://www.compdirinc.com

Annual, fall. Covers approximately 130,000 computer installations; 19 separate volumes for Alaska/Hawaii, Connecticut/New Jersey, Dallas/Ft. Worth, Eastern Seaboard, Far Midwest, Houston, Illinois, Midatlantic, Midcentral, Mideast, Minnesota/Wisconsin, North Central, New England, New York Metro, Northwest, Ohio, Pennsylvania/West Virginia, Southeast, and Southwest Texas. Entries include: Company name, address, phone, fax, email, name and title of contact, hardware used, software application, operating system, programming language, computer graphics, networking system. Arrangement: Geographical. Indexes: Alphabetical, industry, hardware.

★2261★ Directory of Top Computer Executives
Applied Computer Research
PO Box 82266
Phoenix, AZ 85071-2266
Ph: (602)216-9100   Fax: (602)216-9200
Fr: 800-234-2227
URL: http://www.itmarketintelligence.com

Semiannual, June and December. $245.00 for single volume; $420.00 for two-volume set; $625.00 for three-volume set. Covers in three volumes, over 55,000 U.S. and Canadian executives with major information technology or communications responsibilities in over 30,000 U.S. and Canadian companies. Entries include: Company name, address, phone, subsidiary and/or division names, major systems installed, names and titles of top information system executives, number of IT employees, nuimber of PCs, and web address. Arrangement: Geographical within separate eastern, western, and Canadian volumes. Indexes: Industry; alphabetical by company name.

★2262★   *Northwest High Tech*

Resolution Business Press Inc.
12307 NE 149th Ct.
Kirkland, WA 98034
Ph: (425)487-6248   Fax: (425)649-1897
E-mail: info@respress.com
URL: http://www.respress.com

Annual. $34.95. Covers over 2,000 comput-er-related companies in Washington, Ore-gon, and Idaho, and British Columbia and Alberta, Canada. Entries include: Company; name, address, phone, fax; toll-free number; names and titles of key personnel; product/ service, programming languages, financial data, number of employees, operating sys-tems, expansion plans (including hiring and site expansion plans), company market infor-mation, Standard Industrial Classification (SIC) code., internet addresses. Arrange-ment: Geographical. Indexes: Company name, SIC.

★2263★   *Peterson's Hidden Job Market*

Thomson Peterson's
Princeton Pike Corporate Center
2000 Lenox Dr.
PO Box 67005
Lawrenceville, NJ 08648
Ph: (609)896-1800   Fax: 800-277-2465
Fr: 800-338-3282
URL: http://www.petersons.com

Annual, June. $18.95. Covers approximately 2,000 technology firms with under 1,000 employees, which hire at four times the national rate. Entries include: Company name, address, phone, fax, name and title of contact, number of employees, year found-ed, number of employees added in last year, percentage of growth, line of business. Ar-rangement: Geographical by state, then by area code. Indexes: Alphabetical by industry.

★2264★   *Peterson's Job Opportunities in Engineering and Technology*

Thomson Peterson's
PO Box 67005
Lawrenceville, NJ 08648-6105
Fr: 800-338-3282

Compiled by the Peterson's staff. Fourth edition, 1996. $21.95 (paper). 384 pages. Profiles 2,000 high-tech companies looking primarily for technical personnel in such fields as biotechnology, telecommunications, software, computers and peripherals, de-fense, and aerospace. Contains job-search strategies and career options to help match education and expertise to the job market. Indexed geographically, by industry, and by hiring needs.

HANDBOOKS AND MANUALS

★2265★   *America's Top 101 Computer and Technical Jobs*

JIST Publishing
8902 Otis Ave.
Indianapolis, IN 46216-1033
Ph: (317)613-4200   Fax: 800-547-8329

Michael J. Farr. 2004. $15.95. 368 pages. Job hunting in computer and technical indus-tries.

★2266★   *Career Information Center*

Macmillan Publishing Co. Inc.
200 Old Tappan Rd.
Old Tappan, NJ 07675
Fr: 800-428-5331

Visual Education Center Staff. Seventh edi-tion, 1999. $275.00. 2080 pages. This 13-volume set profiles over 600 occupations. Each occupational profile describes job du-ties, educational requirements, how to get the job, advancement possibilities, employ-ment outlook, working conditions, earnings and benefits, and where to write for more information.

★2267★   *Career Opportunities in Computers and Cyberspace*

Facts on File
132 W. 31st St., 17th Fl.
New York, NY 10001-2006
Ph: (212)967-8800   Fax: (212)967-8107
Fr: 800-322-8755

Harry Henderson. 1999. $26.95 (paper). Part of the Career Opportunities Series. 224 pages.

★2268★   *Careers for Computer Buffs and Other Technological Types*

VGM Career Horizons
1221 Avenue of the Americas
New York, NY 10020
Ph: (212)904-2000   Fr: 800-323-4900
E-mail: ntcpub@tribune.com

Marjorie Eberts, Margaret Gisler and Maria Olsen. Second edition, 1999. $14.95; $9.95 (paper).

★2269★   *Careers in the Computer Game Industry*

The Rosen Publishing Group Inc.
29 E. 21st St.
New York, NY 10010
Ph: (212)777-3017   Fax: (212)777-0277
Fr: 800-237-9932

Peter Suciu, David Gerardi. 2004. Careers in mathematics.

★2270★   *Careers in Computers*

VGM Career Horizons
1221 Avenue of the Americas
New York, NY 10020
Ph: (212)904-2000   Fr: 800-323-4900

E-mail: ntcpub@tribune.com

Lila B. Stair and Leslie Stair. Third edition, 2002. $19.95; $14.95 (paper). Describes trends affecting computer careers and ex-plores a wide range of job opportunities from programming to consulting. Provides job qualifications, salary data, job market infor-mation, personal and educational require-ments, career paths, and the place of the job in the organizational structure. Offers advice on education, certification, and job search.

★2271★   *Careers Inside the World of Technology*

Rosen Publishing Group, Inc.
29 E. 21st St.
New York, NY 10010
Ph: (212)777-3017   Fax: 888-436-4643
Fr: 800-237-9932

Jean W. Spencer. Revised edition, 1998. $16.95. 64 pages. Describes computer-relat-ed careers for reluctant readers.

★2272★   *Careers for Number Crunchers and Other Quantitative Types*

McGraw-Hill Trade
2 Penn Plaza
New York, NY 10121
Ph: (212)904-2000   Fr: 800-722-4726
E-mail: ntcpub@tribune.com

Rebecca Burnett. Second edition, 2002. $15.95; $12.95 (paper). 192 pages. Provides information to math-oriented job hunters on how to become statisticians, field research-ers, computer programmers, stock analysts, investment managers, bankers, engineers, accountants, underwriters, economists, mar-ket analysts, mathematicians, systems ana-lysts, and more.

★2273★   *Choosing a Career in Computers*

Rosen Publishing Group, Inc.
29 E. 21st St.
New York, NY 10010
Ph: (212)777-3017   Fax: (212)777-0277
Fr: 800-237-9932

Weigant, Chris. 2000. $17.95.

★2274★   *The Digital Frontier Job & Opportunity Finder*

Moon Lake Media
PO Box 251466
Los Angeles, CA 90025
Ph: (310)535-2453

Don B. Altman. 1996. $19.95 (paper). 256 pages.

★2275★ **Expert Resumes for Computer and Web Jobs**
JIST Publishing
8902 Otis Ave.
Indianapolis, IN 46216-1033
Ph: (317)613-4200   Fax: (317)613-4307
Fr: 800-648-5478

Wendy Enelow and Louis Kursmark. 2001. $16.95 (paper).

★2276★ **Exploring Careers in the Computer Field**
Rosen Publishing Group, Inc.
29 E 21st St.
New York, NY 10010
Ph: (212)777-3017   Fax: 888-436-4643
Fr: 800-237-9932

Joseph Weintraub. Revised edition, 1993. $14.95; $9.95 (paper). Discusses entry into the field, salaries, future trends, and offers job search advice. Surveys the newest growth areas in the computer industry including artificial intelligence, desktop publishing, and personal computers. Out of stock.

★2277★ **Exploring High-Tech Careers**
Rosen Publishing Group, Inc.
29 E. 21st St.
New York, NY 10010
Ph: (212)777-3017   Fax: (212)777-0277
Fr: 800-237-9932

Scott Southworth. Revised edition, 1993. $14.95; $9.95 (paper). 118 pages. Out of print. Gives an orientation to the field of high technology and high-tech jobs. Describes educational preparation and job hunting. Includes a glossary and bibliography.

★2278★ **Get Your IT Career in Gear!**
McGraw-Hill Professional
2 Penn Plaza
New York, NY 10121
Ph: (212)904-2000

Leslie Goff. 2001. $24.99 (paper).

★2279★ **Great Jobs for Computer Science Majors**
McGraw-Hill Companies
1221 Avenue of the Americas
New York, NY 10020
Ph: (212)904-2000   Fr: 800-323-4900
E-mail: ntcpub@tribune.com

Jan Goldberg, Stephen Lambert, Julie De-Galan. 1997. $11.95 (paper). 365 pages.

★2280★ **Job Seekers Guide to Silicon Valley Recruiters**
John Wily and Sons, Inc.
605 Third Ave., 4th Fl.
New York, NY 10158-0012
Ph: (212)850-6276   Fax: (212)850-8641

Christopher W. Hunt, Scott A. Scanlon. First edition, 1998. $19.95 (paper). 371 pages. Includes a list of 2,400 recruiters specializing in high technology positions and explains how to work with them.

★2281★ **The JobBank Guide to Computer and High-Tech Companies**
Adams Media Corp.
57 Littlefield St.
Avon, MA 02322
Ph: (508)427-7100   Fax: (508)427-6790
Fr: 800-872-5627
URL: http://www.adamsmedia.com

Second edition, 1999. $17.95 (paper). 704 pages. Contains profiles of more than 4,500 high-tech employers.

★2282★ **Opportunities in Computer-Aided Design and Computer-Aided Manufacturing**
McGraw-Hill Trade
2 Penn Plaza
New York, NY 10121
Ph: (212)904-2000   Fr: 800-722-4726

Jan Bone. 1994. $14.95; $11.95 (paper). 160 pages. Defines CAD (computer-aided design), CAM (computer-aided manufacturing), and MAP (manufacturing automation protocol). Explains career opportunities in the CAD/CAM field, and education and training needed. Gives job-hunting tips.

★2283★ **Opportunities in Computer Careers**
McGraw-Hill Professional
2 Penn Plaza
New York, NY 10121-2298
Ph: (212)904-2000   Fr: 800-722-4726

Julie Kling Burns. $12.95 (netLibrary). Computer vocational guidance and counseling.

★2284★ **Opportunities in High Tech Careers**
McGraw-Hill Trade
2 Penn Plaza
New York, NY 10121
Ph: (212)904-2000   Fr: 800-722-4726

Gary Colter and Deborah Yanuck. 1995. $14.95; $11.95 (paper). 160 pages. Explores high technology careers. Describes job opportunities, how to make a career decision, how to prepare for high technology jobs, job hunting techniques, and future trends.

★2285★ **Opportunities in Office Occupations**
McGraw-Hill Trade
2 Penn Plaza
New York, NY 10121
Ph: (212)904-2000   Fr: 800-722-4726

Blanche Ettinger. 1994. $14.95; $11.95 (paper). 200 pages. Covers a variety of office positions and discusses trends for the next decade. Describes the job market, opportunities, job duties, educational preparation, the work environment, and earnings.

★2286★ **Preparing for an Outstanding Career in Computers: Questions and Answers for Professionals and Students**
Rafi Systems, Incorporated
750 N. Diamond Bar Blvd., Suite 224
Diamond Bar, CA 91765
Ph: (909)593-8124   Fax: (909)629-1034
Fr: 800-584-6706

Mohamed Rafiquzzaman. 2001. $19.95.

★2287★ **Unlocking the Clubhouse: Women in Computing**
MIT Press
5 Cambridge Ctr., Suite 4
Cambridge, MA 02142-1493
Ph: (617)253-5646   Fax: (617)253-6779
Fr: 800-356-0343

Jane Margolis and Allan Fisher. 2001. $24.95.

★2288★ **The Unofficial Guide to Getting a Job at Microsoft**
McGraw-Hill Education Group
800 Taylor Staion Rd.
Blacklick, OH 43004-0545
Fax: (614)755-5645   Fr: 800-722-4726

Rebecca Smith. 2000. $16.95 (paper).

★2289★ **Winning Resumes for Computer Personnel**
Barron's Educational Series, Inc.
250 Wireless Blvd.
Hauppauge, NY 11788-3917
Ph: (631)434-3311   Fax: (631)434-3723
Fr: 800-645-3476

Anne Hart. Second edition, 1998. $12.95 (paper). 320 pages.

★2290★ **Your Opportunities in Computers**
Energeia Publishing, Inc.
1307 Fairmount Ave., S
Salem, OR 97302-4313
Ph: (503)362-1480   Fax: (503)362-2123
Fr: 800-639-6048

John Tribbett. 1994. $2.50 (paper). 8 pages.

★2291★ **Your Resume: Key to a Better Job**
Hungry Minds, Inc.
10475 Crosspoint Blvd.
Indianapolis, IN 46256
Fax: (317)572-4000   Fr: 800-667-1115

Leonard Corwen. Sixth edition, 1996. $24.95 (paper). 200 pages. Provides guidelines for resume writing; explains what employers look for in a resume, including contents and style. Includes model resumes for high-demand careers such as computer programmers, health administrators, and high-tech professionals. Notes basic job-getting information and strategies.

EMPLOYMENT AGENCIES AND SEARCH FIRMS

★2292★ **The Aspire Group**
52 Second Ave, 1st Fl
Waltham, MA 02451-1129
Fax: (718)890-1810   Fr: 800-546-5675
URL: http://www.bmanet.com
Employment agency.

★2293★ **Carol Maden Group**
2019 Cunningham Dr., Ste. 218
Hampton, VA 23666
Ph: (757)827-9010   Fax: (757)827-9081
Personnel consultants offering placement service in computer technology and engineering, servicing manufacturing and private industries nationwide. Temporary placement servicing clerical and light industrial.

★2294★ **Comsys Inc.**
4 Research Pl., Ste. 300
Rockville, MD 20850
Ph: (301)921-3600   Fax: (301)921-3670
Fr: 800-926-6797
Provides programmers, systems analysts, hardware design engineers, software architects, technical writers, electrical engineers, technicians, and other computer project support personnel to high-tech clients. Such personnel are available for short or long-term projects on an hourly or fixed-price basis. Expertise on all computer makes/ models and software. Specializes in systems design and development.

★2295★ **Data Systems Search Consultants**
1615 Bonanza St., Ste.205
Walnut Creek, CA 94596
Ph: (925)256-0635   Fax: (925)256-9099
E-mail: dsscinfo@dssc.com
URL: http://www.dssc.com
Employment agency. Executive search firm.

★2296★ **The Datafinders Group, Inc.**
25 E Spring Valley Ave.,Fl.3
Maywood, NJ 07607
Ph: (201)845-7700   Fax: (201)845-7365
E-mail: info@datafinders.net
URL: http://www.datafinders.net
Executive search firm.

★2297★ **Dean Associates**
PO Box 1079
Santa Cruz, CA 95061
Ph: (831)423-2931
Executive search firm focused on the high technology industry.

★2298★ **DillonGray**
2333 San Ramon Valley Blvd., Ste. 125
San Ramon, CA 94583
Ph: (925)743-4444   Fax: (925)743-1144
Executive search firm focused on technology related companies.

★2299★ **Huntington Personnel Consultants, Inc.**
PO Box 1077
Huntington, NY 11743-0640
Ph: (516)549-8888
Executive search firm and employment agency.

★2300★ **Jim Ward Associates**
35 Browning Ave.
Toronto, ON, Canada M4K 1V8
Ph: (416)463-1661   Fax: (416)463-1688
Placement service provides careers and contract positions and professionals specifically related to the computing field. Industries served: various industries from government to small business; including banking, service, retail, distribution, manufacturing that use central, distributed or network computing facilities.

★2301★ **M.J. Curran & Associates Inc.**
304 Newbury St., Ste. 509
Boston, MA 02115
Ph: (617)247-7700   Fax: (617)267-6429
Executive search firm.

★2302★ **Romac International, Inc.**
1001 E Palm Ave
Tampa, FL 33605
Ph: (813)552-5239   Fax: (813)552-2122
URL: http://www.romac.com
Executive search firm. More than 30 locations throughout the United States.

★2303★ **Strategic Staffing Solutions Inc.**
Penobscot Bldg.
645 Griswold, Ste. 3446
Detroit, MI 48226-4216
Fax: (313)965-9967   Fr: 888-738-3261
Provides staffing for customized systems development, contract programming, customer specific training programs, and alternate staffing options. Industries served: banking, retail, healthcare, manufacturing, telecommunications, and automotive.

★2304★ **Technical Talent Locators Ltd.**
5570 Sterrett Place, Ste.208
Columbia, MD 21044
Ph: (410)740-0091
URL: http://www.ttlgroup.com
Permanent employment agency working within the following fields: software and database engineering; computer, communication, and telecommunication system engi-

neering; and other computer-related disciplines.

★2305★ **Techsearch Services, Inc.**
46 Wickford Pl.
Madison, CT 06443
Ph: (203)318-1100   Fax: (203)318-8800
E-mail: dtaft@snet.net
URL: http://www.techsearchservices.com
Executive search firm.

★2306★ **TRC Staffing Services Inc.**
2110 15 Mile Rd., Ste. B
Sterling Heights, MI 48310
Ph: (586)939-3210   Fax: (586)978-0572
A full-service executive search company with permanent placements encompassing engineering, industrial sales, financial and computer science positions. Screen, interview, and verify past employment for all candidates prior to referral. Also assist personnel staffs in the attainment of their EEO/AAP goals with the placement of talented individuals in positions which are underutilized with minorities and/or women. In addition, firm has a clerical temporary service division, TRC Temporary Service; and an employment agency, TRC Staffing Services.

★2307★ **Tri-Serv Inc.**
22 W. Padonia Rd., Ste. C-353
Timonium, MD 21093
Ph: (410)561-1740   Fax: (410)252-7417
E-mail: info@tri-serv.coom
URL: http://www.tri-serv.com
Permanent employment agency.

★2308★ **Wallach Associates Inc.**
6101 Executive Blvd., Ste. 380
Rockville, MD 20852-3907
Ph: (301)231-9000   Fax: (301)770-9015
Fr: 800-296-2084
Specialists in recruitment of professional personnel, primarily in electronic systems, energy research and development, management consulting, operations research, computers, defense systems, and programmers. Specializes in Internet and software engineer for intelligence community (DOD, NSA, CIA, DIA, etc.).

★2309★ **Worlco Computer Resources, Inc.**
997 Old Eagle School Rd., Ste. 219
Wayne, PA 19087-1706
Ph: (610)293-9070   Fax: (610)293-1027
E-mail: parisi@worlco.com
URL: http://www.worlco.com
Employment agency and executive search firm. Second location in Cherry Hill, New Jersey.

ONLINE JOB SOURCES AND SERVICES

★2310★ ComputerJobs.com
URL: http://www.computerjobs.com

Description: The site is an employment tool for technology professionals. Information on positions is updated hourly for seekers. Jobs may be searched by skill, or by location nationally or in a specific state or city job market. Contains thousands of job postings. National jobs may be posted for free. Also career resources for IT professionals.

★2311★ Computerwork.com
E-mail: candidate_support@computerwork.com
URL: http://computerwork.com/

Description: Job search and resume submission service for professionals in information technology.

★2312★ Computerworld Careers
URL: http://www.computerworld.com/cwi/careers/

Description: Offers career opportunities for IT (information technology) professionals. Job seekers may search the jobs database, register at the site, and read about job surveys and employment trends. Employers may post jobs.

★2313★ Computing Research Association Job Announcements
URL: http://www.cra.org/main/cra.jobs.html

Description: Contains dated links to national college and university computer technology positions.

★2314★ Dice.com
URL: http://www.dice.com

Description: Job search database for computer consultants and high-tech professionals, listing thousands of high tech permanent contract and consulting jobs for programmers, software engineers, systems administrators, web developers, and hardware engineers. Also free career advice e-mail newsletter and job posting e-alerts.

★2315★ Guru
URL: http://www.guru.com

Description: Job board specializing in contract jobs for creative and information technology professionals. Also provides online incorporation and educational opportunities for independent contractors along with articles and advice.

★2316★ Ittalent.com
E-mail: ewsmith@ITtalent.com
URL: http://www.ittalent.com

Description: Job search and resume submission service for professionals in information technology.

★2317★ Jobs for Programmers
E-mail: prgjobs@jfpresources.com
URL: http://www.prgjobs.com

Description: Job board site for computer programmers that allows them to browse through thousands of programming jobs, even search for special jobs with sign-on bonuses, relocation funding, and 4-day work weeks. Resume posting is free.

★2318★ Softwarejobs.com
E-mail: info@softwarejobs.com
URL: http://softwarejobs.techengine.com

Description: Job search website for software programmers. Registrants can post their resume and search available positions, review career resources, and activate e-mail job alerts. Registration is free.

★2319★ ZDNet Tech Jobs
URL: http://www.zdnet.com/special/filters/techjobs/

Description: Site houses a listing of national employment opportunities for professionals in high tech fields. Also contains resume building tips and relocation resources. Powered by Dice.com

TRADESHOWS

★2320★ CommUnity
Keith Reed Media Events
303 Vintage Park Dr.
Foster City, CA 94404
Ph: (650)578-6897   Fax: (650)525-0193
Fr: 800-488-2883
E-mail: mtrask@zdcf.com

Primary Exhibits: Integrated data, voice and video; presents integrated solutions to the IT professional.

★2321★ Summer Computer Simulation Conference
Society for Computer Simulation
 International
4838 Romsom Ct., Ste. L
PO Box 17900
San Diego, CA 92117
Ph: (619)277-3888   Fax: (619)277-3930

Annual. **Primary Exhibits:** Simulation software and hardware, publications, and books.

★2322★ XPLOR Conference
XPLOR International
24238 Hawthorne Blvd.
Torrance, CA 90505-6505
Ph: (310)791-9521   Fax: (310)375-4240
Fr: 800-669-7567

E-mail: info@xplor.org
URL: http://www.xplor.org

Annual. **Primary Exhibits:** Equipment, supplies, and services for users and manufacturers of advanced electronic document systems.

OTHER SOURCES

★2323★ Association of Computer Professionals (ACP)
9 Forest Dr.
Plainview, NY 11803
Ph: (516)938-8223   Fax: (516)938-3073
E-mail: sybosworth@aol.com

Members: Authors, consultants, programmers, publishers, and teachers in the computer field who provide products or services to users or to other professionals. **Purpose:** Works to advance the art and science of computer professionals through educational means. Encourages education and instruction of the public regarding what the association views as the beneficial use of computers and computer technology. **Activities:** Provides members with information on accounting, business management, creative marketing techniques, law, microcomputer advances, tax matters, technical developments, and special earning opportunities. Addresses issues of software protection, contract law, tax benefits, potential tax problems, and financial subjects such as sources of capital for new ventures and expanding businesses.

★2324★ Association of Information Technology Professionals
401 N Michigan Ave., Ste. 2400
PO Box 809189
Chicago, IL 60611-4267
Ph: (312)245-1070   Fax: (312)527-6636
Fr: 800-224-9371
E-mail: aitp_hq@aitp.org
URL: http://www.aitp.org

Members: Managerial personnel, staff, educators, and individuals interested in the management of information resources. Founder of the Certificate in Data Processing examination program, now administered by an intersociety organization. **Purpose:** Maintains Legislative Communications Network. Professional education programs include EDP-oriented business and management principles self-study courses and a series of videotaped management development seminars. Sponsors student organizations around the country interested in information technology and encourages members to serve as counselors for the Scout computer merit badge. Conducts research projects, including a business information systems curriculum for two- and four-year colleges.

★2325★ Association for Women in Computing (AWC)

41 Sutter St., Ste. 1006
San Francisco, CA 94104
Ph: (415)905-4663
E-mail: info@awc-hq.org
URL: http://www.awc-hq.org

Members: Individuals interested in promoting the education, professional development, and advancement of women in computing.

★2326★ Black Data Processing Associates (BDPA)

6301 Ivy Ln., Ste. 700
Greenbelt, MD 20770
Ph: (301)220-2180   Fax: (301)220-2185
Fr: 800-727-BDPA
E-mail: president@bdpa.org
URL: http://www.bdpa.org

Description: Persons employed in the information processing industry, including electronic data processing, electronic word processing, and data communications; others interested in information processing. Seeks to accumulate and share information processing knowledge and business expertise in order to increase the career and business potential of minorities in the information processing field. Conducts professional seminars, workshops, tutoring services, and community introductions to data processing. Makes annual donation to the United Negro College Fund.

★2327★ COIN Career Guidance System

COIN Educational Products
3361 Executive Pky., Ste. 302
Toledo, OH 43606
Ph: (419)536-5353   Fax: (419)536-7056
Fr: 800-274-8515
URL: http://www.coin3.com/highschool/guidance.asp

CD-ROM. Provides career information through seven cross-referenced files covering postsecondary schools, college majors, vocational programs, military service, apprenticeship programs, financial aid, and scholarships. Apprenticeship file describes national apprenticeship training programs, including information on how to apply, contact agencies, and program content. Military file describes more than 200 military occupations and training opportunities related to civilian employment.

★2328★ Computer Occupations

Delphi Productions
3160 4th St.
Boulder, CO 80304
Fax: (303)443-4022   Fr: 888-443-2400
URL: http://www.delphivideo.com

$95.00. 50 minutes. Part of the Careers for the 21st Century Video Library.

★2329★ Information Technology Occupations

Delphi Productions
3160 4th St.
Boulder, CO 80304
Fax: (303)443-4022   Fr: 888-443-2400
URL: http://www.delphivideo.com

$95.00. 52 minutes. Part of the Emerging Careers Video Library.

★2330★ Information Technology Services

Cambridge Educational
2572 Brunswick Ave.
Lawrenceville, NJ 08648-4128
Fax: 800-FAX-ON-US   Fr: 800-468-4227
URL: http://www.cambridgeeducational.com

$89.95. 2002. 18 minutes. Part of the Career Cluster Series.

★2331★ Institute for Certification of Computing Professionals (ICCP)

2350 E Devon Ave., Ste. 115
Des Plaines, IL 60018-4610
Ph: (847)299-4227   Fax: (847)299-4280
Fr: 800-U-GET-CCP
E-mail: office@iccp.org
URL: http://www.iccp.org

Members: Professional societies united to promote the development of computer examinations which are of high quality, directed toward information technology professionals, and designed to encourage competence and professionalism. Individuals passing the exams automatically become members of the Institute for Certification of Computing Professionals. Individuals passing exams become certified as CCP or ACP. **Activities:** Has developed code of ethics and good practice to which those taking the exams promise to adhere. Maintains speakers' bureau; compiles statistics.

★2332★ Internet Careers: College Not Required

Cambridge Educational
2572 Brunswick Ave.
Lawrenceville, NJ 08648-4128
Fax: 800-FAX-ON-US   Fr: 800-468-4227
URL: http://www.cambridgeeducational.com

Video. 1998. $79.95. 28 minutes. Covers careers and job opportunities related to developing, programming, and managing Internet sites.

★2333★ Resumes for High Tech Careers

Vgm Career Horizons
1221 Avenue of the Americas
New York, NY 10020
Ph: (212)904-2000   Fr: 800-323-4900
E-mail: ntcpub@tribune.com

Second edition, 1997. $9.95 (paper). 462 pages. Demonstrates how to tailor a resume that catches a high tech employer's attention. Part of Resumes for... series.

★2334★ Special Interest Group for Computers and the Physically Handicapped (SIGCAPH)

Church St. Sta.
PO Box 12115
New York, NY 10249
Ph: (212)626-0500   Fax: (212)944-1318
E-mail: chair_sigcaph@acm.org
URL: http://www.acm.org/sigcaph

Description: Promotes the professional interests of computing personnel with physical disabilities and the application of computing & information technology in solving relevant disability problems. Studies to educate the public to support careers for the disabled.

Computer Service Technicians

SOURCES OF HELP-WANTED ADS

★2335★ Communications of the ACM
Association for Computing Machinery
1515 Broadway
New York, NY 10036
Ph: (212)626-0500   Fax: (212)944-1318
Fr: 800-342-6626
URL: http://www.acm.org/about_acm/ov_
pubs.html

Monthly. Computing news magazine.

★2336★ Computerworld
101 Communications
9121 Oakdale Ave.
Chatsworth, CA 91311
Ph: (818)734-1520   Fax: (818)734-1522
URL: http://www.computerworld.com

Weekly. $48.00/year for individuals. News-
paper for information systems executives.

★2337★ Machine Design
Penton Media Inc.
1300 E 9th St.
Cleveland, OH 44114-1503
Ph: (216)696-7000   Fax: (216)931-9799
E-mail: mdeditor@penton.com
URL: http://www.machinedesign.com

$153.00/year for individuals. Magazine on
design engineering function.

★2338★ PC Computing
Ziff-Davis Media Inc.
28 E 28th St.
New York, NY 10016-7930
Ph: (212)503-3500

Monthly. Magazine on personal computers.

★2339★ PC Magazine
Ziff-Davis Media Inc.
28 E 28th St.
New York, NY 10016-7930
Ph: (212)503-3500

Semimonthly. Consumer magazine focusing
on the personal computer industry.

★2340★ PC Week
Ziff-Davis Media Inc.
28 E 28th St.
New York, NY 10016-7930
Ph: (212)503-3500
URL: http://www.pcweek.com

Weekly. Free to qualified subscribers;
$195.00/year for individuals; $250.00/year
for Canada and Mexico; $395.00/year for
other countries; $6.00 for single issue. Tab-
loid featuring microcomputer products and
developments.

★2341★ PC WORLD
101 Communications
9121 Oakdale Ave.
Chatsworth, CA 91311
Ph: (818)734-1520   Fax: (818)734-1522
URL: http://www.pcworld.com

Monthly. $29.90/year for individuals; $5.95
for single issue.

PLACEMENT AND JOB REFERRAL SERVICES

**★2342★ Electronics Technicians
Association, International (ETA-I)**
5 Depot St.
Greencastle, IN 46135
Ph: (765)653-8262   Fax: (765)653-4287
Fr: 800-288-3824
E-mail: eta@tds.net
URL: http://www.eta-sda.com

Description: Skilled electronics technicians.
Provides placement service; offers certification examinations for electronics technicians

and satellite, fiber optics, and data cabling
installers. Compiles wage and manpower
statistics. Administers FCC Commercial License examinations. Certification of computer network systems technicians and web and
internet specialists.

**★2343★ North American Computer
Service Association (NACSA)**
2431 Aloma Ave., No. 124
Winter Park, FL 32792-2540
Ph: (407)657-1000   Fax: (407)657-1010
Fr: 888-666-1160
E-mail: nacdggone@mymailstation.com

Description: Computer service and repair
companies; suppliers to the industry; computer repair schools; professional consultants. Promotes orderly growth for the computer service industry and assists members
with tasks such as contract negotiation,
training, legislative liaison, and parts and
supplies purchasing. Maintains placement
service members and acquisition.

EMPLOYER DIRECTORIES AND NETWORKING LISTS

★2344★ Computer Directory
Computer Directories Inc.
23815 Nichols Sawmill Rd.
Hockley, TX 77447
Ph: (281)259-5959   Fax: (281)356-7980
Fr: 800-234-4353
URL: http://www.compdirinc.com

Annual, fall. Covers approximately 130,000
computer installations; 19 separate volumes
for Alaska/Hawaii, Connecticut/New Jersey,
Dallas/Ft. Worth, Eastern Seaboard, Far
Midwest, Houston, Illinois, Midatlantic, Midcentral, Mideast, Minnesota/Wisconsin,
North Central, New England, New York
Metro, Northwest, Ohio, Pennsylvania/West
Virginia, Southeast, and Southwest Texas.
Entries include: Company name, address,
phone, fax, email, name and title of contact,
hardware used, software application, operating system, programming language, comput-

er graphics, networking system. Arrangement: Geographical. Indexes: Alphabetical, industry, hardware.

★2345★ **Directory of Top Computer Executives**

Applied Computer Research
PO Box 82266
Phoenix, AZ 85071-2266
Ph: (602)216-9100   Fax: (602)216-9200
Fr: 800-234-2227
URL: http://www.itmarketintelligence.com

Semiannual, June and December. $245.00 for single volume; $420.00 for two-volume set; $625.00 for three-volume set. Covers in three volumes, over 55,000 U.S. and Canadian executives with major information technology or communications responsibilities in over 30,000 U.S. and Canadian companies. Entries include: Company name, address, phone, subsidiary and/or division names, major systems installed, names and titles of top information system executives, number of IT employees, nuimber of PCs, and web address. Arrangement: Geographical within separate eastern, western, and Canadian volumes. Indexes: Industry; alphabetical by company name.

HANDBOOKS AND MANUALS

★2346★ **America's Fastest Growing Jobs**

JIST Works, Inc.
8902 Otis Ave.
Indianapolis, IN 46216-1033
Ph: (317)613-4200   Fax: (317)613-4307
Fr: 800-648-5478
E-mail: jistworks@aol.com
URL: http://www.jist.com

Seventh edition, 2002. $16.95 (paper). 438 pages. Each job profile explains the nature of the work, skills and abilities required, employment outlook, average earnings, related occupations, education and training requirements, and employment opportunities. Also contains career planning information and job search tips.

★2347★ **America's Top 101 Computer and Technical Jobs**

JIST Publishing
8902 Otis Ave.
Indianapolis, IN 46216-1033
Ph: (317)613-4200   Fax: 800-547-8329

Michael J. Farr. 2004. $15.95. 368 pages. Job hunting in computer and technical industries.

★2348★ **Career Opportunities in Computers and Cyberspace**

Facts on File
132 W. 31st St., 17th Fl.
New York, NY 10001-2006
Ph: (212)967-8800   Fax: (212)967-8107
Fr: 800-322-8755

Harry Henderson. 1999. $26.95 (paper). Part of the Career Opportunities Series. 224 pages.

★2349★ **Careers for Computer Buffs and Other Technological Types**

VGM Career Horizons
1221 Avenue of the Americas
New York, NY 10020
Ph: (212)904-2000   Fr: 800-323-4900
E-mail: ntcpub@tribune.com

Marjorie Eberts, Margaret Gisler and Maria Olsen. Second edition, 1999. $14.95; $9.95 (paper).

★2350★ **Careers in Computers**

VGM Career Horizons
1221 Avenue of the Americas
New York, NY 10020
Ph: (212)904-2000   Fr: 800-323-4900
E-mail: ntcpub@tribune.com

Lila B. Stair and Leslie Stair. Third edition, 2002. $19.95; $14.95 (paper). Describes trends affecting computer careers and explores a wide range of job opportunities from programming to consulting. Provides job qualifications, salary data, job market information, personal and educational requirements, career paths, and the place of the job in the organizational structure. Offers advice on education, certification, and job search.

★2351★ **Choosing a Career in Computers**

Rosen Publishing Group, Inc.
29 E. 21st St.
New York, NY 10010
Ph: (212)777-3017   Fax: (212)777-0277
Fr: 800-237-9932

Weigant, Chris. 2000. $17.95.

★2352★ **Computer Support Technician**

National Learning Corp.
212 Michael Dr.
Syosset, NY 11791
Ph: (516)921-8888   Fax: (516)921-8743
Fr: 800-645-6337

Jack Rudman. 1997. $34.95. Part of the Career Examination Series.

★2353★ **Computer Technician Career Starter**

LearningExpress, LLC
900 Broadway, Ste. 604
New York, NY 10003
Ph: (212)995-2566   Fax: (212)995-5512
Fr: 800-295-9556

Joan Vaughn. Second edition, 2001. 208 pages. Part of the Career Starters Series.

★2354★ **The Digital Frontier Job & Opportunity Finder**

Moon Lake Media
PO Box 251466
Los Angeles, CA 90025
Ph: (310)535-2453

Don B. Altman. 1996. $19.95 (paper). 256 pages.

★2355★ **Expert Resumes for Computer and Web Jobs**

JIST Publishing
8902 Otis Ave.
Indianapolis, IN 46216-1033
Ph: (317)613-4200   Fax: (317)613-4307
Fr: 800-648-5478

Wendy Enelow and Louis Kursmark. 2001. $16.95 (paper).

★2356★ **Exploring Careers in the Computer Field**

Rosen Publishing Group, Inc.
29 E 21st St.
New York, NY 10010
Ph: (212)777-3017   Fax: 888-436-4643
Fr: 800-237-9932

Joseph Weintraub. Revised edition, 1993. $14.95; $9.95 (paper). Discusses entry into the field, salaries, future trends, and offers job search advice. Surveys the newest growth areas in the computer industry including artificial intelligence, desktop publishing, and personal computers. Out of stock.

★2357★ **Get Your IT Career in Gear!**

McGraw-Hill Professional
2 Penn Plaza
New York, NY 10121
Ph: (212)904-2000

Leslie Goff. 2001. $24.99 (paper).

★2358★ **Great Jobs for Computer Science Majors**

McGraw-Hill Companies
1221 Avenue of the Americas
New York, NY 10020
Ph: (212)904-2000   Fr: 800-323-4900
E-mail: ntcpub@tribune.com

Jan Goldberg, Stephen Lambert, Julie DeGalan. 1997. $11.95 (paper). 365 pages.

★2359★ **How to Be a Successful Computer Consultant**

McGraw-Hill Companies
860 Taylor Station Rd.
Blacklick, OH 43004-0545
Fax: (614)755-5645   Fr: 800-722-4726

Walid Mougayar and Alan R. Simon. Fourth edition, revised, 1998. $29.95 (paper). Out of print.

★2360★ The JobBank Guide to Computer and High-Tech Companies

Adams Media Corp.
57 Littlefield St.
Avon, MA 02322
Ph: (508)427-7100   Fax: (508)427-6790
Fr: 800-872-5627
URL: http://www.adamsmedia.com

Second edition, 1999. $17.95 (paper). 704 pages. Contains profiles of more than 4,500 high-tech employers.

★2361★ Opportunities in Computer Careers

McGraw-Hill Professional
2 Penn Plaza
New York, NY 10121-2298
Ph: (212)904-2000   Fr: 800-722-4726

Julie Kling Burns. $12.95 (netLibrary). Computer vocational guidance and counseling.

★2362★ Opportunities in Computer Maintenance Careers

McGraw-Hill Trade
2 Penn Plaza
New York, NY 10121
Ph: (212)904-2000   Fr: 800-722-4726

Elliott Kanter and Jonathan Yaeger. 1995. $14.95; $11.95 (paper). 204 pages. Offers advice on job hunting and where the jobs are. Illustrated.

★2363★ Opportunities in High Tech Careers

McGraw-Hill Trade
2 Penn Plaza
New York, NY 10121
Ph: (212)904-2000   Fr: 800-722-4726

Gary Colter and Deborah Yanuck. 1995. $14.95; $11.95 (paper). 160 pages. Explores high technology careers. Describes job opportunities, how to make a career decision, how to prepare for high technology jobs, job hunting techniques, and future trends.

★2364★ Preparing for an Outstanding Career in Computers: Questions and Answers for Professionals and Students

Rafi Systems, Incorporated
750 N. Diamond Bar Blvd., Suite 224
Diamond Bar, CA 91765
Ph: (909)593-8124   Fax: (909)629-1034
Fr: 800-584-6706

Mohamed Rafiquzzaman. 2001. $19.95.

★2365★ Unlocking the Clubhouse: Women in Computing

MIT Press
5 Cambridge Ctr., Suite 4
Cambridge, MA 02142-1493
Ph: (617)253-5646   Fax: (617)253-6779
Fr: 800-356-0343

Jane Margolis and Allan Fisher. 2001. $24.95.

★2366★ The Unofficial Guide to Getting a Job at Microsoft

McGraw-Hill Education Group
800 Taylor Staion Rd.
Blacklick, OH 43004-0545
Fax: (614)755-5645   Fr: 800-722-4726

Rebecca Smith. 2000. $16.95 (paper).

★2367★ Where the Jobs Are: The Hottest Careers for the 90s

The Career Press, Inc.
3 Tice Rd.
PO Box 687
Franklin Lakes, NJ 07417-1322
Ph: (201)848-0310   Fax: (201)848-1727
Fr: 800-227-3371

Joyce Hadley. Third edition, 2000. $13.99 (paper). 400 pages. Out of print. Describes careers in fifteen general fields, from accounting to travel and hospitality.

★2368★ Winning Resumes for Computer Personnel

Barron's Educational Series, Inc.
250 Wireless Blvd.
Hauppauge, NY 11788-3917
Ph: (631)434-3311   Fax: (631)434-3723
Fr: 800-645-3476

Anne Hart. Second edition, 1998. $12.95 (paper). 320 pages.

★2369★ Your Opportunities in Computers

Energeia Publishing, Inc.
1307 Fairmount Ave., S
Salem, OR 97302-4313
Ph: (503)362-1480   Fax: (503)362-2123
Fr: 800-639-6048

John Tribbett. 1994. $2.50 (paper). 8 pages.

EMPLOYMENT AGENCIES AND SEARCH FIRMS

★2370★ Carol Maden Group

2019 Cunningham Dr., Ste. 218
Hampton, VA 23666
Ph: (757)827-9010   Fax: (757)827-9081

Personnel consultants offering placement service in computer technology and engineering, servicing manufacturing and private industries nationwide. Temporary placement servicing clerical and light industrial.

★2371★ Jim Ward Associates

35 Browning Ave.
Toronto, ON, Canada M4K 1V8
Ph: (416)463-1661   Fax: (416)463-1688

Placement service provides careers and contract positions and professionals specifically related to the computing field. Industries served: various industries from government to small business; including banking, service, retail, distribution, manufacturing that use central, distributed or network computing facilities.

★2372★ The Murphy Group

245 W Roosevelt Rd., Bldg.15 Ste.101
Chicago, IL 60185
Ph: (630)639-5110   Fax: (630)639-5113
E-mail: info@murphygroup.com
URL: http://www.murphygroup.com

Employment agency. Places personnel in a variety of positions. Additional offices located in Napierville, Park Ridge, and OakBrook.

ONLINE JOB SOURCES AND SERVICES

★2373★ ComputerJobs.com

URL: http://www.computerjobs.com

Description: The site is an employment tool for technology professionals. Information on positions is updated hourly for seekers. Jobs may be searched by skill, or by location nationally or in a specific state or city job market. Contains thousands of job postings. National jobs may be posted for free. Also career resources for IT professionals.

★2374★ Computerwork.com

E-mail: candidate_support@computerwork.com
URL: http://computerwork.com/

Description: Job search and resume submission service for professionals in information technology.

★2375★ Computerworld Careers

URL: http://www.computerworld.com/cwi/careers/

Description: Offers career opportunities for IT (information technology) professionals. Job seekers may search the jobs database, register at the site, and read about job surveys and employment trends. Employers may post jobs.

★2376★ Computing Research Association Job Announcements

URL: http://www.cra.org/main/cra.jobs.html

Description: Contains dated links to national college and university computer technology positions.

★2377★ Guru

URL: http://www.guru.com

Description: Job board specializing in contract jobs for creative and information technology professionals. Also provides online incorporation and educational opportunities for independent contractors along with articles and advice.

★2378★ Ittalent.com
E-mail: ewsmith@ITtalent.com
URL: http://www.ittalent.com

Description: Job search and resume submission service for professionals in information technology.

★2379★ ZDNet Tech Jobs
URL: http://www.zdnet.com/special/filters/techjobs/

Description: Site houses a listing of national employment opportunities for professionals in high tech fields. Also contains resume building tips and relocation resources. Powered by Dice.com

OTHER SOURCES

★2380★ Association of Computer Professionals (ACP)
9 Forest Dr.
Plainview, NY 11803
Ph: (516)938-8223　　Fax: (516)938-3073
E-mail: sybosworth@aol.com

Members: Authors, consultants, programmers, publishers, and teachers in the computer field who provide products or services to users or to other professionals. **Purpose:** Works to advance the art and science of computer professionals through educational means. Encourages education and instruction of the public regarding what the association views as the beneficial use of computers and computer technology. **Activities:** Provides members with information on accounting, business management, creative marketing techniques, law, microcomputer advances, tax matters, technical developments, and special earning opportunities. Addresses issues of software protection, contract law, tax benefits, potential tax problems, and financial subjects such as sources of capital for new ventures and expanding businesses.

★2381★ Association of Information Technology Professionals
401 N Michigan Ave., Ste. 2400
PO Box 809189
Chicago, IL 60611-4267
Ph: (312)245-1070　　Fax: (312)527-6636
Fr: 800-224-9371
E-mail: aitp_hq@aitp.org
URL: http://www.aitp.org

Members: Managerial personnel, staff, educators, and individuals interested in the management of information resources. Founder of the Certificate in Data Processing examination program, now administered by an intersociety organization. **Purpose:** Maintains Legislative Communications Network. Professional education programs include EDP-oriented business and management principles self-study courses and a series of videotaped management development seminars. Sponsors student organizations around the country interested in information technology and encourages members to serve as counselors for the Scout computer merit badge. Conducts research projects, including a business information systems curriculum for two- and four-year colleges.

★2382★ Association for Women in Computing (AWC)
41 Sutter St., Ste. 1006
San Francisco, CA 94104
Ph: (415)905-4663
E-mail: info@awc-hq.org
URL: http://www.awc-hq.org

Members: Individuals interested in promoting the education, professional development, and advancement of women in computing.

★2383★ *Computer Occupations*
Delphi Productions
3160 4th St.
Boulder, CO 80304
Fax: (303)443-4022　　Fr: 888-443-2400
URL: http://www.delphivideo.com

$95.00. 50 minutes. Part of the Careers for the 21st Century Video Library.

★2384★ Institute for Certification of Computing Professionals (ICCP)
2350 E Devon Ave., Ste. 115
Des Plaines, IL 60018-4610
Ph: (847)299-4227　　Fax: (847)299-4280
Fr: 800-U-GET-CCP
E-mail: office@iccp.org
URL: http://www.iccp.org

Members: Professional societies united to promote the development of computer examinations which are of high quality, directed toward information technology professionals, and designed to encourage competence and professionalism. Individuals passing the exams automatically become members of the Institute for Certification of Computing Professionals. Individuals passing exams become certified as CCP or ACP. **Activities:** Has developed code of ethics and good practice to which those taking the exams promise to adhere. Maintains speakers' bureau; compiles statistics.

★2385★ International Society of Certified Electronics Technicians (ISCET)
3608 Pershing Ave.
Fort Worth, TX 76107-4527
Ph: (817)921-9101　　Fax: (817)921-3741
E-mail: info@iscet.org
URL: http://www.iscet.org

Description: Technicians in 50 countries who have been certified by the society. Seeks to provide a fraternal bond among certified electronics technicians, raise their public image, and improve the effectiveness of industry education programs for technicians. Offers training programs in new electronics information. Maintains library of service literature for consumer electronic equipment, including manuals and schematics for out-of-date equipment. Offers all FCC licenses. Sponsors testing program for certification of electronics technicians in the fields of audio, communications, computer, consumer, industrial, medical electronics, radar, radio-television, and video.

★2386★ National Electronics Service Dealers Association (NESDA)
3608 Pershing Ave.
Fort Worth, TX 76107-4527
Ph: (817)921-9061　　Fax: (817)921-3741
E-mail: mack@nesda.com
URL: http://www.nesda.com

Description: Local and state electronic service associations and companies representing 4200 individuals. Provides educational assistance in electronic training to public schools; supplies technical service information on business management training to electronic service dealers. Offers certification, apprenticeship, and training programs through International Society of Certified Electronics Technicians. Compiles statistics on electronics service business; conducts technical service and business management seminars.

★2387★ Special Interest Group for Computers and the Physically Handicapped (SIGCAPH)
Church St. Sta.
PO Box 12115
New York, NY 10249
Ph: (212)626-0500　　Fax: (212)944-1318
E-mail: chair_sigcaph@acm.org
URL: http://www.acm.org/sigcaph

Description: Promotes the professional interests of computing personnel with physical disabilities and the application of computing & information technology in solving relevant disability problems. Studies to educate the public to support careers for the disabled.

★2388★ *Technical & Related Occupations*
Delphi Productions
3160 4th St.
Boulder, CO 80304
Fax: (303)443-4022　　Fr: 888-443-2400
URL: http://www.delphivideo.com

$95.00. 49 minutes. Part of the Careers for the 21st Century Video Library.

Computer Support Specialists

SOURCES OF HELP-WANTED ADS

★2389★ AS/400 Systems Management
Adams Business Media
250 S Wacker Dr., Ste. 1150
Chicago, IL 60606
Ph: (312)977-0999   Fax: (312)980-3135
E-mail: 73222.3344@compuserve.com
URL: http://www.hotlink400.com

Monthly. $42.00/year for individuals. Management-oriented magazine for DP/MIS managers with an IBM AS/400 on site.

★2390★ Communications of the ACM
Association for Computing Machinery
1515 Broadway
New York, NY 10036
Ph: (212)626-0500   Fax: (212)944-1318
Fr: 800-342-6626
URL: http://www.acm.org/about_acm/ov_pubs.html

Monthly. Computing news magazine.

★2391★ Computers in Libraries
Information Today Inc.
143 Old Marlton Pke.
Medford, NJ 08055-8750
Ph: (609)654-6266   Fax: (609)654-4309
Fr: 800-300-9848
URL: http://www.infotoday.com

Monthly. $99.95/year for U.S. $114.00/year for Canada and Mexico; $124.00/year for other countries. Library science and computer magazine.

★2392★ PC Computing
Ziff-Davis Media Inc.
28 E 28th St.
New York, NY 10016-7930
Ph: (212)503-3500

Monthly. Magazine on personal computers.

★2393★ PC Magazine
Ziff-Davis Media Inc.
28 E 28th St.
New York, NY 10016-7930
Ph: (212)503-3500

Semimonthly. Consumer magazine focusing on the personal computer industry.

★2394★ PC Today
Sandhills Publishing
120 W Harvest Dr.
PO Box 85310
Lincoln, NE 68501-5310
Ph: (402)479-2141   Fax: (402)479-2120
Fr: 800-247-4880

Monthly. $24.00/year; $32.00/year for other countries; $2.95/year for single issue; $3.50/year. Magazine for personal computer users.

★2395★ PC WORLD
101 Communications
9121 Oakdale Ave.
Chatsworth, CA 91311
Ph: (818)734-1520   Fax: (818)734-1522
URL: http://www.pcworld.com

Monthly. $29.90/year for individuals; $5.95 for single issue.

EMPLOYER DIRECTORIES AND NETWORKING LISTS

★2396★ Computer Directory
Computer Directories Inc.
23815 Nichols Sawmill Rd.
Hockley, TX 77447
Ph: (281)259-5959   Fax: (281)356-7980
Fr: 800-234-4353
URL: http://www.compdirinc.com

Annual, fall. Covers approximately 130,000 computer installations; 19 separate volumes for Alaska/Hawaii, Connecticut/New Jersey, Dallas/Ft. Worth, Eastern Seaboard, Far Midwest, Houston, Illinois, Midatlantic, Midcentral, Mideast, Minnesota/Wisconsin, North Central, New England, New York Metro, Northwest, Ohio, Pennsylvania/West Virginia, Southeast, and Southwest Texas. Entries include: Company name, address, phone, fax, email, name and title of contact, hardware used, software application, operating system, programming language, computer graphics, networking system. Arrangement: Geographical. Indexes: Alphabetical, industry, hardware.

HANDBOOKS AND MANUALS

★2397★ America's Top 101 Computer and Technical Jobs
JIST Publishing
8902 Otis Ave.
Indianapolis, IN 46216-1033
Ph: (317)613-4200   Fax: 800-547-8329

Michael J. Farr. 2004. $15.95. 368 pages. Job hunting in computer and technical industries.

★2398★ Career Opportunities in Computers and Cyberspace
Facts on File
132 W. 31st St., 17th Fl.
New York, NY 10001-2006
Ph: (212)967-8800   Fax: (212)967-8107
Fr: 800-322-8755

Harry Henderson. 1999. $26.95 (paper). Part of the Career Opportunities Series. 224 pages.

★2399★ Careers Inside the World of Technology
Rosen Publishing Group, Inc.
29 E. 21st St.
New York, NY 10010
Ph: (212)777-3017   Fax: 888-436-4643
Fr: 800-237-9932

Jean W. Spencer. Revised edition, 1998. $16.95. 64 pages. Describes computer-related careers for reluctant readers.

★2400★ Choosing a Career in Computers

Rosen Publishing Group, Inc.
29 E. 21st St.
New York, NY 10010
Ph: (212)777-3017   Fax: (212)777-0277
Fr: 800-237-9932

Weigant, Chris. 2000. $17.95.

★2401★ Computer Support Technician

National Learning Corporation
212 Michael Dr.
Syosset, NY 11791
Ph: (516)921-8888   Fax: (516)921-8743
Fr: 800-645-6337

Rudman, Jack. 1997. $34.95 (Trade paper).

★2402★ The Digital Frontier Job & Opportunity Finder

Moon Lake Media
PO Box 251466
Los Angeles, CA 90025
Ph: (310)535-2453

Don B. Altman. 1996. $19.95 (paper). 256 pages.

★2403★ How to Be a Successful Computer Consultant

McGraw-Hill Companies
860 Taylor Station Rd.
Blacklick, OH 43004-0545
Fax: (614)755-5645   Fr: 800-722-4726

Walid Mougayar and Alan R. Simon. Fourth edition, revised, 1998. $29.95 (paper). Out of print.

★2404★ The JobBank Guide to Computer and High-Tech Companies

Adams Media Corp.
57 Littlefield St.
Avon, MA 02322
Ph: (508)427-7100   Fax: (508)427-6790
Fr: 800-872-5627
URL: http://www.adamsmedia.com

Second edition, 1999. $17.95 (paper). 704 pages. Contains profiles of more than 4,500 high-tech employers.

★2405★ Opportunities in Computer Careers

McGraw-Hill Professional
2 Penn Plaza
New York, NY 10121-2298
Ph: (212)904-2000   Fr: 800-722-4726

Julie Kling Burns. $12.95 (netLibrary). Computer vocational guidance and counseling.

★2406★ Opportunities in Computer Systems Careers

McGraw-Hill Contemporary Books
1221 Avenue of the Americas
New York, NY 10020
Ph: (212)904-2000   Fr: 800-323-4900
E-mail: ntcpub@tribune.com

Julie King Burns. 1996. $14.95; $11.95 (paper). 160 pages.

★2407★ Winning Resumes for Computer Personnel

Barron's Educational Series, Inc.
250 Wireless Blvd.
Hauppauge, NY 11788-3917
Ph: (631)434-3311   Fax: (631)434-3723
Fr: 800-645-3476

Anne Hart. Second edition, 1998. $12.95 (paper). 320 pages.

★2408★ Your Opportunities in Computers

Energeia Publishing, Inc.
1307 Fairmount Ave., S
Salem, OR 97302-4313
Ph: (503)362-1480   Fax: (503)362-2123
Fr: 800-639-6048

John Tribbett. 1994. $2.50 (paper). 8 pages.

EMPLOYMENT AGENCIES AND SEARCH FIRMS

★2409★ Carol Maden Group

2019 Cunningham Dr., Ste. 218
Hampton, VA 23666
Ph: (757)827-9010   Fax: (757)827-9081

Personnel consultants offering placement service in computer technology and engineering, servicing manufacturing and private industries nationwide. Temporary placement servicing clerical and light industrial.

★2410★ Chaves & Associates

1698 Post Rd. E
Westport, CT 06880
Ph: (203)222-2222   Fax: (203)259-5200
E-mail: gen@chaves.com
URL: http://www.in-sitesearch.com

Executive search firm.

★2411★ Jim Ward Associates

35 Browning Ave.
Toronto, ON, Canada M4K 1V8
Ph: (416)463-1661   Fax: (416)463-1688

Placement service provides careers and contract positions and professionals specifically related to the computing field. Industries served: various industries from government to small business; including banking, service, retail, distribution, manufacturing that use central, distributed or network computing facilities.

★2412★ Professional Computer Resources Inc.

328 Rensselaer Ave.
Charlotte, NC 28203
Ph: (704)335-1312   Fax: (704)335-8763
E-mail: resumes@pcr.net
URL: http://www.pcr.net

Executive search firm.

★2413★ TRC Staffing Services Inc.

2110 15 Mile Rd., Ste. B
Sterling Heights, MI 48310
Ph: (586)939-3210   Fax: (586)978-0572

A full-service executive search company with permanent placements encompassing engineering, industrial sales, financial and computer science positions. Screen, interview, and verify past employment for all candidates prior to referral. Also assist personnel staffs in the attainment of their EEO/AAP goals with the placement of talented individuals in positions which are underutilized with minorities and/or women. In addition, firm has a clerical temporary service division, TRC Temporary Service; and an employment agency, TRC Staffing Services.

ONLINE JOB SOURCES AND SERVICES

★2414★ ComputerJobs.com
URL: http://www.computerjobs.com

Description: The site is an employment tool for technology professionals. Information on positions is updated hourly for seekers. Jobs may be searched by skill, or by location nationally or in a specific state or city job market. Contains thousands of job postings. National jobs may be posted for free. Also career resources for IT professionals.

★2415★ Computerwork.com
E-mail: candidate_support@computerwork.com
URL: http://computerwork.com/

Description: Job search and resume submission service for professionals in information technology.

★2416★ Computerworld Careers
URL: http://www.computerworld.com/cwi/careers/

Description: Offers career opportunities for IT (information technology) professionals. Job seekers may search the jobs database, register at the site, and read about job surveys and employment trends. Employers may post jobs.

★2417★ Computing Research Association Job Announcements
URL: http://www.cra.org/main/cra.jobs.html

Description: Contains dated links to national college and university computer technology positions.

★2418★ Guru
URL: http://www.guru.com
Description: Job board specializing in contract jobs for creative and information technology professionals. Also provides online incorporation and educational opportunities for independent contractors along with articles and advice.

★2419★ Ittalent.com
E-mail: ewsmith@ITtalent.com
URL: http://www.ittalent.com
Description: Job search and resume submission service for professionals in information technology.

★2420★ ZDNet Tech Jobs
URL: http://www.zdnet.com/special/filters/techjobs/
Description: Site houses a listing of national employment opportunities for professionals in high tech fields. Also contains resume building tips and relocation resources. Powered by Dice.com

TRADESHOWS

★2421★ XPLOR Conference
XPLOR International
24238 Hawthorne Blvd.
Torrance, CA 90505-6505
Ph: (310)791-9521   Fax: (310)375-4240
Fr: 800-669-7567
E-mail: info@xplor.org
URL: http://www.xplor.org

Annual. **Primary Exhibits:** Equipment, supplies, and services for users and manufacturers of advanced electronic document systems.

OTHER SOURCES

★2422★ Association of Computer Professionals (ACP)
9 Forest Dr.
Plainview, NY 11803
Ph: (516)938-8223   Fax: (516)938-3073
E-mail: sybosworth@aol.com

Members: Authors, consultants, programmers, publishers, and teachers in the computer field who provide products or services to users or to other professionals. **Purpose:** Works to advance the art and science of computer professionals through educational means. Encourages education and instruction of the public regarding what the association views as the beneficial use of computers and computer technology. **Activities:** Provides members with information on accounting, business management, creative marketing techniques, law, microcomputer advances, tax matters, technical developments, and special earning opportunities. Addresses issues of software protection, contract law, tax benefits, potential tax problems, and financial subjects such as sources of capital for new ventures and expanding businesses.

★2423★ Association of Information Technology Professionals
401 N Michigan Ave., Ste. 2400
PO Box 809189
Chicago, IL 60611-4267
Ph: (312)245-1070   Fax: (312)527-6636
Fr: 800-224-9371
E-mail: aitp_hq@aitp.org
URL: http://www.aitp.org

Members: Managerial personnel, staff, educators, and individuals interested in the management of information resources. Founder of the Certificate in Data Processing examination program, now administered by an intersociety organization. **Purpose:** Maintains Legislative Communications Network. Professional education programs include EDP-oriented business and management principles self-study courses and a series of videotaped management development seminars. Sponsors student organizations around the country interested in information technology and encourages members to serve as counselors for the Scout computer merit badge. Conducts research projects, including a business information systems curriculum for two- and four-year colleges.

★2424★ Association for Women in Computing (AWC)
41 Sutter St., Ste. 1006
San Francisco, CA 94104
Ph: (415)905-4663
E-mail: info@awc-hq.org
URL: http://www.awc-hq.org

Members: Individuals interested in promoting the education, professional development, and advancement of women in computing.

★2425★ *Computer Occupations*
Delphi Productions
3160 4th St.
Boulder, CO 80304
Fax: (303)443-4022   Fr: 888-443-2400
URL: http://www.delphivideo.com

$95.00. 50 minutes. Part of the Careers for the 21st Century Video Library.

★2426★ *Information Technology Services*
Cambridge Educational
2572 Brunswick Ave.
Lawrenceville, NJ 08648-4128
Fax: 800-FAX-ON-US   Fr: 800-468-4227
URL: http://www.cambridgeeducational.com

$89.95. 2002. 18 minutes. Part of the Career Cluster Series.

★2427★ Institute for Certification of Computing Professionals (ICCP)
2350 E Devon Ave., Ste. 115
Des Plaines, IL 60018-4610
Ph: (847)299-4227   Fax: (847)299-4280
Fr: 800-U-GET-CCP
E-mail: office@iccp.org
URL: http://www.iccp.org

Members: Professional societies united to promote the development of computer examinations which are of high quality, directed toward information technology professionals, and designed to encourage competence and professionalism. Individuals passing the exams automatically become members of the Institute for Certification of Computing Professionals. Individuals passing exams become certified as CCP or ACP. **Activities:** Has developed code of ethics and good practice to which those taking the exams promise to adhere. Maintains speakers' bureau; compiles statistics.

Computer Systems Analysts

★2440★ PC Computing

Ziff-Davis Media Inc.
28 E 28th St.
New York, NY 10016-7930
Ph: (212)503-3500

Monthly. Magazine on personal computers.

★2441★ PC Magazine

Ziff-Davis Media Inc.
28 E 28th St.
New York, NY 10016-7930
Ph: (212)503-3500

Semimonthly. Consumer magazine focusing on the personal computer industry.

★2442★ PC Today

Sandhills Publishing
120 W Harvest Dr.
PO Box 85310
Lincoln, NE 68501-5310
Ph: (402)479-2141   Fax: (402)479-2120
Fr: 800-247-4880

Monthly. $24.00/year; $32.00/year for other countries; $2.95/year for single issue; $3.50/year. Magazine for personal computer users.

★2443★ PC Week

Ziff-Davis Media Inc.
28 E 28th St.
New York, NY 10016-7930
Ph: (212)503-3500
URL: http://www.pcweek.com

Weekly. Free to qualified subscribers; $195.00/year for individuals; $250.00/year for Canada and Mexico; $395.00/year for other countries; $6.00 for single issue. Tabloid featuring microcomputer products and developments.

★2444★ PC WORLD

101 Communications
9121 Oakdale Ave.
Chatsworth, CA 91311
Ph: (818)734-1520   Fax: (818)734-1522
URL: http://www.pcworld.com

Monthly. $29.90/year for individuals; $5.95 for single issue.

★2445★ Performance Computing

CMP Media L.L.C.
600 Community Dr.
Manhasset, NY 11030
Ph: (516)562-5000
URL: http://www.performance-comput-ing.com

Monthly. Free to qualified subscribers; $55.00/year, nonqualified. Magazine for professional users of UNIX and UNIX-like systems, and Windows NT.

PLACEMENT AND JOB REFERRAL SERVICES

★2446★ American Indian Science and Engineering Society (AISES)

PO Box 9828
Albuquerque, NM 87119-9828
Ph: (505)765-1052   Fax: (505)765-5608
E-mail: info@aises.org
URL: http://www.aises.org

Description: American Indian and non-Indian students and professionals in science, technology, and engineering fields; corporations representing energy, mining, aerospace, electronic, and computer fields. Seeks to motivate and encourage students to pursue undergraduate and graduate studies in science, engineering, and technology. Sponsors science fairs in grade schools, teacher training workshops, summer math/science sessions for 8th-12th graders, professional chapters, and student chapters in colleges. Offers scholarships. Adult members serve as role models, advisers, and mentors for students. Operates placement service.

EMPLOYER DIRECTORIES AND NETWORKING LISTS

★2447★ Computer Directory

Computer Directories Inc.
23815 Nichols Sawmill Rd.
Hockley, TX 77447
Ph: (281)259-5959   Fax: (281)356-7980
Fr: 800-234-4353
URL: http://www.compdirinc.com

Annual, fall. Covers approximately 130,000 computer installations; 19 separate volumes for Alaska/Hawaii, Connecticut/New Jersey, Dallas/Ft. Worth, Eastern Seaboard, Far Midwest, Houston, Illinois, Midatlantic, Midcentral, Mideast, Minnesota/Wisconsin, North Central, New England, New York Metro, Northwest, Ohio, Pennsylvania/West Virginia, Southeast, and Southwest Texas. Entries include: Company name, address, phone, fax, email, name and title of contact, hardware used, software application, operating system, programming language, computer graphics, networking system. Arrangement: Geographical. Indexes: Alphabetical, industry, hardware.

★2448★ Directory of Top Computer Executives

Applied Computer Research
PO Box 82266
Phoenix, AZ 85071-2266
Ph: (602)216-9100   Fax: (602)216-9200
Fr: 800-234-2227
URL: http://www.itmarketintelligence.com

Semiannual, June and December. $245.00 for single volume; $420.00 for two-volume set; $625.00 for three-volume set. Covers in three volumes, over 55,000 U.S. and Canadian executives with major information technology or communications responsibilities in over 30,000 U.S. and Canadian companies. Entries include: Company name, address, phone, subsidiary and/or division names, major systems installed, names and titles of top information system executives, number of IT employees, nuimber of PCs, and web address. Arrangement: Geographical within separate eastern, western, and Canadian volumes. Indexes: Industry; alphabetical by company name.

★2449★ Northwest High Tech

Resolution Business Press Inc.
12307 NE 149th Ct.
Kirkland, WA 98034
Ph: (425)487-6248   Fax: (425)649-1897
E-mail: info@respress.com
URL: http://www.respress.com

Annual. $34.95. Covers over 2,000 computer-related companies in Washington, Oregon, and Idaho, and British Columbia and Alberta, Canada. Entries include: Company; name, address, phone, fax; toll-free number; names and titles of key personnel; product/service, programming languages, financial data, number of employees, operating systems, expansion plans (including hiring and site expansion plans), company market information, Standard Industrial Classification (SIC) code., internet addresses. Arrangement: Geographical. Indexes: Company name, SIC.

★2450★ Peterson's Hidden Job Market

Thomson Peterson's
Princeton Pike Corporate Center
2000 Lenox Dr.
PO Box 67005
Lawrenceville, NJ 08648
Ph: (609)896-1800   Fax: 800-277-2465
Fr: 800-338-3282
URL: http://www.petersons.com

Annual, June. $18.95. Covers approximately 2,000 technology firms with under 1,000 employees, which hire at four times the national rate. Entries include: Company name, address, phone, fax, name and title of contact, number of employees, year founded, number of employees added in last year, percentage of growth, line of business. Arrangement: Geographical by state, then by area code. Indexes: Alphabetical by industry.

★2451★ Peterson's Job Opportunities in Engineering and Technology

Thomson Peterson's
PO Box 67005
Lawrenceville, NJ 08648-6105
Fr: 800-338-3282

Compiled by the Peterson's staff. Fourth edition, 1996. $21.95 (paper). 384 pages. Profiles 2,000 high-tech companies looking primarily for technical personnel in such fields as biotechnology, telecommunications, software, computers and peripherals, defense, and aerospace. Contains job-search strategies and career options to help match education and expertise to the job market.

Indexed geographically, by industry, and by hiring needs.

HANDBOOKS AND MANUALS

★2452★ America's Top 101 Computer and Technical Jobs
JIST Publishing
8902 Otis Ave.
Indianapolis, IN 46216-1033
Ph: (317)613-4200   Fax: 800-547-8329
Michael J. Farr. 2004. $15.95. 368 pages. Job hunting in computer and technical industries.

★2453★ Career Information Center
Macmillan Publishing Co. Inc.
200 Old Tappan Rd.
Old Tappan, NJ 07675
Fr: 800-428-5331
Visual Education Center Staff. Seventh edition, 1999. $275.00. 2080 pages. This 13-volume set profiles over 600 occupations. Each occupational profile describes job duties, educational requirements, how to get the job, advancement possibilities, employment outlook, working conditions, earnings and benefits, and where to write for more information.

★2454★ Career Opportunities in Computers and Cyberspace
Facts on File
132 W. 31st St., 17th Fl.
New York, NY 10001-2006
Ph: (212)967-8800   Fax: (212)967-8107
Fr: 800-322-8755
Harry Henderson. 1999. $26.95 (paper). Part of the Career Opportunities Series. 224 pages.

★2455★ Careers for Computer Buffs and Other Technological Types
VGM Career Horizons
1221 Avenue of the Americas
New York, NY 10020
Ph: (212)904-2000   Fr: 800-323-4900
E-mail: ntcpub@tribune.com
Marjorie Eberts, Margaret Gisler and Maria Olsen. Second edition, 1999. $14.95; $9.95 (paper).

★2456★ Careers in Computers
VGM Career Horizons
1221 Avenue of the Americas
New York, NY 10020
Ph: (212)904-2000   Fr: 800-323-4900
E-mail: ntcpub@tribune.com
Lila B. Stair and Leslie Stair. Third edition, 2002. $19.95; $14.95 (paper). Describes trends affecting computer careers and explores a wide range of job opportunities from programming to consulting. Provides job

qualifications, salary data, job market information, personal and educational requirements, career paths, and the place of the job in the organizational structure. Offers advice on education, certification, and job search.

★2457★ Careers Inside the World of Technology
Rosen Publishing Group, Inc.
29 E. 21st St.
New York, NY 10010
Ph: (212)777-3017   Fax: 888-436-4643
Fr: 800-237-9932
Jean W. Spencer. Revised edition, 1998. $16.95. 64 pages. Describes computer-related careers for reluctant readers.

★2458★ Careers for Number Crunchers and Other Quantitative Types
McGraw-Hill Trade
2 Penn Plaza
New York, NY 10121
Ph: (212)904-2000   Fr: 800-722-4726
E-mail: ntcpub@tribune.com
Rebecca Burnett. Second edition, 2002. $15.95; $12.95 (paper). 192 pages. Provides information to math-oriented job hunters on how to become statisticians, field researchers, computer programmers, stock analysts, investment managers, bankers, engineers, accountants, underwriters, economists, market analysts, mathematicians, systems analysts, and more.

★2459★ Choosing a Career in Computers
Rosen Publishing Group, Inc.
29 E. 21st St.
New York, NY 10010
Ph: (212)777-3017   Fax: (212)777-0277
Fr: 800-237-9932
Weigant, Chris. 2000. $17.95.

★2460★ Coordinator of Computer Services
National Learning Corp.
212 Michael Dr.
Syosset, NY 11791
Ph: (516)921-8888   Fax: (516)921-8743
Fr: 800-645-6337
Jack Rudman. 1997. $39.95 (paper). Part of the Career Examination Series.

★2461★ The Digital Frontier Job & Opportunity Finder
Moon Lake Media
PO Box 251466
Los Angeles, CA 90025
Ph: (310)535-2453
Don B. Altman. 1996. $19.95 (paper). 256 pages.

★2462★ Expert Resumes for Computer and Web Jobs
JIST Publishing
8902 Otis Ave.
Indianapolis, IN 46216-1033
Ph: (317)613-4200   Fax: (317)613-4307
Fr: 800-648-5478
Wendy Enelow and Louis Kursmark. 2001. $16.95 (paper).

★2463★ Exploring Careers in the Computer Field
Rosen Publishing Group, Inc.
29 E 21st St.
New York, NY 10010
Ph: (212)777-3017   Fax: 888-436-4643
Fr: 800-237-9932
Joseph Weintraub. Revised edition, 1993. $14.95; $9.95 (paper). Discusses entry into the field, salaries, future trends, and offers job search advice. Surveys the newest growth areas in the computer industry including artificial intelligence, desktop publishing, and personal computers. Out of stock.

★2464★ Exploring High-Tech Careers
Rosen Publishing Group, Inc.
29 E. 21st St.
New York, NY 10010
Ph: (212)777-3017   Fax: (212)777-0277
Fr: 800-237-9932
Scott Southworth. Revised edition, 1993. $14.95; $9.95 (paper). 118 pages. Out of print. Gives an orientation to the field of high technology and high-tech jobs. Describes educational preparation and job hunting. Includes a glossary and bibliography.

★2465★ Get Your IT Career in Gear!
McGraw-Hill Professional
2 Penn Plaza
New York, NY 10121
Ph: (212)904-2000
Leslie Goff. 2001. $24.99 (paper).

★2466★ Great Jobs for Computer Science Majors
McGraw-Hill Companies
1221 Avenue of the Americas
New York, NY 10020
Ph: (212)904-2000   Fr: 800-323-4900
E-mail: ntcpub@tribune.com
Jan Goldberg, Stephen Lambert, Julie De-Galan. 1997. $11.95 (paper). 365 pages.

★2467★ How to Be a Successful Computer Consultant
McGraw-Hill Companies
860 Taylor Station Rd.
Blacklick, OH 43004-0545
Fax: (614)755-5645   Fr: 800-722-4726
Walid Mougayar and Alan R. Simon. Fourth edition, revised, 1998. $29.95 (paper). Out of print.

★2468★ *Job Seekers Guide to Silicon Valley Recruiters*

John Wily and Sons, Inc.
605 Third Ave., 4th Fl.
New York, NY 10158-0012
Ph: (212)850-6276   Fax: (212)850-8641

Christopher W. Hunt, Scott A. Scanlon. First edition, 1998. $19.95 (paper). 371 pages. Includes a list of 2,400 recruiters specializing in high technology positions and explains how to work with them.

★2469★ *The JobBank Guide to Computer and High-Tech Companies*

Adams Media Corp.
57 Littlefield St.
Avon, MA 02322
Ph: (508)427-7100   Fax: (508)427-6790
Fr: 800-872-5627
URL: http://www.adamsmedia.com

Second edition, 1999. $17.95 (paper). 704 pages. Contains profiles of more than 4,500 high-tech employers.

★2470★ *Opportunities in Computer Careers*

McGraw-Hill Professional
2 Penn Plaza
New York, NY 10121-2298
Ph: (212)904-2000   Fr: 800-722-4726

Julie Kling Burns. $12.95 (netLibrary). Computer vocational guidance and counseling.

★2471★ *Opportunities in Computer Systems Careers*

McGraw-Hill Contemporary Books
1221 Avenue of the Americas
New York, NY 10020
Ph: (212)904-2000   Fr: 800-323-4900
E-mail: ntcpub@tribune.com

Julie King Burns. 1996. $14.95; $11.95 (paper). 160 pages.

★2472★ *Opportunities in High Tech Careers*

McGraw-Hill Trade
2 Penn Plaza
New York, NY 10121
Ph: (212)904-2000   Fr: 800-722-4726

Gary Colter and Deborah Yanuck. 1995. $14.95; $11.95 (paper). 160 pages. Explores high technology careers. Describes job opportunities, how to make a career decision, how to prepare for high technology jobs, job hunting techniques, and future trends.

★2473★ *Opportunities in Office Occupations*

McGraw-Hill Trade
2 Penn Plaza
New York, NY 10121
Ph: (212)904-2000   Fr: 800-722-4726

Blanche Ettinger. 1994. $14.95; $11.95 (paper). 200 pages. Covers a variety of office positions and discusses trends for the next decade. Describes the job market, opportunities, job duties, educational preparation, the work environment, and earnings.

★2474★ *Preparing for an Outstanding Career in Computers: Questions and Answers for Professionals and Students*

Rafi Systems, Incorporated
750 N. Diamond Bar Blvd., Suite 224
Diamond Bar, CA 91765
Ph: (909)593-8124   Fax: (909)629-1034
Fr: 800-584-6706

Mohamed Rafiquzzaman. 2001. $19.95.

★2475★ *Unlocking the Clubhouse: Women in Computing*

MIT Press
5 Cambridge Ctr., Suite 4
Cambridge, MA 02142-1493
Ph: (617)253-5646   Fax: (617)253-6779
Fr: 800-356-0343

Jane Margolis and Allan Fisher. 2001. $24.95.

★2476★ *The Unofficial Guide to Getting a Job at Microsoft*

McGraw-Hill Education Group
800 Taylor Staion Rd.
Blacklick, OH 43004-0545
Fax: (614)755-5645   Fr: 800-722-4726

Rebecca Smith. 2000. $16.95 (paper).

★2477★ *Where the Jobs Are: The Hottest Careers for the 90s*

The Career Press, Inc.
3 Tice Rd.
PO Box 687
Franklin Lakes, NJ 07417-1322
Ph: (201)848-0310   Fax: (201)848-1727
Fr: 800-227-3371

Joyce Hadley. Third edition, 2000. $13.99 (paper). 400 pages. Out of print. Describes careers in fifteen general fields, from accounting to travel and hospitality.

★2478★ *Winning Resumes for Computer Personnel*

Barron's Educational Series, Inc.
250 Wireless Blvd.
Hauppauge, NY 11788-3917
Ph: (631)434-3311   Fax: (631)434-3723
Fr: 800-645-3476

Anne Hart. Second edition, 1998. $12.95 (paper). 320 pages.

★2479★ *Your Opportunities in Computers*

Energeia Publishing, Inc.
1307 Fairmount Ave., S
Salem, OR 97302-4313
Ph: (503)362-1480   Fax: (503)362-2123
Fr: 800-639-6048

John Tribbett. 1994. $2.50 (paper). 8 pages.

EMPLOYMENT AGENCIES AND SEARCH FIRMS

★2480★ **Ashton Computer Professionals Inc.**

15 Chesterfield, Pl. C
North Vancouver, BC, Canada V7M 3K3
Ph: (604)904-0304   Fax: (604)904-0305

Provides personnel recruitment and temporary contract services, specializing in advanced computer technology based fields, i.e., management information services, software engineering, product manufacturing, telecommunications, management personnel in all technology based disciplines. Serves private industries as well as government agencies.

★2481★ **The Aspire Group**

52 Second Ave, 1st Fl
Waltham, MA 02451-1129
Fax: (718)890-1810   Fr: 800-546-5675
URL: http://www.bmanet.com

Employment agency.

★2482★ **Carol Maden Group**

2019 Cunningham Dr., Ste. 218
Hampton, VA 23666
Ph: (757)827-9010   Fax: (757)827-9081

Personnel consultants offering placement service in computer technology and engineering, servicing manufacturing and private industries nationwide. Temporary placement servicing clerical and light industrial.

★2483★ **CNR Search**

4535 Saddlehorn Dr.
Reno, NV 89511
Ph: (775)851-2829   Fax: (775)851-4514

Provides staffing services of permanent and temporary employees. Works primarily on a retained basis. Contingency on a limited basis. Active in providing human resources consulting services. Also active in mergers and acquisitions in high technology firms. Industries served: computer; information services; insurance, pharmaceutical and health care.

★2484★ **Data Systems Search Consultants**

1615 Bonanza St., Ste.205
Walnut Creek, CA 94596
Ph: (925)256-0635   Fax: (925)256-9099
E-mail: dsscinfo@dssc.com
URL: http://www.dssc.com

Employment agency. Executive search firm.

★2485★ **The Datafinders Group, Inc.**

25 E Spring Valley Ave.,Fl.3
Maywood, NJ 07607
Ph: (201)845-7700   Fax: (201)845-7365
E-mail: info@datafinders.net

URL: http://www.datafinders.net

Executive search firm.

★2486★ **Dean Associates**
PO Box 1079
Santa Cruz, CA 95061
Ph: (831)423-2931

Executive search firm focused on the high technology industry.

★2487★ **Jim Ward Associates**
35 Browning Ave.
Toronto, ON, Canada M4K 1V8
Ph: (416)463-1661   Fax: (416)463-1688

Placement service provides careers and contract positions and professionals specifically related to the computing field. Industries served: various industries from government to small business; including banking, service, retail, distribution, manufacturing that use central, distributed or network computing facilities.

★2488★ **Romac International, Inc.**
1001 E Palm Ave
Tampa, FL 33605
Ph: (813)552-5239   Fax: (813)552-2122
URL: http://www.romac.com

Executive search firm. More than 30 locations throughout the United States.

★2489★ **Sullivan and Cogliano**
230 2nd Ave
Waltham, MA 02451
Ph: (781)890-7890   Fr: 888-785-2641
E-mail: contact@sullivansogliano.com
URL: http://www.sullivancogliano.com

Executive search firm.

★2490★ **Technical Talent Locators Ltd.**
5570 Sterrett Place, Ste.208
Columbia, MD 21044
Ph: (410)740-0091
URL: http://www.ttlgroup.com

Permanent employment agency working within the following fields: software and database engineering; computer, communication, and telecommunication system engineering; and other computer-related disciplines.

★2491★ **Techsearch Services, Inc.**
46 Wickford Pl.
Madison, CT 06443
Ph: (203)318-1100   Fax: (203)318-8800
E-mail: dtaft@snet.net
URL: http://www.techsearchservices.com

Executive search firm.

★2492★ **TRC Staffing Services Inc.**
2110 15 Mile Rd., Ste. B
Sterling Heights, MI 48310
Ph: (586)939-3210   Fax: (586)978-0572

A full-service executive search company with permanent placements encompassing engineering, industrial sales, financial and computer science positions. Screen, interview, and verify past employment for all candidates prior to referral. Also assist personnel staffs in the attainment of their EEO/AAP goals with the placement of talented individuals in positions which are underutilized with minorities and/or women. In addition, firm has a clerical temporary service division, TRC Temporary Service; and an employment agency, TRC Staffing Services.

★2493★ **Tri-Serv Inc.**
22 W. Padonia Rd., Ste. C-353
Timonium, MD 21093
Ph: (410)561-1740   Fax: (410)252-7417
E-mail: info@tri-serv.coom
URL: http://www.tri-serv.com

Permanent employment agency.

★2494★ **Worlco Computer Resources, Inc.**
997 Old Eagle School Rd., Ste. 219
Wayne, PA 19087-1706
Ph: (610)293-9070   Fax: (610)293-1027
E-mail: parisi@worlco.com
URL: http://www.worlco.com

Employment agency and executive search firm. Second location in Cherry Hill, New Jersey.

ONLINE JOB SOURCES AND SERVICES

★2495★ **ComputerJobs.com**
URL: http://www.computerjobs.com

Description: The site is an employment tool for technology professionals. Information on positions is updated hourly for seekers. Jobs may be searched by skill, or by location nationally or in a specific state or city job market. Contains thousands of job postings. National jobs may be posted for free. Also career resources for IT professionals.

★2496★ **Computerwork.com**
E-mail: candidate_support@computerwork.com
URL: http://computerwork.com/

Description: Job search and resume submission service for professionals in information technology.

★2497★ **Computerworld Careers**
URL: http://www.computerworld.com/cwi/careers/

Description: Offers career opportunities for IT (information technology) professionals. Job seekers may search the jobs database, register at the site, and read about job surveys and employment trends. Employers may post jobs.

★2498★ **Computing Research Association Job Announcements**
URL: http://www.cra.org/main/cra.jobs.html

Description: Contains dated links to national college and university computer technology positions.

★2499★ **Guru**
URL: http://www.guru.com

Description: Job board specializing in contract jobs for creative and information technology professionals. Also provides online incorporation and educational opportunities for independent contractors along with articles and advice.

★2500★ **Jobs for Programmers**
E-mail: prgjobs@jfpresources.com
URL: http://www.prgjobs.com

Description: Job board site for computer programmers that allows them to browse through thousands of programming jobs, even search for special jobs with sign-on bonuses, relocation funding, and 4-day work weeks. Resume posting is free.

★2501★ **ZDNet Tech Jobs**
URL: http://www.zdnet.com/special/filters/techjobs/

Description: Site houses a listing of national employment opportunities for professionals in high tech fields. Also contains resume building tips and relocation resources. Powered by Dice.com

TRADESHOWS

★2502★ **XPLOR Conference**
XPLOR International
24238 Hawthorne Blvd.
Torrance, CA 90505-6505
Ph: (310)791-9521   Fax: (310)375-4240
Fr: 800-669-7567
E-mail: info@xplor.org
URL: http://www.xplor.org

Annual. **Primary Exhibits:** Equipment, supplies, and services for users and manufacturers of advanced electronic document systems.

OTHER SOURCES

★2503★ Association of Computer Professionals (ACP)

9 Forest Dr.
Plainview, NY 11803
Ph: (516)938-8223   Fax: (516)938-3073
E-mail: sybosworth@aol.com

Members: Authors, consultants, programmers, publishers, and teachers in the computer field who provide products or services to users or to other professionals. **Purpose:** Works to advance the art and science of computer professionals through educational means. Encourages education and instruction of the public regarding what the association views as the beneficial use of computers and computer technology. **Activities:** Provides members with information on accounting, business management, creative marketing techniques, law, microcomputer advances, tax matters, technical developments, and special earning opportunities. Addresses issues of software protection, contract law, tax benefits, potential tax problems, and financial subjects such as sources of capital for new ventures and expanding businesses.

★2504★ Association of Information Technology Professionals

401 N Michigan Ave., Ste. 2400
PO Box 809189
Chicago, IL 60611-4267
Ph: (312)245-1070   Fax: (312)527-6636
Fr: 800-224-9371
E-mail: aitp_hq@aitp.org
URL: http://www.aitp.org

Members: Managerial personnel, staff, educators, and individuals interested in the management of information resources. Founder of the Certificate in Data Processing examination program, now administered by an intersociety organization. **Purpose:** Maintains Legislative Communications Network. Professional education programs include EDP-oriented business and management principles self-study courses and a series of videotaped management development seminars. Sponsors student organizations around the country interested in information technology and encourages members to serve as counselors for the Scout computer merit badge. Conducts research projects, including a business information systems curriculum for two- and four-year colleges.

★2505★ Association for Women in Computing (AWC)

41 Sutter St., Ste. 1006
San Francisco, CA 94104
Ph: (415)905-4663
E-mail: info@awc-hq.org
URL: http://www.awc-hq.org

Members: Individuals interested in promoting the education, professional development, and advancement of women in computing.

★2506★ Black Data Processing Associates (BDPA)

6301 Ivy Ln., Ste. 700
Greenbelt, MD 20770
Ph: (301)220-2180   Fax: (301)220-2185
Fr: 800-727-BDPA
E-mail: president@bdpa.org
URL: http://www.bdpa.org

Description: Persons employed in the information processing industry, including electronic data processing, electronic word processing, and data communications; others interested in information processing. Seeks to accumulate and share information processing knowledge and business expertise in order to increase the career and business potential of minorities in the information processing field. Conducts professional seminars, workshops, tutoring services, and community introductions to data processing. Makes annual donation to the United Negro College Fund.

★2507★ Computer Occupations

Delphi Productions
3160 4th St.
Boulder, CO 80304
Fax: (303)443-4022   Fr: 888-443-2400
URL: http://www.delphivideo.com

$95.00. 50 minutes. Part of the Careers for the 21st Century Video Library.

★2508★ Information Technology Occupations

Delphi Productions
3160 4th St.
Boulder, CO 80304
Fax: (303)443-4022   Fr: 888-443-2400
URL: http://www.delphivideo.com

$95.00. 52 minutes. Part of the Emerging Careers Video Library.

★2509★ Information Technology Services

Cambridge Educational
2572 Brunswick Ave.
Lawrenceville, NJ 08648-4128
Fax: 800-FAX-ON-US   Fr: 800-468-4227

URL: http://www.cambridgeeducational.com

$89.95. 2002. 18 minutes. Part of the Career Cluster Series.

★2510★ Institute for Certification of Computing Professionals (ICCP)

2350 E Devon Ave., Ste. 115
Des Plaines, IL 60018-4610
Ph: (847)299-4227   Fax: (847)299-4280
Fr: 800-U-GET-CCP
E-mail: office@iccp.org
URL: http://www.iccp.org

Members: Professional societies united to promote the development of computer examinations which are of high quality, directed toward information technology professionals, and designed to encourage competence and professionalism. Individuals passing the exams automatically become members of the Institute for Certification of Computing Professionals. Individuals passing exams become certified as CCP or ACP. **Activities:** Has developed code of ethics and good practice to which those taking the exams promise to adhere. Maintains speakers' bureau; compiles statistics.

★2511★ Resumes for High Tech Careers

Vgm Career Horizons
1221 Avenue of the Americas
New York, NY 10020
Ph: (212)904-2000   Fr: 800-323-4900
E-mail: ntcpub@tribune.com

Second edition, 1997. $9.95 (paper). 462 pages. Demonstrates how to tailor a resume that catches a high tech employer's attention. Part of Resumes for... series.

★2512★ Special Interest Group for Computers and the Physically Handicapped (SIGCAPH)

Church St. Sta.
PO Box 12115
New York, NY 10249
Ph: (212)626-0500   Fax: (212)944-1318
E-mail: chair_sigcaph@acm.org
URL: http://www.acm.org/sigcaph

Description: Promotes the professional interests of computing personnel with physical disabilities and the application of computing & information technology in solving relevant disability problems. Studies to educate the public to support careers for the disabled.

Construction and Building Inspectors

SOURCES OF HELP-WANTED ADS

★2513★ American City and County
Primedia Business
6151 Powers Ferry Rd.
Atlanta, GA 30339
Ph: (770)955-2500   Fax: (770)618-0348

Monthly. $67.00/year for individuals. Municipal and county administration magazine.

★2514★ American Professional Constructor
American Institute of Constructors
466 94th Ave. N
St. Petersburg, FL 33702
Ph: (727)578-0317   Fax: (727)578-9982

Biennial. Subscription included in membership; $100.00/year for nonmembers; $50.00 for single issue. Journal covering general interest and technical articles for construction professionals.

★2515★ Architectural West
Dodson Publications Inc.
546 Court St.
Reno, NV 89501
Ph: (775)333-1080   Fax: (775)333-1081
URL: http://www.architecturalwest.com

Bimonthly. $12.00/year for individuals. Trade magazine covering issues for architects and specifiers of exterior building materials in the western United States.

★2516★ BIA News
Brick Industry Association
11490 Commerce Park Dr., Ste. 300
Reston, VA 20191
Ph: (703)620-0010   Fax: (703)620-3928

Monthly. $30.00/year. Trade publication covering issues for the brick industry.

★2517★ Builder
Hanley-Wood L.L.C.
1 Thomas Cir., Ste. 600
Washington, DC 20005
Ph: (202)452-0800   Fax: (202)785-1974
URL: http://www.builderonline.com

Monthly. $29.95/year for individuals. Magazine covering housing and construction industry.

★2518★ CEE News
Primedia Business
9800 Metcalf Ave.
Overland Park, KS 66212
Ph: (913)341-1300   Fax: (913)967-1898

Monthly. Free to qualified subscribers; $52.00/year; $92.00/year for other countries. Electrical construction industry magazine.

★2519★ Civil Engineering-ASCE
American Society of Civil Engineers
1801 Alexander Bell Dr.
Reston, VA 20191
Ph: (703)295-6300   Fax: (703)295-6222
Fr: 800-548-2723
E-mail: ztrem@ce.udel.edu
URL: http://www.pubs.asce.org/ceonline/newce.html

Monthly. $30.00/year for members; $160.00/year for individuals; $160.00/year for institutions, nonmembers; $205.00/year for out of country; $50.00/year for foreign members; $205.00/year for institutions, other countries. Professional magazine.

★2520★ Construction Claims Monthly
Business Publishers Inc.
8737 Colesville Rd., Ste. 1100
Silver Spring, MD 20910-3928
Ph: (301)589-5103   Fax: (301)589-8493
Fr: 800-274-6737
URL: http://ex.bpinews.com/ccm

Description: Monthly. Covers significant legal developments governing contract payment and performance. Features an article on construction claims law; summaries of recent decisions with expert commentary; and highlights of actions by the federal boards of contract appeals and the Comptroller General.

★2521★ Construction Digest
Construction Digest
5804 W 74th St.
Indianapolis, IN 46278
Ph: (317)293-6860   Fax: (317)293-7840
Fr: 888-893-6860

Semimonthly. $3.00 for single issue. Magazine for the public works and construction engineering industries.

★2522★ CONSTRUCTOR
Associated General Contractors Information
333 John Carlyle St., Ste. 200
Alexandria, VA 22314
Ph: (703)837-5355   Fax: (703)837-5402
URL: http://www.agc.org

Monthly. $15.00/year for members; $250.00/year for nonmembers; $4.00/year for single issue except July, November, and December; $25.00/year for single issue-November, December; $325.00 for single issue-July. Management magazine for the Construction Industry.

★2523★ Consulting-Specifying Engineer
Reed Business Information
360 Park Ave. S
New York, NY 10014
Ph: (646)746-7764
URL: http://www.csemag.com/index.asp?webzine=cse&publication=cse

The integrated engineering magazine of the building construction industry.

★2524★ Engineering Times
National Society of Professional Engineers
1420 King St.
Alexandria, VA 22314
Ph: (703)684-2875   Fax: (703)836-4875
E-mail: et@nspe.org
URL: http://http//:www.nspc.org/1et.asp

$30.00/year for individuals; $48.00/year for out of country. Magazine (tabloid) covering professional, legislative, and techology issues for an engineering audience.

★2525★ **ENR: Engineering News-Record**
McGraw-Hill Companies
1221 Avenue of the Americas
New York, NY 10020
Ph: (212)512-2000
URL: http://www.enr.com

Weekly. $74.00/year; $5.00 for single issue. Magazine focusing on engineering and construction.

★2526★ **Home Builder Newsletter**
Home Builders Association of Greater New Orleans
2424 N Arnoult Rd.
Metairie, LA 70001
Ph: (504)837-2700   Fax: (504)837-4663

Description: Monthly. Contains information of interest to the New Orleans area residential construction industry. Covers the activities of the Association. Recurring features include letters to the editor, news of research, a calendar of events, reports of meetings, news of educational opportunities, and job listings.

★2527★ **Kitchen and Bath Business**
VNU Business Media
770 Broadway
New York, NY 10003-9595
Ph: (646)654-5000
URL: http://www.kitchen-bath.com

Monthly. $35.00/year for qualified subscribers; $65.00/year for others. Trade magazine on kitchen and bath remodeling and construction.

★2528★ **The Municipality**
League of Wisconsin Municipalities
202 State St., Ste. 300
Madison, WI 53703-2215
Ph: (608)267-2380   Fax: (608)267-0645
Fr: 800-991-5502

Monthly. $12.00/year. Magazine for officials of Wisconsin's local municipal governments.

★2529★ **NAHRO Monitor**
National Association of Housing and Redevelopment Officials
630 I St. NW
Washington, DC 20001-3736
Ph: (202)289-3500   Fax: (202)289-8181
Fr: 877-866-2476
URL: http://www.nahro.org

Description: Semimonthly. Disseminates news on low-income housing and community development issues. Intended for member professionals and government officials.

★2530★ **The NAWIC Image**
National Association of Women in Construction (NAWIC)
327 S Adams St.
Fort Worth, TX 76104-1002
Ph: (817)877-5551   Fax: (817)877-0324
Fr: 800-552-3506

Description: Bimonthly. Fosters career advancement for women in construction. Features women business owners, training for construction trades and educational programs. Recurring features include columns titled "Issues and Trends," "Road to Success," "Chapter Highlights," "Members on the Move," and "Q&A."

★2531★ **Professional Builder**
Reed Business Information
360 Park Ave. S
New York, NY 10014
Ph: (646)746-7764
URL: http://www.probuilder.com

Monthly. $10.00 for single issue; $139.95/year for by mail.

★2532★ **Remodeling**
Hanley-Wood L.L.C.
1 Thomas Cir., Ste. 600
Washington, DC 20005
Ph: (202)452-0800   Fax: (202)785-1974
URL: http://www.remodeling.hw.net

Monthly. $24.95/year for individuals; $8.00 for single issue. Trade magazine for the professional remodeling industry.

★2533★ **Roofing Contractor**
BNP Media, Inc.
2401 W Big Beaver Rd., Ste. 700
Troy, MI 48084
Ph: (248)362-3700   Fax: (248)362-0317
URL: http://www.roofingcontractor.com/

Monthly. Trade publication covering roofing and the construction industry.

★2534★ **Western City**
League of California Cities
1400 K St., 4th Fl.
Sacramento, CA 95814
Ph: (916)658-8223   Fax: (916)658-8289
Fr: 800-262-1801
URL: http://www.westerncity.com

Monthly. $39.00/year for individuals; $63.00 for two years. Municipal interest magazine.

PLACEMENT AND JOB REFERRAL SERVICES

★2535★ **Building Officials and Code Administrators International (BOCA)**
4051 W Flossmoor Rd.
Country Club Hills, IL 60478
Ph: (708)799-2300   Fax: 800-214-7167
Fr: 800-214-4321

E-mail: webmaster@iccstate.org
URL: http://www.bocai.org

Members: Governmental officials and agencies and other interests concerned with administering or formulating building, fire, mechanical, plumbing, zoning, housing regulations. **Purpose:** Promulgates the BOCA National Codes and the ICC International Codes suitable for adoption by reference by governmental entities. **Activities:** Provides services for maintaining the codes up-to-date. Supplies information on quality and acceptability of building materials and systems and on new construction techniques and materials. Maintains services for all members in connection with codes and their administration; provides consulting, training and education, plan review, and other advisory services; conducts correspondence courses; prepares in-service training programs and assists local organizations in such activities. Maintains placement services.

★2536★ **Professional Women in Construction (PWC)**
315 E. 56th St.
New York, NY 10022-3730
Ph: (212)486-7745   Fax: (212)486-0228
E-mail: pwcusa1@aol.com
URL: http://www.pwcusa.org

Description: Management-level women and men in construction and allied industries; owners, suppliers, architects, engineers, field personnel, office personnel, and bonding/surety personnel. Provides a forum for exchange of ideas and promotion of political and legislative action, education, and job opportunities for women in construction and related fields; forms liaisons with other trade and professional groups; develops research programs. Strives to reform abuses and to assure justice and equity within the construction industry. Sponsors mini-workshops. Maintains Action Line which provides members with current information on pertinent legislation and on the association's activities and job referrals.

EMPLOYER DIRECTORIES AND NETWORKING LISTS

★2537★ **ABC Today-Associated Builders and Contractors National Membership Directory Issue**
Associated Builders & Contractors Inc.
4250 N Fairfax Dr., 9th Fl.
Arlington, VA 22203
Ph: (703)812-2000   Fax: (703)812-8203

Annual, December. $150.00. Publication includes: List of approximately 19,000 member construction contractors and suppliers. Entries include: Company name, address, phone, name of principal executive, code to volume of business, business specialty. Arrangement: Classified by chapter, then by work specialty.

★2538★ Constructor-AGC Directory of Membership and Services Issue

AGC Information Inc.
333 John Carlyle St., Ste. 200
Alexandria, VA 22314
Ph: (703)548-3118   Fax: (703)548-3119
URL: http://www.agc.org

Annual, July. $250.00 for nonmembers; $15.00 for members; $250.00 for other countries. Publication includes: List of over 8,500 member firms and 24,000 national associate member firms engaged in building, highway, heavy, industrial, municipal utilities, and railroad construction (SIC 1541, 1542, 1611, 1622, 1623, 1629); listing of state and local chapter officers. Entries include: For firms-Company name, address, phone, fax, names of principal executives, and code indicating type of construction undertaken. For officers-Name, title, address. Arrangement: Geographical, Alphabetical. Indexes: Company name.

★2539★ ENR-Top 400 Construction Contractors Issue

McGraw-Hill Companies
1221 Ave. of the Americas
New York, NY 10020
Ph: (212)512-2000   Fax: (212)512-3840

Annual, May issue of "Engineering News Record". $10.00. Publication includes: List of 400 United States contractors receiving largest dollar volumes of contracts in preceding calendar year. Separate lists of 50 largest design/construct management firms; 50 largest program and construction managers; 25 building contractors; 25 heavy contractors. Entries include: Company name, headquarters location, total value of contracts received in preceding year, value of foreign contracts, countries in which operated, construction specialities. Arrangement: By total value of contracts received.

★2540★ Inspection Service Directory

infoUSA Inc.
5711 S 86th Cir.
Omaha, NE 68127-0347
Ph: (402)930-3500   Fax: (402)331-0176
Fr: 800-555-6124
URL: http://www.abii.com

Updated continuously; printed on request. Number of listings: 3,189. Entries include: Name, address, phone, size of advertisement, name of owner or manager, number of employees, year first in "Yellow Pages." Compiled from telephone company "Yellow Pages," nationwide. Arrangement: Geographical.

HANDBOOKS AND MANUALS

★2541★ AEC Workforce Guide to Find the Right the Right Job in the Design and Construction Industry

Zweig White
One Apple Hill Dr.
Natick, MA 01760
Ph: (508)651-1559   Fax: (503)653-6522
Fr: 800-466-6275

$23.95. 240 pages. Handbook for job hunters in the design and construction industry.

★2542★ Building Professionals: Creating a Successful Portfolio

Prentice Hall PTR
240 Frisch Ct.
Paramus, NJ 07652-5240
Fax: 800-835-5327   Fr: 800-282-0693

Diane J. Orton, Tammy Freelin, Fresa J. Jacobs, Robin R. Wingo. September 2002. 61 pages.

★2543★ Careers in the Building and Construction Industry

The Rosen Publishing Group, Inc.
29 E. 21st St.
New York, NY 10010
Ph: (212)777-3017   Fax: (212)777-0277
Fr: 800-237-9932

Melanie Ann Apel. December 2004.

★2544★ Exploring Careers in Construction

Prentice Hall PTR
200 Old Tappan Rd.
Old Tappan, NJ 07675
Ph: (201)236-7000   Fr: 800-223-1360

1998. $12.00. 94 pages.

★2545★ Opportunities in Building Construction Trades

McGraw-Hill Trade
2 Penn Plaza
New York, NY 10121
Ph: (212)904-2000   Fr: 800-722-4726

Michael Sumichrast. Second edition, 1998. $14.95; $11.95 (paper). 202 pages. From custom builder to rehabber, the many kinds of companies that employ craftspeople and contractors are explored. Includes job descriptions, requirements, and salaries for dozens of specialties within the construction industry. Contains a complete list of Bureau of Apprenticeship and Training state and area offices. Illustrated.

★2546★ Opportunities in State and Local Government Careers

Vgm Career Horizons
1221 Avenue of the Americas
New York, NY 10020
Ph: (212)904-2000   Fr: 800-323-4900
E-mail: ntcpub@tribune.com

Neale J. Baxter. 1994. $14.95; $10.95 (paper). 160 pages. Points out the incentives and drawbacks of a government career. Describes hiring procedures and provides tips on filling out applications, taking physical and aptitude tests, handling interviews, and finding jobs. Describes the jobs in which 75% of all state and local government workers are employed. For each occupation, covers the nature of the work and the training required.

EMPLOYMENT AGENCIES AND SEARCH FIRMS

★2547★ Callaghan International Inc.

119 W. 57th St., Ste. 1220
New York, NY 10019
Ph: (212)265-9200   Fax: (212)265-0080

Executive search firm.

★2548★ Construction Executives Inc.

PO Box 231360
New Orleans, LA 70183
Ph: 888-800-6952

Executive search firm specifically for construction.

★2549★ Dudley & Associates

PO Box 1835
Addison, TX 75001
Ph: (214)560-2222   Fax: (972)818-1069

Executive search firm focused on construction and real estate industries.

★2550★ Frank Palma Associates

110 S. Jefferson Rd.
Whippany, NJ 07981
Ph: (973)884-1498   Fax: (973)884-1499

Executive search firm.

★2551★ Real Estate Executive Search, Inc.

PO Box 387
San Francisco, CA 94104-0387
Ph: (415)398-4116
E-mail: jhavrees@aol.com

Executive search firm for the real estate and finance fields.

★2552★ Specialized Search Associates

15200 Jog Rd., Ste. 201
Delray Beach, FL 33446
Ph: (561)499-3711   Fax: (561)499-3770
Fr: 888-405-2650
E-mail: lm7880@aol.com

Executive search firm that specializes in construction, engineering, and sales.

★2553★ 20-20 Foresight Executive Search Inc.
One Lincoln Centre
18 W. 140 Butterfield Rd., Fl. 15
Oakbrook Terrace, IL 60181
Ph: (708)246-2100

Executive search firm. Affiliate offices in CA and Washington DC.

ONLINE JOB SOURCES AND SERVICES

★2554★ Construction Education.com
URL: http://www.constructioneducation.com
Description: Includes link page with list of professional resources, employment opportunities listed by company, and construction-related recruiters' pages, as well as general job search websites. Also contains on-site job bank.

TRADESHOWS

★2555★ A/E/C Systems
A/E/C Systems International
356 N. Pottstown Pike, Ste. 200
Exton, PA 19341-2220
Ph: (610)458-7070   Fax: (610)458-7171
Fr: 800-451-1196
E-mail: info@aecsystems.com
URL: http://www.aecsystems.com

Annual. **Primary Exhibits:** Architects, designers, civil engineers, surveyors, power and process engineers, GIS, contractors, facilities managers/owners, mechanical and manufacturing engineers.

★2556★ Cincinnati Construction Expo
Industry Week
Penton Media, Inc.
1300 9th St. Ste. 316
Cleveland, OH 44114-1503
Ph: (513)528-1550   Fax: (513)528-1131
E-mail: exposource1@aol.com
URL: http://www.exposupersite.com

Annual. **Primary Exhibits:** Building products and services for architects, contractors, and builders.

★2557★ SBCCI Research and Education Conference
Southern Building Code Congress, International
900 Montclair Rd.
Birmingham, AL 35213
Ph: (205)591-1853   Fax: (205)591-0775
URL: http://www.sbcci.org

Annual. **Primary Exhibits:** Exhibits relating to uniformity in building regulations.

OTHER SOURCES

★2558★ American Society of Home Inspectors (ASHI)
932 Lee St., No. 101
Des Plaines, IL 60016-6546
Ph: (847)759-2820   Fax: (847)759-1620
Fr: 800-743-2744
E-mail: robp@ashi.org
URL: http://www.ashi.org
Description: Professional home inspectors whose goals are to establish home inspector qualifications, set standards of practice for home inspections, adhere to a code of ethics, keep the concept of "objective third party" intact, inform members of the most advanced methods and techniques. Conducts seminars through local chapters.

★2559★ Associated Builders and Contractors (ABC)
1300 N. 17th St., Ste. 800
Rosslyn, VA 22209
Ph: (703)812-2000   Fax: (703)812-8201
E-mail: info@abc.org
URL: http://www.abc.org
Description: Construction contractors, subcontractors, suppliers, and associates. Aim is to foster and perpetuate the principles of rewarding construction workers and management on the basis of merit. Sponsors management education programs and craft training; also sponsors apprenticeship and skill training programs. Disseminates technological and labor relations information.

★2560★ Associated General Contractors of America (AGC)
333 John Carlyle St., Ste. 200
Alexandria, VA 22314
Ph: (703)548-3118   Fax: (703)548-3119
E-mail: sandhers@agc.org
URL: http://www.agc.org
Description: General construction contractors; subcontractors; industry suppliers; service firms. Provides market services through its divisions. Conducts special conferences and seminars designed specifically for construction firms. Compiles statistics on job accidents reported by member firms. ors. Maintains 65 committees, including joint cooperative committees with other associations and liaison committees with federal agencies.

★2561★ *Construction and Building Inspectors*
Evon Publishing
832 N 7th Ave.
Iron River, MI 49935
Ph: (906)265-3190

Audiocassette. 1996. $16.95. 32 minutes. Part of the Careers and Vocational Guidance Series. Provides information about the nature of the work, educational requirements, employment outlook, earnings, and work conditions as well as additional related information.

★2562★ *The Construction Industry*
Evon Publishing
832 N 7th Ave.
Iron River, MI 49935
Ph: (906)265-3190

Audiocassette. 1996. $16.95. 32 minutes. Part of the Careers and Vocational Guidance Series. Provides information about the nature of the work, educational requirements, employment outlook, earnings, and work conditions as well as additional related information.

★2563★ International Conference of Building Officials (ICBO)
5360 Workman Mill Rd.
Whittier, CA 90601-2298
Ph: (562)699-0541   Fax: 888-329-4226
Fr: 800-284-4406
URL: http://www.icbo.org
Description: Representatives of local, regional, and state governments. Seeks to publish, maintain, and promote the Uniform Building Code and related documents; investigate and research principles underlying safety to life and property in the construction, use, and location of buildings and related structures; develop and promulgate uniformity in regulations pertaining to building construction; educate the building official; formulate guidelines for the administration of building inspection departments. Conducts training programs, courses, and certification programs for code enforcement inspectors. Maintains speakers' bureau.

★2564★ National Association of Home Builders (NAHB)
1201 15th St. NW
Washington, DC 20005
Ph: (202)266-8200   Fax: (202)822-0586
Fr: 800-368-5242
E-mail: info@nahb.com
URL: http://www.nahb.org
Description: Single and multifamily home builders, commercial builders, and others associated with the building industry. Lobbies on behalf of the housing industry and conducts public affairs activities to increase public understanding of housing and the economy. Collects and disseminates data on current developments in home building and home builders' plans through its Economics Department and nationwide Metropolitan Housing Forecast. Maintains NAHB Research Center, which functions as the research arm of the home building industry. Sponsors seminars and workshops on construction, mortgage credit, labor relations, cost reduction, land use, remodeling, and business management. Compiles statistics; offers charitable program, spokesman training, and placement service; maintains speakers' bureau, and Hall of Fame. Subsidiaries include the National Council of the Housing Industry. Maintains over 50 committees in many areas of construction; operates National Commercial Builders Council, National Council of the Multifamily Housing Industry, National Remodelers Council, and National Sales and Marketing Council.

★2565★ National Association of Women in Construction (NAWIC)
327 S Adams St.
Fort Worth, TX 76104
Ph: (817)877-5551   Fax: (817)877-0324
Fr: 800-552-3506
E-mail: nawic@nawic.org
URL: http://www.nawic.org

Description: Seeks to enhance the success of women in the construction industry.

★2566★ National Center for Construction Education and Research
3600 NW 43rd St., Bldg. G
PO Box 141104
Gainesville, FL 32606-1104
Ph: (352)334-0911   Fax: (352)334-0932
Fr: 888-NCCER-20
E-mail: info@nccer.org
URL: http://www.nccer.org

Description: Education foundation committed to the development and publication of Contren(TM) Learning Series, the source of craft training, management education and

safety resources for the construction industry.

★2567★ Southern Building Code Congress, International (SBCCI)
900 Montclair Rd.
Birmingham, AL 35213-1206
Ph: (205)591-1853   Fax: (205)591-0775
Fr: 800-214-4321
E-mail: info@sbcci.org
URL: http://www.sbcci.org

Members: Active members are state, county, municipal, or other government subdivisions (2,500); associate members are trade associations, architects, engineers, contractors, and related groups or persons (13,450). **Purpose:** Seeks to develop, maintain, and promote the adoption of the International Building, Residential Gas, Plumbing, Mechanical, Fire, and property maintenance Codes. Encourages uniformity in building regulations through the International Codes and their application and enforcement. **Activities:** Provides technical and educational services to members and others; participates in the development of nationally recognized

consensus standards. Provides research on new materials and methods of construction; conducts seminars on code enforcement, inspection, and special topics.

★2568★ Women in Building Construction
Her Own Words
PO Box 5264
Madison, WI 53705-0264
Ph: (608)271-7083   Fax: (608)271-0209
URL: http://www.herownwords.com/

Video. Jocelyn Riley. $95.00. 15 minutes. Resource guide also available for $45.00.

★2569★ Women in Nontraditional Careers: An Introduction
Her Own Words
PO Box 5264
Madison, WI 53705
Ph: (608)271-7083   Fax: (608)271-0209
URL: http://www.herownwords.com/

Video. Jocelyn Riley. $95.00. 15 minutes. Resource guide also available for $45.00.

Construction Managers

★2570★ American Professional Constructor

American Institute of Constructors
466 94th Ave. N
St. Petersburg, FL 33702
Ph: (727)578-0317   Fax: (727)578-9982
Biennial. Subscription included in membership; $100.00/year for nonmembers; $50.00 for single issue. Journal covering general interest and technical articles for construction professionals.

★2571★ Architectural West

Dodson Publications Inc.
546 Court St.
Reno, NV 89501
Ph: (775)333-1080   Fax: (775)333-1081
URL: http://www.architecturalwest.com
Bimonthly. $12.00/year for individuals. Trade magazine covering issues for architects and specifiers of exterior building materials in the western United States.

★2572★ BIA News

Brick Industry Association
11490 Commerce Park Dr., Ste. 300
Reston, VA 20191
Ph: (703)620-0010   Fax: (703)620-3928
Monthly. $30.00/year. Trade publication covering issues for the brick industry.

★2573★ CEE News

Primedia Business
9800 Metcalf Ave.
Overland Park, KS 66212
Ph: (913)341-1300   Fax: (913)967-1898
Monthly. Free to qualified subscribers; $52.00/year; $92.00/year for other countries. Electrical construction industry magazine.

★2574★ Construction Claims Monthly

Business Publishers Inc.
8737 Colesville Rd., Ste. 1100
Silver Spring, MD 20910-3928
Ph: (301)589-5103   Fax: (301)589-8493
Fr: 800-274-6737
URL: http://ex.bpinews.com/ccm
Description: Monthly. Covers significant legal developments governing contract payment and performance. Features an article on construction claims law; summaries of recent decisions with expert commentary; and highlights of actions by the federal boards of contract appeals and the Comptroller General.

★2575★ Construction Digest

Construction Digest
5804 W 74th St.
Indianapolis, IN 46278
Ph: (317)293-6860   Fax: (317)293-7840
Fr: 888-893-6860
Semimonthly. $3.00 for single issue. Magazine for the public works and construction engineering industries.

★2576★ Construction Division Newsletter

NSC Press
1121 Spring Lake Dr.
Itasca, IL 60143-3201
Ph: (630)285-1121   Fax: (630)285-1315
Fr: 800-621-7615
URL: http://www.nsc.org
Description: Bimonthly. Focuses on industrial and occupational safety in the construction industry. Carries items on such topics as safe work practices and products; accident prevention; and successful industrial safety programs and policies. Available online only.

★2577★ Contractors Guide

G & M Communications
1050 Illinois Rte. 63, Ste. 200
Bensenville, IL 60106-1096
Ph: (847)588-3333   Fax: (847)647-7055
URL: http://www.constructiongroup.com
Monthly. Free to qualified subscribers; $25.00/year for individuals; $5.00 for single

issue. Trade magazine on roofing and insulation.

★2578★ Design Cost Data

DC & D Technologies Inc.
8602 N 40th St.
Tampa, FL 33604
Ph: (813)989-9300   Fax: (813)980-3982
Fr: 800-533-5680
E-mail: webmaster@dcd.com
URL: http://www.dcd.com
Bimonthly. $84.40/year for individuals. Publication providing real cost data case studies of various types completed around the country for design and building professionals.

★2579★ Kitchen and Bath Business

VNU Business Media
770 Broadway
New York, NY 10003-9595
Ph: (646)654-5000
URL: http://www.kitchen-bath.com
Monthly. $35.00/year for qualified subscribers; $65.00/year for others. Trade magazine on kitchen and bath remodeling and construction.

★2580★ Remodeling

Hanley-Wood L.L.C.
1 Thomas Cir., Ste. 600
Washington, DC 20005
Ph: (202)452-0800   Fax: (202)785-1974
URL: http://www.remodeling.hw.net
Monthly. $24.95/year for individuals; $8.00 for single issue. Trade magazine for the professional remodeling industry.

★2581★ Roofing Contractor

BNP Media, Inc.
2401 W Big Beaver Rd., Ste. 700
Troy, MI 48084
Ph: (248)362-3700   Fax: (248)362-0317
URL: http://www.roofingcontractor.com/
Monthly. Trade publication covering roofing and the construction industry.

EMPLOYER DIRECTORIES AND NETWORKING LISTS

★2582★ Athletic Business-Professional Directory Section

Athletic Business Publications Inc.
4130 Lien Rd.
Madison, WI 53704
Ph: (608)249-0186   Fax: (608)249-1153
Fr: 800-722-8764

Monthly. $8.00. Publication includes: List of architects, engineers, contractors, and consultants in athletic facility planning and construction; all listings are paid. Entries include: Company name, address, phone, fax and short description of company. Arrangement: Alphabetical.

HANDBOOKS AND MANUALS

★2583★ AEC Workforce Guide to Find the Right the Right Job in the Design and Construction Industry

Zweig White
One Apple Hill Dr.
Natick, MA 01760
Ph: (508)651-1559   Fax: (503)653-6522
Fr: 800-466-6275

$23.95. 240 pages. Handbook for job hunters in the design and construction industry.

★2584★ Building Professionals: Creating a Successful Portfolio

Prentice Hall PTR
240 Frisch Ct.
Paramus, NJ 07652-5240
Fax: 800-835-5327   Fr: 800-282-0693

Diane J. Orton, Tammy Freelin, Fresa J. Jacobs, Robin R. Wingo. September 2002. 61 pages.

★2585★ Careers in the Building and Construction Industry

The Rosen Publishing Group, Inc.
29 E. 21st St.
New York, NY 10010
Ph: (212)777-3017   Fax: (212)777-0277
Fr: 800-237-9932

Melanie Ann Apel. December 2004.

★2586★ Construction Manager

National Learning Corporation
212 Michael Dr.
Syosset, NY 11791
Ph: (516)921-8888   Fax: (516)921-8743
Fr: 800-645-6337

Rudman, Jack. 1994. $39.95 (Trade paper).

EMPLOYMENT AGENCIES AND SEARCH FIRMS

★2587★ Adams Executive Search

3416 Fairfield Trail
Clearwater, FL 33761
Ph: (727)772-1536   Fr: (727)772-1537
Executive Search firm.

★2588★ AET Advisors LLC

3495 Piedmont Rd., NE Bldg 11, Ste. 824
Atlanta, GA 30305
Ph: (404)237-8208   Fax: (404)261-6961
Executive search and consultant firm. Focuses on the real estate industry.

★2589★ American Express Tax & Business Services

1 S. Wacker Dr., Ste. 800
Chicago, IL 60606
Ph: (312)634-4715   Fax: (312)634-5527
Executive search firm.

★2590★ The Cherbonnier Group Inc.

1 Riverway, Ste. 1700
Houston, TX 77056
Ph: (713)688-4701
Executive search firm.

★2591★ Commonwealth Resources Inc.

262 Washington St., Ste. 800
Boston, MA 02108
Ph: (617)250-1100   Fax: (617)250-1199
Executive search firm.

★2592★ Construction Executives Inc.

PO Box 231360
New Orleans, LA 70183
Ph: 888-800-6952
Executive search firm specifically for construction.

★2593★ The Consulting Group

366 Madison Ave., Fl. 10
New York, NY 10017
Ph: (212)751-8484   Fax: (212)692-9290
Executive search firm.

★2594★ Contractor Marketing

7600 Dayton Rd.
Fairborn, OH 45324-1904
Ph: (937)864-5854   Fax: (937)865-7017
Executive search firm.

★2595★ Cook Associates Inc.

212 W Kinzie St.
Chicago, IL 60610
Ph: (312)329-0900   Fax: (312)329-2422

Management and executive recruiting specialists offering a commitment to clients to find the best candidates and to find those candidates as efficiently as possible. Approach provides a flexible and effective structure that serves the special needs of both large and small companies. Serves the following industries: industrial, equipment manufacturer, food processing, graphic arts, chemical process, retailing, mechanical products, healthcare services, financial and professional services, legal, consumer products, construction and engineering, packaging, pulp and paper.

★2596★ Crown Advisors Inc.

239 Fort Pitt Blvd.
Pittsburgh, PA 15222
Ph: (412)566-1100   Fax: (412)566-1256
Executive search firm. Branch in Denver, CO.

★2597★ Dudley & Associates

PO Box 1835
Addison, TX 75001
Ph: (214)560-2222   Fax: (972)818-1069
Executive search firm focused on construction and real estate industries.

★2598★ Edward Dellon Associates Inc.

1801 Avenue of the Stars, Ste. 640
Los Angeles, CA 90067
Ph: (310)286-0625   Fax: (310)277-3069
Executive search firm.

★2599★ G Adams Partners

205 W. Wacker Dr., Ste. 810
Chicago, IL 60606
Ph: (312)673-0390   Fax: (312)673-0390
Executive search firm.

★2600★ HardHatJobs.com

1200 Executive Dr. E, Ste. 127-A
Richardson, TX 75081
Ph: (972)808-9200   Fax: (972)808-9203

Executive search and consulting for Commercial Construction, Construction Engineering and Construction Management professionals. Presidents, CEO's, COO's, Business Development, Executive Vice Presidents, VP, CFO's, Program, Project and Construction Managers, Superintendents, Schedulers, Project Accountants, Cost Controllers and Safety Engineers.

★2601★ John Dickerman and Associates

9030 Bronson Dr.
Potomac, MD 20854
Ph: (301)983-2546

Specializes in construction, real estate and housing; marketing of manufactured building materials and products; financing of homes, apartments, and related community elements. Involved in Federal government programs in housing and urban affairs. The firm has done numerous corporate acquisition and investment analyses, management studies, and executive search assignments in the field of building and manufacturing.

★2602★ McNichol Associates

620 Chestnut St., Ste. 1031
Philadelphia, PA 19106
Ph: (215)922-4142   Fax: (215)922-0178

Performs executive search for middle and senior-level management, marketing, and technical personnel for professioanl design firms; construction, management, and general contractors; engineering-construction organizations; environmental firms, and others needing technical mannagement personnel.

★2603★ Oliver & Rozner Associates

598 Madison Ave., Ste. 11
New York, NY 10022
Ph: (212)688-1850

Performs executive search for top tiers of management including presidents, general management, advertising account management, division management, group executive and vice presidential line positions in such areas as marketing, research, operations, sales, finance, human resources, and others; hard-to-find specialists including specific marketing/advertising executives, research and development expertise, computer/data processing knowledge, scientific, physicians-product efficacy and occupational medicine, and engineering. Industries served include pharmaceutical, healthcare, hospital, advertising, consumer products and packaged goods, housewares, direct selling, cosmetics/toiletries, industrial products, high technology products, forest products, engineering, construction, environment/resource recovery, graphic arts, chemical, and government agencies.

★2604★ Robert Howe and Associates

PO Box 450867
Atlanta, GA 31145-0867
Ph: (770)270-1211   Fax: (770)270-1209

Provides consulting services in the area of executive search and recruitment. Industries served: healthcare, hospitality, chemical, metals, electronics, construction, and food processing.

★2605★ The Sharrow Group

531 Ridge Rd. E
Rochester, NY 14621
Ph: (585)266-0993   Fr: 877-759-6910

Executive search firm offers specialized placement in areas of rubber, adhesives, plastic, coatings, paint, information technology, patent and trademark attorneys, and construction executives.

★2606★ 20-20 Foresight Executive Search Inc.

One Lincoln Centre
18 W. 140 Butterfield Rd., Fl. 15
Oakbrook Terrace, IL 60181
Ph: (708)246-2100

Executive search firm. Affiliate offices in CA and Washington DC.

ONLINE JOB SOURCES AND SERVICES

★2607★ Construction Education.com
URL: http://www.constructioneducation.com

Description: Includes link page with list of professional resources, employment opportunities listed by company, and construction-related recruiters' pages, as well as general job search websites. Also contains on-site job bank.

★2608★ Construction Management Association of America
URL: http://www.cmaanet.org

Description: Association website contains a job databank, professional resources books for sale, and career development seminars to attend. Must be a member to fully utilize site, which also includes more project leads, discussion forums, and more.

TRADESHOWS

★2609★ Buildings Show

Merchandise Mart Properties Inc.
The Merchandise Mart, Ste. 470
Chicago, IL 60654
Ph: (312)527-4141   Fax: (312)527-7782
Fr: 800-677-6278

Annual. **Primary Exhibits:** Building products and commercial furnishings and finishes.

★2610★ Cincinnati Construction Expo

Industry Week
Penton Media, Inc.
1300 9th St. Ste. 316
Cleveland, OH 44114-1503
Ph: (513)528-1550   Fax: (513)528-1131
E-mail: exposource1@aol.com

URL: http://www.exposupersite.com

Annual. **Primary Exhibits:** Building products and services for architects, contractors, and builders.

★2611★ CONEXPO-CON/AGG

Association of Equipment Manufacturers (AEM)
111 E. Wisconsin Ave., Ste. 1000
Milwaukee, WI 53202-4806
Ph: (414)272-0943   Fax: (414)272-2672
Fr: 800-867-6060
E-mail: info@conexpoconagg.com
URL: http://www.conexpoconagg.com

Triennial. **Primary Exhibits:** Construction and construction materials industry equipment, supplies, and services. **Dates and Locations:** 2005 Mar 15-19; Las Vegas, NV • 2008 Dates and location not set.

★2612★ Construction Financial Management Association Annual Conference and Exhibition

Construction Financial Management Association
29 Emmons Dr. F-50
Princeton, NJ 08540
Ph: (609)452-8000   Fax: (609)452-0417
URL: http://www.cfma.org

Annual. **Primary Exhibits:** Equipment, supplies, and services for the construction industry. **Dates and Locations:** 2005 Apr 21-25; Boston, MA; Marriott Copley Place • 2006 Apr 20-24; Las Vegas, NV; Caesars Palace.

★2613★ International Association of Structural Movers Convention

International Association of Structural Movers
117 Sylvan St.
PO Box 1213
Elbridge, NY 13060

Annual. **Primary Exhibits:** Heavy structural equipment, trusses, buildings, and machinery.

★2614★ MIACON - Miami International Construction Show/Expo

MIACON Construction Show, Inc.
2921 Coral Way
Miami, FL 33145
Ph: (305)441-2865   Fax: (305)529-9217
E-mail: mail@miacon.com
URL: http://www.miacon.com

Annual. **Primary Exhibits:** Equipment, machinery, building supplies, and services for the construction industry. **Dates and Locations:** 2004 Oct 29-31; Miami, FL.

★2615★ National Association of Demolition Contractors Annual Convention

National Association of Demolition Contractors
16 N. Franklin St., Ste. 203
Doylestown, PA 18901
Ph: (215)348-4949   Fax: (215)348-8422
Fr: 800-541-2412
E-mail: info@demolitionassociation.com
URL: http://www.demolitionassociation.com

Annual. **Primary Exhibits:** Demolition equipment, supplies, and services. **Dates and Locations:** 2005 Mar 06-09; Las Vegas, NV; The Mirage • 2006 Mar 26-29; Nashville, TN; Gaylord Opryland.

★2616★ SBCCI Research and Education Conference

Southern Building Code Congress, International
900 Montclair Rd.
Birmingham, AL 35213
Ph: (205)591-1853   Fax: (205)591-0775
URL: http://www.sbcci.org

Annual. **Primary Exhibits:** Exhibits relating to uniformity in building regulations.

★2617★ Southeast Roofing and Sheet Metal Spectacular Trade Exposition

Florida Roofing, Sheet Metal, and Air Conditioning Contractors Association - FRSA
Box 4850
Winter Park, FL 32793
Ph: (407)671-3772   Fax: (407)679-0010
URL: http://www.floridaroof.com

Annual. **Primary Exhibits:** Roofing and sheet metal supplies, products and services. **Dates and Locations:** 2005 Jul 20-23; Orlando, FL; Orange County Convention Center and Peabody Hotel.

★2618★ 21st Century Building Expo and Conference

North Carolina Home Builders Association
6716 Six Forks Rd.
PO Box 99090
Raleigh, NC 27624
Ph: (919)676-9090   Fax: (919)676-0402
Fr: 800-662-7129

Annual. **Primary Exhibits:** Exhibits relating to the promotion of safe, affordable housing across North Carolina.

★2619★ World Congress of the World Federation of Building Service Contractors

World Federation of Building Service Contractors
10201 Lee Hwy., Ste. 225
Fairfax, VA 22030
Ph: (703)359-7090   Fax: (703)352-0493
Fr: 800-368-3414

Biennial. **Primary Exhibits:** Floor care and carpet care equipment, building service con-tracting equipment, supplies, and services. **Dates and Locations:** 2004 Dates not set; Montreal, QC, Canada • 2006 Dates not set; Buenos Aires, Argentina.

OTHER SOURCES

★2620★ Administration and Management Occupations

Delphi Productions
3160 4th St.
Boulder, CO 80304
Fax: (303)443-4022   Fr: 888-443-2400
URL: http://www.delphivideo.com

$95.00. 50 minutes. Part of the Careers for the 21st Century Video Library.

★2621★ American Society of Home Inspectors (ASHI)

932 Lee St., No. 101
Des Plaines, IL 60016-6546
Ph: (847)759-2820   Fax: (847)759-1620
Fr: 800-743-2744
E-mail: robp@ashi.org
URL: http://www.ashi.org

Description: Professional home inspectors whose goals are to establish home inspector qualifications, set standards of practice for home inspections, adhere to a code of ethics, keep the concept of "objective third party" intact, inform members of the most advanced methods and techniques. Conducts seminars through local chapters.

★2622★ American Society of Professional Estimators (ASPE)

11141 Georgia Ave., Ste. 412
Wheaton, MD 20902
Ph: (301)929-8848   Fax: (301)929-0231
Fr: 888-378-6283
E-mail: info@aspenational.com
URL: http://www.aspenational.org

Description: Construction cost estimators. Develops professional and ethical standards in construction estimating. Offers continuing education to established professionals; provides certification for estimators.

★2623★ Associated Builders and Contractors (ABC)

1300 N. 17th St., Ste. 800
Rosslyn, VA 22209
Ph: (703)812-2000   Fax: (703)812-8201
E-mail: info@abc.org
URL: http://www.abc.org

Description: Construction contractors, sub-contractors, suppliers, and associates. Aim is to foster and perpetuate the principles of rewarding construction workers and management on the basis of merit. Sponsors management education programs and craft training; also sponsors apprenticeship and skill training programs. Disseminates tech-nological and labor relations information.

★2624★ Associated General Contractors of America (AGC)

333 John Carlyle St., Ste. 200
Alexandria, VA 22314
Ph: (703)548-3118   Fax: (703)548-3119
E-mail: sandhers@agc.org
URL: http://www.agc.org

Description: General construction contrac-tors; subcontractors; industry suppliers; ser-vice firms. Provides market services through its divisions. Conducts special conferences and seminars designed specifically for con-struction firms. Compiles statistics on job accidents reported by member firms. ors. Maintains 65 committees, including joint cooperative committees with other associa-tions and liaison committees with federal agencies.

★2625★ The Construction Industry

Evon Publishing
832 N 7th Ave.
Iron River, MI 49935
Ph: (906)265-3190

Audiocassette. 1996. $16.95. 32 minutes. Part of the Careers and Vocational Guidance Series. Provides information about the na-ture of the work, educational requirements, employment outlook, earnings, and work conditions as well as additional related infor-mation.

★2626★ Women in Building Construction

Her Own Words
PO Box 5264
Madison, WI 53705-0264
Ph: (608)271-7083   Fax: (608)271-0209
URL: http://www.herownwords.com/

Video. Jocelyn Riley. $95.00. 15 minutes. Resource guide also available for $45.00.

★2627★ Women in Highway Construction

Her Own Words
PO Box 5264
Madison, WI 53705-0264
Ph: (608)271-7083   Fax: (608)271-0209
URL: http://www.herownwords.com/

Video. Jocelyn Riley. $95.00. 15 minutes. Resource guide also available for $45.00.

★2628★ Women in Nontraditional Careers: An Introduction

Her Own Words
PO Box 5264
Madison, WI 53705
Ph: (608)271-7083   Fax: (608)271-0209
URL: http://www.herownwords.com/

Video. Jocelyn Riley. $95.00. 15 minutes. Resource guide also available for $45.00.

Correction Officers and Parole Officers

SOURCES OF HELP-WANTED ADS

★2629★ ACJS Today
Academy of Criminal Justice Sciences
402 Nunn Hall
Northern Kentucky University
Newport, KY 41099
Ph: (606)572-5634   Fax: (606)572-6665
Fr: 800-757-ACJS

Description: Four issues/year. Contains criminal justice information.

★2630★ American City and County
Primedia Business
6151 Powers Ferry Rd.
Atlanta, GA 30339
Ph: (770)955-2500   Fax: (770)618-0348

Monthly. $67.00/year for individuals. Municipal and county administration magazine.

★2631★ Criminal Justice Newsletter
Pace Publications
1900 L St. NW, Ste. 312
Washington, DC 20036
Ph: (202)835-1770   Fax: (202)835-1772

Description: Semimonthly. Monitors significant developments relating to law enforcement, courts, corrections, planning, research, and theory. Covers criminal justice and juvenile issues. Recurring features include announcements of projects, grants, conferences, courses, and job listings.

★2632★ Law and Order
Law and Order
130 Waukegan Rd., Ste. 202
Deerfield, IL 60015
Ph: (847)444-3300   Fax: (847)444-3333
Fr: 800-843-9764
E-mail: laworder@concentric.net
URL: http://www.lawandordermag.com

Monthly. $22.00/year for individuals. Law enforcement trade magazine.

★2633★ The Municipality
League of Wisconsin Municipalities
202 State St., Ste. 300
Madison, WI 53703-2215
Ph: (608)267-2380   Fax: (608)267-0645
Fr: 800-991-5502

Monthly. $12.00/year. Magazine for officials of Wisconsin's local municipal governments.

★2634★ On the Line
American Correctional Association
4380 Forbes Blvd.
Lanham, MD 20706-4322
Ph: (301)918-1800   Fax: (301)918-1886
Fr: 800-222-5646

Description: Five issues/year. Provides updates on the Association's efforts to improve correctional standards and to develop adequate physical facilities. Presents national news of the corrections field. Recurring features include job listings, news of research, notices of publications available, reports of meetings, and a calendar of events.

★2635★ Western City
League of California Cities
1400 K St., 4th Fl.
Sacramento, CA 95814
Ph: (916)658-8223   Fax: (916)658-8289
Fr: 800-262-1801
URL: http://www.westerncity.com

Monthly. $39.00/year for individuals; $63.00 for two years. Municipal interest magazine.

PLACEMENT AND JOB REFERRAL SERVICES

★2636★ American Society of Criminology (ASC)
1314 Kinnear Rd., Ste. 212
Columbus, OH 43212-1156
Ph: (614)292-9207   Fax: (614)292-6767
E-mail: ceskridge@unl.edu
URL: http://www.asc41.com

Description: Professional and academic criminologists; students of criminology in accredited universities; psychiatrists, psychologists, and sociologists. Works to develop criminology as a science and academic discipline; to aid in the construction of criminological curricula in accredited universities; to upgrade the practitioner in criminological fields (police, prisons, probation, parole, delinquency workers). Conducts research programs; sponsors three student paper competitions. Provides placement service at annual convention.

★2637★ Nine Lives Associates (NLA)
Executive Protection Institute
PO Box 802
Berryville, VA 22611-0802
Ph: (540)554-2540   Fax: (540)554-2558
E-mail: info@personalprotection.com
URL: http://www.personalprotection.com

Description: Law enforcement, correctional, military, and security professionals who have been granted Personal Protection Specialist certification through completion of the protective services program offered by the Executive Protection Institute; conducts research. EPI programs emphasize personal survival skills and techniques for the protection of others. Provides professional recognition for qualified individuals engaged in executive protection assignments. Maintains placement service. Operates speakers' bureau; compiles statistics

EMPLOYER DIRECTORIES AND NETWORKING LISTS

★2638★ Directory of Juvenile and Adult Correctional Departments, Institutions, Agencies, and Probation and Parole Authorities

American Correctional Association
4380 Forbes Blvd.
Lanham, MD 20706-4322
Ph: (301)918-1800   Fax: (301)918-1886
Fr: 800-222-5646

Annual, April; latest edition 2002. $90.00. Covers more than 4,000 adult and juvenile state, federal, provincial, correctional departments, institutions, agencies, programs, paroling authorities, and military correctional facilities in the United States, its territories and Canada. Entries include: Agency name, address, phone, fax, e-mail, web address, name of administrative officers (and other personnel for agencies), length of operation, average number and types of inmates, cost of care, security level, number of staff, accreditation status, and other information. Arrangement: Geographical within authority by states, federal military, Canada. Indexes: Correctional Personnel (U.S. & Canada); Institutions (U.S. & Canada).

★2639★ National Directory of Law Enforcement Administrators, Correctional Institutions & Related Agencies

National Public Safety Information Bureau
601 Main St., Ste. 201
PO Box 365
Stevens Point, WI 54481
Ph: (715)345-2772   Fax: (715)345-7288
Fr: 800-647-7579
URL: http://www.safetysource.com

Annual, June. $129.00. Covers police departments, sheriffs, coroners, criminal prosecutors, child support agencies, state law enforcement and criminal investigation agencies; federal criminal investigation and related agencies; state and federal correctional institutions; campus law enforcement departments; county jails, airport and harbor police, Bureau of Indian Affairs officials, plus new homeland security section. Entries include: Name, address, phone, fax, names and titles of key personnel, number of officers, population served. Arrangement: Separate geographical sections for police chiefs, coroners, sheriffs, prosecutors, prisons and state criminal investigation agencies; also separate sections for federal agencies and miscellaneous law enforcement and related agencies. Indexes: Departments.

HANDBOOKS AND MANUALS

★2640★ America's Fastest Growing Jobs

JIST Works, Inc.
8902 Otis Ave.
Indianapolis, IN 46216-1033
Ph: (317)613-4200   Fax: (317)613-4307
Fr: 800-648-5478
E-mail: jistworks@aol.com
URL: http://www.jist.com

Seventh edition, 2002. $16.95 (paper). 438 pages. Each job profile explains the nature of the work, skills and abilities required, employment outlook, average earnings, related occupations, education and training requirements, and employment opportunities. Also contains career planning information and job search tips.

★2641★ Career Planning in Criminal Justice

Anderson Publishing Co.
2035 Reading Rd.
Cincinnati, OH 45202-1576
Ph: (513)421-4142   Fax: (513)562-8116
Fr: 800-582-7295

Robert C. DeLucia and Thomas J. Doyle. Third edition, 1998. 226 pages. $21.95. Surveys a wide range of career and employment opportunities in law enforcement, the courts, corrections, forensic science, and private security. Contains career planning and job hunting advice.

★2642★ Careers in Law Enforcement and Security

Rosen Publishing Group, Inc.
29 E. 21st St.
New York, NY 10010
Ph: (212)777-3017   Fax: 888-436-4643
Fr: 800-237-9932

Paul Cohen and Shari Cohen. Revised edition, 1994. $18.95. $9.95 (paper), out of print. Describes jobs such as police, sheriff, detective, FBI, CIA, and Secret Service agents, parole and probation officers, security guards, and private investigators. Covers job duties, qualifications, education, training, income, and advancement possibilities. Offers advice about where and how to apply for jobs.

★2643★ The Changing Career of the Correctional Officer

Butterworth-Heinemann
225 Wildwood Ave., Unit B
Woburn, MA 01801
Ph: (781)904-2500   Fax: (781)904-2640
Fr: 800-366-2665

Don A. Josi and Dale K. Sechrest. 1998. $29.99 (paper). 176 pages. Contains information for students considering the profession as well as career develoment issues for administrators, management personnel, and supervisors.

★2644★ Opportunities in Law Enforcement and Criminal Justice Careers

McGraw-Hill Contemporary Books
1221 Avenue of the Americas
New York, NY 10020
Ph: (212)904-2000   Fr: 800-323-4900
E-mail: ntcpub@tribune.com

James Stinchcomb. Revised edition, 1996. $14.95; $11.95 (paper). 160 pages. Offers information on opportunities at the city, county, state, military, and federal levels. Contains bibliography and illustrations.

★2645★ Probation Officer, Parole Officer

Hungry Minds, Inc.
10475 Crosspoint Blvd.
Indianapolis, IN 46256
Ph: (317)572-3000   Fax: (317)572-4000
Fr: 800-667-1115

Hy Hammer. Fifth edition, 1996. $15.95. 192 pages.

★2646★ Real People Working in Law

McGraw-Hill Contemporary Books
1221 Avenue of the Americas
New York, NY 10020
Ph: (212)904-2000   Fr: 800-323-4900
E-mail: ntcpub@tribune.com

Blythe Camenson, Jan Goldberg. 1997. $14.95; $12.95 (paper). 405 pages. Interviews and profiles of working professionals capture a range of opportunities in this field.

TRADESHOWS

★2647★ American Jail Association Training Conference & Jail Expo

American Jail Association
1135, Professional Court
Hagerstown, MD 21740-5853
Ph: (301)790-3930   Fax: (301)790-2941
E-mail: jails@worldnet.att.net
URL: http://www.corrections.com/aja

Annual. **Primary Exhibits:** Jail supplies & services for correctional facilities; construction design; training; officer equipment and correctional equipment, supplies, and services. **Dates and Locations:** 2005 May 15-19; Kansas City, KS • 2006 May 21-25; Salt Lake City, UT • 2007 May 20-24; Nashville, TN • 2008 May 04-08; Sacramento, CA.

★2648★ North Carolina Correctional Association Annual Conference

North Carolina Correctional Association
PO Box 10404
Raleigh, NC 27605
Ph: (910)618-5574   Fax: (910)618-5615

Annual. **Primary Exhibits:** Equipment, supplies, and services for state correctional facilities.

OTHER SOURCES

★2649★ **American Correctional Association (ACA)**
4380 Forbes Blvd.
Lanham, MD 20706
Ph: (301)918-1800   Fax: (301)918-1886
Fr: 800-222-5646
E-mail: jeffw@aca.org
URL: http://www.aca.org/

Description: Correctional administrators, wardens, superintendents, members of prison and parole boards, probation officers, psychologists, educators, sociologists, and other individuals; institutions and associations involved in the correctional field. Promotes improved correctional standards, including selection of personnel, care, supervision, education, training, employment, treatment, and post-release adjustment of inmates. Studies causes of crime and juvenile delinquency and methods of crime control and prevention through grants and contracts. Compiles statistics. Conducts research programs and training of correctional professionals. Offers accreditation of institutions and certification for correctional executive, manager, supervisor, and officer.

★2650★ *Careers in Criminal Justice*
Cambridge Educational
2572 Brunswick Ave.
Lawrenceville, NJ 08648-4128
Fax: 800-FAX-ON-US   Fr: 800-468-4227
URL: http://www.cambridgeeducational.com
$79.95. 2002. 22 minutes.

★2651★ *Human Services Occupations*
Delphi Productions
3160 4th St.
Boulder, CO 80304
Fax: (303)443-4022   Fr: 888-443-2400
URL: http://www.delphivideo.com
$95.00. 50 minutes. Part of the Careers for the 21st Century Video Library.

Cosmetologists and Hairdressers

★2652★ Cosmetics & Toiletries

Allured Publishing Corp.
362 S Schmale Rd.
Carol Stream, IL 60188-2787
Ph: (630)480-2997   Fax: (630)653-2192
E-mail: cosmtoil@allured.com

Monthly. $98.00/year for individuals; $137.00/year for Canada; $189.00/year for other countries. Trade magazine on cosmetic and toiletries manufacturing with an emphasis on product research and development issues.

★2653★ Entertainment Design Magazine

Primedia Business
9800 Metcalf Ave.
Overland Park, KS 66212
Ph: (913)341-1300   Fax: (913)967-1898
E-mail: edld@intertec.com
URL: http://www.etecnyc.net

$37.95/year for individuals; $5.95 for single issue. The business of entertainment technology and design.

★2654★ Global Cosmetic Industry

Allured Publishing Corp.
362 S Schmale Rd.
Carol Stream, IL 60188-2787
Ph: (630)480-2997   Fax: (630)653-2192

Monthly. Trade publication covering the cosmetics industry worldwide.

★2655★ Modern Salon

Vance Publishing Corp.
400 Knightsbridge Pkwy.
Lincolnshire, IL 60069
Ph: (847)634-2600   Fax: (847)634-4343
Fr: 800-621-2845
E-mail: modernsalon.com

Monthly. $20.00/year for individuals; $4.00 for single issue. Magazine focusing on hair-styling salons for men and women.

★2656★ Nailpro

Creative Age Publications Inc.
7628 Densmore Ave.
Van Nuys, CA 91406-2042
Ph: (818)782-7328   Fax: (818)782-7450
Fr: 800-442-5667
E-mail: nailpro@creativeage.com
URL: http://www.nailpro.com

Monthly. $24.00/year for individuals; $5.00 for single issue; $20.00/year for students. Salon owners and nail technicians read Nailpro for continuing education in techniques and services, marketing and management tips, product information and industry news.

★2657★ SalonNews

Fairchild Publications Inc.
7 W 34th St.
New York, NY 10001
Ph: (212)630-4000

Monthly. Trade publication covering the hair and beauty salon industries.

★2658★ Skin Inc.

Allured Publishing Corp.
362 S Schmale Rd.
Carol Stream, IL 60188-2787
Ph: (630)480-2997   Fax: (630)653-2192
E-mail: skininc@allured.com
URL: http://www.skininc.com

$49.00/year for individuals; $10.00 for single issue. The complete business guide for face and body care.

★2659★ Soap and Cosmetics

Chemical Week Associates
110 Williams St., 11th Fl.
New York, NY 10038
Ph: (212)621-4900   Fax: (212)621-4949

Monthly. Trade publication covering the cosmetics industry.

★2660★ Soap/Cosmetics/Chemical Specialties

Cygnus Business Media Inc.
445 Broad Hollow Rd.
Melville, NY 11747
Ph: (631)845-2700   Fax: (631)845-2798
Fr: 800-308-6397

Monthly. Free to qualified subscribers; $60.00/year for individuals. Trade magazine for household and personal care products.

PLACEMENT AND JOB REFERRAL SERVICES

★2661★ World International Nail and Beauty Association (WINBA)

1221 N. Lake View Ave.
Anaheim, CA 92807
Ph: (714)779-9892   Fax: (714)779-9971
Fr: 800-541-9838

Members: Professionals in the nail and skin care industries. **Purpose:** Objectives are to represent the manicure and skin care industry; promote the effective use and application of manicuring and skin care products and equipment; provide a means for mutual communication and joint study; represent the industry before state boards, the Food and Drug Administration, and other regulatory agencies. **Activities:** Conducts seminars; secures discounts on supplies; offers special conducts public relations program; sponsors research and educational programs; compiles statistics. Maintains speakers' bureau and placement service.

EMPLOYER DIRECTORIES AND NETWORKING LISTS

★2662★ American Salon's Green Book
Advanstar Communications Inc.
7500 Old Oak Blvd.
Cleveland, OH 44130-3369
Ph: (440)243-8100   Fax: (440)891-2777
E-mail: directories@advanstar.com
URL: http://www.advanstar.com

Annual, November. $145.00. Covers about 1,300 manufacturers of supplies and equipment for salons and spas; 130 manufacturers' representatives; 3,200 distributors; employment agencies, show management companies, and related trade organizations. Entries include: For manufacturers and agents-Company name, address, phone, names of principal executives, products available. For distributors-Company name, address, phone, branches, name of owner or president, number of sales representatives, trade association affiliation, Metropolitan Statistical Area (MSA) in which located. For representatives-Company name, address, phone, territory covered. Arrangement: Manufacturers are alphabetical; agents, distributors, representatives are geographical. Indexes: Product, trade name.

★2663★ Beauty Salons Directory
infoUSA Inc.
5711 S 86th Cir.
Omaha, NE 68127-0347
Ph: (402)930-3500   Fax: (402)331-0176
Fr: 800-555-6124
URL: http://www.abii.com

Annual. Number of listings: 236,649. Entries include: Salon name, address, phone (including area code), size of advertisement, year first in "Yellow Pages," name of owner or manager, number of employees. Compiled from telephone company "Yellow Pages," nationwide. Arrangement: Geographical.

★2664★ Manicuring Salons Directory
infoUSA Inc.
5711 S 86th Cir.
Omaha, NE 68127-0347
Ph: (402)930-3500   Fax: (402)331-0176
Fr: 800-555-6124
URL: http://www.abii.com

Annual. Number of listings: 52,194. Entries include: Name, address, phone (including area code), size of advertisement, year first in "Yellow Pages," name of owner or manager, number of employees. Regional editions available: Eastern, $645.00; Western, $610.00. Compiled from telephone company "Yellow Pages," nationwide. Arrangement: Geographical.

HANDBOOKS AND MANUALS

★2665★ Career After Cosmetology School: Step-by-Step Guide to a Lucrative Career and Salon Ownership
Step-by-Step Publications
1645 Westmont Ave.
Campbell, CA 95008
Ph: (408)376-0276   Fax: (408)376-0396
Fr: 800-305-2205

Jessica Brooks. 1997. $29.95. 320 pages.

★2666★ Careers for Film Buffs and Other Hollywood Types
VGM Career Horizons
1221 Avenue of the Americas
New York, NY 10020
Ph: (212)904-2000   Fr: 800-323-4900
E-mail: ntcpub@tribune.com

Jaq Greenspon. 1994. $14.95; $9.95 (paper). 250 pages. Describes job descriptions in production, camera, sound, special effects, grips, electrical, makeup, costumes, etc.

★2667★ Careers in Hairdressing and Beauty Therapy
Kogan Page, Ltd.
22 Broad St., Ste. 34
Milford, CT 06460

Alexa Stace and Sheena Fitzsimmons. Seventh edition, 1996. $14.95 (paper). Part of Kogan Page Careers series. Out of print.

★2668★ Cosmetology Career Starter
LearningExpress, LLC
900 Broadway, Ste. 604
New York, NY 10003
Ph: (212)995-2566   Fax: (212)995-5512
Fr: 800-295-9556

Lorraine Korman. Second edition, 2002.

★2669★ Hair, Makeup & Styling Career Guide
Set the Pace Publishing Group
1870 N. Vermont Ave., Ste. 529
Los Angeles, CA 90027
Ph: (213)913-0773   Fax: (213)913-0900

Crystal A. Wright. 1995. $39.95 (paper).

★2670★ How to Get a Job with a Cruise Line
Ticket to Adventure, Inc.
PO Box 41005
St. Petersburg, FL 33743-1005
Ph: (727)822-5029   Fax: (727)821-3409
Fr: 800-929-7447

Mary Fallon Miller. Fifth edition, 2001. $16.95 (paper). 336 pages. Explores jobs with cruise ships, describing duties, responsibilities, benefits, and training. Lists cruise ship lines and schools offering cruise line training. Offers job hunting advice.

★2671★ Opportunities in Beauty Culture Careers
McGraw-Hill Contemporary Books
1221 Avenue of the Americas
New York, NY 10020
Ph: (212)904-2000   Fr: 800-323-4900
E-mail: ntcpub@tribune.com

Susan Wood Gearhart. 1996. $14.95; $11.95 (paper). 205 pages. Outlines how to enter the field and build a career. Independent salon ownership in also covered. Contains bibliography and illustrations.

★2672★ Planning Your Cosmetology Career
Prentice Hall PTR
200 Old Tappan Rd.
Old Tappan, NJ 07675
Ph: (201)236-7000   Fr: 800-223-1360

Mary Murphy-Martin. 1993. $12.90 (paper). 108 pages.

★2673★ The Transition, How to Become a Salon Professional
Thomson Learning
7625 Empire Dr.
Florence, KY 41042
Ph: (859)525-6620   Fax: (859)525-0978
Fr: 800-347-7707

Louise Cotter and Frances L. DuBose. 1996. $19.25. Part of the Cosmetology Series. 352 pages.

TRADESHOWS

★2674★ American Association of Cosmetology Schools Annual Conference
American Association of Cosmetology Schools
15825 N 71st St., Ste. 100
Scottsdale, AZ 85254-1521
Fax: (602)404-8900   Fr: 800-831-1086
URL: http://www.beautyschools.org

Annual. **Primary Exhibits:** Beauty supplies and products, and cosmetology services.

★2675★ American Electrology Association Annual Convention
American Electrology Association
106 Oak Ridge Rd.
Trumbull, CT 06611
Ph: (203)374-6667   Fax: (203)372-7134
URL: http://www.electrology.com

Annual. **Primary Exhibits:** Electrology equipment, supplies, and services.

★2676★ IBS - International Beauty Show, New York

Advanstar Communications Inc.
7500 Old Oak Blvd.
Cleveland, OH 44130
Ph: (440)891-2701   Fax: (440)891-2741
Fr: 800-225-4569
E-mail: info@advantstar.com
URL: http://www.advanstar.com

Annual. **Primary Exhibits:** Beauty and health related equipment, supplies, and services.

★2677★ IBS Seattle - International Beauty Show

Advanstar Communications Inc.
7500 Old Oak Blvd.
Cleveland, OH 44130
Ph: (440)891-2701   Fax: (440)891-2741
Fr: 800-225-4569
E-mail: info@advantstar.com
URL: http://www.advanstar.com

Primary Exhibits: Beauty and healthcare exhibition.

★2678★ Midwest Beauty Show

Chicago Cosmetologists Association
401 N. Michigan
Chicago, IL 60611
Ph: (312)321-6809   Fax: (312)245-1080
Fr: 800-648-2505

Annual. **Primary Exhibits:** Goods and services for the beauty trade.

★2679★ NAILS Show

Bobit Publishing
21061 S. Western Ave.
Torrance, CA 90501
Ph: (310)533-2400   Fax: (310)533-2500

Annual. **Primary Exhibits:** Manicure equipment, supplies, and services.

★2680★ National Beauty Show - HAIRWORLD

National Cosmetology Association
401 N. Michigan Ave.
Chicago, IL 60611-4255
Fr: 800-527-1683
E-mail: nca-now@primary.net
URL: http://www.nca-now.com

Annual. **Primary Exhibits:** Hair products, cosmetics, and jewelry.

OTHER SOURCES

★2681★ Association of Cosmetologists and Hairdressers (ACH)

6872 Arlington
West Bloomfield, MI 48322
Ph: (313)563-0360   Fax: (248)669-0636

Description: Cosmetologists and beauticians; beauty product manufacturers, wholesalers, buyers, and retailers. Seeks to keep members informed of current trends in the beauty culture industry. Conducts demonstrations. Compiles statistics. Sponsors educational programs.

★2682★ Hair International/Associated Master Barbers and Beauticians of America (HI/AMBBA)

2017 Church St.
Lebanon, PA 17046-2733
Fax: (717)838-0796

Members: Barber styling and cosmetology school and business owners and employees; manufacturers. **Activities:** Operates speakers' bureau; conducts hairstyling show, classes, and seminars.

★2683★ National Beauty Culturists' League (NBCL)

25 Logan Cir. NW
Washington, DC 20005
Ph: (202)332-2695   Fax: (202)332-0940
E-mail: info@nbcl.org
URL: http://www.nbcl.net

Members: Beauticians, cosmetologists, and beauty products manufacturers. **Purpose:** Encourages standardized, scientific, and approved methods of hair, scalp, and skin treatments. **Activities:** Offers scholarships and plans to establish a research center. Sponsors: National Institute of Cosmetology, a training course in operating and designing and business techniques; National Beauty Week. Maintains hall of fame; conducts research programs; compiles statistics.

★2684★ National Cosmetology Association (NCA)

401 N Michigan Ave.
Chicago, IL 60611-4255
Ph: (312)527-6757   Fax: (312)464-6118
E-mail: nca1@sba.com
URL: http://www.salonprofessionals.org

Members: Owners of cosmetology salons; cosmetologists. **Activities:** Sponsors National Cosmetology Month and National Beauty Show. Provides special sections for estheticians, school owners, salon owners, and nail technicians. Maintains hall of fame. Conducts educational and charitable programs.

★2685★ *Personal & Building Service Occupations*

Delphi Productions
3160 4th St.
Boulder, CO 80304
Fax: (303)443-4022   Fr: 888-443-2400
URL: http://www.delphivideo.com

$95.00. 48 minutes. Part of the Careers for the 21st Century Video Library.

Cost Estimators

SOURCES OF HELP-WANTED ADS

★2686★ Builder
Hanley-Wood L.L.C.
1 Thomas Cir., Ste. 600
Washington, DC 20005
Ph: (202)452-0800   Fax: (202)785-1974
URL: http://www.builderonline.com

Monthly. $29.95/year for individuals. Magazine covering housing and construction industry.

★2687★ Construction Digest
Construction Digest
5804 W 74th St.
Indianapolis, IN 46278
Ph: (317)293-6860   Fax: (317)293-7840
Fr: 888-893-6860

Semimonthly. $3.00 for single issue. Magazine for the public works and construction engineering industries.

★2688★ CONSTRUCTOR
Associated General Contractors
  Information
333 John Carlyle St., Ste. 200
Alexandria, VA 22314
Ph: (703)837-5355   Fax: (703)837-5402
URL: http://www.agc.org

Monthly. $15.00/year for members; $250.00/year for nonmembers; $4.00/year for single issue except July, November, and December; $25.00/year for single issue-November, December; $325.00 for single issue-July. Management magazine for the Construction Industry.

★2689★ Cost Engineering
AACE International
209 Prairie Ave., Ste. 100
Morgantown, WV 26501
Ph: (304)296-8444   Fax: (304)291-5728
Fr: 800-858-COST
URL: http://www.aacei.org

Monthly. $60.00/year for individuals; $76.00/year for other countries; $8.00 for single issue, members; $12.00 for single issue, nonmembers. Magazine.

★2690★ Design Cost Data
DC & D Technologies Inc.
8602 N 40th St.
Tampa, FL 33604
Ph: (813)989-9300   Fax: (813)980-3982
Fr: 800-533-5680
E-mail: webmaster@dcd.com
URL: http://www.dcd.com

Bimonthly. $84.40/year for individuals. Publication providing real cost data case studies of various types completed around the country for design and building professionals.

★2691★ ENR: Engineering News-Record
McGraw-Hill Companies
1221 Avenue of the Americas
New York, NY 10020
Ph: (212)512-2000
URL: http://www.enr.com

Weekly. $74.00/year; $5.00 for single issue. Magazine focusing on engineering and construction.

★2692★ Professional Builder
Reed Business Information
360 Park Ave. S
New York, NY 10014
Ph: (646)746-7764
URL: http://www.probuilder.com

Monthly. $10.00 for single issue; $139.95/year for by mail.

PLACEMENT AND JOB REFERRAL SERVICES

★2693★ AACE International
209 Prairie Ave., Ste. 100
Morgantown, WV 26501
Ph: (304)296-8444   Fax: (304)291-5728
Fr: 800-858-2678
E-mail: info@aacei.org
URL: http://www.aacei.org

Description: Professional society of cost managers, cost engineers, estimators, schedulers and planners, project managers, educators, representatives of all branches of engineering, engineering students, and others. Conducts technical and educational programs. Offers placement service. Compiles statistics. Operates certification program for certified cost engineers (CCE) or certified cost consultants (CCC), or interim cost consultants (ICC).

★2694★ International Society of Parametric Analysts (ISPA)
PO Box 6402
Town & Country Branch
Chesterfield, MO 63006-6402
Ph: (636)527-2955   Fax: (636)256-8358
E-mail: clydeperry@aol.com
URL: http://www.ispa-cost.org

Members: Engineers, designers, statisticians, estimators, and managers in industry, the military, and government who develop and use computerized, parametric cost-estimating models. **Activities:** Conducts educational activities aimed at promoting usage of parametric modeling techniques for purposes of cost estimating, risk analysis, and technology forecasting. Sponsors placement service.

★2695★ Professional Women in Construction (PWC)
315 E. 56th St.
New York, NY 10022-3730
Ph: (212)486-7745   Fax: (212)486-0228
E-mail: pwcusa1@aol.com
URL: http://www.pwcusa.org

Description: Management-level women and men in construction and allied industries; owners, suppliers, architects, engineers, field personnel, office personnel, and bonding/surety personnel. Provides a forum for exchange of ideas and promotion of political and legislative action, education, and job opportunities for women in construction and related fields; forms liaisons with other trade and professional groups; develops research programs. Strives to reform abuses and to assure justice and equity within the construction industry. Sponsors mini-workshops. Maintains Action Line which provides members with current information on pertinent legislation and on the association's activities and job referrals.

EMPLOYER DIRECTORIES AND NETWORKING LISTS

★2696★ ABC Today-Associated Builders and Contractors National Membership Directory Issue

Associated Builders & Contractors Inc.
4250 N Fairfax Dr., 9th Fl.
Arlington, VA 22203
Ph: (703)812-2000   Fax: (703)812-8203

Annual, December. $150.00. Publication includes: List of approximately 19,000 member construction contractors and suppliers. Entries include: Company name, address, phone, name of principal executive, code to volume of business, business specialty. Arrangement: Classified by chapter, then by work specialty.

★2697★ Constructor-AGC Directory of Membership and Services Issue

AGC Information Inc.
333 John Carlyle St., Ste. 200
Alexandria, VA 22314
Ph: (703)548-3118   Fax: (703)548-3119
URL: http://www.agc.org

Annual, July. $250.00 for nonmembers; $15.00 for members; $250.00 for other countries. Publication includes: List of over 8,500 member firms and 24,000 national associate member firms engaged in building, highway, heavy, industrial, municipal utilities, and railroad construction (SIC 1541, 1542, 1611, 1622, 1623, 1629); listing of state and local chapter officers. Entries include: For firms-Company name, address, phone, fax, names of principal executives, and code indicating type of construction undertaken. For officers-Name, title, address. Arrangement: Geographical, Alphabetical. Indexes: Company name.

★2698★ ENR-Top 500 Design Firms Issue

McGraw-Hill Companies
1221 Ave. of the Americas
New York, NY 10020
Ph: (212)512-2000   Fax: (212)512-3840

Annual, April. $10.00. Publication includes: List of 500 leading architectural, engineering, and specialty design firms selected on basis of annual billings. Entries include: Company name, headquarters location, type of firm, current and prior year rank in billings, types of services, countries in which operated in preceding year. Arrangement: Ranked by billings.

★2699★ ENR-Top 400 Construction Contractors Issue

McGraw-Hill Companies
1221 Ave. of the Americas
New York, NY 10020
Ph: (212)512-2000   Fax: (212)512-3840

Annual, May issue of "Engineering News Record". $10.00. Publication includes: List of 400 United States contractors receiving largest dollar volumes of contracts in preceding calendar year. Separate lists of 50 largest design/construct management firms; 50 largest program and construction managers; 25 building contractors; 25 heavy contractors. Entries include: Company name, headquarters location, total value of contracts received in preceding year, value of foreign contracts, countries in which operated, construction specialities. Arrangement: By total value of contracts received.

★2700★ ENR-Top International Design Firms Issue

McGraw-Hill Companies
1221 Ave. of the Americas
New York, NY 10020
Ph: (212)512-2000   Fax: (212)512-3840

Annual, July issue of "Engineering News Record". $10.00. Publication includes: List of 200 design firms (including United States firms) competing outside their own national borders who received largest dollar volume of foreign contracts in preceding calendar year. Entries include: Company name, headquarters location, type of firm, current and previous year rankings in total billings, types of services, countries in which operated in preceding year. Arrangement: By amount billed to international clients in previous year.

EMPLOYMENT AGENCIES AND SEARCH FIRMS

★2701★ Real Estate Executive Search, Inc.

PO Box 387
San Francisco, CA 94104-0387
Ph: (415)398-4116
E-mail: jhavrees@aol.com

Executive search firm for the real estate and finance fields.

★2702★ Specialized Search Associates

15200 Jog Rd., Ste. 201
Delray Beach, FL 33446
Ph: (561)499-3711   Fax: (561)499-3770
Fr: 888-405-2650
E-mail: lm7880@aol.com

Executive search firm that specializes in construction, engineering, and sales.

OTHER SOURCES

★2703★ American Society of Professional Estimators (ASPE)

11141 Georgia Ave., Ste. 412
Wheaton, MD 20902
Ph: (301)929-8848   Fax: (301)929-0231
Fr: 888-378-6283
E-mail: info@aspenational.com
URL: http://www.aspenational.org

Description: Construction cost estimators. Develops professional and ethical standards in construction estimating. Offers continuing education to established professionals; provides certification for estimators.

★2704★ Associated Builders and Contractors (ABC)

1300 N. 17th St., Ste. 800
Rosslyn, VA 22209
Ph: (703)812-2000   Fax: (703)812-8201
E-mail: info@abc.org
URL: http://www.abc.org

Description: Construction contractors, subcontractors, suppliers, and associates. Aim is to foster and perpetuate the principles of rewarding construction workers and management on the basis of merit. Sponsors management education programs and craft training; also sponsors apprenticeship and skill training programs. Disseminates technological and labor relations information.

★2705★ Associated General Contractors of America (AGC)

333 John Carlyle St., Ste. 200
Alexandria, VA 22314
Ph: (703)548-3118   Fax: (703)548-3119
E-mail: sandhers@agc.org
URL: http://www.agc.org

Description: General construction contractors; subcontractors; industry suppliers; service firms. Provides market services through its divisions. Conducts special conferences and seminars designed specifically for construction firms. Compiles statistics on job accidents reported by member firms. ors. Maintains 65 committees, including joint cooperative committees with other associations and liaison committees with federal agencies.

★2706★ *Financial Occupations*

Delphi Productions
3160 4th St.
Boulder, CO 80304
Fax: (303)443-4022   Fr: 888-443-2400
URL: http://www.delphivideo.com

$95.00. 50 minutes. Part of the Careers for the 21st Century Video Library.

★2707★ National Association of Home Builders (NAHB)

1201 15th St. NW
Washington, DC 20005
Ph: (202)266-8200   Fax: (202)822-0586
Fr: 800-368-5242
E-mail: info@nahb.com
URL: http://www.nahb.org

Description: Single and multifamily home builders, commercial builders, and others associated with the building industry. Lobbies on behalf of the housing industry and conducts public affairs activities to increase public understanding of housing and the economy. Collects and disseminates data on current developments in home building and home builders' plans through its Economics Department and nationwide Metropolitan Housing Forecast. Maintains NAHB Research Center, which functions as the research arm of the home building industry. Sponsors seminars and workshops on construction, mortgage credit, labor relations, cost reduction, land use, remodeling, and business management. Compiles statistics; offers charitable program, spokesman training, and placement service; maintains speakers' bureau, and Hall of Fame. Subsidiaries include the National Council of the Housing Industry. Maintains over 50 committees in many areas of construction; operates National Commercial Builders Council, National Council of the Multifamily Housing Industry, National Remodelers Council, and National Sales and Marketing Council.

★2708★ National Association of Women in Construction (NAWIC)

327 S Adams St.
Fort Worth, TX 76104
Ph: (817)877-5551   Fax: (817)877-0324
Fr: 800-552-3506
E-mail: nawic@nawic.org
URL: http://www.nawic.org

Description: Seeks to enhance the success of women in the construction industry.

★2709★ National Center for Construction Education and Research

3600 NW 43rd St., Bldg. G
PO Box 141104
Gainesville, FL 32606-1104
Ph: (352)334-0911   Fax: (352)334-0932
Fr: 888-NCCER-20
E-mail: info@nccer.org
URL: http://www.nccer.org

Description: Education foundation committed to the development and publication of Contren(TM) Learning Series, the source of craft training, management education and safety resources for the construction industry.

★2710★ Society of Cost Estimating and Analysis (SCEA)

101 S Whiting St., Ste. 201
Alexandria, VA 22304
Ph: (703)751-8069   Fax: (703)461-7328
E-mail: scea@sceaonline.net
URL: http://www.sceaonline.net

Description: Dedicated to improving cost estimating and analysis in government and industry and enhancing the professional competence and achievements of its' members. Administers a professional certification program leading to the designation of Certified Cost Estimator/Analyst; offers extensive literature in the field through its' Professional Development Program. Goals of the Society include enhancing the profession of cost estimating and analysis, fostering the professional growth of its members, enhancing the understanding and application of cost estimating, analysis and related disciplines throughout government and industry and providing forums and media through which current issues of interest to the profession can be addressed and advances in the state-of-the-art can be shared.

Counselors

SOURCES OF HELP-WANTED ADS

★2711★ AAEE Connections

American Association for Employment in
  Education
3040 Riverside Dr., Ste. 125
Columbus, OH 43221
Ph: (614)485-1111   Fax: (614)485-9609

Description: Quarterly. Publishes news of
the Association, whose aim is "to enhance
and promote the concept of career planning
and placement as an integral part of the
educational process and to undertake activities designed to help schools, colleges, and
universities meet their educational staffing
needs." Also concerned with teacher education and the supply of/demand for teachers.
Recurring features include news of members, state and regional news, and announcements of upcoming conferences and
meetings.

**★2712★ Alcoholism: Clinical and
Experimental Research**

Lippincott Williams & Wilkins
530 Walnut St.
Philadelphia, PA 19106
Ph: (215)521-8300   Fax: (215)521-8902
Fr: 800-638-3030
E-mail: jewers@lww.com
URL: http://www.alcoholism-cer.com/

Monthly. $337.00/year for individuals;
$645.00/year for institutions; $411.00/year
for other countries; $736.00/year for institu-
tions, other countries. Publishing original
clinical and research studies on alcoholism
and alcohol-induced organ damage.

★2713★ American Annals of the Deaf

Conference of Educational Administrators
  Serving the Deaf
800 Florida Ave. NE
Washington, DC 20002
Ph: (202)651-5488   Fax: (202)651-5489
URL: http://sehs.gallaudet.edu/annals

$60.00/year for individuals; $66.00/year for

Canada; $80.00/year for other countries.
Journal focusing on education of the deaf.

★2714★ APA Monitor

American Psychological Association
750 1st St. NE
Washington, DC 20002-4242
Ph: (202)336-5500   Fax: (202)336-5620
Fr: 800-374-2721
E-mail: journals@apa.org
URL: http://www.apa.org/monitor/

Monthly.   Free to qualified subscribers;
$46.00/year for nonmembers; $87.00/year
for institutions. Official newspaper of the
APA. Reports on the science, profession,
and social responsibility of psychology, including latest legislative developments affecting mental health, education, and research support.

**★2715★ Career Planning & Adult
Development Network Newsletter**

Career Planning & Adult Development
  Network
4965 Sierra Rd.
San Jose, CA 95132
Ph: (408)441-9100   Fax: (408)441-9101
URL: http://www.careernetwork.org

Description: Bimonthly. Contains features
and news items on career development and
human resources: theory, methodology, research, practices, and techniques. Deals
with manpower, organizational planning,
counseling, training, equal opportunity, career transition, marketing skills, and adult
learning. Recurring features include notices
of resources, materials, publications of interest, conferences, workshops, seminars, employment opportunities, book reviews, network news, and a column on publishers of
career development books.

**★2716★ The Chronicle of Higher
Education**

The Chronicle of Higher Education
1255 23rd St. NW, Ste. 700
Washington, DC 20037-1125
Ph: (202)466-1000   Fax: (202)452-1033
URL: http://chronicle.com

Weekly. $82.50/year for individuals; $3.75
for single issue. Higher education magazine
(tabloid).

★2717★ Counseling Today

American Counseling Association
5999 Stevenson Ave.
Alexandria, VA 22304-3300
Ph: (703)823-9800   Fax: (703)823-0252
Fr: 800-347-6647
E-mail: ct@counseling.org
URL: http://www.counseling.org/ctonline

Description: Monthly. Covers news and
issues relevant to the counseling profession.

**★2718★ Counselor Education and
Supervision**

American Counseling Association
5999 Stevenson Ave.
Alexandria, VA 22304-3300
Ph: (703)823-9800   Fax: (703)823-0252
Fr: 800-347-6647

Quarterly. $50.00/year   for   individuals;
$70.00/year for institutions. Journal covering
counseling theories, techniques, skills,
teaching, training, and trends.

★2719★ Family Therapy News

American Association for Marriage and
  Family Therapy
1133 15th St. NW, Ste. 300
Washington, DC 20005-2710
Ph: (202)452-0109
E-mail: ftn@aamft.org

Bimonthly. $20.00/year   for   individuals;
$35.00/year for institutions, Canada; $10.00/
year for out of country. Newspaper for
professionals in family therapy and mental
health-related issues.

**★2720★ Journal of Career Planning &
Employment**

National Association of Colleges and
  Employers
62 Highland Ave.
Bethlehem, PA 18017
Ph: (610)868-1421   Fax: (610)868-0208
Fr: 800-544-5272

URL: http://www.jobweb.org/

Quarterly. $72.00/year. Journal on career planning, and recruitment of the college educated work force.

★2721★ *Journal of Counseling and Development*

American Counseling Association
5999 Stevenson Ave.
Alexandria, VA 22304-3300
Ph: (703)823-9800   Fax: (703)823-0252
Fr: 800-347-6647
URL: http://www.counseling.org

Quarterly. $40.00/year for individuals; $175.00/year for institutions. Journal for counseling and human development professionals concerning research, empirical data on current issues, and emerging counseling trends.

★2722★ *Journal of Counseling Psychology*

American Psychological Association
750 1st St. NE
Washington, DC 20002-4242
Ph: (202)336-5500   Fax: (202)336-5620
Fr: 800-374-2721
E-mail: journals@apa.org
URL: http://www.apa.org/journals/cou.html

Quarterly. $41.00/year for members; $23.00/year for students; $81.00/year for nonmembers; $199.00/year for institutions. Journal presenting empirical studies about counseling processes and interventions, theoretical articles about counseling, and studies dealing with evaluation of counseling applications and programs.

★2723★ *Journal of Family Issues*

Sage Publications Inc.
2455 Teller Rd.
Thousand Oaks, CA 91320
Ph: (805)499-0721   Fax: (805)499-0871
Fr: 800-818-SAGE
E-mail: advertising@sagepub.com
URL: http://www.sagepub.com/journal.aspx?pid=163

$109.00/year for individuals; $109.00/year for out of country; $699.00/year for institutions; $699.00/year for institutions, other countries; $19.00/year for single issue, individuals; $97.00 for single issue, institutions. Family studies journal.

★2724★ *Journal of Family Psychology*

American Psychological Association
750 1st St. NE
Washington, DC 20002-4242
Ph: (202)336-5500   Fax: (202)336-5620
Fr: 800-374-2721
E-mail: journals@apa.org
URL: http://www.apa.org/journals/fam.html

Quarterly. $49.00/year for members; $30.00/year for students; $99.00/year for nonmembers; $169.00/year for institutions. Journal reporting on theory, research, and clinical practice in family psychology; including articles on family and marital theory and con-

cepts, research and evaluation, therapeutic frameworks and methods, and policies and legal matters concerning family and marriage.

★2725★ *Journal of Family Psychotherapy*

The Haworth Press Inc.
10 Alice St.
Binghamton, NY 13904-1580
Ph: (607)722-5857   Fax: (607)722-1424
Fr: 800-429-6784
URL: http://www.haworthpress.com

Quarterly. $34.00/year for individuals, USA; $75.00/year for institutions, USA; $175.00/year for libraries, USA; $44.20/year for individuals, Canada; $97.50/year for institutions, Canada; $227.50/year for libraries, Canada; $47.60/year for individuals, other countries; $105.00/year for institutions, other countries; $245.00/year for libraries, other countries. Journal includes case studies, treatment reports, and strategies in clinical practice for psychotherapists.

★2726★ *Journal of Family Violence*

Kluwer Academic/Plenum Publishing Corp.
233 Spring St., 7th
New York, NY 10013-1578
Ph: (212)620-8000   Fax: (212)463-0742
Fr: 800-221-9369

Quarterly. $225.00/year for institutions; $265.00/year for institutions, other countries. Psychology journal.

★2727★ *National Association of Advisors for the Health Professions-Advisor*

National Association of Advisors for the Health Professions Inc.
College of Liberal Arts and Sciences
Arizona State University
Tempe, AZ 85287-0701
Ph: (602)965-2365

Description: Quarterly. Intended for college and university faculty who advise undergraduate students on health careers. Focuses on manpower statistics, financial aid, admission procedures, curriculum, advising, recruitment, counseling practice, and ethics. Covers Association and legislative news and announcements from affiliated organizations. Recurring features include interviews, statistics, book reviews, news of research, editorials, opinion, and items on awards, meetings, and membership.

★2728★ *The New Social Worker*

White Hat Communications
PO Box 5390
Harrisburg, PA 17110-0390
Ph: (717)238-3787   Fax: (717)238-2090
URL: http://www.socialworker.com

$15.00/year for individuals. Publication offering career guidance for social work students.

★2729★ *The Nonprofit Times*

NPT Publishing Group Inc.
120 Littleton Rd., Ste. 120
Parsippany, NJ 07054-1803
Ph: (973)394-1800   Fax: (973)734-1771
E-mail: ednchief@nptimes.com
URL: http://www.nptimes.com

$8.95 for single issue; $59.00/year. Trade journal serving nonprofit organizations.

★2730★ *Spectrum*

Association for Counselor Education and Supervision (ACES)
5999 Stevenson Ave.
Alexandria, VA 22304
Ph: (703)823-9800

Description: Quarterly. Focuses on "the need for quality education and supervision of counselors in all work settings," the accreditation process, and professional development activities for counselors. Recurring features include news of the activities, programs, and members of ACES and related organizations.

★2731★ *Washington Counseletter*

Chronicle Guidance Publications Inc.
66 Aurora St.
Moravia, NY 13118-3576
Ph: (315)497-0330   Fax: (315)497-3359
Fr: 800-622-7284

Description: Monthly, October-May. Provides information on new developments in education and the behavioral sciences for guidance counselors. Emphasizes government materials, actions, and issues affecting education. Recurring features include items concerning scholarships, financial aid, and educational and employment opportunities.

PLACEMENT AND JOB REFERRAL SERVICES

★2732★ **Alliance for Children and Families (ACF)**

11700 W Lake Park Dr.
Milwaukee, WI 53224-3099
Ph: (414)359-1040   Fax: (414)359-1074
Fr: 800-221-3726
E-mail: info@alliance1.org
URL: http://www.alliance1.org

Description: Membership organization of local agencies in more than 1000 communities providing family counseling, family life education and family advocacy services, and other programs to help families with parent-child, marital, mental health, and other problems of family living. Assists member agencies in developing and providing effective family services. Works with the media, government, and corporations to promote strong family life. Compiles statistics; conducts research. Maintains extensive files of unpublished materials from member agencies. Offers career placement services.

★2733★ American Association of Psychiatric Technicians (AAPT)

2000 "O" St., Ste. 250
Sacramento, CA 95814-5286
Ph: (916)443-1701   Fax: (916)329-9145
Fr: 800-391-7589
E-mail: hearn@psychtechs.org
URL: http://www.psychtechs.org

Description: Administers the Nationally Certified Psychiatric Technician examination to non-licensed direct-care workers in the fields of mental illness, developmental disabilities and substance abuse.

★2734★ American College Personnel Association (ACPA)

1 Dupont Cir. NW, Ste. 300
Washington, DC 20036-1188
Ph: (202)835-2272   Fax: (202)296-3286
E-mail: info@acpa.nche.edu
URL: http://www.acpa.nche.edu

Description: Individuals employed in higher education and involved in student personnel work, including administration, counseling, research, and teaching. Fosters student development in higher education in areas of service, advocacy, and standards by offering professional programs for educators committed to the overall development of post-secondary students. Sponsors professional and educational activities in cooperation with other organizations. Offers placement services.

★2735★ Association for Multicultural Counseling and Development (AMCD)

5999 Stevenson Ave.
Alexandria, VA 22304
E-mail: rdherring@ualr.edu
URL: http://www.amcd-aca.org

Description: A division of the American Counseling Association. Professionals involved in counseling careers in educational settings, social services, and community agencies; interested individuals; students. Seeks to: develop programs aimed at improving ethnic and racial empathy and understanding; foster personal growth and improve educational opportunities for all minorities in the U.S.; defend human and civil rights; provide in-service and pre-service training for members and others in the profession. Works to enhance members' ability to serve as behavioral change agents. Offers placement service.

★2736★ Association for Specialists in Group Work (ASGW)

202 Education N
Texas A&M Commerce
Commerce, TX 75429
Ph: (903)886-5630   Fax: (903)886-5780
Fr: 800-347-6647
E-mail: george_leddick@tamu-commerce.edu
URL: http://www.asgw.org/

Description: A division of the American Counseling Association. Individuals interested in group counseling holding master's or doctoral degrees, and engaged in practice, teaching, or research in group work; persons holding undergraduate degrees who are interested in group work, but not actively engaged in practice, teaching, or research; students. Seeks to assist and further interests of children, youth, and adults by providing effective services through the group medium, preventing problems, providing maximum development, and remediating disabling behaviors. Sponsors programs to advance group work in schools, clinics, universities, private practice, and mental health institutions. Conducts placement service.

★2737★ International Association of Counselors and Therapists (IACT)

10915 Bonita Beach Rd., Ste. 1101
Bonita Springs, FL 34135-9049
Ph: (239)498-9710   Fax: (239)498-1215
E-mail: iactnow@aol.com
URL: http://www.iact.org

Description: Mental health professionals, medical professionals, social workers, clergy, educators, hypnotherapists, counselors, and individuals interested in the helping professions. Promotes enhanced professional image and prestige for complementary therapy. Provides a forum for exchange of information and ideas among practitioners of traditional and nontraditional therapies and methodologies; fosters unity among "grassroots" practitioners and those with advanced academic credentials. Facilitates the development of new therapy programs. Conducts educational, research, and charitable programs. Awards credits for continuing education. Maintains speakers' bureau and library; operates referral and placement services; compiles statistics. Assists in the development of local chapters.

★2738★ International Educator's Institute (TIE)

PO Box 513
Cummaquid, MA 02637
Ph: (508)362-1414   Fax: (508)362-1411
Fr: 877-375-6668
E-mail: tie@tieonline.com
URL: http://www.tieonline.com

Description: Facilitates the placement of teachers and administrators in American, British, and international schools. Seeks to create a network that provides for professional development opportunities and improved financial security of members. Offers advice and information on international school news, recent educational developments, job placement, and investment, consumer, and professional development opportunities. Makes available insurance and travel benefits. Operates International Schools Internship Program.

★2739★ National Academic Advising Association (NACADA)

Kansas State Univ.
2323 Anderson Ave., Ste. 225
Manhattan, KS 66502
Ph: (785)532-5717   Fax: (785)532-7732
E-mail: nacada@ksu.edu
URL: http://www.nacada.ksu.edu

Members: Academic program advisors, faculty, administrators, counselors, and others concerned with the intellectual, personal, and career development of students in all types of postsecondary educational institutions. **Purpose:** Dedicated to the support and professional growth of academic advising and academic advisers. Provides a forum for discussion, debate, and exchange of ideas regarding academic advising. Serves as advocate for standards and quality programs in academic advising. **Activities:** Operates consultants bureau to assist advising services on college campuses. Maintains placement service, speakers' bureau, and information clearinghouse. Maintains placement service, speakers' bureau, and information clearinghouse.

★2740★ National Council on Rehabilitation Education (NCRE)

Rehabilitation Counseling Program
School of Education and Human Development
California State University - Fresno
5005 N Maple Ave., M.S. 3
Fresno, CA 93740-8025
Ph: (559)278-0325   Fax: (559)278-0098
E-mail: charlesa@csufresno.edu
URL: http://www.rehabeducators.org/

Description: Academic institutions and organizations; professional educators, researchers, and students. Goals are to: assist in the documentation of the effect of education in improving services to persons with disability; determine the skills and training necessary for effective rehabilitation services; develop role models, standards, and uniform licensure and certification requirements for rehabilitation personnel; interact with consumers and public and private sector policy makers. Disseminates information and provides forum for discussion. Sponsors specialized education and placement service. Compiles statistics. Works closely with agencies and associations serving persons with disabilities.

EMPLOYER DIRECTORIES AND NETWORKING LISTS

★2741★ *American Association for Correctional Psychology-Directory*

American Association for Correctional Psychology
c/o Robert Smith, Ed.D.
Marshall University Graduate College
100 Angus E Peyton Dr.
South Charleston, WV 25303-1600
Ph: (304)746-1929   Fax: (304)746-1942

Continuously updated. Covers 400 mental health professionals engaged in correctional and rehabilitative work in prisons, reformatories, juvenile institutions, probation and parole agencies, and in other aspects of criminal justice. Entries include: Name, affiliation, address, phone. Arrangement: Alphabetical.

★2742★ American Group Psychotherapy Association-Membership Directory

American Group Psychotherapy Association Inc.
25 E 21st St., 6th Fl.
New York, NY 10023
Ph: (212)477-2677   Fax: (212)979-6627
Fr: 877-668-AGPA

Biennial, fall. $90.00. Covers 4,500 physicians, psychologists, clinical social workers, psychiatric nurses, and other mental health professionals interested in treatment of emotional problems by group methods. Entries include: Name, office or home address, highest degree held, office or home phone number. Arrangement: Alphabetical. Indexes: Geographical.

★2743★ American Society for Adolescent Psychiatry-Membership Directory

American Society for Adolescent Psychiatry
PO Box 570218
Dallas, TX 75357-0218
Ph: (972)686-6166   Fax: (972)613-5532

Annual, spring. $15.00. Covers 1,500 members. Entries include: Name, office address and phone, fax, home address and phone (when given). Arrangement: Alphabetical. Indexes: Geographical, chapter.

★2744★ Boarding Schools Directory

The Association of Boarding Schools
4455 Connecticut Ave., Ste. A200
Washington, DC 20008
Ph: (202)966-8705   Fax: (202)966-8708
Fr: 800-541-5908
URL: http://www.schools.com

Annual, August. Covers boarding schools that are members of the Association of Boarding Schools. Entries include: School name, address, phone, e-mail and url's, grades for which boarding students are accepted, enrollment, brief description. Arrangement: Classified by type of school. Indexes: Geographical; program; Alphabetical.

★2745★ Career & Vocational Counseling Directory

infoUSA Inc.
5711 S 86th Cir.
Omaha, NE 68127-0347
Ph: (402)930-3500   Fax: (402)331-0176
Fr: 800-555-6124
URL: http://www.abii.com

Annual. Number of listings: 2,971. Entries include: Name, address, phone (including area code), size of advertisement, year first in "Yellow Pages," name of owner or manager, number of employees. Compiled from telephone company "Yellow Pages," nationwide. Arrangement: Geographical.

★2746★ Christian Association for Psychological Studies International-Membership Directory

Christian Association for Psychological Studies
PO Box 310400
New Braunfels, TX 78131-0400
Ph: (830)629-2277   Fax: (830)629-2342
URL: http://www.caps.net/dircoup.htm

Annual, June. $12.00 for other countries. Covers 2,300 Christians involved in psychology, psychiatry, counseling, sociology, social work, ministry, and nursing. Entries include: Name, office address and phone number, highest degree held, area of occupational specialization, and career data. Arrangement: Geographical. Indexes: Alphabetical.

★2747★ Christian Schools International-Directory

Christian Schools International
3350 E Paris Ave. SE
Grand Rapids, MI 49512-3054
Ph: (616)957-1070   Fax: (616)957-5022
Fr: 800-635-8288
URL: http://www.gospelcom.net/csi

Annual, November. $52.00 for nonmembers. Covers nearly 450 Reformed Christian elementary and secondary schools; related associations; societies without schools. Entries include: For schools-School name, address, phone; name, title, and address of officers; names of faculty members. Arrangement: Geographical.

★2748★ Counseling Services Directory

infoUSA Inc.
5711 S 86th Cir.
Omaha, NE 68127-0347
Ph: (402)930-3500   Fax: (402)331-0176
Fr: 800-555-6124
URL: http://www.abii.com

Annual. Number of listings: 13,066. Entries include: Name, address, phone (including area code), size of advertisement, year first in "Yellow Pages," name of owner or manager, number of employees. Compiled from telephone company "Yellow Pages," nationwide. Arrangement: Geographical.

★2749★ Directory of Counseling Services

International Association of Counseling Services
101 S Whiting St., Ste. 211
Alexandria, VA 22304-3416
Ph: (703)823-9840   Fax: (703)823-9843

Annual, September. $50.00. Covers about 200 accredited services in the United States and Canada concerned with psychological, educational, and vocational counseling, including those at colleges and universities, and public and private agencies. Entries include: Name, address, phone, hours of operation, director's name, service, clientele served. Arrangement: Geographical.

★2750★ Directory of Public School Systems in the U.S.

American Association for Employment in Education
3040 Riverside Dr., Ste. 125
Columbus, OH 43221
Ph: (614)485-1111   Fax: (614)485-9609

Annual, Winter. $80.00. Covers about 14,500 public school systems in the United States and their administrative personnel. Entries include: System name, address, phone, website address, name and title of personnel administrator, levels taught and approx. student population. Arrangement: Geographical by state.

★2751★ Directory of Refugee Mental Health Professionals and Paraprofessionals

Refugee Assistance Program–Mental Health Technical Assistance Center
University of Minnesota
Mayo Mail Code 85
420 Delaware St. SE
Minneapolis, MN 55455
Ph: (612)638-0700   Fax: (612)627-4205

$18.00. Covers professionals who specialize in refugee mental health. Entries include: Name, address, phone, geographical area served and area of specialty. Arrangement: Geographical.

★2752★ Directory: Who's Who in Career Services & HR/Staffing

National Association of Colleges and Employers
62 Highland Ave.
Bethlehem, PA 18017
Ph: (610)868-1421   Fax: (610)868-0208
Fr: 800-544-5272
URL: http://www.jobweb.org/

Annual, latest edition January 1999. $47.95. Covers about 1,760 college and university offices concerned with securing employment for graduates and about 1,430 companies with staff assigned to recruiting and hiring college graduates. Entries include: For colleges-College name and address; names, titles, phone, fax, and URL and e-mail addresses of career planning and placement personnel; interview dates for undergraduates and graduates; months of graduation; whether alumni placement is also handled, student enrollment (including minority data), and dates of career/job fairs. For employers-Company name; names, addresses, phone, fax and e-mail addresses of recruitment staff; names of secondary contacts; nature of business; number of employees. Arrangement: Colleges are geographical; employers are alphabetical. Indexes: Institutional name, personal name (college personnel); geographical, personal name (in company recruitment).

★2753★ *The Encyclopedia of Suicide*
Facts On File Inc.
132 W 31st St., 17th Fl.
New York, NY 10001-2006
Ph: (212)967-8800   Fax: 800-678-3633
Fr: 800-322-8755

$65.00. Publication includes: List of national organizations and suicide prevention/crisis intervention groups in the United States and Canada. Principal content of publication is detailed information about the problem and history of suicide. Indexes: Alphabetical.

★2754★ *Fifty State Educational Directories*
Career Guidance Foundation
8090 Engineer Rd., Ste. B
San Diego, CA 92111
Ph: (858)560-8051   Fax: (858)278-8960
Fr: 800-854-2670
URL: http://www.cgf.org

Annual, latest edition June 1996. $89.00. Microfiche. Collection consists of reproductions of the state educational directories published by the departments of education of individual 50 states. Directory contents vary, but the majority contain listings of elementary and secondary schools, colleges and universities, and state education officials. Amount of detail in each also varies. Entries include: Usually, institution name, address, and name of one executive.

★2755★ *Handbook of Private Schools*
Porter Sargent Publishers Inc.
11 Beacon St., Ste. 1400
Boston, MA 02108-3099
Ph: (617)523-1670   Fax: (617)523-1021
Fr: 800-342-7470
E-mail: orders@portersargent.com

Annual, June. $99.00. Covers more than 1,600 elementary and secondary boarding and day schools in the United States. Entries include: School name, address, phone, fax, E-mail, URL, type of school (boarding or day), sex and age range, names and titles of administrators, grades offered, academic orientation, curriculum, new admissions yearly, tests required for admission, enrollment and faculty, graduate record, number of alumni, tuition and scholarship figures, summer session, plant evaluation and endowment, date of establishment, calendar, association membership, description of school's offerings and history, test score averages, uniform requirements, geographical, and demographic date. Arrangement: Geographical. Indexes: Alphabetical by school name, cross indexed by state, region, grade range, sexes accepted, school features and enrollment.

★2756★ *MDR's School Directories*
Market Data Retrieval
1 Forest Pkwy.
Shelton, CT 06484
Ph: (203)926-4800   Fax: (203)926-1826
Fr: 800-333-8802
URL: http://www.schooldata.com

Annual, October. $1,349.00 for set. Covers over 90,000 public, 8,000 Catholic, and 15,000 other private schools (grades K-12) in the United States; over 15,000 school district offices, and 76,000 school librarians; and 27,000 media specialists, 33,000 technology coordinators. Includes names of over 165,000 school district administrators and staff members in county and state education administration. Entries include: For districts: District name and address; telephone and fax number; number of schools; number of teachers in the district; district enrollment; special Ed students; limited-english proficient students; minority percentage by race, college bound students; expenditures per student for instructional materials; poverty level; title 1 dollars; site-based management; district open/close dates; construction indicator; technologies and quantities (instructional computer brands, multimedia computers; networks, VCRs, satellite dish, DVD Player/Drive High-Speed Internet Access URL); district-level adminstrators, *new superintendents shaded.* For schools: School name and address-new public shaded; telephone and fax number; principal new principal shaded; librarian, media specialist and technology coordinator; grade span; special programs and school type; student enrollment; technologies and quantities (instructional computer brand noting predominant brand); Multi-Media Computers; internet connection or access; Tech Sophistication Index. Arrangement: Geographical. Indexes: District County; District Personnel; Principal; New Public Schools and Key Personnel; District and School Telephone; District URLs.

★2757★ *Mental Health Directory*
Office of Consumer, Family & Public Information
Parklawn Bldg.
5600 Fishers Ln.
Rockville, MD 20857
Ph: (301)443-4795   Fax: (301)443-0284

Irregular, previous edition 1990; latest edition 1995. $23.00. Covers hospitals, treatment centers, outpatient clinics, day/night facilities, residential treatment centers for emotionally disturbed children, residential supportive programs such as halfway houses, and mental health centers offering mental health assistance; not included are substance abuse programs, Veteran's Administration programs, nursing homes, programs for the developmentally disabled, and organizations in which fees are retained by individual members. Entries include: Name, address, phone. Arrangement: Geographical.

★2758★ *Mental Health Services Directory*
infoUSA Inc.
5711 S 86th Cir.
Omaha, NE 68127-0347
Ph: (402)930-3500   Fax: (402)331-0176
Fr: 800-555-6124
URL: http://www.abii.com

Annual. Number of listings: 18,282. Entries include: Name, address, phone (including area code), size of advertisement, year first in "Yellow Pages," name of owner or manager, number of employees. Compiled from telephone company "Yellow Pages," nationwide. Arrangement: Geographical.

★2759★ *Mental Help Net*
CenterSite, LLC
570 Metro Place
Dublin, OH 43017
URL: http://www.mentalhelp.net

Covers resources for finding mental help including local therapists and self-help groups; Services including upcoming conferences, professional education, and universities offering degrees in mental health fields.

★2760★ *National Directory of Children, Youth & Families Services*
Penny K. Spencer, Publisher
14 Inverness Dr. E. Ste. D-144
Englewood, CO 80112
Ph: (303)662-8165   Fax: 800-845-6452
Fr: 800-343-6681
URL: http://www.childrenyouthfamilydir.com/

Annual, July. $159.00. Covers more than 45,000 key contacts in the areas of Social Services, Health & Mental Health Services, Juvenile Justice Agencies, Education Departments, Treatment Centers & Hospitals, Referral Networks, child, youth, and family-oriented social services, health and mental health services, and juvenile/family court and youth advocacy services, educational listings in state and private agencies, major cities, and 3,300 counties; also covers runaway youth centers, child abuse projects, congressional committees, clearinghouses, and national organizations concerned with family health and welfare; buyers' guide to specialized services and products. Entries include: Agency listings include agency name, address, phone, fax, after-hours phone, websites, names of principal executives and staff, description of services. Arrangement: Geographical.

★2761★ *National Directory for Employment in Education*
American Association for Employment in Education
3040 Riverside Dr., Ste. 125
Columbus, OH 43221
Ph: (614)485-1111   Fax: (614)485-9609

Annual, Winter. $20.00 for institutions. Covers about 600 placement offices maintained by teacher-training institutions and 300 school district personnel officers and/or superintendents responsible for hiring profesional staff. Entries include: Institution name, address, phone, contact name, email address, and website. Arrangement: Geographical. Indexes: Personal name, subject-field of teacher training, institutions which provide vacancy bulletins and placement services to non-enrolled students.

★2762★ National Register

American Association of Sex Educators, Counselors, and Therapists
PO Box 5488
Richmond, VA 23220-0488
E-mail: aasect@worldnet.att.net

Annual. Covers about 1,600 association members. Entries include: Name, address, phone, highest degree, certification status. Arrangement: Separate geographical sections for educators, therapists, and counselors.

★2763★ Opportunities Abroad for Educators

Fulbright Teacher and Administrator Exchange Program
600 Maryland Ave. SW, Ste. 320
Washington, DC 20024-2520
Ph: (202)314-3527   Fax: (202)479-6806
Fr: 800-726-0479
URL: http://www.fulbrightexchanges.org

Annual. Covers opportunities available for elementary and secondary teachers, and two year college instructors, and school administrators to attend seminars or to teach abroad under the Mutual Educational and Cultural Exchange Act of 1961. Entries include: Countries of placement, dates, eligibility requirements, teaching assignments. Arrangement: Geographical.

★2764★ Private Independent Schools

Bunting and Lyon Inc.
238 N Main St.
Wallingford, CT 06492
Ph: (203)269-3333   Fax: (203)269-5697
URL: http://www.buntingandlyon.com

Annual, February. $110.00. Covers 1,200 English-speaking elementary and secondary private schools and summer programs in North America and abroad. Entries include: School name, address, phone, fax, e-mail, website, enrollment, tuition and other fees, financial aid information, administrator's name and educational background, director of admission, regional accreditation, description of programs, curriculum, activities, learning differences grid. Arrangement: Geographical. Indexes: School name; geographical. Summer programs, general classification grid, learning differences reference grid.

★2765★ Public Human Services Directory

American Public Human Services Association
810 1st St. NE, Ste. 500
Washington, DC 20002
Ph: (202)682-0100   Fax: (202)289-6555
E-mail: pubs@aphsa.org
URL: http://www.aphsa.org

Annual, September. $120.00 for members; $155.00 for out of country. Covers federal, state, territorial, county, and major municipal public human service agencies. Entries include: Agency name, address, phone, fax, e-mail address, web site address, names of key personnel, program area. Arrangement: Geographical.

★2766★ Requirements for Certification of Teachers, Counselors, Librarians, Administrators for Elementary and Secondary Schools

University of Chicago Press
Journals Division
PO Box 37005
Chicago, IL 60637
Ph: (773)753-3347   Fax: (773)753-0811
Fr: 877-705-1878

Annual, June. $44.00. Publication includes: List of state and local departments of education. Entries include: Office name, address, phone. Principal content of publication is summaries of each state's teaching and administrative certification requirements. Arrangement: Geographical.

★2767★ State Vocational Rehabilitation Agencies

U.S. Office of Special Education and Rehabilitative Services
330 C St. SW, Rm. 3211-MES
Washington, DC 20202-2735
Ph: (202)205-8719   Fax: (202)205-9340
URL: http://www.ed.gov/pubs/annualreport2001/index.html

Quarterly. Covers state government agencies responsible for vocational rehabilitation activities. Entries include: Agency name, address, phone, name and title of director, federal Rehabilitation Services Administration region number, fax, tty, and e-mail address. Arrangement: Geographical.

HANDBOOKS AND MANUALS

★2768★ Career Counseling in Schools: Multicultural and Developmental Perspectives

American Counseling Association
5999 Stevenson Ave.
Alexandria, VA 22304-3300
Ph: (703)823-9800   Fax: (703)823-0252
Fr: 800-347-6647

Roger D. Herring. 1998. $45.95 (paper). 348 pages.

★2769★ Career Information Center

Macmillan Publishing Co. Inc.
200 Old Tappan Rd.
Old Tappan, NJ 07675
Fr: 800-428-5331

Visual Education Center Staff. Seventh edition, 1999. $275.00. 2080 pages. This 13-volume set profiles over 600 occupations. Each occupational profile describes job duties, educational requirements, how to get the job, advancement possibilities, employment outlook, working conditions, earnings and benefits, and where to write for more information.

★2770★ Careers for Good Samaritans and Other Humanitarian Types

McGraw-Hill Trade
2 Penn Plaza
New York, NY 10121
Ph: (212)904-2000   Fr: 800-722-4726
E-mail: ntcpub@tribune.com

Marjorie Eberts and Margaret Gisler. Second edition, 1998. $9.95 (paper). 274 pages. Contains hundreds of ideas for turning good work into paid work. Inventories opportunities in service organizations like the Red Cross, Goodwill, and the Salvation Army; religious groups, VISTA, the Peace Corps, and UNICEF; and agencies at all levels of the government. Part of Careers for You series.

★2771★ Careers in Health Care

McGraw-Hill Trade
2 Penn Plaza
New York, NY 10121
Ph: (212)904-2000   Fr: 800-722-4726
E-mail: ntcpub@tribune.com

Barbara M. Swanson. Fourth edition, 2000. $17.95; $13.95 (paper). 320 pages. Describes job duties, work settings, salaries, licensing and certification requirements, educational preparation, and future outlook. Gives ideas on how to secure a job.

★2772★ Careers in Social and Rehabilitation Services

McGraw-Hill Trade
2 Penn Plaza
New York, NY 10121
Ph: (212)904-2000   Fr: 800-722-4726
E-mail: ntcpub@tribune.com

Geraldine O. Garner. Second edition, 2001. $19.95; 14.95 (paper). 128 pages.

★2773★ Clinical Supervision in Alcohol and Drug Abuse Counseling: Principles, Models, Methods

John Wiley & Sons, Incorporated
111 River St.
Hoboken, NJ 07030
Ph: (201)748-6000   Fax: (201)748-6088

David J. Powell, Archie Brodsky. 2004. $40.00. 448 pages.

★2774★ Employment and Training Counselor

National Learning Corporation
212 Michael Dr.
Syosset, NY 11791
Ph: (516)921-8888   Fax: (516)921-8743
Fr: 800-645-6337

Jack Rudman. 2002. $34.95. Career explorations.

★2775★ Great Jobs for Liberal Arts Majors

McGraw-Hill Professional
2 Penn Plaza
New York, NY 10121
Ph: (212)904-2000   Fr: 800-722-4726

E-mail: ntcpub@tribune.com

Blythe Camenson. Second edition, 2001. $14.95 (paper). 256 pages.

★2776★ Great Jobs for Psychology Majors

McGraw-Hill Trade
2 Penn Plaza
New York, NY 10121
Ph: (212)904-2000   Fr: 800-722-4726
E-mail: ntcpub@tribune.com

Julie DeGalan and Stephen Lambert. 1995. $11.95 (paper). 468 pages. Out of print.

★2777★ Guidance Counselor, Elementary School

National Learning Corporation
212 Michael Dr.
Syosset, NY 11791
Ph: (516)921-8888   Fax: (516)921-8743
Fr: 800-645-6337

Jack Rudman. 2002. $49.95.

★2778★ Handbook of Career Counseling Theory and Practice

Davies Black Publishing Inc.
3803 E. Bayshore Rd.
Palo Alto, CA 94303
Ph: (650)969-8901   Fax: (650)969-8608
Fr: 800-624-1765

Mark L. Savickas and W. Bruce Walsh, editors. 1996. $69.95. 480 pages.

★2779★ The Helping Professions: A Careers Sourcebook

Thomson Wadsworth
10 Davis Dr.
Belmont, CA 94002
Ph: (650)598-9757   Fr: 800-354-9706

William Burger and Merrill Youkeles. 1999. $24.95. 206 pages. Part of the Counseling Series. Describes nine major professions in the human services field including a vignette illustrating actual work activities. Gives a realistic picture of the challenges of each profession, salary levels & duties at various levels of training, educational requirements, licensing, certification & an estimated job outlook.

★2780★ How to Get a Job in Education

Adams Media Corp.
57 Littlefield St.
Avon, MA 02322
Ph: (508)427-7100   Fax: (508)427-6790
Fr: 800-872-5627
URL: http://www.adamsmedia.com

Joel Levin. Second edition, 1995. $15.95. 320 pages. Out of print. Prepared for recent college graduates, seasoned educators, and career-changing professionals, this publication guides the job-seeker through the necessary steps to obtaining a job in education at the elementary, secondary, and university levels. Offers advice on how to prepare for state and local examinations, how to locate teaching opportunities nationwide, and how to obtain certification. Includes a nationwide salary survey. Covers public, private, summer, and overseas opportunities.

★2781★ Non-Profits and Education Job Finder

Planning Communications
7215 Oak Ave.
River Forest, IL 60305-1935
Ph: (708)366-5200   Fax: (708)366-5280
Fr: 888-366-5200
URL: http://jobfindersonline.com

Daniel Lauber. 1997. $32.95; $16.95 (paper). 336 pages. Covers 1600 sources. Discusses how to use sources of non-profit sector job vacancies in a number of specialties and state-by-state, including job-matching services, job hotlines, specialty periodicals with job ads, salary surveys, and directories. Covers a variety of fields from education to religion. Includes chapters on resume and cover letter preparation and interviewing.

★2782★ Opportunities in Counseling and Development Careers

McGraw-Hill Contemporary Books
1221 Avenue of the Americas
New York, NY 10020
Ph: (212)904-2000   Fr: 800-323-4900
E-mail: ntcpub@tribune.com

Neale Baxter, Mark U. Toch, and Philip A. Perry. 1997. $14.95; $11.95 (paper). 160 pages. A guide to planning for and seeking opportunities in this challenging field. Illustrated.

★2783★ Opportunities in Health and Medical Careers

McGraw-Hill Trade
2 Penn Plaza
New York, NY 10121
Ph: (212)904-2000   Fr: 800-722-4726

I. Donald Snook, Jr. and Leo D'Orazio. 1997. $14.95; $11.95 (paper). 202 pages. Covers the full range of medical and health occupations. Illustrated.

★2784★ Opportunities in Mental Health Careers

McGraw-Hill Trade
2 Penn Plaza
New York, NY 10121
Ph: (212)904-2000   Fr: 800-722-4726

Philip A. Perry and George Blake. 1996. $14.95; $11.95 (paper). 160 pages.

EMPLOYMENT AGENCIES AND SEARCH FIRMS

★2785★ Educational Placement Service

1001 Craig Rd., Ste. 170
St. Louis, MO 63146
Ph: (314)991-5855   Fax: (314)991-5295
URL: http://www.educatorjobs.com

Employment agency. Focuses on teaching, administrative, and education-related openings.

ONLINE JOB SOURCES AND SERVICES

★2786★ Delta T Group

E-mail: staffing@sdelta-tgroup.com
URL: http://www.delta-tgroup.com

Description: Specialized contract temporary staffing source for healthcare professionals in the fields of social service, psychiatry, mental health, and substance abuse. Organizations may request services and staffing; job seekers may view services provided, submit a resume, or peruse jobs available.

★2787★ RehabWorld

URL: http://www.rehabworld.com

Description: Site for rehabilitation professionals to learn about the profession and locate jobs. Includes user groups, salary surveys, and chat capabilities. **Main files include:** Physical Therapy, Occupational Therapy, Speech Therapy, Mental Health, Employer World, Student World, International World, Forum.

TRADESHOWS

★2788★ American Counseling Association World Conference

American Counseling Association
5999 Stevenson Ave.
Alexandria, VA 22304-3300
Ph: (703)823-9800   Fax: (703)823-0252
Fr: 800-347-6647
E-mail: meetings@counseling.org
URL: http://www.counseling.org

Annual. **Primary Exhibits:** Books, career development information, college selection, student financial aid, testing and measurement techniques, practice management companies, software, rehabilitation aids, and community agencies and private clinics specializing in substance abuse and mental health.

★2789★ **Association for Counselor Education and Supervision National Conference**

Association for Counselor Education and Supervision
c/o American Counseling Association
5999 Stevenson Ave.
Alexandria, VA 22304
Ph: (703)823-9800   Fax: (703)823-0252
Fr: 800-347-6647

Quadrennial. **Primary Exhibits:** Exhibits relating to the professional preparation of counselors.

★2790★ **International Association of Pupil Personnel Workers Conference**

International Association of Pupil Personnel Workers
c/o Bill Chmela
2025 Juneway Dr.
Long Beach, IN 46360
Ph: (219)872-4975
E-mail: w.chmela@attbi.com

Annual. **Primary Exhibits:** Equipment, supplies, and services for school administrators, counselors, attendance officers, and school social workers.

OTHER SOURCES

★2791★ **American Counseling Association (ACA)**

5999 Stevenson Ave.
Alexandria, VA 22304-3300
Ph: (703)823-9800   Fax: (703)823-0252
Fr: 800-347-6647
E-mail: ryep@counseling.org
URL: http://www.counseling.org

Description: Counseling professionals in elementary and secondary schools, higher education, community agencies and organizations, rehabilitation programs, government, industry, business, private practice, career counseling, and mental health counseling. Conducts professional development institutes and provides liability insurance. Maintains Counseling and Human Development Foundation to fund counseling projects.

★2792★ **American Psychological Association (APA)**

750 First St. NE
Washington, DC 20002-4242
Ph: (202)336-5500   Fax: (202)336-6069
Fr: 800-374-2721
E-mail: mhonaker@apa.org
URL: http://www.apa.org/

Members: Scientific and professional society of psychologists. Students participate as affiliates. **Purpose:** Works to advance psychology as a science, a profession, and as a means of promoting human welfare.

★2793★ **Association on Higher Education and Disability (AHEAD)**

PO Box 540666
Waltham, MA 02454
Ph: (781)788-0003   Fax: (781)788-0033
E-mail: ahead@ahead.org
URL: http://www.ahead.org.

Description: Individuals interested in promoting the equal rights and opportunities of disabled postsecondary students, staff, faculty, and graduates. Provides an exchange of communication for those professionally involved with disabled students; collects, evaluates, and disseminates information; encourages and supports legislation for the benefit of disabled students. Conducts surveys on issues pertinent to college students with disabilities; offers resource referral system and employment exchange for positions in disability student services. Conducts research programs; compiles statistics.

★2794★ **Counseling Association for Humanistic Education and Development (C-AHEAD)**

5999 Stevenson Ave.
Alexandria, VA 22304
Ph: (703)823-9800   Fax: 800-473-2329
Fr: 800-347-6647
E-mail: membership@counseling.org
URL: http://www.counseling.org

Description: A division of the American Counseling Association. Teachers, educational administrators, community agency workers, counselors, school social workers, and psychologists; others interested in the area of human development. Aims to assist individuals in improving their quality of life. Provides forum for the exchange of information about humanistically-oriented administrative and instructional practices. Supports humanistic practices and research on instructional and organizational methods for facilitating humanistic education; encourages cooperation among related professional groups.

★2795★ *Counselors*

Evon Publishing
832 N 7th Ave.
Iron River, MI 49935
Ph: (906)265-3190

Audiocassette. 1996. $16.95. 32 minutes. Part of the Careers and Vocational Guidance Series. Provides information about the nature of the work, educational requirements, employment outlook, earnings, and work conditions as well as additional related information.

★2796★ **Employee Assistance Society of North America (EASNA)**

230 E Ohio St., Ste. 400
Chicago, IL 60611-3265
Ph: (312)644-0828   Fax: (312)644-8557
E-mail: easna@bostrom.com
URL: http://www.easna.org

Description: Individuals in the field of employee assistance, including psychiatrists, psychologists, and managers. Facilitates communication among members; provides resource information; serves as a network for employee assistance programs nationwide. Conducts research.

★2797★ **National Association of State Directors of Special Education (NASDSE)**

1800 Diagonal Rd., Ste. 320
Alexandria, VA 22314
Ph: (703)519-3800   Fax: (703)519-3808
E-mail: nasdse@nasdse.org
URL: http://www.nasdse.org

Members: Professional society of state directors; consultants, supervisors, and administrators who have statewide responsibilities for administering special education programs. **Purpose:** Provides services to state agencies to facilitate their efforts to maximize educational outcomes for individuals with disabilities.

★2798★ **National Career Development Association (NCDA)**

10820 E 45th St., Ste. 210
Tulsa, OK 74146
Ph: (918)663-7060   Fax: (918)663-7058
Fr: (866)367-6232
E-mail: dpennington@ncda.org
URL: http://www.ncda.org

Description: A division of the American Counseling Association. **Members:** Professionals and others interested in career development or counseling in various work environments. **Purpose:** Supports counselors, education and training personnel, and allied professionals working in schools, colleges, business/industry, community and government agencies, and in private practice. **Activities:** Provides publications, support for state and local activities, human equity programs, and continuing education and training for these professionals. Provides networking opportunities for career professionals in business, education, and government.

★2799★ **National Council for Accreditation of Teacher Education (NCATE)**

2010 Massachusetts Ave. NW, Ste. 500
Washington, DC 20036-1023
Ph: (202)466-7496   Fax: (202)296-6620
E-mail: ncate@ncate.org
URL: http://www.ncate.org

Members: Representatives from constituent colleges and universities, state departments of education, school boards, teacher, and other professional groups. **Purpose:** Voluntary accrediting body devoted exclusively to evaluation and accreditation of institutions for preparation of elementary and secondary school teachers; preparation of school service personnel, including school principals, supervisors, superintendents, school psychologists, instructional technologists, and other specialists for school-oriented positions.

★2800★ National Employment Counseling Association (NECA)

5999 Stevenson Ave.
Alexandria, VA 22304
Ph: (703)823-9800   Fr: 800-347-6647
E-mail: kbrawley@mindspring.com
URL: http://www.geocities.com/Athens/
Acropolis/6491/neca.html

Description: A division of the American Counseling Association. Those engaged in employment counseling, counselor education, research, administration or supervision in business and industry, colleges and universities, and federal and state governments; students. Offers professional leadership and development services; provides opportunities for professional growth through workshops and special projects.

★2801★ National Rehabilitation Association (NRA)

633 S Washington St.
Alexandria, VA 22314
Ph: (703)836-0850   Fax: (703)836-0848
E-mail: info@nationalrehab.org
URL: http://www.nationalrehab.org/website/
index.html

Description: Providing opportunities through knowledge and diversity for professionals in the fields of rehabilitation of people with disabilities.

★2802★ National Rehabilitation Counseling Association (NRCA)

8807 Sudley Rd., Ste. 102
Manassas, VA 20110-4719
Ph: (703)361-2077   Fax: (703)361-2489
E-mail: nrcaoffice@aol.com
URL: http://nrca-net.org/

Description: A division of the National Rehabilitation Association. Professional and student rehabilitation counselors. Works to expand the role of counselors in the rehabilitation process and seeks to advance members' professional development. Supports legislation favoring the profession.

★2803★ *Opportunities in Psychology Careers*

McGraw-Hill Trade
2 Penn Plaza
New York, NY 10121
Ph: (212)904-2000   Fr: 800-722-4726
E-mail: ntcpub@tribune.com

Donald E. Super and Charles McAfee Super. 1994. $14.95; $11.95 (paper). A guide to planning for and building a career in the field.

Includes bibliography and illustrations. Out of print.

★2804★ *Overseas Employment Opportunities for Educators: Department of Defense Dependents Schools*

DIANE Publishing Co.
PO Box 1428
Collingdale, PA 19023-8428
Ph: (610)461-6200   Fax: (610)461-6130
Fr: 800-782-3833

Barry Leonard, editor. 1999. $20.00. 44 pages. An introduction to teachings positions in the Dept. of Defense Dependents Schools (DoDDS), a worldwide school system, operated by the DoD in 14 countries.

★2805★ *Teaching & Related Occupations*

Delphi Productions
3160 4th St.
Boulder, CO 80304
Fax: (303)443-4022   Fr: 888-443-2400
URL: http://www.delphivideo.com

$95.00. 50 minutes. Part of the Careers for the 21st Century Video Library.

Credit Analysts

★2806★ Accounting Horizons

American Accounting Association
5717 Bessie Dr.
Sarasota, FL 34233
Ph: (941)921-7747   Fax: (941)923-4093

Quarterly. Publication covering the banking, finance, and accounting industries.

★2807★ American Banker

American Banker/Bond Buyer Inc.
1 State St. Plz.
New York, NY 10004
Ph: (212)803-8200   Fax: (212)843-9600
Fr: 800-982-0633
URL: http://www.americanbanker.com

Daily. $775.00/year. Newspaper for senior executives in banking and other financial services industries. Coverage includes trends, analysis, and statistics of the legislative scene in Washington; finance; mortgages; technology; small business; and regional banking.

★2808★ Brookings Papers on Economic Activity

Brookings Institution Press
1775 Massashusetts Ave. NW
Washington, DC 20036
Ph: (202)797-6000   Fax: (202)797-6195
Fr: 800-275-1447

Semiannual. Publication covering economics and business.

★2809★ Business Credit

National Association of Credit
  Management
8840 Columbia 100 Pkwy.
Columbia, MD 21045
Ph: (410)740-5560   Fax: (410)740-5574
Fr: 800-955-8815
E-mail: bcm@nacm.org

Monthly. $54.00/year, US businesses; $48.00/year for libraries; $7.00/year for sin-gle issue. Magazine covering finance, business credit management, providing information for the extension of credit, maintenance of accounts receivable, and cash asset management.

★2810★ Commercial Lending Review

Aspen Publishers Inc.
1185 Avenue of the Americas, 37th Fl.
New York, NY 10036
Ph: (212)597-0200   Fax: (212)597-0390
Fr: 800-447-1717
E-mail: cgreene@world.std.com
URL: http://www.aspenpublishers.com

$325.00/year for individuals. Journal covering all aspects of lending for commercial banks, community and regional banks and other financial institutions.

★2811★ Financial Management

Financial Management Association
School of Business
University of S Florida
Tampa, FL 33620-5500
Ph: (813)974-2084   Fax: (813)974-3318
E-mail: kporto@coba.usf.edu

Quarterly. $95.00/year for individuals; $20.00 for single issue. Journal covering business, economics, finance and management.

★2812★ Northwestern Financial Review

NFR Communications Inc.
4948 Washburn Ave.S.
Minneapolis, MN 55410
Ph: (612)929-8110   Fax: (612)929-8146
E-mail: web@nfrcom.com
URL: http://www.nfrcom.com

Bimonthly. $89.00/year for individuals; $160.00 for two years; $5.00/year for single issue. Trade publication covering commercial banking.

★2813★ U.S. Banker

Thomson Financial
195 Broadway
New York, NY 10007
Ph: (646)822-2000

URL: http://www.electronicbanker.com

Monthly. $59.00/year for individuals. Magazine serving the financial services industry.

★2814★ Commercial Finance Association (CFA)

225 W 34th St., Ste. 1815
New York, NY 10122
Ph: (212)594-3490   Fax: (212)564-6053
E-mail: postmaster@cfa.com
URL: http://www.cfa.com

Members: Organizations engaged in asset-based financial services including commercial financing and factoring and lending money on a secured basis to small- and medium-sized business firms. **Purpose:** Acts as a forum for information and consideration about ideas, opportunities, and legislation concerning asset-based financial services. Seeks to improve the industry's legal and operational procedures. **Activities:** Offers job placement and reference services for members. Sponsors School for Field Examiners and other educational programs. Compiles statistics; conducts seminars and surveys; maintains speakers' bureau and 21 committees.

★2815★ National Association of Federal Credit Unions (NAFCU)

3138 10th St. N
Arlington, VA 22201-2149
Ph: (703)522-4770   Fax: (703)524-1082
Fr: 800-336-4644
E-mail: webmaster@nafcunet.org
URL: http://www.nafcunet.org

Description: Federally chartered credit unions united for financial reform legislation and regulations impacting members. Provides information on the latest industry developments and proposed and final regulations issued by the National Credit Union Administration, the Federal Reserve, and other regulatory agencies. Represents members' interests before federal regulatory bodies and Congress. Maintains speakers' bureau and research information service; offers placement service; compiles statistics and holds educational conferences.

EMPLOYER DIRECTORIES AND NETWORKING LISTS

★2816★ American Banker-Top Commercial Banks by Assets, Deposits

American Banker/Bond Buyer Inc.
1 State St. Plz.
New York, NY 10004
Ph: (212)803-8200   Fax: (212)843-9600
Fr: 800-982-0633

Semiannual, March and September. $25.00. Publication includes: List of the top 300 commercial banks. Entries include: Name of bank, headquarters, amount of deposits at the previous quarter, place in rank at quarter. Arrangement: Ranked by deposits and assets. Indexes: Geographical.

★2817★ American Banker-Top Finance Companies Issue

American Banker/Bond Buyer Inc.
1 State St. Plz.
New York, NY 10004
Ph: (212)803-8200   Fax: (212)843-9600
Fr: 800-982-0633

Annual, December. $25.00. Publication includes: List of top finance companies with $10 million or more in capital funds. Entries include: Finance company name, headquarters, city; rankings of net receivables by type, business, consumer, and other; total capital funds for two preceding years; capital and surplus, total assets, net receivables, net income, deferred income, receivables acquired, and amount of bank credit at end of the preceding year. Arrangement: Ranked by size of capital funds.

★2818★ American Banker-Top 300 Mortgage Companies Issue

American Banker/Bond Buyer Inc.
1 State St. Plz.
New York, NY 10004
Ph: (212)803-8200   Fax: (212)843-9600
Fr: 800-982-0633

Annual, October. $25.00. Entries include: Company name, headquarters city, rank; dollar value of mortgages serviced for current and prior year; prior year's rank and gain in rank; number of mortgages; number of investors. Arrangement: Ranked by total dollar value of mortgages.

★2819★ American Banker-Top 300 Thrifts by Deposits

American Banker/Bond Buyer Inc.
1 State St. Plz.
New York, NY 10004
Ph: (212)803-8200   Fax: (212)843-9600
Fr: 800-982-0633

Semiannual, May and November. $25.00. Publication includes: List of top 300 thrift institutions. Entries include: Name of institution, city, rank; total assets, deposits, and total capital. Arrangement: Ranked by deposits, assets, and risk-based capital ratios.

★2820★ Branches of Your State: Banks, Savings and Loans, Credit Unions, & Savings Banks

Sheshunoff Information Services
807 Las Cimas Pkwy., Ste. 300
Austin, TX 78746
Ph: (512)472-2244   Fax: (512)305-6575
Fr: 800-456-2340

Annual, February. $475.00. Covers in separate state editions, banks, savings and loan branches, and credit unions. For those states without branch banking, individual banks, savings and loan institutions, and credit unions are listed. Entries include: Institution name, address, institution type, deposit totals, percent change over 12 months, percentage share of parent company's total deposits. Arrangement: Geographical.

★2821★ Career Opportunities in Banking, Finance, and Insurance

Facts on File Inc.
132 W 31st St., 17th Fl.
New York, NY 10001
Ph: (212)967-8800   Fax: 800-678-3633
Fr: 800-322-8755

$49.50. Publication includes: Lists of colleges with programs supporting banking, finance, and industry; professional associations; professional certifications; regulatory agencies; and Internet resources for career planning. Principal content of publication is job descriptions for professions in the banking, finance, and insurance industries. Indexes: Alphabetical.

★2822★ Corporate Finance Sourcebook

LexisNexis Group
121 Chanlon Rd.
New Providence, NJ 07974
Ph: (908)464-6800   Fax: (908)771-7704
Fr: 800-526-4902
URL: http://www.financesourcebook.com/cfs_info.htm

Annual, November. $689.00. Covers securities research analysts; major private lenders; investment banking firms; commercial banks; United States-based foreign banks; commercial finance firms; leasing companies; foreign investment bankers in the United States; pension managers; banks that offer master trusts; cash managers; business insurance brokers; business real estate specialists; lists about 3,400 firms; 14,500

key financial experts. Entries include: Firm name, address, phone, e-mail, and names and titles of officers, contacts, or specialists in corporate finance. Additional details are given as appropriate, including names of major clients, number of companies served, services, total assets, branch locations, years in business. Arrangement: Classified by line of business and then alphabetized within that line of business. Indexes: Firm name, personnel name, geographical.

★2823★ Credit Reporting Agencies Directory

infoUSA Inc.
5711 S 86th Cir.
Omaha, NE 68127-0347
Ph: (402)930-3500   Fax: (402)331-0176
Fr: 800-555-6124
URL: http://www.abii.com

Annual. Number of listings: 1,863. Entries include: Name, address, phone (including area code), size of advertisement, year first in "Yellow Pages," name of owner or manager, number of employees. Compiled from telephone company "Yellow Pages," nationwide. Arrangement: Geographical.

★2824★ Credit Union Directory

National Credit Union Administration
1775 Duke St.
Alexandria, VA 22314
Ph: (703)518-6410   Fax: (703)518-6433
URL: http://www.ncua.gov/data/directory/cudir.html

Annual, summer. $15.00. Covers federal credit unions and state-chartered credit unions that are insured by the National Credit Union Share Insurance Fund; coverage includes United States possessions. Entries include: Credit union name, address, phone, charter number, principal operating officer, year-end total assets, number of members. Arrangement: Geographical.

★2825★ Employment Opportunities, USA

Washington Research Associates
1090 Vermont Ave., NW, Ste. 800
Washington, DC 20005
Ph: (202)408-7025

Annual, quarterly updates. $184.00. Publication includes: List of over 1,000 employment contacts in companies and agencies in the banking, arts, telecommunications, education, and 14 other industries and professions, including the federal government. Entries include: Company name, name of representative, address, description of products or services, hiring and recruiting practices, training programs, and year established. Principal content is industry overviews, career news, employment opportunity information on 14 different job markets, and comprehensive guidance to career resources on the Internet. Arrangement: Classified by industry. Indexes: Occupation.

★2826★ **Mergent Bank and Finance Manual**

Mergent Inc.
5250 77 Center Dr., Ste. 150
Charlotte, NC 28217
Ph: (704)559-7601   Fax: (704)559-6945
Fr: 800-342-5647
URL: http://www.mergent.com

Annual, July; supplements in 'Mergent Bank & Finance News Reports'. $2,095.00. Covers in four volumes, over 12,000 national, state, and private banks, savings and loans, mutual funds, unit investment trusts, and insurance and real estate companies in the United States. Entries include: Company name, headquarters and branch offices, phones, names and titles of principal executives, directors, history, Moody's rating, and extensive financial and statistical data. Arrangement: Classified by type of business. Indexes: Company name.

★2827★ **National Bankers Association-Roster of Minority Banking Institutions**

National Bankers Association
1513 P St. NW
Washington, DC 20005
Ph: (202)588-5432   Fax: (202)588-5443

Annual, October. $5.00. Covers about 140 banks owned or controlled by minority group persons or women. Entries include: Bank name, address, phone, name of one executive. Arrangement: Geographical.

★2828★ **NFCC Directory of Members**

National Foundation for Credit Counseling
801 Roeder Rd., Ste. 900
Silver Spring, MD 20910
Ph: (301)589-5600   Fax: (301)495-5623

$5.00 for members; $10.50 for nonmembers. Covers about 1,300 affiliated non-profit Consumer Credit Counseling Services in the United States, Puerto Rico, and Canada, which provide non-profit education, counseling, and debt management programs for financial and housing issues. Entries include: Member name, address, phone, fax, name and title of contact, subsidiary and branch names and locations, names and titles of key personnel, description. Arrangement: Geographical. Indexes: Agency name, name of personnel.

★2829★ **Roster of Minority Financial Institutions**

U.S. Department of the Treasury
1500 Pennsylvania Ave. NW
Washington, DC 20220
Ph: (202)622-2000

Biennial. Covers about 170 commercial, minority-owned and controlled financial institutions participating in the Department of the Treasury's Minority Bank Deposit Program. Entries include: Name of institution, name and title of chief officer, address, phone, fax. Arrangement: Geographical.

★2830★ **Thomson Bank Directory**

Thomson Financial Publishing
4709 W.Golf Rd., Ste. 600
Skokie, IL 60076
Ph: (847)676-9600   Fax: (847)933-8101
Fr: 800-321-3373
URL: http://www.tgbr.com

Semiannual, June and December. $608.00; $509.00 for annual subscription. Covers in three volumes, about 11,000 banks and 50,000 branches of United States banks, and 60,000 foreign banks and branches engaged in foreign banking; Federal Reserve system and other United States government and state government banking agencies; 500 largest North American and International commercial banks; paper and automated clearinghouses. Volumes 1 and 2 contain North American listings; volumes 3 and 4, international listings (also cited as 'Thomson International Bank Directory'); volume 5, Worldwide Correspondents Guide containing key correspondent data to facilitate funds transfer. Entries include: For domestic banks-Bank name, address, phone, telex, cable, date established, routing number, charter type, bank holding company affiliation, memberships in Federal Reserve System and other banking organizations, principal officers by function performed, principal correspondent banks, and key financial data (deposits, etc.). For international banks-Bank name, address, phone, fax, telex, cable, SWIFT address, transit or sort codes within home country, ownership, financial data, names and titles of key personnel, branch locations. For branches-Bank name, address, phone, charter type, ownership and other details comparable to domestic bank listings. Arrangement: Geographical. Indexes: Alphabetical, geographical.

★2831★ **Thomson North American Financial Institutions Directory**

Thomson Financial Publishing
4709 W.Golf Rd., Ste. 600
Skokie, IL 60076
Ph: (847)676-9600   Fax: (847)933-8101
Fr: 800-321-3373

Semiannual. $449.00 for single issue. Covers 15,000 banks and their branches; over 2,000 head offices, and 15,500 branches of savings and loan associations; over 5,500 credit unions with assets over $5 million; Federal Reserve System and other U.S. government and state government banking agencies; bank holding, commercial finance, and leasing companies; coverage includes the United States, Canada, Mexico, and Central America. Entries include: Bank name, address, phone, fax, telex, principal officers and directors, date established, financial data, association memberships, attorney or counsel, correspondent banks, out-of-town branch, holding company affiliation, ABA transit number and routing symbol, MICR number with check digit, credit card(s) issued, trust powers, current par value and dividend of common stock, kind of charter. Arrangement: Geographical. Indexes: Alphabetical.

★2832★ **Who's Who in Finance and Industry**

Marquis Who's Who
121 Chanlon Rd.
New Providence, NJ 07974
Ph: (908)673-1101   Fax: (908)673-1189
Fr: 800-473-7020
URL: http://www.marquiswhoswho.com

Biennial, July of odd years. $292.50. Covers over 21,000 individuals. Entries include: Name, home and office addresses, personal, career, and family data; civic and political activities; memberships, publications, awards. Arrangement: Alphabetical.

HANDBOOKS AND MANUALS

★2833★ **Careers in Banking and Finance**

Rosen Publishing Group, Inc.
29 E. 21st St.
New York, NY 10010
Ph: (212)777-3017   Fax: 888-436-4643
Fr: 800-237-9932

Patricia Haddock. 2001. $16.95 139 pages. Offers advice on job hunting. Describes jobs at all levels in banking and finance. Contains information about the types of financial organizations where the jobs are found, educational requirements, job duties, and salaries.

★2834★ **Opportunities in Banking Careers**

McGraw-Hill Trade
2 Penn Plaza
New York, NY 10121
Ph: (212)904-2000   Fr: 800-722-4726

Philip Perry. 1994. $14.95; $11.95 (paper). 160 pages. Discusses banking opportunities in a variety of settings: commercial banks, savings and loans, finance companies, and mortgage banks.

★2835★ **Opportunities in Hospital Administration Careers**

McGraw-Hill/Contemporary Books
1221 Avenue of the Americas
New York, NY 10020
Ph: (212)904-2000   Fr: 800-323-4900
E-mail: ntcpub@tribune.com

I. Donald Snook. 1997. $14.95; $11.95 (paper). 160 pages. Discusses opportunities for administrators in a variety of management settings: hospital, department, clinic, group practice, HMO, mental health, and extended care facilities.

EMPLOYMENT AGENCIES AND SEARCH FIRMS

★2836★ Alfred Daniels & Associates Inc.
5795 Waverly Ave.
La Jolla, CA 92037
Ph: (858)459-4009

Executive search firm.

★2837★ Bell Wishingrad Partners Inc.
230 Park Ave., Ste. 1000
New York, NY 10169
Ph: (212)949-6666

Executive search firm focused on the financial industry.

★2838★ Butterfass, Pepe & MacCallan Inc.
PO Box 721
Mahwah, NJ 07430
Ph: (201)560-9500   Fax: (201)560-9506

Executive search firm.

★2839★ Cheryl Alexander & Associates
8588 Shadow Creek Dr.
Maple Grove, MN 55311
Ph: (763)416-4570

Executive search firm.

★2840★ Cross Hill Partners LLC
245 Park Ave., Fl. 24
New York, NY 10167
Ph: (212)672-1604   Fax: (212)202-6316

Executive search firm.

★2841★ DBL Associates
1334 Park View Ave., Ste. 100
Manhattan Beach, CA 90266
Ph: (310)546-8121

Executive search firm focused on the financial industry.

★2842★ Douglas-Allen Inc.
1500 Main St., Fl. 24
PO Box 15368
Springfield, MA 01115
Ph: (413)739-0900

Executive search firm.

★2843★ Employment Advisors
815 Nicollet Mall Ste 200
Minneapolis, MN 55402
Ph: (612)339-3944
E-mail: info@collegegraduateregistry.com
URL: http://www.collegegraduateregistry.com

Employment agency. Places candidates in variety of fields.

★2844★ ESearch Group
30 Tower Ln.
Avon, CT 06001
Ph: (860)677-6770

Executive search firm.

★2845★ Financial Professionals
4100 Spring Valley Rd., Ste. 307
Dallas, TX 75244
Ph: (972)991-8999   Fax: (972)702-0776

Executive search consultants with additional offices in Forth Worth and Houston.

★2846★ Foster Partners
230W 41st St.
New York, NY 10036
Ph: (646)452-4601   Fax: (212)893-2309

Executive search firm affiliated with Daubenspeck and Associates Ltd. Branches in Washington, DC and Dallas.

★2847★ The Murphy Group
245 W Roosevelt Rd., Bldg.15 Ste.101
Chicago, IL 60185
Ph: (630)639-5110   Fax: (630)639-5113
E-mail: info@murphygroup.com
URL: http://www.murphygroup.com

Employment agency. Places personnel in a variety of positions. Additional offices located in Napierville, Park Ridge, and OakBrook.

TRADESHOWS

★2848★ Pennsylvania Association of Community Bankers Convention
Pennsylvania Association of Community Bankers
PO Box 5319
Harrisburg, PA 17110-5319
Ph: (717)231-7447   Fax: (717)231-7445

Annual. **Primary Exhibits:** Equipment, supplies, and services for community banks, thrifts, and associate firms.

OTHER SOURCES

★2849★ American Bankers Association (ABA)
1120 Connecticut Ave. NW
Washington, DC 20036
Ph: (202)663-5000   Fax: (202)663-7543
Fr: 800-BAN-KERS
E-mail: mwhitake@aba.com
URL: http://www.aba.com

Members: Principally commercial banks and trust companies; combined assets of members represent approximately 90% of the U.S. banking industry; approximately 94% of members are community banks with less than $500 million in assets. **Purpose:** Seeks to enhance the role of commerical bankers as preeminent providers of financial services through communications, research, legal action, lobbying of federal legislative and regulatory bodies, and education and training programs. Serves as spokesperson for the banking industry; facilitates exchange of information among members. Maintains the American Institute of Banking, an industry-sponsored adult education program. **Activities:** Conducts educational and training programs for bank employees and officers through a wide range of banking schools and national conferences. Maintains liaison with federal bank regulators; lobbies Congress on issues affecting commercial banks; testifies before congressional committees; represents members in U.S. postal rate proceedings. Serves as secretariat of the International Monetary Conference and the Financial Institutions Committee for the American National Standards Institute. Files briefs and lawsuits in major court cases affecting the industry. Conducts teleconferences with state banking associations on such issues as regulatory compliance; works to build consensus and coordinate activities of leading bank and financial service trade groups. Provides services to members including: public advocacy; news media contact; insurance program providing directors and officers with liability coverage, financial institution bond, and trust errors and omissions coverage; research service operated through ABA Center for Banking Information; fingerprint set processing in conjunction with the Federal Bureau of Investigation; discounts on operational and income-producing projects through the Corporation for American Banking. Conducts conferences, forums, and workshops covering subjects such as small business, consumer credit, agricultural and community banking, trust management, bank operations, and automation. Sponsors ABA Educational Foundation and the Personal Economics Program, which educates schoolchildren and the community on banking, economics, and personal finance.

★2850★ American Credit Union Mortgage Association (ACUMA)
PMB 3419, Via Lido, No. 135
Newport Beach, CA 92663
Ph: (949)645-5288   Fax: (949)645-5297
Fr: 877-44-ACUMA
E-mail: info102@acuma.org
URL: http://www.acuma.org

Members: Credit unions providing real estate lending services. **Purpose:** Promotes adherence to high standards of ethics and practice in the issuing of mortgage loans. **Activities:** Represents members' interests before regulatory agencies and industrial associations; conducts research and educational programs; maintains speakers' bureau; compiles statistics.

★2851★ American Financial Services Association (AFSA)

919 18th St. NW
Washington, DC 20006
Ph: (202)296-5544   Fax: (202)223-0321
E-mail: afsa@afsamail.com
URL: http://www.americanfinsvcs.org

Description: Companies whose business is primarily direct credit lending to consumers and/or the purchase of sales finance paper on consumer goods. Some members have insurance and retail subsidiaries; some are themselves subsidiaries of highly diversified parent corporations. Encourages the business of financing individuals and families for necessary and useful purposes, at reasonable charges, including interest; promotes consumer understanding of basic money management principles as well as constructive uses of consumer credit. Educational services include films, textbooks, and study units for the classroom and budgeting guides for individuals and families. Compiles statistical reports; offers seminars.

★2852★ American League of Financial Institutions (ALFI)

900 19th St. NW, Ste. 400
Washington, DC 20006
Ph: (202)857-6176   Fax: (202)296-8716
URL: http://www.alfi.org

Members: Federal and state chartered minority savings and loan associations in 25 states and the District of Columbia. **Purpose:** Undertakes programs to increase the income of and savings flow into the associations including a direct solicitation effort; provides counseling and technical assistance for member associations; offers consultant services to assist individual associations and groups wishing to organize new associations or acquire existing associations with development potential; collects, organizes, and distributes materials that will aid member associations. **Activities:** Conducts research to improve investment capability, resolve common management problems, and evaluate statistical data on an industry-wide basis to develop and institute training programs for management personnel. Conducts research programs.

★2853★ Association for Financial Professionals (AFP)

7315 Wisconsin Ave., Ste. 600W
Bethesda, MD 20814-3211
Ph: (301)907-2862   Fax: (301)907-2864
E-mail: jkaitz@afponline.org
URL: http://www.afponline.org

Purpose: Seeks to establish a national forum for the exchange of concepts and techniques related to improving the management of treasury and the careers of professionals through research, education, publications, and recognition of the treasury management profession through a certification program. **Activities:** Conducts educational programs. Operates career center.

★2854★ Consumer Data Industry Association

1090 Vermont Ave. NW, Ste. 200
Washington, DC 20005-4905
Ph: (202)408-7401   Fax: (202)371-0134
URL: http://www.cdiaonline.org

Description: International association of credit reporting and collection service offices. Maintains hall of fame and biographical archives; conducts specialized educational programs. Offers computerized services and compiles statistics.

★2855★ Credit Professionals International (CPI)

525 B N Laclede Station Rd.
St. Louis, MO 63119
Ph: (314)961-0031   Fax: (314)961-0040
E-mail: creditpro@creditprofessionals.org
URL: http://www.creditprofessionals.org

Description: Individuals employed in credit or collection departments of business firms or professional offices. Conducts educational program in credit work. Sponsors Career Club composed of members who have been involved in credit work at least 25 years.

★2856★ Credit Union Executives Society (CUES)

5510 Research Park Dr.
Madison, WI 53711-5377
Ph: (608)271-2664   Fax: (608)271-2303
Fr: 800-252-2664
E-mail: cues@cues.org
URL: http://www.cues.org

Description: Advances the professional development of credit union CEOs senior management and directors. An international membership associations dedicated to the professional development of credit union CEO's, senior management and directors. Offers from highly acclaimed institues to an array of online services to progressive new strategic solutions.

★2857★ Financial Occupations

Delphi Productions
3160 4th St.
Boulder, CO 80304
Fax: (303)443-4022   Fr: 888-443-2400
URL: http://www.delphivideo.com

$95.00. 50 minutes. Part of the Careers for the 21st Century Video Library.

★2858★ National Association of Credit Management (NACM)

8840 Columbia
100 Parkway
Columbia, MD 21045-2158
Ph: (410)740-5560   Fax: (410)740-5574
Fr: 800-955-8815
E-mail: nacm_info@nacm.org
URL: http://www.nacm.org

Description: Credit and financial executives representing manufacturers, wholesalers, financial institutions, insurance companies, utilities, and other businesses interested in business credit. Promotes sound credit practices and legislation. Conducts Graduate School of Credit and Financial Management at Dartmouth College, Hanover, NH.

★2859★ National Association of Credit Union Services Organizations (NACUSO)

PMB 3419 Via Lido, No.135
Newport Beach, CA 92663
Ph: (949)645-5296   Fax: (949)645-5297
Fr: 888-462-2870
E-mail: bdorsa@nacuso.org
URL: http://www.nacuso.org

Members: Credit union service organizations and their employees. **Purpose:** Promotes professional advancement of credit union service organization staff; seeks to insure adherence to high standards of ethics and practice among members. **Activities:** Conducts research and educational programs; formulates and enforces standards of conduct and practice; maintains speakers' bureau; compiles statistics.

★2860★ National Bankers Association (NBA)

1513 P St. NW
Washington, DC 20005
Ph: (202)588-5432   Fax: (202)588-5443
E-mail: nahart@nationalbankers.org
URL: http://www.nationalbankers.org/

Members: Minority banking institutions owned by minority individuals and institutions. **Purpose:** Serves as an advocate for the minority banking industry. Organizes banking services, government relations, marketing, scholarship, and technical assistance programs. **Activities:** Offers placement services; compiles statistics.

★2861★ Risk Management Association

1 Liberty Pl.
1650 Market St., Ste. 2300
Philadelphia, PA 19103-7398
Ph: (215)446-4000   Fax: (215)446-4101
Fr: 800-677-7621
E-mail: member@rmahq.org
URL: http://www.rmahq.org

Members: Commercial and savings banks, and savings and loan, and other financial services companies. **Activities:** Conducts research and professional development activities in areas of loan administration, asset management, and commercial lending and credit to increase professionalism.

★2862★ Society of Certified Credit Executives (SCCE)

PO Box 390106
Minneapolis, MN 55439-0106
Ph: (952)926-6547   Fax: (952)926-1624
E-mail: scce@collector.com
URL: http://www.acainternational.org

Description: A division of the International Credit Association. Credit executives who have been certified through SCCE's professional certification programs. Seeks to improve industry operations while expanding the knowledge of its members. Maintains placement service.

Dancers and Choreographers

SOURCES OF HELP-WANTED ADS

★2863★ AAHPERD Update

American Alliance for Health, Physical
Education, Recreation & Dance
1900 Association Dr.
Reston, VA 20191
Ph: (703)476-3400   Fax: (703)476-9527
Fr: 800-213-7193
E-mail: update@aahperd.org
URL: http://www.aahperd.org

Description: Six issues/year. Provides
news and information on the Alliance. Discusses current issues and research in the
areas of health, physical education, recreation, dance, fitness, and adapted physical
education. Recurring features include a calendar of events, reports of meetings, news
of educational opportunities, job listings,
notices of publications available, and columns titled President's Message, Membership Corner, and From the EVP's Desk.

★2864★ ArtSEARCH

Theatre Communications Group
520 Eighth Ave., 24th Fl.
New York, NY 10018-4156
Ph: (212)609-5900   Fax: (212)609-5901
E-mail: custserv@tcg.org
URL: http://www.tcg.org

Description: Biweekly. Publishes classified
listings for job opportunities in the arts,
especially theatre, dance, music, and educational institutions. Listings include opportunities in administration, artistic, education,
production, and career development.

★2865★ Back Stage West

VNU Business Media USA
770 Broadway
New York, NY 10003
Ph: (646)654-5000
URL: http://www.vnubusinessmedia.com/

Weekly. $95.00/year. Trade publication cov-
ering the entertainment industry.

★2866★ C Magazine

C The Visual Arts Foundation
PO Box 5, Sta. B
Toronto, ON, Canada M5T 2T2
Ph: (416)539-9495   Fax: (416)539-9903
Fr: 800-745-6312

Quarterly. Periodical covering the visual and
performing arts.

★2867★ Daily Variety

Reed Business Information
5700 Wilshire Blvd., Ste. 120
Los Angeles, CA 90036
Ph: (323)857-6600   Fax: (323)965-2475

Daily. Global entertainment newspaper (tabloid).

★2868★ Dance Magazine

Dance Magazine
111 Myrtle St., Ste. 203
Oakland, CA 94607
Ph: (510)839-6060   Fax: (510)839-6066
E-mail: dancemag@dancemagazine.com
URL: http://www.dancemagazine.com

Monthly. $34.95/year for individuals; $46.95/
year for Canada; $66.95/year for other coun-
tries. Performng arts magazine featuring all
forms of dance with profiles, news, photos,
reviews of performances, and information on
books, videos, films, schools, health, and
technique.

★2869★ Music and Media

VNU Business Media USA
770 Broadway
New York, NY 10003
Ph: (646)654-5000
URL: http://www.vnubusinessmedia.com/
box/bp/div_ent_music_musicm.

Weekly. $175.00/year. Publication covering
the music and entertainment industries.

★2870★ PIX

VNU Business Media USA
770 Broadway
New York, NY 10003
Ph: (646)654-5000

Monthly. Trade publication covering the arts
and entertainment industries.

**★2871★ Ross Reports Television and
Film**

VNU Business Media USA
770 Broadway
New York, NY 10003
Ph: (646)654-5000

Monthly. $59.00/year for individuals; $7.95
for single issue. Trade publication covering
talent agents and casting directors in New
York and Los Angeles, as well as television
and film production. Special national issue
every December. Sister publication to Back
Stage, Back Stage West.

★2872★ Strategies

American Alliance for Health, Physical
Education, Recreation & Dance
1900 Association Dr.
Reston, VA 20191
Ph: (703)476-3400   Fax: (703)476-9527
Fr: 800-213-7193
E-mail: strategies@aahperd.org

$25.00/year for members; $40.00/year for
individuals; $63.00/year for businesses, in-
stitutions, and libraries. Journal providing
practical, hands-on information to physical
educators and coaches.

★2873★ Variety

Reed Business Information
5700 Wilshire Blvd., Ste. 120
Los Angeles, CA 90036
Ph: (323)857-6600   Fax: (323)965-2475

Weekly. $129.00/year. Newspaper (tabloid)
reporting on theatre, television, radio, music,
records, and movies.

PLACEMENT AND JOB REFERRAL SERVICES

★2874★ Dance Notation Bureau (DNB)

151 W 30th St., Rm. 202
New York, NY 10001-4007
Ph: (212)564-0985   Fax: (212)216-9027
E-mail: notation@mindspring.com
URL: http://www.dancenotation.org

Description: Documents and preserves dance works through the use of graphic notation. Awards certification for all levels of Labanotation, Teacher of Labanotation, and Professional Notator. Conducts research into movement-related analysis techniques and programs. Maintains extension at Ohio State University, Columbus. Maintains placement service; assists choreographers in copyrighting, licensing, and restaging of their dance works. Offers service for dance reconstructors and circulating library materials to members. Maintains most substantial archive of original Labanotated dance scores in the world.

★2875★ Institute of American Indian Arts (IAIA)

83 Avan Nu Po Rd.
Santa Fe, NM 87505
Ph: (505)424-2300   Fax: (505)424-4500
Fr: 800-804-6423
E-mail: webmaster@iaiancad.org
URL: http://www.iaiancad.org

Description: Federally chartered private institution. Offers learning opportunities in the arts and crafts to Native American youth (Indian, Eskimo, or Aleut). Emphasis is placed upon Indian traditions as the basis for creative expression in fine arts including painting, sculpture, museum studies, creative writing, printmaking, photography, communications, design, and dance, as well as training in metal crafts, jewelry, ceramics, textiles, and various traditional crafts. Students are encouraged to identify with their heritage and to be aware of themselves as members of a race rich in architecture, the fine arts, music, pageantry, and the humanities. All programs are based on elements of the Native American cultural heritage that emphasize differences between Native American and non-Native Americancultures. Sponsors Indian arts-oriented junior college offering Associate of Fine Arts degrees in various fields as well as seminars, an exhibition program, and traveling exhibits. Maintains extensive library, museum, and biographical archives. Provides placement service

★2876★ Texas International Theatrical Arts Society (TITAS)

3101 N Fitzhugh, Ste. 301
Dallas, TX 75204
Ph: (214)528-6112   Fax: (214)528-2617
E-mail: csantos@titas.org
URL: http://www.titas.org

Description: Theatrical agencies working to book entertainers and international acts into all live music venues. Provides placement service; conducts educational seminars.

★2877★ United States National Institute of Dance (USNID)

38 S Arlington Ave.
PO Box 245
East Orange, NJ 07019
Ph: (973)673-9225

Members: Participants include dance teachers, students, colleges and universities, dance companies, and local and international dance teachers' organizations. **Purpose:** Seeks to: provide dance teachers with international variations and techniques for improving artistic qualities and teaching methods; establish a uniform method of teaching all forms of dance at the highest professional level; provide an international network of consultation and counseling services for dance teachers and dancers. **Activities:** Maintains speakers' bureau; offers placement and children's services; sponsors competitions. Conducts demonstrations, lectures, and certificate correspondence courses. Produces new correspondence course "How to Prevent and Care for Dance Injuries".

★2878★ World Congress of Teachers of Dancing (WCTD)

38 S. Arlington Ave.
PO Box 245
East Orange, NJ 07019

Members: A division of the United States National Institute of Dance. Colleges, universities, professional dance schools, and teachers of dancing. **Purpose:** Seeks to maintain global standards of excellence in dance. **Activities:** Conducts educational programs and examinations; certifies teachers of dancing. Researches and disseminates information on the history and status of dance from local to international levels. Bestows honorary degrees, including Professor of Dance, Companion of Dance, and Danseur/Premier Danseuse Supreme. Maintains placement service and speakers' bureau.

EMPLOYER DIRECTORIES AND NETWORKING LISTS

★2879★ *Contemporary Theatre, Film, and Television*

Thomson Gale
27500 Drake Rd.
Farmington Hills, MI 48331-3535
Ph: (248)699-4253   Fax: (248)699-8065
Fr: 800-877-GALE
URL: http://www.gale.com

Bimonthly. $175.00. Covers in 47 volumes, more than 15,000 leading and up-and-coming performers, directors, writers, producers, designers, managers, choreographers, technicians, composers, executives, and dancers in the United States, Canada, Great Britain and the world. Each volume includes updated biographies for people listed in previous volumes and in "Who's Who in the Theatre," which this series has superseded. Entries include: Name, agent and/or office addresses, personal and career data; stage, film, and television credits; writings, awards, other information. Arrangement: Alphabetical. Indexes: Cumulative name index also covers entries in "Who's Who in the Theatre" editions 1-17 and in "Who Was Who in the Theatre".

★2880★ *Dancing Instruction Directory*

infoUSA Inc.
5711 S 86th Cir.
Omaha, NE 68127-0347
Ph: (402)930-3500   Fax: (402)331-0176
Fr: 800-555-6124
URL: http://www.abii.com

Annual. Number of listings: 14,474. Entries include: Name, address, phone (including area code), size of advertisement, year first in "Yellow Pages," name of owner or manager, number of employees. Compiled from telephone company "Yellow Pages," nationwide. Arrangement: Geographical.

★2881★ *Employment Opportunities, USA*

Washington Research Associates
1090 Vermont Ave., NW, Ste. 800
Washington, DC 20005
Ph: (202)408-7025

Annual, quarterly updates. $184.00. Publication includes: List of over 1,000 employment contacts in companies and agencies in the banking, arts, telecommunications, education, and 14 other industries and professions, including the federal government. Entries include: Company name, name of representative, address, description of products or services, hiring and recruiting practices, training programs, and year established. Principal content is industry overviews, career news, employment opportunity information on 14 different job markets, and comprehensive guidance to career resources on the Internet. Arrangement: Classified by industry. Indexes: Occupation.

★2882★ *Musical America International Directory of the Performing Arts*

Commonwealth Business Media
400 Windsor Corporate Park
50 Millstone Rd., Ste. 200
East Windsor, NJ 08520-1415
Ph: (609)371-7700   Fax: (609)371-7883
Fr: 800-221-5488
E-mail: info@musicalamerican.com
URL: http://www.musicalamerica.com

Annual, December. $115.00. Covers U.S., Canadian, and international orchestras, musicians, singers, performing arts series, dance and opera companies, festivals, contests, foundations and awards, publishers of music, artist managers, booking agents, music magazines, and service and professional music organizations. Section for U.S. and Canada also includes listings of choral groups, music schools and departments, and newspaper music critics; international directory section also lists concert managers. Entries include: Name of organization, institution, address, phone, fax, URL, e-mail addressess, key personnel; most entries include name of contact, manager, conductor, etc. For schools-Number of students and faculty. For orchestras-Number of concerts and seats. Other entries show similar details as appropriate. Arrangement: Geographical. Indexes: Alphabetical and by category.

★2883★ *National Directory of Arts Internships*

National Network for Artist Placement
935 W. Ave. 37
Los Angeles, CA 90065
Ph: (323)222-4035   Fax: (323)225-5711
URL: http://www.artistplacement.com/intern.htm

Biennial, odd years. $85.00. Covers over 5,000 internship opportunities in dance, music, theater, art, design, film, and video & over 1,250 host organizations Entries include: Name of sponsoring organization, address, name of contact; description of positions available, eligibility requirements, stipend or salary (if any), application procedures. Arrangement: Classified by discipline, then geographical.

★2884★ *Regional Theater Directory*

American Theatre Works Inc.
PO Box 510
Dorset, VT 05251
Ph: (802)867-2223   Fax: (802)867-0144
URL: http://www.theatredirectories.com

Annual, May. $20.95. Covers regional theater companies and dinner theatres with employment opportunities in acting, design, production, and management. Entries include: Company name, address, phone, name and title of contact; type of company, activities, and size of house; whether union affiliated, whether nonprofit or commercial; year established; hiring procedure and number of positions hired annually, season; description of stage; internships, description of artistic policy and audience. Arrangement: Geographical. Indexes: Company name, type of plays produced.

★2885★ *Stern's Directory*

Dance Magazine
333 Seventh Ave.,11th Fl.
New York, NY 10001
Ph: (212)979-4803   Fax: (646)674-0102
E-mail: sterns@dancemagazine.com
URL: http://www.dancemagazine.com/

Annual, September, latest edition 2002. $35.00. Covers over 10,000 dance companies, managers and artists' representatives, support services presenting organizations, festivals, funding sources, dance schools, and dance merchandise. Entries include: Company, institution or personal name, address, phone, cable, telex, fax, e-mail address, names of key personnel, and brief descriptions of services offered. Arrangement: Classified by performing arts category

as well as product or service. Indexes: Advertisers.

★2886★ *Summer Theater Directory*

American Theatre Works Inc.
PO Box 510
Dorset, VT 05251
Ph: (802)867-2223   Fax: (802)867-0144
URL: http://www.theatredirectories.com

Annual, December. $20.95. Covers summer theater companies, theme parks and cruise lines that offer employment opportunities in acting, design, production, and management; summer theater training programs. Entries include: Company name, address, phone, name and title of contact; type of company, activities and size of house; whether union affiliated, whether nonprofit or commercial; year established; hiring procedure and number of positions hired annually, season; description of stage; internships; description of company's artistic goals and audience. Arrangement: Geographical. Indexes: Company name.

HANDBOOKS AND MANUALS

★2887★ *The Art of Making Dances*

Textbook Publishers
27315 Jefferson J2
Temecula, CA 92590
Ph: (866)230-7238   Fax: (909)767-0133

Doris Humphrey. January 2003. $29.00. 189 pages.

★2888★ *Ballet Dancers in Career Transition: Sixteen Success Stories*

McFarland & Company, Inc. Publishers
PO Box 611
Jefferson, NC 28640
Ph: (336)246-4460   Fax: (336)246-5018
Fr: 800-253-2187

Nancy Upper. May 2004. $39.95 (paper). Illustrated. 264 Pages.

★2889★ *Career Information Center*

Macmillan Publishing Co. Inc.
200 Old Tappan Rd.
Old Tappan, NJ 07675
Fr: 800-428-5331

Visual Education Center Staff. Seventh edition, 1999. $275.00. 2080 pages. This 13-volume set profiles over 600 occupations. Each occupational profile describes job duties, educational requirements, how to get the job, advancement possibilities, employment outlook, working conditions, earnings and benefits, and where to write for more information.

★2890★ *Career Opportunities in Theater and the Performing Arts*

Facts on File, Inc.
132 W. 31st St., 17th Fl.
New York, NY 10001-2006
Ph: (212)967-8800   Fax: (212)967-9196
Fr: 800-322-8755
URL: http://www.factsonfile.com

Shelly Field. Second edition, 1999. $29.95; $18.95 (paper). 256 pages. Offers a complete range of information about job opportunities in the performing arts. Part of Career Opportunities Series.

★2891★ *Careers for Culture Lovers and Other Artsy Types*

VGM Career Horizons
1221 Avenue of the Americas
New York, NY 10020
Ph: (212)904-2000   Fr: 800-323-4900
E-mail: ntcpub@tribune.com

Marjorie Eberts and Margaret Gisler. Second edition, 1999. $14.95; $9.95 (paper). 234 pages. Describes how to get work in a variety of fields related to art and culture. Opportunities include picture framer, curator, art restorer, symphony manager, disk jockey, music reviewer, dance teacher, choreographer, costume designer, theater manager, light designer, drama teacher, bookstore owner, interior decorator, antique store owner, and others.

★2892★ *Careers for Night Owls and Other Insomniacs*

McGraw-Hill Trade
2 Penn Plaza
New York, NY 10121
Ph: (212)904-2000   Fr: 800-722-4726
E-mail: ntcpub@tribune.com

Louise Miller. 1995. $14.95; $9.95 (paper). 160 pages.

★2893★ *Careers for the Stagestruck and Other Dramatic Types*

McGraw-Hill Contemporary Books
1221 Avenue of the Americas
New York, NY 10020
Ph: (212)904-2000   Fr: 800-323-4900
E-mail: ntcpub@tribune.com

Lucia Mauro, 1997. $14.95; $9.95 (paper). 144 pages. Includes bibliographical references.

★2894★ *High Kicks!: The Essential Guide to Working as a Dancer*

A & C Black
37 Soho Sq.
London W1D 3QZ, United Kingdom
Ph: 020 7758 0200

Donna Rossman. 1999.

★2895★ Opportunities in Entertainment Careers

McGraw-Hill Trade
2 Penn Plaza
New York, NY 10121
Ph: (212)904-2000   Fr: 800-722-4726
E-mail: ntcpub@tribune.com

Jan Goldberg. 1999. $14.95; $11.95 (paper). 160 pages.

★2896★ Resumes for Performing Arts Careers

Vgm Career Horizons
1221 Avenue of the Americas
New York, NY 10020
Ph: (212)904-2000   Fr: 800-323-4900
E-mail: ntcpub@tribune.com

1997. $9.95 (paper). 462 pages.

TRADESHOWS

★2897★ International Society for the Performing Arts Foundation Annual Conference

International Society for the Performing Arts Foundation
17 Purdy Ave.
PO Box 909
Rye, NY 10580
Ph: (914)921-1550   Fax: (914)921-1593
E-mail: info@ispa.org
URL: http://ispa.org

Annual. **Primary Exhibits:** Information of performing artists agents and managers.

★2898★ Texas Association for Health, Physical Education, Recreation, and Dance Annual State Convention

Texas Association for Health, Physical Education, Recreation, and Dance
6300 La Calma Dr., Ste. 100
Austin, TX 78752-3890
Ph: (512)459-1299   Fax: (512)459-1290
Fr: 800-880-7300
URL: http://www.tahperd.org

Annual. **Primary Exhibits:** Publications, equipment, and supplies for health, physical education, recreation, and dance.

OTHER SOURCES

★2899★ American Dance Guild (ADG)

PO Box 2006
Lenox Hill Sta.
New York, NY 10021
Ph: (212)932-2789
E-mail: americandanceguild@hotmail.com
URL: http://www.americandanceguild.org

Description: Teachers, choreographers, therapists, performers, historians, critics, writers, and students in the field of dance, including ballet, modern dance, modern jazz dance, tap dance, and ethnological dance forms. Initiates programs of national significance in the field. Provides the American Dance Guild Harkness Resource for Dance Study Preserves: Significant Dance Works. Presents dance conferences, festivals, seminars, workshops; maintains dance educators network; publishes books and videos in the dance field.

★2900★ Dancers and Choreographers

Evon Publishing
832 N 7th Ave.
Iron River, MI 49935
Ph: (906)265-3190

Audiocassette. 1996. $16.95. 32 minutes. Part of the Careers and Vocational Guidance Series. Provides information about the nature of the work, educational requirements, employment outlook, earnings, and work conditions as well as additional related information.

★2901★ International Tap Association (ITA)

PO Box 356
Boulder, CO 80306
Ph: (303)443-7989   Fax: (303)443-7992
E-mail: ita@tapdance.org
URL: http://www.tapdance.org/tap/ita/index.html

Members: Tap dancers, choreographers, teachers, scholars, students, and interested individuals. **Purpose:** Promotes the understanding, preservation, and development of tap dance as an art form. Encourages the creation of new performance venues, touring circuits, and presentation methods. **Activities:** Maintains biographical and video archives covering historical figures in tap dance. Publishes the ITA newsletter six times per year. Houses information clearing house for tap resources.

★2902★ Media and the Arts Occupations

Delphi Productions
3160 4th St.
Boulder, CO 80304
Fax: (303)443-4022   Fr: 888-443-2400
URL: http://www.delphivideo.com

$95.00. 50 minutes. Part of the Careers for the 21st Century Video Library.

★2903★ National Dance Association (NDA)

1900 Association Dr.
Reston, VA 20191-1599
Ph: (703)476-3421   Fax: (703)476-9527
Fr: 800-213-7193
E-mail: nda@aahperd.org
URL: http://www.aahperd.org/nda

Description: Dance educators, choreographers, schools and dance/arts administrators, researchers, performers, dance medicine/science specialists, technologists, therapists and others associated with dance/arts education. Works with 160 federal and state agencies, arts and education associations, foundations, and businesses and corporations to ensure that: (1) quality dance/arts education is available to all Americans regardless of age, sex, ability, interest, or culture; and (2) quality dance/arts education becomes a part of U.S. education for all children.

Database Administrators

SOURCES OF HELP-WANTED ADS

★2904★ ACM Computing Surveys
Association for Computing Machinery
1515 Broadway
New York, NY 10036
Ph: (212)626-0500   Fax: (212)944-1318
Fr: 800-342-6626
URL: http://www.acm.org

Quarterly. $30.00/year for members; $160.00/year for nonmembers; $25.00/year for students. Journal presenting surveys and tutorials in computer science.

★2905★ Communications of the ACM
Association for Computing Machinery
1515 Broadway
New York, NY 10036
Ph: (212)626-0500   Fax: (212)944-1318
Fr: 800-342-6626
URL: http://www.acm.org/about_acm/ov_pubs.html

Monthly. Computing news magazine.

★2906★ Computerworld
101 Communications
9121 Oakdale Ave.
Chatsworth, CA 91311
Ph: (818)734-1520   Fax: (818)734-1522
URL: http://www.computerworld.com

Weekly. $48.00/year for individuals. Newspaper for information systems executives.

★2907★ Database Programming & Design
CMP Media L.L.C.
600 Community Dr.
Manhasset, NY 11030
Ph: (516)562-5000
E-mail: tgibb@cmp.com
URL: http://www.intelligententerprise.com/dbpdsearch.shtml

Monthly. Computer magazine.

★2908★ Datamation
Reed Business Information
275 Washington St.
Newton, MA 02458
Ph: (617)558-4900   Fax: (617)630-3830
Fr: 800-357-4745
E-mail: bsemich@cahners.com
URL: http://www.datamation.com

Semimonthly. $69.00/year; $10.00 for single issue. Magazine on computers and information processing.

★2909★ Digital News & Review
Reed Business Information
275 Washington St.
Newton, MA 02458
Ph: (617)558-4900   Fax: (617)630-3830
Fr: 800-357-4745

Semimonthly. Free to qualified subscribers.

★2910★ InformationWEEK
CMP Media L.L.C.
600 Community Dr.
Manhasset, NY 11030
Ph: (516)562-5000
E-mail: llally@cmp.com
URL: http://www.mfi.com

Weekly. Free to qualified subscribers. Magazine focusing on data and information processing news and strategies.

★2911★ InfoWorld
InfoWorld
155 Bovet Rd.
San Mateo, CA 94402
Ph: (650)572-7341   Fax: (415)312-0580
Fr: 800-227-8365

Weekly. Free to qualified subscribers; $180.00/year for individuals. Weekly IS publication.

★2912★ NEWS/400
iSeries Network
221 E 29th St.
Loveland, CO 80538
Ph: (970)663-4700   Fax: (970)667-2321
Fr: 800-621-1544
E-mail: letters@iseriesnetwork.com
URL: http://www.iseriesnetwork.com

Monthly. Trade magazine for programmers and data processing managers who use IBM iSeries.

★2913★ Performance Computing
CMP Media L.L.C.
600 Community Dr.
Manhasset, NY 11030
Ph: (516)562-5000
URL: http://www.performance-computing.com

Monthly. Free to qualified subscribers; $55.00/year, nonqualified. Magazine for professional users of UNIX and UNIX-like systems, and Windows NT.

EMPLOYER DIRECTORIES AND NETWORKING LISTS

★2914★ Computer Directory
Computer Directories Inc.
23815 Nichols Sawmill Rd.
Hockley, TX 77447
Ph: (281)259-5959   Fax: (281)356-7980
Fr: 800-234-4353
URL: http://www.compdirinc.com

Annual, fall. Covers approximately 130,000 computer installations; 19 separate volumes for Alaska/Hawaii, Connecticut/New Jersey, Dallas/Ft. Worth, Eastern Seaboard, Far Midwest, Houston, Illinois, Midatlantic, Midcentral, Mideast, Minnesota/Wisconsin, North Central, New England, New York Metro, Northwest, Ohio, Pennsylvania/West Virginia, Southeast, and Southwest Texas. Entries include: Company name, address, phone, fax, email, name and title of contact, hardware used, software application, operating system, programming language, computer graphics, networking system. Arrangement: Geographical. Indexes: Alphabetical, industry, hardware.

★2915★ Information Sources: The IIA Annual Membership Directory

Software & Information Industry Association
1090 Vermont Ave. NW, 6th Fl.
Washington, DC 20005
Ph: (202)289-7442   Fax: (202)289-7097
URL: http://www.siia.net/

Annual, November. $75.00 for members; $300.00 for nonmember. Covers more than 800 companies involved in the creation, distribution, and use of information products, services, and technology. Entries are prepared by companies described. Entries include: Company name, address, phone, names of executives, international partners, regional offices, trade and brand names, and description of products and services. Arrangement: Alphabetical. Indexes: Product, personal name, trade name, geographical, corporate parents, international and niche markets.

★2916★ Northwest High Tech

Resolution Business Press Inc.
12307 NE 149th Ct.
Kirkland, WA 98034
Ph: (425)487-6248   Fax: (425)649-1897
E-mail: info@respress.com
URL: http://www.respress.com

Annual. $34.95. Covers over 2,000 computer-related companies in Washington, Oregon, and Idaho, and British Columbia and Alberta, Canada. Entries include: Company; name, address, phone, fax; toll-free number; names and titles of key personnel; product/service, programming languages, financial data, number of employees, operating systems, expansion plans (including hiring and site expansion plans), company market information, Standard Industrial Classification (SIC) code., internet addresses. Arrangement: Geographical. Indexes: Company name, SIC.

★2917★ Peterson's Hidden Job Market

Thomson Peterson's
Princeton Pike Corporate Center
2000 Lenox Dr.
PO Box 67005
Lawrenceville, NJ 08648
Ph: (609)896-1800   Fax: 800-277-2465
Fr: 800-338-3282
URL: http://www.petersons.com

Annual, June. $18.95. Covers approximately 2,000 technology firms with under 1,000 employees, which hire at four times the national rate. Entries include: Company name, address, phone, fax, name and title of contact, number of employees, year founded, number of employees added in last year, percentage of growth, line of business. Arrangement: Geographical by state, then by area code. Indexes: Alphabetical by industry.

★2918★ Signal Magazine-AFCEA Source Book Issue

Armed Forces Communications & Electronics Association (AFCEA)
4400 Fair Lakes Ct.
Fairfax, VA 22033-3899
Ph: (703)631-6100   Fr: 800-336-4583
E-mail: signal@afcea.org
URL: http://www.afcea.org/sourcebook

Annual, January. $50.00. Publication includes: List of member companies concerned with communications, design, production, maintenance and operation of communications, electronics, command and control, computers, intelligence systems and imagery. Entries include: Company name, address, phone, names and titles of key personnel, financial keys, trade and brand names, products or services, affiliations, description of organizational purpose, objectives. Arrangement: Alphabetical. Indexes: By disciplines.

HANDBOOKS AND MANUALS

★2919★ Careers for Computer Buffs and Other Technological Types

VGM Career Horizons
1221 Avenue of the Americas
New York, NY 10020
Ph: (212)904-2000   Fr: 800-323-4900
E-mail: ntcpub@tribune.com

Marjorie Eberts, Margaret Gisler and Maria Olsen. Second edition, 1999. $14.95; $9.95 (paper).

★2920★ Careers in Computers

VGM Career Horizons
1221 Avenue of the Americas
New York, NY 10020
Ph: (212)904-2000   Fr: 800-323-4900
E-mail: ntcpub@tribune.com

Lila B. Stair and Leslie Stair. Third edition, 2002. $19.95; $14.95 (paper). Describes trends affecting computer careers and explores a wide range of job opportunities from programming to consulting. Provides job qualifications, salary data, job market information, personal and educational requirements, career paths, and the place of the job in the organizational structure. Offers advice on education, certification, and job search.

★2921★ Careers in Electronic Information: An Insider's Guide to the Information Job Market

National Federation of Abstracting and Information Services
1518 Walnut St., Ste. 307
Philadelphia, PA 19102
Ph: (215)893-1561   Fr: (215)893-1564

Wendy K. Wicks. 1997. $39.00 (paper). 184 pages.

★2922★ The Digital Frontier Job & Opportunity Finder

Moon Lake Media
PO Box 251466
Los Angeles, CA 90025
Ph: (310)535-2453

Don B. Altman. 1996. $19.95 (paper). 256 pages.

★2923★ Exploring Careers in the Computer Field

Rosen Publishing Group, Inc.
29 E 21st St.
New York, NY 10010
Ph: (212)777-3017   Fax: 888-436-4643
Fr: 800-237-9932

Joseph Weintraub. Revised edition, 1993. $14.95; $9.95 (paper). Discusses entry into the field, salaries, future trends, and offers job search advice. Surveys the newest growth areas in the computer industry including artificial intelligence, desktop publishing, and personal computers. Out of stock.

★2924★ Great Jobs for Computer Science Majors

McGraw-Hill Companies
1221 Avenue of the Americas
New York, NY 10020
Ph: (212)904-2000   Fr: 800-323-4900
E-mail: ntcpub@tribune.com

Jan Goldberg, Stephen Lambert, Julie De-Galan. 1997. $11.95 (paper). 365 pages.

★2925★ Job Seekers Guide to Silicon Valley Recruiters

John Wily and Sons, Inc.
605 Third Ave., 4th Fl.
New York, NY 10158-0012
Ph: (212)850-6276   Fax: (212)850-8641

Christopher W. Hunt, Scott A. Scanlon. First edition, 1998. $19.95 (paper). 371 pages. Includes a list of 2,400 recruiters specializing in high technology positions and explains how to work with them.

★2926★ The JobBank Guide to Computer and High-Tech Companies

Adams Media Corp.
57 Littlefield St.
Avon, MA 02322
Ph: (508)427-7100   Fax: (508)427-6790
Fr: 800-872-5627
URL: http://www.adamsmedia.com

Second edition, 1999. $17.95 (paper). 704 pages. Contains profiles of more than 4,500 high-tech employers.

★2927★ Peterson's Job Opportunities in Engineering and Technology

Thomson Peterson's
PO Box 67005
Lawrenceville, NJ 08648-6105
Fr: 800-338-3282

Compiled by the Peterson's staff. Fourth edition, 1996. $21.95 (paper). 384 pages.

Profiles 2,000 high-tech companies looking primarily for technical personnel in such fields as biotechnology, telecommunications, software, computers and peripherals, defense, and aerospace. Contains job-search strategies and career options to help match education and expertise to the job market. Indexed geographically, by industry, and by hiring needs.

★2928★ *Your Opportunities in Computers*
Energeia Publishing, Inc.
1307 Fairmount Ave., S
Salem, OR 97302-4313
Ph: (503)362-1480   Fax: (503)362-2123
Fr: 800-639-6048

John Tribbett. 1994. $2.50 (paper). 8 pages.

EMPLOYMENT AGENCIES AND SEARCH FIRMS

★2929★ **Cardinal Mark Inc.**
601 Carlson Pkwy., Ste. 1050
Minnetonka, MN 55305
Ph: (952)449-3005

Executive search firm concentrated on telecommunication industry.

★2930★ **Career Development Services**
706 East Ave.
Rochester, NY 14607-2105
Ph: (585)244-0750   Fax: (585)244-7115
Fr: 800-736-6710
E-mail: info@careerdev.org
URL: http://www.careerdev.org

Employment agency.

★2931★ **Huntington Personnel Consultants, Inc.**
PO Box 1077
Huntington, NY 11743-0640
Ph: (516)549-8888

Executive search firm and employment agency.

ONLINE JOB SOURCES AND SERVICES

★2932★ **ComputerJobs.com**
URL: http://www.computerjobs.com

Description: The site is an employment tool for technology professionals. Information on positions is updated hourly for seekers. Jobs may be searched by skill, or by location nationally or in a specific state or city job market. Contains thousands of job postings. National jobs may be posted for free. Also career resources for IT professionals.

★2933★ **Computerwork.com**
E-mail: candidate_support@computerwork.com
URL: http://computerwork.com/

Description: Job search and resume submission service for professionals in information technology.

★2934★ **Guru**
URL: http://www.guru.com

Description: Job board specializing in contract jobs for creative and information technology professionals. Also provides online incorporation and educational opportunities for independent contractors along with articles and advice.

★2935★ **Ittalent.com**
E-mail: ewsmith@ITtalent.com
URL: http://www.ittalent.com

Description: Job search and resume submission service for professionals in information technology.

★2936★ **ZDNet Tech Jobs**
URL: http://www.zdnet.com/special/filters/techjobs/

Description: Site houses a listing of national employment opportunities for professionals in high tech fields. Also contains resume building tips and relocation resources. Powered by Dice.com

OTHER SOURCES

★2937★ *Computer Occupations*
Delphi Productions
3160 4th St.
Boulder, CO 80304
Fax: (303)443-4022   Fr: 888-443-2400
URL: http://www.delphivideo.com

$95.00. 50 minutes. Part of the Careers for the 21st Century Video Library.

★2938★ *Information Technology Occupations*
Delphi Productions
3160 4th St.
Boulder, CO 80304
Fax: (303)443-4022   Fr: 888-443-2400
URL: http://www.delphivideo.com

$95.00. 52 minutes. Part of the Emerging Careers Video Library.

★2939★ *Information Technology Services*
Cambridge Educational
2572 Brunswick Ave.
Lawrenceville, NJ 08648-4128
Fax: 800-FAX-ON-US   Fr: 800-468-4227
URL: http://www.cambridgeeducational.com

$89.95. 2002. 18 minutes. Part of the Career Cluster Series.

Dental Assistants

SOURCES OF HELP-WANTED ADS

★2940★ American Dental Hygienists' Association Access
American Dental Hygienists' Association
444 N Michigan Ave., Ste. 3400
Chicago, IL 60611
Ph: (312)440-8900   Fax: (312)440-6780
Fr: 800-243-ADHA

Subscription included in membership; $30.00/year for nonmembers. Magazine covering current dental hygiene topics, regulatory and legislative developments, and association news.

★2941★ Bulletin of Dental Education
American Dental Education Association
1625 Massachusetts Ave. NW
Washington, DC 20036-2212
Ph: (202)667-9433   Fax: (202)667-0642

Description: Monthly. Contains news and information on dental education. Recurring features include a calendar of events, reports of meetings, news of educational opportunities, job listings, and notices of publications available.

★2942★ CDS Review
Chicago Dental Society
401 N Michigan Ave., Ste. 300
Chicago, IL 60611-4272
Ph: (312)836-7305   Fax: (312)836-7337
E-mail: reviewvox@aol.com

$25.00/year for individuals; $30.00/year, schools and industry; $45.00/year for other countries; $4.00 for single issue; $6.00/year for November issue. Dental journal.

★2943★ Dental Economics
PennWell Corp.
1421 S Sheridan Rd.
Tulsa, OK 74112
Ph: (918)835-3161   Fax: (918)832-9201
Fr: 800-331-4463
URL: http://www.de.pennnet.com/home.cfm

Monthly. $88.00 for single issue; $10.00 for single issue; $120.00/year for out of country, Mexico/Canada; $168.00/year for other countries; $16.00 for single issue, Mexico/Canada; $18.00/year for single issue, other countries. Magazine featuring business-related articles for dentists.

★2944★ Hawaii Dental Journal
Hawaii Medical Journal
1345 S Beretania St., No. 301
Honolulu, HI 96814-1821

Bimonthly. Dental journal.

★2945★ Illinois Dental Journal
Illinois State Dental Society
1010 S Second St.
PO Box 376
Springfield, IL 62705
Ph: (217)525-1406   Fax: (217)525-8872

Monthly. $25.00/year for members; $45.00/year for nonmembers; $75.00/year for nonmembers, other countries; $5.00 for single issue. Dental magazine.

★2946★ Journal of the American Dental Association
ADA Publishing
211 E Chicago Ave.
Chicago, IL 60611
Ph: (312)440-2810   Fax: (312)440-3538
Fr: 800-621-8099
URL: http://www.ada.org

Monthly. $110.00/year for individuals; $139.00/year for institutions; $13.00 for single issue; $139.00/year for individuals, foreign; $176.00/year for institutions, foreign; $122.00/year for individuals, Canadian; $158.00/year for institutions, Canadian; $69.00/year for nonmembers, student. Trade journal for the dental profession.

★2947★ Journal of the California Dental Association
California Dental Association
1201 'K' St. Mall
PO Box 13749
Sacramento, CA 95853
Ph: (916)443-0505   Fax: (916)443-2943
Fr: 800-736-7071
URL: http://www.cda.org/cda

Monthly. $24.00/year for ADA members; $60.00/year for nonmembers; $10.00/year for single issue ($10.78 July issue); $12.00/year for CDA members. Professional magazine for dentists.

★2948★ Journal of Dental Education
American Dental Education Association
1625 Massachusetts Ave. NW
Washington, DC 20036-2212
Ph: (202)667-9433   Fax: (202)667-0642

Monthly. $75.00/year; $100.00/year for Canada; $125.00/year for other countries. Peer-reviewed journal for scholarly research and reviews on dental education.

★2949★ Journal of Dental Hygiene
American Dental Hygienists' Association
444 N Michigan Ave., Ste. 3400
Chicago, IL 60611
Ph: (312)440-8900   Fax: (312)440-6780
Fr: 800-243-ADHA
E-mail: mail@adha.net

$45.00/year; $65.00/year; $90.00/year. Professional journal on dental hygiene.

★2950★ Journal of Dental Research
International and American Associations for Dental Research
1619 Duke St.
Alexandria, VA 22314-3406
Ph: (703)548-0066   Fax: (703)548-1883
E-mail: research@iadr.org
URL: http://www.dentalresearch.org

Monthly. $402.00/year for individuals; $412.00/year for other countries. Dental science journal.

★2951★ Journal of Dentistry for Children

American Society of Dentistry for Children
875 N Michigan Ave., Ste. 4040
Chicago, IL 60611-1901
Ph: (312)943-1244   Fax: (312)943-5341
Fr: 800-637-2732

Bimonthly. $100.00/year for individuals, domestic; $120.00/year for institutions, domestic; $120.00/year for individuals, other countries; $150.00/year for institutions, other countries. Magazine focusing on dentistry for children.

★2952★ Maryland State Dental Association Newsletter

Maryland State Dental Association
6410F Dobbin Rd.
Columbia, MD 21045-4744
Ph: (410)964-2880   Fax: (410)964-0583

Description: Monthly. Reports on health, legislative, economic, and medical issues that are pertinent to dentistry. Recurring features include letters to the editor, interviews, news of research, a calendar of events, reports of meetings, news of educational opportunities, and job listings.

★2953★ MDS News

Massachusetts Dental Society
Two Willow St., Ste. 200
Southborough, MA 01745-1027
Ph: (508)480-9797   Fax: (508)480-0002
Fr: 800-342-8747

Description: Six issues/year. Provides news on the Society's activities and articles on the dental profession. Recurring features include reports of meetings, news of educational opportunities, job listings, and notices of publications available.

★2954★ Pennsylvania Dental Journal

Pennsylvania Dental Association
Box 3341
Harrisburg, PA 17105
Ph: (717)234-5941   Fax: (717)234-2186
E-mail: rap@padental.org

Bimonthly. $36.00/year for individuals; $60.00/year for other countries. Professional dentistry magazine containing treatment/procedure news, PDA activities information, continuing education courses, and legislation updates.

★2955★ RDH

PennWell Corp.
PO Box 1260
Tulsa, OK 74101-1260
Ph: (918)831-9742   Fax: (918)831-9804
Fr: 800-633-1681

Monthly. $48.00/year. Magazine for dental hygiene professionals covering practice management, patient motivation, practice options, financial planning, personal development, preventive oral health care and treatment, home care instruction, radiology, anesthesia, nutrition, and new products.

PLACEMENT AND JOB REFERRAL SERVICES

★2956★ American Public Health Association (APHA)

800 I St. NW
Washington, DC 20001-3710
Ph: (202)777-2742   Fax: (202)777-2534
E-mail: comments@apha.org
URL: http://www.apha.org

Members: Professional organization of physicians, nurses, educators, academicians, environmentalists, epidemiologists, new professionals, social workers, health administrators, optometrists, podiatrists, pharmacists, dentists, nutritionists, health planners, other community and mental health specialists, and interested consumers. Purpose: Seeks to protect and promote personal, mental, and environmental health. Activities: Services include promulgation of standards; establishment of uniform practices and procedures; development of the etiology of communicable diseases; research in public health; exploration of medical care programs and their relationships to public health. Sponsors job placement service.

EMPLOYER DIRECTORIES AND NETWORKING LISTS

★2957★ American Academy of Pediatric Dentistry-Membership Directory

American Academy of Pediatric Dentistry
211 E Chicago Ave., Ste. 700
Chicago, IL 60611
Ph: (312)337-2169   Fax: (312)337-6329
URL: http://www.aapd.org

Annual, November. $600.00. Covers 5,600 pediatric dentists and several dentists in practice, teaching, and research. Entries include: Name, address, phone. Arrangement: Alphabetical. Indexes: Geographical.

★2958★ Dentists Directory

infoUSA Inc.
5711 S 86th Cir.
Omaha, NE 68127-0347
Ph: (402)930-3500   Fax: (402)331-0176
Fr: 800-555-6124
URL: http://www.abii.com

Annual. Number of listings: 210,919. Entries include: Name, address, phone (including area code), size of advertisement, code indicating specialty, year first in "Yellow Pages," name of owner or manager, number of employees. Regional editions available: North East (Connecticut, Maine Massachusetts, New Hampshire, New Jersey, New York, Pennsylvania, Rhode Island, Vermont), $1310.00; East North Central (Illinois, Indiana, Michigan, Ohio, Wisconsin), $945.00; West North Central (Iowa, Kansas, Minnesota, Missouri, Nebraska, North Dako-

ta, South Dakota), $460.00; South Atlantic (District of Columbia, Delaware, Florida, Georgia, Maryland, North Carolina, South Carolina, Virginia, West Virginia), $845.00; South Central (Alabama, Arkansas, Kentucky, Louisiana, Mississippi, Oklahoma, Tennessee, Texas), $745.00; Mountain (Arizona, Colorado, Idaho, Montana, Nevada, New Mexico, Utah, Wyoming), $380.00; Pacific (Alaska, California, Hawaii, Oregon, Washington), $945,00. Compiled from telephone company "Yellow Pages," nationwide. Arrangement: Geographical.

★2959★ International Association for Orthodontics-Membership Directory

International Association for Orthodontics
735 N Water St., Ste. 617
Milwaukee, WI 53202
Ph: (414)272-2757   Fax: (414)272-2754
Fr: 800-447-8770

Annual, June. $75.00. Covers 2,500 general and children's dentists who also work to correct facial and jaw irregularities. Entries include: Name, office address and phone, orthodontic techniques practiced. Arrangement: Geographical. Indexes: Personal name.

★2960★ Washington Physicians Directory

National Directories Inc.
PO Box 4436
Silver Spring, MD 20914
Ph: (301)384-1506   Fax: (301)384-6854
E-mail: wpd@wpdnetwork.com

Annual, April. $47.00. Covers 9,800 physicians in private practice or on full-time staff at hospitals in the Washington, D.C., metropolitan area. Entries include: Name, medical school and year of graduation; up to four office addresses with phone numbers for each; up to four medical specialties (indicating board certifications), Unique Physician Identification Numbers (UPIN), and e-mail. Arrangement: Alphabetical. Indexes: Geographical (within medical specialty); foreign language.

HANDBOOKS AND MANUALS

★2961★ Careers in Health Care

McGraw-Hill Trade
2 Penn Plaza
New York, NY 10121
Ph: (212)904-2000   Fr: 800-722-4726
E-mail: ntcpub@tribune.com

Barbara M. Swanson. Fourth edition, 2000. $17.95; $13.95 (paper). 320 pages. Describes job duties, work settings, salaries, licensing and certification requirements, educational preparation, and future outlook. Gives ideas on how to secure a job.

★2962★ Competency Skills for the Dental Assistant

Thomson Delmar Learning
PO Box 15015
Albany, NY 12212-5015
Ph: (518)348-2300   Fax: (518)464-0393
Fr: 800-998-7498

Charline M. Dofka. 1995. $43.95. 576 pages.

★2963★ Dental Assisting: A Comprehensive Approach

Thomson Delmar Learning
PO Box 15015
Albany, NY 12212-5015
Ph: (518)348-2300   Fax: (518)373-6345
Fr: 800-998-7498

Donna J. Phinney, Judy Helen Halstead. Second edition. June 2003. $74.95. Illustrated. 864 pages.

★2964★ Dental Assisting Exam Preparation

W.B. Saunders Co.
150 S. Independence Mall W.
The Public Ledger Bldg., Ste. 1250
Philadelphia, PA 19106-3412
Ph: (215)238-5500   Fax: (215)238-8495
Fr: 800-654-2452

Hazel O. Torres and Lois Mazzucchi-Ballard. 1993. $23.00 (paper). 208 pages.

★2965★ Opportunities in Health and Medical Careers

McGraw-Hill Trade
2 Penn Plaza
New York, NY 10121
Ph: (212)904-2000   Fr: 800-722-4726

I. Donald Snook, Jr. and Leo D'Orazio. 1997. $14.95; $11.95 (paper). 202 pages. Covers the full range of medical and health occupations. Illustrated.

★2966★ Opportunities in Paramedical Careers

McGraw-Hill/Contemporary Books
1221 Avenue of the Americas
New York, NY 10020
Ph: (212)904-2000   Fr: 800-323-4900
E-mail: ntcpub@tribune.com

Alex Kacen. Revised, 1999. $14.95; 11.95 (paper). 200 pages. Discusses a variety of opportunities in this field and how to pursue them. Illustrated.

★2967★ Resumes for Health and Medical Careers

McGraw-Hill Trade
2 Penn Plaza
New York, NY 10121
Ph: (212)904-2000   Fr: 800-722-4726
E-mail: ntcpub@tribune.com

1997. $9.95 (paper). 455 pages.

★2968★ Textbook for Dental Nurses

Blackwell Publishing
350 Main St., 6th Fl.
Malden, MA 02148-5018
Ph: (781)388-8200   Fax: (781)388-8210

H. Levinson. Ninth edition. May 2004. Illustrated. 496 Pages. Educational.

EMPLOYMENT AGENCIES AND SEARCH FIRMS

★2969★ Colucci, Blendow & Johnson

643 Main St., Ste. 8
Half Moon Bay, CA 94019-1988
Ph: (650)712-0103   Fax: (650)712-0105

Executive search consultants in the medical technology area that includes pharmaceuticals, medical equipment and device manufacturers, biotechnology, therapeutic supplies, diagnostic laboratory equipment and supplies, diagnostic imaging equipment and supplies, medical services, chemicals, cosmetic and toiletries, dental, veterinarian, and agricultural genetics companies.

★2970★ DDS Staffing Resources, Inc.

9755 Dogwood Rd., Ste. 200
Roswell, GA 30075
Ph: (770)998-7779   Fax: (770)552-0176
URL: http://www.ddsstaffing.com

Employment agency.

★2971★ Legal Medical Staffing Services Inc.

Plz. 1000, Ste. 202, Main St.
Voorhees, NJ 08043
Ph: (856)751-7999   Fax: (856)751-8448

Offers a specialized service providing temporary and full-time support exclusively to the legal, dental, and medical professions.

★2972★ Team Placement Service, Inc.

5113 Leesburg Pike, Ste. 510
Falls Church, VA 22041-3242
Ph: (703)820-8618   Fax: (703)820-3368
Fr: 800-495-6767
E-mail: 4jobs@teamplace.com
URL: http://www.teamplace.com

Temporary agency that also handles some permanent placements.

ONLINE JOB SOURCES AND SERVICES

★2973★ Medhunters.com
E-mail: info@medhunters.com
URL: http://www.medhunters.com

Description: Career search site for jobs in all health care specialties; educational resources; visa and licensing information for relocation; interesting articles; relocation tools; links to professional organizations and general resources.

★2974★ ProHealthJobs
E-mail: sales@prohealthjobs.com
URL: http://www.prohealthjobs.com

Description: Career resources site for the medical and health care field. Lists professional opportunities, product information, continuing education and open positions.

TRADESHOWS

★2975★ American Academy of Pediatric Dentistry Annual Meeting

American Academy of Pediatric Dentistry
211 E Chicago Ave., Ste. 700
Chicago, IL 60611
Ph: (312)337-2169   Fax: (312)337-6329
URL: http://www.aapd.org

Annual. **Primary Exhibits:** Dental products and publications.

★2976★ American Dental Association Annual Session & Technical Exhibition

American Dental Association
211 E. Chicago Ave.
Chicago, IL 60611-2678
Ph: (312)440-2581   Fax: (312)440-2707
E-mail: exhibit@ada.org
URL: http://www.ada.org

Annual. **Primary Exhibits:** Dental equipment, instruments, materials, therapeutics, and services.

★2977★ Star of the North Meeting

Minnesota Dental Association
2236 Marshall Ave.
St. Paul, MN 55104
Ph: (651)646-7454   Fax: (651)646-8246
E-mail: info@mndental.org
URL: http://www.mndental.org

Annual. **Primary Exhibits:** Dental equipment and supplies, dental laboratory equipment, office equipment, and service organizations. **Dates and Locations:** 2005 Apr 29-May 02; St. Paul, MN; RiverCentre • 2006 Apr 28-May 01; St. Paul, MN; RiverCentre.

★2978★ Thomas P. Hinman Dental Meeting & Exhibits

Thomas P. Hinman Dental Society
60 Lenox Pte.
Atlanta, GA 30324
Ph: (404)231-1476   Fax: (404)231-9638

Annual. **Primary Exhibits:** Dental equipment, supplies, and services.

★2979★ Yankee Dental Congress

Massachusetts Dental Society
2 Willow St., Ste. 200
Southborough, MA 01745
Ph: (508)480-9797   Fax: (508)480-0002
Fr: 800-943-9200
E-mail: madental@massdental.org
URL: http://www.massdental.org

Annual. **Primary Exhibits:** Dental products, equipment, and services. **Dates and Locations:** 2005 Jan 27-30; Boston, MA.

OTHER SOURCES

★2980★ American Dental Assistants Association (ADAA)

35 E Wacker Dr., No. 1730
Chicago, IL 60601-2211
Ph: (312)541-1550   Fax: (312)541-1496
E-mail: dmarrell@adaa1.com
URL: http://www.dentalassistant.org

Description: Individuals employed as dental assistants in dental offices, clinics, hospitals, or institutions; instructors of dental assistants; dental students. Sponsors workshops and seminars; maintains governmental liaison. Offers group insurance; maintains scholarship trust fund. Dental Assisting National Board examines members who are candidates for title of Certified Dental Assistant.

★2981★ American Dental Association (ADA)

211 E. Chicago Ave.
Chicago, IL 60611
Ph: (312)440-2500   Fax: (312)440-2800
E-mail: publicinfo@ada.org
URL: http://www.ada.org

Description: Professional society of dentists. Encourages the improvement of the health of the public and promotes the art and science of dentistry in matters of legislation and regulations. Inspects and accredits dental schools and schools for dental hygienists, assistants, and laboratory technicians. Conducts research programs at ADA Foundation Research Institute. Produces most of the dental health education material used in the U.S. Sponsors National Children's Dental Health Month. Compiles statistics on personnel, practice, and dental care needs and attitudes of patients with regard to dental health. Sponsors 13 councils.

★2982★ American Dental Education Association

1625 Massachusetts Ave. NW, Ste. 600
Washington, DC 20036-2212
Ph: (202)667-9433   Fax: (202)667-0642
E-mail: adea@adea.org
URL: http://www.adea.org/

Description: Individuals interested in dental education; schools of dentistry, graduate dentistry, and allied dental education in the U.S., Canada, and Puerto Rico; affiliated institutions of the federal government. To promote better teaching and education in dentistry and dental research and to facilitate exchange of ideas among dental educators. Sponsors meetings, conferences, and workshops; conducts surveys, studies, and special projects and publishes their results. Maintains 39 sections representing teaching and administrative areas of dentistry.

★2983★ American Medical Technologists (AMT)

710 Higgins Rd.
Park Ridge, IL 60068-5765
Ph: (847)823-5169   Fax: (847)823-0458
Fr: 800-275-1268
E-mail: mail@amt1.com
URL: http://www.amt1.com

Description: National professional association and certifying body for medical laboratory technologists, technicians, medical assistants, dental assistants, and phlebotomists. Maintains job information service. Sponsors AMT Institute for Education, evaluates and recommends continuing education programs.

★2984★ American School Health Association (ASHA)

PO Box 708
7263 State Route 43
Kent, OH 44240
Ph: (330)678-1601   Fax: (330)678-4526
Fr: 800-445-2742
E-mail: asha@ashaweb.org
URL: http://www.ashaweb.org

Description: School physicians, school nurses, dentist, nurses, nutritionists, health educators, dental hygienist, school-based professionals and public health workers. Promotes coordinated school health programs that include health education, health services, a healthful school environment, physical education, nutrition services, and psycho-social health services offered in schools collaboratively with families and other members of the community. Offers professional reference materials. Conducts pilot programs that inform materials development, provides technical assistance to school professionals, advocates for school health, and complies statistics.

★2985★ Dental Assistants

Evon Publishing
832 N 7th Ave.
Iron River, MI 49935
Ph: (906)265-3190

Audiocassette. 1996. $16.95. 32 minutes. Part of the Careers and Vocational Guidance Series. Provides information about the nature of the work, educational requirements, employment outlook, earnings, and work conditions as well as additional related information.

★2986★ Exploring Health Occupations

Cambridge Educational
2572 Brunswick Ave.
Lawrenceville, NJ 08648-4128
Fax: 800-FAX-ON-US   Fr: 800-468-4227
URL: http://www.cambridgeeducational.com

Two videos. $139.95. 1999.

★2987★ Health Service Occupations

Delphi Productions
3160 4th St.
Boulder, CO 80304
Fax: (303)443-4022   Fr: 888-443-2400
URL: http://www.delphivideo.com

$95.00. 50 minutes. Part of the Careers for the 21st Century Video Library.

★2988★ Holistic Dental Association (HDA)

PO Box 5007
Durango, CO 81301
Ph: (970)259-1091   Fax: (970)259-1091
E-mail: info@holisticdental.org
URL: http://www.holisticdental.org

Description: Dentists, chiropractors, dental hygienists, physical therapists, and medical doctors. Goals are: to provide a holistic approach to better dental care for patients; to expand techniques, medications, and philosophies that pertain to extractions, anesthetics, fillings, crowns, and orthodontics. Encourages use of homeopathic medications, acupuncture, cranial osteopathy, nutritional techniques, and physical therapy in treating patients in addition to conventional treatments. Sponsors training and educational seminars.

★2989★ Medical Assistants

Evon Publishing
832 N 7th Ave.
Iron River, MI 49935
Ph: (906)265-3190

Audiocassette. 1996. $16.95. 32 minutes. Part of the Careers and Vocational Guidance Series. Provides information about the nature of the work, educational requirements, employment outlook, earnings, and work conditions as well as additional related information.

★2990★ Medical Technicians and Technologists

Cambridge Educational
2572 Brunswick Ave.
Lawrenceville, NJ 08648-4128
Fax: 800-FAX-ON-US   Fr: 800-468-4227
URL: http://www.cambridgeeducational.com

$79.95. 15 minutes. Part of the Exploring Health Occupations Series.

★2991★ Medicine & Related Occupations

Delphi Productions
3160 4th St.
Boulder, CO 80304
Fax: (303)443-4022   Fr: 888-443-2400

URL: http://www.delphivideo.com

$95.00. 45 minutes. Part of the Careers for the 21st Century Video Library.

★2992★ National Association of Dental Assistants (NADA)

900 S Washington St., No. G-13
Falls Church, VA 22046
Ph: (703)237-8616   Fax: (703)533-1153

Members: Professional dental auxiliaries.
Purpose: Seeks to bring added stature and purpose to the profession through continuing education and make available to dental assistants the special benefits normally limited to members of specialized professional and fraternal groups.

★2993★ National Dental Assistants Association (NDA)

3517 16th St. NW
Washington, DC 20010
Ph: (202)588-1697   Fax: (202)588-1244

E-mail: christine.wright@chsys.org
URL: http://www.ndaonline.org/auxillary.htm

Description: An auxiliary of the National Dental Association. Works to encourage education and certification among dental assistants. Conducts clinics and workshops to further the education of members. Bestows annual Humanitarian Award; offers scholarships.

★2994★ National Rural Health Association (NRHA)

1 W Armour Blvd., Ste. 203
Kansas City, MO 64111-2087
Ph: (816)756-3140   Fax: (816)756-3144
E-mail: mail@nrharural.org
URL: http://www.nrharural.org

Description: Administrators, physicians, nurses, physician assistants, health planners, academicians, and others interested or involved in rural health care. Creates a better understanding of health care problems unique to rural areas; utilizes a collective approach in finding positive solutions; articulates and represents the health care needs of rural America; supplies current information to rural health care providers; serves as a liaison between rural health care programs throughout the country. Offers continuing education credits for medical, dental, nursing, and management courses.

★2995★ Women in Dentistry

Her Own Words
PO Box 5264
Madison, WI 53705-0264
Ph: (608)271-7083   Fax: (608)271-0209
URL: http://www.herownwords.com/

Video. Jocelyn Riley. $95.00. 15 minutes. Resource guide also available for $45.00.

Dental Hygienists

★2996★ American Dental Hygienists' Association Access

American Dental Hygienists' Association
444 N Michigan Ave., Ste. 3400
Chicago, IL 60611
Ph: (312)440-8900   Fax: (312)440-6780
Fr: 800-243-ADHA

Subscription included in membership; $30.00/year for nonmembers. Magazine covering current dental hygiene topics, regulatory and legislative developments, and association news.

★2997★ Bulletin of Dental Education

American Dental Education Association
1625 Massachusetts Ave. NW
Washington, DC 20036-2212
Ph: (202)667-9433   Fax: (202)667-0642

Description: Monthly. Contains news and information on dental education. Recurring features include a calendar of events, reports of meetings, news of educational opportunities, job listings, and notices of publications available.

★2998★ CDS Review

Chicago Dental Society
401 N Michigan Ave., Ste. 300
Chicago, IL 60611-4272
Ph: (312)836-7305   Fax: (312)836-7337
E-mail: reviewvox@aol.com

$25.00/year for individuals; $30.00/year, schools and industry; $45.00/year for other countries; $4.00 for single issue; $6.00/year for November issue. Dental journal.

★2999★ Dental Economics

PennWell Corp.
1421 S Sheridan Rd.
Tulsa, OK 74112
Ph: (918)835-3161   Fax: (918)832-9201
Fr: 800-331-4463
URL: http://www.de.pennnet.com/home.cfm

Monthly. $88.00 for single issue; $10.00 for single issue; $120.00/year for out of country, Mexico/Canada; $168.00/year for other countries; $16.00 for single issue, Mexico/Canada; $18.00/year for single issue, other countries. Magazine featuring business-related articles for dentists.

★3000★ Hawaii Dental Journal

Hawaii Medical Journal
1345 S Beretania St., No. 301
Honolulu, HI 96814-1821

Bimonthly. Dental journal.

★3001★ Illinois Dental Journal

Illinois State Dental Society
1010 S Second St.
PO Box 376
Springfield, IL 62705
Ph: (217)525-1406   Fax: (217)525-8872

Monthly. $25.00/year for members; $45.00/year for nonmembers; $75.00/year for nonmembers, other countries; $5.00 for single issue. Dental magazine.

★3002★ Journal of the American Dental Association

ADA Publishing
211 E Chicago Ave.
Chicago, IL 60611
Ph: (312)440-2810   Fax: (312)440-3538
Fr: 800-621-8099
URL: http://www.ada.org

Monthly. $110.00/year for individuals; $139.00/year for institutions; $13.00 for single issue; $139.00/year for individuals, foreign; $176.00/year for institutions, foreign; $122.00/year for individuals, Canadian; $158.00/year for institutions, Canadian; $69.00/year for nonmembers, student. Trade journal for the dental profession.

★3003★ Journal of the California Dental Association

California Dental Association
1201 'K' St. Mall
PO Box 13749
Sacramento, CA 95853
Ph: (916)443-0505   Fax: (916)443-2943
Fr: 800-736-7071
URL: http://www.cda.org/cda

Monthly. $24.00/year for ADA members; $60.00/year for nonmembers; $10.00/year for single issue ($10.78 July issue); $12.00/year for CDA members. Professional magazine for dentists.

★3004★ Journal of Dental Education

American Dental Education Association
1625 Massachusetts Ave. NW
Washington, DC 20036-2212
Ph: (202)667-9433   Fax: (202)667-0642

Monthly. $75.00/year; $100.00/year for Canada; $125.00/year for other countries. Peer-reviewed journal for scholarly research and reviews on dental education.

★3005★ Journal of Dental Hygiene

American Dental Hygienists' Association
444 N Michigan Ave., Ste. 3400
Chicago, IL 60611
Ph: (312)440-8900   Fax: (312)440-6780
Fr: 800-243-ADHA
E-mail: mail@adha.net

$45.00/year; $65.00/year; $90.00/year. Professional journal on dental hygiene.

★3006★ Journal of Dental Research

International and American Associations for Dental Research
1619 Duke St.
Alexandria, VA 22314-3406
Ph: (703)548-0066   Fax: (703)548-1883
E-mail: research@iadr.org
URL: http://www.dentalresearch.org

Monthly. $402.00/year for individuals; $412.00/year for other countries. Dental science journal.

★3007★ Journal of Dentistry for Children

American Society of Dentistry for Children
875 N Michigan Ave., Ste. 4040
Chicago, IL 60611-1901
Ph: (312)943-1244   Fax: (312)943-5341
Fr: 800-637-2732

Bimonthly. $100.00/year for individuals, domestic; $120.00/year for institutions, domestic; $120.00/year for individuals, other countries; $150.00/year for institutions, other countries. Magazine focusing on dentistry for children.

★3008★ Maryland State Dental Association Newsletter

Maryland State Dental Association
6410F Dobbin Rd.
Columbia, MD 21045-4744
Ph: (410)964-2880   Fax: (410)964-0583

Description: Monthly. Reports on health, legislative, economic, and medical issues that are pertinent to dentistry. Recurring features include letters to the editor, interviews, news of research, a calendar of events, reports of meetings, news of educational opportunities, and job listings.

★3009★ MDS News

Massachusetts Dental Society
Two Willow St., Ste. 200
Southborough, MA 01745-1027
Ph: (508)480-9797   Fax: (508)480-0002
Fr: 800-342-8747

Description: Six issues/year. Provides news on the Society's activities and articles on the dental profession. Recurring features include reports of meetings, news of educational opportunities, job listings, and notices of publications available.

★3010★ Pennsylvania Dental Journal

Pennsylvania Dental Association
Box 3341
Harrisburg, PA 17105
Ph: (717)234-5941   Fax: (717)234-2186
E-mail: rap@padental.org

Bimonthly. $36.00/year for individuals; $60.00/year for other countries. Professional dentistry magazine containing treatment/procedure news, PDA activities information, continuing education courses, and legislation updates.

★3011★ RDH

PennWell Corp.
PO Box 1260
Tulsa, OK 74101-1260
Ph: (918)831-9742   Fax: (918)831-9804
Fr: 800-633-1681

Monthly. $48.00/year. Magazine for dental hygiene professionals covering practice management, patient motivation, practice options, financial planning, personal development, preventive oral health care and treatment, home care instruction, radiology, anesthesia, nutrition, and new products.

★3012★ WSDA News

Washington State Dental Association (WSDA)
2033 6th Ave., Ste. 333
Seattle, WA 98121
Ph: (206)448-1914   Fax: (206)443-9266
URL: http://www.wsda.org

Description: Monthly, except October. Contains information of interest to dentists on legislation, regulations, state boards and government, and business of the association. Recurring features include letters to the editor, editorial and op-ed columns, President's message, obituraries, practice opportunities, news of educational opportunities, and job listings.

PLACEMENT AND JOB REFERRAL SERVICES

★3013★ American Public Health Association (APHA)

800 I St. NW
Washington, DC 20001-3710
Ph: (202)777-2742   Fax: (202)777-2534
E-mail: comments@apha.org
URL: http://www.apha.org

Members: Professional organization of physicians, nurses, educators, academicians, environmentalists, epidemiologists, new professionals, social workers, health administrators, optometrists, podiatrists, pharmacists, dentists, nutritionists, health planners, other community and mental health specialists, and interested consumers. **Purpose:** Seeks to protect and promote personal, mental, and environmental health. **Activities:** Services include promulgation of standards; establishment of uniform practices and procedures; development of the etiology of communicable diseases; research in public health; exploration of medical care programs and their relationships to public health. Sponsors job placement service.

EMPLOYER DIRECTORIES AND NETWORKING LISTS

★3014★ American Academy of Pediatric Dentistry-Membership Directory

American Academy of Pediatric Dentistry
211 E Chicago Ave., Ste. 700
Chicago, IL 60611
Ph: (312)337-2169   Fax: (312)337-6329
URL: http://www.aapd.org

Annual, November. $600.00. Covers 5,600 pediatric dentists and several dentists in practice, teaching, and research. Entries include: Name, address, phone. Arrangement: Alphabetical. Indexes: Geographical.

★3015★ Dentists Directory

infoUSA Inc.
5711 S 86th Cir.
Omaha, NE 68127-0347
Ph: (402)930-3500   Fax: (402)331-0176
Fr: 800-555-6124
URL: http://www.abii.com

Annual. Number of listings: 210,919. Entries include: Name, address, phone (including area code), size of advertisement, code indicating specialty, year first in "Yellow Pages," name of owner or manager, number of employees. Regional editions available: North East (Connecticut, Maine Massachusetts, New Hampshire, New Jersey, New York, Pennsylvania, Rhode Island, Vermont), $1310.00; East North Central (Illinois, Indiana, Michigan, Ohio, Wisconsin), $945.00; West North Central (Iowa, Kansas, Minnesota, Missouri, Nebraska, North Dakota, South Dakota), $460.00; South Atlantic (District of Columbia, Delaware, Florida, Georgia, Maryland, North Carolina, South Carolina, Virginia, West Virginia), $845.00; South Central (Alabama, Arkansas, Kentucky, Louisiana, Mississippi, Oklahoma, Tennessee, Texas), $745.00; Mountain (Arizona, Colorado, Idaho, Montana, Nevada, New Mexico, Utah, Wyoming), $380.00; Pacific (Alaska, California, Hawaii, Oregon, Washington), $945,00. Compiled from telephone company "Yellow Pages," nationwide. Arrangement: Geographical.

★3016★ International Association for Orthodontics-Membership Directory

International Association for Orthodontics
735 N Water St., Ste. 617
Milwaukee, WI 53202
Ph: (414)272-2757   Fax: (414)272-2754
Fr: 800-447-8770

Annual, June. $75.00. Covers 2,500 general and children's dentists who also work to correct facial and jaw irregularities. Entries include: Name, office address and phone, orthodontic techniques practiced. Arrangement: Geographical. Indexes: Personal name.

★3017★ Washington Physicians Directory

National Directories Inc.
PO Box 4436
Silver Spring, MD 20914
Ph: (301)384-1506   Fax: (301)384-6854
E-mail: wpd@wpdnetwork.com

Annual, April. $47.00. Covers 9,800 physicians in private practice or on full-time staff at hospitals in the Washington, D.C., metropolitan area. Entries include: Name, medical school and year of graduation; up to four office addresses with phone numbers for each; up to four medical specialties (indicating board certifications), Unique Physician Identification Numbers (UPIN), and e-mail. Arrangement: Alphabetical. Indexes: Geographical (within medical specialty); foreign language.

HANDBOOKS AND MANUALS

★3018★ Careers in Health Care
McGraw-Hill Trade
2 Penn Plaza
New York, NY 10121
Ph: (212)904-2000   Fr: 800-722-4726
E-mail: ntcpub@tribune.com

Barbara M. Swanson. Fourth edition, 2000. $17.95; $13.95 (paper). 320 pages. Describes job duties, work settings, salaries, licensing and certification requirements, educational preparation, and future outlook. Gives ideas on how to secure a job.

★3019★ Dental Assisting: A Comprehensive Approach
Thomson Delmar Learning
PO Box 15015
Albany, NY 12212-5015
Ph: (518)348-2300   Fax: (518)373-6345
Fr: 800-998-7498

Donna J. Phinney, Judy Helen Halstead. Second edition. June 2003. $74.95. Illustrated. 864 pages.

★3020★ Dental Assisting Exam Preparation
W.B. Saunders Co.
150 S. Independence Mall W.
The Public Ledger Bldg., Ste. 1250
Philadelphia, PA 19106-3412
Ph: (215)238-5500   Fax: (215)238-8495
Fr: 800-654-2452

Hazel O. Torres and Lois Mazzucchi-Ballard. 1993. $23.00 (paper). 208 pages.

★3021★ Opportunities in Health and Medical Careers
McGraw-Hill Trade
2 Penn Plaza
New York, NY 10121
Ph: (212)904-2000   Fr: 800-722-4726

I. Donald Snook, Jr. and Leo D'Orazio. 1997. $14.95; $11.95 (paper). 202 pages. Covers the full range of medical and health occupations. Illustrated.

★3022★ Opportunities in Medical Technology Careers
McGraw-Hill/Contemporary Books
1221 Avenue of the Americas
New York, NY 10020
Ph: (212)904-2000   Fr: 800-323-4900
E-mail: ntcpub@tribune.com

Karen R. Karni. Revised, 1996. $14.95; $11.95 (paper). 205 pages. Details opportunities for various technical medical personnel and supplies up-to-date information on salary levels and employment outlook. Appendices list associations and unions in each field. Illustrated.

★3023★ Opportunities in Paramedical Careers
McGraw-Hill/Contemporary Books
1221 Avenue of the Americas
New York, NY 10020
Ph: (212)904-2000   Fr: 800-323-4900
E-mail: ntcpub@tribune.com

Alex Kacen. Revised, 1999. $14.95; 11.95 (paper). 200 pages. Discusses a variety of opportunities in this field and how to pursue them. Illustrated.

★3024★ Resumes for Health and Medical Careers
McGraw-Hill Trade
2 Penn Plaza
New York, NY 10121
Ph: (212)904-2000   Fr: 800-722-4726
E-mail: ntcpub@tribune.com

1997. $9.95 (paper). 455 pages.

★3025★ Textbook for Dental Nurses
Blackwell Publishing
350 Main St., 6th Fl.
Malden, MA 02148-5018
Ph: (781)388-8200   Fax: (781)388-8210

H. Levinson. Ninth edition. May 2004. Illustrated. 496 Pages. Educational.

EMPLOYMENT AGENCIES AND SEARCH FIRMS

★3026★ Colucci, Blendow & Johnson
643 Main St., Ste. 8
Half Moon Bay, CA 94019-1988
Ph: (650)712-0103   Fax: (650)712-0105

Executive search consultants in the medical technology area that includes pharmaceuticals, medical equipment and device manufacturers, biotechnology, therapeutic supplies, diagnostic laboratory equipment and supplies, diagnostic imaging equipment and supplies, medical services, chemicals, cosmetic and toiletries, dental, veterinarian, and agricultural genetics companies.

★3027★ DDS Staffing Resources, Inc.
9755 Dogwood Rd., Ste. 200
Roswell, GA 30075
Ph: (770)998-7779   Fax: (770)552-0176
URL: http://www.ddsstaffing.com

Employment agency.

★3028★ Legal Medical Staffing Services Inc.
Plz. 1000, Ste. 202, Main St.
Voorhees, NJ 08043
Ph: (856)751-7999   Fax: (856)751-8448

Offers a specialized service providing temporary and full-time support exclusively to the legal, dental, and medical professions.

★3029★ Team Placement Service, Inc.
5113 Leesburg Pike, Ste. 510
Falls Church, VA 22041-3242
Ph: (703)820-8618   Fax: (703)820-3368
Fr: 800-495-6767
E-mail: 4jobs@teamplace.com
URL: http://www.teamplace.com

Temporary agency that also handles some permanent placements.

ONLINE JOB SOURCES AND SERVICES

★3030★ Medbulletin Medical Career Resource Center
E-mail: medbulletin@atsmedbulletin.com
URL: http://www.medbulletin.com

Description: Offers free specialized update service, resume posting, recruiter directory, varied job listings, and relocation services.

★3031★ Medhunters.com
E-mail: info@medhunters.com
URL: http://www.medhunters.com

Description: Career search site for jobs in all health care specialties; educational resources; visa and licensing information for relocation; interesting articles; relocation tools; links to professional organizations and general resources.

★3032★ ProHealthJobs
E-mail: sales@prohealthjobs.com
URL: http://www.prohealthjobs.com

Description: Career resources site for the medical and health care field. Lists professional opportunities, product information, continuing education and open positions.

TRADESHOWS

★3033★ American Academy of Pediatric Dentistry Annual Meeting
American Academy of Pediatric Dentistry
211 E Chicago Ave., Ste. 700
Chicago, IL 60611
Ph: (312)337-2169   Fax: (312)337-6329
URL: http://www.aapd.org

Annual. **Primary Exhibits:** Dental products and publications.

★3034★ American Dental Association Annual Session & Technical Exhibition
American Dental Association
211 E. Chicago Ave.
Chicago, IL 60611-2678
Ph: (312)440-2581   Fax: (312)440-2707
E-mail: exhibit@ada.org

URL: http://www.ada.org

Annual. **Primary Exhibits:** Dental equipment, instruments, materials, therapeutics, and services.

★3035★ American Dental Hygienists' Association Convention

American Dental Hygienists' Association
444 N. Michigan Ave., Ste. 3400
Chicago, IL 60611
Ph: (312)440-8900   Fax: (312)440-8929
E-mail: mail@adha.net
URL: http://www.adha.org

Annual. **Primary Exhibits:** Dental hygiene products and services. **Dates and Locations:** 2005 Jun 22-29; Las Vegas, NV; Riviera Hotel • 2006 Jun 21-28; Orlando, FL; Disney's Contemporary Resort.

★3036★ National Dental Association Annual Convention

National Dental Association, Inc.
3517 16th St., NW
Washington, DC 20010
Ph: (202)588-1697   Fax: (202)588-1244
E-mail: admin@ndaonline.org

Annual. **Primary Exhibits:** Dental and Pharmaceutical equipment, supplies, and services.

★3037★ Star of the North Meeting

Minnesota Dental Association
2236 Marshall Ave.
St. Paul, MN 55104
Ph: (651)646-7454   Fax: (651)646-8246
E-mail: info@mndental.org
URL: http://www.mndental.org

Annual. **Primary Exhibits:** Dental equipment and supplies, dental laboratory equipment, office equipment, and service organizations. **Dates and Locations:** 2005 Apr 29-May 02; St. Paul, MN; RiverCentre • 2006 Apr 28-May 01; St. Paul, MN; RiverCentre.

★3038★ Thomas P. Hinman Dental Meeting & Exhibits

Thomas P. Hinman Dental Society
60 Lenox Pte.
Atlanta, GA 30324
Ph: (404)231-1476   Fax: (404)231-9638

Annual. **Primary Exhibits:** Dental equipment, supplies, and services.

★3039★ Three Rivers Dental Conference

Dental Society of Western Pennsylvania
900 Cedar Ave.
Pittsburgh, PA 15212
Ph: (412)321-5810   Fax: (412)321-7719

Annual. **Primary Exhibits:** Dental products and equipment, computers, office equipment, and insurance.

★3040★ Yankee Dental Congress

Massachusetts Dental Society
2 Willow St., Ste. 200
Southborough, MA 01745
Ph: (508)480-9797   Fax: (508)480-0002
Fr: 800-943-9200
E-mail: madental@massdental.org
URL: http://www.massdental.org

Annual. **Primary Exhibits:** Dental products, equipment, and services. **Dates and Locations:** 2005 Jan 27-30; Boston, MA.

OTHER SOURCES

★3041★ American Association of Dental Examiners (AADE)

211 E. Chicago Ave., Ste. 760
Chicago, IL 60611
Ph: (312)440-7464   Fax: (312)440-3525
E-mail: info@aadexam.org
URL: http://www.aadexam.org

Description: Present and past members of state dental examining boards and board administrators. To assist member agencies with problems related to state dental board examinations and licensure, and enforcement of the state dental practice act. Conducts research; compiles statistics.

★3042★ American Dental Association (ADA)

211 E. Chicago Ave.
Chicago, IL 60611
Ph: (312)440-2500   Fax: (312)440-2800
E-mail: publicinfo@ada.org
URL: http://www.ada.org

Description: Professional society of dentists. Encourages the improvement of the health of the public and promotes the art and science of dentistry in matters of legislation and regulations. Inspects and accredits dental schools and schools for dental hygienists, assistants, and laboratory technicians. Conducts research programs at ADA Foundation Research Institute. Produces most of the dental health education material used in the U.S. Sponsors National Children's Dental Health Month. Compiles statistics on personnel, practice, and dental care needs and attitudes of patients with regard to dental health. Sponsors 13 councils.

★3043★ American Dental Education Association

1625 Massachusetts Ave. NW, Ste. 600
Washington, DC 20036-2212
Ph: (202)667-9433   Fax: (202)667-0642
E-mail: adea@adea.org
URL: http://www.adea.org/

Description: Individuals interested in dental education; schools of dentistry, graduate dentistry, and allied dental education in the U.S., Canada, and Puerto Rico; affiliated institutions of the federal government. To promote better teaching and education in dentistry and dental research and to facilitate exchange of ideas among dental educators. Sponsors meetings, conferences, and workshops; conducts surveys, studies, and special projects and publishes their results. Maintains 39 sections representing teaching and administrative areas of dentistry.

★3044★ American Dental Hygienists' Association (ADHA)

444 N Michigan Ave., Ste. 3400
Chicago, IL 60611
Ph: (312)440-8911   Fax: (312)467-1806
Fr: 800-243-ADHA
E-mail: exec.office@adha.net
URL: http://www.adha.org

Description: Professional organization of licensed dental hygienists possessing a degree or certificate in dental hygiene granted by an accredited school of dental hygiene. Makes available scholarships, research grants, and continuing education programs. Maintains accrediting service through the American Dental Association's Commission on Dental Accreditation. Compiles statistics.

★3045★ American School Health Association (ASHA)

PO Box 708
7263 State Route 43
Kent, OH 44240
Ph: (330)678-1601   Fax: (330)678-4526
Fr: 800-445-2742
E-mail: asha@ashaweb.org
URL: http://www.ashaweb.org

Description: School physicians, school nurses, dentist, nurses, nutritionists, health educators, dental hygienist, school-based professionals and public health workers. Promotes coordinated school health programs that include health education, health services, a healthful school environment, physical education, nutrition services, and psycho-social health services offered in schools collaboratively with families and other members of the community. Offers professional reference materials. Conducts pilot programs that inform materials development, provides technical assistance to school professionals, advocates for school health, and complies statistics.

★3046★ *Exploring Health Occupations*

Cambridge Educational
2572 Brunswick Ave.
Lawrenceville, NJ 08648-4128
Fax: 800-FAX-ON-US   Fr: 800-468-4227
URL: http://www.cambridgeeducational.com

Two videos. $139.95. 1999.

★3047★ *Health Service Occupations*

Delphi Productions
3160 4th St.
Boulder, CO 80304
Fax: (303)443-4022   Fr: 888-443-2400
URL: http://www.delphivideo.com

$95.00. 50 minutes. Part of the Careers for the 21st Century Video Library.

★3048★ Health Technologists & Technicians

Delphi Productions
3160 4th St.
Boulder, CO 80304
Fax: (303)443-4022   Fr: 888-443-2400
URL: http://www.delphivideo.com

$95.00. 50 minutes. Part of the Careers for the 21st Century Video Library.

★3049★ Holistic Dental Association (HDA)

PO Box 5007
Durango, CO 81301
Ph: (970)259-1091   Fax: (970)259-1091
E-mail: info@holisticdental.org
URL: http://www.holisticdental.org

Description: Dentists, chiropractors, dental hygienists, physical therapists, and medical doctors. Goals are: to provide a holistic approach to better dental care for patients; to expand techniques, medications, and philosophies that pertain to extractions, anesthetics, fillings, crowns, and orthodontics. Encourages use of homeopathic medications, acupuncture, cranial osteopathy, nutritional techniques, and physical therapy in treating patients in addition to conventional treatments. Sponsors training and educational seminars.

★3050★ Medical Technicians and Technologists

Cambridge Educational
2572 Brunswick Ave.
Lawrenceville, NJ 08648-4128
Fax: 800-FAX-ON-US   Fr: 800-468-4227

URL: http://www.cambridgeeducational.com

$79.95. 15 minutes. Part of the Exploring Health Occupations Series.

★3051★ Medicine & Related Occupations

Delphi Productions
3160 4th St.
Boulder, CO 80304
Fax: (303)443-4022   Fr: 888-443-2400
URL: http://www.delphivideo.com

$95.00. 45 minutes. Part of the Careers for the 21st Century Video Library.

★3052★ National Dental Hygienists' Association (NDHA)

12511 Arbor Dr.
Alsip, IL 60803
E-mail: erylsh@aol.com
URL: http://www.ndhaonline.org

Members: Minority dental hygienists. **Purpose:** To cultivate and promote the art and science of dental hygiene and to enhance the professional image of dental hygienists. Attempts to meet the needs of society through educational, political, and social activities while giving the minority dental hygienist a voice in shaping the profession. Encourages cooperation and mutual support among minority professionals. Seeks to increase opportunities for continuing education and employment in the field of dental hygiene. Works to improve individual and community dental health. **Activities:** Sponsors annual seminar, fundraising events, and scholarship programs; participates in career orientation programs; counsels and assists

students applying for or enrolled in dental hygiene programs. Maintains liaison with American Dental Hygienists' Association.

★3053★ National Rural Health Association (NRHA)

1 W Armour Blvd., Ste. 203
Kansas City, MO 64111-2087
Ph: (816)756-3140   Fax: (816)756-3144
E-mail: mail@nrharural.org
URL: http://www.nrharural.org

Description: Administrators, physicians, nurses, physician assistants, health planners, academicians, and others interested or involved in rural health care. Creates a better understanding of health care problems unique to rural areas; utilizes a collective approach in finding positive solutions; articulates and represents the health care needs of rural America; supplies current information to rural health care providers; serves as a liaison between rural health care programs throughout the country. Offers continuing education credits for medical, dental, nursing, and management courses.

★3054★ Women in Dentistry

Her Own Words
PO Box 5264
Madison, WI 53705-0264
Ph: (608)271-7083   Fax: (608)271-0209
URL: http://www.herownwords.com/

Video. Jocelyn Riley. $95.00. 15 minutes. Resource guide also available for $45.00.

Dental Lab Technicians

SOURCES OF HELP-WANTED ADS

★3055★ American Dental Hygienists' Association Access

American Dental Hygienists' Association
444 N Michigan Ave., Ste. 3400
Chicago, IL 60611
Ph: (312)440-8900   Fax: (312)440-6780
Fr: 800-243-ADHA

Subscription included in membership; $30.00/year for nonmembers. Magazine covering current dental hygiene topics, regulatory and legislative developments, and association news.

★3056★ Bulletin of Dental Education

American Dental Education Association
1625 Massachusetts Ave. NW
Washington, DC 20036-2212
Ph: (202)667-9433   Fax: (202)667-0642

Description: Monthly. Contains news and information on dental education. Recurring features include a calendar of events, reports of meetings, news of educational opportunities, job listings, and notices of publications available.

★3057★ CDS Review

Chicago Dental Society
401 N Michigan Ave., Ste. 300
Chicago, IL 60611-4272
Ph: (312)836-7305   Fax: (312)836-7337
E-mail: reviewvox@aol.com

$25.00/year for individuals; $30.00/year, schools and industry; $45.00/year for other countries; $4.00 for single issue; $6.00/year for November issue. Dental journal.

★3058★ Dental Economics

PennWell Corp.
1421 S Sheridan Rd.
Tulsa, OK 74112
Ph: (918)835-3161   Fax: (918)832-9201
Fr: 800-331-4463
URL: http://www.de.pennnet.com/home.cfm

Monthly. $88.00 for single issue; $10.00 for single issue; $120.00/year for out of country, Mexico/Canada; $168.00/year for other countries; $16.00 for single issue, Mexico/Canada; $18.00/year for single issue, other countries. Magazine featuring business-related articles for dentists.

★3059★ Hawaii Dental Journal

Hawaii Medical Journal
1345 S Beretania St., No. 301
Honolulu, HI 96814-1821

Bimonthly. Dental journal.

★3060★ Illinois Dental Journal

Illinois State Dental Society
1010 S Second St.
PO Box 376
Springfield, IL 62705
Ph: (217)525-1406   Fax: (217)525-8872

Monthly. $25.00/year for members; $45.00/year for nonmembers; $75.00/year for nonmembers, other countries; $5.00 for single issue. Dental magazine.

★3061★ Journal of the California Dental Association

California Dental Association
1201 'K' St. Mall
PO Box 13749
Sacramento, CA 95853
Ph: (916)443-0505   Fax: (916)443-2943
Fr: 800-736-7071
URL: http://www.cda.org/cda

Monthly. $24.00/year for ADA members; $60.00/year for nonmembers; $10.00/year for single issue ($10.78 July issue); $12.00/year for CDA members. Professional magazine for dentists.

★3062★ Journal of Dental Education

American Dental Education Association
1625 Massachusetts Ave. NW
Washington, DC 20036-2212
Ph: (202)667-9433   Fax: (202)667-0642

Monthly. $75.00/year; $100.00/year for Canada; $125.00/year for other countries. Peer-reviewed journal for scholarly research and reviews on dental education.

★3063★ Journal of Dental Hygiene

American Dental Hygienists' Association
444 N Michigan Ave., Ste. 3400
Chicago, IL 60611
Ph: (312)440-8900   Fax: (312)440-6780
Fr: 800-243-ADHA
E-mail: mail@adha.net

$45.00/year; $65.00/year; $90.00/year. Professional journal on dental hygiene.

★3064★ Journal of Dental Research

International and American Associations for Dental Research
1619 Duke St.
Alexandria, VA 22314-3406
Ph: (703)548-0066   Fax: (703)548-1883
E-mail: research@iadr.org
URL: http://www.dentalresearch.org

Monthly. $402.00/year for individuals; $412.00/year for other countries. Dental science journal.

★3065★ Journal of Dentistry for Children

American Society of Dentistry for Children
875 N Michigan Ave., Ste. 4040
Chicago, IL 60611-1901
Ph: (312)943-1244   Fax: (312)943-5341
Fr: 800-637-2732

Bimonthly. $100.00/year for individuals, domestic; $120.00/year for institutions, domestic; $120.00/year for individuals, other countries; $150.00/year for institutions, other countries. Magazine focusing on dentistry for children.

★3066★ The Journal of Prosthetic Dentistry

Mosby Inc.
11830 Westline Industrial Dr.
St. Louis, MO 63146
Ph: (314)872-8370   Fax: (314)432-1380
Fr: 800-325-4177
URL: http://www.mosby.com

Monthly. $169.00/year for individuals; $349.00/year for institutions; $84.00/year for students; $209.00/year for individuals, other countries; $389.00/year for institutions, other countries; $105.00/year for students, other countries. Journal emphasizing new techniques, evaluation of dental materials, pertinent basic science concepts, and patient psychology in restorative dentistry.

★3067★ **Maryland State Dental Association Newsletter**

Maryland State Dental Association
6410F Dobbin Rd.
Columbia, MD 21045-4744
Ph: (410)964-2880   Fax: (410)964-0583

Description: Monthly. Reports on health, legislative, economic, and medical issues that are pertinent to dentistry. Recurring features include letters to the editor, interviews, news of research, a calendar of events, reports of meetings, news of educational opportunities, and job listings.

★3068★ **MDS News**

Massachusetts Dental Society
Two Willow St., Ste. 200
Southborough, MA 01745-1027
Ph: (508)480-9797   Fax: (508)480-0002
Fr: 800-342-8747

Description: Six issues/year. Provides news on the Society's activities and articles on the dental profession. Recurring features include reports of meetings, news of educational opportunities, job listings, and notices of publications available.

★3069★ **Pennsylvania Dental Journal**

Pennsylvania Dental Association
Box 3341
Harrisburg, PA 17105
Ph: (717)234-5941   Fax: (717)234-2186
E-mail: rap@padental.org

Bimonthly. $36.00/year for individuals; $60.00/year for other countries. Professional dentistry magazine containing treatment/procedure news, PDA activities information, continuing education courses, and legislation updates.

EMPLOYER DIRECTORIES AND NETWORKING LISTS

★3070★ **Dental Laboratories Directory**

infoUSA Inc.
5711 S 86th Cir.
Omaha, NE 68127-0347
Ph: (402)930-3500   Fax: (402)331-0176
Fr: 800-555-6124
URL: http://www.abii.com

Annual. Number of listings: 12,026. Entries include: Name, address, phone (including area code), size of advertisement, year first in "Yellow Pages," name of owner of manag-

er, number of employees. Compiled from telephone company "Yellow Pages" nationwide. Arrangement: Geographical.

★3071★ **Dentists Directory**

infoUSA Inc.
5711 S 86th Cir.
Omaha, NE 68127-0347
Ph: (402)930-3500   Fax: (402)331-0176
Fr: 800-555-6124
URL: http://www.abii.com

Annual. Number of listings: 210,919. Entries include: Name, address, phone (including area code), size of advertisement, code indicating specialty, year first in "Yellow Pages," name of owner or manager, number of employees. Regional editions available: North East (Connecticut, Maine Massachusetts, New Hampshire, New Jersey, New York, Pennsylvania, Rhode Island, Vermont), $1310.00; East North Central (Illinois, Indiana, Michigan, Ohio, Wisconsin), $945.00; West North Central (Iowa, Kansas, Minnesota, Missouri, Nebraska, North Dakota, South Dakota), $460.00; South Atlantic (District of Columbia, Delaware, Florida, Georgia, Maryland, North Carolina, South Carolina, Virginia, West Virginia), $845.00; South Central (Alabama, Arkansas, Kentucky, Louisiana, Mississippi, Oklahoma, Tennessee, Texas), $745.00; Mountain (Arizona, Colorado, Idaho, Montana, Nevada, New Mexico, Utah, Wyoming), $380.00; Pacific (Alaska, California, Hawaii, Oregon, Washington), $945,00. Compiled from telephone company "Yellow Pages," nationwide. Arrangement: Geographical.

HANDBOOKS AND MANUALS

★3072★ **Careers in Health Care**

McGraw-Hill Trade
2 Penn Plaza
New York, NY 10121
Ph: (212)904-2000   Fr: 800-722-4726
E-mail: ntcpub@tribune.com

Barbara M. Swanson. Fourth edition, 2000. $17.95; $13.95 (paper). 320 pages. Describes job duties, work settings, salaries, licensing and certification requirements, educational preparation, and future outlook. Gives ideas on how to secure a job.

★3073★ **Dental Laboratory Technology: Basic Sciences**

Gordon Press Publishers
PO Box 459, Bowling Green Sta.
New York, NY 10004
Ph: (212)969-8419   Fax: (718)624-8419
1993. $299.95.

★3074★ **Opportunities in Health and Medical Careers**

McGraw-Hill Trade
2 Penn Plaza
New York, NY 10121
Ph: (212)904-2000   Fr: 800-722-4726

I. Donald Snook, Jr. and Leo D'Orazio. 1997. $14.95; $11.95 (paper). 202 pages. Covers the full range of medical and health occupations. Illustrated.

★3075★ **Opportunities in Medical Technology Careers**

McGraw-Hill/Contemporary Books
1221 Avenue of the Americas
New York, NY 10020
Ph: (212)904-2000   Fr: 800-323-4900
E-mail: ntcpub@tribune.com

Karen R. Karni. Revised, 1996. $14.95; $11.95 (paper). 205 pages. Details opportunities for various technical medical personnel and supplies up-to-date information on salary levels and employment outlook. Appendices list associations and unions in each field. Illustrated.

★3076★ **Opportunities in Paramedical Careers**

McGraw-Hill/Contemporary Books
1221 Avenue of the Americas
New York, NY 10020
Ph: (212)904-2000   Fr: 800-323-4900
E-mail: ntcpub@tribune.com

Alex Kacen. Revised, 1999. $14.95; 11.95 (paper). 200 pages. Discusses a variety of opportunities in this field and how to pursue them. Illustrated.

★3077★ **Resumes for Health and Medical Careers**

McGraw-Hill Trade
2 Penn Plaza
New York, NY 10121
Ph: (212)904-2000   Fr: 800-722-4726
E-mail: ntcpub@tribune.com

1997. $9.95 (paper). 455 pages.

EMPLOYMENT AGENCIES AND SEARCH FIRMS

★3078★ **Colucci, Blendow & Johnson**

643 Main St., Ste. 8
Half Moon Bay, CA 94019-1988
Ph: (650)712-0103   Fax: (650)712-0105

Executive search consultants in the medical technology area that includes pharmaceuticals, medical equipment and device manufacturers, biotechnology, therapeutic supplies, diagnostic laboratory equipment and supplies, diagnostic imaging equipment and supplies, medical services, chemicals, cosmetic and toiletries, dental, veterinarian, and agricultural genetics companies.

★3079★ DDS Staffing Resources, Inc.
9755 Dogwood Rd., Ste. 200
Roswell, GA 30075
Ph: (770)998-7779 Fax: (770)552-0176
URL: http://www.ddsstaffing.com
Employment agency.

★3080★ Legal Medical Staffing Services Inc.
Plz. 1000, Ste. 202, Main St.
Voorhees, NJ 08043
Ph: (856)751-7999 Fax: (856)751-8448
Offers a specialized service providing temporary and full-time support exclusively to the legal, dental, and medical professions.

ONLINE JOB SOURCES AND SERVICES

★3081★ Medhunters.com
E-mail: info@medhunters.com
URL: http://www.medhunters.com
Description: Career search site for jobs in all health care specialties; educational resources; visa and licensing information for relocation; interesting articles; relocation tools; links to professional organizations and general resources.

★3082★ ProHealthJobs
E-mail: sales@prohealthjobs.com
URL: http://www.prohealthjobs.com
Description: Career resources site for the medical and health care field. Lists professional opportunities, product information, continuing education and open positions.

TRADESHOWS

★3083★ Star of the North Meeting
Minnesota Dental Association
2236 Marshall Ave.
St. Paul, MN 55104
Ph: (651)646-7454 Fax: (651)646-8246
E-mail: info@mndental.org
URL: http://www.mndental.org
Annual. **Primary Exhibits:** Dental equipment and supplies, dental laboratory equipment, office equipment, and service organizations. **Dates and Locations:** 2005 Apr 29-May 02; St. Paul, MN; RiverCentre • 2006 Apr 28-May 01; St. Paul, MN; RiverCentre.

★3084★ Yankee Dental Congress
Massachusetts Dental Society
2 Willow St., Ste. 200
Southborough, MA 01745
Ph: (508)480-9797 Fax: (508)480-0002
Fr: 800-943-9200
E-mail: madental@massdental.org
URL: http://www.massdental.org
Annual. **Primary Exhibits:** Dental products, equipment, and services. **Dates and Locations:** 2005 Jan 27-30; Boston, MA.

OTHER SOURCES

★3085★ American Dental Association (ADA)
211 E. Chicago Ave.
Chicago, IL 60611
Ph: (312)440-2500 Fax: (312)440-2800
E-mail: publicinfo@ada.org
URL: http://www.ada.org
Description: Professional society of dentists. Encourages the improvement of the health of the public and promotes the art and science of dentistry in matters of legislation and regulations. Inspects and accredits dental schools and schools for dental hygienists, assistants, and laboratory technicians. Conducts research programs at ADA Foundation Research Institute. Produces most of the dental health education material used in the U.S. Sponsors National Children's Dental Health Month. Compiles statistics on personnel, practice, and dental care needs and attitudes of patients with regard to dental health. Sponsors 13 councils.

★3086★ American Dental Education Association
1625 Massachusetts Ave. NW, Ste. 600
Washington, DC 20036-2212
Ph: (202)667-9433 Fax: (202)667-0642
E-mail: adea@adea.org
URL: http://www.adea.org/
Description: Individuals interested in dental education; schools of dentistry, graduate dentistry, and allied dental education in the U.S., Canada, and Puerto Rico; affiliated institutions of the federal government. To promote better teaching and education in dentistry and dental research and to facilitate exchange of ideas among dental educators. Sponsors meetings, conferences, and workshops; conducts surveys, studies, and special projects and publishes their results. Maintains 39 sections representing teaching and administrative areas of dentistry.

★3087★ Dental Laboratory Technicians
Evon Publishing
832 N 7th Ave.
Iron River, MI 49935
Ph: (906)265-3190
Audiocassette. 1996. $16.95. 32 minutes. Part of the Careers and Vocational Guidance Series. Provides information about the nature of the work, educational requirements, employment outlook, earnings, and work conditions as well as additional related information.

★3088★ Exploring Health Occupations
Cambridge Educational
2572 Brunswick Ave.
Lawrenceville, NJ 08648-4128
Fax: 800-FAX-ON-US Fr: 800-468-4227
URL: http://www.cambridgeeducational.com
Two videos. $139.95. 1999.

★3089★ Health Service Occupations
Delphi Productions
3160 4th St.
Boulder, CO 80304
Fax: (303)443-4022 Fr: 888-443-2400
URL: http://www.delphivideo.com
$95.00. 50 minutes. Part of the Careers for the 21st Century Video Library.

★3090★ Health Technologists & Technicians
Delphi Productions
3160 4th St.
Boulder, CO 80304
Fax: (303)443-4022 Fr: 888-443-2400
URL: http://www.delphivideo.com
$95.00. 50 minutes. Part of the Careers for the 21st Century Video Library.

★3091★ Holistic Dental Association (HDA)
PO Box 5007
Durango, CO 81301
Ph: (970)259-1091 Fax: (970)259-1091
E-mail: info@holisticdental.org
URL: http://www.holisticdental.org
Description: Dentists, chiropractors, dental hygienists, physical therapists, and medical doctors. Goals are: to provide a holistic approach to better dental care for patients; to expand techniques, medications, and philosophies that pertain to extractions, anesthetics, fillings, crowns, and orthodontics. Encourages use of homeopathic medications, acupuncture, cranial osteopathy, nutritional techniques, and physical therapy in treating patients in addition to conventional treatments. Sponsors training and educational seminars.

★3092★ Medical Technicians and Technologists
Cambridge Educational
2572 Brunswick Ave.
Lawrenceville, NJ 08648-4128
Fax: 800-FAX-ON-US Fr: 800-468-4227
URL: http://www.cambridgeeducational.com
$79.95. 15 minutes. Part of the Exploring Health Occupations Series.

★3093★ Medicine & Related Occupations
Delphi Productions
3160 4th St.
Boulder, CO 80304
Fax: (303)443-4022 Fr: 888-443-2400
URL: http://www.delphivideo.com

$95.00. 45 minutes. Part of the Careers for the 21st Century Video Library.

★3094★ **National Association of Dental Assistants (NADA)**
900 S Washington St., No. G-13
Falls Church, VA 22046
Ph: (703)237-8616   Fax: (703)533-1153

Members: Professional dental auxiliaries. **Purpose:** Seeks to bring added stature and purpose to the profession through continuing education and make available to dental assistants the special benefits normally limited to members of specialized professional and fraternal groups.

★3095★ **National Association of Dental Laboratories (NADL)**
1530 Metropolitan Blvd.
Tallahassee, FL 32308
Ph: (850)222-0053   Fax: (850)222-0053
Fr: 800-950-1150
E-mail: nadl@nadl.org
URL: http://www.nadl.org

Description: Represents 2900 commercial dental laboratories, manufacturers/suppliers and educators serving the dental profession. **Purpose:** Develops criteria for ethical dental laboratories. **Activities:** Offers business and personal insurance programs, Hazardous Materials Training Program, and an infectious disease prevention training program, business management and technical education programs. Compiles statistics; maintains speakers' bureau and museum; conducts educational and charitable programs.

★3096★ *Production Occupations*
Delphi Productions
3160 4th St.
Boulder, CO 80304
Fax: (303)443-4022   Fr: 888-443-2400
URL: http://www.delphivideo.com

$95.00. 49 minutes. Part of the Careers for the 21st Century Video Library.

★3097★ *Technical & Related Occupations*
Delphi Productions
3160 4th St.
Boulder, CO 80304
Fax: (303)443-4022   Fr: 888-443-2400
URL: http://www.delphivideo.com

$95.00. 49 minutes. Part of the Careers for the 21st Century Video Library.

Dentists

SOURCES OF HELP-WANTED ADS

★3098★ American Association of Women Dentists-Chronicle

American Association of Women Dentists
645 N Michigan Ave., No. 800
Chicago, IL 60611-4267
Ph: (312)280-9296   Fax: (312)280-9893
Fr: 800-920-2293
URL: http://www.womendentists.org

Description: Quarterly. Includes articles of interest on dentistry, nutrition, research, education, and federal services. Provides information on the association, the practice of dentistry, and women in dentistry.

★3099★ American Dental Hygienists' Association Access

American Dental Hygienists' Association
444 N Michigan Ave., Ste. 3400
Chicago, IL 60611
Ph: (312)440-8900   Fax: (312)440-6780
Fr: 800-243-ADHA

Subscription included in membership; $30.00/year for nonmembers. Magazine covering current dental hygiene topics, regulatory and legislative developments, and association news.

★3100★ American Journal of Orthodontics and Dentofacial Orthopedics

Mosby Inc.
11830 Westline Industrial Dr.
St. Louis, MO 63146
Ph: (314)872-8370   Fax: (314)432-1380
Fr: 800-325-4177
URL: http://www.elsevier.com

Monthly. $172.00/year for individuals; $363.00/year for institutions; $86.00/year for students; $206.00/year for individuals, other countries; $397.00/year for institutions, other countries; $103.00/year for students, other countries. Journal for orthodontists and dentists who include orthodontics as a portion of their practice.

★3101★ Bulletin of Dental Education

American Dental Education Association
1625 Massachusetts Ave. NW
Washington, DC 20036-2212
Ph: (202)667-9433   Fax: (202)667-0642

Description: Monthly. Contains news and information on dental education. Recurring features include a calendar of events, reports of meetings, news of educational opportunities, job listings, and notices of publications available.

★3102★ CDS Review

Chicago Dental Society
401 N Michigan Ave., Ste. 300
Chicago, IL 60611-4272
Ph: (312)836-7305   Fax: (312)836-7337
E-mail: reviewvox@aol.com

$25.00/year for individuals; $30.00/year, schools and industry; $45.00/year for other countries; $4.00 for single issue; $6.00/year for November issue. Dental journal.

★3103★ Dental Economics

PennWell Corp.
1421 S Sheridan Rd.
Tulsa, OK 74112
Ph: (918)835-3161   Fax: (918)832-9201
Fr: 800-331-4463
URL: http://www.de.pennnet.com/home.cfm

Monthly. $88.00 for single issue; $10.00 for single issue; $120.00/year for out of country, Mexico/Canada; $168.00/year for other countries; $16.00 for single issue, Mexico/Canada; $18.00/year for single issue, other countries. Magazine featuring business-related articles for dentists.

★3104★ Hawaii Dental Journal

Hawaii Medical Journal
1345 S Beretania St., No. 301
Honolulu, HI 96814-1821

Bimonthly. Dental journal.

★3105★ Illinois Dental Journal

Illinois State Dental Society
1010 S Second St.
PO Box 376
Springfield, IL 62705
Ph: (217)525-1406   Fax: (217)525-8872

Monthly. $25.00/year for members; $45.00/year for nonmembers; $75.00/year for nonmembers, other countries; $5.00 for single issue. Dental magazine.

★3106★ Journal of the American Dental Association

ADA Publishing
211 E Chicago Ave.
Chicago, IL 60611
Ph: (312)440-2810   Fax: (312)440-3538
Fr: 800-621-8099
URL: http://www.ada.org

Monthly. $110.00/year for individuals; $139.00/year for institutions; $13.00 for single issue; $139.00/year for individuals, foreign; $176.00/year for institutions, foreign; $122.00/year for individuals, Canadian; $158.00/year for institutions, Canadian; $69.00/year for nonmembers, student. Trade journal for the dental profession.

★3107★ Journal of the California Dental Association

California Dental Association
1201 'K' St. Mall
PO Box 13749
Sacramento, CA 95853
Ph: (916)443-0505   Fax: (916)443-2943
Fr: 800-736-7071
URL: http://www.cda.org/cda

Monthly. $24.00/year for ADA members; $60.00/year for nonmembers; $10.00/year for single issue ($10.78 July issue); $12.00/year for CDA members. Professional magazine for dentists.

★3108★ Journal of Dental Education

American Dental Education Association
1625 Massachusetts Ave. NW
Washington, DC 20036-2212
Ph: (202)667-9433   Fax: (202)667-0642

Monthly. $75.00/year; $100.00/year for Canada; $125.00/year for other countries. Peer-reviewed journal for scholarly research and reviews on dental education.

★3109★ Journal of Dental Hygiene

American Dental Hygienists' Association
444 N Michigan Ave., Ste. 3400
Chicago, IL 60611
Ph: (312)440-8900   Fax: (312)440-6780
Fr: 800-243-ADHA
E-mail: mail@adha.net

$45.00/year; $65.00/year; $90.00/year. Professional journal on dental hygiene.

★3110★ Journal of Dental Research

International and American Associations
  for Dental Research
1619 Duke St.
Alexandria, VA 22314-3406
Ph: (703)548-0066   Fax: (703)548-1883
E-mail: research@iadr.org
URL: http://www.dentalresearch.org

Monthly. $402.00/year for individuals; $412.00/year for other countries. Dental science journal.

★3111★ Journal of Dentistry for Children

American Society of Dentistry for Children
875 N Michigan Ave., Ste. 4040
Chicago, IL 60611-1901
Ph: (312)943-1244   Fax: (312)943-5341
Fr: 800-637-2732

Bimonthly. $100.00/year for individuals, domestic; $120.00/year for institutions, domestic; $120.00/year for individuals, other countries; $150.00/year for institutions, other countries. Magazine focusing on dentistry for children.

★3112★ The Journal of Prosthetic Dentistry

Mosby Inc.
11830 Westline Industrial Dr.
St. Louis, MO 63146
Ph: (314)872-8370   Fax: (314)432-1380
Fr: 800-325-4177
URL: http://www.mosby.com

Monthly. $169.00/year for individuals; $349.00/year for institutions; $84.00/year for students; $209.00/year for individuals, other countries; $389.00/year for institutions, other countries; $105.00/year for students, other countries. Journal emphasizing new techniques, evaluation of dental materials, pertinent basic science concepts, and patient psychology in restorative dentistry.

★3113★ Maryland State Dental Association Newsletter

Maryland State Dental Association
6410F Dobbin Rd.
Columbia, MD 21045-4744
Ph: (410)964-2880   Fax: (410)964-0583

Description: Monthly. Reports on health, legislative, economic, and medical issues that are pertinent to dentistry. Recurring features include letters to the editor, interviews, news of research, a calendar of events, reports of meetings, news of educational opportunities, and job listings.

★3114★ MDS News

Massachusetts Dental Society
Two Willow St., Ste. 200
Southborough, MA 01745-1027
Ph: (508)480-9797   Fax: (508)480-0002
Fr: 800-342-8747

Description: Six issues/year. Provides news on the Society's activities and articles on the dental profession. Recurring features include reports of meetings, news of educational opportunities, job listings, and notices of publications available.

★3115★ Pennsylvania Dental Journal

Pennsylvania Dental Association
Box 3341
Harrisburg, PA 17105
Ph: (717)234-5941   Fax: (717)234-2186
E-mail: rap@padental.org

Bimonthly. $36.00/year for individuals; $60.00/year for other countries. Professional dentistry magazine containing treatment/procedure news, PDA activities information, continuing education courses, and legislation updates.

★3116★ RDH

PennWell Corp.
PO Box 1260
Tulsa, OK 74101-1260
Ph: (918)831-9742   Fax: (918)831-9804
Fr: 800-633-1681

Monthly. $48.00/year. Magazine for dental hygiene professionals covering practice management, patient motivation, practice options, financial planning, personal development, preventive oral health care and treatment, home care instruction, radiology, anesthesia, nutrition, and new products.

★3117★ WSDA News

Washington State Dental Association
  (WSDA)
2033 6th Ave., Ste. 333
Seattle, WA 98121
Ph: (206)448-1914   Fax: (206)443-9266
URL: http://www.wsda.org

Description: Monthly, except October. Contains information of interest to dentists on legislation, regulations, state boards and government, and business of the association. Recurring features include letters to the editor, editorial and op-ed columns, President's message, obituaries, practice oppor-

tunities, news of educational opportunities, and job listings.

PLACEMENT AND JOB REFERRAL SERVICES

★3118★ American Public Health Association (APHA)

800 I St. NW
Washington, DC 20001-3710
Ph: (202)777-2742   Fax: (202)777-2534
E-mail: comments@apha.org
URL: http://www.apha.org

Members: Professional organization of physicians, nurses, educators, academicians, environmentalists, epidemiologists, new professionals, social workers, health administrators, optometrists, podiatrists, pharmacists, dentists, nutritionists, health planners, other community and mental health specialists, and interested consumers. **Purpose:** Seeks to protect and promote personal, mental, and environmental health. **Activities:** Services include promulgation of standards; establishment of uniform practices and procedures; development of the etiology of communicable diseases; research in public health; exploration of medical care programs and their relationships to public health. Sponsors job placement service.

★3119★ Ukrainian Medical Association of North America (UMANA)

2247 W. Chicago Ave., 2nd Fl.
Chicago, IL 60622
Ph: (773)278-6262   Fax: (773)278-6962
Fr: 888-RXU-MANA
E-mail: umana@umana.org
URL: http://www.umana.org

Description: Physicians, surgeons, dentists, and persons in related professions who are of Ukrainian descent. Provides assistance to members; sponsors lectures. Maintains placement service, museum, biographical and medical archives, and library of 1800 medical books and journals in Ukrainian.

EMPLOYER DIRECTORIES AND NETWORKING LISTS

★3120★ American Academy of Pediatric Dentistry-Membership Directory

American Academy of Pediatric Dentistry
211 E Chicago Ave., Ste. 700
Chicago, IL 60611
Ph: (312)337-2169   Fax: (312)337-6329
URL: http://www.aapd.org

Annual, November. $600.00. Covers 5,600 pediatric dentists and several dentists in practice, teaching, and research. Entries include: Name, address, phone. Arrangement: Alphabetical. Indexes: Geographical.

★3121★ **Dentists Directory**
infoUSA Inc.
5711 S 86th Cir.
Omaha, NE 68127-0347
Ph: (402)930-3500   Fax: (402)331-0176
Fr: 800-555-6124
URL: http://www.abii.com

Annual. Number of listings: 210,919. Entries include: Name, address, phone (including area code), size of advertisement, code indicating specialty, year first in "Yellow Pages," name of owner or manager, number of employees. Regional editions available: North East (Connecticut, Maine Massachusetts, New Hampshire, New Jersey, New York, Pennsylvania, Rhode Island, Vermont), $1310.00; East North Central (Illinois, Indiana, Michigan, Ohio, Wisconsin), $945.00; West North Central (Iowa, Kansas, Minnesota, Missouri, Nebraska, North Dakota, South Dakota), $460.00; South Atlantic (District of Columbia, Delaware, Florida, Georgia, Maryland, North Carolina, South Carolina, Virginia, West Virginia), $845.00; South Central (Alabama, Arkansas, Kentucky, Louisiana, Mississippi, Oklahoma, Tennessee, Texas), $745.00; Mountain (Arizona, Colorado, Idaho, Montana, Nevada, New Mexico, Utah, Wyoming), $380.00; Pacific (Alaska, California, Hawaii, Oregon, Washington), $945,00. Compiled from telephone company "Yellow Pages," nationwide. Arrangement: Geographical.

★3122★ **Health & Medical Industry Directory**
infoUSA Inc.
5711 S 86th Cir.
Omaha, NE 68127-0347
Ph: (402)930-3500   Fax: (402)331-0176
Fr: 800-555-6124
URL: http://www.abii.com

Released 1993. CD-ROM. Lists over 1.1 million physicians and surgeons, dentists, clinics, health clubs, and other health-related businesses in the U.S. and Canada. Entries include: Name, address, phone. IBM-compatible equipment required.

★3123★ **International Association for Orthodontics-Membership Directory**
International Association for Orthodontics
735 N Water St., Ste. 617
Milwaukee, WI 53202
Ph: (414)272-2757   Fax: (414)272-2754
Fr: 800-447-8770

Annual, June. $75.00. Covers 2,500 general and children's dentists who also work to correct facial and jaw irregularities. Entries include: Name, office address and phone, orthodontic techniques practiced. Arrangement: Geographical. Indexes: Personal name.

★3124★ **Physicians and Dentists Database**
Firstmark Inc.
25 Vintinner Rd.
PO Box 1270
Campton, NH 03223-1270
Ph: (603)726-4800   Fax: (603)726-4840
Fr: 800-729-2600
URL: http://www.firstmark.com/fmkcat/docs+3.htm

Updated continuously; printed on request. Database covers: Over 500,000 physicians and 160,000 dentists nationwide. Entries include: Individual name, address, phone, medical specialty, whether in single or group practice.

★3125★ **Washington Physicians Directory**
National Directories Inc.
PO Box 4436
Silver Spring, MD 20914
Ph: (301)384-1506   Fax: (301)384-6854
E-mail: wpd@wpdnetwork.com

Annual, April. $47.00. Covers 9,800 physicians in private practice or on full-time staff at hospitals in the Washington, D.C., metropolitan area. Entries include: Name, medical school and year of graduation; up to four office addresses with phone numbers for each; up to four medical specialties (indicating board certifications), Unique Physician Identification Numbers (UPIN), and e-mail. Arrangement: Alphabetical. Indexes: Geographical (within medical specialty); foreign language.

HANDBOOKS AND MANUALS

★3126★ **The Art and Science of Being a Dentist: Leading Dentists Reveal the Secrets to Professional and Personal Success**
Aspatore Books, Inc.
264 Beacon St., 2nd Fl.
Boston, MA 02116
Ph: (617)249-1960   Fax: (617)249-1970

August 2003. $37.95. 256 pages.

★3127★ **Barron's Guide to Medical and Dental Schools**
Barron's Educational Series, Inc.
250 Wireless Blvd.
Hauppauge, NY 11788-3917
Ph: (631)434-3311   Fax: (631)434-3723
Fr: 800-645-3476

Saul Wischnitzer and Edith Wischnitzer. Eighth edition, 1997. $16.95. 384 pages. Out of print.

★3128★ **Careers in Medicine, Dentistry and Mental Health**
Kogan Page, Ltd.
22 Broad St., Ste. 34
Milford, CT 06460

Judith Humphries and Loulou Brown. Seventh edition, 1996. $14.95 (paper). Part of the Kogan Page Careers Series. Out of print.

★3129★ **The Dentists' Handbook**
Andent, Inc.
1000 North Ave.
Waukegan, IL 60085
Ph: (847)223-5077

Ellis J. Neiburger and S. Neiburger. 1993. $37.50 (paper). 350 pages.

★3130★ **Healthcare Career Directory-Nurses and Physicians**
Thomson Gale
27500 Drake Rd.
Farmington Hills, MI 48331-3535
Ph: (248)699-GALE   Fax: 800-414-5043
Fr: 800-877-GALE
E-mail: galeord@gale.com
URL: http://www.gale.com

Bradley Morgan. Second edition, 1993. $39.00. 300 pages. Out of print. Essays on specific careers provide an insider's perspective. Features extensive listings of contacts and entry-level job opportunities. Provides information on internships and sources of help-wanted ads.

★3131★ **Opportunities in Health and Medical Careers**
McGraw-Hill Trade
2 Penn Plaza
New York, NY 10121
Ph: (212)904-2000   Fr: 800-722-4726

I. Donald Snook, Jr. and Leo D'Orazio. 1997. $14.95; $11.95 (paper). 202 pages. Covers the full range of medical and health occupations. Illustrated.

★3132★ **REA's Authoritative Guide to Medical Dental School**
Research and Education Association
61 Ethel Rd., W
Piscataway, NJ 08854
Ph: (732)819-8800   Fax: (732)819-8808
Fr: 800-822-0830

1997. $21.95 (paper). 592 pages.

★3133★ **Resumes for Health and Medical Careers**
McGraw-Hill Trade
2 Penn Plaza
New York, NY 10121
Ph: (212)904-2000   Fr: 800-722-4726
E-mail: ntcpub@tribune.com

1997. $9.95 (paper). 455 pages.

EMPLOYMENT AGENCIES AND SEARCH FIRMS

★3134★ Colucci, Blendow & Johnson
643 Main St., Ste. 8
Half Moon Bay, CA 94019-1988
Ph: (650)712-0103   Fax: (650)712-0105
Executive search consultants in the medical technology area that includes pharmaceuticals, medical equipment and device manufacturers, biotechnology, therapeutic supplies, diagnostic laboratory equipment and supplies, diagnostic imaging equipment and supplies, medical services, chemicals, cosmetic and toiletries, dental, veterinarian, and agricultural genetics companies.

★3135★ DDS Staffing Resources, Inc.
9755 Dogwood Rd., Ste. 200
Roswell, GA 30075
Ph: (770)998-7779   Fax: (770)552-0176
URL: http://www.ddsstaffing.com
Employment agency.

★3136★ Legal Medical Staffing Services Inc.
Plz. 1000, Ste. 202, Main St.
Voorhees, NJ 08043
Ph: (856)751-7999   Fax: (856)751-8448
Offers a specialized service providing temporary and full-time support exclusively to the legal, dental, and medical professions.

★3137★ Team Placement Service, Inc.
5113 Leesburg Pike, Ste. 510
Falls Church, VA 22041-3242
Ph: (703)820-8618   Fax: (703)820-3368
Fr: 800-495-6767
E-mail: 4jobs@teamplace.com
URL: http://www.teamplace.com
Temporary agency that also handles some permanent placements.

ONLINE JOB SOURCES AND SERVICES

★3138★ Medbulletin Medical Career Resource Center
E-mail: medbulletin@atsmedbulletin.com
URL: http://www.medbulletin.com
Description: Offers free specialized update service, resume posting, recruiter directory, varied job listings, and relocation services.

★3139★ Medhunters.com
E-mail: info@medhunters.com
URL: http://www.medhunters.com
Description: Career search site for jobs in all health care specialties; educational resources; visa and licensing information for relocation; interesting articles; relocation tools; links to professional organizations and general resources.

★3140★ Medzilla
URL: http://www.medzilla.com
Description: General medical website which matches employers and job hunters to their ideal employees and jobs through search capabilities. **Main files include:** Post Jobs, Search Resumes, Post Resumes, Search Jobs, Head Hunters, Articles, Salary Survey.

★3141★ Monster Healthcare
E-mail: office@atsmedsearch.com
URL: http://myh.monster.com/
Description: H Monster delivers nationwide access to healthcare recruiting. Employers can post job listings or ads. Job seekers can post and code resumes, and search over 150,000 healthcare job listings, healthcare career advice columns, career resources information, and member employer profiles and services.

★3142★ ProHealthJobs
E-mail: sales@prohealthjobs.com
URL: http://www.prohealthjobs.com
Description: Career resources site for the medical and health care field. Lists professional opportunities, product information, continuing education and open positions.

TRADESHOWS

★3143★ Academy of General Dentistry Annual Meeting
Academy of General Dentistry
211 E. Chicago Ave., Ste. 900
Chicago, IL 60611
Ph: (312)440-4300   Fax: (312)440-0513
Fr: 888-243-3368
URL: http://www.agd.org
Annual. **Primary Exhibits:** Dental products and services. **Dates and Locations:** 2005 Jul 14-17; Washington, DC; Marriott Wardman Park.

★3144★ American Academy of Fixed Prosthodontics Scientific Session
American Academy of Fixed Prosthodontics
1930 Sea Way
PO Box 1409
Bodega Bay, CA 94923-1409
Ph: (707)875-3040   Fax: (707)875-2927
Fr: 800-785-9188
E-mail: secaafp@worldnet.att.net
Annual. **Primary Exhibits:** Prosthodontics equipment, supplies, and services. 2005 Feb 25-26; Chicago, IL.

★3145★ American Academy of Gnathologic Orthopedics Conference
American Academy of Gnathologic Orthopedics
1585 N. Barrington Rd., Ste. 106
Hoffman Estates, IL 60194
Ph: (847)884-1220   Fax: (847)884-1638
Annual. **Primary Exhibits:** Exhibits of interest to those in the fields of maxillofacial orthopedics/orthodontics and preventative and corrective orthodontics. **Dates and Locations:** 2004 Sep 22-25; Reno, NV.

★3146★ American Academy of Orofacial Pain Annual Scientific Meeting
American Academy of Orofacial Pain
19 Mantua Rd.
Mount Royal, NJ 08061
Ph: (609)423-7222   Fax: (609)423-3420
Annual. **Primary Exhibits:** Exhibits relating to orofacial pain and temporomandibular disorders.

★3147★ American Academy of Pediatric Dentistry Annual Meeting
American Academy of Pediatric Dentistry
211 E Chicago Ave., Ste. 700
Chicago, IL 60611
Ph: (312)337-2169   Fax: (312)337-6329
URL: http://www.aapd.org
Annual. **Primary Exhibits:** Dental products and publications.

★3148★ American Association of Dental Schools Annual Session and Exposition
American Association of Dental Schools
1625 Massachusetts Ave., NW
Washington, DC 20036
Ph: (202)667-9433   Fax: (202)667-0642
Annual. **Primary Exhibits:** Dental equipment and supplies, publications, video equipment, and computers.

★3149★ American Association of Orthodontists Trade Show and Scientific Session
American Association of Orthodontists
401 N. Lindbergh Blvd.
St. Louis, MO 63141-7816
Ph: (314)993-1700   Fax: (314)997-1745
Fr: 800-424-2841
E-mail: info@aaortho.org
URL: http://www.aaortho.org
Annual. **Primary Exhibits:** Orthodontic equipment and materials.

★3150★ American Association of Public Health Dentistry Conference
American Association of Public Health Dentistry
1224 Centre West, Ste. 400B
Springfield, IL 62704
Ph: (217)391-0218   Fax: (217)793-0041
E-mail: natoff@aaphd.org

URL: http://www.aaphd.org

Annual. **Primary Exhibits:** Dental public health equipment, supplies, and services.

★3151★ American Dental Association Annual Session & Technical Exhibition

American Dental Association
211 E. Chicago Ave.
Chicago, IL 60611-2678
Ph: (312)440-2581   Fax: (312)440-2707
E-mail: exhibit@ada.org
URL: http://www.ada.org

Annual. **Primary Exhibits:** Dental equipment, instruments, materials, therapeutics, and services.

★3152★ American Dental Society of Anesthesiology Scientific Meeting

American Dental Society of Anesthesiology
211 E. Chicago Ave., Ste. 948
Chicago, IL 60611
Ph: (312)664-8270   Fax: (312)642-9713
Fr: 800-722-7788

Annual. **Primary Exhibits:** Anesthetics and anesthesia monitoring equipment.

★3153★ General Session and Exhibition of the IADR

International Association for Dental Research
1619 Duke St.
Alexandria, VA 22314
Ph: (703)548-0066   Fax: (703)548-1883
E-mail: research@iadr.com
URL: http://www.dentalresearch.org

Annual. **Primary Exhibits:** Dentistry equipment, supplies, and services. **Dates and Locations:** 2005 Mar 09-12; Baltimore, MD; Baltimore Convention Center • 2006 Jun 28-Jul 01; Brisbane, QL, Australia; Brisbane Convention Center.

★3154★ International Education Congress of Dental Technology

Dental Laboratory Association of the State of New York
1 Barstow Rd., Ste. P-20
Great Neck, NY 11021-3501
Ph: (516)829-1144   Fax: (516)829-1988
E-mail: dlany@aol.com
URL: http://www.dlany.org

Annual. **Primary Exhibits:** Dental laboratory supplies and services.

★3155★ International Medical and Dental Hypnotherapy Association (IMDHA)

International Medical and Dental Hypnotherapy Association (IMDHA)
4110 Edgeland, Ste. 800
Royal Oak, MI 48073-2285
Ph: (248)549-5594   Fax: (248)549-5421
E-mail: aspencer@infinityinst.com
URL: http://www.infinityinst.com

Annual. **Primary Exhibits:** Hypnotherapy and Holistic Health.

★3156★ Mid-Continent Dental Congress

Greater St. Louis Dental Society
13667 Manchester Rd.
St. Louis, MO 63131
Ph: (314)965-5960   Fax: (314)965-4746
E-mail: gslds@gslds.org

Annual. **Primary Exhibits:** Dental equipment, supplies, and services.

★3157★ National Dental Association Annual Convention

National Dental Association, Inc.
3517 16th St., NW
Washington, DC 20010
Ph: (202)588-1697   Fax: (202)588-1244
E-mail: admin@ndaonline.org

Annual. **Primary Exhibits:** Dental and Pharmaceutical equipment, supplies, and services.

★3158★ Star of the North Meeting

Minnesota Dental Association
2236 Marshall Ave.
St. Paul, MN 55104
Ph: (651)646-7454   Fax: (651)646-8246
E-mail: info@mndental.org
URL: http://www.mndental.org

Annual. **Primary Exhibits:** Dental equipment and supplies, dental laboratory equipment, office equipment, and service organizations. **Dates and Locations:** 2005 Apr 29-May 02; St. Paul, MN; RiverCentre • 2006 Apr 28-May 01; St. Paul, MN; RiverCentre.

★3159★ Thomas P. Hinman Dental Meeting & Exhibits

Thomas P. Hinman Dental Society
60 Lenox Pte.
Atlanta, GA 30324
Ph: (404)231-1476   Fax: (404)231-9638

Annual. **Primary Exhibits:** Dental equipment, supplies, and services.

★3160★ Three Rivers Dental Conference

Dental Society of Western Pennsylvania
900 Cedar Ave.
Pittsburgh, PA 15212
Ph: (412)321-5810   Fax: (412)321-7719

Annual. **Primary Exhibits:** Dental products and equipment, computers, office equipment, and insurance.

★3161★ Yankee Dental Congress

Massachusetts Dental Society
2 Willow St., Ste. 200
Southborough, MA 01745
Ph: (508)480-9797   Fax: (508)480-0002
Fr: 800-943-9200
E-mail: madental@massdental.org
URL: http://www.massdental.org

Annual. **Primary Exhibits:** Dental products, equipment, and services. **Dates and Locations:** 2005 Jan 27-30; Boston, MA.

OTHER SOURCES

★3162★ American Association of Dental Examiners (AADE)

211 E. Chicago Ave., Ste. 760
Chicago, IL 60611
Ph: (312)440-7464   Fax: (312)440-3525
E-mail: info@aadexam.org
URL: http://www.aadexam.org

Description: Present and past members of state dental examining boards and board administrators. To assist member agencies with problems related to state dental board examinations and licensure, and enforcement of the state dental practice act. Conducts research; compiles statistics.

★3163★ American Dental Association (ADA)

211 E. Chicago Ave.
Chicago, IL 60611
Ph: (312)440-2500   Fax: (312)440-2800
E-mail: publicinfo@ada.org
URL: http://www.ada.org

Description: Professional society of dentists. Encourages the improvement of the health of the public and promotes the art and science of dentistry in matters of legislation and regulations. Inspects and accredits dental schools and schools for dental hygienists, assistants, and laboratory technicians. Conducts research programs at ADA Foundation Research Institute. Produces most of the dental health education material used in the U.S. Sponsors National Children's Dental Health Month. Compiles statistics on personnel, practice, and dental care needs and attitudes of patients with regard to dental health. Sponsors 13 councils.

★3164★ American Dental Education Association

1625 Massachusetts Ave. NW, Ste. 600
Washington, DC 20036-2212
Ph: (202)667-9433   Fax: (202)667-0642
E-mail: adea@adea.org
URL: http://www.adea.org/

Description: Individuals interested in dental education; schools of dentistry, graduate dentistry, and allied dental education in the U.S., Canada, and Puerto Rico; affiliated institutions of the federal government. To promote better teaching and education in dentistry and dental research and to facilitate exchange of ideas among dental educators. Sponsors meetings, conferences, and workshops; conducts surveys, studies, and special projects and publishes their results. Maintains 39 sections representing teaching and administrative areas of dentistry.

★3165★ **American School Health Association (ASHA)**
PO Box 708
7263 State Route 43
Kent, OH 44240
Ph: (330)678-1601   Fax: (330)678-4526
Fr: 800-445-2742
E-mail: asha@ashaweb.org
URL: http://www.ashaweb.org

Description: School physicians, school nurses, dentist, nurses, nutritionists, health educators, dental hygienist, school-based professionals and public health workers. Promotes coordinated school health programs that include health education, health services, a healthful school environment, physical education, nutrition services, and psycho-social health services offered in schools collaboratively with families and other members of the community. Offers professional reference materials. Conducts pilot programs that inform materials development, provides technical assistance to school professionals, advocates for school health, and complies statistics.

★3166★ *Exploring Health Occupations*
Cambridge Educational
2572 Brunswick Ave.
Lawrenceville, NJ 08648-4128
Fax: 800-FAX-ON-US   Fr: 800-468-4227
URL: http://www.cambridgeeducational.com

Two videos. $139.95. 1999.

★3167★ *Health Service Occupations*
Delphi Productions
3160 4th St.
Boulder, CO 80304
Fax: (303)443-4022   Fr: 888-443-2400
URL: http://www.delphivideo.com

$95.00. 50 minutes. Part of the Careers for the 21st Century Video Library.

★3168★ **Holistic Dental Association (HDA)**
PO Box 5007
Durango, CO 81301
Ph: (970)259-1091   Fax: (970)259-1091
E-mail: info@holisticdental.org
URL: http://www.holisticdental.org

Description: Dentists, chiropractors, dental hygienists, physical therapists, and medical doctors. Goals are: to provide a holistic approach to better dental care for patients; to expand techniques, medications, and philosophies that pertain to extractions, anesthetics, fillings, crowns, and orthodontics. Encourages use of homeopathic medications, acupuncture, cranial osteopathy, nutritional techniques, and physical therapy in treating patients in addition to conventional treatments. Sponsors training and educational seminars.

★3169★ **International Congress of Oral Implantologists (ICOI)**
248 Lorraine Ave., Ste. 3
Upper Montclair, NJ 07043
Ph: (973)783-6300   Fax: (973)783-1175
Fr: 800-442-0525
E-mail: icoi@dentalimplants.com
URL: http://www.dentalimplants.com

Description: Dentists and oral surgeons dedicated to the teaching of and research in oral implantology (branch of dentistry dealing with dental implants placed into or on top of the jaw bone). Offers fellowship, mastership, and diplomate certification programs. Compiles statistics and maintains registry of current research in the field. Sponsors classes, seminars, and workshops at universities, hospitals, and societies worldwide. Provides consultation and patient information/referral services.

★3170★ *Medicine & Related Occupations*
Delphi Productions
3160 4th St.
Boulder, CO 80304
Fax: (303)443-4022   Fr: 888-443-2400

URL: http://www.delphivideo.com
$95.00. 45 minutes. Part of the Careers for the 21st Century Video Library.

★3171★ **National Rural Health Association (NRHA)**
1 W Armour Blvd., Ste. 203
Kansas City, MO 64111-2087
Ph: (816)756-3140   Fax: (816)756-3144
E-mail: mail@nrharural.org
URL: http://www.nrharural.org

Description: Administrators, physicians, nurses, physician assistants, health planners, academicians, and others interested or involved in rural health care. Creates a better understanding of health care problems unique to rural areas; utilizes a collective approach in finding positive solutions; articulates and represents the health care needs of rural America; supplies current information to rural health care providers; serves as a liaison between rural health care programs throughout the country. Offers continuing education credits for medical, dental, nursing, and management courses.

★3172★ *Women in Dentistry*
Her Own Words
PO Box 5264
Madison, WI 53705-0264
Ph: (608)271-7083   Fax: (608)271-0209
URL: http://www.herownwords.com/

Video. Jocelyn Riley. $95.00. 15 minutes. Resource guide also available for $45.00.

★3173★ *Women in Nontraditional Careers: An Introduction*
Her Own Words
PO Box 5264
Madison, WI 53705
Ph: (608)271-7083   Fax: (608)271-0209
URL: http://www.herownwords.com/

Video. Jocelyn Riley. $95.00. 15 minutes. Resource guide also available for $45.00.

Designers

SOURCES OF HELP-WANTED ADS

★3174★ Builder

Hanley-Wood L.L.C.
1 Thomas Cir., Ste. 600
Washington, DC 20005
Ph: (202)452-0800   Fax: (202)785-1974
URL: http://www.builderonline.com

Monthly. $29.95/year for individuals. Magazine covering housing and construction industry.

★3175★ Design News

Reed Business Information
275 Washington St.
Newton, MA 02458
Ph: (617)558-4900   Fax: (617)630-3830
Fr: 800-357-4745
E-mail: dn@chners.com

Semimonthly. $55.00/year for individuals. Magazine covering design engineering.

★3176★ Design Perspectives

Industrial Designers Society of America
45195 Business Ct., Ste. 250
Dulles, VA 20166-6717
Ph: (703)759-0100   Fax: (703)759-7679
URL: http://www.idsa.org

Description: Monthly. Discusses issues relevant to the profession. Recurring features include reports of chapter and national activities of IDSA, a section on employment opportunities in the field, resource section, and a calendar of events.

★3177★ ENR: Engineering News-Record

McGraw-Hill Companies
1221 Avenue of the Americas
New York, NY 10020
Ph: (212)512-2000
URL: http://www.enr.com

Weekly. $74.00/year; $5.00 for single issue. Magazine focusing on engineering and construction.

★3178★ Entertainment Design Magazine

Primedia Business
9800 Metcalf Ave.
Overland Park, KS 66212
Ph: (913)341-1300   Fax: (913)967-1898
E-mail: edld@intertec.com
URL: http://www.etecnyc.net

$37.95/year for individuals; $5.95 for single issue. The business of entertainment technology and design.

★3179★ Fabric Architecture

Industrial Fabrics Association International
1801 County Rd. B W
Roseville, MN 55113-4061
Ph: (651)222-2508   Fax: (651)225-6966
Fr: 800-225-4324
URL: http://www.ifai.com

Bimonthly. $39.00/year; $43.00/year for Canada and Mexico; $55.00/year for out of country. Magazine specializing in interior and exterior design ideas and technical information for architectural fabric applications in architecture and the landscape.

★3180★ HOW

F & W Publications Inc.
4700 E Galbraith Rd.
Cincinnati, OH 45236-6708
Ph: (513)531-2690   Fax: (513)531-2902
Fr: 800-289-0963
E-mail: editorial@howdesign.com

Bimonthly. $49.00/year for individuals; $7.95 for single issue, Jan/Feb or May/June; $9.95 for single issue, Mar/April or July/Aug; $11.95/year for single issue, Sept/Oct or Nov/Dec. Instructional trade magazine.

★3181★ Hydraulics & Pneumatics

Penton Media Inc.
1300 E 9th St.
Cleveland, OH 44114-1503
Ph: (216)696-7000   Fax: (216)931-9799
URL: http://www.fpweb.com/

$60.00/year; $95.00/year for other countries. Magazine of hydraulic and pneumatic systems and engineering.

★3182★ Jobline News

Graphic Artists Guild
90 John St., Ste. 403
New York, NY 10038
Ph: (212)791-3400   Fax: (212)791-0333
E-mail: jobline@gag.org

Description: Weekly. Lists jobs for freelance and staff artists in areas such as graphic design, illustration, and art education. Lists jobs from across the country; quantity and locales vary weekly.

★3183★ Producers Masterguide

Producers Masterguide
60 E 8th St., 34th Fl.
New York, NY 10003-6514
Ph: (212)777-4002   Fax: (212)777-4101
URL: http://www.producers.masterguide.com

Annual. $145.00/year for U.S.; $155.00/year for Canada; $175.00/year for other countries. An international film and TV production directory and guide for the professional motion picture, broadcast television, feature film, TV commercial, cable/satellite, digital and videotape industries in the U.S., Canada, the UK, the Caribbean Islands, Mexico, Australia, New Zealand, Europe, Israel, Morocco, the Far East, and South America.

★3184★ Professional Builder

Reed Business Information
360 Park Ave. S
New York, NY 10014
Ph: (646)746-7764
URL: http://www.probuilder.com

Monthly. $10.00 for single issue; $139.95/year for by mail.

★3185★ Society for Environmental Graphic Design-Messages

Society for Environmental Graphic Design
1000 Vermont Ave. NW, Ste. 400
Washington, DC 20005
Ph: (202)638-5555   Fax: (202)638-0891
E-mail: segdoffice@aol.com

Description: Bimonthly. Reports on Society program news, member services, resources, and product news.

★3186★ *Visual Merchandising and Store Design*

ST Media Group International Inc.
407 Gilbert Ave.
Cincinnati, OH 45202
Ph: (513)421-2050   Fax: (513)421-5144
Fr: 800-925-1110
E-mail: vmsd@stmediagroup.com
URL: http://www.visualstore.com

Monthly. $42.00/year; $5.50/year, single copy. The leading magazine of the retail design industry covering the latest trends in retail design, store planning, and merchandise presentation.

★3187★ *Wire & Cable Technology International*

Initial Publications Inc.
3869 Darrow Rd., Ste. 109
Stow, OH 44224
Ph: (330)686-9544   Fax: (330)686-9563
E-mail: info@wiretech.com

Bimonthly. $40.00/year for individuals; $90.00/year for other countries. Magazine for manufacturers of ferrous, nonferrous, bare, and insulated wire.

PLACEMENT AND JOB REFERRAL SERVICES

★3188★ **Advertising Production Club of New York (APC)**

276 Bowery
New York, NY 10012
Ph: (212)334-2018   Fax: (212)431-5786
E-mail: admin@apc-ny.org
URL: http://www.apc-ny.org

Description: Production and traffic department personnel from advertising agencies, corporate or retail advertising departments, and publishing companies; college level graphic arts educators. Meetings include educational programs on graphic arts procedures and plant tours. Maintains employment service for members.

★3189★ **American Society of Furniture Designers (ASFD)**

144 Woodland Dr.
New London, NC 28127
Ph: (910)576-1273   Fax: (910)576-1573
E-mail: info@asfd.com
URL: http://www.asfd.com

Members: Professional furniture designers, teachers, students, corporate suppliers of products and services; others who supply products and services related to furniture design. Seeks to promote the profession of furniture design. Conducts and cooperates in educational courses and seminars for furniture designers and persons planning to enter the field. Maintains placement service.

★3190★ **BDA**

2029 Century Park East, Ste. 555
Los Angeles, CA 90067-2906
Ph: (310)789-1509   Fax: (310)712-0039
E-mail: bonnie@promax.tv
URL: http://www.bda.tv

Members: Designers, artists, art directors, illustrators, photographers, animators, and other motion graphic professionals in the electronic media industry; educators and students; commercial and industrial companies that manufacture products related to design. **Purpose:** Objectives are to promote understanding between designers, clients, and management; to stimulate innovative ideas and techniques; to encourage and provide a resource for young talent; and to provide a forum for discussion on industry issues and concerns. **Activities:** Maintains placement service; conducts surveys and compiles statistics.

★3191★ **Professional Services Management Association (PSMA)**

99 Canal Center Plz., Ste. 330
Alexandria, VA 22314
Ph: (703)739-0277   Fax: (703)549-2498
Fr: (866)739-0277
E-mail: info@psmanet.org
URL: http://www.psmanet.org

Members: Individuals responsible for any or all aspects of business management in a professional design firm. **Purpose:** Works to improve the effectiveness of professional design firms through the growth and development of business management skills. Seeks to: provide a forum for the exchange of ideas and information and discussion and resolution of common problems and issues; establish guidelines for approaches to common management concerns; initiate and maintain professional relationships among members; improve recognition and practice of management as a science in professional design firms; advance and improve reputable service to clients; offer a variety of comprehensive educational programs and opportunities. **Activities:** Maintains speakers' bureau and placement service. Holds seminars. Conducts surveys and research programs. Compiles statistics.

★3192★ **University and College Designers Association (UCDA)**

153 Front St.
Smyrna, TN 37167
Ph: (615)459-4559   Fax: (615)459-5229
E-mail: info@ucda.com
URL: http://www.ucda.com

Description: Colleges, universities, junior colleges, or technical institutions that have an interest in visual communication design; individuals who are involved in the active production of such communication design or as teachers or students of these related disciplines. Purposes are to: aid, assist, and educate members through various programs of education; improve members' skills and techniques in communication and design areas such as graphics, photography, signage, films, and other related fields of communication design; be concerned with the

individual members' relationships within their own institutions as well as the larger communities in which they serve; aid and assist members in their efforts to be professionals in their respective fields through programs of education and information. Maintains placement service.

EMPLOYER DIRECTORIES AND NETWORKING LISTS

★3193★ *Black Book Photography*

Black Book Marketing Group
10 Astor Pl., 6th Fl.
New York, NY 10003
Ph: (212)539-9800   Fax: (212)539-9801
Fr: 800-841-1246
URL: http://www.BlackBook.com

Annual, January. $110.00. Publication includes over 19,000 art directors, creative directors, photographers and photographic services, design firms, advertising agencies, and other firms whose products or services are used in advertising. Entries include: Company name, address, phone. Principal content of publication is 4-color samples from the leading commercial photographers. Arrangement: Classified by product/service.

★3194★ *Career Opportunities in the Fashion Industry*

Facts On File Inc.
132 W 31st St., 17th Fl.
New York, NY 10001-2006
Ph: (212)967-8800   Fax: 800-678-3633
Fr: 800-322-8755

$49.50. Publication includes: Lists of Internet resources, educational institutions, organizations, and associations related to the fashion industry. Principal content of publication is information on careers in the fashion world. Indexes: Alphabetical.

★3195★ *ENR-Top 500 Design Firms Issue*

McGraw-Hill Companies
1221 Ave. of the Americas
New York, NY 10020
Ph: (212)512-2000   Fax: (212)512-3840

Annual, April. $10.00. Publication includes: List of 500 leading architectural, engineering, and specialty design firms selected on basis of annual billings. Entries include: Company name, headquarters location, type of firm, current and prior year rank in billings, types of services, countries in which operated in preceding year. Arrangement: Ranked by billings.

★3196★ ENR-Top International Design Firms Issue

McGraw-Hill Companies
1221 Ave. of the Americas
New York, NY 10020
Ph: (212)512-2000   Fax: (212)512-3840

Annual, July issue of "Engineering News Record". $10.00. Publication includes: List of 200 design firms (including United States firms) competing outside their own national borders who received largest dollar volume of foreign contracts in preceding calendar year. Entries include: Company name, headquarters location, type of firm, current and previous year rankings in total billings, types of services, countries in which operated in preceding year. Arrangement: By amount billed to international clients in previous year.

★3197★ Furniture Designers and Custom Builders Directory

infoUSA Inc.
5711 S 86th Cir.
Omaha, NE 68127-0347
Ph: (402)930-3500   Fax: (402)331-0176
Fr: 800-555-6124
URL: http://www.abii.com

Annual. Number of listings: 7,396. Entries include: Name, address, phone (including area code), size of advertisement, year first in "Yellow Pages," name of owner or manager, number of employees. Compiled from telephone company "Yellow Pages," nationwide. Arrangement: Geographical.

HANDBOOKS AND MANUALS

★3198★ AEC Workforce Guide to Find the Right the Right Job in the Design and Construction Industry

Zweig White
One Apple Hill Dr.
Natick, MA 01760
Ph: (508)651-1559   Fax: (503)653-6522
Fr: 800-466-6275

$23.95. 240 pages. Handbook for job hunters in the design and construction industry.

★3199★ Becoming Designers: Education and Influences

Intellect, Ltd.
PO Box 862
Bristol BS99 1DE, United Kingdom
January 2004. $29.95. 160 pages. Study of design.

★3200★ Business and Legal Forms for Graphic Designers

Allworth Press
10 E. 23rd St., Ste. 510
New York, NY 10010
Ph: (212)777-8395   Fax: (212)777-8261
Fr: 800-491-2808

Tad Crawford, Eva Doman Bruck. Third edition. May 2003. $29.95 (CD-ROM, trade cloth). 160 pages.

★3201★ Career Information Center

Macmillan Publishing Co. Inc.
200 Old Tappan Rd.
Old Tappan, NJ 07675
Fr: 800-428-5331

Visual Education Center Staff. Seventh edition, 1999. $275.00. 2080 pages. This 13-volume set profiles over 600 occupations. Each occupational profile describes job duties, educational requirements, how to get the job, advancement possibilities, employment outlook, working conditions, earnings and benefits, and where to write for more information.

★3202★ Career Opportunities in Theater and the Performing Arts

Facts on File, Inc.
132 W. 31st St., 17th Fl.
New York, NY 10001-2006
Ph: (212)967-8800   Fax: (212)967-9196
Fr: 800-322-8755
URL: http://www.factsonfile.com

Shelly Field. Second edition, 1999. $29.95; $18.95 (paper). 256 pages. Offers a complete range of information about job opportunities in the performing arts. Part of Career Opportunities Series.

★3203★ Careers for Color Connoisseurs and Other Visual Types

VGM Career Horizons
1221 Avenue of the Americas
New York, NY 10020
Ph: (212)904-2000   Fr: 800-323-4900
E-mail: ntcpub@tribune.com

Jan Goldberg. 1999. $14.95; $9.95 (paper). 212 pages.

★3204★ Careers for Crafty People and Other Dexterous Types

VGM Career Horizons
1221 Avenue of the Americas
New York, NY 10020
Ph: (212)904-2000   Fr: 800-323-4900
E-mail: ntcpub@tribune.com

Mark Rowh. Second Edition, 2002. $14.95; $9.95 (paper). 192 pages.

★3205★ Careers for Culture Lovers and Other Artsy Types

VGM Career Horizons
1221 Avenue of the Americas
New York, NY 10020
Ph: (212)904-2000   Fr: 800-323-4900
E-mail: ntcpub@tribune.com

Marjorie Eberts and Margaret Gisler. Second edition, 1999. $14.95; $9.95 (paper). 234 pages. Describes how to get work in a variety of fields related to art and culture. Opportunities include picture framer, curator, art restorer, symphony manager, disk jockey, music reviewer, dance teacher, choreographer, costume designer, theater manager, light designer, drama teacher, bookstore owner, interior decorator, antique store owner, and others.

★3206★ Careers for Fashion Plates and Other Trendsetters

VGM Career Horizons
N T C Publishing Group
1221 Avenue of the Americas
New York, NY 10020
Ph: (212)904-2000   Fr: 800-323-4900
E-mail: ntcpub@tribune.com

Lucia Mauro. 1996. $14.95; $9.95 (paper). 205 pages. Describes career opportunities in fashion, entertainment, retail, and promotion, with advice from fashion professionals.

★3207★ Careers for Film Buffs and Other Hollywood Types

VGM Career Horizons
1221 Avenue of the Americas
New York, NY 10020
Ph: (212)904-2000   Fr: 800-323-4900
E-mail: ntcpub@tribune.com

Jaq Greenspon. 1994. $14.95; $9.95 (paper). 250 pages. Describes job descriptions in production, camera, sound, special effects, grips, electrical, makeup, costumes, etc.

★3208★ Careers in the Graphic Arts

Rosen Publishing Group, Inc.
29 E. 21st St.
New York, NY 10010
Ph: (212)777-3017   Fax: 888-436-4643
Fr: 800-237-9932

Erin McGuire-Lytle. Revised edition, 1997. $16.95; $9.95 (paper). 152 pages. Discusses a career in graphic arts; outlines educational requirements, training, and skills needed to become an illustrator, layout artist, designer, and paste-up artist. Gives job hunting advice, describes how to write a resume, prepare a portfolio, and interview preparation. Gives a state-by-state listing of schools offering graphic arts.

★3209★ Careers in the Visual Arts: A Guide to Jobs, Money, Opportunities, and an Artistic Life

Watson-Guptill Publications, Inc.
BPI Communications, Inc.
770 Broadway
New York, NY 10003
Ph: (646)654-5400   Fax: (646)654-5486
Fr: 800-323-9432

Dee Ito. 1993. $14.95 (paper). 320 pages. Out of print. Gives a broad overview of each field included, with educational requirements and employment opportunities. Includes ideas on how to get started.

★3210★ *Careers Without College: Fashion*

Thomson Peterson's
PO Box 67005
Lawrenceville, NJ 08648-6105
Ph: (609)243-9111   Fax: (609)243-9150
Fr: 800-338-3282

Peggy Schmidt. Second edition, 1999. $9.95 (paper). Part of Careers Without College series.

★3211★ *The Creative Business Guide to Running a Graphic Design Business*

W. W. Norton & Company, Incorporated
500 Fifth Ave.
New York, NY 10110-0017
Ph: (212)354-5500   Fax: (212)869-0856
Fr: 800-223-2584

Cameron Foote. 2001. $45.00.

★3212★ *The Designer's Commonsense Business Book*

F & W Publications, Inc.
4700 E Galbraith Rd.
Cincinnati, OH 45236
Ph: (513)531-2690   Fax: (513)531-4082
Fr: 800-289-0963
E-mail: ntcpub@tribune.com

Barbara Ganim. Revised, 1995. $29.95; $27.99 (paper). 180 pages.

★3213★ *Great Jobs for Art Majors*

McGraw-Hill Contemporary Books
1221 Avenue of the Americas
New York, NY 10020
Ph: (212)904-2000   Fr: 800-323-4900
E-mail: ntcpub@tribune.com

Blythe Camenson, Stephen Lambert, Julie DeGalan. 1997. $11.95 (paper). 345 pages. Includes bibliographical references and index.

★3214★ *Great Jobs for Theater Majors*

McGraw-Hill Companies
1221 Avenue of the Americas
New York, NY 10020
Ph: (212)904-2000   Fr: 800-323-4900
E-mail: ntcpub@tribune.com

Jan Goldberg, Stephen Lambert, Julie De-Galan. 1998. $11.95 (paper). 388 pages.

★3215★ *Managing to Make It*

University of Chicago Press
1427 E. 60th St.
Chicago, IL 60637
Ph: (773)702-7700   Fax: (773)702-9756

Frank F. Furstenberg. 1999. $32.50.

★3216★ *New Media Careers for Artists and Designers*

AuthorHouse
1663 Liberty Dr., Ste. 200
Bloomington, IN 47403
Fax: (812)339-8654   Fr: 800-839-8640

Brenda S. Faison. February 2003. $13.95. 136 pages.

★3217★ *100 Habits of Successful Graphic Designers: Insider Secrets from the World's Top Talent*

Rockport Publishers
33 Commercial St.
Gloucester, MA 01930
Ph: (978)282-9590   Fax: (978)283-2742

October 2003. $40.00. Illustrated. 192 pages.

★3218★ *Opportunities in Arts and Crafts Careers*

McGraw-Hill Contemporary Books
1221 Avenue of the Americas
New York, NY 10020
Ph: (212)904-2000   Fr: 800-323-4900
E-mail: ntcpub@tribune.com

Betty Gardner. 1998. $14.95; $11.95 (paper). 202 pages.

★3219★ *Opportunities in Commercial Art and Graphic Design Careers*

McGraw-Hill Trade
2 Penn Plaza
New York, NY 10121
Ph: (212)904-2000   Fr: 800-722-4726

Barbara Gordon. Second edition, 1997. $12.95; $11.95 (paper). 160 pages. Provides a survey of job opportunities in advertising and public relations, publishing, fashion, architecture, and newspapers, as well as in a variety of specialty markets. Illustrated.

★3220★ *Opportunities in Fashion Careers*

McGraw-Hill Trade
2 Penn Plaza
New York, NY 10121
Ph: (212)904-2000   Fr: 800-722-4726

Roslyn Dolber. 1994. $14.95; $11.95 (paper). 160 pages. Covers job opportunities in the textile industry, design and manufacturing, apparel production, and fashion merchandising, and how to pursue them. Illustrated.

★3221★ *Opportunities in Museum Careers*

McGraw-Hill/Contemporary Books
1221 Avenue of the Americas
New York, NY 10020
Ph: (212)904-2000   Fr: 800-323-4900

Blythe Camenson. 1996. $14.95; $11.95 (paper). 160 pages.

★3222★ *Opportunities in Publishing Careers*

McGraw-Hill Professional
2 Penn Plaza
New York, NY 10121
Ph: (212)904-2000   Fr: 800-722-4726
E-mail: ntcpub@tribune.com

Robert A. Carter and S. William Pattis. 1995. $14.95; $11.95 (paper). 160 pages. Covers all positions in book and magazine publishing, including new opportunities in multimedia publishing.

★3223★ *Opportunities in Visual Arts Careers*

McGraw-Hill Trade
2 Penn Plaza
New York, NY 10121
Ph: (212)904-2000   Fr: 800-722-4726
E-mail: ntcpub@tribune.com

Mark Salmon. 1994. $14.95; $11.95 (paper). 160 pages. Points the way to a career in the visual arts, examining opportunities for designers, painters, sculptors, illustrators, animators, photographers, art therapists, educators, and others. Offers a view of the pros and cons of working for an art or design company or on your own.

★3224★ *Power Freelancing: Home-Based Careers for Writers, Designers, & Consultants*

Mid-List Press
4324 12th Ave., S
Minneapolis, MN 55407-3218
Ph: (612)822-3733   Fax: (612)823-8387
Fr: 888-543-1138

George Sorenson. 1995. $14.95 (paper). 192 pages.

★3225★ *Savvy Designers Guide to Success*

F & W Publications Inc.
4700 E. Galbraith Rd.
Cincinnati, OH 45236
Ph: (513)531-2690   Fax: (513)531-4082
Fr: 800-289-0963

Jeff Fisher. December 2004. $24.99.

★3226★ *2002 Artist's & Graphic Designer's Market*

Writer's Digest Books
F & W Publications, Inc.
1507 Dana Ave.
Cincinnati, OH 45207
Ph: (513)531-2690   Fax: (513)531-4082
Fr: 800-289-0963

Mary Cox, editor. 2001. $24.99 (paper). 720 pages.

★3227★ Where the Jobs Are: The Hottest Careers for the 90s

The Career Press, Inc.
3 Tice Rd.
PO Box 687
Franklin Lakes, NJ 07417-1322
Ph: (201)848-0310   Fax: (201)848-1727
Fr: 800-227-3371

Joyce Hadley. Third edition, 2000. $13.99 (paper). 400 pages. Out of print. Describes careers in fifteen general fields, from accounting to travel and hospitality.

EMPLOYMENT AGENCIES AND SEARCH FIRMS

★3228★ ARI Inernational

1501 Ocean Ave.
Seal Beach, CA 90740
Ph: (562)795-5111   Fax: (562)596-9794

International executive search firm.

★3229★ The Aspire Group

52 Second Ave, 1st Fl
Waltham, MA 02451-1129
Fax: (718)890-1810   Fr: 800-546-5675
URL: http://www.bmanet.com

Employment agency.

★3230★ Capitol Search

215 E. Ridgewood Ave., Ste. 205
Ridgewood, NJ 07450
Ph: (201)444-6666

Employment agency.

★3231★ Claremont-Branan, Inc.

1298 Rockbridge Rd., Ste. B
Stone Mountain, GA 30087
Ph: (770)925-2915   Fax: (770)925-2601

Employment agency. Executive search firm.

★3232★ Colli Associates

404 Caboose Ln.
Valrico, FL 33594
Ph: (813)681-2145   Fax: (813)661-5217
E-mail: colli@gte.net

Employment agency. Executive search firm.

★3233★ Gene Kaufman Associates Ltd.

450 7th Ave., Ste. 913
New York, NY 10123-0101
Ph: (212)643-0625   Fax: (212)643-8598

Personnel consultant specializing in recruiting on all levels for the apparel industry in the areas of design, sales, merchandising, production, operations, and administration.

★3234★ Randolph Associates, Inc.

950 Massachusetts Ave., Ste. 105
Cambridge, MA 02139-3174
Ph: (617)441-8777   Fax: (617)441-8778
E-mail: jobs@greatjobs.com
URL: http://www.greatjobs.com

Employment agency. Provides regular or temporary placement of staff.

★3235★ RitaSue Siegel Resources, Inc.

20 E. 46th St.
New York, NY 10017-2417
Ph: (212)682-2100   Fax: (212)682-2946
E-mail: ritasues@ritasue.com
URL: http://www.ritasuesiegelresources.com

Executive search firm specializing in industrial and product design.

★3236★ Search and Recruit International

4455 South Blvd.
Virginia Beach, VA 23452
Ph: (757)490-3151   Fax: (757)497-6503
E-mail: britt@searchandrecruit.com
URL: http://www.searchandrecruit.com

Employment agency. Headquartered in Virginia Beach. Other offices in Bremerton, WA; Charleston, SC; Jacksonville, FL; Memphis, TN; Pensacola, FL; Sacramento, CA; San Bernardino, CA; San Diego, CA.

ONLINE JOB SOURCES AND SERVICES

★3237★ Aquent.com

URL: http://www.aquent.com/work/index.html

Description: Aquent finds contract, project-based, and permanent work for a broad range of creative and information technology professionals. Applicants submit their applications, which are reviewed by an Aquent agent and, if qualifications match job opportunities, they will be called in for an interview and skills assessment. If skills and experience are appropriate, then will then be assigned an Aquent agent who will get to work finding contract or permanent jobs. Also offers free career resources.

★3238★ Guru

URL: http://www.guru.com

Description: Job board specializing in contract jobs for creative and information technology professionals. Also provides online incorporation and educational opportunities for independent contractors along with articles and advice.

TRADESHOWS

★3239★ American Textile Machinery Exhibition International

Textile Hall Corp.
PO Box 5823
Greenville, SC 29606
Ph: (864)331-2277   Fax: (864)331-2282
E-mail: atmei@textilehall.com
URL: http://www.atmei2004.com

Biennial. **Primary Exhibits:** Machinery and supplies for yarn, fiber, and nonwoven manufacturing, weaving, knitting and finishing, and plant maintenance. **Dates and Locations:** 2004 Sep 13-17; Greenville, SC; Palmetto Expo Center • 2006 Oct 1; Atlanta, GA; Georgia World Congress Center.

★3240★ DesigNation

DesigNation, Inc.
300 M St., SW, Ste. N110
Washington, DC 20024
Ph: (202)488-1530   Fax: (202)488-3838
E-mail: info@designation.net
URL: http://www.designation.net

Annual. **Primary Exhibits:** Exhibits of interest to designers holding college degrees who are practicing graphic, industrial, fashion, textile, and interior design.

★3241★ Industrial Fabrics Association International Expo

Industrial Fabrics Association International
1801 County Rd. B W
Roseville, MN 55113-4061
Ph: (651)222-2508   Fax: (651)631-9334
Fr: 800-225-4324

Annual. **Primary Exhibits:** Industrial and commercial fabric equipment, supplies, and services. **Dates and Locations:** 2004 Oct 27-29; Pittsburgh, PA; David L. Lawrence Convention Center.

OTHER SOURCES

★3242★ American Design Drafting Association (ADDA)

105 E Main St.
Newbern, TN 38059
Ph: (731)627-0802   Fax: (731)627-9321
E-mail: corporate@adda.org
URL: http://www.adda.org

Members: Designers, drafters, drafting managers, chief drafters, supervisors, administrators, instructors, and students of design and drafting. **Purpose:** Encourages a continued program of education for self-improvement and professionalism in design and drafting and computer-aided design/drafting. Informs members of effective techniques and materials used in drawings and other graphic presentations. **Activities:** Evaluates curriculum of educational institutions through certification program; sponsors drafter certification program.

★3243★ Designers

Evon Publishing
832 N 7th Ave.
Iron River, MI 49935
Ph: (906)265-3190

Audiocassette. 1996. $16.95. 32 minutes. Part of the Careers and Vocational Guidance Series. Provides information about the nature of the work, educational requirements, employment outlook, earnings, and work conditions as well as additional related information.

★3244★ Home Economics Careers

Cambridge Educational
2572 Brunswick Ave.
Lawrenceville, NJ 08648-4128
Fax: 800-FAX-ON-US   Fr: 800-468-4227
URL: http://www.cambridgeeducational.com
$79.95. 30 minutes. Includes manual.

★3245★ Industrial Designers Society of America (IDSA)

45195 Business Ct., No. 250
Dulles, VA 20166
Ph: (703)707-6000   Fax: (703)787-8501
E-mail: idsa@idsa.org
URL: http://www.idsa.org

Members: Professional society of industrial designers. **Purpose:** Represents the profession in its relations with business, education, government, and international designers; promotes the industrial design profession. Conducts research, educational, and charitable programs. Compiles statistics.

★3246★ Media and the Arts Occupations

Delphi Productions
3160 4th St.
Boulder, CO 80304
Fax: (303)443-4022   Fr: 888-443-2400
URL: http://www.delphivideo.com

$95.00. 50 minutes. Part of the Careers for the 21st Century Video Library.

★3247★ Society of American Florists (SAF)

1601 Duke St.
Alexandria, VA 22314-3406
Ph: (703)836-8700   Fax: (703)836-8705
Fr: 800-336-4743
E-mail: memberinfo@safnow.org
URL: http://www.safnow.org

Description: Growers, wholesalers, retailers, and allied tradesmen in the floral industry. Lobbies Congress on behalf of the industry; sponsors educational programs; promotes the floral industry; prepares materials for consumers and for high school and college students; provides business resources. Sponsors Floricultural Hall of Fame, American Academy of Floriculture, and Professional Floral Commentators - International. Compiles statistics; sponsors competitions.

Desktop Publishers

SOURCES OF HELP-WANTED ADS

★3248★ *The Editorial Eye*
EEI Press
66 Canal Ctr. Plz., Ste. 200
Alexandria, VA 22314
Ph: (703)683-0683   Fax: (703)683-4915
Fr: 800-683-8380
E-mail: eye@eeicom.com
URL: http://www.eeicom.com/eye/

Description: Monthly. Contains articles, tests, and columns that treat the full range of editorial questions, including editing, writing, and style.

★3249★ *Independent Publisher Online*
Jenkins Group Inc.
400 W Front St., No. 4A
Traverse City, MI 49684-2206
Ph: (231)933-0445   Fax: (231)933-0448

Monthly. Free. Online magazine containing book reviews and articles about independent publishing.

★3250★ *Industry Focus*
Association of Business Support Services
  International Inc.
5852 Oak Meadow Dr.
Yorba Linda, CA 92886-5930
Ph: (714)695-9398   Fax: (714)779-8106
Fr: 800-237-1462
E-mail: abssi4you@aol.com

Description: Monthly. Deals with every facet of business-support-service and virtual-assistant operations: pricing, successful new sales techniques for adding clients, dealing with clients and employees, work scheduling, forms and contracts, financial management, equipment and technology. Contains input from ABSSI members.

★3251★ *PMA Newsletter*
Publishers Marketing Association (PMA)
627 Aviation Way
Manhattan Beach, CA 90266
Ph: (310)372-2732   Fax: (310)374-3342

URL: http://www.pma-online.org

Description: Monthly. Informs member entrepreneurial book publishers about upcoming marketing programs and other Association activities aimed at helping independent publishers succeed. Also carries articles on topics such as desktop publishing and typesetting systems. Recurring features include member, committee, and research news, notices of educational and cooperative marketing opportunities, a calendar of events, and columns titled News from the "Net" and From the Director's Desk.

EMPLOYER DIRECTORIES AND NETWORKING LISTS

★3252★ *The Information Professional's Guide to Career Development Online*
Information Today Inc.
143 Old Marlton Pke.
Medford, NJ 08055-8750
Ph: (609)654-6266   Fax: (609)654-4309
Fr: 800-300-9848

$29.50. Covers web sites, professional associations, and conferences for the career development of information professionals. Indexes: Alphabetical.

HANDBOOKS AND MANUALS

★3253★ *Career Opportunities in Computers and Cyberspace*
Facts on File
132 W. 31st St., 17th Fl.
New York, NY 10001-2006
Ph: (212)967-8800   Fax: (212)967-8107
Fr: 800-322-8755

Harry Henderson. 1999. $26.95 (paper). Part of the Career Opportunities Series. 224 pages.

★3254★ *Choosing a Career in Desktop Publishing*
Rosen Publishing Group, Inc.
29 E. 21st St.
New York, NY 10010
Ph: (212)777-3017   Fax: (212)777-0277
Fr: 800-237-9932

Ross, Allison J. 2000. $17.95.

★3255★ *The Complete Help Book for Authors and Publishers*
Hannacroix Creek Books, Incorporated
1127 High Ridge Rd., No. 110
Stamford, CT 06905-1203
Ph: (203)321-8674   Fax: (203)968-0193

Jan Yeager. 2005. $29.95. Explores self-publishing for authors.

★3256★ *Desk-Top Publishing: Writing and Publishing in the Computer Age*
Houghton Mifflin Company
215 Park Ave., S.
New York, NY 10003
Ph: (212)420-5800   Fax: (212)420-5855
Fr: 800-225-3362

Sullivan, David R. 1989.

★3257★ *Exploring Careers in Word Processing and Desktop Publishing*
Rosen Publishing Group Inc.
29 East 21st St.
New York, NY 10010

Jean Spencer. Offers an overview of desktop publishing.

★3258★ *How to Start a Home-Based Desktop Publishing Business*
Globe Pequot Press
246 Gooselane, PO Box 480
Guilford, CT 06437

Louise Kursmark. 240 pages.

★3259★ *Opportunities in Publishing Careers*

McGraw-Hill Professional
2 Penn Plaza
New York, NY 10121
Ph: (212)904-2000   Fr: 800-722-4726
Pattis, S. William, Robert A. Carter, and Blythe Camenson. 2000. $12.95 (Trade paper). 160 pages.

★3260★ *Second Lives: Becoming a Desktop Publisher*

St. Martin's Press LLC
175 Fifth Ave.
New York, NY 10010
Bill Harris. 1999. 117 pages.

ONLINE JOB SOURCES AND SERVICES

★3261★ **Desktop Publisher IQ**
URL: http://www.dtpjournal.com
Description: Offers a variety of resources for desktop publishers.

★3262★ **DesktopPublishing.com**
URL: http://www.desktoppublishing.com
Description: General resource website contains job bank and list of links to resume enhancing and distributing software available for download on the Internet.

★3263★ **Graphic Artists Guild**
URL: http://www.gag.org
Description: JOBLine News section of Guild Resources page contains weekly e-mail newsletter of job listings. **Fee:** Must subscribe to e-mail newsletter non-member six-month rates start at $80. Visitors may download a free sample.

★3264★ **Guru**
URL: http://www.guru.com
Description: Job board specializing in contract jobs for creative and information technology professionals. Also provides online incorporation and educational opportunities for independent contractors along with articles and advice.

★3265★ **National Association of Photoshop Professionals**
URL: http://www.photoshopuser.com
Description: Membership website includes member job bank where visitors can search for available jobs or post their resumes for employer review, along with other career-related resources. **Fee:** Must be member of association to access; dues are $99.

OTHER SOURCES

★3266★ **Association of Computer Professionals (ACP)**
9 Forest Dr.
Plainview, NY 11803
Ph: (516)938-8223   Fax: (516)938-3073

E-mail: sybosworth@aol.com
Members: Authors, consultants, programmers, publishers, and teachers in the computer field who provide products or services to users or to other professionals. **Purpose:** Works to advance the art and science of computer professionals through educational means. Encourages education and instruction of the public regarding what the association views as the beneficial use of computers and computer technology. **Activities:** Provides members with information on accounting, business management, creative marketing techniques, law, microcomputer advances, tax matters, technical developments, and special earning opportunities. Addresses issues of software protection, contract law, tax benefits, potential tax problems, and financial subjects such as sources of capital for new ventures and expanding businesses.

★3267★ **Association for Women in Computing (AWC)**
41 Sutter St., Ste. 1006
San Francisco, CA 94104
Ph: (415)905-4663
E-mail: info@awc-hq.org
URL: http://www.awc-hq.org
Members: Individuals interested in promoting the education, professional development, and advancement of women in computing.

Dietitians and Nutritionists

SOURCES OF HELP-WANTED ADS

★3268★ American Journal of Clinical Nutrition
The American Society for Clinical Nutrition
9650 Rockville Pke.
Bethesda, MD 20814-3998
Ph: (301)530-7110   Fax: (301)571-1863
E-mail: ajcn@ucdavis.edu
URL: http://www.ajcn.org

Monthly. $60.00/year for members; $120.00/year for nonmembers; $190.00/year for institutions; $50.00/year for students. Journal of basic and clinical studies relevant to human nutrition.

★3269★ Chef
Talcott Communications Corp.
2B W Kinzie, 12th Fl.
Chicago, IL 60610
Ph: (312)849-2220   Fax: (312)849-2174
Fr: 800-229-1967
E-mail: chef@talcott.com

$32.00/year for individuals; $2.95/year. Food information for chefs.

★3270★ Dietary Manager Magazine
Dietary Managers Association (DMA)
406 Surrey Woods Dr.
St. Charles, IL 60174
Ph: (630)587-6336   Fax: (630)587-6308
Fr: 800-323-1908

$35.00/year for individuals; $5.00 for single issue. Professional magazine focusing on nutrition and management issues encountered by dietary managers in non-commerical food service.

★3271★ Food Management
Penton Media Inc.
1300 E 9th St.
Cleveland, OH 44114-1503
Ph: (216)696-7000   Fax: (216)931-9799
URL: http://www.foodservicesearch.com/

Monthly. Free. Magazine for foodservice professionals in the onsite "noncommercial" market.

★3272★ FoodService Director
VNU Business Publications
770 Broadway
New York, NY 10003
Ph: (646)654-5000   Fax: (646)654-4977
URL: http://www.fsd.com

Monthly. Tabloid newspaper of the noncommercial foodservice market.

★3273★ Foodservice East
The Newbury Street Group Inc.
165 New Boston St., No. 236
Woburn, MA 01801
Ph: (781)376-9080   Fax: (781)376-0010
Fr: 800-852-5212
E-mail: fdsvceast@.aol.com

$30.00/year for individuals. Compact Tabloid covering trends and analysis of the foodservice industry in the Northeast. A business-to-business publication featuring news, analysis and trends for the Northeast food service professional.

★3274★ Journal of the American Dietetic Association
American Dietetic Association
120 S Riverside Plaza, Ste. 2000
Chicago, IL 60606-6995
Ph: (312)899-0040   Fax: (312)899-4817
Fr: 800-877-1600

Monthly. $115.00/year for individuals; $140.00/year for Canada; $190.00/year for other countries; $9.75 for single issue. Journal reporting original research on nutrition, diet therapy, education and administration.

★3275★ Nutrition Notes
American Society for Nutrition Sciences
9650 Rockville Pke.
Bethesda, MD 20814-3990
Ph: (301)530-7050   Fax: (301)571-1892
E-mail: nnotes@asns.faser.org
URL: http://www.faser.org/asns

Description: Quarterly. Contains updates on nutrition legislation, public affairs, and public information policies. Reviews the results of nutritional research conducted by members of the Institute, which is comprised of nutrition scientists from universities, government, and industry. Recurring features include news of members, letters to the editor, job listings, notices of publications available, information on awards and fellowships, and news of scientific meetings.

★3276★ Nutrition Week
Community Nutrition Institute
910 17th St. NW, No. 413
Washington, DC 20006
Ph: (202)776-0595   Fax: (202)776-0599

Description: Forty-eight issues/year. Reports on federal, state, and local food assistance activities; diet and health policy; and food safety issues. Discusses prices, trends in the food industry, labeling, sustainable agriculture, poverty, and welfare topics. Recurring features include listings of employment opportunities and a calendar of events.

★3277★ Southeast Food Service News
Southeast Publishing Company Inc.
PO Box 47719
Atlanta, GA 30362
Ph: (770)452-1807   Fax: (770)457-3829
E-mail: info@sfsn.com

$36.00/year for individuals. Magazine (tabloid) serving the food industry.

★3278★ Sunbelt Foodservice
Shelby Publishing Company Inc.
517 Green St.
Gainesville, GA 30501
Ph: (770)534-8380   Fax: (770)535-0110

Monthly. $25.00/year for individuals. Trade newspaper (tabloid) covering the food industry geared toward restaurant operators.

★3279★ Vegetarian Times

Sabot Publishing Inc.
301 Concourse Blvd., Ste. 350
Glen Allen, VA 23059-5643
Ph: (804)346-0990   Fax: (804)346-1223

$24.95/year for individuals. Magazine devoted to plant-based foods and related topics such as health, fitness, and the environment.

PLACEMENT AND JOB REFERRAL SERVICES

★3280★ American Public Health Association (APHA)

800 I St. NW
Washington, DC 20001-3710
Ph: (202)777-2742   Fax: (202)777-2534
E-mail: comments@apha.org
URL: http://www.apha.org

Members: Professional organization of physicians, nurses, educators, academicians, environmentalists, epidemiologists, new professionals, social workers, health administrators, optometrists, podiatrists, pharmacists, dentists, nutritionists, health planners, other community and mental health specialists, and interested consumers. **Purpose:** Seeks to protect and promote personal, mental, and environmental health. **Activities:** Services include promulgation of standards; establishment of uniform practices and procedures; development of the etiology of communicable diseases; research in public health; exploration of medical care programs and their relationships to public health. Sponsors job placement service.

★3281★ Dietary Managers Association (DMA)

406 Surrey Woods Drive
St. Charles, IL 60174
Ph: (630)587-6336   Fax: (630)587-6308
Fr: 800-323-1908
URL: http://www.dmaonline.org

Description: Dietary managers united to maintain a high level of competency and quality in dietary departments through continuing education. Provides educational programs and placement service.

EMPLOYER DIRECTORIES AND NETWORKING LISTS

★3282★ AHA Guide to the Health Care Field

American Hospital Association (AHA)
1 N. Franklin St., 27th Fl.
Chicago, IL 60606
Ph: (312)422-2050   Fax: (312)422-4700
Fr: 800-424-4301

Annual, August. $295.00. Covers hospitals,

networks, multi-health care systems, free-standing ambulatory surgery centers, psychiatric facilities, long-term care facilities, substance abuse programs, and other health-related organizations. Entries include: For hospitals-Facility name, address, phone, administrator's name, number of beds, facilities and services, number of employees, expenses, other statistics. For other organizations-Name, address, phone, fax, name and title of contact. Arrangement: Geographical. Indexes: Hospital name.

★3283★ Directory of Hospital Personnel

Thomson Medical Economics
5 Paragon Dr.
Montvale, NJ 07645-1742
Ph: (201)358-7200   Fax: (201)722-2680

Annual, November. $325.00. Covers 200,000 executives at 7,000 U.S. hospitals. Entries include: Name of hospital, address, phone, number of beds, type and JCAHO status of hospital, names and titles of key department heads and staff, medical and nursing school affiliations; number of residents, interns, and nursing students. Arrangement: Geographical. Indexes: Hospital name, personnel, hospital size.

★3284★ Hospital Blue Book

Billian/Transworld Publishing Inc.
2100 Powers Ferry Rd.
Ste. 300
Atlanta, GA 30339
Ph: (770)955-8484   Fax: (770)955-8485
Fr: 800-533-8484
E-mail: blu-book@billian.com

Annual, January. $285.00 for national edition; $160.00 for southern edition. Covers more than 6,687 hospitals; some listings also appear in a separate southern edition of this publication. Entries include: Name of hospital, accreditation, mailing address, phone, fax, number of beds, type of facility (nonprofit, general, state, etc.); list of administrative personnel and chiefs of medical services, with specific titles. Arrangement: Geographical.

★3285★ Medical and Health Information Directory

Thomson Gale
27500 Drake Rd.
Farmington Hills, MI 48331-3535
Ph: (248)699-4253   Fax: (248)699-8065
Fr: 800-877-GALE
E-mail: businessproducts@gale.com

Annual. $285.00 per volume; $675.00 per set. Covers in Volume 1, more than 26,500 medical and health oriented associations, organizations, institutions, and government agencies, including health maintenance organizations (HMOs), preferred provider organizations (PPOs), insurance companies, pharmaceutical companies, research centers, and medical and allied health schools. In Volume 2, over 12,000 medical book publishers; medical periodicals, directories, audiovisual producers and services, medical libraries and information centers, electronic

resources, and health-related internet search engines. In Volume 3, more than 35,500 clinics, treatment centers, care programs, and counseling/diagnostic services for 34 subject areas. Entries include: Institution, service, or firm name, address, phone, fax, email and URL; many include names of key personnel and, when pertinent, descriptive annotation. Volume 3 was formerly listed separately as Health Services Directory. Arrangement: Classified by organization activity, service, etc. Indexes: Each volume has a complete alphabetical name and keyword index.

HANDBOOKS AND MANUALS

★3286★ Career Opportunities in the Food and Beverage Industry

Facts on File, Inc.
132 W. 31st St., 17th Fl.
New York, NY 10001-2006
Ph: (212)967-8800   Fax: (212)967-8107
Fr: 800-322-8755
URL: http://www.factsonfile.com

Barbara Sims-Bell. Second edition, 2001. $18.95 (paper). Provides the job seeker with information about locating and landing 80 skilled and unskilled jobs in the industry. Includes detailed job descriptions for many specific positions and lists trade associations, recruiting organizations, and major agencies. Contains index and bibliography.

★3287★ Careers in Health Care

McGraw-Hill Trade
2 Penn Plaza
New York, NY 10121
Ph: (212)904-2000   Fr: 800-722-4726
E-mail: ntcpub@tribune.com

Barbara M. Swanson. Fourth edition, 2000. $17.95; $13.95 (paper). 320 pages. Describes job duties, work settings, salaries, licensing and certification requirements, educational preparation, and future outlook. Gives ideas on how to secure a job.

★3288★ Careers Inside the World of Health Care

Rosen Publishing Group Inc.
29 E. 21st. St.
New York, NY 10010
Ph: (212)777-3017   Fax: 888-436-4643
Fr: 800-237-9932

Beth Wilkinson. 1999. $17.95. 64 pages.

★3289★ Careers in Social and Rehabilitation Services

McGraw-Hill Trade
2 Penn Plaza
New York, NY 10121
Ph: (212)904-2000   Fr: 800-722-4726
E-mail: ntcpub@tribune.com

Geraldine O. Garner. Second edition, 2001. $19.95; 14.95 (paper). 128 pages.

★3290★ Opportunities in Health and Medical Careers

McGraw-Hill Trade
2 Penn Plaza
New York, NY 10121
Ph: (212)904-2000   Fr: 800-722-4726
I. Donald Snook, Jr. and Leo D'Orazio. 1997. $14.95; $11.95 (paper). 202 pages. Covers the full range of medical and health occupations. Illustrated.

★3291★ Opportunities in Sports Medicine Careers

McGraw-Hill Trade
2 Penn Plaza
New York, NY 10121
Ph: (212)904-2000   Fr: 800-722-4726
E-mail: ntcpub@tribune.com
William Ray Heitzmann. 1995. $14.95; $11.95 (paper). 160 pages. Discusses a variety of opportunities in this field and how to pursue them. Contains bibliography and illustrations.

★3292★ Resumes for Health and Medical Careers

McGraw-Hill Trade
2 Penn Plaza
New York, NY 10121
Ph: (212)904-2000   Fr: 800-722-4726
E-mail: ntcpub@tribune.com
1997. $9.95 (paper). 455 pages.

EMPLOYMENT AGENCIES AND SEARCH FIRMS

★3293★ Harper Associates

29870 Middlebelt
Farmington Hills, MI 48334
Ph: (248)932-1170   Fax: (248)932-1214
E-mail: resumes@harperjobs.com
URL: http://www.harperjobs.com
Executive search firm and employment agency.

★3294★ Professional Placement Associates, Inc.

287 Bowman Ave., Ste. 309
Purchase, NY 10577
Ph: (914)251-1000   Fax: (914)251-1055
E-mail: lschachter@ppasearch.com
URL: http://www.ppasearch.com
Executive search firm specializing in the health and medical field.

★3295★ Ritt-Ritt and Associates

5105 Tollview Dr., Ste. 100
Rolling Meadows, IL 60008
Ph: (847)483-9330   Fax: (847)483-9331
E-mail: info@rittsearch.com
URL: http://www.rittsearch.com

Food service and hospitality employment agency and executive search firm.

ONLINE JOB SOURCES AND SERVICES

★3296★ Institute of Food Technologists - IFT Web Express

E-mail: info@atsift.org
URL: http://www.ift.org/employment/index.shtml
Description: Offers job information and resources for those considering the Food Science and Technology field. Employers may post for full- or part-time positions and have the option of receiving a resume file of current job seekers. IFT members may register for a six-month confidential service to have their credentials reviewed by food industry employers. Job seekers who list credentials will receive the monthly Jobs Available bulletin. **Main files include:** Employment and Salary Information, How to Find Your First Job in the Food Sciences, Resources for Non-US Job Seekers, and more.

★3297★ Medbulletin Medical Career Resource Center

E-mail: medbulletin@atsmedbulletin.com
URL: http://www.medbulletin.com
Description: Offers free specialized update service, resume posting, recruiter directory, varied job listings, and relocation services.

★3298★ Medhunters.com

E-mail: info@medhunters.com
URL: http://www.medhunters.com
Description: Career search site for jobs in all health care specialties; educational resources; visa and licensing information for relocation; interesting articles; relocation tools; links to professional organizations and general resources.

★3299★ ProHealthJobs

E-mail: sales@prohealthjobs.com
URL: http://www.prohealthjobs.com
Description: Career resources site for the medical and health care field. Lists professional opportunities, product information, continuing education and open positions.

TRADESHOWS

★3300★ American Dietetic Association Annual Meeting and Exhibition

American Dietetic Association
120 S Riverside Plaza, Ste. 2000
Chicago, IL 60606-6995
Fr: 800-877-1600

E-mail: exhibit@eatright.org
URL: http://www.eatright.org
Annual. **Primary Exhibits:** Food products, food service equipment, nutrition supplements, health-care books, resource materials, and computers.

★3301★ California Dietetic Association Meeting

California Dietetic Association
7740 Manchester, No. 102
Playa Del Rey, CA 90293-8499
Ph: (310)822-0177   Fax: (310)823-0264
E-mail: cdaep@aol.com
Annual. **Primary Exhibits:** Food and nutrition services.

★3302★ Dietary Managers Association Meeting and Expo

Dietary Managers Association
406 Surrey Woods Dr.
St. Charles, IL 60174-2386
Annual. **Primary Exhibits:** Dietary management equipment, supplies, and services.

OTHER SOURCES

★3303★ American Association of Nutritional Consultants (AANC)

400 Oak Hill Dr.
Winona Lake, IN 46590
Fax: (574)269-4060   Fr: 888-828-2262
E-mail: registrar@aanc.net
URL: http://www.aanc.net
Description: Professional nutritional consultants. Seeks to create a forum for exchange of nutritional information. Offers benefits such as car rental and laboratory discounts.

★3304★ American Dietetic Association (ADA)

120 S Riverside Plz.
Chicago, IL 60606-6995
Ph: (312)899-0040   Fax: (312)899-1979
Fr: 800-877-1600
E-mail: membrshp@eatright.org
URL: http://www.eatright.org
Members: Food and nutrition professionals. Promotes nutrition, health and well-being.

★3305★ American School Health Association (ASHA)

PO Box 708
7263 State Route 43
Kent, OH 44240
Ph: (330)678-1601   Fax: (330)678-4526
Fr: 800-445-2742
E-mail: asha@ashaweb.org
URL: http://www.ashaweb.org
Description: School physicians, school nurses, dentist, nurses, nutritionists, health educators, dental hygienist, school-based professionals and public health workers.

Promotes coordinated school health programs that include health education, health services, a healthful school environment, physical education, nutrition services, and psycho-social health services offered in schools collaboratively with families and other members of the community. Offers professional reference materials. Conducts pilot programs that inform materials development, provides technical assistance to school professionals, advocates for school health, and complies statistics.

★3306★ *Exploring Health Occupations*
Cambridge Educational
2572 Brunswick Ave.
Lawrenceville, NJ 08648-4128
Fax: 800-FAX-ON-US   Fr: 800-468-4227
URL: http://www.cambridgeeducational.com

Two videos. $139.95. 1999.

★3307★ *Health Assessment & Treating Occupations*
Delphi Productions
3160 4th St.
Boulder, CO 80304
Fax: (303)443-4022   Fr: 888-443-2400

URL: http://www.delphivideo.com

$95.00. 50 minutes. Part of the Careers for the 21st Century Video Library.

★3308★ *Health Service Occupations*
Delphi Productions
3160 4th St.
Boulder, CO 80304
Fax: (303)443-4022   Fr: 888-443-2400
URL: http://www.delphivideo.com

$95.00. 50 minutes. Part of the Careers for the 21st Century Video Library.

★3309★ *Home Economics Careers*
Cambridge Educational
2572 Brunswick Ave.
Lawrenceville, NJ 08648-4128
Fax: 800-FAX-ON-US   Fr: 800-468-4227
URL: http://www.cambridgeeducational.com

$79.95. 30 minutes. Includes manual.

★3310★ **IDEA Health and Fitness Association**
6190 Cornerstone Ct. E., Ste. 204
San Diego, CA 92121-3773
Ph: (858)535-8979   Fax: (858)535-8234
Fr: 800-999-IDEA
E-mail: member@ideafit.com
URL: http://www.ideafit.com

Purpose: Provides continuing education for fitness professionals including; fitness instructors, personal trainers, program directors, and club/studio owners. **Activities:** Offers workshops for continuing education credits.

★3311★ *Medicine & Related Occupations*
Delphi Productions
3160 4th St.
Boulder, CO 80304
Fax: (303)443-4022   Fr: 888-443-2400
URL: http://www.delphivideo.com

$95.00. 45 minutes. Part of the Careers for the 21st Century Video Library.

Disc Jockeys

SOURCES OF HELP-WANTED ADS

★3312★ AFTRA Magazine
American Federation of Television and
  Radio Artists
260 Madison Ave.
New York, NY 10016-2402
Ph: (212)532-0800   Fax: (212)532-2242

Membership magazine covering issues in
television and radio broadcasting.

★3313★ Community Radio News
National Federation of Community
  Broadcasters (NFCB)
Fort Mason Ctr., Bldg. D
San Francisco, CA 94123
Ph: (415)771-1160   Fax: (415)771-1160

Description: Monthly. Serves as a medium
of communication for independent, community-licensed radio stations. Contains brief
articles and news items on such topics as
public broadcasting and programming, legislative developments, activities of the Federal
Communications Commission, and local stations. Recurring features include notices of
grants and awards, job openings, and a
calendar of events/conferences for noncommercial broadcasters.

★3314★ Country Airplay Monitor
VNU Business Media USA
770 Broadway
New York, NY 10003
Ph: (646)654-5000
URL: http://www.vnubusinessmedia.com/
box/bp/div_ent_music_airm.ht

Weekly. $295.00/year for individuals. Trade
publication covering the radio and music
industry.

★3315★ Journal of Radio Studies
Broadcast Education Association
1771 N St. NW
Washington, DC 20036
Ph: (202)429-5355   Fax: (202)775-2981

Quarterly. Journal covering issues in broadcasting.

★3316★ R&B Airplay Monitor
VNU Business Media USA
770 Broadway
New York, NY 10003
Ph: (646)654-5000
URL: http://www.vnubusinessmedia.com/
box/bp/div_ent_music_airm.ht

Weekly. $295.00/year for individuals. Trade
publication covering the radio and telecommunications industries.

★3317★ Rock Airplay Monitor
VNU Business Media USA
770 Broadway
New York, NY 10003
Ph: (646)654-5000
URL: http://www.vnubusinessmedia.com/
box/bp/div_ent_music_airm.ht

Weekly. $295.00/year for individuals. Trade
publication covering the music and radio
industries.

EMPLOYER DIRECTORIES AND NETWORKING LISTS

**★3318★ GMA'S Online Christian Music
Networking Guide**
Gospel Music Association
1205 Division St.
Nashville, TN 37203
Ph: (615)242-0303   Fax: (615)254-9755
E-mail: info@gospelmusic.org
URL: http://www.gospelmusic.org

Continuous, January. $39.95 for nonmem-
bers; $19.95 for members. Covers gospel
musicians, composers, and artists; recording

companies, studios, and production companies; booking agencies; publishers; performing rights organizations; television and radio
broadcasting stations; book stores, Bible
supply stores, and other retailers/managers;
publications; ministry organizations, artist
managers, industry related services, christian clubs, concert promoters, distributors.
Entries include: Name, contact address,
phone, fax, E-mail. Broadcasting station
listings include contact, program title, format.
Arrangement: Search engine is flexible.

**★3319★ Radio Stations and
Broadcasting Companies Directory**
infoUSA Inc.
5711 S 86th Cir.
Omaha, NE 68127-0347
Ph: (402)930-3500   Fax: (402)331-0176
Fr: 800-555-6124
URL: http://www.abii.com

Annual. Number of listings: 13,087. Entries
include: Name, address, phone (including
area code), size of advertisement, year first
in "Yellow Pages," name of owner or manager, number of employees. Available by
sinal type. Compiled from telephone company "Yellow Pages," nationwide. Arrangement: Geographical.

HANDBOOKS AND MANUALS

**★3320★ The Best Home-Based
Businesses for the 90s**
Putnam Publishing Group
375 Hudson St.
New York, NY 10014
Ph: (212)366-2000   Fax: (212)366-2643
Fr: 800-331-4624

Paul Edwards and Sarah Edwards. Second
edition, 1991. $11.95 (paper). 272 pages.
Profiles 95 businesses and careers that can
be conducted from one's home. Lists
sources of additional information. Out of
print.

★3321★ Breakin' into the Music Business

Fireside
10 Midland Ave.
PO Box 430
Port Chester, NY 10573
Ph: (914)937-8601   Fax: (914)937-9139
Fr: 800-354-4004

Alan H. Siegel. 1993. $19.95. 276 pages. Describes the record deal; the artist-manager relationship; working with copyrights, demos, and the terminology used in the industry.

★3322★ Build and Manage Your Music Career

artistpro.com, LLC
236 Georgia St., Suite 100
Vallejo, CA 94590
Ph: (707)554-1935   Fax: (707)554-9751

Maurice Johnson. 1999.

★3323★ A Career Handbook for TV, Radio, Film, Video and Interactive Media

A & C Black
37 Soho Sq.
London W1D 3QZ, United Kingdom
Ph: 020 7758 0200

Shiona Llewellyn.

★3324★ Career Opportunities in Radio

Facts on File Inc.
132 W. 31st St., 17th Fl.
New York, NY 10001-2006
Ph: (212)967-8800   Fax: (212)967-9196
Fr: 800-322-8755

Shelly Field. April 2004. $18.95 (paper). Illustrated. 288 pages.

★3325★ Careers for Culture Lovers and Other Artsy Types

VGM Career Horizons
1221 Avenue of the Americas
New York, NY 10020
Ph: (212)904-2000   Fr: 800-323-4900
E-mail: ntcpub@tribune.com

Marjorie Eberts and Margaret Gisler. Second edition, 1999. $14.95; $9.95 (paper). 234 pages. Describes how to get work in a variety of fields related to art and culture. Opportunities include picture framer, curator, art restorer, symphony manager, disk jockey, music reviewer, dance teacher, choreographer, costume designer, theater manager, light designer, drama teacher, bookstore owner, interior decorator, antique store owner, and others.

★3326★ Careers as a Disc Jockey

Rosen Publishing Group, Inc.
29 E. 21st St.
New York, NY 10010
Ph: (212)777-3017   Fax: 888-436-4643
Fr: 800-237-9932

Chris Weigant. 1999. $18.95. 192 pages.

Provides information on getting started and being successful.

★3327★ Careers for Music Lovers and Other Tuneful Types

McGraw-Hill Contemporary Books
N T C Publishing Group
1221 Avenue of the Americas
New York, NY 10020
Ph: (212)904-2000   Fr: 800-323-4900
E-mail: ntcpub@tribune.com

Jeff Johnson. 1996. $14.95; $9.95 (paper). 160 pages. Describes hundreds of music industry jobs and careers.

★3328★ Careers for Talkative Types and Others with the Gift of Gab

McGraw-Hill Trade
2 Penn Plaza
New York, NY 10121
Ph: (212)904-2000   Fr: 800-722-4726
E-mail: ntcpub@tribune.com

Marjorie Eberts and Margaret Gisler. 1998. $14.95; $9.95 (paper). 160 pages.

★3329★ The DJ Cookbook: How to Start and Run a Mobile DJ Service for Profit

Juice Gallery Multimedia
2042 Big Oak Ave.
Chino Hills, CA 91709
Ph: (909)597-0791   Fr: 800-710-0163

$34.95. Self-help on becoming a DJ.

★3330★ Freelance Dee-Jaying: How to Become a Successful Discotheque and Radio Jock

Trans-Atlantic Publications, Inc.
311 Bainbridge St.
Philadelphia, PA 19147
Ph: (215)925-5083   Fax: (215)925-1912

John Clancy. 1996. 136 pages. Part of the Jobs and Careers Series.

★3331★ The Gigs Handbook: A Beginner's Guide to Playing Professionally

Benny Publishing
9403 Lincolnwood Dr.
Evanston, IL 60203
Ph: (847)673-2039

Sharon Black. 2000. $18.95 (paper). "The Gigs Handbook" is for music students who want to earn money through performing, amateurs who want to play professionally, or anyone who can say gig gag giggle 10 times really fast. "The Gigs Handbook" is a beginners guide to playing professionally. The book will help readers learn how to get gigs & become professional musicians, make contacts & promote themselves, deal with problems on the job, play weddings & other special events & begin playing by ear. "The Gigs Handbook" is sure to be enjoyed by anyone interested in music as a career, bettering their musician skills, expanding their repertoire, adding to their styles &

private music teaching. Author, pianist & educator Sharon Black is a seasoned "gigger" who has taught music to all grade levels & holds a Master of Music Degree from Northwestern University. She has written & performed for WBBM & WGN television & is the author/composer of the Halloween musical "Samhain."

★3332★ Great Jobs for Music Majors

McGraw-Hill Companies
1221 Avenue of the Americas
New York, NY 10020
Ph: (212)904-2000   Fr: 800-323-4900
E-mail: ntcpub@tribune.com

Jan Goldberg, Stephen Lambert, Julie De-Galan. 1997. $11.95 (paper). 365 pages.

★3333★ How to Become a Radio DJ: A Guide to Breaking and Entering

Happy Communications
PO Box 443
Troy, MI 48099
Ph: (248)577-0777

Mike Staff. 1998. $39.95 (paper). 140 pages.

★3334★ Increase Your Mobile DJ Business by 30%...Starting Next Month!

B C Productions Inc.
PO Box 42365
Des Moines, IA 50322
Ph: (515)986-3344   Fr: 800-257-7635

Robert Popyk. 2003. $24.95.

★3335★ Inside Broadcasting

Routledge
7625 Empire Dr.
Florence, KY 41042
Fr: 800-634-7064

1997. $24.99. 232 pages. Part of the Career Builders Guide Series.

★3336★ The Lost Soul Companion: Comfort & Constructive Advice for Struggling Actors, Musicians, Artists, Writers & Other Free Spirits

Puckitt Press, Incorporated
P.O. Box 3248
Bloomington, IN 47402-3248
Ph: (812)331-4337

Susan M. Brackney. 2000. $10.00

★3337★ Making It in Broadcasting: An Insider's Guide to Career Opportunities

Macmillan Publishing Co. Inc.
200 Old Tappan Rd.
Old Tappan, NJ 07675
Fr: 800-428-5331

Leonard Mogel. 1994. $15.00 (paper). 320 pages.

★3338★ The Mobile DJ Handbook: How to Start and Run a Profitable Mobile Disc Jockey Service

Butterworth-Heinemann
225 Wildwood Ave., Unit B
Woburn, MA 01801
Ph: (781)904-2500   Fax: (781)904-2640
Fr: 800-366-2665

Stacy Zemon. 1997. $21.95 (paper). 170 pages.

★3339★ Moving up in the Music Business

Allworth Press
10 E. 23rd St., Suite 510
New York, NY 10010
Ph: (212)777-8395   Fax: (212)777-8261
Fr: 800-491-2808

Jodi Summers. 2000. $18.95 (paper).

★3340★ The National Business Employment Weekly Jobs Rated Almanac

John Wiley & Sons Inc.
1 Wiley Dr.
Somerset, NJ 08873
Ph: (732)469-4400   Fr: 800-225-5945

Les Krantz. First edition, 1995. $16.95. 340 pages. Ranks 250 jobs by environment, salary, outlook, physical demands, stress, security, travel opportunities, and geographic location.

★3341★ On-the-Air Anywhere: A Beginner's Guide to Broadcasting

Dorrance Publishing Co., Inc.
643 Smithfield St.
Pittsburgh, PA 15222
Ph: (412)288-4543   Fax: (412)288-1786
Fr: 800-788-7654

Charlie Pullen. 1996. $8.00 (paper). 80 pages.

★3342★ 100 Best Careers in Entertainment

Macmillan Publishing Co. Inc.
200 Old Tappan Rd.
Old Tappan, NJ 07675
Fr: 800-428-5331

Shelly Field. 1995. $14.95 (paper). 352 pages.

★3343★ Opportunities in Broadcasting Careers

McGraw-Hill Trade
2 Penn Plaza
New York, NY 10121
Ph: (212)904-2000   Fr: 800-722-4726

Elmo I. Ellis. 1998. $14.95; $11.95 (paper). Discusses opportunities and job search techniques in broadcasting, television, and radio. Illustrated.

★3344★ Opportunities in Music Careers

McGraw-Hill Professional
2 Penn Plaza
New York, NY 10121
Ph: (212)904-2000   Fr: 800-722-4726

Robert Gerardi. Fourth edition, revised, 2002. $15.95; $11.95 (paper). 160 pages. Describes the job market and where to find work. Covers careers in performing, writing, musical directing, management, and technical areas. Illustrated.

★3345★ Ruthless Self-Promotion in the Music Industry

artistpro.com, LLC
236 Georgia St., Suite 100
Vallejo, CA 94590
Ph: (707)554-1935   Fax: (707)554-9751

Jeffrey P. Fisher. 1999.

★3346★ Secrets of Negotiating a Record Contract: The Musician's Guide to Understanding & Avoiding Sneaky Lawyer Tricks

Backbeat Books
600 Harrison St.
San Francisco, CA 94107
Ph: (408)848-5294   Fax: (408)848-5784
Fr: (866)222-5232

Moses Avalon. 2001. $19.95 (paper).

★3347★ This Business of Music Marketing and Promotion

Watson-Guptill Publications, Incorporated
770 Broadway
New York, NY 10003
Ph: (646)654-5400   Fax: (646)654-5486
Fr: 800-323-9432

Tad Lathrop and Jim Pettigrew, Jr. 1999. $21.95.

★3348★ What's up Dawg: How to Become a Superstar in the Music Business

Hyperion Press
77 W. 66th St., 11th Fl.
New York, NY 10023-6298
Ph: (212)456-0100   Fax: (212)456-0108
Fr: 800-759-0190

Randy Jackson. January 2004. $14.70 (paper). 288 pages.

OTHER SOURCES

★3349★ American Disc Jockey Association (ADJA)

1964 Wagner St.
Pasadena, CA 91107
Ph: (626)844-3204   Fr: 888-723-5776
E-mail: markthomas@adja.org
URL: http://www.adja.org

Members: Mobile and night club disc jockeys. **Purpose:** Seeks to promote the disc jockey as a professional form of entertainment; improves the industry by establishing standards, procedures, and benefits. **Activities:** Assists and trains members; provides forums for professional disc jockeys; conducts educational, charitable, and research programs.

★3350★ Radio and Television Broadcasting

Evon Publishing
832 N 7th Ave.
Iron River, MI 49935
Ph: (906)265-3190

Audiocassette. 1996. $16.95. 32 minutes. Part of the Careers and Vocational Guidance Series. Provides information about the nature of the work, educational requirements, employment outlook, earnings, and work conditions as well as additional related information.

Dispensing Opticians

SOURCES OF HELP-WANTED ADS

★3351★ American Optician
Opticians Association of America
PO Box 6600
Springfield, VA 22150-6600
Ph: (703)916-8856   Fax: (703)916-7966
Fr: 800-443-8997

Quarterly. Subscription included in membership. Professional journal covering optometry.

★3352★ EyeNet
American Academy of Ophthalmology
655 Beach St.
PO Box 7424
San Francisco, CA 94120
Ph: (415)561-8500
E-mail: eyenet@aao.org
URL: http://206.14.84.3/eyenet_mag/

Monthly. $128.00/year for individuals. Professional magazine of the American Academy of Ophthalmology covering clinical, socioeconomic and political trends affecting their practice for members.

★3353★ Optometry
American Optometric Association
243 N Lindbergh Blvd.
St. Louis, MO 63141-7881
Ph: (314)991-4100   Fax: (314)991-4101
E-mail: jdkopp@aoa.org

Monthly. Subscription included in membership; $101.00/year for nonmembers; $5.00/year for nonmembers, single issue. Clinical journal for members of the American Optometric Association.

★3354★ Review of Optometry
Jobson Professional Publications Group
11 Campus Blvd., Ste. 100
Newtown Square, PA 19073
Ph: (610)492-1000   Fax: (610)492-1039
E-mail: reviewofoptometry@jobson.com
URL: http://http:www.revoptom.com

Monthly. $46.00/year for individuals. Journal for the optometric profession and optical industry.

EMPLOYER DIRECTORIES AND NETWORKING LISTS

★3355★ Contact Lenses-Retail Directory
infoUSA Inc.
5711 S 86th Cir.
Omaha, NE 68127-0347
Ph: (402)930-3500   Fax: (402)331-0176
Fr: 800-555-6124
URL: http://www.abii.com

Annual. Number of listings: 13,108. Entries include: Name, address, phone (including area code), size of advertisement, year first in "Yellow Pages," name of owner or manager, number of employees. Compiled from telephone company "Yellow Pages," nationwide. Arrangement: Geographical.

★3356★ Guild of Prescription Opticians of America-Guild Reference Directory
Guild of Prescription Opticians of America, Div.
PO Box 6600
Springfield, VA 22150-6600
Ph: (703)691-8355   Fax: (703)691-3929
Fr: 800-443-8997

Annual, January. $60.00. Covers 250 member firms with a total of 350 retail locations. Entries include: Company name, address, name of manager, services. Arrangement: Geographical.

★3357★ Opticians Directory
infoUSA Inc.
5711 S 86th Cir.
Omaha, NE 68127-0347
Ph: (402)930-3500   Fax: (402)331-0176
Fr: 800-555-6124
URL: http://www.abii.com

Annual. Number of listings: 13,642. Entries include: Company name, address, phone (including area code), size of advertisement, year first in "Yellow Pages," name of owner or manager, number of employees. Compiled from telephone company "Yellow Pages," nationwide. Arrangement: Geographical.

HANDBOOKS AND MANUALS

★3358★ Careers in Health Care
McGraw-Hill Trade
2 Penn Plaza
New York, NY 10121
Ph: (212)904-2000   Fr: 800-722-4726
E-mail: ntcpub@tribune.com

Barbara M. Swanson. Fourth edition, 2000. $17.95; $13.95 (paper). 320 pages. Describes job duties, work settings, salaries, licensing and certification requirements, educational preparation, and future outlook. Gives ideas on how to secure a job.

★3359★ Opportunities in Eye Care Careers
McGraw-Hill Trade
2 Penn Plaza
New York, NY 10121
Ph: (212)904-2000   Fr: 800-722-4726

Kathleen Belkoff. 1998. $14.95; $11.95 (paper). 206 pages. Explores careers in ophthalmology, optometry, and support positions. Describes the work, salary, and employment outlook and opportunities.

★3360★ Opportunities in Health and Medical Careers
McGraw-Hill Trade
2 Penn Plaza
New York, NY 10121
Ph: (212)904-2000   Fr: 800-722-4726

I. Donald Snook, Jr. and Leo D'Orazio. 1997. $14.95; $11.95 (paper). 202 pages. Covers

the full range of medical and health occupations. Illustrated.

EMPLOYMENT AGENCIES AND SEARCH FIRMS

★3361★ Retail Recruiters/Spectrum Consultants, Inc.
10 E Athens Ave., Ste.200
Ardmore, PA 19003
Ph: (610)645-9520
E-mail: rrspectrum@erols.com

Employment agency. Affiliate offices in many locations across the country.

ONLINE JOB SOURCES AND SERVICES

★3362★ Medhunters.com
E-mail: info@medhunters.com
URL: http://www.medhunters.com

Description: Career search site for jobs in all health care specialties; educational resources; visa and licensing information for relocation; interesting articles; relocation tools; links to professional organizations and general resources.

★3363★ ProHealthJobs
E-mail: sales@prohealthjobs.com
URL: http://www.prohealthjobs.com

Description: Career resources site for the medical and health care field. Lists professional opportunities, product information, continuing education and open positions.

TRADESHOWS

★3364★ American Academy of Optometry
American Academy of Optometry
6110 Executive Blvd., Ste. 506
Rockville, MD 20852
Ph: (301)984-1441   Fax: (301)984-4737
E-mail: aaoptom@aol.com

Annual. **Primary Exhibits:** Exhibits focusing on the latest research and patient treatments relating to clinical practice standards, optometric education, and experimental research in visual problems. **Dates and Locations:** 2004 Dec 09-13; Tampa, FL; Convention Center.

★3365★ International Vision Expo and Conference/East
Association Expositions and Services
383 Main Ave.
Norwalk, CT 06851
Ph: (203)840-5600   Fax: (203)840-9600
E-mail: inquiry@shot.reedexpo.com

Annual. **Primary Exhibits:** Equipment, supplies and services for the vision industry.

OTHER SOURCES

★3366★ American Academy of Optometry (AAO)
6110 Executive Blvd., Ste. 506
Rockville, MD 20852
Ph: (301)984-1441   Fax: (301)984-4737
E-mail: aaoptom@aol.com
URL: http://www.aaopt.org

Description: Optometrists, educators, and scientists interested in optometric education, and standards of care in visual problems. Conducts continuing education for optometrists and visual scientists. Sponsors 4-day annual meeting.

★3367★ American Board of Opticianry (ABO)
6506 Loisdale Rd., Ste. 209
Springfield, VA 22150-1815
Ph: (703)719-5800   Fax: (703)719-9144
Fr: 800-296-1379
E-mail: mail@abo-ncle.org
URL: http://www.abo.org

Description: Provides uniform standards for dispensing opticians by administering the National Opticianry Competency Examination and by issuing the Certified Optician Certificate to those passing the exam. Also administers the Master in Ophthalmic Optics Examination and issues certificates to opticians at the advanced level passing the exam. Maintains records of persons certified for competency in eyeglass dispensing. Adopts and enforces continuing education requirements; assists and encourages state licensing boards in the use of the National Opticianry Competency Examination for licensure purposes.

★3368★ American Optometric Association (AOA)
243 N Lindbergh Blvd.
St. Louis, MO 63141
Ph: (314)991-4100   Fax: (314)991-4101
URL: http://www.aoanet.org/

Members: Professional association of optometrists, students of optometry, and paraoptometric assistants and technicians. **Purpose:** Purposes are to improve the quality, availability, and accessibility of eye and vision care; to represent the optometric profession; to help members conduct their practices; to promote the highest standards of patient care. **Activities:** Monitors and promotes legislation concerning the scope of optometric practice, alternate health care delivery systems, health care cost containment, Medicare, and other issues relevant to eye/vision care. Supports the International Library, Archives and Museum of Optometry which includes references on ophthalmic and related sciences with emphasis on the history and socieconomic aspects of optometry. Operates Vision U.S.A. program, which provides free eye care to the working poor. Conducts specialized education programs; operates placement service; compiles statistics. Maintains museum. Conducts Seal of Certification and Acceptance Program.

★3369★ Association of University Professors of Ophthalmology (AUPO)
PO Box 420369
San Francisco, CA 94142-0369
Ph: (415)561-8548   Fax: (415)561-8531
E-mail: aupo@aao.org

Members: Heads of departments or divisions of ophthalmology in accredited medical schools throughout the U.S. and Canada; directors of ophthalmology residency programs in institutions not connected to medical schools. **Purpose:** Promotes medical education, research, and patient care relating to ophthalmology. **Activities:** Operates Ophthalmology Matching Program and faculty placement service, which aids ophthalmologists interested in being associated with university ophthalmology programs to locate such programs.

★3370★ Dispensing Opticians
Evon Publishing
832 N 7th Ave.
Iron River, MI 49935
Ph: (906)265-3190

Audiocassette. 1996. $16.95. 32 minutes. Part of the Careers and Vocational Guidance Series. Provides information about the nature of the work, educational requirements, employment outlook, earnings, and work conditions as well as additional related information.

★3371★ Exploring Health Occupations
Cambridge Educational
2572 Brunswick Ave.
Lawrenceville, NJ 08648-4128
Fax: 800-FAX-ON-US   Fr: 800-468-4227
URL: http://www.cambridgeeducational.com

Two videos. $139.95. 1999.

★3372★ Health Service Occupations
Delphi Productions
3160 4th St.
Boulder, CO 80304
Fax: (303)443-4022   Fr: 888-443-2400
URL: http://www.delphivideo.com

$95.00. 50 minutes. Part of the Careers for the 21st Century Video Library.

★3373★ *Health Technologists &*
Technicians

Delphi Productions
3160 4th St.
Boulder, CO 80304
Fax: (303)443-4022   Fr: 888-443-2400
URL: http://www.delphivideo.com

$95.00. 50 minutes. Part of the Careers for
the 21st Century Video Library.

★3374★ *Medicine & Related*
Occupations

Delphi Productions
3160 4th St.
Boulder, CO 80304
Fax: (303)443-4022   Fr: 888-443-2400
URL: http://www.delphivideo.com

$95.00. 45 minutes. Part of the Careers for
the 21st Century Video Library.

★3375★ **National Academy of**
Opticianry (NAO)

8401 Corporate Dr No. 605
Landover, MD 20785
Ph: (301)577-4828   Fax: (301)577-3880
Fr: 800-229-4828
E-mail: info@nao.org
URL: http://www.nao.org

Description: Offers review courses for national certification and state licensure examinations to members. Maintains speakers'
bureau and Career Progression Program.

★3376★ **National Association of**
Optometrists and Opticians (NAOO)

PO Box 459
Marblehead, OH 43440
Ph: (419)798-2031   Fax: (419)798-8548
E-mail: fdrozak@cros.net

Description: Licensed optometrists, opticians, and corporations. Conducts public
affairs programs of mutual importance to
members; serves as an organizational center for special purpose programs; acts as a
clearinghouse for information affecting the
retail optical industry.

★3377★ **National Contact Lens**
Examiners (NCLE)

6506 Loisdale Rd., Ste.209
Springfield, VA 22150-1815
Ph: (703)719-5800   Fax: (703)719-9144
Fr: 800-296-1379
E-mail: mail@abo-ncle.org
URL: http://www.abo.org

Description: National certifying agency promoting continued development of opticians
and technicians as contact lens fitters by
formulating standards and procedures for
determination of entry-level competency. Assists in the continuation, development, administration, and monitoring of a national
Contact Lens Registry Examination (CLRE),
which verifies entry-level competency of
contact lens fitters. Issues certificates. Activities include maintaining records of those
certified in contact lens fitting; encouraging
state occupational licensing and credentialing agencies to use the CLRE for licensure
purposes; identifying contact lens dispensing
education needs as a result of findings of
examination programs; disseminating information to sponsors of contact lens continuing education programs.

★3378★ **Opticians Association of**
America (OAA)

PO Box 6600
Springfield, VA 22150-6600
Ph: (703)916-8856   Fax: (703)916-7966
Fr: 800-443-8997
E-mail: oaa@opticians.org
URL: http://www.opticians.org

Members: Retail dispensing opticians who
fill prescriptions for glasses or contact lenses
written by a vision care specialist. **Purpose:**
Works to advance the science of ophthalmic
optics. **Activities:** Conducts research and
educational programs. Maintains museum
and speakers' bureau. Compiles statistics.

Drafters

SOURCES OF HELP-WANTED ADS

★3379★ Architectural Record

McGraw-Hill Companies
1221 Avenue of the Americas
New York, NY 10020
Ph: (212)512-2000
URL: http://www.mcgraw-hill.com

$59.00/year for individuals; $7.00 for single issue. Magazine focusing on architecture.

★3380★ Builder

Hanley-Wood L.L.C.
1 Thomas Cir., Ste. 600
Washington, DC 20005
Ph: (202)452-0800   Fax: (202)785-1974
URL: http://www.builderonline.com

Monthly. $29.95/year for individuals. Magazine covering housing and construction industry.

★3381★ Civil Engineering-ASCE

American Society of Civil Engineers
1801 Alexander Bell Dr.
Reston, VA 20191
Ph: (703)295-6300   Fax: (703)295-6222
Fr: 800-548-2723
E-mail: ztrem@ce.udel.edu
URL: http://www.pubs.asce.org/ceonline/newce.html

Monthly. $30.00/year for members; $160.00/year for individuals; $160.00/year for institutions, nonmembers; $205.00/year for out of country; $50.00/year for foreign members; $205.00/year for institutions, other countries. Professional magazine.

★3382★ Construction Digest

Construction Digest
5804 W 74th St.
Indianapolis, IN 46278
Ph: (317)293-6860   Fax: (317)293-7840
Fr: 888-893-6860

Semimonthly. $3.00 for single issue. Maga-zine for the public works and construction engineering industries.

★3383★ CONSTRUCTOR

Associated General Contractors
   Information
333 John Carlyle St., Ste. 200
Alexandria, VA 22314
Ph: (703)837-5355   Fax: (703)837-5402
URL: http://www.agc.org

Monthly. $15.00/year for members; $250.00/year for nonmembers; $4.00/year for single issue except July, November, and December; $25.00/year for single issue-November, December; $325.00 for single issue-July. Management magazine for the Construction Industry.

★3384★ Design News

Reed Business Information
275 Washington St.
Newton, MA 02458
Ph: (617)558-4900   Fax: (617)630-3830
Fr: 800-357-4745
E-mail: dn@chners.com

Semimonthly. $55.00/year for individuals. Magazine covering design engineering.

★3385★ ENR: Engineering News-Record

McGraw-Hill Companies
1221 Avenue of the Americas
New York, NY 10020
Ph: (212)512-2000
URL: http://www.enr.com

Weekly. $74.00/year; $5.00 for single issue. Magazine focusing on engineering and construction.

★3386★ High Technology Careers Magazine

HTC
4701 Patrick Henry Dr., No. 1901
Santa Clara, CA 95054-1847
Ph: (408)970-8800   Fax: (408)567-0242
URL: http://www.hightechcareers.com

Bimonthly. $29.00/year; $35.00/year for Canada; $85.00/year for out of country. Magazine (tabloid) containing employment opportunity information for the engineering and technical community.

★3387★ NSBE Magazine

NSBE Publications
1454 Duke St.
Alexandria, VA 22314
Ph: (703)549-2207   Fax: (703)683-5312

$10.00/year for individuals; $2.00 for single issue. Journal providing information on engineering careers, self-development, and cultural issues for recent graduates with technical majors.

★3388★ Professional Builder

Reed Business Information
360 Park Ave. S
New York, NY 10014
Ph: (646)746-7764
URL: http://www.probuilder.com

Monthly. $10.00 for single issue; $139.95/year for by mail.

EMPLOYER DIRECTORIES AND NETWORKING LISTS

★3389★ Directory of Contract Staffing Firms

C.E. Publications Inc.
PO Box 3006
Bothell, WA 98041-3006
Ph: (425)806-5200   Fax: (425)806-5585
URL: http://www.cjhunter.com/dcsf/overview.html

$15.00. Covers nearly 1,300 contract firms actively engaged in the employment of engineering, IT/IS, and technical personnel for 'temporary' contract assignments throughout the world. Entries include: Company name, address, phone, name of contact, email, web address. Arrangement: Alphabetical. Indexes: Geographical.

★3390★ Drafting Services Directory

infoUSA Inc.
5711 S 86th Cir.
Omaha, NE 68127-0347
Ph: (402)930-3500   Fax: (402)331-0176
Fr: 800-555-6124
URL: http://www.abii.com

Annual. Number of listings: 4,744. Entries include: Name, address, phone (including area code), size of advertisement, year first in "Yellow Pages," name of owner or manager, number of employees. Compiled from telephone company "Yellow Pages," nationwide. Arrangement: Geographical.

★3391★ ENR-Top 500 Design Firms Issue

McGraw-Hill Companies
1221 Ave. of the Americas
New York, NY 10020
Ph: (212)512-2000   Fax: (212)512-3840

Annual, April. $10.00. Publication includes: List of 500 leading architectural, engineering, and specialty design firms selected on basis of annual billings. Entries include: Company name, headquarters location, type of firm, current and prior year rank in billings, types of services, countries in which operated in preceding year. Arrangement: Ranked by billings.

★3392★ ENR-Top International Design Firms Issue

McGraw-Hill Companies
1221 Ave. of the Americas
New York, NY 10020
Ph: (212)512-2000   Fax: (212)512-3840

Annual, July issue of "Engineering News Record". $10.00. Publication includes: List of 200 design firms (including United States firms) competing outside their own national borders who received largest dollar volume of foreign contracts in preceding calendar year. Entries include: Company name, headquarters location, type of firm, current and previous year rankings in total billings, types of services, countries in which operated in preceding year. Arrangement: By amount billed to international clients in previous year.

★3393★ Peterson's Job Opportunities in Engineering and Technology

Thomson Peterson's
PO Box 67005
Lawrenceville, NJ 08648-6105
Fr: 800-338-3282

Compiled by the Peterson's staff. Fourth edition, 1996. $21.95 (paper). 384 pages. Profiles 2,000 high-tech companies looking primarily for technical personnel in such fields as biotechnology, telecommunications, software, computers and peripherals, defense, and aerospace. Contains job-search strategies and career options to help match education and expertise to the job market. Indexed geographically, by industry, and by hiring needs.

★3394★ ProFile: The Architects Sourcebook

Reed Construction Data
30 Technology Pkwy. S
Norcross, GA 30092
Ph: (770)209-3664   Fax: 800-444-1059
Fr: 800-949-0276
E-mail: profile@reedbusiness.com
URL: http://www.firstsourceonl.com

Annual. $225.00. Covers more than 27,000 architectural firms. Entries include: For firms-Firm name, address, phone, fax, year established, key staff and their primary responsibilities (for design, specification, etc.), number of staff personnel by discipline, types of work, geographical area served, projects. "ProFile" is an expanded version of, and replaces, the "Firm Directory." Arrangement: Firms are geographical. Indexes: Firm name, key individuals, specialization by category, consultants.

HANDBOOKS AND MANUALS

★3395★ Career Information Center

Macmillan Publishing Co. Inc.
200 Old Tappan Rd.
Old Tappan, NJ 07675
Fr: 800-428-5331

Visual Education Center Staff. Seventh edition, 1999. $275.00. 2080 pages. This 13-volume set profiles over 600 occupations. Each occupational profile describes job duties, educational requirements, how to get the job, advancement possibilities, employment outlook, working conditions, earnings and benefits, and where to write for more information.

★3396★ Exploring High-Tech Careers

Rosen Publishing Group, Inc.
29 E. 21st St.
New York, NY 10010
Ph: (212)777-3017   Fax: (212)777-0277
Fr: 800-237-9932

Scott Southworth. Revised edition, 1993. $14.95; $9.95 (paper). 118 pages. Out of print. Gives an orientation to the field of high technology and high-tech jobs. Describes educational preparation and job hunting. Includes a glossary and bibliography.

★3397★ Opportunities in Computer-Aided Design and Computer-Aided Manufacturing

McGraw-Hill Trade
2 Penn Plaza
New York, NY 10121
Ph: (212)904-2000   Fr: 800-722-4726

Jan Bone. 1994. $14.95; $11.95 (paper). 160 pages. Defines CAD (computer-aided design), CAM (computer-aided manufacturing), and MAP (manufacturing automation protocol). Explains career opportunities in the CAD/CAM field, and education and training needed. Gives job-hunting tips.

★3398★ Opportunities in Drafting Careers

McGraw-Hill Trade
2 Penn Plaza
New York, NY 10121
Ph: (212)904-2000   Fr: 800-722-4726

Mark Rowh. 1994. $14.95; $11.95 (paper). 298 pages. Provides information on opportunities in mechanical, landscape, marine, and topographical drafting in civil service, architecture, electronics, and other fields. Contains index and illustrations.

★3399★ Opportunities in High Tech Careers

McGraw-Hill Trade
2 Penn Plaza
New York, NY 10121
Ph: (212)904-2000   Fr: 800-722-4726

Gary Colter and Deborah Yanuck. 1995. $14.95; $11.95 (paper). 160 pages. Explores high technology careers. Describes job opportunities, how to make a career decision, how to prepare for high technology jobs, job hunting techniques, and future trends.

EMPLOYMENT AGENCIES AND SEARCH FIRMS

★3400★ Agra Placements, Ltd.

8187 University Blvd.
Clive, IA 50325
Ph: (515)225-6562   Fax: (515)225-7733
E-mail: iowa@agraplacements.com
URL: http://www.agraplacements.com

Executive search firm. Branch offices in Peru, IN, Lincoln, IL, and New Ulm, MN.

★3401★ The Aspire Group

52 Second Ave, 1st Fl
Waltham, MA 02451-1129
Fax: (718)890-1810   Fr: 800-546-5675
URL: http://www.bmanet.com

Employment agency.

★3402★ International Staffing Consultants

2901 W Coast Hwy.,Ste. 200
Newport Beach, CA 92663
Ph: (949)263-5933   Fax: (949)767-5959
E-mail: iscinc@iscworld.com
URL: http://www.iscworld.com

Employment agency. Provides placement on regular or temporary basis. Affiliate office in London.

★3403★ Main Line Personnel Service, Inc.

Pagoda Blding.
100 Presidential Blvd. Ste. 200
Bala Cynwyd, PA 19004-0448
Ph: (610)667-1820   Fax: (610)668-5000

URL: http://www.mlpers.com
Employment agency.

★3404★ Tri-Serv Inc.
22 W. Padonia Rd., Ste. C-353
Timonium, MD 21093
Ph: (410)561-1740   Fax: (410)252-7417
E-mail: info@tri-serv.coom
URL: http://www.tri-serv.com

Permanent employment agency.

OTHER SOURCES

★3405★ American Design Drafting Association (ADDA)
105 E Main St.
Newbern, TN 38059
Ph: (731)627-0802   Fax: (731)627-9321
E-mail: corporate@adda.org
URL: http://www.adda.org

Members: Designers, drafters, drafting managers, chief drafters, supervisors, administrators, instructors, and students of design and drafting. **Purpose:** Encourages a continued program of education for self-improvement and professionalism in design and drafting and computer-aided design/drafting. Informs members of effective techniques and materials used in drawings and other graphic presentations. **Activities:** Evaluates curriculum of educational institutions through certification program; sponsors drafter certification program.

★3406★ Technical & Related Occupations
Delphi Productions
3160 4th St.
Boulder, CO 80304
Fax: (303)443-4022   Fr: 888-443-2400
URL: http://www.delphivideo.com

$95.00. 49 minutes. Part of the Careers for the 21st Century Video Library.

Economists

SOURCES OF HELP-WANTED ADS

★3407★ Brookings Papers on Economic Activity

Brookings Institution Press
1775 Massashusetts Ave. NW
Washington, DC 20036
Ph: (202)797-6000   Fax: (202)797-6195
Fr: 800-275-1447

Semiannual. Publication covering economics and business.

★3408★ Business Insurance

Crain Communications Inc.
711 Third Ave.
New York, NY 10017-4036
Ph: (212)210-0100   Fax: (212)210-0244
Fr: 800-446-1420
URL: http://www.businessinsurance.com

Weekly. $97.00/year for individuals. International newsweekly reporting on corporate risk and employee benefit management news.

★3409★ Economic Perspectives

Federal Reserve Bank of Chicago
Public Affairs Department
230 S LaSalle
Chicago, IL 60604
Ph: (312)322-5860   Fax: (312)322-5515
E-mail: ecucation.chi@chi.frb.org

Quarterly. Publication covering the field of economics.

★3410★ Employment Opportunities for Business Economists

National Association for Business Economics
1233 20th St., Ste. 505
Washington, DC 20036
Ph: (202)463-6223   Fax: (202)463-6239

Description: Bimonthly. Features listings of job openings for business economists and analysts.

★3411★ Financial Management

Financial Management Association
School of Business
University of S Florida
Tampa, FL 33620-5500
Ph: (813)974-2084   Fax: (813)974-3318
E-mail: kporto@coba.usf.edu

Quarterly. $95.00/year for individuals; $20.00 for single issue. Journal covering business, economics, finance and management.

★3412★ Journal of Forensic Economics

National Association of Forensic Economists
PO Box 30067
Kansas City, MO 64112
Ph: (816)235-2833

Quarterly. Journal covering economics and law.

★3413★ Knowledge Management

Freedom Technology Media Group
17666 Fitch
Irvine, CA 92614-6022
Ph: (212)333-7600

Monthly. Publication covering business and economics.

★3414★ McKinsey Quarterly

McKinsey & Company Inc.
55 E 52nd St.
New York, NY 10022

Quarterly. Publication covering business and economics.

★3415★ OECD Observer

Organization for Economic Cooperation and Development
2001 L St. NW, Ste. 650
Washington, DC 20036-4922
Ph: (202)785-6323   Fax: (202)785-0350
Fr: 800-456-6323
URL: http://www.oecdobserver.org

Bimonthly. $50.00/year for individuals. Mag-azine on economic affairs, science, and technology.

★3416★ World Economic Outlook

International Monetary Fund
700 19th St. NW, Ste. 12-607
Washington, DC 20431
Ph: (202)623-7430   Fax: (202)623-7201

Semiannual. Publication covering economics and business issues worldwide.

PLACEMENT AND JOB REFERRAL SERVICES

★3417★ African Studies Association (ASA)

Rutgers the State University of New Jersey
132 George St.- Douglass Campus
New Brunswick, NJ 08901-1400
Ph: (732)932-8173
E-mail: callasa@rci.rutgers.edu

Members: Persons specializing in teaching, writing, or research on Africa including political scientists, historians, geographers, anthropologists, economists, librarians, linguists, and government officials; persons who are studying African subjects; institutional members are universities, libraries, government agencies, and others interested in receiving information about Africa. **Purpose:** Seeks to foster communication and to stimulate research among scholars on Africa. **Activities:** Sponsors placement service; conducts panels and discussion groups; presents exhibits and films.

★3418★ American Agricultural Economics Association (AAEA)

415 S Duff Ave., Ste. C
Ames, IA 50010-6600
Ph: (515)233-3202   Fax: (515)233-3101
E-mail: info@aaea.org
URL: http://www.aaea.org

Members: Professional society of agricultural economists. **Purpose:** Serves to enhance the skills, knowledge and professional contribution of those economists who serve society by solving problems related to agriculture, food, resources, and economic development. **Activities:** Offers placement service.

★3419★ National Association for Business Economics (NABE)

1233 20th St. NW, Ste. 505
Washington, DC 20036
Ph: (202)463-6223   Fax: (202)463-6239
E-mail: nabe@nabe.com
URL: http://www.nabe.com

Description: Professional society of institutions, businesses, and students with an active interest in business economics and individuals who are employed by academic, private, or governmental concerns in the area of business-related economic issues. Maintains placement service for members; conducts several seminars per year. Maintains speakers' bureau.

★3420★ Southern Economic Association (SEA)

Oklahoma State University
College of Bus. Admin.
Stillwater, OK 74078-4011
Ph: (405)744-7645   Fax: (405)744-5180
URL: http://www.okstate.edu/economics/ journal/south1.html

Description: Professional economists in government, business, and academic institutions. Provides placement service for economists.

EMPLOYER DIRECTORIES AND NETWORKING LISTS

★3421★ American Banker-Top Commercial Banks by Assets, Deposits

American Banker/Bond Buyer Inc.
1 State St. Plz.
New York, NY 10004
Ph: (212)803-8200   Fax: (212)843-9600
Fr: 800-982-0633

Semiannual, March and September. $25.00. Publication includes: List of the top 300 commercial banks. Entries include: Name of bank, headquarters, amount of deposits at the previous quarter, place in rank at quarter. Arrangement: Ranked by deposits and assets. Indexes: Geographical.

★3422★ American Banker-Top Finance Companies Issue

American Banker/Bond Buyer Inc.
1 State St. Plz.
New York, NY 10004
Ph: (212)803-8200   Fax: (212)843-9600
Fr: 800-982-0633

Annual, December. $25.00. Publication includes: List of top finance companies with $10 million or more in capital funds. Entries include: Finance company name, headquarters, city; rankings of net receivables by type, business, consumer, and other; total capital funds for two preceding years; capital and surplus, total assets, net receivables, net income, deferred income, receivables acquired, and amount of bank credit at end of the preceding year. Arrangement: Ranked by size of capital funds.

★3423★ American Banker-Top 300 Mortgage Companies Issue

American Banker/Bond Buyer Inc.
1 State St. Plz.
New York, NY 10004
Ph: (212)803-8200   Fax: (212)843-9600
Fr: 800-982-0633

Annual, October. $25.00. Entries include: Company name, headquarters city, rank; dollar value of mortgages serviced for current and prior year; prior year's rank and gain in rank; number of mortgages; number of investors. Arrangement: Ranked by total dollar value of mortgages.

★3424★ American Banker-Top 300 Thrifts by Deposits

American Banker/Bond Buyer Inc.
1 State St. Plz.
New York, NY 10004
Ph: (212)803-8200   Fax: (212)843-9600
Fr: 800-982-0633

Semiannual, May and November. $25.00. Publication includes: List of top 300 thrift institutions. Entries include: Name of institution, city, rank; total assets, deposits, and total capital. Arrangement: Ranked by deposits, assets, and risk-based capital ratios.

★3425★ Association for University Business and Economic Research-Membership Directory

Association for University Business and Economic Research/AUBER
801 W Michigan St.
Indianapolis, IN 46202-5151
Ph: (317)274-2204   Fax: (317)274-3312

Annual, January. $10.00. Covers member institutions in the United States and abroad with centers, bureaus, departments, etc., concerned with business and economic research. Entries include: Name of bureau, center, etc., sponsoring institution name, address, phone, names and titles of director and staff, publications and frequency. Arrangement: Geographical. Indexes: Director name, institution name.

★3426★ Business Economics-Membership Directory Issue

National Association for Business Economics
1233 20th St. NW, Ste. 505
Washington, DC 20036
Ph: (202)463-6223   Fax: (202)463-6239
E-mail: nabe@nabe.com

Annual, March. $125.00 for electronic; $150.00 for print. Publication includes: List of about 3,000 members of the association, including students. Entries include: Name, address, phone, corporate affiliation, economic specialization, industries of research specialization, NABE activities, educational background, work experience. Arrangement: Alphabetical by member name, company, and roundtable affiliation. Indexes: Company, roundtable, and students.

★3427★ Mergent Bank and Finance Manual

Mergent Inc.
5250 77 Center Dr., Ste. 150
Charlotte, NC 28217
Ph: (704)559-7601   Fax: (704)559-6945
Fr: 800-342-5647
URL: http://www.mergent.com

Annual, July; supplements in 'Mergent Bank & Finance News Reports'. $2,095.00. Covers in four volumes, over 12,000 national, state, and private banks, savings and loans, mutual funds, unit investment trusts, and insurance and real estate companies in the United States. Entries include: Company name, headquarters and branch offices, phones, names and titles of principal executives, directors, history, Moody's rating, and extensive financial and statistical data. Arrangement: Classified by type of business. Indexes: Company name.

★3428★ National Association for Business Economics-Membership Directory

National Association for Business Economics
1233 20th St., Ste. 505
Washington, DC 20036
Ph: (202)463-6223   Fax: (202)463-6239

Annual, March. $95.00. Covers about 3,600 members internationally. Entries include: Name, address, phone, company affiliation, educational background, prior employment history, areas of specialization and industries of research specialization, roundtable affiliation, Standard Industrial Classification (SIC) code. Arrangement: Alphabetical. Indexes: Company name, association roundtable affiliation.

★3429★ National Economists Club-Membership Directory

National Economists Club
Box 19281
Washington, DC 20036
Ph: (703)739-9404   Fax: (703)739-9405

Biennial. Covers nearly 800 professional economists and others having an interest in economic subjects. Entries include: Name, address, phone. Arrangement: Alphabetical by organization.

★3430★ Roster of Minority Financial Institutions

U.S. Department of the Treasury
1500 Pennsylvania Ave. NW
Washington, DC 20220
Ph: (202)622-2000

Biennial. Covers about 170 commercial, minority-owned and controlled financial institutions participating in the Department of the Treasury's Minority Bank Deposit Program. Entries include: Name of institution, name and title of chief officer, address, phone, fax. Arrangement: Geographical.

★3431★ Roster of Women Economists

Committee on the Status of Women in the Economics Profession
4901 Tower Ct.
Tallahassee, FL 32303
Ph: (850)562-1211   Fax: (850)562-3838
URL: http://www.cswep.org/f97chair.html

Biennial, odd years. $35.00. Covers 6,000 women in economics. Entries include: Name, address, phone, title, affiliation, degrees, honors, specialty, number of articles and books published. e-mail, fax. Publisher is a standing committee of the American Economic Association. Arrangement: Alphabetical. Indexes: Geographical, employer, fields of specialization.

★3432★ Thomson Bank Directory

Thomson Financial Publishing
4709 W.Golf Rd., Ste. 600
Skokie, IL 60076
Ph: (847)676-9600   Fax: (847)933-8101
Fr: 800-321-3373
URL: http://www.tgbr.com

Semiannual, June and December. $608.00; $509.00 for annual subscription. Covers in three volumes, about 11,000 banks and 50,000 branches of United States banks, and 60,000 foreign banks and branches engaged in foreign banking; Federal Reserve system and other United States government and state government banking agencies; 500 largest North American and International commercial banks; paper and automated clearinghouses. Volumes 1 and 2 contain North American listings; volumes 3 and 4, international listings (also cited as 'Thomson International Bank Directory'); volume 5, Worldwide Correspondents Guide containing key correspondent data to facilitate funds transfer. Entries include: For domestic banks-Bank name, address, phone, telex, cable, date established, routing number, charter type, bank holding company affiliation, memberships in Federal Reserve System and other banking organizations, principal officers by function performed, principal correspondent banks, and key financial data (deposits, etc.). For international banks-Bank name, address, phone, fax, telex, cable, SWIFT address, transit or sort codes within home country, ownership, financial data, names and titles of key personnel, branch locations. For branches-Bank name, address, phone, charter type, ownership and other details comparable to domestic bank listings. Arrangement: Geographical. Indexes: Alphabetical, geographical.

★3433★ Thomson North American Financial Institutions Directory

Thomson Financial Publishing
4709 W.Golf Rd., Ste. 600
Skokie, IL 60076
Ph: (847)676-9600   Fax: (847)933-8101
Fr: 800-321-3373

Semiannual. $449.00 for single issue. Covers 15,000 banks and their branches; over 2,000 head offices, and 15,500 branches of savings and loan associations; over 5,500 credit unions with assets over $5 million; Federal Reserve System and other U.S. government and state government banking agencies; bank holding, commercial finance, and leasing companies; coverage includes the United States, Canada, Mexico, and Central America. Entries include: Bank name, address, phone, fax, telex, principal officers and directors, date established, financial data, association memberships, attorney or counsel, correspondent banks, out-of-town branch, holding company affiliation, ABA transit number and routing symbol, MICR number with check digit, credit card(s) issued, trust powers, current par value and dividend of common stock, kind of charter. Arrangement: Geographical. Indexes: Alphabetical.

★3434★ Who's Who in Finance and Industry

Marquis Who's Who
121 Chanlon Rd.
New Providence, NJ 07974
Ph: (908)673-1101   Fax: (908)673-1189
Fr: 800-473-7020
URL: http://www.marquiswhoswho.com

Biennial, July of odd years. $292.50. Covers over 21,000 individuals. Entries include: Name, home and office addresses, personal, career, and family data; civic and political activities; memberships, publications, awards. Arrangement: Alphabetical.

HANDBOOKS AND MANUALS

★3435★ Careers for Number Crunchers and Other Quantitative Types

McGraw-Hill Trade
2 Penn Plaza
New York, NY 10121
Ph: (212)904-2000   Fr: 800-722-4726
E-mail: ntcpub@tribune.com

Rebecca Burnett. Second edition, 2002. $15.95; $12.95 (paper). 192 pages. Provides information to math-oriented job hunters on how to become statisticians, field researchers, computer programmers, stock analysts, investment managers, bankers, engineers, accountants, underwriters, economists, market analysts, mathematicians, systems analysts, and more.

★3436★ Opportunities in Research and Development Careers

McGraw-Hill/Contemporary Books
1221 Avenue of the Americas
New York, NY 10020
Ph: (212)904-2000   Fr: 800-323-4900
E-mail: ntcpub@tribune.com

Jan Goldberg. 1997. $14.95; $11.95 (paper). 204 pages.

★3437★ Opportunities in Social Science Careers

McGraw-Hill Companies
860 Taylor Station Rd.
Blacklick, OH 43004-0545
Fax: (614)755-5645   Fr: 800-722-4726

Rosanne J. Marek. March 2004. $22.95. 160 Pages. VGM Opportunities Series.

EMPLOYMENT AGENCIES AND SEARCH FIRMS

★3438★ Choi & Burns LLC

590 Madison Ave., Fl. 26
New York, NY 10022
Ph: (212)755-7051   Fax: (212)355-2610

Executive search firm focuses on the financial industry.

★3439★ Cook & Company

12 Masterton Rd.
Bronxville, NY 10708
Ph: (914)779-4838

Executive search firm dedicated to the financial industry.

★3440★ Cromwell Partners Inc.

305 Madison Ave.
New York, NY 10165
Ph: (212)953-3220   Fax: (212)953-4688

Executive search firm.

★3441★ Dussick Management Associates

54 White Birch Rd.
Madison, CT 06443
Ph: (203)245-9311   Fax: (203)245-9570
E-mail: vince@dussick.com
URL: http://www.dussick.com

Executive search firm.

★3442★ Hawkes Peers

224 Fifth Ave., Floor 6
New York, NY 10001
Ph: (212)624-4070   Fax: (212)624-4089
E-mail: info@hawkespeers.com
URL: http://www.hawkespeers.com

Executive search firm specializing in the areas of banking and sales.

★3443★ International Staffing Consultants

2901 W Coast Hwy.,Ste. 200
Newport Beach, CA 92663
Ph: (949)263-5933   Fax: (949)767-5959
E-mail: iscinc@iscworld.com
URL: http://www.iscworld.com

Employment agency. Provides placement on regular or temporary basis. Affiliate office in London.

★3444★ The Murphy Group

245 W Roosevelt Rd., Bldg.15 Ste.101
Chicago, IL 60185
Ph: (630)639-5110   Fax: (630)639-5113
E-mail: info@murphygroup.com
URL: http://www.murphygroup.com

Employment agency. Places personnel in a variety of positions. Additional offices located in Napierville, Park Ridge, and OakBrook.

★3445★ Ritt-Ritt and Associates

5105 Tollview Dr., Ste. 100
Rolling Meadows, IL 60008
Ph: (847)483-9330   Fax: (847)483-9331
E-mail: info@rittsearch.com
URL: http://www.rittsearch.com

Food service and hospitality employment agency and executive search firm.

★3446★ Sales Executives Inc.

755 W. Big Beaver Rd., Ste. 2107
Troy, MI 48084
Ph: (248)362-1900
E-mail: dale@salesexecutives.com
URL: http://www.salesexecutives.com

Employment agency. Executive search firm.

★3447★ Werbin Associates Executive Search, Inc.

140 Riverside Dr., Ste. 10N
New York, NY 10024-2605
Ph: (212)799-6111
E-mail: swerb@bellatlantic.net

Employment agency. Executive search firm.

OTHER SOURCES

★3448★ American Almanac of Jobs and Salaries

Morrow Avon
1350 Avenue of the Americas
New York, NY 10019
Ph: (212)261-6788   Fr: 800-242-7737

John W. Wright. Revised edition, 2000. $20.00 (paper). 672 pages. This is a comprehensive guide to the wages of hundreds of occupations in a wide variety of industries and organizations.

★3449★ American Economic Association (AEA)

2014 Broadway, Ste. 305
Nashville, TN 37203-2418
Ph: (615)322-2595   Fax: (615)343-7590
E-mail: aeainfo@vanderbilt.edu
URL: http://www.vanderbilt.edu/AEA

Members: Educators, business executives, government administrators, journalists, lawyers, and others interested in economics and its application to present-day problems. **Purpose:** Encourages historical and statistical research into actual conditions of industrial life and provides a nonpartisan forum for economic discussion.

★3450★ Committee on the Status of Women in the Economics Profession (CSWEP)

Cornell University
204 Ives Hall
Ithaca, NY 14853
Ph: (607)255-2438   Fax: (607)255-4496
E-mail: cswep@cornell.edu
URL: http://www.cswep.org

Description: A standing committee of American Economic Association. Women economists in the U.S. Purpose is to support and facilitate equality of opportunity for women economists. Disseminates information about job opportunities, research funding, and research related to the status of women in economics. Sponsors technical sessions.

★3451★ Economic Policy Institute (EPI)

1660 L St., NW, Ste. 1200
Washington, DC 20036
Ph: (202)775-8810   Fax: (202)775-0819
E-mail: epi@epinet.org
URL: http://www.epinet.org/

Purpose: Conducts research and provides a forum for the exchange of information on economic policy issues. Promotes educational programs to encourage discussion of economic policy and economic issues, particularly the economics of poverty, unemployment, inflation, American industry, international competitiveness, and problems of economic adjustment as they affect the community and the individual. **Activities:** Sponsors seminars for economists and citizens.

★3452★ Economists

Evon Publishing
832 N 7th Ave.
Iron River, MI 49935
Ph: (906)265-3190

Audiocassette. 1996. $16.95. 32 minutes. Part of the Careers and Vocational Guidance Series. Provides information about the nature of the work, educational requirements, employment outlook, earnings, and work conditions as well as additional related information.

★3453★ Institute for Economic Analysis (IEA)

4 High St., No. 3
Brattleboro, VT 05301
Ph: (802)254-0089   Fax: (802)254-1251
E-mail: atlee@sover.net
URL: http://iea-macro-economics.org

Purpose: Seeks to develop tools for macroeconomic analysis and policy that can maintain stable full employment growth, low inflation, low interest rates and equitable distribution of income and wealth. Integrates GDP and financial accounts for more systematic coordination of monetary and fiscal policy. Special focuses include federal monetary policy, federal budget deficit/surplus, social security, consumer credit, and world economic recovery.

★3454★ International Studies Association (ISA)

324 Social Sciences Bldg.
University of Arizona
Tucson, AZ 85721
Ph: (520)621-7715   Fax: (520)621-5780
E-mail: isa@u.arizona.edu
URL: http://www.isanet.org

Members: Social scientists and other scholars from a wide variety of disciplines who are specialists in international affairs and cross-cultural studies; academicians; government officials; officials in international organizations; business executives; students. **Purpose:** Promotes research, improved teaching, and the orderly growth of knowledge in the field of international studies; emphasizes a multidisciplinary approach to problems. **Activities:** Conducts conventions, workshops and discussion groups.

★3455★ National Council on Economic Education (NCEE)

1140 Avenue of the Americas, 2nd Fl.
New York, NY 10036
Ph: (212)730-7007   Fax: (212)730-1793
Fr: 800-338-1192
E-mail: rduvall@ncee.net
URL: http://www.ncee.net

Description: Economists, educators, and representatives from business, labor, and finance dedicated to improving economic education by improving the quality and increasing the quantity of economics being taught in all levels of schools and colleges. Initiates curriculum development and research; experiments with new economics courses and ways to prepare teachers and students; provides updated teacher-pupil materials; coordinates national and local programs in economics education. Provides consulting services to educators; sponsors workshops; tests new methods in practical school situations.

★3456★ Professional Specialty Occupations

Delphi Productions
3160 4th St.
Boulder, CO 80304
Fax: (303)443-4022   Fr: 888-443-2400

URL: http://www.delphivideo.com

$95.00. 53 minutes. Part of the Careers for

the 21st Century Video Library.

Education Administrators

single issue. Periodical covering issues in education.

SOURCES OF HELP-WANTED ADS

★3457★ AABC Newsletter

Accrediting Association of Bible Colleges
5575 S Semoran Blvd., Ste. 26
Orlando, FL 32822-1781
Ph: (407)207-0808   Fax: (407)207-0840
URL: http://www.aabc.org

Description: Five issues/year (always January, April, June, September, and November). Provides information on issues, events, and resources for Bible college administrators and others interested in Christian higher education. Recurring features include a calendar of events, reports of meetings, news of educational opportunities, book reviews, and notices of publications available.

★3458★ AAEE Connections

American Association for Employment in Education
3040 Riverside Dr., Ste. 125
Columbus, OH 43221
Ph: (614)485-1111   Fax: (614)485-9609

Description: Quarterly. Publishes news of the Association, whose aim is "to enhance and promote the concept of career planning and placement as an integral part of the educational process and to undertake activities designed to help schools, colleges, and universities meet their educational staffing needs." Also concerned with teacher education and the supply of/demand for teachers. Recurring features include news of members, state and regional news, and announcements of upcoming conferences and meetings.

★3459★ Academic Exchange Quarterly

Rapid Intellect Group Inc.
PO Box 131
Stuyvesant Falls, NY 12174
Ph: (518)372-1347
E-mail: AEQ@rapidintellect.com
URL: http://rapidintellect.com/AEQweb/

Quarterly. $156.00/year for individuals; $116.00/year, professional rate; $39.00 for

★3460★ The American School Board Journal

American School Board Journal
1680 Duke St.
Alexandria, VA 22314
Ph: (703)838-6722
URL: http://www.asbj.com

Monthly. $54.00/year for U.S.; $60.00/year for Canada; $79.00/year for other countries. Magazine serving school board members, superintendents, and other administrative officials.

★3461★ American School & University

Primedia Business
9800 Metcalf Ave.
Overland Park, KS 66212
Ph: (913)341-1300   Fax: (913)967-1901
Fr: (866)505-7173
E-mail: asu@primediabusiness.com
URL: http://www.primediabusiness.com

Monthly. $50.00/year for individuals. Trade magazine.

★3462★ ASBSD-Bulletin

Associated School Boards of South Dakota
PO Box 1059
Pierre, SD 57501-1059
Ph: (605)773-2500   Fax: (605)773-2501

Description: Semimonthly. Deals with policymaking, financing, and innovation in public education. Seeks to promote reorganization and adequate financing. Recurring features include letters to the editor, news of research, reports of meetings, news of educational opportunities, job listings, notices of publications available, and columns titled On the Line, Check This, and Board Policies.

★3463★ Change

Heldref Publications
1319 18th St. NW
Washington, DC 20036-1802
Ph: (202)296-6267   Fax: (202)296-5149
Fr: 800-365-9753
URL: http://www.heldref.org/html/chg.html

Bimonthly. $51.00/year for individuals; $103.00/year for institutions. Magazine dealing with contemporary issues in higher learning.

★3464★ The Chronicle of Higher Education

The Chronicle of Higher Education
1255 23rd St. NW, Ste. 700
Washington, DC 20037-1125
Ph: (202)466-1000   Fax: (202)452-1033
URL: http://chronicle.com

Weekly. $82.50/year for individuals; $3.75 for single issue. Higher education magazine (tabloid).

★3465★ Community Colleges Journal

American Association of Community Colleges
1 Dupont Cir. NW, Ste. 410
Washington, DC 20036
Ph: (202)728-0200   Fax: (202)223-9390
Fr: 800-250-6557
URL: http://www.aacc.nche.edu

Educational magazine.

★3466★ Education Week

Editorial Projects in Education Inc.
6935 Arlington Rd., Ste. 100
Bethesda, MD 20814
Ph: (301)280-3100   Fax: (301)280-3250
E-mail: ew@epe.org
URL: http://www.edweek.org

Weekly. $79.94/year for individuals. Professional newspaper for elementary and secondary school educators.

★3467★ Educational Researcher

American Educational Research
 Association
1230 17th St. NW
Washington, DC 20036-3078
Ph: (202)223-9485   Fax: (202)775-1824
URL: http://www.aera.net

$41.00/year for individuals; $8.00 for single
issue; $56.00/year for institutions; $50.00/
year for out of country; free to members of
AERA. Educational research journal.

★3468★ Electronic Learning

Scholastic Library Publishing Inc.
90 Old Sherman Tpke.
Danbury, CT 06816
Ph: (203)797-3500   Fax: (203)797-3657
Fr: 800-621-1115

$19.00/year. Magazine focusing on electron-
ic education.

**★3469★ Journal of Career Planning &
Employment**

National Association of Colleges and
 Employers
62 Highland Ave.
Bethlehem, PA 18017
Ph: (610)868-1421   Fax: (610)868-0208
Fr: 800-544-5272
URL: http://www.jobweb.org/

Quarterly. $72.00/year. Journal on career
planning, and recruitment of the college
educated work force.

**★3470★ Journal of College Teaching
& Learning**

Western Academic Press
PO Box 620760
Littleton, CO 80162
Ph: (303)904-4750   Fax: (303)978-0413

Monthly. $495.00/year for institutions. Refer-
eed academic journal covering all areas of
college level teaching, learning and administration.

**★3471★ Journal of Higher Education
Outreach and Engagement (JHEOE)**

Institute of Higher Education (IHE)
Meigs Hall
Athens, GA 30602-6772
Ph: (706)542-0579   Fax: (706)583-0281
E-mail: jheoe@uga.edu
URL: http://www.uga.edu/jheoe/

$35.00/year for individuals; $45.00/year for
Canada; $60.00/year for elsewhere, surface
mail; $70.00/year for elsewhere, airmail;
$95.00/year for institutions; $105.00/year for
institutions, Canada; $110.00/year for institu-
tions elsewhere, surface mail; $120.00/year
for institutions elsewhere, airmail. Journal
covering higher education outreach and engagement for scholars, practitioners, and
professionals.

**★3472★ Journal of Language, Identity,
and Education**

Lawrence Erlbaum Associates Inc.
10 Industrial Ave.
Mahwah, NJ 07430-2262
Ph: (201)236-9500   Fax: (201)236-0072
Fr: 800-9-BOOKS-9
E-mail: journals@erlbaum.com
URL: http://www.erlbaum.com/shop/
tek9.asp?pg=products&specific=1

Quarterly. $40.00/year for individuals;
$70.00/year for out of country; $225.00/year
for institutions; $255.00/year for institutions,
other countries. Scholarly, interdisciplinary
journal covering issues in language, identity
and education worldwide for academics,
educators and policy specialists in a variety
of disciplines, and others.

**★3473★ Journal of Latinos and
Education**

Lawrence Erlbaum Associates Inc.
10 Industrial Ave.
Mahwah, NJ 07430-2262
Ph: (201)236-9500   Fax: (201)236-0072
Fr: 800-9-BOOKS-9
E-mail: journals@erlbaum.com
URL: http://www.erlbaum.com/shop/
tek9.asp?pg=products&specific=1

Quarterly. $40.00/year for individuals;
$70.00/year for out of country; $195.00/year
for institutions; $225.00/year for institutions,
other countries. Scholarly, multidisciplinary
journal covering educational issues that impact Latinos for researchers, teaching professionals, academics, scholars, institutions,
and others.

★3474★ Journal of Teacher Education

Boston College
McElroy Commons, No. 113
Chestnut Hill, MA 02467
Ph: (617)552-4820   Fax: (617)552-4823

Magazine of interest to educators.

**★3475★ Matrix: The Magazine for
Leaders in Higher Education**

Professional Media Group L.L.C.
36 Clipper Ct., Ste. B
Mystic, CT 06355-2138

Bimonthly. Trade publication covering issues
for higher education professionals.

★3476★ NJEA Review

New Jersey Education Association
180 W State St.
PO Box 1211
Trenton, NJ 08607
Ph: (609)599-4561   Fax: (609)392-6321
E-mail: lgalley@mgea.org

$25.00/year. Educational journal for public
school employees.

★3477★ The Physics Teacher

American Association of Physics
 Teachers
One Physics Ellipse
College Park, MD 20740-3845
Ph: (301)209-3350   Fax: (301)209-0845
E-mail: tpt@appstate.edu
URL: http:///www.aapt.org/tpt

$94.00/year for individuals; $47.00/year. Scientific education magazine.

★3478★ School and Community

Missouri State Teachers Association
PO Box 458
Columbia, MO 65205-0458
Ph: (573)442-3127   Fax: (573)443-5079
Fr: 800-392-0532
E-mail: publications@mail.msta.org
URL: http://www.msta.org

Quarterly. $15.00/year. Education maga-
zine.

★3479★ Tech Directions

Prakken Publications Inc.
PO Box 8623
Ann Arbor, MI 48107-8623
Ph: (734)975-2800   Fax: (734)975-2787
Fr: 800-530-WORD
E-mail: tdedit@techdirections.com
URL: http://www.techdirections.com

Free to qualified subscribers; $30.00/year for
individuals. Magazine covering issues, programs, and projects in industrial education,
technology education, trade and industry,
and vocational-technical career education.
Articles are geared for teacher and administrator use and reference from elementary
school through postsecondary levels.

★3480★ Today's OEA

Oregon Education Association
6900 SW Atlanta St.
Portland, OR 97223-2513
Ph: (503)684-3300   Fax: (503)684-8063

Bimonthly. Free to qualified subscribers;
$10.00/year for nonmembers. Membership
magazine covering educational issues statewide and nationally.

★3481★ Women in Higher Education

Wenniger Co.
1934 Monroe St.
Madison, WI 53711-2027
Ph: (608)251-3232   Fax: (608)284-0601
E-mail: women@wihe.com
URL: http://www.wihe.com

Description: Monthly. Focuses on leadership, career strategies, gender equity, and
harassment of women administrators. Recurring features include interviews, news of
research, reports of meetings and presentations, news of educational opportunities, job
listings, book reviews, notices of publications
available, columns titled Profile, Research
Briefs, Newswatch, What Should She Do?,
Moveable Type, and The Last Laugh.

PLACEMENT AND JOB REFERRAL SERVICES

★3482★ American Association of Christian Schools (AACS)
PO Box 1097
Independence, MO 64051-0597
Ph: (816)252-9900   Fax: (816)252-6700
E-mail: national@aacs.org
URL: http://www.aacs.org

Description: Maintains teacher/administrator certification program and placement service. Participates in school accreditation program. Sponsors National Academic Tournament. Maintains American Christian Honor Society. Compiles statistics; maintains speakers' bureau and placement service.

★3483★ American Association of School Administrators (AASA)
801 N Moore St., Ste. 700
Arlington, VA 22203
Ph: (703)875-0748   Fax: (703)841-1543
E-mail: info@aasa.org
URL: http://www.aasa.org

Description: Professional association of administrators and executives of school systems and educational service agencies; school district superintendents; central, building, and service unit administrators; presidents of colleges, deans, and professors of educational administration; placement officers; executive directors and administrators of education associations. Sponsors numerous professional development conferences annually.

★3484★ American College Personnel Association (ACPA)
1 Dupont Cir. NW, Ste. 300
Washington, DC 20036-1188
Ph: (202)835-2272   Fax: (202)296-3286
E-mail: info@acpa.nche.edu
URL: http://www.acpa.nche.edu

Description: Individuals employed in higher education and involved in student personnel work, including administration, counseling, research, and teaching. Fosters student development in higher education in areas of service, advocacy, and standards by offering professional programs for educators committed to the overall development of post-secondary students. Sponsors professional and educational activities in cooperation with other organizations. Offers placement services.

★3485★ American Education Finance Association (AEFA)
8365 Armadillo Tr.
Evergreen, CO 80439
Ph: (303)674-0857   Fax: (303)670-8986
E-mail: esteinbre@du.edu
URL: http://www.aefa.cc

Members: State and national teacher organizations, university personnel, school administrators, state educational agency personnel, legislators and legislative staff, federal agency personnel, and interested foundations and students. **Purpose:** Facilitates communication among groups and individuals in the field of educational finance including academicians, researchers, and policymakers. Main interests include traditional school finance concepts, public policy issues, and the review and debate of emerging issues of educational finance. **Activities:** Conducts workshop. Compiles statistics. Maintains placement service.

★3486★ Association of College and University Housing Officers International (ACUHO-I)
941 Chatham Lane, Ste. 318
Columbus, OH 43221-2416
Ph: (614)292-0099   Fax: (614)292-3205
E-mail: web@acuho-i.org
URL: http://www.acuho.ohio-state.edu/

Description: Officials of educational institutions in 11 countries concerned with all aspects of student housing and food service operation. Supports and conducts research. Organizes seminars and workshops. Offers internships. Maintains biographical archives; offers placement service. Compiles statistics.

★3487★ Association of Southern Baptist Colleges and Schools (ASBCS)
PO Box 11655
Jackson, TN 38308-0127
Ph: (731)660-3497   Fax: (731)664-6459
E-mail: bob_agee@baptistschools.org
URL: http://www.baptistschools.org

Members: Southern Baptist senior colleges, universities, junior colleges, academies, and Bible schools. **Purpose:** Promotes Christian education through literature, faculty workshops, student recruitment, teacher placement, trustee orientation, statistical information, and other assistance to members.

★3488★ College Media Advisers (CMA)
University of Memphis
MJ-300
Memphis, TN 38152-6661
Ph: (901)678-2403   Fax: (901)678-4798
E-mail: rsplbrgn@memphis.edu
URL: http://www.collegemedia.org

Members: Professional association serving advisers, directors, and chairmen of boards of college student media (newspapers, yearbooks, magazines, handbooks, directories, and radio and television stations); heads of schools and departments of journalism; and others interested in junior college, college, and university student media. **Purpose:** Serves as clearinghouse for student media; acts as consultant on student theses and dissertations on publications. Encourages high school journalism and examines its relationships to college and professional journalism. **Activities:** Conducts national survey of student media in rotation each year by type: newspapers, magazines, and yearbooks; radio and television stations. Compiles statistics. Maintains placement service and speakers' bureau.

★3489★ Council of Educational Facility Planners, International (CEFPI)
9180 E Desert Cove Dr., No. 104
Scottsdale, AZ 85260-6231
Ph: (480)391-0840   Fax: (480)391-0940
E-mail: contact@cefpi.org
URL: http://www.cefpi.com

Members: Individuals and firms who are responsible for planning, designing, creating, maintaining, and equipping the physical environment of education. **Purpose:** Sponsors an exchange of information, professional experiences, best practices research results, and other investigative techniques concerning educational facility planning. **Activities:** Include publication and review of current and emerging practices in educational facility planning; identification and execution of needed research; development of professional training programs; strengthening of planning services on various levels of government and in institutions of higher learning; leadership in the development of higher standards for facility design and the physical environment of education. Operates speakers' bureau; sponsors placement service; compiles statistics.

★3490★ Council for Jewish Education (CJE)
11 Olympia Ln.
Monsey, NY 10952
Ph: (845)368-8657   Fax: (845)369-6538
E-mail: mjscje@aol.com

Description: Teachers of Hebrew in universities; heads of Bureaus of Jewish Education and their administrative departments; faculty members of Jewish teacher training schools. Seeks to: further the cause of Jewish education in America; raise professional standards and practices; promote the welfare and growth of Jewish educational workers; improve and strengthen Jewish life. Conducts educational programs; cosponsors a Personnel Placement Committee with Jewish Education Service of North America.

★3491★ International Educator's Institute (TIE)
PO Box 513
Cummaquid, MA 02637
Ph: (508)362-1414   Fax: (508)362-1411
Fr: 877-375-6668
E-mail: tie@tieonline.com
URL: http://www.tieonline.com

Description: Facilitates the placement of teachers and administrators in American, British, and international schools. Seeks to create a network that provides for professional development opportunities and improved financial security of members. Offers advice and information on international school news, recent educational developments, job placement, and investment, consumer, and professional development opportunities. Makes available insurance and travel benefits. Operates International Schools Internship Program.

★3492★ Jesuit Association of Student Personnel Administrators (JASPA)

1 DuPont Cir., Ste. 405
Washington, DC 20036
Ph: (202)862-9893   Fax: (202)862-8523
E-mail: treynold@regis.edu
URL: http://jaspa.creighton.edu

Description: Administrators of student personnel programs in 28 Jesuit colleges and universities in the United States. Sponsors institutes and seminars for personnel in Jesuit colleges. Bestows Rev. Victor R. Yanitelli Award; compiles statistics. Cooperates with Catholic and non-Catholic educational associations in various projects. Maintains placement service; conducts workshops. Operates organizational archives; compiles statistics.

★3493★ Jewish Educators Assembly (JEA)

300 Forest Dr.
East Hills, NY 11548
Ph: (516)484-9585   Fax: (516)484-9586
E-mail: jewisheducators@aol.com
URL: http://www.jewisheducators.org/

Members: Educational and supervisory personnel serving Jewish educational institutions. **Purpose:** Seeks to advance the development of Jewish education in the congregation on all levels in consonance with the philosophy of the Conservative Movement; cooperate with the United Synagogue of America Commission on Jewish Education as the policy-making body of the educational enterprise; join in cooperative effort with other Jewish educational institutions and organizations; establish and maintain professional standards for Jewish educators; serve as a forum for the exchange of ideas; promote the values of Jewish education as a basis for the creative continuity of the Jewish people. **Activities:** Maintains placement service and speakers' bureau.

★3494★ National Academic Advising Association (NACADA)

Kansas State Univ.
2323 Anderson Ave., Ste. 225
Manhattan, KS 66502
Ph: (785)532-5717   Fax: (785)532-7732
E-mail: nacada@ksu.edu
URL: http://www.nacada.ksu.edu

Members: Academic program advisors, faculty, administrators, counselors, and others concerned with the intellectual, personal, and career development of students in all types of postsecondary educational institutions. **Purpose:** Dedicated to the support and professional growth of academic advising and academic advisers. Provides a forum for discussion, debate, and exchange of ideas regarding academic advising. Serves as advocate for standards and quality programs in academic advising. **Activities:** Operates consultants bureau to assist advising services on college campuses. Maintains placement service, speakers' bureau, and information clearinghouse. Maintains placement service, speakers' bureau, and information clearinghouse.

★3495★ National Alliance of Black School Educators (NABSE)

310 Pennsylvania Ave. SE
Washington, DC 20003
Ph: (202)608-6310   Fax: (202)608-6319
Fr: 800-221-2654
E-mail: nabse@nabse.org
URL: http://www.nabse.org

Description: Black educators from all levels; others indirectly involved in the education of black youth. Purpose is to promote awareness, professional expertise, and commitment among black educators. Goals are to: eliminate and rectify the results of racism in education; work with state, local, and national leaders to raise the academic achievement level of all black students; increase members' involvement in legislative activities; facilitate the introduction of a curriculum that more completely embraces black America; improve the ability of black educators to promote problem resolution; create a meaningful and effective network of strength, talent, and professional support. Sponsors workshops, commission meetings, and special projects. Encourages research, especially as it relates to blacks, and the presentation of papers during national conferences. Plans to establish a National Black Educators Data Bank and offer placement service.

★3496★ National Association of Teachers' Agencies (NATA)

797 Kings Hwy.
Fairfield, CT 06432
Ph: (203)333-0611   Fax: (203)334-7224
E-mail: info@jobsforteachers.com
URL: http://www.jobsforteachers.com

Description: Private employment agencies engaged primarily in the placement of teaching and administration personnel. Works to standardize records and promote a strong ethical sense in the placement field. Maintains speakers' bureau.

★3497★ National Association of Temple Educators (NATE)

633 Third Ave. 7th Fl.
New York, NY 10017-6778
Ph: (212)452-6510   Fax: (212)452-6512
E-mail: nateoff@aol.com
URL: http://rj.org/nate/

Members: Directors of education in Reform Jewish religious schools, principals, heads of departments, supervisors, educational consultants, students, and authors. **Purpose:** Purposes are to: assist in the growth and development of Jewish religious education consistent with the aims of Reform Judaism; stimulate communal interest in Jewish religious education; represent and encourage the profession of temple educator. **Activities:** Conducts surveys on personnel practices, confirmation practices, religious school organization and administration, curricular practices, and other aspects of religious education. Sponsors institutes for principals and educational directors; maintains placement service.

★3498★ National Council of Secondary School Athletic Directors (NCSSAD)

1900 Association Dr.
Reston, VA 20191-1598
Ph: (703)476-3410   Fax: (703)476-8316
Fr: 800-213-7193
E-mail: naspe@aahperd.org
URL: http://www.aahperd.org/naspe

Description: A council of the National Association for Sport and Physical Education, which is a division of the American Alliance for Health, Physical Education, Recreation and Dance. Professional athletic directors in secondary schools. Purposes are to improve the educational aspects of interscholastic athletics; to provide for an exchange of ideas; to establish closer working relationships with related professional groups and promote greater unity; to establish and implement standards for the professional preparation of secondary school athletic directors. Provides in-service training programs. Maintains placement service and speakers' bureau. speakers' bureau. speakers' bureau.

★3499★ School Management Study Group (SMSG)

4948 Rebecca Dr.
Pocatello, ID 83202-1666
Fax: (208)232-2928
E-mail: agdavi@smsg.com

Members: School administrative bodies and college personnel **Purpose:** seeking to improve schools and to involve educators in critical school problems. **Activities:** Offers services for continuing education of professional staff; sponsors seminars and training programs. Areas of interest include integration, policy development, conflict management, evaluation, shared governance, and others, most involving change. Maintains speakers' bureau; conducts research programs; compiles statistics. Operates placement services and hall of fame.

★3500★ Solomon Schecher Day School Association (SSDSA)

155 5th Ave.
New York, NY 10010-6802
Ph: (212)533-7800   Fax: (212)353-9439
E-mail: info@uscj.org
URL: http://www.uscj.org

Description: A division of the United Synagogue of Conservative Judaism Commission on Jewish Education. Jewish elementary day schools and high schools with a total of over 21,500 students. Named for Solomon Schecher (1850-1915), scholar of Talmud and rabbinical literature at Cambridge and founder of the United Synagogue of America and the Jewish Theological Seminary. Provides visitations and consultations regarding education, governance and administration; publication of advisories and position papers, biennial conferences for lay leaders, annual conferences of the principals council, Shibboley Schechter newsletter, listserves for presidents, School heads, Business managers, and development directors. Also provides dissemination of demographics and statistics, chartering and accreditation of schools, seminars and board training for lay leaders, Schechter website, SHAR"R, 7th and 8th grade trips to Israel, placement service, MaToK-TaNaKH curriculum development project for Solomon Schecter Day schools, residency fellowship program to prepare professional leadership (SREL) and a listing of consultants.

★3501★ University Council for Educational Administration (UCEA)

University of MO/Columbia
205 Hill Hall
Columbia, MO 65211-2185
Ph: (573)884-8300   Fax: (573)884-8302
E-mail: execucea@coe.missouri.edu
URL: http://www.ucea.org

Members: Consortium of departments of educational administration in universities. **Purpose:** Promotes and disseminates information on the improvement of pre-service and in-service training of school and higher education administrators. **Activities:** Conducts research and development in educational administration through interuniversity cooperation. Operates placement service.

EMPLOYER DIRECTORIES AND NETWORKING LISTS

★3502★ Accredited Institutions of Postsecondary Education

Oryx Press
1434 E San Miguel Ave.
Phoenix, AZ 85014-2422
Fr: 800-225-5800

Annual, May. $59.95. Covers more than 5,500 accredited institutions and programs of postsecondary education in the United States and U.S.-chartered schools in 14 countries. Entries include: Institution name, address, phone, whether public or private, any religious affiliation, type of institution and student body, branch campuses or affiliated institutions, date of first accreditation and latest reaffirmation of accrediting body, accredited programs in professional fields, level of degrees offered, name of chief executive officer, size and composition of enrollment, type of academic calendar. Arrangement: Geographical. Indexes: Institution.

★3503★ American Universities and Colleges

Walter de Gruyter Inc.
200 Saw Mill River Rd.
Hawthorne, NY 10532
Ph: (914)747-0110   Fax: (914)747-1326
URL: http://www.degruyter.com/rs/

Quadrennial, latest edition 16, 2001. $298.00. Covers over 1,900 accredited four-year and graduate colleges and universities. Includes a list of statewide coordinating boards of higher education. Entries include: For schools-Name, address, history, governing board, calendar, freshmen and general

student body characteristics, distinctive programs, student life, whether it has a reserve officers training corps (ROTC), graduate work, degrees conferred, fees, student financial aid, departments and teaching staff, enrollment, foreign students, publications, library, finances, buildings and grounds, administration; separate descriptions of each major division within a university. For boards-Name, address, name of director. Arrangement: Geographical. Indexes: Institution name, general.

★3504★ Boarding Schools Directory

The Association of Boarding Schools
4455 Connecticut Ave., Ste. A200
Washington, DC 20008
Ph: (202)966-8705   Fax: (202)966-8708
Fr: 800-541-5908
URL: http://www.schools.com

Annual, August. Covers boarding schools that are members of the Association of Boarding Schools. Entries include: School name, address, phone, e-mail and url's, grades for which boarding students are accepted, enrollment, brief description. Arrangement: Classified by type of school. Indexes: Geographical; program; Alphabetical.

★3505★ Christian Schools International-Directory

Christian Schools International
3350 E Paris Ave. SE
Grand Rapids, MI 49512-3054
Ph: (616)957-1070   Fax: (616)957-5022
Fr: 800-635-8288
URL: http://www.gospelcom.net/csi

Annual, November. $52.00 for nonmembers. Covers nearly 450 Reformed Christian elementary and secondary schools; related associations; societies without schools. Entries include: For schools-School name, address, phone; name, title, and address of officers; names of faculty members. Arrangement: Geographical.

★3506★ College and University Professional Association-Membership Directory

College and University Professional Association for Human Resources
Tyson Pl.
2607 Kingston Pk., Ste. 250
Knoxville, TN 37919
Ph: (865)637-7673   Fax: (865)637-7674
E-mail: arothstein@cupahr.org
URL: http://cupahr.org/membersonly.html

Online continually updated; access restricted to members. $150.00. Covers more than 7,000 members interested in college and university human resource administration; over 1,700 institutions. Entries include: For members-Personal name, title, affiliation, address, fax, e-mail, phone. For institutions-Organization name, address, phone, and names/titles of representatives. Arrangement: Members are alphabetical; institutions are geographical.

★3507★ Directory of Education Agencies

Council of Chief State School Officers
1 Massachusetts Ave., NW, Ste. 700
Washington, DC 20001-1431
Ph: (202)336-7000   Fax: (202)408-8072

Annual. $22.00. Covers about 1,500 top officers of federal, state, and territorial education agencies responsible at that level for administration of elementary, secondary, and vocational/technical education. Entries include: Department or agency name, address, phone, names and phone numbers of superintendent or commissioner and principal staff members. Arrangement: Geographical. Indexes: Personal name.

★3508★ Directory of Public Elementary and Secondary Education Agencies

National Center for Education Statistics
1990 K St., NW
Washington, DC 20006
Ph: (202)502-7300   Fr: 800-424-1616

Annual. $22.00. Covers about 17,000 local education agencies in the United States, the District of Columbia, and five territories which operate their own schools or pay tuition to other local education agencies. Also lists intermediate education agencies. Entries include: Agency name, address, phone, county, description of district, grade span, membership, special education students, metropolitan status, number of high school graduates, teachers, and schools. Also available from Superintendent of Documents, U.S. Government Printing Office. Arrangement: Geographical, then by type of agency.

★3509★ Directory of Public School Systems in the U.S.

American Association for Employment in Education
3040 Riverside Dr., Ste. 125
Columbus, OH 43221
Ph: (614)485-1111   Fax: (614)485-9609

Annual, Winter. $80.00. Covers about 14,500 public school systems in the United States and their administrative personnel. Entries include: System name, address, phone, website address, name and title of personnel administrator, levels taught and approx. student population. Arrangement: Geographical by state.

★3510★ Directory: Who's Who in Career Services & HR/Staffing

National Association of Colleges and Employers
62 Highland Ave.
Bethlehem, PA 18017
Ph: (610)868-1421   Fax: (610)868-0208
Fr: 800-544-5272
URL: http://www.jobweb.org/

Annual, latest edition January 1999. $47.95. Covers about 1,760 college and university offices concerned with securing employment for graduates and about 1,430 companies with staff assigned to recruiting and hiring college graduates. Entries include: For colleges-College name and address; names, titles, phone, fax, and URL and e-mail addresses of career planning and placement personnel; interview dates for undergraduates and graduates; months of graduation; whether alumni placement is also handled, student enrollment (including minority data), and dates of career/job fairs. For employers-Company name; names, addresses, phone, fax and e-mail addresses of recruitment staff; names of secondary contacts; nature of business; number of employees. Arrangement: Colleges are geographical; employers are alphabetical. Indexes: Institutional name, personal name (college personnel); geographical, personal name (in company recruitment).

★3511★ *Educational Leadership: A Reference Handbook*

ABC-CLIO
130 Cremona Dr.
Santa Barbara, CA 93117
Ph: (805)968-1911   Fax: (805)685-9685
Fr: 800-368-6868

$45.00. Publication includes: Directory of organizations, institutes, associations, government agencies, and leadership academies. Principal content of publication is a discussion of educational leadership styles and applications. Indexes: Alphabetical.

★3512★ *Employment Opportunities, USA*

Washington Research Associates
1090 Vermont Ave., NW, Ste. 800
Washington, DC 20005
Ph: (202)408-7025

Annual, quarterly updates. $184.00. Publication includes: List of over 1,000 employment contacts in companies and agencies in the banking, arts, telecommunications, education, and 14 other industries and professions, including the federal government. Entries include: Company name, name of representative, address, description of products or services, hiring and recruiting practices, training programs, and year established. Principal content is industry overviews, career news, employment opportunity information on 14 different job markets, and comprehensive guidance to career resources on the Internet. Arrangement: Classified by industry. Indexes: Occupation.

★3513★ *Encyclopedia of Education*

Macmillan/McGraw-Hill
2 Penn Plz.
New York, NY 10121
Ph: (212)904-6749   Fax: (212)904-6637

$850.00. Publication includes: List of assessment and achievement tests with contact information; list of state departments of education; list of Internet resources. Principal content of publication is a variety of topics within the field of education including policy, curriculum, learning, assessment, legislation, history, and standards. Indexes: Alphabetical.

★3514★ *Fifty State Educational Directories*

Career Guidance Foundation
8090 Engineer Rd., Ste. B
San Diego, CA 92111
Ph: (858)560-8051   Fax: (858)278-8960
Fr: 800-854-2670
URL: http://www.cgf.org

Annual, latest edition June 1996. $89.00. Microfiche. Collection consists of reproductions of the state educational directories published by the departments of education of individual 50 states. Directory contents vary, but the majority contain listings of elementary and secondary schools, colleges and universities, and state education officials. Amount of detail in each also varies. Entries include: Usually, institution name, address, and name of one executive.

★3515★ *Ganley's Catholic Schools in America-Elementary/Secondary/College & University*

Fisher Publishing Co.
PO Box 15070
Scottsdale, AZ 85267
Ph: (480)657-9422   Fax: (480)657-9422
Fr: 800-759-7615
URL: http://www.ganleyscatholicschools.com

Annual, summer; latest edition 2003. $51.50. Covers over 8,400 Catholic K-12 Schools. Arrangement: Geographical by state, then alphabetical by Diocese name.

★3516★ *Guide to Technical, Trade, & Business Schools*

Riverside Publishing/Wintergreen Orchard House
425 Springlake Dr.
Itasca, IL 60143-2079
Ph: (630)467-7000   Fax: (630)467-7192
Fr: 800-323-9540

Biennial, even years. $170.00 for national edition; $50.00 for regional edition. Covers over 3,800 accredited public and proprietary post-secondary schools offering programs in auto mechanics, aviation, business, electronics, and other technical, trade, or business fields. Available in a four-volume national edition or as four regional editions. Entries include: School name, address, phone, accrediting body, admissions contact, course offerings, placement services, and profile. Arrangement: Geographical. Indexes: Subject, special programs, sports, professional accreditations.

★3517★ *Handbook of Private Schools*

Porter Sargent Publishers Inc.
11 Beacon St., Ste. 1400
Boston, MA 02108-3099
Ph: (617)523-1670   Fax: (617)523-1021
Fr: 800-342-7470
E-mail: orders@portersargent.com

Annual, June. $99.00. Covers more than 1,600 elementary and secondary boarding and day schools in the United States. Entries include: School name, address, phone, fax, E-mail, URL, type of school (boarding or

day), sex and age range, names and titles of administrators, grades offered, academic orientation, curriculum, new admissions yearly, tests required for admission, enrollment and faculty, graduate record, number of alumni, tuition and scholarship figures, summer session, plant evaluation and endowment, date of establishment, calendar, association membership, description of school's offerings and history, test score averages, uniform requirements, geographical, and demographic date. Arrangement: Geographical. Indexes: Alphabetical by school name, cross indexed by state, region, grade range, sexes accepted, school features and enrollment.

★3518★ *Independent School Guide for Washington DC and Surrounding Area*

Lift Hill Press Inc.
4930-A Eisenhower Ave.
Alexandria, VA 22304
Ph: (703)212-9113   Fax: (703)212-9114
Fr: 800-699-9113
URL: http://www.washingtonbk.com

Biennial. $15.95. Covers over 475 independent schools (including parochial schools) in the Washington, DC area, including Maryland and Virginia. Entries include: School name, address, phone, name and title of contact, number of faculty, geographical area served, tuition, courses, admission procedures, summer programs, LD/ED programs, scholarships available. Arrangement: Alphabetical. Indexes: Geographical.

★3519★ *Independent Schools Association of the Southwest-Membership List*

Independent Schools Association of the Southwest
4700 Bryant Irvin Ct., Ste. 204
Fort Worth, TX 76107
Ph: (817)569-9200   Fax: (817)569-9103
Fr: 800-688-5007
URL: http://www.isasw.org

Annual, August. Covers over 75 independent elementary and secondary schools accredited by the association. Entries include: School name, address, phone, chief administrative officer, structure, and enrollment. Arrangement: Geographical. Indexes: Alphabetical.

★3520★ *MDR's School Directories*

Market Data Retrieval
1 Forest Pkwy.
Shelton, CT 06484
Ph: (203)926-4800   Fax: (203)926-1826
Fr: 800-333-8802
URL: http://www.schooldata.com

Annual, October. $1,349.00 for set. Covers over 90,000 public, 8,000 Catholic, and 15,000 other private schools (grades K-12) in the United States; over 15,000 school district offices, and 76,000 school librarians; and 27,000 media specialists, 33,000 technology coordinators. Includes names of over 165,000 school district administrators and staff members in county and state education administration. Entries include: For districts:

District name and address; telephone and fax number; number of schools; number of teachers in the district; district enrollment; special Ed students; limited-english proficient students; minority percentage by race, college bound students; expenditures per student for instructional materials; poverty level; title 1 dollars; site-based management; district open/close dates; construction indicator; technologies and quantities (instructional computer brands, multimedia computers; networks, VCRs, satellite dish, DVD Player/Drive High-Speed Internet Access URL); district-level adminstrators, *new superintendents shaded*. For schools: School name and address-new public shaded; telephone and fax number; principal new principal shaded; librarian, media specialist and technology coordinator; grade span; special programs and school type; student enrollment; technologies and quantities (instructional computer brand noting predominant brand); Multi-Media Computers; internet connection or access; Tech Sophistication Index. Arrangement: Geographical. Indexes: District County; District Personnel; Principal; New Public Schools and Key Personnel; District and School Telephone; District URLs.

★3521★ **National Association of College Deans, Registrars and Admissions Officers-Directory**

National Association of College Deans, Registrars and Admissions Officers
Albany State University
Albany, GA 31705
Ph: (912)430-4638   Fax: (912)430-2953

Annual, February. $10.00. Covers about 325 member deans, registrars, and admissions officers at nearly 90 predominantly Black schools. Entries include: Institution name, address, phone, names and titles of key personnel, enrollment, whether a public or private institution. Arrangement: Alphabetical.

★3522★ **National Association of College and University Business Officers-Membership Directory**

National Association of College and University Business Officers
2501 M St. NW, Ste. 400
Washington, DC 20037
Ph: (202)861-2500   Fax: (202)861-2583
URL: http://www.nacubo.org

Annual, winter. $500.00 for nonmembers; $49.00 for members. Number of listings: 2,800 institutions; 22,00 people. Entries include: Name of institution, address, names of primary representatives. Arrangement: Alphabetical and regional.

★3523★ **National Association of Teachers' Agencies-Membership Directory**

National Association of Teachers' Agencies
797 Kings Hwy.
Fairfield, CT 06432
Ph: (203)333-0611   Fax: (203)334-7224

URL: http://www.jobsforteachers.com

Annual, January. Covers approximately 20 private employment agencies engaged primarily in the placement of teaching and administrative personnel in education. Entries include: Name, address, phone, names of key officials. Arrangement: Alphabetical.

★3524★ **National Directory of Alternative Schools**

National Coalition of Alternative Community Schools
1289 Jewett St.
Ann Arbor, MI 48104-6201
Ph: (734)668-9171   Fax: (734)769-9629
Fr: 888-771-9171

Biennial, odd years. $18.00. Covers over 500 alternative education programs, including home schools, and state and regional coalitions of alternative schools and colleges; also lists organizations and networks offering services and resources to those working with children; international coverage. Entries include: Name, address, phone, name of contact; many also include descriptions of programs. Arrangement: Schools are geographical. Indexes: Complete index of entries.

★3525★ **National Directory for Employment in Education**

American Association for Employment in Education
3040 Riverside Dr., Ste. 125
Columbus, OH 43221
Ph: (614)485-1111   Fax: (614)485-9609

Annual, Winter. $20.00 for institutions. Covers about 600 placement offices maintained by teacher-training institutions and 300 school district personnel officers and/or superintendents responsible for hiring profesional staff. Entries include: Institution name, address, phone, contact name, email address, and website. Arrangement: Geographical. Indexes: Personal name, subject-field of teacher training, institutions which provide vacancy bulletins and placement services to non-enrolled students.

★3526★ **National School Public Relations Association-Directory**

National School Public Relations Association
15948 Derwood Rd.
Rockville, MD 20855-2123
Ph: (301)519-0496   Fax: (301)519-0494

Annual, January. Covers approximately 2,000 school system public relations directors, school administrators, principals, and others who are members of the National School Public Relations Association. Entries include: Name, affiliation, address, phone. Arrangement: Geographical.

★3527★ **Opportunities Abroad for Educators**

Fulbright Teacher and Administrator Exchange Program
600 Maryland Ave. SW, Ste. 320
Washington, DC 20024-2520
Ph: (202)314-3527   Fax: (202)479-6806
Fr: 800-726-0479
URL: http://www.fulbrightexchanges.org

Annual. Covers opportunities available for elementary and secondary teachers, and two year college instructors, and school administrators to attend seminars or to teach abroad under the Mutual Educational and Cultural Exchange Act of 1961. Entries include: Countries of placement, dates, eligibility requirements, teaching assignments. Arrangement: Geographical.

★3528★ **Patterson's American Education**

Educational Directories Inc.
PO Box 68097
Schaumburg, IL 60168-0097
Ph: (847)891-1250   Fax: (847)891-0945
Fr: 800-357-6183
URL: http://www.ediusa.com

Annual, October; latest edition 2002. $87.00. Covers over 11,400 school districts in the United States; more than 34,000 public, private, and Catholic high schools, middle schools, and junior high schools; approximately 300 parochial superintendents; 400 state department of education personnel. Entries include: For school districts and schools-District and superintendent name, address, phone, fax, grade ranges, enrollment , school names, addresses, phone numbers, grade ranges, enrollment, names of principals. For postsecondary schools-School name, address, phone number, URL, e-mail, names of administrator or director of admissions. For private and Catholic high schools-Name, address, phone, fax, enrollment, grades offered, name of principal. Postsecondary institutions are covered in 'Patterson's Schools Classified'. Arrangement: Geographical by state, then alphabetical by city.

★3529★ **Patterson's Schools Classified**

Educational Directories Inc.
PO Box 68097
Schaumburg, IL 60168-0097
Ph: (847)891-1250   Fax: (847)891-0945
Fr: 800-357-6183
URL: http://www.ediusa.com

Annual, April. $15.00. Covers over 7,000 accredited colleges, universities, community colleges, junior colleges, career schools and teaching hospitals. Entries include: School name, address, phone, URL, e-mail, name of administrator or admissions officer, description, professional accreditation (where applicable). Updated from previous year's edition of 'Patterson's American Education'. Arrangement: Classified by area of study, then geographical by state. Indexes: Alphabetical by name.

★3530★ *Private Independent Schools*

Bunting and Lyon Inc.
238 N Main St.
Wallingford, CT 06492
Ph: (203)269-3333   Fax: (203)269-5697
URL: http://www.buntingandlyon.com

Annual, February. $110.00. Covers 1,200 English-speaking elementary and secondary private schools and summer programs in North America and abroad. Entries include: School name, address, phone, fax, e-mail, website, enrollment, tuition and other fees, financial aid information, administrator's name and educational background, director of admission, regional accreditation, description of programs, curriculum, activities, learning differences grid. Arrangement: Geographical. Indexes: School name; geographical. Summer programs, general classification grid, learning differences reference grid.

★3531★ *Requirements for Certification of Teachers, Counselors, Librarians, Administrators for Elementary and Secondary Schools*

University of Chicago Press
Journals Division
PO Box 37005
Chicago, IL 60637
Ph: (773)753-3347   Fax: (773)753-0811
Fr: 877-705-1878

Annual, June. $44.00. Publication includes: List of state and local departments of education. Entries include: Office name, address, phone. Principal content of publication is summaries of each state's teaching and administrative certification requirements. Arrangement: Geographical.

★3532★ *School Guide*

School Guide Publications
210 N Ave.
New Rochelle, NY 10801
Ph: (914)632-7771   Fax: (914)632-3412
Fr: 800-433-7771
URL: http://www.schoolguides.com

Annual, September. $10.00. Covers over 3,000 colleges, vocational schools, and nursing schools in the United States. Entries include: Institution name, address, phone, courses offered, degrees awarded. Arrangement: Classified by type of institution, then geographical. Indexes: Subject.

★3533★ *Understanding Educational Reform: A Reference Handbook*

ABC-CLIO
130 Cremona Dr.
Santa Barbara, CA 93117
Ph: (805)968-1911   Fax: (805)685-9685
Fr: 800-368-6868

$45.00. Publication includes: List of print and nonprint resources with Web site information regarding educational reform. Principal content of publication is a discussion of a variety of aspects of educational reform including history, politics, and resistance to it.

HANDBOOKS AND MANUALS

★3534★ *Career Information Center*

Macmillan Publishing Co. Inc.
200 Old Tappan Rd.
Old Tappan, NJ 07675
Fr: 800-428-5331

Visual Education Center Staff. Seventh edition, 1999. $275.00. 2080 pages. This 13-volume set profiles over 600 occupations. Each occupational profile describes job duties, educational requirements, how to get the job, advancement possibilities, employment outlook, working conditions, earnings and benefits, and where to write for more information.

★3535★ *Careers in Education*

McGraw-Hill Professional
2 Penn Plaza
New York, NY 10121-2298
Ph: (212)904-2000   Fr: 800-722-4726

Roy A. Edelfelt, Alan Reiman. Fourth edition. $14.95. E-book, netLibrary.

★3536★ *Careers in Focus: Family and Consumer Sciences; Education and Communication, Science and Technology, Human Services, Business, Art*

Goodheart-Wilcox Publisher
18604 W. Creek Dr.
Tinley Park, IL 60477-6243
Ph: (708)687-5000   Fax: 888-409-3900
Fr: 888-409-3900

Lee Jackson. September 2003. $45.00. Illustrated. 399 pages.

★3537★ *Educator's Job Search: The Ultimate Guide to Finding Positions in Education*

National Education Association
PO Box 2035
Annapolis Junction, MD 20701
Fr: 800-229-4200

Martin Kimeldorf. 1993. $15.95 (paper). 88 pages.

★3538★ *How to Get a Job in Education*

Adams Media Corp.
57 Littlefield St.
Avon, MA 02322
Ph: (508)427-7100   Fax: (508)427-6790
Fr: 800-872-5627
URL: http://www.adamsmedia.com

Joel Levin. Second edition, 1995. $15.95. 320 pages. Out of print. Prepared for recent college graduates, seasoned educators, and career-changing professionals, this publication guides the job-seeker through the necessary steps to obtaining a job in education at the elementary, secondary, and university levels. Offers advice on how to prepare for state and local examinations, how to locate teaching opportunities nationwide, and how

to obtain certification. Includes a nationwide salary survey. Covers public, private, summer, and overseas opportunities.

★3539★ *Non-Profits and Education Job Finder*

Planning Communications
7215 Oak Ave.
River Forest, IL 60305-1935
Ph: (708)366-5200   Fax: (708)366-5280
Fr: 888-366-5200
URL: http://jobfindersonline.com

Daniel Lauber. 1997. $32.95; $16.95 (paper). 336 pages. Covers 1600 sources. Discusses how to use sources of non-profit sector job vacancies in a number of specialties and state-by-state, including job-matching services, job hotlines, specialty periodicals with job ads, salary surveys, and directories. Covers a variety of fields from education to religion. Includes chapters on resume and cover letter preparation and interviewing.

★3540★ *Opportunities in State and Local Government Careers*

Vgm Career Horizons
1221 Avenue of the Americas
New York, NY 10020
Ph: (212)904-2000   Fr: 800-323-4900
E-mail: ntcpub@tribune.com

Neale J. Baxter. 1994. $14.95; $10.95 (paper). 160 pages. Points out the incentives and drawbacks of a government career. Describes hiring procedures and provides tips on filling out applications, taking physical and aptitude tests, handling interviews, and finding jobs. Describes the jobs in which 75% of all state and local government workers are employed. For each occupation, covers the nature of the work and the training required.

★3541★ *Real People Working in Education*

McGraw-Hill Contemporary Books
1221 Avenue of the Americas
New York, NY 10020
Ph: (212)904-2000   Fr: 800-323-4900
E-mail: ntcpub@tribune.com

Blythe Camenson, Jan Goldberg. 1997. $17.95; $12.95 (paper). Interviews and profiles of working professionals capture a range of opportunities in this field.

★3542★ *Where the Jobs Are: The Hottest Careers for the 90s*

The Career Press, Inc.
3 Tice Rd.
PO Box 687
Franklin Lakes, NJ 07417-1322
Ph: (201)848-0310   Fax: (201)848-1727
Fr: 800-227-3371

Joyce Hadley. Third edition, 2000. $13.99 (paper). 400 pages. Out of print. Describes careers in fifteen general fields, from accounting to travel and hospitality.

★3543★ Who Is Leading Our Schools?: An Overview of School Administrators and their Careers

Rand Corporation
1700 Main St.
Santa Monica, CA 90407-2138
Ph: (310)393-0411   Fax: (310)451-6996

Katherine Chung, Karen Ross. June 2003. $28.50. Illustrated. 258 pages.

EMPLOYMENT AGENCIES AND SEARCH FIRMS

★3544★ Auerbach Associates Inc.

65 Franklin St., Ste. 400
Boston, MA 02110
Ph: (617)451-0095   Fax: (617)451-5199

Executive search firm focused on non-profit and higher education industries.

★3545★ Berardi & Associates

1140 Avenue of the Americas, Fl. 8
New York, NY 10036
Ph: (212)403-6180   Fax: (212)764-9690

Executive search firm.

★3546★ Educational Placement Service

1001 Craig Rd., Ste. 170
St. Louis, MO 63146
Ph: (314)991-5855   Fax: (314)991-5295
URL: http://www.educatorjobs.com

Employment agency. Focuses on teaching, administrative, and education-related openings.

★3547★ Norman Roberts & Associates Inc.

1800 Century Park E, Ste. 430
Los Angeles, CA 90067-1507
Ph: (310)552-1112   Fax: (310)552-1113

Specializes in nationwide recruitments for: public sector, not-for-profit, transportation, utilities, engineering, healthcare and education. Recruits in all functional areas within these industries. Over 25 years of executive search experience.

★3548★ Perez-Arton Consultants Inc.

23 Spring St., Ste. 304
Ossining, NY 10562
Ph: (914)762-2100

Executive searches for major academic/administrative units. Conducts institutional evaluations and executive staff assessments. Firm works for colleges, universities and educationally related non-profits only.

★3549★ R.H. Perry & Associates

2607 31st St. NW
Washington, DC 20008
Ph: (202)965-6464   Fax: (202)338-3953

Search counsel to higher education, serving a wide range of colleges and universities. Specializing in presidential and senior-level administrative search. Offers an interim service for presidential and vice-presidential transitions.

TRADESHOWS

★3550★ Accrediting Association of Bible Colleges Annual Meeting

Accrediting Association of Bible Colleges
5575 S. Semoran Blvd., Ste. 26
Orlando, FL 32822-1781
Ph: (407)207-0808   Fax: (407)207-0840
URL: http://www.aabc.org

Annual. **Primary Exhibits:** Publications, office equipment, travel information, educational resources, fundraising services, computers, Bible literature, films, and related material for educational institutions.

★3551★ American Association of School Administrators Annual Conference and Exposition

American Association of School Administrators (AASA)
1801 N. Moore St.
Arlington, VA 22209
Ph: (703)875-0748   Fax: (703)841-1543
URL: http://www.aasa.org

Annual. **Primary Exhibits:** Educational equipment and services. **Dates and Locations:** 2005 Feb 17-20; San Antonio, TX • 2006 Feb 23-26; San Diego, CA.

★3552★ Association of School Business Officials International Annual Meeting and Exhibits

Association of School Business Officials International
11401 N. Shore Dr.
Reston, VA 20190
Ph: (703)478-0405   Fax: (703)478-0205
E-mail: info@asbointl.org
URL: http://www.asbointl.org

Annual. **Primary Exhibits:** Equipment, supplies, and services for school districts. **Dates and Locations:** 2005 Oct 21-25; Boston, MA.

★3553★ International Association of Pupil Personnel Workers Conference

International Association of Pupil Personnel Workers
c/o Bill Chmela
2025 Juneway Dr.
Long Beach, IN 46360
Ph: (219)872-4975
E-mail: w.chmela@attbi.com

Annual. **Primary Exhibits:** Equipment, supplies, and services for school administrators, counselors, attendance officers, and school social workers.

★3554★ National Association of Elementary School Principals Annual Convention and Exhibition

National Association of Elementary School Principals
1615 Duke St.
Alexandria, VA 22314
Ph: (703)684-3345   Fax: (703)518-6281
Fr: 800-386-2877
URL: http://www.naesp.org

Annual. **Primary Exhibits:** Textbooks publishers, classroom supplies and equipment; playground equipment; incentive/fundraising programs; curriculum; technology; professional/staff development. **Dates and Locations:** 2004 Apr 17-19; San Francisco, CA • 2005 Apr 16-18; Baltimore, MD.

★3555★ National Association of Secondary School Principals Annual Convention

National Association of Secondary School Principals
1904 Association Dr.
Reston, VA 20191
Ph: (703)860-1332   Fax: (703)476-5490
Fr: 800-253-1746
URL: http://www.nassp.org

Annual. **Primary Exhibits:** School furnishings, supplies and equipment, fund raising, school jewelry, awards, yearbooks, textbooks.

★3556★ National Rural Education Research Forum and Conference

National Rural Education Association
c/o Bob Mooneyham
820 Van Vleet Oval
University of Oklahoma
Norman, OK 73019
Ph: (405)325-7959   Fax: (405)325-7959
E-mail: bmooneyham@ou.edu

Annual. **Primary Exhibits:** Exhibits for rural education programs.

★3557★ Southwestern Federation of Administrative Disciplines Convention

Southwestern Federation of Administrative Disciplines
2700 Bay Area Blvd.
Houston, TX 77058
Ph: (713)283-3122   Fax: (713)283-3951
URL: http://www.swfao.swt.edu

Annual. **Primary Exhibits:** Educational materials and services.

★3558★ UCEA Convention

University Council for Educational
  Administration
c/o Dr. Michelle Young
205 Hill Hall
Columbia, MO 65211-2185
Ph: (573)884-8300
E-mail: admnucea@coe.missouri.edu
URL: http://www.ucea.org

Annual. **Primary Exhibits:** Publications related to educational administration in universities.

OTHER SOURCES

★3559★ ACE Fellows Program

1 Dupont Cir. NW, 8th Fl.
Washington, DC 20036-1193
Ph: (202)939-9300   Fax: (202)785-8056
E-mail: fellows@ace.nche.edu
URL: http://www.acenet.edu

Description: Service of the American Council on Education to strengthen leadership in American postsecondary education by identifying and preparing individuals who have shown promise for responsible positions in higher education administration. **Purpose:** Objectives are: to encourage and prepare individuals making higher education administration their professional career; to provide opportunities for planned observation and experience in decision making; to identify and develop potential leaders. Arranges internships whereby senior faculty and administrators are given the opportunity to study higher education leadership as an intern at a host institution. The stipulations are that the fellow will do certain assigned reading in higher education administration, focus on a strategic learning project and serve at the home institution for the academic year following the internship. Provides services for alumni of the program.

★3560★ Administration and Management Occupations

Delphi Productions
3160 4th St.
Boulder, CO 80304
Fax: (303)443-4022   Fr: 888-443-2400
URL: http://www.delphivideo.com

$95.00. 50 minutes. Part of the Careers for the 21st Century Video Library.

★3561★ American Almanac of Jobs and Salaries

Morrow Avon
1350 Avenue of the Americas
New York, NY 10019
Ph: (212)261-6788   Fr: 800-242-7737

John W. Wright. Revised edition, 2000. $20.00 (paper). 672 pages. This is a comprehensive guide to the wages of hundreds of occupations in a wide variety of industries and organizations.

★3562★ American Association of Collegiate Registrars and Admissions Officers (AACRAO)

1 Dupont Cir. NW, Ste. 520
Washington, DC 20036
Ph: (202)293-9161   Fax: (202)872-8857
E-mail: info@aacrao.org
URL: http://www.aacrao.org

Members: Degree-granting postsecondary institutions (2400), government agencies, and higher education coordinating boards, private educational organizations, and education-oriented businesses. **Purpose:** Promotes higher education and furthers the professional development of members working in admissions, enrollment management, institutional research, records, and registration.

★3563★ American Association for Women in Community Colleges (AAWCC)

1202 W Thomas Rd.
Phoenix, AZ 85013
Ph: (602)285-7449   Fax: (602)285-7832
E-mail: aawcc@pcmail.maricopa.edu
URL: http://www.pc.maricopa.edu/aawcc

Description: Women faculty members, administrators, staff members, students, and trustees of community colleges. Objectives are to: develop communication and disseminate information among women in community, junior, and technical colleges; encourage educational program development; obtain grants for educational projects for community college women. Disseminates information on women's issues and programs. Conducts regional and state professional development workshops and forums. Recognizes model programs that assist women in community colleges. A council of the American Association of Community Colleges.

★3564★ American Federation of School Administrators (AFSA)

1729 21st St. NW
Washington, DC 20009-1101
Ph: (202)986-4209   Fax: (202)986-4211
E-mail: afsa@admin.org
URL: http://www.admin.org

Description: Principals, vice-principals, directors, supervisors, and administrators involved in pedagogical education. Purposes are to: achieve the highest goals in education; maintain and improve standards, benefits, and conditions for personnel without regard to color, race, sex, background, or national origin; obtain job security; protect seniority and merit; cooperate with all responsible organizations in education; promote understanding, participation, and support of the public, communities, and agencies; be alert to resist attacks and campaigns that would create or entrench a spoils system; promote democratic society by supporting full educational opportunities for every child and student in the nation.

★3565★ Association of Christian Schools International (ACSI)

731 Chapel Hills Dr.
Colorado Springs, CO 80920-1027
Ph: (719)528-6906   Fax: (719)531-0631
Fr: 800-367-0798
E-mail: info@acsi.org
URL: http://www.acsi.org

Description: Seeks to enable Christian educators and schools worldwide to effectively prepare students for life.

★3566★ Association of Departments of English (ADE)

26 Broadway, 3rd Fl.
New York, NY 10004-1789
Ph: (646)576-5130   Fax: (646)834-4045
E-mail: dlaurence@mla.org
URL: http://www.ade.org

Description: Administrators of college and university departments of English, humanities, rhetoric, and communications. To improve the teaching of English and the administration of English departments. Conducts studies and surveys of literature and writing courses. Sponsors sessions at major English conventions and conferences nationwide. Sponsored by Modern Language Association of America.

★3567★ Association on Higher Education and Disability (AHEAD)

PO Box 540666
Waltham, MA 02454
Ph: (781)788-0003   Fax: (781)788-0033
E-mail: ahead@ahead.org
URL: http://www.ahead.org.

Description: Individuals interested in promoting the equal rights and opportunities of disabled postsecondary students, staff, faculty, and graduates. Provides an exchange of communication for those professionally involved with disabled students; collects, evaluates, and disseminates information; encourages and supports legislation for the benefit of disabled students. Conducts surveys on issues pertinent to college students with disabilities; offers resource referral system and employment exchange for positions in disability student services. Conducts research programs; compiles statistics.

★3568★ Association for the Study of Higher Education (ASHE)

202 Hill Hall
Columbia, MO 65211-2190
Ph: (573)882-9645   Fax: (573)884-2197
E-mail: ashe@coe.missouri.edu
URL: http://www.ashe.missouri.edu

Description: Professors, researchers, administrators, policy analysts, graduate students, and others concerned with the study of higher education. Purposes are to advance the study of higher education and facilitate and encourage discussion of priority issues for research in the study of higher education.

★3569★ Convention of American Instructors of the Deaf (CAID)

PO Box 377
Bedford, TX 76095-0377
Ph: (817)354-8414
E-mail: caid@swbell.net
URL: http://www.caid.org/

Members: Professional organization of teachers, administrators, and professionals in allied fields related to education of the deaf and hard-of-hearing. **Purpose:** Objectives are to provide opportunities for a free interchange of views concerning methods and means of educating the deaf and hard-of-hearing; to promote such education by the publication of reports, essays, and other information; to develop more effective methods of teaching deaf and hard-of-hearing children.

★3570★ Counseling Association for Humanistic Education and Development (C-AHEAD)

5999 Stevenson Ave.
Alexandria, VA 22304
Ph: (703)823-9800   Fax: 800-473-2329
Fr: 800-347-6647
E-mail: membership@counseling.org
URL: http://www.counseling.org

Description: A division of the American Counseling Association. Teachers, educational administrators, community agency workers, counselors, school social workers, and psychologists; others interested in the area of human development. Aims to assist individuals in improving their quality of life. Provides forum for the exchange of information about humanistically-oriented administrative and instructional practices. Supports humanistic practices and research on instructional and organizational methods for facilitating humanistic education; encourages cooperation among related professional groups.

★3571★ *Education and Training*

Cambridge Educational
2572 Brunswick Ave.
Lawrenceville, NJ 08648-4128
Fax: 800-FAX-ON-US   Fr: 800-468-4227
URL: http://www.cambridgeeducational.com

$89.95. 2002. 18 minutes.

★3572★ Friends Council on Education (FCE)

1507 Cherry St.
Philadelphia, PA 19102
Ph: (215)241-7245   Fax: (215)241-7299
E-mail: quakered@aol.com
URL: http://www.friendscouncil.org

Members: Representatives appointed by Friends Yearly Meetings; heads of Quaker secondary and elementary schools and colleges; members-at-large. **Purpose:** Acts as a clearinghouse for information on Quaker schools and colleges. **Activities:** Holds meetings and conferences on education and provides in-service training for teachers, administrators, and trustees in Friends schools.

★3573★ NAFSA/Association of International Educators (NAFSA)

1307 New York Ave. NW, 8th Fl.
Washington, DC 20005
Ph: (202)737-3699   Fax: (202)737-3657
E-mail: inbox@nafsa.org
URL: http://www.nafsa.org

Description: Individuals, organizations, and institutions dealing with international educational exchange, including foreign student advisers, overseas educational advisers, credentials and admissions officers, administrators and teachers of English as a second language, community support personnel, study-abroad administrators, and embassy cultural or educational personnel. Promotes self-regulation standards and responsibilities in international educational exchange; offers professional development opportunities primarily through publications, workshops, grants, and regional and national conferences. Advocates for increased awareness and support of international education and exchange on campuses, in government, and in communities. Offers services including: a job registry for employers and professionals involved with international education; a consultant referral service. Sponsors joint liaison activities with a variety of other educational and government organizations to conduct a census of foreign student enrollment in the U.S.; conducts workshops about specific subjects and countries.

★3574★ National Association of College and University Business Officers (NACUBO)

2501 M St., NW, Ste. 400
Washington, DC 20037-1308
Ph: (202)861-2500   Fax: (202)861-2583
URL: http://www.nacubo.org

Members: Colleges, universities, and companies that are members of a regional association. **Purpose:** Develops and maintains national interest in improving the principles and practices of business and financial administration in higher education. **Activities:** Sponsors workshops in fields such as cash management, grant and contract maintenance, accounting, investment, student loan administration, and costing. Conducts research and information exchange programs between college and university personnel; compiles statistics.

★3575★ National Association of Elementary School Principals (NAESP)

1615 Duke St.
Alexandria, VA 22314
Ph: (703)684-3345   Fax: (703)549-5568
Fr: 800-386-2377
E-mail: naesp@naesp.org
URL: http://www.naesp.org

Description: Professional association of principals, assistant or vice principals, and aspiring principals; persons engaged in educational research and in the professional education of elementary and middle school administrators. Sponsors National Distinguished Principals Program, President's Award for Educational Excellence, American

Student Council Association. Offers annual national convention and exhibition, on-site and internet professional development workshops throughout the year. Recently expanded professional publications offered through the National Principals' Resource Center.

★3576★ National Association of Episcopal Schools (NAES)

815 2nd Ave., Ste. 313
New York, NY 10017-4594
Ph: (212)716-6134   Fax: (212)286-9366
Fr: 800-334-7626
E-mail: info@episcopalschools.org
URL: http://www.naes.org

Description: Episcopal day and boarding schools and preschools. Promotes the educational ministry of the Episcopal Church. Provides publications, consultation services and conference focusing on Episcopal identity of schools, worship, religious education, spirituality, leadership development and governance for heads/directors, administrators, chaplains and teachers of religion, trustees, rectors and other church and school leaders.

★3577★ National Association of Independent Schools (NAIS)

1620 L St. NW, Ste. 1100
Washington, DC 20036-5695
Ph: (202)973-9700   Fax: (202)973-9790
E-mail: info@nais.org
URL: http://www.nais.org

Description: Independent elementary and secondary school members; regional associations of independent schools and related associations. Provides curricular and administrative research and services. Conducts educational programs; compiles statistics.

★3578★ National Association of Secondary School Principals (NASSP)

1904 Association Dr.
Reston, VA 20191-1537
Ph: (703)860-0200   Fax: (703)476-5432
Fr: 800-253-7746
URL: http://www.principals.org

Description: Middle level and high school principals, assistant principals, and aspiring school leaders, others engaged in secondary school administration and/or supervision; college professors teaching courses in secondary education. Sponsors National Association of Student Councils (NASC), National Honor Society (NHS), and National Junior Honor Society (NJHS).

★3579★ National Association of State Directors of Special Education (NASDSE)

1800 Diagonal Rd., Ste. 320
Alexandria, VA 22314
Ph: (703)519-3800   Fax: (703)519-3808
E-mail: nasdse@nasdse.org
URL: http://www.nasdse.org

Members: Professional society of state directors; consultants, supervisors, and administrators who have statewide responsibilities for administering special education programs. **Purpose:** Provides services to state agencies to facilitate their efforts to maximize educational outcomes for individuals with disabilities.

★3580★ **National Association of Student Personnel Administrators (NASPA)**
1875 Connecticut Ave., NW - Ste. 418
Washington, DC 20009
Ph: (202)265-7500   Fax: (202)797-1157
E-mail: office@naspa.org
URL: http://www.naspa.org

Description: Representatives of degree-granting institutions of higher education which have been fully accredited. Works to enrich the educational experience of all students. Serves colleges and universities by providing leadership and professional growth opportunities for the senior student affairs officer and other professionals who consider higher education and student affairs issues from an institutional perspective. Provides professional development; improves information and research; acts as an advocate for students in higher education. Promotes diversity in NASPA and the profession. Maintains career service and conducts the Richard F. Stevens Institute. Supports minority undergraduate fellows program.

★3581★ **National Community Education Association (NCEA)**
3929 Old Lee Hwy., Ste. 91-A
Fairfax, VA 22030
Ph: (703)359-8973   Fax: (703)359-0972
E-mail: ncea@ncea.com
URL: http://www.ncea.com

Description: Community school directors, principals, superintendents, professors, teachers, students, and laypeople. **Purpose:** Promotes and establishes community schools as an integral part of the educational plan of every community. Emphasizes community and parent involvement in the schools, lifelong learning, and enrichment of K-12 and adult education. Serves as a clearinghouse for the exchange of ideas and information, and the sharing of efforts. **Activities:** Offers leadership training.

★3582★ **National Council for Accreditation of Teacher Education (NCATE)**
2010 Massachusetts Ave. NW, Ste. 500
Washington, DC 20036-1023
Ph: (202)466-7496   Fax: (202)296-6620
E-mail: ncate@ncate.org
URL: http://www.ncate.org

Members: Representatives from constituent colleges and universities, state departments of education, school boards, teacher, and other professional groups. **Purpose:** Voluntary accrediting body devoted exclusively to evaluation and accreditation of institutions for preparation of elementary and secondary school teachers; preparation of school service personnel, including school principals, supervisors, superintendents, school psychologists, instructional technologists, and other specialists for school-oriented positions.

★3583★ *Overseas Employment Opportunities for Educators: Department of Defense Dependents Schools*
DIANE Publishing Co.
PO Box 1428
Collingdale, PA 19023-8428
Ph: (610)461-6200   Fax: (610)461-6130
Fr: 800-782-3833

Barry Leonard, editor. 1999. $20.00. 44 pages. An introduction to teachings positions in the Dept. of Defense Dependents Schools (DoDDS), a worldwide school system, operated by the DoD in 14 countries.

★3584★ *Teaching & Related Occupations*
Delphi Productions
3160 4th St.
Boulder, CO 80304
Fax: (303)443-4022   Fr: 888-443-2400
URL: http://www.delphivideo.com

$95.00. 50 minutes. Part of the Careers for the 21st Century Video Library.

EEG Technologists and Technicians

EMPLOYER DIRECTORIES AND NETWORKING LISTS

★3585★ AHA Guide to the Health Care Field

American Hospital Association (AHA)
1 N. Franklin St., 27th Fl.
Chicago, IL 60606
Ph: (312)422-2050   Fax: (312)422-4700
Fr: 800-424-4301

Annual, August. $295.00. Covers hospitals, networks, multi-health care systems, free-standing ambulatory surgery centers, psychiatric facilities, long-term care facilities, substance abuse programs, and other health-related organizations. Entries include: For hospitals-Facility name, address, phone, administrator's name, number of beds, facilities and services, number of employees, expenses, other statistics. For other organizations-Name, address, phone, fax, name and title of contact. Arrangement: Geographical. Indexes: Hospital name.

★3586★ Directory of Hospital Personnel

Thomson Medical Economics
5 Paragon Dr.
Montvale, NJ 07645-1742
Ph: (201)358-7200   Fax: (201)722-2680

Annual, November. $325.00. Covers 200,000 executives at 7,000 U.S. hospitals. Entries include: Name of hospital, address, phone, number of beds, type and JCAHO status of hospital, names and titles of key department heads and staff, medical and nursing school affiliations; number of residents, interns, and nursing students. Arrangement: Geographical. Indexes: Hospital name, personnel, hospital size.

★3587★ Guide to Careers in the Health Professions

The Princeton Review
1745 Broadway
New York, NY 10019
Ph: (212)829-6928   Fax: (212)940-7400
Fr: 800-733-3000

Published January, 2001. $24.95. Presents advice and information for those searching for satisfying careers in the health professions. Publication includes: Directory of schools and academic programs. Entries include: Name, address, phone, tuition, program details, employment profiles.

★3588★ Hospital Blue Book

Billian/Transworld Publishing Inc.
2100 Powers Ferry Rd.
Ste. 300
Atlanta, GA 30339
Ph: (770)955-8484   Fax: (770)955-8485
Fr: 800-533-8484
E-mail: blu-book@billian.com

Annual, January. $285.00 for national edition; $160.00 for southern edition. Covers more than 6,687 hospitals; some listings also appear in a separate southern edition of this publication. Entries include: Name of hospital, accreditation, mailing address, phone, fax, number of beds, type of facility (nonprofit, general, state, etc.); list of administrative personnel and chiefs of medical services, with specific titles. Arrangement: Geographical.

★3589★ Medical and Health Information Directory

Thomson Gale
27500 Drake Rd.
Farmington Hills, MI 48331-3535
Ph: (248)699-4253   Fax: (248)699-8065
Fr: 800-877-GALE
E-mail: businessproducts@gale.com

Annual. $285.00 per volume; $675.00 per set. Covers in Volume 1, more than 26,500 medical and health oriented associations, organizations, institutions, and government agencies, including health maintenance organizations (HMOs), preferred provider organizations (PPOs), insurance companies, pharmaceutical companies, research centers, and medical and allied health schools. In Volume 2, over 12,000 medical book publishers; medical periodicals, directories, audiovisual producers and services, medical libraries and information centers, electronic resources, and health-related internet search engines. In Volume 3, more than 35,500 clinics, treatment centers, care programs, and counseling/diagnostic services for 34 subject areas. Entries include: Institution, service, or firm name, address, phone, fax, email and URL; many include names of key personnel and, when pertinent, descriptive annotation. Volume 3 was formerly listed separately as Health Services Directory. Arrangement: Classified by organization activity, service, etc. Indexes: Each volume has a complete alphabetical name and keyword index.

HANDBOOKS AND MANUALS

★3590★ Careers in Health Care

McGraw-Hill Trade
2 Penn Plaza
New York, NY 10121
Ph: (212)904-2000   Fr: 800-722-4726
E-mail: ntcpub@tribune.com

Barbara M. Swanson. Fourth edition, 2000. $17.95; $13.95 (paper). 320 pages. Describes job duties, work settings, salaries, licensing and certification requirements, educational preparation, and future outlook. Gives ideas on how to secure a job.

★3591★ Opportunities in Health and Medical Careers

McGraw-Hill Trade
2 Penn Plaza
New York, NY 10121
Ph: (212)904-2000   Fr: 800-722-4726

I. Donald Snook, Jr. and Leo D'Orazio. 1997. $14.95; $11.95 (paper). 202 pages. Covers the full range of medical and health occupations. Illustrated.

★3592★ Opportunities in Medical Imaging Careers

McGraw-Hill/Contemporary Books
1221 Ave Of The Americas
New York, NY 10020
Ph: (212)904-2000   Fax: (973)302-2300
Fr: 800-225-5945

Clifford J. Sherry. 1993. $14.95. 160 pages.

★3593★ Opportunities in Medical Technology Careers

McGraw-Hill/Contemporary Books
1221 Avenue of the Americas
New York, NY 10020
Ph: (212)904-2000   Fr: 800-323-4900
E-mail: ntcpub@tribune.com

Karen R. Karni. Revised, 1996. $14.95; $11.95 (paper). 205 pages. Details opportunities for various technical medical personnel and supplies up-to-date information on salary levels and employment outlook. Appendices list associations and unions in each field. Illustrated.

★3594★ Resumes for Health and Medical Careers

McGraw-Hill Trade
2 Penn Plaza
New York, NY 10121
Ph: (212)904-2000   Fr: 800-722-4726
E-mail: ntcpub@tribune.com

1997. $9.95 (paper). 455 pages.

EMPLOYMENT AGENCIES AND SEARCH FIRMS

★3595★ Shiloh Careers International, Inc.

7105 Peach Ct., Ste102
PO Box 831
Brentwood, TN 37024-0831
Ph: (615)373-3090   Fax: (615)373-3480
E-mail: maryann@shilohcareers.com
URL: http://www.shilohcareers.com

Employment agency serving the industry field.

ONLINE JOB SOURCES AND SERVICES

★3596★ Medbulletin Medical Career Resource Center

E-mail: medbulletin@atsmedbulletin.com
URL: http://www.medbulletin.com
Description: Offers free specialized update service, resume posting, recruiter directory, varied job listings, and relocation services.

★3597★ Medhunters.com

E-mail: info@medhunters.com
URL: http://www.medhunters.com
Description: Career search site for jobs in all health care specialties; educational resources; visa and licensing information for relocation; interesting articles; relocation tools; links to professional organizations and general resources.

★3598★ ProHealthJobs

E-mail: sales@prohealthjobs.com
URL: http://www.prohealthjobs.com
Description: Career resources site for the medical and health care field. Lists professional opportunities, product information, continuing education and open positions.

TRADESHOWS

★3599★ American Association of Electrodiagnostic Medicine Annual Scientific Meeting

American Association of Electrodiagnostic Medicine
421 1st Ave. SW, Ste. 300E
Rochester, MN 55902-3018
Ph: (507)288-0100   Fax: (507)288-1225
E-mail: aaem@aaem.net
URL: http://www.aaem.net

Annual. **Primary Exhibits:** Electromyographic and electrodiagnostic equipment and accessories, pharmaceutical companies, and publishers. **Dates and Locations:** 2004 Nov 3-6; Savannah, GA; Savannah International Trade and Convention Center.

★3600★ American Clinical Neurophysiology Society Annual Meeting and Short Courses

American Clinical Neurophysiology Society
1 Regency Dr.
PO Box 30
Bloomfield, CT 06002
Ph: (860)243-3977   Fax: (860)286-0787
E-mail: acns@ssmgt.com
URL: http://www.acns.org

Annual. **Primary Exhibits:** Electroencephalographic and neurophysiology equipment, supplies, and services.

OTHER SOURCES

★3601★ American Society of Electroneurodiagnostic Technologists (ASET)

426 West 42nd St.
Kansas City, MO 64111
Ph: (816)931-1120   Fax: (816)931-1145
E-mail: info@aset.org
URL: http://www.aset.org

Members: Persons engaged in clinical electroencephalographic (EEG) technology, evoked potential responses, nerve conduction studies, and polysomnography (sleep studies). **Purpose:** Objective is the advancement of electroneurodiagnostic technology education and practice standards.

★3602★ EEG Technologists and Technicians

Evon Publishing
832 N 7th Ave.
Iron River, MI 49935
Ph: (906)265-3190

Audiocassette. 1996. $16.95. 32 minutes. Part of the Careers and Vocational Guidance Series. Provides information about the nature of the work, educational requirements, employment outlook, earnings, and work conditions as well as additional related information.

★3603★ Exploring Health Occupations

Cambridge Educational
2572 Brunswick Ave.
Lawrenceville, NJ 08648-4128
Fax: 800-FAX-ON-US   Fr: 800-468-4227
URL: http://www.cambridgeeducational.com

Two videos. $139.95. 1999.

★3604★ Health Service Occupations

Delphi Productions
3160 4th St.
Boulder, CO 80304
Fax: (303)443-4022   Fr: 888-443-2400
URL: http://www.delphivideo.com

$95.00. 50 minutes. Part of the Careers for the 21st Century Video Library.

★3605★ Health Technologists & Technicians

Delphi Productions
3160 4th St.
Boulder, CO 80304
Fax: (303)443-4022   Fr: 888-443-2400
URL: http://www.delphivideo.com

$95.00. 50 minutes. Part of the Careers for the 21st Century Video Library.

★3606★ Medical Technicians and Technologists

Cambridge Educational
2572 Brunswick Ave.
Lawrenceville, NJ 08648-4128
Fax: 800-FAX-ON-US   Fr: 800-468-4227
URL: http://www.cambridgeeducational.com

$79.95. 15 minutes. Part of the Exploring Health Occupations Series.

★3607★ Medicine & Related Occupations

Delphi Productions
3160 4th St.
Boulder, CO 80304
Fax: (303)443-4022   Fr: 888-443-2400

URL: http://www.delphivideo.com

$95.00. 45 minutes. Part of the Careers for

the 21st Century Video Library.

EKG Technicians

SOURCES OF HELP-WANTED ADS

★3608★ American Heart Journal

Mosby Inc.
The Curtis Ctr., 3rd Fl.
Independence Sq. W
Philadelphia, PA 19106-3399
Ph: (215)235-7800   Fax: (215)238-7883
Fr: 800-523-1649
URL: http://www.mosby.com/ahs

Monthly. $190.00/year for individuals; $406.00/year for institutions; $95.00/year for students; $238.00/year for individuals, other countries; $454.00/year for institutions, other countries; $119.00/year for students, other countries. Medical journal serving practicing cardiologists, university-affiliated clinicians, and physicians keeping abreast of developments in the diagnosis and management of cardiovascular disease.

★3609★ The American Journal of Cardiology

Excerpta Medica Inc.
655 Avenue of the Americas
New York, NY 10010
Ph: (212)989-5800

Semimonthly. $66.00/year. Journal for heart specialists.

★3610★ Clinical Cardiology

Clinical Cardiology Publishing Company Inc.
PO Box 832
Mahwah, NJ 07430-0832
Ph: (201)818-1010   Fax: (201)818-0086
Fr: 800-443-0263
E-mail: clinicalcardiology@fams.org
URL: http://www.clinicalcardiology.org

Monthly. $80.00/year; $126.50/year for other countries. Peer-reviewed indexed medical journal.

★3611★ Heart and Lung

Mosby Inc.
Curtis Ctr., 3rd Fl.
170 S. Independence Mall W
Philadelphia, PA 19106-3399
Ph: (215)238-7800
URL: http://www.mosby.com/hrtlng

Bimonthly. $66.00/year for individuals; $217.00/year for institutions. Journal offering articles prepared by nurse and physician members of the critical care team, recognizing the nurse's role in the care and management of major organ-system conditions in critically ill patients.

★3612★ Journal of the American Society of Echocardiography

Mosby
The Curtis Ctr., 3rd Fl.
Independence Sq. W
Philadelphia, PA 19106-3399
Ph: (215)235-7800   Fax: (215)238-7883
Fr: 800-523-1649
URL: http://www.mosby.com/echo

Monthly. $180.00/year for individuals; $253.00/year for institutions; $90.00/year for students; $228.00/year for individuals, out of country; $301.00/year for institutions, out of country; $114.00/year for students, out of country. Official journal of the American Society of Echocardiography serving as a source of information on the technical basis and clinical application of echocardiography. Peer-reviewed publication featuring research, reviews, and case studies.

★3613★ Journal of Cardiopulmonary Rehabilitation

Lippincott Williams & Wilkins
530 Walnut St.
Philadelphia, PA 19106
Ph: (215)521-8300   Fax: (215)521-8902
Fr: 800-638-3030
E-mail: gregg@breuningnagle.com
URL: http://www.jcrjournal.com/

Bimonthly. $99.95/year for individuals; $249.95/year for institutions; $99.95/year for other countries; $301.95/year for institutions, other countries. Medical journal.

EMPLOYER DIRECTORIES AND NETWORKING LISTS

★3614★ AHA Guide to the Health Care Field

American Hospital Association (AHA)
1 N. Franklin St., 27th Fl.
Chicago, IL 60606
Ph: (312)422-2050   Fax: (312)422-4700
Fr: 800-424-4301

Annual, August. $295.00. Covers hospitals, networks, multi-health care systems, freestanding ambulatory surgery centers, psychiatric facilities, long-term care facilities, substance abuse programs, and other health-related organizations. Entries include: For hospitals-Facility name, address, phone, administrator's name, number of beds, facilities and services, number of employees, expenses, other statistics. For other organizations-Name, address, phone, fax, name and title of contact. Arrangement: Geographical. Indexes: Hospital name.

★3615★ Directory of Hospital Personnel

Thomson Medical Economics
5 Paragon Dr.
Montvale, NJ 07645-1742
Ph: (201)358-7200   Fax: (201)722-2680

Annual, November. $325.00. Covers 200,000 executives at 7,000 U.S. hospitals. Entries include: Name of hospital, address, phone, number of beds, type and JCAHO status of hospital, names and titles of key department heads and staff, medical and nursing school affiliations; number of residents, interns, and nursing students. Arrangement: Geographical. Indexes: Hospital name, personnel, hospital size.

★3616★ Guide to Careers in the Health Professions

The Princeton Review
1745 Broadway
New York, NY 10019
Ph: (212)829-6928   Fax: (212)940-7400
Fr: 800-733-3000

Published January, 2001. $24.95. Presents advice and information for those searching for satisfying careers in the health professions. Publication includes: Directory of schools and academic programs. Entries include: Name, address, phone, tuition, program details, employment profiles.

★3617★ Hospital Blue Book

Billian/Transworld Publishing Inc.
2100 Powers Ferry Rd.
Ste. 300
Atlanta, GA 30339
Ph: (770)955-8484   Fax: (770)955-8485
Fr: 800-533-8484
E-mail: blu-book@billian.com

Annual, January. $285.00 for national edition; $160.00 for southern edition. Covers more than 6,687 hospitals; some listings also appear in a separate southern edition of this publication. Entries include: Name of hospital, accreditation, mailing address, phone, fax, number of beds, type of facility (nonprofit, general, state, etc.); list of administrative personnel and chiefs of medical services, with specific titles. Arrangement: Geographical.

★3618★ Medical and Health Information Directory

Thomson Gale
27500 Drake Rd.
Farmington Hills, MI 48331-3535
Ph: (248)699-4253   Fax: (248)699-8065
Fr: 800-877-GALE
E-mail: businessproducts@gale.com

Annual. $285.00 per volume; $675.00 per set. Covers in Volume 1, more than 26,500 medical and health oriented associations, organizations, institutions, and government agencies, including health maintenance organizations (HMOs), preferred provider organizations (PPOs), insurance companies, pharmaceutical companies, research centers, and medical and allied health schools. In Volume 2, over 12,000 medical book publishers; medical periodicals, directories, audiovisual producers and services, medical libraries and information centers, electronic resources, and health-related internet search engines. In Volume 3, more than 35,500 clinics, treatment centers, care programs, and counseling/diagnostic services for 34 subject areas. Entries include: Institution, service, or firm name, address, phone, fax, email and URL; many include names of key personnel and, when pertinent, descriptive annotation. Volume 3 was formerly listed separately as Health Services Directory. Arrangement: Classified by organization activity, service, etc. Indexes: Each volume has a complete alphabetical name and keyword index.

HANDBOOKS AND MANUALS

★3619★ Careers in Health Care

McGraw-Hill Trade
2 Penn Plaza
New York, NY 10121
Ph: (212)904-2000   Fr: 800-722-4726
E-mail: ntcpub@tribune.com

Barbara M. Swanson. Fourth edition, 2000. $17.95; $13.95 (paper). 320 pages. Describes job duties, work settings, salaries, licensing and certification requirements, educational preparation, and future outlook. Gives ideas on how to secure a job.

★3620★ The Only EKG Book You'll Ever Need

Lippincott-Raven Publishers
227 E. Washington Sq.
Philadelphia, PA 19106-3780
Ph: (215)238-4436   Fax: (215)238-4227
Fr: 800-777-2295

Third edition, 1999.

★3621★ Opportunities in Health and Medical Careers

McGraw-Hill Trade
2 Penn Plaza
New York, NY 10121
Ph: (212)904-2000   Fr: 800-722-4726

I. Donald Snook, Jr. and Leo D'Orazio. 1997. $14.95; $11.95 (paper). 202 pages. Covers the full range of medical and health occupations. Illustrated.

★3622★ Opportunities in Medical Imaging Careers

McGraw-Hill/Contemporary Books
1221 Ave Of The Americas
New York, NY 10020
Ph: (212)904-2000   Fax: (973)302-2300
Fr: 800-225-5945

Clifford J. Sherry. 1993. $14.95. 160 pages.

★3623★ Opportunities in Medical Technology Careers

McGraw-Hill/Contemporary Books
1221 Avenue of the Americas
New York, NY 10020
Ph: (212)904-2000   Fr: 800-323-4900
E-mail: ntcpub@tribune.com

Karen R. Karni. Revised, 1996. $14.95; $11.95 (paper). 205 pages. Details opportunities for various technical medical personnel and supplies up-to-date information on salary levels and employment outlook. Appendices list associations and unions in each field. Illustrated.

★3624★ Resumes for Health and Medical Careers

McGraw-Hill Trade
2 Penn Plaza
New York, NY 10121
Ph: (212)904-2000   Fr: 800-722-4726

E-mail: ntcpub@tribune.com
1997. $9.95 (paper). 455 pages.

EMPLOYMENT AGENCIES AND SEARCH FIRMS

★3625★ Shiloh Careers International, Inc.

7105 Peach Ct., Ste102
PO Box 831
Brentwood, TN 37024-0831
Ph: (615)373-3090   Fax: (615)373-3480
E-mail: maryann@shilohcareers.com
URL: http://www.shilohcareers.com

Employment agency serving the industry field.

★3626★ Team Placement Service, Inc.

5113 Leesburg Pike, Ste. 510
Falls Church, VA 22041-3242
Ph: (703)820-8618   Fax: (703)820-3368
Fr: 800-495-6767
E-mail: 4jobs@teamplace.com
URL: http://www.teamplace.com

Temporary agency that also handles some permanent placements.

ONLINE JOB SOURCES AND SERVICES

★3627★ Medhunters.com
E-mail: info@medhunters.com
URL: http://www.medhunters.com

Description: Career search site for jobs in all health care specialties; educational resources; visa and licensing information for relocation; interesting articles; relocation tools; links to professional organizations and general resources.

★3628★ ProHealthJobs
E-mail: sales@prohealthjobs.com
URL: http://www.prohealthjobs.com

Description: Career resources site for the medical and health care field. Lists professional opportunities, product information, continuing education and open positions.

TRADESHOWS

★3629★ American Association of Electrodiagnostic Medicine Annual Scientific Meeting
American Association of Electrodiagnostic Medicine
421 1st Ave. SW, Ste. 300E
Rochester, MN 55902-3018
Ph: (507)288-0100 Fax: (507)288-1225
E-mail: aaem@aaem.net
URL: http://www.aaem.net

Annual. **Primary Exhibits:** Electromyographic and electrodiagnostic equipment and accessories, pharmaceutical companies, and publishers. **Dates and Locations:** 2004 Nov 3-6; Savannah, GA; Savannah International Trade and Convention Center.

★3630★ American Clinical Neurophysiology Society Annual Meeting and Short Courses
American Clinical Neurophysiology Society
1 Regency Dr.
PO Box 30
Bloomfield, CT 06002
Ph: (860)243-3977 Fax: (860)286-0787
E-mail: acns@ssmgt.com
URL: http://www.acns.org

Annual. **Primary Exhibits:** Electroencephalographic and neurophysiology equipment, supplies, and services.

★3631★ American College of Cardiology Annual Scientific Session
American College of Cardiology
9111 Old Georgetown Rd.
Bethesda, MD 20814-1699
Ph: (301)897-5400 Fax: (301)897-9745
Fr: 800-253-4636
URL: http://www.acc.org

Annual. **Primary Exhibits:** Products and services related to cardiovascular medicine.

OTHER SOURCES

★3632★ Alliance of Cardiovascular Professionals
4356 Benney Rd., Ste. 2-103
Virginia Beach, VA 23452
Ph: (757)497-1225 Fax: (757)497-0010
E-mail: seanmce@aol.com
URL: http://www.acp-online.org

Description: Dedicated to meeting educational needs, developing programs to meet those needs, and providing a structure to offer the cardiovascular and pulmonary technology professional a key to the future as a valuable member of the medical team. Seeks advancement for members through communication and education. Provides coordinated programs to orient the newer professional to his field and continuing educational opportunities for technologist personnel. Has established guidelines for educational programs in the hospital and university setting. Works with educators and physicians to provide basic, advanced, and in-service programs for technologists. Sponsors registration and certification programs which provide technology professionals with further opportunity to clarify their level of expertise.Compiles statistics

★3633★ EKG Technicians
Evon Publishing
832 N 7th Ave.
Iron River, MI 49935
Ph: (906)265-3190

Audiocassette. 1996. $16.95. 32 minutes. Part of the Careers and Vocational Guidance Series. Provides information about the nature of the work, educational requirements, employment outlook, earnings, and work conditions as well as additional related information.

★3634★ Exploring Health Occupations
Cambridge Educational
2572 Brunswick Ave.
Lawrenceville, NJ 08648-4128
Fax: 800-FAX-ON-US Fr: 800-468-4227

URL: http://www.cambridgeeducational.com
Two videos. $139.95. 1999.

★3635★ Health Service Occupations
Delphi Productions
3160 4th St.
Boulder, CO 80304
Fax: (303)443-4022 Fr: 888-443-2400
URL: http://www.delphivideo.com

$95.00. 50 minutes. Part of the Careers for the 21st Century Video Library.

★3636★ Health Technologists & Technicians
Delphi Productions
3160 4th St.
Boulder, CO 80304
Fax: (303)443-4022 Fr: 888-443-2400
URL: http://www.delphivideo.com

$95.00. 50 minutes. Part of the Careers for the 21st Century Video Library.

★3637★ Medical Technicians and Technologists
Cambridge Educational
2572 Brunswick Ave.
Lawrenceville, NJ 08648-4128
Fax: 800-FAX-ON-US Fr: 800-468-4227
URL: http://www.cambridgeeducational.com

$79.95. 15 minutes. Part of the Exploring Health Occupations Series.

★3638★ Medicine & Related Occupations
Delphi Productions
3160 4th St.
Boulder, CO 80304
Fax: (303)443-4022 Fr: 888-443-2400
URL: http://www.delphivideo.com

$95.00. 45 minutes. Part of the Careers for the 21st Century Video Library.

Electrical and Electronic Equipment Repairers

SOURCES OF HELP-WANTED ADS

★3639★ Appliance Service News

Gamit Enterprises Inc.
1917 S St.
Geneva, IL 60134
Ph: (630)845-9481   Fax: (630)845-9483
Fr: 877-747-1625
E-mail: asnews@cin.net
URL: http://asnews.com

Monthly. $59.95/year for individuals. Magazine for appliance technicians.

★3640★ Electric Light & Power

PennWell Corp.
1421 S Sheridan Rd.
Tulsa, OK 74112
Ph: (918)835-3161   Fax: (918)832-9201
Fr: 800-331-4463
URL: http://uaelp.pennnet.com/articles/print_toc.cfm?p=34

Monthly. Free to qualified subscribers; $70.00/year for institutions; $78.00/year for Canada; $194.00/year for other countries. Tabloid providing news of electric utility industry developments and activities and coverage of new products and technology.

★3641★ Electronic Servicing & Technology

Mainly Marketing
403 Main St.
PO Box 748
Port Washington, NY 11050
Ph: (516)883-3382   Fax: (516)883-2162
Fr: 800-462-4659
E-mail: cpersedit@aol.com

Monthly. $29.95/year for individuals. Consumer electronics servicing magazine.

★3642★ Engineering Economist

Institute of Industrial Engineers
3577 Pkwy. Ln., Ste. 200
Norcross, GA 30092
Ph: (770)449-0461   Fax: (770)263-8532
Fr: 800-494-0460

Quarterly. Publication covering business issues in the energy, petroleum and mining industries.

★3643★ High Tech News and Satellite Journal

Electronic Technicians Association (ETA)
502 N Jackson St.
Greencastle, IN 46135
Ph: (765)653-4301   Fax: (765)653-8262
Fr: 800-288-3824

Description: Monthly. Serves member technicians with news of the Association and the electronics industry, including items on service, education, employment, management, and events. Contains information on membership, management, telecommunications, and business and technical training programs. Recurring features include editorials, news of research, letters to the editor, book reviews, and a calendar of events.

★3644★ Journal of Vacuum Science and Technology A & B

American Institute of Physics
1 Physics Ellipse
College Park, MD 20740-3843
Ph: (301)209-3000   Fax: (301)209-0842
E-mail: jvst@mcnc.org

Monthly. $670.00/year for individuals. Journal containing research review articles in all areas of vacuum science.

★3645★ Machine Design

Penton Media Inc.
1300 E 9th St.
Cleveland, OH 44114-1503
Ph: (216)696-7000   Fax: (216)931-9799
E-mail: mdeditor@penton.com
URL: http://www.machinedesign.com

$153.00/year for individuals. Magazine on design engineering function.

★3646★ Poptronics

Gernsback Publications Inc.
Box 51866
Boulder, CO 80322
URL: http://www.poptronics.com

Monthly. $19.99/year; $4.99 for single issue. Electronics magazine featuring audio and video electronics, computers, construction, and how-to information.

★3647★ Security Sales

Bobit Publishing
21061 S Western Ave.
Torrance, CA 90501
Ph: (310)533-2400   Fax: (310)533-2500
E-mail: secsales@bobit.com
URL: http://www.securitysales.com

Monthly. $35.00/year for individuals; $42.00/year for Canada; $53.00/year for other countries. Magazine covering the security industry.

PLACEMENT AND JOB REFERRAL SERVICES

★3648★ Electronics Technicians Association, International (ETA-I)

5 Depot St.
Greencastle, IN 46135
Ph: (765)653-8262   Fax: (765)653-4287
Fr: 800-288-3824
E-mail: eta@tds.net
URL: http://www.eta-sda.com

Description: Skilled electronics technicians. Provides placement service; offers certification examinations for electronics technicians and satellite, fiber optics, and data cabling installers. Compiles wage and manpower statistics. Administers FCC Commercial License examinations. Certification of computer network systems technicians and web and internet specialists.

EMPLOYER DIRECTORIES AND NETWORKING LISTS

★3649★ AM-Appliance Manufacturer-Directory Issue

Business News Publishing Co.
5900 Harper Rd., No. 105
Solon, OH 44139-1835
Ph: (440)349-3060   Fax: (440)498-9121
E-mail: amlindac@nowoline.net
URL: http://www.ammagazine.com

Annual, December. $25.00. Publication includes: Directory of 4,500 manufacturers and suppliers of equipment, material, and components to the appliance industry; trade associations. Entries include: Company name, address, phone, fax, website, and e-mail. Arrangement: Classified by product or service, and by company name. Indexes: Product/service, company.

★3650★ American Electronics Association-Directory

American Electronics Association
601 Pennsylvania Ave. NW, N Bldg., Ste. 600
Washington, DC 20004
Ph: (202)682-9110   Fax: (202)682-9111
Fr: 800-284-4232
URL: http://www.aeanet.org

Annual, June. $195.00 for nonmembers; $95.00 for members. Covers over 3,000 member electronics and high-technology companies and 500 associate member firms including financial institutions, law firms, and accounting firms. Entries include: Company name, address, phone, World Wide Web addresses, cable address, fax, names of executives, number of employees, list of products or services, date founded, whether a public or private company, stock market where traded, ticker symbol. Arrangement: Alphabetical. Indexes: Geographical, product.

★3651★ Appliances Dealers-Major Household Directory

infoUSA Inc.
5711 S 86th Cir.
Omaha, NE 68127-0347
Ph: (402)930-3500   Fax: (402)331-0176
Fr: 800-555-6124
URL: http://www.abii.com

Annual. Number of listings: 18,485(U.S. edition); 4,166 (Canadian edition). Entries include: Company name, address, phone (including area code), size of advertisement, year first in "Yellow Pages," name of owner or manager, number of employees. Compiled from telephone company "Yellow Pages," nationwide. Arrangement: Geographical.

★3652★ Buyer's Guide & Membership Directory

Independent Electrical Contractors Inc.
4401 Ford Ave., Ste. 1100
Alexandria, VA 22302-1432
Ph: (703)549-7351   Fax: (703)549-7448
Fr: 800-456-4324

Annual. $75.00. Covers member electrical contracting firms, electrical manufacturers, and distributors. Entries include: Name of company, address, names of principals. Arrangement: Geographical.

★3653★ Electric Equipment Manufacturers Directory

infoUSA Inc.
5711 S 86th Cir.
Omaha, NE 68127-0347
Ph: (402)930-3500   Fax: (402)331-0176
Fr: 800-555-6124
URL: http://www.abii.com

Annual. Number of listings: 4,294. Entries include: Name, address, phone (including area code). Compiled from telephone company "Yellow Pages," nationwide. Arrangement: Geographical.

★3654★ Television/Radio Service & Repair Directory

infoUSA Inc.
5711 S 86th Cir.
Omaha, NE 68127-0347
Ph: (402)930-3500   Fax: (402)331-0176
Fr: 800-555-6124
URL: http://www.abii.com

Annual. Number of listings: 10,166. Entries include: Name, address, phone (including area code), size of advertisement, year first in "Yellow Pages," name of owner or manager, number of employees. Compiled from telephone company "Yellow Pages," nationwide. Arrangement: Geographical.

HANDBOOKS AND MANUALS

★3655★ America's Fastest Growing Jobs

JIST Works, Inc.
8902 Otis Ave.
Indianapolis, IN 46216-1033
Ph: (317)613-4200   Fax: (317)613-4307
Fr: 800-648-5478
E-mail: jistworks@aol.com
URL: http://www.jist.com

Seventh edition, 2002. $16.95 (paper). 438 pages. Each job profile explains the nature of the work, skills and abilities required, employment outlook, average earnings, related occupations, education and training requirements, and employment opportunities. Also contains career planning information and job search tips.

★3656★ The Complete Guide to Electronics Troubleshooting

Thomson Delmar Learning
PO Box 15015
Albany, NY 12212-5015
Ph: (518)348-2300   Fax: (518)464-0393
Fr: 800-998-7498

James Perozzo. 1994. $57.50.

★3657★ Opportunities in Electrical Trades

McGraw-Hill/Contemporary Books
1221 Avenue of the Americas
New York, NY 10020
Ph: (212)904-2000   Fr: 800-323-4900
E-mail: ntcpub@tribune.com

Robert Wood and Kenneth R. Edwards. 1996. $14.95; $11.95 (paper). 160 pages. Offers advice on job hunting and where the jobs are. Includes index, bibliography, and illustrations.

★3658★ Opportunities in Electronics Careers

McGraw-Hill Trade
2 Penn Plaza
New York, NY 10121
Ph: (212)904-2000   Fr: 800-722-4726

Mark Rowh. 1999. $14.95; $11.95 (paper). 160 pages. Discusses career opportunities in commercial and industrial electronics equipment repair, electronics home entertainment repair, electronics engineering, and engineering technology. Includes job outlook and how to get off to a good start on the job.

★3659★ Opportunities in High Tech Careers

McGraw-Hill Trade
2 Penn Plaza
New York, NY 10121
Ph: (212)904-2000   Fr: 800-722-4726

Gary Colter and Deborah Yanuck. 1995. $14.95; $11.95 (paper). 160 pages. Explores high technology careers. Describes job opportunities, how to make a career decision, how to prepare for high technology jobs, job hunting techniques, and future trends.

★3660★ Opportunities in Installation and Repair Careers

McGraw-Hill Trade
2 Penn Plaza
New York, NY 10121
Ph: (212)904-2000   Fr: 800-722-4726

Mark Rowh. 1995. $14.95; $11.95 (paper). 160 pages.

★3661★ Troubleshooting Electrical/Electronic Systems

American Technical Publishers, Inc.
1155 W. 175th St.
Homewood, IL 60430
Ph: (708)957-1100   Fax: (708)957-1137
Fr: 800-323-3471

Glen A. Mazur and Thomas E. Proctor. 1994. $42.00. 476 pages.

★3662★ Troubleshooting and Repairing Major Appliances
McGraw-Hill Education Group
T A B Books
PO Box 545
Blacklick, OH 43004-0545
Fr: 800-338-3987
Eric Kleinert. 1995. $44.95; $29.95 (paper).

EMPLOYMENT AGENCIES AND SEARCH FIRMS

★3663★ Omni Recruiting Group, Inc.
600 Galleria Parkway. Ste.1900-78
Atlanta, GA 30339
Ph: (770)261-8680   Fax: (770)980-0700
URL: http://www.omnirecruiting.com
Executive search firm specializing in sales.

★3664★ S.D. Kelly and Associates, Inc.
541 Washington St.
Canton, MA 02021-3001
Ph: (781)326-8038   Fax: (781)562-0194
E-mail: info@sdkelly.com
URL: http://www.sdkelly.com
Employment agency.

TRADESHOWS

★3665★ Electronic Distribution Show and Conference
Electronic Distribution Show Corp.
222 S. Riverside Plaza, Ste. 2160
Chicago, IL 60606
Ph: (312)648-1140   Fax: (312)648-4282
E-mail: eds@edsc.org
URL: http://www.edsc.org
Annual. **Primary Exhibits:** Electronic products.

★3666★ E3 - Electronic Entertainment Expo
IDG Expo Management Co.
PO Box 620
Medfield, MA 02052-0620
URL: http://www.idgexpos.com
Annual. **Primary Exhibits:** Interactive entertainment equipment, supplies, and services.

★3667★ International CES
CEMA - Consumer Electronics Manufacturers Association
2500 Wilson Blvd.
Arlington, VA 22201-3834
Ph: (866)233-7968   Fax: (703)907-7601
E-mail: CESinfo@CE.org
URL: http://www.cesweb.org/about_ces/

fact_sheet.asp
Annual. **Primary Exhibits:** Electronic equipment, supplies, and services. **Dates and Locations:** 2005 Jan 06-09 • 2006 Jan 05-08.

★3668★ NUCA - National Utility Contractors Association Convention
VNU Expositions, Inc. - Bill Communications, Inc.
1199 S. Belt Line Rd., Ste. 100
Coppell, TX 75019
Ph: (972)906-6500   Fax: (972)906-6501
E-mail: jjames@vnuexpo.com
URL: http://www.vnuexpo.com
Annual. **Primary Exhibits:** Equipment, supplies, and services for the construction of utility lines (pipes for storm and sanitary sewers and drainage, water lines, cables, ducts, conduits, and other utility work).

★3669★ POWER-GEN International
PennWell Conferences and Exhibitions (Oklahoma)
1421 S. Sheridan Rd.
Tulsa, OK 74112
Ph: (918)835-3161   Fax: (918)831-9497
URL: http://www.pennwell.com
Annual. **Primary Exhibits:** Equipment and services for power generation industries.

OTHER SOURCES

★3670★ COIN Career Guidance System
COIN Educational Products
3361 Executive Pky., Ste. 302
Toledo, OH 43606
Ph: (419)536-5353   Fax: (419)536-7056
Fr: 800-274-8515
URL: http://www.coin3.com/highschool/guidance.asp
CD-ROM. Provides career information through seven cross-referenced files covering postsecondary schools, college majors, vocational programs, military service, apprenticeship programs, financial aid, and scholarships. Apprenticeship file describes national apprenticeship training programs, including information on how to apply, contact agencies, and program content. Military file describes more than 200 military occupations and training opportunities related to civilian employment.

★3671★ Electronic Industries
Evon Publishing
832 N 7th Ave.
Iron River, MI 49935
Ph: (906)265-3190
Audiocassette. 1996. $16.95. 32 minutes. Part of the Careers and Vocational Guidance Series. Provides information about the nature of the work, educational requirements,

employment outlook, earnings, and work conditions as well as additional related information.

★3672★ Electronic Industries Alliance (EIA)
2500 Wilson Blvd.
Arlington, VA 22201
Ph: (703)907-7500   Fax: (703)907-7501
URL: http://www.eia.org
Description: Committed to the competitiveness of the American producer, EIA represents all companies involved in the design and manufacture of electronic components, parts, systems and equipment for communications, industrial, government and consumer uses. Has represented U.S. electronics manufacturers for more than 73 years.

★3673★ International Society of Certified Electronics Technicians (ISCET)
3608 Pershing Ave.
Fort Worth, TX 76107-4527
Ph: (817)921-9101   Fax: (817)921-3741
E-mail: info@iscet.org
URL: http://www.iscet.org
Description: Technicians in 50 countries who have been certified by the society. Seeks to provide a fraternal bond among certified electronics technicians, raise their public image, and improve the effectiveness of industry education programs for technicians. Offers training programs in new electronics information. Maintains library of service literature for consumer electronic equipment, including manuals and schematics for out-of-date equipment. Offers all FCC licenses. Sponsors testing program for certification of electronics technicians in the fields of audio, communications, computer, consumer, industrial, medical electronics, radar, radio-television, and video.

★3674★ Mechanics & Repairers
Delphi Productions
3160 4th St.
Boulder, CO 80304
Fax: (303)443-4022   Fr: 888-443-2400
URL: http://www.delphivideo.com
$95.00. 50 minutes. Part of the Careers for the 21st Century Video Library.

★3675★ National Electronics Service Dealers Association (NESDA)
3608 Pershing Ave.
Fort Worth, TX 76107-4527
Ph: (817)921-9061   Fax: (817)921-3741
E-mail: mack@nesda.com
URL: http://www.nesda.com
Description: Local and state electronic service associations and companies representing 4200 individuals. Provides educational assistance in electronic training to public schools; supplies technical service information on business management training to electronic service dealers. Offers certification, apprenticeship, and training programs through International Society of Certified

Electronics Technicians. Compiles statistics on electronics service business; conducts technical service and business management seminars.

★3676★ *Scientific, Engineering, and Technical Services*
Cambridge Educational
2572 Brunswick Ave.
Lawrenceville, NJ 08648-4128

Fax: 800-FAX-ON-US   Fr: 800-468-4227
URL: http://www.cambridgeeducational.com
$89.95. 2002. 18 minutes. Part of the Career Cluster Series.

Electrical and Electronics Engineers

★3677★ AWIS Magazine

Association for Women in Science
1200 New York Ave. NW, Ste. 650
Washington, DC 20005
Ph: (202)326-8940   Fax: (202)326-8960
Fr: 800-886-AWIS

Description: Bimonthly. Covers issues, legislation, and trends related to science education for girls, women, and minorities. Includes information on grants and fellowships, job openings, educational programs, events, and notices of publications available.

★3678★ CEE News

Primedia Business
9800 Metcalf Ave.
Overland Park, KS 66212
Ph: (913)341-1300   Fax: (913)967-1898

Monthly. Free to qualified subscribers; $52.00/year; $92.00/year for other countries. Electrical construction industry magazine.

★3679★ Circuits Assembly

UP Media Group Inc.
2018 Powers Ferry Rd., Ste. 600
Atlanta, GA 30339
Ph: (678)589-8800   Fax: (678)589-8850
E-mail: ca@up-mediagroup.com
URL: http://www.circuitsassembly.com

Monthly. Free to qualified subscribers; $135.00/year for other countries. Serves the PCB assembly marketplace.

★3680★ Communications of the ACM

Association for Computing Machinery
1515 Broadway
New York, NY 10036
Ph: (212)626-0500   Fax: (212)944-1318
Fr: 800-342-6626
URL: http://www.acm.org/about_acm/ov_pubs.html

Monthly. Computing news magazine.

★3681★ Community Radio News

National Federation of Community
  Broadcasters (NFCB)
Fort Mason Ctr., Bldg. D
San Francisco, CA 94123
Ph: (415)771-1160   Fax: (415)771-1160

Description: Monthly. Serves as a medium of communication for independent, community-licensed radio stations. Contains brief articles and news items on such topics as public broadcasting and programming, legislative developments, activities of the Federal Communications Commission, and local stations. Recurring features include notices of grants and awards, job openings, and a calendar of events/conferences for noncommercial broadcasters.

★3682★ Computer Design

PennWell Corp.
98 Spit Brook Rd.
Nashua, NH 03062-5737
Ph: (603)891-0123   Fax: (603)891-0574

Free to qualified subscribers; $88.00/year, others. Printed in two editions: magazine covers microprocessor-based systems design; news edition covers the systems time-to-market team.

★3683★ Connector Specifier

PennWell Corp.
100 S Atkinson Rd., Ste. 382
Grayslake, IL 60030-7817
Ph: (847)876-5602   Fax: (847)634-4240
URL: http://www.csmag.com

Free to qualified subscribers. Magazine for electronic engineers on the use of connectors and interconnection products.

★3684★ Consulting-Specifying Engineer

Reed Business Information
360 Park Ave. S
New York, NY 10014
Ph: (646)746-7764
URL: http://www.csemag.com/index.asp?webzine=cse&publication=cse

The integrated engineering magazine of the building construction industry.

★3685★ Defense & Security Electronics

Primedia Business
6151 Powers Ferry Rd.
Atlanta, GA 30339
Ph: (770)955-2500   Fax: (770)618-0348
E-mail: mgibbs@mindspring.com
URL: http://www.internetview.com

Monthly. $38.00/year for individuals. Defense and security electronics magazine.

★3686★ ECN (Electronic Component News)

Reed Business Information
360 Park Ave. S
New York, NY 10014
Ph: (646)746-7764
URL: http://www.e-insite.net/ecnmag/

Monthly. Free to qualified subscribers. Magazine (tabloid) for electronics design engineers and engineering management.

★3687★ EDN Products and Careers

Reed Business Information
275 Washington St.
Newton, MA 02458
Ph: (617)558-4900   Fax: (617)630-3830
Fr: 800-357-4745

Biweekly. Free to qualified subscribers. Newspaper (tabloid) of technology, products, and careers for engineers and engineering managers.

★3688★ EE Evaluation Engineering

Nelson Publishing Inc.
2500 Tamiami Trl. N
Nokomis, FL 34275-3482
Ph: (941)966-9521   Fax: (941)966-2590
Fr: 800-226-6113
E-mail: ee@nelsonpub.com
URL: http://www.nelsonpub.com/ee/

Monthly. $99.00/year for individuals; $140.00/year for other countries; $9.50 for single issue. Trade magazine covering electronic engineering, evaluation and test.

★3689★ **Electric Light & Power**

PennWell Corp.
1421 S Sheridan Rd.
Tulsa, OK 74112
Ph: (918)835-3161   Fax: (918)832-9201
Fr: 800-331-4463
URL: http://uaelp.pennnet.com/articles/
print_toc.cfm?p=34

Monthly. Free to qualified subscribers; $70.00/year for institutions; $78.00/year for Canada; $194.00/year for other countries. Tabloid providing news of electric utility industry developments and activities and coverage of new products and technology.

★3690★ **The Electrochemical Society Interface**

Electrochemical Society Inc.
65 S Main St.
Pennington, NJ 08534-2839
Ph: (609)737-1902   Fax: (609)737-2743
E-mail: interface@electrochem.org
URL: http://www.electrochem.org

Quarterly. $40.00/year; $10.00 for single issue. Publication featuring news and articles of interest to members of the Electrochemical Society.

★3691★ **Electronic Design**

Penton Technology and Lifestyle Media, Inc.
45 Eisenhower Dr., 5th Fl.
Paramus, NJ 07652
Ph: (201)845-2490   Fax: (201)845-2496
Fr: 800-526-6052
URL: http://www.penton.com/ed

Biweekly. Professional magazine covering current information in the field of electronic design.

★3692★ **Electronic Engineering Times**

CMP Media L.L.C.
600 Community Dr.
Manhasset, NY 11030
Ph: (516)562-5000
E-mail: rkeane@cmp.com
URL: http://www.eetimes.com/

Weekly. $280.00/year for individuals; $324.00/year for Canada; $449.00/year for other countries; $519.00/year, Asia and Australia. Weekly trade newspaper.

★3693★ **Electronic Products**

Hearst Business Communications/UTP Div.
645 Stewart Ave.
Garden City, NY 11530
Ph: (516)227-1300   Fax: (516)227-1453
Fr: 800-833-7138
E-mail: lens@electronicproducts.com
URL: http://www.electronicproducts.com

Free to qualified subscribers. Magazine for electronic design engineers and management.

★3694★ **Electronic Servicing & Technology**

Mainly Marketing
403 Main St.
PO Box 748
Port Washington, NY 11050
Ph: (516)883-3382   Fax: (516)883-2162
Fr: 800-462-4659
E-mail: cpersedit@aol.com

Monthly. $29.95/year for individuals. Consumer electronics servicing magazine.

★3695★ **Engineering Economist**

Institute of Industrial Engineers
3577 Pkwy. Ln., Ste. 200
Norcross, GA 30092
Ph: (770)449-0461   Fax: (770)263-8532
Fr: 800-494-0460

Quarterly. Publication covering business issues in the energy, petroleum and mining industries.

★3696★ **Engineering Times**

National Society of Professional Engineers
1420 King St.
Alexandria, VA 22314
Ph: (703)684-2875   Fax: (703)836-4875
E-mail: et@nspe.org
URL: http://httpl/:www.nspc.org/1et.asp

$30.00/year for individuals; $48.00/year for out of country. Magazine (tabloid) covering professional, legislative, and techology issues for an engineering audience.

★3697★ **ENR: Engineering News-Record**

McGraw-Hill Companies
1221 Avenue of the Americas
New York, NY 10020
Ph: (212)512-2000
URL: http://www.enr.com

Weekly. $74.00/year; $5.00 for single issue. Magazine focusing on engineering and construction.

★3698★ **Graduating Engineer & Computer Careers**

Career Recruitment Media
211 W. Wacker Dr., No. 900
Chicago, IL 60606
Ph: (312)525-3100
URL: http://www.graduatingengineer.com

$16.00/year for individuals. Magazine focusing on employment, education, and career development for entry-level engineers and computer scientists.

★3699★ **High Tech News and Satellite Journal**

Electronic Technicians Association (ETA)
502 N Jackson St.
Greencastle, IN 46135
Ph: (765)653-4301   Fax: (765)653-8262
Fr: 800-288-3824

Description: Monthly. Serves member technicians with news of the Association and the electronics industry, including items on service, education, employment, management, and events. Contains information on membership, management, telecommunications, and business and technical training programs. Recurring features include editorials, news of research, letters to the editor, book reviews, and a calendar of events.

★3700★ **High Technology Careers Magazine**

HTC
4701 Patrick Henry Dr., No. 1901
Santa Clara, CA 95054-1847
Ph: (408)970-8800   Fax: (408)567-0242
URL: http://www.hightechcareers.com

Bimonthly. $29.00/year; $35.00/year for Canada; $85.00/year for out of country. Magazine (tabloid) containing employment opportunity information for the engineering and technical community.

★3701★ **IEEE Spectrum**

Institute of Electrical and Electronics Engineers Inc.
3 Park Ave., 17th Fl.
New York, NY 10016-5997
Ph: (212)419-7900   Fax: (212)752-4929
E-mail: spectrum-webmaster@eee.org
URL: http://www.spectrum.leee.org

$195.00/year for individuals; $245.00/year, print and electronic rate for U.S., Canada, and Mexico; $25.00 for single issue outside U.S., Canada and Mexico. Magazine for the scientific and engineering professional. Provides information on developments and trends in engineering, physics, mathematics, chemistry, medicine/biology, and the nuclear sciences.

★3702★ **Journal of Electronic Materials**

IEEE Electron Devices Society
c/o IEEE Operation Center
445 Hoes Ln.
Piscataway, NJ 08855-1331
Ph: (732)981-0060   Fax: (732)981-1721

Bimonthly. Professional journal covering electronics engineering issues.

★3703★ **Machine Design**

Penton Media Inc.
1300 E 9th St.
Cleveland, OH 44114-1503
Ph: (216)696-7000   Fax: (216)931-9799
E-mail: mdeditor@penton.com
URL: http://www.machinedesign.com

$153.00/year for individuals. Magazine on design engineering function.

★3704★ **Microwave Journal**

Horizon House Publications Inc.
685 Canton St.
Norwood, MA 02062
Ph: (781)769-9750   Fax: (781)769-9884
Fr: 800-541-5970
E-mail: mwj@mwjournal.com

URL: http://www.mwjournal.com

Monthly. Free to qualified subscribers; $115.00/year for individuals; $175.00 for two years; $190.00/year for other countries; $355.00 for two years, other countries; $10.00 for single issue; $20.00 for single issue, other countries. Electronic engineering magazine.

★3705★ **NSBE Magazine**
NSBE Publications
1454 Duke St.
Alexandria, VA 22314
Ph: (703)549-2207   Fax: (703)683-5312

$10.00/year for individuals; $2.00 for single issue. Journal providing information on engineering careers, self-development, and cultural issues for recent graduates with technical majors.

★3706★ **PE & RS Photogrammetric Engineering & Remote Sensing**
The Imaging and Geospatial Information Society
5410 Grosvenor Ln., Ste. 210
Bethesda, MD 20814
Ph: (301)493-0290   Fax: (301)493-0208
E-mail: asprs@asprs.org

Monthly. $130.00/year. Journal covering photogrammetry, remote sensing, geographic information systems, cartography, and surveying, global positioning systems, digital photogrammetry.

★3707★ **Power**
McGraw-Hill Companies
1221 Avenue of the Americas
New York, NY 10020
Ph: (212)512-2000

Monthly. $19.00/year; $5.00 for single issue. Magazine for engineers in electric utilities, process and manufacturing plants, commercial and service establishments, and consulting, design, and construction engineering firms working in the power technology field.

★3708★ **Printed Circuit Design & Manufacture**
CMP Media L.L.C.
600 Community Dr.
Manhasset, NY 11030
Ph: (516)562-5000
E-mail: wgiffor@upmediagroup.com
URL: http://www.pcdandm.com/pcdmag

Monthly. Free to qualified subscribers. Magazine for engineers and designers of PCBs and related technologies.

★3709★ **RF Design**
Primedia Business
9800 Metcalf Ave.
Overland Park, KS 66212
Ph: (913)341-1300   Fax: (913)967-1898

Monthly. $42.00/year for individuals; $62.00/year for other countries; $102.00/year by mail. Magazine covering the R.F. engineering field.

★3710★ **Semiconductor International**
Reed Business Information
360 Park Ave. S
New York, NY 10014
Ph: (646)746-7764
URL: http://www.e-insite.net/semiconductor/

Monthly. Magazine profiling semiconductor manufacturing issues.

★3711★ **SMT**
PennWell Corp.
100 S Atkinson Rd., Ste. 382
Grayslake, IL 60030-7817
Ph: (847)876-5602   Fax: (847)634-4240
URL: http://smt.pennnet.com

Monthly. Free to qualified subscribers. Trade magazine for professional engineers involved in surface mount technology circuit design and board assembly.

★3712★ **Solid State Technology**
PennWell Corp.
98 Spit Brook Rd.
Nashua, NH 03062-5737
Ph: (603)891-0123   Fax: (603)891-0574
URL: http://sst.pennnet.com/home.cfm

Monthly. $217.00/year for individuals in USA; $302.00/year for individuals in Canada and Mexico; $364.00/year for individuals in other countries; $346.00 for two years in USA; $481.00/year for two years in Canada and Mexico; $580.00 for two years in other countries. Magazine containing electronic and semiconductor engineering news and information.

★3713★ **SWE**
Society of Women Engineers
230 E Ohio St., No. 400
2135 Lamberton Rd.
Chicago, IL 60611-3265
Ph: (312)596-5223   Fax: (312)596-5252
E-mail: hq@swe.org
URL: http://www.swe.org

Bimonthly. $30.00/year for nonmembers. Magazine for engineering students and for women and men working in the engineering and technology fields. Covers career guidance, continuing development and topical issues.

★3714★ **Technology Review**
Technology Review
201 Vassar St.
Cambridge, MA 02139
Ph: (617)253-8250   Fax: (617)258-5850
E-mail: trcomments@mit.edu

$30.00/year for individuals; $42.00/year for other countries; $4.95/year for single issue. Magazine reviewing new developments in technology with an emphasis on economic, political, and social implications. Not a new product publication.

★3715★ **Test & Measurement World**
Reed Business Information
275 Washington St.
Newton, MA 02458-1630
Ph: (617)964-3030
E-mail: tmworld@tmworld.com
URL: http://www.tmworld.com

Monthly. $93.99/year for nonmembers. Electronic engineering magazine specializing in test, measurement, and inspection of electronic products

★3716★ **Transmission and Distribution World**
Primedia Business
9800 Metcalf Ave.
Overland Park, KS 66212
Ph: (913)341-1300   Fax: (913)967-1898
URL: http://www.tdworld.com

Monthly. Free to qualified subscribers; $32.00/year; $6.00 for single issue. Magazine about powerline construction, transmission, and distribution.

★3717★ **WEPANEWS**
Women in Engineering Programs & Advocates Network
Castle Point on the Hudson
Hoboken, NJ 07030
Ph: (201)216-5245   Fax: (201)216-5175
URL: http://www.wepan.org/newsletter.html

Description: Two issues/year. Seeks to provide greater access for women to careers in engineering. Includes news of graduate, undergraduate, freshmen, pre-college, and re-entry engineering programs for women. Recurring features include job listings, faculty, grant, and conference news, international engineering program news, action group news, notices of publications available, and a column titled Kudos.

PLACEMENT AND JOB REFERRAL SERVICES

★3718★ **American Indian Science and Engineering Society (AISES)**
PO Box 9828
Albuquerque, NM 87119-9828
Ph: (505)765-1052   Fax: (505)765-5608
E-mail: info@aises.org
URL: http://www.aises.org

Description: American Indian and non-Indian students and professionals in science, technology, and engineering fields; corporations representing energy, mining, aerospace, electronic, and computer fields. Seeks to motivate and encourage students to pursue undergraduate and graduate studies in science, engineering, and technology. Sponsors science fairs in grade schools, teacher training workshops, summer math/science sessions for 8th-12th graders, professional chapters, and student chapters in colleges. Offers scholarships. Adult members serve as role models, advisers, and mentors for students. Operates placement service.

★3719★ American Society of Test Engineers (ASTE)

PO Box 389
Nutting Lake, MA 01865-0389
E-mail: aste@earthlink.net
URL: http://www.astetest.org

Members: Companies involved in the electronic testing industry and instrumentation are corporate members; engineers who work in test engineering related fields are regular members. **Purpose:** Seeks to foster improved communication among individuals and companies in the testing industry. **Activities:** Offers job referral service.

★3720★ Association for the Advancement of Medical Instrumentation (AAMI)

1110 N Glebe Rd., No. 220
Arlington, VA 22201-4795
Ph: (703)525-4890   Fax: (703)525-1424
Fr: 800-332-2264
URL: http://www.aami.org

Description: Clinical engineers, biomedical equipment technicians, physicians, hospital administrators, consultants, engineers, manufacturers of medical devices, nurses researchers and others interested in medical instrumentation. Purpose is to improve the quality of medical care through the application, development, and management of technology. Maintains placement service. Offers certification programs for biomedical equipment technicians and clinical engineers. Produces numerous standards and recommended practices on medical devices and procedures. Offers educational programs.

★3721★ Engineering Society of Detroit (ESD)

26100 American Dr., Ste. 500
Southfield, MI 48034-6184
Ph: (248)355-2910   Fax: (248)355-1492
E-mail: esd@esd.org
URL: http://esd.org

Description: Engineers from all disciplines; scientists and technologists. Conducts technical programs and engineering refresher courses; sponsors conferences and expositions. Maintains speakers' bureau; offers placement services. Although based in Detroit, MI, society membership is international.

★3722★ International Microelectronic and Packaging Society

611 2nd St. NE
Washington, DC 20002
Ph: (202)548-4001   Fax: (202)548-6115
E-mail: imaps@imaps.org
URL: http://www.imaps.org

Description: Electronics engineers and specialists in industry, business, and education. Encourages the exchange of information across boundaries of fields of specialization; supports close interactions between the complementary technologies of ceramics,

thick and thin films, semiconductor packaging, discrete semiconductor devices, and monolithic circuits. Promotes and assists in the development and expansion of microelectronics instruction in schools and departments of electrical and electronic engineering. Conducts seminars at international, national, regional, and chapter levels.

★3723★ Korean Scientists and Engineers Association in America (KSEA)

1952 Gallows Rd., Ste. 300
Vienna, VA 22182
Ph: (703)748-1221   Fax: (703)748-1331
E-mail: sejong@ksea.org
URL: http://www.ksea.org

Description: Scientists and engineers holding single or advanced degrees. Goals are to: promote friendship and mutuality among Korean and American scientists and engineers; contribute to Korea's scientific, technological, industrial, and economic developments; strengthen the scientific, technological, and cultural bonds between Korea and the U.S. Sponsors symposium. Maintains speakers' bureau, placement service, and biographical archives. Compiles statistics. Maintains 100 volume library of scientific handbooks and yearbooks in Korean.

★3724★ Robotics International of the Society of Manufacturing Engineers (RI/SME)

One SME Dr.
PO Box 930
Dearborn, MI 48121
Ph: (313)271-1500   Fax: (313)271-2861
Fr: 800-733-4763
E-mail: service@sme.org
URL: http://www.sme.org/ri

Description: Engineers, managers, educators, and government officials in 50 countries working or interested in the field of robotics. Promotes efficient and effective use of current and future robot technology. Serves as a clearinghouse for the industry trends and developments. Areas of interest include: aerospace; assembly systems; casting and forging; education and training; human factors and safety; human and food service; material handling; military systems; nontraditional systems; research and development; small shop applications; welding. Offers professional certification. Operates placement service; compiles statistics. Maintains speakers' bureau.

★3725★ Society of Hispanic Professional Engineers (SHPE)

5400 E Olympic Blvd., Ste. 210
Los Angeles, CA 90022
Ph: (323)725-3970   Fax: (323)725-0316
E-mail: shpenational@shpe.org
URL: http://www.shpe.org

Description: Engineers, student engineers, and scientists seeking to increase the number of Hispanic engineers by providing motivation and support to students. Sponsors competitions and educational programs.

Maintains placement service and speakers' bureau; compiles statistics.

EMPLOYER DIRECTORIES AND NETWORKING LISTS

★3726★ American Electronics Association-Directory

American Electronics Association
601 Pennsylvania Ave. NW, N Bldg., Ste. 600
Washington, DC 20004
Ph: (202)682-9110   Fax: (202)682-9111
Fr: 800-284-4232
URL: http://www.aeanet.org

Annual, June. $195.00 for nonmembers; $95.00 for members. Covers over 3,000 member electronics and high-technology companies and 500 associate member firms including financial institutions, law firms, and accounting firms. Entries include: Company name, address, phone, World Wide Web addresses, cable address, fax, names of executives, number of employees, list of products or services, date founded, whether a public or private company, stock market where traded, ticker symbol. Arrangement: Alphabetical. Indexes: Geographical, product.

★3727★ American Men and Women of Science

Thomson Gale
27500 Drake Rd.
Farmington Hills, MI 48331-3535
Ph: (248)699-4253   Fax: (248)699-8065
Fr: 800-877-GALE
E-mail: amws@galegroup.com

Biennial, latest edition December 2002. $975.00. Covers over 129,700 U.S. and Canadian scientists active in the physical, biological, mathematical, computer science, and engineering fields; includes references to previous edition for deceased scientists and nonrespondents. Entries include: Name, address, education, personal and career data, memberships, honors and awards, research interest. Arrangement: Alphabetical. Indexes: Discipline (in separate volume).

★3728★ Careers in Focus: Engineering

Ferguson Publishing Co.
200 W Jackson Blvd.
Chicago, IL 60606
Ph: (312)692-0109

2nd edition, 2002. $22.95. Publication includes: List of resources to consult for more information. Principal content of publication is job descriptions, advancement opportunities, educational requirements, employment outlook, salary information, and working conditions for careers in the field of engineering. Indexes: Alphabetical.

★3729★ Design News OEM Directory

Reed Business Information
275 Washington St.
Newton, MA 02458
Ph: (617)558-4712   Fax: (617)558-4512
Fr: 800-357-4745
E-mail: dn@cahners.com
URL: http://www.dnoemdirectory.com

Annual, November. $50.00. Covers about 5,000 manufacturers and suppliers of power transmission products, fluid power products, and electrical/electronic components to the OEM (original equipment manufacturer) market in SIC groups 34-39. Entries include: Company name, address, phone, fax, url, e-mail. Arrangement: Alphabetical. Indexes: Product locator, Trade Name, supplier locator.

★3730★ Directory of Contract Staffing Firms

C.E. Publications Inc.
PO Box 3006
Bothell, WA 98041-3006
Ph: (425)806-5200   Fax: (425)806-5585
URL: http://www.cjhunter.com/dcsf/overview.html

$15.00. Covers nearly 1,300 contract firms actively engaged in the employment of engineering, IT/IS, and technical personnel for 'temporary' contract assignments throughout the world. Entries include: Company name, address, phone, name of contact, email, web address. Arrangement: Alphabetical. Indexes: Geographical.

★3731★ Electric Equipment Manufacturers Directory

infoUSA Inc.
5711 S 86th Cir.
Omaha, NE 68127-0347
Ph: (402)930-3500   Fax: (402)331-0176
Fr: 800-555-6124
URL: http://www.abii.com

Annual. Number of listings: 4,294. Entries include: Name, address, phone (including area code). Compiled from telephone company "Yellow Pages," nationwide. Arrangement: Geographical.

★3732★ Engineers-Electrical Directory

infoUSA Inc.
5711 S 86th Cir.
Omaha, NE 68127-0347
Ph: (402)930-3500   Fax: (402)331-0176
Fr: 800-555-6124
URL: http://www.abii.com

Updated continuously; printed on request. Number of listings: 2,608. Entries include: Name, address, phone (including area code), size of advertisement, year first in "Yellow Pages," name of owner or manager, number of employees. Compiled from telephone company "Yellow Pages," nationwide. Arrangement: Geographical.

★3733★ Indiana Society of Professional Engineers-Directory

Indiana Society of Professional Engineers
PO Box 20806
Indianapolis, IN 46220
Ph: (317)255-2267   Fax: (317)255-2530

Annual, fall. $55.00. Covers member registered engineers, land surveyors, engineering students, and engineers in training. Entries include: Member name, address, phone, type of membership, business information, specialty. Arrangement: Alpha by chapter area.

★3734★ International Association of Electrical Inspectors-Membership Directory

International Association of Electrical Inspectors (IAEI)
901 Waterfall Way, Ste. 602
Richardson, TX 75080-7702
Ph: (972)235-1455   Fax: (972)235-3855

Annual, April. $11.95. Covers 26,000 state and federal government, industrial, utility, and insurance electrical inspectors, and, as associate members, electricians, manufacturers, engineers, architects, and wiremen. Entries include: Name, title, type of member, address, company affiliation. Arrangement: Geographical, then by division, chapter, or section, and type of membership, then alphabetical. Indexes: Committees; personal name.

★3735★ International Directory of Engineering Societies and Related Organizations

American Association of Engineering Societies
1828 L St. NW, Ste. 906
Washington, DC 20036
Ph: (202)296-2237   Fax: (202)296-1151
Fr: 888-400-AAES

Irregular, latest edition December 1998. $240.00. Covers about 1,370 national, regional, Canadian, and international organizations concerned with engineering and related fields. Entries include: Name, address, phone, fax, e-mail, key personnel, objectives, publications, activities, mailing lists, federation memberships, meeting and convention dates, and budget data. Arrangement: Alphabetical. Indexes: Acronym, geographical, area of specialization.

★3736★ Peterson's Job Opportunities in Engineering and Technology

Thomson Peterson's
PO Box 67005
Lawrenceville, NJ 08648-6105
Fr: 800-338-3282

Compiled by the Peterson's staff. Fourth edition, 1996. $21.95 (paper). 384 pages. Profiles 2,000 high-tech companies looking primarily for technical personnel in such fields as biotechnology, telecommunications, software, computers and peripherals, defense, and aerospace. Contains job-search strategies and career options to help match education and expertise to the job market.

Indexed geographically, by industry, and by hiring needs.

HANDBOOKS AND MANUALS

★3737★ The Best Resumes for Scientists and Engineers

John Wiley & Sons Inc.
1 Wiley Dr.
Somerset, NJ 08873
Ph: (732)469-4400   Fr: 800-225-5945

Adele Lewis and David J. Moore. Second edition, 1993. $37.50; $19.95 (paper). 224 pages. Presents an extensive collection of scientific and engineering resumes, highlighting the important differences between these and resumes written for other occupations.

★3738★ Engineering Your Job Search: A Job-Finding Resource for Engineering Professionals

Professional Publications, Inc.
1250 5th Ave.
Belmont, CA 94002
Ph: (650)593-9119   Fax: (650)592-4519
Fr: 800-426-1178

Compiled by Professional Publications, editors. 1995. $24.95 (paper). 154 pages. Out of print.

★3739★ The I Hate Selling Book: Business-Building Advice for Consultants, Attorneys, Accountants, Engineers, Architects, and Other Professionals

Allan Boress & Associates
1500 University Dr., Suite 239
Coral Springs, FL 33071
Ph: (954)345-4666   Fax: (954)344-2453

Allan S. Boress. 2001. $29.95.

★3740★ Keys to Engineering Success

Prentice Hall PTR
One Lake St.
Upper Saddle River, NJ 07458
Ph: (201)236-7000

Jill S. Tietjen, Kristy A. Schloss, Carol Carter, Joyce Bishop, and Sarah Lyman. 2000. $32.00 (paper).

★3741★ Majoring in Engineering: How to Get from Your Freshman Year to Your First Job

Farrar, Straus & Giroux, Inc.
19 Union Sq., W
New York, NY 10003
Ph: (212)741-6900   Fax: (212)633-9385
Fr: 888-330-8477

John Garcia and Carol Carter, editors. 2000. $20.00; $10.00 (paper). 134 pages.

★3742★ *The New Engineer's Guide to Career Growth & Professional Awareness*

Institute of Electrical & Electronics
Engineers Inc.
445 Hoes Ln.
PO Box 1331
Piscataway, NJ 08855-1331
Ph: (732)562-3967   Fax: (732)981-9334
Fr: 800-678-4333

Irving J. Gabelman, editor. 1996. $39.95 (paper). 275 pages.

★3743★ *On Becoming an Engineer: A Guide to Career Paths*

Institute of Electrical and Electronics
Engineers, Inc.
445 Hoes Ln.
PO Box 1331
Piscataway, NJ 08855-1331
Ph: (732)562-3967   Fax: (732)981-9334
Fr: 800-678-4333

David J. Irwin. 1997. $19.95. 152 pages.

★3744★ *Opportunities in Electronics Careers*

McGraw-Hill Trade
2 Penn Plaza
New York, NY 10121
Ph: (212)904-2000   Fr: 800-722-4726

Mark Rowh. 1999. $14.95; $11.95 (paper). 160 pages. Discusses career opportunities in commercial and industrial electronics equipment repair, electronics home entertainment repair, electronics engineering, and engineering technology. Includes job outlook and how to get off to a good start on the job.

★3745★ *Opportunities in Engineering Careers*

McGraw-Hill Contemporary Books
1221 Avenue of the Americas
New York, NY 10020
Ph: (212)904-2000   Fr: 800-323-4900
E-mail: ntcpub@tribune.com

Nicholas Basta. Revised, 1995. $14.95; $11.95 (paper). 200 pages. Outlines typical job titles, salaries, career paths, and employment prospects.

★3746★ *Opportunities in High Tech Careers*

McGraw-Hill Trade
2 Penn Plaza
New York, NY 10121
Ph: (212)904-2000   Fr: 800-722-4726

Gary Colter and Deborah Yanuck. 1995. $14.95; $11.95 (paper). 160 pages. Explores high technology careers. Describes job opportunities, how to make a career decision, how to prepare for high technology jobs, job hunting techniques, and future trends.

★3747★ *Opportunities in Research and Development Careers*

McGraw-Hill/Contemporary Books
1221 Avenue of the Americas
New York, NY 10020
Ph: (212)904-2000   Fr: 800-323-4900
E-mail: ntcpub@tribune.com

Jan Goldberg. 1997. $14.95; $11.95 (paper). 204 pages.

★3748★ *Real People Working in Engineering*

McGraw-Hill Contemporary Books
1221 Avenue of the Americas
New York, NY 10020
Ph: (212)904-2000   Fr: 800-323-4900
E-mail: ntcpub@tribune.com

Blythe Camenson, Jan Goldberg. 1997. $14.95; $12.95 (paper). Interviews and profiles of working professionals capture a range of opportunities in this field.

★3749★ *Resumes for Engineering Careers*

McGraw-Hill Trade
2 Penn Plaza
New York, NY 10121
Ph: (212)904-2000   Fr: 800-722-4726
E-mail: ntcpub@tribune.com

2000. $10.95 (paper). 456 pages. Contains sample resumes and cover letters applicable to any engineering field.

★3750★ *Resumes for Scientific and Technical Careers*

McGraw-Hill Contemporary Books
1221 Avenue of the Americas
New York, NY 10020
Ph: (212)904-2000   Fr: 800-323-4900
E-mail: ntcpub@tribune.com

1999. $9.95 (paper). 450 pages. Provides resume advice for individuals interested in working in scientific and technical careers. Includes sample resumes and cover letters.

★3751★ *Where the Jobs Are: The Hottest Careers for the 90s*

The Career Press, Inc.
3 Tice Rd.
PO Box 687
Franklin Lakes, NJ 07417-1322
Ph: (201)848-0310   Fax: (201)848-1727
Fr: 800-227-3371

Joyce Hadley. Third edition, 2000. $13.99 (paper). 400 pages. Out of print. Describes careers in fifteen general fields, from accounting to travel and hospitality.

EMPLOYMENT AGENCIES AND SEARCH FIRMS

★3752★ **Artgo Inc.**
12 Public Square
Willoughby, OH 44094-7843
Ph: (440)942-0597

Executive search firm.

★3753★ **The Aspire Group**
52 Second Ave, 1st Fl
Waltham, MA 02451-1129
Fax: (718)890-1810   Fr: 800-546-5675
URL: http://www.bmanet.com

Employment agency.

★3754★ **The Bedford Group**
154 Quicksand Pond Rd.
Little Compton, RI 02837
Ph: (401)635-0293   Fax: (401)635-8466

Executive search firm.

★3755★ **Bell Oaks Co.**
10 Glenlake Parkway, Ste. 300
Atlanta, GA 30328
Ph: (678)287-2000   Fax: (678)287-2001
E-mail: atlantacareers@belloaks.com
URL: http://www.belloaks.com

Personnel service firm.

★3756★ **Claremont-Branan, Inc.**
1298 Rockbridge Rd., Ste. B
Stone Mountain, GA 30087
Ph: (770)925-2915   Fax: (770)925-2601

Employment agency. Executive search firm.

★3757★ **Colli Associates**
404 Caboose Ln.
Valrico, FL 33594
Ph: (813)681-2145   Fax: (813)661-5217
E-mail: colli@gte.net

Employment agency. Executive search firm.

★3758★ **Electronic Careers**
21355 Pacific Coast Hwy., Ste. 100
Malibu, CA 90265
Ph: (310)317-6115   Fax: (310)317-6119

Executive search firm.

★3759★ **Engineer One, Inc.**
PO Box 23037
Knoxville, TN 37933
Fax: (865)691-0110
E-mail: engineerone@engineerone.com
URL: http://www.engineerone.com

Employment agency.

★3760★ Executive Recruiters Agency
14 Office Park Dr., Ste. 100
PO Box 21810
Little Rock, AR 72221-1810
Ph: (501)224-7000   Fax: (501)224-8534
E-mail: grogers@execrecruit.com
URL: http://www.execrecruit.com

Personnel service firm.

★3761★ James Bangert & Associates Inc.
15500 Wayzata Blvd., Ste. 1030 F
Wayzata, MN 55391
Ph: (952)475-3454   Fax: (952)473-4306

Executive search firm.

★3762★ Louis Rudzinsky Associates Inc.
394 Lowell St.
PO Box 640
Lexington, MA 02420
Ph: (781)862-6727   Fax: (781)862-6868

Provides recruitment, placement, and executive search to industry (software, electronics, optics) covering positions in general management, manufacturing, engineering, and marketing. Personnel consulting activities include counsel to small and startup companies. Industries served: electronics, aerospace, optical, laser, computer, software, imaging, electro-optics, biotechnology, advanced materials, and solid-state/semiconductor.

★3763★ Main Line Personnel Service, Inc.
Pagoda Blding.
100 Presidential Blvd. Ste. 200
Bala Cynwyd, PA 19004-0448
Ph: (610)667-1820   Fax: (610)668-5000
URL: http://www.mlpers.com

Employment agency.

★3764★ Rand Personnel
1200 Truxtun, Ste. 130
Bakersfield, CA 93301
Ph: (805)325-0751   Fax: (805)325-4120

Personnel service firm serving a variety of fields.

★3765★ Search and Recruit International
4455 South Blvd.
Virginia Beach, VA 23452
Ph: (757)490-3151   Fax: (757)497-6503
E-mail: britt@searchandrecruit.com
URL: http://www.searchandrecruit.com

Employment agency. Headquartered in Virginia Beach. Other offices in Bremerton, WA; Charleston, SC; Jacksonville, FL; Memphis, TN; Pensacola, FL; Sacramento, CA; San Bernardino, CA; San Diego, CA.

★3766★ Technical Talent Locators Ltd.
5570 Sterrett Place, Ste.208
Columbia, MD 21044
Ph: (410)740-0091
URL: http://www.ttlgroup.com

Permanent employment agency working within the following fields: software and database engineering; computer, communication, and telecommunication system engineering; and other computer-related disciplines.

★3767★ Techtronix Technical Search
PO Box 17713
Milwaukee, WI 53217-0173
Ph: (414)466-3100   Fax: (414)466-3598

Firm specializes in recruiting executives for the engineering, information systems, manufacturing, marketing, finance, and human resources industries.

★3768★ Tri-Serv Inc.
22 W. Padonia Rd., Ste. C-353
Timonium, MD 21093
Ph: (410)561-1740   Fax: (410)252-7417
E-mail: info@tri-serv.coom
URL: http://www.tri-serv.com

Permanent employment agency.

★3769★ Winters Technical Staffing Services
2025 Sheppard Ave. E, Ste. 4110
Willowdale, ON, Canada M2T 1V7
Ph: (416)495-7422   Fax: (416)495-8479

Technical staffing service for permanent and contract positions in all facets of engineering. Serves government agencies, consulting engineers, and all areas of manufacturing in Canada and northeast U.S.

ONLINE JOB SOURCES AND SERVICES

★3770★ Spherion Workforce Architects
URL: http://www.spherion.com

Description: Recruitment firm specializing in accounting and finance, sales and marketing, interim executives, technology, engineering, retail and human resources.

TRADESHOWS

★3771★ American Society for Engineering Education Annual Conference and Exposition
American Society for Engineering Education
1818 N St., Ste. 600
Washington, DC 20036
Ph: (202)331-3500   Fax: (202)265-8504
URL: http://www.asee.org

Annual. **Primary Exhibits:** Publications, engineering supplies and equipment, computers, software, and research companies all products and services related to engineering education. **Dates and Locations:** 2005 Jun 12-15; Portland, OR • 2006 Jun 18-21; Chicago, IL • 2007 Jun 24-27; Honolulu, HI.

★3772★ Electronic Imaging International
SPIE - International Society for Optical Engineering
PO Box 10
Bellingham, WA 98227-0010
Ph: (360)676-3290   Fax: (360)647-1445
E-mail: spie@spie.org
URL: http://www.spie.org/

Annual. **Primary Exhibits:** Equipment, supplies, and services for image processing computer graphics, fiber optics, high definition television, electronic printing and publishing, military electronics, medical tomography industries, and electronic imaging products.

★3773★ O-E/LASE - Optoelectronics and Laser Applications in Science and Engineering Exhibit
SPIE - International Society for Optical Engineering
PO Box 10
Bellingham, WA 98227-0010
Ph: (360)676-3290   Fax: (360)647-1445
E-mail: spie@spie.org
URL: http://www.spie.org/

Annual. **Primary Exhibits:** Laser applications, science, and engineering; optics and optomechanics; optical computing and holography; and mass data optical storage.

★3774★ PCB Design Conference West
CMP Media LLC (San Francisco)
2800 Campus Dr.
San Mateo, CA 94403
Ph: (650)513-4400   Fax: (650)513-4646
URL: http://www.cmp.com

Annual. **Primary Exhibits:** Provides circuit board designers education and information about the industry, including tools and techniques.

OTHER SOURCES

★3775★ Aircraft Electronics Association (AEA)

4217 S. Hocker
Independence, MO 64055-0963
Ph: (816)373-6565   Fax: (816)478-3100
E-mail: info@aea.net
URL: http://www.aea.net

Members: Companies engaged in the sales, engineering, installation, and service of electronic aviation equipment and systems. **Purpose:** Seeks to advance the science of aircraft electronics; promote uniform and stable regulations and uniform standards of performance; establish and maintain a code of ethics; gather and disseminate technical data; advance the education of members and the public in the science of aircraft electronics. **Activities:** Is active in the areas of supplement type certificates, test equipment licensing, temporary FCC licensing for new installations, spare parts availability and pricing, audiovisual technician training, equipment and spare parts loan, profitable installation, and service facility operation. Provides employment information, equipment exchange information and service assistance on member installations anywhere in the world.

★3776★ American Almanac of Jobs and Salaries

Morrow Avon
1350 Avenue of the Americas
New York, NY 10019
Ph: (212)261-6788   Fr: 800-242-7737

John W. Wright. Revised edition, 2000. $20.00 (paper). 672 pages. This is a comprehensive guide to the wages of hundreds of occupations in a wide variety of industries and organizations.

★3777★ American Association of Engineering Societies (AAES)

1828 L St. NW, No. 906
Washington, DC 20036
Ph: (202)296-2237   Fax: (202)296-1151
Fr: 888-400-2237
E-mail: tprice@aaes.org
URL: http://www.aaes.org

Description: Coordinates the efforts of the member societies in the provision of reliable and objective information to the general public concerning issues which affect the engineering profession and the field of engineering as a whole; to collect, analyze, document, and disseminate data which will inform the general public of the relationship between engineering and the national welfare; to provide a forum for the engineering societies to exchange and discuss their views on matters of common interest; and to represent the U.S. engineering community abroad through representation in WFEO and UPADI.

★3778★ ASPRS - The Imaging and Geospatial Information Society

5410 Grosvenor Ln., Ste. 210
Bethesda, MD 20814-2160
Ph: (301)493-0290   Fax: (301)493-0208
E-mail: asprs@asprs.org
URL: http://www.asprs.org

Members: Firms, individuals, government employees, and academicians engaged in photogrammetry, photointerpretation, remote sensing, and geographic information systems and their application to such fields as archaeology, geographic information systems, military reconnaissance, urban planning, engineering, traffic surveys, meteorological observations, medicine, geology, forestry, agriculture, construction, and topographic mapping. Mission is to advance knowledge and improve understanding of these sciences and to promote responsible applications. **Activities:** Offers voluntary certification program open to persons associated with one or more functional area of photogrammetry, remote sensing, and GIS. Surveys the profession of private firms in photogrammetry and remote sensing in the areas of productsand services

★3779★ Association for International Practical Training (AIPT)

10400 Little Patuxent Pkwy., Ste. 250
Columbia, MD 21044-3519
Ph: (410)997-2200   Fax: (410)992-3924
E-mail: aipt@aipt.org
URL: http://www.aipt.org

Description: Providers worldwide on-the-job training programs for students and professionals seeking international career development and life-changing experiences. Arranges workplace exchanges in hundreds of professional fields, bringing employers and trainees together from around the world. Client list ranges from small farming communities to Fortune 500 companies.

★3780★ Electrical and Electronics Engineers

Evon Publishing
832 N 7th Ave.
Iron River, MI 49935
Ph: (906)265-3190

Audiocassette. 1996. $16.95. 32 minutes. Part of the Careers and Vocational Guidance Series. Provides information about the nature of the work, educational requirements, employment outlook, earnings, and work conditions as well as additional information.

★3781★ Electronic Industries

Evon Publishing
832 N 7th Ave.
Iron River, MI 49935
Ph: (906)265-3190

Audiocassette. 1996. $16.95. 32 minutes. Part of the Careers and Vocational Guidance Series. Provides information about the nature of the work, educational requirements, employment outlook, earnings, and work conditions as well as additional related information.

★3782★ Electronic Industries Alliance (EIA)

2500 Wilson Blvd.
Arlington, VA 22201
Ph: (703)907-7500   Fax: (703)907-7501
URL: http://www.eia.org

Description: Committed to the competitiveness of the American producer, EIA represents all companies involved in the design and manufacture of electronic components, parts, systems and equipment for communications, industrial, government and consumer uses. Has represented U.S. electronics manufacturers for more than 73 years.

★3783★ Engineering Occupations

Delphi Productions
3160 4th St.
Boulder, CO 80304
Fax: (303)443-4022   Fr: 888-443-2400
URL: http://www.delphivideo.com

$95.00. 50 minutes. Part of the Careers for the 21st Century Video Library.

★3784★ Institute of Electrical and Electronics Engineers (IEEE)

445 Hoes Lane
Piscataway, NJ 08854
Ph: (732)981-0060   Fax: (732)981-9667
Fr: 800-678-4333
E-mail: corporate-communications@ieee.org
URL: http://www.ieee.org

Description: Engineers and scientists in electrical engineering, electronics, and allied fields; membership includes 58,000 students. Conducts lecture courses at the local level on topics of current engineering and scientific interest. Assists student groups. Supports Engineering Societies Library in New York City in conjunction with other groups.

★3785★ ISA - Instrumentation, Systems, and Automation Society

67 Alexander Dr.
PO Box 12277
Research Triangle Park, NC 27709
Ph: (919)549-8411   Fax: (919)549-8288
E-mail: info@isa.org
URL: http://www.isa.org

Purpose: Fosters advancement in the theory, design, manufacture, and use of instruments, computers, and systems for measurement and control.

★3786★ National Action Council for Minorities in Engineering (NACME)

Empire State Bldg., Ste. 2212
350 Fifth Ave.
New York, NY 10118-2299
Ph: (212)279-2626   Fax: (212)629-5178
E-mail: webmaster@nacme.org
URL: http://www.nacme.org/

Description: Leads the national effort to increase access to careers in engineering and other science-based disciplines. Supported by the nation's leading technology-intensive companies, NACME conducts research and public policy analysis, develops and operates national demonstration programs at precollege and university levels, and disseminates information through publications, conferences, and electronic media. NACME is also the nation's largest privately funded source of scholarships for minority students in engineering.

★3787★ **National Society of Professional Engineers (NSPE)**
1420 King St.
Alexandria, VA 22314
Ph: (703)684-2800   Fax: (703)836-4875
Fr: 888-285-6773
E-mail: custserv@nspe.org
URL: http://www.nspe.org

Description: Professional engineers and engineers-in-training in all fields registered in accordance with the laws of states or territories of the U.S. or provinces of Canada; qualified graduate engineers, student members, and registered land surveyors. Is concerned with social, professional, ethical, and economic considerations of engineering as a profession; encompasses programs in public relations, employment practices, ethical con-

siderations, education, and career guidance. Monitors legislative and regulatory actions of interest to the engineering profession.

★3788★ *Scientific, Engineering, and Technical Services*
Cambridge Educational
2572 Brunswick Ave.
Lawrenceville, NJ 08648-4128
Fax: 800-FAX-ON-US   Fr: 800-468-4227
URL: http://www.cambridgeeducational.com

$89.95. 2002. 18 minutes. Part of the Career Cluster Series.

★3789★ **Society of Women Engineers (SWE)**
230 E Ohio St., No. 400
Chicago, IL 60611-3265
Ph: (312)596-5223   Fax: (312)596-5252
E-mail: hq@swe.org
URL: http://www.swe.org

Description: Educational and service organization representing both students and professional women in engineering and technical fields.

★3790★ **SPIE - The International Society for Optical Engineering (SPIE)**
PO Box 10
Bellingham, WA 98227-0010
Ph: (360)676-3290   Fax: (360)647-1445
E-mail: spie@spie.org
URL: http://www.spie.org

Description: Dedicated to advancing scientific research and engineering applications of optical, photonic, imaging and optoelectronic technologies through meetings, education programs, and publications.

★3791★ *Women in Engineering*
Her Own Words
PO Box 5264
Madison, WI 53705-0264
Ph: (608)271-7083   Fax: (608)271-0209
URL: http://www.herownwords.com/

Video. Jocelyn Riley. $95.00. 15 minutes. Resource guide also available for $45.00.

Electricians

SOURCES OF HELP-WANTED ADS

★3792★ Builder

Hanley-Wood L.L.C.
1 Thomas Cir., Ste. 600
Washington, DC 20005
Ph: (202)452-0800   Fax: (202)785-1974
URL: http://www.builderonline.com

Monthly. $29.95/year for individuals. Magazine covering housing and construction industry.

★3793★ CEE News

Primedia Business
9800 Metcalf Ave.
Overland Park, KS 66212
Ph: (913)341-1300   Fax: (913)967-1898

Monthly. Free to qualified subscribers; $52.00/year; $92.00/year for other countries. Electrical construction industry magazine.

★3794★ Construction Digest

Construction Digest
5804 W 74th St.
Indianapolis, IN 46278
Ph: (317)293-6860   Fax: (317)293-7840
Fr: 888-893-6860

Semimonthly. $3.00 for single issue. Magazine for the public works and construction engineering industries.

★3795★ CONSTRUCTOR

Associated General Contractors Information
333 John Carlyle St., Ste. 200
Alexandria, VA 22314
Ph: (703)837-5355   Fax: (703)837-5402
URL: http://www.agc.org

Monthly. $15.00/year for members; $250.00/year for nonmembers; $4.00/year for single issue except July, November, and December; $25.00/year for single issue-November, December; $325.00 for single issue-July. Management magazine for the Construction Industry.

★3796★ Electric Light & Power

PennWell Corp.
1421 S Sheridan Rd.
Tulsa, OK 74112
Ph: (918)835-3161   Fax: (918)832-9201
Fr: 800-331-4463
URL: http://uaelp.pennnet.com/articles/print_toc.cfm?p=34

Monthly. Free to qualified subscribers; $70.00/year for institutions; $78.00/year for Canada; $194.00/year for other countries. Tabloid providing news of electric utility industry developments and activities and coverage of new products and technology.

★3797★ Engineering Economist

Institute of Industrial Engineers
3577 Pkwy. Ln., Ste. 200
Norcross, GA 30092
Ph: (770)449-0461   Fax: (770)263-8532
Fr: 800-494-0460

Quarterly. Publication covering business issues in the energy, petroleum and mining industries.

★3798★ High Tech News and Satellite Journal

Electronic Technicians Association (ETA)
502 N Jackson St.
Greencastle, IN 46135
Ph: (765)653-4301   Fax: (765)653-8262
Fr: 800-288-3824

Description: Monthly. Serves member technicians with news of the Association and the electronics industry, including items on service, education, employment, management, and events. Contains information on membership, management, telecommunications, and business and technical training programs. Recurring features include editorials, news of research, letters to the editor, book reviews, and a calendar of events.

★3799★ Professional Builder

Reed Business Information
360 Park Ave. S
New York, NY 10014
Ph: (646)746-7764
URL: http://www.probuilder.com

Monthly. $10.00 for single issue; $139.95/year for by mail.

★3800★ WIT

Northern New England Tradeswomen
189 N Main St., Ste. 9
Barre, VT 05641-4173
Ph: (802)476-4040   Fax: (802)476-3346

Description: Three issues/year. Provides a network of support, information, and skill sharing for women in skilled trades professions.

EMPLOYER DIRECTORIES AND NETWORKING LISTS

★3801★ ABC Today-Associated Builders and Contractors National Membership Directory Issue

Associated Builders & Contractors Inc.
4250 N Fairfax Dr., 9th Fl.
Arlington, VA 22203
Ph: (703)812-2000   Fax: (703)812-8203

Annual, December. $150.00. Publication includes: List of approximately 19,000 member construction contractors and suppliers. Entries include: Company name, address, phone, name of principal executive, code to volume of business, business specialty. Arrangement: Classified by chapter, then by work specialty.

★3802★ Buyer's Guide & Membership Directory

Independent Electrical Contractors Inc.
4401 Ford Ave., Ste. 1100
Alexandria, VA 22302-1432
Ph: (703)549-7351   Fax: (703)549-7448
Fr: 800-456-4324

Annual. $75.00. Covers member electrical contracting firms, electrical manufacturers, and distributors. Entries include: Name of company, address, names of principals. Arrangement: Geographical.

★3803★ Constructor-AGC Directory of Membership and Services Issue

AGC Information Inc.
333 John Carlyle St., Ste. 200
Alexandria, VA 22314
Ph: (703)548-3118   Fax: (703)548-3119
URL: http://www.agc.org

Annual, July. $250.00 for nonmembers; $15.00 for members; $250.00 for other countries. Publication includes: List of over 8,500 member firms and 24,000 national associate member firms engaged in building, highway, heavy, industrial, municipal utilities, and railroad construction (SIC 1541, 1542, 1611, 1622, 1623, 1629); listing of state and local chapter officers. Entries include: For firms-Company name, address, phone, fax, names of principal executives, and code indicating type of construction undertaken. For officers-Name, title, address. Arrangement: Geographical, Alphabetical. Indexes: Company name.

★3804★ Electric Contractors Directory

infoUSA Inc.
5711 S 86th Cir.
Omaha, NE 68127-0347
Ph: (402)930-3500   Fax: (402)331-0176
Fr: 800-555-6124
URL: http://www.abii.com

Annual. Number of listings: 63,261. Entries include: Name, address, phone (including area code), size of advertisement, year first in "Yellow Pages," name of owner or manager, number of employees. Regional editions available. Compiled from telephone company "Yellow Pages," nationwide. Arrangement: Geographical.

★3805★ ENR-Top 400 Construction Contractors Issue

McGraw-Hill Companies
1221 Ave. of the Americas
New York, NY 10020
Ph: (212)512-2000   Fax: (212)512-3840

Annual, May issue of "Engineering News Record". $10.00. Publication includes: List of 400 United States contractors receiving largest dollar volumes of contracts in preceding calendar year. Separate lists of 50 largest design/construct management firms; 50 largest program and construction managers; 25 building contractors; 25 heavy contractors. Entries include: Company name, headquarters location, total value of contracts received in preceding year, value of foreign contracts, countries in which operated, construction specialities. Arrangement: By total value of contracts received.

★3806★ International Association of Electrical Inspectors-Membership Directory

International Association of Electrical Inspectors (IAEI)
901 Waterfall Way, Ste. 602
Richardson, TX 75080-7702
Ph: (972)235-1455   Fax: (972)235-3855

Annual, April. $11.95. Covers 26,000 state and federal government, industrial, utility, and insurance electrical inspectors, and, as associate members, electricians, manufacturers, engineers, architects, and wiremen. Entries include: Name, title, type of member, address, company affiliation. Arrangement: Geographical, then by division, chapter, or section, and type of membership, then alphabetical. Indexes: Committees; personal name.

HANDBOOKS AND MANUALS

★3807★ Audel Questions and Answers for Electricians' Examinations

Hungry Minds, Inc.
10475 Crosspoint Blvd.
Indianapolis, IN 46256
Fax: (317)572-4000   Fr: 800-667-1115

Paul Rosenberg. First edition, revised, 1999. $20.00. 256 pages.

★3808★ Electrician's Exam Preparation Guide

Craftsman Book Co.
6058 Corte del Cedro
Carlsbad, CA 92009
Ph: (760)438-7828   Fax: (760)438-0398
Fr: 800-829-8123

John E. Traister. 2002. $34.50 (paper). 352 pages. Based on the 1996 NEC.

★3809★ Exploring Careers in the Construction Industry

Rosen Publishing Group Inc.
29 E. 21st St.
New York, NY 10010
Ph: (212)777-3017   Fax: 888-436-4643
Fr: 800-237-9932

Elizabeth Stewart Lytle. Revised edition, 1994. $16.95; $9.95 (paper). Out of print.

★3810★ Exploring Careers as an Electrician

Rosen Publishing Group Inc.
29 E. 21st St.
New York, NY 10010
Ph: (212)777-3017   Fax: 888-436-4643
Fr: 800-237-9932

Elizabeth S. Lytle. Revised edition, 1999. $18.95. 148 pages. Details the steps one takes in becoming an electrician, starting with apprenticeship and ending with full-time electrician work.

★3811★ How to Start and Manage a Construction Electrician Business: Step-by-Step Guide to Business Success

Lewis and Renn Associates
4860 E. Main St., No. A128
Mesa, AZ 85205
Fax: (480)830-1187

Leslie D. Renn and Jerre G. Lewis. 1994. $16.95 (paper). 120 pages.

★3812★ The New Handbook for Electricians

Prentice Hall PTR
200 Old Tappan Rd.
Old Tappan, NJ 07675
Ph: (201)236-7000   Fr: 800-223-1360

Martin Clifford. Second edition, 1996. $50.00; $37.50 (paper). 400 pages. Out of print.

★3813★ Opportunities in Building Construction Trades

McGraw-Hill Trade
2 Penn Plaza
New York, NY 10121
Ph: (212)904-2000   Fr: 800-722-4726

Michael Sumichrast. Second edition, 1998. $14.95; $11.95 (paper). 202 pages. From custom builder to rehabber, the many kinds of companies that employ craftspeople and contractors are explored. Includes job descriptions, requirements, and salaries for dozens of specialties within the construction industry. Contains a complete list of Bureau of Apprenticeship and Training state and area offices. Illustrated.

★3814★ Opportunities in Electrical Trades

McGraw-Hill/Contemporary Books
1221 Avenue of the Americas
New York, NY 10020
Ph: (212)904-2000   Fr: 800-323-4900
E-mail: ntcpub@tribune.com

Robert Wood and Kenneth R. Edwards. 1996. $14.95; $11.95 (paper). 160 pages. Offers advice on job hunting and where the jobs are. Includes index, bibliography, and illustrations.

TRADESHOWS

★3815★ AMRA International Symposium

Automatic Meter Reading Association
60 Revere Dr., Ste. 500
Northbrook, IL 60062
Ph: (847)480-9628   Fax: (847)480-9282
Fr: 888-612-2672
E-mail: amra@amra-intl.org
URL: http://www.amra-intl.org

Annual. **Primary Exhibits:** Utilities meter reading equipment, supplies, and services. **Dates and Locations:** 2004 Sep 26-29; Kissimmee, FL; Gaylord Palms Resort and Convention Center.

★3816★ Edison Electric Institute Convention and Expo

Edison Electric Institute
5203 Leesburg Pike, Ste. 1305
Falls Church, VA 20004-2696
Ph: (703)998-9864   Fax: (703)998-7163
E-mail: mambert@verizon.ne
URL: http://www.eei.org

Annual. **Primary Exhibits:** Exhibits directed to investor-owned electric utility companies operating in the U.S. and abroad.

★3817★ Electric Expo
Comprehensive Show Management, Inc.
PO Box 297
Springfield, PA 19064
Ph: (610)544-5775   Fax: (610)544-9808
E-mail: sally.oshea@verizon.net

Biennial. **Primary Exhibits:** Electrical equipment, supplies, and services.

★3818★ Electri...FYI - Upstate Electrical Show
Electrical Association of Rochester
PO Box 20219
Rochester, NY 14602-0219
Ph: (716)334-4730   Fax: (716)334-1919
E-mail: electrifyi@earoch.com
URL: http://www.earoch.com

Triennial. **Primary Exhibits:** Electrical supplies and services. **Dates and Locations:** 2006 Apr 02; Rochester, NY.

★3819★ ICCON - International Commercial Construction Exposition
National Association of Home Builders of the United States
1201 15th St. NW
Washington, DC 20005-2800
Ph: (202)266-8109   Fax: (202)266-8223
Fr: 800-368-5242
E-mail: exposales@nahb.com
URL: http://www.buildersshow.com

Primary Exhibits: Equipment, supplies, and services for the construction industries.

★3820★ Independent Electrical Contractors Annual Convention and Expo
Independent Electrical Contractors Inc.
4401 Ford Ave. Ste 1100
Alexandria, VA 22302-1432
Ph: (703)549-7352   Fax: (703)549-7448
Fr: 800-456-4324
E-mail: bmathisen@ieci.org
URL: http://www.ieci.org

Annual. **Primary Exhibits:** Equipment, supplies, and services for independent electrical contractors.

★3821★ The NECA Show
National Electrical Contractors Association
3 Bethesda Metro Center, Ste. 1100
Bethesda, MD 20814
Ph: (301)215-4507   Fax: (301)215-4553
E-mail: neca@necanet.org
URL: http://www.necanet.org

Annual. **Primary Exhibits:** Electrical products, publications, computers, software, tools, and equipment.

★3822★ Upper Midwest Electrical Expo
North Central Electrical League
2901 Metro Dr., Ste. 203
Bloomington, MN 55425-1556
Ph: (952)854-4405   Fax: (952)854-7076
Fr: 800-925-4985
E-mail: expo@ncel.org
URL: http://www.ncel.org

Biennial. **Primary Exhibits:** Electrical equipment, supplies, and services. **Dates and Locations:** 2006 Apr; Minneapolis, MN; Minnealpolis Convention Center.

OTHER SOURCES

★3823★ Associated Builders and Contractors (ABC)
1300 N. 17th St., Ste. 800
Rosslyn, VA 22209
Ph: (703)812-2000   Fax: (703)812-8201
E-mail: info@abc.org
URL: http://www.abc.org

Description: Construction contractors, subcontractors, suppliers, and associates. Aim is to foster and perpetuate the principles of rewarding construction workers and management on the basis of merit. Sponsors management education programs and craft training; also sponsors apprenticeship and skill training programs. Disseminates technological and labor relations information.

★3824★ Associated General Contractors of America (AGC)
333 John Carlyle St., Ste. 200
Alexandria, VA 22314
Ph: (703)548-3118   Fax: (703)548-3119
E-mail: sandhers@agc.org
URL: http://www.agc.org

Description: General construction contractors; subcontractors; industry suppliers; service firms. Provides market services through its divisions. Conducts special conferences and seminars designed specifically for construction firms. Compiles statistics on job accidents reported by member firms. ors. Maintains 65 committees, including joint cooperative committees with other associations and liaison committees with federal agencies.

★3825★ Associated Specialty Contractors (ASC)
3 Bethesda Metro Ctr., Ste. 1100
Bethesda, MD 20814
Ph: (301)657-3110   Fax: (301)215-4500
E-mail: dgw@necanet.org
URL: http://www.assoc-spec-con.org

Description: Subcontractor associations with a total of 25,000 members representing electrical, heating, piping, mechanical, air conditioning, sheet metal, plumbing, ventilating, painting and decorating, and roofing and insulation contractors. Promotes liaison with general contractors, architects, and engineers on inter-industry matters, codes, bid-

ding, and contracting procedures. Coordinates governmental affairs, research, and educational matters.

★3826★ Building Trades
Delphi Productions
3160 4th St.
Boulder, CO 80304
Fax: (303)443-4022   Fr: 888-443-2400
URL: http://www.delphivideo.com

$95.00. 46 minutes. Part of the Careers for the 21st Century Video Library.

★3827★ COIN Career Guidance System
COIN Educational Products
3361 Executive Pky., Ste. 302
Toledo, OH 43606
Ph: (419)536-5353   Fax: (419)536-7056
Fr: 800-274-8515
URL: http://www.coin3.com/highschool/guidance.asp

CD-ROM. Provides career information through seven cross-referenced files covering postsecondary schools, college majors, vocational programs, military service, apprenticeship programs, financial aid, and scholarships. Apprenticeship file describes national apprenticeship training programs, including information on how to apply, contact agencies, and program content. Military file describes more than 200 military occupations and training opportunities related to civilian employment.

★3828★ Electrician
Cambridge Educational
2572 Brunswick Ave.
Lawrenceville, NJ 08648-4128
Fax: 800-FAX-ON-US   Fr: 800-468-4227
URL: http://www.cambridgeeducational.com

$39.95. 1993. Part of the Career Connections video series.

★3829★ Independent Electrical Contractors (IEC)
4401 Ford Ave., Ste. 1100
Alexandria, VA 22302-1432
Ph: (703)549-7351   Fax: (703)549-7448
Fr: 800-456-4324
E-mail: wrmathisen@ieci.org
URL: http://www.ieci.org

Members: Independent electrical contractors, small and large, primarily open shop. **Purpose:** Promotes the interests of members; works to eliminate "unwise and unfair business practices" and to protect its members against "unfair or unjust taxes and legislative enactments." **Activities:** Sponsors electrical apprenticeship programs; conducts educational programs on cost control and personnel motivation. Represents independent electrical contractors to the National Electrical Code panel. Conducts surveys on volume of sales and purchases and on type of products used. Has formulated National Pattern Standards for Apprentice Training for Electricians.

★3830★ National Association of Home Builders (NAHB)
1201 15th St. NW
Washington, DC 20005
Ph: (202)266-8200   Fax: (202)822-0586
Fr: 800-368-5242
E-mail: info@nahb.com
URL: http://www.nahb.org

Description: Single and multifamily home builders, commercial builders, and others associated with the building industry. Lobbies on behalf of the housing industry and conducts public affairs activities to increase public understanding of housing and the economy. Collects and disseminates data on current developments in home building and home builders' plans through its Economics Department and nationwide Metropolitan Housing Forecast. Maintains NAHB Research Center, which functions as the research arm of the home building industry. Sponsors seminars and workshops on construction, mortgage credit, labor relations, cost reduction, land use, remodeling, and business management. Compiles statistics; offers charitable program, spokesman training, and placement service; maintains speakers' bureau, and Hall of Fame. Subsidiaries include the National Council of the Housing Industry. Maintains over 50 committees in many areas of construction; operates National Commercial Builders Council, National Council of the Multifamily Housing Industry, National Remodelers Council, and National Sales and Marketing Council.

★3831★ National Association of Women in Construction (NAWIC)
327 S Adams St.
Fort Worth, TX 76104
Ph: (817)877-5551   Fax: (817)877-0324
Fr: 800-552-3506
E-mail: nawic@nawic.org
URL: http://www.nawic.org

Description: Seeks to enhance the success of women in the construction industry.

★3832★ National Electrical Contractors Association (NECA)
3 Bethesda Metro Ctr., Ste. 1100
Bethesda, MD 20814
Ph: (301)657-3110   Fax: (301)215-4500
E-mail: webmaster@necanet.org
URL: http://www.necanet.org

Members: Contractors erecting, installing, repairing, servicing, and maintaining electric wiring, equipment, and appliances. **Activities:** Provides management services and labor relations programs for electrical contractors; conducts seminars for contractor sales and training. Conducts research and educational programs; compiles statistics. Sponsors honorary society, the Academy of Electrical Contracting.

★3833★ *Women in Building Construction*
Her Own Words
PO Box 5264
Madison, WI 53705-0264
Ph: (608)271-7083   Fax: (608)271-0209
URL: http://www.herownwords.com/

Video. Jocelyn Riley. $95.00. 15 minutes. Resource guide also available for $45.00.

Emergency Medical Technicians

SOURCES OF HELP-WANTED ADS

★3834★ Ambulatory Outreach

Society for Ambulatory Care Professionals
1 N Franklin, 31st Fl.
Chicago, IL 60606
Fax: (312)422-4577

Quarterly. Subscription included in membership; $95.00/year for nonmembers. Professional journal for ambulatory care personnel.

★3835★ American Fire Journal

American Fire Journal
9072 E Artesia Blvd., Ste. 7
Bellflower, CA 90706-6299
Ph: (562)866-1664   Fax: (562)867-6434

Monthly. $22.95/year for individuals; $42.00/year for individuals, other countries; $3.50/year for single issue. Magazine about fire protection.

★3836★ ASRT Scanner

American Society of Radiologic
 Technologists
15000 Central Ave. SE
Albuquerque, NM 87123-3917
Ph: (505)298-4500   Fax: (505)298-5063
Fr: 800-444-2778

Monthly. Subscription included in membership. Professional magazine covering issues in radiology and medical technology. Includes calendar of events, member profiles, state affiliate news, educational opportunities, and research updates.

★3837★ Dispatch Monthly

Gary Allen
PO Box 8387
Berkeley, CA 94707-8387
Ph: (510)528-7830   Fax: (510)558-3109
Fr: 877-370-3477
E-mail: editor@dispatchmonthly.com
URL: http://www.911dispatch.com

Description: Monthly. Provides focused news for public safety emergency (911)

dispatchers. Recurring features include letters to the editor, interviews, news of research, a calendar of events, reports of meetings, news of educational opportunities, job listings, book reviews, and notices of publications available.

★3838★ Emergency Medical Services

Summer Communications Inc.
7626 Densmore Ave.
Van Nuys, CA 91406-2042
Ph: (818)786-4367   Fax: (818)786-9246
Fr: 800-224-4367
E-mail: emsmag@earthlink.net
URL: http://www.emsmagazine.com

Monthly. $19.95/year for individuals. Magazine covering emergency care, rescue and transportation.

★3839★ Health Care Weekly Review

The Martin Group Inc.
24901 Northwestern Hwy., Ste. 316A
Southfield, MI 48075
Ph: (248)440-6080   Fax: (248)352-4801
E-mail: hcwr@compuserve.com

Weekly. $48.00/year for individuals. Professional newspaper covering the health care industry.

★3840★ Hospitals & Health Networks

Health Forum L.L.C.
One N Franklin
Chicago, IL 60606
Ph: (312)893-6800   Fax: (312)422-4600
Fr: 800-621-6902
E-mail: hhn@healthforum.com
URL: http://www.hhnmag.com

Monthly. Publication covering the health care industry.

★3841★ Journal of the American Society of Podiatric Medical Assistants

American Society of Podiatric Medical
 Assistants
2124 S Austin Blvd.
Cicero, IL 60804
Ph: (708)863-6303   Fax: (708)863-5375
Fr: 888-88A-SPMA

Quarterly. Subscription included in membership. Professional journal covering issues in podiatry.

★3842★ Journal of Health and Hospital Law

American Health Lawyers Association
1025 Connecticut NW, Ste. 600
Washington, DC 20036
Ph: (202)833-1100   Fax: (202)833-1105

Quarterly. $150.00/year. Professional journal covering healthcare issues and cases and their impact on the health care arena.

★3843★ Medicine and Health

Thomson Financial
195 Broadway
New York, NY 10007
Ph: (646)822-2000

Weekly. Professional publication covering the health care industry.

★3844★ Minority Health Today

Heritage Information Holdings Inc.
1101 Pennsylvania Ave. NW, Ste. 820
Washington, DC 20001

Bimonthly. Publication covering minority issues in health.

★3845★ The Municipality

League of Wisconsin Municipalities
202 State St., Ste. 300
Madison, WI 53703-2215
Ph: (608)267-2380   Fax: (608)267-0645
Fr: 800-991-5502

Monthly. $12.00/year. Magazine for officials of Wisconsin's local municipal governments.

★3846★ Research in Healthcare Financial Management

International Society for Research in Healthcare Financial Management Ltd.
305 W Chesapeake Ave.
CSBA Ste. L-096
Towson, MD 21204

Annual. Publication covering issues in the healthcare industry.

★3847★ State Health Monitor

Atlantic Information Services Inc.
1100 17th St. NW, No. 300
Washington, DC 20036
Ph: (202)775-9008   Fax: (202)331-9542
Fr: 800-521-4323
E-mail: customerserv@aispub.com

Monthly. Publication covering health care.

★3848★ Trauma Reports

Thomson Medical Economics
5 Paragon Dr.
Montvale, NJ 07645-1742
Ph: (201)358-7200   Fax: (201)722-2680
URL: http://www.ahcpub.com/ahc_root_html/products/newsletters/tr.

Bimonthly. $239.00/year for individuals. Professional publication covering health care.

PLACEMENT AND JOB REFERRAL SERVICES

★3849★ National Association of Emergency Medical Technicians (NAEMT)

132-A E Northside Dr.
Clinton, MS 39056
Ph: (601)924-7744   Fax: (601)924-7325
Fr: 800-34-NAEMT
E-mail: president@naemt.org
URL: http://www.naemt.org

Description: Represents and supports EMTS, paramedics and other professionals working in pre-hospital emergency medicine working in all sectors of EMS, including government third-service agencies, fire departments, hospital-based ambulance services, private companies, industrial, special operations settings, and in the military. Acts as a voice for EMS personnel in Washington, DC regarding decisions affecting EMS; speaks on behalf of all EMS providers; representatives sit on boards, associations, expert panels, and commissions to ensure that EMS is represented in decisions affecting health care and public safety; works on behalf of members in the areas of compensation and recognition, recruitment and retention, safety, and education and training.

EMPLOYER DIRECTORIES AND NETWORKING LISTS

★3850★ AHA Guide to the Health Care Field

American Hospital Association (AHA)
1 N. Franklin St., 27th Fl.
Chicago, IL 60606
Ph: (312)422-2050   Fax: (312)422-4700
Fr: 800-424-4301

Annual, August. $295.00. Covers hospitals, networks, multi-health care systems, free-standing ambulatory surgery centers, psychiatric facilities, long-term care facilities, substance abuse programs, and other health-related organizations. Entries include: For hospitals-Facility name, address, phone, administrator's name, number of beds, facilities and services, number of employees, expenses, other statistics. For other organizations-Name, address, phone, fax, name and title of contact. Arrangement: Geographical. Indexes: Hospital name.

★3851★ Directory of Hospital Personnel

Thomson Medical Economics
5 Paragon Dr.
Montvale, NJ 07645-1742
Ph: (201)358-7200   Fax: (201)722-2680

Annual, November. $325.00. Covers 200,000 executives at 7,000 U.S. hospitals. Entries include: Name of hospital, address, phone, number of beds, type and JCAHO status of hospital, names and titles of key department heads and staff, medical and nursing school affiliations; number of residents, interns, and nursing students. Arrangement: Geographical. Indexes: Hospital name, personnel, hospital size.

★3852★ Guide to Careers in the Health Professions

The Princeton Review
1745 Broadway
New York, NY 10019
Ph: (212)829-6928   Fax: (212)940-7400
Fr: 800-733-3000

Published January, 2001. $24.95. Presents advice and information for those searching for satisfying careers in the health professions. Publication includes: Directory of schools and academic programs. Entries include: Name, address, phone, tuition, program details, employment profiles.

★3853★ Hospital Blue Book

Billian/Transworld Publishing Inc.
2100 Powers Ferry Rd.
Ste. 300
Atlanta, GA 30339
Ph: (770)955-8484   Fax: (770)955-8485
Fr: 800-533-8484
E-mail: blu-book@billian.com

Annual, January. $285.00 for national edition; $160.00 for southern edition. Covers more than 6,687 hospitals; some listings

also appear in a separate southern edition of this publication. Entries include: Name of hospital, accreditation, mailing address, phone, fax, number of beds, type of facility (nonprofit, general, state, etc.); list of administrative personnel and chiefs of medical services, with specific titles. Arrangement: Geographical.

★3854★ The JobBank Guide to Health Care Companies

Adams Media Corp.
57 Littlefield St.
Avon, MA 02322
Ph: (508)427-7100   Fax: (508)427-6790
Fr: 800-872-5627

$17.95. Covers Jobs nationwide in health care companies. Entries include: Firm or organization name, address, phone, name and title of contact; description of organization, headquarters location, typical titles for entry- and middle-level positions, educational backgrounds desired, fringe benefits offered, stock exchange listing, training programs, internships, parent company, number of employees, revenues, e-mail and web address, projected number of hires. Indexes: Alphabetical.

★3855★ Medical and Health Information Directory

Thomson Gale
27500 Drake Rd.
Farmington Hills, MI 48331-3535
Ph: (248)699-4253   Fax: (248)699-8065
Fr: 800-877-GALE
E-mail: businessproducts@gale.com

Annual. $285.00 per volume; $675.00 per set. Covers in Volume 1, more than 26,500 medical and health oriented associations, organizations, institutions, and government agencies, including health maintenance organizations (HMOs), preferred provider organizations (PPOs), insurance companies, pharmaceutical companies, research centers, and medical and allied health schools. In Volume 2, over 12,000 medical book publishers; medical periodicals, directories, audiovisual producers and services, medical libraries and information centers, electronic resources, and health-related internet search engines. In Volume 3, more than 35,500 clinics, treatment centers, care programs, and counseling/diagnostic services for 34 subject areas. Entries include: Institution, service, or firm name, address, phone, fax, email and URL; many include names of key personnel and, when pertinent, descriptive annotation. Volume 3 was formerly listed separately as Health Services Directory. Arrangement: Classified by organization activity, service, etc. Indexes: Each volume has a complete alphabetical name and keyword index.

★3856★ National Directory of Fire Chiefs & EMS Administrators

National Public Safety Information Bureau
601 Main St., Ste. 201
PO Box 365
Stevens Point, WI 54481
Ph: (715)345-2772   Fax: (715)345-7288
Fr: 800-647-7579
URL: http://www.safetysource.com

Annual, December. $129.00. Covers over 36,000 fire and emergency departments in the U.S. Entries include: Department name, address, phone, fax, county, name of chief, type of department, financial structure. Arrangement: Geographical.

★3857★ Registry of Ambulance Services

Emergency Medical Services Div.
1000 NE., 10th St., Rm. 1104
Oklahoma City, OK 73117
Ph: (405)271-5600   Fax: (405)271-4240

Annual, August. Covers approximately 200 licensed ambulance services in Oklahoma. Entries include: Company, name, address, phone, geographical area served, names and titles of key personnel, number of employees, number of vehicles, description of service, number of primary hospitals. An abridged version containing only names and addresses is available for $38.50. Arrangement: Alphabetical by county and city.

HANDBOOKS AND MANUALS

★3858★ Careers in the Emergency Medical Response Team's Search and Rescue Unit

The Rosen Publishing Group, Inc.
29 E. 21st St.
New York, NY 10010
Ph: (212)777-3017   Fax: (212)777-0277
Fr: 800-237-9932

Jeri Freedman. December 2002. $26.50. Illustrated. 64 pages.

★3859★ Careers in Health Care

McGraw-Hill Trade
2 Penn Plaza
New York, NY 10121
Ph: (212)904-2000   Fr: 800-722-4726
E-mail: ntcpub@tribune.com

Barbara M. Swanson. Fourth edition, 2000. $17.95; $13.95 (paper). 320 pages. Describes job duties, work settings, salaries, licensing and certification requirements, educational preparation, and future outlook. Gives ideas on how to secure a job.

★3860★ Careers for Night Owls and Other Insomniacs

McGraw-Hill Trade
2 Penn Plaza
New York, NY 10121
Ph: (212)904-2000   Fr: 800-722-4726

E-mail: ntcpub@tribune.com

Louise Miller. 1995. $14.95; $9.95 (paper). 160 pages.

★3861★ Opportunities in Health and Medical Careers

McGraw-Hill Trade
2 Penn Plaza
New York, NY 10121
Ph: (212)904-2000   Fr: 800-722-4726

I. Donald Snook, Jr. and Leo D'Orazio. 1997. $14.95; $11.95 (paper). 202 pages. Covers the full range of medical and health occupations. Illustrated.

★3862★ Opportunities in Paramedical Careers

McGraw-Hill/Contemporary Books
1221 Avenue of the Americas
New York, NY 10020
Ph: (212)904-2000   Fr: 800-323-4900
E-mail: ntcpub@tribune.com

Alex Kacen. Revised, 1999. $14.95; 11.95 (paper). 200 pages. Discusses a variety of opportunities in this field and how to pursue them. Illustrated.

★3863★ Opportunities in State and Local Government Careers

Vgm Career Horizons
1221 Avenue of the Americas
New York, NY 10020
Ph: (212)904-2000   Fr: 800-323-4900
E-mail: ntcpub@tribune.com

Neale J. Baxter. 1994. $14.95; $10.95 (paper). 160 pages. Points out the incentives and drawbacks of a government career. Describes hiring procedures and provides tips on filling out applications, taking physical and aptitude tests, handling interviews, and finding jobs. Describes the jobs in which 75% of all state and local government workers are employed. For each occupation, covers the nature of the work and the training required.

★3864★ The Paramedic Review

Thomson Delmar Learning
P.O. Box 15015
Albany, NY 12212-5015
Ph: (518)348-2300   Fax: (518)464-0393
Fr: 800-998-7498

Bob Elling and Kirsten Elling. 2002.

★3865★ Resumes for Health and Medical Careers

McGraw-Hill Trade
2 Penn Plaza
New York, NY 10121
Ph: (212)904-2000   Fr: 800-722-4726
E-mail: ntcpub@tribune.com

1997. $9.95 (paper). 455 pages.

EMPLOYMENT AGENCIES AND SEARCH FIRMS

★3866★ JPM International

26060 Acero
Mission Viejo, CA 92691
Ph: (949)699-4300   Fax: (949)699-4333
Fr: 800-685-7856
E-mail: leslieo@jpmintl.com
URL: http://www.jpmintl.com

Executive search firm and employment agency.

ONLINE JOB SOURCES AND SERVICES

★3867★ Medhunters.com
E-mail: info@medhunters.com
URL: http://www.medhunters.com

Description: Career search site for jobs in all health care specialties; educational resources; visa and licensing information for relocation; interesting articles; relocation tools; links to professional organizations and general resources.

★3868★ ProHealthJobs
E-mail: sales@prohealthjobs.com
URL: http://www.prohealthjobs.com

Description: Career resources site for the medical and health care field. Lists professional opportunities, product information, continuing education and open positions.

OTHER SOURCES

★3869★ Commission on Accreditation of Allied Health Education Programs (CAAHEP)

35 E. Wacker Dr., Ste. 1970
Chicago, IL 60601-2208
Ph: (312)553-9355   Fax: (312)553-9616
E-mail: caahep@caahep.org
URL: http://www.caahep.org

Description: Serves as a nationally recognized accrediting agency for allied health programs in 18 occupational areas.

★3870★ Emergency Medical Technicians

Evon Publishing
832 N 7th Ave.
Iron River, MI 49935
Ph: (906)265-3190

Audiocassette. 1996. $16.95. 32 minutes. Part of the Careers and Vocational Guidance Series. Provides information about the nature of the work, educational requirements, employment outlook, earnings, and work conditions as well as additional related information.

★3871★ *EMTs, Nurses, Therapists, and Assistants*

Cambridge Educational
2572 Brunswick Ave.
Lawrenceville, NJ 08648-4128
Fax: 800-FAX-ON-US   Fr: 800-468-4227
URL: http://www.cambridgeeducational.com

$79.95. 1999. Part of the series "Exploring Health Occupations."

★3872★ *Exploring Health Occupations*

Cambridge Educational
2572 Brunswick Ave.
Lawrenceville, NJ 08648-4128
Fax: 800-FAX-ON-US   Fr: 800-468-4227
URL: http://www.cambridgeeducational.com

Two videos. $139.95. 1999.

★3873★ *Health Service Occupations*

Delphi Productions
3160 4th St.
Boulder, CO 80304
Fax: (303)443-4022   Fr: 888-443-2400
URL: http://www.delphivideo.com

$95.00. 50 minutes. Part of the Careers for the 21st Century Video Library.

★3874★ *Health Technologists & Technicians*

Delphi Productions
3160 4th St.
Boulder, CO 80304
Fax: (303)443-4022   Fr: 888-443-2400
URL: http://www.delphivideo.com

$95.00. 50 minutes. Part of the Careers for the 21st Century Video Library.

★3875★ *Medical Technicians and Technologists*

Cambridge Educational
2572 Brunswick Ave.
Lawrenceville, NJ 08648-4128
Fax: 800-FAX-ON-US   Fr: 800-468-4227
URL: http://www.cambridgeeducational.com

$79.95. 15 minutes. Part of the Exploring Health Occupations Series.

★3876★ *Medicine & Related Occupations*

Delphi Productions
3160 4th St.
Boulder, CO 80304
Fax: (303)443-4022   Fr: 888-443-2400
URL: http://www.delphivideo.com

$95.00. 45 minutes. Part of the Careers for the 21st Century Video Library.

★3877★ National Registry of Emergency Medical Technicians (NREMT)

Rocco V. Morando Bldg.
6610 Busch Blvd.
PO Box 29233
Columbus, OH 43229
Ph: (614)888-4484   Fax: (614)888-8920
E-mail: webmaster@nremt.org
URL: http://www.nremt.org

Purpose: Promotes the improved delivery of emergency medical services by assisting in the development and evaluation of educational programs to train emergency medical technicians; establishing qualifications for eligibility to apply for registration; preparing and conducting examinations designed to assure the competency of emergency medical technicians and paramedics; establishing a system for biennial registration; establishing procedures for revocation of certificates of registration for cause; maintaining a directory of registered emergency medical technicians.

★3878★ *Women in Firefighting*

Her Own Words
PO Box 5264
Madison, WI 53705-0264
Ph: (608)271-7083   Fax: (608)271-0209
URL: http://www.herownwords.com/

Video. Jocelyn Riley. $95.00. 15 minutes. Resource guide also available for $45.00.

Employment Interviewers

SOURCES OF HELP-WANTED ADS

★3879★ *Checkpoint*
Russell Staffing Resources
PO Box 6279
San Rafael, CA 94903-0279
Fax: (415)986-6003

Description: Quarterly. Designed to meet the needs of persons responsible for hiring and employment. Includes updates on hot trends, technologies, laws, new human resource tools, techniques, advice, and columns titled You Heard It Here First and It's Enough to Drive You Batty.

★3880★ *Journal of Staff Development*
National Staff Development Council
PO Box 240
Oxford, OH 45056
Ph: (513)523-6029   Fax: (513)523-0638
Fr: 800-727-7288

Quarterly. Professional journal covering administration issues.

★3881★ *Recruiting Trends*
Kennedy Information Inc.
One Pheonix Mill Ln., 5th Fl.
Peterborough, NH 03458
Ph: (603)924-1006   Fax: (603)924-4034
Fr: 800-531-0007

Description: Bimonthly. Provides strategies and tactics for creating and maintaining a competitive work force.

★3882★ *Workforce*
ACC Communications Inc.
245 Fischer Ave., B-2
Costa Mesa, CA 92626
Ph: (714)751-1883   Fax: (714)751-4106
E-mail: mailroom@workforcemag.com
URL: http://www.workforceonline.com

Monthly. $59.00/year for individuals; $99.00/year for Canada. A Business magazine for human resources management leaders.

PLACEMENT AND JOB REFERRAL SERVICES

★3883★ **Association of Career Management Consulting Firms International (AOCFI)**
204 E St. NE
Washington, DC 20002
Ph: (202)547-6344   Fax: (202)547-6348
E-mail: aocfi@aocfi.org
URL: http://www.aocfi.org

Members: Firms providing displaced employees, who are sponsored by their organization, with counsel and assistance in job searching and the techniques and practices of choosing a career. **Purpose:** To develop, improve, and encourage the art and science of outplacement consulting and the professional standards of competence, objectivity, and integrity in the service of clients. Cooperates with other industrial, technical, educational, professional, and governmental bodies in areas of mutual interest and concern.

★3884★ **International Association of Personnel in Employment Security (IAPES)**
1801 Louisville Rd.
Frankfort, KY 40601
Fax: (502)223-4127   Fr: 888-898-9960
E-mail: iapes@iapes.org
URL: http://www.iapes.org

Description: Officials and others engaged in job placement, unemployment compensation, and labor market information administration through municipal, state, provincial, and federal government employment agencies and unemployment compensation agencies. Conducts workshops and research. Offers professional development program of study guides and tests.

EMPLOYER DIRECTORIES AND NETWORKING LISTS

★3885★ *The Directory of Executive Recruiters*
Kennedy Information Inc.
1 Kennedy Pl.
Rte. 12 S.
Fitzwilliam, NH 03447
Ph: (603)585-3101   Fax: (603)585-6401
Fr: 800-531-0007

First edition, 2001. $179.95. 2100 pages. Lists and describes more than 3,200 firms in North America and indexes these by function, industry, and geographic area. Names key principals of recruiting firms. Includes narrative section on executive search and how it affects job candidates. Also available: Corporate Edition, expanded for use by corporate staffs, $99.00 (hardcover).

★3886★ *Employment Agencies & Opportunities Directory*
infoUSA Inc.
5711 S 86th Cir.
Omaha, NE 68127-0347
Ph: (402)930-3500   Fax: (402)331-0176
Fr: 800-555-6124
URL: http://www.abii.com

Annual. Number of listings: 30,462. Entries include: Name, address, phone (including area code), size of advertisement, year first in "Yellow Pages," name of owner or manager, number of employees. Compiled from telephone company "Yellow Pages," nationwide. Arrangement: Geographical.

★3887★ *Employment Contractors-Temporary Help Directory*
infoUSA Inc.
5711 S 86th Cir.
Omaha, NE 68127-0347
Ph: (402)930-3500   Fax: (402)331-0176
Fr: 800-555-6124
URL: http://www.abii.com

Annual. Number of listings: 22,959. Entries include: Name, address, phone (including area code), size of advertisement, year first in "Yellow Pages," name of owner or manager, number of employees. Compiled from telephone company "Yellow Pages," nationwide. Arrangement: Geographical.

★3888★ **Executive Recruitment Firms**

JNN International Inc.
6821 Sutherland Ct.
Mentor, OH 44060

Annual, September. $7.00. Covers firms providing services such as executive search, job counseling, and marketing (resume preparation, mailing, etc.); personnel agencies and job registers. Published in 18 industry-specific volumes under title "Executive Recruitment Firms Specializing in (industry name)" and a general volume titled "Executive Recruitment Firms Specializing in Most Industries." Entries include: Company name, contact name, address. Arrangement: Separate geographical sections for firms that do not charge fees and those that do charge.

★3889★ **Executive Search Consultants Directory**

infoUSA Inc.
5711 S 86th Cir.
Omaha, NE 68127-0347
Ph: (402)930-3500   Fax: (402)331-0176
Fr: 800-555-6124
URL: http://www.abii.com

Annual. Number of listings: 8,320. Entries include: Name, address, phone (including area code), size of advertisement, year first in "Yellow Pages," name of owner or manager, number of employees. Compiled from telephone company "Yellow Pages," nationwide. Arrangement: Geographical.

★3890★ **Executive Search Research Directory**

Recruiting & Search Report
PO Box 9433
Panama City, FL 32417
Ph: (850)235-3733   Fax: (850)233-9695
Fr: 800-634-4548
E-mail: esrd11@aol.com
URL: http://www.rsronline.com

Biennial, with yearly updates; May 2004, 11th Edition. $100.00. Covers over 400 freelance executive search researchers that specialize in candidate locating, screening, and development for executive recruiters and corporate (in-house) recruiters; publishers of directories, books, periodicals, and other resources related to recruitment research. Entries include: For researchers-Name, address, phone, rates, year established, first year listed, a description of services and specialties, hourly rates. Arrangement: Researchers are geographical by zip code. Indexes: Geographical; means of industry or functional concentration; unusual expertise; specialty.

★3891★ **International Association for Personnel Women-Membership Roster**

National Human Resources Association (NHRA)
PO Box 803
Pewaukee, WI 53072-0803
Fax: (414)475-5959   Fr: (866)523-4417

Latest edition November, 1994. $150.00. Covers 1,200 members-at-large and members of affiliated chapters. Entries include: Individual name, title, company name, mailing address, office phone. Arrangement: Classified by type of membership.

★3892★ **National Directory of Personnel Service Firms**

National Association of Personnel Services
10905 Fort Washington Rd., Ste. 400
Fort Washington, MD 20744-5807
Ph: (301)203-6700   Fax: (301)203-4346

Annual, spring. $15.95. Covers Over 1,100 member private (for-profit) personnel service firms and temporary service firms. Entries include: Firm name, address, phone, fax, contact, area of specialization. Arrangement: Same information given geographically by employment specialty.

HANDBOOKS AND MANUALS

★3893★ **Hiring: More Than a Gut Feeling (Build Your Business)**

Career Press, Inc.
3 Tice Rd.,
Franklin Lakes, NJ 07417-1322
Ph: (201)848-0310   Fax: (201)848-1727
Fr: 800-227-3371

Richard S. Deems. 1995. $12.99 (paper). 128 pages.

★3894★ **How to Become a Skillful Interviewer (Worksmart Series)**

AMACOM
1601 Broadway, 12th Fl.
New York, NY 10019-7420
Ph: (518)891-1500   Fax: (518)903-8168
Fr: 800-250-5308

Randi Toler Sachs. 1994. $12.95 (paper). 83 pages.

★3895★ **How to Spot a Liar in a Job Interview**

Management Advantage, Incorporated
P.O. Box 3708
Walnut Creek, CA 94598-0708
Ph: (925)671-0404   Fax: (925)825-3930
Fr: 888-671-0404

Wayne D. Ford. 1999. $14.95 (paper).

★3896★ **How to Succeed in Employee Development: Moving from Vision to Results**

The McGraw-Hill Companies
860 Taylor Station Rd.
Blacklick, OH 43004-0545
Fr: 800-722-4726

Edward Moorby. Third edition, 1998. 183 pages. Part of the Training Series.

★3897★ **The Human Resource Professional's Career Guide: Building a Position of Strength**

John Wiley & Sons, Inc.
111 River St
Hoboken, NJ 07030
Ph: (201)748-6000   Fax: (201)748-6088
Fr: 800-255-5945

Jeanne Palmer, Martha I. Finney. June 2004. $35.00. 264 pages.

★3898★ **Interviewer Approaches**

Ashgate Publishing Co.
2252 Ridge Rd.
Brookfield, VT 05036-9704
Ph: (802)276-3162   Fax: (802)276-3651
Fr: 800-535-9544

Jean Morton-Williams. 1993. $89.95. 239 pages.

★3899★ **The Interviewer's Pocketbook**

Management Pocketbooks
Laurel Hse., Station Approach
London SO24 9JH, United Kingdom
Ph: 440 1962 735573   Fax: 440 1962 733637

John Townsend. 1999.

★3900★ **Interviewing Skills for Managers**

Piatkus Books
5 Windmill St.
London W1P 1HF, United Kingdom
Ph: 020 7631 0710   Fax: 020 7436 7137

Tony Pont and Gillian Pont. 1999.

★3901★ **Interviewing the World's Top Interviewers: The Inside Story of Journalism's Most Momentous Revelations**

Sure Seller, Inc.
136 W. 22nd St.
New York, NY 10011
Ph: (212)633-2022   Fax: (212)633-2123

Jack Huper and Dean Diggins. 1993. $5.50 (paper)

★3902★ **96 Great Interview Questions to Ask Before You Hire**

AMACOM
1601 Broadway, 12th Fl.
New York, NY 10019-7420
Ph: (518)891-1500   Fax: (518)903-8168

Paul Falcone. 2000. $10.95.

★3903★ Real-Resumes for Human-Resources and Personnel Jobs: Including Real Resumes Used to Change Careers and Transfer Skills to Other Industries
PREP Publishing
1110 1/2 Hay St., PMB 66
Fayetteville, NC 28305
Ph: (910)483-6611   Fax: (910)483-2439
Fr: 800-533-2814

Anne McKinney. September 2002. $16.95.

★3904★ Up Is Not the Only Way: A Guide to Developing Workforce Talent
Davies-Black Publishers, Inc.
3803 E. Bayshore Rd.
Palo Alto, CA 94303
Ph: (650)969-8901   Fax: (650)969-8608
Fr: 800-624-1765

Beverly L. Kaye. Second Edition. 2002. $22.95. 320 pages.

★3905★ Where the Jobs Are: The Hottest Careers for the 90s
The Career Press, Inc.
3 Tice Rd.
PO Box 687
Franklin Lakes, NJ 07417-1322
Ph: (201)848-0310   Fax: (201)848-1727
Fr: 800-227-3371

Joyce Hadley. Third edition, 2000. $13.99 (paper). 400 pages. Out of print. Describes careers in fifteen general fields, from accounting to travel and hospitality.

EMPLOYMENT AGENCIES AND SEARCH FIRMS

★3906★ Abbott Smith Associates, Inc.
PO Box 318
3290 Franklin Ave.
Millbrook, NY 12545
Ph: (845)677-5300   Fax: (845)677-3315
E-mail: abbottsmith@prodigy.net

Executive search firm. Affiliate offices in Chicago and London.

★3907★ Abel Fuller & Zedler LLC
4550 Post Oak Pl., Ste. 141
Houston, TX 77027
Ph: (713)961-3330   Fax: (713)961-3337

Executive Search Firm.

★3908★ The Andre Group Inc.
500 N. Gulph Rd., Ste. 210
King of Prussia, PA 19406
Ph: (610)337-0600   Fax: (610)337-1333

Executive search firm. Focused on the human resource field.

★3909★ The Aspire Group
52 Second Ave., 1st Fl
Waltham, MA 02451-1129
Fax: (718)890-1810   Fr: 800-546-5675
URL: http://www.bmanet.com

Employment agency.

★3910★ Campbell/Carlson LLC
The Addison Bldg.
831 E. Moorehead St., Ste. 750
Charlotte, NC 28202
Ph: (704)373-0234   Fax: (704)373-0232

Executive search firm.

★3911★ Dankowski and Associates, Inc.
6479 Stoney Ridge Rd.NE, Ste. 200
PO Box 39478
North Ridgeville, OH 44039-0478
Ph: (440)327-8717   Fax: (440)327-1853
E-mail: dankowski@aol.com
URL: http://www.samkowskiassociates.com

Executive search firm.

★3912★ The Enfield Company
1605 Juliet St.
Austin, TX 78704
Ph: (512)444-9921

Executive search firm.

★3913★ Executive Search Inc.
5401 Gamble Dr., Ste. 275
Minneapolis, MN 55416
Ph: (952)541-9153

Executive search firm.

★3914★ FM Industries
10125 Crosstown Circle, Ste. 300
Eden Prairie, MN 55344
Ph: (952)941-0966   Fax: (952)941-4462

Executive search firm.

★3915★ John J. Davis & Associates Inc.
521 5th Ave., Ste. 1740
New York, NY 10175
Ph: (212)286-9489   Fax: (973)467-3706

Executive search firm.

★3916★ Karras Personnel, Inc.
2 Central Ave.
Madison, NJ 07940
Ph: (973)966-6800
E-mail: karraspersonnel@mindspring.com
URL: http://www.karraspersonnel.home.mindspring.com

Executive search firm specializing in human resources recruiting.

★3917★ Philip Conway Management
320 Hampton Place
Hinsdale, IL 60521-3823
Ph: (630)655-4566

Executive search firm.

★3918★ Protocol Agency Inc.
2659 Townsgate Rd., Ste.203
Westlake Village, CA 91361-2774
Ph: (626)449-2214   Fax: (805)371-0048
E-mail: wiv@protocalagency.com
URL: http://www.protocolagency.com

Executive search firm focusing on a variety of placements.

★3919★ Willmott and Associates
922 Waltham St., Ste. 103
Lexington, MA 02421-8019
Ph: (781)863-5400   Fax: (781)863-8000
E-mail: willmont@willmont.com
URL: http://www.willmott.com

Executive search firm and permanent employment agency. Also fills some temporary placements.

ONLINE JOB SOURCES AND SERVICES

★3920★ Spherion Workforce Architects
URL: http://www.spherion.com
Description: Recruitment firm specializing in accounting and finance, sales and marketing, interim executives, technology, engineering, retail and human resources.

OTHER SOURCES

★3921★ American Almanac of Jobs and Salaries
Morrow Avon
1350 Avenue of the Americas
New York, NY 10019
Ph: (212)261-6788   Fr: 800-242-7737

John W. Wright. Revised edition, 2000. $20.00 (paper). 672 pages. This is a comprehensive guide to the wages of hundreds of occupations in a wide variety of industries and organizations.

★3922★ American Staffing Association (ASA)
277 S. Washington St., Ste. 200
Alexandria, VA 22314-3646
Ph: (703)253-2020   Fax: (703)253-2053
E-mail: asa@staffingtoday.net
URL: http://www.staffingtoday.net

Description: Promotes and represents the staffing industry through legal and legislative advocacy, public relations, education, and the establishment of high standards of ethical conduct.

★3923★ Employment Interviewers

Evon Publishing
832 N 7th Ave.
Iron River, MI 49935
Ph: (906)265-3190

Audiocassette. 1996. $16.95. 32 minutes. Part of the Careers and Vocational Guidance Series. Provides information about the nature of the work, educational requirements, employment outlook, earnings, and work conditions as well as additional related information.

★3924★ Employment Support Center (ESC)

1556 Wisconsin Ave., NW
Washington, DC 20007
Ph: (202)628-2919   Fax: (202)628-2920

E-mail: jobclubs@hotmail.com
URL: http://www.angelfire.com/biz/jobclubs/

Description: Trains individuals to facilitate support groups for job-seekers. Operates a job bank for employment assistance; helps people learn to network for job contacts; provides technical assistance to employment support self help groups. Maintains speakers' bureau. Provides job-search skills training.

★3925★ HR Policy Association

1015 15th St. NW, Ste. 1200
Washington, DC 20005-2605
Ph: (202)789-8670   Fax: (202)789-0064
E-mail: info@hrpolicy.org
URL: http://www.hrpolicy.org

Description: Senior human resource executives of Fortune 500 companies. Conducts research and publishes findings on matters relating to federal human resources policy and its application and effects. Maintains task forces to study pending employment issues; conducts seminars, and offers a suite of labor relations and HR effectiveness training courses.

★3926★ National Association of Personnel Services (NAPS)

10905 Fort Washington Rd., Ste. 400
Fort Washington, MD 20744
Ph: (301)203-6700   Fax: (301)203-4346
E-mail: dcallis@recruitinglife.com
URL: http://www.napsweb.org

Description: Private employment and temporary service firms. Compiles statistics on professional agency growth and development; conducts certification program and educational programs. Association is distinct from former name of National Association of Personnel Consultants.

Engineering Technicians

★3927★ Connector Specifier
PennWell Corp.
100 S Atkinson Rd., Ste. 382
Grayslake, IL 60030-7817
Ph: (847)876-5602   Fax: (847)634-4240
URL: http://www.csmag.com

Free to qualified subscribers. Magazine for electronic engineers on the use of connectors and interconnection products.

★3928★ EE Evaluation Engineering
Nelson Publishing Inc.
2500 Tamiami Trl. N
Nokomis, FL 34275-3482
Ph: (941)966-9521   Fax: (941)966-2590
Fr: 800-226-6113
E-mail: ee@nelsonpub.com
URL: http://www.nelsonpub.com/ee/

Monthly. $99.00/year for individuals; $140.00/year for other countries; $9.50 for single issue. Trade magazine covering electronic engineering, evaluation and test.

★3929★ Electronic Engineering Times
CMP Media L.L.C.
600 Community Dr.
Manhasset, NY 11030
Ph: (516)562-5000
E-mail: rkeane@cmp.com
URL: http://www.eetimes.com/

Weekly. $280.00/year for individuals; $324.00/year for Canada; $449.00/year for other countries; $519.00/year, Asia and Australia. Weekly trade newspaper.

★3930★ Electronic Products
Hearst Business Communications/UTP Div.
645 Stewart Ave.
Garden City, NY 11530
Ph: (516)227-1300   Fax: (516)227-1453
Fr: 800-833-7138
E-mail: lens@electronicproducts.com
URL: http://www.electronicproducts.com

Free to qualified subscribers. Magazine for electronic design engineers and management.

★3931★ Engineering Times
National Society of Professional Engineers
1420 King St.
Alexandria, VA 22314
Ph: (703)684-2875   Fax: (703)836-4875
E-mail: et@nspe.org
URL: http://http//:www.nspc.org/1et.asp

$30.00/year for individuals; $48.00/year for out of country. Magazine (tabloid) covering professional, legislative, and techology issues for an engineering audience.

★3932★ ENR: Engineering News-Record
McGraw-Hill Companies
1221 Avenue of the Americas
New York, NY 10020
Ph: (212)512-2000
URL: http://www.enr.com

Weekly. $74.00/year; $5.00 for single issue. Magazine focusing on engineering and construction.

★3933★ High Technology Careers Magazine
HTC
4701 Patrick Henry Dr., No. 1901
Santa Clara, CA 95054-1847
Ph: (408)970-8800   Fax: (408)567-0242
URL: http://www.hightechcareers.com

Bimonthly. $29.00/year; $35.00/year for Canada; $85.00/year for out of country. Magazine (tabloid) containing employment opportunity information for the engineering and technical community.

★3934★ Mechanical Engineering
American Society of Mechanical Engineers
3 Park Ave.
New York, NY 10016-5990
Ph: (212)591-7000   Fax: (212)591-7674
Fr: 800-843-2763
E-mail: memag@asme.org
URL: http://www.memagazine.org

Monthly. $25.00 for single issue. Mechanical Engineering featuring technical and industry related technological advancements and news.

★3935★ Microwave Journal
Horizon House Publications Inc.
685 Canton St.
Norwood, MA 02062
Ph: (781)769-9750   Fax: (781)769-9884
Fr: 800-541-5970
E-mail: mwj@mwjournal.com
URL: http://www.mwjournal.com

Monthly. Free to qualified subscribers; $115.00/year for individuals; $175.00 for two years; $190.00/year for other countries; $355.00 for two years, other countries; $10.00 for single issue; $20.00 for single issue, other countries. Electronic engineering magazine.

★3936★ Modern Metals
Trend Publishing
One E Erie, Ste. 401
Chicago, IL 60611
Ph: (312)654-2300   Fax: (312)654-2323
Fr: 800-278-7363
URL: http://www.modernmetals.com

Monthly. $85.00/year for individuals; $14.00 for single issue. Metals fabrication magazine.

★3937★ NSBE Magazine
NSBE Publications
1454 Duke St.
Alexandria, VA 22314
Ph: (703)549-2207   Fax: (703)683-5312

$10.00/year for individuals; $2.00 for single issue. Journal providing information on engineering careers, self-development, and cultural issues for recent graduates with technical majors.

★3938★ *Power*

McGraw-Hill Companies
1221 Avenue of the Americas
New York, NY 10020
Ph: (212)512-2000

Monthly. $19.00/year; $5.00 for single issue. Magazine for engineers in electric utilities, process and manufacturing plants, commercial and service establishments, and consulting, design, and construction engineering firms working in the power technology field.

★3939★ *Printed Circuit Design & Manufacture*

CMP Media L.L.C.
600 Community Dr.
Manhasset, NY 11030
Ph: (516)562-5000
E-mail: wgiffor@upmediagroup.com
URL: http://www.pcdandm.com/pcdmag

Monthly. Free to qualified subscribers. Magazine for engineers and designers of PCBs and related technologies.

★3940★ *SMT*

PennWell Corp.
100 S Atkinson Rd., Ste. 382
Grayslake, IL 60030-7817
Ph: (847)876-5602   Fax: (847)634-4240
URL: http://smt.pennnet.com

Monthly. Free to qualified subscribers. Trade magazine for professional engineers involved in surface mount technology circuit design and board assembly.

★3941★ *SWE*

Society of Women Engineers
230 E Ohio St., No. 400
2135 Lamberton Rd.
Chicago, IL 60611-3265
Ph: (312)596-5223   Fax: (312)596-5252
E-mail: hq@swe.org
URL: http://www.swe.org

Bimonthly. $30.00/year for nonmembers. Magazine for engineering students and for women and men working in the engineering and technology fields. Covers career guidance, continuing development and topical issues.

★3942★ *Technology Review*

Technology Review
201 Vassar St.
Cambridge, MA 02139
Ph: (617)253-8250   Fax: (617)258-5850
E-mail: trcomments@mit.edu

$30.00/year for individuals; $42.00/year for other countries; $4.95/year for single issue. Magazine reviewing new developments in technology with an emphasis on economic, political, and social implications. Not a new product publication.

★3943★ *Test & Measurement World*

Reed Business Information
275 Washington St.
Newton, MA 02458-1630
Ph: (617)964-3030
E-mail: tmworld@tmworld.com
URL: http://www.tmworld.com

Monthly. $93.99/year for nonmembers. Electronic engineering magazine specializing in test, measurement, and inspection of electronic products

★3944★ *33 Metal Producing*

Penton Media Inc.
1300 E 9th St.
Cleveland, OH 44114-1503
Ph: (216)696-7000   Fax: (216)931-9799
E-mail: infor@mdna.com
URL: http://www.33metalproducing.com/default.asp?Section=home

$35.00/year for individuals; $38.00/year for Canada; $48.00/year for other countries. Magazine covering the metalproducing industry.

★3945★ *Tooling & Production*

Nelson Publishing Inc.
2500 Tamiami Trl. N
Nokomis, FL 34275-3482
Ph: (941)966-9521   Fax: (941)966-2590
Fr: 800-226-6113
URL: http://www.toolingandproduction.com

Monthly. $90.00/year for individuals. Magazine concerning metalworking.

PLACEMENT AND JOB REFERRAL SERVICES

★3946★ **American Indian Science and Engineering Society (AISES)**

PO Box 9828
Albuquerque, NM 87119-9828
Ph: (505)765-1052   Fax: (505)765-5608
E-mail: info@aises.org
URL: http://www.aises.org

Description: American Indian and non-Indian students and professionals in science, technology, and engineering fields; corporations representing energy, mining, aerospace, electronic, and computer fields. Seeks to motivate and encourage students to pursue undergraduate and graduate studies in science, engineering, and technology. Sponsors science fairs in grade schools, teacher training workshops, summer math/science sessions for 8th-12th graders, professional chapters, and student chapters in colleges. Offers scholarships. Adult members serve as role models, advisers, and mentors for students. Operates placement service.

★3947★ **Electronics Technicians Association, International (ETA-I)**

5 Depot St.
Greencastle, IN 46135
Ph: (765)653-8262   Fax: (765)653-4287
Fr: 800-288-3824
E-mail: eta@tds.net
URL: http://www.eta-sda.com

Description: Skilled electronics technicians. Provides placement service; offers certification examinations for electronics technicians and satellite, fiber optics, and data cabling installers. Compiles wage and manpower statistics. Administers FCC Commercial License examinations. Certification of computer network systems technicians and web and internet specialists.

★3948★ **Engineering Society of Detroit (ESD)**

26100 American Dr., Ste. 500
Southfield, MI 48034-6184
Ph: (248)355-2910   Fax: (248)355-1492
E-mail: esd@esd.org
URL: http://esd.org

Description: Engineers from all disciplines; scientists and technologists. Conducts technical programs and engineering refresher courses; sponsors conferences and expositions. Maintains speakers' bureau; offers placement services. Although based in Detroit, MI, society membership is international.

★3949★ **Robotics International of the Society of Manufacturing Engineers (RI/SME)**

One SME Dr.
PO Box 930
Dearborn, MI 48121
Ph: (313)271-1500   Fax: (313)271-2861
Fr: 800-733-4763
E-mail: service@sme.org
URL: http://www.sme.org/ri

Description: Engineers, managers, educators, and government officials in 50 countries working or interested in the field of robotics. Promotes efficient and effective use of current and future robot technology. Serves as a clearinghouse for the industry trends and developments. Areas of interest include: aerospace; assembly systems; casting and forging; education and training; human factors and safety; human and food service; material handling; military systems; nontraditional systems; research and development; small shop applications; welding. Offers professional certification. Operates placement service; compiles statistics. Maintains speakers' bureau.

★3950★ **Society of Hispanic Professional Engineers (SHPE)**

5400 E Olympic Blvd., Ste. 210
Los Angeles, CA 90022
Ph: (323)725-3970   Fax: (323)725-0316
E-mail: shpenational@shpe.org
URL: http://www.shpe.org

Description: Engineers, student engineers, and scientists seeking to increase the number of Hispanic engineers by providing motivation and support to students. Sponsors competitions and educational programs. Maintains placement service and speakers' bureau; compiles statistics.

★3951★ **Society for Mining, Metallurgy, and Exploration (SME)**
8307 Shaffer Pky.
PO Box 277002
Littleton, CO 80127-7002
Ph: (303)973-9550   Fax: (303)973-3845
Fr: 800-763-3132
E-mail: sme@smenet.org
URL: http://www.smenet.org

Description: A member society of the American Institute of Mining, Metallurgical and Petroleum Engineers. Persons engaged in the finding, exploitation, treatment, and marketing of all classes of minerals (metal ores, industrial minerals, and solid fuels) except petroleum. Promotes the arts and sciences connected with the production of useful minerals and metals. Offers specialized education programs; compiles enrollment and graduation statistics from schools offering engineering degrees in mining, mineral, mineral processing/metallurgical, geological, geophysical, and mining technology. Provides placement service and sponsors charitable programs.

EMPLOYER DIRECTORIES AND NETWORKING LISTS

★3952★ **Directory of Contract Staffing Firms**
C.E. Publications Inc.
PO Box 3006
Bothell, WA 98041-3006
Ph: (425)806-5200   Fax: (425)806-5585
URL: http://www.cjhunter.com/dcsf/overview.html

$15.00. Covers nearly 1,300 contract firms actively engaged in the employment of engineering, IT/IS, and technical personnel for 'temporary' contract assignments throughout the world. Entries include: Company name, address, phone, name of contact, email, web address. Arrangement: Alphabetical. Indexes: Geographical.

★3953★ **Engineers-Mechanical Directory**
infoUSA Inc.
5711 S 86th Cir.
Omaha, NE 68127-0347
Ph: (402)930-3500   Fax: (402)331-0176
Fr: 800-555-6124
URL: http://www.abii.com

Updated continuously; printed on request. Number of listings: 2,635. Entries include: Name, address, phone (including area code), size of advertisement, year first in "Yellow Pages," name of owner or manager, number of employees. Compiled from telephone company "Yellow Pages," nationwide. Arrangement: Geographical.

★3954★ **ENR-Top 500 Design Firms Issue**
McGraw-Hill Companies
1221 Ave. of the Americas
New York, NY 10020
Ph: (212)512-2000   Fax: (212)512-3840

Annual, April. $10.00. Publication includes: List of 500 leading architectural, engineering, and specialty design firms selected on basis of annual billings. Entries include: Company name, headquarters location, type of firm, current and prior year rank in billings, types of services, countries in which operated in preceding year. Arrangement: Ranked by billings.

★3955★ **International Directory of Engineering Societies and Related Organizations**
American Association of Engineering Societies
1828 L St. NW, Ste. 906
Washington, DC 20036
Ph: (202)296-2237   Fax: (202)296-1151
Fr: 888-400-AAES

Irregular, latest edition December 1998. $240.00. Covers about 1,370 national, regional, Canadian, and international organizations concerned with engineering and related fields. Entries include: Name, address, phone, fax, e-mail, key personnel, objectives, publications, activities, mailing lists, federation memberships, meeting and convention dates, and budget data. Arrangement: Alphabetical. Indexes: Acronym, geographical, area of specialization.

★3956★ **Peterson's Job Opportunities for Engineering and Computer Science Majors**
Thomson Thomson Peterson's
Princeton Pke. Corporate Ctr., 2000 Lenox Dr.
PO Box 67005
Lawrenceville, NJ 08648
Ph: (609)896-1800   Fax: (609)896-4531
Fr: 800-338-3282

Annual, latest edition 1999. $18.95. Covers approximately 2,000 research, consulting, manufacturing, government, and technical services organizations hiring colleges graduates in the fields of engineering, telecommunications, biotechnology, software, and consumer electronics. Entries include: Organization name, address, phone, name and title of contact, type of organization, number of employees, Standard Industrial Classification (SIC) code, description of opportunities available, level of education required, starting salary, location, level of experience accepted, benefits.

★3957★ **Peterson's Job Opportunities in Engineering and Technology**
Thomson Peterson's
PO Box 67005
Lawrenceville, NJ 08648-6105
Fr: 800-338-3282

Compiled by the Peterson's staff. Fourth edition, 1996. $21.95 (paper). 384 pages. Profiles 2,000 high-tech companies looking primarily for technical personnel in such fields as biotechnology, telecommunications, software, computers and peripherals, defense, and aerospace. Contains job-search strategies and career options to help match education and expertise to the job market. Indexed geographically, by industry, and by hiring needs.

HANDBOOKS AND MANUALS

★3958★ **Career Information Center**
Macmillan Publishing Co. Inc.
200 Old Tappan Rd.
Old Tappan, NJ 07675
Fr: 800-428-5331

Visual Education Center Staff. Seventh edition, 1999. $275.00. 2080 pages. This 13-volume set profiles over 600 occupations. Each occupational profile describes job duties, educational requirements, how to get the job, advancement possibilities, employment outlook, working conditions, earnings and benefits, and where to write for more information.

★3959★ **Engineering Your Job Search: A Job-Finding Resource for Engineering Professionals**
Professional Publications, Inc.
1250 5th Ave.
Belmont, CA 94002
Ph: (650)593-9119   Fax: (650)592-4519
Fr: 800-426-1178

Compiled by Professional Publications, editors. 1995. $24.95 (paper). 154 pages. Out of print.

★3960★ **Majoring in Engineering: How to Get from Your Freshman Year to Your First Job**
Farrar, Straus & Giroux, Inc.
19 Union Sq., W
New York, NY 10003
Ph: (212)741-6900   Fax: (212)633-9385
Fr: 888-330-8477

John Garcia and Carol Carter, editors. 2000. $20.00; $10.00 (paper). 134 pages.

★3961★ Opportunities in Electronics Careers

McGraw-Hill Trade
2 Penn Plaza
New York, NY 10121
Ph: (212)904-2000　　Fr: 800-722-4726

Mark Rowh. 1999. $14.95; $11.95 (paper). 160 pages. Discusses career opportunities in commercial and industrial electronics equipment repair, electronics home entertainment repair, electronics engineering, and engineering technology. Includes job outlook and how to get off to a good start on the job.

★3962★ Opportunities in Science Technician Careers

McGraw-Hill Contemporary Books
1221 Avenue of the Americas
New York, NY 10020
Ph: (212)904-2000　　Fr: 800-323-4900

JoAnn Chirico. 1996. $11.95 (paper). Part of Opportunities In... Series. 205 pages.

★3963★ Professional Development for Technicians

Thomson Delmar Learning
PO Box 15015
Albany, NY 12212-5015
Ph: (518)348-2300　　Fax: (518)464-0393
Fr: 800-998-7498

Johnson. 1997. $110.00.

★3964★ Real People Working in Engineering

McGraw-Hill Contemporary Books
1221 Avenue of the Americas
New York, NY 10020
Ph: (212)904-2000　　Fr: 800-323-4900
E-mail: ntcpub@tribune.com

Blythe Camenson, Jan Goldberg. 1997. $14.95; $12.95 (paper). Interviews and profiles of working professionals capture a range of opportunities in this field.

★3965★ Resumes for Engineering Careers

McGraw-Hill Trade
2 Penn Plaza
New York, NY 10121
Ph: (212)904-2000　　Fr: 800-722-4726
E-mail: ntcpub@tribune.com

2000. $10.95 (paper). 456 pages. Contains sample resumes and cover letters applicable to any engineering field.

★3966★ Resumes for Scientific and Technical Careers

McGraw-Hill Contemporary Books
1221 Avenue of the Americas
New York, NY 10020
Ph: (212)904-2000　　Fr: 800-323-4900
E-mail: ntcpub@tribune.com

1999. $9.95 (paper). 450 pages. Provides resume advice for individuals interested in working in scientific and technical careers. Includes sample resumes and cover letters.

★3967★ Where the Jobs Are: The Hottest Careers for the 90s

The Career Press, Inc.
3 Tice Rd.
PO Box 687
Franklin Lakes, NJ 07417-1322
Ph: (201)848-0310　　Fax: (201)848-1727
Fr: 800-227-3371

Joyce Hadley. Third edition, 2000. $13.99 (paper). 400 pages. Out of print. Describes careers in fifteen general fields, from accounting to travel and hospitality.

EMPLOYMENT AGENCIES AND SEARCH FIRMS

★3968★ Advanced Employment Resources

3040 Charlevoix Dr.
Grand Rapids, MI 49546
Ph: (616)942-9950　　Fax: (616)942-9950

Executive search firm.

★3969★ AmiTech Group

6405 Metcalf Ave., Ste. 107
Overland Park, KS 66202
Ph: (913)384-9150

Executive search firm. Focuses on technology and engineering.

★3970★ Andrew Associates Executive Search Inc.

PO Box 2029
Lake Oswego, OR 97035
Ph: (503)635-7222　　Fr: (866)294-1301

Executive search firm.

★3971★ The Aspire Group

52 Second Ave, 1st Fl
Waltham, MA 02451-1129
Fax: (718)890-1810　　Fr: 800-546-5675
URL: http://www.bmanet.com

Employment agency.

★3972★ Brandywine Management Group

8 Drawbridge Rd.
Berlin, MD 21811
Ph: (410)208-9791　　Fax: (410)208-9792

Executive search firm.

★3973★ Cadillac Engineering and Manufacturing Inc.

7909 Latchington Ct.
Charlotte, NC 28227
Ph: (704)568-6825　　Fax: (704)568-6825

Provides engineering consulting services and engineering personnel to the manufacturing, plastics, and chemical industries.

★3974★ Colli Associates

404 Caboose Ln.
Valrico, FL 33594
Ph: (813)681-2145　　Fax: (813)661-5217
E-mail: colli@gte.net

Employment agency. Executive search firm.

★3975★ Copier Careers

PO Box 300140
Minneapolis, MN 55403
Ph: (612)332-4888　　Fax: 800-464-3434
Fr: 888-733-4868

Executive search firm focused on technicians.

★3976★ Emplex Associates

PO Box 2497
Southfield, MI 48037
Ph: (248)352-6362　　Fr: 888-203-1010

Executive search firm.

★3977★ Ethos Consulting Inc.

50 California St., Ste. 1500
San Francisco, CA 94111
Ph: (415)277-5450　　Fax: (415)244-5451

Executive search firm. Second branch in Scottsdale, AZ.

★3978★ Executive Directions Inc.

PO Box 223
Foxboro, MA 02035
Ph: (508)698-3030　　Fax: (508)543-6047

Executive search firm.

★3979★ The Fawcett Group

39 Ross Rd.
Swampscott, MA 01907
Ph: (781)592-9555　　Fax: (661)457-2083

Executive search firm.

★3980★ Main Line Personnel Service, Inc.

Pagoda Blding.
100 Presidential Blvd. Ste. 200
Bala Cynwyd, PA 19004-0448
Ph: (610)667-1820　　Fax: (610)668-5000
URL: http://www.mlpers.com

Employment agency.

★3981★ Search and Recruit International

4455 South Blvd.
Virginia Beach, VA 23452
Ph: (757)490-3151　　Fax: (757)497-6503
E-mail: britt@searchandrecruit.com
URL: http://www.searchandrecruit.com

Employment agency. Headquartered in Virginia Beach. Other offices in Bremerton, WA; Charleston, SC; Jacksonville, FL; Memphis, TN; Pensacola, FL; Sacramento, CA; San Bernardino, CA; San Diego, CA.

★**3982**★ **Tri-Serv Inc.**

22 W. Padonia Rd., Ste. C-353
Timonium, MD 21093
Ph: (410)561-1740   Fax: (410)252-7417
E-mail: info@tri-serv.coom
URL: http://www.tri-serv.com

Permanent employment agency.

OTHER SOURCES

★**3983**★ **Aircraft Electronics Association (AEA)**

4217 S. Hocker
Independence, MO 64055-0963
Ph: (816)373-6565   Fax: (816)478-3100
E-mail: info@aea.net
URL: http://www.aea.net

Members: Companies engaged in the sales, engineering, installation, and service of electronic aviation equipment and systems. **Purpose:** Seeks to advance the science of aircraft electronics; promote uniform and stable regulations and uniform standards of performance; establish and maintain a code of ethics; gather and disseminate technical data; advance the education of members and the public in the science of aircraft electronics. **Activities:** Is active in the areas of supplement type certificates, test equipment licensing, temporary FCC licensing for new installations, spare parts availability and pricing, audiovisual technician training, equipment and spare parts loan, profitable installation, and service facility operation. Provides employment information, equipment exchange information and service assistance on member installations anywhere in the world.

★**3984**★ **American Association of Engineering Societies (AAES)**

1828 L St. NW, No. 906
Washington, DC 20036
Ph: (202)296-2237   Fax: (202)296-1151
Fr: 888-400-2237
E-mail: tprice@aaes.org
URL: http://www.aaes.org

Description: Coordinates the efforts of the member societies in the provision of reliable and objective information to the general public concerning issues which affect the engineering profession and the field of engineering as a whole; to collect, analyze, document, and disseminate data which will inform the general public of the relationship between engineering and the national welfare; to provide a forum for the engineering societies to exchange and discuss their views on matters of common interest; and to represent the U.S. engineering community aborad through representation in WFEO and UPADI.

★**3985**★ **American Society of Certified Engineering Technicians (ASCET)**

PO Box 1348
Flowery Branch, GA 30542-0023
Ph: (770)967-9173   Fax: (770)967-8049
E-mail: general_manager@ascet.org
URL: http://www.ascet.org

Members: Certified and noncertified engineering technicians and technologists. Persons are certified by societies such as the American Concrete Institute, American Society for Nondestructive Testing, American Welding Society, National Institute for Certification in Engineering Technologies, and National Association of Radio and Telecommunications Engineers, National Association of Industrial Technology, the American Society for Quality Control, the Canadian Council of Technicians and Technologists, Manufacturing Engineers Certification Institute, American Construction Inspectors Association, City and Guilds of London Institute, American Construction Inspectors Association, Washington Area Council of Engineering Laboratories, and the Electronics Technicians Association International, as skilled technicians or technologists whose training and experience qualify them to provide technical support and assistance to registered professional engineers and engineering departments. **Purpose:** Works to obtain recognition of the contribution of engineering technicians and engineering technologists as an essential part of the engineering-scientific team; cooperate with engineering and scientific societies; improve the utilization of the engineering technician and technologist; assist the educational, social, economic, and ethical development of the engineering technician and technologist. **Activities:** Conducts triennial survey among members to determine employer support, pay scales, and fringe benefits. Offers referral service. Offers referral service.

★**3986**★ **Association for International Practical Training (AIPT)**

10400 Little Patuxent Pky., Ste. 250
Columbia, MD 21044-3519
Ph: (410)997-2200   Fax: (410)992-3924
E-mail: aipt@aipt.org
URL: http://www.aipt.org

Description: Providers worldwide on-the-job training programs for students and professionals seeking international career development and life-changing experiences. Arranges workplace exchanges in hundreds of professional fields, bringing employers and trainees together from around the world. Client list ranges from small farming communities to Fortune 500 companies.

★**3987**★ *Engineering Technicians*

Evon Publishing
832 N 7th Ave.
Iron River, MI 49935
Ph: (906)265-3190

Audiocassette. 1996. $16.95. 32 minutes. Part of the Careers and Vocational Guidance Series. Provides information about the nature of the work, educational requirements, employment outlook, earnings, and work conditions as well as additional related information.

★**3988**★ **International Society of Certified Electronics Technicians (ISCET)**

3608 Pershing Ave.
Fort Worth, TX 76107-4527
Ph: (817)921-9101   Fax: (817)921-3741
E-mail: info@iscet.org
URL: http://www.iscet.org

Description: Technicians in 50 countries who have been certified by the society. Seeks to provide a fraternal bond among certified electronics technicians, raise their public image, and improve the effectiveness of industry education programs for technicians. Offers training programs in new electronics information. Maintains library of service literature for consumer electronic equipment, including manuals and schematics for out-of-date equipment. Offers all FCC licenses. Sponsors testing program for certification of electronics technicians in the fields of audio, communications, computer, consumer, industrial, medical electronics, radar, radio-television, and video.

★**3989**★ **ISA - Instrumentation, Systems, and Automation Society**

67 Alexander Dr.
PO Box 12277
Research Triangle Park, NC 27709
Ph: (919)549-8411   Fax: (919)549-8288
E-mail: info@isa.org
URL: http://www.isa.org

Purpose: Fosters advancement in the theory, design, manufacture, and use of instruments, computers, and systems for measurement and control.

★**3990**★ **National Institute for Certification in Engineering Technologies (NICET)**

1420 King St.
Alexandria, VA 22314-2794
Ph: (703)548-1518   Fax: (703)682-2756
Fr: 888-IS-NICET
URL: http://www.nicet.org

Description: Grants and issues certificates to engineering technicians and technologists who voluntarily apply for certification and satisfy competency criteria through examinations and verification of work experience. (More than 100,000 technicians and 1,000 technologists have been certified.) Requirements for certification involve work experience in terms of job task proficiency and length of progressively more responsible experience. Levels of certification are Technician Trainee, Associate Engineering Technician, Engineering Technician, Senior Engineering Technician, Associate Engineering Technologist, and Certified Engineering Technologist.

★3991★ *Scientific, Engineering, and Technical Services*
Cambridge Educational
2572 Brunswick Ave.
Lawrenceville, NJ 08648-4128
Fax: 800-FAX-ON-US   Fr: 800-468-4227
URL: http://www.cambridgeeducational.com
$89.95. 2002. 18 minutes. Part of the Career Cluster Series.

★3992★ Society of Women Engineers (SWE)
230 E Ohio St., No. 400
Chicago, IL 60611-3265
Ph: (312)596-5223   Fax: (312)596-5252
E-mail: hq@swe.org
URL: http://www.swe.org

Description: Educational and service organization representing both students and professional women in engineering and technical fields.

★3993★ *Technical & Related Occupations*
Delphi Productions
3160 4th St.
Boulder, CO 80304
Fax: (303)443-4022   Fr: 888-443-2400
URL: http://www.delphivideo.com
$95.00. 49 minutes. Part of the Careers for the 21st Century Video Library.

★3994★ *Women in Engineering*
Her Own Words
PO Box 5264
Madison, WI 53705-0264
Ph: (608)271-7083   Fax: (608)271-0209
URL: http://www.herownwords.com/
Video. Jocelyn Riley. $95.00. 15 minutes. Resource guide also available for $45.00.

Environmental Engineers

Magazine dealing with water supply resources, treatment, and distribution.

★4005★ **Journal of Environmental Engineering**
American Society of Civil Engineers
1801 Alexander Bell Dr.
Reston, VA 20191
Ph: (703)295-6300   Fax: (703)295-6222
Fr: 800-548-2723
E-mail: ztrem@ce.udel.edu
URL: http://www.pubs.asce.org/journals/sub03ee.html

Monthly. $520.00/year for institutions; $167.00/year for individuals; $111.00/year for members; $568.00/year for institutions, other countries; $159.00/year for members, international. Journal on the practice and status of research in environmental engineering science, systems engineering, and sanitation.

★4006★ **Journal of Environmental Health**
National Environmental Health Association
720 S Colorado Blvd., Ste. 970, S Twr.
Denver, CO 80246-1925
Ph: (303)756-9090   Fax: (303)691-9490
E-mail: staff@neha.org
URL: http://www.umi.com/proquest

Free to qualified subscribers; $100.00/year for individuals; single issues available. Journal presenting environmental health and protection issues.

★4007★ **MainStream**
American Water Works Association (AWWA)
6666 W Quincy Ave.
Denver, CO 80235
Ph: (303)347-6272   Fax: (303)794-7310
URL: http://www.awwa.org/mainstream

Description: Biweekly, online; print issue is quarterly. Carries news of the Association and features about the drinking water industry, including regulations, legislation, conservation, treatment, quality, distribution, management, and utility operations. Recurring features include letters to the editor, a calendar of events, reports of meetings, news of educational opportunities, notices of publications available, education and job opportunities in the industry and legislative news.

★4008★ **SWE**
Society of Women Engineers
230 E Ohio St., No. 400
2135 Lamberton Rd.
Chicago, IL 60611-3265
Ph: (312)596-5223   Fax: (312)596-5252
E-mail: hq@swe.org
URL: http://www.swe.org

Bimonthly. $30.00/year for nonmembers. Magazine for engineering students and for women and men working in the engineering and technology fields. Covers career guidance, continuing development and topical issues.

★4009★ **Technology Review**
Technology Review
201 Vassar St.
Cambridge, MA 02139
Ph: (617)253-8250   Fax: (617)258-5850
E-mail: trcomments@mit.edu

$30.00/year for individuals; $42.00/year for other countries; $4.95/year for single issue. Magazine reviewing new developments in technology with an emphasis on economic, political, and social implications. Not a new product publication.

★4010★ **Water Environment Research**
Water Environment Federation
601 Wythe St.
Alexandria, VA 22314-1994
Ph: (703)684-2400   Fax: (703)684-2492
Fr: 800-666-0206
E-mail: msc@wef.org

Bimonthly. $40.00/year for members; $158.00/year for nonmembers. Technical journal covering municipal and industrial water pollution control, water quality, and hazardous wastes.

★4011★ **WEPANEWS**
Women in Engineering Programs & Advocates Network
Castle Point on the Hudson
Hoboken, NJ 07030
Ph: (201)216-5245   Fax: (201)216-5175
URL: http://www.wepan.org/newsletter.html

Description: Two issues/year. Seeks to provide greater access for women to careers in engineering. Includes news of graduate, undergraduate, freshmen, pre-college, and re-entry engineering programs for women. Recurring features include job listings, faculty, grant, and conference news, international engineering program news, action group news, notices of publications available, and a column titled Kudos.

PLACEMENT AND JOB REFERRAL SERVICES

★4012★ **American Indian Science and Engineering Society (AISES)**
PO Box 9828
Albuquerque, NM 87119-9828
Ph: (505)765-1052   Fax: (505)765-5608
E-mail: info@aises.org
URL: http://www.aises.org

Description: American Indian and non-Indian students and professionals in science, technology, and engineering fields; corporations representing energy, mining, aerospace, electronic, and computer fields. Seeks to motivate and encourage students to pursue undergraduate and graduate studies in science, engineering, and technology. Sponsors science fairs in grade schools, teacher training workshops, summer math/science sessions for 8th-12th graders, professional chapters, and student chapters in

colleges. Offers scholarships. Adult members serve as role models, advisers, and mentors for students. Operates placement service.

★4013★ **Engineering Society of Detroit (ESD)**
26100 American Dr., Ste. 500
Southfield, MI 48034-6184
Ph: (248)355-2910   Fax: (248)355-1492
E-mail: esd@esd.org
URL: http://esd.org

Description: Engineers from all disciplines; scientists and technologists. Conducts technical programs and engineering refresher courses; sponsors conferences and expositions. Maintains speakers' bureau; offers placement services. Although based in Detroit, MI, society membership is international.

★4014★ **Environmental Careers Organization (ECO)**
179 South St.
Boston, MA 02111
Ph: (617)426-4375   Fax: (617)423-0998
E-mail: info@eco.org
URL: http://www.eco.org

Description: Seeks to protect and enhance the environment through the development of professionals, the promotion of careers, and the inspiration of individual action. Offers paid internships, career development educational programs and related publications. Participants in programs are mostly upper-level undergraduate, graduate, and doctoral students, or recent graduates seeking professional experience relevant to careers in the environmental fields. Individual subject areas of placement service include biology, chemistry, community development, hazardous waste, natural resources, pollution, public/occupational health, transportation, and wildlife.

★4015★ **Korean Scientists and Engineers Association in America (KSEA)**
1952 Gallows Rd., Ste. 300
Vienna, VA 22182
Ph: (703)748-1221   Fax: (703)748-1331
E-mail: sejong@ksea.org
URL: http://www.ksea.org

Description: Scientists and engineers holding single or advanced degrees. Goals are to: promote friendship and mutuality among Korean and American scientists and engineers; contribute to Korea's scientific, technological, industrial, and economic developments; strengthen the scientific, technological, and cultural bonds between Korea and the U.S. Sponsors symposium. Maintains speakers' bureau, placement service, and biographical archives. Compiles statistics. Maintains 100 volume library of scientific handbooks and yearbooks in Korean.

★4016★ Society of Hispanic Professional Engineers (SHPE)

5400 E Olympic Blvd., Ste. 210
Los Angeles, CA 90022
Ph: (323)725-3970   Fax: (323)725-0316
E-mail: shpenational@shpe.org
URL: http://www.shpe.org

Description: Engineers, student engineers, and scientists seeking to increase the number of Hispanic engineers by providing motivation and support to students. Sponsors competitions and educational programs. Maintains placement service and speakers' bureau; compiles statistics.

EMPLOYER DIRECTORIES AND NETWORKING LISTS

★4017★ American Men and Women of Science

Thomson Gale
27500 Drake Rd.
Farmington Hills, MI 48331-3535
Ph: (248)699-4253   Fax: (248)699-8065
Fr: 800-877-GALE
E-mail: amws@galegroup.com

Biennial, latest edition December 2002. $975.00. Covers over 129,700 U.S. and Canadian scientists active in the physical, biological, mathematical, computer science, and engineering fields; includes references to previous edition for deceased scientists and nonrespondents. Entries include: Name, address, education, personal and career data, memberships, honors and awards, research interest. Arrangement: Alphabetical. Indexes: Discipline (in separate volume).

★4018★ Association of Conservation Engineers-Membership Directory

Association of Conservation Engineers
c/o John Bruner Secretary
Wyoning State Parks and Historic Sites
2301 Central Ave., 4th Fl. S
Cheyenne, WY 82002
Ph: (307)777-6325   Fax: (307)777-6472
E-mail: jbrune@state.wy.us

Annual, June. Covers 280 persons with administrative or engineering background in conservation. Entries include: Member name, address, phone, company or institution name. Arrangement: Alphabetical.

★4019★ Directory of Contract Staffing Firms

C.E. Publications Inc.
PO Box 3006
Bothell, WA 98041-3006
Ph: (425)806-5200   Fax: (425)806-5585
URL: http://www.cjhunter.com/dcsf/overview.html

$15.00. Covers nearly 1,300 contract firms actively engaged in the employment of engineering, IT/IS, and technical personnel for 'temporary' contract assignments throughout the world. Entries include: Company name,

address, phone, name of contact, email, web address. Arrangement: Alphabetical. Indexes: Geographical.

★4020★ Engineers-Environmental Directory

infoUSA Inc.
5711 S 86th Cir.
Omaha, NE 68127-0347
Ph: (402)930-3500   Fax: (402)331-0176
Fr: 800-555-6124
URL: http://www.abii.com

Updated continuously; printed on request. Number of listings: 3,932. Entries include: Name, address, phone, size of advertisement, name of owner or manager, number of employees, year first in "Yellow Pages." Compiled from telephone company "Yellow Pages," nationwide. Arrangement: Geographical.

★4021★ Indiana Society of Professional Engineers-Directory

Indiana Society of Professional Engineers
PO Box 20806
Indianapolis, IN 46220
Ph: (317)255-2267   Fax: (317)255-2530

Annual, fall. $55.00. Covers member registered engineers, land surveyors, engineering students, and engineers in training. Entries include: Member name, address, phone, type of membership, business information, specialty. Arrangement: Alpha by chapter area.

★4022★ Who's Who in Environmental Engineering

American Academy of Environmental Engineers
130 Holiday Ct., Ste. 100
Annapolis, MD 21401
Ph: (410)266-3311   Fax: (410)266-7653

Annual, April. $75.00. Covers about 2,400 licensed professional environmental engineers that have been certified by examination in one or more of seven specialties: air pollution control, general environmental engineering, industrial hygiene, hazardous waste management, radiation protection, solid waste management, water supply and wastewater. Entries include: Name, affiliation, address, phone, area of specialization, biographical data. Arrangement: Alphabetical, geographical, area of specialization.

HANDBOOKS AND MANUALS

★4023★ The Best Resumes for Scientists and Engineers

John Wiley & Sons Inc.
1 Wiley Dr.
Somerset, NJ 08873
Ph: (732)469-4400   Fr: 800-225-5945

Adele Lewis and David J. Moore. Second edition, 1993. $37.50; $19.95 (paper). 224

pages. Presents an extensive collection of scientific and engineering resumes, highlighting the important differences between these and resumes written for other occupations.

★4024★ Careers in the Environment

VGM Career Horizons
N T C Publishing Group
1221 Avenue of the Americas
New York, NY 10020
Ph: (212)904-2000   Fr: 800-323-4900
E-mail: ntcpub@tribune.com

Michael Fasulo and Paul Walker. Second edition, 2000. $17.95; $13.95 (paper). 275 pages. Comprehensive information on the diverse career opportunities available in environmental services.

★4025★ Careers in Environmental Geoscience

American Association of Petroleum Geologists
PO Box 979
Tulsa, OK 74101-0979
Ph: (918)584-2555   Fax: (918)560-2652
Fr: 800-364-2274

Robert R. Jordan, Rima Petrossian, and William J. Murphy. 1996. $5.00 (paper). DEP Publications Series. 54 pages.

★4026★ Careers for Environmental Types and Others Who Respect the Earth

VGM Career Horizons
N T C Publishing Group
1221 Avenue of the Americas
New York, NY 10020
Ph: (212)904-2000   Fr: 800-323-4900
E-mail: ntcpub@tribune.com

Jane Kinney and Mike Fasulo. Second edition, 2001. $15.95; $12.95 (paper). 192 pages. Describes environmentally friendly positions with corporations, government, and environmental organizations.

★4027★ Careers Inside the World of Environmental Science

Rosen Publishing Group, Inc.
29 E. 21st St.
New York, NY 10010
Ph: (212)777-3017   Fax: 888-436-4643
Fr: 800-237-9932

Robert Gartner. 1995. $16.95. 64 pages. Describes jobs in environmental studies and related fields for reluctant readers.

★4028★ Careers in Science and Engineering

National Academies Press
500 5th St. NW
Washington, DC 20055
Ph: (202)334-3180   Fax: (202)334-2793
Fr: 800-624-6242

1996. $11.95. 160 pages. Covers planning for graduate school and beyond.

★4029★ The Complete Guide to Environmental Careers in the 21st Century

Island Press
PO Box 7
Covelo, CA 95428
Ph: (707)983-6432   Fax: (707)983-6414
Fr: 800-828-1302

Kevin Doyle, et al, editors. 1998. Third edition. $18.00 (paper). 463 pages. A completely revised and updated edition of the standard reference on environmental careers.

★4030★ Engineering Your Job Search: A Job-Finding Resource for Engineering Professionals

Professional Publications, Inc.
1250 5th Ave.
Belmont, CA 94002
Ph: (650)593-9119   Fax: (650)592-4519
Fr: 800-426-1178

Compiled by Professional Publications, editors. 1995. $24.95 (paper). 154 pages. Out of print.

★4031★ Great Jobs for Engineering Majors

McGraw-Hill Professional
McGraw-Hill Higher Education
2 Penn Plaza
New York, NY 10121
Ph: (212)904-2000   Fr: 800-722-4726
E-mail: ntcpub@tribune.com

Geraldine O. Garner. Second edition, 2002. $14.95. 256 pages. Covers all the career options open to students majoring in engineering.

★4032★ Hidden Job Market

Thomson Peterson's
PO Box 67005
Lawrenceville, NJ 08648-6105
Fr: 800-338-3282

Ninth edition, 1999. $18.95 (paper). 319 pages. Guide to 2,000 fast-growing companies that are hiring now. Focuses on high technology companies in such fields as environmental consulting, genetic engineering, home health care, telecommunications, alternative energy systems, and others. Part of Peterson's Hidden Job Market series.

★4033★ How to Succeed as an Engineer: A Practical Guide to Enhance Your Career

Institute of Electrical & Electronics
  Engineers Inc.
PO Box 87204
Vancouver, WA 98687
Ph: (360)253-9532   Fax: (360)253-4084
Todd Yuzuriha. 1999. $29.95 (paper). 367 pages.

★4034★ Job Opportunities in the Environment 1995

Thomson Peterson's
PO Box 67005
Lawrenceville, NJ 08648-6105
Fr: 800-338-3282

Second edition, 1994. $18.95 (paper). 265 pages. Out of print.

★4035★ Keys to Engineering Success

Prentice Hall PTR
One Lake St.
Upper Saddle River, NJ 07458
Ph: (201)236-7000

Jill S. Tietjen, Kristy A. Schloss, Carol Carter, Joyce Bishop, and Sarah Lyman. 2000. $32.00 (paper).

★4036★ Majoring in Engineering: How to Get from Your Freshman Year to Your First Job

Farrar, Straus & Giroux, Inc.
19 Union Sq., W
New York, NY 10003
Ph: (212)741-6900   Fax: (212)633-9385
Fr: 888-330-8477

John Garcia and Carol Carter, editors. 2000. $20.00; $10.00 (paper). 134 pages.

★4037★ Nature (Career Portraits)

McGraw-Hill Trade
2 Penn Plaza
New York, NY 10121
Ph: (212)904-2000   Fax: (212)755-5645
Fr: 800-722-4726

Marjorie Eberts. 1996. $13.95. 310 pages. Highlights a range of careers that focus on the environment, with descriptions of a typical day on the job and interactive exercises for readers.

★4038★ The New Engineer's Guide to Career Growth & Professional Awareness

Institute of Electrical & Electronics
  Engineers Inc.
445 Hoes Ln.
PO Box 1331
Piscataway, NJ 08855-1331
Ph: (732)562-3967   Fax: (732)981-9334
Fr: 800-678-4333

Irving J. Gabelman, editor. 1996. $39.95 (paper). 275 pages.

★4039★ Opportunities in Engineering Careers

McGraw-Hill Contemporary Books
1221 Avenue of the Americas
New York, NY 10020
Ph: (212)904-2000   Fr: 800-323-4900
E-mail: ntcpub@tribune.com

Nicholas Basta. Revised, 1995. $14.95; $11.95 (paper). 200 pages. Outlines typical job titles, salaries, career paths, and employment prospects.

★4040★ Opportunities in Environmental Careers

McGraw-Hill Trade
2 Penn Plaza
New York, NY 10121
Ph: (212)904-2000   Fr: 800-722-4726
E-mail: ntcpub@tribune.com

Odom Fanning. Revised, 2002. $12.95 (paper). 160 pages. Describes a broad range of opportunities in fields such as environmental health, recreation, physics, and hygiene, and provides job search advice. Part of Opportunities in...Series.

★4041★ Peterson's Job Opportunities in Engineering and Technology

Thomson Peterson's
PO Box 67005
Lawrenceville, NJ 08648-6105
Fr: 800-338-3282

Compiled by the Peterson's staff. Fourth edition, 1996. $21.95 (paper). 384 pages. Profiles 2,000 high-tech companies looking primarily for technical personnel in such fields as biotechnology, telecommunications, software, computers and peripherals, defense, and aerospace. Contains job-search strategies and career options to help match education and expertise to the job market. Indexed geographically, by industry, and by hiring needs.

★4042★ Real People Working in Engineering

McGraw-Hill Contemporary Books
1221 Avenue of the Americas
New York, NY 10020
Ph: (212)904-2000   Fr: 800-323-4900
E-mail: ntcpub@tribune.com

Blythe Camenson, Jan Goldberg. 1997. $14.95; $12.95 (paper). Interviews and profiles of working professionals capture a range of opportunities in this field.

★4043★ Resumes for Engineering Careers

McGraw-Hill Trade
2 Penn Plaza
New York, NY 10121
Ph: (212)904-2000   Fr: 800-722-4726
E-mail: ntcpub@tribune.com

2000. $10.95 (paper). 456 pages. Contains sample resumes and cover letters applicable to any engineering field.

★4044★ Resumes for Environmental Careers

McGraw-Hill Trade
2 Penn Plaza
New York, NY 10121
Ph: (212)904-2000   Fr: 800-722-4726
E-mail: ntcpub@tribune.com

2002. $9.95 (paper). 160 pages. Provides resume advice tailored to people pursuing careers focusing on the environment. Includes sample resumes and cover letters.

★4045★ Resumes for Scientific and Technical Careers

McGraw-Hill Contemporary Books
1221 Avenue of the Americas
New York, NY 10020
Ph: (212)904-2000   Fr: 800-323-4900
E-mail: ntcpub@tribune.com

1999. $9.95 (paper). 450 pages. Provides resume advice for individuals interested in working in scientific and technical careers. Includes sample resumes and cover letters.

★4046★ Where the Jobs Are: The Hottest Careers for the 90s

The Career Press, Inc.
3 Tice Rd.
PO Box 687
Franklin Lakes, NJ 07417-1322
Ph: (201)848-0310   Fax: (201)848-1727
Fr: 800-227-3371

Joyce Hadley. Third edition, 2000. $13.99 (paper). 400 pages. Out of print. Describes careers in fifteen general fields, from accounting to travel and hospitality.

EMPLOYMENT AGENCIES AND SEARCH FIRMS

★4047★ Amtec Engineering Corp.

2749 Saturn St.
Brea, CA 92821
Ph: (714)993-1900   Fax: (714)993-2419
E-mail: staffing@amtec-eng.com
URL: http://www.amtec-eng.com

Employment agency.

★4048★ The Angus Group Ltd.

250 W. Court St., Ste. 100E
Cincinnati, OH 45202-1088
Ph: (513)961-5575   Fax: (513)961-5616

Executive search firm.

★4049★ Bell Oaks Co.

10 Glenlake Parkway, Ste. 300
Atlanta, GA 30328
Ph: (678)287-2000   Fax: (678)287-2001
E-mail: atlantacareers@belloaks.com
URL: http://www.belloaks.com

Personnel service firm.

★4050★ The Borton Wallace Company

PO Box 8816
Asheville, NC 28814-0989
Ph: (828)258-1831   Fax: (828)251-0989

Executive search firm.

★4051★ Career Center, Inc.

194 Passaic St.
Hackensack, NJ 07601
Ph: (201)342-1777   Fax: (201)342-1776
Fr: 800-227-3379
E-mail: career@careercenterinc.com
URL: http://www.careercenterinc.com

Employment agency.

★4052★ Carlyle & Conlan Inc.

630 Davis Dr., Ste. 260
Morrisville, NC 27560
Ph: (919)474-0771   Fax: (919)474-0682

Executive search firm.

★4053★ The Carter Group LLC

PO Box 850303
Mobile, AL 36685-0303
Ph: (251)342-0999   Fax: (251)342-7999

Executive search firm. Branch in Alpharetta GA.

★4054★ Clarey/Napier International

1221 McKinney, Ste. 3112
Houston, TX 77010
Ph: (713)238-6705   Fax: (713)236-4778

Executive search firm.

★4055★ COBA Executive Search

14947 E. Wagon Trail Place
Aurora, CO 80015
Ph: (303)693-8382

Executive search firm.

★4056★ Corporate Environment Ltd.

PO Box 798
Crystal Lake, IL 60039-0798
Ph: (815)455-6070   Fax: (815)455-0124

Executive search firm.

★4057★ The Elliot Company

534 Maison Pl.
Bryn Mawr, PA 19010
Ph: (610)527-1840

Executive search firm.

★4058★ Erspamer Associates

4010 W. 65th St., Ste. 100
Edina, MN 55435
Ph: (952)925-3747   Fax: (952)925-4022
E-mail: hdhuntrel@aol.com

Executive search firm specializing in technical management.

★4059★ Executive Recruiters Agency

14 Office Park Dr., Ste. 100
PO Box 21810
Little Rock, AR 72221-1810
Ph: (501)224-7000   Fax: (501)224-8534
E-mail: grogers@execrecruit.com

URL: http://www.execrecruit.com

Personnel service firm.

★4060★ High Employee Services Ltd.

525 Greenfield Rd., 2nd Fl.
Lancaster, PA 17601
Ph: (717)396-7701   Fax: (717)396-7779

Personnel consultants serving all industries including business and finance, engineering, sales and marketing, and focusing on manufacturing, industrial, and transportation operations. Conducts full time, contract staffing, and temporary (clerical and skilled) placements. Serves private industries as well as government agencies.

★4061★ JPM International

26060 Acero
Mission Viejo, CA 92691
Ph: (949)699-4300   Fax: (949)699-4333
Fr: 800-685-7856
E-mail: leslieo@jpmintl.com
URL: http://www.jpmintl.com

Executive search firm and employment agency.

★4062★ Rand Personnel

1200 Truxtun, Ste. 130
Bakersfield, CA 93301
Ph: (805)325-0751   Fax: (805)325-4120

Personnel service firm serving a variety of fields.

★4063★ Randolph Associates, Inc.

950 Massachusetts Ave., Ste. 105
Cambridge, MA 02139-3174
Ph: (617)441-8777   Fax: (617)441-8778
E-mail: jobs@greatjobs.com
URL: http://www.greatjobs.com

Employment agency. Provides regular or temporary placement of staff.

★4064★ Search North America Inc.

PO Box 3577
Sunriver, OR 97707-0577
Ph: (503)222-6461   Fax: (503)227-2804

An executive search and recruiting firm whose focus is placing engineers, operations and maintenance managers, sales and marketing management, financial and general management executives (both domestic and international). Industries served: forest products, pulp and paper, waste to energy, environmental services, consulting and equipment suppliers for above related industries.

★4065★ Techtronix Technical Search

PO Box 17713
Milwaukee, WI 53217-0173
Ph: (414)466-3100   Fax: (414)466-3598

Firm specializes in recruiting executives for the engineering, information systems, manufacturing, marketing, finance, and human resources industries.

★**4066**★ **TRC Staffing Services Inc.**
2110 15 Mile Rd., Ste. B
Sterling Heights, MI 48310
Ph: (586)939-3210   Fax: (586)978-0572

A full-service executive search company with permanent placements encompassing engineering, industrial sales, financial and computer science positions. Screen, interview, and verify past employment for all candidates prior to referral. Also assist personnel staffs in the attainment of their EEO/AAP goals with the placement of talented individuals in positions which are underutilized with minorities and/or women. In addition, firm has a clerical temporary service division, TRC Temporary Service; and an employment agency, TRC Staffing Services.

★**4067**★ **Winters Technical Staffing Services**
2025 Sheppard Ave. E, Ste. 4110
Willowdale, ON, Canada M2T 1V7
Ph: (416)495-7422   Fax: (416)495-8479

Technical staffing service for permanent and contract positions in all facets of engineering. Serves government agencies, consulting engineers, and all areas of manufacturing in Canada and northeast U.S.

ONLINE JOB SOURCES AND SERVICES

★**4068**★ **Spherion Workforce Architects**
URL: http://www.spherion.com
Description: Recruitment firm specializing in accounting and finance, sales and marketing, interim executives, technology, engineering, retail and human resources.

TRADESHOWS

★**4069**★ **Air and Waste Management Association Annual Conference and Exhibition**
Air and Waste Management Association
One Gateway Center, 3rd Fl.
Pittsburgh, PA 15222
Ph: (412)232-3444   Fax: (412)232-3450
Fr: 800-270-3444
E-mail: info@awma.org
URL: http://www.awma.org

Annual. **Primary Exhibits:** Instrumentation, environmental control products, and services.

★**4070**★ **American Society for Engineering Education Annual Conference and Exposition**
American Society for Engineering Education
1818 N St., Ste. 600
Washington, DC 20036
Ph: (202)331-3500   Fax: (202)265-8504
URL: http://www.asee.org

Annual. **Primary Exhibits:** Publications, engineering supplies and equipment, computers, software, and research companies all products and services related to engineering education. **Dates and Locations:** 2005 Jun 12-15; Portland, OR • 2006 Jun 18-21; Chicago, IL • 2007 Jun 24-27; Honolulu, HI.

★**4071**★ **National Water Resources Association Annual Conference**
National Water Resources Association
3800 N. Fairfax Dr., Ste. 4
Arlington, VA 22203
Ph: (703)524-1544   Fax: (703)524-1548
E-mail: nwra@dgs.dgsys.com

Annual. **Primary Exhibits:** Exhibits relating to the development, control, conservation, and utilization of water resources in the reclamation states (17 western states).

★**4072**★ **NGWA Annual Convention/ Exposition**
National Ground Water Association
601 Dempsey Rd.
Westerville, OH 43081
Ph: (614)898-7791   Fax: (614)898-7786
Fr: 800-551-7379
E-mail: gphelps@ngwa.org
URL: http://www.ngwa.org

Annual. **Primary Exhibits:** Equipment, products and technology for the ground water industry. **Dates and Locations:** 2004 Dec 13-15; Las Vegas, NV; Las Vegas Convention Center • 2005 Dec 14-16; Atlanta, GA; Cobb Galleria.

★**4073**★ **Texas Ground Water Association Trade Show and Convention**
Texas Ground Water Association (TGWA)
221 E. 9th St., Ste. 206
Austin, TX 78701
Ph: (512)472-7437   Fax: (512)472-0537

Annual. **Primary Exhibits:** Water well equipment, including drills.

★**4074**★ **Water Quality Association Convention**
Water Quality Association
4151 Naperville Rd.
Lisle, IL 60532
Ph: (630)505-0160   Fax: (630)505-9637

Annual. **Primary Exhibits:** Water treatment equipment and related articles.

★**4075**★ **WEFTEC**
Water Environment Federation
601 Wythe St.
Alexandria, VA 22314-1994
Ph: (703)684-2443   Fax: (703)684-2475
E-mail: expoinfo@wef.org
URL: http://www.weftec.org

Annual. **Primary Exhibits:** Water treatment equipment, supplies, and services. **Dates and Locations:** 2004 Oct 02-06; New Orleans, LA; Ernest N. Norial Convention Center • 2005 Oct 29 - Nov 02; Washington, DC; Washington Convention Center • 2006 Oct 21-25; Dallas, TX; Dallas Convention Center.

OTHER SOURCES

★**4076**★ **Air and Waste Management Association (A&WMA)**
1 Gateway Ctr., 3rd Fl.
420 Duquesne Blvd.
Pittsburgh, PA 15222
Ph: (412)232-3444   Fax: (412)232-3450
Fr: 800-270-3444
E-mail: info@awma.org
URL: http://www.awma.org

Description: Environmental, educational, and technical organization. **Purpose:** Seeks to provide a neutral forum for the exchange of technical information on a wide variety of environmental topics.

★**4077**★ **American Academy of Environmental Engineers (AAEE)**
130 Holiday Ct., No. 100
Annapolis, MD 21401
Ph: (410)266-3311   Fax: (410)266-7653
E-mail: academy@aaee.net
URL: http://www.aaee.net

Members: Environmentally oriented registered professional engineers certified by examination as Diplomates of the Academy. **Purpose:** Works to improve the standards of environmental engineering; to certify those with special knowledge of environmental engineering; to furnish lists of those certified to the public. **Activities:** Maintains speakers' bureau. Recognizes areas of specialization: Air Pollution Control; General Environmental; Hazardous Waste Management; Industrial Hygiene; Radiation Protection; Solid Waste Management; Water Supply and Wastewater. Requires written and oral examinations for certification. Works with other professional organizations on environmentally oriented activities. Identifies potential employment candidates through Talent Search Service.

★**4078**★ **American Association of Engineering Societies (AAES)**
1828 L St. NW, No. 906
Washington, DC 20036
Ph: (202)296-2237   Fax: (202)296-1151
Fr: 888-400-2237
E-mail: tprice@aaes.org

URL: http://www.aaes.org

Description: Coordinates the efforts of the member societies in the provision of reliable and objective information to the general public concerning issues which affect the engineering profession and the field of engineering as a whole; to collect, analyze, document, and disseminate data which will inform the general public of the relationship between engineering and the national welfare; to provide a forum for the engineering societies to exchange and discuss their views on matters of common interest; and to represent the U.S. engineering community aborad through representation in WFEO and UPADI.

★4079★ **Environmental Industry Associations**

4301 Connecticut Ave., NW, Ste. 300
Washington, DC 20008
Ph: (202)244-4700   Fax: (202)966-4818
Fr: 800-424-2869
E-mail: eii@envasns.org
URL: http://www.envasns.org

Activities: Compiles statistics; conducts research and educational programs.

★4080★ *Environmental Occupations: Professional*

Delphi Productions
3160 4th St.
Boulder, CO 80304
Fax: (303)443-4022   Fr: 888-443-2400
URL: http://www.delphivideo.com

$95.00. 49 minutes. Part of the Emerging Careers Video Library.

★4081★ *Environmental Occupations: Technical*

Delphi Productions
3160 4th St.
Boulder, CO 80304
Fax: (303)443-4022   Fr: 888-443-2400
URL: http://www.delphivideo.com

$95.00. 48 minutes. Part of the Emerging Careers Video Library.

★4082★ **National Action Council for Minorities in Engineering (NACME)**

Empire State Bldg., Ste. 2212
350 Fifth Ave.
New York, NY 10118-2299
Ph: (212)279-2626   Fax: (212)629-5178
E-mail: webmaster@nacme.org
URL: http://www.nacme.org/

Description: Leads the national effort to increase access to careers in engineering and other science-based disciplines. Supported by the nation's leading technology-intensive companies, NACME conducts research and public policy analysis, develops and operates national demonstration programs at precollege and university levels, and disseminates information through publications, conferences, and electronic media. NACME is also the nation's largest privately funded source of scholarships for minority students in engineering.

★4083★ **National Society of Professional Engineers (NSPE)**

1420 King St.
Alexandria, VA 22314
Ph: (703)684-2800   Fax: (703)836-4875
Fr: 888-285-6773
E-mail: custserv@nspe.org
URL: http://www.nspe.org

Description: Professional engineers and engineers-in-training in all fields registered in accordance with the laws of states or territories of the U.S. or provinces of Canada; qualified graduate engineers, student members, and registered land surveyors. Is concerned with social, professional, ethical, and economic considerations of engineering as a profession; encompasses programs in public relations, employment practices, ethical considerations, education, and career guidance. Monitors legislative and regulatory actions of interest to the engineering profession.

★4084★ *Resumes for High Tech Careers*

Vgm Career Horizons
1221 Avenue of the Americas
New York, NY 10020
Ph: (212)904-2000   Fr: 800-323-4900
E-mail: ntcpub@tribune.com

Second edition, 1997. $9.95 (paper). 462 pages. Demonstrates how to tailor a resume that catches a high tech employer's attention. Part of Resumes for... series.

★4085★ *Scientific, Engineering, and Technical Services*

Cambridge Educational
2572 Brunswick Ave.
Lawrenceville, NJ 08648-4128
Fax: 800-FAX-ON-US   Fr: 800-468-4227
URL: http://www.cambridgeeducational.com

$89.95. 2002. 18 minutes. Part of the Career Cluster Series.

★4086★ **Society of Women Engineers (SWE)**

230 E Ohio St., No. 400
Chicago, IL 60611-3265
Ph: (312)596-5223   Fax: (312)596-5252
E-mail: hq@swe.org
URL: http://www.swe.org

Description: Educational and service organization representing both students and professional women in engineering and technical fields.

★4087★ *Women in Engineering*

Her Own Words
PO Box 5264
Madison, WI 53705-0264
Ph: (608)271-7083   Fax: (608)271-0209
URL: http://www.herownwords.com/

Video. Jocelyn Riley. $95.00. 15 minutes. Resource guide also available for $45.00.

Event Planners

★4088★ *Association News*

Schneider Publishing Co.
11835 W Olympic Blvd., 12th Fl.
Los Angeles, CA 90064
Ph: (310)577-3700   Fax: (310)577-3715
Fr: 877-577-3700

Monthly. $48.00/year for individuals. Magazine containing management and meeting plan information for association executives and meeting planners.

★4089★ *Meeting News*

Bill Communications Inc.
770 Broadway
New York, NY 10003-9595
Ph: (646)654-4500   Fax: (646)654-7212
URL: http://www.meetingnews.com

Free to qualified subscribers; $65.00/year. The newspaper for conventions, meetings, incentive travel and trade show professionals.

★4090★ *Special Events*

Miramar Communications Inc.
23805 Stuart Ranch Rd., Ste. 235
PO Box 8987
Malibu, CA 90265-8987
Ph: (310)317-4522   Fax: (310)317-0264
Fr: 800-543-4116
URL: http://www.specialevents.com

Monthly. Free to qualified subscribers. Magazine for special event professionals.

EMPLOYER DIRECTORIES AND NETWORKING LISTS

★4091★ *Meeting Professionals International Membership Directory*

Meeting Professionals International
4455 LBJ Fwy., Ste. 1200
Dallas, TX 75244-5903
Ph: (972)702-3000   Fax: (972)702-3070
URL: http://www.mpiweb.org

Annual. Free for members; $155.00 for nonmembers. Covers profiles of the members of Meeting Professionals International.

★4092★ *National Coalition of Black Meeting Planners-Directory*

National Coalition of Black Meeting
  Planners
8630 Fenton St., Ste. 126
Silver Spring, MD 20910
Ph: (202)628-3952   Fax: (301)588-0011
URL: http://www.ncbmp.com

Annual. Included in membership. Covers all members, associations, and meeting planners in the National Coalition of Black Meeting Planners.

★4093★ *Party Planning Service Directory*

infoUSA Inc.
5711 S 86th Cir.
Omaha, NE 68127-0347
Ph: (402)930-3500   Fax: (402)331-0176
Fr: 800-555-6124
URL: http://www.abii.com

Annual. Number of listings: 8,789. Entries include: Name, address, phone (including area code), size of advertisement, year first in "Yellow Pages," name of owner or manager, number of employees. Compiled from telephone company "Yellow Pages," nationwide. Arrangement: Geographical.

HANDBOOKS AND MANUALS

★4094★ *The Business of Event Planning: Behind-the-Scenes Secrets of Successful Special Events*

John Wiley & Sons Co.
10475 Crosspoint Blvd.
Indianapolis, IN 46256
Fax: 800-597-3299   Fr: 877-762-2974

Judy Allen. 2002. 320 pages. Provides expert advice for professional event planners.

★4095★ *How to Start a Home-Based Event Planning Business*

Globe Pequot Press
246 Goose Lane
Guilford, CT 06437
Ph: 888-249-7586   Fr: 800-820-2329
URL: http://www.globepequot.com

Jill Moran. 2004. $12.57. 197 pages. This insider's handbook reveals how to start a successful business planning a wide variety of events from home.

★4096★ *Opportunities in Event Planning Careers*

McGraw-Hill Companies
2 Penn Plaza
New York, NY 10121

Blyth Camenson. 2002. 160 pages. Details how to get started as an independent or corporate event planner. Includes training advice and salary statistics.

ONLINE JOB SOURCES AND SERVICES

★4097★ *Event Planner*
URL: http://www.event-planner.com
Description: Industry news and employment opportunities.

★4098★ Event Planner Directory
URL: http://www.eventplannerdirectory.com
Description: Vendor resources.

OTHER SOURCES

★4099★ Association of Collegiate Conference and Events Directors-International (ACCED-I)
Colorado State University
8037 Campus Delivery
Fort Collins, CO 80523-8037
Ph: (970)491-3772   Fax: (970)491-0667
Fr: 877-502-2233
E-mail: dbacced@lamar.colostate.edu
URL: http://acced-i.org

Members: University conference and special events directors; professionals who design, coordinate, and market conferences and special events on college and university campuses. **Purpose:** Dedicated to the professional development of its members; promotes the growth and distinction of the profession by uniting personnel and encouraging camaraderie. Promotes high standards of business and ethical conduct; works to foster communication, cooperation, and information sharing. **Activities:** Conducts research programs; collaborates with sister associations. Provides leadership opportunities through committee and board participation. Acts as an information clearinghouse; compiles statistics.

★4100★ Association for Convention Operations Management (ACOM)
PO Box 659
Avondale Estates, GA 30002
Ph: (404)292-3514   Fax: (404)292-2931
E-mail: info@acomonline.org
URL: http://www.acomonline.org/

Description: Convention service directors and managers of hotels, convention centers, and convention bureaus; suppliers of services and products to the convention and meetings industry are affiliate members. Works to increase the effectiveness, productivity, and quality of meetings, conventions, and exhibitions. Works to establish high ethical standards, improve professional management techniques, and increase awareness of client, employer, and provider needs. Maintains speakers' bureau, resource center, and placement services; compiles statistics. Conducts research and educational programs.

★4101★ Canadian Special Events Society
7950 Suncrest Dr.
Burnaby, BC, Canada V5C 1A5
Ph: (604)438-3687   Fax: (604)431-6775
URL: http://www.cses.ca/

Description: Provides a networking forum for members; offers professional development opportunities; disseminates industry developments.

★4102★ Connected International Meeting Professionals Association (CIMPA)
9200 Bayard Pl.
Fairfax, VA 22032
Ph: (703)286-2142   Fax: (703)291-2292
E-mail: info@meetingprofessionals.org
URL: http://www.cimpa.org

Members: Meeting planners, incentive organizers, travel agents, tour operators, and seminar organizers in 42 countries. **Purpose:** Works to improve the skills of professional conference and convention planners. Serves as a clearinghouse of information on new travel destinations and planning technologies, techniques, and strategies. **Activities:** Facilitates exchange of information among Internet professionals. Produces a television program on travel and meetings. Conducts educational courses and awards Certified Internet Meeting Professional designation. Conducts research programs and placement service. Sponsors training courses on the Internet.

★4103★ GCG Event Partners
125 Main St., Ste. H
Stoneham, MA 02180
Ph: (781)279-9887   Fax: (781)279-9875

Description: Network of event planning professionals.

★4104★ International Association of Fairs and Expositions
PO Box 985
Springfield, MO 65801
Fr: 800-516-0313
URL: http://www.fairsandexpos.com/about.aspx

Description: Individuals, corporations, and organizations involved with the planning and management of fairs, expositions.

★4105★ International Festivals and Events Association
2601 Eastover Terrace
Boise, ID 83706
Ph: (208)433-0950   Fax: (208)433-9812
URL: http://www.ifea.com

Description: Provides professional development opportunities and fundraising ideas for individuals involved in the special events industry.

★4106★ International Society of Meeting Planners (ISMP)
1224 No. Nokomis NE
Alexandria, MN 56308-5072
Ph: (320)763-4919   Fax: (320)763-9290
E-mail: ismp@iami.org
URL: http://www.iami.org/ismp.cfm

Members: Meeting planners and related industries. **Purpose:** Works to improve professionalism and competency in the industry as well as create new business opportunities for members. **Activities:** Provides networking opportunities. Offers professional designations: the RMP - Registered Meeting

Planner, CDS - Certified Destination Specialist, ITS - Incentive Travel Specialist, and CEP - Certified Event Planner.

★4107★ International Special Events Society
401 N. Michigan Ave.
Chicago, IL 60611
Fr: 800-688-4737
URL: http://www.ises.com

Description: Fosters performance through education. Represents special event producers.

★4108★ National Coalition of Black Meeting Planners (NCBMP)
8630 Fenton St., Ste. 126
Silver Spring, MD 20910
Ph: (202)628-3952   Fax: (301)588-0011
URL: http://www.ncbmp.com

Description: Black meeting planners. Purposes are to act as liaison with hotels, airlines, convention centers, and bureaus in an effort to assess the impact of minorities in these fields; assess the needs of the convention industry and how best to meet these needs; enhance members' sophistication in planning meetings; maximize employment of minorities in the convention industry. Maintains speakers' bureau. Conducts educational and research programs and compiles statistics on demographic employment of minorities in the convention industry. Maintains placement service.

★4109★ Professional Convention Management Association (PCMA)
2301 S Lake Shore Dr., Ste. 1001
Chicago, IL 60616-1419
Ph: (312)423-7262   Fax: (312)423-7222
Fr: 877-827-7262
E-mail: president@pcma.org
URL: http://www.pcma.org

Members: Convention, meeting, and exhibition planners, managers, and CEOs of nonprofit organizations. Promotes professional convention management; offers educational programs.

★4110★ Religious Conference Management Association (RCMA)
One RCA Dome, Ste. 120
Indianapolis, IN 46225
Ph: (317)632-1888   Fax: (317)632-7909
E-mail: rcma@rcmaweb.org
URL: http://www.rcmaweb.org

Description: Persons responsible for planning and/or managing religious conventions, meetings, and assemblies; associate members are individuals who directly support the logistics of religious meetings. Promotes professional excellence through exchange of ideas, techniques, and methods of management.

★4111★ Society of Corporate Meeting Professionals (SCMP)
217 Ridgemont Ave.
San Antonio, TX 78209
Ph: (210)353-8037   Fax: (210)822-9838
E-mail: info@scmp.org
URL: http://www.scmp.org

Members: Company and corporate meeting planners and conference center or hotel convention service managers and independent corporate meeting and special event planners united to promote continuing education and high standards among members.

Activities: Maintains databank of past meeting site selections and related information. Sponsors educational meetings and lectures.

★4112★ Society of Government Meeting Professionals (SGMP)
908 King St.
Alexandria, VA 22314
Ph: (703)549-0892   Fax: (703)549-0708
Fr: 800-827-8916
E-mail: carl.c.thompson@worldnet.att.net
URL: http://www.sgmp.org

Description: Individuals involved in planning government meetings on a full- or part-time basis; suppliers of services to government planners. Provides education in basic and advanced areas of meeting planning and facilitates professional contact with other government planners and suppliers knowledgeable in government contracting. Maintains referral network of planning resources, information on latest techniques, and opportunities to inspect conference facilities.

Fashion Models

SOURCES OF HELP-WANTED ADS

★4113★ Daily Variety

Reed Business Information
5700 Wilshire Blvd., Ste. 120
Los Angeles, CA 90036
Ph: (323)857-6600   Fax: (323)965-2475

Daily. Global entertainment newspaper (tabloid).

★4114★ JQ

Adams Business Media
420 S Palm Canyon Dr.
Palm Springs, CA 92262-7304
Ph: (760)318-7000   Fax: (760)416-7107

Bimonthly. Trade publication covering the fashion and retail industries.

EMPLOYER DIRECTORIES AND NETWORKING LISTS

★4115★ Black Book Photography

Black Book Marketing Group
10 Astor Pl., 6th Fl.
New York, NY 10003
Ph: (212)539-9800   Fax: (212)539-9801
Fr: 800-841-1246
URL: http://www.BlackBook.com

Annual, January. $110.00. Publication includes over 19,000 art directors, creative directors, photographers and photographic services, design firms, advertising agencies, and other firms whose products or services are used in advertising. Entries include: Company name, address, phone. Principal content of publication is 4-color samples from the leading commercial photographers. Arrangement: Classified by product/service.

★4116★ Model & Talent Directory

Peter Glenn Publications
6040 NW 43rd Ter.
Boca Raton, FL 33496-4043
Ph: (561)999-8930   Fax: (561)999-8931
Fr: 888-332-6700
URL: http://www.pgdirect.com

Annual. $24.95. Covers over 2,200 listings of model and talent agencies worldwide. Arrangement: Geographical.

★4117★ Modeling Agencies Directory

infoUSA Inc.
5711 S 86th Cir.
Omaha, NE 68127-0347
Ph: (402)930-3500   Fax: (402)331-0176
Fr: 800-555-6124
URL: http://www.abii.com

Updated continuously; printed on request. Number of listings: 1,604. Entries include: Name, address, phone, size of advertisement, name of owner or manager, number of employees, year first in "Yellow Pages." Compiled from telephone company "Yellow Pages," nationwide. Arrangement: Geographical.

★4118★ New York City Model Agency Directory

Peter Glenn Publications
6040 NW 43rd Ter.
Boca Raton, FL 33496-4043
Ph: (561)999-8930   Fax: (561)999-8931
Fr: 888-332-6700
URL: http://www.pgdirect.com

Annual. $13.95. Covers about 80 modeling agencies in New York City. Entries include: Company name, address, phone, fax, name and title of contact, type of modeling work handled, interview information, years of operation. Arrangement: Alphabetical. Indexes: Name.

★4119★ The Official Southwest Talent Directory

Cobb-Rendish Publishing
1920 Abrams Pkwy., Ste. 419
Dallas, TX 75214-6271
Fax: (214)855-0643

Annual, latest edition March, 1995. $25.00. Covers over 500 adult and juvenile actors, actresses, and models; motion picture and audio/videotape production facilities in the Southwest. Entries include: Name, acting or performing specialties, and agency contact; production services are presented in individual suppliers' ads. Arrangement: Talent classified by sex and age of performers; production sources classified by product or service. Indexes: Personal name, ethnic group, talent abilities.

HANDBOOKS AND MANUALS

★4120★ Beginner's Guide to Model Photography: Techniques for the Photographer and Tips for the Aspiring Model

Reference Desk Books
430 Quintana Rd., Ste. 146
Morro Bay, CA 93442
Ph: (805)772-8806   Fax: (805)528-0218

Valentine DelVecchio. 1993. $29.95 (paper). 128 pages.

★4121★ Careers for Fashion Plates and Other Trendsetters

VGM Career Horizons
N T C Publishing Group
1221 Avenue of the Americas
New York, NY 10020
Ph: (212)904-2000   Fr: 800-323-4900
E-mail: ntcpub@tribune.com

Lucia Mauro. 1996. $14.95; $9.95 (paper). 205 pages. Describes career opportunities in fashion, entertainment, retail, and promotion, with advice from fashion professionals.

★4122★ Hollywood, Here I Come!: An Insider's Guide to a Successful Acting & Modeling Career in Los Angeles

Yellow Deer Press
P.O. Box 7309A
Santa Monica, CA 90406-7309
Ph: (213)871-8755   Fr: 800-437-3267

Cynthia Hunter. 1999. $19.95.

★4123★ The Model's Work Book: A Hollywood Agents 20-Step Guide to Launching Your Modeling Career

Miller Boulay, Inc.
9367 Otchipwe Ave.
Stillwater, MN 55082
Ph: (651)430-9235   Fax: (651)351-7615

Laura Boulay, William Squire. January 2003. $29.95. Illustrated. 120 Pages.

★4124★ Opportunities in Beauty and Modeling Careers

McGraw-Hill Companies
860 Taylor Station Rd.
Blacklick, OH 43004-0545
Fax: (614)755-5645   Fr: 800-722-4726

Susan Wood Gearhart. September 2004. $13.95. 160 pages.

★4125★ Opportunities in Modeling Careers

McGraw-Hill Trade
2 Penn Plaza
New York, NY 10121
Ph: (212)904-2000   Fr: 800-722-4726

Susan Wood Gearhart. 1999. $14.95; $11.95 (paper). 146 pages. Addresses opportunities in modeling, ranging from artist's model to photographic model. Includes bibliography and illustrations.

★4126★ Real-Resumes for Retailing, Modeling, Fashion and Beauty Jobs: Including Real Resumes Used to Change Careers and Transfer Skills to Other Industries

PREP Publishing
1110 1/2 Hay St., PMB 66
Fayetteville, NC 28305
Ph: (910)483-6611   Fax: (910)483-2439
Fr: 800-533-2814

October 2002. $16.95.

★4127★ So, You Want to Be a Fashion Model?

InterScout, LLC
PO Box 965
Estes Park, CO 80517

Marcia Rothschild Moellers. 2003. $27.50. 166 Pages.

★4128★ Your Modeling Career: You Don't Have to Be a Superstar to Succeed

Allworth Press
10 E. 23rd St., Suite 510
New York, NY 10010
Ph: (212)777-8395   Fax: (212)777-8261
Fr: 800-491-2808

Debbie Press and Skip Press. 2000. $14.95 (paper).

ONLINE JOB SOURCES AND SERVICES

★4129★ Talent Network.com
URL: http://www.photographynetwork.com/
Description: A business-to-business portal for the fashion, arts, and entertainment industries. Online site contains a industry listings, portfolios and news items.

Financial Managers

★4130★ *Accounting Horizons*
American Accounting Association
5717 Bessie Dr.
Sarasota, FL 34233
Ph: (941)921-7747   Fax: (941)923-4093
Quarterly. Publication covering the banking, finance, and accounting industries.

★4131★ *American Banker*
American Banker/Bond Buyer Inc.
1 State St. Plz.
New York, NY 10004
Ph: (212)803-8200   Fax: (212)843-9600
Fr: 800-982-0633
URL: http://www.americanbanker.com
Daily. $775.00/year. Newspaper for senior executives in banking and other financial services industries. Coverage includes trends, analysis, and statistics of the legislative scene in Washington; finance; mortgages; technology; small business; and regional banking.

★4132★ *Barron's*
Dow Jones & Company Inc.
200 Liberty St.
New York, NY 10281
Ph: (212)416-2000   Fax: (212)416-2658
Fr: 800-832-1234
E-mail: editors@barrons.com
URL: http://www.barrons.com
Weekly. $145.00/year for individuals; $3.50 for single issue. Business and finance magazine.

★4133★ *Business Credit*
National Association of Credit
  Management
8840 Columbia 100 Pkwy.
Columbia, MD 21045
Ph: (410)740-5560   Fax: (410)740-5574
Fr: 800-955-8815
E-mail: bcm@nacm.org

Monthly. $54.00/year, US businesses; $48.00/year for libraries; $7.00/year for single issue. Magazine covering finance, business credit management, providing information for the extension of credit, maintenance of accounts receivable, and cash asset management.

★4134★ *Business Insurance*
Crain Communications Inc.
711 Third Ave.
New York, NY 10017-4036
Ph: (212)210-0100   Fax: (212)210-0244
Fr: 800-446-1420
URL: http://www.businessinsurance.com
Weekly. $97.00/year for individuals. International newsweekly reporting on corporate risk and employee benefit management news.

★4135★ *CFO*
CFO Publishing
253 Summer St.
Boston, MA 02210
Ph: (617)345-9700   Fax: (617)951-9306
Monthly. $19.00/year; $5.00 for single issue. Business magazine for small to mid-sized companies.

★4136★ *Financial Management*
Financial Management Association
School of Business
University of S Florida
Tampa, FL 33620-5500
Ph: (813)974-2084   Fax: (813)974-3318
E-mail: kporto@coba.usf.edu
Quarterly. $95.00/year for individuals; $20.00 for single issue. Journal covering business, economics, finance and management.

★4137★ *Forbes*
Forbes Magazine
60 5th Ave.
New York, NY 10011
Ph: (212)620-2200   Fax: (212)206-5174
URL: http://www.forbes.com

Biweekly. $52.00/year; $4.95 for single issue. Magazine reporting on industry, business and finance management.

★4138★ *Investment Dealers' Digest*
Securities Data Publishing
195 Broadway, 10th Fl.
New York, NY 10007
Fr: 800-455-5844
E-mail: subscribe@iddis.com
Weekly. $625.00/year for individuals. Magazine focusing on securities and finance.

★4139★ *Journal of Accountancy*
The American Institute of Certified Public
  Accountants
1211 Avenue of the Americas
New York, NY 10036-8775
Ph: (212)596-6200   Fax: (212)596-6213
Fr: 888-777-7077
E-mail: joaed@aicpa.org
URL: http://www.aicpa.org
Monthly. $56.00/year for individuals. Accounting journal.

★4140★ *Journal of Financial and
  Quantitative Analysis*
Journal of Financial & Quantitative
  Analysis
University of Washington
School of Business Administration
115 Lewis Hall
PO Box 353200
Seattle, WA 98195
Ph: (206)543-4598   Fax: (206)616-1894
E-mail: jfqa@u.washington.edu
URL: http://weber.u.washington.edu/~jfqa
Quarterly. $40.00/year; $25.00/year for students; $85.00/year. Journal on research in finance.

★4141★ *The Journal of Taxation*
RIA Group
395 Hudson St., 4th Fl.
New York, NY 10014
Ph: (212)352-2746   Fax: (212)367-6314
Fr: 800-431-9025

URL: http://checkpoint.riag.com

Monthly. $250.00/year for individuals. Journal for sophisticated tax practitioners.

★4142★ **Mortgage Banking Magazine**
Mortgage Bankers Association of America
1919 Pennsylvania Ave. NW
Washington, DC 20006-3438
Ph: (202)557-2700   Fax: (202)721-0245
Fr: 800-793-MBAA
URL: http://www.mortgagebankingmagazine.com/

Monthly. $15.00 for single issue; $69.95/year for nonmembers; $110.00/year for two years; $74.95/year for Canada and foreign subscriptions. Magazine of the real estate finance industry.

★4143★ **National Mortgage News**
Thomson Financial
195 Broadway
New York, NY 10007
Ph: (646)822-2000
E-mail: nmnews@aol.com

$198.00/year for individuals. Newspaper for mortgage lenders and investment bankers.

★4144★ **Northwestern Financial Review**
NFR Communications Inc.
4948 Washburn Ave.S.
Minneapolis, MN 55410
Ph: (612)929-8110   Fax: (612)929-8146
E-mail: web@nfrcom.com
URL: http://www.nfrcom.com

Bimonthly. $89.00/year for individuals; $160.00 for two years; $5.00/year for single issue. Trade publication covering commercial banking.

★4145★ **PENSION Management**
Primedia Business
6151 Powers Ferry Rd.
Atlanta, GA 30339
Ph: (770)955-2500   Fax: (770)618-0348

Monthly. $68.00/year for individuals. Magazine on pension investment and fund administration.

★4146★ **Pensions & Investments**
Crain Communications Inc.
711 Third Ave.
New York, NY 10017-4036
Ph: (212)210-0100   Fax: (212)210-0244
Fr: 800-446-1420

Biweekly. $205.00/year. Magazine containing news and features on investment management, pension management, corporate finance, and cash management.

★4147★ **Servicing Management**
LDJ Corp.
70 Edwin Ave.
PO Box 2330
Waterbury, CT 06722
Ph: (203)755-0158   Fax: (203)755-3480
Fr: 800-325-6745

Monthly. $48.00/year for individuals; $8.00 for single issue. Trade magazine for mortgage professionals involved with mortgage loan servicing.

★4148★ **Strategic Finance**
Institute of Management Accountants
10 Paragon Dr.
Montvale, NJ 07645-1760
Ph: (201)573-9000   Fax: (201)474-1603
Fr: 800-638-4427
E-mail: sfmag@imanet.org
URL: http://www.proquest.umi.com

Monthly. $145.00/year for individuals; $73.00/year, non-profit libraries. Magazine reporting on corporate finance, accounting, cash management, and budgeting.

★4149★ **U.S. Banker**
Thomson Financial
195 Broadway
New York, NY 10007
Ph: (646)822-2000
URL: http://www.electronicbanker.com

Monthly. $59.00/year for individuals. Magazine serving the financial services industry.

★4150★ **World Economic Outlook**
International Monetary Fund
700 19th St. NW, Ste. 12-607
Washington, DC 20431
Ph: (202)623-7430   Fax: (202)623-7201

Semiannual. Publication covering economics and business issues worldwide.

PLACEMENT AND JOB REFERRAL SERVICES

★4151★ **Commercial Finance Association (CFA)**
225 W 34th St., Ste. 1815
New York, NY 10122
Ph: (212)594-3490   Fax: (212)564-6053
E-mail: postmaster@cfa.com
URL: http://www.cfa.com

Members: Organizations engaged in asset-based financial services including commercial financing and factoring and lending money on a secured basis to small- and medium-sized business firms. **Purpose:** Acts as a forum for information and consideration about ideas, opportunities, and legislation concerning asset-based financial services. Seeks to improve the industry's legal and operational procedures. **Activities:** Offers job placement and reference services for members. Sponsors School for Field

Examiners and other educational programs. Compiles statistics; conducts seminars and surveys; maintains speakers' bureau and 21 committees.

★4152★ **Financial Management Association International (FMA)**
College of Business Administration, Ste. 3331
University of South Florida
Tampa, FL 33620-5500
Ph: (813)974-2084   Fax: (813)974-3318
E-mail: fma@coba.usf.edu
URL: http://www.fma.org

Members: Professors of financial management; corporate financial officers. **Purpose:** Facilitates exchange of ideas among persons involved in financial management or the study thereof. **Activities:** Conducts workshops for comparison of current research projects and development of cooperative ventures in writing and research. Sponsors honorary society for superior students at 300 colleges and universities. Offers placement services.

★4153★ **National Bankers Association (NBA)**
1513 P St. NW
Washington, DC 20005
Ph: (202)588-5432   Fax: (202)588-5443
E-mail: nahart@nationalbankers.org
URL: http://www.nationalbankers.org/

Members: Minority banking institutions owned by minority individuals and institutions. **Purpose:** Serves as an advocate for the minority banking industry. Organizes banking services, government relations, marketing, scholarship, and technical assistance programs. **Activities:** Offers placement services; compiles statistics.

EMPLOYER DIRECTORIES AND NETWORKING LISTS

★4154★ **American Banker-Top Commercial Banks by Assets, Deposits**
American Banker/Bond Buyer Inc.
1 State St. Plz.
New York, NY 10004
Ph: (212)803-8200   Fax: (212)843-9600
Fr: 800-982-0633

Semiannual, March and September. $25.00. Publication includes: List of the top 300 commercial banks. Entries include: Name of bank, headquarters, amount of deposits at the previous quarter, place in rank at quarter. Arrangement: Ranked by deposits and assets. Indexes: Geographical.

★4155★ *American Banker-Top Finance Companies Issue*

American Banker/Bond Buyer Inc.
1 State St. Plz.
New York, NY 10004
Ph: (212)803-8200   Fax: (212)843-9600
Fr: 800-982-0633

Annual, December. $25.00. Publication includes: List of top finance companies with $10 million or more in capital funds. Entries include: Finance company name, headquarters, city; rankings of net receivables by type, business, consumer, and other; total capital funds for two preceding years; capital and surplus, total assets, net receivables, net income, deferred income, receivables acquired, and amount of bank credit at end of the preceding year. Arrangement: Ranked by size of capital funds.

★4156★ *American Banker-Top 300 Mortgage Companies Issue*

American Banker/Bond Buyer Inc.
1 State St. Plz.
New York, NY 10004
Ph: (212)803-8200   Fax: (212)843-9600
Fr: 800-982-0633

Annual, October. $25.00. Entries include: Company name, headquarters city, rank; dollar value of mortgages serviced for current and prior year; prior year's rank and gain in rank; number of mortgages; number of investors. Arrangement: Ranked by total dollar value of mortgages.

★4157★ *American Banker-Top 300 Thrifts by Deposits*

American Banker/Bond Buyer Inc.
1 State St. Plz.
New York, NY 10004
Ph: (212)803-8200   Fax: (212)843-9600
Fr: 800-982-0633

Semiannual, May and November. $25.00. Publication includes: List of top 300 thrift institutions. Entries include: Name of institution, city, rank; total assets, deposits, and total capital. Arrangement: Ranked by deposits, assets, and risk-based capital ratios.

★4158★ *America's Corporate Finance Directory*

LexisNexis Group
121 Chanlon Rd.
New Providence, NJ 07974
Ph: (908)464-6800   Fax: (908)771-7704
Fr: 800-526-4902
URL: http://www.lexisnexis.com/corpfinancedir/default.asp

Annual, September. $799.99. Covers financial personnel and outside financial services relationships of 5,000 leading United States corporations and their wholly-owned United States subsidiaries. Entries include: Company name, address, phone, fax, telex, e-mail addresses, stock exchange information, earnings, total assets, size of pension/profit-sharing fund portfolio, number of employees, description of business, wholly-owned U.S. subsidiaries of parent company; name and title of key executives; outside suppliers of financial services. Arrangement: Alphabetical. Indexes: Financial responsibilities, Standard Industrial Classification (SIC) code, geographical, personnel, private companies, company name.

★4159★ *Association for Investment Management & Research-Membership Directory*

Association for Investment Management & Research
560 Ray C. Hunt Dr.
PO Box 3668
Charlottesville, VA 22903-0668
Ph: (434)951-5499   Fax: (434)951-5262
Fr: 800-247-8132
URL: http://www.aimr.org

Annual, January. $150.00. Covers 38,000 security and financial analysts who are practicing investment analysis. Entries include: Name, firm affiliation and address, phone, fax, e-mail. Arrangement: Alphabetical.

★4160★ *Branches of Your State: Banks, Savings and Loans, Credit Unions, & Savings Banks*

Sheshunoff Information Services
807 Las Cimas Pkwy., Ste. 300
Austin, TX 78746
Ph: (512)472-2244   Fax: (512)305-6575
Fr: 800-456-2340

Annual, February. $475.00. Covers in separate state editions, banks, savings and loan branches, and credit unions. For those states without branch banking, individual banks, savings and loan institutions, and credit unions are listed. Entries include: Institution name, address, institution type, deposit totals, percent change over 12 months, percentage share of parent company's total deposits. Arrangement: Geographical.

★4161★ *Career Opportunities in Banking, Finance, and Insurance*

Facts on File Inc.
132 W 31st St., 17th Fl.
New York, NY 10001
Ph: (212)967-8800   Fax: 800-678-3633
Fr: 800-322-8755

$49.50. Publication includes: Lists of colleges with programs supporting banking, finance, and industry; professional associations; professional certifications; regulatory agencies; and Internet resources for career planning. Principal content of publication is job descriptions for professions in the banking, finance, and insurance industries. Indexes: Alphabetical.

★4162★ *Corporate Finance Sourcebook*

LexisNexis Group
121 Chanlon Rd.
New Providence, NJ 07974
Ph: (908)464-6800   Fax: (908)771-7704
Fr: 800-526-4902
URL: http://www.financesourcebook.com/cfs_info.htm

Annual, November. $689.00. Covers securities research analysts; major private lenders; investment banking firms; commercial banks; United States-based foreign banks; commercial finance firms; leasing companies; foreign investment bankers in the United States; pension managers; banks that offer master trusts; cash managers; business insurance brokers; business real estate specialists; lists about 3,400 firms; 14,500 key financial experts. Entries include: Firm name, address, phone, e-mail, and names and titles of officers, contacts, or specialists in corporate finance. Additional details are given as appropriate, including names of major clients, number of companies served, services, total assets, branch locations, years in business. Arrangement: Classified by line of business and then alphabetized within that line of business. Indexes: Firm name, personnel name, geographical.

★4163★ *Employment Opportunities, USA*

Washington Research Associates
1090 Vermont Ave., NW, Ste. 800
Washington, DC 20005
Ph: (202)408-7025

Annual, quarterly updates. $184.00. Publication includes: List of over 1,000 employment contacts in companies and agencies in the banking, arts, telecommunications, education, and 14 other industries and professions, including the federal government. Entries include: Company name, name of representative, address, description of products or services, hiring and recruiting practices, training programs, and year established. Principal content is industry overviews, career news, employment opportunity information on 14 different job markets, and comprehensive guidance to career resources on the Internet. Arrangement: Classified by industry. Indexes: Occupation.

★4164★ *4 Data Base*

Hunt-Scanlon Publishing
20 Signal Rd.
Stamford, CT 06902-7907
Ph: (203)352-2920   Fax: (203)352-2930

Annual. $1,350.00 for individuals. Database covers more than 100,000 top and middle management professionals in human resources, finance, sales and marketing, and information technology at over 10,000 companies in the U.S. Entries include: Company name, address, phone, number of employees, SIC codes, revenues, individual name, title, phone number, industry specialization.

★4165★ *Mergent Bank and Finance Manual*

Mergent Inc.
5250 77 Center Dr., Ste. 150
Charlotte, NC 28217
Ph: (704)559-7601   Fax: (704)559-6945
Fr: 800-342-5647
URL: http://www.mergent.com

Annual, July; supplements in 'Mergent Bank & Finance News Reports'. $2,095.00. Covers in four volumes, over 12,000 national, state, and private banks, savings and loans, mutual funds, unit investment trusts, and insurance and real estate companies in the United States. Entries include: Company name, headquarters and branch offices, phones, names and titles of principal executives, directors, history, Moody's rating, and extensive financial and statistical data. Arrangement: Classified by type of business. Indexes: Company name.

★4166★ National Bankers Association-Roster of Minority Banking Institutions

National Bankers Association
1513 P St. NW
Washington, DC 20005
Ph: (202)588-5432   Fax: (202)588-5443

Annual, October. $5.00. Covers about 140 banks owned or controlled by minority group persons or women. Entries include: Bank name, address, phone, name of one executive. Arrangement: Geographical.

★4167★ NFCC Directory of Members

National Foundation for Credit Counseling
801 Roeder Rd., Ste. 900
Silver Spring, MD 20910
Ph: (301)589-5600   Fax: (301)495-5623

$5.00 for members; $10.50 for nonmembers. Covers about 1,300 affiliated non-profit Consumer Credit Counseling Services in the United States, Puerto Rico, and Canada, which provide non-profit education, counseling, and debt management programs for financial and housing issues. Entries include: Member name, address, phone, fax, name and title of contact, subsidiary and branch names and locations, names and titles of key personnel, description. Arrangement: Geographical. Indexes: Agency name, name of personnel.

★4168★ Peterson's Job Opportunities for Business Majors

Thomson Peterson's
Princeton Pke. Corporate Ctr., 2000 Lenox Dr.
PO Box 67005
Lawrenceville, NJ 08648
Ph: (609)896-1800   Fax: (609)896-4531
Fr: 800-338-3282
URL: http://www.petersons.com

Irregular, latest edition 2000 - 16th ed. $18.95. Covers the 2,000 largest U.S. employers hiring in several fields, including financial services, management consulting, consumer products, and media/ entertainment. Entries include: Organization name, address, phone, name and title of contact, number of employees, type of organization. Arrangement: Alphabetical. Indexes: Type of organization.

★4169★ Roster of Minority Financial Institutions

U.S. Department of the Treasury
1500 Pennsylvania Ave. NW
Washington, DC 20220
Ph: (202)622-2000

Biennial. Covers about 170 commercial, minority-owned and controlled financial institutions participating in the Department of the Treasury's Minority Bank Deposit Program. Entries include: Name of institution, name and title of chief officer, address, phone, fax. Arrangement: Geographical.

★4170★ Thomson Bank Directory

Thomson Financial Publishing
4709 W.Golf Rd., Ste. 600
Skokie, IL 60076
Ph: (847)676-9600   Fax: (847)933-8101
Fr: 800-321-3373
URL: http://www.tgbr.com

Semiannual, June and December. $608.00; $509.00 for annual subscription. Covers in three volumes, about 11,000 banks and 50,000 branches of United States banks, and 60,000 foreign banks and branches engaged in foreign banking; Federal Reserve system and other United States government and state government banking agencies; 500 largest North American and International commercial banks; paper and automated clearinghouses. Volumes 1 and 2 contain North American listings; volumes 3 and 4, international listings (also cited as 'Thomson International Bank Directory'); volume 5, Worldwide Correspondents Guide containing key correspondent data to facilitate funds transfer. Entries include: For domestic banks-Bank name, address, phone, telex, cable, date established, routing number, charter type, bank holding company affiliation, memberships in Federal Reserve System and other banking organizations, principal officers by function performed, principal correspondent banks, and key financial data (deposits, etc.). For international banks-Bank name, address, phone, fax, telex, cable, SWIFT address, transit or sort codes within home country, ownership, financial data, names and titles of key personnel, branch locations. For branches-Bank name, address, phone, charter type, ownership and other details comparable to domestic bank listings. Arrangement: Geographical. Indexes: Alphabetical, geographical.

★4171★ Thomson North American Financial Institutions Directory

Thomson Financial Publishing
4709 W.Golf Rd., Ste. 600
Skokie, IL 60076
Ph: (847)676-9600   Fax: (847)933-8101
Fr: 800-321-3373

Semiannual. $449.00 for single issue. Covers 15,000 banks and their branches; over 2,000 head offices, and 15,500 branches of savings and loan associations; over 5,500 credit unions with assets over $5 million; Federal Reserve System and other U.S. government and state government banking agencies; bank holding, commercial finance, and leasing companies; coverage includes

the United States, Canada, Mexico, and Central America. Entries include: Bank name, address, phone, fax, telex, principal officers and directors, date established, financial data, association memberships, attorney or counsel, correspondent banks, out-of-town branch, holding company affiliation, ABA transit number and routing symbol, MICR number with check digit, credit card(s) issued, trust powers, current par value and dividend of common stock, kind of charter. Arrangement: Geographical. Indexes: Alphabetical.

★4172★ Who's Who in Finance and Industry

Marquis Who's Who
121 Chanlon Rd.
New Providence, NJ 07974
Ph: (908)673-1101   Fax: (908)673-1189
Fr: 800-473-7020
URL: http://www.marquiswhoswho.com

Biennial, July of odd years. $292.50. Covers over 21,000 individuals. Entries include: Name, home and office addresses, personal, career, and family data; civic and political activities; memberships, publications, awards. Arrangement: Alphabetical.

HANDBOOKS AND MANUALS

★4173★ Best Websites for Financial Professionals, Business Appraisers, & Accountants

John Wiley & Sons Inc.
111 River St.
Hoboken, NJ 07030-5774
Ph: (201)748-6000   Fax: (201)748-5774

Eva M. Lang. 2001. $39.95 (paper).

★4174★ Careers in Banking and Finance

Rosen Publishing Group, Inc.
29 E. 21st St.
New York, NY 10010
Ph: (212)777-3017   Fax: 888-436-4643
Fr: 800-237-9932

Patricia Haddock. 2001. $16.95 139 pages. Offers advice on job hunting. Describes jobs at all levels in banking and finance. Contains information about the types of financial organizations where the jobs are found, educational requirements, job duties, and salaries.

★4175★ Careers in Finance

McGraw-Hill Professional
2 Penn Plaza
New York, NY 10121-2298
Ph: (212)904-2000   Fr: 800-722-4726

Trudy Ring. 1994. $15.95 (paper). 192 pages. Vocational guidance in the banking and financial industries.

★4176★ Careers for Financial Mavens and Other Money Movers
McGraw-Hill Trade
2 Penn Plaza
New York, NY 10121
Ph: (212)904-2000 Fr: 800-722-4726
E-mail: ntcpub@tribune.com
Marjorie Eberts and Margaret Gisler. 1998. $14.95; $9.95 (paper). 232 pages.

★4177★ Careers for Number Crunchers and Other Quantitative Types
McGraw-Hill Trade
2 Penn Plaza
New York, NY 10121
Ph: (212)904-2000 Fr: 800-722-4726
E-mail: ntcpub@tribune.com
Rebecca Burnett. Second edition, 2002. $15.95; $12.95 (paper). 192 pages. Provides information to math-oriented job hunters on how to become statisticians, field researchers, computer programmers, stock analysts, investment managers, bankers, engineers, accountants, underwriters, economists, market analysts, mathematicians, systems analysts, and more.

★4178★ Great Jobs for Business Majors
McGraw-Hill Trade
2 Penn Plaza
New York, NY 10121
Ph: (212)904-2000 Fr: 800-722-4726
E-mail: ntcpub@tribune.com
Stephen Lambert. 1996. $11.95 (paper). 462 pages.

★4179★ Job Seekers Guide to Wall Street Recruiters
John Wiley & Sons Inc.
1 Wiley Dr.
Somerset, NJ 08873
Ph: (732)469-4400 Fr: 800-225-5945
Christopher W. Hunt and Scott A. Scanlon. 1998. $19.95 (paper). Lists recruiters covering investment banking, investment management, and the securities industry.

★4180★ Opportunities in Banking Careers
McGraw-Hill Trade
2 Penn Plaza
New York, NY 10121
Ph: (212)904-2000 Fr: 800-722-4726
Philip Perry. 1994. $14.95; $11.95 (paper). 160 pages. Discusses banking opportunities in a variety of settings: commercial banks, savings and loans, finance companies, and mortgage banks.

★4181★ Opportunities in Financial Careers
McGraw-Hill Trade
2 Penn Plaza
New York, NY 10121
Ph: (212)904-2000 Fr: 800-722-4726
Michael Sumichrast. 1997. $14.95; $11.95 (paper). 210 pages. A guide to planning for and seeking opportunities in this challenging field.

★4182★ Opportunities in Hospital Administration Careers
McGraw-Hill/Contemporary Books
1221 Avenue of the Americas
New York, NY 10020
Ph: (212)904-2000 Fr: 800-323-4900
E-mail: ntcpub@tribune.com
I. Donald Snook. 1997. $14.95; $11.95 (paper). 160 pages. Discusses opportunities for administrators in a variety of management settings: hospital, department, clinic, group practice, HMO, mental health, and extended care facilities.

★4183★ Resumes for Banking and Financial Careers
McGraw-Hill Contemporary Books
1221 Avenue of the Americas
New York, NY 10020
Ph: (212)904-2000 Fr: 800-323-4900
E-mail: ntcpub@tribune.com
2001. $10.95 (paper). 468 pages.

★4184★ Where the Jobs Are: The Hottest Careers for the 90s
The Career Press, Inc.
3 Tice Rd.
PO Box 687
Franklin Lakes, NJ 07417-1322
Ph: (201)848-0310 Fax: (201)848-1727
Fr: 800-227-3371
Joyce Hadley. Third edition, 2000. $13.99 (paper). 400 pages. Out of print. Describes careers in fifteen general fields, from accounting to travel and hospitality.

EMPLOYMENT AGENCIES AND SEARCH FIRMS

★4185★ A-L Associates Inc.
546 5th Ave., Fl. 6
New York, NY 10036
Ph: (212)878-9000 Fax: (212)878-9096
Executive search firm.

★4186★ Abbott Associates
20880 Fish Rd.
Wilder, ID 83676
Ph: (208)482-4303
Executive search firm with focus on senior level.

★4187★ Abel Fuller & Zedler LLC
4550 Post Oak Pl., Ste. 141
Houston, TX 77027
Ph: (713)961-3330 Fax: (713)961-3337
Executive Search Firm.

★4188★ Accu Staff Inc.
2350 W River Park Dr.
Tucson, AZ 85705
Ph: (520)690-6630
Services provided include recruiting, temporary help, retained search, outplacement, testing and consulting. Specialties include management, executive, administrative, accounting/bookkeeping, data processing, financial, sales, marketing, technical, manufacturing, industrial and secretarial/office support. Serves private industries as well as government agencies.

★4189★ Aegis Consulting
633 3rd Ave., Fl. 27
New York, NY 10017
Ph: (212)687-2200 Fax: (212)687-0079
Executive search firm.

★4190★ Ahrensdorf & Associates
PO Box 7494
St. Davids, PA 19087-7494
Ph: (610)971-0500 Fax: (610)971-9530
Executive search firm.

★4191★ AKS Associates Ltd.
175 Derby St., Ste. 27
Hingham, MA 02043-4054
Ph: (781)740-1704 Fax: (781)740-4383
Senior search firm. Concentrates on the financial industry.

★4192★ Alexander Edwards International Inc.
501 Madison Ave., Ste. 401
New York, NY 10022
Ph: (212)242-6881 Fax: (212)989-2810
Fr: 800-590-3001
Global executive search firm. Second location in Maryland.

★4193★ Alfred Daniels & Associates Inc.
5795 Waverly Ave.
La Jolla, CA 92037
Ph: (858)459-4009
Executive search firm.

★4194★ Allard Associates Inc.
425 Market St., Ste. 2200
San Francisco, CA 94105
Ph: (530)661-7562 Fax: 800-526-7791
Fr: 800-291-5279
Executive search firm. Focuses on financial

placement surrounding the credit card industry.

★4195★ Allen Evans Klein International
305 Madison Ave., Ste. 1650
New York, NY 10165
Ph: (212)983-9300   Fax: (212)983-9272
Global Executive search firm.

★4196★ Allen Personnel Agency Inc.
170 Broadway, Rm. 211
New York, NY 10038
Ph: (212)571-1150   Fax: (212)766-1015
Fr: 800-486-1150
Personnel consultants specializing in business and finance recruitment, specifically insurance, banking, stock brokerage, law and accounting.

★4197★ Allerton Heneghan & O'Neill
1 Tower Ln., Ste. 1700
Oakbrook Terrace, IL 60181
Ph: (630)645-2294   Fax: (630)645-2298
Executive Search firm.

★4198★ Ambler Associates
14881 Quorum Dr., Ste. 450
Dallas, TX 75254-7018
Ph: (972)404-8712   Fax: (972)404-8761
Fr: 800-728-8712
Executive search firm.

★4199★ American Executive Management Inc.
30 Federal St.
Salem, MA 01970
Ph: (978)477-5923
Executive search firm. Second location in Boston.

★4200★ American Human Resources Associates Ltd. (AHRA)
PO Box 18269
Cleveland, OH 44118-0269
Ph: (440)995-7120   Fr: 877-342-5833
Executive search firm. Focused on real estate, banking and credit & collection.

★4201★ The Angus Group Ltd.
250 W. Court St., Ste. 100E
Cincinnati, OH 45202-1088
Ph: (513)961-5575   Fax: (513)961-5616
Executive search firm.

★4202★ Arlene Clapp Ltd.
4250 Park Glen Rd.
Minneapolis, MN 55416
Ph: (952)928-7474   Fax: (952)928-7475
Executive search firm.

★4203★ The Bankers Register
1140 Avenue of the Americas
New York, NY 10036
Ph: (212)840-0800   Fax: (212)840-7039
Specialists in the recruitment and placement of men and women in the banking community. Committed exclusively to: commercial banking, international banking, trust/investments, and thrift/mortgage banking.

★4204★ Barkstone Group LLC
113 South St.
PO Box 218
Litchfield, CT 06759-0218
Ph: (860)567-2400   Fax: (860)567-1466
Executive search firm focused on the banking industry.

★4205★ Bartholdi Partners
12020 Sunrise Valley Dr., Ste. 160
Reston, VA 20191
Ph: (703)476-5519   Fax: (703)476-6473
Executive search firm. Affiliates in San Francisco, San Jose, Phoenix, Scottsdale, Parker CO, and Framingham MA.

★4206★ Bartram/Taylor Group LLC
60 E. 42nd St., Ste. 3204
New York, NY 10165
Ph: (212)692-9644   Fax: (212)370-3627
Executive search firm concentrating on finance.

★4207★ The Beam Group
11 Penn Ctr., Ste. 502
Philadelphia, PA 19103
Ph: (215)988-2100   Fax: (215)988-1558
Executive search firm.

★4208★ Bell Wishingrad Partners Inc.
230 Park Ave., Ste. 1000
New York, NY 10169
Ph: (212)949-6666
Executive search firm focused on the financial industry.

★4209★ The Bennett Group Inc.
5640 Professional Circle, Ste. A8
Indianapolis, IN 46241
Ph: (317)247-1240   Fax: (317)247-6533
Executive search firm.

★4210★ Bialecki Inc.
780 3rd Ave., Ste. 4203
New York, NY 10017
Ph: (212)755-1090
Senior executive search firm focused on the financial industry.

★4211★ BMF Reynolds Inc.
336 Nassau St.
Princeton, NJ 08540
Ph: (609)688-8700
Executive search firm.

★4212★ Bonell Ryan Inc.
444 Madison Ave., Ste. 3202
New York, NY 10022
Ph: (212)754-0700   Fax: (702)995-9935
Executive search firm.

★4213★ Bowden & Company Inc.
5000 Rockside Rd.
Cleveland, OH 44131
Ph: (216)447-1800   Fax: (216)447-1803
Executive search consultants who specialize in filling positions for chief executive officers, directors, executive and managerial team members in all functional areas. Industries served: manufacturing, financial services, professional services, and venture capital firms.

★4214★ Brandjes Associates
721 Cliveden Rd.
PO Box 5971
Baltimore, MD 21208-4715
Ph: (410)484-5423   Fax: (410)484-6140
Fr: 877-485-8193
Executive recruiting for the financial services industry.

★4215★ Brush Creek Partners
1133 W. Main St.
Blue Springs, MO 64015
Ph: (816)228-9192   Fax: (816)228-6740
Executive search firm.

★4216★ The Burling Group Ltd.
191 N. Wacker Dr., Ste. 2300
Chicago, IL 60606
Ph: (312)346-0888
Executive search firm.

★4217★ Butterfass, Pepe & MacCallan Inc.
PO Box 721
Mahwah, NJ 07430
Ph: (201)560-9500   Fax: (201)560-9506
Executive search firm.

★4218★ Buxbaum/Rink Consulting L.L.C.
1 Bradley Rd., Ste. 901
Woodbridge, CT 06525
Ph: (203)389-5949   Fax: (203)397-0615
Personnel consulting firms offer contingency search, recruitment and placement of accounting/finance, as well as other business management positions. In addition to serving these two major career areas, also provides

similar services to operations, marketing and human resources executives. Industries served: manufacturing, financial services, and service.

★4219★ Cannellos-Smartt Associates
23 Davenport Way
Hillsborough, NJ 08844-2923
Ph: (908)359-8319
Executive search firm with another office in Hillborough.

★4220★ Canny, Bowen Inc.
280 Park Ave., Fl. 30 W
New York, NY 10017
Ph: (212)949-6611   Fax: (212)949-5191
Executive search firm.

★4221★ Career Specialists Inc.
155 108th Ave. NE, Ste. 200
Bellevue, WA 98004
Ph: (425)455-0582   Fax: (425)646-9738
Executive search firm.

★4222★ Carrington & Carrington Ltd
39 S. LaSalle St., Ste. 700
Chicago, IL 60603
Ph: (312)606-0015   Fax: (312)606-0501
Executive search firm.

★4223★ CarterBaldwin
300 Colonial Center Pkwy., Ste. 240
Roswell, GA 30076
Ph: (678)448-0000   Fax: (770)552-1088
Executive search firm.

★4224★ Caruthers & Company LLC
1175 Post Rd. East
Westport, CT 06880
Ph: (203)221-3234   Fax: (203)221-7300
Executive search firm.

★4225★ Chanko-Ward Ltd.
2 W 45th St., Ste. 1201
New York, NY 10036
Ph: (212)869-4040   Fax: (212)869-0281
Primarily engaged in executive recruiting for individuals and corporations, where disciplines of accounting, planning, mergers/acquisitions, finance, or MIS are required. In addition will function as the internal personnel department of a corporation, either to augment present staff or in a situation where there is no formal personnel department. Serves private industries as well as government agencies.

★4226★ Chicago Consulting Partners Ltd.
930 4th Ave. South
Libertyville, IL 60048
Ph: (847)680-0416
Executive search firm concentrated in the financial industry.

★4227★ Chiron Advisors Inc.
1 Rockefeller Plaza, Ste. 1007
New York, NY 10020
Ph: (212)698-1161   Fax: (212)698-1167
Executive search firm focused on the financial industry.

★4228★ Choi & Burns LLC
590 Madison Ave., Fl. 26
New York, NY 10022
Ph: (212)755-7051   Fax: (212)355-2610
Executive search firm focuses on the financial industry.

★4229★ Christian & Timbers
1 Corporate Exchange
25825 Science Park Dr., Ste. 400
Cleveland, OH 44122
Ph: (216)464-8710   Fax: (216)464-6160
Fr: 800-380-9444
Executive search firm. Eight branches spanning the USA.

★4230★ CMSI Consulting LLC
14580 SW 87th Ave., Ste. 1G
Miami, FL 33176
Ph: (305)969-0683   Fax: (212)202-4096
Fr: 800-713-0093
Executive search firm.

★4231★ Coffou Partners Inc.
1 IBM Plaza
330 N. Wabash Ave., Ste. 2111
Chicago, IL 60611
Ph: (312)464-0896   Fax: (312)464-0322
Executive search firm.

★4232★ Connexus Group LLC
225 W. 34th St., Ste. 1800
New York, NY 10122-0499
Ph: (212)563-3382
Executive search firm.

★4233★ Conspectus Inc.
222 Purchase St., Ste. 318
Rye, NY 10580
Ph: (914)925-0600
Executive search firm concentrated on the financial industry.

★4234★ Consultants to Executive Management Company Ltd.
2 1st National Plz., Ste. 610
Chicago, IL 60603
Ph: (312)855-1500   Fax: (312)855-1510
Fr: 800-800-2362
National personnel consultancy specializes in executive search with focus on accounting and finance, management information systems, professional medical, and real estate fields.

★4235★ The Consulting Group
366 Madison Ave., Fl. 10
New York, NY 10017
Ph: (212)751-8484   Fax: (212)692-9290
Executive search firm.

★4236★ Cook & Company
12 Masterton Rd.
Bronxville, NY 10708
Ph: (914)779-4838
Executive search firm dedicated to the financial industry.

★4237★ Cornell Global
PO Box 7113
Wilton, CT 06897
Ph: (203)762-0730   Fax: (203)761-9507
Executive search firm.

★4238★ Cornell Group International Consulting Inc.
1 Corwin Ct., Ste. 200
Newburgh, NY 12550
Ph: (845)565-8905   Fax: (845)565-5688
Executive search firm.

★4239★ The Corporate Source Group Inc.
280 S. Main St.
Andover, MA 01810
Ph: (987)475-6400   Fax: (987)475-6800
Executive search firm branches in Phoenix, AZ; Tampa, Fl; North Potomac, MD; McMurray, PA.

★4240★ CP Consulting
674 Hideout
Lake Ariel, PA 18436
Ph: (570)698-8321   Fax: (570)698-8321
Executive search firm.

★4241★ Deerfield Associates
572 Washington St., Ste. 15
Wellesley, MA 02482
Fax: (781)237-5600
Executive search firm.

★4242★ Dellosso and Greenberg
525 E. 82nd St., Ste. 2B
New York, NY 10028
Ph: (212)570-5350   Fax: (212)861-8050
Executive search firm.

★4243★ DGL Consultants
189 S. Main St.
PO Box 450
Richford, VT 05476
Ph: (802)848-7764   Fax: (802)848-3117
Executive search firm.

★4244★ DLG Associates Inc.
1515 Mockingbird Ln., Ste. 560
Charlotte, NC 28209
Ph: (704)522-9993   Fax: (704)522-7730
Executive search firm.

★4245★ Dotson & Associates
412 E. 55th St., Ste. 8A
New York, NY 10022
Ph: (212)593-4274
Executive search firm.

★4246★ Douglas-Allen Inc.
1500 Main St., Fl. 24
PO Box 15368
Springfield, MA 01115
Ph: (413)739-0900
Executive search firm.

★4247★ Eileen Finn & Associates Inc.
230 Park Ave., Fl. 10
New York, NY 10169
Ph: (212)687-1260   Fax: (212)551-1473
Executive search firm.

★4248★ Epsen, Fuller & Associates LLC
10 Park Place On the Green, Ste. 420
Morristown, NJ 07960
Ph: (973)359-9929   Fax: (973)359-9928
Executive search firm.

★4249★ Essex Consulting Group Inc.
PO Box 550
Essex, MA 01929
Ph: (978)768-0030
Executive search firm.

★4250★ Ethos Consulting Inc.
50 California St., Ste. 1500
San Francisco, CA 94111
Ph: (415)277-5450   Fax: (415)244-5451
Executive search firm. Second branch in Scottsdale, AZ.

★4251★ Executive Dimensions
5820 Main St., Ste. 403
Williamsville, NY 14221
Ph: (716)632-9034   Fax: (716)632-2889
Executive search firm.

★4252★ Executive Search Consultants International Inc.
Empire State Bldg.
3505th Ave., Ste. 5501
New York, NY 10118
Ph: (212)330-1900   Fax: (212)330-1906
Executive search firm.

★4253★ The Executive Source Inc.
55 5th Ave., Fl. 19
New York, NY 10003-4301
Ph: (212)691-5505   Fax: (212)691-9839
Executive search firm.

★4254★ Fagan & Company
PO Box 611
Ligonier, PA 15658
Ph: (724)238-9571
Executive search firm.

★4255★ Faircastle Technology Group LLC
27 Wells Rd., Ste. 1117
Monroe, CT 06468-1266
Ph: (203)459-0631
Executive search firm focused on high technology.

★4256★ Fast Start Inc.
15 Pelican Pl.
Belleair, FL 33756-1512
Ph: (727)581-2224   Fax: (727)581-4743
Small consulting firm offering consulting, and broker/dealer referral services for the registered representative and the broker dealer. Offers assistance in areas of: practice management, broker/dealer selection, start-up interfacing, and career guidance.

★4257★ Ferrari Search Group
24200 Chagrin Blvd., Ste. 1
Cleveland, OH 44122
Ph: (216)491-1122   Fax: (216)491-1510
Executive search firm.

★4258★ Financial Professionals
4100 Spring Valley Rd., Ste. 307
Dallas, TX 75244
Ph: (972)991-8999   Fax: (972)702-0776
Executive search consultants with additional offices in Forth Worth and Houston.

★4259★ Flagship Global Inc.
Flagship Wharf
197 8th St.
Boston, MA 02129
Ph: (617)241-9000
Executive search firm focused on the financial industry.

★4260★ Flynn, Hancock Inc.
1001 Farmington Ave.
West Hartford, CT 06107-2121
Ph: (860)521-5005   Fax: (860)561-5294
Executive search firm.

★4261★ Fogec Consultants Inc.
PO Box 28806
Milwaukee, WI 53228
Ph: (414)427-0690
Executive search firm focused on the financial industry.

★4262★ Foster Associates
The Livery
209 Cooper Ave.
Upper Montclair, NJ 07043
Ph: (973)746-2800   Fax: (973)746-9712
Executive search firm.

★4263★ Frank Palma Associates
110 S. Jefferson Rd.
Whippany, NJ 07981
Ph: (973)884-1498   Fax: (973)884-1499
Executive search firm.

★4264★ The Hanover Consulting Group
11707 Hunters Run Dr.
Hunt Valley, MD 21030
Ph: (410)785-1912   Fax: (410)785-1913
Specialize in finding, evaluating, and selecting top talent for the banking and trust industries.

★4265★ Houser Martin Morris
110 110th Ave. NE, Ste. 580
PO Box 90015
Bellevue, WA 98004-9015
Ph: (425)453-2700   Fax: (425)453-8726
Focus is in the areas of retained executive search, professional and technical recruiting. Areas of specialization include software engineering, sales and marketing, information technology, legal, human resources, accounting and finance, manufacturing, factory automation, and engineering.

★4266★ J Nicolas Arthur
77 Franklin St., Fl. 3
Boston, MA 02110
Ph: (617)204-9000   Fax: (617)303-8934
Executive search firm specializing in the finance industry.

★4267★ J.R. Scott and Associates

1 S Wacker Dr., Ste. 1616
Chicago, IL 60606-4616
Ph: (312)795-4300   Fax: (312)795-4329
E-mail: mark@esquirestaffing.com
URL: http://www.esquirestaffing.com

Executive search firm specializing in retail securities sales, investment banking, and equity and debt trading. A division of Esquire Personnel Services, Inc.

★4268★ Michael Anthony Associates Inc.

42 Washington St., Ste. 301
Wellesley, MA 02481-1803
Ph: (781)237-4950   Fax: (781)237-6811
Fr: 800-337-4950

Applications development, systems programming, communications, and database specialists servicing the IBM mainframe, midrange, and PC marketplace. Provides technical expertise of conversions, system software installation and upgrades, performance and tuning, capacity planning, and data communications. In addition to contract services also provides retained search and contingency placement of computer professionals ranging from senior staff to senior management. Also act as brokers for independent consultants and small consulting firms requiring the services of marketing specialists. Industries served: banking, financial services, hospitals, HMO's, manufacturers, software development, universities, defense, and consulting firms.

★4269★ Minority Search Inc.

777 S R.L. Thornton Fwy., Ste. 105
Dallas, TX 75203
Ph: (214)948-6116   Fax: (214)948-6118

Firm recruits executives for the banking, manufacturing, insurance, marketing, and consulting industries.

★4270★ The Murphy Group

245 W Roosevelt Rd., Bldg.15 Ste.101
Chicago, IL 60185
Ph: (630)639-5110   Fax: (630)639-5113
E-mail: info@murphygroup.com
URL: http://www.murphygroup.com

Employment agency. Places personnel in a variety of positions. Additional offices located in Napierville, Park Ridge, and OakBrook.

★4271★ Paul Falcone Associates

PO Box 115
Mount Freedom, NJ 07970
Ph: (973)895-5200   Fax: (973)895-5266

Executive search firm.

★4272★ Penn Hill Associates Inc.

PO Box 1367
Pawleys Island, SC 29585
Ph: (843)237-8988   Fax: (843)237-9220

Offers executive search services for consumer finance companies. Industries served: consumer finance, home equity, and auto financing.

★4273★ Penn Search Inc.

997 Old Eagle School Rd., Ste. 202
Wayne, PA 19087-1706
Ph: (610)964-8820   Fax: (610)964-8916

Offers Information Technology, Accounting and Financial executive search services.

★4274★ Princeton Executive Search

1 Eves Dr., Ste. 115
PO Box Box 7373
Marlton, NJ 08053
Ph: (856)596-3300   Fax: (856)596-8866

Provides search and placement for management level professions. Specializes in accounting, banking, engineering and human resources. Industries served: financial, research and development, insurance, manufacturing, banking, and government agencies.

★4275★ Raines International Inc.

250 Park Ave., 17th Fl.
New York, NY 10177
Ph: (212)997-1100   Fax: (212)944-7585

International generalist firm specializing in middle to upper management executives. Concentrations include general management, finance and accounting, information technology (MIS), operations/procurement, strategic planning, investment banking, real estate/finance, human resources, insurance, and legal.

★4276★ Rocky Mountain Recruiters, Inc.

2000 S Colorado Blvd., Ste. 200
The Annex Bldg.
Denver, CO 80222
Ph: (303)296-2000   Fax: (303)296-2223
E-mail: miket@rmrecruiters.com
URL: http://www.rmrecruiters.com

Accounting, financial, and executive search firm.

★4277★ Romac International, Inc.

1001 E Palm Ave
Tampa, FL 33605
Ph: (813)552-5239   Fax: (813)552-2122
URL: http://www.romac.com

Executive search firm. More than 30 locations throughout the United States.

★4278★ Spherion Corp.

2050 Spectrum Blvd.
Fort Lauderdale, FL 33309
Ph: (954)938-7600   Fax: (954)938-7666
Fr: 800-976-7678

A worldwide leader in recruiting, assessing and deploying talent. It provides the widest range of services available including consulting, managed staffing, outsourcing, search/recruitment and flexible staffing. The company has expertise in industries such as information technology, outsourcing, accounting and finance, law, manufacturing and human resources as well as clerical, administrative and light industrial.

★4279★ 306 Search Advisors Inc.

230 Park Ave., Ste. 1000
New York, NY 10169
Ph: (646)435-5796

Executive search firm.

★4280★ TRC Staffing Services Inc.

2110 15 Mile Rd., Ste. B
Sterling Heights, MI 48310
Ph: (586)939-3210   Fax: (586)978-0572

A full-service executive search company with permanent placements encompassing engineering, industrial sales, financial and computer science positions. Screen, interview, and verify past employment for all candidates prior to referral. Also assist personnel staffs in the attainment of their EEO/AAP goals with the placement of talented individuals in positions which are underutilized with minorities and/or women. In addition, firm has a clerical temporary service division, TRC Temporary Service; and an employment agency, TRC Staffing Services.

★4281★ 20-20 Foresight Executive Search Inc.

One Lincoln Centre
18 W. 140 Butterfield Rd., Fl. 15
Oakbrook Terrace, IL 60181
Ph: (708)246-2100

Executive search firm. Affiliate offices in CA and Washington DC.

★4282★ Val Executive Resources Group

100 Merrick Rd., Ste. 302E
Rockville Centre, NY 11570-4801
Ph: (516)764-9000   Fax: (516)764-9122

Personnel consultants recruiting on contingency and retained search basis specializing in Banking and Finance, to include: Corporate, Commercial and Consumer Banking, Private Banking, Trust, Investments, Human Resources, Marketing, focusing on lower, middle, and senior management positions. Industries served: banking, finance, brokerage, insurance.

ONLINE JOB SOURCES AND SERVICES

★4283★ Accountingjobs.com

E-mail: jobs@atsaccountingjobs.com
URL: http://www.accountingjobs.com

Description: Site holds national employment opportunities for accounting and finance professionals. Job seekers may search over 1,000 available positions posted by employers. Employers may browse through resumes posted by the job seekers. Employer profiles are also housed on the site, as well as links to other financial/accounting resources on the web.

★4284★ American Association of Finance and Accounting
E-mail: feedback@aafa.com
URL: http://www.aafa.com
Description: AAFA is the largest and oldest alliance of executive search firms specializing in the recruitment and placement of finance and accounting professionals. Contains career opportunities site with job board for both job seekers and hiring employers. One does not have to be a member to search for jobs.

★4285★ Careers in Business
E-mail: wtunstall@careerselector.com
URL: http://careers-in-business.com
Description: Job search site with concentration in business, finance, consulting, marketing and non-profit related careers. Seekers may search database or post resume, plus review resources list for further information.

★4286★ The Digital Financier
URL: http://www.dfin.com
Description: Job postings from financial companies. Offers links to major job search websites. Has leads for further training and allows companies to post their own job links.

★4287★ Financial Executives International
E-mail: ncatazarno@fei.org
URL: http://www.fei.org
Description: Member site for financial executives professional association contains job board and field-related information. **Fee:** Must be member to access services. Annual membership dues $485.

★4288★ Financial Job Network
E-mail: info@atsfjn.com
URL: http://www.fjn.com
Description: Contains information on international and national employment opportunities for those in the financial job market. Job listings may be submitted, as well as resumes. **Main files include:** Testimonials, Calendar, Corporate Listings, FJN Clients, more. **Fee:** Free to candidates.

★4289★ Spherion Workforce Architects
URL: http://www.spherion.com
Description: Recruitment firm specializing in accounting and finance, sales and marketing, interim executives, technology, engineering, retail and human resources.

TRADESHOWS

★4290★ Consumer Bankers Association Executive Conference
Consumer Bankers Association
1000 Wilson Blvd., Ste. 3012
Arlington, VA 22209-3908
Ph: (703)276-1750   Fax: (703)528-1290
Annual. **Primary Exhibits:** Banking equipment, supplies, and services.

★4291★ FIM-National - Financial Investment Management Exposition and Conference
Flagg Management, Inc.
353 Lexington Ave.
New York, NY 10016
Ph: (212)286-0333   Fax: (212)286-0086
E-mail: flaggmgmt@msn.com
URL: http://www.flaggmgmt.com
Annual. **Primary Exhibits:** Online investment systems internet information series, portfolio management systems, online trading and execution systems. Investment industry professionals and information and technology systems management.

★4292★ Independent Bankers Association of America National Convention and Techworld
Independent Community Bankers of America (ICBA)
1 Thomas Circle NW, Ste. 400
Washington, DC 20005
Ph: (202)659-8111   Fax: (202)659-9216
Fr: 800-422-8439
E-mail: info@ibaa.org
URL: http://www.ibaa.org
Annual. **Primary Exhibits:** Banking related goods and services, including computers, software, and paper products.

★4293★ Pennsylvania Association of Community Bankers Convention
Pennsylvania Association of Community Bankers
PO Box 5319
Harrisburg, PA 17110-5319
Ph: (717)231-7447   Fax: (717)231-7445
Annual. **Primary Exhibits:** Equipment, supplies, and services for community banks, thrifts, and associate firms.

★4294★ Tecnobanca Expo
Marketing International Corp.
200 N. Glebe Rd., Ste. 900
Arlington, VA 22203
Ph: (703)527-8000   Fax: (703)527-8006
E-mail: micexpos@aol.com
Annual. **Primary Exhibits:** Equipment, supplies, and services for the banking industry.

OTHER SOURCES

★4295★ Administration and Management Occupations
Delphi Productions
3160 4th St.
Boulder, CO 80304
Fax: (303)443-4022   Fr: 888-443-2400
URL: http://www.delphivideo.com
$95.00. 50 minutes. Part of the Careers for the 21st Century Video Library.

★4296★ American Bankers Association (ABA)
1120 Connecticut Ave. NW
Washington, DC 20036
Ph: (202)663-5000   Fax: (202)663-7543
Fr: 800-BAN-KERS
E-mail: mwhitake@aba.com
URL: http://www.aba.com
Members: Principally commercial banks and trust companies; combined assets of members represent approximately 90% of the U.S. banking industry; approximately 94% of members are community banks with less than $500 million in assets. **Purpose:** Seeks to enhance the role of commerical bankers as preeminent providers of financial services through communications, research, legal action, lobbying of federal legislative and regulatory bodies, and education and training programs. Serves as spokesperson for the banking industry; facilitates exchange of information among members. Maintains the American Institute of Banking, an industry-sponsored adult education program. **Activities:** Conducts educational and training programs for bank employees and officers through a wide range of banking schools and national conferences. Maintains liaison with federal bank regulators; lobbies Congress on issues affecting commercial banks; testifies before congressional committees; represents members in U.S. postal rate proceedings. Serves as secretariat of the International Monetary Conference and the Financial Institutions Committee for the American National Standards Institute. Files briefs and lawsuits in major court cases affecting the industry. Conducts teleconferences with state banking associations on such issues as regulatory compliance; works to build consensus and coordinate activities of leading bank and financial service trade groups. Provides services to members including: public advocacy; news media contact; insurance program providing directors and officers with liability coverage, financial institution bond, and trust errors and omissions coverage; research service operated through ABA Center for Banking Information; fingerprint set processing in conjunction with the Federal Bureau of Investigation; discounts on operational and income-producing projects through the Corporation for American Banking. Conducts conferences, forums, and workshops covering subjects such as small business, consumer credit, agricultural and community banking, trust management, bank operations, and automation. Sponsors ABA Educational Foundation and the Personal Economics Program, which

educates schoolchildren and the community on banking, economics, and personal finance.

★4297★ American Financial Services Association (AFSA)

919 18th St. NW
Washington, DC 20006
Ph: (202)296-5544   Fax: (202)223-0321
E-mail: afsa@afsamail.com
URL: http://www.americanfinsvcs.org

Description: Companies whose business is primarily direct credit lending to consumers and/or the purchase of sales finance paper on consumer goods. Some members have insurance and retail subsidiaries; some are themselves subsidiaries of highly diversified parent corporations. Encourages the business of financing individuals and families for necessary and useful purposes, at reasonable charges, including interest; promotes consumer understanding of basic money management principles as well as constructive uses of consumer credit. Educational services include films, textbooks, and study units for the classroom and budgeting guides for individuals and families. Compiles statistical reports; offers seminars.

★4298★ American League of Financial Institutions (ALFI)

900 19th St. NW, Ste. 400
Washington, DC 20006
Ph: (202)857-6176   Fax: (202)296-8716
URL: http://www.alfi.org

Members: Federal and state chartered minority savings and loan associations in 25 states and the District of Columbia. **Purpose:** Undertakes programs to increase the income of and savings flow into the associations including a direct solicitation effort; provides counseling and technical assistance for member associations; offers consultant services to assist individual associations and groups wishing to organize new associations or acquire existing associations with development potential; collects, organizes, and distributes materials that will aid member associations. **Activities:** Conducts research to improve investment capability, resolve common management problems, and evaluate statistical data on an industry-wide basis to develop and institute training programs for management personnel. Conducts research programs.

★4299★ Association for Financial Professionals (AFP)

7315 Wisconsin Ave., Ste. 600W
Bethesda, MD 20814-3211
Ph: (301)907-2862   Fax: (301)907-2864
E-mail: jkaitz@afponline.org
URL: http://www.afponline.org

Purpose: Seeks to establish a national forum for the exchange of concepts and techniques related to improving the management of treasury and the careers of professionals through research, education, publications, and recognition of the treasury management profession through a certifica-

tion program. **Activities:** Conducts educational programs. Operates career center.

★4300★ Bank Administration Institute (BAI)

1 N. Franklin St., Ste. 1000
Chicago, IL 60606
Ph: (312)653-2464   Fax: (312)683-2373
E-mail: info@bai.org
URL: http://www.bai.org

Description: Works to improve the competitive position of banking companies through strategic research and educational offerings.

★4301★ Eastern Finance Association

Department of Finance
University of Mississippi
PO Box 1848
University, MS 38677
Ph: (662)915-7721
E-mail: mwalker@bus.olemiss.edu
URL: http://www.easternfinance.org

Description: College and university professors and financial officers (1200); libraries (450). Provides a meeting place for persons interested in any aspect of finance, including financial management, investments, and banking. Sponsors research competitions.

★4302★ Financial Executives International (FEI)

200 Campus Dr.
PO Box 1938
Florham Park, NJ 07932
Ph: (973)765-1025   Fax: (973)898-4649
E-mail: csayther@fei.org
URL: http://www.fei.org

Members: Professional organization of corporate financial executives performing duties of chief financial officer, controller, treasurer, or vice-president-finance. **Activities:** Sponsors research activities through its affiliated Financial Executives Research Foundation. Maintains offices in Toronto, Canada, and Washington, DC.

★4303★ Financial Managers Society (FMS)

100 W Monroe, Ste. 810
Chicago, IL 60603
Ph: (312)578-1300   Fax: (312)578-1308
Fr: 800-275-4367
E-mail: info@fmsinc.org
URL: http://www.fmsinc.org

Purpose: Technical information exchange for financial managers of financial institutions.

★4304★ Financial Occupations

Delphi Productions
3160 4th St.
Boulder, CO 80304
Fax: (303)443-4022   Fr: 888-443-2400
URL: http://www.delphivideo.com

$95.00. 50 minutes. Part of the Careers for the 21st Century Video Library.

★4305★ Financial Women's Association of New York (FWA)

215 Park Ave. S, Ste. 1713
New York, NY 10003
Ph: (212)533-2141   Fax: (212)982-3008
E-mail: fwaoffice@fwa.org
URL: http://www.fwa.org

Members: Persons of professional status in the field of finance in the New York metropolitan area. **Purpose:** Works to promote and maintain high professional standards in the financial and business communities; provide an opportunity for members to enhance one another's professional contacts; achieve recognition of the contribution of women to the financial and business communities; encourage other women to seek professional positions within the financial and business communities. **Activities:** Activities include educational trips to foreign countries; college internship program including foreign student exchange; high school mentorship program; Washington and international briefings; placement service for members. Maintains speakers' bureau.

★4306★ National Association of Corporate Treasurers (NACT)

12100 Sunset Hills Rd., Ste. 130
Reston, VA 20190-5202
Ph: (703)437-4377   Fax: (703)435-4390
E-mail: nact@nact.org
URL: http://www.nact.org

Description: Serves as a forum for high-level finance executives who perform all or a substantial part of the duties of corporate treasureship. Seeks to produce and facilitate the exchange of information relevant to the management of corporate treasury operations. Sponsors general sessions on such topics as Cash Management Issues for the 90s, Corporate Finance, Data Processing/Electronic Services, International Liquidity Management. Offers job clearinghouse services.

★4307★ Risk and Insurance Management Society (RIMS)

655 3rd Ave., 2nd Fl.
New York, NY 10017
Ph: (212)286-9292   Fax: (212)986-9716
E-mail: jhampton@rims.org
URL: http://www.rims.org

Description: Business association serving corporate risk and insurance managers. Dedicated to advancing the practice of risk management, a discipline that protects physical, financial, and human resources.

★4308★ Risk Management Association

1 Liberty Pl.
1650 Market St., Ste. 2300
Philadelphia, PA 19103-7398
Ph: (215)446-4000   Fax: (215)446-4101
Fr: 800-677-7621
E-mail: member@rmahq.org
URL: http://www.rmahq.org

Members: Commercial and savings banks, and savings and loan, and other financial services companies. **Activities:** Conducts research and professional development activities in areas of loan administration, asset management, and commercial lending and credit to increase professionalism.

★4309★ Society of Cost Estimating and Analysis (SCEA)
101 S Whiting St., Ste. 201
Alexandria, VA 22304
Ph: (703)751-8069   Fax: (703)461-7328

E-mail: scea@sceaonline.net
URL: http://www.sceaonline.net

Description: Dedicated to improving cost estimating and analysis in government and industry and enhancing the professional competence and achievements of its' members. Administers a professional certification program leading to the designation of Certified Cost Estimator/Analyst; offers extensive literature in the field through its' Professional Development Program. Goals of the Society include enhancing the profession of cost estimating and analysis, fostering the professional growth of its members, enhancing the understanding and application of cost estimating, analysis and related disciplines throughout government and industry and providing forums and media through which current issues of interest to the profession can be addressed and advances in the state-of-the-art can be shared.

Fire Fighters

★4310★ American City and County

Primedia Business
6151 Powers Ferry Rd.
Atlanta, GA 30339
Ph: (770)955-2500   Fax: (770)618-0348

Monthly. $67.00/year for individuals. Municipal and county administration magazine.

★4311★ American Fire Journal

American Fire Journal
9072 E Artesia Blvd., Ste. 7
Bellflower, CA 90706-6299
Ph: (562)866-1664   Fax: (562)867-6434

Monthly. $22.95/year for individuals; $42.00/year for individuals, other countries; $3.50/year for single issue. Magazine about fire protection.

★4312★ Firehouse Magazine

Cygnus Business Media Inc.
445 Broad Hollow Rd.
Melville, NY 11747
Ph: (631)845-2700   Fax: (631)845-2798
Fr: 800-308-6397
E-mail: subscribe@firehouse.com
URL: http://www.firehouse.com

Monthly. $48.00/year for individuals. Magazine focusing on fire protection.

★4313★ ICHIEFS On Scene

International Association of Fire Chiefs
  Inc.
4025 Fair Ridge Dr.
Fairfax, VA 22033-2868
Ph: (703)273-0911   Fax: (703)273-9363
E-mail: onscene@ichiefs.org
URL: http://www.ichiefs.org

Description: Semimonthly. Covers management, technical, and legislative issues that affect fire fighting professionals, including volunteers. Recurring features include letters to the editor, interviews, news of research, reports of meetings, news of educational opportunities, job listings, notices of publications available, and columns titled Executive Director's Column, Comm Center, Announcements, Section News, President's Column, and Staying Out of Trouble-A Case Study.

★4314★ International Fire Fighter

International Association of Fire Fighters
1750 New York Ave. NW
Washington, DC 20006
Ph: (202)737-8484   Fax: (202)737-8418
E-mail: kshelton@iaff.org

Bimonthly. Free to qualified subscribers; $18.00/year for individuals. Union tabloid.

★4315★ The Municipality

League of Wisconsin Municipalities
202 State St., Ste. 300
Madison, WI 53703-2215
Ph: (608)267-2380   Fax: (608)267-0645
Fr: 800-991-5502

Monthly. $12.00/year. Magazine for officials of Wisconsin's local municipal governments.

★4316★ NFPA Journal

National Fire Protection Association
1 Batterymarch Park
PO Box 9101
Quincy, MA 02269-9101
Ph: (617)984-7323   Fax: (617)984-7090
Fr: 800-344-3555

Bimonthly. $95.00/year for individuals. Magazine concerning fire protection, prevention.

★4317★ Western City

League of California Cities
1400 K St., 4th Fl.
Sacramento, CA 95814
Ph: (916)658-8223   Fax: (916)658-8289
Fr: 800-262-1801
URL: http://www.westerncity.com

Monthly. $39.00/year for individuals; $63.00 for two years. Municipal interest magazine.

★4318★ American Fire Services

American Fire Services
139 Selden Hill Dr.
West Hartford, CT 06107
Ph: (860)521-7056   Fax: (860)521-3714

Reported as biennial, Jan. of odd years; latest edition Nov. 1993. $50.00. Covers approximately 2,700 municipal fire departments; coverage includes Canada. Entries include: Department name, headquarters address, fire station locations, number of employees, population, units geographical area served, description of operations, radio frequencies, chief/administrator, phone, statistics. Arrangement: Geographical. Indexes: Department name, geographical.

★4319★ Fellowship of Christian Firefighters International-Directory

Fellowship of Christian Firefighters
  International
Box 901
Fort Collins, CO 80522-0901
Fax: (970)407-0083   Fr: 800-322-9848
URL: http://
www.fellowshipofchristianfirefighters.com

Biennial, Odd years. Covers about 2,000 member Christian firefighters. Entries include: Name, address, phone. Arrangement: Alphabetical. Indexes: Local chapter.

★4320★ National Directory of Fire Chiefs & EMS Administrators

National Public Safety Information Bureau
601 Main St., Ste. 201
PO Box 365
Stevens Point, WI 54481
Ph: (715)345-2772   Fax: (715)345-7288
Fr: 800-647-7579
URL: http://www.safetysource.com

Annual, December. $129.00. Covers over 36,000 fire and emergency departments in the U.S. Entries include: Department name, address, phone, fax, county, name of chief, type of department, financial structure. Arrangement: Geographical.

HANDBOOKS AND MANUALS

★4321★ Fire Service Administration

National Fire Protection Association
1 Batterymarch Pk.
Quincy, MA 02269
Ph: (617)770-3000   Fax: (617)770-0700
Fr: 800-344-3555

Nancy K. Grant and David Hoover. 1994. $53.50. 442 pages. Out of print.

★4322★ Firefighter Career Starter

LearningExpress, LLC
900 Broadway, Ste. 604
New York, NY 10003
Ph: (212)995-2566   Fax: (212)995-5512
Fr: 800-295-9556

Mary Masi and Lauren B. Starkey. Second edition, 2001. $15.95 (paper). 208 pages. Part of the Career Starters Series.

★4323★ Opportunities in Fire Protection Services

McGraw-Hill/Contemporary Books
1221 Avenue of the Americas
New York, NY 10020
Ph: (212)904-2000   Fr: 800-323-4900
E-mail: ntcpub@tribune.com

Ronny J. Coleman. 1997. $14.95; $11.95 (paper). 160 pages. Surveys opportunities in local, state, and federal fire departments and forestry services, as well as with fire equipment and fire insurance companies. Contains bibliography and illustrations.

★4324★ Real-Resumes for Firefighting Jobs

PREP Publishing
1110 1/2 Hay St., PMB 66
Fayetteville, NC 28305
Ph: (910)483-6611   Fax: (910)483-2439
Fr: 800-533-2814

April 2004. $16.95. Illustrated. 192 pages. Firefighting careers.

TRADESHOWS

★4325★ Fire-Rescue International

International Association of Fire Chiefs Inc.
4025 Fair Ridge Dr.
Fairfax, VA 22033-2868
Ph: (703)273-0911   Fax: (703)273-9363
URL: http://www.iafc.org

Annual. **Primary Exhibits:** Fire safety and emergency medical service equipment, supplies, and services; related training and support materials.

OTHER SOURCES

★4326★ Human Services Occupations

Delphi Productions
3160 4th St.
Boulder, CO 80304
Fax: (303)443-4022   Fr: 888-443-2400
URL: http://www.delphivideo.com

$95.00. 50 minutes. Part of the Careers for the 21st Century Video Library.

★4327★ International Association of Fire Chiefs (IAFC)

4025 Fair Ridge Dr.
Fairfax, VA 22033-2868
Ph: (703)273-0911   Fax: (703)273-9363
Fr: 800-661-3336

URL: http://www.ichiefs.org

Members: Fire Dept. chief officers, emergency services administrators and emergency medical services directors/managers and supervisors, career, volunteer, municipal and private, who are interested in improving fire, rescue, and EMS coverage to the general public. **Purpose:** Provides leadership to career and volunteer chiefs, chief fire officers and managers of emergency service organizations throughout the international community through vision, information, education, services and representation to enhance their professionalism and capabilities.

★4328★ Math at Work: Women in Nontraditional Careers

Her Own Words
PO Box 5264
Madison, WI 53705-0264
Ph: (608)271-7083   Fax: (608)271-0209
URL: http://www.herownwords.com/

Video. Jocelyn Riley. $95.00. 15 minutes. Resource guide also available for $45.00.

★4329★ Women in Firefighting

Her Own Words
PO Box 5264
Madison, WI 53705-0264
Ph: (608)271-7083   Fax: (608)271-0209
URL: http://www.herownwords.com/

Video. Jocelyn Riley. $95.00. 15 minutes. Resource guide also available for $45.00.

★4330★ Women in Nontraditional Careers: An Introduction

Her Own Words
PO Box 5264
Madison, WI 53705
Ph: (608)271-7083   Fax: (608)271-0209
URL: http://www.herownwords.com/

Video. Jocelyn Riley. $95.00. 15 minutes. Resource guide also available for $45.00.

Fitness Trainers

SOURCES OF HELP-WANTED ADS

★4331★ AAHPERD Update
American Alliance for Health, Physical
  Education, Recreation & Dance
1900 Association Dr.
Reston, VA 20191
Ph: (703)476-3400   Fax: (703)476-9527
Fr: 800-213-7193
E-mail: update@aahperd.org
URL: http://www.aahperd.org

Description: Six issues/year. Provides
news and information on the Alliance. Discusses current issues and research in the
areas of health, physical education, recreation, dance, fitness, and adapted physical
education. Recurring features include a calendar of events, reports of meetings, news
of educational opportunities, job listings,
notices of publications available, and columns titled President's Message, Membership Corner, and From the EVP's Desk.

★4332★ ACE FitnessMatters
American Council on Exercise
4851 Paramount Dr.
San Diego, CA 92133
Fr: 800-825-3636
E-mail: gdpbm@gale.acecom

Bimonthly. $25.00/year for individuals. Con-
sumer magazine covering health and fitness
news.

★4333★ NSCA Bulletin
National Strength & Conditioning
  Association (NSCA)
1885 Bob Johnson Dr.
Colorado Springs, CO 80906-4000
Ph: (719)632-6722   Fax: (719)632-6367
Fr: 800-815-6826

Description: Six issues/year. Tracks Association activities. Recurring features include
interviews, a calendar of events, reports of
meetings, news of educational opportunities,
job listings, book reviews, and notices of
publications available.

PLACEMENT AND JOB REFERRAL SERVICES

**★4334★ Exercise Safety Association
(ESA)**
PO Box 547916
Orlando, FL 32854-9716
Ph: (407)246-5090   Fax: (407)246-5090
E-mail: askesa@aol.com
URL: http://www.exercisesafety.com

Description: Fitness instructors, personal
trainers, health spas, YMCAs, community
recreation departments, and hospital
wellness programs. Purposes are: to improve the qualifications of exercise instructors; to train instructors to develop safe
exercise programs that will help people
avoid injury while exercising; to prepare
instructors for national certification. Offers
training in aerobics and exercise and on the
physiological aspects of exercise. Conducts
exercise safety and research programs.
Sponsors charitable program; maintains
speakers' bureau. Offers instructor placement services.

**★4335★ National Athletic Trainers
Association (NATA)**
2952 Stemmons Fwy., Ste. 200
Dallas, TX 75247-6196
Ph: (214)637-6282   Fax: (214)637-2206
Fr: 800-879-6282
E-mail: ebd@nata.org
URL: http://www.nata.org

Members: Athletic trainers from universities,
colleges, and junior colleges; professional
football, baseball, basketball, and ice hockey; high schools, preparatory schools, military establishments, sports medicine clinics,
and business/industrial health programs. **Activities:** Maintains hall of fame and placement service. Conducts research programs;
compiles statistics.

EMPLOYER DIRECTORIES AND NETWORKING LISTS

**★4336★ Exercise and Physical Fitness
Programs Directory**
infoUSA Inc.
5711 S 86th Cir.
Omaha, NE 68127-0347
Ph: (402)930-3500   Fax: (402)331-0176
Fr: 800-555-6124
URL: http://www.abii.com

Annual. Number of listings: 8,412. Entries
include: Name, address, phone (including
area code), size of advertisement, year first
in "Yellow Pages," name of owner or manager, number of employees. Compiled from
telephone company "Yellow Pages," nationwide. Arrangement: Geographical.

**★4337★ Health Clubs Studios &
Gymnasiums Directory**
infoUSA Inc.
5711 S 86th Cir.
Omaha, NE 68127-0347
Ph: (402)930-3500   Fax: (402)331-0176
Fr: 800-555-6124
URL: http://www.abii.com

Updated continuously; printed on request.
Number of listings: 17,012. Entries include:
Name, address, phone (including area
code). Compiled from telephone company
"Yellow Pages," nationwide. Arrangement:
Geographical.

**★4338★ Health & Fitness Program
Consultants Directory**
infoUSA Inc.
5711 S 86th Cir.
Omaha, NE 68127-0347
Ph: (402)930-3500   Fax: (402)331-0176
Fr: 800-555-6124
URL: http://www.abii.com

Annual. Number of listings: 4,627. Entries
include: Name, address, phone (including
area code), size of advertisement, year first
in "Yellow Pages," name of owner or manager, number of employees. Compiled from

telephone company "Yellow Pages," nationwide. Arrangement: Geographical.

★4339★ National Sports and Fitness Association-Fitness Directory
National Sports & Fitness Association
1945 Palo Verde, Ste. 202
Long Beach, CA 90815-3445
Ph: (562)682-3559   Fax: (562)799-3355

Annual, summer. Entries include: Name, address, phone, products or services, geographical area covered, sports and fitness interests. Arrangement: Alphabetical.

★4340★ Who's Who in Sports & Fitness
National Sports & Fitness Association
1945 Palo Verde, Ste. 202
Long Beach, CA 90815-3445
Ph: (562)682-3559   Fax: (562)799-3355

Annual, January. Entries include: Name, address, phone, biographical data, products or services, geographical area covered. Arrangement: Alphabetical. Indexes: Geographical.

HANDBOOKS AND MANUALS

★4341★ Athlete's Guide to Career Planning
Human Kinetics Publishers
PO Box 5076
Champaign, IL 61825-5076
Ph: (217)351-5076   Fax: (217)351-2674
Fr: 800-747-4457

Al Petitpas, Delight Champagne, Judy Chartrand, Shane Murphy and Steven Danish. 1997. $17.95 (paper). 240 pages.

★4342★ The Best Home-Based Businesses for the 90s
Putnam Publishing Group
375 Hudson St.
New York, NY 10014
Ph: (212)366-2000   Fax: (212)366-2643
Fr: 800-331-4624

Paul Edwards and Sarah Edwards. Second edition, 1991. $11.95 (paper). 272 pages. Profiles 95 businesses and careers that can be conducted from one's home. Lists sources of additional information. Out of print.

★4343★ Careers for Health Nuts and Others Who Like to Stay Fit
McGraw-Hill Trade
2 Penn Plaza
New York, NY 10121
Ph: (212)904-2000   Fr: 800-722-4726
E-mail: ntcpub@tribune.com

Blythe Camenson. 1996. $14.95; $9.95 (paper). 160 pages.

★4344★ Careers Without College: Fitness
Thomson Peterson's
PO Box 67005
Lawrenceville, NJ 08648-6105
Fr: 800-338-3282

Maura R. Curless. 1992. $7.95 (paper).

★4345★ Certified Fitness Instructor Career Starter: Finding and Getting a Great Job
LearningExpress, LLC
900 Broadway, Ste. 604
New York, NY 10003
Ph: (212)995-2566   Fax: (212)995-5512
Fr: 800-295-9556

Lauren B. Starkey. December 2002. $16.94. Illustrated. 224 Pages. Career Starters Series.

★4346★ It's More Than Just Making Them Sweat: A Career Training Guide for Personal Fitness Trainers
Robert D. Reed Publishers
750 La Playa St., Suite 647
San Francisco, CA 94121-3262
Ph: (650)994-6570   Fax: (650)994-6579
Fr: 800-774-7336

Ed Thornton. 2001 (paper).

★4347★ Opportunities in Fitness Careers
McGraw-Hill Contemporary Books
1221 Avenue of the Americas
New York, NY 10020
Ph: (212)904-2000   Fr: 800-323-4900
E-mail: ntcpub@tribune.com

Mary Miller. 1998. $14.95; $11.95 (paper). 160 pages. Surveys fitness related careers. Describes career opportunities, education and experience needed, how to get into entry-level jobs and what income to expect. Schools are listed in the appendix.

★4348★ Personal Trainer Manual: The Resource for Fitness Instructors
American Council on Exercise
4851 Paramount Dr.
San Diego, CA 92133
Fr: 800-825-3636

Richard T. Cotton, editor. 1997. $34.95. 552 pages. Out of print.

OTHER SOURCES

★4349★ American Athletic Trainers Association and Certification Board (AATA)
146 E. Duarte Rd.
Arcadia, CA 91006
Ph: (626)445-1978   Fax: (626)574-1999
E-mail: americansportsmedicine@hotmail.com

Purpose: Works to qualify and certify active athletic trainers; to establish minimum competence standards for individuals participating in the prevention and care of athletic injuries; to inform communities nationwide of the importance of having competent leadership in the area of athletic training. **Activities:** Conducts continuing education and charitable programs; maintains placement service. Oldest athletic trainers association in the nation.

★4350★ American College of Sports Medicine (ACSM)
401 W Michigan St.
Indianapolis, IN 46202-3233
Ph: (317)637-9200   Fax: (317)634-7817
E-mail: publicinfo@acsm.org
URL: http://www.acsm.org

Purpose: Promotes and integrates scientific research, education, and practical applications of sports medicine and exercise science to maintain and enhance physical performance, fitness, health, and quality of life. **Activities:** Certifies fitness leaders, fitness instructors, exercise test technologists, exercise specialists, health/fitness program directors, and U.S. military fitness personnel. Grants continuing medical education (CME) and continuing education credits (CEC). Operates more than 50 committees.

★4351★ American Council on Exercise (ACE)
4851 Paramount Dr.
San Diego, CA 92123
Ph: (858)279-8227   Fax: (858)279-8064
Fr: 800-825-3636
E-mail: kristiep@acefitness.org
URL: http://www.acefitness.org

Members: Certifies fitness professionals and non-profit organizations. **Purpose:** Keeps them aware of new information in the health and fitness industry. **Activities:** Offers continuing education programs. Sponsors children's services. Provides consumers with health and fitness research and information.

★4352★ IDEA Health and Fitness Association
6190 Cornerstone Ct. E., Ste. 204
San Diego, CA 92121-3773
Ph: (858)535-8979   Fax: (858)535-8234
Fr: 800-999-IDEA
E-mail: member@ideafit.com
URL: http://www.ideafit.com

Purpose: Provides continuing education for fitness professionals including; fitness instructors, personal trainers, program directors, and club/studio owners. **Activities:** Offers workshops for continuing education credits.

★4353★ National Federation of Professional Trainers

PO Box 4579
Lafayette, IN 47903-4579
Ph: (765)471-7372   Fax: (765)471-7369
Fr: 800-729-6378
E-mail: info@nfpt.com
URL: http://www.nfpt.com

Purpose: Offers affordable, convenient, comprehensive, and applicable information to those seeking personal fitness trainer certification. Offers organizational certification credentials for consumer recognition of competence; provide certified affiliates with ongoing education; establish a network of support, and provide professional products and services to trainers and consumers', and facilitate and encourage the exchange of ideas, knowledge, business experiences, and financial opportunities between all fitness administrators internationally. **Activities:** Offers educational programs.

★4354★ Personal & Building Service Occupations

Delphi Productions
3160 4th St.
Boulder, CO 80304
Fax: (303)443-4022   Fr: 888-443-2400
URL: http://www.delphivideo.com

$95.00. 48 minutes. Part of the Careers for the 21st Century Video Library.

Flight Attendants

SOURCES OF HELP-WANTED ADS

★4355★ Airport Highlights

Airports Council International/North
  America
1775 K St. NW, No. 500
Washington, DC 20006-1502
Ph: (202)293-8500   Fax: (202)887-5365
E-mail: publicaffairs@aci-na.org

Description: Monthly. Spotlights airport
news, regulatory and Congressional developments, domestic and international aviation
news, industry issues, and employment and
business opportunities.

**★4356★ Commuter/Regional Airline
News**

PBI Media L.L.C.
1201 Seven Locks Rd., Ste. 300
Potomac, MD 20854
Ph: (301)354-2000   Fax: (301)309-3847
Fr: 800-777-5006
URL: http://www.phillips.com

Description: Weekly. Covers the commuter/
regional airline industry, including airline
management, marketing, labor, personnel
changes, aircraft acquisitions, new products,
and the financial and operational environment. Recurring features include interviews,
news of research, a calendar of events,
reports of meetings, job listings, and notices
of publications available.

★4357★ Flying

Hachette Filipacchi Media U.S. Inc.
1633 Broadway
New York, NY 10019
Ph: (212)767-6000

Monthly. $26.00/year; $3.95 for single issue.
General aviation magazine.

EMPLOYER DIRECTORIES AND NETWORKING LISTS

★4358★ Airline Companies Directory

infoUSA Inc.
5711 S 86th Cir.
Omaha, NE 68127-0347
Ph: (402)930-3500   Fax: (402)331-0176
Fr: 800-555-6124
URL: http://www.abii.com

Annual. Number of listings: 2,335 (U.S.
edition); 684 (Canadian edition). Entries include: Name, address, phone (including area
code), size of advertisement, year first in
"Yellow Pages," name of owner or manager,
number of employees. Compiled from telephone company "Yellow Pages," nationwide. Arrangement: Geographical.

**★4359★ National Air Transportation
Association-Official Membership
Directory**

National Air Transportation Association
4226 King St.
Alexandria, VA 22302
Ph: (703)845-9000   Fax: (703)845-8176
Fr: 800-808-6282

Annual, October. $95.00. Covers more than
1,000 regular, associate, and affiliate members; regular members include airport service organizations, air taxi operators, and
commuter airlines. Entries include: Company
name, address, phone, fax number, name
and title of contact. Arrangement: Regular
members are classified by service; associate
and affiliate members are alphabetical in
separate sections. Indexes: Geographical.

**★4360★ World Aviation Directory &
Aerospace Database**

Aviation Week
1200 G St. NW, Ste. 200
Washington, DC 20005
Ph: (202)383-2484   Fax: (202)383-2478
Fr: 800-551-2015
E-mail: wad@mcgraw-hill.com
URL: http://www.wadaviation.com

Semiannual,   March   and   September.

$245.00 for print; $995.00 for online version.
Key statistics on the database include
19,000 airlines, manufacturers, MRO stations, airports military/government and dis-
tributors/suppliers; 6,000 product/service categories and 150,000 listings; 60,000 avia-
tion/aerospace professionals; 500,000 users
across all 3 platforms/formats and, Commercial, Military & Business Aviation Fleet Data
Arrangement: Classified by major activity
(manufacturers, airlines, etc.). Indexes:
Company and organization, personnel, product, trade name.

HANDBOOKS AND MANUALS

**★4361★ America's Fastest Growing
Jobs**

JIST Works, Inc.
8902 Otis Ave.
Indianapolis, IN 46216-1033
Ph: (317)613-4200   Fax: (317)613-4307
Fr: 800-648-5478
E-mail: jistworks@aol.com
URL: http://www.jist.com

Seventh edition, 2002. $16.95 (paper). 438
pages. Each job profile explains the nature
of the work, skills and abilities required,
employment outlook, average earnings, related occupations, education and training
requirements, and employment opportunities. Also contains career planning information and job search tips.

**★4362★ Careers as a Flight Attendant:
Flight to the Future**

Rosen Publishing Group, Inc.
29 E. 21st St.
New York, NY 10010
Ph: (212)777-3017   Fax: 888-436-4643
Fr: 800-237-9932

Catherine Okray Lobus. Revised edition,
1995. $16.95. Discusses the work, personal
characteristics of successful flight attendants, physical and educational qualifications, the application process, and airline
training programs. Lists major airlines and

outlines their application processes, policies and benefits, and training programs.

★4363★ **Careers for Night Owls and Other Insomniacs**

McGraw-Hill Trade
2 Penn Plaza
New York, NY 10121
Ph: (212)904-2000   Fr: 800-722-4726
E-mail: ntcpub@tribune.com

Louise Miller. 1995. $14.95; $9.95 (paper). 160 pages.

★4364★ **Careers in Travel, Tourism, and Hospitality**

McGraw-Hill Contemporary Books
1221 Avenue of the Americas
New York, NY 10020
Ph: (212)904-2000   Fr: 800-323-4900
E-mail: ntcpub@tribune.com

Marjorie Eberts, Linda Brothers, and Ann Gisler. 1997. $17.95; 13.95 (paper). 192 pages.

★4365★ **The Flight Attendant Career Guide**

TK Enterprises
PO Box 6455
Delray Beach, FL 33482-6455
Ph: (561)495-4604   Fax: (561)495-5027
Fr: 800-735-4448
URL: http://jobfindersonline.com

Tim Kirkwood. 1993. $14.95. This step-by-step guide, written by a flight attendant, explains the real-life aspects of the job, & helps the applicant decide if this is the career for them. Chapter topics include: History of Flight Attendants, Minimum Requirements, Types of Airlines, Applying & Interviewing, Training, Scheduling, A Typical 3-Day Trip. In addition, the guide lists the hiring requirements of over 75 US airlines, including salary, languages, age, domiciles, AND application addresses for each.

★4366★ **Flight Attendant Career: Your Key to Your Office in the Skies**

Morris Publishing
3212 E. Hwy. 30
PO Box 2110
Kearney, NE 68847
Ph: (308)236-7888   Fax: (308)237-0263
Fr: 800-650-7888

Tom Janovsky. 1998. $14.95 (paper). 228 pages.

★4367★ **Flight Attendant Job Finder and Career Guide**

Planning Communications
7215 Oak Ave.
River Forest, IL 60305-1935
Ph: (708)366-5200   Fax: (708)366-5280
Fr: 888-366-5200

Tim Kirkwood. 1999. $32.95.

★4368★ **Follow Your Dreams?: Secrets to Getting Hired As a Flight Attendant**

AuthorHouse
1663 Liberty Dr., Ste. 20
Bloomington, IN 47403
Fax: (812)339-8654   Fr: 800-839-8640

Tammy Clark. January 2003. $13.95. 120 pages.

★4369★ **Opportunities in Airline Careers**

McGraw-Hill Contemporary Books
1221 Avenue of the Americas
New York, NY 10020
Ph: (212)904-2000   Fr: 800-323-4900
E-mail: ntcpub@tribune.com

Adrian A. Paradis. 1997. $14.95; $11.95 (paper). 205 pages.

★4370★ **Opportunities in Travel Careers**

McGraw-Hill Contemporary Books
1221 Avenue of the Americas
New York, NY 10020
Ph: (212)904-2000   Fr: 800-323-4900
E-mail: ntcpub@tribune.com

Robert Scott Milne. 1996. $14.95; $11.95 (paper). 198 pages. Discusses what the jobs are and where to find them in airlines, shipping lines, and railroads. Discusses related opportunities in hotels, motels, resorts, travel agencies, public relation firms, and recreation departments. Illustrated.

★4371★ **Ready to Fly: An Insider's Guide to Becoming a Flight Attendant**

iUniverse Inc.
2021 Pine Lake Rd., Ste. 100
Lincoln, NE 68512
Ph: (402)323-7800   Fax: (402)323-7824
Fr: 877-288-4737

Peter Conrad Joseph. November 2002. $13.95. 148 pages.

★4372★ **Vault Guide to Flight Attendant Careers**

Vault.com
150 W. 22nd St., 5th Fl.
New York, NY 10011
Ph: (212)366-4212   Fax: (212)366-6117
Fr: 888-562-8285

Mark Gazdik. November 2004. $29.95. 128 pages.

★4373★ **Welcome Aboard!: Your Career As a Flight Attendant**

Cage Consulting Inc.
3333 Quebec, Ste. 1022
Denver, CO 80207
Ph: (303)329-0656   Fax: (303)329-5426
Fr: 888-899-2243

Becky S. Bock and Cheryl A. Cage. 1998. $14.95 (paper).

ONLINE JOB SOURCES AND SERVICES

★4374★ **AirlineCareer.com**
URL: http://www.airlinecareer.com
Web-based training center. Provides flight attendant job placement services.

OTHER SOURCES

★4375★ **Association of Flight Attendants - CWA (AFA)**
1275 K St. NW, Ste. 500
Washington, DC 20005
URL: http://www.afanet.org

Description: Labor union organized by flight attendants. AFA represents over 50,000 flight attendants at 26 airlines, serving as a voice for flight attendants at their workplace, in the industry, and in the media.

★4376★ **Flight Attendants**
Evon Publishing
832 N 7th Ave.
Iron River, MI 49935
Ph: (906)265-3190

Audiocassette. 1996. $16.95. 32 minutes. Part of the Careers and Vocational Guidance Series. Provides information about the nature of the work, educational requirements, employment outlook, earnings, and work conditions as well as additional related information.

★4377★ **Personal & Building Service Occupations**
Delphi Productions
3160 4th St.
Boulder, CO 80304
Fax: (303)443-4022   Fr: 888-443-2400
URL: http://www.delphivideo.com

$95.00. 48 minutes. Part of the Careers for the 21st Century Video Library.

Florists

SOURCES OF HELP-WANTED ADS

★4378★ The Extra Touch Online
Extra Touch Florists
33031 Schoolcraft Rd.
Livonia, MI 48150
URL: http://www.etfassociation.org
Monthly. Online publication for retail florists.

★4379★ Florists' Review
PO Box 4368
Topeka, KS 66604
Ph: (785)266-0888   Fax: (785)266-0333
Fr: 800-367-4708
Monthly guidebook for operating a successful floral business.

★4380★ Grower Talks
Ball Publishing
PO Box 9
Batavia, IL 60510
Ph: (630)208-9080   Fax: (630)208-9350
Fr: 888-888-0013
E-mail: info@ballpublishing.com
URL: http://www.growertalks.com
Monthly. $29.00/year for individuals. Trade magazine covering issues for commercial greenhouse growers with a focus on North American production.

EMPLOYER DIRECTORIES AND NETWORKING LISTS

★4381★ Florists-Retail Directory
infoUSA Inc.
5711 S 86th Cir.
Omaha, NE 68127-0347
Ph: (402)930-3500   Fax: (402)331-0176
Fr: 800-555-6124
URL: http://www.abii.com
Annual. Number of listings: 50,501. Entries include: Name, address, phone (including area code), size of advertisement, year first in "Yellow Pages," name of owner or manager, number of employees. Regional editions available. Compiled from telephone company "Yellow Pages," nationwide. Arrangement: Geographical.

★4382★ Florists-Wholesale Directory
infoUSA Inc.
5711 S 86th Cir.
Omaha, NE 68127-0347
Ph: (402)930-3500   Fax: (402)331-0176
Fr: 800-555-6124
URL: http://www.abii.com
Annual. Number of listings: 3,286. Entries include: Name, address, phone (including area code), size of advertisement, year first in "Yellow Pages," name of owner of manager, number of employees. Compiled from telephone company "Yellow Pages," nationwide. Arrangement: Geographical.

★4383★ Michigan Florist-Membership Directory
Michigan Floral Association
1152 Haslett Rd.
Haslett, MI 48840-9778
URL: http://www.michiganfloral.org
Annual, fall. $75.00. Publication includes: List of about 1,100 member floral retailers and wholesalers, nurseries and garden centers, and individual members. Entries include: Company name, owner's name, address, phone, type of business. Arrangement: Separate geographical and alphabetical lists.

★4384★ National Flower Shop Directory
PO Box 247
Navesink, NJ 07752
E-mail: info@floral-directory.com
URL: http://www.floral-directory.com/detail.htm
Annual. $149.00. Provides directory of local florist shops. List phone numbers, addresses. Also has an online service with direct links to local florist shops.

★4385★ Professional Floral Communicators-International-Directory
Professional Floral Communicators-International
1601 Duke St.
Alexandria, VA 22314
Ph: (703)836-8700   Fax: (703)836-8705
Fr: 800-336-4743
E-mail: keidam@safnow.org
URL: http://www.safnow.org
Covers about 80 member floral presenters and educators. Entries include: Name, address, phone, professional affiliation, education, career data, interests, design and presentation techniques. Arrangement: Alphabetical/geographic/area of expertise.

★4386★ Teleflora Subscribers Directory
Teleflora
11444 W Olympic Blvd.
Los Angeles, CA 90064
Ph: (310)231-9199   Fax: (310)966-3610
Fr: 800-321-2665
Bimonthly. Covers about 20,000 florists who subscribe to Teleflora, a flower delivery wire service; military bases and installations; Teleflora Canada; foreign affiliates; and suppliers of flower arranging materials and equipment. Entries include: For subscribers-Shop or company name, address, phone, amount of minimum order, special promotions stocked, hours, principals. For foreign affiliates-Shop name, address, cable address, amount of minimum order. For suppliers-Company name, address, phone. Arrangement: Subscribers and affiliates are geographical; suppliers are classified. Indexes: Foreign cities served through headquarters only.

★4387★ Wholesale Florists & Florist Supplier Association-Membership Directory
Wholesale Florist & Florist Supplier Association
147 Old Solomons Island Rd., Ste. 302
Annapolis, MD 21401
Ph: (410)573-0400   Fax: (410)573-5001
Fr: 888-289-3372
E-mail: jwanko@wffsa.org

Biennial, Summer/Winter. $100.00. Number of listings: 1,275. Entries include: Company name, address, phone, names of executives, list of products or services. Arrangement: Geographical. Indexes: Alphabetical.

HANDBOOKS AND MANUALS

★4388★ *Careers in Horticulture and Botany*
McGraw-Hill Trade
2 Penn Plaza
New York, NY 10121
Ph: (212)904-2000   Fr: 800-722-4726
E-mail: ntcpub@tribune.com

Jerry Garner. 1996. $17.95; 13.95 (paper). 255 pages. Includes bibliographical references

★4389★ *Careers for Plant Lovers and Other Green Thumb Types*
Vgm Career Horizons
N T C Publishing Group
1221 Avenue of the Americas
New York, NY 10020
Ph: (212)904-2000   Fr: 800-323-4900
E-mail: ntcpub@tribune.com

Blythe Camenson. 1995. $14.95; $9.95 (paper). 160 pages. Describes careers for people who love working with plants and flowers.

★4390★ *Fabjob Guide to Become a Florist*
FabJob
4603 NE University Village, No. 224
Seattle, WA 98105

2004. $29.95. Offers a step-by-step guide to becoming a florist.

★4391★ *How to Start and Manage a Flower and Plant Store Business*
Lewis & Renn Associates
4860 E. Main St., No. A128
Mesa, AZ 85205
Fax: (480)830-1187

Jerre G. Lewis and Leslie Renn. 1999. $18.95 (paper).

★4392★ *How to Start and Manage a Retail Florist Business: Step by Step Guide to Starting and Managing Your Own Business*
Lewis & Renn Associates
4860 E. Main St., No. A128
Mesa, AZ 85205
Fax: (480)830-1187

Jerre G. Lewis and Leslie Renn. 1999. $18.95 (paper).

★4393★ *The National Business Employment Weekly Jobs Rated Almanac*
John Wiley & Sons Inc.
1 Wiley Dr.
Somerset, NJ 08873
Ph: (732)469-4400   Fr: 800-225-5945

Les Krantz. First edition, 1995. $16.95. 340 pages. Ranks 250 jobs by environment, salary, outlook, physical demands, stress, security, travel opportunities, and geographic location.

★4394★ *Opportunities in Horticulture Careers*
McGraw-Hill Trade
2 Penn Plaza
New York, NY 10121
Ph: (212)904-2000   Fr: 800-722-4726

Jan Goldberg. 1994. $14.95; $11.95 (paper). 160 pages. Describes careers in horticulture, the nursery industry, and floriculture, among others.

★4395★ *The Profit Minded Florist*
American Floral Services, Inc.
P.O. Box 12309
Oklahoma City, OK 73157-2309
Ph: (405)947-3373   Fax: (405)943-7131
Fr: 800-456-7890

American Floral Services, Inc. Staff, Paul Goodman, and Marie Ackerman. 2000. $99.95 (paper).

★4396★ *The Retail Florist Business*
Interstate Publishers, Inc.
PO Box 50
Danville, IL 61834-0050
Ph: (217)446-0500   Fax: (217)446-9706
Fr: 800-843-4774

Peter B. Pfahl. Fifth edition, 1994. $48.75. 336 pages.

OTHER SOURCES

★4397★ *Florist*
Cambridge Educational
2572 Brunswick Ave.
Lawrenceville, NJ 08648-4128
Fax: 800-FAX-ON-US   Fr: 800-468-4227
URL: http://www.cambridgeeducational.com

$39.95. 15 minutes. Part of the Vocational Visions Career series.

★4398★ *Society of American Florists (SAF)*
1601 Duke St.
Alexandria, VA 22314-3406
Ph: (703)836-8700   Fax: (703)836-8705
Fr: 800-336-4743
E-mail: memberinfo@safnow.org
URL: http://www.safnow.org

Description: Growers, wholesalers, retailers, and allied tradesmen in the floral industry. Lobbies Congress on behalf of the industry; sponsors educational programs; promotes the floral industry; prepares materials for consumers and for high school and college students; provides business resources. Sponsors Floricultural Hall of Fame, American Academy of Floriculture, and Professional Floral Commentators - International. Compiles statistics; sponsors competitions.

Forensic Scientists

SOURCES OF HELP-WANTED ADS

★4399★ Forensic Examiner
American College of Forensic Examiners
2750 E Sunshine Rd.
Springfield, MO 65802
Bimonthly. Publication covering issues in forensic exam.

★4400★ Journal of the American Society of Questioned Document Examiners
American Society of Questioned
 Document Examiners
PO Box 382684
Germantown, TN 38183-2684
Ph: (901)759-0729   Fax: (901)737-2643
Quarterly. Subscription included in membership. Professional journal covering forensic sciences.

★4401★ Journal of Forensic Identification
American Society for Testing and
 Materials
100 Barr Harbor Dr.
West Conshohocken, PA 19428
6/year. $249.00. A scientific journal that provides over 115 pages of articles related to forensics. Also offers information regarding training and educational events, job postings and announcements.

★4402★ Journal of Forensic Sciences
American Academy of Forensic Sciences
PO Box 669
Colorado Springs, CO 80901
Ph: (719)636-1100   Fax: (719)636-1993
Bimonthly. $32.00/year for members; $124.00/year for nonmembers. Journal covering professional and scientific articles on forensics.

★4403★ Journal of Intelligent and Robotic Systems
Kluwer Academic/Plenum Publishing Corp.
233 Spring St., 7th Fl.
New York, NY 10013-1578
Ph: (212)620-8000   Fax: (212)463-0742
Fr: 800-221-9369
URL: http://www.wkap.nl/jouralhome.htm/0921-0296
Monthly. $900.00/year for institutions, print or online edition only; $570.00/year for individuals. Journal covering systems and control science with artificial intelligence and computer science concepts.

★4404★ Science
American Association for the
 Advancement of Science
1200 New York Ave. NW
Washington, DC 20005
Ph: (202)326-6400   Fax: (202)371-9849
URL: http://htpp://www.sciencemag.org
Weekly. $105.00/year for individuals; $7.00 for single issue. Magazine devoted to science, scientific research, and public policy.

EMPLOYER DIRECTORIES AND NETWORKING LISTS

★4405★ American Academy of Forensic Sciences-Membership Directory
American Academy of Forensic Sciences
PO Box 669
Colorado Springs, CO 80901
Ph: (719)636-1100   Fax: (719)636-1993
Annual, May. Covers 3,800 persons qualified in forensic sciences, including law, pathology, biology, odontology, physical anthropology, psychiatry, questioned documents, criminalistics, engineering, and toxicology. Entries include: Name, office address and phone, highest degree held, professional title, type of certification. Arrangement: Alphabetical. Indexes: Geographical, subject.

★4406★ Encyclopedia of Forensic Science: A Compendium of Detective Fact and Fiction
Oryx Press
1434 E San Miguel Ave.
Phoenix, AZ 85014-2422
Fr: 800-225-5800
$64.95. Publication includes: List of Web sites related to forensic science. Principal content of publication is entries on people and events dealing with forensic science. Arrangement: Alphabetical. Indexes: Alphabetical.

★4407★ Forensic Services Directory
National Forensic Center
17 Temple Ter.
Lawrenceville, NJ 08648
Ph: (609)883-0550   Fax: (609)883-7622
Fr: 800-526-5177
URL: http://expertindex.com
Annual, January. $134.50 for out of state; $142.27 for New Jersey residents. Covers about 5,000 individuals willing to serve as expert witnesses or consultants during litigation; also associations, societies, and institutes with specialized information. Entries include: For individuals-Name, address, phone, degrees, affiliation, professional license (if any), specialties; many listings include biographical data. For organizations-Name, address, phone, areas of interest, information service available. Arrangement: Alphabetical by individual or organization name, then by consulting field or specialty (aviation, chemistry, testing laboratories).

★4408★ International Association for Identification-Membership Directory
International Association for Identification
2535 Pilot Knob Rd., Ste. 117
Mendota Heights, MN 55120-1120
Ph: (651)681-8566   Fax: (651)681-8443
Annual, December. Covers about 5,000 police officials, identification personnel, and others engaged in forensic identification, investigation, and scientific crime detection. Entries include: Name, preferred mailing address. Arrangement: Geographical. Indexes: Alphabetical.

★4409★ Opportunities in Forensic Science

The McGraw-Hill Cos.
P.O. Box 182604
Columbus, OH 43272
Ph: 877-833-5524   Fax: (614)759-3759
Fr: 800-257-0993

$15.00 for cloth; $12.00 for paper. Publication includes: a list of colleges and universities offering graduate programs and internships in the field of forensic science. Principal content of publication is is information on career opportunities in the forensic sciences, including educational requirements, qualifications needed, and salary. Publisher also offers a catalog card kit for this title.

HANDBOOKS AND MANUALS

★4410★ Career Planning in Criminal Justice

Anderson Publishing Co.
2035 Reading Rd.
Cincinnati, OH 45202-1576
Ph: (513)421-4142   Fax: (513)562-8116
Fr: 800-582-7295

Robert C. DeLucia and Thomas J. Doyle. Third edition, 1998. 226 pages. $21.95. Surveys a wide range of career and employment opportunities in law enforcement, the courts, corrections, forensic science, and private security. Contains career planning and job hunting advice.

★4411★ DNA Technology in Forensic Science

National Academies Press
500 Fifth Street, NW
Washington, DC 20055
Ph: (202)334-3313

$34.16. 200 pages. Offers recommendations for resolving crucial questions that are emerging as DNA typing becomes more widespread.

★4412★ Forensic Science Handbook

Prentice Hall PRT
One Lake Street
Upper Saddle River, NJ 07458
Ph: (201)236-7616   Fax: (201)236-7696

Reference source for the field of criminalistics. Each chapter offers a review of a particular aspect of the field written by noted experts.

★4413★ Guide to Nontraditional Careers in Science

Hemisphere Publishing Corp.
325 Chestnut St., 8th Fl.
Philadelphia, PA 19106
Ph: (215)785-5800   Fax: (215)269-0363
Fr: 800-821-8312

Karen Young Kreeger. 1998. $38.95 (paper). 263 pages.

★4414★ Principles and Practice of Criminalistics: The Profession of Forensic Science

CRC Press LLC
2000 NW Corporate Blvd
Boca Raton, FL 33431
Ph: (561)994-0555   Fax: (561)994-0555

Keith Inman and Norah Rudin. 2000. $89.95. 392 pages. Outlines a logical framework for the examination of physical evidence in a criminalistics laboratory.

TRADESHOWS

★4415★ American Academy of Forensic Sciences Annual Scientific Meeting

American Academy of Forensic Sciences
410 N. 21st St., Ste. 203
PO Box 669
Colorado Springs, CO 80901-0669
Ph: (719)636-1100   Fax: (719)636-1993
E-mail: membship@aafs.org

Annual. **Primary Exhibits:** Scientific instruments.

OTHER SOURCES

★4416★ American Academy of Forensic Sciences (AAFS)

410 N 21st St.
PO Box 669
Colorado Springs, CO 80904-2798
Ph: (719)636-1100   Fax: (719)636-1993
E-mail: awarren@aafs.org
URL: http://www.aafs.org

Description: Professional society of criminalists, scientists, members of the bench and bar, pathologists, biologists, psychiatrists, examiners of questioned documents, toxicologists, odontologists, anthropologists, and engineers. Works to encourage the study, improve the practice, elevate the standards, and advance the cause of the forensic sciences; improve the quality of scientific techniques, tests, and criteria; plan, organize, and administer meetings, reports, and other projects for the stimulation and advancement of these and related purposes. Maintains Forensic Sciences Job Listing; conducts selected research for the government; offers forensic expert referral service.

★4417★ American Board of Criminalistics (ABC)

PO Box 1123
Wausau, WI 54402-1123
Ph: (715)845-3684   Fax: (715)845-4156
E-mail: abcreg@dwave.net
URL: http://www.criminalistics.com/ABC/A.php

Members: Regional and national organiza-

tions of forensic scientists and criminalists. **Purpose:** Offers certificates of Professional Competency in Criminalistics as well as in specialty disciplines of forensic biology, drug chemistry, fire debris analysis, and various areas of trace evidence examination. Works to establish professional standards and promote growth within the industry. **Activities:** Answers questions regarding the certification process.

★4418★ American Board of Forensic Toxicology (ABFT)

PO Box 669
Colorado Springs, CO 80901-0669
Ph: (719)636-1100   Fax: (719)636-1993
URL: http://www.abft.org/

Description: Works to establish, enhance, and revise as necessary, standards of qualification for those who practice forensic toxicology, and to certify as qualified specialists those applicants who comply with the requirements of the Board.

★4419★ American College of Forensic Examiners

2750 E Sunshine
Springfield, MO 65804
Ph: (417)881-3818   Fax: (417)881-4702
Fr: 800-423-9737
E-mail: cao@acfei.com
URL: http://www.acfei.com

Members: Professionals in the field of forensic examination, including the following disciplines: accounting, accident reconstruction, criminology, crisis intervention, counselors, social work, nursing and law enforcement hypnosis, all medical fields, physics, psychiatry, psychology, and toxicology. **Purpose:** Works to advance the profession of forensic examination through education, training, and certification.

★4420★ American Society of Crime Laboratory Directors

PO Box 2710
Largo, FL 33779
Ph: (727)541-2982   Fax: (727)547-2692

Description: Nonprofit professional society dedicated to providing excellence in forensic science analysis through leadership in the management of forensic science. The purpose of the organization is to foster professional interests; assist the development of laboratory management principles and techniques; acquire, preserve and disseminate forensic based information; maintain and improve communications among crime laboratory directors; and to promote, encourage and maintain the highest standards of practice in the field.

★4421★ Evidence Photographers International Council (EPIC)

600 Main St.
Honesdale, PA 18431
Ph: (570)253-5450   Fax: (570)253-5011
Fr: 800-356-3742
E-mail: headquarters@epic-photo.org

URL: http://www.epic-photo.org

Members: Law enforcement and civil evidence photographers; others in related fields. **Purpose:** Objectives are to: aid in the worldwide advancement of forensic photography; assist in research and development of new techniques; enhance professional education; inform members of new procedures. **Activities:** Maintains speakers' bureau. Offers certification upon satisfactory completion of an oral or written examination by a three-member panel, receipt of a minimum of 30 prints for review, and a $150 application fee. Provides an honors program to recognize those who have shown expertise in the field of forensic photography, and service to EPIC. Sponsors the EPIC Witness Referral Service. Referral Service. Referral Service.

★4422★ Forensic Sciences Foundation (FSF)

410 N 21st St., Ste. 203
Colorado Springs, CO 80904
Ph: (719)636-1100   Fax: (719)636-1993
URL: http://www.aafs.org

Purpose: Works to conduct research in the procedures and standards utilized in the practice of forensic sciences; develop and implement useful educational and training programs and methods of benefit to forensic sciences; conduct programs of public education concerning issues of importance to the forensic sciences; engage in activities which will promote, encourage, and assist the development of the forensic sciences. **Activities:** Provides referral service for forensic scientists. Compiles statistics. Operates the Forensic Sciences Foundation Press.

★4423★ International Association for Identification (IAI)

2535 Pilot Knob Rd., Ste. 117
Mendota Heights, MN 55120-1120
Ph: (651)681-8566   Fax: (651)681-8443
E-mail: iaisecty@theiai.org
URL: http://www.theiai.org/

Description: Individuals engaged in forensic identification, investigation, and scientific crime detection. Strives to improve methods of scientific identification techniques used in criminal investigations.

★4424★ National Forensic Center (NFC)

17 Temple Terrace
Lawrenceville, NJ 08648
Ph: (609)883-0550   Fr: 800-526-5177
E-mail: forenexpts@worldnet.att.net
URL: http://www.expertindex.com

Description: Expert witnesses and litigation consultants who serve attorneys, insurance companies, and government agencies. Trains consultants to work with attorneys and to testify in court; trains individuals to serve as expert witnesses and litigation consultants. Makes speakers available upon request. Compiles statistics on experts' fees.

★4425★ National Forensic Science Technology Center

7881 114th Avenue North
Largo, FL 33773
Ph: (727)549-6067   Fax: (727)549-6070
E-mail: info@nfstc.org
URL: http://www.nfstc.org/index.htm

Description: Provides systems support, training and education to the forensic science community in the United States.

★4426★ Society of Forensic Toxicologists (SOFT)

PO Box 5543
Mesa, AZ 85211-5543
Ph: (480)839-9106   Fax: (480)839-9106
E-mail: c8toxi@www.cuyahoga.oh.us
URL: http://www.soft-tox.org

Description: Scientists who analyze tissue and body fluids for drugs and poisons and interpret the information for judicial purposes; students and other interested individuals. Objectives are to establish uniform qualifications and requirements for certification of forensic toxicologists and promote support mechanisms for continued certification; to stimulate research and development; to provide review board for cases involving differences of professional opinion; to cooperate with institutions of higher learning in providing forensic toxicology education and training programs; to act on administrative and career problems affecting forensic toxicologists. Serves as clearinghouse; conducts proficiency testing programs; provides information on case histories and job opportunities. Sponsors American Board of Forensic Toxicology.

Foresters and Conservation Scientists

★4427★ Appalachian Trailway News

Appalachian Trail Conference
PO Box 807
Harpers Ferry, WV 25425
Ph: (304)535-6331   Fax: (304)535-2667
Fr: 888-287-8673

$15.00/year for individuals. Magazine on hiking, Appalachian Trail protection, and general conservation issues.

★4428★ AWIS Magazine

Association for Women in Science
1200 New York Ave. NW, Ste. 650
Washington, DC 20005
Ph: (202)326-8940   Fax: (202)326-8960
Fr: 800-886-AWIS

Description: Bimonthly. Covers issues, legislation, and trends related to science education for girls, women, and minorities. Includes information on grants and fellowships, job openings, educational programs, events, and notices of publications available.

★4429★ CJE Newsletter

Coalition for Jobs and the Environment
PO Box 645
Abingdon, VA 24210-0645
Description: Bimonthly. Covers issues relating to employment, jobs, and environmental safety. Recurring features include letters to the editor, news, interviews, a calendar of events, news of members, and columns titled Action Needed and Resources.

★4430★ Drinking Water & Backflow Prevention

Drinking Water & Backflow Prevention
PO Box 33209
Northglenn, CO 80233
Ph: (303)451-0978   Fax: (303)452-9776
Fr: 888-367-3927
E-mail: backflow@dwbp-online.com
URL: http://www.dunbq-online.com

Description: Monthly. Presents articles directed toward "individuals, companies, organizations, agencies, and municipalities with an interest in drinking water protection and backflow prevention." Contains information on safety standards, water system protection, training programs, cross-connection control, and all issues related to preventing the contamination of potable drinking water supplies with backflow prevention devices. Recurring features include case studies, letters to the editor, news of research, columns titled Test Your Investigative Skills and Backflow Prevention Device Repairs, and reports of meetings. Also carries news of educational opportunities, job listings, notices of publications available, and a calendar of events.

★4431★ Endangered Species Bulletin

U.S. Fish and Wildlife Service
4401 N Fairfax Dr., Rm. 670
Rm. 670
Arlington, VA 22203
Ph: (703)358-2029   Fax: (703)358-1826

Bimonthly. Publication covering wildlife conservation and environmental issues.

★4432★ Environment (News)

Global Information Network
146 W 29th St., Ste. 7E
New York, NY 10001
Ph: (212)244-3123   Fax: (212)244-3522
URL: http://www.globalinfo.org

Daily. $750.00/year. Publication covering environmental issues.

★4433★ Fisheries

American Fisheries Society
5410 Grosvenor Ln., Ste. 110
Bethesda, MD 20814-2199
Ph: (301)897-8616   Fax: (301)897-8096
URL: http://www.fisheries.org

Monthly. $76.00/year for individuals; $76.00/year for Canada and Mexico; $88.00/year for other countries; $38.00/year for students and retirees; $38.00/year for Canada and Mexico, students and retirees; $44.00/year for other countries, students and retirees. Magazine covering fisheries management and aquatic resource issues.

★4434★ The Job Seeker

The Job Seeker
24313 Destiny Ave.
Tomah, WI 54660-4367
Ph: (608)378-4450   Fax: (608)378-4450

Description: Semimonthly. Specializes "in environmental and natural resource vacancies nationwide." Lists current vacancies from federal, state, local, private, and nonprofit employers. Also available via e-mail.

★4435★ Journal of Forestry

Society of American Foresters
5400 Grosvenor Ln.
Bethesda, MD 20814-2198
Ph: (301)897-8720   Fax: (301)897-3690
URL: http://www.safnet.org

Monthly. $55.00/year; $100.00/year for institutions. Journal of forestry serves to advance the profession by keeping professionals informed about significant developments and ideas in forest science, natural resource management, and forest policy.

★4436★ Nature International Weekly Journal of Science

Nature Publishing Group
345 Park Ave. S
New York, NY 10010-1707
Ph: (212)726-9200   Fax: (212)689-9711
Fr: 888-331-6288
E-mail: nature@natureny.com
URL: http://www.nature.com

Weekly. $145.00/year for individuals; $495.00/year for institutions. Magazine covering science and technology, including the fields of biology, biochemistry, genetics, medicine, earth sciences, physics, pharmacology, and behavioral sciences.

★4437★ The Northeastern Naturalist

Humboldt Field Research Institute
PO Box 9
Steuben, ME 04680-0009
Ph: (207)546-2821   Fax: (207)546-3042

URL: http://www.eaglehill.us/jngeninf.html

Quarterly. $40.00/year for individuals; $60.00/year for institutions; $45.00/year for individuals, Canada; $65.00/year for institutions, Canada; $49.00/year for individuals, other countries; $69.00/year for institutions, other countries. Peer-reviewed interdisciplinary scientific journal covering field ecology, biology, behavior, biogeography, taxonomy, anatomy, physiology, geology and related fields in the northeastern United States.

★4438★ Northern Logger and Timber Processor

N.L. Publishing Inc.
PO Box 69
Old Forge, NY 13420
Ph: (315)369-3078   Fax: (315)369-3736

Monthly. $10.00/year for individuals. Magazine for the logging and lumber industries.

★4439★ OnEarth

Natural Resources Defense Council
40 W 20 St.
New York, NY 10011
Ph: (212)727-2700   Fax: (212)727-1773

Quarterly. Periodical covering environmental issues.

★4440★ Ornithological Newsletter

Dr. Cheryl L. Trine
3889 E Valley View
Berrien Springs, MI 49103
Ph: (616)471-7886
URL: http://birds.cornell.edu/OSNA/orn-newsl.htm

Description: Bimonthly. Provides information of interest to ornithologists. Recurring features include listings of available grants and awards, news of members, a calendar of events, activities of sponsoring societies, and notices of publications available. Notices of employment opportunities are also available on the Web version.

★4441★ PE & RS Photogrammetric Engineering & Remote Sensing

The Imaging and Geospatial Information Society
5410 Grosvenor Ln., Ste. 210
Bethesda, MD 20814
Ph: (301)493-0290   Fax: (301)493-0208
E-mail: asprs@asprs.org

Monthly. $130.00/year. Journal covering photogrammetry, remote sensing, geographic information systems, cartography, and surveying, global positioning systems, digital photogrammetry.

★4442★ The Southeastern Naturalist

Humboldt Field Research Institute
PO Box 9
Steuben, ME 04680-0009
Ph: (207)546-2821   Fax: (207)546-3042
URL: http://www.eaglehill.us/jngeninf.html

Quarterly. $40.00/year for individuals;

$60.00/year for institutions; $45.00/year for individuals, Canada; $65.00/year for institutions, Canada; $49.00/year for individuals, other countries; $69.00/year for institutions, other countries. Peer-reviewed interdisciplinary scientific journal covering field ecology, biology, behavior, biogeography, taxonomy, anatomy, physiology, geology and related fields in the southeastern United States.

★4443★ Wetlands

Society of Wetland Scientists
1313, Dolley Madison Blvd.Ste.402
McLean, VA 22101
Ph: (703)790-1745   Fax: (703)790-2672
Fr: 800-627-0629
URL: http://www.sws.org/wetlands/

Quarterly. $50.00/year for individuals, includes SWS membership; $25.00/year for students, includes SWS membership; $250.00/year for institutions, includes SWS membership; $125.00/year for libraries, includes SWS membership; $65.00/year for family, includes SWS membership; $35.00/year for emeritus, includes SWS membership. Scholarly journal covering all aspects of wetlands biology, ecology, hydrology, water chimstry, soil and sediment characteristics, management, and laws and regulations.

★4444★ The Wildlifer

The Wildlife Society
5410 Grosvenor Ln.
Bethesda, MD 20814-2197
Ph: (301)897-9770   Fax: (301)530-2471

Description: Bimonthly. Serves as the Society's official publication of record. Contains items on section and chapter activities, meetings of interest, career notes, job opportunities, and timely articles on significant developments in conservation issues. Recurring features include editorials, news of members, letters to the editor, a calendar of events, and a column titled Call for Papers.

PLACEMENT AND JOB REFERRAL SERVICES

★4445★ Korean Scientists and Engineers Association in America (KSEA)

1952 Gallows Rd., Ste. 300
Vienna, VA 22182
Ph: (703)748-1221   Fax: (703)748-1331
E-mail: sejong@ksea.org
URL: http://www.ksea.org

Description: Scientists and engineers holding single or advanced degrees. Goals are to: promote friendship and mutuality among Korean and American scientists and engineers; contribute to Korea's scientific, technological, industrial, and economic development; strengthen the scientific, technological, and cultural bonds between Korea and the U.S. Sponsors symposium. Maintains

speakers' bureau, placement service, and biographical archives. Compiles statistics. Maintains 100 volume library of scientific handbooks and yearbooks in Korean.

★4446★ Natural Science for Youth Foundation (NSYF)

130 Azalea Dr.
Roswell, GA 30075
Ph: (770)594-9367   Fax: (770)594-7738
E-mail: info@slpt.org

Description: Sponsors natural science centers, junior nature museums, native animal parks, and trailside museums. Provides information service. Conducts training courses in museum and nature center management. Maintains museum and placement service.

★4447★ Society for Range Management (SRM)

445 Union Blvd., Ste. 230
Lakewood, CO 80228
Ph: (303)986-3309   Fax: (303)986-3892
E-mail: srmweb@rangelands.org
URL: http://www.rangelands.org/

Members: Professional international society of scientists, technicians, ranchers, administrators, teachers, and students interested in the study, use, and management of rangeland resources for livestock, wildlife, watershed, and recreation. Activities: Sponsors placement service.

EMPLOYER DIRECTORIES AND NETWORKING LISTS

★4448★ American Men and Women of Science

Thomson Gale
27500 Drake Rd.
Farmington Hills, MI 48331-3535
Ph: (248)699-4253   Fax: (248)699-8065
Fr: 800-877-GALE
E-mail: amws@galegroup.com

Biennial, latest edition December 2002. $975.00. Covers over 129,700 U.S. and Canadian scientists active in the physical, biological, mathematical, computer science, and engineering fields; includes references to previous edition for deceased scientists and nonrespondents. Entries include: Name, address, education, personal and career data, memberships, honors and awards, research interest. Arrangement: Alphabetical. Indexes: Discipline (in separate volume).

★4449★ Association of Consulting Foresters-Membership Specialization Directory

Association of Consulting Foresters
732 N Washington St., Ste. 4A
Alexandria, VA 22314-1921
Ph: (703)548-0990   Fax: (703)548-6395

Annual, August. Free. Covers nearly 500 member forestry consulting firms and professional foresters who earn the largest part of their income from consulting. Entries include: Name, address, phone, specialties, background, career data, staff (if a consulting firm), geographic area served, capabilities, including equipment available and foreign language proficiency. Arrangement: Alphabetical. Indexes: Name, office location, language, international capability.

★4450★ **Conservation Directory**

National Wildlife Federation
11100 Wildlife Center Dr.
Reston, VA 20190
Ph: (703)638-6000   Fax: (703)438-6061
E-mail: cdadmin@nwf.org
URL: http://www.nwf.org/conservationdirectory

Annual, January. $70.00. Covers over 3,000 organizations, agencies, colleges and universities with conservation programs and more than 18,000 officials concerned with environmental conservation, education, and natural resource use and management. Entries include: Agency name, address, branch or subsidiary office name and address, names and titles of key personnel, descriptions of program areas, size of membership (where appropriate), telephone, fax, e-mail and URL addresses. Arrangement: Classified by type of organization. Indexes: Personal name, keyword, geographic, organization.

★4451★ **National Parks: Index**

U.S. National Park Service
Harpers Ferry Center
PO Box 50
Harpers Ferry, WV 25425-0050
Ph: (202)208-4747   Fax: (304)535-6144
URL: http://www.nps.gov/

Biennial, odd years. $6.50. Covers over 379 areas administered by the National Park Service, including parks, shores, historic sites, 80 national trails, and wild and scenic rivers. Entries include: Name, location, address, acreage (federal, non-federal, and gross), federal facilities, brief description. Arrangement: Most areas are alphabetical by state; geographical and historical by state; wild and scenic rivers and national trails are alphabetical by state. Indexes: Alphabetical by state.

★4452★ **Peterson's Job Opportunities in Engineering and Technology**

Thomson Peterson's
PO Box 67005
Lawrenceville, NJ 08648-6105
Fr: 800-338-3282

Compiled by the Peterson's staff. Fourth edition, 1996. $21.95 (paper). 384 pages. Profiles 2,000 high-tech companies looking primarily for technical personnel in such fields as biotechnology, telecommunications, software, computers and peripherals, defense, and aerospace. Contains job-search strategies and career options to help match education and expertise to the job market. Indexed geographically, by industry, and by hiring needs.

★4453★ **Seasonal Employment**

U.S. National Park Service
Harpers Ferry Center
PO Box 50
Harpers Ferry, WV 25425-0050
Ph: (202)208-4747   Fax: (304)535-6144
URL: http://www.nps.gov

Updated as needed; go to "InfoZone" to access. Publication includes: List of 10 regional offices and branches of the National Park Service that accept applications for seasonal jobs. Entries include: Name, address, phone, geographical area served. Principal content of publication is information on seasonal jobs offered by the National Park Services, with description of duties, qualifications, and application procedures for each type of job offered. Arrangement: Geographical.

HANDBOOKS AND MANUALS

★4454★ **The Best Resumes for Scientists and Engineers**

John Wiley & Sons Inc.
1 Wiley Dr.
Somerset, NJ 08873
Ph: (732)469-4400   Fr: 800-225-5945

Adele Lewis and David J. Moore. Second edition, 1993. $37.50; $19.95 (paper). 224 pages. Presents an extensive collection of scientific and engineering resumes, highlighting the important differences between these and resumes written for other occupations.

★4455★ **Career Information Center**

Macmillan Publishing Co. Inc.
200 Old Tappan Rd.
Old Tappan, NJ 07675
Fr: 800-428-5331

Visual Education Center Staff. Seventh edition, 1999. $275.00. 2080 pages. This 13-volume set profiles over 600 occupations. Each occupational profile describes job duties, educational requirements, how to get the job, advancement possibilities, employment outlook, working conditions, earnings and benefits, and where to write for more information.

★4456★ **Careers in the Environment**

VGM Career Horizons
N T C Publishing Group
1221 Avenue of the Americas
New York, NY 10020
Ph: (212)904-2000   Fr: 800-323-4900
E-mail: ntcpub@tribune.com

Michael Fasulo and Paul Walker. Second edition, 2000. $17.95; $13.95 (paper). 275 pages. Comprehensive information on the diverse career opportunities available in environmental services.

★4457★ **Careers for Environmental Types and Others Who Respect the Earth**

VGM Career Horizons
N T C Publishing Group
1221 Avenue of the Americas
New York, NY 10020
Ph: (212)904-2000   Fr: 800-323-4900
E-mail: ntcpub@tribune.com

Jane Kinney and Mike Fasulo. Second edition, 2001. $15.95; $12.95 (paper). 192 pages. Describes environmentally friendly positions with corporations, government, and environmental organizations.

★4458★ **Careers for Health Nuts and Others Who Like to Stay Fit**

McGraw-Hill Trade
2 Penn Plaza
New York, NY 10121
Ph: (212)904-2000   Fr: 800-722-4726
E-mail: ntcpub@tribune.com

Blythe Camenson. 1996. $14.95; $9.95 (paper). 160 pages.

★4459★ **The Complete Guide to Environmental Careers in the 21st Century**

Island Press
PO Box 7
Covelo, CA 95428
Ph: (707)983-6432   Fax: (707)983-6414
Fr: 800-828-1302

Kevin Doyle, et al, editors. 1998. Third edition. $18.00 (paper). 463 pages. A completely revised and updated edition of the standard reference on environmental careers.

★4460★ **Job Opportunities in the Environment 1995**

Thomson Peterson's
PO Box 67005
Lawrenceville, NJ 08648-6105
Fr: 800-338-3282

Second edition, 1994. $18.95 (paper). 265 pages. Out of print.

★4461★ **Nature (Career Portraits)**

McGraw-Hill Trade
2 Penn Plaza
New York, NY 10121
Ph: (212)904-2000   Fax: (212)755-5645
Fr: 800-722-4726

Marjorie Eberts. 1996. $13.95. 310 pages. Highlights a range of careers that focus on the environment, with descriptions of a typical day on the job and interactive exercises for readers.

★4462★ Opportunities in Agriculture Careers

McGraw-Hill Trade
2 Penn Plaza
New York, NY 10121
Ph: (212)904-2000   Fr: 800-722-4726
William C. White and Donald N. Collins. 1995. $13.95. 160 pages.

★4463★ Opportunities in Biological Science Careers

McGraw-Hill Trade
2 Penn Plaza
New York, NY 10121
Ph: (212)904-2000   Fr: 800-722-4726
E-mail: ntcpub@tribune.com

Charles A. Winter. 1998. $14.95; $11.95 (paper). 200 pages. Identifies employers and outlines opportunities in plant and animal biology, biological specialties, biomedical sciences, applied biology, and other areas. Illustrated.

★4464★ Opportunities in Energy Careers

McGraw-Hill Trade
2 Penn Plaza
New York, NY 10121
Ph: (212)904-2000   Fr: 800-722-4726
E-mail: ntcpub@tribune.com

Nicholas Basta. 1995. $13.95; $10.95 (paper). 160 pages. Discusses opportunities in a variety of fields, including petroleum, nuclear, and thermal energy, and how to pursue employment. Illustrated. Out of print.

★4465★ Opportunities in Environmental Careers

McGraw-Hill Trade
2 Penn Plaza
New York, NY 10121
Ph: (212)904-2000   Fr: 800-722-4726
E-mail: ntcpub@tribune.com

Odom Fanning. Revised, 2002. $12.95 (paper). 160 pages. Describes a broad range of opportunities in fields such as environmental health, recreation, physics, and hygiene, and provides job search advice. Part of Opportunities in...Series.

★4466★ Opportunities in Farming and Agriculture Careers

McGraw-Hill Trade
2 Penn Plaza
New York, NY 10121
Ph: (212)904-2000   Fr: 800-722-4726
William C. White and Donald N. Collins. Revised, 1995. $14.95; $11.95 (paper). 205 pages. Covers opportunities in such fields as agricultural engineering, management, experimental farming, agricultural sales, teaching, and others, and provides job-hunting advice. Illustrated. Out of print.

★4467★ Opportunities in Forestry Careers

McGraw-Hill Trade
2 Penn Plaza
New York, NY 10121
Ph: (212)904-2000   Fr: 800-722-4726
E-mail: ntcpub@tribune.com

Christopher M. Wille. 1998. $11.95 (paper). 204 pages. Describes the forestry opportunities available in governmental agencies, commercial enterprises, education, and private conservation association, and how to pursue openings. Illustrated. Part of Opportunities in...Series.

★4468★ Opportunities in State and Local Government Careers

Vgm Career Horizons
1221 Avenue of the Americas
New York, NY 10020
Ph: (212)904-2000   Fr: 800-323-4900
E-mail: ntcpub@tribune.com

Neale J. Baxter. 1994. $14.95; $10.95 (paper). 160 pages. Points out the incentives and drawbacks of a government career. Describes hiring procedures and provides tips on filling out applications, taking physical and aptitude tests, handling interviews, and finding jobs. Describes the jobs in which 75% of all state and local government workers are employed. For each occupation, covers the nature of the work and the training required.

★4469★ Resumes for Environmental Careers

McGraw-Hill Trade
2 Penn Plaza
New York, NY 10121
Ph: (212)904-2000   Fr: 800-722-4726
E-mail: ntcpub@tribune.com

2002. $9.95 (paper). 160 pages. Provides resume advice tailored to people pursuing careers focusing on the environment. Includes sample resumes and cover letters.

★4470★ Resumes for Scientific and Technical Careers

McGraw-Hill Contemporary Books
1221 Avenue of the Americas
New York, NY 10020
Ph: (212)904-2000   Fr: 800-323-4900
E-mail: ntcpub@tribune.com

1999. $9.95 (paper). 450 pages. Provides resume advice for individuals interested in working in scientific and technical careers. Includes sample resumes and cover letters.

★4471★ View from the Top: Forest Service Research

Forest History Society, Inc.
701 William Vickers Ave.
Durham, NC 27701
Ph: (919)682-9319   Fax: (919)682-2349
R. Keith Arnold, M. B. Dickerman, Robert E. Buckman, and Harold H. Steen. 1994. $16.95 (paper). 365 pages.

TRADESHOWS

★4472★ Forest Products Machinery & Equipment Exposition

Southern Forest Products Association
2900 Indiana Ave.
Kenner, LA 70065
Ph: (504)443-4464   Fax: (504)443-6612
E-mail: mail@sfpa.org
URL: http://www.sfpa.org

Biennial. **Primary Exhibits:** Equipment, supplies, and services for the forest products industry. Includes lumber, panels, engineered wood products, plywood, secondary processing, forestry and land management.

★4473★ Northeastern Forest Products Equipment Expo

Northeastern Loggers Association
PO Box 69
Old Forge, NY 13420
Ph: (315)369-3078   Fax: (315)369-3736

Annual. **Primary Exhibits:** Forest industry services, equipment, and associated products. **Dates and Locations:** 2005 May 10-12.

★4474★ Pacific Logging Congress

Pacific Logging Congress
PO Box 1281
Maple Valley, WA 98038
Ph: (425)413-2808   Fax: (425)413-1359
E-mail: pacificlogging@aol.com
URL: http://www.pacificloggingcongress.com

Annual. **Primary Exhibits:** Logging and allied industry equipment. **Dates and Locations:** 2004 Nov 03-05; Scottsdale, AZ • 2005 Dates not set; Victoria, BC, Canada.

★4475★ Redwood Region Logging Conference

Redwood Region Logging Conference
5601 S. Broadway
Eureka, CA 95503
Ph: (707)443-4091   Fax: (707)443-0926
E-mail: rrlc@rrlc.net
URL: http://www.rrlc.net

Annual. **Primary Exhibits:** Logging equipment, supplies and services.

★4476★ Society of American Foresters National Convention

Society of American Foresters
5400 Grosvenor Ln.
Bethesda, MD 20814
Ph: (301)897-8720   Fax: (301)897-3690

Annual. **Primary Exhibits:** Forestry equipment, publications, hardware and software, chemicals, machinery, and geographic information systems.

★4477★ **Western Forestry Conference**

Western Forestry and Conservation
 Association
4033 SW Canyon Rd.
Portland, OR 97221
Ph: (503)226-4562   Fax: (503)226-2515
E-mail: wfca@teleport.com

Annual. **Primary Exhibits:** Forestry equipment, including firefighting equipment and supplies, remote sensing services, computer hardware and software, safety equipment, nursery supplies and services.

OTHER SOURCES

★4478★ **American Forests**

PO Box 2000
Washington, DC 20013
Ph: (202)955-4500   Fax: (202)955-4588
Fr: 800-368-5748
E-mail: dgangloff@amfor.org
URL: http://www.americanforests.org

Description: A citizens' conservation and tree-planting organization working to advance the intelligent management and use of forests, soil, water, wildlife, and all other natural resources. Promotes public appreciation of natural resources and the part they play in the social, recreational, and economic life of the U.S.

★4479★ **ASPRS - The Imaging and Geospatial Information Society**

5410 Grosvenor Ln., Ste. 210
Bethesda, MD 20814-2160
Ph: (301)493-0290   Fax: (301)493-0208
E-mail: asprs@asprs.org
URL: http://www.asprs.org

Members: Firms, individuals, government employees, and academicians engaged in photogrammetry, photointerpretation, remote sensing, and geographic information systems and their application to such fields as archaeology, geographic information systems, military reconnaissance, urban planning, engineering, traffic surveys, meteorological observations, medicine, geology, forestry, agriculture, construction, and topographic mapping. Mission is to advance knowledge and improve understanding of these sciences and to promote responsible applications. **Activities:** Offers voluntary certification program open to persons associated with one or more functional area of photogrammetry, remote sensing, and GIS. Surveys the profession of private firms in photogrammetry and remote sensing in the areas of productsand services

★4480★ **Association of Consulting Foresters of America (ACF)**

732 N Washington St., Ste. 4A
Alexandria, VA 22314-1921
Ph: (703)548-0990   Fax: (703)548-6395
E-mail: director@acf-foresters.com
URL: http://www.acf-foresters.com

Members: Professional foresters in the field of applied forestry and forest utilization who work for private landowners or industry on a contract or contingency basis. Members must be graduates of an association-approved forestry school and have five years experience in forest administration and management. **Activities:** Provides client referral service. Compiles statistics.

★4481★ **Association for International Practical Training (AIPT)**

10400 Little Patuxent Pky., Ste. 250
Columbia, MD 21044-3519
Ph: (410)997-2200   Fax: (410)992-3924
E-mail: aipt@aipt.org
URL: http://www.aipt.org

Description: Providers worldwide on-the-job training programs for students and professionals seeking international career development and life-changing experiences. Arranges workplace exchanges in hundreds of professional fields, bringing employers and trainees together from around the world. Client list ranges from small farming communities to Fortune 500 companies.

★4482★ *Environmental Occupations: Professional*

Delphi Productions
3160 4th St.
Boulder, CO 80304
Fax: (303)443-4022   Fr: 888-443-2400
URL: http://www.delphivideo.com

$95.00. 49 minutes. Part of the Emerging Careers Video Library.

★4483★ *Environmental Occupations: Technical*

Delphi Productions
3160 4th St.
Boulder, CO 80304
Fax: (303)443-4022   Fr: 888-443-2400
URL: http://www.delphivideo.com

$95.00. 48 minutes. Part of the Emerging Careers Video Library.

★4484★ *Foresters and Conservation Scientists*

Evon Publishing
832 N 7th Ave.
Iron River, MI 49935
Ph: (906)265-3190

Audiocassette. 1996. $16.95. 32 minutes. Part of the Careers and Vocational Guidance Series. Provides information about the nature of the work, educational requirements, employment outlook, earnings, and work conditions as well as additional related information.

★4485★ **Minority Women In Science (MWIS)**

Directorate for Education and Human
 Resources Programs
1200 New York Ave. NW
Washington, DC 20005
Ph: (202)326-7019   Fax: (202)371-9849
E-mail: sassefa@aaas.org

Description: A national network group of the American association for the Advancement of Science (AAAS), Education and Human Resources Directorate. The objectives of this group are: to identify and share information on resources and programs that could help in mentoring young women and minorities interested in science and engineering careers, and to strengthen communication among women and minorities in science and education.

★4486★ **National Association of Conservation Districts (NACD)**

509 Capitol Ct. NE
Washington, DC 20002-4946
Ph: (202)547-6223   Fax: (202)547-6450
E-mail: washington@nacdnet.org
URL: http://www.nacdnet.org

Description: Soil and water conservation districts organized by the citizens of watersheds, counties, or communities under provisions of state laws. Directs and coordinates, through local self-government efforts, the conservation and development of soil, water, and related natural resources. Districts include over 90% of the nation's privately owned land. Conducts educational programs and children's services.

★4487★ *Scientific, Engineering, and Technical Services*

Cambridge Educational
2572 Brunswick Ave.
Lawrenceville, NJ 08648-4128
Fax: 800-FAX-ON-US   Fr: 800-468-4227
URL: http://www.cambridgeeducational.com

$89.95. 2002. 18 minutes. Part of the Career Cluster Series.

★4488★ *Scientific Occupations*

Delphi Productions
3160 4th St.
Boulder, CO 80304
Fax: (303)443-4022   Fr: 888-443-2400
URL: http://www.delphivideo.com

$95.00. 60 minutes. Part of the Careers for the 21st Century Video Library.

★4489★ **Society of American Foresters (SAF)**

5400 Grosvenor Ln.
Bethesda, MD 20814-2198
Ph: (301)897-8720   Fax: (301)897-3690
E-mail: safweb@safnet.org
URL: http://www.safnet.org

Description: National scientific and educational organization representing forestry in the United States. Aims to advance the science, education, technology, and practice of forestry. Supports 28 subject-oriented working groups.

★4490★ Student Conservation Association (SCA)

PO Box 550
Charlestown, NH 03603
Ph: (603)543-1700   Fax: (603)543-1828
E-mail: ask-us@theSCA.org
URL: http://www.theSCA.org

Description: Works to build the next generation of conservation leaders and inspire lifelong stewardship of the environment and communities by engaging young people in hands-on service to the land. Provides conservation service opportunities, outdoor education and leadership development for young people. Offers college and graduate students, as well as older adults expense-paid conservation internships. These positions include wildlife research, wilderness patrols and interpretive opportunities and provide participants with valuable hands-on career experience. Also places 15-19 year old high school students in four-week volunteer conservation crews in national parks forests and refuges across the country each summer to accomplish a range of trail building and habitat conservation projects. Offers year-round diversity conservation programs for young women and young persons of color in leading metropolitan areas of U.S.

Fuel Cell Engineers

SOURCES OF HELP-WANTED ADS

★4491★ Advanced Fuel Cell Technology

Seven Mountains Scientific Inc.
PO Box 650
Boalsburg, PA 16827

Monthly. Covers research on fuel cell technology and the people and companies involved with the development of such technology.

★4492★ Energy User News

BNP Media, Inc.
2401 W Big Beaver Rd., Ste. 700
Troy, MI 48084
Ph: (248)362-3700   Fax: (248)362-0317
URL: http://www.energyusernews.com

Monthly. Magazine exreporting on the energy management market as it relates to commercial, industrial, and institutional facilites.

★4493★ Engineering Times

National Society of Professional Engineers
1420 King St.
Alexandria, VA 22314
Ph: (703)684-2875   Fax: (703)836-4875
E-mail: et@nspe.org
URL: http://http//:www.nspc.org/1et.asp

$30.00/year for individuals; $48.00/year for out of country. Magazine (tabloid) covering professional, legislative, and techology issues for an engineering audience.

★4494★ ENR: Engineering News-Record

McGraw-Hill Companies
1221 Avenue of the Americas
New York, NY 10020
Ph: (212)512-2000
URL: http://www.enr.com

Weekly. $74.00/year; $5.00 for single issue.

Magazine focusing on engineering and construction.

★4495★ Fuel Cell Industry Report

Alexander Communications Group
28 West 25th St., 8th Fl.
New York, NY 10010

Information for manufacturers, integrators, suppliers, and end users.

★4496★ Fuel Cell Magazine

Webcom Communications Corp.
7355 E. Orchard Road, Ste. 100
Greenwood Village, CO 80111
Fr: 800-803-9488

Trade journal.

★4497★ High Technology Careers Magazine

HTC
4701 Patrick Henry Dr., No. 1901
Santa Clara, CA 95054-1847
Ph: (408)970-8800   Fax: (408)567-0242
URL: http://www.hightechcareers.com

Bimonthly. $29.00/year; $35.00/year for Canada; $85.00/year for out of country. Magazine (tabloid) containing employment opportunity information for the engineering and technical community.

★4498★ National Engineer

National Association of Power Engineers
One Springfield St.
Chicopee, MA 01013-2624
Ph: (413)592-6273   Fax: (413)592-1998

Bimonthly. $25.00/year for individuals; $3.00 for single issue.

★4499★ National Fuel Cell Research Center Journal

National Fuel Cell Research Center
University of California Irvine
221 Engineering Lab Facility, Bldg. 323
Irvine, CA 92697

Quarterly. $60/year. Provides a forum for the discussion of information related to high

efficiency, environmentally sensitive energy and power technologies.

★4500★ NSBE Magazine

NSBE Publications
1454 Duke St.
Alexandria, VA 22314
Ph: (703)549-2207   Fax: (703)683-5312

$10.00/year for individuals; $2.00 for single issue. Journal providing information on engineering careers, self-development, and cultural issues for recent graduates with technical majors.

★4501★ SWE

Society of Women Engineers
230 E Ohio St., No. 400
2135 Lamberton Rd.
Chicago, IL 60611-3265
Ph: (312)596-5223   Fax: (312)596-5252
E-mail: hq@swe.org
URL: http://www.swe.org

Bimonthly. $30.00/year for nonmembers. Magazine for engineering students and for women and men working in the engineering and technology fields. Covers career guidance, continuing development and topical issues.

★4502★ WEPANEWS

Women in Engineering Programs & Advocates Network
Castle Point on the Hudson
Hoboken, NJ 07030
Ph: (201)216-5245   Fax: (201)216-5175
URL: http://www.wepan.org/newsletter.html

Description: Two issues/year. Seeks to provide greater access for women to careers in engineering. Includes news of graduate, undergraduate, freshmen, pre-college, and re-entry engineering programs for women. Recurring features include job listings, faculty, grant, and conference news, international engineering program news, action group news, notices of publications available, and a column titled Kudos.

EMPLOYER DIRECTORIES AND NETWORKING LISTS

★4503★ Careers in Focus: Engineering

Ferguson Publishing Co.
200 W Jackson Blvd.
Chicago, IL 60606
Ph: (312)692-0109

2nd edition, 2002. $22.95. Publication includes: List of resources to consult for more information. Principal content of publication is job descriptions, advancement opportunities, educational requirements, employment outlook, salary information, and working conditions for careers in the field of engineering. Indexes: Alphabetical.

HANDBOOKS AND MANUALS

★4504★ The Best Resumes for Scientists and Engineers

John Wiley & Sons Inc.
1 Wiley Dr.
Somerset, NJ 08873
Ph: (732)469-4400   Fr: 800-225-5945

Adele Lewis and David J. Moore. Second edition, 1993. $37.50; $19.95 (paper). 224 pages. Presents an extensive collection of scientific and engineering resumes, highlighting the important differences between these and resumes written for other occupations.

★4505★ Great Jobs for Engineering Majors

McGraw-Hill Professional
McGraw-Hill Higher Education
2 Penn Plaza
New York, NY 10121
Ph: (212)904-2000   Fr: 800-722-4726
E-mail: ntcpub@tribune.com

Geraldine O. Garner. Second edition, 2002. $14.95. 256 pages. Covers all the career options open to students majoring in engineering.

★4506★ Keys to Engineering Success

Prentice Hall PTR
One Lake St.
Upper Saddle River, NJ 07458
Ph: (201)236-7000

Jill S. Tietjen, Kristy A. Schloss, Carol Carter, Joyce Bishop, and Sarah Lyman. 2000. $32.00 (paper).

★4507★ Majoring in Engineering: How to Get from Your Freshman Year to Your First Job

Farrar, Straus & Giroux, Inc.
19 Union Sq., W
New York, NY 10003
Ph: (212)741-6900   Fax: (212)633-9385
Fr: 888-330-8477

John Garcia and Carol Carter, editors. 2000. $20.00; $10.00 (paper). 134 pages.

★4508★ The New Engineer's Guide to Career Growth & Professional Awareness

Institute of Electrical & Electronics Engineers Inc.
445 Hoes Ln.
PO Box 1331
Piscataway, NJ 08855-1331
Ph: (732)562-3967   Fax: (732)981-9334
Fr: 800-678-4333

Irving J. Gabelman, editor. 1996. $39.95 (paper). 275 pages.

★4509★ Resumes for Engineering Careers

McGraw-Hill Trade
2 Penn Plaza
New York, NY 10121
Ph: (212)904-2000   Fr: 800-722-4726
E-mail: ntcpub@tribune.com

2000. $10.95 (paper). 456 pages. Contains sample resumes and cover letters applicable to any engineering field.

EMPLOYMENT AGENCIES AND SEARCH FIRMS

★4510★ The Corban Group

5050 Research Ct., Ste. 600
Suwanee, GA 30024
Ph: (678)638-6000

Executive search firm.

★4511★ High Employee Services Ltd.

525 Greenfield Rd., 2nd Fl.
Lancaster, PA 17601
Ph: (717)396-7701   Fax: (717)396-7779

Personnel consultants serving all industries including business and finance, engineering, sales and marketing, and focusing on manufacturing, industrial, and transportation operations. Conducts full time, contract staffing, and temporary (clerical and skilled) placements. Serves private industries as well as government agencies.

★4512★ Techtronix Technical Search

PO Box 17713
Milwaukee, WI 53217-0173
Ph: (414)466-3100   Fax: (414)466-3598

Firm specializes in recruiting executives for the engineering, information systems, manufacturing, marketing, finance, and human resources industries.

★4513★ TRC Staffing Services Inc.

2110 15 Mile Rd., Ste. B
Sterling Heights, MI 48310
Ph: (586)939-3210   Fax: (586)978-0572

A full-service executive search company with permanent placements encompassing engineering, industrial sales, financial and computer science positions. Screen, interview, and verify past employment for all candidates prior to referral. Also assist personnel staffs in the attainment of their EEO/AAP goals with the placement of talented individuals in positions which are underutilized with minorities and/or women. In addition, firm has a clerical temporary service division, TRC Temporary Service; and an employment agency, TRC Staffing Services.

★4514★ Winters Technical Staffing Services

2025 Sheppard Ave. E, Ste. 4110
Willowdale, ON, Canada M2T 1V7
Ph: (416)495-7422   Fax: (416)495-8479

Technical staffing service for permanent and contract positions in all facets of engineering. Serves government agencies, consulting engineers, and all areas of manufacturing in Canada and northeast U.S.

ONLINE JOB SOURCES AND SERVICES

★4515★ Fuel Cell Information Resource

URL: http://www.fuelcells.org

Description: Provides news, educational resources, and job postings.

★4516★ Fuel Cell Online

URL: http://www.fuelcellonline.com

Description: Industry products, events, and employment links.

TRADESHOWS

★4517★ American Society for Engineering Education Annual Conference and Exposition

American Society for Engineering Education
1818 N St., Ste. 600
Washington, DC 20036
Ph: (202)331-3500   Fax: (202)265-8504
URL: http://www.asee.org

Annual. **Primary Exhibits:** Publications, engineering supplies and equipment, computers, software, and research companies all products and services related to engineering education. **Dates and Locations:** 2005 Jun 12-15; Portland, OR • 2006 Jun 18-21; Chicago, IL • 2007 Jun 24-27; Honolulu, HI.

OTHER SOURCES

★4518★ American Association of Blacks in Energy (AABE)

927 15th St. NW, Ste. 200
Washington, DC 20005
Ph: (202)371-9530   Fax: (202)371-9218
Fr: 800-466-0204
E-mail: aabe@aabe.org
URL: http://www.aabe.org

Description: Blacks in energy-related professions, including engineers, scientists, consultants, academicians, and entrepreneurs; government officials and public policymakers; interested students. Represents blacks and other minorities in matters involving energy use and research, the formulation of energy policy, the ownership of energy resources, and the development of energy technologies. Seeks to increase the knowledge, understanding, and awareness of the minority community in energy issues by serving as an energy information source for policymakers, recommending blacks and other minorities to appropriate energy officials and executives, encouraging students to pursue professional careers in the energy industry, and advocating the participation of blacks and other minorities in energy programs and policymaking activities. Updates members on key legislation and regulations being developed by the Department of Energy, the Department of Interior, the Department of Commerce, the Small Business Administration, and other federal and state agencies. Offers information on current job openings

★4519★ American Association of Engineering Societies (AAES)

1828 L St. NW, No. 906
Washington, DC 20036
Ph: (202)296-2237   Fax: (202)296-1151
Fr: 888-400-2237
E-mail: tprice@aaes.org
URL: http://www.aaes.org
Description: Coordinates the efforts of the

member societies in the provision of reliable and objective information to the general public concerning issues which affect the engineering profession and the field of engineering as a whole; to collect, analyze, document, and disseminate data which will inform the general public of the relationship between engineering and the national welfare; to provide a forum for the engineering societies to exchange and discuss their views on matters of common interest; and to represent the U.S. engineering community aborad through representation in WFEO and UPADI.

★4520★ American Engineering Association (AEA)

PO Box 820473
Fort Worth, TX 76182-0473
Ph: (972)264-6248
E-mail: info@aea.org
URL: http://www.aea.org

Description: Engineers and engineering professionals. Works to advance the engineering profession and U.S. engineering capabilities. Issues of concern include age discrimination, immigration laws, trade agreements, loss of U.S. manufacturing and engineering capability, and recruitment of foreign students. Testifies before Congress.

★4521★ American Hydrogen Association

1739 W. 7th Ave.
Mesa, AZ 85202
Ph: (480)827-7915
URL: http://www.clean-air.org

Description: Seeks to stimulate interest and help establish the renewable hydrogen energy economy.

★4522★ American Institute of Engineers (AIE)

4630 Appian Way, Ste. 206
El Sobrante, CA 94803-1875
Ph: (510)758-6240   Fax: (510)758-6240
E-mail: aie@members-aie.org
URL: http://www.members-aie.org

Description: Professional Association for engineers, scientists, and mathematicians. Multi-disciplined, non-technical Association whose mission statement is to improve the stature and image of engineers, scientists, and mathematicians. Provides endorsements, awards and opportunities for small business start-ups within the AIE Councils. Sponsors "LA Engineer," a comedy-drama television series; produces annual "Academy Hall of Fame".

★4523★ Association of Energy Engineers

4025 Pleasantdale Rd., Ste. 420
Atlanta, GA 30340
Ph: (770)447-5083   Fax: (770)446-3969
URL: http://www.aeecenter.org

Description: Provides information on energy efficiency, utility deregulation, facility management, plant engineering, and envi-

ronmental compliance. Offers resources such as seminars, tradeshows, and certification programs.

★4524★ California Fuel Cell Partnership

3300 Industrial Blvd., Ste. 1000
West Sacramento, CA 95691
Ph: (916)371-2870   Fax: (916)375-2008
URL: http://www.fuelcellpartnership.org

Description: Auto manufacturers, energy companies, fuel cell technology companies, and government agencies striving to advance new vehicle technology.

★4525★ *Engineering Occupations*

Delphi Productions
3160 4th St.
Boulder, CO 80304
Fax: (303)443-4022   Fr: 888-443-2400
URL: http://www.delphivideo.com

$95.00. 50 minutes. Part of the Careers for the 21st Century Video Library.

★4526★ Engineering Society of Detroit (ESD)

26100 American Dr., Ste. 500
Southfield, MI 48034-6184
Ph: (248)355-2910   Fax: (248)355-1492
E-mail: esd@esd.org
URL: http://esd.org

Description: Engineers from all disciplines; scientists and technologists. Conducts technical programs and engineering refresher courses; sponsors conferences and expositions. Maintains speakers' bureau; offers placement services. Although based in Detroit, MI, society membership is international.

★4527★ Engineering Workforce Commission (EWC)

1828 L St. NW, Ste. 906
Washington, DC 20036-5110
Ph: (202)296-2237   Fax: (202)296-1151
Fr: 888-400-AAES
E-mail: mdoster@aaes.org
URL: http://www.ewc-online.org

Description: Commissioners appointed by member societies of the American Association of Engineering Societies to engage in studies and analyses of the supply, demand, use, and remuneration of engineering and technical personnel. Provides representation to government groups dealing with professional manpower policy; consults with industry. Gathers and disseminates information on the engineering profession. Conducts surveys of engineering school enrollments, degrees, and salaries; monitors federal labor statistics.

★4528★ Fuel Cell Power Association

PO Box 7574
Arlington, VA 22207
Description: Promotes the interests of the fuel cell industry by educating the govern-

ment and the public on the benefits of fuel power.

★4529★ International Federation of Professional and Technical Engineers (IFPTE)

8630 Fenton St., No. 400
Silver Spring, MD 20910-3803
Ph: (301)565-9016   Fax: (301)565-0018
URL: http://www.ifpte.org

Description: Labor union representing engineers, scientists, architects, technicians.

★4530★ Korean Scientists and Engineers Association in America (KSEA)

1952 Gallows Rd., Ste. 300
Vienna, VA 22182
Ph: (703)748-1221   Fax: (703)748-1331
E-mail: sejong@ksea.org
URL: http://www.ksea.org

Description: Scientists and engineers holding single or advanced degrees. Goals are to: promote friendship and mutuality among Korean and American scientists and engineers; contribute to Korea's scientific, technological, industrial, and economic developments; strengthen the scientific, technological, and cultural bonds between Korea and the U.S. Sponsors symposium. Maintains speakers' bureau, placement service, and biographical archives. Compiles statistics. Maintains 100 volume library of scientific handbooks and yearbooks in Korean.

★4531★ National Action Council for Minorities in Engineering (NACME)

Empire State Bldg., Ste. 2212
350 Fifth Ave.
New York, NY 10118-2299
Ph: (212)279-2626   Fax: (212)629-5178
E-mail: webmaster@nacme.org
URL: http://www.nacme.org/

Description: Leads the national effort to increase access to careers in engineering and other science-based disciplines. Supported by the nation's leading technology-intensive companies, NACME conducts research and public policy analysis, develops and operates national demonstration programs at precollege and university levels, and disseminates information through publications, conferences, and electronic media. NACME is also the nation's largest privately funded source of scholarships for minority students in engineering.

★4532★ National Society of Professional Engineers (NSPE)

1420 King St.
Alexandria, VA 22314
Ph: (703)684-2800   Fax: (703)836-4875
Fr: 888-285-6773
E-mail: custserv@nspe.org
URL: http://www.nspe.org

Description: Professional engineers and engineers-in-training in all fields registered in accordance with the laws of states or territories of the U.S. or provinces of Canada; qualified graduate engineers, student members, and registered land surveyors. Is concerned with social, professional, ethical, and economic considerations of engineering as a profession; encompasses programs in public relations, employment practices, ethical considerations, education, and career guidance. Monitors legislative and regulatory actions of interest to the engineering profession.

★4533★ Scientific, Engineering, and Technical Services

Cambridge Educational
2572 Brunswick Ave.
Lawrenceville, NJ 08648-4128
Fax: 800-FAX-ON-US   Fr: 800-468-4227
URL: http://www.cambridgeeducational.com

$89.95. 2002. 18 minutes. Part of the Career Cluster Series.

★4534★ Society of Engineering Science (SES)

College of Engineering
Virginia Tech
Blacksburg, VA 24061
Ph: (540)231-9171   Fax: (540)231-3031
E-mail: henneke@vt.edu
URL: http://www.sesinc.org

Members: Individuals with at least a baccalaureate degree who are engaged in any aspect of engineering science or in other pursuits that contribute to the advancement of engineering science. Purpose: Works to foster and promote the interchange of ideas and information among the various fields of engineering science and among engineering science and the fields of theoretical and applied physics, chemistry, and mathematics. Is dedicated to the advancement of interdisciplinary research and to the establishment of a bridge between science and engineering.

★4535★ Society of Hispanic Professional Engineers (SHPE)

5400 E Olympic Blvd., Ste. 210
Los Angeles, CA 90022
Ph: (323)725-3970   Fax: (323)725-0316
E-mail: shpenational@shpe.org
URL: http://www.shpe.org

Description: Engineers, student engineers, and scientists seeking to increase the number of Hispanic engineers by providing motivation and support to students. Sponsors competitions and educational programs. Maintains placement service and speakers' bureau; compiles statistics.

★4536★ Society of Women Engineers (SWE)

230 E Ohio St., No. 400
Chicago, IL 60611-3265
Ph: (312)596-5223   Fax: (312)596-5252
E-mail: hq@swe.org
URL: http://www.swe.org

Description: Educational and service organization representing both students and professional women in engineering and technical fields.

★4537★ United Engineering Foundation (UEF)

3 Park Ave., 27th Fl.
New York, NY 10016-5902
Ph: (212)591-7829   Fax: (212)591-7441
E-mail: engfnd@aol.com
URL: http://www.engfnd.org

Description: Federation of 5 major national engineering societies: American Institute of Chemical Engineers; American Institute of Mining, Metallurgical and Petroleum Engineers; American Society of Civil Engineers; American Society of Mechanical Engineers; Institute of Electrical and Electronics Engineers. Supports research in engineering and advances the engineering arts and sciences through its conference program.

★4538★ US Fuel Cell Council

1625 K Street
Washington, DC 20006

Description: Dedicated to fostering the commercialization of fuel cells in the United States. Provides technical advice, collects information and issues reports on the industry, and raises public awareness of fuel cells and their potential.

Fund Raisers

SOURCES OF HELP-WANTED ADS

★4539★ *The Chronicle of Philanthropy*
The Chronicle of Philanthropy
1255 23rd St. NW, Ste. 700
Washington, DC 20037
Ph: (202)466-1200   Fax: (202)466-2078
E-mail: editor@philanthropy.com
URL: http://philanthropy.com

Biweekly. $69.50/year for individuals. Magazine covering fundraising, philanthropy, and non-profit organizations. Includes information on tax rulings, new grants, and statistics, reports on grant makers, and profiles of foundations.

★4540★ *Community Radio News*
National Federation of Community
  Broadcasters (NFCB)
Fort Mason Ctr., Bldg. D
San Francisco, CA 94123
Ph: (415)771-1160   Fax: (415)771-1160

Description: Monthly. Serves as a medium of communication for independent, community-licensed radio stations. Contains brief articles and news items on such topics as public broadcasting and programming, legislative developments, activities of the Federal Communications Commission, and local stations. Recurring features include notices of grants and awards, job openings, and a calendar of events/conferences for noncommercial broadcasters.

★4541★ *DM News*
DM News
100 6th Ave.of the Americas
New York, NY 10013
Ph: (212)925-7300   Fax: (212)925-8752
E-mail: inquiry@dmnews.com
URL: http://www.dmnews.com

Weekly. $75.00/year. Tabloid newspaper for publishers, fund raisers, financial marketers, catalogers, package goods advertisers and their agencies, and other marketers who use direct mail, mail order advertising, catalogs, or other direct response media to sell their products or services.

★4542★ *The Nonprofit Times*
NPT Publishing Group Inc.
120 Littleton Rd., Ste. 120
Parsippany, NJ 07054-1803
Ph: (973)394-1800   Fax: (973)734-1771
E-mail: ednchief@nptimes.com
URL: http://www.nptimes.com

$8.95 for single issue; $59.00/year. Trade journal serving nonprofit organizations.

EMPLOYER DIRECTORIES AND NETWORKING LISTS

★4543★ *American Association of Fund-Raising Counsel Membership Directory*
American Association of Fund-Raising
  Counsel Inc.
10293 N Meridian St., Ste. 175
Indianapolis, IN 46290

Annual. Covers member fund-raising consulting firms. Entries include: Company name, address, phone, fax, geographical area served, types of clients, description of services. Arrangement: Alphabetical.

★4544★ *Complete Guide to Public Employment*
Impact Publications
9104 Manassas Dr., Ste. N
Manassas Park, VA 20111-5211
Ph: (703)361-7300   Fax: (703)335-9486

Triennial, latest edition 1994. $34.95 for cloth copy; $19.95 for paper copy. Publication includes: List of federal, state, and local government agencies and departments, trade and professional associations, contracting and consulting firms, nonprofit organizations, foundations, research organizations, political support groups, and other organizations offering public service career opportunities. Entries include: Organization name, address, phone, name and title of contact. Complete title is "Complete Guide to Public Employment: Opportunities and Strategies with Federal, State, and Local Government; Trade and Professional Associations; Contracting and and Consulting Firms; Foundations; Research Organizations; and Political Support Groups." Arrangement: Classified by type of service. Indexes: Subject.

★4545★ *Fund Raising Counselors & Organizations Directory*
infoUSA Inc.
5711 S 86th Cir.
Omaha, NE 68127-0347
Ph: (402)930-3500   Fax: (402)331-0176
Fr: 800-555-6124
URL: http://www.abii.com

Updated continuously; printed on request. Number of listings: 3,796. Covers name, address, phone (including area code), size of advertisement, year first in "Yellow Pages," name of owner or manager, number of employees. Compiled from telephone company "Yellow Pages," nationwide. Arrangement: Geographical.

★4546★ *National Directory of Nonprofit Organizations*
The Taft Group
27500 Drake Rd.
Farmington Hills, MI 48331-3535
Ph: (248)699-4253   Fax: (248)699-8052
Fr: 800-877-GALE
E-mail: businessproducts@gale.com
URL: http://www.gale.com

Annual. $650.00. Covers over 265,000 nonprofit organizations; volume 1 covers organizations with annual incomes of over $100,000; volume 2 covers organizations with incomes between $25,000 and $99,999. Entries include: Organization name, address, phone, annual income, IRS filing status, employer identification number, tax deductible status, activity description. Arrangement: Alphabetical. Indexes: Area of activity, geographical.

★4547★ NSFRE Directory

National Society of Fund Raising
  Executives
1101 King St., Ste. 700
Alexandria, VA 22314
Ph: (703)684-0410   Fax: (703)684-0540
Fr: 800-666-FUND

Annual, January. Database covers: Approximately 18,000 fund raisers and development officers for private and public not-for-profit organizations. Entries include: Name, organization name, address, phone, fax, e-mail. Database is housed in the members only section of our web site. Arrangement: Classified by chapter, then alphabetical.

HANDBOOKS AND MANUALS

★4548★ Careers for Good Samaritans and Other Humanitarian Types

McGraw-Hill Trade
2 Penn Plaza
New York, NY 10121
Ph: (212)904-2000   Fr: 800-722-4726
E-mail: ntcpub@tribune.com

Marjorie Eberts and Margaret Gisler. Second edition, 1998. $9.95 (paper). 274 pages. Contains hundreds of ideas for turning good work into paid work. Inventories opportunities in service organizations like the Red Cross, Goodwill, and the Salvation Army; religious groups, VISTA, the Peace Corps, and UNICEF; and agencies at all levels of the government. Part of Careers for You series.

★4549★ Fund Raisers: Their Careers, Stories, Concerns, and Accomplishments

Jossey-Bass Inc. Publishers
350 Sansome St., 5th Fl.
San Francisco, CA 94104-1342
Ph: (415)433-1740   Fax: (415)433-0499
Fr: 800-956-7739

Margaret A. Duronio and Eugene R. Temple. 1996. $37.00. 221 pages. Part of the Nonprofit Sector Series. Helps professional fund raisers examine their work environment and make smarter choices about their careers. Based on results from a three-year national study that included a survey of 1,700 professional fund raisers and 82 personal interviews. Reveals compensation practices, factors involved in entering and advancing in the field, the status of women and minorities in fund raising, and reasons for turnover. Other areas discussed include accountability, ethical practice, and licensing and regulation.

★4550★ Fund-Raising Fundamentals: A Guide to Annual Giving for Professionals and Volunteers

John Wiley & Sons Inc.
1 Wiley Dr.
Somerset, NJ 08873
Ph: (732)469-4400   Fr: 800-225-5945

James M. Greenfield. 1994. $31.95 (paper). 432 pages.

★4551★ Fund Raising 101: How to Raise Money for Charities

John Wiley & Sons Inc.
1 Wiley Dr.
Somerset, NJ 08873
Ph: (732)469-4400   Fr: 800-225-5945

William L. Doyle. 1993. $34.50. 237 pages.

★4552★ Fundraising As a Profession: Advancements and Challenges in the Field

John Wiley & Sons, Inc.
111 River St.
Hoboken, NJ 07030
Ph: (201)748-6000   Fax: (201)748-6088
Fr: 800-255-5945

PF Staff. January 2004. $29.00. 104 pages. Part of the J-B PF Single Issue Philanthropic Fundraising Series.

★4553★ Great Jobs for Liberal Arts Majors

McGraw-Hill Professional
2 Penn Plaza
New York, NY 10121
Ph: (212)904-2000   Fr: 800-722-4726
E-mail: ntcpub@tribune.com

Blythe Camenson. Second edition, 2001. $14.95 (paper). 256 pages.

★4554★ How to Successfully Start a Grassroots Non-Profit Organization

Achievement U.S.A. Corporation
P.O. Box 9328
Washington, DC 20005
Ph: (202)319-9057   Fr: 800-891-3296

Darryl Webster. 2001. $20.00 The author provides a unique grassroots perspective on the pros & cons in getting started in the non-profit world. This book was written to save its reader's money, time & energy looking for information to help them start a non-profit organization. Some of the subjects covered in the book are: incorporating, obtaining tax exemption, garnering community support, marketing, proposal writing for grants, fundraising, getting publicity, giving interviews, & also comments on the significance & impact that grass-roots' citizens are having in the non-profit sector. Students, teachers, professors, community organizers, & citizens of all persuasions will greatly benefit from this book. Webster graduated from George Washington University (1987) & Catholic University of America (MSW/PA). A grass-roots community organizer who started a non-profit organization that won him numerous awards & honors, including: 1991 National Achievement Against the Odds Award; 1989 USA Today News: Hero Award; 1989 Washingtonian of the Year; Ebony Magazine: Future Leader of America. Highly recommended for both academic & public libraries. Volume discounts available from the publisher.

★4555★ Jobs & Careers with Nonprofit Organizations

Impact Publications
9104 Manassas Dr., Ste. N
Manassas Park, VA 20111-5211
Ph: (703)361-7300   Fax: (703)335-9486

Ronald L. Krannich and Caryl R. Krannich. Second edition, 1998. $17.95 (paper). 450 pages. Out of print.

★4556★ Non-Profits and Education Job Finder

Planning Communications
7215 Oak Ave.
River Forest, IL 60305-1935
Ph: (708)366-5200   Fax: (708)366-5280
Fr: 888-366-5200
URL: http://jobfindersonline.com

Daniel Lauber. 1997. $32.95; $16.95 (paper). 336 pages. Covers 1600 sources. Discusses how to use sources of non-profit sector job vacancies in a number of specialties and state-by-state, including job-matching services, job hotlines, specialty periodicals with job ads, salary surveys, and directories. Covers a variety of fields from education to religion. Includes chapters on resume and cover letter preparation and interviewing.

★4557★ Opportunities in Nonprofit Organizations

McGraw-Hill Trade
2 Penn Plaza
New York, NY 10121
Ph: (212)904-2000   Fr: 800-722-4726

Adrian Paradis. 1994. $14.95; $11.95 (paper). 160 pages. Covers a range of career opportunities with nonprofit organizations.

OTHER SOURCES

★4558★ Association of Professional Researchers for Advancement (APRA)

40 Shumsn Blvd., Ste. 325
Naperville, IL 60563
Ph: (630)717-8160   Fax: (630)717-8354
E-mail: info@aprahome.org

Description: Individuals involved in educational, medical, cultural, and religious organizations; fundraising consultants. Facilitates education and dissemination of information about prospect research; encourages professional development and cooperative relationships among members. (Prospect research is aimed at securing gifts, grants, and charitable donations for nonprofit organizations.)

★4559★ **Society for Nonprofit Organizations (SNPO)**
5820 Canton Rd., No. 165
Canton, MI 48187-2683
Ph: (734)451-3582   Fax: (734)451-5935

E-mail: info@snpo.org
URL: http://www.snpo.org

Description: Dedicated to bringing together those who serve in the nonprofit world in order to build a strong network of professionals throughout the country; provides a forum for the exchange of information, knowledge, and ideas on strengthening and increasing productivity within nonprofit organizations and among their leaders. Mission is accomplished through the publication of Nonprofit World magazine, educational programs offered by the Learning Institute, and other communications with its members.

Funeral Directors

SOURCES OF HELP-WANTED ADS

★4560★ AFDS Today

Associated Funeral Directors International
PO Box 5788
Kingsport, TN 37663-0788
Ph: (423)392-1985   Fax: (423)392-1179
Fr: 800-346-7151

Bimonthly. $29.95/year. Trade magazine covering issues for funeral directors.

★4561★ Cemetery & Funeral Business and Legal Guide

CB Legal Publishing Corp.
PO Box 1327
Northbrook, IL 60065-1327
Ph: (847)509-0501   Fax: (847)509-1027

Description: Ten issues/year. Discusses business and legal problems pertinent to the funeral service and cemetary industry. Covers such topics as antitrust issues, tax matters, consumer trade practice, government regulations, environmental concerns, and cremations.

★4562★ Funeral Monitor

Abbott & Hast Publications
761 Lighthouse Ave., Ste. A
Monterey, CA 93940-1033
Ph: (831)657-9403   Fax: (831)657-9137
Fr: 800-453-1199
E-mail: info@funeralmonitor.com
URL: http://www.funeralmonitor.com

Description: Weekly. Provides information on the funeral industry.

★4563★ Funeral Service 'Insider'

United Communications Group
11300 Rockville Pke., Ste. 1100
Rockville, MD 20852
Ph: (301)816-8950   Fax: (301)816-8945
Fr: 800-929-4824
E-mail: layers@ucg.com

Description: Forty-eight issues/year. Covers the latest trends in funeral service educa-

tion, legislation, franchising, marketing, and consumer purchasing. Recurring features include editorials, news of research, letters to the editor, and a calendar of events.

★4564★ NFDA Bulletin

National Funeral Directors Association
13625 Bishop's Dr.
Brookfield, WI 53005
Ph: (262)789-1880   Fax: (262)789-6977
URL: http://www.nfda.org

Description: Monthly. Covers association activities and funeral business management topics. Reports on association news, government regulation, public relations issues, and local developments.

HANDBOOKS AND MANUALS

★4565★ Choosing a Career in Mortuary Science & the Funeral Industry

Rosen Publishing Group, Inc.
29 E. 21st St.
New York, NY 10010
Ph: (212)777-3017   Fax: (212)777-0277
Fr: 800-237-9932

Stair, Nancy. 2002. 64 pages.

★4566★ Funeral Directing Investigator

National Learning Corporation
212 Michael Dr.
Syosset, NY 11791
Ph: (516)921-8888   Fax: (516)921-8743
Fr: 800-645-6337

Rudman, Jack. 1994. $34.95 (Trade paper).

★4567★ Opportunities in Funeral Services Careers

McGraw-Hill Trade
2 Penn Plaza
New York, NY 10121
Ph: (212)904-2000

Sacks, Terence J. 1997. $11.95 (Trade paper). 205 pages.

ONLINE JOB SOURCES AND SERVICES

★4568★ FuneralNet.com

URL: http://www.funeralnet.com

Description: General mortuary science information site contains Funeral Careers section with information on continuing education and classifieds section with postings for internship and employment opportunities.

★4569★ National Funeral Directors Association

E-mail: nfda@nfda.org
URL: http://www.nfda.org

Description: Contains employment classifieds and career resources such as licensing and educational requirements, continuing education credit opportunities and more for those interested in finding a position as a funeral director.

TRADESHOWS

★4570★ Monument Builders of North America Conference

Monument Builders of North America
3158 Des Plaines Ave., Ste. 224
Des Plaines, IL 60018
Ph: (708)803-8800   Fax: (708)803-8823
Fr: 800-233-4472

Annual. Primary Exhibits: Equipment, supplies, and services for modern and religious memorial designs.

★4571★ **National Funeral Directors Association Annual Convention & Expo**

National Funeral Directors Association
13625 Bishop's Dr.
Brookfield, WI 53005-6607
Ph: (262)789-1880   Fax: (262)789-6977
Fr: 800-228-6332
E-mail: nfda@nfda.org
URL: http://www.nfda.org

Annual. **Primary Exhibits:** Equipment, supplies, and services for funeral directors and morticians.

★4572★ **New Jersey State Funeral Directors Association Convention**

New Jersey State Funeral Directors Association
PO Box L
Manasquan, NJ 08736
Ph: (732)974-9444   Fax: (732)974-8144

Annual. **Primary Exhibits:** Funeral industry equipment, supplies, and services.

★4573★ **South Dakota Funeral Directors Association Annual Convention**

South Dakota Funeral Directors Association
106 W. Capitol Ave.
PO Box 1037
Pierre, SD 57501
Ph: (605)224-1353   Fax: (605)224-7426

Annual. **Primary Exhibits:** Caskets, chemical supplies, publications, clothing, coaches, accounting services, computer services, vaults, funeral vehicles, and cemetery monument dealers. **Dates and Locations:** 2005 May 09-10; Sioux Falls, SD; Ramkota Hotel and Convention Center • 2006 May 15-16; Sioux Falls, SD; Ramkota Hotel and Convention Center.

★4574★ **Texas Funeral Directors Association Convention**

Texas Funeral Directors Association
1513 S. Interstate 35
Austin, TX 78741
Ph: (512)442-2304   Fax: (512)443-3559

Annual. **Primary Exhibits:** Caskets, chemicals, and funeral home supplies. **Dates and Locations:** 2004 Jun 07-11; Austin, TX • 2005 Jun 13-17; Galveston, TX.

★4575★ **Virginia Funeral Directors Association Convention**

Virginia Funeral Directors Association
5803 Staples Mill Rd.
Richmond, VA 23228-5427
Ph: (804)264-0505   Fax: (804)264-3260

Annual. **Primary Exhibits:** Equipment, supplies, and services for funeral homes.

Gaming Services Workers

SOURCES OF HELP-WANTED ADS

★4576★ Gaming Morning Report

Delaware Gaming Investments
PO Box 1676
Dover, DE 19903
Fr: (866)683-4357

Daily. News, research, and analysis for industry executives.

EMPLOYER DIRECTORIES AND NETWORKING LISTS

★4577★ American Casino Guide

Casino Vacations
PO Box 703
Dania, FL 33004
Ph: (954)989-2766   Fax: (954)966-7048
Fr: 800-741-1596
URL: http://www.americancasinoguide.com

Annual, November. $12.70. Covers more than 600 casino/resorts, riverboat casinos, and Indian casinos in the United States. Entries include: Casino name, address, phone, toll-free number, room rates, dining information, games offered, features, web site addresses. Arrangement: Geographical. Indexes: Name.

★4578★ Career Opportunities in Casinos and Casino Hotels

Facts on File Inc.
132 W 31st St., 17th Fl.
New York, NY 10001
Ph: (212)967-8800   Fax: 800-678-3633
Fr: 800-322-8755
URL: http://www.factsonfile.com

Irregular. $49.50; $44.55 for libraries. Publication includes a directory of casinos and cruise lines, gaming conferences and expos, seminars, workshops, and industry Web sites. Principal content of publication is 100 occupations in 10 employment sections on careers in gaming, administration, management, security, entertainment, hotel management, and food and beverage service in the casino industry.

★4579★ Casinos Directory

infoUSA Inc.
5711 S 86th Cir.
Omaha, NE 68127-0347
Ph: (402)930-3500   Fax: (402)331-0176
Fr: 800-555-6124
URL: http://www.abii.com

Annual. Number of listings: 1,792. Entries include: Name, address, phone, size of advertisement, name of owner or manager, number of employees, year first in "Yellow Pages." Compiled from telephone company "Yellow Pages," nationwide. Arrangement: Geographical.

★4580★ Gambler's Digest

Krause Publications Inc.
700 E. State St.
Iola, WI 54990-0001
Ph: (715)445-2214   Fax: (715)445-4087
Fr: 800-258-0929

$24.95. Lists more than 1,200 gaming destinations in the U.S., including casinos, horse tracks, dog tracks, riverboats and gambling cruises. Offers articles and tips on gaming success as well as a list of gaming-related books, magazines, videos, gaming web sites and other reference sources. Publication includes: Directory details for each destination, including name, address, phone, prices, entertainment, restaurants and hotel accommodations.

★4581★ Gambling in America

ABC-CLIO
130 Cremona Dr.
Santa Barbara, CA 93117
Ph: (805)968-1911   Fax: (805)685-9685
Fr: 800-368-6868
URL: http://www.abc-clio.com

Latest edition 1997. $85.00 for print; $50.00 for e-book. Publication includes: List of agencies and organizations concerned with legalized gambling issues. Entries include: Organization name, address, phone. Principal content of publication is examination of sanctioned gambling and its impact upon economics, crime, government, laws and regulations, public attitudes, and other elements of political debate. Part of "Contemporary World Issues Series." Arrangement: Directory of government and private organizations, selected print resources, internet, film resources.

★4582★ Gaming Products and Services-Buyers Guide Issue

RCM Enterprises Inc.
1161 Wayzata Blvd. E, Ste. 205
Wayzata, MN 55391-1935
Ph: (651)523-0666   Fax: (651)523-0665
Fr: 800-451-9278

Annual, May. $25.00. Publication includes: List of companies providing products and services for the gaming industry; international coverage. Entries include: Company name, address, phone, fax, sales office location, description, geographical area served, product/service. Principal content of publication is information on gaming products. Arrangement: Alphabetical by company name. Indexes: Product/service; trade name.

★4583★ International Gaming Resource Guide

Gem Communications
1771 E. Flamingo Rd., No. 208A
Las Vegas, NV 89119
Fax: (702)794-0799
URL: http://www.igwb.com/resource-guide.htm

Annual. $50.00. Publication includes: Lists of 1,800 organizations concerned with gaming and wagering establishments, including casinos, lotteries, racing commissions, race tracks, jai alai frontons, etc.; and regulatory agencies. Entries include: Listings in the 'Corporate Profiles' section (which expand selected other listings) include name, parent company name, address, mailing address (if different), phone, names and titles of key personnel. Other listings show name, address, and phone only. Arrangement: Alphabetical.

★4584★ Thoroughbred Racing Associations of North America-Directory and Record Book

Thoroughbred Racing Associations
420 Fair Hill Dr., Ste. 1
Elkton, MD 21921-2573
Ph: (410)392-9200   Fax: (410)398-1366

Annual, April. $17.00. Covers features on member thoroughbred racetracks in the United States and Canada, and the Eclipse Awards. Entries include: For member tracks-Corporate name, track name, address, phone, names of officers and staff, track data, equipment data, capacity, prices, and brief history of the track. Listings for non-member tracks do not include descriptive data or history. Arrangement: Alphabetical by track name.

EMPLOYMENT AGENCIES AND SEARCH FIRMS

★4585★ The IMC Group of Cos.

14 E 60th St., Ste. 1200
New York, NY 10022
Ph: (212)838-9535   Fax: (212)486-2964

International executive recruiting and management consulting company providing leading-edge services for the hospitality, leisure, entertainment, gaming, and new media industries throughout the U.S., Europe, Africa, Asia Pacific, and Latin America.

TRADESHOWS

★4586★ IGBE - International Gaming Business Exposition

Ascend Media Gaming Group
1771 E. Flamingo Road, No. 208A
Las Vegas, NV 89119
URL: http://www.gemcommunications.com

Annual. **Primary Exhibits:** Products, equipment, and services for the gaming industry, including casino equipment, game supplies, and accessories.

★4587★ North American Association of State and Provincial Lotteries Conference and Trade Show

North American Association of State and Provincial Lotteries
2775 Bishop Rd., Ste. B
Wickliffe, OH 44092-2683
Ph: (216)241-2310   Fax: (216)241-4350
E-mail: nasplhq@aol.com
URL: http://www.naspl.org

Annual. **Primary Exhibits:** Lottery equipment, supplies, and services. **Dates and Locations:** 2004 Oct 04; Quebec City, QC, Canada; Quebec City Convention Center.

★4588★ World Gaming Congress and Expo

Ascend Media Gaming Group
1771 E. Flamingo Road, No. 208A
Las Vegas, NV 89119
URL: http://www.gemcommunications.com

Primary Exhibits: Casino operations equipment, supplies, and services. Hotel, & resort systems, services. Decorative furnishings and fixtures.

OTHER SOURCES

★4589★ American Gaming Association

555 13th St. NW
Washington, DC 20004
Ph: (202)637-6500
URL: http://www.americangaming.org

Description: Represents the commercial casino entertainment industry by addressing federal legislative and regulatory issues affecting its members and their employees and customers, such as federal taxation, regulatory issues, and travel and tourism matters.

★4590★ Gaming Standards Association (GSA)

39355 California St., Ste. 307
Fremont, CA 94538
Ph: (510)774-4007
E-mail: info@gamingstandards.com
URL: http://www.gamingstandards.com/

Description: Gaming manufacturers, suppliers and operators. Promotes identification, definition, development, and implementation of open standards to facilitate innovation, education and communication for the gaming industry.

★4591★ International Simulation and Gaming Association (ISAGA)

George Washington University
School of Business and Public Management
Monroe Hall
Washington, DC 20052
Ph: (202)994-6918   Fax: (202)994-4930
E-mail: lobuts@gwu.edu
URL: http://isaga.pm.it-chiba.ac.jp

Description: Individuals interested in any facet of simulation and gaming. Maintains resource lists; conducts specialized education; sponsors workshops, symposia, and research activities.

★4592★ North American Gaming Regulators Association

26 E. Exchange St.
St. Paul, MN 55101
Ph: (651)203-7244   Fax: (651)290-8866
E-mail: info@nagra.org

Description: Brings together agencies that regulate gaming activities and provides a forum for the mutual exchange of regulatory information and techniques. Collects and disseminates regulatory and enforcement information, procedures, and experiences from all jurisdictions provided on-going gaming education and training for all members.

General Managers and Top Executives

SOURCES OF HELP-WANTED ADS

★4593★ Association News

Schneider Publishing Co.
11835 W Olympic Blvd., 12th Fl.
Los Angeles, CA 90064
Ph: (310)577-3700   Fax: (310)577-3715
Fr: 877-577-3700

Monthly. $48.00/year for individuals. Magazine containing management and meeting plan information for association executives and meeting planners.

★4594★ CFO

CFO Publishing
253 Summer St.
Boston, MA 02210
Ph: (617)345-9700   Fax: (617)951-9306

Monthly. $19.00/year; $5.00 for single issue. Business magazine for small to mid-sized companies.

★4595★ Commuter/Regional Airline News

PBI Media L.L.C.
1201 Seven Locks Rd., Ste. 300
Potomac, MD 20854
Ph: (301)354-2000   Fax: (301)309-3847
Fr: 800-777-5006
URL: http://www.phillips.com

Description: Weekly. Covers the commuter/regional airline industry, including airline management, marketing, labor, personnel changes, aircraft acquisitions, new products, and the financial and operational environment. Recurring features include interviews, news of research, a calendar of events, reports of meetings, job listings, and notices of publications available.

★4596★ Executive Leadership

National Institute of Business
  Management
1750 Old Meadow Rd., Ste. 302
McLean, VA 22102
Ph: (703)905-8000   Fax: (703)905-8042
Fr: 800-543-2049
URL: http://www.nibm.net/

Description: Monthly. Shows the reader how to become a better leader. Contains information on taking charge in the workplace, enjoying a wider business perspective, leading organizations to more efficiency and greater success, and rising faster in the field of management.

★4597★ Forbes

Forbes Magazine
60 5th Ave.
New York, NY 10011
Ph: (212)620-2200   Fax: (212)206-5174
URL: http://www.forbes.com

Biweekly. $52.00/year; $4.95 for single issue. Magazine reporting on industry, business and finance management.

★4598★ Franchising World

International Franchise Association
1350 New York Ave. NW, Ste. 900
Washington, DC 20005-4709
Ph: (202)628-8000   Fax: (202)628-0812
Fr: 800-543-1038

$18.00/year for individuals; $3.50 for single issue. Trade magazine covering topics of interest to franchise company executives and the business world.

★4599★ IndustryWeek

Penton Media Inc.
1300 E 9th St.
Cleveland, OH 44114-1503
Ph: (216)696-7000   Fax: (216)931-9799
E-mail: iwinfo@industryweek.com
URL: http://www.industryweek.com

Semimonthly. Magazine containing articles to help industry executives sharpen their managerial skills and increase their effectiveness.

★4600★ Journal of Staff Development

National Staff Development Council
PO Box 240
Oxford, OH 45056
Ph: (513)523-6029   Fax: (513)523-0638
Fr: 800-727-7288

Quarterly. Professional journal covering administration issues.

★4601★ The Los Angeles Business Journal

The Los Angeles Business Journal
5700 Wilshire, No. 170
Los Angeles, CA 90036
Ph: (213)549-5225   Fax: (213)549-5255
E-mail: labjtalk@aol.com

Weekly. $79.95/year for individuals. Newspaper (tabloid) covering local business news, business trends, executive profiles, and information for the Los Angeles area executive.

★4602★ Organizations and Change

International Registry of Organization
  Development Professionals
11234 Walnut Ridge Rd.
Chesterland, OH 44026
Ph: (440)729-7419
URL: http://members.aol.com/odinst

Description: Monthly. Serves organization development professionals, teachers of organizational behavior, management consultants, personnel directors and executives by carrying news items, interest surveys, economic information, and committee reports. Recurring features include announcements of conferences, meetings, publications, consulting opportunities, and employment openings. Subscription includes annual publication titled *The International Registry of Organization Development Professionals and Organization Development Handbook*, and copies of *The Organizational Development Journal*.

★4603★ San Diego Business Journal

San Diego Business Journal
4909 Murphy Canyon Rd., No. 200
San Diego, CA 92123
Ph: (858)277-6359   Fax: (858)571-3628

Weekly (Mon.). $58.00/year for individuals. Metropolitan business newspaper specializing in investigative and enterprise reporting on San Diego County businesses and related issues.

★4604★ San Diego Daily Transcript

San Diego Daily Transcript
2131 3rd Ave.
Box 85469
San Diego, CA 92101
Ph: (619)232-4381   Fax: (619)231-4866
Fr: 800-697-6397
E-mail: webmaster@sddt.com
URL: http://www.sddt.com

Daily. $200.00/year for individuals; $337.50 for two years. Local business newspaper.

★4605★ San Francisco Business Times

American City Business Journals Inc.
120 W Morehead St., Ste. 200
Charlotte, NC 28202
Ph: (704)973-1000   Fax: (704)973-1001
E-mail: sanfrancisco@bizjournals.com
URL: http://www.sanfrancisco.bcentral.com

$88.00/year for individuals; $140.00 for two years. Local business newspaper (tabloid) serving the San Francisco Bay Area.

★4606★ Supply Chain Management Review

Reed Business Information
275 Washington St.
Newton, MA 02458-1630
Ph: (617)964-3030

Bimonthly. Publication covering business and management.

PLACEMENT AND JOB REFERRAL SERVICES

★4607★ National Black MBA Association (NBMBAA)

180 N Michigan Ave., Ste. 1400
Chicago, IL 60601
Ph: (312)236-2622   Fax: (312)236-0390
E-mail: mail@nbmbaa.org
URL: http://www.nbmbaa.org

Description: Business professionals, lawyers, accountants, and engineers concerned with the role of blacks who hold advanced management degrees. Works to create economic and intellectual wealth for the black community. Encourages blacks to pursue continuing business education; assists students preparing to enter the business world. Provides programs for minority youths, students, and professionals, and entrepreneurs

including workshops, panel discussions, and Destination MBA seminar. Sponsors job fairs. Works with graduate schools. Operates job placement service.

EMPLOYER DIRECTORIES AND NETWORKING LISTS

★4608★ D & B Million Dollar Directory

Dun & Bradstreet
3 Sylvan Way
Parsippany, NJ 07054-3896
Fax: (973)605-6911   Fr: 800-526-0651
URL: http://www.dnbmdd.com

Annual. $1,395.00. Covers 1,600,000 public and private businesses with either a net worth of $500,000 or more, 250 or more employees at that location, or $25,000,000 or more in sales volume; includes industrial corporations, utilities, transportation companies, bank and trust companies, stock brokers, mutual and stock insurance companies, wholesalers, retailers, and domestic subsidiaries of foreign corporations. Entries include: Company name, address, phone, state of incorporation; annual sales; number of employees, company ticker symbol on stock exchange, Standard Industrial Classification (SIC) number, line of business; principal bank, accounting firm; parent company name, current ownership date, division names and functions, directors or trustees; names, titles, functions of principal executives, number of employees, import/export designation. Arrangement: Alphabetical, cross referenced geographically and by industry classification. Indexes: Geographical (with address and SIC), product by SIC (with address).

★4609★ Forbes-Up-and-Comers 200: Best Small Companies in America Issue

Forbes Magazine
60 5th Ave.
New York, NY 10011
Ph: (212)620-2200   Fax: (212)206-5174
URL: http://www.forbes.com

Weekly. $6.99. Publication includes: List of 200 small companies judged to be high quality and fast-growing on the basis of 5-year return on equity and other qualitative measurements. Also includes a list of the 100 best small companies outside the U.S. Note: Issue does not carry address or CEO information for the foreign companies. Entries include: Company name, shareholdings data on chief executive officer; financial data. Arrangement: Alphabetical. Indexes: Ranking.

★4610★ Inc.-The Inc. 500 Issue

Gruner & Jahr USA Publishing
375 Lexington Ave., 10th Fl.
New York, NY 10017-4024
Ph: (212)499-2119   Fax: (212)499-2097
URL: http://www.inc.com

Annual, October. $3.50. Publication includes: List of 500 fastest-growing privately held companies based on percentage increase in sales over the five year period prior to compilation of current year's list. Entries include: Company name, headquarters city, description of business, year founded, number of employees, sales five years earlier and currently, profitability range, and growth statistics. Arrangement: Ranked by sales growth.

★4611★ MBA Employment Guide Report

Association of MBA Executives Inc.
388 E Main St., Ste. A
Branford, CT 06405-3527
Ph: (203)315-5221   Fax: (203)483-6186

Continuous. Database covers more than 4,000 firms that employ persons with Master of Business Administration degrees. More detailed profiles are given for 100 firms selected on the basis of their on-campus recruitment activity. Custom reports are issued upon request at $10.00 per report. Database includes: For companies covered in detail-Name, headquarters location, description of business, current recruitment objectives, employment policies, benefits offered, name and address of employment representative, financial data. For others-Name, location, contact person and telephone number, parent company (if any), code for primary line of business.

★4612★ Peterson's Job Opportunities for Business Majors

Thomson Peterson's
Princeton Pke. Corporate Ctr., 2000 Lenox Dr.
PO Box 67005
Lawrenceville, NJ 08648
Ph: (609)896-1800   Fax: (609)896-4531
Fr: 800-338-3282
URL: http://www.petersons.com

Irregular, latest edition 2000 - 16th ed. $18.95. Covers the 2,000 largest U.S. employers hiring in several fields, including financial services, management consulting, consumer products, and media/ entertainment. Entries include: Organization name, address, phone, name and title of contact, number of employees, type of organization. Arrangement: Alphabetical. Indexes: Type of organization.

★4613★ Standard & Poor's Register of Corporations, Directors and Executives

Standard & Poor's
55 Water St.
New York, NY 10041
Ph: (212)438-1000
URL: http://www2.standardandpoors.com/

Annual, January; supplements in April, July, and October. $675.00. Covers over 55,000 public and privately held corporations in the United States, including names and titles of over 400,000 officials (Volume 1); 70,000 biographies of directors and executives (Volume 2). Entries include: For companies-Name, address, phone, names of principal executives and accountants; primary bank, primary law firm, number of employees, estimated annual sales, outside directors, Standard Industrial Classification (SIC) code, product or service provided. For directors and executives-Name, home and principal business addresses, date and place of birth, fraternal organization memberships, business affiliations. Arrangement: Alphabetical. Indexes: Volume 3 indexes companies geographically, by Standard Industrial Classification (SIC) code, and by corporate family groups.

HANDBOOKS AND MANUALS

★4614★ Better Resumes for Executives and Professionals

Barron's Educational Series, Inc.
250 Wireless Blvd.
PO Box 8040
Hauppauge, NY 11788-3917
Ph: (631)434-3311   Fax: (631)434-3723
Fr: 800-645-3476

Robert F. Wilson and Adele Lewis. Fourth edition, 2000. $13.95 (paper). Explains how to write resumes and cover letters for executives and professionals in most fields.

★4615★ Careers in International Business

McGraw-Hill Trade
2 Penn Plaza
New York, NY 10121
Ph: (212)904-2000   Fr: 800-722-4726
E-mail: ntcpub@tribune.com

Ed Halloran. 1996. $17.95; 13.95 (paper). 160 pages.

★4616★ The Directory of Executive Recruiters 2004

Kennedy Information, Inc.
One Phoenix Mill Ln., 5th Fl.
Peterborough, NH 03458
Ph: (603)924-0900   Fax: (603)924-4460
Fr: 800-531-0007

November 2003. $49.95 (CD-ROM, paper).

★4617★ The Executive Job Search: A Comprehensive Handbook for Seasoned Professionals

McGraw-Hill Companies
860 Taylor Station Rd.
Blacklick, OH 43004-0545
Fax: (614)755-5645   Fr: 800-722-4726

Orrin G. Wood. $15.95 (paper). Illustrated. 256 pages. Executive job search manual.

★4618★ Executive Search Firms and Employment Agencies in Seattle: Job-Search Resources for the Executive, Manager and Professional

Barrett Street Productions
PO Box 99642
Seattle, WA 98199
Ph: (206)284-8202   Fax: (206)352-0944

Linda Carlson. 1998. $21.95 (paper). 192 pages. Contains information regarding employment agencies, recruiting and job hunting in Seattle, Washington area.

★4619★ Expert Resumes for Managers and Executives

JIST Publishing
8902 Otis Ave.
Indianapolis, IN 46216-1033
Ph: (317)613-4200   Fax: 800-547-8329

Wendy S. Enelow, Louise M. Kursmark. 2003. $16.95. 269 pages.

★4620★ Job Seekers Guide to Executive Recruiters

John Wiley & Sons Inc.
1 Wiley Dr.
Somerset, NJ 08873
Ph: (732)469-4400   Fr: 800-225-5945

Christopher W. Hunt. Scott A. Scanlon. 1997. $34.95 (paper). 516 pages.

★4621★ Making a Life, Making a Living: Reclaiming Your Purpose and Passion in Business and in Life

Warner Books, Incorporated
1271 Avenue of the Americas
New York, NY 10020
Ph: (212)522-7200

Mark Albion. 2000.

★4622★ Opportunities in Business Management Careers

McGraw-Hill Contemporary Books
1221 Avenue of the Americas
New York, NY 10020
Ph: (212)904-2000   Fr: 800-323-4900
E-mail: ntcpub@tribune.com

Irene Place and Lewis Baratz. 1997. $14.95; $11.95 (paper). 160 pages. Provides guidance on the most effective channels to management positions.

★4623★ The Resilient Candidate: A Definitive Guide to Securing Executive Jobs While Unemployed

Proactive Publishing, LLC
5739 Sandhill Dr.
Middleton, WI 53562-0533
Ph: (608)824-0085   Fax: (608)827-8515

December 2003. Marketed towards college students.

★4624★ Resume Guide for $100,000 Executive Jobs: Careerjournal.com from Wall Street Journal

John Wiley & Sons, Inc.
111 River St.
Hoboken, NJ 07030
Ph: (201)748-6000   Fax: (201)748-6088
Fr: 800-255-5945

William E. Montag. August 2002. $16.95. Illustrated. 360 pages.

★4625★ The Secrets of Executive Search: Professional Strategies for Managing Your personal Job Search

John Wiley & Sons, Inc.
111 River St.
Hoboken, NJ 07030
Ph: (201)748-6000   Fax: (201)748-6088
Fr: 800-255-5945

Robert Melancon. September 2002. $16.95. 175 pages.

★4626★ The Ultimate CV for Managers and Professionals: Win Senior Managerial Positions with an Outstanding CV

How To Books
3 Newtec Pl., Magdalen Rd.
Oxford OX4 1RE, United Kingdom

Rachel Bishop-Firth. January 2004. $17.50. Illustrated. 144 pages. Jobs and Career Series.

EMPLOYMENT AGENCIES AND SEARCH FIRMS

★4627★ A-L Associates Inc.

546 5th Ave., Fl. 6
New York, NY 10036
Ph: (212)878-9000   Fax: (212)878-9096

Executive search firm.

★4628★ Abeln, Magy & Associates

800 E. Wayzata Blvd., Ste. 200
Wayzata, MN 55391
Ph: (952)476-4938   Fax: (952)404-7470

Executive search firm.

★4629★ ADA Executive Search Inc.

4134 Gulf of Mexico Dr.
PO Box 9
Longboat Key, FL 34228
Ph: (941)387-8700

Executive search firm.

★4630★ **Adams & Associates International**
520 Shorely Dr. 201, PO Box 129
Barrington, IL 60011-0129
Ph: (847)304-5300
Global executive search firm.

★4631★ **Adams Executive Search**
3416 Fairfield Trail
Clearwater, FL 33761
Ph: (727)772-1536   Fr: (727)772-1537
Executive Search firm.

★4632★ **The Adkins Group Inc.**
3105 Manchaca Rd., Ste. A
Austin, TX 78704
Ph: (512)916-9600   Fax: (512)916-9665
Executive search firm.

★4633★ **Adler Management Inc.**
66 Witherspoon St., Ste. 315
Princeton, NJ 08542
Ph: (609)443-3300   Fax: (609)443-4439
Executive Search Firm.

★4634★ **Advanced Employment Resources**
3040 Charlevoix Dr.
Grand Rapids, MI 49546
Ph: (616)942-9950   Fax: (616)942-9950
Executive search firm.

★4635★ **Advantage Partners Inc.**
29225 Chagrin Blvd., Ste. 275
Cleveland, OH 44122
Ph: (216)514-1212   Fax: (216)514-1213
Executive search firm.

★4636★ **Aegis Consulting**
633 3rd Ave., Fl. 27
New York, NY 10017
Ph: (212)687-2200   Fax: (212)687-0079
Executive search firm.

★4637★ **Aegis Group Search Consultants LLC**
23875 Novi Rd.
Novi, MI 48375-3243
Ph: (248)344-1450   Fax: (248)347-2231
Executive search and consultant firm. Focuses on the medical industry.

★4638★ **AET Advisors LLC**
3495 Piedmont Rd., NE Bldg 11, Ste. 824
Atlanta, GA 30305
Ph: (404)237-8208   Fax: (404)261-6961
Executive search and consultant firm. Focuses on the real estate industry.

★4639★ **Ahern Search Partners**
3982 Powell Rd. Ste. 205
Powell, OH 43065
Ph: (614)880-9136   Fax: (614)436-4125
Executive search firm. Concentrates on the healthcare market.

★4640★ **Ahrensdorf & Associates**
PO Box 7494
St. Davids, PA 19087-7494
Ph: (610)971-0500   Fax: (610)971-9530
Executive search firm.

★4641★ **AKS Associates Ltd.**
175 Derby St., Ste. 27
Hingham, MA 02043-4054
Ph: (781)740-1704   Fax: (781)740-4383
Senior search firm. Concentrates on the financial industry.

★4642★ **Alexander Associates**
993 Lenox Dr., Ste. 200
Lawrenceville, NJ 08648
Ph: (609)844-7597   Fax: (609)844-7589
Executive search firm for the Boston to DC area.

★4643★ **Alexander & Company**
8308 Barber Oak Dr.
Plano, TX 75025
Ph: 877-495-8300
Executive search firm.

★4644★ **Alexander Edwards International Inc.**
501 Madison Ave., Ste. 401
New York, NY 10022
Ph: (212)242-6881   Fax: (212)989-2810
Fr: 800-590-3001
Global executive search firm. Second location in Maryland.

★4645★ **The Alexander Group**
2700 Post Oak Blvd., Ste. 2400
Houston, TX 77056
Ph: (713)993-7900   Fax: (713)993-7979
Executive search firm. Second location in San Francisco.

★4646★ **Alexander Ross & Company**
21 E 40th St.
New York, NY 10016
Ph: (212)889-9333   Fax: (212)481-3565
Executive search firm.

★4647★ **Alexander, Woolman & Stark**
1835 Market St., Ste. 1140
Philadelphia, PA 19103
Ph: (267)256-0721   Fax: (267)256-0725
Executive search firm. Branches in Massachusetts and Vermont.

★4648★ **The Alfus Group Inc.**
353 Lexington Ave., Fl. 8
New York, NY 10016
Ph: (212)599-1000   Fax: (212)599-1523
Executive search firm. Specializes in the hospitality industry.

★4649★ **Allard Associates Inc.**
425 Market St., Ste. 2200
San Francisco, CA 94105
Ph: (530)661-7562   Fax: 800-526-7791
Fr: 800-291-5279
Executive search firm. Focuses on financial placement surrounding the credit card industry.

★4650★ **Allen Associates**
650 Westlake Ctr.
Cincinnati, OH 45242
Ph: (513)563-3040
Executive senior-level search firm.

★4651★ **Allen Austin**
4543 Post Oak Pl., Ste. 217
Houston, TX 77027
Ph: (713)355-1900   Fax: (713)355-1901
Executive search firm. Branches in North Carolina and Dallas.

★4652★ **Allen Evans Klein International**
305 Madison Ave., Ste. 1650
New York, NY 10165
Ph: (212)983-9300   Fax: (212)983-9272
Global Executive search firm.

★4653★ **Allerton Heneghan & O'Neill**
1 Tower Ln., Ste. 1700
Oakbrook Terrace, IL 60181
Ph: (630)645-2294   Fax: (630)645-2298
Executive Search firm.

★4654★ **Alliance Search Management Inc.**
1717 Woodstead Ct., Ste. 106
The Woodlands, TX 77380
Ph: (281)367-8630   Fr: 800-444-0573
Employment agency.

★4655★ **AllianceSource LLC**
865 United Nations Plaza, Fl. 13A
New York, NY 10017
Ph: (212)308-1095
Executive search firm.

★4656★ **Ambler Associates**
14881 Quorum Dr., Ste. 450
Dallas, TX 75254-7018
Ph: (972)404-8712   Fax: (972)404-8761
Fr: 800-728-8712
Executive search firm.

★4657★ American Executive Management Inc.
30 Federal St.
Salem, MA 01970
Ph: (978)477-5923
Executive search firm. Second location in Boston.

★4658★ American Express Tax & Business Services
1 S. Wacker Dr., Ste. 800
Chicago, IL 60606
Ph: (312)634-4715   Fax: (312)634-5527
Executive search firm.

★4659★ American Incite
917 Hillfield Ct.
Oceanside, CA 92054-7013
Ph: (760)754-2444   Fax: (760)754-2453
Executive Search firm.

★4660★ American Physician Network Inc.
2794 Tennis Club Dr., Ste. 204
PO Box 222352
West Palm Beach, FL 33422-2352
Fax: 888-699-5512   Fr: 800-245-8227
Employment agency focused on the healthcare industry.

★4661★ American Research Systems
PO Box 45155
Omaha, NE 68145-0155
Ph: (402)333-8333
Employment agency.

★4662★ Ames & Ames LLC
PO Box 4704
Menlo Park, CA 94026
Ph: (650)218-7404
Executive search firm.

★4663★ AmiTech Group
6405 Metcalf Ave., Ste. 107
Overland Park, KS 66202
Ph: (913)384-9150
Executive search firm. Focuses on technology and engineering.

★4664★ Anderson & Associates
112 S. Tyron St.
Charlotte, NC 28284
Ph: (704)347-0090   Fax: (704)347-0064
Executive search firm. Branch in Cumming, Georgia.

★4665★ Anderson Bradshaw Associates Inc.
PO Box 924045
Houston, TX 77292-4045
Ph: (713)869-6789
Domestic and international search firm.

★4666★ Anderson Executive Search Inc.
1460 Woodland Trace
Cumming, GA 30041
Ph: (678)455-0691
Executive search firm.

★4667★ Andre David & Associates Inc.
PO Box 700967
Dallas, TX 75370
Ph: (972)250-1986   Fax: (972)250-2243
Executive search firm.

★4668★ The Andre Group Inc.
500 N. Gulph Rd., Ste. 210
King of Prussia, PA 19406
Ph: (610)337-0600   Fax: (610)337-1333
Executive search firm. Focused on the human resource field.

★4669★ Andrew Associates Executive Search Inc.
PO Box 2029
Lake Oswego, OR 97035
Ph: (503)635-7222   Fr: (866)294-1301
Executive search firm.

★4670★ The Angus Group Ltd.
250 W. Court St., Ste. 100E
Cincinnati, OH 45202-1088
Ph: (513)961-5575   Fax: (513)961-5616
Executive search firm.

★4671★ APA Search Inc.
1 Byram Brook Pl., Ste. 201
Armonk, NY 10504
Ph: (914)273-6000   Fax: (914)273-8025
Employment agency specializing in the automotive, retail, and hardware industries.

★4672★ The Arcus Group Inc.
325 N. Saint Paul, Ste. 1340
Dallas, TX 75201
Ph: (214)871-3332   Fax: (214)871-1338
Executive search firm. Branch in Chicago.

★4673★ Argus National Inc.
98 Mill Plain Rd., Ste. 301
Danbury, CT 06811-5148
Ph: (203)790-8420
Executive search firm.

★4674★ ARI Inernational
1501 Ocean Ave.
Seal Beach, CA 90740
Ph: (562)795-5111   Fax: (562)596-9794
International executive search firm.

★4675★ ARI Management Consultants - Executive Search
241 W. 36th St., Fl. 6
New York, NY 10018
Ph: (212)736-9114   Fax: (212)658-9958
Executive firm specializing in American-European searches.

★4676★ Ariel Associates
141 E. 89 St., Ste. 9-H
New York, NY 10128-2330
Ph: (212)348-9600
Executive search firm specializing in media, advertising and publishing.

★4677★ Artgo Inc.
12 Public Square
Willoughby, OH 44094-7843
Ph: (440)942-0597
Executive search firm.

★4678★ Arthur Diamond Associates Inc.
4630 Montgomery Ave., Ste. 200
Bethesda, MD 20814-3436
Ph: (301)657-8866   Fax: (301)657-8876
Executive search firm.

★4679★ Ashworth Consultants Inc.
53 Fulton St.
Boston, MA 02109-1401
Ph: (617)720-0350
Executive search firm.

★4680★ Asset Group Inc.
PO Box 211
Verona, NJ 07044
Ph: (973)571-1367   Fax: (973)571-1387
International executive search firm.

★4681★ Association Executive Resources Group
PO Box 3880
Gaithersburg, MD 20885-3880
Ph: (301)417-7045   Fax: (301)417-7049
Executive search firm. Concentrates on nonprofits.

★4682★ Association Strategies
1111 N. Fairfax St.
Fairfax, VA 22314
Ph: (703)683-0580
Employment agency.

★4683★ AST Partners Ltd.
1 Atlantic St.
Stamford, CT 06901
Ph: (203)975-7188   Fax: (203)975-7353
Executive search firm.

★4684★ Aster Search Group
555 Madison Ave
New York, NY 10022
Ph: (212)888-6182
Executive search firm focused on the health-care industry.

★4685★ Atlanta Executive Partners Inc.
PO Box W
Teaticket, MA 02536
Ph: (508)495-4300
Executive search firm.

★4686★ Aubin International Inc.
30 Rowes Wharf
Boston, MA 02110
Ph: (617)443-9922   Fax: (617)443-9955
Executive search firm.

★4687★ Auguston and Associates Inc.
1010 S. Ocean Blvd., Ste. 601
Pompano Beach, FL 33062
Ph: (954)943-0503   Fax: (954)784-1660
Fr: 888-244-5598
Executive search firm focused on medical devices.

★4688★ Austin Group Inernational
117 Laura Lane, Ste. 200
Austin, TX 78746
Ph: (512)329-8077
Executive search firm.

★4689★ Austin-McGregor Inernational
3500 Oak Lawn Ave., Ste. 550
Dallas, TX 75219
Ph: (972)488-0500   Fax: (972)488-0535
Executive search firm. Branch located in Mattoon, IL.

★4690★ Avery Associates
3 N. Santa Cruz Ave., Ste. A
Los Gatos, CA 95030
Ph: (408)399-4424   Fax: (408)399-4423
Administration search firm.

★4691★ Avery James Inc.
6601 Center Dr. W., Ste. 500
Los Angeles, CA 90045
Ph: (310)342-8224
Executive search firm.

★4692★ The Ayers Group
370 Lexington Ave.
New York, NY 10017
Ph: (212)599-5656   Fax: (212)661-7910
Executive search firm. Location in Norwalk, CT and two locations in New Jersey.

★4693★ The Baer Group
3161 Coleridge Rd., Ste. 300
Cleveland, OH 44118
Ph: (216)371-9982
Executive search firm.

★4694★ Baker, Nelms & Montgomery
980 N. Michigan Ave., Ste. 930
Chicago, IL 60611
Ph: (312)397-8833   Fax: (312)397-9631
Executive search firm.

★4695★ Baker, Parker & Associates Inc.
5 Concourse Pkwy., Ste. 2440
Atlanta, GA 30328-5347
Ph: (770)804-1996   Fax: (770)804-1917
Executive search firm.

★4696★ Baldwin Associates LLC
3 Goose Cove Rd.
Bath, ME 04530-4017
Ph: (207)442-7070   Fax: (207)442-8995
Executive search firm focused on the high-technology industry.

★4697★ Bales Partners Inc.
980 N. Michigan Ave., Ste. 1400
Chicago, IL 60611
Ph: (312)214-3998   Fax: (312)214-3981
Executive search firm.

★4698★ Ballein Search Partners
PO Box 5204
Oak Brook, IL 60522
Ph: (630)322-9220   Fax: (630)322-9221
Executive search firm focused in the health-care industry.

★4699★ Ballos & Company Inc.
45 Fieldstone Dr.
Morristown, NJ 07960-2634
Ph: (973)538-4753
Executive search firm.

★4700★ Banister International
1 Commerce Square
2005 Market St., Ste. 820
Philadelphia, PA 19103
Ph: (267)256-2300   Fax: (267)330-0333
Executive search firm.

★4701★ Banyan Group ESC Ltd.
411 Theodore Fremd Ave., Fl. 2
Rye, NY 10580
Ph: (914)921-1010   Fax: (914)921-1011
Executive search firm.

★4702★ The Barack Group Inc.
Grand Central Station
PO Box 4407
New York, NY 10163
Ph: (212)867-9700   Fax: (212)681-9555
Executive search firm.

★4703★ Barger & Sargeant Inc.
131 Windermere Rd., Ste. 600
PO Box 1420
Center Harbor, NH 03226-1420
Ph: (603)253-4700
Executive search firm.

★4704★ Barkstone Group LLC
113 South St.
PO Box 218
Litchfield, CT 06759-0218
Ph: (860)567-2400   Fax: (860)567-1466
Executive search firm focused on the bank-ing industry.

★4705★ Barnes Development Group LLC
1045 W. Glen Oak Lane, Ste. 4
Mequon, WI 53092
Ph: (262)241-8468   Fr: (262)241-8438
Executive search firm.

★4706★ Barone-O'Hara Associates Inc.
34 Fackler Rd.
Princeton, NJ 08540
Ph: (609)683-5566   Fax: (609)683-8077
Executive search firm focused on medical devices.

★4707★ Barro Global Search Inc.
10951 Pico Blvd., Ste. 316
Los Angeles, CA 90064
Ph: (310)441-5305
Executive search firm focused on healthcare and hospitals.

★4708★ Bartholdi Partners
12020 Sunrise Valley Dr., Ste. 160
Reston, VA 20191
Ph: (703)476-5519   Fax: (703)476-6473
Executive search firm. Affiliates in San Fran-cisco, San Jose, Phoenix, Scottsdale, Parker CO, and Framingham MA.

★4709★ Barton Associates Inc.
4314 Yoakum Blvd.
Houston, TX 77006
Ph: (713)961-9111   Fax: (713)993-9399
Executive search firm. Affiliate in Houston, TX.

★4710★ Battalia Winston International
555 Madison Ave.
New York, NY 10022
Ph: (212)308-8080   Fax: (212)308-1309
Executive search firm. Branches in Los Angeles, Chicago, Wellesley Hills MA, Edison NJ.

★4711★ Beach Executive Search Inc.
11324 NW 12th Ct.
Coral Springs, FL 33071-6494
Ph: (954)340-7337
Executive search firm.

★4712★ The Beam Group
11 Penn Ctr., Ste. 502
Philadelphia, PA 19103
Ph: (215)988-2100   Fax: (215)988-1558
Executive search firm.

★4713★ The Bedford Group
154 Quicksand Pond Rd.
Little Compton, RI 02837
Ph: (401)635-0293   Fax: (401)635-8466
Executive search firm.

★4714★ Behavioral Science Associates Inc.
2135 E. University Dr., Ste. 121
Mesa, AZ 85213
Ph: (480)833-2629   Fax: (480)833-1029
Fr: 800-233-4318
Executive search firm.

★4715★ Bell Wishingrad Partners Inc.
230 Park Ave., Ste. 1000
New York, NY 10169
Ph: (212)949-6666
Executive search firm focused on the financial industry.

★4716★ Bench International Search Inc.
120 S. Doheny Dr.
Beverly Hills, CA 90211
Ph: (310)854-9900   Fax: (310)854-9000
Executive search firm.

★4717★ Bender Executive Search Management Consulting
45 N. Station Plaza, Ste. 315
Great Neck, NY 11021
Ph: (516)773-4300   Fax: (516)482-5355
Executive search firm.

★4718★ Bennett Associates
335 Washington St., Ste. 12
Norwell, MA 02061-1900
Ph: (781)659-9950   Fax: (781)659-9969
Executive search firm. Branches in Northbrook, IL and Rye, NY.

★4719★ The Bennett Group Inc.
5640 Professional Circle, Ste. A8
Indianapolis, IN 46241
Ph: (317)247-1240   Fax: (317)247-6533
Executive search firm.

★4720★ Bennett Search & Consulting Company Inc.
285-1 W. Naomi Dr.
Naples, FL 34104
Ph: (239)352-0219   Fax: (239)353-7719
Executive search firm.

★4721★ Bennett Wheelless Group Ltd.
30 S. Wacker Dr., Fl. 22
Chicago, IL 60606
Ph: (312)596-8388   Fax: (801)697-5227
Executive search firm focused on direct marketing positions.

★4722★ Berkana International Ltd.
20021 Ballinger Way NE, Ste. C
Seattle, WA 98155
Ph: (206)363-6970   Fax: (206)547-3843
Executive search firm.

★4723★ Berkhemer Clayton Inc.
Figueroa Courtyard
221 S. Figueroa St., Ste. 240
Los Angeles, CA 90012
Ph: (213)621-2300   Fax: (213)621-2309
Executive search firm.

★4724★ Bert Davis Executive Search Inc.
425 Madison Ave., Fl. 14
New York, NY 10017
Ph: (212)838-4000   Fax: (212)888-3823
Executive search firm.

★4725★ Best, Coleman and Partners
1085 Commonwealth Ave., Ste. 325
Boston, MA 02115
Executive search firm. Focused on wholesale and retail industries.

★4726★ Bethesda Pharmaceuticals Ltd.
PO Box 30557
Bethesda, MD 20824
Ph: (301)907-8838
Executive search firm.

★4727★ BFL Associates Ltd.
12 Greenway Plaza, Ste. 1222
Houston, TX 77046-1203
Ph: (713)965-2112   Fax: (713)965-2114
Executive search firm.

★4728★ Bialecki Inc.
780 3rd Ave., Ste. 4203
New York, NY 10017
Ph: (212)755-1090
Senior executive search firm focused on the financial industry.

★4729★ Bialla & Associates Inc.
4000 Bridgeway, Ste. 201
Sausalito, CA 94965
Ph: (415)332-7111   Fax: (415)332-3964
Executive search firm.

★4730★ Billington & Associates
3250 Wilshire Blvd., Ste. 900
Los Angeles, CA 90010
Ph: (213)386-7511   Fax: (213)386-7025
Executive search firm.

★4731★ Blackshaw, Olmstead, Lynch & Koenig
730 Monarch Plaza
Atlanta, GA 30326
Ph: (404)261-7770   Fax: (404)261-4469
Executive search firm. Branches in Woodland Hills, CA; Fairfield, CT; and Chicago, IL.

★4732★ Blake/Hansen & Schmidt Ltd.
5514 Ridgeway Ct.
Westlake Village, CA 91362
Ph: (805)879-1192
Executive search firm specializing in plastics, rubber and packaging.

★4733★ Blaney Executive Search
Damonmill Square
Concord, MA 01742
Ph: (978)371-2192
Executive search firm.

★4734★ Blumenthal-Hart LLC
53 W. Jackson Blvd., Ste. 1307
Chicago, IL 60604
Ph: (312)663-0090   Fax: (312)663-0405
Executive search firm.

★4735★ Board Search Partners LLC
700 Larkspur Landing Circle, Ste. 199
Larkspur, CA 94939
Ph: (415)462-8100   Fax: (415)462-8101
Executive search firm focused on placing board members.

★4736★ Boettcher Associates
120 Bishops Way, Ste. 126
Brookfield, WI 53005
Ph: (262)782-2205
Executive search firm.

★4737★ Bonell Ryan Inc.
444 Madison Ave., Ste. 3202
New York, NY 10022
Ph: (212)754-0700   Fax: (702)995-9935
Executive search firm.

★4738★ Bonnell Associates Ltd.
12 Summer Hill Rd.
Westport, CT 06880
Ph: (203)319-7214   Fax: (203)319-7219
Executive search firm.

★4739★ The Bonner Group
59 E. Mill Rd.
PO Box 15
Long Valley, NJ 07853
Ph: (908)876-5200   Fax: (908)876-9275
Executive search firm.

★4740★ Bosland Gray Associates
Waterview Plaza
2001 Rte. 46, Ste. 310
Parsippany, NJ 07054
Ph: (973)402-4964
Executive search firm.

★4741★ Boston Search Group Inc.
224 Clarendon St., Ste. 41
Boston, MA 02116-3729
Ph: (617)266-4333   Fax: (781)735-0562
Executive search firm.

★4742★ Boulware & Associates Inc.
175 W. Jackson Blvd., Ste. 621
Chicago, IL 60604
Ph: (312)322-0088   Fax: (312)322-0092
Executive search firm.

★4743★ Boyden
360 Lexington Ave., Ste. 1300
New York, NY 10532-1217
Ph: (212)949-9850   Fax: (212)949-5905
E-mail: jrice@boyden.com
URL: http://www.boyden.com/newyork
Executive search firm. Affiliate offices across the country and abroad.

★4744★ Boyle & Associates Retained Search Group
238 Chester St., Ste. 200
St. Paul, MN 55107
Ph: (651)223-5050   Fax: (651)297-6286
Executive search firm.

★4745★ The Bradbury Group Inc.
2112 Vizcaya Way, Ste. 200
Campbell, CA 95008
Ph: (408)377-5400   Fax: (408)377-1112
Executive search firm

★4746★ Brady Associates International Inc.
PO Box 1892
New York, NY 10021
Ph: (412)934-2228   Fax: (724)935-8059
Executive search firm focused on the energy and utilities industry.

★4747★ The Brand Company Inc.
181 Shores Dr.
Vero Beach, FL 32963
Ph: (561)231-1807
Executive search firm.

★4748★ Brandywine Consulting Group
5 Great Valley Pkwy., Ste. 322
Malvern, PA 19355
Ph: (610)407-4600
Executive search firm. An Affiliate of Brandywine Management Group in Berlin, MD.

★4749★ Brandywine Management Group
8 Drawbridge Rd.
Berlin, MD 21811
Ph: (410)208-9791   Fax: (410)208-9792
Executive search firm.

★4750★ Branthover Associates
360 Lexington Ave., Ste. 1300
New York, NY 10017
Ph: (212)949-9400   Fax: (212)949-5905
Executive search firm.

★4751★ Brault & Associated Ltd.
18417 Lanier Island Sq.
Leesburg, VA 20176
Ph: (703)771-0200   Fax: (703)771-0270
Executive search firm.

★4752★ The Brazik Group LLC
1444 N. Farnsworth Ave., Ste. 105
Aurora, IL 60505
Ph: (630)820-0785
Executive search firm. Branches in Tinley Park, IL and Union Pier, MI.

★4753★ Brenner Executive Resources Inc.
1230 Avenue of the Americas, Fl. 3
New York, NY 10036
Ph: (917)639-4035
Executive search firm focused on information technology.

★4754★ The Brentwood Group Inc.
170 Kinnelon Rd., Ste. 7
Kinnelon, NJ 07405
Ph: (973)283-1000   Fax: (973)283-1220
Executive search firm.

★4755★ The Brentwood Group Ltd.
4949 SW Meadows Rd., Ste. 140
Lake Oswego, OR 97035
Ph: (503)697-8136   Fax: (503)697-8161
Executive search firm focused on the high technology industry.

★4756★ Brentwood International
9841 Airport Blvd., Ste. 420
Los Angeles, CA 90045
Ph: (310)216-0033   Fax: (310)338-5484
Executive search firm with focus on information technology. Branch in Fairfield, CA.

★4757★ Briant Associates Inc.
18 E. Dundee Rd. Bldg 2, Ste. 202
Barrington, IL 60010
Ph: (847)382-5725   Fax: (847)382-7265
Executive search firm.

★4758★ BridgeGate LLC
18401 Von Karman Ave., Ste. 440
Irvine, CA 92612
Ph: (949)553-9200
Executive search firm.

★4759★ The Brimeyer Group Inc.
50 S. 9th Ave., Ste. 101
Hopkins, MN 55343
Ph: (952)945-0246
Executive search firm.

★4760★ Brooke Chase Associates Inc.
1443 Tallevast Rd.
Sarasota, FL 34243
Ph: (941)358-3111   Fax: (941)358-3311
Executive search firm. Branches in San Rafael, CA; Chicago; and Charlotte, NC.

★4761★ Brown Venture Associates Inc.
3000 Sand Hill Rd., Bldg. 3, Ste. 110
Menlo Park, CA 94025
Ph: (650)233-0205   Fax: (650)233-1902
Executive search firm.

★4762★ Brownson & Associates LP
2825 Wilcrest, Ste. 656
Houston, TX 77042
Ph: (713)626-4790   Fax: (713)877-1745
Executive search firm.

★4763★ **Bruce Edwards & Associates Inc.**
PO Box 51206
Durham, NC 27717-1206
Ph: (919)489-5368
Executive search firm.

★4764★ **Brush Creek Partners**
1133 W. Main St.
Blue Springs, MO 64015
Ph: (816)228-9192   Fax: (816)228-6740
Executive search firm.

★4765★ **Buffkin & Associates LLC**
730 Cool Springs Blvd., Ste. 120
Franklin, TN 37067
Ph: (615)771-0098   Fax: (615)771-0099
Executive search firm.

★4766★ **Burke, O'Brien & Bishop Associates Inc.**
301 N. Harrison St., Ste. 111
Princeton, NJ 08540
Ph: (609)921-3510   Fax: (609)683-1578
Executive search firm.

★4767★ **The Burling Group Ltd.**
191 N. Wacker Dr., Ste. 2300
Chicago, IL 60606
Ph: (312)346-0888
Executive search firm.

★4768★ **Burton & Grove Inc.**
1600 Golf Rd., Ste. 1200
Rolling Meadows, IL 60008
Ph: (847)981-7690
Executive search firm.

★4769★ **Busch International**
5150 El Camino Real, Ste. A-30
Los Altos, CA 94022
Ph: (650)623-0990
Executive search firm focused solely on high-technology electronics.

★4770★ **Byron Leonard International**
99 Long Ct., Ste. 201
Thousand Oaks, CA 91360
Ph: (805)373-7500   Fr: (818)222-2744
Executive search firm.

★4771★ **CAA Search**
5469 Sunbird Dr.
Loves Park, IL 61111
Ph: (815)654-8535   Fax: (815)654-0469
Executive search firm.

★4772★ **Cabot Consultants**
1750 Tysons Blvd., Ste. 250
McLean, VA 22102
Ph: (703)584-2310
Executive search firm.

★4773★ **The Caler Group**
23337 Lago Mar Circle
Boca Raton, FL 33433
Ph: (561)394-8045   Fax: (561)394-4645
Executive search firm.

★4774★ **Caliber Associates**
5090 Shoreham Pl., Ste. 201
San Diego, CA 92122
Ph: (858)551-7880   Fax: (858)551-7887
Executive search firm.

★4775★ **Callaghan International Inc.**
119 W. 57th St., Ste. 1220
New York, NY 10019
Ph: (212)265-9200   Fax: (212)265-0080
Executive search firm.

★4776★ **Callan Associates Ltd.**
2021 Spring Rd., Ste. 175
Oak Brook, IL 60523
Fax: (630)574-3099
Executive search firm.

★4777★ **Calland & Company**
2296 Henderson Mill Rd., Ste. 222
Atlanta, GA 30345
Ph: (770)270-9100   Fax: (770)270-9300
Executive search firm focused on senior management and healthcare.

★4778★ **Cameron Consulting Group**
1245 Q St.
Sacramento, CA 95814
Ph: (916)447-9015
Executive search firm.

★4779★ **Campbell/Carlson LLC**
The Addison Bldg.
831 E. Moorehead St., Ste. 750
Charlotte, NC 28202
Ph: (704)373-0234   Fax: (704)373-0232
Executive search firm.

★4780★ **Cannellos-Smartt Associates**
23 Davenport Way
Hillsborough, NJ 08844-2923
Ph: (908)359-8319
Executive search firm with another office in Hillborough.

★4781★ **Cantor Executive Search Solutions Inc.**
315 W. 57 St., Ste. 207
New York, NY 10019
Ph: (212)333-3000   Fax: (212)245-1012
Executive search firm. Branch in Fairfield, CT.

★4782★ **Capodice & Associates**
Midtown Plaza
1243 S. Tamiami Trail
Sarasota, FL 34239
Ph: (941)906-1990   Fax: (941)906-1991
Executive search firm. Branch in Carlisle, MA.

★4783★ **Caprio & Associates Inc.**
1415 W. 22nd St., Tower Fl.
Oak Brook, IL 60523
Ph: (630)705-9101   Fax: (630)705-9102
Executive search firm.

★4784★ **Capstone Consulting Inc.**
723 S. Dearborn St., Printers Row
Chicago, IL 60605
Ph: (312)922-9556   Fax: (312)922-9558
Executive search firm.

★4785★ **Capstone Inc.**
971 Albany Shaker Rd.
Latham, NY 12110
Ph: (518)783-9300   Fax: (518)783-9328
Executive search firm.

★4786★ **Career Consulting International**
550 Brickell Ave., Ste. 502
Miami, FL 33131-2508
Ph: (305)361-2174
Executive search firm.

★4787★ **Career Specialists Inc.**
155 108th Ave. NE, Ste. 200
Bellevue, WA 98004
Ph: (425)455-0582   Fax: (425)646-9738
Executive search firm.

★4788★ **Carlson & Czeswik**
740 Mississippi River Blvd., Ste. 18-G
St. Paul, MN 55116
Ph: (651)698-6400
Executive search firm.

★4789★ **Carlson Research Group**
5051 Castello Dr., Ste. 211
Naples, FL 34103
Ph: (239)649-7576   Fax: (239)649-8058
Executive search firm.

★4790★ Carrington & Carrington Ltd
39 S. LaSalle St., Ste. 700
Chicago, IL 60603
Ph: (312)606-0015   Fax: (312)606-0501
Executive search firm.

★4791★ Carris, Jackowitz Associates
201 E. 79th St.
New York, NY 10021
Ph: (212)879-5482
Executive search firm.

★4792★ CarterBaldwin
300 Colonial Center Pkwy., Ste. 240
Roswell, GA 30076
Ph: (678)448-0000   Fax: (770)552-1088
Executive search firm.

★4793★ Caruso & Associates Inc.
1509 N. Military Trail, Ste. 216
West Palm Beach, FL 33409
Ph: (561)683-2336
Executive search firm.

★4794★ Cary & Associates
PO Box 2043
Winter Park, FL 32790
Ph: (407)647-1145
Executive search firm.

★4795★ Catalyx Group
303 W. 42nd St., Ste. 607
New York, NY 10036
Ph: (212)956-3525
Executive search firm.

★4796★ Caywood Partners Ltd.
6484 Washington St., Ste. B
Yountville, CA 94599
Ph: (707)945-1340
Executive search firm. Focuses on networking industries.

★4797★ Cendea
13740 Research Blvd., Bldg. O-1
Austin, TX 78750
Ph: (512)219-6000
Executive search firm.

★4798★ Chaitin & Associates Inc.
22543 Ventura Blvd., Ste. 220
Woodland Hills, CA 91364
Ph: (818)225-8655   Fax: (818)225-8660
Executive search firm.

★4799★ Chase Hunter Group Inc.
1143 W. North Shore Ave.
Chicago, IL 60626
Ph: (773)338-7865
Executive search firm focused around the healthcare industry.

★4800★ The Cherbonnier Group Inc.
1 Riverway, Ste. 1700
Houston, TX 77056
Ph: (713)688-4701
Executive search firm.

★4801★ Cheryl Alexander & Associates
8588 Shadow Creek Dr.
Maple Grove, MN 55311
Ph: (763)416-4570
Executive search firm.

★4802★ Chicago Research Group Inc.
PO Box 3757
Chapel Hill, NC 27515
Ph: (919)968-0120
Executive search firm.

★4803★ Chiron Advisors Inc.
1 Rockefeller Plaza, Ste. 1007
New York, NY 10020
Ph: (212)698-1161   Fax: (212)698-1167
Executive search firm focused on the financial industry.

★4804★ Chrisman & Company Inc.
350 S. Figueroa St., Ste. 550
Los Angeles, CA 90071
Ph: (213)620-1192
Executive search firm.

★4805★ Christian & Timbers
1 Corporate Exchange
25825 Science Park Dr., Ste. 400
Cleveland, OH 44122
Ph: (216)464-8710   Fax: (216)464-6160
Fr: 800-380-9444
Executive search firm. Eight branches spanning the USA.

★4806★ Clarey Andrews & Klein Inc.
1200 Shermer Rd., Ste. 108
Northbrook, IL 60062
Ph: (847)498-2870
Executive search firm.

★4807★ Cole, Warren & Long Inc.
2 Penn Center Plaza, Ste. 312
Philadelphia, PA 19102
Ph: (215)563-0701   Fax: (215)563-2907
Executive search firm with international placement.

★4808★ Coleman Lew & Associates Inc.
326 W. 10th St.
Charlotte, NC 28202
Ph: (704)377-0362   Fax: (704)377-0424
Executive search firm.

★4809★ Columbia Consulting Group
Sun Life Bldg.
20 S. Charles St., Fl. 9
Baltimore, MD 21201
Ph: (410)385-2525   Fax: (410)385-0044
Executive search firm. Branches in Ft. Lauderdale, FL; Jupiter, FL; and New York, NY.

★4810★ Compton Graham International Inc.
14262 Devington Way
Ft. Myers, FL 33912
Ph: (239)433-4660
Executive search firm. Second location in Toronto, Canada.

★4811★ Conard Associates Inc.
74 Northeastern Blvd., Unit 22A
Nashua, NH 03062
Ph: (603)886-0600   Fax: (603)886-8886
Executive search firm.

★4812★ Conex
150 E. 52nd St., Fl. 2
New York, NY 10022
Ph: (212)371-3737
Executive search firm.

★4813★ Connexus Group LLC
225 W. 34th St., Ste. 1800
New York, NY 10122-0499
Ph: (212)563-3382
Executive search firm.

★4814★ Conway & Associates
1007 Church St., Ste. 307
Evanston, IL 60201
Ph: (847)866-6832   Fax: (847)866-6265
Executive search firm.

★4815★ The Cooke Group Inc.
1001 W. Glen Oaks Lane, Ste. 102
Mequon, WI 53092
Ph: (262)241-9843   Fax: (262)241-1004
Fr: 888-432-7800
Executive search firm.

★4816★ The Cooper Executive Search Group Inc.
PO Box 375
Wales, WI 53183-0375
Ph: (262)968-9049   Fax: (262)968-9059
Executive search firm.

★4817★ Core Management Search LLC
5130 Saratoga Ln. N., Ste. 201
Minneapolis, MN 55442
Ph: (763)559-0977   Fax: (763)559-1664
Executive search firm.

★4818★ Cornell Group International Consulting Inc.
1 Corwin Ct., Ste. 200
Newburgh, NY 12550
Ph: (845)565-8905   Fax: (845)565-5688
Executive search firm.

★4819★ Courtright & Associates Inc.
PO Box 503
Clarks Summit, PA 18411-0503
Ph: (570)586-0735   Fax: (570)586-3969
Executive search firm.

★4820★ CraigSearch
901 Waterfall Way, Ste. 107
Richardson, TX 75080
Ph: (972)644-3264
Executive search firm.

★4821★ Creative-Leadership Inc.
16980 Via Tazon, Ste. 260
San Diego, CA 92127
Ph: (858)592-0506   Fax: (858)592-0413
Fr: 800-875-5323
Executive search firm.

★4822★ Crest Associates Inc.
366 Crest Ave.
Alamo, CA 94507
Ph: (925)945-7374   Fax: (925)935-9170
Executive search firm.

★4823★ Crist Associates
2 Salt Creek Ln., Ste. 102
Hinsdale, IL 60521
Ph: (630)321-1110   Fax: (630)321-1112
Executive search firm.

★4824★ Cristal Partners
311 S. Wacker Dr., Ste. 4550
Chicago, IL 60606
Ph: (312)444-9499   Fax: (312)697-4915
Executive search firm.

★4825★ Cross Hill Partners LLC
245 Park Ave., Fl. 24
New York, NY 10167
Ph: (212)672-1604   Fax: (212)202-6316
Executive search firm.

★4826★ Crown Advisors Inc.
239 Fort Pitt Blvd.
Pittsburgh, PA 15222
Ph: (412)566-1100   Fax: (412)566-1256
Executive search firm. Branch in Denver, CO.

★4827★ CTR
581 Bellwood Dr., Ste. 100
Santa Clara, CA 95054
Ph: (408)980-8082
Executive search firm.

★4828★ Cullen International Executive Search Inc.
50 Northcrest Dr.
Newnan, GA 30265-1200
Ph: (678)423-1556   Fax: (678)423-1718
Executive search firm.

★4829★ Curran Partners Inc.
1 Landmark Sq., Fl. 18
Stamford, CT 06901
Ph: (203)363-5350   Fax: (203)363-5353
Executive search firm.

★4830★ Curry Company
25 Eastfield Rd.
Mount Vernon, NY 10552
Ph: (914)667-5735
Executive search firm.

★4831★ Custom Research Solutions
5450 Katella, Ste. 104
Los Alamitos, CA 90720
Ph: (562)431-6690
Executive search firm.

★4832★ Cyntal International Ltd.
405 Lexington Ave., Ste. 2600-19
New York, NY 10174
Ph: (917)368-8181
Executive search firm.

★4833★ Dahl-Morrow International
608 S. King, Ste. 103
Leesburg, VA 20175
Ph: (703)779-5600   Fax: (703)779-5678
Executive search firm specializes in high technology.

★4834★ DAL Partners
4 Corporate Dr., Ste. 482
Shelton, CT 06484-6263
Ph: (203)225-7800   Fax: (203)225-7807
Executive search firm.

★4835★ Daly & Company Inc.
175 Federal St.
Boston, MA 02110-2210
Ph: (617)262-2800   Fax: (617)728-4477
Executive search firm.

★4836★ David Allen Associates
PO Box 56
Haddonfield, NJ 08033-0048
Ph: (856)795-6470   Fax: (856)795-0175
Executive search firm.

★4837★ David Erickson-Pearson
8008 S. Madison Way
Centennial, CO 80122
Ph: (303)703-6165   Fax: (303)703-8144
Executive search firm.

★4838★ Deborah Bishop & Associates
883 Island Dr., Ste. 212
Alameda, CA 94502
Ph: (510)523-2305
Executive search firm. Concentrates on the high-tech industry only.

★4839★ Denney & Company Inc.
Gateway Ctr.
PO Box 22156
Pittsburgh, PA 15201
Ph: (412)441-9636
Executive search firm.

★4840★ Derba & Derba
7 Whispering Pines
Andover, MA 01810
Ph: (978)470-8270   Fax: (978)470-4592
Executive search firm focused on the hospitality industry.

★4841★ DHR International
10 S. Riverside Plaza, Ste. 2220
Chicago, IL 60606
Ph: (312)782-1581   Fax: (312)782-2096
Executive search firm. International organization with a variety of affiliate offices.

★4842★ The Dieck Group Inc.
114 W. Monroe St.
Mauston, WI 53948-1130
Ph: (608)847-3400   Fax: (608)847-5799
Executive search firm focused on pulp, paper and the packaging industries.

★4843★ The Diestel Group
2755 E. Cottonwood Pkwy., Ste. 580
Salt Lake City, UT 84121
Ph: (801)365-0400   Fax: (801)365-0401
Executive search firm.

★4844★ Dinte Resources Inc.
8300 Greensboro Dr., Ste. 750
McLean, VA 22102
Ph: (703)448-3300   Fax: (703)448-0215
Executive search firm.

★4845★ DLB Associates
271 Madison Ave., Ste. 1406
New York, NY 10016
Ph: (212)953-6460   Fax: (212)953-6764
Executive search firm.

★4846★ DNPitchon Associates
60 W. Ridgewood Ave.
Ridgewood, NJ 07450
Ph: (201)612-8350
Executive search firm.

★4847★ Doherty International Inc.
899 Skokie Blvd., Ste. 430
Northbrook, IL 60062
Ph: (847)564-1753   Fax: (847)564-1763
Executive search firm.

★4848★ Donahue/Patterson Associates
33 N. LaSalle St., Ste. 2600
Chicago, IL 60602
Ph: (312)732-0999
Executive search firm.

★4849★ Dressler Associates
624 University Ave.
Palo Alto, CA 94301
Ph: (650)323-0456   Fax: (650)323-2904
Executive search firm.

★4850★ Drinkwater & Associates
167 West St.
Beverly, MA 01915
Ph: (978)922-3676
Executive search firm.

★4851★ Dunhill Professional Search
150 Motor Pkwy.
Hauppauge, NY 11788-5111
Ph: (631)952-3000   Fax: (631)952-3500
E-mail: info@dunhillstaff.com
URL: http://www.dunhillstaff.com
Executive search firm. Over 180 affiliated locations coast-to-coast.

★4852★ Dunlap & Sullivan Associates
29 Pearl St. NW, Ste. 227
Grand Rapids, MI 49503
Ph: (616)458-4142   Fax: (616)458-4203
Executive search firm with second location in Hobe Sound, FL.

★4853★ DuVall & Associates
4203 Costa Salada
San Clemente, CA 92673
Ph: (949)488-8790   Fax: (949)488-8793
Executive search firm specializing in management team placement.

★4854★ Dynamic Synergy Corp.
600 Entrada Dr., Fl. 2
Santa Monica, CA 90402
Ph: (310)573-7300
Executive search firm.

★4855★ Eastman & Beaudine Inc.
5700 W. Plano Pkwy., Ste. 2800
Plano, TX 75093
Ph: (972)267-8891   Fax: (972)267-8008
Executive search firm. Second location in Alpharetta, GA.

★4856★ EFL Associates
7101 College Blvd., Ste. 550
Overland Park, KS 66210-1891
Ph: (913)451-8866   Fax: (913)451-3219
Executive search firm. Locations in Englewood, CO and Lake Forest, IL.

★4857★ Egan & Associates Inc.
White House Ctr.
128 S. 6th Ave.
West Bend, WI 53095
Ph: (262)335-0707   Fax: (262)335-0625
Executive search firm.

★4858★ The Elliot Company
534 Maison Pl.
Bryn Mawr, PA 19010
Ph: (610)527-1840
Executive search firm.

★4859★ Elwell & Associates Inc.
31920 Nottingwood
Farmington Hills, MI 48334
Ph: (248)488-9750   Fax: (248)488-9751
Executive search firm.

★4860★ Erlanger Holdings Inc.
2 Soundview Dr.
Greenwich, CT 06830
Ph: (203)629-5410   Fax: (203)629-5444
Executive search firm with second location in North Palm Beach, FL.

★4861★ ESA
141 Durham Rd., Ste. 16
Madison, CT 06443
Ph: (203)245-1983   Fax: (203)245-8428
Executive search firm.

★4862★ ET Search Inc.
1250 Prospect St., Ste. 101
La Jolla, CA 92037-3618
Ph: (858)459-3443   Fax: (858)459-4147
Executive search firm focused on the tax industry.

★4863★ ETI Search International
980 Hammond Dr., Ste. 650
Atlanta, GA 30328
Ph: (770)399-8492   Fax: (770)399-8487
Executive search firm.

★4864★ Executive Careers Ltd.
1801 Avenue of the Stars, Fl. 6
Los Angeles, CA 90067
Ph: (310)552-3455   Fax: (310)578-7524
Executive search firm.

★4865★ Executive Resources International LLC
Boston Harbor
63 Atlantic Ave.
Boston, MA 02110
Ph: (617)742-8970   Fax: (617)523-9093
Executive search firm.

★4866★ The Executive Roundtable
PO Box 64421
Souderton, PA 18964
Ph: (215)721-1650   Fax: (215)721-8650
Fr: 888-315-1150
Executive search firm.

★4867★ Executive Search Inc.
5401 Gamble Dr., Ste. 275
Minneapolis, MN 55416
Ph: (952)541-9153
Executive search firm.

★4868★ Executive Search World
Harbor Ct.
66 Queen St., Ste. 1802
Honolulu, HI 96813
Ph: (808)526-3812   Fax: (808)523-9356
Executive search firm for Hawaii.

★4869★ Executives Unlimited Inc.
6475 E. Pacific Coast Hwy., Ste. 369
Long Beach, CA 90803
Ph: (562)597-4466   Fr: (866)957-4466
Executive search firm. Branches in Western Springs, IL; Scotch Plains, NJ; Long Beach, CA.

★4870★ Ferneborg & Associates Inc.
160 Bovet Rd., Ste. 210
San Mateo, CA 94402
Ph: (650)577-0100   Fax: (650)577-0122
Executive search firm.

★4871★ First Advisory Services International
20626 W. Liberty Rd.
White Hall, MD 21161-9063
Ph: (410)329-2033
Executive search firm.

★4872★ Fitzgibbon & Associates
PO Box 1108
Media, PA 19063
Ph: (610)565-7566
Executive search firm focused on the communications industry.

★4873★ FM Industries
10125 Crosstown Circle, Ste. 300
Eden Prairie, MN 55344
Ph: (952)941-0966   Fax: (952)941-4462
Executive search firm.

★4874★ Forray Associates Inc.
2 Penn Plaza, Ste. 1910
New York, NY 10121
Ph: (212)279-0404
Executive search firm.

★4875★ Foster Partners
230W 41st St.
New York, NY 10036
Ph: (646)452-4601   Fax: (212)893-2309
Executive search firm affiliated with Daubenspeck and Associates Ltd. Branches in Washington, DC and Dallas.

★4876★ Fox-Morris
1617 JFK Blvd., Ste. 210
Philadelphia, PA 19103
Ph: (215)561-6300
Executive search firm. Branch locations in many states throughout the U.S.

★4877★ Franchot Cohen & Associates Inc.
810 Lake St. East
Wayzata, MN 55391
Ph: (952)253-0080   Fax: (952)253-0081
Executive search firm.

★4878★ Francis & Associates
6923 Vista Dr.
West Des Moines, IA 50266
Ph: (515)221-9800   Fax: (515)221-9806
Executive search firm.

★4879★ G Adams Partners
205 W. Wacker Dr., Ste. 810
Chicago, IL 60606
Ph: (312)673-0390   Fax: (312)673-0390
Executive search firm.

★4880★ Harvey Bell & Associates
700 Lindsay Ave.
Rohnert Park, CA 94928
Ph: (707)795-0650   Fax: (707)795-0655
Executive search firm.

★4881★ Heidrick and Struggles, Inc.
233 S. Wacker Dr., Ste. 4200
Sears Tower
Chicago, IL 60606-6303
Ph: (312)496-1200   Fax: (312)496-1290
URL: http://www.heidrick.com
Executive search firm. International organization with a variety of affiliate offices.

★4882★ J. Burkey Associates
900 Laurel Ave.
River Edge, NJ 07661
Ph: (201)262-7990   Fax: (201)262-7955
Executive search firm.

★4883★ J H Dugan & Company
225 Crossroads Blvd., Ste. 416
Carmel, CA 93923
Ph: (831)655-5880   Fax: (831)655-5588
Executive search firm.

★4884★ J Nicolas Arthur
77 Franklin St., Fl. 3
Boston, MA 02110
Ph: (617)204-9000   Fax: (617)303-8934
Executive search firm specializing in the finance industry.

★4885★ James Bangert & Associates Inc.
15500 Wayzata Blvd., Ste. 1030 F
Wayzata, MN 55391
Ph: (952)475-3454   Fax: (952)473-4306
Executive search firm.

★4886★ James Drury Partners
875 N. Michigan Ave., Ste. 3805
Chicago, IL 60611
Ph: (312)654-6708   Fax: (312)654-6710
Executive search firm.

★4887★ John C. Boone & Company
1807 Henley St.
Glenview, IL 60025
Ph: (847)998-1905
Executive search firm.

★4888★ John J. Davis & Associates Inc.
521 5th Ave., Ste. 1740
New York, NY 10175
Ph: (212)286-9489   Fax: (973)467-3706
Executive search firm.

★4889★ Joseph R. Burns & Associates Inc.
8 Stafford Dr.
Madison, NJ 07940
Ph: (973)377-1350   Fax: (973)377-9350
Executive search firm.

★4890★ Joy Reed Belt Search Consultants Inc.
5804 Grand Blvd.
PO Box 54410
Oklahoma City, OK 73154
Ph: (405)842-5155   Fax: (405)842-6357
Executive search firm. Branch in Tulsa, OK.

★4891★ J.R. Bechtle & Company
112 Water St., Ste. 500
Boston, MA 02109
Ph: (617)722-9980   Fax: (617)722-4130
Executive search firm.

★4892★ JT Brady & Associates
10900 Perry Hwy. 12203
Wexford, PA 15090
Ph: (412)934-2228   Fax: (724)935-8059
Executive search firm.

★4893★ Judith Cushman & Associates
1275 12th Ave. NW, Ste. 14
Issaquah, WA 98027
Ph: (425)392-8660   Fax: (425)391-9190
Executive search firm.

★4894★ JW Barleycorn & Associates Inc.
1614 Lancaster Ave.
Reynoldsburg, OH 43068
Ph: (614)861-4400   Fax: (614)861-5558
Executive search firm.

★4895★ Korn/Ferry International
200 Park Ave., Floor 37
New York, NY 10166
Ph: (212)687-1834   Fax: (212)986-5684
URL: http://www.kornferry.com
Executive search firm. International organization with a variety of affiliate offices.

★4896★ Management Recruiters International, Inc. (MRI)
200 Public Sq., Fl 31
Cleveland, OH 44122-2301
Ph: (216)696-1122   Fax: (216)696-3221
Fr: 800-875-4000
E-mail: allen.salikof@brilliantpeople.com
URL: http://ww.brilliantpeople.com
Executive search firm. More than 300 offices throughout the U.S.

★4897★ **Martin H. Bauman Associates LLC**
375 Park Ave., Ste. 2002
New York, NY 10152
Ph: (212)752-6580   Fax: (212)755-1096
Executive search firm.

★4898★ **Neil Fink Associates**
Ghirardelli Square
900 N. Point St., Ste. 210
San Francisco, CA 94109-1192
Ph: (415)441-3777   Fax: (415)775-4925
Executive search firm.

★4899★ **Neil Frank & Company**
PO Box 3570
Redondo Beach, CA 90277-1570
Ph: (310)543-1611   Fax: (310)540-2639
Executive search firm.

★4900★ **Paul Bodner & Associates Inc.**
1808 Taos Estates St.
Las Vegas, NV 89128
Ph: (702)386-9007   Fax: (702)386-9016
Executive search firm. Second branch in Denver, CO.

★4901★ **Paul Falcone Associates**
PO Box 115
Mount Freedom, NJ 07970
Ph: (973)895-5200   Fax: (973)895-5266
Executive search firm.

★4902★ **Paul J. Biestek Associates Inc.**
800 E. NW Hwy., Ste. 700
PO Box 101
Palatine, IL 60074
Ph: (847)825-5131
Executive search firm.

★4903★ **Philip Conway Management**
320 Hampton Place
Hinsdale, IL 60521-3823
Ph: (630)655-4566
Executive search firm.

★4904★ **Polly Brown Associates Inc.**
230 Park Ave., Ste. 1152
New York, NY 10169
Ph: (212)661-7575   Fax: (212)808-4126
Executive search firm.

★4905★ **R Gaines Baty Associates Inc.**
12750 Merit Dr., Ste. 990
Dallas, TX 75251
Ph: (972)386-7900   Fax: (972)387-2224
Executive search firm.

★4906★ **R J Dishaw & Associates**
PO Box 671262
Dallas, TX 75367-1262
Ph: (972)924-5000   Fax: (972)924-5003
Executive search firm.

★4907★ **Richard Clark & Associates Inc.**
9 W. 95th St., Ste. C
New York, NY 10025
Ph: (212)222-5600
Executive search firm.

★4908★ **Robert W. Dingman Company Inc.**
650 Hampshire Rd., Ste. 116
Westlake Village, CA 91361
Ph: (805)778-1777   Fax: (805)778-9288
Executive search firm with a second office in Black Forest, CO.

★4909★ **Roth Young of Minneapolis**
6212 Vernon Ct.
Minneapolis, MN 55436-1669
Ph: (952)831-6655   Fax: (952)831-7413
E-mail: info@rymn.com
URL: http://www.rymn.com
Executive search firm. Over 25 affiliated offices across the nation.

★4910★ **Russell Reynolds Associates, Inc.**
200 Park Ave., Ste. 2300
New York, NY 10166-0002
Ph: (212)351-2000   Fax: (212)370-0896
E-mail: info@russellreynolds.com
URL: http://www.russelreynolds.com
Executive search firm. Affiliate offices across the country and abroad.

★4911★ **Sanford Rose Associates (SRA Intern)**
3737 Embassy Pkwy. , Ste.200
Akron, OH 44333-8369
Ph: (330)670-9797   Fax: (330)670-9798
Fr: 800-731-7724
E-mail: hw@sanfordrose.com
URL: http://www.sanfordrose.com
Executive search firm. Over 80 franchised office locations nationwide.

★4912★ **Snelling and Snelling, Inc.**
6555 NW 9th Ave., Ste. 203
Ft. Lauderdale, FL 33309
Ph: (954)771-0090   Fax: (954)771-8583
Fr: 800-393-0090
E-mail: snelling@bellsouth.net
URL: http://www.snelling.com/ftlauderdale
Employment agency. Over 50 offices across the country.

★4913★ **Sunny Bates Associates**
345 7th Ave., Fl. 8
New York, NY 10001
Ph: (212)691-5252   Fax: (212)691-3133
Executive search firm.

★4914★ **306 Search Advisors Inc.**
230 Park Ave., Ste. 1000
New York, NY 10169
Ph: (646)435-5796
Executive search firm.

★4915★ **Valerie Fredrickson & Company**
800 Menlo Ave., Ste. 220
Menlo Park, CA 94025
Ph: (650)614-0220   Fax: (650)614-0223
Executive search firm.

★4916★ **William B. Arnold Associates Inc.**
600 S. Cherry St., Ste. 1105
Denver, CO 80246-1716
Ph: (303)393-6662
Executive search firm.

★4917★ **William J. Christopher Associates Inc.**
307 N. Walnut St.
West Chester, PA 19380
Ph: (610)696-4397
Executive search firm.

ONLINE JOB SOURCES AND SERVICES

★4918★ **American Society of Association Executives**
E-mail: career@asaenet.org
URL: http://www.asaenet.org
Description: Membership site for executives of non-profit associations. "Career Headquarters" section contains resources both for searching for employees and new positions. Executives can also search resumes and review a list of executive recruiters, plus read information on a number of employment-related issues. You do not have to be a member to view job boards.

★4919★ **A.T. Kearney Executive Search**
E-mail: executive_search@atkearney.com
URL: http://www.executivesearch.atkearney.com
Description: A.T. Kearney is an innovative, corporate-focused management consulting firm that ensures clients receive superior value in the digital economy. Executives may also submit their resumes through e-mail for

consideration for present and future searches conducted by Kearney.

★4920★ Christian & Timbers
E-mail: comments@ctnet.com
URL: http://www.ctnet.com

Description: Established in 1980, Christian & Timbers is considered one of the top retained executive search firms. Focusing on CEO, Board director and senior-level executive search and selection, their clients span high-profile early-stage companies to the Fortune 50 and EuroTop 500. Site contains information on recent job trends and articles on choosing an executive level recruiter.

★4921★ ExecuNet
URL: http://www.execunet.com

Description: Job site dedicated to the 100,000+K executive job seeker. Members may access job bank, recruiter and employer information, have their resumes reviewed, attend networking meetings, and access cutting-edge career information and references. **Fee:** Must become member to access services, cost is $219 for six-month membership.

★4922★ ExecutivesOnly
URL: http://Executivesonly.com

Description: Job site specializing in executive positions netting an annual salary of $70K or more. Members can view job bank and set up daily e-mail alerts. They may also choose to recruit the help of a senior adviser who can help review resumes and distribute them to recruiters. **Fee:** Must become member to access services.

★4923★ Heidrick & Struggles Management Search
URL: http://www.heidrick.com/default.aspx

Description: Executive search firm that will distribute registered resumes to recruiters with suitable positions available.

★4924★ MBA Careers
E-mail: support@mbacareers.com
URL: http://www.mbacareers.com

Description: Job site that provides resume posting, databank search and e-mail alert services to MBA and other advanced graduate degree holders.

★4925★ NetShare.com
E-mail: netshare@netshare.com
URL: http://www.netshare.com

Description: Members-only resource for $100,000+ executives who are actively searching for new positions or passively tracking the job market. Listings that match posted profile will be e-mailed. **Fee:** Fees vary by level of service; annual basic level dues are $325.

★4926★ Ray & Berndtson
E-mail: marketing@rayberndtson.com
URL: http://www.rayberndtson.com/

Description: Ray & Berndtson is an international executive search firm, specializing in recruiting services for top-level executives in the automotive, business and professional services, consumer products and services, e-business, energy and utilities, financial services, healthcare and life sciences, industrial products and services, education/not-for-profit, and technology industries.

★4927★ 6Figurejobs.com
E-mail: info@6figurejobs.com
URL: http://www.6figurejobs.com

Description: 6FigureJobs provides executives and experienced professionals with access to some of the most exclusive executive jobs, executive recruiters and career management tools available. Includes tools for both posting and viewing jobs, resume refinement, company research and more.

★4928★ SpencerStuart.com
E-mail: contact@spenserstuart.com
URL: http://www.spencerstuart.com

Description: Executive search firm; contains professionalism resources and assessment tools for career management. Seekers can post their resume online and receive e-mail alerts about newly posted positions, along with industry news and event announcements. Must sign up for membership to take full advantage of resources.

★4929★ Spherion Workforce Architects
URL: http://www.spherion.com

Description: Recruitment firm specializing in accounting and finance, sales and marketing, interim executives, technology, engineering, retail and human resources.

★4930★ Transearch.com
E-mail: contact@transearch.com
URL: http://www.transearch.com

Description: International executive search firm concentrating in searches for executives in retail, real estate, information technology, industry, life sciences and financial services. Seekers may search job board and submit their resume for recruiter review.

★4931★ WSA Executive Job Search Center
E-mail: info@atswsacorp.com
URL: http://www.wsacorp.com/index.asp

Description: A site intended for $50K-$700K range executives. Offers resume preparation, critiques and distribution, and interview preparation.

OTHER SOURCES

★4932★ Administration and Management Occupations
Delphi Productions
3160 4th St.
Boulder, CO 80304
Fax: (303)443-4022   Fr: 888-443-2400
URL: http://www.delphivideo.com

$95.00. 50 minutes. Part of the Careers for the 21st Century Video Library.

★4933★ American Almanac of Jobs and Salaries
Morrow Avon
1350 Avenue of the Americas
New York, NY 10019
Ph: (212)261-6788   Fr: 800-242-7737

John W. Wright. Revised edition, 2000. $20.00 (paper). 672 pages. This is a comprehensive guide to the wages of hundreds of occupations in a wide variety of industries and organizations.

★4934★ American Chamber of Commerce Executives (ACCE)
4875 Eisenhower Ave., Ste. 250
Alexandria, VA 22304-4850
Ph: (703)998-0072   Fax: (703)212-9512
E-mail: mfleming@acce.org
URL: http://www.acce.org

Members: Professional society of chamber of commerce executives and staff members.

★4935★ American Management Association (AMA)
1601 Broadway
New York, NY 10019-7420
Ph: (212)586-8100   Fax: (212)903-8168
Fr: 800-262-9699
E-mail: customerservice@amanet.org
URL: http://www.amanet.org

Members: American Management Association provides educational forums worldwide where members and their colleagues learn superior, practical business skills and explore best practices of world-class organizations through interaction with each other and expert faculty practitioners. **Purpose:** AMA's publishing program provides tools individuals use to extend learning beyond the classroom in a process of life-long professional growth and development through education.

★4936★ American Society of Association Executives (ASAE)
1575 I St. NW
Washington, DC 20005-1103
Ph: (202)626-2723   Fax: (202)371-8825
Fr: 888-950-2723
E-mail: pr@asaenet.org
URL: http://www.asaenet.org

Members: Professional society of paid executives of international, national, state, and local trade, professional, and philanthropic associations. **Purpose:** Seeks to educate association executives on effective management, including: the proper objectives, functions, and activities of associations; the basic principles of association management; the legal aspects of association activity; policies relating to association management; efficient methods, procedures, and techniques of association management; the responsibilities and professional standards of association executives. Maintains information resource center. **Activities:** Conducts resume, guidance, and consultation services; compiles statistics in the form of reports, surveys, and studies; carries out research and education. Maintains ASAE Services Corporation to provide special services and ASAE Foundation to do future-oriented research and make grant awards. Offers executive search services and insurance programs. Provides CEO center for chief staff executives. Conducts Certified Association Executive (CAE) program.

★4937★ **Center for Creative Leadership (CCL)**
PO Box 26300
One Leadership Pl.
Greensboro, NC 27438-6300
Ph: (336)545-2810   Fax: (336)282-3284
E-mail: info@leaders.ccl.org
URL: http://www.ccl.org

Description: Promotes behavioral science research and leadership education.

★4938★ **The International Alliance for Women (TIAW)**
8405 Greensboro Dr., Ste. 800
McLean, VA 22102
Ph: (703)506-3284   Fax: (703)506-3266
E-mail: info@tiaw.org
URL: http://www.tiaw.org

Members: Local networks (32) comprising 10,000 professional and executive women in 12 countries; individual businesswomen without a network affiliation (225) are alliance associates. Seeks to promote recognition of the achievements of women in business; encourage placement of women in senior executive positions; maintain high standards of professional competence among members. Facilitates communication on an international scale among professional women's networks and their members. Represents members' interests before policymake business and government. **Activities:** Sponsors programs that support equal opportunity and enhance members' business and professional skills Operates appointments and directors service. Maintains speakers' bureau.

★4939★ **National Association of Corporate Directors (NACD)**
1828 L St. NW, Ste. 801
Washington, DC 20036
Ph: (202)775-0509   Fax: (202)775-4857
E-mail: info@nacdonline.org
URL: http://www.nacdonline.org

Members: Corporate directors and boards of directors; chief executive officers, presidents, accountants, lawyers, consultants, and other executives are members. **Activities:** Conducts research, surveys, and seminars.

★4940★ **National Management Association (NMA)**
2210 Arbor Blvd.
Dayton, OH 45439
Ph: (937)294-0421   Fax: (937)294-2374
E-mail: nma@nma1.org
URL: http://www.nma1.org

Description: Business and industrial management personnel; membership comes from supervisory level, with the remainder from middle management and above. Seeks to develop and recognize management as a profession and to promote the free enterprise system. Prepares chapter programs on basic management, management policy and practice, communications, human behavior, industrial relations, economics, political education, and liberal education. Maintains speakers' bureau and hall of fame. Maintains educational, charitable, and research programs. Sponsors charitable programs.

★4941★ **National Society of Hispanic MBAs (NSHMBA)**
1303 W Walnut Hill Ln., Ste. 300
Irving, TX 75038
Fax: (214)596-9325   Fr: 877-467-4622
E-mail: agonzalez@nshmba.org
URL: http://www.nshmba.org

Description: Hispanic MBA professional business network dedicated to economic and philanthropic advancement.

★4942★ **Women in Management (WIM)**
PO Box 9560
Springfield, IL 62791-9560
Fax: (217)544-2706   Fr: 877-946-6285
E-mail: nationalwim@aol.com
URL: http://www.wimonline.org

Description: Support network of women in professional and management positions that facilitates the exchange of experience and ideas. Promotes self-growth in management; provides speakers who are successful in management; sponsors workshops and special interest groups to discuss problems and share job experiences.

Geographers

Sources of Help-Wanted Ads

★4943★ AAG Newsletter

Association of American Geographers
1710 16th St. NW
Washington, DC 20009-3198
Ph: (202)234-1450   Fax: (202)234-2744

Description: Monthly. Publishes items of interest to Association members and persons in related disciplines. Contains news of research, news of members, listings of publications, information on grant and employment opportunities, notices of field courses and seminars, calls for papers, and a calendar of events.

★4944★ Base Line

Map and Geography Round Table
c/o James A. Coombs
SW Missiouri State Univ.
Maps Library
Springfield, MO 65804-0095
Ph: (417)280-3205   Fax: (417)280-3257
Fr: 800-545-2433
URL: http://magert.whoi.edu:8000/

Description: Bimonthly. Provides current information on cartographic materials, publications of interest to map and geography librarians, related government activities, and map librarianship. Recurring features include conference and meeting information, news of research, job listings, and columns by the Division chair and the editor.

★4945★ Geographical Review

American Geographical Society
120 Wall St., Ste. 100
New York, NY 10005
Ph: (212)422-5456   Fax: (212)422-5480

Quarterly. $76.00/year for individuals; $25.00 for single issue; $126.00/year for institutions; $147.00/year, foreign; $38.00/year for students. Periodical covering the field of geography.

★4946★ PE & RS Photogrammetric Engineering & Remote Sensing

The Imaging and Geospatial Information
  Society
5410 Grosvenor Ln., Ste. 210
Bethesda, MD 20814
Ph: (301)493-0290   Fax: (301)493-0208
E-mail: asprs@asprs.org

Monthly. $130.00/year. Journal covering photogrammetry, remote sensing, geographic information systems, cartography, and surveying, global positioning systems, digital photogrammetry.

★4947★ The Professional Geographer

San Diego State University
5500 Campanile Dr.
San Diego, CA 92182-7700
Ph: (619)594-4199   Fax: (619)594-7277
E-mail: progeog@mail.sdsu.edu

Quarterly. $132.00/year for individuals; $154.00/year. Geographical journal.

Placement and Job Referral Services

★4948★ African Studies Association (ASA)

Rutgers the State University of New
  Jersey
132 George St.- Douglass Campus
New Brunswick, NJ 08901-1400
Ph: (732)932-8173
E-mail: callasa@rci.rutgers.edu

Members: Persons specializing in teaching, writing, or research on Africa including political scientists, historians, geographers, anthropologists, economists, librarians, linguists, and government officials; persons who are studying African subjects; institutional members are universities, libraries, government agencies, and others interested in receiving information about Africa. **Purpose:** Seeks to foster communication and to stimulate research among scholars on Africa. **Activities:** Sponsors placement service; conducts panels and discussion groups; presents exhibits and films.

Employer Directories and Networking Lists

★4949★ Guide to Programs in Geography in the United States and Canada/AAG Handbook and Directory of Geographers

Association of American Geographers
1710 16th St. NW
Washington, DC 20009-3198
Ph: (202)234-1450   Fax: (202)234-2744
E-mail: guide@aag.org

Annual, September. $50.00; $25.00 for students. Covers approximately 300 institutions and 7,000 individuals. Entries include: For institutions-Department, address, and phone, contact person, requirements, programs, facilities, financial aid, faculty, titles of dissertations and theses completed. For individuals-Name, address, birth date, degrees received, place of employment. Arrangement: Geographical. Indexes: Department specialty; ZIP code.

Handbooks and Manuals

★4950★ Careers Using Geography

Kogan Page
120 Pentonville Rd.
London N1 9JN, United Kingdom

Patrick Talbot. March 2000. Includes practical tips, case studies, and contact points for getting further information.

★4951★ Opportunities in Social Science Careers

McGraw-Hill Companies
860 Taylor Station Rd.
Blacklick, OH 43004-0545
Fax: (614)755-5645   Fr: 800-722-4726

Rosanne J. Marek. March 2004. $22.95. 160 Pages. VGM Opportunities Series.

★4952★ Research Opportunities in Geography at the U.S. Geological Survey

National Academies Press
500 Fifth St. NW
Washington, DC 20055
Ph: (202)334-3313   Fax: (202)334-2451
Fr: 888-624-7654

October 2002. $32.00. Illustrated. 144 pages. Earth Sciences.

OTHER SOURCES

★4953★ American Geographical Society

120 Wall St., Ste. 100
New York, NY 10005
Ph: (212)422-5456
URL: http://www.amergeog.org

Description: Industry professionals and other interested individuals.

★4954★ ASPRS - The Imaging and Geospatial Information Society

5410 Grosvenor Ln., Ste. 210
Bethesda, MD 20814-2160
Ph: (301)493-0290   Fax: (301)493-0208
E-mail: asprs@asprs.org
URL: http://www.asprs.org

Members: Firms, individuals, government employees, and academicians engaged in photogrammetry, photointerpretation, remote sensing, and geographic information systems and their application to such fields as archaeology, geographic information systems, military reconnaissance, urban planning, engineering, traffic surveys, meteorological observations, medicine, geology, forestry, agriculture, construction, and topographic mapping. Mission is to advance knowledge and improve understanding of these sciences and to promote responsible applications. **Activities:** Offers voluntary certification program open to persons associated with one or more functional area of photogrammetry, remote sensing, and GIS. Surveys the profession of private firms in photogrammetry and remote sensing in the areas of productsand services

★4955★ Association of American Geographers (AAG)

1710 16th St. NW
Washington, DC 20009-3198
Ph: (202)234-1450   Fax: (202)234-2744
E-mail: gaia@aag.org
URL: http://www.aag.org

Description: Professional society of educators and scientists in the field of geography. Seeks to further professional investigations in geography and to encourage the application of geographic research in education, government, and business. Conducts research; compiles statistics.

★4956★ Geography Education National Implementation Project

Texas A & M University
College Station, TX 77843
Ph: (979)845-1579   Fax: (979)862-4487
URL: http://genip.tamu.edu

Description: Consortium of geographic associations committed to improving the status and quality of geography education.

★4957★ National Council for Geographic Education (NCGE)

206A Martin Hall
Jacksonville State University
Jacksonville, AL 36265-1602
Ph: (256)782-5293   Fax: (256)782-5336
E-mail: ncge@jsucc.jsu.edu
URL: http://www.ncge.org

Description: Teachers of geography and social studies in elementary and secondary schools, colleges, and universities; geographers in governmental agencies and private businesses. Encourages the training of teachers in geographic concepts, practices, teaching methods, and techniques; works to develop effective geographic educational programs in schools and colleges and with adult groups; stimulates the production and use of accurate and understandable geographic teaching aids and materials.

★4958★ Scientific, Engineering, and Technical Services

Cambridge Educational
2572 Brunswick Ave.
Lawrenceville, NJ 08648-4128
Fax: 800-FAX-ON-US   Fr: 800-468-4227
URL: http://www.cambridgeeducational.com

$89.95. 2002. 18 minutes. Part of the Career Cluster Series.

Geologists and Geophysicists

SOURCES OF HELP-WANTED ADS

★4959★ *AAPG Bulletin*
American Association of Petroleum
 Geologists
1444 S Boulder
PO Box 979
Tulsa, OK 74101-0979
Ph: (918)584-2555   Fax: (918)560-2636
Fr: 800-364-AAPG
E-mail: bulletin@aapg.org
URL: http://www.aapg.org

Monthly. $290.00/year for individuals;
$320.00/year for other countries; $375.00/
year for other countries by airmail; $16.00 for
single issue, members; $25.00 for single
issue, nonmembers. Peer-reviewed journal
on the application of geological and geophysical principles to exploration and production
for the development of energy resources.
Subjects include petroleum geology, oil sha-
le, coal, uranium, and geothermal energy.

★4960★ *AAPG Explorer*
American Association of Petroleum
 Geologists
1444 S Boulder
PO Box 979
Tulsa, OK 74101-0979
Ph: (918)584-2555   Fax: (918)560-2636
Fr: 800-364-AAPG
E-mail: postmaster@aapq.org
URL: http://www.aapg.org

Monthly. $63.00/year for individuals; $7.00
for single issue. Magazine containing articles
about energy issues with an emphasis on
exploration for hydrocarbons and energy
minerals.

★4961★ *AEG News*
Association of Engineering Geologists
PO Box 460518
Denver, CO 80246
Ph: (303)757-2926   Fax: (303)757-2969
Description: Bimonthly. Covers news of the
engineering geology profession and the Association, whose members are engineering
geologists and geological engineers worldwide. Recurring features include letters to
the editor, a calendar of events, news of
research, and short articles of technical
interest.

★4962★ *AWIS Magazine*
Association for Women in Science
1200 New York Ave. NW, Ste. 650
Washington, DC 20005
Ph: (202)326-8940   Fax: (202)326-8960
Fr: 800-886-AWIS
Description: Bimonthly. Covers issues, legislation, and trends related to science education for girls, women, and minorities. Includes information on grants and fellowships, job openings, educational programs,
events, and notices of publications available.

★4963★ *Engineering and Mining
Journal*
Primedia Business
9800 Metcalf Ave.
Overland Park, KS 66212
Ph: (913)341-1300   Fax: (913)967-1898
URL: http://www.e-mj.com

Monthly. $79.00/year, Canada and U.S.;
$129.00/year for other countries. Provides
professionals in metallic and nonmetallic
ores and minerals industries with news and
technical economic information.

★4964★ *Gaea*
Association for Women Geoscientists
PO Box 280
Broomfield, CO 80038-0280
E-mail: gaea@awg.org
Description: Bimonthly. Serves as an exchange of technical and professional information for the purpose of enhancing the
professional growth and advancement of
women in the geosciences. Explores opportunities and careers available in the geosciences and announces workshops and seminars on job hunting techniques, management skills, and career and life planning.
Recurring features include news of members, Association updates, and notices of
awards granted.

★4965★ *Geology*
Geological Society of America Inc.
PO Box 9140
Boulder, CO 80301-9140
Ph: (303)447-2020   Fax: (303)357-1070
Fr: 800-472-1988
URL: http://www.geosociety.org

Monthly. $350.00/year for U.S., Canada, and
Mexico; $360.00/year for other countries.
Geology journal.

★4966★ *Nature International Weekly
Journal of Science*
Nature Publishing Group
345 Park Ave. S
New York, NY 10010-1707
Ph: (212)726-9200   Fax: (212)689-9711
Fr: 888-331-6288
E-mail: nature@natureny.com
URL: http://www.nature.com

Weekly. $145.00/year for individuals;
$495.00/year for institutions. Magazine cov-
ering science and technology, including the
fields of biology, biochemistry, genetics,
medicine, earth sciences, physics, pharmacology, and behavioral sciences.

★4967★ *Oil & Gas Journal*
PennWell Corp.
1700 W Loop S, Ste. 1000
Houston, TX 77027
Ph: (713)621-9720   Fax: (713)963-6296
Fr: 800-736-6935
URL: http://www.ogjonline.com

Weekly. $79.00/year for individuals. Trade
magazine serving engineers and managers
in international petroleum operations.

★4968★ *PE & RS Photogrammetric
Engineering & Remote Sensing*
The Imaging and Geospatial Information
 Society
5410 Grosvenor Ln., Ste. 210
Bethesda, MD 20814
Ph: (301)493-0290   Fax: (301)493-0208
E-mail: asprs@asprs.org

Monthly. $130.00/year. Journal covering
photogrammetry, remote sensing, geographic information systems, cartography, and

surveying, global positioning systems, digital photogrammetry.

★4969★ *PRISCUM*

Paleontological Society
118 Ozark Hall
Department of Geology
University of Arkansas
Fayetteville, AR 72701
Ph: (501)575-3370   Fax: (501)575-3846

Description: Semiannual. Carries news of membership activities and announcements of events, publications, employment opportunities, and activities pertaining to geology and paleontology. Recurring features include notices of awards, available sources of research funding, notices of new journals and books available, and book reviews.

★4970★ *The Scientist*

The Scientist Inc.
3535 Market St., Ste. 200
Philadelphia, PA 19104-2645
Ph: (215)386-9601   Fax: (215)386-7542
Fr: 800-258-6008
E-mail: info@the-scientist.com
URL: http://www.the-scientist.com

Biweekly. $49.00/year for individuals; $149.00/year for institutions; $24.00/year for students; $82.00/year for other countries; $49.00/year for students, other countries; $174.00/year for institutions, other countries. News journal (tabloid) for life scientists featuring news, opinions, research, and professional section.

PLACEMENT AND JOB REFERRAL SERVICES

★4971★ **American Geophysical Union (AGU)**

2000 Florida Ave. NW
Washington, DC 20009-1277
Ph: (202)462-6900   Fax: (202)328-0566
Fr: 800-966-AGU1
E-mail: service@agu.org
URL: http://www.agu.org

Members: Individuals professionally associated with the field of geophysics; supporting institutional members are companies and other organizations whose work involves geophysics. **Purpose:** Promotes the study of problems concerned with the figure and physics of the earth; initiates and coordinates research that depends upon national and international cooperation and provides for scientific discussion of research results. **Activities:** Sponsors placement service at semiannual meeting.

★4972★ **Geological Society of America (GSA)**

3300 Penrose Pl.
PO Box 9140
Boulder, CO 80301-9140
Ph: (303)447-2020   Fax: (303)357-1070
Fr: 888-443-4472
E-mail: gsa@geosociety.org
URL: http://www.geosociety.org

Description: Professional society of earth scientists. Promotes the science of geology. Maintains placement service.

★4973★ **Korean Scientists and Engineers Association in America (KSEA)**

1952 Gallows Rd., Ste. 300
Vienna, VA 22182
Ph: (703)748-1221   Fax: (703)748-1331
E-mail: sejong@ksea.org
URL: http://www.ksea.org

Description: Scientists and engineers holding single or advanced degrees. Goals are to: promote friendship and mutuality among Korean and American scientists and engineers; contribute to Korea's scientific, technological, industrial, and economic developments; strengthen the scientific, technological, and cultural bonds between Korea and the U.S. Sponsors symposium. Maintains speakers' bureau, placement service, and biographical archives. Compiles statistics. Maintains 100 volume library of scientific handbooks and yearbooks in Korean.

★4974★ **National Ground Water Association (NGWA)**

601 Dempsey Rd.
Westerville, OH 43081
Ph: (614)898-7791   Fax: (614)898-7786
Fr: 800-551-7379
E-mail: ngwa@ngwa.org
URL: http://www.ngwa.org

Description: Ground water drilling contractors; manufacturers and suppliers of drilling equipment; ground water scientists such as geologists, engineers, public health officials, and others interested in the problems of locating, developing, preserving, and using ground water supplies. Conducts seminars, and continuing education programs. Encourages scientific education, research, and the development of standards; offers placement services; compiles market statistics. Offers charitable program. Maintains speakers bureau.

EMPLOYER DIRECTORIES AND NETWORKING LISTS

★4975★ *American Men and Women of Science*

Thomson Gale
27500 Drake Rd.
Farmington Hills, MI 48331-3535
Ph: (248)699-4253   Fax: (248)699-8065
Fr: 800-877-GALE

E-mail: amws@galegroup.com

Biennial, latest edition December 2002. $975.00. Covers over 129,700 U.S. and Canadian scientists active in the physical, biological, mathematical, computer science, and engineering fields; includes references to previous edition for deceased scientists and nonrespondents. Entries include: Name, address, education, personal and career data, memberships, honors and awards, research interest. Arrangement: Alphabetical. Indexes: Discipline (in separate volume).

★4976★ *Directory of Certified Petroleum Geologists*

American Association of Petroleum Geologists
1444 S Boulder
PO Box 979
Tulsa, OK 74101-0979
Ph: (918)584-2555   Fax: (918)560-2636
Fr: 800-364-AAPG

Covers about 3,400 members of the association. Entries include: Name, address; education and career data; whether available for consulting. Arrangement: Alphabetical. Indexes: Geographical.

★4977★ *Directory of Physics, Astronomy, and Geophysics Staff*

American Institute of Physics
1 Physics Ellipse
College Park, MD 20740-3843
Ph: (301)209-3100   Fax: (301)209-0843
URL: http://www.aip.org/catalog/books/dpags.html

Biennial. $65.00. Covers 31,000 staff members at 2,300 colleges, universities, and laboratories throughout North America that employ physicists and astronomers; list of foreign organizations. Entries include: Name, address, phone, fax, email address. Arrangement: Separate alphabetical sections for individuals, academic institutions, and laboratories. Indexes: Academic institution location, type of laboratory.

★4978★ *The Geophysical Directory*

Geophysical Directory Inc.
PO Box 130508
Houston, TX 77219
Ph: (713)529-8789   Fax: (713)529-3646
Fr: 800-929-2462
E-mail: info@geophysicaldirectory.com

Annual, March. $125.00 within USA; $140.00 outside USA. Covers about 4,000 companies that provide geophysical equipment, supplies, or services, and mining and petroleum companies that use geophysical techniques; international coverage. Entries include: Company name, address, phone, fax, names of principal executives, operations, and sales personnel; similar information for branch locations. Arrangement: Classified by product or service. Indexes: Company name, personal name.

★4979★ Geophysicists: A Directory of AGU Members

American Geophysical Union
2000 Florida Ave. NW
Washington, DC 20009
Ph: (202)462-6900   Fax: (202)328-0566
Fr: 800-966-2481
URL: http://www.agu.org

Covers 40,000 member geophysicists. Entries include: Name, address, office and home phone numbers, fax, email addresses, type of membership, year joined, and section affiliation. Arrangement: Alphabetical.

★4980★ The Oil & Gas Directory

Geophysical Directory Inc.
PO Box 130508
Houston, TX 77219
Ph: (713)529-8789   Fax: (713)529-3646
Fr: 800-929-2462
E-mail: info@theoilandandgasdirectory.com

Annual, October. $105.00 within USA; $120.00 outside of USA. Covers about 9,000 companies worldwide involved in petroleum exploration, drilling, and production, and suppliers to the industry. Entries include: Company name, address, phone, fax, names of principal personnel, branch office addresses, phone numbers, and key personnel. Arrangement: Classified by activity. Indexes: Company name, personal name.

★4981★ Peterson's Job Opportunities in Engineering and Technology

Thomson Peterson's
PO Box 67005
Lawrenceville, NJ 08648-6105
Fr: 800-338-3282

Compiled by the Peterson's staff. Fourth edition, 1996. $21.95 (paper). 384 pages. Profiles 2,000 high-tech companies looking primarily for technical personnel in such fields as biotechnology, telecommunications, software, computers and peripherals, defense, and aerospace. Contains job-search strategies and career options to help match education and expertise to the job market. Indexed geographically, by industry, and by hiring needs.

★4982★ Society of Exploration Geophysicists-Yearbook

Society of Exploration Geophysicists
8801 S. Yale Ave., Ste.500
Tulsa, OK 74137-3575
Ph: (918)497-5500   Fax: (918)497-5557
URL: http://seg.org/publications/yearbook/

Annual, May. $40.00. Publication includes: Membership roster of nearly 14,500 geophysicists, corporations, and students. Entries include: Name, address, phone, fax, e-mail type of member; affiliation given for individuals. Arrangement: Alphabetical; geographical.

HANDBOOKS AND MANUALS

★4983★ Becoming an Independent Geologist: Thriving in Good Times & Bad

American Association of Petroleum Geologist
PO Box 979
Tulsa, OK 74101-9979
Fax: (918)560-2632

James A. Gibbs. 1999. $12.00 (paper).

★4984★ The Best Resumes for Scientists and Engineers

John Wiley & Sons Inc.
1 Wiley Dr.
Somerset, NJ 08873
Ph: (732)469-4400   Fr: 800-225-5945

Adele Lewis and David J. Moore. Second edition, 1993. $37.50; $19.95 (paper). 224 pages. Presents an extensive collection of scientific and engineering resumes, highlighting the important differences between these and resumes written for other occupations.

★4985★ Career Information Center

Macmillan Publishing Co. Inc.
200 Old Tappan Rd.
Old Tappan, NJ 07675
Fr: 800-428-5331

Visual Education Center Staff. Seventh edition, 1999. $275.00. 2080 pages. This 13-volume set profiles over 600 occupations. Each occupational profile describes job duties, educational requirements, how to get the job, advancement possibilities, employment outlook, working conditions, earnings and benefits, and where to write for more information.

★4986★ Careers in Environmental Geoscience

American Association of Petroleum Geologists
PO Box 979
Tulsa, OK 74101-0979
Ph: (918)584-2555   Fax: (918)560-2652
Fr: 800-364-2274

Robert R. Jordan, Rima Petrossian and William J. Murphy. 1996. $5.00 (paper). 54 pages.

★4987★ Guide to Nontraditional Careers in Science

Hemisphere Publishing Corp.
325 Chestnut St., 8th Fl.
Philadelphia, PA 19106
Ph: (215)785-5800   Fax: (215)269-0363
Fr: 800-821-8312

Karen Young Kreeger. 1998. $38.95 (paper). 263 pages.

★4988★ Guiding Your Career As a Professional Geologist

American Association of Petroleum Geologists
PO Box 979
Tulsa, OK 74101-0979
Ph: (918)584-2555   Fax: (918)560-2652
Fr: 800-364-2274

Peter R. Rose, editor. 1994. $5.00 (paper). 78 pages.

★4989★ Opportunities in Research and Development Careers

McGraw-Hill/Contemporary Books
1221 Avenue of the Americas
New York, NY 10020
Ph: (212)904-2000   Fr: 800-323-4900
E-mail: ntcpub@tribune.com

Jan Goldberg. 1997. $14.95; $11.95 (paper). 204 pages.

★4990★ Resumes for Scientific and Technical Careers

McGraw-Hill Contemporary Books
1221 Avenue of the Americas
New York, NY 10020
Ph: (212)904-2000   Fr: 800-323-4900
E-mail: ntcpub@tribune.com

1999. $9.95 (paper). 450 pages. Provides resume advice for individuals interested in working in scientific and technical careers. Includes sample resumes and cover letters.

★4991★ To Boldly Go: A Practical Career Guide for Scientists

American Geophysical Union
2000 Florida Ave., NW
Washington, DC 20009
Ph: (202)462-6900   Fax: (202)328-0566
Fr: 800-966-2481

Peter S. Fiske. 1996. $19.00 (paper).

TRADESHOWS

★4992★ Geological Society of America Annual Meeting and GeoScience Expo

Geological Society of America Inc.
3300 Penrose Pl.
PO Box 9140
Boulder, CO 80301
Ph: (303)447-2020   Fax: (303)447-0648
Fr: 800-472-1988
E-mail: mball@geosociety.org
URL: http://www.geosociety.org

Annual. **Primary Exhibits:** Geology equipment, supplies, and services including instrumentation and computer hardware and software.

★4993★ **Society of Exploration Geophysicists Annual International Meeting and Exposition**

Society of Exploration Geophysicists
PO Box 702740
Tulsa, OK 74170
Ph: (918)497-5539   Fax: (918)497-5552
URL: http://www.seg.org

Annual. **Primary Exhibits:** Geophysical products and services, computer hardware and software, data storage, visualization technology. **Dates and Locations:** 2004 Oct 10-15; Denver, CO; Denver Convention Center • 2005 Nov 06-11; Houston, TX; George R. Brown Convention Center.

OTHER SOURCES

★4994★ *American Almanac of Jobs and Salaries*

Morrow Avon
1350 Avenue of the Americas
New York, NY 10019
Ph: (212)261-6788   Fr: 800-242-7737

John W. Wright. Revised edition, 2000. $20.00 (paper). 672 pages. This is a comprehensive guide to the wages of hundreds of occupations in a wide variety of industries and organizations.

★4995★ **American Geological Institute (AGI)**

4220 King St.
Alexandria, VA 22302-1502
Ph: (703)379-2480   Fax: (703)379-7563
E-mail: agi@agiweb.org
URL: http://www.agiweb.org

Members: Federation of national scientific and technical societies in the earth sciences. **Purpose:** Seeks to stimulate public understanding of geological sciences; improve teaching of the geological sciences in schools, colleges, and universities; maintain high standards of professional training and conduct; work for the general welfare of members. **Activities:** Provides career guidance program.

★4996★ **American Institute of Professional Geologists (AIPG)**

8703 Yates Dr., Ste. 200
Westminster, CO 80031
Ph: (303)412-6205   Fax: (303)253-9220
E-mail: aipg@aipg.org
URL: http://www.aipg.org

Members: Geologists. **Purpose:** Provides certification to geologists attesting to their competence and integrity. Represents the geologic profession before government bodies and the public.

★4997★ **ASPRS - The Imaging and Geospatial Information Society**

5410 Grosvenor Ln., Ste. 210
Bethesda, MD 20814-2160
Ph: (301)493-0290   Fax: (301)493-0208
E-mail: asprs@asprs.org
URL: http://www.asprs.org

Members: Firms, individuals, government employees, and academicians engaged in photogrammetry, photointerpretation, remote sensing, and geographic information systems and their application to such fields as archaeology, geographic information systems, military reconnaissance, urban planning, engineering, traffic surveys, meteorological observations, medicine, geology, forestry, agriculture, construction, and topographic mapping. Mission is to advance knowledge and improve understanding of these sciences and to promote responsible applications. **Activities:** Offers voluntary certification program open to persons associated with one or more functional area of photogrammetry, remote sensing, and GIS. Surveys the profession of private firms in photogrammetry and remote sensing in the areas of products and services

★4998★ **Association of Engineering Geologists (AEG)**

720 S Colorado Blvd., Ste. 960-S
PO Box 460518
Denver, CO 80246
Ph: (303)757-2926   Fax: (303)757-2969
E-mail: aeg@aegweb.org
URL: http://www.aegweb.org

Members: Graduate geologists and geological engineers; full members must have five years experience in the field of engineering geology. **Purpose:** Seeks to provide a forum for the discussion and dissemination of technical and scientific information; encourage the advancement of professional recognition, scientific research, and high ethical and professional standards. Has compiled information on engineering geology curricula of colleges and universities. Promotes public understanding, health, safety, and welfare, and acceptance of the engineering geology profession. **Activities:** Conducts technical sessions, symposia, abstracts, and short courses; cosponsors seminars and conferences with other professional and technical societies and organizations.

★4999★ **Association of Ground Water Scientists and Engineers - A Division of National Ground Water Association (AGWSE)**

601 Dempsey Rd.
Westerville, OH 43081
Ph: (614)898-7791   Fax: (614)898-7786
Fr: 800-551-7379
E-mail: ngwa@ngwa.org
URL: http://www.ngwa.org/membership/ag-benft.html

Description: A technical division of the National Ground Water Association. Hydrogeologists, geologists, hydrologists, civil and environmental engineers, geochemists, biologists, and scientists in related fields. Seek to provide leadership and guidance for scientific, economical, and beneficial groundwater development; promote the use, protection, and management of the world's groundwater resources. Conducts educational programs, seminars, short courses, symposia, and field research projects. Maintains speakers' bureau and museum; offers placement service; sponsors competitions; compiles statistics.

★5000★ **Association for International Practical Training (AIPT)**

10400 Little Patuxent Pky., Ste. 250
Columbia, MD 21044-3519
Ph: (410)997-2200   Fax: (410)992-3924
E-mail: aipt@aipt.org
URL: http://www.aipt.org

Description: Providers worldwide on-the-job training programs for students and professionals seeking international career development and life-changing experiences. Arranges workplace exchanges in hundreds of professional fields, bringing employers and trainees together from around the world. Client list ranges from small farming communities to Fortune 500 companies.

★5001★ **Association for Women Geoscientists (AWG)**

PO Box 30645
Lincoln, NE 68503-0645
Fax: (402)489-8122
E-mail: office@awg.org
URL: http://www.awg.org

Members: Men and women geologists, geophysicists, petroleum engineers, geological engineers, hydrogeologists, paleontologists, geochemists, and other geoscientists. **Purpose:** Aims to: encourage the participation of women in the geosciences; exchange educational, technical, and professional information; enhance the professional growth and advancement of women in the geosciences. Provides information through web site on opportunities and careers available to women in the geosciences. **Activities:** Sponsors educational booths and programs at geological society conventions. Operates charitable program. Maintains speakers' bureau, and Association for Women Geoscientists Foundation (educational arm).

★5002★ *Environmental Occupations: Professional*

Delphi Productions
3160 4th St.
Boulder, CO 80304
Fax: (303)443-4022   Fr: 888-443-2400
URL: http://www.delphivideo.com

$95.00. 49 minutes. Part of the Emerging Careers Video Library.

★5003★ *Environmental Occupations: Technical*

Delphi Productions
3160 4th St.
Boulder, CO 80304
Fax: (303)443-4022   Fr: 888-443-2400
URL: http://www.delphivideo.com

$95.00. 48 minutes. Part of the Emerging Careers Video Library.

★5004★ Marine Technology Society (MTS)

5565 Sterrett Pl., No. 108
Columbia, MD 21044
Ph: (410)884-5330   Fax: (410)884-9060
E-mail: mtsmbrship@erols.com
URL: http://www.mtsociety.org

Description: Scientists, engineers, educators, and others with professional interests in the marine sciences or related fields; includes institutional and corporate members. Disseminates marine scientific and technical information, including institutional, environmental, physical, and biological aspects; fosters a deeper understanding of the world's seas and attendant technologies. Maintains 13 sections and 29 professional committees. Conducts tutorials.

★5005★ Minority Women In Science (MWIS)

Directorate for Education and Human
  Resources Programs
1200 New York Ave. NW
Washington, DC 20005
Ph: (202)326-7019   Fax: (202)371-9849
E-mail: sassefa@aaas.org

Description: A national network group of the American association for the Advancement of Science (AAAS), Education and Human Resources Directorate. The objectives of this group are: to identify and share information on resources and programs that could help in mentoring young women and minorities interested in science and engineering careers, and to strengthen communication among women and minorities in science and education.

★5006★ The Petroleum Industry

Evon Publishing
832 N 7th Ave.
Iron River, MI 49935
Ph: (906)265-3190

Audiocassette. 1996. $16.95. 32 minutes. Part of the Careers and Vocational Guidance Series. Provides information about the nature of the work, educational requirements, employment outlook, earnings, and work conditions as well as additional related information.

★5007★ Scientific, Engineering, and Technical Services

Cambridge Educational
2572 Brunswick Ave.
Lawrenceville, NJ 08648-4128
Fax: 800-FAX-ON-US   Fr: 800-468-4227
URL: http://www.cambridgeeducational.com

$89.95. 2002. 18 minutes. Part of the Career Cluster Series.

★5008★ Scientific Occupations

Delphi Productions
3160 4th St.
Boulder, CO 80304
Fax: (303)443-4022   Fr: 888-443-2400
URL: http://www.delphivideo.com

$95.00. 60 minutes. Part of the Careers for the 21st Century Video Library.

★5009★ Society of Exploration Geophysicists (SEG)

8801 S Yale
PO Box 702740
Tulsa, OK 74170
Ph: (918)497-5500   Fax: (918)497-5557
E-mail: web@seg.org
URL: http://www.seg.org

Description: Individuals having eight years of education and experience in exploration geophysics or geology. Promotes the science of geophysics, especially as it applies to the exploration for petroleum and other minerals. Encourages high professional standards among members; supports the common interests of members. Maintains SEG Foundation, which receives contributions from companies and individuals and distributes them in the form of scholarships to students of geophysics and related subjects. Offers short continuing education courses to geophysicists and geologists. Maintains 37 committees, including: Development and Production; Engineering and Groundwater Geophysics; Mining and Geothermal; Offshore Exploration and Oceanography.

Graphic Artists

★5010★ **ACM Transactions on Graphics**

Association for Computing Machinery
1515 Broadway
New York, NY 10036
Ph: (212)626-0500   Fax: (212)944-1318
Fr: 800-342-6626
URL: http://www.acm.org/

Quarterly. $45.00/year for members; $170.00/year for nonmembers; $40.00/year for students. Computer graphics journal.

★5011★ **Computer Graphics World**

PennWell Corp.
98 Spit Brook Rd.
Nashua, NH 03062-5737
Ph: (603)891-0123   Fax: (603)891-0574
URL: http://cgw.pennnet.com/home.cfm

Monthly. $55.00/year for individuals; $75.00/year for Canada and Mexico; $115.00/year for other countries; $90.00 for two years; $104.00 for two years, Canada and Mexico; $160.00/year for two years, other countries. Publication reporting on the use of modeling, animation, and multimedia in the areas of science and engineering, art and entertainment, and presentation and training.

★5012★ **Creative Business**

Creative Business
275 Newbury St.
Boston, MA 02116
Ph: (617)424-1368   Fax: (617)353-1391
E-mail: edit@creativebusiness.com
URL: http://www.creativebusiness.com

Description: Ten issues/year. Provides business information for freelance graphic designers and studio principals.

★5013★ **Design Perspectives**

Industrial Designers Society of America
45195 Business Ct., Ste. 250
Dulles, VA 20166-6717
Ph: (703)759-0100   Fax: (703)759-7679

URL: http://www.idsa.org

Description: Monthly. Discusses issues relevant to the profession. Recurring features include reports of chapter and national activities of IDSA, a section on employment opportunities in the field, resource section, and a calendar of events.

★5014★ **Graphic Arts Monthly**

Reed Business Information
360 Park Ave. S
New York, NY 10010
Ph: (646)746-7395   Fax: (646)746-7434
URL: http://www.gammag.com

Monthly. $99.90/year for U.S. and territories; $176.90/year for Canada; $154.90/year for Mexico; $212.90/year for foreign, surface mail; $260.90/year for foreign, air mail. Magazine featuring commercial printing and graphic arts, including digital technologies.

★5015★ **Graphic Communicator**

Graphic Communications International
   Union
1900 L St. NW
Washington, DC 20036
Ph: (202)462-1400   Fax: (202)721-0600
URL: http://www.gciu.org

$12.00/year for individuals in the U.S.; $15.00/year for elsewhere. Trade newspaper of the Graphic Communications International Union.

★5016★ **IEEE Computer Graphics and Applications**

IEEE Computer Society
PO Box 3014
Los Alamitos, CA 90720-1264
Ph: (714)821-8380   Fax: (714)821-4010
Fr: 800-272-6657
E-mail: rbaldwin@computer.org
URL: http://www.computer.org/cga/

Bimonthly. $32.00/year for members; $320.00/year for institutions. Magazine addressing the interests and needs of professional designers and users of computer graphics hardware, software, and systems.

★5017★ **Jobline News**

Graphic Artists Guild
90 John St., Ste. 403
New York, NY 10038
Ph: (212)791-3400   Fax: (212)791-0333
E-mail: jobline@gag.org

Description: Weekly. Lists jobs for freelance and staff artists in areas such as graphic design, illustration, and art education. Lists jobs from across the country; quantity and locales vary weekly.

★5018★ **Journal of Graphics Tools**

A.K. Peters Ltd.
63 S Ave.
Natick, MA 01760
Ph: (508)655-9933   Fax: (508)655-5847
E-mail: jgt@akpeters.com
URL: http://www.acm.org/jgt

Quarterly. $50.00/year for individuals; $120.00/year for institutions, U.S. and Canada; $40.00 for single issue; $7.50/year for U.S., postage and handling; $25.00/year for elsewhere, postage and handling; $15.00/year for Canada, postage and handling. Journal containing research ideas for computer graphics professionals.

★5019★ **Modernism Magazine**

David Rago
333 N Main St.
Lambertville, NJ 08530
Ph: (609)397-4104   Fax: (609)397-9377
Fr: 888-847-6464
E-mail: info@modernismmagazine.com

Quarterly. $19.95/year for individuals; $6.95 for single issue. Publication covering the visual arts and design.

★5020★ **Society for Environmental Graphic Design-Messages**

Society for Environmental Graphic Design
1000 Vermont Ave. NW, Ste. 400
Washington, DC 20005
Ph: (202)638-5555   Fax: (202)638-0891
E-mail: segdoffice@aol.com

Description: Bimonthly. Reports on Society program news, member services, resources, and product news.

★5021★ Trace: AIGA Journal of Design

American Institute of Graphic Arts
164 5th Ave.
New York, NY 10010
Ph: (212)255-4004   Fax: (212)807-1799

Triennial. Free; $22.00/year for individuals; $14.00/year for single issue. Journal of design and visual culture.

PLACEMENT AND JOB REFERRAL SERVICES

★5022★ Advertising Production Club of New York (APC)

276 Bowery
New York, NY 10012
Ph: (212)334-2018   Fax: (212)431-5786
E-mail: admin@apc-ny.org
URL: http://www.apc-ny.org

Description: Production and traffic department personnel from advertising agencies, corporate or retail advertising departments, and publishing companies; college level graphic arts educators. Meetings include educational programs on graphic arts procedures and plant tours. Maintains employment service for members.

EMPLOYER DIRECTORIES AND NETWORKING LISTS

★5023★ American Showcase Illustration

American Showcase Inc.
915 Broadway, 14th Fl.
New York, NY 10010
Ph: (212)673-6600   Fax: (212)673-9795
Fr: 800-894-7469

Annual. $95.00. Covers illustrators and graphic designers. Entries include: Name, address, phone, sample of work. Arrangement: Geographical.

★5024★ Artist's & Graphic Designer's Market

Writer's Digest Books
4700 E Galbraith Rd.
Cincinnati, OH 45236
Ph: (513)531-2690   Fr: 800-289-0963
E-mail: artdesign@fwpubs.com

Annual, September. $24.99. Covers 2,500 buyers of free-lance art work, including ad agencies, art studios, galleries, clip art firms, audiovisual firms, television film producers, periodicals, record companies, book publishers; coverage includes Canada. Entries include: Name of buyer, address, phone, payment rates, special submission requirements, reporting time, how to break in. Arrangement: Classified by type of market.

★5025★ Chicago Sourcebook

Black Book Marketing Group
10 Astor Pl., 6th Fl.
New York, NY 10003-6935
Ph: (212)539-9800   Fax: (212)539-9801

Annual, November. Covers commercial artists and photographers and graphic designers in Chicago, Illinois area. Entries include: Firm name, address, phone; other details as provided by firm. Arrangement: Alphabetical.

★5026★ Contemporary Designers

St. James Press
27500 Drake Rd.
Farmington Hills, MI 48331-3535
Ph: (248)699-4253   Fax: (248)699-8062
Fr: 800-877-4253

Irregular, 3rd edition 1996. $190.00. Covers 685 living designers and outstanding deceased designers from the recent past in the fields of art, architecture, industry, environment, textile, fashion, furniture, theater, film, graphic arts, and interior design; international coverage. Entries include: Name, date and place of birth, address, spouse's and children's names, educational background, area of specialization, projects completed, exhibitions, memberships; bibliography of materials by or about the entrant; signed critical essay. Arrangement: Alphabetical. Indexes: Nationality, designer type.

★5027★ Graphic Arts Blue Book

Reed Business Information
360 Park Ave. S
New York, NY 10010
Ph: (646)746-7395   Fax: (646)746-7434
E-mail: bluebook@reedbusiness.com
URL: http://www.gabb.com

Annual. $95.00. Covers printing plants, bookbinders, imagesetters, platemakers, paper merchants, paper manufacturers, printing machinery manufacturers and dealers, and others serving the graphic arts industry (Standard Industrial Classification (SIC) code 2600, 2700). Eight editions: New York edition (7,000 establishments) covers metropolitan New York and the state of New Jersey; Southeastern edition (10,500 establishments) covers Kentucky, Tennessee, Alabama, Mississippi, Virginia (except Washington suburbs), North Carolina, South Carolina, Georgia, and Florida; Northeastern edition (6,000 establishments) covers Connecticut, Maine, Massachusetts, New Hampshire, New York (upstate only), Rhode Island, and Vermont and the eastern Canadian provinces; Delaware Valley-Ohio edition (8,500 establishments) covers Pennsylvania, Maryland, Delaware, District of Columbia and its Virginia suburbs, and Ohio; Midwestern edition (13,000 establishments) covers Illinois, Indiana, Iowa, Michigan, Minnesota, Missouri, Wisconsin, North and South Dakota; Southwestern edition (5,500 establishments) covers Arizona, southern California, Hawaii, southern Nevada; Pacific Northwestern edition (5,500 establishments), covers northern California, northern Nevada, Oregon, Washington, Montana, Idaho, Wyoming, Utah, Alaska, and the western provinces of Canada. Texas central edition (8000 establish-

ments) covering Texas, Colorado, New Mexico, Oklahoma, Louisiana, Kansas, Missouri, and Nebraska. Entries include: Company name, address, phone, names and titles of executives, name of buyer, list of products or services, year established. Arrangement: Same information given geographically, classified by product/service, and classified by paper brand name/watermark. Indexes: Alphabetical.

★5028★ Klik! Showcase Photography

American Showcase Inc.
915 Broadway, 14th Fl.
New York, NY 10010
Ph: (212)673-6600   Fax: (212)673-9795
Fr: 800-894-7469
URL: http://www.americanshowcase.com/pages/k9_branding.html

Annual. $55.00. Covers 9,500 photographers, and related companies. Entries include: Name, address, phone, sample of work. Illustrators and graphic designers are described in 'American Showcase Illustration'. Arrangement: Geographical. Indexes: Specialty.

★5029★ Printworld Directory of Contemporary Prints and Prices

Printworld International Inc.
PO Box 1957
West Chester, PA 19380
Ph: (610)431-6654   Fax: (610)431-6653
Fr: 800-788-9101
URL: http://www.printworlddirectory.com

Irregular, previous edition 1991; latest edition 2003, 10th edition. $285.00. Publication includes: Biographical data on 5,000 international artists in contemporary printmaking; thousands of galleries who handle prints and hundreds of print publishers, and 600,000 print/price listings. Entries include: For artists-Name, address, personal and educational data, major exhibits, collections, publishers, printers, galleries, awards, teaching positions and documentation of prints. For galleries and publishers-Name, address. Arrangement: Alphabetical. Indexes: Artist name, printer/print workshop, publisher, gallery, art appraiser.

★5030★ RSVP: The Directory of Illustration and Design

RSVP: The Directory of Illustration and Design
253 Washington Ave., No. D4
Brooklyn, NY 11205
Ph: (718)857-9267   Fax: (718)783-2376
URL: http://www.rsvpdirectory.com

Annual, January/February latest edition 2003. $20.00. Covers about 250 illustrators and designers in the graphic arts industry. All listings are paid. Entries include: Name, address, phone, sample of work. Arrangement: Separate sections for illustrators and designers; each subdivided into color and black and white. Indexes: Specialty (with phone), geographical, alphabetical.

★5031★ Self-Employed Writers and Artists Network-Directory

Self-Employed Writers and Artists Network Inc.
PO Box 440
Paramus, NJ 07653
Ph: (201)967-1313
URL: http://www.swan-net.com

Annual, spring. Covers over 135 freelance writers, graphic designers, illustrators, photographers, and other graphic arts professionals in northern New Jersey and New York city providing services in advertising, marketing, sales promotion, public relations, and telecommunications. Entries include: Name, address, phone, biographical data, description of services provided. Arrangement: Alphabetical. Indexes: Line of business.

★5032★ Who's Who in SGIA

Screenprinting and Graphic Imaging Association International
10015 Main St.
Fairfax, VA 22031
Ph: (703)385-1335   Fax: (703)273-0456
Fr: 888-385-3588

Annual, August. Covers about 3,800 screen printers and graphic imaging companies, suppliers of screen printing equipment and graphic imaging materials, and investors in the Screen Printing Technical Foundation; international coverage. Entries include: Company name, address, phone, fax, e-mail, name of contact, products or services. Arrangement: Classified by type of business, then geographical. Indexes: Alphabetical by company, within state or country.

★5033★ The Workbook

Scott & Daughters Publishing Inc.
940 N Highland Ave., Ste. A
Los Angeles, CA 90038
Ph: (323)856-0008   Fax: (323)856-0443
Fr: 800-547-2688
URL: http://www.workbook.com

Annual, February. $120.00. Covers 49,000 advertising agencies, art directors, photographers, freelance illustrators and designers, artists' representatives, interactive designers, pre-press services, and other graphic arts services in the U.S. Entries include: Company or individual name, address, phone, specialty. National in scope. Arrangement: Classified by product or service.

HANDBOOKS AND MANUALS

★5034★ Becoming a Computer Graphics Designer Artist

John Wiley and Sons, Inc.
1 Wiley Dr.
Somerset, NJ 08875-1272
Ph: (732)469-4400   Fax: (732)302-2300
Fr: 800-225-5945

Gardner. 2000. $29.95 (paper). 288 pages. Part of Design and Graphic Design series.

★5035★ Becoming a Graphic Designer

John Wiley and Sons, Inc.
1 Wiley Dr.
Somerset, NJ 08875-1272
Ph: (732)469-4400   Fax: (732)302-2300
Fr: 800-225-5945

Steven Heller and Teresa Fernandes. 2002. $35.00 (paper). 336 pages.

★5036★ Becoming a Successful Artist

F & W Publications, Inc.
4700 E Galbraith Rd.
Cincinnati, OH 45236
Ph: (513)531-2690   Fax: (513)531-4082
Fr: 800-289-0963

Lewis B. Lehrman. 1996. $24.99 (paper). 144 pages.

★5037★ Careers for Color Connoisseurs and Other Visual Types

VGM Career Horizons
1221 Avenue of the Americas
New York, NY 10020
Ph: (212)904-2000   Fr: 800-323-4900
E-mail: ntcpub@tribune.com

Jan Goldberg. 1999. $14.95; $9.95 (paper). 212 pages.

★5038★ Careers for Crafty People and Other Dexterous Types

VGM Career Horizons
1221 Avenue of the Americas
New York, NY 10020
Ph: (212)904-2000   Fr: 800-323-4900
E-mail: ntcpub@tribune.com

Mark Rowh. Second Edition, 2002. $14.95; $9.95 (paper). 192 pages.

★5039★ Careers by Design: A Headhunter's Secrets for Success and Survival in Graphic Design

Allworth Press
10 E. 23rd St., Ste. 510
New York, NY 10010
Ph: (212)777-8395   Fax: (212)777-8261
Fr: 800-491-2808

Roz Goldfarb. Third edition, 2002. 256 pages.

★5040★ Careers for Film Buffs and Other Hollywood Types

VGM Career Horizons
1221 Avenue of the Americas
New York, NY 10020
Ph: (212)904-2000   Fr: 800-323-4900
E-mail: ntcpub@tribune.com

Jaq Greenspon. 1994. $14.95; $9.95 (paper). 250 pages. Describes job descriptions in production, camera, sound, special effects, grips, electrical, makeup, costumes, etc.

★5041★ Careers in the Graphic Arts

Rosen Publishing Group, Inc.
29 E. 21st St.
New York, NY 10010
Ph: (212)777-3017   Fax: 888-436-4643
Fr: 800-237-9932

Erin McGuire-Lytle. Revised edition, 1997. $16.95; $9.95 (paper). 152 pages. Discusses a career in graphic arts; outlines educational requirements, training, and skills needed to become an illustrator, layout artist, designer, and paste-up artist. Gives job hunting advice, describes how to write a resume, prepare a portfolio, and interview preparation. Gives a state-by-state listing of schools offering graphic arts.

★5042★ Careers in Graphic Communications: A Resource Book

GATF Press
PO Box 1020
Sewickley, PA 15143-1020
Ph: (412)741-5733   Fax: (412)741-0609
Fr: 800-662-3916

Sally A. Flecker and Pamela J. Groff. 1998. $35.00 (paper). 200 pages.

★5043★ Careers for Night Owls and Other Insomniacs

McGraw-Hill Trade
2 Penn Plaza
New York, NY 10121
Ph: (212)904-2000   Fr: 800-722-4726
E-mail: ntcpub@tribune.com

Louise Miller. 1995. $14.95; $9.95 (paper). 160 pages.

★5044★ Careers in the Visual Arts: A Guide to Jobs, Money, Opportunities, and an Artistic Life

Watson-Guptill Publications, Inc.
BPI Communications, Inc.
770 Broadway
New York, NY 10003
Ph: (646)654-5400   Fax: (646)654-5486
Fr: 800-323-9432

Dee Ito. 1993. $14.95 (paper). 320 pages. Out of print. Gives a broad overview of each field included, with educational requirements and employment opportunities. Includes ideas on how to get started.

★5045★ Chronicle Artistic Occupations Guidebook

Chronicle Guidance Publications, Inc.
66 Aurora St.
Moravia, NY 13118-3576
Fax: (315)497-3359   Fr: 800-899-0454

Paul Downes, editor. Revised, 1994. $81.80.

★5046★ The Education of a Graphic Designer

Allworth Press
10 E. 23rd St., Ste. 510
New York, NY 10010
Ph: (212)777-8395   Fax: (212)777-8261
Fr: 800-491-2808

Steven Heller, editor. 1998. $18.95 (paper). 288 pages. Designers discuss how they acquired knowledge of design and then succeeded in applying this academic training to practical solutions in their careers.

★5047★ Graphic Design: A Career Guide and Educational Directory

American Institute of Graphic Arts
164 Fifth Ave.
New York, NY 10010-5900
Ph: (212)807-1990

Sharon H. Poggenpohl, editor. 1993. $25.00 (paper). 160 pages.

★5048★ Graphic Designer's Ultimate Resource Directory

F & W Publications, Inc.
4700 E Galbraith Rd.
Cincinnati, OH 45236
Ph: (513)531-2690   Fax: (513)531-4082
Fr: 800-289-0963

Poppy Evans. 1999. $28.99 (paper). 192 pages.

★5049★ Great Jobs for Art Majors

McGraw-Hill Contemporary Books
1221 Avenue of the Americas
New York, NY 10020
Ph: (212)904-2000   Fr: 800-323-4900
E-mail: ntcpub@tribune.com

Blythe Camenson, Stephen Lambert, Julie DeGalan. 1997. $11.95 (paper). 345 pages. Includes bibliographical references and index.

★5050★ How to Be a Successful Cartoonist

F & W Publications Inc.
4700 E Galbraith Rd.
Cincinnati, OH 45236
Ph: (513)531-2690   Fax: (513)531-4082
Fr: 800-289-0963

Randy Glasbergen. 1996. $19.99. 128 pages. Explains how to get started and what the opportunities are, among other topics.

★5051★ How to Start and Operate Your Own Design Firm

McGraw-Hill Companies
2 Penn Plaza
New York, NY 10121-2298
Ph: (212)904-4509   Fr: 800-338-3987

Albert W. Rubeling, Jr. 1994. $33.00. 192 pages.

★5052★ How to Survive and Prosper as an Artist: Selling Yourself Without Selling Your Soul

Henry Holt and Co., LLC
115 W. 18th St., 5th Fl.
New York, NY 10011
Ph: (212)886-9200   Fax: (212)633-0748
Fr: 800-672-2054

Caroll Michels. Fourth edition, 1997. $16.00. 336 pages. Includes index and bibliographical references.

★5053★ New Media Careers for Artists and Designers

AuthorHouse
1663 Liberty Dr., Ste. 200
Bloomington, IN 47403
Fax: (812)339-8654   Fr: 800-839-8640

Brenda S. Faison. February 2003. $13.95. 136 pages.

★5054★ 100 Best Careers for Writers and Artists

Thomson Peterson's
PO Box 67005
Lawrenceville, NJ 08648-6105
Fr: 800-338-3282

Shelly Field. 1997. $15.95 (paper). 288 pages. Identifies job opportunities in communications and the arts.

★5055★ Opportunities in Arts and Crafts Careers

McGraw-Hill Contemporary Books
1221 Avenue of the Americas
New York, NY 10020
Ph: (212)904-2000   Fr: 800-323-4900
E-mail: ntcpub@tribune.com

Betty Gardner. 1998. $14.95; $11.95 (paper). 202 pages.

★5056★ Opportunities in Commercial Art and Graphic Design Careers

McGraw-Hill Trade
2 Penn Plaza
New York, NY 10121
Ph: (212)904-2000   Fr: 800-722-4726

Barbara Gordon. Second edition, 1997. $12.95; $11.95 (paper). 160 pages. Provides a survey of job opportunities in advertising and public relations, publishing, fashion, architecture, and newspapers, as well as in a variety of specialty markets. Illustrated.

★5057★ Opportunities in Desktop Publishing Careers

McGraw-Hill Trade
2 Penn Plaza
New York, NY 10121
Ph: (212)904-2000   Fr: 800-722-4726

Kenny Schiff. 1994. $14.95; $11.95 (paper). 160 pages. Out of stock.

★5058★ Opportunities in Drafting Careers

McGraw-Hill Trade
2 Penn Plaza
New York, NY 10121
Ph: (212)904-2000   Fr: 800-722-4726

Mark Rowh. 1994. $14.95; $11.95 (paper). 298 pages. Provides information on opportunities in mechanical, landscape, marine, and topographical drafting in civil service, architecture, electronics, and other fields. Contains index and illustrations.

★5059★ Opportunities in Visual Arts Careers

McGraw-Hill Trade
2 Penn Plaza
New York, NY 10121
Ph: (212)904-2000   Fr: 800-722-4726
E-mail: ntcpub@tribune.com

Mark Salmon. 1994. $14.95; $11.95 (paper). 160 pages. Points the way to a career in the visual arts, examining opportunities for designers, painters, sculptors, illustrators, animators, photographers, art therapists, educators, and others. Offers a view of the pros and cons of working for an art or design company or on your own.

★5060★ Power Freelancing: Home-Based Careers for Writers, Designers, & Consultants

Mid-List Press
4324 12th Ave, S
Minneapolis, MN 55407-3218
Ph: (612)822-3733   Fax: (612)823-8387
Fr: 888-543-1138

George Sorenson. 1995. $14.95 (paper). 192 pages.

★5061★ Resumes for Advertising Careers

McGraw-Hill Contemporary Books
1221 Avenue of the Americas
New York, NY 10020
Ph: (212)904-2000   Fr: 800-323-4900
E-mail: ntcpub@tribune.com

1998. $9.95 (paper). 392 pages. Aimed at job seekers trying to enter or advance in advertising. Provides sample resumes for copywriters, art directors, account managers, ad managers, and media people at all levels of experience. Furnishes sample cover letters.

★5062★ Taking the Leap: Building a Career as a Visual Artist

Chronicle Books LLC
85 Second St.
San Francisco, CA 94105
Ph: (415)537-4200   Fax: (415)537-4460
Fr: 800-722-6657

Cay Lang. 1998. $16.95. 224 pages.

★5063★ 2002 Artist's & Graphic Designer's Market

Writer's Digest Books
F & W Publications, Inc.
1507 Dana Ave.
Cincinnati, OH 45207
Ph: (513)531-2690   Fax: (513)531-4082
Fr: 800-289-0963

Mary Cox, editor. 2001. $24.99 (paper). 720 pages.

EMPLOYMENT AGENCIES AND SEARCH FIRMS

★5064★ Caprio & Associates Inc.

1415 W. 22nd St., Tower Fl.
Oak Brook, IL 60523
Ph: (630)705-9101   Fax: (630)705-9102

Executive search firm.

★5065★ Cook Associates Inc.

212 W Kinzie St.
Chicago, IL 60610
Ph: (312)329-0900   Fax: (312)329-2422

Management and executive recruiting specialists offering a commitment to clients to find the best candidates and to find those candidates as efficiently as possible. Approach provides a flexible and effective structure that serves the special needs of both large and small companies. Serves the following industries: industrial, equipment manufacturer, food processing, graphic arts, chemical process, retailing, mechanical products, healthcare services, financial and professional services, legal, consumer products, construction and engineering, packaging, pulp and paper.

★5066★ Gordon Wahls Executive Search Co.

450 Park Way
PO Box 386
Broomall, PA 19008-0386
Ph: (610)359-8800   Fax: (610)359-8803
Fr: 800-523-7112

Offers executive search services for the printing, packaging, publishing and graphic arts industry.

★5067★ Graphic Arts Employment Service, Inc.

409 N Pacific Coast Hwy., Ste.455
Redondo Beach, CA 90277
Ph: (310)316-1246   Fax: (310)937-3760
Fr: 800-499-9722
E-mail: info@gaes.com
URL: http://www.gaes.com

Employment agency specializing in the publishing and packaging industries.

★5068★ Graphic Search Associates Inc.

PO Box 373
Newtown Square, PA 19073
Ph: (610)359-1234   Fax: (610)353-8120
Fr: 800-342-1777
E-mail: info@graphsrch.com
URL: http://www.graphsrch.com

Executive search firm for the graphic arts industry.

★5069★ LandaJob Advertising Staffing Specialists

8177 Wornall Rd.
Kansas City, MO 64114
Ph: (816)523-1881   Fax: (816)523-1876
Fr: 800-931-8806

Personnel consultants and recruiters for advertising, marketing, and communications positions. Industries served: advertising, communications, marketing, graphic arts, printing, and publishing.

★5070★ Lloyd Staffing

445 Broad Hollow Rd., Ste.119
Melville, NY 11747
Ph: (631)777-7600   Fax: (631)777-7626
Fr: 888-292-6678
E-mail: info@lloydstaffing.com
URL: http://www.lloydstaffing.com

Personnel agency and search firm.

★5071★ Oliver & Rozner Associates

598 Madison Ave., Ste. 11
New York, NY 10022
Ph: (212)688-1850

Performs executive search for top tiers of management including presidents, general management, advertising account management, division management, group executive and vice presidential line positions in such areas as marketing, research, operations, sales, finance, human resources, and others; hard-to-find specialists including specific marketing/advertising executives, research and development expertise, computer/data processing knowledge, scientific, physicians-product efficacy and occupational medicine, and engineering. Industries served include pharmaceutical, healthcare, hospital, advertising, consumer products and packaged goods, housewares, direct selling, cosmetics/toiletries, industrial products, high technology products, forest products, engineering, construction, environment/resource recovery, graphic arts, chemical, and government agencies.

★5072★ Printemps

18 Avery Pl.
Westport, CT 06880
Ph: (203)226-6869   Fax: (203)226-1594

Specializes in providing temporary support for graphic design, document management and the electronic printing industry. Provides permanent placement for professionals and production personnel. Consults with printers and in-house printshops for greater produc-tion efficiency. Handles personnel management and policy programs as well. Industries served: printing, advertising, manufacturing, insurance, banking, and government agencies.

ONLINE JOB SOURCES AND SERVICES

★5073★ Graphic Artists Guild

URL: http://www.gag.org

Description: JOBLine News section of Guild Resources page contains weekly e-mail newsletter of job listings. **Fee:** Must subscribe to e-mail newsletter non-member six-month rates start at $80. Visitors may download a free sample.

★5074★ PrintJobs.com

PO Box 135
Bowmansville, NY 14026
Ph: (716)686-9251   Fax: (716)686-9258
E-mail: newhouse@atsprintjobs.com
URL: http://www.printjobs.com

Description: Aims to find suitable graphic arts jobs for qualified candidates. Over a hundred jobs are maintained and updated on the site. **Fee:** Must be paid by employers using the site; no registration charge for job hunters.

OTHER SOURCES

★5075★ American Artists Professional League (AAPL)

47 5th Ave.
New York, NY 10003
Ph: (212)645-1345   Fax: (212)645-1345

Description: Professional painters, sculptors, and graphic artists.

★5076★ American Institute of Graphic Arts (AIGA)

164 5th Ave.
New York, NY 10010
Ph: (212)807-1990   Fax: (212)807-1799
Fr: 800-548-1634
E-mail: comments@aiga.org
URL: http://www.aiga.org

Description: Graphic designers, art directors, art directors, illustrators, packaging designers. Sponsors exhibits and projects in the public interest. Sponsors traveling exhibitions. Operates gallery. Maintains library of design books and periodicals; offers slide archives.

★5077★ Art Directors Club (ADC)

106 W 29th St.
New York, NY 10001
Ph: (212)643-1440   Fax: (212)643-4266
E-mail: info@adcny.org
URL: http://www.adcny.org

Members: Art directors of advertising magazines and agencies, visual information specialists, and graphic designers; associate members are artists, cinematographers, photographers, copywriters, educators, journalists, and critics. **Purpose:** Promotes and stimulates interest in the practice of art direction. **Activities:** Sponsors Annual Exhibition of Advertising, Editorial and Television Art and Design; International Traveling Exhibition; Hall of Fame. Provides educational, professional, and entertainment programs; on-premise art exhibitions; portfolio review program. Conducts panels for students and faculty.

★5078★ Association for Graphic Arts Training

Banta Publications
100 Banta Rd.
Long Prairie, MN 56347
Ph: (320)732-7915   Fax: (320)732-7415
Fr: 800-214-1120
E-mail: bbense@banta.com
URL: http://www.agatweb.org/

Members: Full- and part-time graphics art trainers at printing and pre-press companies; graphic arts teachers; and other interested individuals and companies. **Purpose:** Seeks to increase the productivity of graphic arts trainers through effective, efficient education and training with support from suppliers, educational institutions, associations, non-profit organizations, and consultants. Aims to: establish a networking opportunities for trainers; share performance challenges, solutions, and resources; improve members' skills, knowledge, and professionalism; align training with corporate strategies; increase awareness of the importance of training; and create guidelines for training materials used in the industry.

★5079★ Graphic Arts Technical Foundation (GATF)

200 Deer Run Rd.
Sewickley, PA 15143-2600
Ph: (412)741-6860   Fax: (412)741-2311
Fr: 800-910-GATF
E-mail: info@gatf.org
URL: http://www.gatf.org

Description: Scientific, research, technical, and educational organization serving the international graphic communications industries. Conducts research in all graphic processes and their commercial applications. Conducts seminars, workshops, and forums on graphic arts and environmental subjects. Conducts educational programs, including the publishing of graphic arts textbooks and learning modules, videotapes and CD-ROMs and broadcast video seminars. Conducts the GATF training and certification program in sheet-fed offset press operating, Web Offset press operating, Image Assembly, and desktop publishing. Produces test images and quality control devices for the industry. Performs technical services for the graphic arts industry, including problem-solving, material evaluation, and plant audits. A partner of the Printing Industries of America (PIA).

★5080★ *Graphic Designer*

Cambridge Educational
2572 Brunswick Ave.
Lawrenceville, NJ 08648-4128
Fax: 800-FAX-ON-US   Fr: 800-468-4227
URL: http://www.cambridgeeducational.com

$39.95. 1993. Part of the Career Connections video series.

★5081★ Gravure Education Foundation (GEF)

1200A Scottsville Rd.
Rochester, NY 14624
Ph: (585)436-2150   Fax: (585)436-7689
E-mail: rwagner@gaa.org
URL: http://www.gaa.org/GEF/index.htm

Purpose: Objectives are to establish gravure curricula with graphic arts educational facilities at all educational levels; provide financial assistance to students; develop new resources for conducting educational programs; encourage postgraduate projects and research within the graphic arts; provide career orientation at the high school level; provide for internships throughout the gravure industry. Seeks to serve as a catalyst within the framework of established institutions and to provide encouragement to enterprising individuals.

★5082★ International Association of Printing House Craftsmen (IAPHC)

7042 Brooklyn Blvd.
Minneapolis, MN 55429-1370
Ph: (763)560-1620   Fax: (763)560-1350
Fr: 800-466-4274
E-mail: headquarters@iaphc.org
URL: http://www.iaphc.org

Members: Individuals world-wide employed or interested in any facet of the graphic arts. **Activities:** Conducts field trips; maintains speakers' bureau; sponsors educational programs. Sponsors International Printing Week and International Gallery of Superb Printing.

★5083★ International Graphic Arts Education Association (IGAEA)

1899 Preston White Dr.
Reston, VA 20191-4367
Ph: (703)758-0595
E-mail: pdaniel@southsuburbancollege.edu
URL: http://www.igaea.org

Description: Graphic arts and printing teachers. To develop an integrated and comprehensive system of graphic arts education in schools and colleges of the U.S. Assists organizations in arranging lectures or other programs relating to graphic arts. Sponsors annual Graphic Communications Week; Visual Communication Journal; conducts research programs.

★5084★ *Media and the Arts Occupations*

Delphi Productions
3160 4th St.
Boulder, CO 80304
Fax: (303)443-4022   Fr: 888-443-2400
URL: http://www.delphivideo.com

$95.00. 50 minutes. Part of the Careers for the 21st Century Video Library.

★5085★ Type Directors Club (TDC)

127 W 25th St., Fl. 8
New York, NY 10001
Ph: (212)633-8943   Fax: (212)633-8944
E-mail: director@tdc.org
URL: http://www.tdc.org

Description: Professional society of typographic designers, type directors, and teachers of typography; sustaining members are individuals with interests in typographic education. Seeks to stimulate research and disseminate information. Provides speakers and offers presentations on new developments in typography.

★5086★ Typophiles

35 Schermerhorn St.
Brooklyn, NY 11201-4826

Description: Designers, printers, book collectors, artists, calligraphers, private press owners, wood engravers, and others interested in graphic arts.

Hazardous Waste Management Specialists

SOURCES OF HELP-WANTED ADS

★5087★ BioCycle

The JG Press Inc.
419 State Ave.
Emmaus, PA 18049
Ph: (610)967-4135

Monthly. $69.00/year; $97.00/year for out of country; $113.00/year for two years; $169.00/year for two years, other countries. Magazine focusing on management of city and industrial wastes by recycling and composting.

★5088★ Drinking Water & Backflow Prevention

Drinking Water & Backflow Prevention
PO Box 33209
Northglenn, CO 80233
Ph: (303)451-0978   Fax: (303)452-9776
Fr: 888-367-3927
E-mail: backflow@dwbp-online.com
URL: http://www.dunbq-online.com

Description: Monthly. Presents articles directed toward "individuals, companies, organizations, agencies, and municipalities with an interest in drinking water protection and backflow prevention." Contains information on safety standards, water system protection, training programs, cross-connection control, and all issues related to preventing the contamination of potable drinking water supplies with backflow prevention devices. Recurring features include case studies, letters to the editor, news of research, columns titled Test Your Investigative Skills and Backflow Prevention Device Repairs, and reports of meetings. Also carries news of educational opportunities, job listings, notices of publications available, and a calendar of events.

★5089★ Industrial Hygiene News

Rimbach Publishing Inc.
8650 Babcock Blvd.
Pittsburgh, PA 15237
Ph: (412)364-5366   Fax: (412)369-9720
Fr: 800-245-3182

Bimonthly. Free to qualified subscribers. Magazine covering industrial hygiene, occupational health, and safety.

★5090★ Journal of Applied Ground Water Protection

Ground Water Protection Council
13308 N Macarthur Blvd.
Oklahoma City, OK 73142-3019
Ph: (405)516-4972   Fax: (405)516-4973

Semiannual. Journal covering issues in water and waste management.

★5091★ Occupational Hazards

Penton Media Inc.
1300 E 9th St.
Cleveland, OH 44114-1503
Ph: (216)696-7000   Fax: (216)931-9799
URL: http://www.occupationalhazards.com

Monthly. $55.00/year; $5.00 for single issue. Monthly publication for safety professionals featuring information to meet OSHA and EPA compliance requirements, improve management of safety, industrial hygiene and environmental programs and find products and services to protect employees and property.

★5092★ Operations Forum

Water Environment Federation
601 Wythe St.
Alexandria, VA 22314-1994
Ph: (703)684-2400   Fax: (703)684-2492
Fr: 800-666-0206

Monthly. $79.00/year for nonmembers. Magazine covering operation/maintenance of WWTPs and wastewater collections systems.

★5093★ Pollution Engineering

Reed Business Information
360 Park Ave. S
New York, NY 10014
Ph: (646)746-7764
URL: http://www.pollutionengineering.com/

Magazine focusing on pollution control, air, water, solid waste, and toxic/hazardous waste.

★5094★ Pollution Equipment News

Rimbach Publishing Inc.
8650 Babcock Blvd.
Pittsburgh, PA 15237
Ph: (412)364-5366   Fax: (412)369-9720
Fr: 800-245-3182

Free to qualified subscribers. Pollution control equipment and products magazine (tabloid).

★5095★ Public Works

Public Works Journal Corp.
PO Box 688
200 S Broad St.
Ridgewood, NJ 07451
Ph: (201)445-5800   Fax: (201)445-5170
Fr: 800-524-2364
URL: http://www.pwmag.com

Monthly. Free to qualified subscribers; $60.00/year for others. Trade magazine covering the public works industry nationwide for city, county, and state.

★5096★ Water Engineering & Management

Scranton Gillette Communications Inc.
380 E NW Hwy., Ste. 200
Des Plaines, IL 60016-2282
Ph: (847)298-6622   Fax: (847)390-0408
E-mail: wemeditor@gcmail.com
URL: http://www.waterinfocenter.com

Monthly. $40.00/year for individuals; $6.00 for single issue; $64.00 for two years; $150.00 for two years, other countries. Trade magazine dedicated to the advancement of the state of the art and the transfer of technology in the field of municipal, county and regional water supply and water pollution control. Serves consulting sanitary engineers and managers of water/wastewater facilities who specify/buy products and services.

★5097★ Water Environment Research

Water Environment Federation
601 Wythe St.
Alexandria, VA 22314-1994
Ph: (703)684-2400   Fax: (703)684-2492
Fr: 800-666-0206
E-mail: msc@wef.org

Bimonthly. $40.00/year for members; $158.00/year for nonmembers. Technical journal covering municipal and industrial water pollution control, water quality, and hazardous wastes.

★5098★ Water & Wastes Digest

Scranton Gillette Communications Inc.
380 E NW Hwy., Ste. 200
Des Plaines, IL 60016-2282
Ph: (847)298-6622   Fax: (847)390-0408

Bimonthly. $10.00/year for individuals; $13.00/year for other countries; $2.00 for single issue. Magazine (tabloid) featuring product news for decision makers in the municipal and industrial water and water pollution control industries.

PLACEMENT AND JOB REFERRAL SERVICES

★5099★ Environmental Technology Council (ETC)

734 15th St. NW, Ste. 720
Washington, DC 20005-1013
Ph: (202)783-0870   Fax: (202)737-2038
E-mail: comments@etc.org
URL: http://www.etc.org

Description: Firms dedicated to the use of high technology treatment in the management of hazardous wastes and to the restricted use of land disposal facilities in the interests of protecting human health and the environment. Advocates minimization of hazardous wastes and the use of alternative technologies in their treatment, including chemical and biological treatments, fixation, neutralization, reclamation, recycling, and thermal treatments such as incineration. Encourages land disposal prohibitions. Promotes reductions in the volume of hazardous waste generated annually and expansion of EPA hazardous waste list. Advocates use of treatment technology as a more cost-effective approach to Superfund site cleanups. Works with state, national, and international officials and firms to assist in development of programs that utilize treatment and minimize land disposal. Provides technical and placement assistance to members; sponsors special studies, technical seminars, and workshops; participates in federal legislation, litigation, and regulatory development. Maintains library of materials on new technolo-

gies; operates speakers' bureau; compiles statistics and mailing list.

★5100★ Spill Control Association of America (SCAA)

32500 Scenic Ln.
Franklin, MI 48025
Ph: (248)851-1936   Fax: (313)849-1623
E-mail: info@scaa-spill.org
URL: http://www.scaa-spill.org

Description: Third party contractors; manufacturers or suppliers of pollution control and containment equipment; individuals in private or governmental capacities involved with spill clean-up and containment operations; associate companies. To provide information on the oil and hazardous material emergency response and remediation industry's practices, trends, and achievements; to establish liaison with local, state, and federal government agencies responsible for laws and regulations regarding pollution caused by oil and hazardous materials; to cooperate in the development of industry programs and efforts so that pollutants are properly controlled and removed from land and water. Provides certification for hazardous material technicians. Maintains Spill Control Institute, Technical Services Division; collects and disseminates educational and technical information. Operates speakers' bureau; conducts research. Maintains placement service.

EMPLOYER DIRECTORIES AND NETWORKING LISTS

★5101★ Asbestos Removal Service Directory

infoUSA Inc.
5711 S 86th Cir.
Omaha, NE 68127-0347
Ph: (402)930-3500   Fax: (402)331-0176
Fr: 800-555-6124
URL: http://www.abii.com

Annual. Number of listings: 2,383. Entries include: Name, address, phone (including area code), size of advertisement, year first in "Yellow Pages," name of owner or manager, number of employees. Compiled from telephone company "Yellow Pages," nationwide. Arrangement: Geographical.

★5102★ EI Environmental Services Directory

Environmental Information Ltd.
5775 Wazata Blvd., Ste. 820
St. Louis Park, MN 55416-1234
Ph: (952)831-2473   Fax: (952)831-6550
URL: http://www.envirobiz.com

Annual. $995.00. Covers over 620 waste-handling facilities, 600 transportation firms, 500 spill response firms, 2,100 consultants, 470 laboratories, 450 soil boring/well drilling firms; also includes incineration services, polychlorinated biphenyl (PCB) detoxification

and mobile solvent-recovery services, asbestos services and underground tank services, summaries of states' regulatory programs. Entries include: Company name, address, phone, description of services, regulatory status, on and off site processes used, type of waste handled. Arrangement: Geographical. Indexes: Service.

★5103★ Hazardous Materials Advisory Council-Directory

Hazardous Materials Advisory Council
1101 Vermont Ave. NW, Ste. 301
Washington, DC 20005-3521
Ph: (202)289-4550   Fax: (202)289-4074

Annual, July. Covers about 300 members, shippers, and carriers of hazardous materials; manufacturers of hazardous materials containers; and related organizations. Entries include: Company name, address, phone, fax, representative name. Arrangement: Classified by line of business. Indexes: Geographical; member representative.

★5104★ Hazardous Waste Consultant-Directory of Commercial Hazardous Waste Management Facilities Issue

Elsevier Science Inc.
360 Park Ave. S, No. 11
New York, NY 10010-1710
Ph: (212)989-5800

Semiannual. $115.00. Publication includes: List of 170 licensed commercial facilities that treat and/or dispose of hazardous waste in North America. Entries include: Facility name, address, phone, contact name, type of waste handled, methods of on-site treatment and/or disposal, Environmental Protection Agency permit status and identification number, restrictions, description of other services. Arrangement: Geographical. Indexes: Organization name.

★5105★ HWAC Directory: The Leading Engineering and Science Firms Practicing in Multimedia Environmental Management and Remediation

Hazardous Waste Action Coalition
c/o American Consulting Engineers Council
1015 15th St. NW, Ste. 802
Washington, DC 20005
Ph: (202)347-7474   Fax: (202)898-0076
URL: http://www.hwac.org

Annual. $35.00. Covers HWAC's 100 member engineering firms responsible for designing cleanup solutions for hazardous waste sites. Entries include: Company name, address, phone, office locations, corporate data, firm activities. Arrangement: Geographical.

★5106★ **Peterson's Job Opportunities in Engineering and Technology**

Thomson Peterson's
PO Box 67005
Lawrenceville, NJ 08648-6105
Fr: 800-338-3282

Compiled by the Peterson's staff. Fourth edition, 1996. $21.95 (paper). 384 pages. Profiles 2,000 high-tech companies looking primarily for technical personnel in such fields as biotechnology, telecommunications, software, computers and peripherals, defense, and aerospace. Contains job-search strategies and career options to help match education and expertise to the job market. Indexed geographically, by industry, and by hiring needs.

★5107★ **Who's Who in Environmental Engineering**

American Academy of Environmental Engineers
130 Holiday Ct., Ste. 100
Annapolis, MD 21401
Ph: (410)266-3311   Fax: (410)266-7653

Annual, April. $75.00. Covers about 2,400 licensed professional environmental engineers that have been certified by examination in one or more of seven specialties: air pollution control, general environmental engineering, industrial hygiene, hazardous waste management, radiation protection, solid waste management, water supply and wastewater. Entries include: Name, affiliation, address, phone, area of specialization, biographical data. Arrangement: Alphabetical, geographical, area of specialization.

HANDBOOKS AND MANUALS

★5108★ **The Best Resumes for Scientists and Engineers**

John Wiley & Sons Inc.
1 Wiley Dr.
Somerset, NJ 08873
Ph: (732)469-4400   Fr: 800-225-5945

Adele Lewis and David J. Moore. Second edition, 1993. $37.50; $19.95 (paper). 224 pages. Presents an extensive collection of scientific and engineering resumes, highlighting the important differences between these and resumes written for other occupations.

★5109★ **Hazardous Materials & Waste Management: A Guide for the Professional Hazards Manager**

Noyes Data Corp.
169 Kinderkamack Rd., Ste. 5
Park Ridge, NJ 07656-1338
Ph: (201)666-2121   Fax: (201)666-5111

Paul N. Cheremisinoff and Nicholas P. Cheremisinoff. 1995. $98.00. 265 pages.

★5110★ **Opportunities in Waste Management Careers**

McGraw-Hill Trade
2 Penn Plaza
New York, NY 10121
Ph: (212)904-2000   Fr: 800-722-4726
E-mail: ntcpub@tribune.com

Mark Rowh. 1994. $14.95; $11.95 (paper). 160 pages. Outlines the diverse opportunities in waste management and examines the duties, working conditions, salaries, and future of a variety of positions. Profiles jobs and opportunities in solid waste and waste water management, environmental engineering, soil and wildlife conservation, and related career areas.

EMPLOYMENT AGENCIES AND SEARCH FIRMS

★5111★ **The Energists**

10260 Westheimer Blvd., Ste. 300
Houston, TX 77042
Ph: (713)781-6881   Fax: (713)781-2998
E-mail: search@energists.com
URL: http://www.energists.com

Executive search firm.

★5112★ **Intech Summit Group, Inc.**

5075 Shoreham Pl., Ste. 280
San Diego, CA 92122
Ph: (858)452-2100   Fax: (858)452-8500
E-mail: isg@isgsearch.com
URL: http://www.isgsearch.com

Employment agency and executive recruiter with a branch in Carlsbad, CA.

★5113★ **Lybrook Associates, Inc.**

PO Box 741
Bristol, RI 02809
Ph: (401)254-5840   Fax: (401)254-5088
E-mail: chemistry@lybrook.com
URL: http://www.lybrook.com

Executive search firm specializing in the field of chemistry.

★5114★ **Search Consultants International, Inc.**

4545 Post Oak Pl., Ste. 208
Houston, TX 77027
Ph: (713)622-9188   Fax: (713)622-9186
E-mail: info@searchconsultants.com
URL: http://www.searchconsultants.com

Management executive search firm.

OTHER SOURCES

★5115★ **Air and Waste Management Association (A&WMA)**

1 Gateway Ctr., 3rd Fl.
420 Duquesne Blvd.
Pittsburgh, PA 15222
Ph: (412)232-3444   Fax: (412)232-3450
Fr: 800-270-3444
E-mail: info@awma.org
URL: http://www.awma.org

Description: Environmental, educational, and technical organization. **Purpose:** Seeks to provide a neutral forum for the exchange of technical information on a wide variety of environmental topics.

★5116★ **American Academy of Environmental Engineers (AAEE)**

130 Holiday Ct., No. 100
Annapolis, MD 21401
Ph: (410)266-3311   Fax: (410)266-7653
E-mail: academy@aaee.net
URL: http://www.aaee.net

Members: Environmentally oriented registered professional engineers certified by examination as Diplomates of the Academy. **Purpose:** Works to improve the standards of environmental engineering; to certify those with special knowledge of environmental engineering; to furnish lists of those certified to the public. **Activities:** Maintains speakers' bureau. Recognizes areas of specialization: Air Pollution Control; General Environmental; Hazardous Waste Management; Industrial Hygiene; Radiation Protection; Solid Waste Management; Water Supply and Wastewater. Requires written and oral examinations for certification. Works with other professional organizations on environmentally oriented activities. Identifies potential employment candidates through Talent Search Service.

★5117★ **Environmental Industry Associations**

4301 Connecticut Ave., NW, Ste. 300
Washington, DC 20008
Ph: (202)244-4700   Fax: (202)966-4818
Fr: 800-424-2869
E-mail: eii@envasns.org
URL: http://www.envasns.org

Activities: Compiles statistics; conducts research and educational programs.

★5118★ **Environmental Occupations: Professional**

Delphi Productions
3160 4th St.
Boulder, CO 80304
Fax: (303)443-4022   Fr: 888-443-2400
URL: http://www.delphivideo.com

$95.00. 49 minutes. Part of the Emerging Careers Video Library.

★5119★ *Environmental Occupations: Technical*

Delphi Productions
3160 4th St.
Boulder, CO 80304
Fax: (303)443-4022   Fr: 888-443-2400
URL: http://www.delphivideo.com

$95.00. 48 minutes. Part of the Emerging Careers Video Library.

★5120★ *Scientific, Engineering, and Technical Services*

Cambridge Educational
2572 Brunswick Ave.
Lawrenceville, NJ 08648-4128
Fax: 800-FAX-ON-US   Fr: 800-468-4227
URL: http://www.cambridgeeducational.com

$89.95. 2002. 18 minutes. Part of the Career Cluster Series.

★5121★ **Water Environment Federation (WEF)**

601 Wythe St.
Alexandria, VA 22314-1994
Ph: (703)684-2452   Fax: (703)684-2492
Fr: 800-666-0206
E-mail: csc@wef.org
URL: http://www.wef.org

Description: Technical societies representing chemists, biologists, ecologists, geologists, operators, educational and research personnel, industrial wastewater engineers, consultant engineers, municipal officials, equipment manufacturers, and university professors and students dedicated to the enhancement and preservation of water quality and resources. Seeks to advance fundamental and practical knowledge concerning the nature, collection, treatment, and disposal of domestic and industrial wastewaters, and the design, construction, operation, and management of facilities for these purposes. Disseminates technical information; promotes good public relations and regulations that improve water quality and the status of individuals working in this field. Conducts educational and research programs.

Health Services Managers and Hospital Administrators

SOURCES OF HELP-WANTED ADS

★5122★ AABB Weekly Report

American Association of Blood Banks
8101 Glenbrook Rd.
Bethesda, MD 20814
Ph: (301)907-6977   Fax: (301)907-6895
E-mail: sales@aabb.org
URL: http://www.aabb.org

Description: Forty-four issues/year. Reports on developments in the area of blood banking and transfusion medicine. Covers scientific, regulatory, legislative, and legal information. Recurring features include news summaries and notices of employment positions.

★5123★ AAOHN News

American Association of Occupational
  Health Nurses Inc.
2920 Brandywine Rd., Ste. 100
Atlanta, GA 30341
Ph: (770)455-7757   Fax: (770)455-7271

Description: Monthly. Covers Association events as well as trends and legislation affecting occupational and enivornmental health nursing. Recurring features include news of research, a calendar of events, reports of meetings, news of educational opportunities, job listings, notices of publications available, resources for career-building, briefs on governmental issues concerning occupational and environment health, and a President's column.

★5124★ Administrative Radiology Journal

Glendale Publishing Corp.
934 W Glenoaks Blvd., Ste. 1
Glendale, CA 91202-2755
Ph: (818)500-1872
E-mail: arjournal@aol.com

Monthly. $96.00/year for individuals; $126.00/year for Canada and Mexico; $196.00/year for other countries; $15.00 for single issue. Monthly Journal of Imaging Administration for Chief Imaging M.D.'s, Im-aging Department Managers, Radiation Oncology Directors, and Healthcare Administrators.

★5125★ Ambulatory Outreach

Society for Ambulatory Care Professionals
1 N Franklin, 31st Fl.
Chicago, IL 60606
Fax: (312)422-4577

Quarterly. Subscription included in membership; $95.00/year for nonmembers. Professional journal for ambulatory care personnel.

★5126★ American Dental Hygienists' Association Access

American Dental Hygienists' Association
444 N Michigan Ave., Ste. 3400
Chicago, IL 60611
Ph: (312)440-8900   Fax: (312)440-6780
Fr: 800-243-ADHA

Subscription included in membership; $30.00/year for nonmembers. Magazine covering current dental hygiene topics, regulatory and legislative developments, and association news.

★5127★ Applied Occupational & Environmental Hygiene

Applied Industrial Hygiene Inc.
1330 Kemper Meadow Dr., Ste. 600
Cincinnati, OH 45240
Ph: (513)742-2020   Fax: (513)742-3355
E-mail: comm@acgih.org

Monthly. $159.00/year for individuals; $269.00/year for institutions. Peer-reviewed journal presenting applied solutions for the prevention of occupational and environmental disease and injury.

★5128★ ASRT Scanner

American Society of Radiologic
  Technologists
15000 Central Ave. SE
Albuquerque, NM 87123-3917
Ph: (505)298-4500   Fax: (505)298-5063
Fr: 800-444-2778

Monthly. Subscription included in member-ship. Professional magazine covering issues in radiology and medical technology. Includes calendar of events, member profiles, state affiliate news, educational opportunities, and research updates.

★5129★ CAP Today

College of American Pathologists
325 Waukegan Rd.
Northfield, IL 60093-2750
Ph: (847)832-7000   Fax: (847)832-8150
Fr: 800-323-4040
URL: http://www.cap.org

Monthly. $60.00/year for individuals, U.S.; $75.00/year, Canada; $130.00/year, foreign. Magazine covering advances in pathology tests and equipment, clinical lab management and operations trends, and related regulatory and legislative changes.

★5130★ Catholic Health World

Catholic Health Association of the United
  States
4455 Woodson Rd.
St. Louis, MO 63134-3797
Ph: (314)427-2500   Fax: (314)253-3540
URL: http://www.chausa.org

$35.00/year for individuals; $40.00/year for other countries. Tabloid containing national and regional news stories, human interest items, healthcare legislation articles, and photos of interest to administrators of U.S. Catholic hospitals, medical centers, and long-term care facilities.

★5131★ Group Practice Journal

American Medical Group Association
1422 Duke St.
Alexandria, VA 22314
Ph: (703)838-0033   Fax: (703)548-1890
E-mail: srozga@amga.org
URL: http://www.amga.org

$92.00/year; $171.00 for two years. Magazine covering the business of medicine.

★5132★ Health Care Weekly Review

The Martin Group Inc.
24901 Northwestern Hwy., Ste. 316A
Southfield, MI 48075
Ph: (248)440-6080   Fax: (248)352-4801
E-mail: hcwr@compuserve.com

Weekly. $48.00/year for individuals. Professional newspaper covering the health care industry.

★5133★ Health Education Reports

Chester Associates Inc.
4401-A Connecticut Ave. NW, PMB 212
Washington, DC 20008
Ph: (703)960-6859   Fax: (703)960-0189
Description: Biweekly. Focuses on developments relating to public health and wellness programs and government health policy. Covers activities at Centers for Disease Control around the U.S. and subjects such as health promotion, disease prevention, and medical studies. Recurring features include interviews, news of educational opportunities, job listings, book reviews and notices of publications available, reports of meetings, and a calendar of events.

★5134★ Health Facilities Management

HealthForum
1 N Franklin St., 28th Fl.
Chicago, IL 60606-3421
Ph: (312)893-6800   Fax: (312)422-4500
Fr: 800-621-6902
E-mail: mhrickiewicz@healthforum.com
URL: http://www.hfmmagazine.com

Monthly. $40.00/year; $70.00/year for other countries; $5.00/year for single issue. Trade journal.

★5135★ Health Progress

Catholic Health Association of the United States
4455 Woodson Rd.
St. Louis, MO 63134-3797
Ph: (314)427-2500   Fax: (314)253-3540
E-mail: hpeditor@chausa.org
URL: http://www.chausa.org

Free to qualified subscribers; free to subscribers from CHA; $50.00/year for individuals; $60.00/year for other countries; $10.00 for single issue. Magazine for administrative-level and other managerial personnel in Catholic healthcare and related organizations. Featured are articles on management concepts, legislative and regulatory trends, and theological, sociological, ethical, legal, and technical issues.

★5136★ Hospitals & Health Networks

Health Forum L.L.C.
One N Franklin
Chicago, IL 60606
Ph: (312)893-6800   Fax: (312)422-4600
Fr: 800-621-6902
E-mail: hhn@healthforum.com
URL: http://www.hhnmag.com

Monthly. Publication covering the health care industry.

★5137★ Journal of the American Society of Podiatric Medical Assistants

American Society of Podiatric Medical Assistants
2124 S Austin Blvd.
Cicero, IL 60804
Ph: (708)863-6303   Fax: (708)863-5375
Fr: 888-88A-SPMA

Quarterly. Subscription included in membership. Professional journal covering issues in podiatry.

★5138★ Journal of Health Administration Education

Association of University Programs in Health Administration
730 11th St. NW, 4th Fl.
Washington, DC 20001-4510
Ph: (202)638-1448   Fax: (202)638-3429

Quarterly. Journal covering health administration education.

★5139★ Journal of Health and Hospital Law

American Health Lawyers Association
1025 Connecticut NW, Ste. 600
Washington, DC 20036
Ph: (202)833-1100   Fax: (202)833-1105

Quarterly. $150.00/year. Professional journal covering healthcare issues and cases and their impact on the health care arena.

★5140★ Journal of Healthcare Information Management

Healthcare Information and Management Systems Society
230 E Ohio St., Ste. 500
Chicago, IL 60611
Ph: (312)664-4467   Fax: (312)664-6143

Quarterly. Subscription included in membership. Journal covering research and opinions in the healthcare information management industry.

★5141★ Journal for Healthcare Quality

National Association for Healthcare Quality
4700 W Lake Ave.
Glenview, IL 60025
Fax: 877-218-7939   Fr: 800-966-9392
E-mail: jhq@nahq.org
URL: http://www.nahq.org/

Bimonthly. $125.00/year; $20.00 for single issue. Professional publication that explores safe, cost-effective, quality healthcare.

★5142★ Journal of Nursing Scholarship

Sigma Theta Tau International Honor Society of Nursing
550 W N St.
Indianapolis, IN 46202
Ph: (317)634-8171   Fax: (317)634-8188
Fr: 888-634-7575

Quarterly. $39.00/year for individuals;

$20.00 for single issue; $63.00/year for institutions; $81.00/year for out of country. Peer-reviewed journal covering nursing.

★5143★ Journal of Trauma Nursing

Nursecom Inc.
1211 Locust St.
Philadelphia, PA 19107-5409
Ph: (215)545-7222   Fax: (215)545-8107
Fr: 800-242-6757

Quarterly. Professional publication covering nursing.

★5144★ Medicine and Health

Thomson Financial
195 Broadway
New York, NY 10007
Ph: (646)822-2000

Weekly. Professional publication covering the health care industry.

★5145★ MEEN Imaging Technology News

Reilly Communications Group
16 E Schaumburg Rd.
Schaumburg, IL 60194
Ph: (847)882-6336   Fax: (847)519-0166
URL: http://www.ITNonline.net

Bimonthly. $50.00/year for individuals; $80.00/year for Canada; $110.00/year for other countries, air mail; $10.00 for single issue. Trade magazine (tabloid) serving users and buyers of medical imaging technologies and services.

★5146★ Minnesota Medicine

Minnesota Medical Association
1300 Godward St. NE, Ste. 2500
Minneapolis, MN 55413
Ph: (612)378-1875   Fax: (612)378-3875
Fr: 800-DIAL-MMA
E-mail: mm@mnmed.org

Monthly. $45.00/year for individuals; $5.00 for single issue; $80.00/year for out of country. Magazine on medical, socioeconomic, public health, medical-legal, and biomedical ethics issues of interest to physicians.

★5147★ Minority Health Today

Heritage Information Holdings Inc.
1101 Pennsylvania Ave. NW, Ste. 820
Washington, DC 20001

Bimonthly. Publication covering minority issues in health.

★5148★ Modern Healthcare

Crain Communications Inc.
360 N Michigan Ave.
Chicago, IL 60601
Ph: (312)649-5200   Fax: (312)280-3174
Fr: 800-678-2724
E-mail: mhcedit@crain.com
URL: http://www.modernhealthcare.com

Weekly. $135.00/year. Weekly Business news magazine for Healthcare Management

★5149★ *Nursing Economics*
Jannetti Publications Inc.
E Holly Ave.
Box 56
Pitman, NJ 08071-0056
Ph: (856)256-2300   Fax: (856)589-7463
E-mail: nejrnl@ajj.com

Bimonthly. $49.00/year; $85.00/year for institutions; $10.00/year for single issue. Business magazine for nursing administrators.

★5150★ *Research in Healthcare Financial Management*
International Society for Research in Healthcare Financial Management Ltd.
305 W Chesapeake Ave.
CSBA Ste. L-096
Towson, MD 21204
Annual. Publication covering issues in the healthcare industry.

★5151★ *State Health Monitor*
Atlantic Information Services Inc.
1100 17th St. NW, No. 300
Washington, DC 20036
Ph: (202)775-9008   Fax: (202)331-9542
Fr: 800-521-4323
E-mail: customerserv@aispub.com

Monthly. Publication covering health care.

★5152★ *Trauma Reports*
Thomson Medical Economics
5 Paragon Dr.
Montvale, NJ 07645-1742
Ph: (201)358-7200   Fax: (201)722-2680
URL: http://www.ahcpub.com/ahc_root_html/products/newsletters/tr.

Bimonthly. $239.00/year for individuals. Professional publication covering health care.

★5153★ *Trustee*
Health Forum L.L.C.
One N Franklin
Chicago, IL 60606
Ph: (312)893-6800   Fax: (312)422-4600
Fr: 800-621-6902

$40.00/year for individuals. Magazine for hospital and health care system governing board members containing information about events and issues affecting the health care industry.

PLACEMENT AND JOB REFERRAL SERVICES

★5154★ American Academy of Medical Administrators (AAMA)
701 Lee St., Ste. 600
Des Plaines, IL 60016
Ph: (847)759-8601   Fax: (847)759-8602
E-mail: info@aameda.org
URL: http://www.aameda.org

Description: Serve healthcare management at all levels, within all types of healthcare organizations by providing solid solutions, unique connections, resources and professional recognition that healthcare professionals need to navigate today's complex healthcare environment and stay competitive. Has 7 specialty groups: American College of Cardiovascular Administrators; American College of Oncology Administrators; American College of Contingency Planners; Federal Sector; Small or Rural Healthcare; American College of Managed Care Administrators; and American College of Healthcare Information Administrators.

★5155★ American Academy of Medical Administrators Research and Educational Foundation (AAMA)
701 Lee St., Ste. 600
Des Plaines, IL 60016
Ph: (847)759-8601   Fax: (847)759-8602
E-mail: info@aameda.org
URL: http://www.aameda.org/AboutAAMA/aboutfoundation.html

Description: Individuals with health care backgrounds. Conducts research in the health care field and seminars geared toward professional development. Maintains placement services.

★5156★ American College Health Association (ACHA)
PO Box 28937
Baltimore, MD 21240-8937
Ph: (410)859-1500   Fax: (410)859-1510
E-mail: pcrone@acha.org
URL: http://www.acha.org

Members: Institutions (930) and individuals (2500). **Purpose:** Provides an organization in which institutions of higher education and interested individuals may work together to promote health in its broadest aspects for students and all other members of the college community. **Activities:** Offers continuing education programs for health professionals. Maintains placement listings for physicians and other personnel seeking positions in college health. Compiles statistics. Conducts seminars and training programs.

★5157★ American College of Health Care Administrators (ACHCA)
300 N Lee St., No. 301
Alexandria, VA 22314
Ph: (703)739-7900   Fax: (703)739-7901
Fr: 888-88-ACHCA
E-mail: mtn@achca.org

URL: http://www.achca.org

Members: Persons actively engaged in the administration of long-term care facilities, such as nursing homes, retirement communities, assisted living facilities, and subacute care programs. **Purpose:** ACHCA administers professional certification programs for assisted living, subacute and nursing home administrators. Works to elevate the standards in the field and to develop and promote a code of ethics and standards of education and training. Seeks to inform allied professions and the public that good administration of long-term care facilities calls for special formal academic training and experience. Encourages research in all aspects of geriatrics, the chronically ill, and administration. **Activities:** Maintains placement service. Holds special education programs; facilitates networking among administrators.

★5158★ American College of Managed Care Administrators (ACMCA)
701 Lee St., No. 600
Des Plaines, IL 60016-4516
Ph: (847)759-8601   Fax: (847)759-8602
URL: http://www.aameda.org

Description: Specialty college of the American Academy of Medical Administrators. **Members:** Managers of professionals who are directly or indirectly providing managed healthcare. **Purpose:** Works to promote the advancement of members' professional standing, education, and personal achievement and develop innovative concepts in managed care administration. **Activities:** Conducts an employment referral and educational programs.

★5159★ American College of Medical Quality (ACMQ)
4334 Montgomery Ave.
Bethesda, MD 20814
Ph: (301)913-9149   Fax: (301)913-9142
Fr: 800-924-2149
E-mail: ACMQ@acmq.org
URL: http://www.acmq.org

Members: Physicians, affiliates, and institutions. **Purpose:** Seeks to educate and set standards of competence in the field of quality improvement and management. Offers a core curriculum in quality. Maintains speakers' bureau.

★5160★ American Correctional Health Services Association (BCHSA)
250 Gatsby Pl.
Alpharetta, GA 30022-6161
Fax: (770)650-5789   Fr: 877-918-1842
E-mail: achsa@mindspring.com
URL: http://www.corrections.com/achsa

Members: Health care providers, individuals, or organizations interested in improving the quality of correctional health services. **Purpose:** Aims are to promote the provision of health services to incarcerated persons consistent in quality and quantity with acceptable health care practices; to promote and encourage continuing education and provide technical and professional guidance for correctional health care personnel; to establish a forum for the sharing and discussion of correctional health care issues. **Activities:** Conducts conferences on correctional health care management, nursing, mental health, juvenile corrections, dentistry, and related subjects. Maintains placement service.

★5161★ American Public Health Association (APHA)

800 I St. NW
Washington, DC 20001-3710
Ph: (202)777-2742   Fax: (202)777-2534
E-mail: comments@apha.org
URL: http://www.apha.org

Members: Professional organization of physicians, nurses, educators, academicians, environmentalists, epidemiologists, new professionals, social workers, health administrators, optometrists, podiatrists, pharmacists, dentists, nutritionists, health planners, other community and mental health specialists, and interested consumers. **Purpose:** Seeks to protect and promote personal, mental, and environmental health. **Activities:** Services include promulgation of standards; establishment of uniform practices and procedures; development of the etiology of communicable diseases; research in public health; exploration of medical care programs and their relationships to public health. Sponsors job placement service.

★5162★ American Society of Ophthalmic Administrators (ASOA)

4000 Legato Rd., No. 850
Fairfax, VA 22033
Ph: (703)591-2220   Fax: (703)591-0614
Fr: 800-451-1339
E-mail: asoa@asoa.org
URL: http://www.asoa.org

Members: A division of the American Society of Cataract and Refractive Surgery. Persons involved with the administration of an ophthalmic office or clinic. **Purpose:** Facilitates the exchange of ideas and information in order to improve management practices and working conditions. **Activities:** Offers placement services.

★5163★ Association for the Advancement of Medical Instrumentation (AAMI)

1110 N Glebe Rd., No. 220
Arlington, VA 22201-4795
Ph: (703)525-4890   Fax: (703)525-1424
Fr: 800-332-2264
URL: http://www.aami.org

Description: Clinical engineers, biomedical equipment technicians, physicians, hospital administrators, consultants, engineers, manufacturers of medical devices, nurses researchers and others interested in medical instrumentation. Purpose is to improve the quality of medical care through the application, development, and management of technology. Maintains placement service. Offers certification programs for biomedical equipment technicians and clinical engineers.

Produces numerous standards and recommended practices on medical devices and procedures. Offers educational programs.

★5164★ Radiology Business Management Association (RBMA)

65 Enterprise
Aliso Viejo, CA 92656
Ph: 888-224-RBMA   Fax: (949)330-6461
E-mail: info@rbma.org
URL: http://www.rbma.org

Description: Business managers for private radiology groups; corporate members include: vendors of equipment, services, or supplies. Purposes are to improve business administration of radiologists' practices to better serve patients and the medical profession; and to provide opportunities for professional development and recognition. Offers extensive educational and networking opportunities and informal placement service. Maintains information services emphasizing those aspects unique to the business of radiology.

★5165★ Society for Radiation Oncology Administrators (SROA)

PO Box 51687
Albuquerque, NM 87181-1687
Fax: (505)298-5063   Fr: (866)458-7762
E-mail: sroa@asrt.org
URL: http://www.sroa.org/

Members: Individuals with managerial responsibilities in radiation oncology at the executive, divisional, or departmental level, and whose functions include personnel, budget, and development of operational procedures and guidelines for therapeutic radiology departments. **Purpose:** Strives to improve the administration of the business and nonmedical management aspects of therapeutic radiology, to promote the field of therapeutic radiology administration, to provide a forum for communication among members, and to disseminate information among members. **Activities:** Maintains speakers' bureau; offers placement service.

EMPLOYER DIRECTORIES AND NETWORKING LISTS

★5166★ AHA Guide to the Health Care Field

American Hospital Association (AHA)
1 N. Franklin St., 27th Fl.
Chicago, IL 60606
Ph: (312)422-2050   Fax: (312)422-4700
Fr: 800-424-4301

Annual, August. $295.00. Covers hospitals, networks, multi-health care systems, free-standing ambulatory surgery centers, psychiatric facilities, long-term care facilities, substance abuse programs, and other health-related organizations. Entries include: For hospitals-Facility name, address, phone, administrator's name, number of beds, facili-

ties and services, number of employees, expenses, other statistics. For other organizations-Name, address, phone, fax, name and title of contact. Arrangement: Geographical. Indexes: Hospital name.

★5167★ Directory of Hospital Personnel

Thomson Medical Economics
5 Paragon Dr.
Montvale, NJ 07645-1742
Ph: (201)358-7200   Fax: (201)722-2680

Annual, November. $325.00. Covers 200,000 executives at 7,000 U.S. hospitals. Entries include: Name of hospital, address, phone, number of beds, type and JCAHO status of hospital, names and titles of key department heads and staff, medical and nursing school affiliations; number of residents, interns, and nursing students. Arrangement: Geographical. Indexes: Hospital name, personnel, hospital size.

★5168★ Directory of Personnel Responsible for Radiological Health Programs

Conference of Radiation Control Program Directors Inc.
205 Capital Ave.
Frankfort, KY 40601-2832
Ph: (502)227-4543   Fax: (502)227-7862
URL: http://www.crcpd.org

Annual, January. $45.00. Covers about 350 individuals who conduct radiological health program activities in federal, state, and local government agencies; members of the conferences. Entries include: For directors-Name and title, name of agency address, phone; office hours listed with state heading. For members-name, address, phone, affiliation, department, and title. Arrangement: Directors are by level of agency and geographical. Indexes: Personal name, agency, state.

★5169★ Guide to Careers in the Health Professions

The Princeton Review
1745 Broadway
New York, NY 10019
Ph: (212)829-6928   Fax: (212)940-7400
Fr: 800-733-3000

Published January, 2001. $24.95. Presents advice and information for those searching for satisfying careers in the health professions. Publication includes: Directory of schools and academic programs. Entries include: Name, address, phone, tuition, program details, employment profiles.

★5170★ Health Professions Career and Education Directory

American Medical Association Alliance
515 N. State St.
Chicago, IL 60610
Ph: (312)464-5000   Fax: (312)464-5020
Fr: 800-621-8335
E-mail: dorothy-grant@ama-assn.org
URL: http://ama-assn.org/hpe-letter

Annual, January. $55.00 for members; $65.00 for nonmembers. Covers more than 6,500 health career educational programs in over 64 health occupations at 2,800 sponsoring institutions. Entries include: Occupational descriptions, employment characteristics, and information on education programs, such as length, curriculum, and prerequisites. Arrangement: Classified by occupation, then geographical. Indexes: Institution name, program name.

★5171★ **Hospital Blue Book**
Billian/Transworld Publishing Inc.
2100 Powers Ferry Rd.
Ste. 300
Atlanta, GA 30339
Ph: (770)955-8484   Fax: (770)955-8485
Fr: 800-533-8484
E-mail: blu-book@billian.com

Annual, January. $285.00 for national edition; $160.00 for southern edition. Covers more than 6,687 hospitals; some listings also appear in a separate southern edition of this publication. Entries include: Name of hospital, accreditation, mailing address, phone, fax, number of beds, type of facility (nonprofit, general, state, etc.); list of administrative personnel and chiefs of medical services, with specific titles. Arrangement: Geographical.

★5172★ **The JobBank Guide to Health Care Companies**
Adams Media Corp.
57 Littlefield St.
Avon, MA 02322
Ph: (508)427-7100   Fax: (508)427-6790
Fr: 800-872-5627

$17.95. Covers Jobs nationwide in health care companies. Entries include: Firm or organization name, address, phone, name and title of contact; description of organization, headquarters location, typical titles for entry- and middle-level positions, educational backgrounds desired, fringe benefits offered, stock exchange listing, training programs, internships, parent company, number of employees, revenues, e-mail and web address, projected number of hires. Indexes: Alphabetical.

★5173★ **Medical and Health Information Directory**
Thomson Gale
27500 Drake Rd.
Farmington Hills, MI 48331-3535
Ph: (248)699-4253   Fax: (248)699-8065
Fr: 800-877-GALE
E-mail: businessproducts@gale.com

Annual. $285.00 per volume; $675.00 per set. Covers in Volume 1, more than 26,500 medical and health oriented associations, organizations, institutions, and government agencies, including health maintenance organizations (HMOs), preferred provider organizations (PPOs), insurance companies, pharmaceutical companies, research centers, and medical and allied health schools. In Volume 2, over 12,000 medical book

publishers; medical periodicals, directories, audiovisual producers and services, medical libraries and information centers, electronic resources, and health-related internet search engines. In Volume 3, more than 35,500 clinics, treatment centers, care programs, and counseling/diagnostic services for 34 subject areas. Entries include: Institution, service, or firm name, address, phone, fax, email and URL; many include names of key personnel and, when pertinent, descriptive annotation. Volume 3 was formerly listed separately as Health Services Directory. Arrangement: Classified by organization activity, service, etc. Indexes: Each volume has a complete alphabetical name and keyword index.

HANDBOOKS AND MANUALS

★5174★ **Career Opportunities in Health Care (Career Opportunities)**
Facts on File
132 W. 31st St., 17th Fl.
New York, NY 10001-2006
Ph: (212)967-8800   Fax: (212)967-8107
Fr: 800-322-8755

Shelly Field. Arthur E. Weintraub. 2002. Reprint. $18.95. 243 pages. Part of the Career Opportunities Series.

★5175★ **Great Jobs for Business Majors**
McGraw-Hill Trade
2 Penn Plaza
New York, NY 10121
Ph: (212)904-2000   Fr: 800-722-4726
E-mail: ntcpub@tribune.com

Stephen Lambert. 1996. $11.95 (paper). 462 pages.

★5176★ **Great Jobs for Psychology Majors**
McGraw-Hill Trade
2 Penn Plaza
New York, NY 10121
Ph: (212)904-2000   Fr: 800-722-4726
E-mail: ntcpub@tribune.com

Julie DeGalan and Stephen Lambert. 1995. $11.95 (paper). 468 pages. Out of print.

★5177★ **Health Care Career Starter: Finding and Getting a Great Job**
LearningExpress, LLC
900 Broadway, Ste. 604
New York, NY 10003
Ph: (212)995-2566   Fax: (212)995-5512
Fr: 800-295-9556

Cheryl Jean Hancock. Brigit Dermott. Reprint. 2002. $15.95 (paper). 216 pages. Part of the Heath Care Career Starters Series.

★5178★ **Opportunities in Health and Medical Careers**
McGraw-Hill Trade
2 Penn Plaza
New York, NY 10121
Ph: (212)904-2000   Fr: 800-722-4726

I. Donald Snook, Jr. and Leo D'Orazio. 1997. $14.95; $11.95 (paper). 202 pages. Covers the full range of medical and health occupations. Illustrated.

★5179★ **Opportunities in Hospital Administration Careers**
McGraw-Hill/Contemporary Books
1221 Avenue of the Americas
New York, NY 10020
Ph: (212)904-2000   Fr: 800-323-4900
E-mail: ntcpub@tribune.com

I. Donald Snook. 1997. $14.95; $11.95 (paper). 160 pages. Discusses opportunities for administrators in a variety of management settings: hospital, department, clinic, group practice, HMO, mental health, and extended care facilities.

★5180★ **Resumes for Health and Medical Careers**
McGraw-Hill Trade
2 Penn Plaza
New York, NY 10121
Ph: (212)904-2000   Fr: 800-722-4726
E-mail: ntcpub@tribune.com

1997. $9.95 (paper). 455 pages.

★5181★ **Where the Jobs Are: The Hottest Careers for the 90s**
The Career Press, Inc.
3 Tice Rd.
PO Box 687
Franklin Lakes, NJ 07417-1322
Ph: (201)848-0310   Fax: (201)848-1727
Fr: 800-227-3371

Joyce Hadley. Third edition, 2000. $13.99 (paper). 400 pages. Out of print. Describes careers in fifteen general fields, from accounting to travel and hospitality.

★5182★ **Your Resume: Key to a Better Job**
Hungry Minds, Inc.
10475 Crosspoint Blvd.
Indianapolis, IN 46256
Fax: (317)572-4000   Fr: 800-667-1115

Leonard Corwen. Sixth edition, 1996. $24.95 (paper). 200 pages. Provides guidelines for resume writing; explains what employers look for in a resume, including contents and style. Includes model resumes for high-demand careers such as computer programmers, health administrators, and high-tech professionals. Notes basic job-getting information and strategies.

EMPLOYMENT AGENCIES AND SEARCH FIRMS

★5183★ Abbott Associates
20880 Fish Rd.
Wilder, ID 83676
Ph: (208)482-4303
Executive search firm with focus on senior level.

★5184★ Aegis Group Search Consultants LLC
23875 Novi Rd.
Novi, MI 48375-3243
Ph: (248)344-1450   Fax: (248)347-2231
Executive search and consultant firm. Focuses on the medical industry.

★5185★ Ahern Search Partners
3982 Powell Rd. Ste. 205
Powell, OH 43065
Ph: (614)880-9136   Fax: (614)436-4125
Executive search firm. Concentrates on the healthcare market.

★5186★ Ahrensdorf & Associates
PO Box 7494
St. Davids, PA 19087-7494
Ph: (610)971-0500   Fax: (610)971-9530
Executive search firm.

★5187★ Alan Darling Consulting
374 Dover Rd., Ste. 18
South Newfane, VT 05351
Ph: (802)348-6365
Executive search firm focused on the healthcare industry.

★5188★ Alexander, Woolman & Stark
1835 Market St., Ste. 1140
Philadelphia, PA 19103
Ph: (267)256-0721   Fax: (267)256-0725
Executive search firm. Branches in Massachusetts and Vermont.

★5189★ Alliance Search Management Inc.
1717 Woodstead Ct., Ste. 106
The Woodlands, TX 77380
Ph: (281)367-8630   Fr: 800-444-0573
Employment agency.

★5190★ American Group Practice
1016 5th Ave.
New York, NY 10028
Ph: (212)371-3091
Employment agency focused on the healthcare industry.

★5191★ American Physician Network Inc.
2794 Tennis Club Dr., Ste. 204
PO Box 222352
West Palm Beach, FL 33422-2352
Fax: 888-699-5512   Fr: 800-245-8227
Employment agency focused on the healthcare industry.

★5192★ American Research Systems
PO Box 45155
Omaha, NE 68145-0155
Ph: (402)333-8333
Employment agency.

★5193★ Anderson & Associates
112 S. Tyron St.
Charlotte, NC 28284
Ph: (704)347-0090   Fax: (704)347-0064
Executive search firm. Branch in Cumming, Georgia.

★5194★ ARI Management Consultants - Executive Search
241 W. 36th St., Fl. 6
New York, NY 10018
Ph: (212)736-9114   Fax: (212)658-9958
Executive firm specializing in American-European searches.

★5195★ Aster Search Group
555 Madison Ave
New York, NY 10022
Ph: (212)888-6182
Executive search firm focused on the healthcare industry.

★5196★ Ballein Search Partners
PO Box 5204
Oak Brook, IL 60522
Ph: (630)322-9220   Fax: (630)322-9221
Executive search firm focused in the healthcare industry.

★5197★ Barro Global Search Inc.
10951 Pico Blvd., Ste. 316
Los Angeles, CA 90064
Ph: (310)441-5305
Executive search firm focused on healthcare and hospitals.

★5198★ The Bauman Group
220 Main St., Ste. 200
Los Altos, CA 94022
Ph: (650)941-0800   Fax: (650)941-1729
Executive search firm.

★5199★ Boone-Scaturro Associates Inc.
1122 Cambridge Sq., Ste. A
Alpharetta, GA 30004-3806
Ph: (770)740-1216   Fax: (770)475-5055
Fr: 800-749-1884
Executive search firm focused in the healthcare industry.

★5200★ The Brazik Group LLC
1444 N. Farnsworth Ave., Ste. 105
Aurora, IL 60505
Ph: (630)820-0785
Executive search firm. Branches in Tinley Park, IL and Union Pier, MI.

★5201★ Breitner Clark & Hall Inc.
1017 Turnpike St., Ste. 22A
Canton, MA 02021
Ph: (781)828-6411   Fax: (781)828-6431
Fr: 800-331-7004
Executive search firm focused on the healthcare industry.

★5202★ Calland & Company
2296 Henderson Mill Rd., Ste. 222
Atlanta, GA 30345
Ph: (770)270-9100   Fax: (770)270-9300
Executive search firm focused on senior management and healthcare.

★5203★ Caplan Associates Inc.
77 Bull Path
PO Box 4227
East Hampton, NY 11937
Ph: (631)907-9700   Fax: (631)907-0444
Executive search firm.

★5204★ The Caplan Taylor Group
897 Oak Park Blvd.
PMB 308
Pismo Beach, CA 93449-3287
Ph: (805)481-3000
Executive search firm.

★5205★ Capodice & Associates
Midtown Plaza
1243 S. Tamiami Trail
Sarasota, FL 34239
Ph: (941)906-1990   Fax: (941)906-1991
Executive search firm. Branch in Carlisle, MA.

★5206★ Carson Kolb Healthcare Group Inc.
20301 Birch St., Ste. 101
Newport Beach, CA 92660-1754
Ph: (949)476-2988   Fax: (949)476-2155
Fr: 800-606-9439
Executive search firm focused on the healthcare industry.

★5207★ The Cassie-Shipherd Group
26 Main St.
Toms River, NJ 08753
Ph: (732)473-1779   Fax: (732)473-1023
Executive search firm. Branches in San Diego; Bridgewater, NJ; New Bern, NC; and Salt Lake City.

★5208★ Cejka Search
222 S. Central, Ste. 400
St. Louis, MO 63105
Ph: (314)727-6650   Fax: (314)863-1705
Fr: 800-678-7858
Executive search firm for the healthcare industry. Branch in Norcross, GA.

★5209★ Chase Hunter Group Inc.
1143 W. North Shore Ave.
Chicago, IL 60626
Ph: (773)338-7865
Executive search firm focused around the healthcare industry.

★5210★ Compass Group Ltd.
Birmingham Place Bldg.
401 S. Old Woodward, Ste. 460
Birmingham, MI 48009-6613
Ph: (248)540-9110   Fax: (248)647-8288
Executive search firm. Second location in Oak Brook, IL.

★5211★ Conyngham Partners LLC
PO Box 94
Ridgewood, NJ 07451
Ph: (201)652-3444   Fax: (201)652-6357
Executive search firm.

★5212★ Criterion Search Group Inc.
PO Box 466
Wayne, PA 19087
Ph: (610)581-0590   Fax: (610)581-0594
Executive search firm.

★5213★ The Custer Group
6005 Tattersall Ct.
Brentwood, TN 37027
Ph: (615)309-0577   Fr: (509)847-7762
Executive search firm.

★5214★ Dan Ford Consulting
PO Box 68726
Oro Valley, AZ 85737
Ph: (520)742-0004   Fax: (520)742-0005
Executive search firm.

★5215★ D'Antoni Partners Inc.
1825 Walnut Hill Ln., Ste. 120
Irving, TX 75038
Ph: (972)331-2585   Fax: (972)252-7913
Executive search firm.

★5216★ Daudlin, De Beaupre & Company Inc.
18530 Mack Ave., Ste. 315
Grosse Pointe Farms, MI 48236
Ph: (313)885-1235   Fax: (313)885-1247
Executive search firm focused on the healthcare industry.

★5217★ Diversified Health Resources Inc.
875 N Michigan Ave., Ste. 3250
Chicago, IL 60611-1901
Ph: (312)266-0466   Fax: (312)266-0715
Offers healthcare consulting for hospitals, nursing homes (including homes for the aged), and other health-related facilities and companies. Specializes in planning and marketing. Also conducts executive searches for top level healthcare administrative positions. Serves private industries as well as government agencies.

★5218★ DPSI Medical One
5105 Clinton St., Ste. 2
Erie, PA 16509
Ph: (814)868-0961
Executive search firm.

★5219★ Drew Associates International
25 Pompton Ave., Ste. 305
Verona, NJ 07044
Ph: (973)571-9735
Executive search firm focused on the healthcare industry.

★5220★ ENI
3705 S. Long Beach Blvd.
Holgate, NJ 08008
Ph: (609)207-1376
Executive search firm.

★5221★ Eton Technology Partners
1 Baltimore Pl., Ste. 130
Atlanta, GA 30308
Ph: (404)872-6413   Fax: (404)685-9208
Executive search firm.

★5222★ Executive Dimensions
5820 Main St., Ste. 403
Williamsville, NY 14221
Ph: (716)632-9034   Fax: (716)632-2889
Executive search firm.

★5223★ Fitzgerald Associates
21 Muzzey St.
Lexington, MA 02421
Ph: (781)863-1945   Fax: (781)863-8872
Executive search firm specifically for the healthcare industry.

★5224★ Flannery, Sarna & Associates LLC
N14 W23777 Stone Ridge Dr., Ste. 120
Waukesha, WI 53188
Ph: (262)523-1206   Fax: (262)523-1873
Executive search firm.

★5225★ Foley Proctor Yoskowitz LLC
1 Cattano Ave.
Morristown, NJ 07960-6820
Ph: (973)605-1000   Fax: (973)605-1020
Fr: 800-238-1123
Executive search firm for the healthcare industry. Second location in New York, NY.

★5226★ Forager
1516 Sudeenew Dr.
McHenry, IL 60050
Ph: (815)344-0006
Executive search firm. Branches in Alta Loma, CA; Littleton, CO; and North Barrington, IL.

★5227★ The Ford Group Inc.
295 E. Swedesford Rd., Ste. 282
Wayne, PA 19087
Ph: (610)296-5205
Executive search firm.

★5228★ Joseph R. Burns & Associates Inc.
8 Stafford Dr.
Madison, NJ 07940
Ph: (973)377-1350   Fax: (973)377-9350
Executive search firm.

★5229★ JPM International
26060 Acero
Mission Viejo, CA 92691
Ph: (949)699-4300   Fax: (949)699-4333
Fr: 800-685-7856
E-mail: leslieo@jpmintl.com
URL: http://www.jpmintl.com
Executive search firm and employment agency.

★5230★ Lee Calhoon & Company Inc.
1621 Birchrun Rd.
PO Box 201
Birchrunville, PA 19421
Ph: (610)469-9000   Fax: (610)469-0398
Fr: 800-469-0896
Executive search firm.

★5231★ Minority Executive Search Inc.
PO Box 18063
Cleveland, OH 44118
Ph: (216)932-2022   Fax: (216)932-7988
Firm specializes in finding executives for the consumer, financial, military, automotive, medical, legal, and telecommunications industries.

★5232★ Pate Resources Group Inc.
595 Orleans, Ste. 707
Beaumont, TX 77701
Ph: (409)833-4514　　Fax: (409)833-4646
Fr: 800-669-4514

Offers executive search and recruiting services to professionals who include physicians, healthcare administrators, engineers, accounting and financial disciplines, legal, outplacement, sales and marketing. Industries served: healthcare, petrochemicals, accounting, utility, legal, and municipalities.

★5233★ Paul Bodner & Associates Inc.
1808 Taos Estates St.
Las Vegas, NV 89128
Ph: (702)386-9007　　Fax: (702)386-9016

Executive search firm. Second branch in Denver, CO.

★5234★ Roberson & Co.
PO Box 12222
Glendale, AZ 85318
Ph: (623)362-8855　　Fax: (623)561-2369

A contingency professional and executive recruiting firm working the national and international marketplace. Specialize in accounting, finance, data processing and information services, healthcare, environmental and mining, engineering, manufacturing, human resources, and sales and marketing.

★5235★ Theken Associates Inc.
Ridge Rd.
PO Box 307
Randolph, VT 05060
Ph: (802)728-3145　　Fax: (802)728-5996

Executive search firm for nursing administrators. Consulting services include emphasis on organizational development in the healthcare field and interim leadership in patient care services across the continuum.

★5236★ Tyler & Co.
375 Northridge Rd., Ste. 400
Atlanta, GA 30350-3299
Ph: (770)396-3939　　Fax: (770)396-6693
Fr: 800-989-6789

Retained executive search for the healthcare, food, market research, manufacturing and insurance industries.

★5237★ Vine and Associates
225 W Broadway, Ste. 120
Glendale, CA 91204
Ph: (818)550-9802　　Fax: (818)550-9806

Engaged in executive search and management consulting for healthcare in both the United States and overseas. In addition, the company develops feasibility and strategic planning for its clients who are primarily engaged in staffing, joint ventures and operations of institutions connected with the health industry.

★5238★ Weatherby Locum
6451 N Federal Hwy. , Ste. 80
Fort Lauderdale, FL 33308
Ph: (203)866-1144　　Fax: 800-463-2985
Fr: 800-365-8900
E-mail: info@weatherbylocums.com
URL: http://www.weatherbylocums.com

Executive search firm for physicians. Branch office in Fairfax, VA.

★5239★ Witt/Kieffer, Ford, Hadelman & Lloyd
2015 Spring Rd., Ste. 510
Oak Brook, IL 60523
Ph: (630)990-1370　　Fax: (630)990-1382

Executive search firm that specializes in hospitals and health systems, including those with faith-based sponsors, as well as managed care and insurance companies; specialty, venture-capital-backed and e-Health corporations; physician group practices; colleges and universities and not-for-profit community service and cultural organizations.

ONLINE JOB SOURCES AND SERVICES

★5240★ Health Care Job Store
395 South End Ave., Ste. 15-D
New York, NY 10280
Ph: (212)912-0175
E-mail: jobs@atshealthcarejobstore.com
URL: http://www.healthcarejobstore.com/adag.html

Description: Job sites include every job title in the healthcare industry,every healthcare industry and every geographic location in the U.S.

★5241★ HealthCareerWeb
URL: http://www.healthcareerweb.com/

Description: Advertises jobs for healthcare professionals. **Main files include:** Jobs, Employers, Resumes, Jobwire. Relocation tools and career guidance resources available.

★5242★ Medhunters.com
E-mail: info@medhunters.com
URL: http://www.medhunters.com

Description: Career search site for jobs in all health care specialties; educational resources; visa and licensing information for relocation; interesting articles; relocation tools; links to professional organizations and general resources.

★5243★ Medzilla
URL: http://www.medzilla.com
Description: General medical website which matches employers and job hunters to their ideal employees and jobs through

search capabilities. **Main files include:** Post Jobs, Search Resumes, Post Resumes, Search Jobs, Head Hunters, Articles, Salary Survey.

★5244★ ProHealthJobs
E-mail: sales@prohealthjobs.com
URL: http://www.prohealthjobs.com

Description: Career resources site for the medical and health care field. Lists professional opportunities, product information, continuing education and open positions.

TRADESHOWS

★5245★ American Academy of Medical Administrators Annual Conference and Convocation
American Academy of Medical Administrators
701 Lee St., Ste. 600
Des Plaines, IL 60016
Ph: (847)759-8601　　Fax: (847)759-8602
E-mail: info@aameda.org
URL: http://www.aameda.org

Annual. **Primary Exhibits:** Equipment, supplies, and services related to health care.

★5246★ American Association for Continuity of Care Annual Conference
American Association for Continuity of Care
638 Prospect Ave.
Hartford, CT 06105-4250
Ph: (203)586-7525　　Fax: (203)586-7550
E-mail: lpiorek@csunet.ctstateu.edu

Annual. **Primary Exhibits:** Health care delivery resources, products, and services.

★5247★ American Health Care Association Annual Convention and Exposition
American Health Care Association
1201 L St. NW
Washington, DC 20005
Ph: (202)842-4444　　Fax: (202)842-3860
E-mail: abraden@ahca.org
URL: http://www.ahca.org

Annual. **Primary Exhibits:** Supplies for the long-term health care industry.

★5248★ American Hospital Association Convention
Dallas Hyatt Regency
300 Reunion Blvd.
Dallas, TX 75267
E-mail: ashhra@aha.org
URL: http://www.aha.org

Primary Exhibits: Equipment, supplies, and services for the medical, hospital industry.

★5249★ Federation of American Health Systems Annual Convention & Business Exposition

Federation of American Health Systems
1405 N. Pierce, Ste. 311
Little Rock, AR 72217-8708
Ph: (501)661-9555   Fax: (501)663-4903
Fr: 800-880-FAHS

Annual. **Primary Exhibits:** Hospital, health care, and educational equipment, supplies, and services.

★5250★ Joint Clinical Conference on Hospice & Palliative Care

National Hospice Organization
1700 Diagonal Rd., Ste. 625
Alexandria, VA 22314-2848
Ph: (703)837-1500   Fax: (703)837-1233
Fr: 800-646-6460
E-mail: conferences@nhpco.org
URL: http://www.nhpco.org

Annual. **Primary Exhibits:** equipment, supplies, and services for hospice organizations.

OTHER SOURCES

★5251★ AAHP-HIAA

601 Pennsylvania Ave. NW, South Bldg., Ste. 500
Washington, DC 20004
Ph: (202)778-3200   Fax: (202)331-7487
E-mail: webmaster@aahp.org
URL: http://www.aahp-hiaa.org

Description: Represents the private sector in health care. Member companies provide health, long-term care, dental, disability, and supplemental coverage to more than 200 million Americans.

★5252★ Administration and Management Occupations

Delphi Productions
3160 4th St.
Boulder, CO 80304
Fax: (303)443-4022   Fr: 888-443-2400
URL: http://www.delphivideo.com

$95.00. 50 minutes. Part of the Careers for the 21st Century Video Library.

★5253★ American Almanac of Jobs and Salaries

Morrow Avon
1350 Avenue of the Americas
New York, NY 10019
Ph: (212)261-6788   Fr: 800-242-7737

John W. Wright. Revised edition, 2000. $20.00 (paper). 672 pages. This is a comprehensive guide to the wages of hundreds of occupations in a wide variety of industries and organizations.

★5254★ American College of Healthcare Executives (ACHE)

1 N Franklin, Ste. 1700
Chicago, IL 60606-4425
Ph: (312)424-2800   Fax: (312)424-0023
E-mail: ache@ache.org
URL: http://www.ache.org

Description: Healthcare executives. Conducts credentialing and educational programs and an annual Congress on Healthcare Management. Conducts ground-breaking research and career development and public policy programs. Publishing division, Health Administration Press, publishes books and journals on health services management and textbooks for use in college and university courses. Works toward goal of improving the health status of society by advancing healthcare leadership management excellence.

★5255★ American College of Medical Administrators (ACMA)

701 Lee St., Ste. 600
Des Plaines, IL 60016
Ph: (847)759-8601   Fax: (847)759-8602
URL: http://www.aameda.org

Description: Specialty College of the American Academy of Medical Administrators. **Members:** Healthcare information leaders serving in management positions. **Purpose:** Works to promote the advancement of members' knowledge, professional standing, credentialing, and personal achievements in information technology, management, and strategic planning. **Activities:** Conducts educational programs.

★5256★ American Health Care Association (AHCA)

1201 L St. NW
Washington, DC 20005
Ph: (202)842-4444   Fax: (202)842-3860
URL: http://www.ahca.org

Description: Federation of state associations of long-term health care facilities. Promotes standards for professionals in long-term health care delivery and quality care for patients and residents in a safe environment. Focuses on issues of availability, quality, affordability, and fair payment. Operates as liaison with governmental agencies, Congress, and professional associations. Compiles statistics.

★5257★ American Hospital Association (AHA)

1 N. Franklin
Chicago, IL 60606-3421
Ph: (312)422-3000   Fax: (312)422-4796
URL: http://www.aha.org

Description: Health care provider organizations. Seeks to advance the health of individuals and communities. Leads, represents, and serves health care provider organizations that are accountable to the community and committed to health improvement.

★5258★ American Society for Healthcare Environmental Services of the American Hospital Association (ASHES)

1 N Franklin St.
Chicago, IL 60606
Ph: (312)422-3860   Fax: (312)422-4572
E-mail: ashes@aha.org
URL: http://www.hospitalconnect.com

Description: Managers and directors of hospital environmental services, laundry and linen services, as well as housekeeping departments and waste management (non-hazardous and hazardous), in government or university settings. Provides a forum for discussion among members of common challenges, Professional development, and career advancement. Maintains liaison between members and governmental and standards setting bodies. Bestows Accolades Awards, Phoenix Award, Years of Service Award. Certified Healthcare Environmental Services Professional (CHESP) available through education and Examination.

★5259★ Association of Healthcare Internal Auditors (AHIA)

PO Box 10
Adrian, MI 49221-0010
Ph: (517)467-7729   Fax: (517)467-6104
E-mail: ahia@ahia.org
URL: http://www.ahia.org

Members: Health care internal auditors and other interested individuals. **Purpose:** Promotes cost containment and increased productivity in health care institutions through internal auditing. Serves as a forum for the exchange of experience, ideas, and information among members; provides continuing professional education courses and informs members of developments in health care internal auditing. **Activities:** Offers employment clearinghouse services.

★5260★ Food and Drug Law Institute (FDLI)

1000 Vermont Ave. NW, Ste. 200
Washington, DC 20005-4903
Ph: (202)371-1420   Fax: (202)371-0649
Fr: 800-956-6293
E-mail: comments@fdli.org
URL: http://www.fdli.org

Description: Provides forum regarding laws, regulations and policies related to drugs, medical devices, other health care technologies.

★5261★ Health Service Occupations

Delphi Productions
3160 4th St.
Boulder, CO 80304
Fax: (303)443-4022   Fr: 888-443-2400
URL: http://www.delphivideo.com

$95.00. 50 minutes. Part of the Careers for the 21st Century Video Library.

★5262★ International Executive Housekeepers Association (IEHA)

1001 Eastwind Dr., Ste. 301
Westerville, OH 43081-3361
Ph: (614)895-7166   Fax: (614)895-1248
Fr: 800-200-6342
E-mail: excel@ieha.org
URL: http://www.ieha.org

Description: Persons engaged in facility housekeeping management in hospitals, hotels and motels, schools, and industrial establishments. Has established educational standards. Sponsors certificate and collegiate degree programs. Holds annual International Housekeepers Week celebration during the second full week in September.

★5263★ Medical Group Management Association (MGMA)

104 Inverness Terr. E
Englewood, CO 80112-5306
Ph: (303)799-1111   Fax: (303)643-4439
Fr: 877-275-6462
E-mail: infocenter@mgma.com
URL: http://www.mgma.com

Description: For professionals involved in the management of medical group practices and administration of other ambulatory healthcare facilities. Products and services include education, benchmarking, surveys, national advocacy and networking opportunities for members.

★5264★ *Medicine & Related Occupations*

Delphi Productions
3160 4th St.
Boulder, CO 80304
Fax: (303)443-4022   Fr: 888-443-2400
URL: http://www.delphivideo.com

$95.00. 45 minutes. Part of the Careers for the 21st Century Video Library.

★5265★ National Association of Health Services Executives (NAHSE)

8630 Fenton Street, No. 126
Silver Spring, MD 20910
Ph: (202)628-3953
E-mail: nationalHQ@nahse.org

Description: Black health care executive managers, planners, educators, advocates, providers, organizers, researchers, and consumers participating in academic ventures, educational forums, seminars, workshops, systems design, legislation, and other activities. Conducts National Work-Study Program and sponsors educational programs.

★5266★ National Association for Healthcare Quality (NAHQ)

4700 W Lake Ave.
Glenview, IL 60025-1485
Ph: (847)375-4720   Fax: 877-218-7939
Fr: 800-966-9392
E-mail: dsimmons@nahq.com
URL: http://www.nahq.org

Description: Healthcare professionals in quality assessment and improvement, utilization and risk management, case management, infection control, managed care, nursing, and medical records. Objectives are: to encourage, develop, and provide continuing education for all persons involved in health care quality; to give the patient primary consideration in all actions affecting his or her health and welfare; to promote the sharing of knowledge and encourage a high degree of professional ethics in health care quality. Offers accredited certification in the field of healthcare quality, utilization, and risk management. Facilitates communication and cooperation among members, medical staff, and health care government agencies. Conducts educational seminars and conferences.

★5267★ National Health Council (NHC)

1730 M St. NW, Ste. 500
Washington, DC 20036
Ph: (202)785-3910   Fax: (202)785-5923
E-mail: info@nhcouncil.org
URL: http://www.nhcouncil.org

Description: National membership association of voluntary and professional societies in the health field; national organizations and business groups with strong health interests. Seeks to improve the health of patients, particularly those with chronic diseases, through conferences, publications, policy briefings and special projects. Distributes printed material on health careers and related subjects. Promotes standardization of financial reporting for voluntary health groups.

★5268★ National Rural Health Association (NRHA)

1 W Armour Blvd., Ste. 203
Kansas City, MO 64111-2087
Ph: (816)756-3140   Fax: (816)756-3144
E-mail: mail@nrharural.org
URL: http://www.nrharural.org

Description: Administrators, physicians, nurses, physician assistants, health planners, academicians, and others interested or involved in rural health care. Creates a better understanding of health care problems unique to rural areas; utilizes a collective approach in finding positive solutions; articulates and represents the health care needs of rural America; supplies current information to rural health care providers; serves as a liaison between rural health care programs throughout the country. Offers continuing education credits for medical, dental, nursing, and management courses.

Heating, Air-Conditioning, and Refrigeration Mechanics

SOURCES OF HELP-WANTED ADS

★5269★ Air Conditioning, Heating and Refrigeration News
BNP Media, Inc.
2401 W Big Beaver Rd., Ste. 700
Troy, MI 48084
Ph: (248)362-3700   Fax: (248)362-0317
URL: http://www.achrnews.com/

$44.00/year for individuals. Tabloid for HVAC and commercial refrigeration contractors, wholesalers, manufacturers, engineers, and owners/managers.

★5270★ ASHRAE Journal
American Society of Heating,
   Refrigerating and Air-Conditioning
   Engineers Inc.
1791 Tullie Cir. NE
Atlanta, GA 30329
Ph: (404)636-8400   Fax: (404)321-5478
Fr: 800-527-4723

Monthly. $59.00/year for individuals; $8.00 for single issue. Magazine for the heating, refrigeration, and air conditioning trade.

★5271★ Contractor Magazine
Penton Media Inc.
2700 S River Rd., Ste. 109
Des Plaines, IL 60018
Ph: (847)299-3101   Fax: (847)299-3018
URL: http://www.contractormag.com

Industry news and management how-to magazine for heating, plumbing, piping, fire sprinkler, and other mechanical specialties contracting firms.

★5272★ Heating/Piping/Air Conditioning Engineering (HPAC)
Penton Media Inc.
1300 E 9th St.
Cleveland, OH 44114-1503
Ph: (216)696-7000   Fax: (216)931-9799
URL: http://www.hpac.com/

Monthly. $65.00/year; $105.00/year for other countries.

★5273★ Industrial Heating
Business News Publishing Co.
Manor Oak One
1910 Cochran Rd., Ste. 450
Pittsburgh, PA 15220
Ph: (412)531-3370   Fax: (412)531-3375

Monthly. $25.00/year for Canada; $50.00/year for other countries. Magazine.

★5274★ Reeves Journal
Business News Publishing Co.
23211 S Pointe Dr., Ste. 101
PO Box 30700
Laguna Hills, CA 92653
Ph: (949)830-0881   Fax: (949)859-7845
URL: http://www.reevesjournal.com

Monthly. Free to qualified subscribers. Regional plumbing, heating, and cooling magazine.

★5275★ Service and Contracting (S & C)
BNP Media, Inc.
2401 W Big Beaver Rd., Ste. 700
Troy, MI 48084
Ph: (248)362-3700   Fax: (248)362-0317
E-mail: 103145.3653@compuserve.com

Monthly. $36.00/year; $51.00/year for other countries. Reporting on service, repair, installation, and replacement articles.

★5276★ Snips Magazine
Snips Magazine
755 W Big Beaver., Ste. 1000
Troy, MI 48084-4903
Ph: (248)362-3700   Fax: (248)362-0317
URL: http://www.snipsmag.com

Monthly. Magazine for the sheet metal, warm-air heating, ventilating, and air conditioning industry.Provides helpful hints for contractors.

★5277★ Southern PHC Magazine
Southern Trade Publications Inc.
Box 7344
Greensboro, NC 27417
Ph: (336)454-3516   Fax: (336)454-3649

Bimonthly. Free to qualified subscribers; $10.00/year for others. Trade magazine covering plumbing, heating, and air conditioning, targeted to contractors and wholesalers in 14 southern states.

★5278★ WIT
Northern New England Tradeswomen
189 N Main St., Ste. 9
Barre, VT 05641-4173
Ph: (802)476-4040   Fax: (802)476-3346

Description: Three issues/year. Provides a network of support, information, and skill sharing for women in skilled trades professions.

EMPLOYER DIRECTORIES AND NETWORKING LISTS

★5279★ ABC Today-Associated Builders and Contractors National Membership Directory Issue
Associated Builders & Contractors Inc.
4250 N Fairfax Dr., 9th Fl.
Arlington, VA 22203
Ph: (703)812-2000   Fax: (703)812-8203

Annual, December. $150.00. Publication includes: List of approximately 19,000 member construction contractors and suppliers. Entries include: Company name, address, phone, name of principal executive, code to volume of business, business specialty. Arrangement: Classified by chapter, then by work specialty.

★5280★ Air Conditioning Contractors of America-Membership Directory

Air Conditioning Contractors of America
2800 Shirlington Rd., Ste. 300
Arlington, VA 22206
Ph: (703)575-4477   Fax: (703)575-4449
Fr: 888-290-2220
URL: http://www.acca.org

Annual, Summer. $50.00 for nonmembers. Covers member air conditioning and heating contractors, manufacturers, vocational technical schools. Entries include: Company name, address, phone, fax, names and titles of key personnel, description of fields, and types of work performed. Arrangement: Geographical. Indexes: Alphabetical.

★5281★ Air Conditioning Equipment Repair Directory

infoUSA Inc.
5711 S 86th Cir.
Omaha, NE 68127-0347
Ph: (402)930-3500   Fax: (402)331-0176
Fr: 800-555-6124
URL: http://www.abii.com

Annual. Covers approximately 9,982 companies that specialize in equipment for air conditioning repair. Entries include: Company name, address, phone (including area code), size of advertisement, year first in "Yellow Pages," name of owner or manager, number of employees. Compiled from telephone company "Yellow Pages," nationwide. Arrangement: Geographical.

★5282★ Air Conditioning, Heating & Refrigeration News-Directory Issue

Business News Publishing Co.
2401 W Big Weaver Rd., Ste. 700
Troy, MI 48084
Ph: (248)362-3700   Fax: (248)362-0317
E-mail: wraym@bnp.com
URL: http://www.achrnews.com

Annual, January. $35.00. Publication includes: Lists of about 2,086 manufacturers, 4,383 wholesalers and factory outlets, 1,667 HVACR products, exporters specializing in the industry; related trade organizations; manufacturers representatives, consultants, services; videos and software. Entries include: For manufacturers-Company name, address, phone, fax, e-mail, URL, names of key personnel, brand names, list of products; similar information for other categories. Arrangement: Manufacturers and exporters are alphabetical; wholesalers and representatives are geographical. Indexes: Product, trade name.

★5283★ Constructor-AGC Directory of Membership and Services Issue

AGC Information Inc.
333 John Carlyle St., Ste. 200
Alexandria, VA 22314
Ph: (703)548-3118   Fax: (703)548-3119
URL: http://www.agc.org

Annual, July. $250.00 for nonmembers; $15.00 for members; $250.00 for other countries. Publication includes: List of over 8,500 member firms and 24,000 national associate member firms engaged in building, highway, heavy, industrial, municipal utilities, and railroad construction (SIC 1541, 1542, 1611, 1622, 1623, 1629); listing of state and local chapter officers. Entries include: For firms-Company name, address, phone, fax, names of principal executives, and code indicating type of construction undertaken. For officers-Name, title, address. Arrangement: Geographical, Alphabetical. Indexes: Company name.

★5284★ ENR-Top 400 Construction Contractors Issue

McGraw-Hill Companies
1221 Ave. of the Americas
New York, NY 10020
Ph: (212)512-2000   Fax: (212)512-3840

Annual, May issue of "Engineering News Record". $10.00. Publication includes: List of 400 United States contractors receiving largest dollar volumes of contracts in preceding calendar year. Separate lists of 50 largest design/construct management firms; 50 largest program and construction managers; 25 building contractors; 25 heavy contractors. Entries include: Company name, headquarters location, total value of contracts received in preceding year, value of foreign contracts, countries in which operated, construction specialities. Arrangement: By total value of contracts received.

★5285★ Heating Contractors Directory

infoUSA Inc.
5711 S 86th Cir.
Omaha, NE 68127-0347
Ph: (402)930-3500   Fax: (402)331-0176
Fr: 800-555-6124
URL: http://www.abii.com

Annual. Number of listings: 46,724. Entries include: Name, address, phone (including area code), size of advertisement, year first in "Yellow Pages," coding indicating brands carried, specialties, or franchises held. Regional editions also available. Compiled from telephone company "Yellow Pages," nationwide. Arrangement: Geographical.

★5286★ Mechanical Contractors Directory

infoUSA Inc.
5711 S 86th Cir.
Omaha, NE 68127-0347
Ph: (402)930-3500   Fax: (402)331-0176
Fr: 800-555-6124
URL: http://www.abii.com

Annual. Number of listings: 6,849. Entries include: Name, address, phone (including area code), size of advertisement, year first in "Yellow Pages," name of owner or manager, number of employees. Compiled from telephone company "Yellow Pages," nationwide. Arrangement: Geographical.

★5287★ Michigan Plumbing and Mechanical Contractors Association-Membership Directory

Michigan Plumbing and Mechanical Contractors Association (MPMCA)
400 N Walnut St.
Lansing, MI 48933
Ph: (517)484-5500   Fax: (517)484-5225

Annual. Covers member firms, industry and auxiliary associations, legislative and regulatory agencies in the plumbing and heating industry of Michigan. Entries include: Organization name, address, phone, names and titles of key personnel. Arrangement: Separate sections for members, industry associations, legislative and regulatory, and auxiliaries; members are geographical. Indexes: Company name (members), president name (members).

★5288★ Minnesota P-H-C Contractor-Membership Directory Issue

Minnesota Association of Plumbing-Heating-Cooling Contractors
6300 Shingle Creek Pkwy., No. 275
Brooklyn Center, MN 55430-2183

Annual, July. Publication includes: List of 450 member firms and associates. Entries include: Name of company, address, phone, fax, code indicating type of work, local association affiliation (chapter memberships and other), name and title of owner or officer. Arrangement: Alphabetical. Indexes: Alphabetical by business.

★5289★ National Refrigeration Contractors Association-Membership Directory

National Refrigeration Contractors Association
1900 Arch St.
Philadelphia, PA 19103-1498
Ph: (215)564-3484   Fax: (215)963-9785

Annual, Spring. Covers about 100 member refrigeration contracting companies. Entries include: Company name, address, phone, names and titles of key personnel, branch office or subsidiary names and addresses. Arrangement: Geographical. Indexes: Company name.

★5290★ Northamerican Heating, Refrigeration & Airconditioning Wholesalers Association-Membership Directory

Northamerican Heating, Refrigeration, and Airconditioning Wholesalers Association
1389 Dublin Rd.
Columbus, OH 43215-1084
Ph: (614)488-1835   Fax: (614)488-0482

Annual, spring. Covers about 2,000 wholesalers and distributors. Entries include: Company name, address, phone and names of executives. Arrangement: Alphabetical.

★5291★ **Refrigerating Equipment-Commercial Service Directory**

infoUSA Inc.
5711 S 86th Cir.
Omaha, NE 68127-0347
Ph: (402)930-3500   Fax: (402)331-0176
Fr: 800-555-6124
URL: http://www.abii.com

Annual. Number of listings: 1,476. Entries include: Name, address, phone (including area code), size of advertisement, year first in "Yellow Pages," name of owner or manager, number of employees. Compiled from telephone company "Yellow Pages," nationwide. Arrangement: Geographical.

★5292★ **Who's Who in the Plumbing-Heating-Cooling Contracting Business**

National Association of Plumbing, Heating, Cooling Contractors
180 S Washington St.
PO Box 6808
Falls Church, VA 22040
Ph: (703)237-8100   Fax: (703)237-7442
Fr: 800-533-7694

Annual. $75.00. Covers 4,000 professional plumbing/heating/cooling contractors and member firms. Entries include: Name, address, phone, fax, contact. Arrangement: Geographical. Indexes: Individual member.

HANDBOOKS AND MANUALS

★5293★ **Opportunities in Building Construction Trades**

McGraw-Hill Trade
2 Penn Plaza
New York, NY 10121
Ph: (212)904-2000   Fr: 800-722-4726

Michael Sumichrast. Second edition, 1998. $14.95; $11.95 (paper). 202 pages. From custom builder to rehabber, the many kinds of companies that employ craftspeople and contractors are explored. Includes job descriptions, requirements, and salaries for dozens of specialties within the construction industry. Contains a complete list of Bureau of Apprenticeship and Training state and area offices. Illustrated.

★5294★ **Opportunities in Plumbing and Pipefitting Careers**

McGraw-Hill Trade
2 Penn Plaza
New York, NY 10121
Ph: (212)904-2000   Fr: 800-722-4726

Patrick J. Galvin. 1993. $14.95; $10.95 (paper). 160 pages. Provides information on getting into the trade, apprenticeship programs, and how to build a career in a variety of settings. Illustrated.

TRADESHOWS

★5295★ **AHR Expo - International Air-Conditioning, Heating, Refrigerating Exposition**

International Exposition Co., Inc.
15 Franklin St.
Westport, CT 06880-5958
Ph: (203)221-9232   Fax: (203)221-9260

Annual. **Primary Exhibits:** Industrial, commercial, and residential heating, refrigeration, air conditioning, and ventilation equipment and components. **Dates and Locations:** 2005 Feb 07-09; Orlando, FL; Orange County Convention Center • 2006 Dates not set; Chicago, IL; McCormick Place.

★5296★ **Illinois Association of Plumbing, Heating, and Cooling Contractors Convention and Expo**

Illinois Association of Plumbing, Heating, and Cooling Contractors
821 S. Grand Ave., W.
Springfield, IL 62704
Ph: (217)522-7219   Fax: (217)522-4315
Fr: 800-795-7422
E-mail: iaphcc@aol.com
URL: http://ilphcc.com

Annual. **Primary Exhibits:** Plumbing, heating, and air conditioning products.

★5297★ **IMACA Convention and Trade Show**

International Mobile Air Conditioning Association
6410 Southwest Blvd., Ste. 212
Benbrook, TX 76109-3920
E-mail: imaca@iamerica.net

Annual. **Primary Exhibits:** Air-conditioning systems and other installed accessories for automobiles, and light trucks.

★5298★ **Massachusetts Association of Plumbing/Heating/Cooling Contractors Convention and Tradeshow**

Massachusetts Association of Plumbing/Heating/Cooling Contractors
178 Forbes Rd., Ste. 218
Braintree, MA 02184
Ph: (617)843-3800   Fax: (781)843-1178
Fr: 800-542-7422
E-mail: phcc@shore.net

Annual. **Primary Exhibits:** Plumbing, heating and cooling equipment, supplies, and services.

★5299★ **Mobile Air Conditioning Society Worldwide Convention and Trade Show**

Mobile Air Conditioning Society Worldwide
PO Box 100
East Greenville, PA 18041
Ph: (215)679-2220   Fax: (215)541-4635

Annual. **Primary Exhibits:** Parts and products for the air-conditioning trade.

★5300★ **NEX - North American Exposition**

American Supply Association
222 Merchandise Mart, Ste. 1400
Chicago, IL 60654-1202
Ph: (312)464-0090   Fax: (312)464-0091
Fr: 800-464-0314
E-mail: info@asa.net
URL: http://www.asa.net

Biennial. **Primary Exhibits:** Plumbing, heating, and cooling, piping, hydronic heating, tools, software.

★5301★ **North American Heating and Air Conditioning Wholesalers Association**

North American Heating and Air Conditioning Wholesalers Association
1389 Dublin Rd.
Columbus, OH 43215-1084
Ph: (614)488-1835   Fax: (614)488-0482

Annual. **Primary Exhibits:** Heating and air conditioning equipment, supplies, and services.

★5302★ **Refrigeration Service Engineers Society Educational Conference**

Refrigeration Service Engineers Society
1666 Rand Rd.
Des Plaines, IL 60016-3552
Ph: (847)297-6464   Fax: (847)297-5038
Fr: 800-297-5660
E-mail: general@rsec.org
URL: http://www.rses.org

Annual. **Primary Exhibits:** Equipment, supplies, and services for refrigeration, air-conditioning and heating installation, service, sales, and maintenance.

OTHER SOURCES

★5303★ **Air Conditioning Contractors of America (ACCA)**

2800 Shirlington Rd., Ste. 300
Arlington, VA 22206
Ph: (703)575-4477   Fax: (703)575-4449
E-mail: info@acca.org
URL: http://www.acca.org

Members: Contractors involved in installation and service of heating, air conditioning, and refrigeration systems. Associate members are utilities, manufacturers, wholesalers, and other market-oriented businesses. **Purpose:** Monitors utility competition and operating practices of HVAC manufacturers and wholesalers. **Activities:** Provides consulting services, technical training, and instructor certification program; offers management seminars. Operates annual educational institute.

★5304★ Associated Builders and Contractors (ABC)

1300 N. 17th St., Ste. 800
Rosslyn, VA 22209
Ph: (703)812-2000   Fax: (703)812-8201
E-mail: info@abc.org
URL: http://www.abc.org

Description: Construction contractors, subcontractors, suppliers, and associates. Aim is to foster and perpetuate the principles of rewarding construction workers and management on the basis of merit. Sponsors management education programs and craft training; also sponsors apprenticeship and skill training programs. Disseminates technological and labor relations information.

★5305★ Associated Specialty Contractors (ASC)

3 Bethesda Metro Ctr., Ste. 1100
Bethesda, MD 20814
Ph: (301)657-3110   Fax: (301)215-4500
E-mail: dgw@necanet.org
URL: http://www.assoc-spec-con.org

Description: Subcontractor associations with a total of 25,000 members representing electrical, heating, piping, mechanical, air conditioning, sheet metal, plumbing, ventilating, painting and decorating, and roofing and insulation contractors. Promotes liaison with general contractors, architects, and engineers on inter-industry matters, codes, bidding, and contracting procedures. Coordinates governmental affairs, research, and educational matters.

★5306★ Building Trades

Delphi Productions
3160 4th St.
Boulder, CO 80304
Fax: (303)443-4022   Fr: 888-443-2400
URL: http://www.delphivideo.com

$95.00. 46 minutes. Part of the Careers for the 21st Century Video Library.

★5307★ COIN Career Guidance System

COIN Educational Products
3361 Executive Pky., Ste. 302
Toledo, OH 43606
Ph: (419)536-5353   Fax: (419)536-7056
Fr: 800-274-8515
URL: http://www.coin3.com/highschool/guidance.asp

CD-ROM. Provides career information through seven cross-referenced files covering postsecondary schools, college majors, vocational programs, military service, apprenticeship programs, financial aid, and scholarships. Apprenticeship file describes national apprenticeship training programs, including information on how to apply, contact agencies, and program content. Military file describes more than 200 military occupations and training opportunities related to civilian employment.

★5308★ Heating, Air-Conditioning and Refrigeration Mechanics

Evon Publishing
832 N 7th Ave.
Iron River, MI 49935
Ph: (906)265-3190

Audiocassette. 1996. $16.95. 32 minutes. Part of the Careers and Vocational Guidance Series. Provides information about the nature of the work, educational requirements, employment outlook, earnings, and work conditions as well as additional related information.

★5309★ HVAC

Cambridge Educational
2572 Brunswick Ave.
Lawrenceville, NJ 08648-4128
Fax: 800-FAX-ON-US   Fr: 800-468-4227
URL: http://www.cambridgeeducational.com

$39.95. 1993. Part of the Career Connections Series.

★5310★ Mechanical Contractors Association of America (MCAA)

1385 Piccard Dr.
Rockville, MD 20850-4329
Ph: (301)869-5800   Fax: (301)990-9690
Fr: 800-556-3653
E-mail: jgentille@mcaa.org
URL: http://www.mcaa.org

Members: Contractors who furnish, install, and service piping systems and related equipment for heating, cooling, refrigeration, ventilating, and air conditioning systems. **Purpose:** Works to standardize materials and methods used in the industry. Conducts business overhead, labor wage, and statistical surveys. Maintains dialogue with key officials in building trade unions. Promotes apprenticeship training programs. Conducts seminars on contracts, labor estimating, job cost control, project management, marketing, collective bargaining, contractor insurance, and other management topics. Promotes methods to conserve energy in new and existing buildings. Sponsors Industrial Relations Council for the Plumbing and Pipe Fitting Industry.

★5311★ Mechanics & Repairers

Delphi Productions
3160 4th St.
Boulder, CO 80304
Fax: (303)443-4022   Fr: 888-443-2400
URL: http://www.delphivideo.com

$95.00. 50 minutes. Part of the Careers for the 21st Century Video Library.

★5312★ National Association of Home Builders (NAHB)

1201 15th St. NW
Washington, DC 20005
Ph: (202)266-8200   Fax: (202)822-0586
Fr: 800-368-5242
E-mail: info@nahb.com
URL: http://www.nahb.org

Description: Single and multifamily home builders, commercial builders, and others associated with the building industry. Lobbies on behalf of the housing industry and conducts public affairs activities to increase public understanding of housing and the economy. Collects and disseminates data on current developments in home building and home builders' plans through its Economics Department and nationwide Metropolitan Housing Forecast. Maintains NAHB Research Center, which functions as the research arm of the home building industry. Sponsors seminars and workshops on construction, mortgage credit, labor relations, cost reduction, land use, remodeling, and business management. Compiles statistics; offers charitable program, spokesman training, and placement service; maintains speakers' bureau, and Hall of Fame. Subsidiaries include the National Council of the Housing Industry. Maintains over 50 committees in many areas of construction; operates National Commercial Builders Council, National Council of the Multifamily Housing Industry, National Remodelers Council, and National Sales and Marketing Council.

★5313★ National Association of Women in Construction (NAWIC)

327 S Adams St.
Fort Worth, TX 76104
Ph: (817)877-5551   Fax: (817)877-0324
Fr: 800-552-3506
E-mail: nawic@nawic.org
URL: http://www.nawic.org

Description: Seeks to enhance the success of women in the construction industry.

★5314★ Plumbing-Heating-Cooling Contractors Association (APHCC)

180 S Washington St.
PO Box 6808
Falls Church, VA 22046
Ph: (703)237-8100   Fax: (703)237-7442
Fr: 800-533-7694
E-mail: naphcc@naphcc.org
URL: http://www.phccweb.org

Members: Federation of state and local associations of plumbing, heating, and cooling contractors. **Purpose:** Seeks to advance sanitation, encourage sanitary laws, and generally improve the plumbing, heating, ventilating, and air conditioning industries. **Activities:** Conducts apprenticeship training programs, workshops, and seminars; political action committee. Conducts educational and research programs.

★5315★ Refrigeration Service Engineers Society (RSES)

1666 Rand Rd.
Des Plaines, IL 60016-3552
Ph: (847)297-6464   Fax: (847)297-5038
E-mail: general@rses.org
URL: http://www.rses.org

Members: Persons engaged in refrigeration, air-conditioning and heating installation, service, sales, and maintenance. **Activities:** Conducts training courses and certification testing. Maintains a hall of fame and a speakers' bureau.

Historians

SOURCES OF HELP-WANTED ADS

★5316★ American Studies Association Newsletter

American Studies Association
1120 19th St. NW, Ste. 301
Washington, DC 20036
Ph: (202)467-4783   Fax: (202)467-4786
URL: http://www.georgetown.edu/crossroads

Description: Four issues/year. Promotes the interdisciplinary study of American culture. Presents news of research, publications, and conferences. Also includes information on grants, employment opportunities, and Association activities.

★5317★ Classical Antiquity

University of California Press/Journals
2120 Berkeley Way
Berkeley, CA 94720
Ph: (510)642-4247   Fax: (510)643-7127
URL: http://www.ucpress.edu/journals/ca/index.htm

Semiannual. $36.00/year for individuals; $95.00/year for institutions; $21.00/year for students. Scholarly journal covering interdisciplinary research and issues in Classics-Greek and Roman literature, history, art, philosophy, archaeology, and philology.

★5318★ Dispatch

American Association for State & Local History
1717 Church St.
Nashville, TN 37203-2991
Ph: (615)320-3203   Fax: (615)327-9013

Description: Monthly. Offers general information about state and local historical societies and the study of state and local history in the U.S. and Canada. Informs members of new training programs, seminars, and exhibits in the field. Recurring features include information on grant opportunities, updates on legislation, Association activities, and historical society personnel, interviews, job listings, and notices of publications available.

★5319★ History News

American Association for State & Local History
1717 Church St.
Nashville, TN 37203-2991
Ph: (615)320-3203   Fax: (615)327-9013
URL: http://www.aaslh.org

Quarterly. $50.00/year, includes membership; $75.00/year for institutions, includes membership. Magazine for employees of historic sites, museums, and public history agencies. Coverage includes museum education programs and techniques for working with volunteers.

★5320★ The Minnesota History Interpreter

Minnesota Historical Society
345 Kellogg Blvd. W
St. Paul, MN 55102
Ph: (651)296-5460   Fax: (651)282-2374
URL: http://www.mnhs.org

Description: Nine issues/year. Promotes the preservation of Minnesota history. Explores statewide Historical Society activities, providing news of exhibits, programs, seminars, conferences, and research findings. Recurring features include news of meetings, Heritage Preservation Commission News, news of members, job listings, book reviews, individual/organization profiles, and "how to" articles on topics such as museum work.

★5321★ Oral History Review

University of California Press/Journals
2120 Berkeley Way
Berkeley, CA 94720
Ph: (510)642-4247   Fax: (510)643-7127
URL: http://www.ucpress.edu/journals/ohr/

Semiannual. $60.00/year for individuals; $35.00/year for students; $80.00/year for contributing individuals; $92.00/year for member institutions; $120.00/year for sponsoring institutions. Scholarly journal of the Oral History Association covering oral history of people who have participated in important political, cultural, and economic social developments in modern times.

★5322★ Preservation

National Trust for Historic Preservation
1785 Massachusetts Ave. NW
Washington, DC 20036-2117
Ph: (202)588-6296   Fax: (202)588-6223
Fr: 800-944-6847
URL: http://www.nthp.org

Bimonthly. $20.00/year. Magazine featuring historic preservation.

★5323★ Presidential Studies Quarterly

Blackwell Publishing
350 Main St.
Malden, MA 02148
Ph: (781)388-8200   Fax: (781)388-8210
Fr: 800-759-6102
E-mail: center@thepresidency.org
URL: http://www.blackwell-synergy.com

Quarterly. Publication covering political science and history.

★5324★ Sea History Gazette

National Maritime Historical Society
5 John Walsh Blvd.
PO Box 68
Peekskill, NY 10566
Ph: (914)737-7878   Fax: (914)737-7816
E-mail: editorial@seahistory.org

Description: Six issues/year. Carries news from the fields of maritime history and preservation, including items on ship preservation, marine archaeology, sail training, and museum and exhibit openings. Designed for the layman and professional involved with the maritime heritage community. Recurring features include a calendar of events, reports of meetings, job listings, and book reviews.

★5325★ Southern Association for Women Historians Newsletter

Southern Association for Women Historians
c/o Dr. Melissa Walker
Dept. of History and Politics
Converse College
Spartanburg, SC 29302
E-mail: h-sawh@h-net.msu.edu

Description: Three issues/year. Informs members of the Association's activities aimed at advancing the professional development of women historians and historians of women. Carries minutes of the annual meeting, announcements of awards and prizes available for work published in a variety of areas, and calls for papers at various conferences. Recurring features include notices of publications available, job listings, and member updates.

★5326★ **White House Studies**
Nova Science Publishers Inc.
400 Oser Ave., Ste. 1600
Hauppauge, NY 11788-3619
Ph: (631)231-7269   Fax: (631)231-8175
Annual. Publication covering political science and history.

PLACEMENT AND JOB REFERRAL SERVICES

★5327★ **African Studies Association (ASA)**
Rutgers the State University of New Jersey
132 George St.- Douglass Campus
New Brunswick, NJ 08901-1400
Ph: (732)932-8173
E-mail: callasa@rci.rutgers.edu

Members: Persons specializing in teaching, writing, or research on Africa including political scientists, historians, geographers, anthropologists, economists, librarians, linguists, and government officials; persons who are studying African subjects; institutional members are universities, libraries, government agencies, and others interested in receiving information about Africa. **Purpose:** Seeks to foster communication and to stimulate research among scholars on Africa. **Activities:** Sponsors placement service; conducts panels and discussion groups; presents exhibits and films.

★5328★ **Flag Research Center (FRC)**
PO Box 580
Winchester, MA 01890
Ph: (781)729-9410   Fax: (781)721-4817
E-mail: vexor@attbi.com

Description: Professional and amateur vexillologists (flag historians) seeking to coordinate flag research activities and promote vexillology as a historical discipline and hobby and to increase knowledge of and appreciation for flags of all kinds. Provides data and gives lectures on flag history, etiquette, design, symbolism, and uses. Operates speakers' bureau; offers children's services and placement service; compiles statistics. Plans to establish museum.

EMPLOYER DIRECTORIES AND NETWORKING LISTS

★5329★ **Directory of Federal Historical Programs and Activities**
American Historical Association
400 A St., S.E.
Washington, DC 20003-3889
Ph: (202)544-2422   Fax: (202)544-8307
URL: http://www.historians.org/pubs/directories.htm

Triennial, latest edition 2003. $8.00 for members; $10.00 for nonmembers. Covers about 1,700 federally employed historians and federal government agencies operating historical programs. Entries include: For historians-Name, phone, area of expertise, historical program. For programs-Name, address, functions of historians.

★5330★ **Grants, Fellowships, and Prizes of Interest to Historians**
American Historical Association
400 A St., S.E.
Washington, DC 20003-3889
Ph: (202)544-2422   Fax: (202)544-8307
E-mail: grantguide@theaha.org
URL: http://www.theaha.org/members/grants/index.cfm

Annual, September. Covers over 450 sources of funding (scholarships, fellowships, internships, awards, and book and essay prizes) in the United States and abroad for graduate students, postdoctoral researchers, and institutions in the humanities. Entries include: Name of source, institution name or contact, address, phone, eligibility and proposal requirements, award or stipend amount, location requirements for research, application deadlines. Arrangement: Alphabetical in three categories: support for individual research and teaching; grants for groups and organizations for research and education; and book, article, essay, and manuscript prizes.

★5331★ **Newsletter-Society for Historical Archaeology Membership Directory Issue**
Society for Historical Archaeology
19 Mantua Rd.
Mount Royal, NJ 08061
Ph: (856)224-0995   Fax: (856)423-3420

Annual, June. Publication includes: List of about 2,100 member archaeologists, historians, anthropologists, and ethnohistorians, and other individuals and institutions having an interest in historical archeology or allied fields. Entries include: Name, address. Arrangement: Alphabetical.

★5332★ **Official Museum Directory**
LexisNexis Group
121 Chanlon Rd.
New Providence, NJ 07974
Ph: (908)464-6800   Fax: (908)771-7704
Fr: 800-526-4902

Annual, December. $245.00. Covers approx-

imately 7,850 institutions of art, history, and science in the United States, including general museums, college and university museums, children's and junior museums, company museums, national park and nature center displays, and highly specialized museums. Also includes a separate volume of 2,000 suppliers of services and products to museums. Entries include: For museums-Name, address, phone, date established, personnel, governing authority, brief description of museum and type of collections, facilities, activities, publications, hours of operation, admission prices, membership fees, attendance figures. For suppliers-Company name, address, phone, name and title of contact. Arrangement: Museums are geographical; suppliers are by specialty. Indexes: Museum personnel (with name, title, affiliation, city, and state); type of museum (with name, city, and state); alphabetical; special collection.

★5333★ **Perspectives-Employment Information Section**
American Historical Association
400 A St., S.E.
Washington, DC 20003-3889
Ph: (202)544-2422   Fax: (202)544-8307
URL: http://www.historians.org/members/eib/search.cfm?requesttimeout

Nine issues per year. $120.00 for institutions annually; $3.00 per issue. Publication includes: List of over 1000 job openings per year for historians; international coverage. Entries include: Institution or organization name, address, department name, name and title of contact, responsibilities, application deadline. Arrangement: Geographical.

HANDBOOKS AND MANUALS

★5334★ **Careers for History Buffs & Others Who Learn from the Past**
McGraw-Hill Trade
2 Penn Plaza
New York, NY 10121
Ph: (212)904-2000   Fr: 800-722-4726
E-mail: ntcpub@tribune.com

Blythe Camenson. Second edition, 2002. $15.95; $9.95 (paper). 192 pages.

★5335★ **Designing a Career in Public History: Becoming a Professional Historian**
Krieger Publishing Co.
PO Box 9542
Melbourne, FL 32902-9542
Ph: (407)724-9542   Fax: (407)951-3671
Fr: 800-724-0025

Donna M. Neary.

★5336★ Great Jobs for History Majors

McGraw-Hill Trade
2 Penn Plaza
New York, NY 10121
Ph: (212)904-2000   Fr: 800-722-4726
E-mail: ntcpub@tribune.com

Julie DeGalan and Stephen Lambert. 1994. $11.95 (paper). 442 pages.

★5337★ Opportunities in Social Science Careers

McGraw-Hill Companies
860 Taylor Station Rd.
Blacklick, OH 43004-0545
Fax: (614)755-5645   Fr: 800-722-4726

Rosanne J. Marek. March 2004. $22.95. 160 Pages. VGM Opportunities Series.

TRADESHOWS

★5338★ American Association for State and Local History Annual Meeting

American Association for State and Local History
1717 Church St.
Nashville, TN 37203-2991
Ph: (615)320-3203   Fax: (615)327-9013
E-mail: history@aaslh.org
URL: http://www.aaslh.org

Annual. **Primary Exhibits:** Products and services directed toward the museum and history field, including publications, fund-raising devices, software, exhibit design, historic preservation, historic research and technical information. **Dates and Locations:** 2004 Sep 29-Oct 02.

★5339★ American Historical Association Annual Meeting

American Historical Association
400 A St. SE
Washington, DC 20003
Ph: (202)544-2422   Fax: (202)544-8307
E-mail: aha@theaha.org
URL: http://www.theaha.org

Annual. **Primary Exhibits:** Books and journals from commercial publishers and university presses. **Dates and Locations:** 2005 Jan 6-9; Seattle, WA; Washington State Convention Center • 2006 Jan 5-8; Philadelphia, PA; Philadelphia Marriott and Loews Philadelphia • 2007 Jan 04-07; Atlanta, GA; Hilton Atlanta, Atlanta Marriott, Hyatt Regency.

★5340★ American Society for Ethnohistory Conference

American Society for Ethnohistory
c/o R. David Edmunds, Pres.
University of Texas at Dallas
2601 N Floyd Rd.
Richardson, TX 75080

Annual. **Primary Exhibits:** Exhibits relating to the cultural history of ethnic groups world-wide. **Dates and Locations:** 2004 Dates not set; Chicago, IL • 2005 Dates not set; Santa Fe, NM.

★5341★ Congress of the International Society for Human Ethology

International Society for Human Ethology
c/o Dr. Peter Lafrenieve
362 Little Hall
Department of Psychology
University of Maine
Orono, ME 04469
Ph: (207)581-2044   Fax: (207)581-6128
E-mail: peterlaf@maine.edu
URL: http://evolution.humb.univie.ac.at

Biennial. **Primary Exhibits:** Books, journals, and equipment for observational research.

★5342★ Oral History Association Conference

Oral History Association
Dickinson College
PO Box 1773
Carlisle, PA 17013-2896
Ph: (717)245-1036   Fax: (717)245-1046
E-mail: oha@dickinson.edu
URL: http://www.dickinson.edu/oha

Annual. **Primary Exhibits:** Equipment, supplies, and services related to recording, transcribing, and preserving conversations constituting oral history.

★5343★ Organization of American Historians Annual Meeting

Organization of American Historians
112 N. Bryan St.
Bloomington, IN 47408-4199
Ph: (812)855-7311   Fax: (812)855-0696
E-mail: oah@oah.org
URL: http://www.oah.org

Annual. **Primary Exhibits:** Equipment, supplies, and services of interest to historians, including textbooks and computer software.

★5344★ Southern Historical Association Meeting

Southern Historical Association
Dept. of History
University of Georgia
Athens, GA 30602
Ph: (706)542-8848   Fax: (706)542-2455
URL: http://www.uga.edu/~sha

Annual. **Primary Exhibits:** Publications. **Dates and Locations:** 2004 Nov 03-06; Memphis, TN; Memphis Marriott Downtown • 2005 Nov 02-05; Atlanta, GA; Westin Peachtree Plaza • 2006 Nov 17-20; New Orleans, LA; Fairmont Hotel.

OTHER SOURCES

★5345★ American Association for State and Local History (AASLH)

1717 Church St.
Nashville, TN 37203-2921
Ph: (615)320-3203   Fax: (615)327-9013
E-mail: history@aaslh.org
URL: http://www.aaslh.org

Description: Organization of educators, historians, writers, and other individuals; state and local historical societies; agencies and institutions interested in improving the study of state and local history in the United States and Canada, and assisting historical organizations in improving their public services.

★5346★ American Catholic Historical Association (ACHA)

Mullen Library, Rm. 320
Catholic University of America
Washington, DC 20064
Ph: (202)319-5079   Fax: (202)319-5079
E-mail: cua-chracha@cua.edu

Description: Professional society of historians, educators, students, and others interested in the history of the Catholic church in the United States and abroad and in the promotion of historical scholarship among Catholics. Has sponsored the publication of the papers of John Carroll, first Bishop and Archbishop of Baltimore, MD.

★5347★ American Historical Association (AHA)

400 A St. SE
Washington, DC 20003-3889
Ph: (202)544-2422   Fax: (202)544-8307
E-mail: aha@theaha.org
URL: http://www.theaha.org

Members: Professional historians, educators, and others interested in promoting historical studies and collecting and preserving historical manuscripts. **Activities:** Conducts research and educational programs.

★5348★ American Institute for Conservation of Historic and Artistic Works (AIC)

1717 K St. NW, Ste. 200
Washington, DC 20006
Ph: (202)452-9545   Fax: (202)452-9328
E-mail: info@aic-faic.org
URL: http://aic.stanford.edu

Members: Professionals, scientists, administrators, and educators in the field of art conservation; interested individuals. **Purpose:** Advances the practice and promotes the importance of the preservation of cultural property. **Activities:** Coordinates the exchange of knowledge, research, and publications. Establishes and upholds professional standards. Publishes conservation literature. Compiles statistics. Represents membership to allied professional associations and advocates on conservation-related issues. Solicits and dispenses money exclusively for charitable, scientific, and educational objectives.

★5349★ American Society for Eighteenth-Century Studies (ASECS)
Wake Forest University
PO Box 7867
Winston-Salem, NC 27109
Ph: (336)727-4694   Fax: (336)727-4697
E-mail: asecs@wfu.edu
URL: http://asecs.press.jhu.edu/

Description: Scholars and others interested in the cultural history of the 18th century. Encourages and advances study and research in this area; promotes the interchange of information and ideas among scholars from different disciplines (such as librarianship and bibliography) who are interested in the 18th century. Cosponsors seven fellowship programs; sponsors Graduate Student Caucus.

★5350★ American Society of Psychopathology of Expression (ASPE)
74 Lawton St.
Brookline, MA 02446
Ph: (617)738-9821   Fax: (617)975-0411

Description: Psychiatrists, psychologists, art therapists, sociologists, art critics, artists, social workers, linguists, educators, criminologists, writers, and historians. At least two-thirds of the members must be physicians. Fosters collaboration among specialists in the United States who are interested in the problems of expression and in the artistic activities connected with psychiatric, sociological, and psychological research. Disseminates information about research and clinical applications in the field of psychopathology of expression. Sponsors consultations, seminars, and lectures on art therapy.

★5351★ International Studies Association (ISA)
324 Social Sciences Bldg.
University of Arizona
Tucson, AZ 85721
Ph: (520)621-7715   Fax: (520)621-5780
E-mail: isa@u.arizona.edu
URL: http://www.isanet.org

Members: Social scientists and other scholars from a wide variety of disciplines who are specialists in international affairs and cross-cultural studies; academicians; government officials; officials in international organizations; business executives; students. **Purpose:** Promotes research, improved teaching, and the orderly growth of knowledge in the field of international studies; emphasizes a multidisciplinary approach to problems. **Activities:** Conducts conventions, workshops and discussion groups.

★5352★ National Coalition for History (NCH)
310 Auditorium Bldg.
Michigan State University
East Lansing, MI 48824
Ph: (517)355-9300   Fax: (517)355-8363
E-mail: rbcraig@historycoalition.org
URL: http://www.h-net.org/~nch/

Description: Archival and historical organizations such as: American Historical Association; Organization of American Historians; Phi Alpha Theta; Society of American Archivists; Western History Association. Serves as central advocacy office and information clearinghouse for history/archival related topics affecting government agencies, legislative aides, and professional history and archival associations; develops network of constituent contacts in districts and states; testifies before congressional committees; monitors employment opportunities.

★5353★ National Council on Public History (NCPH)
Indiana University - Purdue University at Indianapolis
327 Cavanaugh
425 University Blvd.
Indianapolis, IN 46202
Ph: (317)274-2716   Fax: (317)278-5230
E-mail: ncph@iupui.edu
URL: http://www.ncph.org

Description: Objectives are to encourage a broader interest in professional history and to stimulate national interest in public history by promoting its use at all levels of society. (Public history deals with nonacademic history. History is brought to the public rather than the classroom through museum work, public displays, and federal, local, and corporate historians.) Serves as an information clearinghouse; sponsors training programs, local and regional colloquia, projects, and panels. Offers advice to departments of history, historical associations, and others seeking information on public history, professional standards, opportunities, and internships. Conducts surveys and analyses.

★5354★ Newcomen Society of the United States (NSUS)
211 Welsh Pool Rd., Ste. 240
Exton, PA 19341-1321
Ph: (610)363-6600   Fax: (610)363-0612
E-mail: info@newcomen.org

Members: Business and professional people in education and industry in the United States and Canada. **Purpose:** Studies material history, as distinguished from political history, in terms of the beginnings, growth, and contributions of industry, transportation, communication, mining, agriculture, banking, insurance, medicine, education, invention, law, and related historical fields. Maintains Thomas Newcomen Memorial Museum in Steam Technology and Industrial History in Chester County, PA. Society named for Thomas Newcomen (1663-1729), British pioneer who invented the first atmospheric steam engine.

★5355★ Organization of American Historians (OAH)
112 N. Bryan Ave.
Bloomington, IN 47408-4199
Ph: (812)855-7311   Fax: (812)855-0696
E-mail: oah@oah.org
URL: http://www.oah.org

Description: Professional historians, including college faculty members, secondary school teachers, graduate students, and other individuals in related fields; institutional subscribers are college, university, high school and public libraries, and historical agencies. Promotes historical research and study. Sponsors 12 prize programs for historical writing; maintains speakers' bureau. Conducts educational programs.

★5356★ United States Capitol Historical Society (USCHS)
200 Maryland Ave. NE
Washington, DC 20002
Ph: (202)543-8919   Fax: (202)544-8244
E-mail: uschs@uschs.org
URL: http://www.uschs.org

Description: A private non-profit, non-partisan educational organization chartered by Congress to preserve and communicate the history and heritage of the U.S. Capital, its institutions, and the individuals who have served in Congress. Society activities include educational programs, popular & scholarly symposia & publications, enhancement of the Capitol's collection of art & artifacts, & research in the U.S. Capitol & the U.S. Congress.

Home Health Aides

★5357★ **ADVANCE for Nurse Practitioners**

Merion Publications Inc.
2900 Horizon Dr.
PO Box 61556
King of Prussia, PA 19406-0956
Ph: (610)278-1400
URL: http://www.advancefornp.com

Monthly. Free to qualified subscribers. For practicing nurse practitioner students with senior status.

★5358★ **Ambulatory Outreach**

Society for Ambulatory Care Professionals
1 N Franklin, 31st Fl.
Chicago, IL 60606
Fax: (312)422-4577

Quarterly. Subscription included in membership; $95.00/year for nonmembers. Professional journal for ambulatory care personnel.

★5359★ **American Dental Hygienists' Association Access**

American Dental Hygienists' Association
444 N Michigan Ave., Ste. 3400
Chicago, IL 60611
Ph: (312)440-8900   Fax: (312)440-6780
Fr: 800-243-ADHA

Subscription included in membership; $30.00/year for nonmembers. Magazine covering current dental hygiene topics, regulatory and legislative developments, and association news.

★5360★ **American Journal of Nursing**

American Journal of Nursing
c/o Lippincott, Williams, & Wilkins
530 Walnut
Philadelphia, PA 19106
Fr: 800-627-0484
URL: http://www.nursingcenter.com

Monthly. $29.95/year. Journal for staff nurses, nurse managers, and clinical nurse specialists. Focuses on patient care in hospitals, hospital ICUs and homes. Provides news coverage of health care from the nursing perspective.

★5361★ **The American Nurse**

American Nurses Association
600 Maryland Ave. SW, Ste. 100 W
Washington, DC 20024-2571
Ph: (202)651-7000   Fax: (202)651-7000
Fr: 800-284-2378
E-mail: adsales@anan.org

$10.00/year for students; $20.00/year for nonmembers; $30.00/year for other countries. Newspaper (tabloid) for the nursing profession.

★5362★ **ASRT Scanner**

American Society of Radiologic
  Technologists
15000 Central Ave. SE
Albuquerque, NM 87123-3917
Ph: (505)298-4500   Fax: (505)298-5063
Fr: 800-444-2778

Monthly. Subscription included in membership. Professional magazine covering issues in radiology and medical technology. Includes calendar of events, member profiles, state affiliate news, educational opportunities, and research updates.

★5363★ **Cancer Nursing**

Lippincott Williams & Wilkins
530 Walnut St.
Philadelphia, PA 19106
Ph: (215)521-8300   Fax: (215)521-8902
Fr: 800-638-3030
E-mail: ashcr@nursing.ufl.edu
URL: http://www.cancernursingonline.com/

Bimonthly. $82.95/year for individuals; $122.95/year for other countries; $192.95/year for institutions; $222.95/year for institutions, other countries. Medical journal covering problems arising in the care and support of cancer patients.

★5364★ **Geriatric Nursing**

Mosby Inc.
10801 Executive Center Dr., Ste. 509
Little Rock, AR 72211
Ph: (501)223-5165   Fax: (501)223-0519
URL: http://www.mosby.com/gerinurs

Bimonthly. $54.00/year for individuals; $105.00/year for institutions. Magazine for nurses in geriatric and gerontologic nursing practice, the primary professional providers of care for the aging. Provides news on issues affecting elders and clinical information on techniques and procedures.

★5365★ **Health Care Weekly Review**

The Martin Group Inc.
24901 Northwestern Hwy., Ste. 316A
Southfield, MI 48075
Ph: (248)440-6080   Fax: (248)352-4801
E-mail: hcwr@compuserve.com

Weekly. $48.00/year for individuals. Professional newspaper covering the health care industry.

★5366★ **Home Health Agency Insider**

American Federation of Home Health
  Agencies
1320 Fenwick Ln., Ste. 100
Silver Spring, MD 20910
Ph: (301)588-1454   Fax: (301)588-4732

Description: Every three weeks. Provides information on regulatory and legislative issues of concern to home health agencies. Discusses employment topics and the issues of providing care. Recurring features include current legislation, regulatory developments, and news of meetings.

★5367★ **Home Healthcare Nurse**

Lippincott Williams & Wilkins
530 Walnut St.
Philadelphia, PA 19106
Ph: (215)521-8300   Fax: (215)521-8902
Fr: 800-638-3030
E-mail: hhnedit@bellsouth.net
URL: http://
www.homehealthcarenurseonline.com/

Monthly. $49.95/year for individuals; $198.95/year for institutions; $102.95/year for other countries; $232.95/year for institutions, other countries. Magazine for the practicing professional nurse working in the home health, community health, and public health areas.

★5368★ HomeCare Magazine
Miramar Communications Inc.
23805 Stuart Ranch Rd., Ste. 235
PO Box 8987
Malibu, CA 90265-8987
Ph: (310)317-4522   Fax: (310)317-0264
Fr: 800-543-4116
URL: http://www.homecaremag.com

Monthly. Magazine serving home medical equipment suppliers, including independent and chain centers specializing in home care, pharmacies or chain drug stores with home care products, and joint-ventured hospital home health care businesses. Contains industry news and new product launches and marketing strategies.

★5369★ Hospitals & Health Networks
Health Forum L.L.C.
One N Franklin
Chicago, IL 60606
Ph: (312)893-6800   Fax: (312)422-4600
Fr: 800-621-6902
E-mail: hhn@healthforum.com
URL: http://www.hhnmag.com

Monthly. Publication covering the health care industry.

★5370★ Journal of the American Society of Podiatric Medical Assistants
American Society of Podiatric Medical Assistants
2124 S Austin Blvd.
Cicero, IL 60804
Ph: (708)863-6303   Fax: (708)863-5375
Fr: 888-88A-SPMA

Quarterly. Subscription included in membership. Professional journal covering issues in podiatry.

★5371★ Journal of Gerontological Nursing
SLACK Inc.
6900 Grove Rd.
Thorofare, NJ 08086-9447
Ph: (856)848-1000   Fax: (856)853-5991
Fr: 800-257-8290
E-mail: jgn@slackinc.com

Monthly. $59.00/year; $109.00/year for institutions; $19.00/year for single issue. Gerontological nursing journal.

★5372★ Journal of Health and Hospital Law
American Health Lawyers Association
1025 Connecticut NW, Ste. 600
Washington, DC 20036
Ph: (202)833-1100   Fax: (202)833-1105

Quarterly. $150.00/year. Professional journal covering healthcare issues and cases and their impact on the health care arena.

★5373★ Journal of Nursing Scholarship
Sigma Theta Tau International Honor Society of Nursing
550 W N St.
Indianapolis, IN 46202
Ph: (317)634-8171   Fax: (317)634-8188
Fr: 888-634-7575

Quarterly. $39.00/year for individuals; $20.00 for single issue; $63.00/year for institutions; $81.00/year for out of country. Peer-reviewed journal covering nursing.

★5374★ Journal of Trauma Nursing
Nursecom Inc.
1211 Locust St.
Philadelphia, PA 19107-5409
Ph: (215)545-7222   Fax: (215)545-8107
Fr: 800-242-6757

Quarterly. Professional publication covering nursing.

★5375★ McKnight's Long-Term Care News
McKnight's Long-Term Care News
Two Northfield Plz., Ste. 300
Northfield, IL 60093-1219
Ph: (847)784-8706   Fax: (847)441-3701
E-mail: ltcnews@medec.com

Monthly. Free to qualified subscribers in U.S.; $5.00/year for single issue; $9.00 for single back issue; $54.95/year for Canada; $59.95/year, foreign. Professional magazine.

★5376★ Medicine and Health
Thomson Financial
195 Broadway
New York, NY 10007
Ph: (646)822-2000

Weekly. Professional publication covering the health care industry.

★5377★ Minority Health Today
Heritage Information Holdings Inc.
1101 Pennsylvania Ave. NW, Ste. 820
Washington, DC 20001

Bimonthly. Publication covering minority issues in health.

★5378★ Modern Healthcare
Crain Communications Inc.
360 N Michigan Ave.
Chicago, IL 60601
Ph: (312)649-5200   Fax: (312)280-3174
Fr: 800-678-2724

E-mail: mhcedit@crain.com
URL: http://www.modernhealthcare.com

Weekly. $135.00/year. Weekly Business news magazine for Healthcare Management

★5379★ Nursing 96
Lippincott Williams & Wilkins
530 Walnut St.
Philadelphia, PA 19106
Ph: (215)521-8300   Fax: (215)521-8902
Fr: 800-638-3030
E-mail: nursing@springnet.com

Monthly. $42.00/year for individuals; $4.00 for single issue. Practical journal for nurses. Includes special sections for hospital critical-care and home health.

★5380★ Nursing Outlook
Mosby Inc.
10801 Executive Center Dr., Ste. 509
Little Rock, AR 72211
Ph: (501)223-5165   Fax: (501)223-0519
URL: http://www.mosby.com

Bimonthly. $57.00/year for individuals; $106.00/year for institutions. Official journal of the American Academy of Nursing, reporting on trends and issues in nursing.

★5381★ Physical & Occupational Therapy in Geriatrics
The Haworth Press Inc.
10 Alice St.
Binghamton, NY 13904-1580
Ph: (607)722-5857   Fax: (607)722-1424
Fr: 800-429-6784
URL: http://www.haworthpress.com

Quarterly. $40.00/year for individuals, USA; $160.00/year for institutions, USA; $225.00/year for libraries, USA; $52.00/year for individuals, Canada; $208.00/year for institutions, Canada; $292.52/year for libraries, Canada; $56.00/year for individuals, other countries; $224.00/year for institutions, other countries; $315.00/year for libraries, other countries. Journal for allied health professionals focusing on current practice and emerging issues in the health care of and rehabilitation of the older client.

★5382★ Provider
American Health Care Association
1201 L St. NW
Washington, DC 20005
Ph: (202)842-4444   Fax: (202)842-3860
Fr: 800-321-4444
E-mail: provider@ahca.org

Monthly. $48.00/year for nonmembers. Provider Magazine.

★5383★ Rehabilitation Nursing
Rehabilitation Nursing
4700 W Lake Ave.
Glenview, IL 60025
Ph: (847)375-4710   Fax: 877-734-9384
Fr: 800-229-7530
E-mail: info@rehabnurse.org

Bimonthly. $95.00/year for individuals; $125.00/year for institutions; $135.00/year for other countries; $18.00 for single issue; $125.00/year for Canada. Magazine focusing on rehabilitation nursing involving clinical practice, research, education, and administration.

★5384★ **Research in Healthcare Financial Management**

International Society for Research in
  Healthcare Financial Management Ltd.
305 W Chesapeake Ave.
CSBA Ste. L-096
Towson, MD 21204

Annual. Publication covering issues in the healthcare industry.

★5385★ **State Health Monitor**

Atlantic Information Services Inc.
1100 17th St. NW, No. 300
Washington, DC 20036
Ph: (202)775-9008   Fax: (202)331-9542
Fr: 800-521-4323
E-mail: customerserv@aispub.com

Monthly. Publication covering health care.

★5386★ **Trauma Reports**

Thomson Medical Economics
5 Paragon Dr.
Montvale, NJ 07645-1742
Ph: (201)358-7200   Fax: (201)722-2680
URL: http://www.ahcpub.com/ahc_root_
html/products/newsletters/tr.

Bimonthly. $239.00/year for individuals. Professional publication covering health care.

PLACEMENT AND JOB REFERRAL SERVICES

★5387★ **American Public Health Association (APHA)**

800 I St. NW
Washington, DC 20001-3710
Ph: (202)777-2742   Fax: (202)777-2534
E-mail: comments@apha.org
URL: http://www.apha.org

Members: Professional organization of physicians, nurses, educators, academicians, environmentalists, epidemiologists, new professionals, social workers, health administrators, optometrists, podiatrists, pharmacists, dentists, nutritionists, health planners, other community and mental health specialists, and interested consumers. **Purpose:** Seeks to protect and promote personal, mental, and environmental health. **Activities:** Services include promulgation of standards; establishment of uniform practices and procedures; development of the etiology of communicable diseases; research in public health; exploration of medical care programs and their relationships to public health. Sponsors job placement service.

EMPLOYER DIRECTORIES AND NETWORKING LISTS

★5388★ **American Journal of Nursing-Career Guide**

American Journal of Nursing
c/o Lippincott, Williams, & Wilkins
530 Walnut St.
Philadelphia, PA 19106-3621
Ph: (215)521-8300   Fax: (215)521-8902
Fr: 800-627-0484
URL: http://www.nursingcenter.com

Annual, April. $13.95. Publication includes: List of nursing organizations and agencies. Entries include: Name, address, names of officers or nursing representative. Arrangement: Classified by type of organization.

★5389★ **Home Health Service Directory**

infoUSA Inc.
5711 S 86th Cir.
Omaha, NE 68127-0347
Ph: (402)930-3500   Fax: (402)331-0176
Fr: 800-555-6124
URL: http://www.abii.com

Annual. Number of listings: 21,158. Entries include: Name, address, phone (including area code), size of advertisement, year first in "Yellow Pages," name of owl her or manager, number of employees. Compiled from telephone company "Yellow Pages," nationwide. Arrangement: Geographical.

★5390★ **The JobBank Guide to Health Care Companies**

Adams Media Corp.
57 Littlefield St.
Avon, MA 02322
Ph: (508)427-7100   Fax: (508)427-6790
Fr: 800-872-5627

$17.95. Covers Jobs nationwide in health care companies. Entries include: Firm or organization name, address, phone, name and title of contact; description of organization, headquarters location, typical titles for entry- and middle-level positions, educational backgrounds desired, fringe benefits offered, stock exchange listing, training programs, internships, parent company, number of employees, revenues, e-mail and web address, projected number of hires. Indexes: Alphabetical.

★5391★ **Medical and Health Information Directory**

Thomson Gale
27500 Drake Rd.
Farmington Hills, MI 48331-3535
Ph: (248)699-4253   Fax: (248)699-8065
Fr: 800-877-GALE
E-mail: businessproducts@gale.com

Annual. $285.00 per volume; $675.00 per set. Covers in Volume 1, more than 26,500 medical and health oriented associations, organizations, institutions, and government agencies, including health maintenance or-

ganizations (HMOs), preferred provider organizations (PPOs), insurance companies, pharmaceutical companies, research centers, and medical and allied health schools. In Volume 2, over 12,000 medical book publishers; medical periodicals, directories, audiovisual producers and services, medical libraries and information centers, electronic resources, and health-related internet search engines. In Volume 3, more than 35,500 clinics, treatment centers, care programs, and counseling/diagnostic services for 34 subject areas. Entries include: Institution, service, or firm name, address, phone, fax, email and URL; many include names of key personnel and, when pertinent, descriptive annotation. Volume 3 was formerly listed separately as Health Services Directory. Arrangement: Classified by organization activity, service, etc. Indexes: Each volume has a complete alphabetical name and keyword index.

★5392★ **Nurses and Nurses' Registries Directory**

infoUSA Inc.
5711 S 86th Cir.
Omaha, NE 68127-0347
Ph: (402)930-3500   Fax: (402)331-0176
Fr: 800-555-6124
URL: http://www.abii.com

Annual. Number of listings: 10,949. Entries include: Name, address, phone (including area code), size of advertisement, year first in "Yellow Pages," name of owner or manager, number of employees. Compiled from telephone company "Yellow Pages," nationwide. Arrangement: Geographical.

★5393★ **Peterson's Job Opportunities for Health and Science Majors**

Thomson Peterson's
Princeton Pke. Corporate Ctr., 2000
  Lenox Dr.
PO Box 67005
Lawrenceville, NJ 08648
Ph: (609)896-1800   Fax: (609)896-4531
Fr: 800-338-3282
URL: http://www.petersons.com

Irregular, latest edition 1999. $18.95. Covers approximately 1,300 research, consulting, government, and non-profit and profit service organizations that hire college and university graduates in science and health-related majors. Entries include: Organization name, address, phone, name and title of contact, type of organization, number of employees, Standard Industrial Classification (SIC) code; description of opportunities available including disciplines, level of education required, starting locations and salaries, level of experience accepted, benefits.

HANDBOOKS AND MANUALS

★5394★ America's Fastest Growing Jobs

JIST Works, Inc.
8902 Otis Ave.
Indianapolis, IN 46216-1033
Ph: (317)613-4200   Fax: (317)613-4307
Fr: 800-648-5478
E-mail: jistworks@aol.com
URL: http://www.jist.com

Seventh edition, 2002. $16.95 (paper). 438 pages. Each job profile explains the nature of the work, skills and abilities required, employment outlook, average earnings, related occupations, education and training requirements, and employment opportunities. Also contains career planning information and job search tips.

★5395★ Being a Long-Term Care Nursing Assistant

Prentice Hall PTR
200 Old Tappan Rd.
Old Tappan, NJ 07675
Ph: (201)236-7000   Fr: 800-223-1360
Connie Will-Black and Judith B. Eighmy. Fifth edition, 2001. $48.00 (paper). 560 pages.

★5396★ Being a Nursing Assistant

Prentice Hall PTR
200 Old Tappan Rd.
Old Tappan, NJ 07675
Ph: (201)236-7000   Fr: 800-223-1360
Eighth edition, 1999. $26.60 (paper).

★5397★ Careers for Caring People and Other Sensitive Types

VGM Career Horizons
1221 Avenue of the Americas
New York, NY 10020
Ph: (212)904-2000   Fr: 800-323-4900
E-mail: ntcpub@tribune.com

Adrian Paradis. 1995. $14.95; $9.95 (paper). 205 pages.

★5398★ Careers in Health Care

McGraw-Hill Trade
2 Penn Plaza
New York, NY 10121
Ph: (212)904-2000   Fr: 800-722-4726
E-mail: ntcpub@tribune.com

Barbara M. Swanson. Fourth edition, 2000. $17.95; $13.95 (paper). 320 pages. Describes job duties, work settings, salaries, licensing and certification requirements, educational preparation, and future outlook. Gives ideas on how to secure a job.

★5399★ Health Care Career Starter: Finding and Getting a Great Job

LearningExpress, LLC
900 Broadway, Ste. 604
New York, NY 10003
Ph: (212)995-2566   Fax: (212)995-5512
Fr: 800-295-9556

Cheryl Jean Hancock. Brigit Dermott. Reprint. 2002. $15.95 (paper). 216 pages. Part of the Heath Care Career Starters Series.

★5400★ How to Be a Nurse Assistant: Career Training in Long Term Care

American Health Care Association
1201 L St. NW
Washington, DC 20005
Ph: (202)842-4444   Fax: (202)842-3860
Fr: 800-325-4177

Margaret Casey, editor. 1994. $23.95 (paper). 480 pages. Out of print.

★5401★ The Long-Term Care Nursing Assistant Training Manual

Health Professions Press
PO Box 10624
Baltimore, MD 21285-0624
Ph: (410)337-9585   Fax: (410)337-8539
Fr: 888-337-8808

Mary A. Anderson, Karen W. Beaver and Kathleen R. Culliton, editors. Second edition, 1996. $29.95 (paper). 352 pages.

★5402★ The Nurses' Career Guide: Discovering New Horizons in Health Care

Sovereignty Press
1241 Johnson Ave., No. 353
San Luis Obispo, CA 93401
Ph: (805)543-6100   Fax: (805)543-1085
Fr: 888-201-2501

Zardoya E. Eagles and Marti Kock. 1999. $17.95 (paper). Helps the reader identify work skills and achievements, clarify values and goals, explore career options, develop a personal action plan, prepare cover letters and resumes, and conduct informational and job interviews. Also addresses the dramatic changes that nurses currently face in the workplace. Includes a 65-page resource section which lists references, samples of resumes and letters, professional magazines, organizations, and online resources.

★5403★ Nursing Today: Transition and Trends

W.B. Saunders Co.
150 S. Independence Mall W
The Public Ledger Bldg., Ste. 1250
Philadelphia, PA 19106-3412
Ph: (215)238-5500   Fax: (215)238-8495
Fr: 800-654-2452

JoAnn Zerwekh and Jo C. Claborn, editors. Second edition, 1997.

★5404★ Opportunities in Health and Medical Careers

McGraw-Hill Trade
2 Penn Plaza
New York, NY 10121
Ph: (212)904-2000   Fr: 800-722-4726
I. Donald Snook, Jr. and Leo D'Orazio. 1997. $14.95; $11.95 (paper). 202 pages. Covers the full range of medical and health occupations. Illustrated.

★5405★ Opportunities in Homecare Services Careers

McGraw-Hill Trade
2 Penn Plaza
New York, NY 10121
Ph: (212)904-2000   Fr: 800-722-4726
Anna deSola Cardoza. 1994. $14.95; $11.95 (paper). 160 pages. Professional child care careers, including various types of therapy and post-intensive surgery assistance.

★5406★ Opportunities in Mental Health Careers

McGraw-Hill Trade
2 Penn Plaza
New York, NY 10121
Ph: (212)904-2000   Fr: 800-722-4726
Philip A. Perry and George Blake. 1996. $14.95; $11.95 (paper). 160 pages.

★5407★ Real People Working in Health Care

McGraw-Hill Contemporary Books
1221 Avenue of the Americas
New York, NY 10020
Ph: (212)904-2000   Fr: 800-323-4900
E-mail: ntcpub@tribune.com

Blythe Camenson, Jan Goldberg. 1996. $17.95; $12.95 (paper). Interviews and profiles of working professionals capture a range of opportunities in this field.

★5408★ Real People Working in the Helping Professions

McGraw-Hill Contemporary Books
1221 Avenue of the Americas
New York, NY 10020
Ph: (212)904-2000   Fr: 800-323-4900
E-mail: ntcpub@tribune.com

Blythe Camenson, Jan Goldberg. 1997. $17.95; $12.95 (paper). Interviews and profiles of working professionals capture a range of opportunities in this field.

★5409★ Reinventing Your Nursing Career: A Handbook for Success in the Age of Managed Care

Jones and Bartlett Publishing
200 Orchard Ridge Dr., Ste. 200
Gaithersburg, MD 20878
Ph: (301)417-7500   Fax: (301)695-7931
Fr: 800-638-8437

Michael Newell and Mario Pinardo. 1997. $37.00 (paper). 272 pages. Helps nurses identify career goals and take practical steps to realize them using self-surveys, goal-setting methods, personal action plans, and networking techniques.

★5410★ **Resumes for Health and Medical Careers**
McGraw-Hill Trade
2 Penn Plaza
New York, NY 10121
Ph: (212)904-2000   Fr: 800-722-4726
E-mail: ntcpub@tribune.com

1997. $9.95 (paper). 455 pages.

★5411★ **Where the Jobs Are: The Hottest Careers for the 90s**
The Career Press, Inc.
3 Tice Rd.
PO Box 687
Franklin Lakes, NJ 07417-1322
Ph: (201)848-0310   Fax: (201)848-1727
Fr: 800-227-3371

Joyce Hadley. Third edition, 2000. $13.99 (paper). 400 pages. Out of print. Describes careers in fifteen general fields, from accounting to travel and hospitality.

★5412★ **Working in Care Settings**
Nelson Thornes
Delta Pl., 27 Beth Rd.
Cheltenham GL53 7TH, United Kingdom
Val Michie. February 2004. $18.75. Illustrated. 206 pages.

EMPLOYMENT AGENCIES AND SEARCH FIRMS

★5413★ **Boone-Scaturro Associates Inc.**
1122 Cambridge Sq., Ste. A
Alpharetta, GA 30004-3806
Ph: (770)740-1216   Fax: (770)475-5055
Fr: 800-749-1884

Executive search firm focused in the healthcare industry.

★5414★ **Dan Ford Consulting**
PO Box 68726
Oro Valley, AZ 85737
Ph: (520)742-0004   Fax: (520)742-0005

Executive search firm.

★5415★ **Medical Personnel Services, Inc.**
1707 L St. NW, Ste. 760
Washington, DC 20036
Ph: (202)466-2955

Employment agency specializing in permanent health/medical placements.

★5416★ **Professional Placement Associates, Inc.**
287 Bowman Ave., Ste. 309
Purchase, NY 10577
Ph: (914)251-1000   Fax: (914)251-1055
E-mail: lschachter@ppasearch.com
URL: http://www.ppasearch.com

Executive search firm specializing in the health and medical field.

ONLINE JOB SOURCES AND SERVICES

★5417★ **HealthCareerWeb**
URL: http://www.healthcareerweb.com/
Description: Advertises jobs for healthcare professionals. **Main files include:** Jobs, Employers, Resumes, Jobwire. Relocation tools and career guidance resources available.

★5418★ **Medhunters.com**
E-mail: info@medhunters.com
URL: http://www.medhunters.com

Description: Career search site for jobs in all health care specialties; educational resources; visa and licensing information for relocation; interesting articles; relocation tools; links to professional organizations and general resources.

★5419★ **ProHealthJobs**
E-mail: sales@prohealthjobs.com
URL: http://www.prohealthjobs.com

Description: Career resources site for the medical and health care field. Lists professional opportunities, product information, continuing education and open positions.

TRADESHOWS

★5420★ **American Association for Continuity of Care Annual Conference**
American Association for Continuity of Care
638 Prospect Ave.
Hartford, CT 06105-4250
Ph: (203)586-7525   Fax: (203)586-7550
E-mail: lpiorek@csunet.ctstateu.edu

Annual. **Primary Exhibits:** Health care delivery resources, products, and services.

★5421★ **American Association of Office Nurses Annual Meeting and Convention**
American Association of Office Nurses
109 Kinderkamack Rd.
Montvale, NJ 07645
Ph: (201)391-2600   Fax: (201)573-8543
Fr: 800-457-7504

E-mail: aaonmail@aaon.org
URL: http://www.aaon.org

Annual. **Primary Exhibits:** Exhibits of interest to nurses.

★5422★ **The HME Industry's Future Show**
National Association of Medical Equipment Services
625 Slaters Ln., Ste. 200
Alexandria, VA 22314
Ph: (703)836-6263   Fax: (703)836-6730
E-mail: info@names.org
URL: http://www.names.org

Annual. **Primary Exhibits:** Home medical equipment.

★5423★ **HOMECARExpo**
National Association for Home Care
228 7th St. SE
Washington, DC 20003
Ph: (202)547-7424   Fax: (202)547-3540

Annual. **Primary Exhibits:** General home health products, emergency response systems, computers, uniforms, publications, surgical and medical supplies, pharmaceuticals, durable and home medical equipment.

★5424★ **International Society of Psychiatric-Mental Health Nurses Annual Conference**
International Society of Psychiatric - Mental Health Nurses
1211 Locust St.
Philadelphia, PA 19107
Ph: (215)545-2843   Fax: (215)545-8107
Fr: 800-826-2950
E-mail: ispn@nursecominc.com
URL: http://www.ispn-psych.org

Annual. **Primary Exhibits:** Psychiatric nursing equipment, supplies, and services.

OTHER SOURCES

★5425★ **American Assembly for Men in Nursing (AAMN)**
11 Cornell Rd.
Latham, NY 12110-1499
Ph: (518)782-9400   Fax: (518)782-9530
E-mail: aamn@aamn.org
URL: http://aamn.org

Members: Registered nurses. **Purpose:** Works to help eliminate prejudice in nursing; interest men in the nursing profession; provide opportunities for the discussion of common problems; encourage education and promote further professional growth; advise and assist in areas of professional inequity; help develop sensitivities to various social needs; promote the principles and practices of positive health care. **Activities:** Acts as a clearinghouse for information on men in nursing. Conducts educational programs.

Promotes education and research about men's health issues.

★5426★ American Health Care Association (AHCA)
1201 L St. NW
Washington, DC 20005
Ph: (202)842-4444   Fax: (202)842-3860
URL: http://www.ahca.org

Description: Federation of state associations of long-term health care facilities. Promotes standards for professionals in long-term health care delivery and quality care for patients and residents in a safe environment. Focuses on issues of availability, quality, affordability, and fair payment. Operates as liaison with governmental agencies, Congress, and professional associations. Compiles statistics.

★5427★ *Exploring Health Occupations*
Cambridge Educational
2572 Brunswick Ave.
Lawrenceville, NJ 08648-4128
Fax: 800-FAX-ON-US   Fr: 800-468-4227
URL: http://www.cambridgeeducational.com

Two videos. $139.95. 1999.

★5428★ *Health Service Occupations*
Delphi Productions
3160 4th St.
Boulder, CO 80304
Fax: (303)443-4022   Fr: 888-443-2400
URL: http://www.delphivideo.com

$95.00. 50 minutes. Part of the Careers for the 21st Century Video Library.

★5429★ *Medicine & Related Occupations*
Delphi Productions
3160 4th St.
Boulder, CO 80304
Fax: (303)443-4022   Fr: 888-443-2400

URL: http://www.delphivideo.com

$95.00. 45 minutes. Part of the Careers for the 21st Century Video Library.

★5430★ National Association of Professional Geriatric Care Managers (PGCM)
1604 N Country Club Rd.
Tucson, AZ 85716-3102
Ph: (520)881-8008   Fax: (520)325-7925
E-mail: info@caremanager.org
URL: http://www.caremanager.org

Description: Promotes quality services and care for elderly citizens. Provides referral service and distributes information to individuals interested in geriatric care management. Maintains referral network.

★5431★ National League for Nursing (NLN)
61 Broadway 33rd Fl.
New York, NY 10006-2701
Ph: (212)363-5555   Fax: (212)812-0393
Fr: 800-669-1656
E-mail: rcorcor@nln.org
URL: http://www.nln.org

Description: Champions the pursuit of quality nursing education. A professional association of nursing faculty, education agencies, healthcare agencies, allied/public agencies, and public members whose mission is to advance quality nursing education that prepares the nursing workforce to meet the needs of diverse populations in an ever-changing health care environment. Serves as the primary source of information about every type of nursing education, from the LVN and LPN to the EDD and PHD. There are 33 affiliated constituent leagues that provide a local forum for members. The National League for Nursing Accrediting Commission is an independent corporate affiliate of the NLN, responsible for providing accreditation services to all levels of nursing education. NLN's bimonthly update is avail-

able free of charge on the website and by email.

★5432★ National Rural Health Association (NRHA)
1 W Armour Blvd., Ste. 203
Kansas City, MO 64111-2087
Ph: (816)756-3140   Fax: (816)756-3144
E-mail: mail@nrharural.org
URL: http://www.nrharural.org

Description: Administrators, physicians, nurses, physician assistants, health planners, academicians, and others interested or involved in rural health care. Creates a better understanding of health care problems unique to rural areas; utilizes a collective approach in finding positive solutions; articulates and represents the health care needs of rural America; supplies current information to rural health care providers; serves as a liaison between rural health care programs throughout the country. Offers continuing education credits for medical, dental, nursing, and management courses.

★5433★ Visiting Nurse Associations of America (VNAA)
99 Summer St., Ste. 1700
Boston, MA 02110
Ph: (617)737-3200   Fax: (617)737-1144
Fr: 800-426-2547
E-mail: vnaa@vnaa.org
URL: http://www.vnaa.org

Members: Voluntary, nonprofit home health care agencies. **Purpose:** Develops competitive strength among community-based nonprofit visiting nurse organizations; works to strengthen business resources and economic programs through contracting, marketing, governmental affairs and publications.

Hotel Managers and Assistants

SOURCES OF HELP-WANTED ADS

★5434★ **Hotel & Motel Management**
Advanstar Communications Inc.
7500 Old Oak Blvd.
Cleveland, OH 44130-3369
Ph: (440)243-8100   Fax: (440)891-2777
URL: http://https://www.advanstar.com/index_allpubs.html

Magazine (tabloid) covering the global lodging industry.

★5435★ **HOTELS**
Reed Business Information
360 Park Ave. S
New York, NY 10014
Ph: (646)746-7764
URL: http://www.hotelsmag.com/

Magazine covering management and operations as well as foodservice and design in the hospitality industry.

★5436★ **LH (Lodging Hospitality)**
Penton Media Inc.
1300 E 9th St.
Cleveland, OH 44114-1503
Ph: (216)696-7000   Fax: (216)931-9799
URL: http://www.lhonline.com

Free to qualified US and Canadian residents. Magazine serving managers of independent, franchise, chain-owned, and referral groups in the hospitality industry.

★5437★ **Restaurants & Institutions**
Reed Business Information
360 Park Ave. S
New York, NY 10014
Ph: (646)746-7764
E-mail: gdrummond@reedbusiness.com
URL: http://www.rimag.com

Magazine focusing on foodservice and lodging management.

★5438★ **Trends in the Hotel Industry**
Pannell Kerr Forster
420 Lexington Ave.
New York, NY 10170
Ph: (212)867-8000

Quarterly. Trade publication covering the hotel industry.

PLACEMENT AND JOB REFERRAL SERVICES

★5439★ **Association for Convention Operations Management (ACOM)**
PO Box 659
Avondale Estates, GA 30002
Ph: (404)292-3514   Fax: (404)292-2931
E-mail: info@acomonline.org
URL: http://www.acomonline.org/

Description: Convention service directors and managers of hotels, convention centers, and convention bureaus; suppliers of services and products to the convention and meetings industry are affiliate members. Works to increase the effectiveness, productivity, and quality of meetings, conventions, and exhibitions. Works to establish high ethical standards, improve professional management techniques, and increase awareness of client, employer, and provider needs. Maintains speakers' bureau, resource center, and placement services; compiles statistics. Conducts research and educational programs.

★5440★ **National Association of Black Hospitality Professionals (NABHP)**
PO Box 8132
Columbus, GA 31908-8132
Ph: (334)298-4802
E-mail: nabhp@aol.com

Description: Works to develop global educational and economic opportunities for the hospitality industry through the expansion and diversification of minority involvement in the industry. Encourages professional development and opportunity in the industry

through the design and implementation of workshops and seminars. Seeks to increase the number, size, and capability of minority-owned businesses within the hospitality and tourism industries. Offers placement service; conducts research and educational programs; compiles statistics.

EMPLOYER DIRECTORIES AND NETWORKING LISTS

★5441★ **Career Opportunities in Casinos and Casino Hotels**
Facts on File Inc.
132 W 31st St., 17th Fl.
New York, NY 10001
Ph: (212)967-8800   Fax: 800-678-3633
Fr: 800-322-8755
URL: http://www.factsonfile.com

Irregular. $49.50; $44.55 for libraries. Publication includes a directory of casinos and cruise lines, gaming conferences and expos, seminars, workshops, and industry Web sites. Principal content of publication is 100 occupations in 10 employment sections on careers in gaming, administration, management, security, entertainment, hotel management, and food and beverage service in the casino industry.

★5442★ **Directory of Chain Restaurant Operators**
Chain Store Guide
3922 Coconut Palm Dr.
Tampa, FL 33619
Ph: (813)627-6800   Fax: (813)627-6882
Fr: 800-927-9292
URL: http://www.csgis.com

Annual, April. $775.00 for CD-ROM; $975.00 for CD-ROM and directory. Covers chain restaurant operators, chain hotel operators, nontraditional foodservice operators and food service management operators who operate 2 or more food service locations. Entries include: For chain restaurant operators-company name, address, phone and fax numbers; e-mail and web addresses; type of business; listing type; total annual sales; food service sales; system wide sales; percent of sales of alcohol; percent of sales from Internet; alcohol types served; total units; company owned units; units franchised to and from; trade names; co-branded names and numbers; food service management location types; trading areas; foreign trading areas; units by primary menu types and type of foodservice; self distributing and catering services indicators; franchise affiliations names and locations; primary distributors names and locations; parent and subsidiary company names and locations; regional; divisional; and branch office locations; distribution centers locations; year founded; public company indicator; key personnel with titles. For chain hotel operators-includes number of restaurants in hotels. For food service management operators-includes number of food service management accounts and total number of locations served. Arrangement: Geographical. Indexes: Alphabetical, type of food service, menu type, franchisee, food service management, state, exclusions.

★5443★ Directory of Hotel & Motel Companies

HealthForum
1 N Franklin St., 28th Fl.
Chicago, IL 60606-3421
Ph: (312)893-6800   Fax: (312)422-4500
Fr: 800-621-6902

Annual, March. $79.00. Covers over 1,025 hotel, motel, and resort chain companies owning, managing, or franchising worldwide. Entries include: Company name, address, phone, fax, e-mail, website, names of executives, properties owned and their locations, numbers of rooms, annual gross sales. Arrangement: Alphabetical.

★5444★ Lodging Hospitality-400 Top Performers Issue

Penton Media Inc.
The Penton Media Bldg. .
1300 E. 9th St
Cleveland, OH 44114-1503
Ph: (216)696-7000   Fax: (216)696-1752

Annual, August. $5.00. Publication includes: Top 400 hotels, motels, inns, and lodges based on total sales per room, and top 50 chains and franchises based on number of rooms. Entries include: For hotels-Hotel name, location, number of guestrooms and suites, rank based on amount of total sales, total sales per room, average occupancy; listings also include data on food and beverage sales, other revenues, number of employees. For chains-Name, number of properties and rooms in the United States and total, status of properties, rate and occupancy data. Arrangement: Hotels in separate sections for convention/commercial, resort, suburban, roadside, and airport units, then ranked by total sales per room; chains ranked by number of rooms.

★5445★ Official Hotel Guide

Northstar Travel Media
500 Plaza Dr.
Secaucus, NJ 07094
Ph: (201)902-2000   Fax: (201)902-7764
Fr: 877-410-1484
URL: http://www.northstartravelmedia.com/pages/ohg.html

Annual. $385.00. Covers in four volumes, 29,000 hotels, motels, and resorts worldwide. Volume 1 covers most of the U.S.; Volume 2 covers the rest of the U.S. and the Western Hemisphere; Volume 3 covers Europe, the Middle East, Asia, and Africa. Volume 4 specialty travel guide includes listings of golf and tennis resorts; health spas, dude ranches, bed and breakfasts, and casino & hotels in the United States; also includes lists of hotels in the Caribbean with golf, tennis, casinos, and all-inclusive. Entries include: Hotel/motel/resort name, address, phone, fax, CRS's, number of rooms or units, rates, brief description of facilities, ratings, codes indicating credit cards accepted, email and website addresses, and travel agent's commission, if any. Arrangement: Geographical.

★5446★ Peterson's Job Opportunities for Business Majors

Thomson Peterson's
Princeton Pke. Corporate Ctr., 2000 Lenox Dr.
PO Box 67005
Lawrenceville, NJ 08648
Ph: (609)896-1800   Fax: (609)896-4531
Fr: 800-338-3282
URL: http://www.petersons.com

Irregular, latest edition 2000 - 16th ed. $18.95. Covers the 2,000 largest U.S. employers hiring in several fields, including financial services, management consulting, consumer products, and media/ entertainment. Entries include: Organization name, address, phone, name and title of contact, number of employees, type of organization. Arrangement: Alphabetical. Indexes: Type of organization.

★5447★ Resorts Directory

infoUSA Inc.
5711 S 86th Cir.
Omaha, NE 68127-0347
Ph: (402)930-3500   Fax: (402)331-0176
Fr: 800-555-6124
URL: http://www.abii.com

Annual. Number of listings: 10,368. Entries include: Name, address, phone (including area code), size of advertisement, year first in "Yellow Pages," name of owner or manager, number of employees. Compiled from telephone company "Yellow Pages," nationwide. Arrangement: Geographical.

HANDBOOKS AND MANUALS

★5448★ Best Impressions in Hospitality: Your Professional Image for Excellence

Thomson Delmar Learning
PO Box 15015
Albany, NY 12212-5015
Ph: (518)348-2300   Fr: 800-998-7498

Angie Michael. 1999. $22.50 (paper). 240 pages.

★5449★ Career Opportunities in Travel and Tourism

Checkmark Books, Inc.
132 W. 31st St., 17th Fl.
New York, NY 10001-2006
Ph: (212)967-8800   Fax: (212)967-9196
Fr: 800-322-8755
URL: http://www.factsonfile.com

John K. Hawks. 1996. $18.95 (paper). 224 pages. Includes detailed job descriptions, educational requirements, salary ranges, and advancement prospects for 70 different job opportunities in this fast-paced industry. Contains index and bibliography.

★5450★ Careers in Catering, Hotel Administration and Management

Kogan Page, Ltd.
22 Broad St., Ste. 34
Milford, CT 06460

Russell Joseph. Fifth edition, 1997. $14.95 (paper). Part of the Kogan Page Careers Series. Out of print.

★5451★ Careers for Night Owls and Other Insomniacs

McGraw-Hill Trade
2 Penn Plaza
New York, NY 10121
Ph: (212)904-2000   Fr: 800-722-4726
E-mail: ntcpub@tribune.com

Louise Miller. 1995. $14.95; $9.95 (paper). 160 pages.

★5452★ Careers in Travel, Tourism, and Hospitality

McGraw-Hill Contemporary Books
1221 Avenue of the Americas
New York, NY 10020
Ph: (212)904-2000   Fr: 800-323-4900
E-mail: ntcpub@tribune.com

Marjorie Eberts, Linda Brothers, and Ann Gisler. 1997. $17.95; 13.95 (paper). 192 pages.

★5453★ Hospitality Skill Sets: Supplement to Creating Your Career Portfolio At-a-Glance Guide

Prentice Hall PRT
200 Old Tappan Rd.
Old Tappan, NJ 07675
Fr: 800-223-1360

Anna Graf Williams and Karen J. Hall. 1997. $23.00 (paper). 80 pages. Out of print.

★5454★ Hospitality and Tourism Careers

Prentice Hall PTR
200 Old Tappan Rd.
Old Tappan, NJ 07675
Ph: (201)236-7000   Fr: 800-223-1360

Melissa Dallas and Carl Riegel. First edition, 1997. $20.85 (paper). 252 pages.

★5455★ How to Get a Job with a Cruise Line

Ticket to Adventure, Inc.
PO Box 41005
St. Petersburg, FL 33743-1005
Ph: (727)822-5029   Fax: (727)821-3409
Fr: 800-929-7447

Mary Fallon Miller. Fifth edition, 2001. $16.95 (paper). 336 pages. Explores jobs with cruise ships, describing duties, responsibilities, benefits, and training. Lists cruise ship lines and schools offering cruise line training. Offers job hunting advice.

★5456★ Opportunities in Hotel and Motel Careers

McGraw-Hill Trade
2 Penn Plaza
New York, NY 10121
Ph: (212)904-2000   Fr: 800-722-4726

Shepard Henkin. Revised, 2000. $12.95 (paper). 160 pages.

★5457★ Opportunities in Travel Careers

McGraw-Hill Contemporary Books
1221 Avenue of the Americas
New York, NY 10020
Ph: (212)904-2000   Fr: 800-323-4900
E-mail: ntcpub@tribune.com

Robert Scott Milne. 1996. $14.95; $11.95 (paper). 198 pages. Discusses what the jobs are and where to find them in airlines, shipping lines, and railroads. Discusses related opportunities in hotels, motels, resorts, travel agencies, public relation firms, and recreation departments. Illustrated.

★5458★ Quality Service: What Every Hospitality Manager Needs to Know

Prentice Hall, PTR
One Lake St.
Upper Saddle River, NJ 07458
Ph: (201)236-7000

Martin. 2001. $22.67.

★5459★ Real-Resumes for Restaurant Food Service and Hotel Jobs: Including Real Resumes Used to Change Careers and Transfer Skills to Other Industries

PREP Publishing
1110 1/2 Hay St., PMB 66
Fayetteville, NC 28305
Ph: (910)483-2439   Fax: (910)483-2439
Fr: 800-533-2814

September 2002. $16.95. Real-Resumes Series.

★5460★ So-You Want to Be an Innkeeper

Chronicle Books LLC
85 Second St.
San Francisco, CA 94105
Ph: (415)537-4200   Fax: (415)537-4460
Fr: 800-722-6657

Susan Brown, et al. Fourth edition, 2004. $16.95 (paper). 336 pages.

★5461★ Working in Hotels and Catering

Thomson Learning
7625 Empire Dr.
Florence, KY 41042
Ph: (859)525-6620   Fax: (859)525-0978
Fr: 800-347-7707

Roy Woods. Second edition, 1997. $35.95 (paper). 252 pages.

★5462★ Working in Hotels and Catering: How to Find Great Employment Opportunities Worldwide

Trans-Atlantic Publications, Inc.
311 Bainbridge St.
Philadelphia, PA 19147
Ph: (215)925-5083   Fax: (215)925-1912

Mark Hempshell. 1997. $19.95 (paper). Part of the Jobs and Careers Series. 174 pages.

EMPLOYMENT AGENCIES AND SEARCH FIRMS

★5463★ The Alfus Group Inc.

353 Lexington Ave., Fl. 8
New York, NY 10016
Ph: (212)599-1000   Fax: (212)599-1523

Executive search firm. Specializes in the hospitality industry.

★5464★ Bowman & Associates

1660 S Amphlett Blvd., Ste. 245
San Mateo, CA 94402
Ph: (650)573-0188   Fax: (650)573-8209

Executive search firm specializing in the hospitality industry.

★5465★ ChaseAmerica Inc.

7100-39 Fairway Dr., Ste. 223
Palm Beach Gardens, FL 33418
Ph: (561)622-1120

Executive search firm.

★5466★ Classic Consultants Inc.

8051 N. Tamiami Trail
Sarasota, FL 34243
Ph: (941)351-3500   Fr: 800-949-6107

Executive search firm.

★5467★ DSA-Dixie Search Associates

670 Village Trace, Bldg. 19, Ste. D
Marietta, GA 30067
Ph: (770)850-0250   Fax: (770)850-9295

Conducts employee recruitment and placement for U.S. and international firms within the food, beverage and hospitality industries.

★5468★ Eastman & Beaudine Inc.

5700 W. Plano Pkwy., Ste. 2800
Plano, TX 75093
Ph: (972)267-8891   Fax: (972)267-8008

Executive search firm. Second location in Alpharetta, GA.

★5469★ The Elliot Group LLC

505 White Plains Rd., Ste. 228
Tarrytown, NY 10591
Ph: (914)631-4904   Fax: (914)631-6481

Executive search firm. Eight locations throughout the United States.

★5470★ Employment Advisors

815 Nicollet Mall Ste 200
Minneapolis, MN 55402
Ph: (612)339-3944
E-mail: info@collegegraduateregistry.com
URL: http://www.collegegraduateregistry.com

Employment agency. Places candidates in variety of fields.

★5471★ Executive Search Consultants LLC

149 Shortwoods Rd.
New Fairfield, CT 06812
Ph: (203)746-7265   Fax: (203)746-7265

Executive search firm.

★5472★ Harper Associates

29870 Middlebelt
Farmington Hills, MI 48334
Ph: (248)932-1170   Fax: (248)932-1214
E-mail: resumes@harperjobs.com
URL: http://www.harperjobs.com

Executive search firm and employment agency.

★5473★ Hospitality International
23 W 73rd St., Ste.100
New York, NY 10023
Ph: (212)769-8800   Fax: (212)769-2138
E-mail: jar@hospitalityinternational.com
URL: http://
www.hospitalityinternational.com

Executive search firm. Branch office in New York, NY.

★5474★ The IMC Group of Cos.
14 E 60th St., Ste. 1200
New York, NY 10022
Ph: (212)838-9535   Fax: (212)486-2964

International executive recruiting and management consulting company providing leading-edge services for the hospitality, leisure, entertainment, gaming, and new media industries throughout the U.S., Europe, Africa, Asia Pacific, and Latin America.

★5475★ J.D. Hersey and Associates
1695 Old Henderson Rd.
Columbus, OH 43220
Ph: (614)459-4555   Fax: (614)459-4544
E-mail: info@jdhersey.com
URL: http://www.jdhersey.com

Executive search firm for permanent and contingency placements.

★5476★ The Personnel Network, Inc.
1246 Lake Murray Blvd.
PO Box 1426
Irmo, SC 29063
Ph: (803)781-2087   Fax: (803)732-7986
E-mail: chuckirmo@aol.com

Executive search firm.

★5477★ Ritt-Ritt and Associates
5105 Tollview Dr., Ste. 100
Rolling Meadows, IL 60008
Ph: (847)483-9330   Fax: (847)483-9331
E-mail: info@rittsearch.com
URL: http://www.rittsearch.com

Food service and hospitality employment agency and executive search firm.

★5478★ Robert Howe and Associates
PO Box 450867
Atlanta, GA 31145-0867
Ph: (770)270-1211   Fax: (770)270-1209

Provides consulting services in the area of executive search and recruitment. Industries served: healthcare, hospitality, chemical, metals, electronics, construction, and food processing.

★5479★ Robert W. Dingman Company Inc.
650 Hampshire Rd., Ste. 116
Westlake Village, CA 91361
Ph: (805)778-1777   Fax: (805)778-9288

Executive search firm with a second office in Black Forest, CO.

★5480★ Sales Recruiters International Ltd.
660 White Plains Rd., 5th Fl.
Tarrytown, NY 10591
Ph: (914)631-0090   Fax: (914)631-1089
Fr: 800-836-0881

Offers management and consulting services including recruitment, selection, and retention of sales and marketing personnel, and teambuilding. Industries served: office products, telecommunications, data processing, financial, contract interiors, food service, hospitality, consumer products, and graphic arts.

ONLINE JOB SOURCES AND SERVICES

★5481★ Bristol Associates, Inc.
URL: http://www.bristolassoc.com
Description: Executive search firm specializing in direct marketing, hospitality and food industries. Applicants can post their resumes online for recruiters' viewing and search current job databank. Also contains job tools and resources.

TRADESHOWS

★5482★ American Hotel and Motel Association Annual Conference and Leadership Forum
American Hotel and Lodging Association
1201 New York Ave. NW, Ste. 600
Washington, DC 20005-3931
Ph: (202)289-3111   Fax: (202)289-3158
Fr: 800-252-2462
URL: http://www.ahla.com

Annual. **Primary Exhibits:** Hotel and motel supplies and equipment.

★5483★ Annual Hotel, Motel, and Restaurant Supply Show of the Southeast
Leisure Time Unlimited, Inc.
708 Main St.
PO Box 332
Myrtle Beach, SC 29578
Ph: (843)448-9483   Fax: (843)626-1513
Fr: 800-261-5591
E-mail: ltushows@aol.com
URL: http://www.dickenschristmashow.com

Annual. **Primary Exhibits:** Carpeting, furniture, coffee makers, produce companies, wine and beer and food companies, and services to motels, hotels, and restaurants. **Dates and Locations:** 2005 Jan 25-27; Myrtle Beach, SC.

★5484★ IH/M & RS - International Hotel/Motel & Restaurant Show
George Little Management, LLC (New York)
10 Bank St.
White Plains, NY 10606-1954
Ph: (914)421-3200   Fax: (914)948-2867
Fr: 800-272-SHOW
URL: http://www.glmshows.com

Annual. **Primary Exhibits:** Products and services for lodging and food serving properties including technology, uniforms, linens and bedding, tabletop accessories, guest amenities and services, food and beverages, cleaning maintenance, foodservice equipment and supplies, franchising information, finance and management furnishings and fixtures, fitness equipment, and leisure and entertainment services.

★5485★ Northeast Food Service and Lodging Exposition and Conference
Reed Exhibitions (North American Headquarters)
383 Main Ave.
PO Box 6059
Norwalk, CT 06851
Ph: (203)840-5402   Fax: (203)840-9402
E-mail: inquiry@reedexpo.com
URL: http://www.reedexpo.com

Annual. **Primary Exhibits:** Food services, operating equipment, and services for the hospitality and institutional foodservice industry.

★5486★ Southeastern Restaurant, Hospitality & Foodservice Show
Reed Exhibitions (North American Headquarters)
383 Main Ave.
PO Box 6059
Norwalk, CT 06851
Ph: (203)840-5402   Fax: (203)840-9402
E-mail: inquiry@reedexpo.com
URL: http://www.reedexpo.com

Annual. **Primary Exhibits:** Equipment, supplies, and services for hotels, restaurants, and travel-related businesses.

★5487★ Upper Midwest Hospitality, Restaurant, and Lodging Show - UP Show
Hospitality Minnesota - Minnesota's Restaurant, Hotel, and Resort Associations
305 E. Roselawn Ave.
St. Paul, MN 55117
Ph: (651)778-2400   Fax: (651)778-2424
E-mail: info@hospitalitymn.com
URL: http://www.hospitalitymn.com

Annual. **Primary Exhibits:** Food, beverages, hospitality business services, lodging supplies, and foodservice equipment. **Dates and Locations:** 2004 Feb 22-24; Minneapolis, MN; Minneapolis Convention Center.

OTHER SOURCES

★5488★ Administration and Management Occupations

Delphi Productions
3160 4th St.
Boulder, CO 80304
Fax: (303)443-4022   Fr: 888-443-2400
URL: http://www.delphivideo.com

$95.00. 50 minutes. Part of the Careers for the 21st Century Video Library.

★5489★ American Almanac of Jobs and Salaries

Morrow Avon
1350 Avenue of the Americas
New York, NY 10019
Ph: (212)261-6788   Fr: 800-242-7737

John W. Wright. Revised edition, 2000. $20.00 (paper). 672 pages. This is a comprehensive guide to the wages of hundreds of occupations in a wide variety of industries and organizations.

★5490★ American Hotel and Lodging Association

1201 New York Ave. NW, Ste. 600
Washington, DC 20005-3931
Ph: (202)289-3100   Fax: (202)289-3199
E-mail: info@ahla.com
URL: http://www.ahla.com

Description: AHLA is a 91-year-old federation of state lodging associations throughout the United States with some 13,000 property members worldwide, representing more than 1.7 million guest rooms. Provides its members with assistance in operations, education and communications and lobbies on Capitol Hill to provide a business climate in which the industry can continue to prosper. Individual state associations provide representation at the state level and offer many additional cost-saving benefits.

★5491★ Association for International Practical Training (AIPT)

10400 Little Patuxent Pky., Ste. 250
Columbia, MD 21044-3519
Ph: (410)997-2200   Fax: (410)992-3924
E-mail: aipt@aipt.org
URL: http://www.aipt.org

Description: Providers worldwide on-the-job training programs for students and professionals seeking international career development and life-changing experiences. Arranges workplace exchanges in hundreds of professional fields, bringing employers and trainees together from around the world. Client list ranges from small farming communities to Fortune 500 companies.

★5492★ Behind the Scenes: Hospitality/Hotels

Cambridge Educational
2572 Brunswick Ave.
Lawrenceville, NJ 08648-4128
Fax: 800-FAX-ON-US   Fr: 800-468-4227
URL: http://www.cambridgeeducational.com

$89.95. 21 minutes. Part of the series "Behind the Scenes: Industrial Field Trips."

★5493★ Club Managers Association of America (CMAA)

1733 King St.
Alexandria, VA 22314-2720
Ph: (703)739-9500   Fax: (703)739-0124
E-mail: cmaa@cmaa.org
URL: http://www.cmaa.org

Members: Professional managers and assistant managers of private golf, yacht, athletic, city, country, luncheon, university, and military clubs. **Purpose:** Encourages education and advancement of members and promotes efficient and successful club operations. **Activities:** Provides reprints of articles on club management. Supports courses in club management. Compiles statistics; maintains management referral service.

★5494★ Hotel Managers and Assistants

Evon Publishing
832 N 7th Ave.
Iron River, MI 49935
Ph: (906)265-3190

Audiocassette. 1996. $16.95. 32 minutes. Part of the Careers and Vocational Guidance Series. Provides information about the nature of the work, educational requirements, employment outlook, earnings, and work conditions as well as additional related information.

★5495★ International Council on Hotel, Restaurant, and Institutional Education (CHRIE)

2613 N Parham Rd., 2nd Fl.
Richmond, VA 23294
Ph: (804)346-4800   Fax: (804)346-5009
E-mail: info@chrie.org
URL: http://www.chrie.org

Description: Schools and colleges offering specialized education and training in hospitals, recreation, tourism and hotel, restaurant, and institutional administration; individuals, executives, and students. Provides networking opportunities and professional development.

★5496★ International Executive Housekeepers Association (IEHA)

1001 Eastwind Dr., Ste. 301
Westerville, OH 43081-3361
Ph: (614)895-7166   Fax: (614)895-1248
Fr: 800-200-6342
E-mail: excel@ieha.org
URL: http://www.ieha.org

Description: Persons engaged in facility housekeeping management in hospitals, hotels and motels, schools, and industrial establishments. Has established educational standards. Sponsors certificate and collegiate degree programs. Holds annual International Housekeepers Week celebration during the second full week in September.

Human Services Workers

SOURCES OF HELP-WANTED ADS

★5497★ *EAP Digest*
Performance Resource Press Inc.
1270 Rankin Dr., Ste. F
Troy, MI 48083-2843
Ph: (248)588-7733   Fax: (248)588-6633
Fr: 800-453-7733

Quarterly. $10.00 for single issue; $36.00/year, U.S.; $45.00/year, Canada, Hawaii, and Alaska; $55.00/year for other countries; $65.00/year for air mail, other countries. Magazine covering planning, development, and administration of employee assistance programs.

★5498★ *Journal of Jewish Communal Service*
Jewish Communal Service Association
3084 State Hwy. 27, Ste. 9
Kendall Park, NJ 08824-1657
Ph: (732)821-1871   Fax: (732)821-5335

Quarterly. $30.00/year for individuals. Journal covering Jewish communal service and social work.

★5499★ *The Lutheran*
Augsburg Fortress, Publishers
100 S Fifth St., Ste. 700
Minneapolis, MN 55402
Ph: (612)330-3300   Fax: (612)330-3521
Fr: 800-426-0115
E-mail: lutheran@elca.org
URL: http://www.thelutheran.org

Monthly. $15.95/year for individuals; $1.50 for single issue. Magazine of the Evangelical Lutheran Church in America.

★5500★ *The Nonprofit Times*
NPT Publishing Group Inc.
120 Littleton Rd., Ste. 120
Parsippany, NJ 07054-1803
Ph: (973)394-1800   Fax: (973)734-1771
E-mail: ednchief@nptimes.com
URL: http://www.nptimes.com

$8.95 for single issue; $59.00/year. Trade journal serving nonprofit organizations.

PLACEMENT AND JOB REFERRAL SERVICES

★5501★ American Humanics (AH)
4601 Madison Ave.
Kansas City, MO 64112
Ph: (816)561-6415   Fax: (816)531-3527
Fr: 800-343-6466
E-mail: kstroup@humanics.org
URL: http://www.humanics.org

Description: Individuals, corporations, and foundations supporting AH work in preparing young people for professional leadership in youth and human service agencies. Provides leadership for co-curricular program on 71 campuses. Conducts research, compiles statistics.

★5502★ American Public Health Association (APHA)
800 I St. NW
Washington, DC 20001-3710
Ph: (202)777-2742   Fax: (202)777-2534
E-mail: comments@apha.org
URL: http://www.apha.org

Members: Professional organization of physicians, nurses, educators, academicians, environmentalists, epidemiologists, new professionals, social workers, health administrators, optometrists, podiatrists, pharmacists, dentists, nutritionists, health planners, other community and mental health specialists, and interested consumers. **Purpose:** Seeks to protect and promote personal, mental, and environmental health. **Activities:** Services include promulgation of standards; establishment of uniform practices and procedures; development of the etiology of communicable diseases; research in public health; exploration of medical care programs and their relationships to public health. Sponsors job placement service.

★5503★ Council for Health and Human Services Ministries, United Church of Christ (CHHSM)
700 Prospect Ave.
Cleveland, OH 44115
Ph: (216)736-2253   Fax: (216)736-2251
E-mail: sickbert@chhsm.org
URL: http://www.chhsm.org

Members: Health and human service institutions related to the United Church of Christ. **Purpose:** Seeks to study, plan, and implement a program in health and human services; assist members in developing and providing quality services and in financing institutional and noninstitutional health and human service ministries; stimulate awareness of and support for these programs; inform the UCC of policies that affect the needs, problems, and conditions of patients; cooperate with interdenominational agencies and others in the field. **Activities:** Maintains placement service and hall of fame. Compiles statistics; provides specialized education programs.

EMPLOYER DIRECTORIES AND NETWORKING LISTS

★5504★ *Directory of Catholic Charities USA Directories*
Catholic Charities USA
1731 King St.
Alexandria, VA 22314
Ph: (703)549-1390   Fax: (703)549-1656
URL: http://www.catholiccharitiesusa.org

Annual. $25.00 for members; $40.00 for nonmembers. Covers nearly 1,200 Catholic community and social service agencies. Listings include diocesan agencies, state Catholic conferences. Entries include: Organization name, address, name and title of director, phone, fax. Arrangement: Geographical by state, then classified by diocese.

★5505★ **Mental Health Directory**
Office of Consumer, Family & Public
Information
Parklawn Bldg.
5600 Fishers Ln.
Rockville, MD 20857
Ph: (301)443-4795   Fax: (301)443-0284

Irregular, previous edition 1990; latest edition 1995. $23.00. Covers hospitals, treatment centers, outpatient clinics, day/night facilities, residential treatment centers for emotionally disturbed children, residential supportive programs such as halfway houses, and mental health centers offering mental health assistance; not included are substance abuse programs, Veteran's Administration programs, nursing homes, programs for the developmentally disabled, and organizations in which fees are retained by individual members. Entries include: Name, address, phone. Arrangement: Geographical.

★5506★ **Mental Health Services Directory**
infoUSA Inc.
5711 S 86th Cir.
Omaha, NE 68127-0347
Ph: (402)930-3500   Fax: (402)331-0176
Fr: 800-555-6124
URL: http://www.abii.com

Annual. Number of listings: 18,282. Entries include: Name, address, phone (including area code), size of advertisement, year first in "Yellow Pages," name of owner or manager, number of employees. Compiled from telephone company "Yellow Pages," nationwide. Arrangement: Geographical.

★5507★ **National Directory of Children, Youth & Families Services**
Penny K. Spencer, Publisher
14 Inverness Dr. E. Ste. D-144
Englewood, CO 80112
Ph: (303)662-8165   Fax: 800-845-6452
Fr: 800-343-6681
URL: http://
www.childrenyouthfamilydir.com/

Annual, July. $159.00. Covers more than 45,000 key contacts in the areas of Social Services, Health & Mental Health Services, Juvenile Justice Agencies, Education Departments, Treatment Centers & Hospitals, Referral Networks, child, youth, and family-oriented social services, health and mental health services, and juvenile/family court and youth advocacy services, educational listings in state and private agencies, major cities, and 3,300 counties; also covers runaway youth centers, child abuse projects, congressional committees, clearinghouses, and national organizations concerned with family health and welfare; buyers' guide to specialized services and products. Entries include: Agency listings include agency name, address, phone, fax, after-hours phone, websites, names of principal executives and staff, description of services. Arrangement: Geographical.

★5508★ **National Directory of Private Social Agencies**
Croner Publications Inc.
10951 Sorrento Valley Rd., Ste. 1D
San Diego, CA 92121-1616
Ph: (619)546-1894   Fax: (858)546-1955
Fr: 800-441-4033
URL: http://www.sdic.net/croner

Base edition supplied upon order; monthly updates. $100.00. Number of listings: Over 10,000. Entries include: Agency name, address, phone, name and title of contact, description of services. Arrangement: Geographical. Indexes: Service, agency type.

★5509★ **Public Human Services Directory**
American Public Human Services
Association
810 1st St. NE, Ste. 500
Washington, DC 20002
Ph: (202)682-0100   Fax: (202)289-6555
E-mail: pubs@aphsa.org
URL: http://www.aphsa.org

Annual, September. $120.00 for members; $155.00 for out of country. Covers federal, state, territorial, county, and major municipal public human service agencies. Entries include: Agency name, address, phone, fax, e-mail address, web site address, names of key personnel, program area. Arrangement: Geographical.

HANDBOOKS AND MANUALS

★5510★ **Careers for Caring People and Other Sensitive Types**
VGM Career Horizons
1221 Avenue of the Americas
New York, NY 10020
Ph: (212)904-2000   Fr: 800-323-4900
E-mail: ntcpub@tribune.com

Adrian Paradis. 1995. $14.95; $9.95 (paper). 205 pages.

★5511★ **Careers in Counseling & Human Services**
Taylor and Francis
325 Chestnut St., 8t Fl.
Philadelphia, PA 19106
Ph: (215)625-2919   Fax: (215)269-0363
Fr: 800-821-8312

Brooke B. Collison and Nancy J. Garfield, editors. Second edition, 1995. $19.95 (paper). 153 pages.

★5512★ **Careers in Focus: Family and Consumer Sciences; Education and Communication, Science and Technology, Human Services, Business, Art**
Goodheart-Wilcox Publisher
18604 W. Creek Dr.
Tinley Park, IL 60477-6243
Ph: (708)687-5000   Fax: 888-409-3900
Fr: 888-409-3900

Lee Jackson. September 2003. $45.00. Illustrated. 399 pages.

★5513★ **Careers for Good Samaritans and Other Humanitarian Types**
McGraw-Hill Trade
2 Penn Plaza
New York, NY 10121
Ph: (212)904-2000   Fr: 800-722-4726
E-mail: ntcpub@tribune.com

Marjorie Eberts and Margaret Gisler. Second edition, 1998. $9.95 (paper). 274 pages. Contains hundreds of ideas for turning good work into paid work. Inventories opportunities in service organizations like the Red Cross, Goodwill, and the Salvation Army; religious groups, VISTA, the Peace Corps, and UNICEF; and agencies at all levels of the government. Part of Careers for You series.

★5514★ **Careers in Health Care**
McGraw-Hill Trade
2 Penn Plaza
New York, NY 10121
Ph: (212)904-2000   Fr: 800-722-4726
E-mail: ntcpub@tribune.com

Barbara M. Swanson. Fourth edition, 2000. $17.95; $13.95 (paper). 320 pages. Describes job duties, work settings, salaries, licensing and certification requirements, educational preparation, and future outlook. Gives ideas on how to secure a job.

★5515★ **Great Jobs for Liberal Arts Majors**
McGraw-Hill Professional
2 Penn Plaza
New York, NY 10121
Ph: (212)904-2000   Fr: 800-722-4726
E-mail: ntcpub@tribune.com

Blythe Camenson. Second edition, 2001. $14.95 (paper). 256 pages.

★5516★ **Interviewing in Health & Human Services**
Thomson Wadsworth
10 Davis Dr.
Belmont, CA 94002
Ph: (650)598-9757   Fr: 800-347-7707

Krishna Samantrai. 1996. $19.50 (paper). 159 pages.

★5517★ Non-Profits and Education Job Finder

Planning Communications
7215 Oak Ave.
River Forest, IL 60305-1935
Ph: (708)366-5200   Fax: (708)366-5280
Fr: 888-366-5200
URL: http://jobfindersonline.com

Daniel Lauber. 1997. $32.95; $16.95 (paper). 336 pages. Covers 1600 sources. Discusses how to use sources of non-profit sector job vacancies in a number of specialties and state-by-state, including job-matching services, job hotlines, specialty periodicals with job ads, salary surveys, and directories. Covers a variety of fields from education to religion. Includes chapters on resume and cover letter preparation and interviewing.

★5518★ Opportunities in Gerontology and Aging Services Careers

McGraw-Hill Trade
2 Penn Plaza
New York, NY 10121
Ph: (212)904-2000   Fr: 800-722-4726

Ellen Williams. 1995. $14.95; $11.95 (paper). 200 pages. Covers jobs in community, health and medical programs, financial, legal, residential, travel and tourism, and counseling, and how to go after them. Includes bibliography and illustrations.

★5519★ Opportunities in Mental Health Careers

McGraw-Hill Trade
2 Penn Plaza
New York, NY 10121
Ph: (212)904-2000   Fr: 800-722-4726

Philip A. Perry and George Blake. 1996. $14.95; $11.95 (paper). 160 pages.

★5520★ Opportunities in Social Work Careers

McGraw-Hill/Contemporary Books
1221 Avenue of the Americas
New York, NY 10020
Ph: (212)904-2000   Fr: 800-323-4900
E-mail: ntcpub@tribune.com

Renee Wittenberg. 1997. 205 pages. $14.95; $11.95 (paper).

★5521★ Real-Resumes for Social Work and Counseling Jobs

Prep Publishing
1110 1/2 Hay St., PMB 66
Fayetteville, NC 28305
Ph: (910)483-2439   Fax: (910)483-2439
Fr: 800-533-2814

April 2002. $16.95. 192 pages. Real-Resumes Series.

TRADESHOWS

★5522★ EAPA Annual Conference

Employee Assistance Professionals Association
2101 Wilson Blvd., Ste. 500
Arlington, VA 22201-3062
Ph: (703)387-1000   Fax: (703)522-4585
E-mail: eapamain@aol.com
URL: http://www.eap-association.com

Annual. **Primary Exhibits:** Exhibits geared toward persons employed full-time in the development or operation of employee assistance programs (EAPs) as administrators, consultants, or motivational counselors.

OTHER SOURCES

★5523★ Association on Higher Education and Disability (AHEAD)

PO Box 540666
Waltham, MA 02454
Ph: (781)788-0003   Fax: (781)788-0033
E-mail: ahead@ahead.org
URL: http://www.ahead.org.

Description: Individuals interested in promoting the equal rights and opportunities of disabled postsecondary students, staff, faculty, and graduates. Provides an exchange of communication for those professionally involved with disabled students; collects, evaluates, and disseminates information; encourages and supports legislation for the benefit of disabled students. Conducts surveys on issues pertinent to college students with disabilities; offers resource referral system and employment exchange for positions in disability student services. Conducts research programs; compiles statistics.

★5524★ Center for the Child Care Workforce, A Project of the American Federation of Teachers Educational Foundation (CCW/AFTEF)

555 New Jersey Ave. NW
Washington, DC 20001
Ph: (202)662-8005   Fax: (202)662-8006
E-mail: ccw@aft.org
URL: http://www.ccw.org

Purpose: Works to develop innovative solutions to the child care crisis to improve salaries, working conditions, and status of child care workers; to increase public awareness about the importance of child care work and the training and skill it demands; to develop resources and create an information sharing network for child care workers nationwide. **Activities:** Gathers current information on salaries and benefits; offers consultation services. Sponsors research projects; compiles statistics; operates speakers' bureau. Maintains extensive file of materials on working conditions and research on child care workers.

★5525★ Child Life Council (CLC)

11820 Parklawn Dr., Ste. 202
Rockville, MD 20852-2529
Ph: (301)881-7090   Fax: (301)881-7092
Fr: 800-CLC-4515
E-mail: clcstaff@childlife.org
URL: http://www.childlife.org

Members: Professional organization representing child life personnel, patient activities specialists, and students in the field. **Purpose:** Promotes psychological well-being and optimum development of children, adolescents, and their families in health care settings. **Activities:** Works to minimize the stress and anxiety of illness and hospitalization. Addresses professional issues such as program standards, competencies, and core curriculum. Provides resources and conducts research and educational programs. Offers a Job Bank Service listing employment openings.

★5526★ Child Welfare League of America (CWLA)

440 1st St. NW, 3rd Fl.
Washington, DC 20001
Ph: (202)638-2952   Fax: (202)638-4004
E-mail: jjohnson@cwla.org
URL: http://www.cwla.org

Purpose: Works to improve care and services for abused, dependent, or neglected children, youth, and their families. **Activities:** Provides training and consultation; conducts research; maintains information service; develops standards for child welfare practice.

★5527★ Human Service Workers

Evon Publishing
832 N 7th Ave.
Iron River, MI 49935
Ph: (906)265-3190

Audiocassette. 1996. $16.95. 32 minutes. Part of the Careers and Vocational Guidance Series. Provides information about the nature of the work, educational requirements, employment outlook, earnings, and work conditions as well as additional related information.

★5528★ Human Services Occupations

Delphi Productions
3160 4th St.
Boulder, CO 80304
Fax: (303)443-4022   Fr: 888-443-2400
URL: http://www.delphivideo.com

$95.00. 50 minutes. Part of the Careers for the 21st Century Video Library.

★5529★ National Organization for Human Service Education (NOHSE)

Fort Greene SNAP
375 Myrtle Ave.
Brooklyn, NY 11205
Ph: (718)694-6957   Fax: (718)694-6958
E-mail: ftg_snap@hotmail.com
URL: http://www.nohse.com

Description: Human service professionals,

faculty, and students. Works to foster excellence in teaching, research and curriculum planning in the human service area; to encourage and support the development of local, state, and national human services organizations; to aid faculty and professional members in their career development. Provides a medium for cooperation and communication among members; maintains registry of qualified consultants in human service education. Conducts professional development workshop; operates speakers' bureau.

Image Consultants

HANDBOOKS AND MANUALS

★5530★ The Best Home-Based Businesses for the 90s

Putnam Publishing Group
375 Hudson St.
New York, NY 10014
Ph: (212)366-2000   Fax: (212)366-2643
Fr: 800-331-4624

Paul Edwards and Sarah Edwards. Second edition, 1991. $11.95 (paper). 272 pages. Profiles 95 businesses and careers that can be conducted from one's home. Lists sources of additional information. Out of print.

★5531★ Careers for Fashion Plates and Other Trendsetters

VGM Career Horizons
N T C Publishing Group
1221 Avenue of the Americas
New York, NY 10020
Ph: (212)904-2000   Fr: 800-323-4900
E-mail: ntcpub@tribune.com

Lucia Mauro. 1996. $14.95; $9.95 (paper). 205 pages. Describes career opportunities in fashion, entertainment, retail, and promotion, with advice from fashion professionals.

★5532★ Careers for Film Buffs and Other Hollywood Types

VGM Career Horizons
1221 Avenue of the Americas
New York, NY 10020
Ph: (212)904-2000   Fr: 800-323-4900
E-mail: ntcpub@tribune.com

Jaq Greenspon. 1994. $14.95; $9.95 (paper). 250 pages. Describes job descriptions in production, camera, sound, special effects, grips, electrical, makeup, costumes, etc.

★5533★ FabJob Guide to Become an Image Consultant: Discover How to Start a Business as an Image, Wardrobe or Makeover Consultant for Women, Men or Companies

FabJob.com
19 Horizon View Ct.
Calgary, AB, Canada T3B 4V7
Ph: (403)949-4980   Fax: (403)949-4980

July 2004. $29.95 (CD-ROM, Paper).

★5534★ The 10 Hottest Consulting Practices: What They Are, How to Get into Them

John Wiley & Sons, Inc.
111 River St.
Hoboken, NJ 07030-5774
Ph: (201)748-6000   Fax: (201)748-6088
Fr: 800-225-5945

Ron Tepper. 1995. $27.95. 210 pages.

OTHER SOURCES

★5535★ About Face Image Consulting

9673-205A St.
Langley, BC, Canada V1M 2H4
Ph: (604)888-9260   Fax: (604)648-9763
URL: http://www.aboutfaceimage.com/

Description: Specializes in coaching individuals, small business owners and corporate staff on image, particularly those experiencing downsizing and career transitions.

★5536★ Anderson Research Center for Image and Etiquette

304 Park Avenue South
New York, NY 12180
Ph: (212)861-2093   Fr: (866)203-6670

Description: Offers a full range of services to assess image and create a personal style strategy that coincides with an individual's body type, lifestyle and goals. Services are available as personalized, one-to-one consultations and coaching, or as seminars and workshops for groups of all sizes, corporate or personal.

★5537★ Association of Image Consultants International (AICI)

12300 Ford Rd., Ste. 135
Dallas, TX 75234
Ph: (972)755-1503   Fax: (972)755-2561
Fr: 877-247-3319
E-mail: info@aici.org
URL: http://www.aici.org

Description: Personal color, style, wardrobe, and image planning consultants. Promotes quality service for clients; aids in establishing working relations between retail stores and consultants; assists community colleges in offering accredited image consulting programs; maintains standards of professionalism for members in the image consulting industry. Provides continuing education and training; maintains speakers' bureau.

★5538★ Image Industry Council International

PO Box 190007
San Francisco, CA 94119
Ph: (415)863-2573   Fax: (928)223-0507
E-mail: info@image360.com
URL: http://www.image360.com

Activities: Maintains speakers' bureau. Conducts educational and research programs.

★5539★ Professional Image Management

65 Coon Rd.
New York, NY 12180
Ph: (518)279-9388
E-mail: image3@mucap.rr.com
URL: http://www.professionalimagemgt.com

Description: Provides executive coaching in professional image.

Industrial Engineers

SOURCES OF HELP-WANTED ADS

★5540★ Applied Occupational & Environmental Hygiene

Applied Industrial Hygiene Inc.
1330 Kemper Meadow Dr., Ste. 600
Cincinnati, OH 45240
Ph: (513)742-2020   Fax: (513)742-3355
E-mail: comm@acgih.org

Monthly. $159.00/year for individuals; $269.00/year for institutions. Peer-reviewed journal presenting applied solutions for the prevention of occupational and environmental disease and injury.

★5541★ AWIS Magazine

Association for Women in Science
1200 New York Ave. NW, Ste. 650
Washington, DC 20005
Ph: (202)326-8940   Fax: (202)326-8960
Fr: 800-886-AWIS

Description: Bimonthly. Covers issues, legislation, and trends related to science education for girls, women, and minorities. Includes information on grants and fellowships, job openings, educational programs, events, and notices of publications available.

★5542★ Engineering Times

National Society of Professional
 Engineers
1420 King St.
Alexandria, VA 22314
Ph: (703)684-2875   Fax: (703)836-4875
E-mail: et@nspe.org
URL: http://http//:www.nspc.org/1et.asp

$30.00/year for individuals; $48.00/year for out of country. Magazine (tabloid) covering professional, legislative, and techology issues for an engineering audience.

★5543★ ENR: Engineering News-Record

McGraw-Hill Companies
1221 Avenue of the Americas
New York, NY 10020
Ph: (212)512-2000
URL: http://www.enr.com

Weekly. $74.00/year; $5.00 for single issue. Magazine focusing on engineering and construction.

★5544★ Graduating Engineer & Computer Careers

Career Recruitment Media
211 W. Wacker Dr., No. 900
Chicago, IL 60606
Ph: (312)525-3100
URL: http://www.graduatingengineer.com

$16.00/year for individuals. Magazine focusing on employment, education, and career development for entry-level engineers and computer scientists.

★5545★ High Technology Careers Magazine

HTC
4701 Patrick Henry Dr., No. 1901
Santa Clara, CA 95054-1847
Ph: (408)970-8800   Fax: (408)567-0242
URL: http://www.hightechcareers.com

Bimonthly. $29.00/year; $35.00/year for Canada; $85.00/year for out of country. Magazine (tabloid) containing employment opportunity information for the engineering and technical community.

★5546★ IIE Solutions

Institute of Industrial Engineers
3577 Pkwy. Ln., Ste. 200
Norcross, GA 30092
Ph: (770)449-0461   Fax: (770)263-8532
Fr: 800-494-0460
E-mail: advertising@iienet.org
URL: http://solutions.iienet.org

Monthly. $60.00/year for individuals; $7.00 for single issue. Magazine covering industrial engineering, facilities design, systems integration, production control, material handling, quality, productivity, management, and other industrial engineering topics.

★5547★ Managing Automation

Thomas Publishing Co.
5 Penn Plz.
New York, NY 10001
Ph: (212)695-0500   Fax: (212)290-7362
URL: http://www.managingautomation.com

Monthly. $60.00/year for individuals; $8.00 for single issue. Managing Automation covers advanced manufacturing technology including automation, integrated manufacturing, enterprise applications, and IT and e-business for the manufacturing enterprise.

★5548★ NSBE Magazine

NSBE Publications
1454 Duke St.
Alexandria, VA 22314
Ph: (703)549-2207   Fax: (703)683-5312

$10.00/year for individuals; $2.00 for single issue. Journal providing information on engineering careers, self-development, and cultural issues for recent graduates with technical majors.

★5549★ Plant Engineering

Reed Business Information
360 Park Ave. S
New York, NY 10014
Ph: (646)746-7764
E-mail: planteng@cahners.com
URL: http://www.plantengineering.com

Free to qualified subscribers. Magazine focusing on engineering support and maintenance in industry.

★5550★ Power

McGraw-Hill Companies
1221 Avenue of the Americas
New York, NY 10020
Ph: (212)512-2000

Monthly. $19.00/year; $5.00 for single issue. Magazine for engineers in electric utilities, process and manufacturing plants, commercial and service establishments, and consulting, design, and construction engineering firms working in the power technology field.

★5551★ SWE

Society of Women Engineers
230 E Ohio St., No. 400
2135 Lamberton Rd.
Chicago, IL 60611-3265
Ph: (312)596-5223   Fax: (312)596-5252
E-mail: hq@swe.org
URL: http://www.swe.org

Bimonthly. $30.00/year for nonmembers. Magazine for engineering students and for women and men working in the engineering and technology fields. Covers career guidance, continuing development and topical issues.

★5552★ Technology Review

Technology Review
201 Vassar St.
Cambridge, MA 02139
Ph: (617)253-8250   Fax: (617)258-5850
E-mail: trcomments@mit.edu

$30.00/year for individuals; $42.00/year for other countries; $4.95/year for single issue. Magazine reviewing new developments in technology with an emphasis on economic, political, and social implications. Not a new product publication.

★5553★ WEPANEWS

Women in Engineering Programs &
 Advocates Network
Castle Point on the Hudson
Hoboken, NJ 07030
Ph: (201)216-5245   Fax: (201)216-5175
URL: http://www.wepan.org/newsletter.html

Description: Two issues/year. Seeks to provide greater access for women to careers in engineering. Includes news of graduate, undergraduate, freshmen, pre-college, and re-entry engineering programs for women. Recurring features include job listings, faculty, grant, and conference news, international engineering program news, action group news, notices of publications available, and a column titled Kudos.

★5554★ Wire & Cable Technology International

Initial Publications Inc.
3869 Darrow Rd., Ste. 109
Stow, OH 44224
Ph: (330)686-9544   Fax: (330)686-9563
E-mail: info@wiretech.com

Bimonthly. $40.00/year for individuals; $90.00/year for other countries. Magazine for manufacturers of ferrous, nonferrous, bare, and insulated wire.

PLACEMENT AND JOB REFERRAL SERVICES

★5555★ American Indian Science and Engineering Society (AISES)

PO Box 9828
Albuquerque, NM 87119-9828
Ph: (505)765-1052   Fax: (505)765-5608
E-mail: info@aises.org
URL: http://www.aises.org

Description: American Indian and non-Indian students and professionals in science, technology, and engineering fields; corporations representing energy, mining, aerospace, electronic, and computer fields. Seeks to motivate and encourage students to pursue undergraduate and graduate studies in science, engineering, and technology. Sponsors science fairs in grade schools, teacher training workshops, summer math/science sessions for 8th-12th graders, professional chapters, and student chapters in colleges. Offers scholarships. Adult members serve as role models, advisers, and mentors for students. Operates placement service.

★5556★ Association for Finishing Processes of the Society of Manufacturing Engineers (AFP/SME)

1 SME Dr.
PO Box 930
Dearborn, MI 48121-0930
Ph: (313)271-1500   Fax: (313)271-2861
Fr: 800-733-4SME
URL: http://www.sme.org/afp

Description: Promotes the technology, process, and management aspects of the cleaning and coating of metal or plastic manufactured products. Conducts clinics and expositions. Offers professional certification. Maintains placement service with free listings for members.

★5557★ Engineering Society of Detroit (ESD)

26100 American Dr., Ste. 500
Southfield, MI 48034-6184
Ph: (248)355-2910   Fax: (248)355-1492
E-mail: esd@esd.org
URL: http://esd.org

Description: Engineers from all disciplines; scientists and technologists. Conducts technical programs and engineering refresher courses; sponsors conferences and expositions. Maintains speakers' bureau; offers placement services. Although based in Detroit, MI, society membership is international.

★5558★ Korean Scientists and Engineers Association in America (KSEA)

1952 Gallows Rd., Ste. 300
Vienna, VA 22182
Ph: (703)748-1221   Fax: (703)748-1331
E-mail: sejong@ksea.org
URL: http://www.ksea.org

Description: Scientists and engineers holding single or advanced degrees. Goals are to: promote friendship and mutuality among Korean and American scientists and engineers; contribute to Korea's scientific, technological, industrial, and economic developments; strengthen the scientific, technological, and cultural bonds between Korea and the U.S. Sponsors symposium. Maintains speakers' bureau, placement service, and biographical archives. Compiles statistics. Maintains 100 volume library of scientific handbooks and yearbooks in Korean.

★5559★ Society of Hispanic Professional Engineers (SHPE)

5400 E Olympic Blvd., Ste. 210
Los Angeles, CA 90022
Ph: (323)725-3970   Fax: (323)725-0316
E-mail: shpenational@shpe.org
URL: http://www.shpe.org

Description: Engineers, student engineers, and scientists seeking to increase the number of Hispanic engineers by providing motivation and support to students. Sponsors competitions and educational programs. Maintains placement service and speakers' bureau; compiles statistics.

EMPLOYER DIRECTORIES AND NETWORKING LISTS

★5560★ American Men and Women of Science

Thomson Gale
27500 Drake Rd.
Farmington Hills, MI 48331-3535
Ph: (248)699-4253   Fax: (248)699-8065
Fr: 800-877-GALE
E-mail: amws@galegroup.com

Biennial, latest edition December 2002. $975.00. Covers over 129,700 U.S. and Canadian scientists active in the physical, biological, mathematical, computer science, and engineering fields; includes references to previous edition for deceased scientists and nonrespondents. Entries include: Name, address, education, personal and career data, memberships, honors and awards, research interest. Arrangement: Alphabetical. Indexes: Discipline (in separate volume).

★5561★ Careers in Focus: Engineering

Ferguson Publishing Co.
200 W Jackson Blvd.
Chicago, IL 60606
Ph: (312)692-0109

2nd edition, 2002. $22.95. Publication includes: List of resources to consult for more information. Principal content of publication is job descriptions, advancement opportunities, educational requirements, employment outlook, salary information, and working conditions for careers in the field of engineering. Indexes: Alphabetical.

★5562★ **Directory of Contract Staffing Firms**

C.E. Publications Inc.
PO Box 3006
Bothell, WA 98041-3006
Ph: (425)806-5200   Fax: (425)806-5585
URL: http://www.cjhunter.com/dcsf/over-view.html

$15.00. Covers nearly 1,300 contract firms actively engaged in the employment of engineering, IT/IS, and technical personnel for 'temporary' contract assignments throughout the world. Entries include: Company name, address, phone, name of contact, email, web address. Arrangement: Alphabetical. Indexes: Geographical.

★5563★ **Engineers-Structural Directory**

infoUSA Inc.
5711 S 86th Cir.
Omaha, NE 68127-0347
Ph: (402)930-3500   Fax: (402)331-0176
Fr: 800-555-6124
URL: http://www.abii.com

Annual. Number of listings: 5,023. Entries include: Name, address, phone (including area code), size of advertisement, year first in "Yellow Pages," name of owner or manager, number of employees. Compiled from telephone company "Yellow Pages," nationwide. Arrangement: Geographical.

★5564★ **International Directory of Engineering Societies and Related Organizations**

American Association of Engineering Societies
1828 L St. NW, Ste. 906
Washington, DC 20036
Ph: (202)296-2237   Fax: (202)296-1151
Fr: 888-400-AAES

Irregular, latest edition December 1998. $240.00. Covers about 1,370 national, regional, Canadian, and international organizations concerned with engineering and related fields. Entries include: Name, address, phone, fax, e-mail, key personnel, objectives, publications, activities, mailing lists, federation memberships, meeting and convention dates, and budget data. Arrangement: Alphabetical. Indexes: Acronym, geographical, area of specialization.

★5565★ **Peterson's Job Opportunities in Engineering and Technology**

Thomson Peterson's
PO Box 67005
Lawrenceville, NJ 08648-6105
Fr: 800-338-3282

Compiled by the Peterson's staff. Fourth edition, 1996. $21.95 (paper). 384 pages. Profiles 2,000 high-tech companies looking primarily for technical personnel in such fields as biotechnology, telecommunications, software, computers and peripherals, defense, and aerospace. Contains job-search strategies and career options to help match education and expertise to the job market. Indexed geographically, by industry, and by hiring needs.

HANDBOOKS AND MANUALS

★5566★ **The Best Resumes for Scientists and Engineers**

John Wiley & Sons Inc.
1 Wiley Dr.
Somerset, NJ 08873
Ph: (732)469-4400   Fr: 800-225-5945

Adele Lewis and David J. Moore. Second edition, 1993. $37.50; $19.95 (paper). 224 pages. Presents an extensive collection of scientific and engineering resumes, highlighting the important differences between these and resumes written for other occupations.

★5567★ **Engineering Your Job Search: A Job-Finding Resource for Engineering Professionals**

Professional Publications, Inc.
1250 5th Ave.
Belmont, CA 94002
Ph: (650)593-9119   Fax: (650)592-4519
Fr: 800-426-1178

Compiled by Professional Publications, editors. 1995. $24.95 (paper). 154 pages. Out of print.

★5568★ **Great Jobs for Engineering Majors**

McGraw-Hill Professional
McGraw-Hill Higher Education
2 Penn Plaza
New York, NY 10121
Ph: (212)904-2000   Fr: 800-722-4726
E-mail: ntcpub@tribune.com

Geraldine O. Garner. Second edition, 2002. $14.95. 256 pages. Covers all the career options open to students majoring in engineering.

★5569★ **The I Hate Selling Book: Business-Building Advice for Consultants, Attorneys, Accountants, Engineers, Architects, and Other Professionals**

Allan Boress & Associates
1500 University Dr., Suite 239
Coral Springs, FL 33071
Ph: (954)345-4666   Fax: (954)344-2453

Allan S. Boress. 2001. $29.95.

★5570★ **Majoring in Engineering: How to Get from Your Freshman Year to Your First Job**

Farrar, Straus & Giroux, Inc.
19 Union Sq., W
New York, NY 10003
Ph: (212)741-6900   Fax: (212)633-9385
Fr: 888-330-8477

John Garcia and Carol Carter, editors. 2000. $20.00; $10.00 (paper). 134 pages.

★5571★ **Opportunities in Engineering Careers**

McGraw-Hill Contemporary Books
1221 Avenue of the Americas
New York, NY 10020
Ph: (212)904-2000   Fr: 800-323-4900
E-mail: ntcpub@tribune.com

Nicholas Basta. Revised, 1995. $14.95; $11.95 (paper). 200 pages. Outlines typical job titles, salaries, career paths, and employment prospects.

★5572★ **Opportunities in High Tech Careers**

McGraw-Hill Trade
2 Penn Plaza
New York, NY 10121
Ph: (212)904-2000   Fr: 800-722-4726

Gary Colter and Deborah Yanuck. 1995. $14.95; $11.95 (paper). 160 pages. Explores high technology careers. Describes job opportunities, how to make a career decision, how to prepare for high technology jobs, job hunting techniques, and future trends.

★5573★ **Opportunities in Research and Development Careers**

McGraw-Hill/Contemporary Books
1221 Avenue of the Americas
New York, NY 10020
Ph: (212)904-2000   Fr: 800-323-4900
E-mail: ntcpub@tribune.com

Jan Goldberg. 1997. $14.95; $11.95 (paper). 204 pages.

★5574★ **Real People Working in Engineering**

McGraw-Hill Contemporary Books
1221 Avenue of the Americas
New York, NY 10020
Ph: (212)904-2000   Fr: 800-323-4900
E-mail: ntcpub@tribune.com

Blythe Camenson, Jan Goldberg. 1997. $14.95; $12.95 (paper). Interviews and profiles of working professionals capture a range of opportunities in this field.

★5575★ **Resumes for Engineering Careers**

McGraw-Hill Trade
2 Penn Plaza
New York, NY 10121
Ph: (212)904-2000   Fr: 800-722-4726
E-mail: ntcpub@tribune.com

2000. $10.95 (paper). 456 pages. Contains sample resumes and cover letters applicable to any engineering field.

★5576★ **Resumes for Scientific and Technical Careers**

McGraw-Hill Contemporary Books
1221 Avenue of the Americas
New York, NY 10020
Ph: (212)904-2000   Fr: 800-323-4900
E-mail: ntcpub@tribune.com

1999. $9.95 (paper). 450 pages. Provides

resume advice for individuals interested in working in scientific and technical careers. Includes sample resumes and cover letters.

★5577★ Review for the Professional Engineer's Examination for Industrial Engineers

Institute of Electrical and Electronics Engineers, Inc.
25 Technology Pk.
Norcross, GA 30092-2988
Ph: (770)449-0460   Fax: (770)441-3295
Fr: 800-494-0460

Donovan Young. 1996. $49.95 (paper). 402 pages.

★5578★ Where the Jobs Are: The Hottest Careers for the 90s

The Career Press, Inc.
3 Tice Rd.
PO Box 687
Franklin Lakes, NJ 07417-1322
Ph: (201)848-0310   Fax: (201)848-1727
Fr: 800-227-3371

Joyce Hadley. Third edition, 2000. $13.99 (paper). 400 pages. Out of print. Describes careers in fifteen general fields, from accounting to travel and hospitality.

EMPLOYMENT AGENCIES AND SEARCH FIRMS

★5579★ The Aspire Group

52 Second Ave, 1st Fl
Waltham, MA 02451-1129
Fax: (718)890-1810   Fr: 800-546-5675
URL: http://www.bmanet.com

Employment agency.

★5580★ Auguston and Associates Inc.

1010 S. Ocean Blvd., Ste. 601
Pompano Beach, FL 33062
Ph: (954)943-0503   Fax: (954)784-1660
Fr: 888-244-5598

Executive search firm focused on medical devices.

★5581★ Bell Oaks Co.

10 Glenlake Parkway, Ste. 300
Atlanta, GA 30328
Ph: (678)287-2000   Fax: (678)287-2001
E-mail: atlantacareers@belloaks.com
URL: http://www.belloaks.com

Personnel service firm.

★5582★ The Brand Company Inc.

181 Shores Dr.
Vero Beach, FL 32963
Ph: (561)231-1807

Executive search firm.

★5583★ CEO Resources Inc.

200 E. State St., Ste. 101
Media, PA 19063
Ph: (610)565-9767

Executive search firm.

★5584★ C.H. Cowles Associates

93 W Alyssa Canyon Pl.
Oro Valley, AZ 85737-1636
Ph: (520)297-7608   Fax: (520)297-7608

Provides services in industrial engineering and industrial management including long-range planning, facilities planning, work improvement, profit improvement, executive search, quality assurance, manufacturing engineering and staff reorganization. Site search and site planning.

★5585★ Christopher-Westmont & Associates Inc.

PO Box 470188
Broadview Heights, OH 44147
Ph: (440)877-0510   Fax: (440)877-0511

Executive search firm.

★5586★ Cizek Associates Inc.

2415 E. Camelback Rd., Ste. 700
Camelback Esplanade I
Phoenix, AZ 85016
Ph: (602)553-1066   Fax: (602)553-1166

Executive search firm.

★5587★ Colli Associates

404 Caboose Ln.
Valrico, FL 33594
Ph: (813)681-2145   Fax: (813)661-5217
E-mail: colli@gte.net

Employment agency. Executive search firm.

★5588★ Davis & Company

3419 Via Lido, Ste. 615
Newport Beach, CA 92663
Ph: (949)376-6995   Fax: (949)376-6995
Fr: 800-600-4417

Executive search firm. Branch in Lake Mary, FL.

★5589★ Dean Associates

PO Box 1079
Santa Cruz, CA 95061
Ph: (831)423-2931

Executive search firm focused on the high technology industry.

★5590★ Dinte Resources Inc.

8300 Greensboro Dr., Ste. 750
McLean, VA 22102
Ph: (703)448-3300   Fax: (703)448-0215

Executive search firm.

★5591★ Electronic Careers

21355 Pacific Coast Hwy., Ste. 100
Malibu, CA 90265
Ph: (310)317-6115   Fax: (310)317-6119

Executive search firm.

★5592★ Elite Resources Group

PO Box 13113
Fairlawn, OH 44334
Ph: (330)867-9412   Fax: (330)867-0468

Executive search firm.

★5593★ Engineer One, Inc.

PO Box 23037
Knoxville, TN 37933
Fax: (865)691-0110
E-mail: engineerone@engineerone.com
URL: http://www.engineerone.com

Employment agency.

★5594★ Executive Recruiters Agency

14 Office Park Dr., Ste. 100
PO Box 21810
Little Rock, AR 72221-1810
Ph: (501)224-7000   Fax: (501)224-8534
E-mail: grogers@execrecruit.com
URL: http://www.execrecruit.com

Personnel service firm.

★5595★ Executive Resource Group Inc.

2470 Windy Hill Rd., Ste. 300
Marietta, GA 30067
Ph: (770)955-1811

Executive search firm.

★5596★ Executive Search Services (ESS)

2925 4th St., Ste. 11
Santa Monica, CA 90405

Executive search firm.

★5597★ Fischer Group International Inc.

296 Country Club Dr., Bldg A
Avon, CT 06001
Ph: (860)404-7700   Fax: (860)404-7799

Executive search firm.

★5598★ Fisher Personnel Management Services

1862 Torrance Blvd.
PO Box 9076
Torrance, CA 90508
Ph: (310)320-6667   Fax: (310)320-1060

Executive search firm.

★5599★ Fowler & Associates

6427 Laurel Valley Rd.
Dallas, TX 75248
Ph: (972)490-5096   Fax: (972)490-5096

Executive search firm.

★5600★ International Staffing Consultants

2901 W Coast Hwy.,Ste. 200
Newport Beach, CA 92663
Ph: (949)263-5933   Fax: (949)767-5959
E-mail: iscinc@iscworld.com
URL: http://www.iscworld.com

Employment agency. Provides placement on regular or temporary basis. Affiliate office in London.

★5601★ Main Line Personnel Service, Inc.

Pagoda Blding.
100 Presidential Blvd. Ste. 200
Bala Cynwyd, PA 19004-0448
Ph: (610)667-1820   Fax: (610)668-5000
URL: http://www.mlpers.com

Employment agency.

★5602★ Mfg/Search, Inc.

431 E Colfax Ave., Ste.120
South Bend, IN 46617
Ph: (574)282-2547   Fr: 800-782-7976
E-mail: mfg@mfgsearch.com
URL: http://www.mfgsearch.com

Executive search firm. Offices in GA, IL, MI, NY.

★5603★ Rand Personnel

1200 Truxtun, Ste. 130
Bakersfield, CA 93301
Ph: (805)325-0751   Fax: (805)325-4120

Personnel service firm serving a variety of fields.

★5604★ Search and Recruit International

4455 South Blvd.
Virginia Beach, VA 23452
Ph: (757)490-3151   Fax: (757)497-6503
E-mail: britt@searchandrecruit.com
URL: http://www.searchandrecruit.com

Employment agency. Headquartered in Virginia Beach. Other offices in Bremerton, WA; Charleston, SC; Jacksonville, FL; Memphis, TN; Pensacola, FL; Sacramento, CA; San Bernardino, CA; San Diego, CA.

★5605★ Techtronix Technical Search

PO Box 17713
Milwaukee, WI 53217-0173
Ph: (414)466-3100   Fax: (414)466-3598

Firm specializes in recruiting executives for the engineering, information systems, manufacturing, marketing, finance, and human resources industries.

★5606★ TRC Staffing Services Inc.

2110 15 Mile Rd., Ste. B
Sterling Heights, MI 48310
Ph: (586)939-3210   Fax: (586)978-0572

A full-service executive search company with permanent placements encompassing engineering, industrial sales, financial and computer science positions. Screen, interview, and verify past employment for all candidates prior to referral. Also assist personnel staffs in the attainment of their EEO/AAP goals with the placement of talented individuals in positions which are underutilized with minorities and/or women. In addition, firm has a clerical temporary service division, TRC Temporary Service; and an employment agency, TRC Staffing Services.

★5607★ Tri-Serv Inc.

22 W. Padonia Rd., Ste. C-353
Timonium, MD 21093
Ph: (410)561-1740   Fax: (410)252-7417
E-mail: info@tri-serv.coom
URL: http://www.tri-serv.com

Permanent employment agency.

ONLINE JOB SOURCES AND SERVICES

★5608★ Spherion Workforce Architects
URL: http://www.spherion.com

Description: Recruitment firm specializing in accounting and finance, sales and marketing, interim executives, technology, engineering, retail and human resources.

TRADESHOWS

★5609★ American Society for Engineering Education Annual Conference and Exposition

American Society for Engineering Education
1818 N St., Ste. 600
Washington, DC 20036
Ph: (202)331-3500   Fax: (202)265-8504
URL: http://www.asee.org

Annual. **Primary Exhibits:** Publications, engineering supplies and equipment, computers, software, and research companies all products and services related to engineering education. **Dates and Locations:** 2005 Jun 12-15; Portland, OR • 2006 Jun 18-21; Chicago, IL • 2007 Jun 24-27; Honolulu, HI.

OTHER SOURCES

★5610★ American Almanac of Jobs and Salaries

Morrow Avon
1350 Avenue of the Americas
New York, NY 10019
Ph: (212)261-6788   Fr: 800-242-7737

John W. Wright. Revised edition, 2000. $20.00 (paper). 672 pages. This is a comprehensive guide to the wages of hundreds of occupations in a wide variety of industries and organizations.

★5611★ American Association of Engineering Societies (AAES)

1828 L St. NW, No. 906
Washington, DC 20036
Ph: (202)296-2237   Fax: (202)296-1151
Fr: 888-400-2237
E-mail: tprice@aaes.org
URL: http://www.aaes.org

Description: Coordinates the efforts of the member societies in the provision of reliable and objective information to the general public concerning issues which affect the engineering profession and the field of engineering as a whole; to collect, analyze, document, and disseminate data which will inform the general public of the relationship between engineering and the national welfare; to provide a forum for the engineering societies to exchange and discuss their views on matters of common interest; and to represent the U.S. engineering community aborad through representation in WFEO and UPADI.

★5612★ American Supplier Institute (ASI)

4050 Legato Rd.
Fairfax, VA 22033
Ph: (734)464-1395   Fax: (734)464-1399
Fr: 800-462-4500
E-mail: asi@asiusa.com
URL: http://www.amsup.com

Description: Seeks to encourage change in U.S. industry through development and implementation of advanced manufacturing and engineering technologies such as Taguchi Methods, Quality Function Deployment, Statistical Process Control, and Total Quality Management. Offers educational courses, training seminars, and workshops to improve quality, reduce cost, and enhance competitive position of U.S. products. Maintains international network of affiliates for developing training specialists and technologies curriculum. Has government contract to provide training services to government supplier companies.

★5613★ Association for International Practical Training (AIPT)

10400 Little Patuxent Pky., Ste. 250
Columbia, MD 21044-3519
Ph: (410)997-2200   Fax: (410)992-3924
E-mail: aipt@aipt.org

URL: http://www.aipt.org

Description: Providers worldwide on-the-job training programs for students and professionals seeking international career development and life-changing experiences. Arranges workplace exchanges in hundreds of professional fields, bringing employers and trainees together from around the world. Client list ranges from small farming communities to Fortune 500 companies.

★5614★ *Engineering Occupations*

Delphi Productions
3160 4th St.
Boulder, CO 80304
Fax: (303)443-4022   Fr: 888-443-2400
URL: http://www.delphivideo.com

$95.00. 50 minutes. Part of the Careers for the 21st Century Video Library.

★5615★ *Industrial Engineers*

Evon Publishing
832 N 7th Ave.
Iron River, MI 49935
Ph: (906)265-3190

Audiocassette. 1996. $16.95. 32 minutes. Part of the Careers and Vocational Guidance Series. Provides information about the nature of the work, educational requirements, employment outlook, earnings, and work conditions as well as additional related information.

★5616★ **Institute of Industrial Engineers (IIE)**

3577 Parkway Ln., Ste. 200
Norcross, GA 30092
Fax: (770)441-3295   Fr: 800-494-0460
E-mail: jpowers@iienet.org
URL: http://www.iienet.org

Description: Professional society of industrial engineers. Concerned with the design, improvement, and installation of integrated systems of people, materials, equipment, and energy. Draws upon specialized knowledge and skill in the mathematical, physical, and social sciences together with the principles and methods of engineering analysis and design, to specify, predict, and evaluate the results obtained from such systems. Maintains technical societies and divisions.

★5617★ **National Action Council for Minorities in Engineering (NACME)**

Empire State Bldg., Ste. 2212
350 Fifth Ave.
New York, NY 10118-2299
Ph: (212)279-2626   Fax: (212)629-5178
E-mail: webmaster@nacme.org
URL: http://www.nacme.org/

Description: Leads the national effort to increase access to careers in engineering and other science-based disciplines. Supported by the nation's leading technology-intensive companies, NACME conducts research and public policy analysis, develops and operates national demonstration programs at precollege and university levels, and disseminates information through publications, conferences, and electronic media. NACME is also the nation's largest privately funded source of scholarships for minority students in engineering.

★5618★ **National Society of Professional Engineers (NSPE)**

1420 King St.
Alexandria, VA 22314
Ph: (703)684-2800   Fax: (703)836-4875
Fr: 888-285-6773
E-mail: custserv@nspe.org
URL: http://www.nspe.org

Description: Professional engineers and engineers-in-training in all fields registered in accordance with the laws of states or territories of the U.S. or provinces of Canada; qualified graduate engineers, student members, and registered land surveyors. Is concerned with social, professional, ethical, and economic considerations of engineering as a profession; encompasses programs in public relations, employment practices, ethical considerations, education, and career guidance. Monitors legislative and regulatory actions of interest to the engineering profession.

★5619★ *Scientific, Engineering, and Technical Services*

Cambridge Educational
2572 Brunswick Ave.
Lawrenceville, NJ 08648-4128
Fax: 800-FAX-ON-US   Fr: 800-468-4227
URL: http://www.cambridgeeducational.com

$89.95. 2002. 18 minutes. Part of the Career Cluster Series.

★5620★ **Society of Women Engineers (SWE)**

230 E Ohio St., No. 400
Chicago, IL 60611-3265
Ph: (312)596-5223   Fax: (312)596-5252
E-mail: hq@swe.org
URL: http://www.swe.org

Description: Educational and service organization representing both students and professional women in engineering and technical fields.

★5621★ **SOLE - The International Society of Logistics (SOLE)**

8100 Professional Pl., Ste. 111
Hyattsville, MD 20785
Ph: (301)459-8446   Fax: (301)459-1522
E-mail: solehq@erols.com
URL: http://www.sole.org

Description: Corporate and individual management and technical practitioners in the field of logistics, including scientists, engineers, educators, managers, and other specialists in commerce, aerospace, and other industries, government, and the military. (Logistics is the art and science of management engineering and technical activities concerned with requirements, and designing, supplying, and maintaining resources to support objectives, plans, and operations.) Covers every logistics specialty, including maintainability, systems and equipment maintenance, maintenance support equipment, human factors, training and training equipment, spare parts, overhaul and repair, handbooks, field site activation and operation, field engineering, facilities, packaging, materials handling, and transportation. Sponsors job referral service; conducts specialized education programs; operates speakers' bureau. Sponsors the Logistics Education Foundation.

★5622★ *Women in Engineering*

Her Own Words
PO Box 5264
Madison, WI 53705-0264
Ph: (608)271-7083   Fax: (608)271-0209
URL: http://www.herownwords.com/

Video. Jocelyn Riley. $95.00. 15 minutes. Resource guide also available for $45.00.

Industrial Production Managers

SOURCES OF HELP-WANTED ADS

★5623★ *The Finishing Line*
Association for Finishing Processes
PO Box 930
One SME Dr.
Dearborn, MI 48121-0930
Ph: (313)271-1500   Fax: (313)240-8255
Fr: 800-733-4SME
URL: http://www.sme.org/cgi-bin/new-gethtml.pl?afp

Description: Quarterly. Concerned with topics related to industrial finishes, such as powder coating, radiation curing, water-borne, high solids, coating and finishing of plastics, and surface preparation. Provides information on government regulations, new products and technology, and educational opportunities in the field of finishing.

★5624★ *Journal of Staff Development*
National Staff Development Council
PO Box 240
Oxford, OH 45056
Ph: (513)523-6029   Fax: (513)523-0638
Fr: 800-727-7288

Quarterly. Professional journal covering administration issues.

★5625★ *Supply Chain Management Review*
Reed Business Information
275 Washington St.
Newton, MA 02458-1630
Ph: (617)964-3030

Bimonthly. Publication covering business and management.

HANDBOOKS AND MANUALS

★5626★ *Getting and Keeping the Job: Success in Business and Technical Careers*
Prentice Hall PTR
One Lake St.
Upper Saddle River, NJ 07458
Ph: (201)236-7000   Fax: 800-445-6991
Fr: 800-567-3800

Clark, Val. 2001. $28.00 (Trade paper). 208 pages.

★5627★ *Materials Manager*
National Learning Corporation
212 Michael Dr.
Syosset, NY 11791
Ph: (516)921-8888   Fax: (516)921-8743
Fr: 800-645-6337

Rudman, Jack. 1994. $34.95 (Trade paper).

EMPLOYMENT AGENCIES AND SEARCH FIRMS

★5628★ **Abel Fuller & Zedler LLC**
4550 Post Oak Pl., Ste. 141
Houston, TX 77027
Ph: (713)961-3330   Fax: (713)961-3337
Executive Search Firm.

★5629★ **Aegis Consulting**
633 3rd Ave., Fl. 27
New York, NY 10017
Ph: (212)687-2200   Fax: (212)687-0079
Executive search firm.

★5630★ **APA Search Inc.**
1 Byram Brook Pl., Ste. 201
Armonk, NY 10504
Ph: (914)273-6000   Fax: (914)273-8025
Employment agency specializing in the automotive, retail, and hardware industries.

★5631★ **Blake/Hansen & Schmidt Ltd.**
5514 Ridgeway Ct.
Westlake Village, CA 91362
Ph: (805)879-1192
Executive search firm specializing in plastics, rubber and packaging.

★5632★ **Boyden**
360 Lexington Ave., Ste 1300
New York, NY 10017
Ph: (212)949-9850   Fax: (212)949-5905
URL: http://www.boyden.com
Executive search firm.

★5633★ **Boyle Ogata Bregman**
18301 Von Karman Ave., Ste. 810
Irvine, CA 92612
Ph: (949)474-0115   Fax: (949)474-2204
E-mail: info@bobsearch.com
URL: http://www.bobsearch.com
Executive search firm.

★5634★ **Bruce Lowery & Associates**
PO Box 166
Ada, MI 49301-0166
Ph: (616)676-3500   Fax: (616)676-3516
E-mail: blowery@iserv.net
Executive search firm.

★5635★ **C.H. Cowles Associates**
93 W Alyssa Canyon Pl.
Oro Valley, AZ 85737-1636
Ph: (520)297-7608   Fax: (520)297-7608
Provides services in industrial engineering and industrial management including long-range planning, facilities planning, work improvement, profit improvement, executive search, quality assurance, manufacturing

engineering and staff reorganization. Site search and site planning.

★5636★ Cochran, Cochran & Yale LLC
955 E. Henrietta Rd.
Rochester, NY 14623
Ph: (585)424-6060   Fax: (585)424-6069
Executive search firm. Branches in Denver, CO; Williamsville, NY.

★5637★ Conboy, Sur & Associates Inc.
545 5th Ave., Ste. 630
New York, NY 10017
Ph: (212)687-4460   Fax: (212)687-4584
Executive search firm.

★5638★ The Corban Group
5050 Research Ct., Ste. 600
Suwanee, GA 30024
Ph: (678)638-6000
Executive search firm.

★5639★ Crowder & Company
40950 Woodward Ave., Ste. 335
Bloomfield Hills, MI 48304
Ph: (248)645-0909   Fax: (248)645-2366
Executive search firm.

★5640★ The Dieck Group Inc.
114 W. Monroe St.
Mauston, WI 53948-1130
Ph: (608)847-3400   Fax: (608)847-5799
Executive search firm focused on pulp, paper and the packaging industries.

★5641★ Eyler Associates Inc.
400 Locust St., Ste. 170
Des Moines, IA 50309
Ph: (515)245-4244
Executive search firm.

★5642★ Ferneborg & Associates Inc.
160 Bovet Rd., Ste. 210
San Mateo, CA 94402
Ph: (650)577-0100   Fax: (650)577-0122
Executive search firm.

★5643★ First Call Professional Services
6910 Hillsdale Ct.
Indianapolis, IN 46250
Ph: (317)596-3254   Fax: (317)596-3258
E-mail: jkolumbus@fcqs.com
URL: http://www.topechelon.com/firstcall
Executive search firm.

★5644★ Forest People International Search Ltd.
800-1100 Melville St.
Vancouver, BC, Canada V6E 4A6
Ph: (604)669-5635   Fax: (604)698-4972
E-mail: people@forestpeople.com
URL: http://www.forestpeople.com
Executive search firm.

★5645★ Fowler & Associates
6427 Laurel Valley Rd.
Dallas, TX 75248
Ph: (972)490-5096   Fax: (972)490-5096
Executive search firm.

★5646★ FPC of Savannah
PO Box 8846
Savannah, GA 31412
Ph: (912)233-4556   Fax: (912)223-8633
E-mail: execsearch@fpcsav.com
URL: http://www.fpcnationl.com/savannah
Executive search firm.

★5647★ FPC of Southwest Missouri
5309 S Golden Ave.
Springfield, MO 65810
Ph: (417)887-6737   Fax: (417)887-6955
E-mail: info@fpcswmo.com
URL: http://www.fpcswmo.com
Executive search firm.

★5648★ Heller Kil Associates Inc.
2060 S Halifax Dr.
Daytona Beach, FL 32118
Ph: (386)761-5100   Fax: (386)761-7206
E-mail: pheller@bellsouth.net
Executive search firm.

★5649★ JB Linde & Associates
1116 Rock Creek Elementary Dr
O'Fallon, MO 63336
Ph: (636)281-8040   Fax: (636)281-8049
E-mail: jblinde@inlink.com
Executive search firm.

★5650★ John R. Williams & Associates Inc.
338 N Elm St., Rm. 213
Greensboro, NC 27401
Ph: (336)279-8800
Executive search firm.

★5651★ John Wylie Associates Inc.
1727 E 71st St.
Tulsa, OK 74136
Ph: (918)496-2100
E-mail: jlwylie@inetmail.att.net
Executive search firm.

★5652★ K.S. Frary & Associates
16 Schooner Ridge, Ste. 301
Marblehead, MA 01945
Ph: (781)631-2464   Fax: (781)631-2465
Executive search firm.

★5653★ Lange & Associates
107 W Market St.
Wabash, IN 46992
Ph: (260)563-7402   Fax: (260)563-3897
E-mail: langeassoc@ctlnet.com
Executive search firm.

★5654★ London Executive Consultants Inc.
380 Wellington St., Ste. 1420
London, ON, Canada N6A 5B5
Ph: (519)434-9167   Fax: (519)434-6318
E-mail: info@londonexecutive.com
URL: http://www.londonexecutive.com
Executive search firm.

★5655★ Michigan Consulting Group
49945 Streamwood
Novi, MI 48374
Ph: (989)386-2219   Fax: (989)386-2219
E-mail: mcg@provide.net
Executive search firm.

★5656★ Miller Personnel Consultants Inc.
931 E 86th St., Ste. 103
Indianapolis, IN 46240
Ph: (317)251-5938   Fax: (317)251-3762
Fr: 800-851-5938
URL: http://www.millerpersonnel.com
Executive search firm.

★5657★ MRI of Dearborn
3 Parklane Blvd., Ste. 1210W
Dearborn, MI 48126
Ph: (313)336-6650   Fax: (313)336-7436
E-mail: visitus@mridearborn.com
URL: http://www.mridearborn.com
Executive search firm.

★5658★ 1 Exec Street
201 Post St., Ste. 401
San Francisco, CA 94108
Ph: (415)982-0555   Fax: (415)982-0550
Executive search firm.

★5659★ Recruiting Services Group Inc.
3107 E Corporate Edge Dr
Germantown, TN 38138
Ph: (901)367-0778   Fax: (901)367-0868
E-mail: resumes@rsghunt.com
URL: http://www.rsghunt.com
Executive search firm.

★5660★ RGT Associates Inc.
2 Greenleaf Woods Dr., Ste.101
PO Box 1032
Portsmouth, NH 03802
Ph: (603)431-9500   Fax: (603)431-6984
E-mail: recruitrgt@aol.com
Executive search firm.

★5661★ Riley Cole
PO Box 10635
Oakland, CA 94610
Ph: (510)336-2333   Fax: (510)336-2777
E-mail: riled@pacbell.net
Executive search firm.

★5662★ Ronald Dukes Associates LLC
20 N. Wacker Dr., Ste. 2010
Chicago, IL 60606
Ph: (312)357-2895   Fax: (312)357-2897
Executive search firm focus on the industrial and automotive industries.

★5663★ Russ Hadick & Associates Inc.
77 W Elmwood, Ste 100
Centerville, OH 45459
Ph: (937)439-7700   Fax: (937)439-7705
E-mail: rhadick@rharecruiters.com
URL: http://www.rharecruiters.com
Executive search firm.

★5664★ Sanford Rose Associates
211 Century Dr., Ste. 106D
Greenville, SC 29607
Ph: (864)233-6100   Fax: (305)946-2946
E-mail: greenvillesc@sanfordrose.com
URL: http://www.sanfordrose.com
Executive search firm.

★5665★ Southern Recruiters & Consultants Inc.
PO Box 2745
Aiken, SC 29802
Ph: (803)648-7834

E-mail: recruiters@southernrecruiters.com
URL: http://www.southernrecruiters.com
Executive search firm.

★5666★ Stiles Associates LLC
276 Newport Rd., Ste. 208
The Gallery
New London, NH 03257
Ph: (603)526-6566   Fax: (603)526-6185
Fr: 800-322-5185
E-mail: tberio@leanexecs.com
URL: http://www.leanexecs.com
Executive search firm.

★5667★ Summit Group Consultants Inc.
16 Voight Ln.
Lafayette, NJ 07848
Ph: (973)875-3300
E-mail: garyp@nac.net
Executive search firm.

★5668★ Teknon Employment Resources Inc.
17 S St. Clair St., Ste. 300
Dayton, OH 45402-2137
Ph: (937)222-5300   Fax: (937)222-6311
E-mail: teknon@teknongroup.cp
URL: http://www.teknongroup.com
Executive search firm.

★5669★ Thorsen Associates Inc.
2020 Grand Ave.
Baldwin, NY 11510
Ph: (516)868-6500   Fax: (516)868-7842
E-mail: info@thorsenassociates.com
URL: http://www.thorsenassociates.com
Executive search firm.

★5670★ William J. Christopher Associates Inc.
307 N. Walnut St.
West Chester, PA 19380
Ph: (610)696-4397
Executive search firm.

TRADESHOWS

★5671★ ITSC - International Thermal Spray Conference and Exposition
ASM International
9639 Kinsman Rd.
Materials Park, OH 44073-0002
Ph: (440)338-5151   Fax: (440)338-4634
Fr: 800-336-5152
E-mail: cast-sru@asminternational.org
URL: http://www.asminternational.org
Annual. **Primary Exhibits:** Thermal spray and welding equipment, supplies, and services.

OTHER SOURCES

★5672★ *Administration and Management Occupations*
Delphi Productions
3160 4th St.
Boulder, CO 80304
Fax: (303)443-4022   Fr: 888-443-2400
URL: http://www.delphivideo.com
$95.00. 50 minutes. Part of the Careers for the 21st Century Video Library.

★5673★ *Production Occupations*
Delphi Productions
3160 4th St.
Boulder, CO 80304
Fax: (303)443-4022   Fr: 888-443-2400
URL: http://www.delphivideo.com
$95.00. 49 minutes. Part of the Careers for the 21st Century Video Library.

Inspectors and Compliance Officers, Except Construction

SOURCES OF HELP-WANTED ADS

★5674★ American City and County

Primedia Business
6151 Powers Ferry Rd.
Atlanta, GA 30339
Ph: (770)955-2500   Fax: (770)618-0348

Monthly. $67.00/year for individuals. Municipal and county administration magazine.

★5675★ American Industrial Hygiene Association Journal

American Industrial Hygiene Association
2700 Prosperity Ave., Ste. 250
Fairfax, VA 22031-4319
Ph: (703)849-8888   Fax: (703)207-3561
E-mail: journal@aiha.org

Monthly. $130.00/year; $155.00/year, Canada and Mexico; $195.00/year for other countries. Journal providing a forum for peer-reviewed articles in the field of industrial hygiene.

★5676★ Applied Occupational & Environmental Hygiene

Applied Industrial Hygiene Inc.
1330 Kemper Meadow Dr., Ste. 600
Cincinnati, OH 45240
Ph: (513)742-2020   Fax: (513)742-3355
E-mail: comm@acgih.org

Monthly. $159.00/year for individuals; $269.00/year for institutions. Peer-reviewed journal presenting applied solutions for the prevention of occupational and environmental disease and injury.

★5677★ Cal-OSHA Reporter

Commanon Corp.
PO Box 1100
Grass Valley, CA 95945-1100
Ph: (530)470-7500   Fax: (530)470-7600

Description: Fifty issues/year. Reports on laws, regulations, court cases, and other issues of interest to occupational safety and health professionals. Recurring features include a calendar of events, reports of meetings, news of educational opportunities, job listings, and notices of publications available. Reviews all Cal-OSHA cases.

★5678★ Food Production Management

CTI Publications Inc.
2 Oakway Rd.
Timonium, MD 21093-4247
Ph: (410)308-2080   Fax: (410)308-2079
E-mail: fpmeditorial@ctipubs.com

Monthly. $40.00/year for individuals; $15.00 for single issue. Magazine on food processing and individual packing news for management, sales, and production personnel in the canning, glass packing, aseptic, and frozen food industries.

★5679★ Industrial Hygiene News

Rimbach Publishing Inc.
8650 Babcock Blvd.
Pittsburgh, PA 15237
Ph: (412)364-5366   Fax: (412)369-9720
Fr: 800-245-3182

Bimonthly. Free to qualified subscribers. Magazine covering industrial hygiene, occupational health, and safety.

★5680★ Journal of Occupational and Environmental Medicine

Lippincott Williams & Wilkins
530 Walnut St.
Philadelphia, PA 19106
Ph: (215)521-8300   Fax: (215)521-8902
Fr: 800-638-3030
URL: http://www.joem.org

Monthly. $250.00/year for individuals; $318.00/year for institutions; $32.00 for single issue; $319.00/year for other countries; $387.00/year for institutions, other countries; $32.00 for single issue, other countries. Occupational and environmental medicine journal.

★5681★ Occupational Health & Safety

Stevens Publishing Corp.
5151 Belt Line Rd., 10th Fl.
Dallas, TX 75254
Ph: (972)687-6700   Fax: (972)687-6799
E-mail: jlaws@stevenspublishing.com
URL: http://www/.ohsonline.com

Monthly. $99.00/year. Magazine covering federal and state regulation of occupational health and safety.

★5682★ Pharmaceutical Technology

Advanstar Communications Inc.
Raritan Plz. III
101 Fieldcrest Ave.
Edison, NJ 08837
Ph: (732)225-9500   Fax: (732)225-0211
E-mail: ptpress@advanstar.com

Monthly. Free to qualified subscribers; $54.00/year. Magazine on applied technology for pharmaceutical firms.

★5683★ SafetyHealth

National Safety Council
1121 Spring Lake Dr.
Itasca, IL 60143-3201
Ph: (630)285-1121   Fax: (630)285-1315
Fr: 800-621-7615

Monthly. $56.00/year; $5.00 for single issue. Publication focusing on workplace safety and health issues.

PLACEMENT AND JOB REFERRAL SERVICES

★5684★ American Public Health Association (APHA)

800 I St. NW
Washington, DC 20001-3710
Ph: (202)777-2742   Fax: (202)777-2534
E-mail: comments@apha.org
URL: http://www.apha.org

Members: Professional organization of physicians, nurses, educators, academicians, environmentalists, epidemiologists, new professionals, social workers, health administrators, optometrists, podiatrists, pharmacists, dentists, nutritionists, health planners, other community and mental health specialists, and interested consumers. **Purpose:** Seeks to protect and promote personal, mental, and environmental health. **Activities:** Services include promulgation of standards; establishment of uniform practices and procedures; development of the etiology of communicable diseases; research in public health; exploration of medical care programs and their relationships to public health. Sponsors job placement service.

★5685★ American Society of Safety Engineers (ASSE)
1800 E. Oakton St.
Des Plaines, IL 60018
Ph: (847)699-2929   Fax: (847)768-3434
E-mail: customerservice@asse.org
URL: http://www.asse.org

Description: Professional society of safety engineers, safety directors, and others concerned with accident prevention, environmental protection and safety and health programs. Sponsors National Safety Month conducts research and educational programs. Develops/publishes ANSI safety-related standatds & other technical literature. Compiles statistics; maintains job placement service.

EMPLOYER DIRECTORIES AND NETWORKING LISTS

★5686★ American Industrial Hygiene Association-Directory
American Industrial Hygiene Association
2700 Prosperity, Ste. 250
Fairfax, VA 22031
Ph: (703)849-8888   Fax: (703)207-3561

Annual, September. Covers approximately 12,000 members concerned with the study and control of environmental factors affecting people at work. Entries include: Name, address, phone, affiliation. Arrangement: Alphabetical. Indexes: Employer, geographical.

★5687★ Carroll's State Directory
Carroll Publishing
145 Taylor St., NE
Washington, DC 20017
Ph: (202)281-2410   Fax: (202)281-2408
Fr: 800-336-4240
URL: http://www.carrollpub.com

Three times per year. $350.00. Covers about 43,000 state government officials in all branches of government; officers, committees and members of state legislatures; managers of boards and authorities. Entries include: Name, address, phone, fax,title. Arrangement: Geographical; separate sections for state offices and legislatures. In-

dexes: Personal name (with phone and e-mail address), organizational, keyword.

★5688★ Federal Career Opportunities
Federal Research Service Inc.
7360 McWhorter Pl., Ste. 201
PO Box 1708
Annandale, VA 22003
Ph: (703)281-0200   Fax: (703)281-7639
Fr: 800-822-5627
URL: http://www.fedjobs.com/index.html

Biweekly. $7.95 per copy. Covers more than 3,000 current federal job vacancies in the United States and overseas; includes permanent, part-time, and temporary positions. Entries include: Position title, location, series and grade, job requirements, special forms, announcement number, closing date, application address. Arrangement: Classified by occupation.

★5689★ Federal Jobs Digest
Federal Jobs Digest
325 Pennsylvania Ave. SE
Washington, DC 20003
Ph: (914)366-0333   Fax: (914)366-0059
Fr: 800-824-5000
URL: http://www.jobsfed.com

Biweekly. $5.50 per issue; $34.00 for three months; $125.00 for year. Covers over 10,000 specific job openings in the federal government in each issue. Vacancies from over 300 Federal Agencies are covered. Entries include: Position name, title, General Schedule (GS) grade, and Wage Grade (WG), closing date for applications, announcement number, application address, phone, and name of contact. Arrangement: By federal department or agency, then geographical.

★5690★ Federal Staff Directory
CQ Press
1255 22nd St. NW, Ste. 400
Washington, DC 20037
Ph: (202)729-1800   Fax: 800-380-3810
Fr: (866)427-7737
URL: http://www.cqdirectories.com

3x/year. $379.00. Covers approximately 45,000 persons in federal government offices and independent agencies, with biographies of 2,600 key executives; includes officials at policy level in agencies of the Office of the President, Cabinet-level departments, independent and regulatory agencies, military commands, federal information centers, and libraries, and United States attorneys, marshals, and ambassadors. Entries include: Name, title, location (indicating building, address, and/or room), phone, fax, e-mail address, website, symbols indicating whether position is a presidential appointment and whether senate approval is required. Arrangement: Classified by department/agency. Indexes: Personal name, subject.

HANDBOOKS AND MANUALS

★5691★ Opportunities in State and Local Government Careers
Vgm Career Horizons
1221 Avenue of the Americas
New York, NY 10020
Ph: (212)904-2000   Fr: 800-323-4900
E-mail: ntcpub@tribune.com

Neale J. Baxter. 1994. $14.95; $10.95 (paper). 160 pages. Points out the incentives and drawbacks of a government career. Describes hiring procedures and provides tips on filling out applications, taking physical and aptitude tests, handling interviews, and finding jobs. Describes the jobs in which 75% of all state and local government workers are employed. For each occupation, covers the nature of the work and the training required.

★5692★ Start Your Own Home Inspection Service
McGraw-Hill Companies
860 Taylor Station Rd.
Blacklick, OH 43004-0545
Fax: (614)755-5645   Fr: 800-722-4726

December 2003. $12.95. Illustrated. 128 pages. Entrepreneur Magazine's Start Up Series.

EMPLOYMENT AGENCIES AND SEARCH FIRMS

★5693★ Summit Executive Search Consultants, Inc.
Ingraham Bldg.
25 SE 2nd Ave., Ste 338
Miami, FL 33131
Ph: (305)379-5008   Fax: (305)379-5150
E-mail: summitsearch@compuserve.com

Executive search firm serving a variety of industries.

TRADESHOWS

★5694★ National Safety Council Congress and Expo
National Safety Council
1121 Spring Lake Dr.
Itasca, IL 60143
Ph: (630)285-1121   Fax: (630)285-0798
Fr: 800-621-7619
URL: http://www.congress.nsc.org

Annual. **Primary Exhibits:** Safety- and health-related products and services, including protective clothing, footwear, consulting services, breathing apparatuses, educational materials, films and related equipment, supplies, and services. **Dates and Locations:**

2004 Sep 10-17; New Orleans, LA; Morial Convention Center • 2005 Sep 18-25; Orlando, FL; Orange City Convention Center.

OTHER SOURCES

★5695★ *Inspectors and Compliance Officers, Except Construction*

Evon Publishing
832 N 7th Ave.
Iron River, MI 49935
Ph: (906)265-3190

Audiocassette. 1996. $16.95. 32 minutes. Part of the Careers and Vocational Guidance Series. Provides information about the nature of the work, educational requirements, employment outlook, earnings, and work conditions as well as additional related information.

★5696★ **National Environmental Health Association (NEHA)**

720 S Colorado Blvd., Ste. 970, S Tower
Denver, CO 80246-1925
Ph: (303)756-9090   Fax: (303)691-9490
E-mail: staff@neha.org
URL: http://www.neha.org

Description: Represents all professionals in environmental health and protection, including Registered Sanitarians, Registered Environmental Health Specialists, Registered Environmental Technicians, Certified Environmental Health Technicians, Registered Hazardous Substances Professionals and Registered Hazardous Substances Specialists. NEHA's mission is to advance the environmental health and protection profession for the purpose of providing a healthful environment for all. Educational materials, publications, credentials and meetings are available to NEHA members and non-member professionals who strive to improve the environment.

★5697★ *Production Occupations*

Delphi Productions
3160 4th St.
Boulder, CO 80304
Fax: (303)443-4022   Fr: 888-443-2400
URL: http://www.delphivideo.com

$95.00. 49 minutes. Part of the Careers for the 21st Century Video Library.

Insurance Sales Agents

SOURCES OF HELP-WANTED ADS

★5698★ ASCnet Quarterly
Applied Systems Client Network
801 Douglas Ave., Ste. 205
Altamonte Springs, FL 32714
Ph: (407)869-0404   Fax: (407)869-0418
Quarterly. Subscription included in membership. Professional magazine covering technical information, association news, and industry information for insurance professionals.

★5699★ Best's Review
A.M. Best Co.
Ambest Rd.
Oldwick, NJ 08858
Fax: (908)439-2200
E-mail: best'sreview@ambest.com
URL: http://www.bestreview.com
Monthly. $21.00/year for individuals; $7.50 for single issue. Magazine covering issues and trends for the management personnel of life/health insurers, the agents, and brokers who market their products.

★5700★ Business Insurance
Crain Communications Inc.
711 Third Ave.
New York, NY 10017-4036
Ph: (212)210-0100   Fax: (212)210-0244
Fr: 800-446-1420
URL: http://www.businessinsurance.com
Weekly. $97.00/year for individuals. International newsweekly reporting on corporate risk and employee benefit management news.

★5701★ CLAIMS
Claims
15112 64th Ave. W
Edmonds, WA 98026
Ph: (425)745-6394
E-mail: editor@claimsmag.com
URL: http://www.claimsmag.com
Monthly. $42.00/year for individuals; $8.00 for single issue. Magazine for the property-casualty insurance claims industry.

★5702★ National Underwriter Property and Casualty/Risk and Benefits Management
National Underwriter Co.
5081 Olympic Blvd.
Erlanger, KY 41018
Ph: (859)692-2100   Fax: 800-874-1916
Fr: 800-543-0874
E-mail: nup&c@nuco.com
Weekly. $89.00/year. Newsweekly for agents, brokers, executives, and managers in risk and benefit insurance.

★5703★ The Standard
Standard Publishing Corp.
155 Federal St., 13th Fl.
Boston, MA 02110
Ph: (617)457-0600   Fax: (617)482-7820
Fr: 800-682-5759
E-mail: stnd@earthlink.net
Weekly. $55.00/year for individuals. Trade newspaper covering insurance events, legislation, regulatory hearings, and court sessions for independent insurance agents in New England.

★5704★ Today's Insurance Woman
National Association of Insurance Women
  (International)
1847 E 15th St.
Tulsa, OK 74104-4610
Ph: (918)744-5195   Fax: (918)743-1968
Fr: 800-766-NAIW
URL: http://www.naiw.org
Bimonthly. $15.00/year. Magazine on insurance and professional development topics for men and women in the risk and insurance field.

PLACEMENT AND JOB REFERRAL SERVICES

★5705★ American Agents Association (AAA)
PO Box 7079
Hilton Head Island, SC 29938
Fax: (803)785-9068   Fr: 800-248-9288
E-mail: american@hargray.com
Members: Licensed insurance agents. **Purpose:** Works to provide programs to enhance the security of insurance agents and their families and to take advantage of programs designed for insurance agents. **Activities:** Offers placement services; compiles statistics. Plans to establish a scholarship program for members' children. Conducts seminars and classes on markets and marketing. Maintains hall of fame.

★5706★ American Association of Insurance Management Consultants (AAIMCO)
3925 Fern Rd.
Medina, OH 44256
Ph: (330)725-8946   Fax: (330)723-6270
E-mail: lavelle@zoominternet.com
URL: http://www.aaimco.com
Description: Insurance companies, agents, and brokers; professors of insurance; accountants and attorneys; personnel management specialists; and those with advanced degrees in management. Advises and assists the insurance industry and seeks to achieve professional recognition for insurance management consultants. Mediates the exchange of ideas; sets standards of service and performance; maintains a code of ethics; offers a referral service and a series of educational conferences and seminars. Operates speakers' bureau; offers placement services; compiles statistics.

EMPLOYER DIRECTORIES AND NETWORKING LISTS

★5707★ Best's Insurance Reports

A.M. Best Co.
Ambest Rd.
Oldwick, NJ 08858
Ph: (908)439-2200   Fax: (908)439-2688
URL: http://www.ambest.com

Annual, summer. $1,495.00 for CD-ROM; $830.00 for print. Published in three editions: Life-health insurance, covering about 1,750 companies, property-casualty insurance, covering over 3,200 companies; and international, covering more than 1,200 insurers. Each edition lists state insurance commissioners and related companies and agencies (mutual funds, worker compensation funds, underwriting agencies, etc.). Entries include: For each company-Company name, address, phone; history; states in which licensed; names of officers and directors; financial data; financial analysis and Best's rating. Arrangement: Alphabetical.

★5708★ Business Insurance-Agent/ Broker Profiles Issue

Business Insurance
360 N Michigan Ave.
Chicago, IL 60601-3806
Ph: (312)649-5319   Fax: (312)280-3174
Fr: 800-678-2724
URL: http://www.businessinsurance.com/cgi-bin/page.pl?pageId=121

Annual, July. $15.00. Publication includes: List of approximately 200 insurance agents and brokers specializing in commercial insurance. Entries include: Firm name, address, phone, fax, branch office locations, year established, names of subsidiaries, gross revenues, premium volume, number of employees, principal officers, percent of revenue generated by commercial retail brokerage, acquisitions. Arrangement: Alphabetical, by company. Indexes: Geographical.

★5709★ Insurance Almanac

Underwriter Printing and Publishing Co.
50 E Palisade Ave.
Englewood, NJ 07631
Ph: (201)569-8808   Fax: (201)569-8817
Fr: 800-526-4700

Annual, July. $175.00. Covers over 3,000 insurance companies that write fire, casualty, accident and health, life, and Lloyd's policies; also lists mutual and reciprocal companies. Includes national, state, and local insurance associations; state insurance officials; and about 800 agents, brokers, actuaries, and adjusters. Entries include: For companies-Company name, address, phone, names of officers and directors, lines written, territory covered; for larger firms, some history and financial data. For associations-Name, address, names of staff and officers, place and date of meetings. For agents, brokers, etc.-Name, address. Arrangement: Classified by insurance lines,

type of activity, etc. Indexes: Company name.

★5710★ Insurance Consultants & Advisors Directory

infoUSA Inc.
5711 S 86th Cir.
Omaha, NE 68127-0347
Ph: (402)930-3500   Fax: (402)331-0176
Fr: 800-555-6124
URL: http://www.abii.com

Annual. Number of listings: 11,032. Entries include: Name, address, phone (including area code), size of advertisement, year first in "Yellow Pages," name of owner or manager, number of employees. Compiled from telephone company "Yellow Pages," nationwide. Arrangement: Geographical.

★5711★ Insurance Directory

infoUSA Inc.
5711 S 86th Cir.
Omaha, NE 68127-0347
Ph: (402)930-3500   Fax: (402)331-0176
Fr: 800-555-6124
URL: http://www.abii.com

Annual. Number of listings: 236,715. Entries include: Name, address, phone, size of advertisement, name of owner or manager, number of employees, year first in "Yellow Pages.". Compiled from telephone company "Yellow Pages," nationwide. Arrangement: Geographical.

★5712★ Insurance Phone Book and Directory

Douglas Publications Inc.
2807 N Parham Rd.,64 Bldg., Ste. 200
Richmond, VA 23294
Ph: (804)762-9600   Fax: (804)217-8999
Fr: 800-794-6086
URL: http://www.douglaspublications.com

Annual. $99.50. Covers about 4,000 life, accident and health, worker's compensation, auto, fire and casualty, marine, surety, and other insurance companies. Entries include: Company name, address, phone, fax, toll-free number, type of insurance provided. Arrangement: Alphabetical.

★5713★ Kirshner's Insurance Directories

National Underwriter Co.
5081 Olympic Blvd.
Erlanger, KY 41018
Ph: (859)692-2100   Fax: 800-874-1916
Fr: 800-543-0874
URL: http://www.nationalunderwriter.com/kirschners/

Annual, all editions except California and Pacific Northwest (semiannual). $19.95. Covers Insurance agents and agencies in all 50 states and the District of Columbia. Published in 24 separate editions for Southern California, Northern California, Pacific Northwest (AK, ID, HI, OR, WA, MT), Michigan, Illinois, New England states (CT, ME, MA, NH, RI, VT), Ohio, Rocky Mountain states (AZ, CO, NV, NM, UT, WY), South

Central states (GA, AL, MS), Indiana, Texas, Kentucky/Tennessee, East Central states (VA, WV, NC, SC), South Central West states (AR, OK, LA), Wisconsin, Central states (KS, MO, NE), North Central states (IA, MN, ND, SD), Mid-Atlantic states (DE, MD, NJ, DC), Pennsylvania, Florida. Entries include: For companies-Name, address, key personnel (with addresses abd phone numbers). Arrangement: Separate alphabetical sections for insurance companies, wholesalers, field agents, and agencies. Indexes: Type of insurance.

★5714★ Mergent Bank and Finance Manual

Mergent Inc.
5250 77 Center Dr., Ste. 150
Charlotte, NC 28217
Ph: (704)559-7601   Fax: (704)559-6945
Fr: 800-342-5647
URL: http://www.mergent.com

Annual, July; supplements in 'Mergent Bank & Finance News Reports'. $2,095.00. Covers in four volumes, over 12,000 national, state, and private banks, savings and loans, mutual funds, unit investment trusts, and insurance and real estate companies in the United States. Entries include: Company name, headquarters and branch offices, phones, names and titles of principal executives, directors, history, Moody's rating, and extensive financial and statistical data. Arrangement: Classified by type of business. Indexes: Company name.

★5715★ National Insurance Association-Member Roster

National Insurance Association
411 Chapel Hill St.
Durham, NC 27701

Annual, June. Covers about 13 insurance companies owned or controlled by African-Americans. Entries include: Company name, address, phone, date founded, states in which licensed, officers. Arrangement: Alphabetical.

★5716★ New Jersey Telephone Tickler

Underwriter Printing and Publishing Co.
50 E Palisade Ave.
Englewood, NJ 07631
Ph: (201)569-8808   Fax: (201)569-8817
Fr: 800-526-4700

Annual, June. $12.50. Covers insurance companies, brokers, agents, and related suppliers in New Jersey. Entries include: Company name, address, phone. Arrangement: Alphabetical. Indexes: Product/service.

★5717★ New York Telephone Tickler

Underwriter Printing and Publishing Co.
50 E Palisade Ave.
Englewood, NJ 07631
Ph: (201)569-8808   Fax: (201)569-8817
Fr: 800-526-4700

Annual, November. $25.00. Covers insurance companies, brokers, agents, and related suppliers in the New York city area. Entries include: Company name, address, phone. Arrangement: Alphabetical. Indexes: Product/service.

★5718★ *Who's Who in Insurance*

Underwriter Printing and Publishing Co.
50 E Palisade Ave.
Englewood, NJ 07631
Ph: (201)569-8808   Fax: (201)569-8817
Fr: 800-526-4700

Annual, February. $150.00. Covers over 5,000 insurance officials, brokers, agents, and buyers. Entries include: Name, title, company name, address, home address, educational background, professional club and association memberships, personal and career data. Arrangement: Alphabetical.

★5719★ *Yearbook*

American Association of Managing
  General Agents
PO Box 26547
Overland Park, KS 66225-6547
URL: http://www.iix.com/aamga

Annual, spring. Covers 250 managing general agents of insurance companies and their more than 500 branch offices; coverage includes Canada. Entries include: Name, address, names and titles of principal and contact, insurance companies represented. Arrangement: Geographical.

HANDBOOKS AND MANUALS

★5720★ *The Adjuster: Making Insurance Claims Pay*

Cargo Publishing Co.
PO Box 75146
Houston, TX 77234
Ph: (713)484-1880   Fax: (713)484-8887
Fr: 800-725-2468

Gordon G. Smith. 1998. $39.95 (paper). 350 pages.

★5721★ *Opportunities in Insurance Careers*

McGraw-Hill/Contemporary Books
1221 Avenue of the Americas
New York, NY 10020
Ph: (212)904-2000   Fr: 800-323-4900
E-mail: ntcpub@tribune.com

Robert Schrayer. Revised, 1999. $14.95; $11.95 (paper). 148 pages. A guide to planning for and seeking opportunities in the field. Contains bibliography and illustrations.

EMPLOYMENT AGENCIES AND SEARCH FIRMS

★5722★ **Barger & Sargeant Inc.**

131 Windermere Rd., Ste. 600
PO Box 1420
Center Harbor, NH 03226-1420
Ph: (603)253-4700

Executive search firm.

★5723★ **Burkholder Group Inc.**

101 N. Cascade Ave., Ste. 410
Colorado Springs, CO 80903
Ph: (719)867-1222   Fax: (719)632-6060

Executive search firm focused on the insurance industry.

★5724★ **De Funiak & Edwards**

1602 Hidden Hills Trail
Long Beach, IN 46360
Fax: (219)874-5347

Executive search firm.

★5725★ **Eggers Consulting Company Inc.**

Eggers Plz., 11272 Elm St.
Omaha, NE 68144
Ph: (402)333-3480   Fax: (402)333-9759

Executive search consulting firm. Industries served: insurance, data processing, retail and banking.

★5726★ **Employment Advisors**

815 Nicollet Mall Ste 200
Minneapolis, MN 55402
Ph: (612)339-3944
E-mail: info@collegegraduateregistry.com
URL: http://www.collegegraduateregistry.com

Employment agency. Places candidates in variety of fields.

★5727★ **Godfrey Personnel Inc.**

300 W. Adams, Ste. 612
Chicago, IL 60606-5194
Ph: (312)236-4455   Fax: (312)580-6292
E-mail: jim@godfreypersonnel.com
URL: http://ww.godfreypersonnel.com

Search firm specializing in insurance industry.

★5728★ **International Insurance Consultants Inc.**

1191 E Newport Ctr. Dr., Ste. 206
Deerfield Beach, FL 33442
Ph: (954)421-0122   Fax: (954)421-3332

Offers executive search to the insurance industry. Clients include insurance companies, brokers, consultants and investment banks. Industries served: insurance and financial services industries.

★5729★ **International Insurance Personnel, Inc.**

300 W. Wieuca Rd., Bldg. 2, Ste. 101
Atlanta, GA 30342
Ph: (404)255-9710
E-mail: info@intlinspersonnel.com
URL: http://www.intlinspersonnel.com/inter-imstafing.htm

Employment agency specializing in the area of insurance.

★5730★ **Questor Consultants, Inc.**

2515 N. Broad St.
Colmar, PA 18915
Ph: (215)997-9262   Fax: (215)997-9226
E-mail: jobs@questorconsultants.com
URL: http://www.questorconsultants.com

Executive search firm specializing in the insurance and legal fields.

★5731★ **Quirk-Corporon and Associates Inc.**

1229 N Jackson, Ste. 205
Milwaukee, WI 53202
Ph: (414)224-9399   Fax: (414)224-9472

Employment agency specializing in all disciplines of the insurance and financial industries.

★5732★ **SHS of Cherry Hill**

929 N Kings Hwy.
Cherry Hill, NJ 08034
Ph: (856)779-9030   Fax: (856)779-0898

Personnel recruiters operating in the disciplines of accounting, sales, insurance, engineering, and administration. Industries served: insurance, distribution, manufacturing, and service.

★5733★ **Tyler & Co.**

375 Northridge Rd., Ste. 400
Atlanta, GA 30350-3299
Ph: (770)396-3939   Fax: (770)396-6693
Fr: 800-989-6789

Retained executive search for the healthcare, food, market research, manufacturing and insurance industries.

ONLINE JOB SOURCES AND SERVICES

★5734★ **Great Insurance Jobs**
URL: http://www.greatinsurancejobs.com
Description: Contains varied insurance positions. Job seekers may browse employee profiles, post resumes, and read descriptions of hundreds of recently-posted insurance jobs.

★5735★ Insurance National Search, Inc.

E-mail: stacy@atsinsurancerecruiters.com
URL: http://www.insurancerecruiters.com

Description: Contains lists of recruiters (listed by department and line of business) and available insurance positions. **Main files include:** Recruiter Resources, Recruiters Roundtable Discussion Forum, Job Listing Submission Form, Candidate Listing Submission Form. Visitors can also search by job position.

★5736★ Premier Careers, Inc.

1345 S. Missouri Ave., Ste. 120
Clearwater, FL 33756
Ph: (727)467-0220   Fax: (727)467-0222
E-mail: info@atspremiercareers.com
URL: http://www.premiercareers.com

Description: Contains a database with information on candidates searching for jobs in the property and casualty insurance industry and with national sales organizations. Houses resumes and letters of reference. Candidate searches may be run by industry, geography, job title, years of experience, compensation, education, and/or accreditation. Also offers resume writing and interviewing tips to job hunters.

TRADESHOWS

★5737★ Independent Insurance Agents of Indiana Annual Convention

Independent Insurance Agents of Indiana
3435 W. 96th St.
Indianapolis, IN 46268
Ph: (317)824-3780   Fax: (317)824-3786
Fr: 800-438-4424
E-mail: mason@bigi.org
URL: http://www.iiaa.org

Annual. **Primary Exhibits:** Small business supplies, automation equipment, solutions, insurance service, coverage providers and carriers.

★5738★ Missouri Association of Insurance Agents Exhibition

Missouri Association of Insurance Agents
2701 Industrial Dr.
PO Box 1785
Jefferson City, MO 65102
Ph: (573)893-4301   Fax: (573)893-3708

Annual. **Primary Exhibits:** Insurance related equipment, supplies, and services.

★5739★ National Association of Independent Life Brokerage Agencies Conference

National Association of Independent Life Brokerage Agencies
8201 Greensboro Dr., Ste. 300
McLean, VA 22102-3810
Ph: (703)610-9020   Fax: (703)610-9005
E-mail: jmn@nailba.com

Annual. **Primary Exhibits:** Equipment, supplies, and services for licensed independent life brokerage agencies that represent at least three insurance companies, but are not controlled or owned by an underwriting company.

★5740★ National Association of Mutual Insurance Companies Annual Convention and Exposition

National Association of Mutual Insurance Companies
3601 Vincennes Rd.
PO Box 68700
Indianapolis, IN 46268-0700
Ph: (317)875-5250   Fax: (317)879-8408
Fr: 800-33-NAMIC
E-mail: exhibitshow@namic.org
URL: http://www.namic.org

Annual. **Primary Exhibits:** Mutual property and casualty insurance equipment, supplies, and services.

★5741★ Professional Independent Insurance Agents of Illinois Annual Convention

Professional Independent Insurance Agents of Illinois
4360 Wabash Ave.
Springfield, IL 62707-7009
Ph: (217)793-6660   Fax: (217)793-6744
Fr: 800-628-6436

Annual. **Primary Exhibits:** Insurance-related products, including computers and office supplies, restoration sevices and cell phones.

★5742★ Professional Insurance Agents of Wisconsin Convention

Professional Insurance Agents of Wisconsin
6401 Odana Rd.
Madison, WI 53719
Ph: (608)274-8188   Fax: (608)274-8195

Annual. **Primary Exhibits:** Insurance equipment, supplies, and services.

★5743★ Public Agency Risk Managers Association Convention

Public Agency Risk Managers Association
PO Box 6810
San Jose, CA 95150
Ph: (408)865-6930   Fax: 888-412-5913
Fr: 888-907-2762
E-mail: BFrancis@PARMA.com

Annual. **Primary Exhibits:** Risk management equipment, supplies, and services.

★5744★ Risk and Insurance Management Society Annual Conference

Risk and Insurance Management Society
655 3rd Ave., 2nd Fl.
New York, NY 10017-5617
Ph: (212)286-9292   Fax: (212)986-9716
URL: http://www.rims.org

Annual. **Primary Exhibits:** Insurance industry related equipment, supplies, and services.

★5745★ Sales Congress of National Association of Insurance and Financial Adviors - New Hampshire

National Association of Insurance and Financial Advisors - New Hampshire
76 S. State St.
Concord, NH 03301-3520
Ph: (603)223-9973   Fax: (603)228-2118
Fr: 800-480-8719
E-mail: assnrhg@aol.com

Annual. **Primary Exhibits:** Equipment, supplies, and services for life and health insurance agents, brokers, and managers.

★5746★ Society of Insurance Trainers and Educators Conference

Society of Insurance Trainers and Educators
c/o Lois A Markovich, CPCU, AIM
2120 Market St., Ste. 108
San Francisco, CA 94114-1395
Ph: (415)621-2830   Fax: (415)621-0889
E-mail: socinstred@aol.com
URL: http://www.insurancetrainers.org

Annual. **Primary Exhibits:** Insurance education equipment, supplies, and services. **Dates and Locations:** 2005 Jun 25-29; Seattle, WA.

OTHER SOURCES

★5747★ American Council of Life Insurers (ACLI)

101 Constitution Ave., NW, Ste. 700
Washington, DC 20001-2133
Ph: (202)624-2000   Fax: (202)624-2319
E-mail: acli@acli.com
URL: http://www.acli.com

Description: National trade association that represents the interests of legal reserve life insurance companies in legislative, regulatory and judicial matters at the federal, state and municipal levels of government and at the NAIC. Its member companies hold the overwhelming majority of the life insurance in force in the United States.

★5748★ American Institute for CPCU (CPCU)

720 Providence Rd.
PO Box 3016
Malvern, PA 19355-0716
Ph: (610)644-2100   Fax: (610)640-9576
Fr: 800-644-2101
E-mail: cserv@cpcuiia.org
URL: http://www.aicpcu.org

Purpose: Determines qualifications for professional certification of insurance personnel; conducts examinations and awards designation of Chartered Property Casualty Underwriter (CPCU).

★5749★ **APIW**
551 5th Ave., Ste. 1625
New York, NY 10176
Ph: (212)867-0228   Fax: (212)867-2544
E-mail: info@apiw.org
URL: http://www.apiw.org

Members: Professional women from the insurance/reinsurance industry. **Purpose:** Promotes cooperation and understanding among members; maintains high professional standards in the insurance industry; provides a strong network of professional contacts and educational aid; recognizes the contributions of women to insurance; encourages women to seek employment in the insurance community.

★5750★ *Business and Administration Support Occupations*
Delphi Productions
3160 4th St.
Boulder, CO 80304
Fax: (303)443-4022   Fr: 888-443-2400
URL: http://www.delphivideo.com

$95.00. 42 minutes. Part of the Careers for the 21st Century Video Library.

★5751★ **GAMA International**
2901 Telestar Ct., Ste. 140
Falls Church, VA 22042-1205
Ph: (703)770-8184   Fax: (703)770-8182
Fr: 800-345-2687
E-mail: mmyers@gama.naifa.org
URL: http://www.gamaweb.com

Description: Provides world-class education and training resources for individuals, companies and organizations involved with the recruitment and development of field managers, representatives and staff in the life insurance and financial services industry; advocates of the value-added role of field management and representatives in the ethical distribution of life insurance and financial products and services industry.

★5752★ **Independent Insurance Agents and Brokers of America (IIABA)**
127 S. Peyton
Alexandria, VA 22314
Ph: (703)683-4422   Fax: (703)683-7556
Fr: 800-221-7917
E-mail: info@iiaba.org
URL: http://www.independentagent.com

Description: Sales agencies handling property, fire, casualty, and surety insurance. Organizes technical and sales courses for new and established agents. Sponsors Independent Insurance Agent Junior Classic Golf Tournament.

★5753★ *Insurance Agent*
Cambridge Educational
2572 Brunswick Ave.
Lawrenceville, NJ 08648-4128
Fax: 800-FAX-ON-US   Fr: 800-468-4227
URL: http://www.cambridgeeducational.com

$39.95. 15 minutes. Part of the Vocational Visions Career Series.

★5754★ **Insurance Information Institute (III)**
110 William St.
New York, NY 10038
Ph: (212)346-5500   Fax: (212)791-1807
Fr: 800-331-9146
E-mail: info@iii.org
URL: http://www.iii.org

Description: Property and casualty insurance companies. Provides information and educational services to mass media, educational institutions, trade associations, businesses, government agencies, and the public.

★5755★ *Insurance Sales Workers*
Evon Publishing
832 N 7th Ave.
Iron River, MI 49935
Ph: (906)265-3190

Audiocassette. 1996. $16.95. 32 minutes. Part of the Careers and Vocational Guidance Series. Provides information about the nature of the work, educational requirements, employment outlook, earnings, and work conditions as well as additional related information.

★5756★ **LOMA**
2300 Windy Ridge Pkwy., Ste. 600
Atlanta, GA 30339-8443
Ph: (770)951-1770   Fax: (770)984-0441
E-mail: marketing@loma.org
URL: http://www.loma.org/

Description: Life and health insurance companies and financial services in the U.S. and Canada; and overseas in 45 countries; affiliate members are firms that provide professional support to member companies. Provides research, information, training, and educational activities in areas of operations and systems, human resources, financial planning and employee development. Administers FLMI Insurance Education Program, which awards FLMI (Fellow, Life Management Institute) designation to those who complete the ten-examination program.

★5757★ *Marketing & Sales Occupations*
Delphi Productions
3160 4th St.
Boulder, CO 80304
Fax: (303)443-4022   Fr: 888-443-2400
URL: http://www.delphivideo.com

$95.00. 50 minutes. Part of the Careers for the 21st Century Video Library.

★5758★ **National Association of Health Underwriters (NAHU)**
200 N 14th St., Ste. 450
Arlington, VA 22201
Ph: (703)276-0220   Fax: (703)841-7797
E-mail: nahu@atsnahu.org
URL: http://www.nahu.org

Description: Insurance agents and brokers engaged in the promotion, sale, and administration of disability income and health insurance. Sponsors advanced health insurance underwriting and research seminars. Testifies before federal and state committees on pending health insurance legislation. Sponsors Leading Producers Roundtable Awards for leading salesmen. Maintains a speakers' bureau and a political action committee.

★5759★ **National Association of Insurance Women International (NAIW)**
1847 E 15th St.
PO Box 4410
Tulsa, OK 74104
Fax: (918)743-1968   Fr: 800-766-6249
E-mail: joinnaiw@naiw.org
URL: http://www.naiw.org

Members: Insurance industry professionals. **Purpose:** Promotes continuing education and networking for the professional advancement of its members. **Activities:** Offers education programs, meetings, services, and leadership opportunities. Provides a forum to learn about other disciplines in the insurance industry.

★5760★ **National Association of Professional Insurance Agents (PIA)**
400 N Washington St.
Alexandria, VA 22314
Ph: (703)836-9340   Fax: (703)836-1279
E-mail: piaweb@pianet.org
URL: http://www.pianet.com

Description: Represents independent agents in all 50 states, Puerto Rico and the District of Columbia. Represents members' interests in government and industry; provides educational programs; compiles statistics; conducts research programs; develops products/services unique to independent agencies; provides information and networking opportunities.

★5761★ **Society of Financial Service Professionals (SFSP)**
270 S Bryn Mawr Ave.
Bryn Mawr, PA 19010-2195
Ph: (610)526-2500   Fax: (610)527-1499
Fr: 800-927-2427
E-mail: custserv@financialpro.org
URL: http://www.financialpro.org

Description: Professional society of insurance and financial advisers. Foster dedication to continuing professional development and adherence to a strict code of ethical business practices.

Interior Designers

SOURCES OF HELP-WANTED ADS

★5762★ Custom Home
Hanley-Wood L.L.C.
1 Thomas Cir., Ste. 600
Washington, DC 20005
Ph: (202)452-0800   Fax: (202)785-1974

Bimonthly. $24.00/year for individuals; $10.00 for single issue; $36.00/year for other countries. Trade publication.

★5763★ Design Cost Data
DC & D Technologies Inc.
8602 N 40th St.
Tampa, FL 33604
Ph: (813)989-9300   Fax: (813)980-3982
Fr: 800-533-5680
E-mail: webmaster@dcd.com
URL: http://www.dcd.com

Bimonthly. $84.40/year for individuals. Publication providing real cost data case studies of various types completed around the country for design and building professionals.

★5764★ Interior Design
Reed Business Information
275 Washington St.
Newton, MA 02458
Ph: (617)558-4900   Fax: (617)630-3830
Fr: 800-357-4745

Monthly. $47.95/year. Interior designing and furnishings magazine.

★5765★ INTERIORS
VNU Business Media USA
770 Broadway
New York, NY 10003
Ph: (646)654-5000

Monthly. $40.00/year for individuals. Magazine for interior designers and architects.

★5766★ Kitchen and Bath Business
VNU Business Media
770 Broadway
New York, NY 10003-9595
Ph: (646)654-5000
URL: http://www.kitchen-bath.com

Monthly. $35.00/year for qualified subscribers; $65.00/year for others. Trade magazine on kitchen and bath remodeling and construction.

★5767★ Kitchen and Bath Design News
Cygnus Business Media Inc.
445 Broad Hollow Rd.
Melville, NY 11747
Ph: (631)845-2700   Fax: (631)845-2798
Fr: 800-308-6397
E-mail: kbdneditor@aol.com
URL: http://www.kitchen-bath-design.com/

Monthly. Trade journal.

★5768★ LDB Interior Textiles
E.W. Williams Publications
2125 Center Ave., Ste. 305
Fort Lee, NJ 07024
Ph: (201)592-7007   Fax: (201)592-7171

Monthly. $72.00/year for individuals; $115.00/year for other countries; $7.00 for single issue; $125.00/year for Canada; $150.00/year for elsewhere. Magazine for buyers of home fashions, including bed, bath and table linens, hard and soft window treatments, home fragrances, decorative pillows and home accessories, accent rugs, and decorative fabrics.

★5769★ Qualified Remodeler Magazine
Cygnus Business Media
1233 Janesville Ave.
Fort Atkinson, WI 53538
Fr: 800-547-7377
URL: http://www.qualifiedremodeler.com

Monthly. Free to qualified subscribers; $66.00/year for individuals. Magazine for remodeling contractor/distributors.

★5770★ Remodeling
Hanley-Wood L.L.C.
1 Thomas Cir., Ste. 600
Washington, DC 20005
Ph: (202)452-0800   Fax: (202)785-1974
URL: http://www.remodeling.hw.net

Monthly. $24.95/year for individuals; $8.00 for single issue. Trade magazine for the professional remodeling industry.

★5771★ Visual Merchandising and Store Design
ST Media Group International Inc.
407 Gilbert Ave.
Cincinnati, OH 45202
Ph: (513)421-2050   Fax: (513)421-5144
Fr: 800-925-1110
E-mail: vmsd@stmediagroup.com
URL: http://www.visualstore.com

Monthly. $42.00/year; $5.50/year, single copy. The leading magazine of the retail design industry covering the latest trends in retail design, store planning, and merchandise presentation.

★5772★ Window Fashions
Grace McNamara Inc.
4215 White Bear Pkwy., Ste. 100
St. Paul, MN 55110
Ph: (651)293-1544   Fax: (651)653-4308
Fr: 800-869-6882
E-mail: wfedit@gwmenamara.com

Monthly. $39.00/year for individuals. Design and merchandizing magazine for specialty retailers, dealers and designers in the business of custom window treatments. Provides design, fashion, and color trend info as well as installation techniques and practical business information.

PLACEMENT AND JOB REFERRAL SERVICES

★5773★ Council of Educational Facility Planners, International (CEFPI)

9180 E Desert Cove Dr., No. 104
Scottsdale, AZ 85260-6231
Ph: (480)391-0840   Fax: (480)391-0940
E-mail: contact@cefpi.org
URL: http://www.cefpi.com

Members: Individuals and firms who are responsible for planning, designing, creating, maintaining, and equipping the physical environment of education. **Purpose:** Sponsors an exchange of information, professional experiences, best practices research results, and other investigative techniques concerning educational facility planning. **Activities:** Include publication and review of current and emerging practices in educational facility planning; identification and execution of needed research; development of professional training programs; strengthening of planning services on various levels of government and in institutions of higher learning; leadership in the development of higher standards for facility design and the physical environment of education. Operates speakers' bureau; sponsors placement service; compiles statistics.

★5774★ Institute of Store Planners

25 N Broadway
Tarrytown, NY 10591
Ph: (914)332-1806   Fax: (914)332-1541
Fr: 800-379-9912
E-mail: adminisp@ispo.org
URL: http://www.ispo.org

Description: Persons active in store planning and design; visual merchandisers, students, and educators; contractors and suppliers to the industry. Dedicated to the professional growth of members while providing service to the public through improvement of the retail environment. Provides forum for debate and discussion by store design experts, retailers, and public figures. Makes available speakers for store planning and design courses at the college level; develops programs for store planning courses. Sponsors student design competitions and annual international store design competition with awards in 10 categories. Maintains placement service.

EMPLOYER DIRECTORIES AND NETWORKING LISTS

★5775★ Almanac of Architecture and Design

Greenway Consulting
30 Technology Pkwy. S, Ste. 200
Norcross, GA 30092
Ph: (770)209-3770   Fax: (770)209-3778

Annual. $37.50. Publication includes: Lists of professional organizations, degree programs, and leading firms in architecture and design. Principal content of publication is a collection of information regarding architecture and design.

★5776★ Association of University Interior Designers-Membership Chairperson

Association of University Interior Designers
c/o Terri Smith-Wright
Purdue University
The Office of Purchasing
West Lafayette, IN 47907
Ph: (765)494-9603   Fax: (765)496-1579

Twice yearly, June and October. Covers nearly 100 in-house interior designers, landscape designers, architects, and purchasing agents associated with universities. Entries include: Name, title, affiliation, address, phone. Arrangement: Alphabetical.

★5777★ Contemporary Designers

St. James Press
27500 Drake Rd.
Farmington Hills, MI 48331-3535
Ph: (248)699-4253   Fax: (248)699-8062
Fr: 800-877-4253

Irregular, 3rd edition 1996. $190.00. Covers 685 living designers and outstanding deceased designers from the recent past in the fields of art, architecture, industry, environment, textile, fashion, furniture, theater, film, graphic arts, and interior design; international coverage. Entries include: Name, date and place of birth, address, spouse's and children's names, educational background, area of specialization, projects completed, exhibitions, memberships; bibliography of materials by or about the entrant; signed critical essay. Arrangement: Alphabetical. Indexes: Nationality, designer type.

★5778★ Directory of Interior Design Programs Accredited by FIDER

Foundation for Interior Design Education Research
146 Monroe Center NW, Ste. 1318
Grand Rapids, MI 49503-2822
Ph: (616)458-0400   Fax: (616)458-0460
URL: http://www.fider.org

Semiannual, June and November. Covers 128 interior design programs in the United States and Canada in conformance with the accreditation standards of the foundation. Entries include: Type of program, name of institution, name of department chair or program head, phone, dates of last and next accreditation review, degrees offered, e-mail and web address. Arrangement: Geographical, degree level offered, then alphabetical by institution name.

★5779★ ENR-Top 500 Design Firms Issue

McGraw-Hill Companies
1221 Ave. of the Americas
New York, NY 10020
Ph: (212)512-2000   Fax: (212)512-3840

Annual, April. $10.00. Publication includes: List of 500 leading architectural, engineering, and specialty design firms selected on basis of annual billings. Entries include: Company name, headquarters location, type of firm, current and prior year rank in billings, types of services, countries in which operated in preceding year. Arrangement: Ranked by billings.

★5780★ ENR-Top International Design Firms Issue

McGraw-Hill Companies
1221 Ave. of the Americas
New York, NY 10020
Ph: (212)512-2000   Fax: (212)512-3840

Annual, July issue of "Engineering News Record". $10.00. Publication includes: List of 200 design firms (including United States firms) competing outside their own national borders who received largest dollar volume of foreign contracts in preceding calendar year. Entries include: Company name, headquarters location, type of firm, current and previous year rankings in total billings, types of services, countries in which operated in preceding year. Arrangement: By amount billed to international clients in previous year.

★5781★ Interior Decorators, Designers & Consultants Directory

infoUSA Inc.
5711 S 86th Cir.
Omaha, NE 68127-0347
Ph: (402)930-3500   Fax: (402)331-0176
Fr: 800-555-6124
URL: http://www.abii.com

Annual. Number of listings: 33,751. Entries include: Name, address, phone (including area code), size of advertisement, year first in "Yellow Pages," name of owner or manager, number of employees. Compiled from telephone company "Yellow Pages," nationwide. Arrangement: Geographical.

★5782★ Interior Design Sourcebook: A Guide to Resources on the History and Practice of Interior Design

Omnigraphics Inc.
615 Griswold St., Ste. 1400
Detroit, MI 48226
Ph: (313)961-1340   Fax: (313)961-1383
Fr: 800-234-1340

$22.50. Publication includes: Resource listing for interior design, including publishers and bookstores, professional and trade organizations, government agencies, research centers, and national product expositions and conferences. Entries include: Address, telephone, fax, e-mail address, and URL. Indexes: Name/organization; subject.

HANDBOOKS AND MANUALS

★5783★ Becoming an Interior Designer: A Visual Career Guide

John Wiley & Sons, Inc.
111 River St.
Hoboken, NJ 07030
Ph: (201)748-6000   Fax: (201)748-6088

Christine M. Piotrowski. December 2003. $35.00 (paper). Illustrated. 288 pages.

★5784★ Career Information Center

Macmillan Publishing Co. Inc.
200 Old Tappan Rd.
Old Tappan, NJ 07675
Fr: 800-428-5331

Visual Education Center Staff. Seventh edition, 1999. $275.00. 2080 pages. This 13-volume set profiles over 600 occupations. Each occupational profile describes job duties, educational requirements, how to get the job, advancement possibilities, employment outlook, working conditions, earnings and benefits, and where to write for more information.

★5785★ Careers for Color Connoisseurs and Other Visual Types

VGM Career Horizons
1221 Avenue of the Americas
New York, NY 10020
Ph: (212)904-2000   Fr: 800-323-4900
E-mail: ntcpub@tribune.com

Jan Goldberg. 1999. $14.95; $9.95 (paper). 212 pages.

★5786★ Careers for Culture Lovers and Other Artsy Types

VGM Career Horizons
1221 Avenue of the Americas
New York, NY 10020
Ph: (212)904-2000   Fr: 800-323-4900
E-mail: ntcpub@tribune.com

Marjorie Eberts and Margaret Gisler. Second edition, 1999. $14.95; $9.95 (paper). 234 pages. Describes how to get work in a variety of fields related to art and culture. Opportunities include picture framer, curator, art restorer, symphony manager, disk jockey, music reviewer, dance teacher, choreographer, costume designer, theater manager, light designer, drama teacher, bookstore owner, interior decorator, antique store owner, and others.

★5787★ The Creative Business Guide to Running a Graphic Design Business

W. W. Norton & Company, Incorporated
500 Fifth Ave.
New York, NY 10110-0017
Ph: (212)354-5500   Fax: (212)869-0856
Fr: 800-223-2584

Cameron Foote. 2001. $45.00.

★5788★ Managing to Make It

University of Chicago Press
1427 E. 60th St.
Chicago, IL 60637
Ph: (773)702-7700   Fax: (773)702-9756

Frank F. Furstenberg. 1999. $32.50.

★5789★ Opportunities in Interior Design and Decorating Careers

McGraw-Hill Trade
2 Penn Plaza
New York, NY 10121
Ph: (212)904-2000   Fr: 800-722-4726

Victoria Ball and David Stearns. Second edition, revised, 2001. $15.95; $12.95 (paper). 160 pages. Covers opportunities and job search techniques in interior design. Addresses working for a design house, contract work, and starting a business. Illustrated.

★5790★ Professional Interior Design: A Career Guide

iUniverse, Inc.
2021 Pine Lake Rd., Ste. 100
Lincoln, NE 68512
Ph: (402)323-7800   Fax: (402)323-9235
Fr: 877-288-4737

Jason Znoy, ASID Illinois Association. May 2004. $9.95 (paper). 64 pages.

★5791★ Start Your Own Interior Design Business and Keep It Growing!

Touch of Design
5342 Elsinore St.
Oceanside, CA 92056
Ph: (619)945-7909   Fax: (619)945-4283

Linda M. Ramsay. 1994. $39.99 (paper). 384 pages.

EMPLOYMENT AGENCIES AND SEARCH FIRMS

★5792★ Claremont-Branan, Inc.

1298 Rockbridge Rd., Ste. B
Stone Mountain, GA 30087
Ph: (770)925-2915   Fax: (770)925-2601

Employment agency. Executive search firm.

★5793★ Randolph Associates, Inc.

950 Massachusetts Ave., Ste. 105
Cambridge, MA 02139-3174
Ph: (617)441-8777   Fax: (617)441-8778
E-mail: jobs@greatjobs.com
URL: http://www.greatjobs.com

Employment agency. Provides regular or temporary placement of staff.

★5794★ RitaSue Siegel Resources, Inc.

20 E. 46th St.
New York, NY 10017-2417
Ph: (212)682-2100   Fax: (212)682-2946
E-mail: ritasues@ritasue.com
URL: http://www.ritasuesiegelresources.com

Executive search firm specializing in industrial and product design.

TRADESHOWS

★5795★ Coverings

TSI, Inc.
11940 US Hwy. 1, Ste. 200
North Palm Beach, FL 33408-2803
Ph: (561)776-0600   Fax: (561)776-7466
Fr: 800-881-9400
E-mail: info@coverings.com
URL: http://www.coverings.com

Annual. **Primary Exhibits:** Residential and commercial covering industries: flooring, ceramic tile, natural stone and related products and services. Also hardwood flooring, laminate flooring, resilient flooring and related adhesives, grouts, sealants, tools and allied products.

★5796★ DesigNation

DesigNation, Inc.
300 M St., SW, Ste. N110
Washington, DC 20024
Ph: (202)488-1530   Fax: (202)488-3838
E-mail: info@designation.net
URL: http://www.designation.net

Annual. **Primary Exhibits:** Exhibits of interest to designers holding college degrees who are practicing graphic, industrial, fashion, textile, and interior design.

★5797★ Paint and Paper Pro Show

Painting and Decorating Contractors of America
3913 Old Lee Hwy., Ste. 33B
Fairfax, VA 22030
Ph: (703)359-0826   Fax: (703)359-2576
Fr: 800-332-7322

Annual. **Primary Exhibits:** Wallpaper, paint, and related products.

★5798★ Surfaces

World Floor Covering Association
2211 E. Howell Ave.
Anaheim, CA 92806-6033
Ph: (714)978-6440   Fax: (714)978-6440
Fr: 800-624-6880
E-mail: surfaces@wfca.org
URL: http://www.wfca.org

Annual. **Primary Exhibits:** Floor covering equipment, supplies, and services.

OTHER SOURCES

★5799★ *Home Economics Careers*
Cambridge Educational
2572 Brunswick Ave.
Lawrenceville, NJ 08648-4128
Fax: 800-FAX-ON-US   Fr: 800-468-4227
URL: http://www.cambridgeeducational.com
$79.95. 30 minutes. Includes manual.

★5800★ **Interior Design Society (IDS)**
PO Box 2396
High Point, NC 27261
Fax: (336)801-6110   Fr: 800-888-9590

E-mail: info@interiordesignsociety.org
URL: http://www.interiordesignsociety.org

Description: Independent designers and decorators, retail designers and sales people, design-oriented firms, and manufacturers. Grants accreditation and recognition to qualified residential interior designers and retail home furnishing stores. Conducts educational seminars in design, sales training, and marketing. Offers products and publications for designers and a correspondence course for home furnishing sales people.

★5801★ **International Interior Design Association (IIDA)**
Merchandise Mart, Ste. 13-500
Chicago, IL 60654-1104
Ph: (312)467-1950   Fax: (312)467-0779
Fr: 888-799-IIDA
E-mail: iidahq@iida.org
URL: http://www.iida.org

Purpose: Professional interior designers, including designers of commercial, healthcare, hospitality, government, retail, residential facilities; educators; researchers; representatives of allied manufacturing sources.
Activities: Conducts research, student programs, and continuing education programs for members. Has developed a code of ethics for the professional design membership.

Jewelers

SOURCES OF HELP-WANTED ADS

★5802★ Couture International Jeweler
VNU Business Media USA
770 Broadway
New York, NY 10003
Ph: (646)654-5000
E-mail: mestevez@vnubuspubs.com
URL: http://www.vnubusinessmedia.com/box/bp/div_mmr_jg_cij.html

Bimonthly. $60.00/year for U.S.; $105.00/year for other countries; $10.00 for single issue. Trade magazine covering the jewelry and retail industry.

★5803★ Diamond Intelligence Briefs
VNU Business Media USA
770 Broadway
New York, NY 10003
Ph: (646)654-5000
URL: http://www.diamondintelligence.com/DIB.asp

$520.00/year for individuals. Trade publication for the diamond and jewelry industry.

★5804★ Fashion Accessories
S.C.M. Publications Inc.
PO Box 859
Mahwah, NJ 07430
Ph: (201)684-9222   Fax: (201)684-9228

Monthly. $24.00/year for individuals. Magazine focusing on fashion jewelry and accessories for women and men.

★5805★ JCK's High-Volume Jeweler
Reed Business Information
Valley Forge Park Pl.
1018 W 9th Ave., 3rd Fl.
King of Prussia, PA 19406-1225
Ph: (610)205-1000   Fax: (610)205-1139

Bimonthly. Professional publication covering the jewelry industry.

★5806★ Jewelers' Circular-Keystone
Reed Business Information
360 Park Ave. S
New York, NY 10014
Ph: (646)746-7764
URL: http://www.jckgroup.com

Monthly. Retail jewelers trade magazine.

★5807★ National Jeweler
VNU Business Media
770 Broadway
New York, NY 10003-9595
Ph: (646)654-5000
E-mail: jwynn@mfi.com
URL: http://www.national-jeweler/com

Biweekly. $45.00/year for one year; $71.00 for two years. Jewelry industry magazine.

★5808★ New York Diamonds
Reed Business Information
360 Park Ave. S
New York, NY 10010
Ph: (646)746-7395   Fax: (646)746-7434

Bimonthly. Publication covering the jewelry trade.

★5809★ Watch & Clock Review
Golden Bell Press
2403 Champa St.
Denver, CO 80205
Ph: (303)296-1600   Fax: (303)295-2159

$19.50/year; $3.00 for single issue. Magazine on watches and clocks.

PLACEMENT AND JOB REFERRAL SERVICES

★5810★ Gemological Institute of America (GIA)
5345 Armada Dr.
Carlsbad, CA 92008
Ph: (760)603-4000   Fax: (760)603-4080
Fr: 800-421-7250
E-mail: president@gia.edu
URL: http://www.gia.edu

Description: Alumni are sustaining members. Conducts home study programs, resident courses, and traveling seminars in identification and quality analysis of diamonds and other gemstones and pearls, and in jewelry making and repair, jewelry designing, and jewelry sales. Through subsidiaries, manufactures and sells gem testing and diamond grading equipment and audiovisual gemstone presentations. Maintains gem testing and research laboratories in Carlsbad, CA and New York City. Offers job placement service; organizes gemological study tours. Awards diplomas as Gemologist, Graduate Gemologist, Graduate Jeweler, and Graduate Jeweler Gemologist; also awards Diamonds Certificate, Colored Stones Certificate, Jewelry Display Certificate, Fine Jewelry Sales Certificate, Jewelry Design Certificate, and Pearls Certificate. Operates speakers' bureau.

★5811★ Women's Jewelry Association (WJA)
333 B Route 46 West, Ste. B-201
Fairfield, NJ 07004
Ph: (973)575-7190   Fax: (973)575-1445
E-mail: info@womensjewelry.org
URL: http://www.womensjewelry.org

Description: Those involved in jewelry design, manufacture, retail, and advertising. Aims to: enhance the status of women in the jewelry industry; make known the contribution of women to the industry; provide a network for women involved with fine jewelry. Maintains hall of fame.

EMPLOYER DIRECTORIES AND NETWORKING LISTS

★5812★ Diamonds Directory

infoUSA Inc.
5711 S 86th Cir.
Omaha, NE 68127-0347
Ph: (402)930-3500   Fax: (402)331-0176
Fr: 800-555-6124
URL: http://www.abii.com

Updated continuously; printed on request. Number of listings: 4,831. Entries include: Name, address, phone (including area code), size of advertisement, year first in "Yellow Pages," name of owner or manager, number of employees. Compiled from telephone company "Yellow Pages," nationwide. Arrangement: Geographical.

★5813★ Jewelers Board of Trade-Confidential Reference Book

Jewelers Board of Trade
95 Jefferson Blvd.
Warwick, RI 02888-1046
Ph: (401)438-0750

Semiannual, March and September. Covers about 45,000 jewelry manufacturers, importers, distributors, and retailers. Entries include: Company name, address, phone, whether a wholesaler, retailer, or manufacturer, credit rating. Arrangement: Geographical.

★5814★ Jewelers' Circular/Keystone-Jewelers' Directory Issue

Reed Business Information
Valley Forge Park Pl.
1018 W 9th Ave., 3rd Fl.
King of Prussia, PA 19406-1225
Ph: (610)205-1000   Fax: (610)205-1139

Annual, December. $33.95. Publication includes: About 8,500 manufacturers, importers, and wholesale jewelers providing merchandise and supplies to the jewelry retailing industry; and related trade organizations. Entries include: For all companies-Company name, address, phone, toll-free phone, fax, e-mail, URL, distribution methods. Arrangement: Classified by product/service, then alphabetical. Indexes: Alphabetical.

★5815★ Jewelers Retail Directory

infoUSA Inc.
5711 S 86th Cir.
Omaha, NE 68127-0347
Ph: (402)930-3500   Fax: (402)331-0176
Fr: 800-555-6124
URL: http://www.abii.com

Annual. Number of listings: 46,547. Entries include: Name, address, phone (including area code), size of advertisement, year first in "Yellow Pages," name of owner or manager, number of employees. Regional editions available. Compiled from telephone company "Yellow Pages," nationwide. Arrangement: Geographical.

★5816★ Jewelers Wholesale Directory

infoUSA Inc.
5711 S 86th Cir.
Omaha, NE 68127-0347
Ph: (402)930-3500   Fax: (402)331-0176
Fr: 800-555-6124
URL: http://www.abii.com

Annual. Number of listings: 6,235. Entries include: Name, address, phone (including area code), size of advertisement, year first in "Yellow Pages," name of owner or manager, number of employees. Compiled from telephone company "Yellow Pages," nationwide. Arrangement: Geographical.

★5817★ Jewelry Manufacturers Directory

infoUSA Inc.
5711 S 86th Cir.
Omaha, NE 68127-0347
Ph: (402)930-3500   Fax: (402)331-0176
Fr: 800-555-6124
URL: http://www.abii.com

Annual. Number of listings: 6,488. Entries include: Name, address, phone (including area code), size of advertisement, year first in "Yellow Pages," name of owner or manager, number of employees. Compiled from telephone company "Yellow Pages," nationwide. Arrangement: Geographical.

★5818★ National Association of Jewelry Appraisers-Membership Directory

National Association of Jewelry
  Appraisers Inc.
PO Box 18
Rego Park, NY 11374-0818
Ph: (718)896-1536

Annual, April. Covers nearly 750 members. Entries include: Name, address, phone, business affiliation, area of specialization. Arrangement: Alphabetical, with seperate georgraphical listing. Indexes: Specialty.

★5819★ National Jeweler-Industry Yellow Pages

VNU Business Media
770 Broadway
New York, NY 10003-9595
Ph: (646)654-5000

Annual, December. $10.00. Covers approximately 5,000 companies providing products and services in the jewelry and watch industries. Entries include: Company name, address, phone, fax, branch office or subsidiary names and addresses, description of product/service provided. Arrangement: Alphabetical by company name. Indexes: Product/service.

HANDBOOKS AND MANUALS

★5820★ How to Be Successful in the Bead Jewelry Business

Kate Drew-Wilkinson Designs
PO Box 1803
Bisbee, AZ 85603
Ph: (520)432-7818   Fax: (520)432-7117

Kate Drew-Wilkinson. 1994. $24.00; $9.95 (paper). 135 pages.

★5821★ JCK's Jewelers' Management Series

Jewelers' Circular-Keystone
1018 W. Ninth Ave.
King of Prussia, PA 19406
Ph: (610)205-1110

1993. $319.70. Out of print. Series includes the Brand Name & Trademark Guide: Jewelry & Kindred Trades, 12th edition, which identifies nearly 15,000 names & symbols used by over 5,000 makers of jewelry store products. It also contains an alphabetical name & address listing of all the manufacturers represented.

TRADESHOWS

★5822★ Jewelers International Showcase

Jewelers International Showcase, Inc.
6405 Congress Ave., Ste. 125
Boca Raton, FL 33487-2827
Ph: (561)998-0205   Fax: (561)998-0209
E-mail: jisshow@aol.com
URL: http://www.jisshow.com

3/year. **Primary Exhibits:** Fine jewelry, fashion jewelry, and related products and services to jewelry trade members. **Dates and Locations:** 2004 Oct 16-18; Miami Beach, FL; Miami Beach Convention Center.

★5823★ Memphis Gift and Jewelry Show Spring

Helen Brett Enterprises, Inc.
5111 Academy Dr.
Lisle, IL 60532-4182
Ph: (630)241-9865   Fax: (630)241-9870
Fr: 800-541-8171
E-mail: rbkolinek@us5.global.ibmail.com

Semiannual. **Primary Exhibits:** Giftware and jewelry, apparel, home decor, novelties, silk flowers, fine/costume jewelry and accessories.

★5824★ MJSA Expo Providence

Manufacturing Jewelers and Suppliers of
  America
45 Royal Little Dr.
Providence, RI 02904-1861
Ph: (401)274-3840   Fax: (401)274-0265
Fr: 800-444-6572

E-mail: mjsa@mjsainc.com
URL: http://mjsa.polygon.net

Biennial. **Primary Exhibits:** Jewelry manufacturing equipment, supplies, machinery and tools, components, and business services.

★5825★ New Orleans Gift and Jewelry Show Fall

Helen Brett Enterprises, Inc.
5111 Academy Dr.
Lisle, IL 60532-4182
Ph: (630)241-9865   Fax: (630)241-9870
Fr: 800-541-8171
E-mail: rbkolinek@us5.global.ibmail.com

Semiannual. **Primary Exhibits:** Giftware and jewelry, apparel, home decor, rugs, silk plants, fine jewelry, costume jewelry, loose gemstones.

OTHER SOURCES

★5826★ American Watchmakers and Clockmakers Institute (AWI)

701 Enterprise Dr.
Harrison, OH 45030
Ph: (513)367-9800   Fax: (513)367-1414
Fr: (866)367-2924
E-mail: jlubic@awi-net.org
URL: http://www.awi-net.org

Members: Jewelers, watchmakers, clockmakers, watch and clock engineers, scientists, repairmen, and others in the watch, clock, and jewelry industry. **Purpose:** Examines and certifies master watchmakers and clockmakers. Maintains a museum displaying horological items, and the National Watch Mark Identification Bureau. Conducts home study course in clock repairing and bench courses for watchmakers in most major U.S. cities. Disseminates career information to vocational counselors in the form of brochures and filmstrips.

★5827★ Jewelers

Evon Publishing
832 N 7th Ave.
Iron River, MI 49935
Ph: (906)265-3190

Audiocassette. 1996. $16.95. 32 minutes. Part of the Careers and Vocational Guidance Series. Provides information about the nature of the work, educational requirements, employment outlook, earnings, and work conditions as well as additional related information.

★5828★ Jewelers of America (JA)

52 Vanderbilt Ave., 19th Fl.
New York, NY 10017-3808
Ph: (646)658-0246   Fax: (646)658-0256
Fr: 800-223-0673
E-mail: info@jewelers.org
URL: http://www.Jewelers.org

Members: Retailers of jewelry, watches, silver, and allied merchandise. **Activities:** Conducts surveys and compiles statistics. Conducts educational programs. Provides information to consumers.

★5829★ Manufacturing Jewelers and Suppliers of America (MJSA)

45 Royal Little Dr.
Providence, RI 02904
Ph: (401)274-3840   Fax: (401)274-0265
Fr: 800-444-MJSA
E-mail: mjsa@mjsainc.com
URL: http://www.mjsainc.com

Description: American manufacturers and suppliers within the jewelry industry. Seeks to foster long-term stability and prosperity of the jewelry industry. Provides leadership in government affairs and industry education.

★5830★ National Association of Jewelry Appraisers (NAJA)

PO Box 6558
Annapolis, MD 21401-0558
Ph: (410)897-0889

Members: Gem and jewelry appraisers, jewelers, importers, brokers, manufacturers, gemological students, and others professionally interested in jewelry appraisal. **Purpose:** Seeks to recognize and make available to the public the services of highly qualified, experienced, independent, and reliable jewelry appraisers. Conducts seminars on jewelry appraisal techniques, methods, and pricing for members and the public. Supports legislation to establish minimum standards of competency and licensing of jewelry appraisers; maintains code of professional ethics. **Activities:** Operates appraiser referral program; sponsors ongoing public relations campaign. Offers equipment discounts, new appraisal forms, travel discounts, insurance, and professional aids for members only. Compiles statistics.

Kindergarten and Elementary School Teachers

SOURCES OF HELP-WANTED ADS

★5831★ AAEE Connections

American Association for Employment in
  Education
3040 Riverside Dr., Ste. 125
Columbus, OH 43221
Ph: (614)485-1111   Fax: (614)485-9609

Description: Quarterly. Publishes news of the Association, whose aim is "to enhance and promote the concept of career planning and placement as an integral part of the educational process and to undertake activities designed to help schools, colleges, and universities meet their educational staffing needs." Also concerned with teacher education and the supply of/demand for teachers. Recurring features include news of members, state and regional news, and announcements of upcoming conferences and meetings.

★5832★ Academic Exchange Quarterly

Rapid Intellect Group Inc.
PO Box 131
Stuyvesant Falls, NY 12174
Ph: (518)372-1347
E-mail: AEQ@rapidintellect.com
URL: http://rapidintellect.com/AEQweb/

Quarterly. $156.00/year for individuals; $116.00/year, professional rate; $39.00 for single issue. Periodical covering issues in education.

★5833★ The American Biology Teacher

National Association of Biology Teachers
12030 Sunrise Valley Dr., Ste. 110
Reston, VA 20191
Ph: (703)264-9696   Fax: (703)264-7778
Fr: 800-406-0775
E-mail: publication@nabt.org
URL: http://www.nabt.org

$125.00/year; $135.00/year for other countries; $10.00 for single issue. Journal featuring articles on biology, science, and education for elementary, high school and college level biology teachers. Includes audio-visual, book, computer, and research reviews.

★5834★ Education Week

Editorial Projects in Education Inc.
6935 Arlington Rd., Ste. 100
Bethesda, MD 20814
Ph: (301)280-3100   Fax: (301)280-3250
E-mail: ew@epe.org
URL: http://www.edweek.org

Weekly. $79.94/year for individuals. Professional newspaper for elementary and secondary school educators.

★5835★ Educational Researcher

American Educational Research
  Association
1230 17th St. NW
Washington, DC 20036-3078
Ph: (202)223-9485   Fax: (202)775-1824
URL: http://www.aera.net

$41.00/year for individuals; $8.00 for single issue; $56.00/year for institutions; $50.00/year for out of country; free to members of AERA. Educational research journal.

★5836★ Electronic Learning

Scholastic Library Publishing Inc.
90 Old Sherman Tpke.
Danbury, CT 06816
Ph: (203)797-3500   Fax: (203)797-3657
Fr: 800-621-1115

$19.00/year. Magazine focusing on electronic education.

★5837★ Journal of Language, Identity, and Education

Lawrence Erlbaum Associates Inc.
10 Industrial Ave.
Mahwah, NJ 07430-2262
Ph: (201)236-9500   Fax: (201)236-0072
Fr: 800-9-BOOKS-9
E-mail: journals@erlbaum.com
URL: http://www.erlbaum.com/shop/
tek9.asp?pg=products&specific=1

Quarterly. $40.00/year for individuals; $70.00/year for out of country; $225.00/year for institutions; $255.00/year for institutions, other countries. Scholarly, interdisciplinary journal covering issues in language, identity and education worldwide for academics, educators and policy specialists in a variety of disciplines, and others.

★5838★ Journal of Latinos and Education

Lawrence Erlbaum Associates Inc.
10 Industrial Ave.
Mahwah, NJ 07430-2262
Ph: (201)236-9500   Fax: (201)236-0072
Fr: 800-9-BOOKS-9
E-mail: journals@erlbaum.com
URL: http://www.erlbaum.com/shop/
tek9.asp?pg=products&specific=1

Quarterly. $40.00/year for individuals; $70.00/year for out of country; $195.00/year for institutions; $225.00/year for institutions, other countries. Scholarly, multidisciplinary journal covering educational issues that impact Latinos for researchers, teaching professionals, academics, scholars, institutions, and others.

★5839★ Journal of Learning Disabilities

PRO-ED Inc.
8700 Shoal Creek Blvd.
Austin, TX 78757-6897
Ph: (512)451-3246   Fax: (512)451-8542
Fr: 800-897-3202

$49.00/year for individuals; $105.00/year for institutions; $115.00/year for other countries. Special education journal.

★5840★ Journal of Teacher Education

Boston College
McElroy Commons, No. 113
Chestnut Hill, MA 02467
Ph: (617)552-4820   Fax: (617)552-4823

Magazine of interest to educators.

★5841★ Learning

The Education Center Inc.
3515 W Market St., Ste. 200
Greensboro, NC 27403
Ph: (336)851-8351   Fax: (336)851-8365
Fr: 800-334-0298
URL: http://www.theeducationcenter.com

$4.95 for single issue. Definitive guide to products and services for K-6 grade teachers in the classroom.

★5842★ Matrix: The Magazine for Leaders in Higher Education

Professional Media Group L.L.C.
36 Clipper Ct., Ste. B
Mystic, CT 06355-2138

Bimonthly. Trade publication covering issues for higher education professionals.

★5843★ Music Educators Journal

MENC: The National Association for Music Education
1806 Robert Fulton Dr.
Reston, VA 20191
Ph: (703)860-4000   Fr: 800-336-3768

Bimonthly. Journal covering all levels of music education. Published on alternate months with Teaching Music.

★5844★ NJEA Review

New Jersey Education Association
180 W State St.
PO Box 1211
Trenton, NJ 08607
Ph: (609)599-4561   Fax: (609)392-6321
E-mail: lgalley@mgea.org

$25.00/year. Educational journal for public school employees.

★5845★ The Physics Teacher

American Association of Physics Teachers
One Physics Ellipse
College Park, MD 20740-3845
Ph: (301)209-3350   Fax: (301)209-0845
E-mail: tpt@appstate.edu
URL: http:///www.aapt.org/tpt

$94.00/year for individuals; $47.00/year. Scientific education magazine.

★5846★ School and Community

Missouri State Teachers Association
PO Box 458
Columbia, MO 65205-0458
Ph: (573)442-3127   Fax: (573)443-5079
Fr: 800-392-0532
E-mail: publications@mail.msta.org
URL: http://www.msta.org

Quarterly. $15.00/year. Education magazine.

★5847★ The Science Teacher

National Science Teachers Association
1840 Wilson Blvd.
Arlington, VA 22201-3000
Ph: (703)243-7100   Fax: (703)243-7177
Fr: 800-722-6782
E-mail: thescienceteacher@nsta.org
URL: http://www.nsta.org

$65.00/year for individuals. Journal on science education.

★5848★ Strategies

American Alliance for Health, Physical Education, Recreation & Dance
1900 Association Dr.
Reston, VA 20191
Ph: (703)476-3400   Fax: (703)476-9527
Fr: 800-213-7193
E-mail: strategies@aahperd.org

$25.00/year for members; $40.00/year for individuals; $63.00/year for businesses, institutions, and libraries. Journal providing practical, hands-on information to physical educators and coaches.

★5849★ Teacher Magazine

Editorial Projects in Education Inc.
6935 Arlington Rd., Ste. 100
Bethesda, MD 20814
Ph: (301)280-3100   Fax: (301)280-3250
E-mail: tm@epe.org
URL: http://www.teachermagazine.org

$17.94/year; $3.00 for single issue. Professional magazine for elementary and secondary school teachers.

★5850★ Teaching Children Mathematics

National Council of Teachers of Mathematics
1906 Association Dr.
Reston, VA 20191-1502
Ph: (703)620-9840   Fax: (703)476-2970
Fr: 800-235-7566

$65.00/year for individuals; $95.00/year for institutions; $7.50/year for single issue. Journal covering mathematics content and methods for pre-service and in-service teachers of grades pre-kindergarten through 6th.

★5851★ Teaching Exceptional Children

Council for Exceptional Children
1110 N Glebe Rd., Ste. 300
Arlington, VA 22201
Ph: (703)620-3660   Fax: (703)264-9494
Fr: 888-232-7733
E-mail: tec@bc.edu

$58.00/year for individuals; $66.00/year for other countries by surface mail; $95.00/year for other countries by airmail; $10.50 for single issue. Journal exploring practical methods for teaching students who have exceptionalities and those who are gifted and talented.

★5852★ Teaching/K-8

Teaching/K-8
40 Richards Ave.
Norwalk, CT 06854-2509
Ph: (203)855-2650   Fax: (203)855-2656
Fr: 800-249-9363
E-mail: teachingk8@aol.com
URL: http://www.teachingk-8.com

$14.99/year for individuals. Magazine for elementary teachers.

★5853★ Tech Directions

Prakken Publications Inc.
PO Box 8623
Ann Arbor, MI 48107-8623
Ph: (734)975-2800   Fax: (734)975-2787
Fr: 800-530-WORD
E-mail: tdedit@techdirections.com
URL: http://www.techdirections.com

Free to qualified subscribers; $30.00/year for individuals. Magazine covering issues, programs, and projects in industrial education, technology education, trade and industry, and vocational-technical career education. Articles are geared for teacher and administrator use and reference from elementary school through postsecondary levels.

★5854★ Today's OEA

Oregon Education Association
6900 SW Atlanta St.
Portland, OR 97223-2513
Ph: (503)684-3300   Fax: (503)684-8063

Bimonthly. Free to qualified subscribers; $10.00/year for nonmembers. Membership magazine covering educational issues statewide and nationally.

PLACEMENT AND JOB REFERRAL SERVICES

★5855★ American Alliance for Health, Physical Education, Recreation and Dance (AAHPERD)

1900 Association Dr.
Reston, VA 20191-1598
Ph: (703)476-3400   Fax: (703)476-9527
Fr: 800-213-7193
URL: http://www.aahperd.org

Members: Students and educators in physical education, dance, health, athletics, safety education, recreation, and outdoor education. **Purpose:** Works to improve its fields of education at all levels through such services as consultation, periodicals and special publications, leadership development, determination of standards, and research. Sponsors placement service.

★5856★ American Association of Christian Schools (AACS)

PO Box 1097
Independence, MO 64051-0597
Ph: (816)252-9900   Fax: (816)252-6700

E-mail: national@aacs.org
URL: http://www.aacs.org

Description: Maintains teacher/administrator certification program and placement service. Participates in school accreditation program. Sponsors National Academic Tournament. Maintains American Christian Honor Society. Compiles statistics; maintains speakers' bureau and placement service.

★5857★ **American Association of Teachers of French (A.A.T.F.)**
Mail Code 4510
Southern Illinois University
Carbondale, IL 62901-4510
Ph: (618)453-5731   Fax: (618)453-5733
E-mail: abrate@siu.edu
URL: http://www.frenchteachers.org

Members: Teachers of French in public and private elementary and secondary schools, colleges, and universities. **Activities:** Sponsors National French Week each November to take French out of the classroom and into the schools and community. Conducts National French Contest in elementary and secondary schools and awards prizes at all levels. Maintains Materials Center with promotional and pedagogical materials; National French Honor Society (high school), Placement Bureau, Pen Pal Bureau, summer scholarships.

★5858★ **American Association of Teachers of Spanish and Portuguese (AATSP)**
423 Exton Commons
Exton, PA 19341-2951
Ph: (610)363-7005   Fax: (610)363-7116
E-mail: corporate@aatsp.org
URL: http://www.aatsp.org

Description: Teachers of Spanish and Portuguese languages and literatures and others interested in Hispanic culture. Operates placement bureau and maintains pen pal registry. Sponsors honor society, Sociedad Honoraria Hispanica and National Spanish Examinations for secondary school students.

★5859★ **American Montessori Society (AMS)**
281 Park Ave. S, 6th Fl.
New York, NY 10010
Ph: (212)358-1250   Fax: (212)358-1256
E-mail: east@amshq.org
URL: http://www.amshq.org

Description: School affiliates and teacher training affiliates; heads of schools, teachers, parents, non-Montessori educators, and other interested individuals dedicated to stimulating the use of the Montessori teaching approach and promoting better education for all children. Formed to meet demands of growing interest in the Montessori approach to early learning. Developed in Italy in 1907 by Dr. Maria Montessori, the system "is based on the young child's instinctive love and need for purposeful work realized in an environment prepared with auto-educative, multi-sensory, manipulative learning devices for language, math, science, and practical

life. Freedom within limits and individual growth fostered in classes with three year age mix and peer stimulation. Teacher's role is that of observer and catalyst." Assists in establishing schools; supplies information and limited services to member schools in other countries. Maintains school consultation and accreditation service; provides information service; assists research and gathers statistical data; offers placement service. Maintains Montessori and related materials exhibit.

★5860★ **Association for Direct Instruction (ADI)**
PO Box 10252
Eugene, OR 97440
Ph: (541)485-1293   Fax: (541)683-7543
Fr: 800-995-2464
E-mail: info@adihome.org
URL: http://www.adihome.org

Members: Public school regular and special education teachers and university instructors. **Purpose:** Encourages, promotes, and engages in research aimed at improving educational methods. Promotes dissemination of developmental information and skills that facilitate the education of adults and children. **Activities:** Administers a preschool for developmentally delayed children. Offers educational training workshops for instructors. Maintains speakers' bureau, and placement service.

★5861★ **Christian Schools International (CSI)**
3350 E Paris Ave. SE
Grand Rapids, MI 49512-3054
Ph: (616)957-1070   Fax: (616)957-5022
Fr: 800-635-8288
E-mail: info@csionline.org
URL: http://community.gospelcom.net/Brix?pageID=2831

Description: Christian elementary and secondary schools enrolling 100,000 pupils and employing 7800 teachers. Purposes are: to provide a medium for a united witness regarding the role of Christian schools in contemporary society; to promote the establishment of Christian schools; to help members function more effectively in areas of promotion, organization, administration, and curriculum; to help establish standards and criteria to guide the operation of its members; to foster high professional ideals and economic well-being among Christian school personnel; to establish and maintain communication with member schools, colleges, churches, government agencies, and the public. Encourages study, research, and writing that embodies Christian theories of education; conducts salary studies, research, andsurveys on operating costs; offers expert and confidential analysis of member school programs and operation. Sponsors meetings, workshops, and seminars; offers placement service. Administers the Christian School Pension and Trust Funds, Group Insurance Plans, and Life and Insurance Plans and Trust Funds.

★5862★ **Independent Educational Services (IES)**
221 S Alfred St.
Alexandria, VA 22314-3647
Ph: (703)548-9700   Fax: (703)548-7171

Description: Nonprofit consulting, head search, and teacher recruitment organization. Furnishes to independent (private) schools dossiers of qualified candidates for teaching and administrative positions. Offers to teachers and prospective teachers information concerning current requirements and qualifications for positions in the field of education and vacancies for which they qualify. Conducts searches for heads of schools. Offers specialized placement workshops, consulting, and in-service programs to independent schools.

★5863★ **International Educator's Institute (TIE)**
PO Box 513
Cummaquid, MA 02637
Ph: (508)362-1414   Fax: (508)362-1411
Fr: 877-375-6668
E-mail: tie@tieonline.com
URL: http://www.tieonline.com

Description: Facilitates the placement of teachers and administrators in American, British, and international schools. Seeks to create a network that provides for professional development opportunities and improved financial security of members. Offers advice and information on international school news, recent educational developments, job placement, and investment, consumer, and professional development opportunities. Makes available insurance and travel benefits. Operates International Schools Internship Program.

★5864★ **Jewish Educators Assembly (JEA)**
300 Forest Dr.
East Hills, NY 11548
Ph: (516)484-9585   Fax: (516)484-9586
E-mail: jewisheducators@aol.com
URL: http://www.jewisheducators.org/

Members: Educational and supervisory personnel serving Jewish educational institutions. **Purpose:** Seeks to advance the development of Jewish education in the congregation on all levels in consonance with the philosophy of the Conservative Movement; cooperate with the United Synagogue of America Commission on Jewish Education as the policy-making body of the educational enterprise; join in cooperative effort with other Jewish educational institutions and organizations; establish and maintain professional standards for Jewish educators; serve as a forum for the exchange of ideas; promote the values of Jewish education as a basis for the creative continuity of the Jewish people. **Activities:** Maintains placement service and speakers' bureau.

★5865★ National Association for Sport and Physical Education (NASPE)

1900 Association Dr.
Reston, VA 20191
Ph: (703)476-3410   Fax: (703)476-8316
Fr: 800-213-7193
E-mail: naspe@aahperd.org
URL: http://www.aahperd.org

Description: Men and women professionally involved with physical activity and sports. Seeks to improve the total sport and physical activity experience in America. Conducts research and education programs in such areas as sport psychology, curriculum development, kinesiology, history, philosophy, sport sociology, and the biological and behavioral basis of human activity. Develops and distributes public information materials which explain the value of physical education programs. Supports councils involved in organizing and supporting elementary, secondary, and college physical education and sport programs; administers the National Council of Athletic Training in conjunction with the National Association for Girls and Women in Sport; serves the professional interests of coaches, trainers, and officials. Maintains hall of fame, placement service, and media resource center for public information and professional preparation. Member benefits include group insurance and discounts.

★5866★ National Association of Teachers' Agencies (NATA)

797 Kings Hwy.
Fairfield, CT 06432
Ph: (203)333-0611   Fax: (203)334-7224
E-mail: info@jobsforteachers.com
URL: http://www.jobsforteachers.com

Description: Private employment agencies engaged primarily in the placement of teaching and administration personnel. Works to standardize records and promote a strong ethical sense in the placement field. Maintains speakers' bureau.

★5867★ National Communication Association (NCA)

1765 N St. NW
Washington, DC 20036
Ph: (202)464-4622   Fax: (202)464-4600
E-mail: smorreale@natcom.org
URL: http://www.natcom.org

Members: Elementary, secondary, college, and university teachers, speech clinicians, media specialists, communication consultants, students, theater directors, and other interested persons; libraries and other institutions. **Purpose:** To promote study, criticism, research, teaching, and application of the artistic, humanistic, and scientific principles of communication, particularly speech communication. Sponsors the publication of scholarly volumes in speech. **Activities:** Conducts international debate tours in the U.S. and abroad. Maintains placement service.

★5868★ U.S.-China Education Foundation (USCEF)

4140 Oceanside Blvd.
PMB 112, No. 159
Oceanside, CA 92056-6005
Ph: (760)644-0977
E-mail: SAGE.Kennedypres@cex.net
URL: http://www.sage-usa.net

Members: A project of the Society for the Advancement of Global Education. **Purpose:** Purposes are to promote the learning of the Chinese languages (including Mandarin, Cantonese, and minority languages such as Mongolian) by Americans, and the learning of English by Chinese. **Activities:** Conducts short-term travel-study program to prepare Americans and Chinese for stays of four, six, or eight months or one to four years in China or the U.S., respectively. Operates teacher placement service and speakers' bureau. A project of S.A.G.E. the Society for the Development of Global Education.

EMPLOYER DIRECTORIES AND NETWORKING LISTS

★5869★ Boarding Schools Directory

The Association of Boarding Schools
4455 Connecticut Ave., Ste. A200
Washington, DC 20008
Ph: (202)966-8705   Fax: (202)966-8708
Fr: 800-541-5908
URL: http://www.schools.com

Annual, August. Covers boarding schools that are members of the Association of Boarding Schools. Entries include: School name, address, phone, e-mail and url's, grades for which boarding students are accepted, enrollment, brief description. Arrangement: Classified by type of school. Indexes: Geographical; program; Alphabetical.

★5870★ Christian Schools International-Directory

Christian Schools International
3350 E Paris Ave. SE
Grand Rapids, MI 49512-3054
Ph: (616)957-1070   Fax: (616)957-5022
Fr: 800-635-8288
URL: http://www.gospelcom.net/csi

Annual, November. $52.00 for nonmembers. Covers nearly 450 Reformed Christian elementary and secondary schools; related associations; societies without schools. Entries include: For schools-School name, address, phone; name, title, and address of officers; names of faculty members. Arrangement: Geographical.

★5871★ Directory of Day Schools in the United States and Canada

Torah Umesorah National Society for Hebrew Day Schools
5723 18th Ave.
Brooklyn, NY 11204
Ph: (718)259-1223   Fax: (718)259-1795

E-mail: mail@tupublications.com

Annual, latest edition 2003. $15.00. Covers over 700 elementary and secondary Hebrew day schools in the U.S. and Canada. Entries include: School name, address, phone, names of administrative personnel, grades taught, language of instruction, year established (fax numbers and e-mail addresses when available). Arrangement: Geographical. Indexes: Schools & personnel.

★5872★ Directory of Public Elementary and Secondary Education Agencies

National Center for Education Statistics
1990 K St., NW
Washington, DC 20006
Ph: (202)502-7300   Fr: 800-424-1616

Annual. $22.00. Covers about 17,000 local education agencies in the United States, the District of Columbia, and five territories which operate their own schools or pay tuition to other local education agencies. Also lists intermediate education agencies. Entries include: Agency name, address, phone, county, description of district, grade span, membership, special education students, metropolitan status, number of high school graduates, teachers, and schools. Also available from Superintendent of Documents, U.S. Government Printing Office. Arrangement: Geographical, then by type of agency.

★5873★ Directory of Public School Systems in the U.S.

American Association for Employment in Education
3040 Riverside Dr., Ste. 125
Columbus, OH 43221
Ph: (614)485-1111   Fax: (614)485-9609

Annual, Winter. $80.00. Covers about 14,500 public school systems in the United States and their administrative personnel. Entries include: System name, address, phone, website address, name and title of personnel administrator, levels taught and approx. student population. Arrangement: Geographical by state.

★5874★ Educators Resource Directory

Grey House Publishing
PO Box 860
Millerton, NY 12546-0860
Ph: (518)789-8700   Fax: (518)789-0556
Fr: 800-562-2139
URL: http://www.greyhouse.com/education.htm

Biennial, latest edition 5th, 2003/04. $145.00 for softcover; $195.00 for online database; $280.00 for book and online database. Covers publishing opportunities, state by state information on enrollment, funding and grant resources, associations and conferences, teaching jobs abroad all geared toward elementary and secondary school professionals. Also covers online databases, textbook publishers, school suppliers, plus state and federal agencies. Entries include: Contact name, address, phone, fax, description, publications. A unique compilation of over

6,200 educational resources and over 130 tables and charts of education statistics and rankings Arrangement: By subject catagories. Indexes: Entry, subject, publisher.

★5875★ **Employment Opportunities, USA**

Washington Research Associates
1090 Vermont Ave., NW, Ste. 800
Washington, DC 20005
Ph: (202)408-7025

Annual, quarterly updates. $184.00. Publication includes: List of over 1,000 employment contacts in companies and agencies in the banking, arts, telecommunications, education, and 14 other industries and professions, including the federal government. Entries include: Company name, name of representative, address, description of products or services, hiring and recruiting practices, training programs, and year established. Principal content is industry overviews, career news, employment opportunity information on 14 different job markets, and comprehensive guidance to career resources on the Internet. Arrangement: Classified by industry. Indexes: Occupation.

★5876★ **Encyclopedia of Education**

Macmillan/McGraw-Hill
2 Penn Plz.
New York, NY 10121
Ph: (212)904-6749   Fax: (212)904-6637

$850.00. Publication includes: List of assessment and achievement tests with contact information; list of state departments of education; list of Internet resources. Principal content of publication is a variety of topics within the field of education including policy, curriculum, learning, assessment, legislation, history, and standards. Indexes: Alphabetical.

★5877★ **Fifty State Educational Directories**

Career Guidance Foundation
8090 Engineer Rd., Ste. B
San Diego, CA 92111
Ph: (858)560-8051   Fax: (858)278-8960
Fr: 800-854-2670
URL: http://www.cgf.org

Annual, latest edition June 1996. $89.00. Microfiche. Collection consists of reproductions of the state educational directories published by the departments of education of individual 50 states. Directory contents vary, but the majority contain listings of elementary and secondary schools, colleges and universities, and state education officials. Amount of detail in each also varies. Entries include: Usually, institution name, address, and name of one executive.

★5878★ **Ganley's Catholic Schools in America-Elementary/Secondary/College & University**

Fisher Publishing Co.
PO Box 15070
Scottsdale, AZ 85267
Ph: (480)657-9422   Fax: (480)657-9422
Fr: 800-759-7615
URL: http://www.ganleyscatholicschools.com

Annual, summer; latest edition 2003. $51.50. Covers over 8,400 Catholic K-12 Schools. Arrangement: Geographical by state, then alphabetical by Diocese name.

★5879★ **Handbook of Private Schools**

Porter Sargent Publishers Inc.
11 Beacon St., Ste. 1400
Boston, MA 02108-3099
Ph: (617)523-1670   Fax: (617)523-1021
Fr: 800-342-7470
E-mail: orders@portersargent.com

Annual, June. $99.00. Covers more than 1,600 elementary and secondary boarding and day schools in the United States. Entries include: School name, address, phone, fax, E-mail, URL, type of school (boarding or day), sex and age range, names and titles of administrators, grades offered, academic orientation, curriculum, new admissions yearly, tests required for admission, enrollment and faculty, graduate record, number of alumni, tuition and scholarship figures, summer session, plant evaluation and endowment, date of establishment, calendar, association membership, description of school's offerings and history, test score averages, uniform requirements, geographical, and demographic date. Arrangement: Geographical. Indexes: Alphabetical by school name, cross indexed by state, region, grade range, sexes accepted, school features and enrollment.

★5880★ **Independent School Guide for Washington DC and Surrounding Area**

Lift Hill Press Inc.
4930-A Eisenhower Ave.
Alexandria, VA 22304
Ph: (703)212-9113   Fax: (703)212-9114
Fr: 800-699-9113
URL: http://www.washingtonbk.com

Biennial. $15.95. Covers over 475 independent schools (including parochial schools) in the Washington, DC area, including Maryland and Virginia. Entries include: School name, address, phone, name and title of contact, number of faculty, geographical area served, tuition, courses, admission procedures, summer programs, LD/ED programs, scholarships available. Arrangement: Alphabetical. Indexes: Geographical.

★5881★ **Independent Schools Association of the Southwest-Membership List**

Independent Schools Association of the Southwest
4700 Bryant Irvin Ct., Ste. 204
Fort Worth, TX 76107
Ph: (817)569-9200   Fax: (817)569-9103
Fr: 800-688-5007
URL: http://www.isasw.org

Annual, August. Covers over 75 independent elementary and secondary schools accredited by the association. Entries include: School name, address, phone, chief administrative officer, structure, and enrollment. Arrangement: Geographical. Indexes: Alphabetical.

★5882★ **MDR's School Directories**

Market Data Retrieval
1 Forest Pkwy.
Shelton, CT 06484
Ph: (203)926-4800   Fax: (203)926-1826
Fr: 800-333-8802
URL: http://www.schooldata.com

Annual, October. $1,349.00 for set. Covers over 90,000 public, 8,000 Catholic, and 15,000 other private schools (grades K-12) in the United States; over 15,000 school district offices, and 76,000 school librarians; and 27,000 media specialists, 33,000 technology coordinators. Includes names of over 165,000 school district administrators and staff members in county and state education administration. Entries include: For districts: District name and address; telephone and fax number; number of schools; number of teachers in the district; district enrollment; special Ed students; limited-english proficient students; minority percentage by race, college bound students; expenditures per student for instructional materials; poverty level; title 1 dollars; site-based management; district open/close dates; construction indicator; technologies and quantities (instructional computer brands, multimedia computers; networks, VCRs, satellite dish, DVD Player/Drive High-Speed Internet Access URL); district-level adminstrators, *new superintendents shaded*. For schools: School name and address-new public shaded; telephone and fax number; principal new principal shaded; librarian, media specialist and technology coordinator; grade span; special programs and school type; student enrollment; technologies and quantities (instructional computer brand noting predominant brand); Multi-Media Computers; internet connection or access; Tech Sophistication Index. Arrangement: Geographical. Indexes: District County; District Personnel; Principal; New Public Schools and Key Personnel; District and School Telephone; District URLs.

★5883★ **National Association of Teachers' Agencies-Membership Directory**

National Association of Teachers' Agencies
797 Kings Hwy.
Fairfield, CT 06432
Ph: (203)333-0611   Fax: (203)334-7224

URL: http://www.jobsforteachers.com

Annual, January. Covers approximately 20 private employment agencies engaged primarily in the placement of teaching and administrative personnel in education. Entries include: Name, address, phone, names of key officials. Arrangement: Alphabetical.

★5884★   **National Directory of Alternative Schools**

National Coalition of Alternative
  Community Schools
1289 Jewett St.
Ann Arbor, MI 48104-6201
Ph: (734)668-9171   Fax: (734)769-9629
Fr: 888-771-9171

Biennial, odd years. $18.00. Covers over 500 alternative education programs, including home schools, and state and regional coalitions of alternative schools and colleges; also lists organizations and networks offering services and resources to those working with children; international coverage. Entries include: Name, address, phone, name of contact; many also include descriptions of programs. Arrangement: Schools are geographical. Indexes: Complete index of entries.

★5885★   **National Directory for Employment in Education**

American Association for Employment in
  Education
3040 Riverside Dr., Ste. 125
Columbus, OH 43221
Ph: (614)485-1111   Fax: (614)485-9609

Annual, Winter. $20.00 for institutions. Covers about 600 placement offices maintained by teacher-training institutions and 300 school district personnel officers and/or superintendents responsible for hiring professional staff. Entries include: Institution name, address, phone, contact name, email address, and website. Arrangement: Geographical. Indexes: Personal name, subject-field of teacher training, institutions which provide vacancy bulletins and placement services to non-enrolled students.

★5886★   **Nursery Schools & Kindergartens Directory**

infoUSA Inc.
5711 S 86th Cir.
Omaha, NE 68127-0347
Ph: (402)930-3500   Fax: (402)331-0176
Fr: 800-555-6124
URL: http://www.abii.com

Annual. Number of listings: 44,016. Entries include: Name, address, phone (including area code), size of advertisement, year first in "Yellow Pages," name of owner or manager, number of employees. Regional editions available. Compiled from telephone company "Yellow Pages," nationwide. Arrangement: Geographical.

★5887★   **Opportunities Abroad for Educators**

Fulbright Teacher and Administrator
  Exchange Program
600 Maryland Ave. SW, Ste. 320
Washington, DC 20024-2520
Ph: (202)314-3527   Fax: (202)479-6806
Fr: 800-726-0479
URL: http://www.fulbrightexchanges.org

Annual. Covers opportunities available for elementary and secondary teachers, and two year college instructors, and school administrators to attend seminars or to teach abroad under the Mutual Educational and Cultural Exchange Act of 1961. Entries include: Countries of placement, dates, eligibility requirements, teaching assignments. Arrangement: Geographical.

★5888★   **Patterson's American Education**

Educational Directories Inc.
PO Box 68097
Schaumburg, IL 60168-0097
Ph: (847)891-1250   Fax: (847)891-0945
Fr: 800-357-6183
URL: http://www.ediusa.com

Annual, October; latest edition 2002. $87.00. Covers over 11,400 school districts in the United States; more than 34,000 public, private, and Catholic high schools, middle schools, and junior high schools; approximately 300 parochial superintendents; 400 state department of education personnel. Entries include: For school districts and schools-District and superintendent name, address, phone, fax, grade ranges, enrollment , school names, addresses, phone numbers, grade ranges, enrollment, names of principals. For postsecondary schools-School name, address, phone number, URL, e-mail, names of administrator or director of admissions. For private and Catholic high schools-Name, address, phone, fax, enrollment, grades offered, name of principal. Postsecondary institutions are covered in 'Patterson's Schools Classified'. Arrangement: Geographical by state, then alphabetical by city.

★5889★   **Patterson's Elementary Education**

Educational Directories Inc.
PO Box 68097
Schaumburg, IL 60168-0097
Ph: (847)891-1250   Fax: (847)891-0945
Fr: 800-357-6183
URL: http://www.ediusa.com/PattersonsElementaryEducation.htm

Annual, October; latest edition 2002. $87.00. Covers over 13,400 public school districts; more than 82,447 public, private, and Catholic elementary and middle schools; and 400 state department of education personnel. Entries include: County name, city, population, public school district name, enrollment, grade range; superintendent name, address, phone, fax, names of public schools, address, phone, fax, principal's name, enrollment; private and Catholic school listings include school name, enrollment, grade ranges, principal's name, address, phone,

fax. Arrangement: Geographical by state, then alphabetical by city.

★5890★   **Private Independent Schools**

Bunting and Lyon Inc.
238 N Main St.
Wallingford, CT 06492
Ph: (203)269-3333   Fax: (203)269-5697
URL: http://www.buntingandlyon.com

Annual, February. $110.00. Covers 1,200 English-speaking elementary and secondary private schools and summer programs in North America and abroad. Entries include: School name, address, phone, fax, e-mail, website, enrollment, tuition and other fees, financial aid information, administrator's name and educational background, director of admission, regional accreditation, description of programs, curriculum, activities, learning differences grid. Arrangement: Geographical. Indexes: School name; geographical. Summer programs, general classification grid, learning differences reference grid.

★5891★   **QED's State-by-State School Guides**

Quality Education Data Inc.
1625 Broadway, Ste. 250
Denver, CO 80202
Ph: (303)209-9400   Fax: (303)209-9444
Fr: 800-525-5811
URL: http://www.qeddata.com/school-guide.htm

Annual, October. $1,345.00 for national set; $3,565.00 for electronic version; $4,175.00 for print and electronic. Covers over 100,000 public and private elementary and secondary schools in 16,000 school districts; in 52 volumes (national set). Entries include: School district name, address, phone, district enrollment, identification of site-based managed schools, number of teachers, number of schools, financial data, minority enrollment statistics, names and educational specializations of key personnel, list of member schools, including school name, address, phone, name of principal, name of librarian, grade levels taught, enrollment, services outsourced, number and brands of microcomputers used. Arrangement: Geographical - county within state. Indexes: School name, district name, geographical (county name), personal name.

★5892★   **Requirements for Certification of Teachers, Counselors, Librarians, Administrators for Elementary and Secondary Schools**

University of Chicago Press
Journals Division
PO Box 37005
Chicago, IL 60637
Ph: (773)753-3347   Fax: (773)753-0811
Fr: 877-705-1878

Annual, June. $44.00. Publication includes: List of state and local departments of education. Entries include: Office name, address, phone. Principal content of publication is summaries of each state's teaching and administrative certification requirements. Arrangement: Geographical.

HANDBOOKS AND MANUALS

★5893★ *The ABC's of Job-Hunting for Teachers: An A-Z Guide to Landing the Perfect Job*

Kappa Delta Pi, Int'l Honor Society in Education
3707 Woodview Trace
Indianapolis, IN 46268-1158
Ph: (317)871-4900   Fax: (317)704-2323
Fr: 800-284-3167

Mary C. Clement. May 2003. $10.95 (paper). Illustrated. 96 pages.

★5894★ *Becoming a Teacher*

Pearson Allyn & Bacon
1230 Ave. of the Americas
New York, NY 10020
Ph: (212)782-3300   Fr: 800-634-7064

Gary Borich. 1995. $24.95 (paper). 140 pages. Part of The Falmer Press Teachers' Library Series No. 7.

★5895★ *Career Information Center*

Macmillan Publishing Co. Inc.
200 Old Tappan Rd.
Old Tappan, NJ 07675
Fr: 800-428-5331

Visual Education Center Staff. Seventh edition, 1999. $275.00. 2080 pages. This 13-volume set profiles over 600 occupations. Each occupational profile describes job duties, educational requirements, how to get the job, advancement possibilities, employment outlook, working conditions, earnings and benefits, and where to write for more information.

★5896★ *Customizing Your Resume for Teaching Positions*

Rowman and Littlefield
4720 Boston Way
Lanham, MD 20706
Ph: (301)459-3366   Fax: (301)459-2118
Fr: 800-462-6420

Edward G. Pultorak. 1993. 52 pages.

★5897★ *Developing a Teaching Style: Methods for Elementary School Teachers*

HarperCollins College Div.
PO Box 400
Prospect Heights, IL 60070
Ph: (847)634-0081   Fax: (847)634-9501

Robert D. Louisell and Jorge Descamps. Second edition, 2000. $39.95 (paper).

★5898★ *Educator's Job Search: The Ultimate Guide to Finding Positions in Education*

National Education Association
PO Box 2035
Annapolis Junction, MD 20701
Fr: 800-229-4200

Martin Kimeldorf. 1993. $15.95 (paper). 88 pages.

★5899★ *Great Jobs for Music Majors*

McGraw-Hill Companies
1221 Avenue of the Americas
New York, NY 10020
Ph: (212)904-2000   Fr: 800-323-4900
E-mail: ntcpub@tribune.com

Jan Goldberg, Stephen Lambert, Julie De-Galan. 1997. $11.95 (paper). 365 pages.

★5900★ *Handbook for Christian EFL Teachers: Christian Teacher-Preparation Programs, Overseas Teaching Opportunities, Instructional Materials and Resources*

Institute for Cross-Cultural Training, Billy Graham Center, Wheaton College; Berry Pub. Services
PO Box 794
Wheaton, IL 60189
Ph: (630)752-7158   Fax: (630)752-7155

Lonna J. Dickerson and Dianne F. Dow. 1997. $9.00 (paper). 96 pages. Part of the Monograph Series.

★5901★ *How to Get a Job in Education*

Adams Media Corp.
57 Littlefield St.
Avon, MA 02322
Ph: (508)427-7100   Fax: (508)427-6790
Fr: 800-872-5627
URL: http://www.adamsmedia.com

Joel Levin. Second edition, 1995. $15.95. 320 pages. Out of print. Prepared for recent college graduates, seasoned educators, and career-changing professionals, this publication guides the job-seeker through the necessary steps to obtaining a job in education at the elementary, secondary, and university levels. Offers advice on how to prepare for state and local examinations, how to locate teaching opportunities nationwide, and how to obtain certification. Includes a nationwide salary survey. Covers public, private, summer, and overseas opportunities.

★5902★ *How to Get the Teaching Position You Want: Teacher Candidate Guide*

Educational Enterprises
PO Box 1836
Spring Valley, CA 91979
Ph: (619)660-7720

Phyllis Murton. Second edition, revised, 1996. $9.95 (paper). 110 pages. This book provides a comprehensive guide for the teacher candidate's job search, as the format offers information that includes: inter-

view questions most often asked in the teaching interview (grade-level & subject-matter specific); sample forms for applications, cover letters, & resumes that will impact principals & district personnel; strategies on preparing for the teaching interview; interview follow-up techniques; inside tips from a superintendent, a principal & a counselor.

★5903★ *The Inside Secrets of Finding a Teaching Job*

JIST Publishing
8902 Otis Ave.
Indianapolis, IN 46216
Ph: (317)613-4200   Fax: (317)613-4307
Fr: 800-648-5478
E-mail: jistworks@aol.com
URL: http://www.jist.com

Burt Beers, Jack Warner, Clyde Bryan and Diane Warner. 1997. $14.95. 186 pages. Tips from educators on finding an entry-level teaching position.

★5904★ *Job Hunting in Education: An Insider's Guide to Success*

Scarecrow Press, Inc.
4501 Forbes Blvd., Ste. 200
Lanham, MD 20706-4310
Ph: (301)459-3366   Fax: (301)429-5747

Herbert F. Pandiscio. April 2004. $39.95 (paper). 192 pages.

★5905★ *The New Elementary Teacher's Handbook: (Almost) Everything You Need to Know for Your First Years of Teaching*

Corwin Press, Inc.
2455 Teller Rd.
Thousand Oaks, CA 91320-2218
Ph: (805)499-9734   Fax: (805)499-0871

Kathleen F. Jonson. 1997. $32.95 (paper). 224 pages.

★5906★ *Non-Profits and Education Job Finder*

Planning Communications
7215 Oak Ave.
River Forest, IL 60305-1935
Ph: (708)366-5200   Fax: (708)366-5280
Fr: 888-366-5200
URL: http://jobfindersonline.com

Daniel Lauber. 1997. $32.95; $16.95 (paper). 336 pages. Covers 1600 sources. Discusses how to use sources of non-profit sector job vacancies in a number of specialties and state-by-state, including job-matching services, job hotlines, specialty periodicals with job ads, salary surveys, and directories. Covers a variety of fields from education to religion. Includes chapters on resume and cover letter preparation and interviewing.

★5907★ Opportunities in State and Local Government Careers

Vgm Career Horizons
1221 Avenue of the Americas
New York, NY 10020
Ph: (212)904-2000   Fr: 800-323-4900
E-mail: ntcpub@tribune.com

Neale J. Baxter. 1994. $14.95; $10.95 (paper). 160 pages. Points out the incentives and drawbacks of a government career. Describes hiring procedures and provides tips on filling out applications, taking physical and aptitude tests, handling interviews, and finding jobs. Describes the jobs in which 75% of all state and local government workers are employed. For each occupation, covers the nature of the work and the training required.

★5908★ Opportunities in Teaching Careers

McGraw-Hill/Contemporary Books
1221 Avenue of the Americas
New York, NY 10020
Ph: (212)904-2000   Fr: 800-323-4900
E-mail: ntcpub@tribune.com

Janet Fine. 2000. $14.95; $11.95 (paper). 200 pages. Discusses licensing and accreditation programs, sources of placement information, job-seeking correspondence, selection procedures, and paths to advancement. Also covers professional associations, non-traditional teaching opportunities, and jobs abroad.

★5909★ A Practical Guide to Elementary Instruction: From Plan to Delivery

Pearson Allyn & Bacon
1230 Ave. of the Americas
New York, NY 10020
Ph: (212)782-3300   Fax: 800-445-6991
Fr: 800-666-9433

Suzanne Borman and Joel M. Levine. 1997. Out of print.

★5910★ Real People Working in Education

McGraw-Hill Contemporary Books
1221 Avenue of the Americas
New York, NY 10020
Ph: (212)904-2000   Fr: 800-323-4900
E-mail: ntcpub@tribune.com

Blythe Camenson, Jan Goldberg. 1997. $17.95; $12.95 (paper). Interviews and profiles of working professionals capture a range of opportunities in this field.

★5911★ The Teaching Career

Teachers College Press, Teachers
  College, Columbia University
1234 Amsterdam Ave.
New York, NY 10027
Ph: (212)678-3929   Fax: (212)678-4149

John I. Goodlad, Timothy J. McMannon. February 2004. $24.95 (paper). Illustrated. 224 pages. The Series in School Reform.

★5912★ Teaching (Career Portraits)

Vgm Career Horizons
1221 Avenue of the Americas
New York, NY 10020
Ph: (212)904-2000   Fr: 800-323-4900
E-mail: ntcpub@tribune.com

Marjorie Eberts and Margaret Gisler. 1994. $13.95. 320 pages.

★5913★ Where the Jobs Are: The Hottest Careers for the 90s

The Career Press, Inc.
3 Tice Rd.
PO Box 687
Franklin Lakes, NJ 07417-1322
Ph: (201)848-0310   Fax: (201)848-1727
Fr: 800-227-3371

Joyce Hadley. Third edition, 2000. $13.99 (paper). 400 pages. Out of print. Describes careers in fifteen general fields, from accounting to travel and hospitality.

★5914★ Why Choose a Career in Teaching?

The Graduate Group
PO Box 370351
West Hartford, CT 06137-0351
Fr: 800-484-7280

James Abbott. April 2004. $30.00 (paper).

EMPLOYMENT AGENCIES AND SEARCH FIRMS

★5915★ Educational Placement Service

1001 Craig Rd., Ste. 170
St. Louis, MO 63146
Ph: (314)991-5855   Fax: (314)991-5295
URL: http://www.educatorjobs.com

Employment agency. Focuses on teaching, administrative, and education-related openings.

TRADESHOWS

★5916★ Association for Childhood Education International Annual International Conference & Exhibition

Association for Childhood Education
  International
17904 Georgia Ave., Ste. 215
Olney, MD 20832
Ph: (301)570-2111   Fax: (301)570-2212
Fr: 800-423-3563
E-mail: aceimc@aol.com
URL: http://www.acei.org

Annual. **Primary Exhibits:** Commercial and educational exhibits of interest to teachers, teacher educators, college students, day care personnel and other care givers.

★5917★ National Art Education Association Convention

National Art Education Association
1916 Association Dr.
Reston, VA 20191
Ph: (703)860-8000   Fax: (703)860-2960
E-mail: naea@dgs.dgsys.com
URL: http://www.naea-reston.org

Annual. **Primary Exhibits:** Art materials; art-related books and magazines; art career education information; arts and crafts supplies. **Dates and Locations:** 2005 Mar 04-08; Boston, MA • 2006 Mar 22-26; Chicago, IL • 2004 Mar 14-18; New York, NY.

★5918★ National Association for the Education of Young Children Annual Conference

National Association for the Education of
  Young Children
1509 16th St., NW
Washington, DC 20036
Ph: (202)232-8777   Fax: (202)328-1846
Fr: 800-424-2460
E-mail: conference@naevc.org
URL: http://www.naevc.org

Annual. **Primary Exhibits:** Educational materials and equipment designed for children ages birth through eight years old. **Dates and Locations:** 2004 Nov 10-13; Anaheim, CA; Anaheim Convention Center.

OTHER SOURCES

★5919★ American Association for Health Education (AAHE)

1900 Association Dr.
Reston, VA 20191
Ph: (703)476-3437   Fax: (703)476-6638
Fr: 800-213-7193
E-mail: aahe@aahperd.org
URL: http://www.aahperd.org/aahe

Members: Professionals who have responsibility for health education in schools, colleges, communities, hospitals and clinics, and industries. **Purpose:** Works for the advancement of health education through program activities and federal legislation; encouragement of close working relationships between all health education and health service organizations; achievement of good health and well-being for all Americans automatically, without conscious thought and endeavor. Member of the American Alliance for Health, Physical Education, Recreation and Dance.

★5920★ American Association of Teachers of German (AATG)

112 Haddontowne Ct., No. 104
Cherry Hill, NJ 08034-3668
Ph: (856)795-5553   Fax: (856)795-9398
E-mail: headquarters@aatg.org
URL: http://www.aatg.org

Description: Teachers of German at all levels; individuals interested in German language and culture. Offers in-service teacher-training workshops, materials, student honor society, national German examination, and stipends/scholarships.

★5921★ **American Federation of Teachers (AFT)**
555 New Jersey Ave. NW
Washington, DC 20001
Ph: (202)879-4400   Fax: (202)879-4545
Fr: 800-238-1133
E-mail: online@aft.org
URL: http://www.aft.org

Description: Affiliated with the AFL-CIO. Works with teachers and other educational employees at the state and local level in organizing, collective bargaining, research, educational issues, and public relations. Conducts research in areas such as educational reform, teacher certification, and national assessments and standards. Represents members' concerns through legislative action; offers technical assistance. Also serves professionals with concerns similar to those of teachers, including state employees, healthcare workers, and paraprofessionals.

★5922★ **Association of Christian Schools International (ACSI)**
731 Chapel Hills Dr.
Colorado Springs, CO 80920-1027
Ph: (719)528-6906   Fax: (719)531-0631
Fr: 800-367-0798
E-mail: info@acsi.org
URL: http://www.acsi.org

Description: Seeks to enable Christian educators and schools worldwide to effectively prepare students for life.

★5923★ *Career Close-ups: School Teacher*
AIMS Multimedia
9710 DeSoto Ave.
Chatsworth, CA 91311
Ph: (818)773-4300   Fax: (818)341-6700
Fr: 800-367-2467
URL: http://www.aimsmultimedia.com

Video. 1994. $69.95. 27 minutes. Profiles of outstanding teachers.

★5924★ **Center for the Child Care Workforce, A Project of the American Federation of Teachers Educational Foundation (CCW/AFTEF)**
555 New Jersey Ave. NW
Washington, DC 20001
Ph: (202)662-8005   Fax: (202)662-8006
E-mail: ccw@aft.org
URL: http://www.ccw.org

Purpose: Works to develop innovative solutions to the child care crisis to improve salaries, working conditions, and status of child care workers; to increase public awareness about the importance of child care work and the training and skill it demands; to develop resources and create an information sharing network for child care workers nationwide. **Activities:** Gathers current infor-

mation on salaries and benefits; offers consultation services. Sponsors research projects; compiles statistics; operates speakers' bureau. Maintains extensive file of materials on working conditions and research on child care workers.

★5925★ **Convention of American Instructors of the Deaf (CAID)**
PO Box 377
Bedford, TX 76095-0377
Ph: (817)354-8414
E-mail: caid@swbell.net
URL: http://www.caid.org/

Members: Professional organization of teachers, administrators, and professionals in allied fields related to education of the deaf and hard-of-hearing. **Purpose:** Objectives are to provide opportunities for a free interchange of views concerning methods and means of educating the deaf and hard-of-hearing; to promote such education by the publication of reports, essays, and other information; to develop more effective methods of teaching deaf and hard-of-hearing children.

★5926★ *Education and Training*
Cambridge Educational
2572 Brunswick Ave.
Lawrenceville, NJ 08648-4128
Fax: 800-FAX-ON-US   Fr: 800-468-4227
URL: http://www.cambridgeeducational.com
$89.95. 2002. 18 minutes.

★5927★ **Friends Council on Education (FCE)**
1507 Cherry St.
Philadelphia, PA 19102
Ph: (215)241-7245   Fax: (215)241-7299
E-mail: quakered@aol.com
URL: http://www.friendscouncil.org

Members: Representatives appointed by Friends Yearly Meetings; heads of Quaker secondary and elementary schools and colleges; members-at-large. **Purpose:** Acts as a clearinghouse for information on Quaker schools and colleges. **Activities:** Holds meetings and conferences on education and provides in-service training for teachers, administrators, and trustees in Friends schools.

★5928★ **International Reading Association (IRA)**
800 Barksdale Rd.
PO Box 8139
Newark, DE 19714-8139
Ph: (302)731-1600   Fax: (302)731-1057
E-mail: pubinfo@reading.org
URL: http://www.reading.org

Description: Teachers, reading specialists, consultants, administrators, supervisors, researchers, psychologists, librarians, and parents interested in promoting literacy. Seeks to improve the quality of reading instruction and promote literacy worldwide. Disseminates information pertaining to research on reading, including information on adult litera-

cy, early childhood and literacy development, international education, literature for children and adolescents, and teacher education and professional development. Maintains over 40 special interest groups and over 70 committees.

★5929★ **International Technology Education Association - Council for Supervisors (ITEA-CS)**
Virginia Department of Education
PO Box 2120, 21st Fl.
Richmond, VA 23218-2120
Ph: (804)225-2839   Fax: (804)371-2456
URL: http://www.iteawww.org

Description: Technology education supervisors from the U.S. Office of Education; local school department chairpersons; state departments of education, local school districts, territories, provinces, and foreign countries. Works to improve instruction and supervision of programs in technology education. Conducts research; compiles statistics. Sponsors competitions. Maintains speakers' bureau.

★5930★ **Jewish Education Service of North America (JESNA)**
111 8th Ave., 11th Fl.
New York, NY 10011-5201
Ph: (212)284-6950   Fax: (212)284-6951
E-mail: jwoocher@jesna.org
URL: http://www.jesna.org

Description: Widely recognized leader in the areas of research and program evaluation, organizational change and innovative program design and dissemination. Operates the Mandell J. Berman Jewish Heritage Center for Research and Evaluation. Supports the Convenant Foundation, a joint venture with the Crown Family, which makes awards and grants for creativity in Jewish education.

★5931★ *Kindergarten and Elementary School Teachers*
Evon Publishing
832 N 7th Ave.
Iron River, MI 49935
Ph: (906)265-3190

Audiocassette. 1996. $16.95. 32 minutes. Part of the Careers and Vocational Guidance Series. Provides information about the nature of the work, educational requirements, employment outlook, earnings, and work conditions as well as additional related information.

★5932★ **NAFSA/Association of International Educators (NAFSA)**
1307 New York Ave. NW, 8th Fl.
Washington, DC 20005
Ph: (202)737-3699   Fax: (202)737-3657
E-mail: inbox@nafsa.org
URL: http://www.nafsa.org

Description: Individuals, organizations, and institutions dealing with international educational exchange, including foreign student advisers, overseas educational advisers, credentials and admissions officers, administrators and teachers of English as a second language, community support personnel, study-abroad administrators, and embassy cultural or educational personnel. Promotes self-regulation standards and responsibilities in international educational exchange; offers professional development opportunities primarily through publications, workshops, grants, and regional and national conferences. Advocates for increased awareness and support of international education and exchange on campuses, in government, and in communities. Offers services including: a job registry for employers and professionals involved with international education; a consultant referral service. Sponsors joint liaison activities with a variety of other educational and government organizations to conduct a census of foreign student enrollment in the U.S.; conducts workshops about specific subjects and countries.

★5933★ National Alliance of Black School Educators (NABSE)

310 Pennsylvania Ave. SE
Washington, DC 20003
Ph: (202)608-6310   Fax: (202)608-6319
Fr: 800-221-2654
E-mail: nabse@nabse.org
URL: http://www.nabse.org

Description: Black educators from all levels; others indirectly involved in the education of black youth. Purpose is to promote awareness, professional expertise, and commitment among black educators. Goals are to: eliminate and rectify the results of racism in education; work with state, local, and national leaders to raise the academic achievement level of all black students; increase members' involvement in legislative activities; facilitate the introduction of a curriculum that more completely embraces black America; improve the ability of black educators to promote problem resolution; create a meaningful and effective network of strength, talent, and professional support. Sponsors workshops, commission meetings, and special projects. Encourages research, especially as it relates to blacks, and the presentation of papers during national conferences. Plans to establish a National Black Educators Data Bank and offer placement service.

★5934★ National Art Education Association (NAEA)

1916 Association Dr.
Reston, VA 20191-1590
Ph: (703)860-8000   Fax: (703)860-2960
E-mail: naea@dgs.dgsys.com
URL: http://www.naea-reston.org

Members: Teachers of art at elementary, middle, secondary, and college levels; colleges, libraries, museums, and other educational institutions. **Purpose:** Studies problems of teaching art; encourages research and experimentation. **Activities:** Serves as clearinghouse for information on art education programs, materials, and methods of instruction. Sponsors special institutes. Cooperates with other national organizations for the furtherance of creative art experiences for youth.

★5935★ National Association of Blind Teachers (NABT)

1155 15th St. NW, Ste. 1004
Washington, DC 20005
Ph: (202)467-5081   Fax: (202)467-5085
Fr: 800-424-8666
E-mail: info@acb.org
URL: http://www.acb.org

Description: Public school teachers, college and university professors, and teachers in residential schools for the blind. Purpose is to promote employment and professional goals of blind persons entering the teaching profession or those established in their respective teaching fields. Serves as a vehicle for the dissemination of information and the exchange of ideas addressing special problems of members. Compiles statistics.

★5936★ National Association of Catholic School Teachers (NACST)

1700 Sansom St., Ste. 903
Philadelphia, PA 19103
Ph: (215)665-0993   Fax: (215)568-8270
Fr: 800-99-NACST
E-mail: nacst.nacst@verizon.net
URL: http://www.nacst.com

Description: Catholic school teachers. Purpose is to unify, advise, and assist Catholic school teachers in matters of collective bargaining. Promotes the welfare and rights of Catholic schools and teachers; determines needs of Catholic schools and teachers. Monitors legislation, trends, and statistics concerning Catholic education; promotes legislation favorable to nonpublic schools and Catholic school teachers; offers legal advice and addresses issues such as unemployment compensation; assists teachers in organizing and negotiating contracts. Maintains speakers' bureau.

★5937★ National Association for the Education of Young Children (NAEYC)

1509 16th St. NW
Washington, DC 20036
Ph: (202)232-8777   Fax: (202)328-1846
Fr: 800-424-2460
E-mail: naeyc@naeyc.org
URL: http://www.naeyc.org

Description: Teachers and directors of preschool and primary schools, kindergartens, child care centers, and early other learning programs for young childhood; early childhood education and child development educators, trainers, and researchers and other professionals dedicated to young children's healthy development.

★5938★ National Association of Episcopal Schools (NAES)

815 2nd Ave., Ste. 313
New York, NY 10017-4594
Ph: (212)716-6134   Fax: (212)286-9366
Fr: 800-334-7626
E-mail: info@episcopalschools.org
URL: http://www.naes.org

Description: Episcopal day and boarding schools and preschools. Promotes the edu-

cational ministry of the Episcopal Church. Provides publications, consultation services and conference focusing on Episcopal identity of schools, worship, religious education, spirituality, leadership development and governance for heads/directors, administrators, chaplains and teachers of religion, trustees, rectors and other church and school leaders.

★5939★ National Association of Independent Schools (NAIS)

1620 L St. NW, Ste. 1100
Washington, DC 20036-5695
Ph: (202)973-9700   Fax: (202)973-9790
E-mail: info@nais.org
URL: http://www.nais.org

Description: Independent elementary and secondary school members; regional associations of independent schools and related associations. Provides curricular and administrative research and services. Conducts educational programs; compiles statistics.

★5940★ National Association for Research in Science Teaching (NARST)

319A Erickson Hall
Michigan State University
East Lansing, MI 48824
Ph: (517)432-4648
E-mail: jwtillot@syr.edu
URL: http://www2.educ.sfu.ca/narstsite/

Description: Science teachers, supervisors, and science educators specializing in research and teacher education. Promotes and coordinates science education research and interprets and reports the results.

★5941★ National Association of State Directors of Special Education (NASDSE)

1800 Diagonal Rd., Ste. 320
Alexandria, VA 22314
Ph: (703)519-3800   Fax: (703)519-3808
E-mail: nasdse@nasdse.org
URL: http://www.nasdse.org

Members: Professional society of state directors; consultants, supervisors, and administrators who have statewide responsibilities for administering special education programs. **Purpose:** Provides services to state agencies to facilitate their efforts to maximize educational outcomes for individuals with disabilities.

★5942★ National Community Education Association (NCEA)

3929 Old Lee Hwy., Ste. 91-A
Fairfax, VA 22030
Ph: (703)359-8973   Fax: (703)359-0972
E-mail: ncea@ncea.com
URL: http://www.ncea.com

Description: Community school directors, principals, superintendents, professors, teachers, students, and laypeople. **Purpose:** Promotes and establishes community schools as an integral part of the educational plan of every community. Emphasizes community and parent involvement in the schools, lifelong learning, and enrichment of K-12 and adult education. Serves as a clearinghouse for the exchange of ideas and information, and the sharing of efforts. **Activities:** Offers leadership training.

★5943★ National Council for Accreditation of Teacher Education (NCATE)
2010 Massachusetts Ave. NW, Ste. 500
Washington, DC 20036-1023
Ph: (202)466-7496   Fax: (202)296-6620
E-mail: ncate@ncate.org
URL: http://www.ncate.org

Members: Representatives from constituent colleges and universities, state departments of education, school boards, teacher, and other professional groups. **Purpose:** Voluntary accrediting body devoted exclusively to evaluation and accreditation of institutions for preparation of elementary and secondary school teachers; preparation of school service personnel, including school principals, supervisors, superintendents, school psychologists, instructional technologists, and other specialists for school-oriented positions.

★5944★ National Council for Geographic Education (NCGE)
206A Martin Hall
Jacksonville State University
Jacksonville, AL 36265-1602
Ph: (256)782-5293   Fax: (256)782-5336
E-mail: ncge@jsucc.jsu.edu
URL: http://www.ncge.org

Description: Teachers of geography and social studies in elementary and secondary schools, colleges, and universities; geographers in governmental agencies and private businesses. Encourages the training of teachers in geographic concepts, practices, teaching methods, and techniques; works to develop effective geographic educational programs in schools and colleges and with adult groups; stimulates the production and use of accurate and understandable geographic teaching aids and materials.

★5945★ National Council of Teachers of Mathematics (NCTM)
1906 Association Dr.
Reston, VA 20191-1502
Ph: (703)620-9840   Fax: (703)476-2970
Fr: 800-235-7566
E-mail: orders@nctm.org
URL: http://www.nctm.org

Description: Dedicated to improving teach-

ing and learning of mathematics. Toll-free number is for orders only.

★5946★ Overseas Employment Opportunities for Educators: Department of Defense Dependents Schools
DIANE Publishing Co.
PO Box 1428
Collingdale, PA 19023-8428
Ph: (610)461-6200   Fax: (610)461-6130
Fr: 800-782-3833

Barry Leonard, editor. 1999. $20.00. 44 pages. An introduction to teachings positions in the Dept. of Defense Dependents Schools (DoDDS), a worldwide school system, operated by the DoD in 14 countries.

★5947★ Teaching & Related Occupations
Delphi Productions
3160 4th St.
Boulder, CO 80304
Fax: (303)443-4022   Fr: 888-443-2400
URL: http://www.delphivideo.com

$95.00. 50 minutes. Part of the Careers for the 21st Century Video Library.

Landscape Architects

★5948★ Architectural Record

McGraw-Hill Companies
1221 Avenue of the Americas
New York, NY 10020
Ph: (212)512-2000
URL: http://www.mcgraw-hill.com

$59.00/year for individuals; $7.00 for single issue. Magazine focusing on architecture.

★5949★ Fabric Architecture

Industrial Fabrics Association International
1801 County Rd. B W
Roseville, MN 55113-4061
Ph: (651)222-2508   Fax: (651)225-6966
Fr: 800-225-4324
URL: http://www.ifai.com

Bimonthly. $39.00/year; $43.00/year for Canada and Mexico; $55.00/year for out of country. Magazine specializing in interior and exterior design ideas and technical information for architectural fabric applications in architecture and the landscape.

★5950★ Grounds Maintenance

Primedia Business
9800 Metcalf Ave.
Overland Park, KS 66212
Ph: (913)341-1300   Fax: (913)967-1898
E-mail: gm_editorial@intertec.com
URL: http://www.grounds-mag.com

Monthly. Free to qualified subscribers; $36.00/year for individuals; $10.00/year for single issue; $10.00/year for back issues (plus postage). Trade magazine on landscape design, maintenance, and installation.

★5951★ Interiorscape

Brantwood Publications Inc.
2410 Northside Dr.
Clearwater, FL 33761
Ph: (727)786-9771   Fax: (727)791-4126

Bimonthly. $12.00/year for individuals; $3.00 for single issue. Interior landscape design magazine.

★5952★ Landscape Architecture

American Society of Landscape Architects
636 Eye St. NW
Washington, DC 20001-3736
Ph: (202)898-2444   Fax: (202)898-1185
URL: http://www.asla.org/members/land/index.cfm

Bimonthly. Professional magazine covering land planning and design.

★5953★ The Landscape Contractor

Illinois Landscape Contractor Association
2625 Butterfield Rd., Ste. 204-W
Oak Brook, IL 60523-1257
Ph: (630)472-2851   Fax: (630)472-3150

Monthly. $65.00/year for individuals. Magazine for the landscape trade.

★5954★ Landscape Design

Adams Business Media/Green Media
833 W Jackson Blvd., 7th fl.
Chicago, IL 60607
Ph: (312)846-4300   Fax: (312)846-4638
URL: http://www.greenindustrynet.com

Quarterly. Free to qualified subscribers. Magazine for licensed landscape architects.

★5955★ Landscape & Irrigation

Adams Business Media/Green Media
833 W Jackson Blvd., 7th fl.
Chicago, IL 60607
Ph: (312)846-4300   Fax: (312)846-4638
URL: http://www.greenmediaonline.com

Monthly. Free to qualified subscribers; $40.00/year for individuals. Magazine for the landscape and irrigation contracting industry.

★5956★ Landscape Management

Advanstar Communications Inc.
7500 Old Oak Blvd.
Cleveland, OH 44130-3369
Ph: (440)243-8100   Fax: (440)891-2777
URL: http://https://www.advanstar.com/index_allpubs.html

Magazine for professionals in landscape, grounds management and lawn care, construction, and maintenance.

★5957★ Nursery News

Cenflo Inc.
205 W Wacker Dr., Ste. 1040
Chicago, IL 60606-3508
Ph: (312)739-5000   Fax: (312)739-0739
Fr: 800-732-4581
URL: http://www.nurserynews.com

Monthly. $20.00/year; $28.00 for two years. Trade newspaper (tabloid) for nursery industry.

★5958★ Qualified Remodeler Magazine

Cygnus Business Media
1233 Janesville Ave.
Fort Atkinson, WI 53538
Fr: 800-547-7377
URL: http://www.qualifiedremodeler.com

Monthly. Free to qualified subscribers; $66.00/year for individuals. Magazine for remodeling contractor/distributors.

★5959★ Remodeling

Hanley-Wood L.L.C.
1 Thomas Cir., Ste. 600
Washington, DC 20005
Ph: (202)452-0800   Fax: (202)785-1974
URL: http://www.remodeling.hw.net

Monthly. $24.95/year for individuals; $8.00 for single issue. Trade magazine for the professional remodeling industry.

PLACEMENT AND JOB REFERRAL SERVICES

★5960★ American Society of Landscape Architects (ASLA)

636 Eye St. NW
Washington, DC 20001-3736
Ph: (202)898-2444   Fax: (202)898-1185
Fr: 888-999-2752
E-mail: jlofton@asla.org
URL: http://www.asla.org/

Description: Professional society of landscape architects. Purpose is to promote the advancement of education and skill in the art of landscape architecture as an instrument in service to the public welfare. Seeks to strengthen existing and proposed university programs in landscape architecture. Offers counsel to new and emerging programs; encourages state registration of landscape architects. Sponsors annual educational exhibit. Offers placement service; conducts specialized education and research.

EMPLOYER DIRECTORIES AND NETWORKING LISTS

★5961★ American Society of Landscape Architects-Members' Handbook

American Society of Landscape Architects
636 Eye St. NW
Washington, DC 20001-3736
Ph: (202)898-2444   Fax: (202)898-1185
E-mail: handbook@asla.org
URL: http://www.asla.org

Annual, November. $250.00. Covers 11,000 member landscape architects and affiliates. Entries include: Name, address, phone, chapter, membership category, year joined, type of practice. Arrangement: Alphabetical. Indexes: Geographical.

★5962★ Association of University Interior Designers-Membership Chairperson

Association of University Interior Designers
c/o Terri Smith-Wright
Purdue University
The Office of Purchasing
West Lafayette, IN 47907
Ph: (765)494-9603   Fax: (765)496-1579

Twice yearly, June and October. Covers nearly 100 in-house interior designers, landscape designers, architects, and purchasing agents associated with universities. Entries include: Name, title, affiliation, address, phone. Arrangement: Alphabetical.

★5963★ California Landscape Contractors Association-Roster

California Landscape Contractors Association
1491 River Park Dr. Ste. 100
Sacramento, CA 95815
Ph: (916)448-2522   Fax: (916)448-7692
Fr: 800-448-CLCA

Annual, January. $50.00. Covers about 2,000 member landscape contractors and suppliers of products and services to the landscape contracting industry. Entries include: Name of firm, address, phone, representative to the association, chapter, products and services offered. Arrangement: Geographical. Indexes: Product/service.

★5964★ Directory of Public Garden Internships

American Association of Botanical Gardens and Arboreta (AABGA)
100 W 10th St., Ste. 614
Wilmington, DE 19801-6604
Ph: (302)655-7100   Fax: (302)655-8100
E-mail: bvincent@aabga.org

Annual, November. $10.00 for members; $15.00 for nonmembers. Covers 700 student internships and summer jobs at public gardens throughout North America. Entries include: Name of institution, address, name of contact, deadline for application, number of students hired, whether internships are available, employment period, hours, rate of pay, whether housing is available, other comments. Arrangement: Alphabetical. Indexes: By position, by state/province.

★5965★ Grounds Maintenance-Buyers' Guide Issue

Primedia Business
9800 Metcalf Ave.
Overland Park, KS 66212
Ph: (913)341-1300   Fax: (913)967-1898
E-mail: gm_editorial@intertec.com
URL: http://www.grounds-mag.com

Annual, December. $5.00. Publication includes: List of manufacturers, growers, and suppliers of materials for landscaping design, construction, and maintenance; landscaping associations. Entries include: Company name, address, phone. Arrangement: Alphabetical/product. Indexes: Product.

★5966★ Landscape Contractors Directory

infoUSA Inc.
5711 S 86th Cir.
Omaha, NE 68127-0347
Ph: (402)930-3500   Fax: (402)331-0176
Fr: 800-555-6124
URL: http://www.abii.com

Annual. Number of listings: 51,298. Entries include: Name, address, phone (including area code), size of advertisement, year first in "Yellow Pages," name of owner or manager, number of employees. Regional editions available: Eastern, $845.00; Western, $515.00. Compiled from telephone company "Yellow Pages," nationwide. Arrangement: Geographical.

★5967★ Landscape Designers Directory

infoUSA Inc.
5711 S 86th Cir.
Omaha, NE 68127-0347
Ph: (402)930-3500   Fax: (402)331-0176
Fr: 800-555-6124
URL: http://www.abii.com

Annual. Number of listings: 12,799. Entries include: Name, address, phone (including area code), size of advertisement, year first in "Yellow Pages," name of owner or manager, number of employees. Compiled from telephone company "Yellow Pages," nationwide. Arrangement: Geographical.

★5968★ New York State Nursery/ Landscape Association-Directory

New York State Nursery/Landscape Assoc. Inc.
PO Box 657
Baldwinsville, NY 13027
Ph: (315)635-5008   Fax: (315)635-4874
Fr: 800-647-0384

Annual, January. Covers over 800 member nursery, landscape, gardening, and lawn maintenance firms in New York. Entries include: Company name, address, phone, name. Arrangement: Alphabetical.

★5969★ ProFile: The Architects Sourcebook

Reed Construction Data
30 Technology Pkwy. S
Norcross, GA 30092
Ph: (770)209-3664   Fax: 800-444-1059
Fr: 800-949-0276
E-mail: profile@reedbusiness.com
URL: http://www.firstsourceonl.com

Annual. $225.00. Covers more than 27,000 architectural firms. Entries include: For firms-Firm name, address, phone, fax, year established, key staff and their primary responsibilities (for design, specification, etc.), number of staff personnel by discipline, types of work, geographical area served, projects. "ProFile" is an expanded version of, and replaces, the "Firm Directory." Arrangement: Firms are geographical. Indexes: Firm name, key individuals, specialization by category, consultants.

HANDBOOKS AND MANUALS

★5970★ Career Information Center

Macmillan Publishing Co. Inc.
200 Old Tappan Rd.
Old Tappan, NJ 07675
Fr: 800-428-5331

Visual Education Center Staff. Seventh edition, 1999. $275.00. 2080 pages. This 13-volume set profiles over 600 occupations. Each occupational profile describes job duties, educational requirements, how to get the job, advancement possibilities, employment outlook, working conditions, earnings and benefits, and where to write for more information.

★5971★ Careers for Health Nuts and Others Who Like to Stay Fit
McGraw-Hill Trade
2 Penn Plaza
New York, NY 10121
Ph: (212)904-2000   Fr: 800-722-4726
E-mail: ntcpub@tribune.com

Blythe Camenson. 1996. $14.95; $9.95 (paper). 160 pages.

★5972★ Careers in Horticulture and Botany
McGraw-Hill Trade
2 Penn Plaza
New York, NY 10121
Ph: (212)904-2000   Fr: 800-722-4726
E-mail: ntcpub@tribune.com

Jerry Garner. 1996. $17.95; 13.95 (paper). 255 pages. Includes bibliographical references

★5973★ Opportunities in Environmental Careers
McGraw-Hill Trade
2 Penn Plaza
New York, NY 10121
Ph: (212)904-2000   Fr: 800-722-4726
E-mail: ntcpub@tribune.com

Odom Fanning. Revised, 2002. $12.95 (paper). 160 pages. Describes a broad range of opportunities in fields such as environmental health, recreation, physics, and hygiene, and provides job search advice. Part of Opportunities in...Series.

★5974★ Opportunities in Landscape Architecture, Botanical Gardens, and Arboreta Careers
McGraw-Hill/Contemporary Books
1221 Avenue of the Americas
New York, NY 10020
Ph: (212)904-2000   Fr: 800-323-4900
E-mail: ntcpub@tribune.com

Blythe Cameron. 1998. $14.95; $11.95 (paper). 202 pages. Includes bibliography.

★5975★ Opportunities in Real Estate Careers
McGraw-Hill Professional
2 Penn Plaza
New York, NY 10121
Ph: (212)904-2000   Fr: 800-722-4726
E-mail: ntcpub@tribune.com

Mariwyn Evans. 2002. $15.95; $11.95 (paper). 160 pages.

★5976★ The Perfect Guide to Making $ in Landscaping and Maintenance: A How-To Book
Moran Publishing
210 Lazy River
Sealy, TX 77474
Fr: 800-223-0351

Gene Yezak. $9.95 (paper). 220 pages.

★5977★ Professional Practice for Landscape Architects
Butterworth-Heinemann
225 Wildwood Ave., Unit B
Woburn, MA 01801
Ph: (781)904-2500   Fax: (781)904-2640
Fr: 800-366-2665

Tennant, Garmory, and Winsch. 2001. $32.95 (paper).

EMPLOYMENT AGENCIES AND SEARCH FIRMS

★5978★ Claremont-Branan, Inc.
1298 Rockbridge Rd., Ste. B
Stone Mountain, GA 30087
Ph: (770)925-2915   Fax: (770)925-2601

Employment agency. Executive search firm.

ONLINE JOB SOURCES AND SERVICES

★5979★ American Society of Landscape Architects JobLink
American Society of Landscape Architects
636 Eye St. NW
Washington, DC 20001-3736
Ph: (202)898-2444   Fax: (202)898-1185
URL: http://www.asla.org/nonmembers/joblink.cfm

Description: A job-search site of the American Society of Landscape Architects. **Fee:** Resume postings cost $100 (nonmembers) or $10 (members) for a two-month listing. Job postings cost $450 (nonmembers) or $200 (members) for a two-month listing.

TRADESHOWS

★5980★ American Society of Landscape Architects Annual Meeting and Expo
American Society of Landscape Architects
636 Eye St., NW
Washington, DC 20015
Ph: (202)898-2444   Fax: (202)898-1185
Fr: 800-787-ASLA

URL: http://www.asla.org

Annual. **Primary Exhibits:** Irrigation supplies, outdoor lighting, park and playground equipment, paving and ground cover, street and park furniture, landscape maintenance equipment, computer hardware and software, architectural finishing materials, construction materials, historic preservation services, surveying and mapping equipment, and related equipment, supplies, and services.

OTHER SOURCES

★5981★ American Association of Botanical Gardens and Arboreta (AABGA)
100 W 10th St., Ste. 614
Wilmington, DE 19801-6604
Ph: (302)655-7100   Fax: (302)655-8100
E-mail: pallenstein@aabga.org
URL: http://www.aabga.org

Members: Directors and staffs of botanical gardens, arboreta, institutions maintaining or conducting horticultural courses, and others. **Purpose:** Seeks to serve North American public gardens and horticultural organizations by promoting professional development through its publications and meetings, advocating the interests of public gardens in political, corporate, foundation, and community arenas, and encouraging gardens to adhere to professional standards in their programs and operations.

★5982★ International Society of Arboriculture (ISA)
PO Box 3129
Champaign, IL 61826-3129
Ph: (217)355-9411   Fax: (217)355-9516
Fr: 888-472-8733
E-mail: isa@isa-arbor.com
URL: http://www.isa-arbor.com/

Description: Individuals engaged in commercial, municipal, and utility arboriculture; city, state, and national government employees; municipal and commercial arborists; others interested in shade tree welfare. Disseminates information on the care and preservation of shade and ornamental trees. Supports research projects at educational institutions.

★5983★ Landscape Architects
Evon Publishing
832 N 7th Ave.
Iron River, MI 49935
Ph: (906)265-3190

Audiocassette. 1996. $16.95. 32 minutes. part of the Careers and Vocational Guidance Series. Provides information about the nature of the work, educational requirements, employment outlook, earnings, and work conditions as well as additional related information.

★5984★ **Landscape Architecture Foundation (LAF)**
818 18th St. NW, Ste. 810
Washington, DC 20006
Ph: (202)331-7070   Fax: (202)331-7079
E-mail: severett@lafoundation.org
URL: http://www.lafoundation.org

Description: Education and research vehicle for the landscape architecture profession in the U.S. Combines the capabilities of landscape architects, interests of environmentalists, and needs of agencies and resource foundations. To encourage development of environmental research; to support and disseminate information on landscape architecture. Provides for the preparation and dissemination of educational and scientific information through publications, exhibits, lectures, and seminars. Solicits and expends gifts, legacies, and grants; has established an endowment fund; finances new programs. Sponsors California Landscape Architectural Student Scholarship Fund; endows and establishes professorships at colleges and universities. Develops programmed teaching materials in landscape architectural planning and construction; encourages submittal of proposals for unique and/or interdisciplinary educational research projects. Prepares slide, film, and tape presentations; operates charitable program. Has conducted a study of the profession to establish goals in terms of education, research needs, practice, and formulation of public policy.

★5985★ *Professional Specialty Occupations*
Delphi Productions
3160 4th St.
Boulder, CO 80304
Fax: (303)443-4022   Fr: 888-443-2400
URL: http://www.delphivideo.com

$95.00. 53 minutes. Part of the Careers for the 21st Century Video Library.

Landscapers

SOURCES OF HELP-WANTED ADS

★5986★ American City and County
Primedia Business
6151 Powers Ferry Rd.
Atlanta, GA 30339
Ph: (770)955-2500   Fax: (770)618-0348
Monthly. $67.00/year for individuals. Municipal and county administration magazine.

★5987★ American Nurseryman
American Nurseryman Publishing Co.
223 W Jackson Blvd., Ste. 500
Chicago, IL 60606-6904
Ph: (312)427-7339   Fax: (312)427-7346
Fr: 800-621-5727
E-mail: editors@amerinursery.com
Semimonthly. $48.00/year for individuals; $80.00/year for other countries; $85.60/year for Canada; $5.00 for single issue. Magazine containing information on horticulture: nursery, landscape and garden center management.

★5988★ Grounds Maintenance
Primedia Business
9800 Metcalf Ave.
Overland Park, KS 66212
Ph: (913)341-1300   Fax: (913)967-1898
E-mail: gm_editorial@intertec.com
URL: http://www.grounds-mag.com
Monthly. Free to qualified subscribers; $36.00/year for individuals; $10.00/year for single issue; $10.00/year for back issues (plus postage). Trade magazine on landscape design, maintenance, and installation.

★5989★ Grower Talks
Ball Publishing
PO Box 9
Batavia, IL 60510
Ph: (630)208-9080   Fax: (630)208-9350
Fr: 888-888-0013
E-mail: info@ballpublishing.com
URL: http://www.growertalks.com

Monthly. $29.00/year for individuals. Trade magazine covering issues for commercial greenhouse growers with a focus on North American production.

★5990★ Interiorscape
Brantwood Publications Inc.
2410 Northside Dr.
Clearwater, FL 33761
Ph: (727)786-9771   Fax: (727)791-4126
Bimonthly. $12.00/year for individuals; $3.00 for single issue. Interior landscape design magazine.

★5991★ Job Line...and News from CPRS
California Park & Recreation Society Inc.
7971 Freeport Blvd.
Sacramento, CA 95832-9701
Ph: (916)665-2777   Fax: (916)665-9149
Description: Monthly. Discusses parks and recreation news of interest.

★5992★ The Landscape Contractor
Illinois Landscape Contractor Association
2625 Butterfield Rd., Ste. 204-W
Oak Brook, IL 60523-1257
Ph: (630)472-2851   Fax: (630)472-3150
Monthly. $65.00/year for individuals. Magazine for the landscape trade.

★5993★ Landscape Design
Adams Business Media/Green Media
833 W Jackson Blvd., 7th fl.
Chicago, IL 60607
Ph: (312)846-4300   Fax: (312)846-4638
URL: http://www.greenindustrynet.com
Quarterly. Free to qualified subscribers. Magazine for licensed landscape architects.

★5994★ Landscape & Irrigation
Adams Business Media/Green Media
833 W Jackson Blvd., 7th fl.
Chicago, IL 60607
Ph: (312)846-4300   Fax: (312)846-4638

URL: http://www.greenmediaonline.com
Monthly. Free to qualified subscribers; $40.00/year for individuals. Magazine for the landscape and irrigation contracting industry.

★5995★ Landscape Management
Advanstar Communications Inc.
7500 Old Oak Blvd.
Cleveland, OH 44130-3369
Ph: (440)243-8100   Fax: (440)891-2777
URL: http://https://www.advanstar.com/index_allpubs.html
Magazine for professionals in landscape, grounds management and lawn care, construction, and maintenance.

★5996★ Lawn & Landscape Magazine
G.I.E. Media, MC
4012 Bridge Ave.
Cleveland, OH 44113
Ph: (216)961-4130   Fax: (216)961-0364
Fr: 800-456-0707
URL: http://www.gie.net
Monthly. Free to qualified subscribers; $5.00 for single issue; $30.00/year for U.S.; $35.00/year for Canada; $98.00/year for international. Magazine for commercial and residential lawn and landscape contracting professionals.

★5997★ The Municipality
League of Wisconsin Municipalities
202 State St., Ste. 300
Madison, WI 53703-2215
Ph: (608)267-2380   Fax: (608)267-0645
Fr: 800-991-5502
Monthly. $12.00/year. Magazine for officials of Wisconsin's local municipal governments.

★5998★ NRPA Job Bulletin
National Recreation and Park Association, Professional Services Div.
22377 Belmont Ridge Rd.
Ashburn, VA 20148
Ph: (703)858-0784   Fax: (703)858-0707
Fr: 800-626-6772
URL: http://www.nrpa.org

Description: Semimonthly. Provides listings of employment opportunities in the park, recreation, and leisure services field.

★**5999**★ *Nursery Business Retailer*

Brantwood Publications Inc.
2410 Northside Dr.
Clearwater, FL 33761
Ph: (727)786-9771   Fax: (727)791-4126
Bimonthly. $15.00/year for individuals; $3.00 for single issue. Wholesale and retail nursery operations magazine.

★**6000**★ *Nursery Management and Production*

Branch-Smith Inc.
120 St. Louis Ave.
PO Box 1868
Fort Worth, TX 76101
Ph: (817)882-4120   Fax: (817)882-4121
Fr: 800-433-5612
E-mail: tdavis@branchsmith.com
URL: http://www.greenbeam.com
Monthly. $96.00/year; $8.00 for single issue. Trade journal covering nursery growing, landscape distribution and landscaping.

★**6001**★ *Nursery News*

Cenflo Inc.
205 W Wacker Dr., Ste. 1040
Chicago, IL 60606-3508
Ph: (312)739-5000   Fax: (312)739-0739
Fr: 800-732-4581
URL: http://www.nurserynews.com
Monthly. $20.00/year; $28.00 for two years. Trade newspaper (tabloid) for nursery industry.

★**6002**★ *Pro*

Cygnus Business Media
1233 Janesville Ave.
Fort Atkinson, WI 53538
Fr: 800-547-7377
URL: http://www.promagazine.com
Magazine for landscape service firms.

★**6003**★ *Western City*

League of California Cities
1400 K St., 4th Fl.
Sacramento, CA 95814
Ph: (916)658-8223   Fax: (916)658-8289
Fr: 800-262-1801
URL: http://www.westerncity.com
Monthly. $39.00/year for individuals; $63.00 for two years. Municipal interest magazine.

★**6004**★ *Yard and Garden*

Cygnus Business Media
1233 Janesville Ave.
Fort Atkinson, WI 53538
Fr: 800-547-7377
URL: http://www.cygnusexpos.com/PropertyPub.cfm?PropertyID=117

Yard and garden magazine featuring product news and retailer success stories.

EMPLOYER DIRECTORIES AND NETWORKING LISTS

★**6005**★ *California Landscape Contractors Association-Roster*

California Landscape Contractors Association
1491 River Park Dr. Ste. 100
Sacramento, CA 95815
Ph: (916)448-2522   Fax: (916)448-7692
Fr: 800-448-CLCA
Annual, January. $50.00. Covers about 2,000 member landscape contractors and suppliers of products and services to the landscape contracting industry. Entries include: Name of firm, address, phone, representative to the association, chapter, products and services offered. Arrangement: Geographical. Indexes: Product/service.

★**6006**★ *Directory of Public Garden Internships*

American Association of Botanical Gardens and Arboreta (AABGA)
100 W 10th St., Ste. 614
Wilmington, DE 19801-6604
Ph: (302)655-7100   Fax: (302)655-8100
E-mail: bvincent@aabga.org
Annual, November. $10.00 for members; $15.00 for nonmembers. Covers 700 student internships and summer jobs at public gardens throughout North America. Entries include: Name of institution, address, name of contact, deadline for application, number of students hired, whether internships are available, employment period, hours, rate of pay, whether housing is available, other comments. Arrangement: Alphabetical. Indexes: By position, by state/province.

★**6007**★ *Grounds Maintenance-Buyers' Guide Issue*

Primedia Business
9800 Metcalf Ave.
Overland Park, KS 66212
Ph: (913)341-1300   Fax: (913)967-1898
E-mail: gm_editorial@intertec.com
URL: http://www.grounds-mag.com
Annual, December. $5.00. Publication includes: List of manufacturers, growers, and suppliers of materials for landscaping design, construction, and maintenance; landscaping associations. Entries include: Company name, address, phone. Arrangement: Alphabetical/product. Indexes: Product.

★**6008**★ *Landscape Contractors Directory*

infoUSA Inc.
5711 S 86th Cir.
Omaha, NE 68127-0347
Ph: (402)930-3500   Fax: (402)331-0176
Fr: 800-555-6124
URL: http://www.abii.com
Annual. Number of listings: 51,298. Entries include: Name, address, phone (including area code), size of advertisement, year first in "Yellow Pages," name of owner or manager, number of employees. Regional editions available: Eastern, $845.00; Western, $515.00. Compiled from telephone company "Yellow Pages," nationwide. Arrangement: Geographical.

★**6009**★ *Landscape Designers Directory*

infoUSA Inc.
5711 S 86th Cir.
Omaha, NE 68127-0347
Ph: (402)930-3500   Fax: (402)331-0176
Fr: 800-555-6124
URL: http://www.abii.com
Annual. Number of listings: 12,799. Entries include: Name, address, phone (including area code), size of advertisement, year first in "Yellow Pages," name of owner or manager, number of employees. Compiled from telephone company "Yellow Pages," nationwide. Arrangement: Geographical.

★**6010**★ *New York State Nursery/ Landscape Association-Directory*

New York State Nursery/Landscape Assoc. Inc.
PO Box 657
Baldwinsville, NY 13027
Ph: (315)635-5008   Fax: (315)635-4874
Fr: 800-647-0384
Annual, January. Covers over 800 member nursery, landscape, gardening, and lawn maintenance firms in New York. Entries include: Company name, address, phone, name. Arrangement: Alphabetical.

★**6011**★ *Seasonal Employment*

U.S. National Park Service
Harpers Ferry Center
PO Box 50
Harpers Ferry, WV 25425-0050
Ph: (202)208-4747   Fax: (304)535-6144
URL: http://www.nps.gov
Updated as needed; go to "InfoZone" to access. Publication includes: List of 10 regional offices and branches of the National Park Service that accept applications for seasonal jobs. Entries include: Name, address, phone, geographical area served. Principal content of publication is information on seasonal jobs offered by the National Park Services, with description of duties, qualifications, and application procedures for each type of job offered. Arrangement: Geographical.

★6012★ **Who's Who in Landscape Contracting**

Associated Landscape Contractors of America
150 Elden St., Ste. 270
Herndon, VA 20170
Ph: (703)736-9666   Fax: (703)736-9668
Fr: 800-395-2522
E-mail: kathywemhoff@alca.org
URL: http://www.alca.org

Annual, winter. $50.00. Covers 2,500 member exterior and interior landscape contractors, related suppliers, affiliates, state associations, students, and student chapters. Entries include: Company name, address, phone, fax, Web site, e-mail, and names of key personnel, specialties. Arrangement: Alphabetical. Indexes: Interior contractor location, exterior contractor location, personal name.

HANDBOOKS AND MANUALS

★6013★ **Careers in Horticulture and Botany**

McGraw-Hill Trade
2 Penn Plaza
New York, NY 10121
Ph: (212)904-2000   Fr: 800-722-4726
E-mail: ntcpub@tribune.com

Jerry Garner. 1996. $17.95; 13.95 (paper). 255 pages. Includes bibliographical references

★6014★ **Opportunities in Landscape Architecture, Botanical Gardens, and Arboreta Careers**

McGraw-Hill/Contemporary Books
1221 Avenue of the Americas
New York, NY 10020
Ph: (212)904-2000   Fr: 800-323-4900
E-mail: ntcpub@tribune.com

Blythe Cameron. 1998. $14.95; $11.95 (paper). 202 pages. Includes bibliography.

★6015★ **The Perfect Guide to Making $ in Landscaping and Maintenance: A How-To Book**

Moran Publishing
210 Lazy River
Sealy, TX 77474
Fr: 800-223-0351

Gene Yezak. $9.95 (paper). 220 pages.

TRADESHOWS

★6016★ **Green Industry Expo**

Professional Lawn Care Association of America
1000 Johnson Ferry Rd., Ste. C-135
Marietta, GA 30068
Ph: (770)973-2019   Fax: (770)579-3835
Fr: 800-458-3466
URL: http://www.qieonline.com

Annual. **Primary Exhibits:** Lawn care equipment, supplies, and services, including fertilizers, weed control materials, insurance information, and power equipment. **Dates and Locations:** 2004 Nov 03-06; Charlotte, NC; Charlotte Convention Center.

★6017★ **International Lawn, Garden, and Power Equipment Expo**

Sellers Expositions
222 Pearl St., Ste. 300
New Albany, IN 47150-3416
Ph: (812)949-9200   Fax: (812)949-9600
Fr: 800-558-8767

Annual. **Primary Exhibits:** Lawn, garden, and power equipment. **Dates and Locations:** 2004 Sep 24-26; Louisville, KY; Kentucky Exposition Center • 2005 Oct 10; Louisville, KY; Kentucky Exposition Center.

★6018★ **Mid-Atlantic Nursery Trade Show**

The Mid-Atlantic Nursery Trade Show, Inc. (MANTS)
PO Box 818
Brooklandville, MD 21022
Ph: (410)296-6959   Fax: (410)296-8288
Fr: 800-431-0066
E-mail: mantsinc@aol.com
URL: http://mants.com

Annual. **Primary Exhibits:** Equipment, supplies, and services relating to all aspects of nursery, landscaping, and garden center businesses.

★6019★ **The World's Showcase of Horticulture**

Southern Nursery Association
1827 Powers Ferry Rd., Bldg. 4, Ste. 100
Atlanta, GA 30339
Ph: (770)953-3311   Fax: (770)953-4411
E-mail: mail@mail.sna.org
URL: http://www.sna.org

Annual. **Primary Exhibits:** Nursery products, including plants, chemicals, machinery and equipment, soil and soil supplements, and plant containers. **Dates and Locations:** 2004 Jul 29-31; Atlanta, GA; Georgia World Congress Center • 2005 Aug 04-06; Atlanta, GA; Georgia World Congress Center • 2006 Aug 03-05; Atlanta, GA; Georgia World Congress Center.

OTHER SOURCES

★6020★ **American Association of Botanical Gardens and Arboreta (AABGA)**

100 W 10th St., Ste. 614
Wilmington, DE 19801-6604
Ph: (302)655-7100   Fax: (302)655-8100
E-mail: pallenstein@aabga.org
URL: http://www.aabga.org

Members: Directors and staffs of botanical gardens, arboreta, institutions maintaining or conducting horticultural courses, and others. **Purpose:** Seeks to serve North American public gardens and horticultural organizations by promoting professional development through its publications and meetings, advocating the interests of public gardens in political, corporate, foundation, and community arenas, and encouraging gardens to adhere to professional standards in their programs and operations.

★6021★ **American Nursery and Landscape Association (ANLA)**

1000 Vermont Ave., No. 300
Washington, DC 20005-4914
Ph: (202)789-2900   Fax: (202)789-1893
URL: http://www.anla.org

Members: Vertical organization of wholesale growers; landscape firms; garden centers; mail order nurseries; suppliers. Promotes the industry and its products. Offers management and consulting services and public relations programs. Provides government representation and bank card plan for members. Maintains hall of fame.

★6022★ **Associated Landscape Contractors of America (ALCA)**

150 Elden St., Ste. 270
Herndon, VA 20170
Ph: (703)736-9666   Fax: (703)736-9668
Fr: 800-395-2522
E-mail: information@alca.org
URL: http://www.alca.org

Members: Landscape contractors. **Purpose:** Works to represent, lead, and unify the interior and exterior landscape industry by working together on a national basis; addressing environmental and legislative issues; and creating increased opportunities in business. **Activities:** Provides forum to encourage members' profitability, personal growth, and professional advancement.

★6023★ **International Society of Arboriculture (ISA)**

PO Box 3129
Champaign, IL 61826-3129
Ph: (217)355-9411   Fax: (217)355-9516
Fr: 888-472-8733
E-mail: isa@isa-arbor.com
URL: http://www.isa-arbor.com/

Description: Individuals engaged in commercial, municipal, and utility arboriculture; city, state, and national government employees; municipal and commercial arborists;

others interested in shade tree welfare. Disseminates information on the care and preservation of shade and ornamental trees. Supports research projects at educational institutions.

★6024★ National Landscape Association (NLA)
1250 I St. NW, Ste. 500
Washington, DC 20005-3922
Ph: (202)789-2900   Fax: (202)789-1893
E-mail: leagle@anla.org
URL: http://www.anla.org/about/nla/nla.htm

Members: Landscape firms. **Purpose:** Works to enhance the professionalism of its member firms in designing, building, and maintaining quality landscapes in a profitable and environmentally responsible manner; represent the landscape perspective within the industry. **Activities:** Sponsors annual

landscape tour in conjunction with American Association of Nurserymen.

★6025★ Personal & Building Service Occupations
Delphi Productions
3160 4th St.
Boulder, CO 80304
Fax: (303)443-4022   Fr: 888-443-2400
URL: http://www.delphivideo.com

$95.00. 48 minutes. Part of the Careers for the 21st Century Video Library.

★6026★ Professional Grounds Management Society (PGMS)
720 Light St.
Baltimore, MD 21230
Ph: (410)223-2861   Fax: (410)752-8295
Fr: 800-609-7467

E-mail: pgms@assnhqtrs.com
URL: http://www.pgms.org

Description: Professional society of grounds managers of large institutions of all sorts and independent landscape contractors. Establishes grounds management as a profession; secures opportunities for professional advancement of well-qualified grounds managers; acquaints the public with "the distinction between competent ground managers, equipped through practical experience and systematic study, and self-styled °maintenance' personnel, lacking these essentials." Sponsors contests. Conducts research and surveys; sponsors certification program for professional grounds managers and grounds keepers. Takes action with the legislative and executive branches of government on issues affecting grounds managers; keeps members informed on matters affecting the profession.

Law Enforcement Officers

SOURCES OF HELP-WANTED ADS

★6027★ ACJS Today
Academy of Criminal Justice Sciences
402 Nunn Hall
Northern Kentucky University
Newport, KY 41099
Ph: (606)572-5634   Fax: (606)572-6665
Fr: 800-757-ACJS

Description: Four issues/year. Contains criminal justice information.

★6028★ American City and County
Primedia Business
6151 Powers Ferry Rd.
Atlanta, GA 30339
Ph: (770)955-2500   Fax: (770)618-0348

Monthly. $67.00/year for individuals. Municipal and county administration magazine.

★6029★ Criminal Justice Newsletter
Pace Publications
1900 L St. NW, Ste. 312
Washington, DC 20036
Ph: (202)835-1770   Fax: (202)835-1772

Description: Semimonthly. Monitors significant developments relating to law enforcement, courts, corrections, planning, research, and theory. Covers criminal justice and juvenile issues. Recurring features include announcements of projects, grants, conferences, courses, and job listings.

★6030★ Journal of Forensic Economics
National Association of Forensic Economists
PO Box 30067
Kansas City, MO 64112
Ph: (816)235-2833

Quarterly. Journal covering economics and law.

★6031★ Journal of Health and Hospital Law
American Health Lawyers Association
1025 Connecticut NW, Ste. 600
Washington, DC 20036
Ph: (202)833-1100   Fax: (202)833-1105

Quarterly. $150.00/year. Professional journal covering healthcare issues and cases and their impact on the health care arena.

★6032★ Law Enforcement Technology
Cygnus Business Media
1233 Janesville Ave.
Fort Atkinson, WI 53538
Fr: 800-547-7377
URL: http://www.cygnusexpos.com/PropertyPub.cfm?PropertyID=124

Monthly. Magazine for police technology and management.

★6033★ Law and Order
Law and Order
130 Waukegan Rd., Ste. 202
Deerfield, IL 60015
Ph: (847)444-3300   Fax: (847)444-3333
Fr: 800-843-9764
E-mail: laworder@concentric.net
URL: http://www.lawandordermag.com

Monthly. $22.00/year for individuals. Law enforcement trade magazine.

★6034★ The Municipality
League of Wisconsin Municipalities
202 State St., Ste. 300
Madison, WI 53703-2215
Ph: (608)267-2380   Fax: (608)267-0645
Fr: 800-991-5502

Monthly. $12.00/year. Magazine for officials of Wisconsin's local municipal governments.

★6035★ Police & Security News
Days Communications
1208 Juniper St.
Quakertown, PA 18951-1520
Ph: (215)538-1240   Fax: (215)538-1208
E-mail: advertising@policeandsecuritynews.com

Bimonthly. $18.00/year; $54.00/year for other countries; $3.00 for single issue. Tabloid for the law enforcement and private security industries. Includes articles on training, new products, and new technology.

★6036★ Western City
League of California Cities
1400 K St., 4th Fl.
Sacramento, CA 95814
Ph: (916)658-8223   Fax: (916)658-8289
Fr: 800-262-1801
URL: http://www.westerncity.com

Monthly. $39.00/year for individuals; $63.00 for two years. Municipal interest magazine.

PLACEMENT AND JOB REFERRAL SERVICES

★6037★ American Police Academy (APA)
6350 Horizon Dr.
Titusville, FL 32780
Ph: (321)264-0911   Fax: (321)264-0033
E-mail: policeinfo@aphf.org
URL: http://www.aphf.org

Description: Educational arm of the American Federation of Police and National Association of Chiefs of Police. Law enforcement officers who have completed advanced training offered by the academy for on-duty police officers and security personnel. Establishes professional certification standards for career officers. Conducts home study programs. Operates speakers' bureau and placement service; compiles statistics.

★6038★ American Society of Criminology (ASC)
1314 Kinnear Rd., Ste. 212
Columbus, OH 43212-1156
Ph: (614)292-9207   Fax: (614)292-6767
E-mail: ceskridge@unl.edu
URL: http://www.asc41.com

Description: Professional and academic

criminologists; students of criminology in accredited universities; psychiatrists, psychologists, and sociologists. Works to develop criminology as a science and academic discipline; to aid in the construction of criminological curricula in accredited universities; to upgrade the practitioner in criminological fields (police, prisons, probation, parole, delinquency workers). Conducts research programs; sponsors three student paper competitions. Provides placement service at annual convention.

★6039★ **National Association of Investigative Specialists (NAIS)**

PO Box 33244
Austin, TX 78764
Ph: (512)719-3595   Fax: (512)719-3594
E-mail: rthomas007@aol.com
URL: http://www.pimall.com/nais

Members: Private investigators, automobile repossessors, bounty hunters, and law enforcement officers. **Purpose:** Promotes professionalism and provides for information exchange among private investigators. Lobbies for investigative regulations. Offers training programs and issues certificates of completion. **Activities:** Sponsors charitable programs; compiles statistics; maintains speakers' bureau and placement service. Operates Investigators' Hall of Fame of Private Investigators. Offers seminars on cassette tape.

★6040★ **Nine Lives Associates (NLA)**

Executive Protection Institute
PO Box 802
Berryville, VA 22611-0802
Ph: (540)554-2540   Fax: (540)554-2558
E-mail: info@personalprotection.com
URL: http://www.personalprotection.com

Description: Law enforcement, correctional, military, and security professionals who have been granted Personal Protection Specialist certification through completion of the protective services program offered by the Executive Protection Institute; conducts research. EPI programs emphasize personal survival skills and techniques for the protection of others. Provides professional recognition for qualified individuals engaged in executive protection assignments. Maintains placement service. Operates speakers' bureau; compiles statistics

EMPLOYER DIRECTORIES AND NETWORKING LISTS

★6041★ *Association of Former Agents of the U.S. Secret Service- Membership Directory*

Association of Former Agents of the U.S. Secret Service
PO Box 1670
Millersville, MD 21108-4670
Ph: (703)256-0188

Annual, March. Entries include: Name, home address. Arrangement: Alphabetical.

★6042★ *International Association of Chiefs of Police Membership Directory*

International Association of Chiefs of Police
515 N Washington St.
Alexandria, VA 22314
Ph: (703)836-6767   Fax: (703)836-4543
Fr: 800-843-4227

Annual, October. $75.00. Covers 20,000 members in command and administrative positions in federal, state, and local law enforcement and related fields; includes county police and sheriffs; international, national, and regional law enforcement agencies and related organizations. Entries include: For officers-Name, title, name of law enforcement agency, address, phone. For agencies and organizations-Name, address, names and titles of key personnel, publications. Arrangement: Geographical and alphabetical.

★6043★ *National Directory of Law Enforcement Administrators, Correctional Institutions & Related Agencies*

National Public Safety Information Bureau
601 Main St., Ste. 201
PO Box 365
Stevens Point, WI 54481
Ph: (715)345-2772   Fax: (715)345-7288
Fr: 800-647-7579
URL: http://www.safetysource.com

Annual, June. $129.00. Covers police departments, sheriffs, coroners, criminal prosecutors, child support agencies, state law enforcement and criminal investigation agencies; federal criminal investigation and related agencies; state and federal correctional institutions; campus law enforcement departments; county jails, airport and harbor police, Bureau of Indian Affairs officials, plus new homeland security section. Entries include: Name, address, phone, fax, names and titles of key personnel, number of officers, population served. Arrangement: Separate geographical sections for police chiefs, coroners, sheriffs, prosecutors, prisons and state criminal investigation agencies; also separate sections for federal agencies and miscellaneous law enforcement and related agencies. Indexes: Departments.

★6044★ *United States Probation and Pretrial Services Officers Directory*

Probation Div.
1 Columbus Cir. NE, Ste. 4-300
Washington, DC 20544
Ph: (202)502-2600   Fax: (202)273-1603

Annual, latest edition December, 1994. Covers federal probation offices and pretrial services offices; federal prisons; members of the United States Parole Commission and the Federal Bureau of Prisons. Entries include: For district offices-District name, address, phone, Federal Telephone System phone; names and titles of chief, other key officials, and probation officers and chiefs; home phone of chief; counties served. For prisons-Name, address, phone; number of male and female inmates. For government agencies-Name, address, phone, FTS phone; names, titles, and phone numbers of board members; regional offices with addresses, phone numbers, and names of commissioners. Arrangement: District offices are by district; prisons are by type of prison, then by city.

HANDBOOKS AND MANUALS

★6045★ *Arco Police Officer*

Hungry Minds, Inc.
909 Third Ave.
New York, NY 10022
Ph: (212)884-5000   Fax: (212)884-5400
Fr: 800-667-1115

Hugh O'Neill, Eve P. Steinberg and Hy Hammer. First edition, 1998. $13.95. Part of Arco Police Officer series.

★6046★ *Become an Officer in Law Enforcement: Getting the Edge*

Career Publishing, Inc.
PO Box 5486
Orange, CA 92863
Ph: (714)771-5155   Fax: (714)532-0180
Fr: 800-854-4014

Robert J. Piel and Paul C. Van Der Linden. 1996. $14.95 (paper). 132 pages.

★6047★ *Career Planning in Criminal Justice*

Anderson Publishing Co.
2035 Reading Rd.
Cincinnati, OH 45202-1576
Ph: (513)421-4142   Fax: (513)562-8116
Fr: 800-582-7295

Robert C. DeLucia and Thomas J. Doyle. Third edition, 1998. 226 pages. $21.95. Surveys a wide range of career and employment opportunities in law enforcement, the courts, corrections, forensic science, and private security. Contains career planning and job hunting advice.

★6048★ Careers in Law Enforcement: Interviewing for Results

The Graduate Group
PO Box 370351
West Hartford, CT 06137-0351
Fr: 800-484-7280

Jim Nelson. 1996. $30.00 (paper).

★6049★ Careers in Law Enforcement and Security

Rosen Publishing Group, Inc.
29 E. 21st St.
New York, NY 10010
Ph: (212)777-3017   Fax: 888-436-4643
Fr: 800-237-9932

Paul Cohen and Shari Cohen. Revised edition, 1994. $18.95. $9.95 (paper), out of print. Describes jobs such as police, sheriff, detective, FBI, CIA, and Secret Service agents, parole and probation officers, security guards, and private investigators. Covers job duties, qualifications, education, training, income, and advancement possibilities. Offers advice about where and how to apply for jobs.

★6050★ Careers for Legal Eagles and Other Law-and-Order Types

McGraw-Hill Trade
2 Penn Plaza
New York, NY 10121
Ph: (212)904-2000   Fr: 800-722-4726
E-mail: ntcpub@tribune.com

Blythe Camenson. 1998. $14.95; $9.95 (paper). 220 pages.

★6051★ Careers for Mystery Buffs and Other Snoops and Sleuths

McGraw-Hill Trade
2 Penn Plaza
New York, NY 10121
Ph: (212)904-2000   Fr: 800-722-4726
E-mail: ntcpub@tribune.com

Blythe Camenson. 1996. $14.95; $9.95 (paper). 210 pages.

★6052★ Criminal Justice Career Opportunities in Ohio

Kendall/Hunt Publishing Company
4050 Westmark Dr.
Dubuque, IA 52002
Ph: (563)589-1000   Fax: 800-772-9165
Fr: 800-228-0810

Katherine Steinbeck, Daniel Ponstingle. January 2003. $20.95. Illustrated. 185 pages.

★6053★ Federal Jobs in Law Enforcement

Impact Publications
9104 Manassas Dr., Ste. N
Manassas Park, VA 20111-5211
Ph: (703)361-7300   Fax: (703)335-9486
Russ Smith. 1996. $14.95 (paper). 208 pages.

★6054★ Guide to Careers in Criminal Justice

Thomson Wadsworth
10 Davis Dr.
Belmont, CA 94002
Ph: (650)598-9757   Fax: (859)525-0978
Fr: 800-347-7707

Wadsworth. 2000. $5.25.

★6055★ Guide to Law Enforcement Careers

Barron's Educational Series, Inc.
250 Wireless Blvd.
Hauppauge, NY 11788-3917
Ph: (631)434-3311   Fax: (631)434-3723
Fr: 800-645-3476

Donald B. Hutton and Anna Mydlarz. Second edition, 2001. $14.95 (paper).

★6056★ How to Be a Great Cop

Prentice Hall PTR
One Lake St.
Upper Saddle River, NJ 07458
Ph: (201)236-7000

Neal E. Trautman. 2000. $28.00 (paper).

★6057★ Inside Jobs: A Realistic Guide to Criminal Justice Careers for College Graduates

Sheffield Publishing Co.
PO Box 359
Salem, WI 53168
Ph: (262)843-2281   Fax: (262)843-3683
Stuart Henry, editor. 1994. $16.95 (paper). 264 pages. Out of print.

★6058★ Law Enforcement Career Guide California

LearningExpress, LLC
900 Broadway, Ste. 604
New York, NY 10003
Ph: (212)995-2566   Fax: (212)995-5512
Fr: 800-295-9556

1996. $20.00 (paper). 144 pages.

★6059★ Law Enforcement Career Guide Florida

LearningExpress, LLC
900 Broadway, Ste. 604
New York, NY 10003
Ph: (212)995-2566   Fax: (212)995-5512
Fr: 800-295-9556

1996. $20.00 (paper). 144 pages.

★6060★ Law Enforcement Career Guide New Jersey

LearningExpress, LLC
900 Broadway,Ste. 604
New York, NY 10003
Ph: (212)995-2566   Fax: (212)995-5512
Fr: 800-295-9556

1996. $20.00 (paper). 144 pages.

★6061★ Law Enforcement Career Guide New York

LearningExpress, LLC
900 Broadway, Ste. 604
New York, NY 10003
Ph: (212)995-2566   Fax: (212)995-5512
Fr: 800-295-9556

1996. $20.00 (paper). 144 pages.

★6062★ Law Enforcement Career Guide Texas

LearningExpress, LLC
900 Broadway, Ste. 604
New York, NY 10003
Ph: (212)995-2566   Fax: (212)995-5512
Fr: 800-295-9556

1996. $20.00 (paper). 144 pages.

★6063★ The Law Enforcement Manual

Princeton Educational Research Institute
239 Hillside Ave.
Cranford, NJ 07016
Ph: (908)276-5101   Fax: (908)931-0210

Mark Adamson, Michael A. Petrillo and Daniel R. DelBagno. Third edition, revised, 1999. $39.95. 341 pages.

★6064★ 100 Best Careers in Crimefighting

Thomson Peterson's
P.O. Box 67005
Lawrenceville, NJ 08648-6105
Fr: 800-338-3282

Mary P. Lee. 1997. $15.95 (paper). 200 pages. Covers private security careers, government law enforcement positions, and more, with information on employment opportunities.

★6065★ Opportunities in Law Enforcement and Criminal Justice Careers

McGraw-Hill Contemporary Books
1221 Avenue of the Americas
New York, NY 10020
Ph: (212)904-2000   Fr: 800-323-4900
E-mail: ntcpub@tribune.com

James Stinchcomb. Revised edition, 1996. $14.95; $11.95 (paper). 160 pages. Offers information on opportunities at the city, county, state, military, and federal levels. Contains bibliography and illustrations.

★6066★ Real People Working in Law

McGraw-Hill Contemporary Books
1221 Avenue of the Americas
New York, NY 10020
Ph: (212)904-2000   Fr: 800-323-4900
E-mail: ntcpub@tribune.com

Blythe Camenson, Jan Goldberg. 1997. $14.95; $12.95 (paper). 405 pages. Interviews and profiles of working professionals capture a range of opportunities in this field.

EMPLOYMENT AGENCIES AND SEARCH FIRMS

★6067★ Ferrari Search Group
24200 Chagrin Blvd., Ste. 1
Cleveland, OH 44122
Ph: (216)491-1122   Fax: (216)491-1510
Executive search firm.

TRADESHOWS

★6068★ International Association of Chiefs of Police Annual Conference
International Association of Chiefs of Police
515 N. Washington St.
Alexandria, VA 22314-2357
Ph: (703)836-6767   Fax: (703)836-4543
Fr: 800-THE-IACP

Annual. **Primary Exhibits:** Law enforcement equipment, supplies, and services.

★6069★ National Sheriffs' Association Annual Conference
National Sheriff Association
1450 Duke St.
Alexandria, VA 22314-3490
Ph: (703)836-7827   Fax: (703)683-6541
Fr: 800-424-7827
URL: http://www.sheriffs.org

Annual. **Primary Exhibits:** Exhibits of interest to local law enforcement professionals.

OTHER SOURCES

★6070★ American Federation of Police and Concerned Citizens (AFP&CC)
3801 Biscayne Blvd.
Miami, FL 33137
Ph: (305)573-0070   Fax: (305)573-9819
E-mail: policeinfo@aphf.org
URL: http://www.aphf.org

Members: Governmental and private law enforcement officers (paid, part-time, or volunteer) united for the prevention of crime and the apprehension of criminals. Offers death benefits and training programs to members and police survivors. **Activities:** Sponsors American Police Academy. Maintains hall of fame. Conducts workshops.

★6071★ Careers in Criminal Justice
Cambridge Educational
2572 Brunswick Ave.
Lawrenceville, NJ 08648-4128
Fax: 800-FAX-ON-US   Fr: 800-468-4227
URL: http://www.cambridgeeducational.com
$79.95. 2002. 22 minutes.

★6072★ Federal Criminal Investigators Association (FCIA)
PO Box 23400
Washington, DC 20026
Fax: 800-528-3492   Fr: 800-961-7753
E-mail: info@fedcia.org
URL: http://www.fedcia.org

Description: Professional fraternal organization dedicated to the advancement of federal law enforcement officers and the citizens they serve. Their mission is to ensure law enforcement professionals have the tools and support network to meet the challenges of future criminal investigations while becoming more community oriented. Intends to pursue mission through promoting professionalism, enhancing the image of federal officers, fostering cooperation among all law enforcement professionals, providing a fraternal environment for the advancement of the membership and community. Deeply involved in charitable programs and organizations.

★6073★ Human Services Occupations
Delphi Productions
3160 4th St.
Boulder, CO 80304
Fax: (303)443-4022   Fr: 888-443-2400
URL: http://www.delphivideo.com

$95.00. 50 minutes. Part of the Careers for the 21st Century Video Library.

★6074★ International Association of Campus Law Enforcement Administrators (IACLEA)
342 W Main St.
West Hartford, CT 06117-2507
Ph: (860)586-7517   Fax: (860)586-7550
E-mail: info@iaclea.org
URL: http://www.iaclea.org

Description: Advances public safety for educational institutions by providing educational resources, advocacy, and professional development. Dedicated to promoting professional ideals and standards in the administration of campus security/public safety/law enforcement. Goal is to make campus security/public safety/law enforcement an integral part of the educational community.

★6075★ International Security and Detective Alliance (ISDA)
PO Box 6303
Corpus Christi, TX 78466-6303
Fax: (361)888-8060

Members: Private investigators and security professionals, investigative reporters and writers, researchers, military personnel, and some interested laypersons. **Purpose:** Seeks to maintain an international registry of investigators for purpose of referral; support a more positive and accurate media image of P.I.s and security officers; provide a professional association for freelance operators; provide continuing education courses and materials. **Activities:** Provides professional certification in numerous specialty areas of investigation and security.

★6076★ International Society of Stress Analysts (ISSA)
9 Westchester Dr.
Kissimmee, FL 34744
Ph: (407)933-4839   Fax: (407)935-0911
E-mail: diogenesfl@aol.com

Members: Jurists, attorneys, physicians, private detectives, law enforcement personnel, security personnel, scholar/researchers, and individuals interested in stress analysis for lie detection/truth verification. **Purpose:** Works to promote the science of psychological stress evaluation and the efficient administration of justice; aid indigent persons, without cost, who may be wrongfully accused; develop and maintain high educational standards; observe and evaluate training programs for the purpose of accreditation and endorsement. **Activities:** Sponsors and certifies schools; offers workshops and research and educational programs; conducts forums. Offers expertise, consultation, and advice; invites inquiries.

★6077★ Math at Work: Women in Nontraditional Careers
Her Own Words
PO Box 5264
Madison, WI 53705-0264
Ph: (608)271-7083   Fax: (608)271-0209
URL: http://www.herownwords.com/

Video. Jocelyn Riley. $95.00. 15 minutes. Resource guide also available for $45.00.

★6078★ National Association of Traffic Accident Reconstructionists and Investigators (NATARI)
PO Box 398
Chadds Ford, PA 19317
Ph: (610)558-5176   Fax: (610)558-5176
E-mail: lizgurn@aol.com
URL: http://www.actar.org/natari.htm

Description: Engineers, attorneys, police officers, private investigators, medical examiners, and other individuals involved in the analysis of motor vehicle traffic accidents. Gathers and disseminates information on techniques and equipment of potential use to members; reviews literature in the field. Participating Organization of the Accreditation Commission for Traffic Accident Reconstruction.

★6079★ National Organization of Black Law Enforcement Executives (NOBLE)
4609 Pinecrest Office Park Dr., Ste. F
Alexandria, VA 22312-1442
Ph: (703)658-1529   Fax: (703)658-9479
E-mail: noble@noblenatl.org
URL: http://www.noblenational.org

Members: Law enforcement executives above the rank of lieutenant; police educators; academy directors; interested individuals and organizations. **Purpose:** Goals are to provide a platform from which the concerns and opinions of minority law enforcement executives and command-level officers can be expressed; to facilitate the exchange of programmatic information among minority law enforcement executives; to increase minority participation at all levels of law enforcement; to eliminate racism in the field of criminal justice; to secure increased cooperation from criminal justice agencies; to reduce urban crime and violence. Seeks to develop and maintain channels of communication between law enforcement agencies and the community; encourages coordinated community efforts to prevent and abate crime and its causes. Offers on-site technical assistance and training to police departments; develops model policies, practices, and procedures designed to decrease racial and religious violence and harassment. **Activities:** Provides job referral services to organizations seeking minority executives. Conducts research and training and offers technical assistance in crime victim assistance, community oriented policing, domestic violence, use of deadly force, reduction of fear of crime, airport security assessment, and minority recruitment. Offers internships; operates speakers' bureau.

★6080★ **Society of Professional Investigators (SPI)**
PO Box 1128
Bellmore, NY 11710
Ph: (516)781-1000   Fax: (516)783-0000
E-mail: info@spionline.org
URL: http://www.spionline.org

Description: Persons with at least 5 years' investigative experience for an official federal, state, or local government agency or for a quasi-official agency formed for law enforcement or related activities. Seeks to advance knowledge of the science and technology of professional investigation, law enforcement, and police science; maintains high standards and ethics; promotes efficiency of investigators in the services they perform.

★6081★ *Women in Nontraditional Careers: An Introduction*
Her Own Words
PO Box 5264
Madison, WI 53705
Ph: (608)271-7083   Fax: (608)271-0209
URL: http://www.herownwords.com/

Video. Jocelyn Riley. $95.00. 15 minutes. Resource guide also available for $45.00.

★6082★ *Women in Policing*
Her Own Words
PO Box 5264
Madison, WI 53705
Ph: (608)271-7083   Fax: (608)271-0209
URL: http://www.herownwords.com/

Video. Jocelyn Riley. $95.00. 15 minutes. Resource guide also available for $45.00.

Lawyers

SOURCES OF HELP-WANTED ADS

★6083★ California Lawyer

Daily Journal Corp.
915 E 1st St.
Los Angeles, CA 90012-4050
Ph: (213)229-5300   Fax: (213)680-3682
Fr: (866)226-8740

Monthly. $60.00/year for individuals. Law magazine.

★6084★ Chicago Lawyer

Law Bulletin Publishing Co.
415 N State St.
Chicago, IL 60610-4674
Ph: (312)644-7800   Fax: (312)644-4255
E-mail: displayads@lbc.com

Monthly. $40.00/year. Legal magazine (tabloid).

★6085★ Cornerstone

National Legal Aid & Defender
  Association
1140 Connecticut Ave. NW, Ste. 900
Washington, DC 20036
Ph: (202)452-0620   Fax: (202)872-1031
E-mail: cornerstone@nlada.org
URL: http://www.nlada.org/

Description: Four issues/year. Monitors current issues affecting legal aid attorneys and public defenders. Recurring features include job listings, conference and training updates, news of research, book reviews, and news of members.

★6086★ Job Announcements

National Center for State Courts
300 Newport Ave.(23185)
PO Box 8798
Williamsburg, VA 23187-8798
Ph: (757)253-2000   Fax: (757)220-0449
Fr: 800-877-1233
URL: http://www.ncsconline.org/

Description: Semimonthly. Provides lists of court-related job openings in the United States and its territories.

★6087★ Journal of Forensic Economics

National Association of Forensic
  Economists
PO Box 30067
Kansas City, MO 64112
Ph: (816)235-2833

Quarterly. Journal covering economics and law.

★6088★ Journal of Health and Hospital Law

American Health Lawyers Association
1025 Connecticut NW, Ste. 600
Washington, DC 20036
Ph: (202)833-1100   Fax: (202)833-1105

Quarterly. $150.00/year. Professional journal covering healthcare issues and cases and their impact on the health care arena.

★6089★ Journal of the Missouri Bar

The Missouri Bar
326 Monroe St.
PO Box 119
Jefferson City, MO 65101-3158
Ph: (573)635-4128   Fax: (573)635-2811

Bimonthly. $12.00/year; $3.00 for single issue. Magazine featuring short, practical articles on legal subjects for practicing attorneys.

★6090★ The Journal of Taxation

RIA Group
395 Hudson St., 4th Fl.
New York, NY 10014
Ph: (212)352-2746   Fax: (212)367-6314
Fr: 800-431-9025
URL: http://checkpoint.riag.com

Monthly. $250.00/year for individuals. Journal for sophisticated tax practitioners.

★6091★ Kentucky Bench & Bar Magazine

Kentucky Bar Association
514 W Main St.
Frankfort, KY 40601-1883
Ph: (502)564-3795   Fax: (502)564-3225

Bimonthly. $20.00/year for individuals. Kentucky law journal.

★6092★ Lawyers Job E-Bulletin Board

Federal Bar Association
2215 M St. NW
Washington, DC 20037
Ph: (202)785-1614   Fax: (202)785-1568
E-mail: pubs@fedbar.org

Description: Semimonthly. Provides a listing of job openings for attorneys, usually in the federal sector. Recurring features include a calendar of events. Available only via e-mail.

★6093★ Legal Times

American Lawyer Media L.P.
1730 M St. NW, Ste. 802
Washington, DC 20036
Ph: (202)457-0686   Fax: (202)785-4539
Fr: 800-933-4317
E-mail: legaltimes@legaltimes.com
URL: http://www.law.com/dc

Weekly. $318.00/year. Legal publication covering law and lobbying in the nation's capitol.

★6094★ Los Angeles Lawyer

Los Angeles County Bar Association
261 S Figueroa St., Ste. 300
Los Angeles, CA 90012
Ph: (213)627-2727   Fax: (213)896-6500
URL: http://www.lacba.org

Monthly. Magazine featuring scholarly legal articles.

★6095★ Massachusetts Lawyers Weekly

Lawyers Weekly Publications
41 W St.
Boston, MA 02111
Ph: (617)451-7300   Fax: (617)451-7324
Fr: 800-444-5297
E-mail: natsales@lweekly.com
URL: http://www.masslaw.com

Weekly. $299.00/year for individuals. News-paper (tabloid) reporting Massachusetts legal news.

★6096★ Michigan Bar Journal

State Bar of Michigan
306 Townsend St.
Lansing, MI 48933
Ph: (517)372-9030   Fax: (517)482-6248

Monthly. $45.00/year for individuals; $55.00/year for other countries. Legal magazine.

★6097★ The National Law Journal

The New York Law Journal
345 Park Ave. S
New York, NY 10010
Ph: (212)779-9200   Fax: (212)481-8110
Fr: 800-888-8300
URL: http://nlj.com

Weekly. $138.00/year. Tabloid focusing on the practice of law and trends in law.

★6098★ New Jersey Law Journal

New Jersey Law Journal
238 Mulberry St.
PO Box 20081
Newark, NJ 07101-6081
Ph: (973)642-0075   Fax: (973)642-0920
URL: http://www.law.com/nj

Weekly. $385.00/year for individuals; $10.00 for single issue. Journal containing digests of court opinions, notes, and orders to the bar from New Jersey Supreme Court and federal district court. Includes news articles on legal topics and commentary by legal specialists.

★6099★ Public Interest Employment Service Job Alert!

Public Interest Clearinghouse
47 Kearny St., Ste. 705
San Francisco, CA 94108
Ph: (415)834-0100   Fax: (415)834-0202
E-mail: pies@pic.org

Description: Semimonthly. Lists job openings in legal aid offices and public interest law organizations.

★6100★ The Recorder

American Lawyer Media L.P.
10 United Nations Plz., 3rd Fl.
San Francisco, CA 94102-4911
Ph: (415)749-5400   Fax: (415)749-5449
Fr: 800-244-5399
E-mail: recorder@counsel.com
URL: http://www.therecorder.com

Daily. $520.00/year for individuals. Legal newspaper.

★6101★ Texas Bar Journal

State Bar of Texas
1414 Colorado
Austin, TX 78701
Ph: (512)463-1463   Fax: (512)463-3802
Fr: 800-204-2222

Monthly. $12.00/year; $2.50 for single issue. Legal news journal for the legal profession.

★6102★ The Washington Lawyer

The District of Columbia Bar
1250 H St. NW, 6th Fl.
Washington, DC 20005-5937
Ph: (202)737-4700   Fax: (202)626-3472
URL: http://www.dcbar.org

Monthly. $30.00/year. Forum for articles and news items for the Washington legal community.

★6103★ Wisconsin Lawyer

State Bar of Wisconsin
5302 Eastpark Blvd.
PO Box 7158
Madison, WI 53707-7158
Ph: (608)257-3838   Fax: (608)257-5502
Fr: 800-444-9404
E-mail: wislawyer@wisbar.org
URL: http://www.wisbar.org/wislawmag/

Monthly. $42.00/year for individuals; $24.00/year for law libraries, educational groups, law students. Magazine for Wisconsin legal professionals.

PLACEMENT AND JOB REFERRAL SERVICES

★6104★ American Board of Professional Liability Attorneys (ABPLA)

1010 Northern Blvd., Ste. 208
Great Neck, NY 11021
Ph: (718)631-1400   Fax: (718)631-1456
E-mail: info@abpla.org
URL: http://www.abpla.org

Description: Accredited by the American Bar Association to certify Attorneys in the areas of medical, legal or accounting professional. **Members:** Liability litigation attorneys who have satisfied requirements of litigation experience and who have passed the ABPLA written liability examination. **Purpose:** Promotes and improves ethical and technical standards of advocacy and litigation practice in professional liability litigation; establish basic standards for training, qualification, and recognition of specialists; foster efficient administration of justice. **Activities:** Provides graduated training program for licensed attorneys desiring certification as specialists in the field. Offers placement service; compiles statistics. Maintains file of abstracts and program transcripts.

★6105★ Association of American Law Schools (AALS)

1201 Connecticut Ave. NW, Ste. 800
Washington, DC 20036-2605
Ph: (202)296-8851   Fax: (202)296-8869
E-mail: aals@aals.org
URL: http://www.aals.org

Description: Law schools association. Seeks to improve the legal profession through legal education. Interacts for law professors with state and federal government, other legal education and professional associations, and other national higher education and learned society organizations. Compiles statistics; sponsors teacher placement service. Presents professional development programs.

★6106★ Christian Management Association (CMA)

PO Box 4090
San Clemente, CA 92674-4090
Ph: (949)487-0900   Fax: (949)487-0927
Fr: 800-727-4CMA
E-mail: CMA@cmaonline.org
URL: http://www.christianity.com/cma

Description: CEO's, key leaders and managers who serve Christian organizations and churches. Provides management information, leadership training and strategic networking. management through its annual national conference, the Christian Management Institute. Holds bimonthly fellowship meeting for training and information reports. Provides job referral and professional referral service to assist Christian managment personnel.

★6107★ Computer Law Association (CLA)

3028 Javier Rd., Ste. 402
Fairfax, VA 22031
Ph: (703)560-7747   Fax: (703)207-7028
E-mail: askcla@cla.org
URL: http://www.cla.org

Members: Lawyers, law students, and others interested in legal problems related to computer-communications technology. **Purpose:** Aids in contracting for computer-communications goods and services; perfecting and protecting proprietary rights chiefly in software; taxing computer-communications goods, services, and transactions; and liability for acquisition and use of computer-communications goods and services. **Activities:** Provides specialized educational programs; offers limited placement service. Holds Annual Computer Law Update.

★6108★ Decalogue Society of Lawyers (DSL)

39 S LaSalle St., No. 410
Chicago, IL 60603
Ph: (312)263-6493   Fax: (312)263-6512

Description: Lawyers of the Jewish faith. Seeks to promote and cultivate social and professional relations among members of the legal profession. Conducts a forum on topics of general and Jewish interest. Maintains placement service to help members find employment and office facilities.

★6109★ Franchise Consultants International Association (FCIA)

5147 S Angela Rd.
Memphis, TN 38117
Ph: (901)368-3361   Fax: (901)368-1144
E-mail: franmark@msn.com

Members: Individuals and corporations involved in franchising including attorneys, consultants, brokers, sales personnel, suppliers, Universities, consultants, advertisers, and developers. **Purpose:** To provide standardized information for the franchise industry. Seeks to coordinate effective and professional franchise consulting and to educate members in franchise law and logistics. Serves as a clearinghouse of approved literature on franchising. **Activities:** Operates archive and hall of fame; compiles statistics. Provides placement service, charitable program, and speakers' bureau. Has extensive library. Expert witness specialists.

★6110★ National Association for Law Placement (NALP)

1025 Connecticut Ave. NW , Ste. 1110
Washington, DC 20036
Ph: (202)835-1001   Fax: (202)835-1112
E-mail: info@nalp.org
URL: http://www.nalp.org

Description: Law schools, legal employers, and bar associations actively engaged in the legal employment process. Purposes are to: provide for the creation and maintenance of standards and ethical procedures to guide law schools and employers in career services and recruitment; promote the exchange of ideas, information, and experiences; develop resource materials and educational programs; enlist employers and law schools in developing well-coordinated placement and recruiting services; provide means for member organizations to participate in an affirmative policy against discrimination in employment. Conducts annual survey of law school graduates and other research.

★6111★ National/Black Law Student Association (NBLSA)

1225 11th St. NW
Washington, DC 20001-4217
URL: http://www.nblsa.org/

Description: Black law students united to meet the needs of black people within the legal profession and to work for the benefit of the black community. Objectives are to: articulate and promote professional competence, needs, and goals of black law students; focus on the relationship between black students and attorneys and the American legal system; instill in black law students and attorneys a greater commitment to the black community; encourage the legal community to bring about change to meet the needs of the black community. Supports black law students at Harvard University who recently called for a boycott of a course on racial discrimination to protest the law

school's faculty-hiring practices. Sponsors the Frederick Douglass Moot Court Competition; offers placement service.

★6112★ Scandanavian American Lawyers Association

4177 Garrick
Warren, MI 48091
Ph: (586)757-4177   Fax: (313)557-6367
E-mail: anton_the_lord_hartforth@msn.com

Members: Professional association of Scandanavian-American attorneys. **Purpose:** Provides a forum to discuss and address issues of interest to members. **Activities:** Maintains a placement service.

EMPLOYER DIRECTORIES AND NETWORKING LISTS

★6113★ American Bar Association-Directory

American Bar Association
750 N Lake Shore Dr.
Chicago, IL 60611
Ph: (312)988-5000   Fr: 800-285-2221

Annual, October. $14.95. Covers approximately 7,500 lawyers active in the affairs of the Association, including officers, members of Boards of Governors and House of Delegates, section officers and council members, committee leaders, headquarters staff, state and local bars, affiliated and other legal organizations. Entries include: Section, council, or other unit name; names, addresses, and phone numbers of officers or chairpersons and members. Arrangement: Classified by position in ABA. Indexes: Alphabetical, Geographical committee.

★6114★ The American Bar Including The Canadian Bar, The Mexican Bar, and The International Bar

Forster Long Inc.
3280 Ramos Cir.
Sacramento, CA 95827
Ph: (916)362-3276   Fax: (916)362-5643
Fr: 800-328-5091
URL: http://www.americanbar.com

Annual, March. $405.00. Lists top law firms in the United States and 100 other countries with individual attorney biographies; selected state administrative offices. Entries include: Firm name, type of practice, address, phone, names, educational data, and memberships of partners and associates. State offices' listings include address, phone. See separate listing, "Law Lists." Arrangement: Geographical, alphabetical, separate sections for Canadian, Mexican and international lawyers. Indexes: Personal name; firm name and location; practice areas.

★6115★ American Lawyers Quarterly

The American Lawyers Co.
853 Westpoint Pkwy., Ste. 710
Cleveland, OH 44145-1595
Ph: (440)871-8700   Fax: (440)871-9997
Fr: 800-843-4000

Semiannual, January and July; monthly supplements. A commercial law list. Arrangement: Geographical.

★6116★ Attorney Jobs Online

Federal Reports Inc.
1010 Vermont Ave. NW, Ste. 408
Washington, DC 20005
Ph: (202)393-3311   Fax: (202)393-1553
Fr: 800-296-9611
URL: http://www.attorneyjobsonline.com

Monthly. $147.00 for individuals per year; $202.00 for institutions per year. Publication includes: Listings of approximately 600 current attorney and law-related job opportunities with the U.S. government and other public and private employers in Washington D.C., nationwide, and abroad. Arrangement: Geographical.

★6117★ Attorneys Directory

infoUSA Inc.
5711 S 86th Cir.
Omaha, NE 68127-0347
Ph: (402)930-3500   Fax: (402)331-0176
Fr: 800-555-6124
URL: http://www.abii.com

Annual. Number of listings: 502,206. Entries include: Name, address, phone (including area code), size of advertisement, year first in "Yellow Pages," name of owner or manager, number of employees. Regional editions available: North East (Connecticut, Maine, Massachusetts, New Hampshire, New Jersey, Pennsylvania, Rhode Island, Vermont), $3,265.00; East North Central (Illinois, Indiana, Michigan, Ohio, Wisconsin), $2,515.00; West North Central (Iowa, Kansas, Minnesota, Missouri, Nebraska, North Dakota, South Dakota), $1,090.00; South Atlantic (Washington D.C., Delaware, Florida, Georgia, Maryland, North Carolina, South Carolina, Virginia, West Virginia), $2580.00; South Central (Alabama, Arkansas, Kentucky, Louisiana, Mississippi, Oklahoma, Tennessee, Texas), $2,195.00; Mountain (Arizona, Colorado, Idaho, Montana, Nevada, New Mexico, Utah, Wyoming), $920.00; Pacific (Alaska, California, Hawaii, Oregon, Washington), $2,330.00. Compiled from telephone company "Yellow Pages," nationwide. Arrangement: Geographical.

★6118★ Attorneys' Service Bureaus Directory

infoUSA Inc.
5711 S 86th Cir.
Omaha, NE 68127-0347
Ph: (402)930-3500   Fax: (402)331-0176
Fr: 800-555-6124
URL: http://www.abii.com

Updated continuously; printed on request. Number of listings: 2,765. Entries include:

Name, address, phone, size of advertisement, name of owner or manager, number of employees, year first in "Yellow Pages." Compiled from telephone company "Yellow Pages," nationwide. Arrangement: Geographical.

★6119★ **Best Lawyers in America**

Woodward/White Inc.
129 1st Ave. SE
Aiken, SC 29801
Ph: (803)648-0300   Fax: (803)641-1709
Fr: (803)641-1710
URL: http://www.bestlawyers.com

Biennial, January of odd years. $200.00. Covers approximately 15,000 attorneys selected as 'the best' in their specialties by a survey of their peers. Entries include: Individual or firm name, address, phone, and subspecialties of interest. Arrangement: Geographical, then classified by legal specialty. Indexes: Name index.

★6120★ **Career Opportunities in Law and the Legal Industry**

Facts On File Inc.
132 W 31st St., 17th Fl.
New York, NY 10001-2006
Ph: (212)967-8800   Fax: 800-678-3633
Fr: 800-322-8755

$49.50. Publication includes: Lists of industry associations and organizations, educational institutions, and web sites related to the legal industry. Principal content of publication is information on careers in the legal field. Indexes: Alphabetical.

★6121★ **Decalogue Society of Lawyers-Directory of Members**

Decalogue Society of Lawyers
39 S La Salle, No. 410
Chicago, IL 60603
Ph: (312)263-6493   Fax: (312)263-6512

Annual. Covers about 1,500 lawyers of the Jewish faith. Entries include: Name, address, phone, fax, area of speciality. Arrangement: Alphabetical and by special area of law.

★6122★ **Gale Encyclopedia of Everyday Law**

Thomson Gale
27500 Drake Rd.
Farmington Hills, MI 48331-3535
Ph: (248)699-4253   Fax: (248)699-8065
Fr: 800-877-GALE
URL: http://www.gale.com

Published October 2002. $295.00. Publication includes: Listing of law-related organizations. Principal content of publication is approximately 200 articles covering specific legal issues of interest to a layperson in the United States and includes details on their background, historical cases, profiles of U.S. laws and regulations, differentiation between states, and further reading.

★6123★ **Insider's Guide to Law Firms**

Mobius Press Inc.
575 Gillaspie Dr.
Boulder, CO 80305-5803
Ph: (303)543-9429   Fax: (303)499-5289
Fr: 800-529-5627
URL: http://www.mobius-press.com

Annual, summer. $32.95. Covers approximately 160 major law firms throughout eight U.S. cities: Atlanta, Boston, Chicago, Los Angeles, New York, Philadelphia, San Francisco/Palo Alto, and Washington. Entries include: Firm name, address, phone, name and title of contact, names and titles of key personnel, number of partners and associates, salary information, percentage of pro bono work, summer opportunities, areas of practice, well known clients, recent deals, management training routines, firm culture. Arrangement: Geographical. Indexes: Firm name.

★6124★ **International Law and Practice-Leadership Directory**

International Law and Practice Section
740 15th St. NW
Washington, DC 20005-1019
Ph: (202)662-1000

Annual. Covers over 300 member lawyers, academics, law students, and international associates in leadership positions in the section. Entries include: Name, address, phone, fax and e-mail address.

★6125★ **International Municipal Lawyers Association-Directory of Officers and Sections**

International Municipal Lawyer Association (IMLA)
1110 Vermont Ave. NW, Ste. 200
Washington, DC 20005
Ph: (202)466-5424   Fax: (202)785-0152
URL: http://www.imladc.org

Bimonthly, winter. Covers members of IMLA committees. Entries include: Name and title of member, address, phone, fax. Arrangement: Classified by sections, officers, and membership departments.

★6126★ **Law Firms Yellow Book**

Leadership Directories Inc.
104 5th Ave.
New York, NY 10011
Ph: (212)627-4140   Fax: (212)645-0931
E-mail: lawfirms@leadershipdirectories.com
URL: http://www.leadershipdirectories.com

Semiannual. $261.00; $182.00 for additional subscriptions. Covers approximately 850 large law firms and over 24,000 attorneys and administrators at more than 3,000 domestic and foreign offices, subsidiaries, and affiliates. Entries include: Firm name, address, phone, telex, year founded; description of practice; officers' names, titles, phone numbers, and law schools attended, addresses, phone numbers, and principal officials at branch offices, e-mails. Arrangement: Alphabetical by firm name. Indexes: Geographical, law school, individual name, law firm, practice area.

★6127★ **Law and Legal Information Directory**

Thomson Gale
27500 Drake Rd.
Farmington Hills, MI 48331-3535
Ph: (248)699-4253   Fax: (248)699-8065
Fr: 800-877-GALE
E-mail: businessproducts@gale.com

Biennial. $405.00. Covers more than 19,000 national and international organizations, bar associations, federal and highest state courts, federal regulatory agencies, law schools, firms and organizations offering continuing legal education, paralegal education, sources of scholarships and grants, awards and prizes, special libraries, information systems and services, research centers, publishers of legal periodicals, books, and audiovisual materials, lawyer referral services, legal aid offices, public defender offices, legislature manuals and registers, small claims courts, corporation departments of state, state law enforcement agencies, state agencies, including disciplinary agencies, and state bar requirements. Entries include: All entries include institution or firm name, address, phone; many include names and titles of key personnel and, when pertinent, descriptive annotations. Contents based in part on information selected from several other Gale directories. Arrangement: Classified by type of organization, activity, service, etc. Indexes: Individual sections have special indexes as required.

★6128★ **Lawyers' List**

Commercial Publishing Company Inc.
8706 Commerce Dr., Ste. 4
Easton, MD 21601
Ph: (410)820-8089   Fax: (410)820-4474
Fr: 800-824-9911
E-mail: info@thelawyerslist.com
URL: http://www.thelawyerslist.com/about.shtml

Annual, May. $75.00. Covers about 2,500 lawyers in general, corporate, trial, patent, trademark, and copywrite practices internationally. Entries include: Firm name, address, phone, fax, e-mail, website, areas of practice, branch offices, names of representative clients, names of partners and associates. A general law list. Arrangement: Geographical.

★6129★ **Lawyer's Register International by Specialties and Fields of Law Including a Directory of Corporate Counsel**

Lawyer's Register Publishing Co.
26310 Emery Rd.
Cleveland, OH 44128
Ph: (216)591-1492   Fax: (216)591-0265
Fr: 800-477-6345

Annual. $399.00. Covers corporate legal staffs worldwide; legal firms; independent practicing attorneys each identified as a specialist in one or more fields of law. Entries include: In corporate section-Corporation, subsidiary, and department names; address, phone, fax; names and titles of legal staff, law schools attended, specialties. In fields of law sections-Name, address, phone, fax, specialties (identified by Standard Industrial Classification (SIC) codes), personal data. A general international/corporate law list. See separate listing, "Law Lists." Arrangement: Separate sections for specializing lawyers and their firms and corporate counsel. Indexes: Lawyers and firms by areas, corporations, more indexes.

★6130★ **The Legal Information Buyer's Guide and Reference Manual**
Kendall Svengalis
Dept. of Library and Information Science
Univ. of Rhode Island
Kingston, RI 02881

$105.00. Publication includes: Appendix listing publishers, distributors, used book dealers, and state bar associations. Principal content of publication is information to help librarians and legal professionals choose legal research materials. Indexes: Alphabetical.

★6131★ **Martindale-Hubbell Bar Register of Preeminent Lawyers**
Martindale-Hubbell Inc.
121 Chanlon Rd.
New Providence, NJ 07974
Ph: (908)464-6800   Fax: (908)771-8704
Fr: 800-526-4902
URL: http://www.martindale.com

Annual. $195.00. Covers over 10,000 of today's most skilled attorneys and law partnerships and firms. Entries include: Firm name, telephone, fax, e-mail, URL, members, associate clients, and name and title of contact. Arrangement: Geographical.

★6132★ **Martindale-Hubbell Canadian Law Directory**
Martindale-Hubbell Inc.
121 Chanlon Rd.
New Providence, NJ 07974
Ph: (908)464-6800   Fax: (908)771-8704
Fr: 800-526-4902
E-mail: canada@martindale.com
URL: http://www.canada.martindale.com

Annual. $85.00. Covers thousands of Canadian attorneys, law firms, and corporate law departments, as well as U.S. laywers interested in receiving referrals from Canada. Arrangement: Geographical. Indexes: Alphabetical, Area of Practice.

★6133★ **Martindale-Hubbell Law Directory**
Martindale-Hubbell Inc.
121 Chanlon Rd.
New Providence, NJ 07974
Ph: (908)464-6800   Fax: (908)771-8704
Fr: 800-526-4902
URL: http://www.martindale.com

Annual. $675.00. Covers lawyers and law firms in the United States, its possessions, and Canada, plus leading law firms worldwide; includes a biographical section by firm, and a separate list of patent lawyers, attorneys in government service, in-house counsel, and services, suppliers, and consultants

to the legal profession. Entries include: For non-subscribing lawyers-Name, year of birth and of first admission to bar, code indicating college and law school attended and first degree, firm name (or other affiliation, if any) and relationship to firm, whether practicing other than as individual or in partnership. For subscribing lawyers-Above information plus complete address, phone, fax, e-mail and URL, type of practice, clients, plus additional personal details (education, certifications, etc.). A general law list. Arrangement: Geographical. Indexes: Alphabetical, area of practice.

★6134★ **National Directory of Prosecuting Attorneys**
National District Attorneys Association
99 Canal Center Plz., Ste. 510
Alexandria, VA 22314
Ph: (703)549-9222   Fax: (703)836-3195
E-mail: cathy.yates@ndaa-apri.org
URL: http://www.ndaa-apri.org/publications/ndaa/index.html

Biennial. $35.00 for members; $50.00 for nonmembers. Covers about 2,800 elected or appointed local prosecuting attorneys. Entries include: Name, address, phone, jurisdiction, fax, email. Arrangement: Geographical. Indexes: Alphabetical.

★6135★ **National Hispanic American Attorney Directory**
Hispanic National Bar Association (HNBA)
c/o Carlos Ortiz
Goya Foods Inc.
100 Seaview Dr.
Secaucus, NJ 07096
Ph: (201)348-4900   Fax: (201)348-9437

Irregular, previous edition January 1994; latest edition 1998. Covers approximately 8,000 Hispanic American lawyers. Entries include: Name, business address, phone, fax, home phone, area of practice. Arrangement: Alphabetical. Indexes: Geographical; area of practice.

★6136★ **NLADA Directory of Legal Aid and Defender Offices in the United States and Territories**
National Legal Aid & Defender Association
1140 Connecticut Ave. NW, Ste. 900
Washington, DC 20036
Ph: (202)452-0620   Fax: (202)872-1031
URL: http://www.nlada.org/Member_Svcs/Publications/Directory/

Biennial, Spring of even years. $30.00 for program member; $50.00 for individual member; $90.00 for nonmembers. Covers approximately 3,600 civil legal aid and indigent defense organizations in the United States; includes programs for specific groups such as prisoners, senior citizens, the disabled, etc. Entries include: Agency name, address, phone, director's name. Arrangement: Geographical. Indexes: Type of service.

★6137★ **Russell Law List**
Commercial Publishing Company Inc.
8706 Commerce Dr., Ste. 4
Easton, MD 21601
Ph: (410)820-8089   Fax: (410)820-4474
Fr: 800-824-9911
E-mail: russell@internetconnection.com
URL: http://internetconnection.com/russells/

Annual, June. Covers law offices (limited one to a city) in general practice, worldwide. Entries include: Name, address, phone, telex, fax, cable address e-mail, website, areas of practice, partners, and representative clients. A general law list. Arrangement: Geographical.

★6138★ **USBD-United States Bar Directory**
Attorneys National Clearing House Co.
PO Box 142828
Gainesville, FL 32614-2828
Ph: (352)336-3344   Fax: (866)859-2624
Fr: (866)860-2624
E-mail: usbd@usbardirectory.com
URL: http://www.usbardirectory.com

Annual, January. $19.95. Covers Over 3,000 general and specialized practice attorneys employed through correspondence (letter, phone, fax or e-mail). Entries include: Firm name, address, phone, preferred fields of practice, fax, email, Web site. Arrangement: Geographical.

★6139★ **Who's Who in American Law**
Marquis Who's Who
121 Chanlon Rd.
New Providence, NJ 07974
Ph: (908)673-1101   Fax: (908)673-1189
Fr: 800-473-7020
E-mail: law@renp.com
URL: http://www.marquiswhoswho.com

Biennial, Winter of odd years. $310.50. Covers over 23,000 lawyers, judges, law school deans and professors, and other legal professionals. Entries include: Name, home and office addresses, place and date of birth, educational background, career history, civic positions, professional memberships, publications, awards, special achievements. Arrangement: Alphabetical. Indexes: Fields of practice, professional area.

★6140★ **Wright-Holmes Law List**
Wright-Holmes Inc.
1020 8th Ave., S., Ste. 10
Naples, FL 34102-6959
Ph: (239)434-8880   Fax: (239)434-5983
Fr: 800-882-5478
URL: http://www.collectioncenter.com/index.htm

Annual, April. Covers over 1,400 law firms throughout the U.S., Canada and 35 other countries. Entries include: Firm name, address, phone. A commercial law list. Arrangement: Geographical.

HANDBOOKS AND MANUALS

★6141★ Administration of Justice: An Internship Guide to the Quest for Justice
Kendall Hunt Publishing Co.
4050 Westmark Dr.
PO Box 1840
Dubuque, IA 52002
Ph: (319)589-1000   Fax: (319)589-1046
Fr: 800-228-0810

Carol Fine. 2000. $55.95 (paper). 340 pages.

★6142★ Attorney's Career Guide
Thomson Delmar Learning
PO Box 15015
Albany, NY 12212-5015
Ph: (518)348-2300   Fax: (518)373-6345
Fr: 800-998-7498

Chere B. Estrin. July 2003. $23.95 (paper). Vocational guidance in law.

★6143★ Career Information Center
Macmillan Publishing Co. Inc.
200 Old Tappan Rd.
Old Tappan, NJ 07675
Fr: 800-428-5331

Visual Education Center Staff. Seventh edition, 1999. $275.00. 2080 pages. This 13-volume set profiles over 600 occupations. Each occupational profile describes job duties, educational requirements, how to get the job, advancement possibilities, employment outlook, working conditions, earnings and benefits, and where to write for more information.

★6144★ Careers in Law
McGraw-Hill Contemporary Books
1221 Avenue of the Americas
New York, NY 10020
Ph: (212)904-2000   Fr: 800-323-4900
E-mail: ntcpub@tribune.com

Gary Munneke. Second edition, 1997. $17.95; $13.95 (paper). 406 pages. Overview of opportunities available to lawyers in private practice, corporate law, in federal, state, and local governments, and in teaching. Provides information on the typical law school curriculum plus opportunities in internships and clerkships.

★6145★ Careers for Legal Eagles and Other Law-and-Order Types
McGraw-Hill Trade
2 Penn Plaza
New York, NY 10121
Ph: (212)904-2000   Fr: 800-722-4726
E-mail: ntcpub@tribune.com

Blythe Camenson. 1998. $14.95; $9.95 (paper). 220 pages.

★6146★ Careers for Mystery Buffs and Other Snoops and Sleuths
McGraw-Hill Trade
2 Penn Plaza
New York, NY 10121
Ph: (212)904-2000   Fr: 800-722-4726
E-mail: ntcpub@tribune.com

Blythe Camenson. 1996. $14.95; $9.95 (paper). 210 pages.

★6147★ Great Jobs for Liberal Arts Majors
McGraw-Hill Professional
2 Penn Plaza
New York, NY 10121
Ph: (212)904-2000   Fr: 800-722-4726
E-mail: ntcpub@tribune.com

Blythe Camenson. Second edition, 2001. $14.95 (paper). 256 pages.

★6148★ Guide to Careers in World Affairs
Impact Publications
9104-N Manassas Dr., Ste. N
Manassas Park, VA 20111-5211
Ph: (703)361-7300   Fax: (703)335-9486

Foreign Affairs Association Staff and Pamela Gerard. Third edition. 1993. $14.95. 331 pages. Out of print. Describes jobs in business, government, and nonprofit organizations. Explains the methods and credentials required to secure a job in many fields, including international law and journalism. Contains sections on internships and graduate programs.

★6149★ A Guide to a Successful Legal Internship
Anderson Publishing Co.
2035 Reading Rd.
Cincinnati, OH 45202-1576
Ph: (513)421-4142   Fax: (513)562-8116
Fr: 800-582-7295

Hedi Nasheri and Peter C. Kratcoski. 1996. $22.95 (paper). 176 pages.

★6150★ The I Hate Selling Book: Business-Building Advice for Consultants, Attorneys, Accountants, Engineers, Architects, and Other Professionals
Allan Boress & Associates
1500 University Dr., Suite 239
Coral Springs, FL 33071
Ph: (954)345-4666   Fax: (954)344-2453

Allan S. Boress. 2001. $29.95.

★6151★ Law School 101: Survival Techniques from First Year to Finding the Right Job
Sourcebooks, Inc.
1935 Brookdale Rd., Ste. 139
Naperville, IL 60563
Ph: (630)961-3900   Fax: (630)961-2168
Fr: 800-432-7444

R. Stephanie Good. May 2004.

★6152★ The Lawyer's Almanac, 2000
Panel Publishers
1185 Ave. of the Americas, 37th Fl.
New York, NY 10036
Ph: (212)597-0200   Fax: (212)597-0334
Fr: 800-447-1717

Aspen Publishers Staff. 2001. $162.00. 1262 pages.

★6153★ The Lawyer's Career Change Handbook: More Than 300 Things You Can Do with a Law Degree
Morrow Avon
1350 Ave. of the Americas
New York, NY 10019
Ph: (212)261-6788   Fr: 800-242-7737

Hindi Greenberg. 1998. $14.00 (paper). 320 pages.

★6154★ Lawyer's Desk Book
Prentice Hall PTR
200 Old Tappan Rd.
Old Tappan, NJ 07675
Fax: 800-445-6991   Fr: 800-223-1360

Shilling. First edition, supplementary. 2001. $39.95. 384 pages.

★6155★ Letters to a Young Lawyer
Basic Books
10 E. 53rd St.
New York, NY 10022-5299
Ph: (212)207-7600   Fax: (212)207-7703

Alan Dershowitz. 2001. $22.00.

★6156★ My First Year As a Lawyer: Real-World Stories from America's Lawyers
Walker & Co.
435 Hudson St.
New York, NY 10014-3941
Ph: (212)727-8300   Fax: (212)727-0984
Fr: 800-289-2553

Mark Simenhoff, editor. 1994. $19.95. 120 pages. Part of the First Year Career Series.

★6157★ Opportunities in Gerontology and Aging Services Careers
McGraw-Hill Trade
2 Penn Plaza
New York, NY 10121
Ph: (212)904-2000   Fr: 800-722-4726

Ellen Williams. 1995. $14.95; $11.95 (paper). 200 pages. Covers jobs in community, health and medical programs, financial, legal, residential, travel and tourism, and counseling, and how to go after them. Includes bibliography and illustrations.

★6158★ Opportunities in Law Careers
McGraw-Hill Trade
2 Penn Plaza
New York, NY 10121
Ph: (212)904-2000   Fr: 800-722-4726

Gary A. Munneke. 1994. $14.95; $11.95 (paper). 160 pages. Covers the entire range of careers in law, from admission to law school to finding the job in private practice, corporate law, public interest law, or teaching.

★6159★ **Opportunities in State and Local Government Careers**
Vgm Career Horizons
1221 Avenue of the Americas
New York, NY 10020
Ph: (212)904-2000   Fr: 800-323-4900
E-mail: ntcpub@tribune.com

Neale J. Baxter. 1994. $14.95; $10.95 (paper). 160 pages. Points out the incentives and drawbacks of a government career. Describes hiring procedures and provides tips on filling out applications, taking physical and aptitude tests, handling interviews, and finding jobs. Describes the jobs in which 75% of all state and local government workers are employed. For each occupation, covers the nature of the work and the training required.

★6160★ **Real People Working in Law**
McGraw-Hill Contemporary Books
1221 Avenue of the Americas
New York, NY 10020
Ph: (212)904-2000   Fr: 800-323-4900
E-mail: ntcpub@tribune.com

Blythe Camenson, Jan Goldberg. 1997. $14.95; $12.95 (paper). 405 pages. Interviews and profiles of working professionals capture a range of opportunities in this field.

★6161★ **Real-Resumes for Legal and Paralegal Jobs**
PREP Publishing
1110 1/2 Hay St., PMB 66
Fayetteville, NC 28305
Ph: (910)483-6611   Fax: (910)483-2439
Fr: 800-533-2814

March 2004. $16.95 (paper). 192 pages. Real-Resumes Series.

★6162★ **Resumes for Law Careers**
McGraw-Hill Professional
2 Penn Plaza
New York, NY 10121
Ph: (212)904-2000   Fr: 800-722-4726
E-mail: ntcpub@tribune.com

2001. $10.95 (paper). 160 pages.

★6163★ **Vault Guide to Bankruptcy Law Careers**
Vault.com
150 W 22nd St., 5th Fl.
New York, NY 10011
Ph: (212)366-4212   Fax: (212)366-6117
Fr: 888-562-8285

Seth A. Stuhl. November 2003. $29.95 (paper). 128 pages. Vault Career Library.

★6164★ **Vault Guide to Careers in Labor and Employment Law**
Vault.com
150 W. 22nd St., 5th Fl.
New York, NY 10011
Ph: (212)366-4212   Fax: (212)366-6117
Fr: 888-562-8285

Timothy Grubb. October 2003. $29.95 (paper). 96 pages. Part of the Vault Career Library series.

★6165★ **Vault Guide to Careers in Litigation**
Vault.com
150 W. 22nd St., 5th Fl.
New York, NY 10011
Ph: (212)366-4212   Fax: (212)366-6117
Fr: 888-562-8285

Kristin Nichols, Neeraja Viswanathan. November 2003. $29.95 (paper). 128 pages.

★6166★ **Vault Guide to Corporate Law Careers**
Vault.com
150 W. 22nd St., 5th Fl.
New York, NY 10011
Ph: (212)366-4212   Fax: (212)366-6117
Fr: 888-562-8285

Zahie El Kouri. November 2003. $29.95 (paper). 128 pages. Vault Career Library.

★6167★ **Vault Guide to the Top Boston Law Firms**
Vault.com
150 W. 22nd St., 5th Fl.
New York, NY 10011
Ph: (212)366-4212   Fax: (212)366-6117
Fr: 888-562-8285

Brook Moshan, Hussam Hamadeh, Mark Oldman, Tyya N. Turner, Marcy Lerner. March 2003. $29.95 (paper). 136 pages. Part of the Vault Career Library series.

★6168★ **Vault Guide to the Top Chicago Law Firms**
Vault.com
150 W. 22nd St., 5th Fl.
New York, NY 10011
Ph: (212)366-4212   Fax: (212)366-6117
Fr: 888-562-8285

Brook Moshan, Hussam Hamadeh, Mark Oldman, Tyya N. Turner, Mercy Lerner. March 2003. $29.95 (paper). 208 pages. Part of the Vault Career Library series.

★6169★ **Vault Guide to the Top Government and Non-Profit Legal Employers**
Vault.com
150 W. 22nd St., 5th Fl.
New York, NY 10011
Ph: (212)366-4212   Fax: (212)366-6117
Fr: 888-562-8285

Marcy Lerner. October 2003. $29.95 (paper). 176 pages. Part of the Vault Career Library Series.

★6170★ **Vault Guide to the Top Texas Law Firms**
Vault.com
150 W. 22nd St., 5th Fl.
New York, NY 10011
Ph: (212)366-4212   Fax: (212)366-6117
Fr: 888-562-8285

Brook Moshan, Hussam Hamadeh, Mark Oldman, Tyya N. Turner, Marcy Lerner. March 2003. $29.95 (paper). 160 pages. Part of the Vault Career Library series.

★6171★ **What Can You Do with a Law Degree?: A Lawyer's Guide to Career Alternatives Inside, Outside and Around the Law**
Niche Press
PO Box 99477
Seattle, WA 98199
Ph: (206)285-5239   Fax: (206)213-0750

Deborah L. Arron. Fourth edition, 1997. $29.95 (paper). 400 pages.

★6172★ **Where the Jobs Are: The Hottest Careers for the 90s**
The Career Press, Inc.
3 Tice Rd.
PO Box 687
Franklin Lakes, NJ 07417-1322
Ph: (201)848-0310   Fax: (201)848-1727
Fr: 800-227-3371

Joyce Hadley. Third edition, 2000. $13.99 (paper). 400 pages. Out of print. Describes careers in fifteen general fields, from accounting to travel and hospitality.

EMPLOYMENT AGENCIES AND SEARCH FIRMS

★6173★ **Allen Personnel Agency Inc.**
170 Broadway, Rm. 211
New York, NY 10038
Ph: (212)571-1150   Fax: (212)766-1015
Fr: 800-486-1150

Personnel consultants specializing in business and finance recruitment, specifically insurance, banking, stock brokerage, law and accounting.

★6174★ **Attorney Resources, Inc.**
750 North St. Paul, Ste. 540
Dallas, TX 75201
Ph: (512)922-8050   Fax: (512)871-3041
Fr: 800-324-4828
E-mail: dallas@attorneyresource.com
URL: http://www.attorneyresource.com

Employment agency. Offices in Fort Worth, TX, and Tulsa, OK. Provides staffing assistance on regular or temporary basis.

★6175★ Bader Research Corp.
60 E. 42nd St., Ste. 565
New York, NY 10165
Ph: (212)682-4750   Fax: (212)682-4758
Executive search firm.

★6176★ Beverly Hills Bar Association Personnel Service
300 S. Beverly Dr., Ste. 214
Beverly Hills, CA 90212-4805
Ph: (310)553-4575   Fax: (310)553-6940
URL: http://www.bhba.org
Employment agency.

★6177★ Bishop Partners
708 3rd Ave., Ste. 2200
New York, NY 10017
Ph: (212)986-3419   Fr: (212)986-3350
Executive search firm focuses on legal and accounting fields.

★6178★ Coleman Legal Search Consultants
1535 JFK Blvd., Ste. 1010
Philadelphia, PA 19102
Ph: (215)864-2700   Fax: (215)864-2709
E-mail: cls@colemanlegal.com
URL: http://www.colemanlegal.com
Executive search firm.

★6179★ Combined Resources Inc.
3996 Tennyson Ln.
North Olmsted, OH 44070
Ph: (440)759-5920
Executive search firm focused on the legal field.

★6180★ DiMarchi Partners Inc.
PO Box 1147
Niwot, CO 80544-1147
Ph: (303)415-9300
Executive search firm focused on the legal industry.

★6181★ Early Cochran & Olson LLC
401 N. Michigan Ave., Ste. 2010
Chicago, IL 60611-4206
Ph: (312)595-4200   Fax: (312)595-4209
Executive search firm focused specifically on the legal field.

★6182★ Fergus Partnership Consulting Inc.
1325 Avenue of the Americas, Ste. 2302
New York, NY 10019-6026
Ph: (212)767-1775   Fax: (212)315-0351
An executive search firm for lawyers. Over 15 years of experience with prestigious law firms worldwide. Experienced in international business and finance.

★6183★ Gibson Arnold & Associates Inc.
1776 Yorktown St., No. 350
Houston, TX 77056-4182
Ph: (713)572-3000   Fax: (713)572-4664
Fr: 800-879-2007
Legal temporary service supplies attorneys, paralegals, and production clerks to major law firms and corporations nationwide. Also maintains a full-time placement division. Assists law firms and corporations with staffing any in-house needs.

★6184★ Gillard Associates Legal Search
202 Bussey St.
Dedham, MA 02026
Ph: (781)329-4731   Fax: (617)329-1357
E-mail: gillardlgl@aol.com
Search firm.

★6185★ Ingle-Terrell & Associates
3100 Sunset Dr.
Charlotte, NC 28209-1208
Ph: (704)333-8400
Provides assistance in recruitment and placement of personnel. Industries served: insurance and law.

★6186★ Interquest Inc.
98 Cuttermill Rd.
Great Neck, NY 11021
Ph: (212)319-0790   Fax: (212)753-0596
Offers retained executive search and other consulting services for the legal profession, with primary focus being general counsel searches for corporations, law firm members and lateral movement of partners for law firms.

★6187★ Legal Medical Staffing Services Inc.
Plz. 1000, Ste. 202, Main St.
Voorhees, NJ 08043
Ph: (856)751-7999   Fax: (856)751-8448
Offers a specialized service providing temporary and full-time support exclusively to the legal, dental, and medical professions.

★6188★ Legal Placement Services, Inc.
740 N Plankinton Ave., Ste.430
Milwaukee, WI 53203
Ph: (414)276-6689   Fax: (414)276-1418
E-mail: info@legalplacementservices.com
URL: http://www.legalplacementservices.com
Employment agency. Periodically fills temporary placements as well.

★6189★ Major, Hagen, and Africa
500 Washington St., Floor 5
San Francisco, CA 94111
Ph: (415)956-1010   Fr: 877-482-1010
E-mail: infosf@nhaglobal.com

URL: http://www.mhaglobal.com
Executive search firm. Affiliate offices in Atlanta, GA, Chicago, IL, and New York, NY.

★6190★ Phyllis Hawkins and Associates
105 E Northern Ave.
Phoenix, AZ 85020
Ph: (602)263-0248   Fax: (602)678-1564
E-mail: phassoc@qweat.com
URL: http://www.azlawsearch.com
Executive search firm focusing on attorney searches.

★6191★ The Sharrow Group
531 Ridge Rd. E
Rochester, NY 14621
Ph: (585)266-0993   Fr: 877-759-6910
Executive search firm offers specialized placement in areas of rubber, adhesives, plastic, coatings, paint, information technology, patent and trademark attorneys, and construction executives.

★6192★ Weiss & Associates
407 Wekiva Springs Rd.
PO Box 915656
Winter Park, FL 32789
Ph: (407)774-1212   Fax: (407)774-0084
Executive and legal search consultants and recruiters for major law firms and multinational corporations throughout North America and Europe. Special expertise with tax attorneys and "key" tax executives in addition to experienced partners with significant portable business. Also specialize in mergers and outplacement services.

ONLINE JOB SOURCES AND SERVICES

★6193★ EmpLawyerNet.com
E-mail: membership@emplawyernet.com
URL: http://www.emplawyernet.com/
Description: Career resource site for lawyers. Contains career information, resume posting and job board search, along with links to CLE events, online bookstores, and recruiter directories. **Fee:** Limited access permitted with free basic membership. Premier membership is $59 or $14.95/month and includes free CLE courses, e-mail alerts, networking opportunities and personal career advice.

★6194★ Headhunt.com: The Counsel Network
E-mail: snash@headhunt.com
URL: http://www.thecounselnetwork.com/
Description: Job search and career resource site for attorneys. Search for jobs, post profile, contact recruiters and consul-

tants, download PDF career guides, and more. Registration is free.

★6195★ Law.com: Law Jobs
URL: http://www.lawjobs.com

Description: Visitors can post job openings for attorneys, legal support staff and temporary workers. Also resources for legal recruiters and temporary staffing agencies.

★6196★ The Legal Employment Search Site
E-mail: webmaster@legalemploy.com
URL: http://www.legalemploy.com

Description: Contains links to job search and career-related websites for lawyers and legal support staff.

TRADESHOWS

★6197★ American Bar Association Annual Meeting/ABA Expo
American Bar Association
750 N. Lake Shore Dr.
Chicago, IL 60611
Ph: (312)988-5000   Fax: (312)988-6338
Fr: 800-238-2667
E-mail: askaba@abanet.org
URL: http://www.abanet.org

Annual. **Primary Exhibits:** Law books, computers, data processing equipment, and other products and services related to the legal profession.

★6198★ Association of American Law Schools Annual Meeting
Association of American Law Schools
1201 Connecticut Ave., NW, Ste. 800
Washington, DC 20036-2605
Ph: (202)296-8851   Fax: (202)296-8869
E-mail: aals@aals.org

Annual. **Primary Exhibits:** Law books, personal computers and hardware and software, video equipment, and communication technology.

★6199★ Association of Legal Administrators Meeting
Association of Legal Administrators
175 E. Hawthorne Pkwy., Ste. 325
Vernon Hills, IL 60061
Ph: (708)816-1212   Fax: (708)816-1213

Annual. **Primary Exhibits:** Computers, hardware, and software; office equipment and supplies; publications, printers, and engravers; insurance; travel consultants; litigation support; facilities management; hotels; and coffee suppliers.

★6200★ Association of Trial Lawyers of America Convention/Exposition
Association of Trial Lawyers of America
1050 31st St., NW
Washington, DC 20007
Ph: (202)965-3500   Fax: (202)625-7313
Fr: 800-424-2725
URL: http://www.atlanet.org

Semiannual. **Primary Exhibits:** Legal product/service providers, including computer animation videos, computer software/hardware, demonstrative evidence products, expert witness services and marketing firms, as well as high end consumer gifts. Online services, structured settlement services, litigation support, legal publishing.

★6201★ National Bar Association Annual Convention & Exhibits
National Bar Association
1225 11th St., NW
Washington, DC 20001
Ph: (202)842-3900   Fax: (202)289-6170
URL: http://www.nationalbar.org

Annual. **Primary Exhibits:** Computers and legal software; office products; accounting services; financial planners, temporary employment agencies; legal publications; travel agencies; luggage and leather goods; fine arts and jewelry.

★6202★ Virginia Trial Lawyers Association Conference
Virginia Trial Lawyers Association
700 E. Main St., Ste. 1510
Richmond, VA 23219
Ph: (804)343-1143   Fax: (804)343-7124
Fr: 800-267-8852
E-mail: vtla@vtla.com
URL: http://www.vtla.com

Annual. **Primary Exhibits:** Equipment, supplies, and services for trial lawyers, including clothiers, printers, financial investors, and mediators. 2005 Mar 31-Apr 03; Hot Springs, VA; The Homestead • 2006 Mar 30-Apr 02; Hot Springs, VA; The Homestead.

OTHER SOURCES

★6203★ American Almanac of Jobs and Salaries
Morrow Avon
1350 Avenue of the Americas
New York, NY 10019
Ph: (212)261-6788   Fr: 800-242-7737

John W. Wright. Revised edition, 2000. $20.00 (paper). 672 pages. This is a comprehensive guide to the wages of hundreds of occupations in a wide variety of industries and organizations.

★6204★ American Association of Nurse Attorneys (TAANA)
7794 Grow Dr.
Pensacola, FL 32514
Ph: (850)474-3646   Fax: (850)484-8762
Fr: 877-532-2262
E-mail: taana@puetzamc.com
URL: http://www.taana.org

Members: Nurse attorneys, nurses in law school, and attorneys in nursing school. **Purpose:** Aims to better nurse attorneys and inform the public on matters of nursing, health care, and law. Goals are to facilitate communication and information sharing between professional groups; to establish an employment network; to assist new and potential nurse attorneys; to develop the profession; to promote the image of nurse attorneys as experts and consultants in nursing and law. **Activities:** Maintains educational foundation.

★6205★ American Bar Association (ABA)
541 N. Fairbanks Ct, Service Center
750 North Lake Shore Dr.
Chicago, IL 60611
Ph: (312)988-5000   Fax: (312)988-5522
Fr: 800-285-2221
E-mail: service@abanet.org
URL: http://www.abanet.org

Description: Attorneys in good standing of the bar of any state. Conducts research and educational projects and activities to: encourage professional improvement; provide public services; improve the administration of civil and criminal justice; increase the availability of legal services to the public. Sponsors Law Day USA. Administers numerous standing and special committees such as Committee on Soviet and East European Law, providing seminars and newsletters. Operates 25 sections, including Criminal Justice, Economics of Law Practice, and Family Law. Sponsors essay competitions. Maintains library.

★6206★ American Blind Lawyers Association (ABLA)
1155 15th St., NW, Ste. 1004
Washington, DC 20005
Ph: (202)467-5081   Fax: (202)467-5085
Fr: 800-424-8666
E-mail: info@acb.org
URL: http://www.acb.org/affiliates/abla.htm

Description: Blind lawyers and blind law students. Seeks to provide a forum for discussion of the special problems encountered by blind persons licensed to practice law and by blind students training for the legal profession; protect the interests of blind members of the legal profession; acquire, preserve, and maintain law libraries and periodicals of special interest to blind lawyers and blind law students; promote the production of and disseminate information concerning legal materials in braille or recorded form; advance the legal profession. Conducts educational, research, and professional training programs. Operates speakers' bureau. Maintains index of legal material in braille and on cassette; reproduces items from the American Bar Journal and related publications on cassettes.

★6207★ **American Intellectual Property Law Association (AIPLA)**
2001 Jefferson Davis Hwy., Ste. 203
Arlington, VA 22202
Ph: (703)415-0780   Fax: (703)415-0786
E-mail: aipla@aipla.org
URL: http://www.aipla.org

Description: Voluntary bar association of lawyers practicing in the fields of patents, trademarks, copyrights, and trade secrets. Aids in the operation and improvement of U.S. patent, trademark, and copyright systems, including the laws by which they are governed and rules and regulations under which federal agencies administer those laws. Sponsors moot court and legal writing competitions.

★6208★ **Association of Family and Conciliation Courts (AFCC)**
6515 Grand Teton Plaza, Ste. 210
Madison, WI 53719-1048
Ph: (608)664-3750   Fax: (608)664-3751
E-mail: afcc@afccnet.org
URL: http://www.afccnet.org

Members: Judges, counselors, family court personnel, attorneys, mediators, researchers, and teachers concerned with the resolution of family disputes as they affect children. **Purpose:** Proposes to develop and improve the practice of dispute resolution procedure as a complement to judicial procedures. Aims to strengthen the family unit and minimize family strife by improving the process of marriage, family, and divorce counseling; and to provide an interdisciplinary forum for the exchange of ideas, for the creation of new approaches to child custody matters and solutions to problems of family discord. Collaborates with the National Council of Juvenile and Family Court Judges, National Judicial College, the National Center for State Courts, the American Bar Association. Several universities, lawschools, and state organizations responsible for providing ongoing training for attorneys, judges, and family therapists. **Activities:** Conducts research and offers technical assistance and training to courts, legal associations, judicial organizations, and behavioral science professionals

★6209★ **Careers in Criminal Justice**
Cambridge Educational
2572 Brunswick Ave.
Lawrenceville, NJ 08648-4128
Fax: 800-FAX-ON-US   Fr: 800-468-4227
URL: http://www.cambridgeeducational.com

$79.95. 2002. 22 minutes.

★6210★ **Equal Justice Works**
2120 L St., Ste. 450
Washington, DC 20037
Ph: (202)466-3686   Fax: (202)429-9766
E-mail: dstern@equaljusticeworks.org
URL: http://www.napil.org

Description: Dedicated to surmounting barriers to equal justice that affect millions of low-income individuals and families. Engaged in organizing, training, and supporting public service-minded law students and creates summer and postgraduate public interest jobs.

★6211★ **Food and Drug Law Institute (FDLI)**
1000 Vermont Ave. NW, Ste. 200
Washington, DC 20005-4903
Ph: (202)371-1420   Fax: (202)371-0649
Fr: 800-956-6293
E-mail: comments@fdli.org
URL: http://www.fdli.org

Description: Provides forum regarding laws, regulations and policies related to drugs, medical devices, other health care technologies.

★6212★ **International Society of Stress Analysts (ISSA)**
9 Westchester Dr.
Kissimmee, FL 34744
Ph: (407)933-4839   Fax: (407)935-0911
E-mail: diogenesfl@aol.com

Members: Jurists, attorneys, physicians, private detectives, law enforcement personnel, security personnel, scholar/researchers, and individuals interested in stress analysis for lie detection/truth verification. **Purpose:** Works to promote the science of psychological stress evaluation and the efficient administration of justice; aid indigent persons, without cost, who may be wrongfully accused; develop and maintain high educational standards; observe and evaluate training programs for the purpose of accreditation and endorsement. **Activities:** Sponsors and certifies schools; offers workshops and research and educational programs; conducts forums. Offers expertise, consultation, and advice; invites inquiries.

★6213★ **Law**
Evon Publishing
832 N 7th Ave.
Iron River, MI 49935
Ph: (906)265-3190

Audiocassette. 1996. $16.95. 32 minutes. Part of the Careers and Vocational Guidance Series. Provides information about the nature of the work, educational requirements, employment outlook, earnings, and work conditions as well as additional related information.

★6214★ **Media Law Resource Center**
80 Eighth Ave., Ste. 200
New York, NY 10011-5126
Ph: (212)337-0200   Fax: (212)337-9893
E-mail: ldrc@ldrc.com
URL: http://www.medialaw.org

Description: Provides support for media defendants in libel and privacy cases, including development of statistical and empirical data, assistance in locating expert witnesses

or consultants, and help in coordinating amicus curiae briefs by supporting organizations. Maintains a brief, pleading, and information bank; collects and disseminates information on pending libel and privacy cases for use in legal defense against claims. Serves as a liaison with media organizations, attorneys, and other groups working to advance the defense of libel and privacy claims. Prepares bulletins and reports on current developments and cases, legal theories, privileges, and defenses. Compiles statistics on the incidence and cost of libel and privacy litigation. Provides employment for law student interns. Conducts educational and training workshops and programs; has established fellowship program in libel law. Operates LDRC Institute.

★6215★ **National Association of Legal Investigators (NALI)**
11643 Saginaw St.
PO Box 905
Grand Blanc, MI 48439
Fax: (810)694-7109   Fr: 800-266-6254
E-mail: laccardo@gfn.org
URL: http://www.nalionline.org/

Description: Legal investigators, both independent and law firm staff, who specialize in investigation of personal injury matters for the plaintiff and criminal defense. Goal is the professionalization of the legal investigator, accomplished by seminars and a professional certification program. Provides nationwide network of contact among members. Compiles statistics.

★6216★ **National Association of Traffic Accident Reconstructionists and Investigators (NATARI)**
PO Box 398
Chadds Ford, PA 19317
Ph: (610)558-5176   Fax: (610)558-5176
E-mail: lizgurn@aol.com
URL: http://www.actar.org/natari.htm

Description: Engineers, attorneys, police officers, private investigators, medical examiners, and other individuals involved in the analysis of motor vehicle traffic accidents. Gathers and disseminates information on techniques and equipment of potential use to members; reviews literature in the field. Participating Organization of the Accreditation Commission for Traffic Accident Reconstruction.

★6217★ **Professional Specialty Occupations**
Delphi Productions
3160 4th St.
Boulder, CO 80304
Fax: (303)443-4022   Fr: 888-443-2400
URL: http://www.delphivideo.com

$95.00. 53 minutes. Part of the Careers for the 21st Century Video Library.

★6218★ Puerto Rican Legal Defense and Education Fund (PRLDEF)
99 Hudson St., 14th Fl.
New York, NY 10013-2815
Ph: (212)219-3360   Fax: (212)431-4276
Fr: 800-328-2322
E-mail: info@prldef.org
URL: http://www.prldef.org

Description: Seeks to secure, promote and protect the civil and human rights of the Puerto Rican and wider Latino community. Three divisions, Legal, Policy and Education, carry out the core program areas - Civil & Human Rights, Civic Engagement & Empowerment, Civil Society & Culture and Equitable Educational Opportunities. the pursuit of a legal career for Puerto Ricans and other minorities via its LSAT prep course, Law Day and other programs.

★6219★ U.S. Travel Data Center (USTDC)
1100 New York Ave. NW, Ste. 450
Washington, DC 20005-3934
Ph: (202)408-8422   Fax: (202)408-1255
URL: http://www.tia.org/Travel/default.asp

Description: Conducts statistical, economic, and market research concerning travel; encourages standardized travel research terminology and techniques. Program objectives include: monitoring trends in travel activity and the travel industry; measuring the economic impact of travel on geographic areas; evaluating the effect of government programs on travel and the travel industry; measuring the cost of travel in the U.S., forecasting travel activity and expenditures.

Legal Assistants

SOURCES OF HELP-WANTED ADS

★6220★ California Lawyer
Daily Journal Corp.
915 E 1st St.
Los Angeles, CA 90012-4050
Ph: (213)229-5300   Fax: (213)680-3682
Fr: (866)226-8740

Monthly. $60.00/year for individuals. Law magazine.

★6221★ Chicago Lawyer
Law Bulletin Publishing Co.
415 N State St.
Chicago, IL 60610-4674
Ph: (312)644-7800   Fax: (312)644-4255
E-mail: displayads@lbc.com

Monthly. $40.00/year. Legal magazine (tabloid).

★6222★ Cornerstone
National Legal Aid & Defender
  Association
1140 Connecticut Ave. NW, Ste. 900
Washington, DC 20036
Ph: (202)452-0620   Fax: (202)872-1031
E-mail: cornerstone@nlada.org
URL: http://www.nlada.org/

Description: Four issues/year. Monitors current issues affecting legal aid attorneys and public defenders. Recurring features include job listings, conference and training updates, news of research, book reviews, and news of members.

★6223★ Geriatric Nursing
Mosby Inc.
10801 Executive Center Dr., Ste. 509
Little Rock, AR 72211
Ph: (501)223-5165   Fax: (501)223-0519
URL: http://www.mosby.com/gerinurs

Bimonthly. $54.00/year for individuals; $105.00/year for institutions. Magazine for nurses in geriatric and gerontologic nursing practice, the primary professional providers of care for the aging. Provides news on issues affecting elders and clinical information on techniques and procedures.

★6224★ Job Announcements
National Center for State Courts
300 Newport Ave.(23185)
PO Box 8798
Williamsburg, VA 23187-8798
Ph: (757)253-2000   Fax: (757)220-0449
Fr: 800-877-1233
URL: http://www.ncsconline.org/

Description: Semimonthly. Provides lists of court-related job openings in the United States and its territories.

★6225★ Journal of Forensic Economics
National Association of Forensic
  Economists
PO Box 30067
Kansas City, MO 64112
Ph: (816)235-2833

Quarterly. Journal covering economics and law.

★6226★ Journal of Health and Hospital Law
American Health Lawyers Association
1025 Connecticut NW, Ste. 600
Washington, DC 20036
Ph: (202)833-1100   Fax: (202)833-1105

Quarterly. $150.00/year. Professional journal covering healthcare issues and cases and their impact on the health care arena.

★6227★ Journal of the Missouri Bar
The Missouri Bar
326 Monroe St.
PO Box 119
Jefferson City, MO 65101-3158
Ph: (573)635-4128   Fax: (573)635-2811

Bimonthly. $12.00/year; $3.00 for single issue. Magazine featuring short, practical articles on legal subjects for practicing attorneys.

★6228★ The Journal of Taxation
RIA Group
395 Hudson St., 4th Fl.
New York, NY 10014
Ph: (212)352-2746   Fax: (212)367-6314
Fr: 800-431-9025
URL: http://checkpoint.riag.com

Monthly. $250.00/year for individuals. Journal for sophisticated tax practitioners.

★6229★ Kentucky Bench & Bar Magazine
Kentucky Bar Association
514 W Main St.
Frankfort, KY 40601-1883
Ph: (502)564-3795   Fax: (502)564-3225

Bimonthly. $20.00/year for individuals. Kentucky law journal.

★6230★ Legal Times
American Lawyer Media L.P.
1730 M St. NW, Ste. 802
Washington, DC 20036
Ph: (202)457-0686   Fax: (202)785-4539
Fr: 800-933-4317
E-mail: legaltimes@legaltimes.com
URL: http://www.law.com/dc

Weekly. $318.00/year. Legal publication covering law and lobbying in the nation's capitol.

★6231★ Los Angeles Lawyer
Los Angeles County Bar Association
261 S Figueroa St., Ste. 300
Los Angeles, CA 90012
Ph: (213)627-2727   Fax: (213)896-6500
URL: http://www.lacba.org

Monthly. Magazine featuring scholarly legal articles.

★6232★ Michigan Bar Journal
State Bar of Michigan
306 Townsend St.
Lansing, MI 48933
Ph: (517)372-9030   Fax: (517)482-6248

Monthly. $45.00/year for individuals; $55.00/year for other countries. Legal magazine.

★6233★ The National Law Journal

The New York Law Journal
345 Park Ave. S
New York, NY 10010
Ph: (212)779-9200   Fax: (212)481-8110
Fr: 800-888-8300
URL: http://nlj.com

Weekly. $138.00/year. Tabloid focusing on the practice of law and trends in law.

★6234★ National Paralegal Reporter

National Federation of Paralegal
 Associations Inc.
PO Box 33108
Kansas City, MO 64114-0108
Ph: (816)941-4000   Fax: (816)941-2725
URL: http://www.paralegals.org

Description: Six issues/year. Focuses on issues of concern to the paralegal profession such as responsibility and ethics, new developments in the field, and educational opportunities. Promotes the recognition and advancement of paralegals and provides information on programs and help offered by paralegal associations. Reports regional NFPA news and news of paralegal associations throughout the U.S. Recurring features include book reviews, news of research, and President's Column.

★6235★ New Jersey Law Journal

New Jersey Law Journal
238 Mulberry St.
PO Box 20081
Newark, NJ 07101-6081
Ph: (973)642-0075   Fax: (973)642-0920
URL: http://www.law.com/nj

Weekly. $385.00/year for individuals; $10.00 for single issue. Journal containing digests of court opinions, notes, and orders to the bar from New Jersey Supreme Court and federal district court. Includes news articles on legal topics and commentary by legal specialists.

★6236★ Public Interest Employment Service Job Alert!

Public Interest Clearinghouse
47 Kearny St., Ste. 705
San Francisco, CA 94108
Ph: (415)834-0100   Fax: (415)834-0202
E-mail: pies@pic.org

Description: Semimonthly. Lists job openings in legal aid offices and public interest law organizations.

★6237★ The Recorder

American Lawyer Media L.P.
10 United Nations Plz., 3rd Fl.
San Francisco, CA 94102-4911
Ph: (415)749-5400   Fax: (415)749-5449
Fr: 800-244-5399
E-mail: recorder@counsel.com
URL: http://www.therecorder.com

Daily. $520.00/year for individuals. Legal newspaper.

★6238★ The Washington Lawyer

The District of Columbia Bar
1250 H St. NW, 6th Fl.
Washington, DC 20005-5937
Ph: (202)737-4700   Fax: (202)626-3472
URL: http://www.dcbar.org

Monthly. $30.00/year. Forum for articles and news items for the Washington legal community.

★6239★ Wisconsin Lawyer

State Bar of Wisconsin
5302 Eastpark Blvd.
PO Box 7158
Madison, WI 53707-7158
Ph: (608)257-3838   Fax: (608)257-5502
Fr: 800-444-9404
E-mail: wislawyer@wisbar.org
URL: http://www.wisbar.org/wislawmag/

Monthly. $42.00/year for individuals; $24.00/year for law libraries, educational groups, law students. Magazine for Wisconsin legal professionals.

PLACEMENT AND JOB REFERRAL SERVICES

★6240★ National Paralegal Association

PO Box 406
Solebury, PA 18963
Ph: (215)297-8333   Fax: (215)297-8358
E-mail: admin@nationalparalegal.org
URL: http://www.nationalparalegal.org

Description: Paralegals, paralegal students, educators, supervisors, paralegal schools, administrators, law librarians, law clinics, and attorneys. Objective is to advance the paralegal profession by promoting recognition, economic benefits, and high standards. Registers paralegals; maintains speakers' bureau, job bank, and placement service; offers resume preparation assistance. Offers free job bank nationally. Sponsors commercial exhibits. Operates mail order bookstore and gift shop. Compiles statistics. Is developing promotion and public relations, insurance, certification, and computer bank programs.

EMPLOYER DIRECTORIES AND NETWORKING LISTS

★6241★ American Bar Association-Directory

American Bar Association
750 N Lake Shore Dr.
Chicago, IL 60611
Ph: (312)988-5000   Fr: 800-285-2221

Annual, October. $14.95. Covers approximately 7,500 lawyers active in the affairs of the Association, including officers, members of Boards of Governors and House of Delegates, section officers and council members, committee leaders, headquarters staff, state and local bars, affiliated and other legal organizations. Entries include: Section, council, or other unit name; names, addresses, and phone numbers of officers or chairpersons and members. Arrangement: Classified by position in ABA. Indexes: Alphabetical, Geographical committee.

★6242★ American Lawyers Quarterly

The American Lawyers Co.
853 Westpoint Pkwy., Ste. 710
Cleveland, OH 44145-1595
Ph: (440)871-8700   Fax: (440)871-9997
Fr: 800-843-4000

Semiannual, January and July; monthly supplements. A commercial law list. Arrangement: Geographical.

★6243★ Attorney Jobs Online

Federal Reports Inc.
1010 Vermont Ave. NW, Ste. 408
Washington, DC 20005
Ph: (202)393-3311   Fax: (202)393-1553
Fr: 800-296-9611
URL: http://www.attorneyjobsonline.com

Monthly. $147.00 for individuals per year; $202.00 for institutions per year. Publication includes: Listings of approximately 600 current attorney and law-related job opportunities with the U.S. government and other public and private employers in Washington D.C., nationwide, and abroad. Arrangement: Geographical.

★6244★ Career Opportunities in Law and the Legal Industry

Facts On File Inc.
132 W 31st St., 17th Fl.
New York, NY 10001-2006
Ph: (212)967-8800   Fax: 800-678-3633
Fr: 800-322-8755

$49.50. Publication includes: Lists of industry associations and organizations, educational institutions, and web sites related to the legal industry. Principal content of publication is information on careers in the legal field. Indexes: Alphabetical.

★6245★ Federal Law-Related Careers Directory

Federal Reports Inc.
1010 Vermont Ave. NW, Ste. 408
Washington, DC 20005
Ph: (202)393-3311   Fax: (202)393-1553
Fr: 800-296-9611
URL: http://www.attorneyjobs.com

Irregular, previous edition 1991; latest edition October 1994. $27.45 for individuals; $52.50 for institutions. Publication includes: Listings of over 1,000 federal government recruiting offices. Entries include: Agency name, address, how to apply, and hiring procedure. Principal content of publication is the description of over 150 law-related careers in the U.S. government for which a law degree is an asset, but not a requirement, including contract specialist, criminal investigator, legal research analyst, and labor relations specialist. Arrangement: Classified by subject. Indexes: Subject.

★6246★ Gale Encyclopedia of Everyday Law

Thomson Gale
27500 Drake Rd.
Farmington Hills, MI 48331-3535
Ph: (248)699-4253   Fax: (248)699-8065
Fr: 800-877-GALE
URL: http://www.gale.com

Published October 2002. $295.00. Publication includes: Listing of law-related organizations. Principal content of publication is approximately 200 articles covering specific legal issues of interest to a layperson in the United States and includes details on their background, historical cases, profiles of U.S. laws and regulations, differentiation between states, and further reading.

★6247★ Law Firms Yellow Book

Leadership Directories Inc.
104 5th Ave.
New York, NY 10011
Ph: (212)627-4140   Fax: (212)645-0931
E-mail: lawfirms@leadershipdirectories.com
URL: http://www.leadershipdirectories.com

Semiannual. $261.00; $182.00 for additional subscriptions. Covers approximately 850 large law firms and over 24,000 attorneys and administrators at more than 3,000 domestic and foreign offices, subsidiaries, and affiliates. Entries include: Firm name, address, phone, fax, telex, year founded, description of practice; officers' names, titles, phone numbers, and law schools attended, addresses, phone numbers, and principal officials at branch offices, e-mails. Arrangement: Alphabetical by firm name. Indexes: Geographical, law school, individual name, law firm, practice area.

★6248★ Law and Legal Information Directory

Thomson Gale
27500 Drake Rd.
Farmington Hills, MI 48331-3535
Ph: (248)699-4253   Fax: (248)699-8065
Fr: 800-877-GALE
E-mail: businessproducts@gale.com

Biennial. $405.00. Covers more than 19,000 national and international organizations, bar associations, federal and highest state courts, federal regulatory agencies, law schools, firms and organizations offering continuing legal education, paralegal education, sources of scholarships and grants, awards and prizes, special libraries, information systems and services, research centers, publishers of legal periodicals, books, and audiovisual materials, lawyer referral services, legal aid offices, public defender offices, legislature manuals and registers, small claims courts, corporation departments of state, state law enforcement agencies, state agencies, including disciplinary agencies, and state bar requirements. Entries include: All entries include institution or firm

name, address, phone; many include names and titles of key personnel and, when pertinent, descriptive annotations. Contents based in part on information selected from several other Gale directories. Arrangement: Classified by type of organization, activity, service, etc. Indexes: Individual sections have special indexes as required.

★6249★ Lawyer's Register International by Specialties and Fields of Law Including a Directory of Corporate Counsel

Lawyer's Register Publishing Co.
26310 Emery Rd.
Cleveland, OH 44128
Ph: (216)591-1492   Fax: (216)591-0265
Fr: 800-477-6345

Annual. $399.00. Covers corporate legal staffs worldwide; legal firms; independent practicing attorneys each identified as a specialist in one or more fields of law. Entries include: In corporate section-Corporation, subsidiary, and department names; address, phone, fax; names and titles of legal staff, law schools attended, specialties. In fields of law sections-Name, address, phone, fax, specialties (identified by Standard Industrial Classification (SIC) codes), personal data. A general international/corporate law list. See separate listing, "Law Lists." Arrangement: Separate sections for specializing lawyers and their firms and corporate counsel. Indexes: Lawyers and firms by areas, corporations, more indexes.

★6250★ The Legal Information Buyer's Guide and Reference Manual

Kendall Svengalis
Dept. of Library and Information Science
Univ. of Rhode Island
Kingston, RI 02881

$105.00. Publication includes: Appendix listing publishers, distributors, used book dealers, and state bar associations. Principal content of publication is information to help librarians and legal professionals choose legal research materials. Indexes: Alphabetical.

★6251★ Martindale-Hubbell Canadian Law Directory

Martindale-Hubbell Inc.
121 Chanlon Rd.
New Providence, NJ 07974
Ph: (908)464-6800   Fax: (908)771-8704
Fr: 800-526-4902
E-mail: canada@martindale.com
URL: http://www.canada.martindale.com

Annual. $85.00. Covers thousands of Canadian attorneys, law firms, and corporate law departments, as well as U.S. laywers interested in receiving referrals from Canada. Arrangement: Geographical. Indexes: Alphabetical, Area of Practice.

★6252★ Martindale-Hubbell Law Directory

Martindale-Hubbell Inc.
121 Chanlon Rd.
New Providence, NJ 07974
Ph: (908)464-6800   Fax: (908)771-8704
Fr: 800-526-4902
URL: http://www.martindale.com

Annual. $675.00. Covers lawyers and law firms in the United States, its possessions, and Canada, plus leading law firms worldwide; includes a biographical section by firm, and a separate list of patent lawyers, attorneys in government service, in-house counsel, and services, suppliers, and consultants to the legal profession. Entries include: For non-subscribing lawyers-Name, year of birth and of first admission to bar, code indicating college and law school attended and first degree, firm name (or other affiliation, if any) and relationship to firm, whether practicing other than as individual or in partnership. For subscribing lawyers-Above information plus complete address, phone, fax, e-mail and URL, type of practice, clients, plus additional personal details (education, certifications, etc.). A general law list. Arrangement: Geographical. Indexes: Alphabetical, area of practice.

★6253★ NLADA Directory of Legal Aid and Defender Offices in the United States and Territories

National Legal Aid & Defender Association
1140 Connecticut Ave. NW, Ste. 900
Washington, DC 20036
Ph: (202)452-0620   Fax: (202)872-1031
URL: http://www.nlada.org/Member_Svcs/Publications/Directory/

Biennial, Spring of even years. $30.00 for program member; $50.00 for individual member; $90.00 for nonmembers. Covers approximately 3,600 civil legal aid and indigent defense organizations in the United States; includes programs for specific groups such as prisoners, senior citizens, the disabled, etc. Entries include: Agency name, address, phone, director's name. Arrangement: Geographical. Indexes: Type of service.

★6254★ Russell Law List

Commercial Publishing Company Inc.
8706 Commerce Dr., Ste. 4
Easton, MD 21601
Ph: (410)820-8089   Fax: (410)820-4474
Fr: 800-824-9911
E-mail: russell@internetconnection.com
URL: http://internetconnection.com/russells/

Annual, June. Covers law offices (limited one to a city) in general practice, worldwide. Entries include: Name, address, phone, telex, fax, cable address e-mail, website, areas of practice, partners, and representative clients. A general law list. Arrangement: Geographical.

★6255★ USBD-United States Bar Directory

Attorneys National Clearing House Co.
PO Box 142828
Gainesville, FL 32614-2828
Ph: (352)336-3344   Fax: (866)859-2624
Fr: (866)860-2624
E-mail: usbd@usbardirectory.com
URL: http://www.usbardirectory.com

Annual, January. $19.95. Covers Over 3,000 general and specialized practice attorneys employed through correspondence (letter, phone, fax or e-mail). Entries include: Firm name, address, phone, preferred fields of practice, fax, email, Web site. Arrangement: Geographical.

★6256★ Who's Who in American Law

Marquis Who's Who
121 Chanlon Rd.
New Providence, NJ 07974
Ph: (908)673-1101   Fax: (908)673-1189
Fr: 800-473-7020
E-mail: law@renp.com
URL: http://www.marquiswhoswho.com

Biennial, Winter of odd years. $310.50. Covers over 23,000 lawyers, judges, law school deans and professors, and other legal professionals. Entries include: Name, home and office addresses, place and date of birth, educational background, career history, civic positions, professional memberships, publications, awards, special achievements. Arrangement: Alphabetical. Indexes: Fields of practice, professional area.

★6257★ Wright-Holmes Law List

Wright-Holmes Inc.
1020 8th Ave., S., Ste. 10
Naples, FL 34102-6959
Ph: (239)434-8880   Fax: (239)434-5983
Fr: 800-882-5478
URL: http://www.collectioncenter.com/index.htm

Annual, April. Covers over 1,400 law firms throughout the U.S., Canada and 35 other countries. Entries include: Firm name, address, phone. A commercial law list. Arrangement: Geographical.

HANDBOOKS AND MANUALS

★6258★ Basic Administrative Law for Paralegals

Aspen Publishers Inc.
1185 Avenue of the Americas, 37th Fl.
New York, NY 10036
Ph: (212)597-0200   Fax: (212)597-0338
Fr: 800-234-1660

Anne Adams. 2002. $70.95. 358 Pages. Explore the basics of Administrative Law.

★6259★ Career Information Center

Macmillan Publishing Co. Inc.
200 Old Tappan Rd.
Old Tappan, NJ 07675
Fr: 800-428-5331

Visual Education Center Staff. Seventh edition, 1999. $275.00. 2080 pages. This 13-volume set profiles over 600 occupations. Each occupational profile describes job duties, educational requirements, how to get the job, advancement possibilities, employment outlook, working conditions, earnings and benefits, and where to write for more information.

★6260★ Career Opportunities for Writers

Checkmark Books
132 W. 31st St., 17th Fl.
New York, NY 10001-2006
Ph: (212)967-8800   Fax: (212)967-9196
Fr: 800-322-8755
URL: http://www.factsonfile.com

Rosemary Ellen Guiley and Janet Frick. Fourth edition, 2000. $45.00. Part of the Career Opportunities Series. Describes more than 100 jobs in eight major fields, offering such details as duties, salaries, perquisites, employment and advancement opportunities, organizations to join, and opportunities for women and minorities.

★6261★ Careers in Law

McGraw-Hill Contemporary Books
1221 Avenue of the Americas
New York, NY 10020
Ph: (212)904-2000   Fr: 800-323-4900
E-mail: ntcpub@tribune.com

Gary Munneke. Second edition, 1997. $17.95; $13.95 (paper). 406 pages. Overview of opportunities available to lawyers in private practice, corporate law, in federal, state, and local governments, and in teaching. Provides information on the typical law school curriculum plus opportunities in internships and clerkships.

★6262★ CLA Review Manual: A Practical Guide to CLA Exam Preparation

West Publishing Co.
College and School Div.
610 Opperman Dr.
PO Box 64526
St. Paul, MN 55123
Ph: (651)687-7000   Fax: (651)687-5827
Fr: 800-328-9424

Virginia Koerselman. Second edition, 1997. $104.95 (paper). 979 pages. This manual is a comprehensive study tool for the Certified Legal Assistant (CLA) Examination administered by the National Association of Legal Assistants, Inc. The manual thoroughly covers each section of the exam with extensive outlines, examples, facts & charts for review. Sample tests and tips for studying are included.

★6263★ Effective Interviewing for Paralegals

Anderson Publishing Co.
2035 Reading Rd.
Cincinnati, OH 45202-1576
Ph: (513)421-4142   Fax: (513)562-8116
Fr: 800-582-7295

Fred E. Jandt. Second edition, 1995. $28.95. 300 pages.

★6264★ Everything You Need to Know About Being a Legal Assistant

Thomson Delmar Learning
PO Box 15015
Albany, NY 12212-5015
Ph: (518)348-2300   Fax: (518)464-0393
Fr: 800-998-7498

Chere B. Estrin. 1995. $23.75 (paper). 206 pages.

★6265★ A Guide to a Successful Legal Internship

Anderson Publishing Co.
2035 Reading Rd.
Cincinnati, OH 45202-1576
Ph: (513)421-4142   Fax: (513)562-8116
Fr: 800-582-7295

Hedi Nasheri and Peter C. Kratcoski. 1996. $22.95 (paper). 176 pages.

★6266★ How to Find a Job As a Paralegal: A Step-by-Step Job Search

West Publishing Co.
College and School Div.
610 Opperman Dr.
St. Paul, MN 55123
Ph: (651)687-7000   Fax: (651)687-6857
Fr: 800-328-9424

Marie Kisiel. 1996. $36.95. 200 pages.

★6267★ The Independent Paralegal's Handbook

Nolo.com
950 Parker St.
Berkeley, CA 94710
Ph: (510)549-1976   Fax: (510)548-5902
Fr: 800-992-6656

Ralph E. Warner, Stephen Elias and Catherine Elias-Jermany. Fifth edition, 2001. $29.95. 352 pages. Part of the Independent Paralegal's Handbook Series.

★6268★ Introduction to Paralegalism

Thomson Delmar Learning
PO Box 15015
Albany, NY 12212-5015
Ph: (518)348-2300   Fax: (518)464-0393
Fr: 800-998-7498

Angela Schneeman. 1997. $20.95.

★6269★ Introduction to Paralegalism: Perspectives, Problems, & Skills

West Publishing Co.
College and School Division
610 Opperman Dr.
St. Paul, MN 55123
Ph: (651)687-7000   Fax: (651)687-6857
Fr: 800-328-9424

William P. Statsky. 1997. $88.95. 1054 pages.

★6270★ Life Outside the Law Firm: Non-Traditional Careers for Paralegals

Thomson Delmar Learning
PO Box 15015
Albany, NY 12212-5015
Ph: (518)348-2300   Fax: (518)464-0393
Fr: 800-998-7498

Karen Treffinger. 1995. $26.75 (paper). 237 pages.

★6271★ Opportunities in Paralegal Careers

McGraw-Hill/Contemporary Books
1221 Avenue of the Americas
New York, NY 10020
Ph: (212)904-2000   Fr: 800-323-4900
E-mail: ntcpub@tribune.com

Alice Fins. 1999. $14.95; $11.95 (paper). 200 pages. Defines job opportunities and provides advice about identifying and obtaining positions. Includes bibliography and illustrations.

★6272★ Paralegal Career Guide

Prentice Hall PTR
200 Old Tappan Rd.
Old Tappan, NJ 07675
Ph: (201)236-7000   Fr: 800-567-3800

Chere B. Estrin. Third edition, 2001. $33.40 (paper). 464 pages. Includes information on jobhunting contacts, sample resumes, and salary data.

★6273★ Paralegal Career Starter

LearningExpress, LLC
900 Broadway, Ste. 604
New York, NY 10003
Ph: (212)995-2566   Fax: (212)995-5512
Fr: 800-295-9556

Lauren B. Starkey. Second edition, 2002.

★6274★ Paralegal Internships: Finding, Managing & Transitioning Your Career

Thomson Delmar Learning
PO Box 15015
Albany, NY 12212-5015
Ph: (518)348-2300   Fax: (518)464-0393
Fr: 800-998-7498

Post. 1998. $27.95 (paper). 267 pages. Part of the Paralegal Series. Text covers all stages of the internship experience, including identifying learning objectives, finding the "right office," managing "office politics," self-

monitoring & documentation & finally how to use the internship to land a permanent job.

★6275★ Paralegal Practice and Procedure: A Practical Guide for The Legal Assistant

Prentice Hall PTR
200 Old Tappan Rd.
Old Tappan, NJ 07675
Ph: (201)909-6200   Fax: (201)909-6360
Fr: 800-223-2336

Deborah E. Larbalestier. Third edition, 1994. $27.95 (paper). 576 pages.

★6276★ A Paralegal Primer

Forbes Custom Publishing
60 Fifth Ave.
New York, NY 10011
Ph: (212)367-4873   Fax: (212)367-4862
Fr: 800-242-8786

Scott A. Hatch. 1998. $19.00 (paper).

★6277★ The Paralegal's Guide to U.S. Government Jobs: How to Land a Job in 140 Law-Related Career Fields

Federal Reports, Inc.
1010 Vermont Ave. NW, Ste. 408
Washington, DC 20005
Ph: (202)393-3311

Richard L. Hermann, Jeanette J. Sobajian and Linda P. Sutherland. Seventh edition, 1996. $19.95. 140 pages. Explains U.S. Government procedures and describes 140 law-related federal careers for which paralegals may qualify. Includes a directory of several hundred Federal Agency personnel offices that hire the most paralegal and law-related talents.

★6278★ Real People Working in Law

McGraw-Hill Contemporary Books
1221 Avenue of the Americas
New York, NY 10020
Ph: (212)904-2000   Fr: 800-323-4900
E-mail: ntcpub@tribune.com

Blythe Camenson, Jan Goldberg. 1997. $14.95; $12.95 (paper). 405 pages. Interviews and profiles of working professionals capture a range of opportunities in this field.

★6279★ Real-Resumes for Legal and Paralegal Jobs

PREP Publishing
1110 1/2 Hay St., PMB 66
Fayetteville, NC 28305
Ph: (910)483-6611   Fax: (910)483-2439
Fr: 800-533-2814

March 2004. $16.95 (paper). 192 pages. Real-Resumes Series.

★6280★ Starting and Managing Your Own Business: A Freelancing Guide for Paralegals

Aspen Publishers, Inc.
200 Orchard Ridge Dr., Ste. 200
Gaithersburg, MD 20878
Ph: (301)417-7500   Fax: (301)695-7931
Fr: 800-638-8437

Dorothy Secol. 1999. $52.00 (paper).

★6281★ Style and Sense For the Legal Profession: A Handbook for Court Reporters, Transcribers, Paralegals and Secretaries

ETC Publications
700 E. Vereda del Sur
Palm Springs, CA 92262
Ph: (760)325-5352   Fax: (760)325-8841
Fr: 800-382-7869

Audrey Fatooh and Barbara R. Mauk. Revised, 1996. $22.95.

★6282★ The Successful Paralegal Job Search Guide

Thomson Delmar Learning
P.O. Box 15015
Albany, NY 12212-5015
Ph: (518)348-2300   Fax: (518)464-0393
Fr: 800-998-7498

Chere B. Estrin and Stacey Hunt. 2000. $32.95.

★6283★ Where the Jobs Are: The Hottest Careers for the 90s

The Career Press, Inc.
3 Tice Rd.
PO Box 687
Franklin Lakes, NJ 07417-1322
Ph: (201)848-0310   Fax: (201)848-1727
Fr: 800-227-3371

Joyce Hadley. Third edition, 2000. $13.99 (paper). 400 pages. Out of print. Describes careers in fifteen general fields, from accounting to travel and hospitality.

★6284★ Your Opportunities in Legal Support

Energeia Publishing, Inc.
1307 Fairmount Ave., S
Salem, OR 97302-4313
Ph: (503)362-1480   Fax: (503)362-2123
Fr: 800-639-6048

Laurie Bean. 1994. $2.50 (paper). 8 pages.

EMPLOYMENT AGENCIES AND SEARCH FIRMS

★6285★ Attorney Resources, Inc.

750 North St. Paul, Ste. 540
Dallas, TX 75201
Ph: (512)922-8050   Fax: (512)871-3041
Fr: 800-324-4828

E-mail: dallas@attorneyresource.com
URL: http://www.attorneyresource.com
Employment agency. Offices in Fort Worth, TX, and Tulsa, OK. Provides staffing assistance on regular or temporary basis.

★6286★ **Beverly Hills Bar Association Personnel Service**
300 S. Beverly Dr., Ste. 214
Beverly Hills, CA 90212-4805
Ph: (310)553-4575   Fax: (310)553-6940
URL: http://www.bhba.org
Employment agency.

★6287★ **Bill Young and Associates**
273 Oak Dale Ln.
Stuarts Draft, VA 24477
Ph: (540)337-5268
E-mail: byoung@billyoung.com
URL: http://www.billyoung.com
Employment agency. Executive recruiter.

★6288★ **Bishop Partners**
708 3rd Ave., Ste. 2200
New York, NY 10017
Ph: (212)986-3419   Fr: (212)986-3350
Executive search firm focuses on legal and accounting fields.

★6289★ **Coleman Legal Search Consultants**
1535 JFK Blvd., Ste. 1010
Philadelphia, PA 19102
Ph: (215)864-2700   Fax: (215)864-2709
E-mail: cls@colemanlegal.com
URL: http://www.colemanlegal.com
Executive search firm.

★6290★ **Cook Associates Inc.**
212 W Kinzie St.
Chicago, IL 60610
Ph: (312)329-0900   Fax: (312)329-2422
Management and executive recruiting specialists offering a commitment to clients to find the best candidates and to find those candidates as efficiently as possible. Approach provides a flexible and effective structure that serves the special needs of both large and small companies. Serves the following industries: industrial, equipment manufacturer, food processing, graphic arts, chemical process, retailing, mechanical products, healthcare services, financial and professional services, legal, consumer products, construction and engineering, packaging, pulp and paper.

★6291★ **DiMarchi Partners Inc.**
PO Box 1147
Niwot, CO 80544-1147
Ph: (303)415-9300
Executive search firm focused on the legal industry.

★6292★ **Early Cochran & Olson LLC**
401 N. Michigan Ave., Ste. 2010
Chicago, IL 60611-4206
Ph: (312)595-4200   Fax: (312)595-4209
Executive search firm focused specifically on the legal field.

★6293★ **Gibson Arnold & Associates Inc.**
1776 Yorktown St., No. 350
Houston, TX 77056-4182
Ph: (713)572-3000   Fax: (713)572-4664
Fr: 800-879-2007
Legal temporary service supplies attorneys, paralegals, and production clerks to major law firms and corporations nationwide. Also maintains a full-time placement division. Assists law firms and corporations with staffing any in-house needs.

★6294★ **Gillard Associates Legal Search**
202 Bussey St.
Dedham, MA 02026
Ph: (781)329-4731   Fax: (617)329-1357
E-mail: gillardlgl@aol.com
Search firm.

★6295★ **Ingle-Terrell & Associates**
3100 Sunset Dr.
Charlotte, NC 28209-1208
Ph: (704)333-8400
Provides assistance in recruitment and placement of personnel. Industries served: insurance and law.

★6296★ **Interquest Inc.**
98 Cuttermill Rd.
Great Neck, NY 11021
Ph: (212)319-0790   Fax: (212)753-0596
Offers retained executive search and other consulting services for the legal profession, with primary focus being general counsel searches for corporations, law firm members and lateral movement of partners for law firms.

★6297★ **Karen Dexter & Associates**
1740 Ridge Ave.
Evanston, IL 60201
Ph: (847)733-7103   Fax: (847)733-9254
Training and development consultant offering interpersonal skills training and one-on-one performance counseling for employees of large organizations. Industries served: advertising, banking and finance, consumer products, entertainment, food and beverage, healthcare, legal profession, manufacturing, government agencies, publishing and broadcasting.

★6298★ **Legal Medical Staffing Services Inc.**
Plz. 1000, Ste. 202, Main St.
Voorhees, NJ 08043
Ph: (856)751-7999   Fax: (856)751-8448
Offers a specialized service providing temporary and full-time support exclusively to the legal, dental, and medical professions.

★6299★ **Legal Placement Services, Inc.**
740 N Plankinton Ave., Ste.430
Milwaukee, WI 53203
Ph: (414)276-6689   Fax: (414)276-1418
E-mail: info@legalplacementservices.com
URL: http://www.legalplacementservices.com
Employment agency. Periodically fills temporary placements as well.

★6300★ **Synectics for Management Decisions Inc.**
1901 N Moore St., Ste. 900
Arlington, VA 22209
Ph: (703)528-2772   Fax: (703)528-2857
Organizational analysis and development consulting firm specializing in economic and international expertise, executive search, management information systems, data processing, training, economic expertise to legal profession, business brokerage, mergers and acquisitions, and leasing services. Serves private industries as well as government agencies.

ONLINE JOB SOURCES AND SERVICES

★6301★ **EmpLawyerNet.com**
E-mail: membership@emplawyernet.com
URL: http://www.emplawyernet.com/
Description: Career resource site for lawyers. Contains career information, resume posting and job board search, along with links to CLE events, online bookstores, and recruiter directories. **Fee:** Limited access permitted with free basic membership. Premier membership is $59 or $14.95/month and includes free CLE courses, e-mail alerts, networking opportunities and personal career advice.

★6302★ **Law.com: Law Jobs**
URL: http://www.lawjobs.com
Description: Visitors can post job openings for attorneys, legal support staff and temporary workers. Also resources for legal recruiters and temporary staffing agencies.

★6303★ **The Legal Employment Search Site**
E-mail: webmaster@legalemploy.com
URL: http://www.legalemploy.com

Description: Contains links to job search and career-related websites for lawyers and legal support staff.

TRADESHOWS

★6304★ American Association for Paralegal Education Convention

American Association for Paralegal Education
407 Wekiva Springs Rd., Ste. 241
Longwood, FL 32779
Ph: (407)834-6688   Fax: (407)834-4747

Annual. **Primary Exhibits:** Computer hardware and software; paralegal publications and educational materials; related supplies.

★6305★ Association of Legal Administrators Meeting

Association of Legal Administrators
175 E. Hawthorne Pkwy., Ste. 325
Vernon Hills, IL 60061
Ph: (708)816-1212   Fax: (708)816-1213

Annual. **Primary Exhibits:** Computers, hardware, and software; office equipment and supplies; publications, printers, and engravers; insurance; travel consultants; litigation support; facilities management; hotels; and coffee suppliers.

OTHER SOURCES

★6306★ American Almanac of Jobs and Salaries

Morrow Avon
1350 Avenue of the Americas
New York, NY 10019
Ph: (212)261-6788   Fr: 800-242-7737

John W. Wright. Revised edition, 2000. $20.00 (paper). 672 pages. This is a comprehensive guide to the wages of hundreds of occupations in a wide variety of industries and organizations.

★6307★ Computer Law Association (CLA)

3028 Javier Rd., Ste. 402
Fairfax, VA 22031
Ph: (703)560-7747   Fax: (703)207-7028
E-mail: askcla@cla.org
URL: http://www.cla.org

Members: Lawyers, law students, and others interested in legal problems related to computer-communications technology. **Purpose:** Aids in contracting for computer-communications goods and services; perfecting and protecting proprietary rights chiefly in software; taxing computer-communications goods, services, and transactions; and liabili-

ty for acquisition and use of computer-communications goods and services. **Activities:** Provides specialized educational programs; offers limited placement service. Holds Annual Computer Law Update.

★6308★ Legal Assistants

Evon Publishing
832 N 7th Ave.
Iron River, MI 49935
Ph: (906)265-3190

Audiocassette. 1996. $16.95. 32 minutes. Part of the Careers and Vocational Guidance Series. Provides information about the nature of the work, educational requirements, employment outlook, earnings, and work conditions as well as additional related information.

★6309★ Media Law Resource Center

80 Eighth Ave., Ste. 200
New York, NY 10011-5126
Ph: (212)337-0200   Fax: (212)337-9893
E-mail: ldrc@ldrc.com
URL: http://www.medialaw.org

Description: Provides support for media defendants in libel and privacy cases, including development of statistical and empirical data, assistance in locating expert witnesses or consultants, and help in coordinating amicus curiae briefs by supporting organizations. Maintains a brief, pleading, and information bank; collects and disseminates information on pending libel and privacy cases for use in legal defense against claims. Serves as a liaison with media organizations, attorneys, and other groups working to advance the defense of libel and privacy claims. Prepares bulletins and reports on current developments and cases, legal theories, privileges, and defenses. Compiles statistics on the incidence and cost of libel and privacy litigation. Provides employment for law student interns. Conducts educational and training workshops and programs; has established fellowship program in libel law. Operates LDRC Institute.

★6310★ National Association of Legal Assistants (NALA)

1516 S Boston, Ste. 200
Tulsa, OK 74119
Ph: (918)587-6828   Fax: (918)582-6772
E-mail: nalanet@nala.org
URL: http://www.nala.org

Members: Professional paralegals employed for over six months; graduates or students of legal assistant training programs; attorneys. Members subscribe to and are bound by the NALA Code of Ethics and Professional Responsibility. **Purpose:** Cooperates with local, state, and national bar associations in setting standards and guidelines for legal assistants. Promotes the profession and attempts to broaden public understanding of the function of the legal assistant. **Activities:** Offers continuing education for legal assistants both nationwide and statewide, and professional certification

on a national basis to members and non-members who meet certain criteria. Conducts regional seminars; publishes books, quarterly journal, and on-line seminars.

★6311★ National Association of Legal Investigators (NALI)

11643 Saginaw St.
PO Box 905
Grand Blanc, MI 48439
Fax: (810)694-7109   Fr: 800-266-6254
E-mail: laccardo@gfn.org
URL: http://www.nalionline.org/

Description: Legal investigators, both independent and law firm staff, who specialize in investigation of personal injury matters for the plaintiff and criminal defense. Goal is the professionalization of the legal investigator, accomplished by seminars and a professional certification program. Provides nationwide network of contact among members. Compiles statistics.

★6312★ National Federation of Paralegal Associations (NFPA)

PO Box 33108
Kansas City, MO 64114-0108
Ph: (816)941-4000   Fax: (816)941-2725
E-mail: info@paralegals.org
URL: http://www.paralegals.org

Members: State and local paralegal associations and other organizations supporting the goals of the federation (60); individual paralegals (15,000). **Purpose:** To serve as a national voice of the paralegal profession; to advance, foster, and promote the paralegal concept; to monitor and participate in developments in the paralegal profession; to maintain a nationwide communications network among paralegal associations and other members of the legal community. **Activities:** Provides a resource center of books, publications, and literature of the field. Monitors activities of local, state, and national bar associations and legislative bodies; presents testimony on matters affecting the profession. Developed PACE exam for Registerd Paralegal credentials.

★6313★ Paralegal

Cambridge Educational
2572 Brunswick Ave.
Lawrenceville, NJ 08648-4128
Fax: 800-FAX-ON-US   Fr: 800-468-4227
URL: http://www.cambridgeeducational.com

$39.95. 15 minutes. Part of the Vocational Visions Career Series.

★6314★ Technical & Related Occupations

Delphi Productions
3160 4th St.
Boulder, CO 80304
Fax: (303)443-4022   Fr: 888-443-2400
URL: http://www.delphivideo.com

$95.00. 49 minutes. Part of the Careers for the 21st Century Video Library.

Librarians

SOURCES OF HELP-WANTED ADS

★6315★ AALL Spectrum

American Association of Law Libraries
53 W Jackson Blvd., Ste. 940
Chicago, IL 60604
Ph: (312)939-4764   Fax: (312)431-1097
URL: http://www.aallnet.org

Description: Ten issues/year. Presents news of interest to law libraries. Includes job listings and announcements from the Association's officers, chapters, and committees.

★6316★ The Abbey Newsletter

Abbey Publications Inc.
7105 Geneva Dr.
Austin, TX 78723-1510
Ph: (512)929-3992   Fax: (512)929-3995
URL: http://palimpsest.stanford.edu/byorg/abbey/

Description: Six issues/year. Encourages the development of library and archival conservation, particularly technical advances and cross-disciplinary research in the field. Covers book repair and the conservation of books, papers, photographs, and non-paper materials. Recurring features include book reviews, news of research, job listings, convention reports, a calendar of events, and an occasional column about equipment and supplies.

★6317★ American Theological Library Association Newsletter

American Theological Library Association
250 S Wacker Dr., Ste. 1600
Chicago, IL 60606
Ph: (312)454-5100   Fax: (312)454-5505
Fr: 888-665-ATLA
E-mail: newsletter@atla.com

Description: Quarterly. Presents news of interest to library professionals at theological schools. Recurring features include notices of publications available and job listings. also available via e-mail.

★6318★ Base Line

Map and Geography Round Table
c/o James A. Coombs
SW Missiouri State Univ.
Maps Library
Springfield, MO 65804-0095
Ph: (417)280-3205   Fax: (417)280-3257
Fr: 800-545-2433
URL: http://magert.whoi.edu:8000/

Description: Bimonthly. Provides current information on cartographic materials, publications of interest to map and geography librarians, related government activities, and map librarianship. Recurring features include conference and meeting information, news of research, job listings, and columns by the Division chair and the editor.

★6319★ Book Marks

Elizabeth Fox
Box 2115
S Dakota State University
Brookings, SD 57007-1098
Ph: (605)668-5569   Fax: (605)688-6133

Description: Bimonthly. Carries news by and for South Dakota public, school, academic, and special libraries. Discusses statewide library issues, reviews South Dakota books, and advises members of continuing education opportunities. Recurring features include columns, a calendar of events, news from libraries, and job listings.

★6320★ Change

Heldref Publications
1319 18th St. NW
Washington, DC 20036-1802
Ph: (202)296-6267   Fax: (202)296-5149
Fr: 800-365-9753
URL: http://www.heldref.org/html/chg.html

Bimonthly. $51.00/year for individuals; $103.00/year for institutions. Magazine dealing with contemporary issues in higher learning.

★6321★ The Chronicle of Higher Education

The Chronicle of Higher Education
1255 23rd St. NW, Ste. 700
Washington, DC 20037-1125
Ph: (202)466-1000   Fax: (202)452-1033
URL: http://chronicle.com

Weekly. $82.50/year for individuals; $3.75 for single issue. Higher education magazine (tabloid).

★6322★ Computers in Libraries

Information Today Inc.
143 Old Marlton Pke.
Medford, NJ 08055-8750
Ph: (609)654-6266   Fax: (609)654-4309
Fr: 800-300-9848
URL: http://www.infotoday.com

Monthly. $99.95/year for U.S. $114.00/year for Canada and Mexico; $124.00/year for other countries. Library science and computer magazine.

★6323★ Information Today

Information Today Inc.
143 Old Marlton Pke.
Medford, NJ 08055-8750
Ph: (609)654-6266   Fax: (609)654-4309
Fr: 800-300-9848
URL: http://www.infotoday.com

$69.95/year for U.S.; $93.00/year for Canada and Mexico; $102.00/year for other countries. User and producer magazine (tabloid) covering electronic and optical information services.

★6324★ Inter-Com

District of Columbia Library Association (DCLA)
7117 Poplar Ave.
Takoma Park, MD 20912

Description: Eleven issues/year (monthly with July/August combined). Deals with libraries and librarians in the Washington D.C., area. Recurring features include a calendar of events, reports of meetings, job listings, and notices of publications available.

★6325★ Law Librarians' Bulletin Board

Legal Information Services
6609 Glen Forest Dr.
Chapel Hill, NC 27517
Ph: (919)672-3035   Fax: (919)408-0267

Description: Eight issues/year. Tracks current events in law librarianship. Recurring features include job listings.

★6326★ Library Journal

Reed Business Information
360 Park Ave. S
New York, NY 10010
Ph: (646)746-6400   Fax: (646)746-6734
E-mail: ljinfo@reedbusiness.com

$94.50/year for individuals. Library management and book selection journal.

★6327★ MLA News

Medical Library Association Inc.
65 E Wacker Dr., Ste. 1900
Chicago, IL 60601-7298
Ph: (312)419-9094   Fax: (312)419-8950
URL: http://www.mlanet.org/publications/mlanews

Description: Monthly, except June/July and November/December, which are combined issues. Covers topics about the association, the health sciences information industry, legislation, and international events. Regular features include updates and reviews of new information technology, medical publication trends, classifieds, educational opportunities, and Internet resources.

★6328★ The Outrider

Wyoming State Library
2301 Capitol Ave.
Cheyenne, WY 82002-0060
Ph: (307)777-5915   Fax: (307)777-6289
URL: http://will.state.wy.us/slpub/index.html

Description: Biennial. Provides news about the activities of the Wyoming State Library, its board, other tax-supported libraries in the state, the American Library Association, and the library field in general. Recurring features include job listings, meetings, workshops, and other events; personnel news; reports on consultant activities and acquisitions news; and columns titled News Briefs, Around the State.

★6329★ The Reference Librarian

The Haworth Press Inc.
10 Alice St.
Binghamton, NY 13904-1580
Ph: (607)722-5857   Fax: (607)722-1424
Fr: 800-429-6784
URL: http://www.haworthpress.com

$60.00/year for individuals; $120.00/year for libraries. Journal for librarians and students, providing information on the changing field of reference librarianship.

★6330★ School Library Journal

Reed Business Information
360 Park Ave. S
New York, NY 10010
Ph: (646)746-6400   Fax: (646)746-6734
E-mail: slj@cahners.com

$87.50/year for individuals; $129.00/year for Canada.

★6331★ SLA Geography & Map Division-Bulletin

Geography & Map Div.
c/o Pat Allen, Physics Library
Physics Bldg., Rm. 1396
Purdue University
West Lafayette, IN 47907
Ph: (317)494-2858   Fax: (317)494-0706

Description: Three issues/year. Provides a medium of exchange of information, news, and research in the field of geographic and cartographic bibliography, literature, and libraries. Recurring features include a letters to the editor, news of research, a calendar of events, reports of meetings, news of educational opportunities, job listings, book reviews, and notices of publications available.

★6332★ TEST Engineering & Management

The Mattingley Publishing Company Inc.
3756 Grand Ave., Ste. 205
Oakland, CA 94610-1545
Ph: (510)839-0909   Fax: (510)839-2950

Bimonthly. $40.00/year for individuals; $55.00/year for other countries; $5.00 for single issue. Trade publication that covers physical and mechanical testing and environmental simulation; edited for test engineering professionals.

★6333★ Wisconsin Lawyer

State Bar of Wisconsin
5302 Eastpark Blvd.
PO Box 7158
Madison, WI 53707-7158
Ph: (608)257-3838   Fax: (608)257-5502
Fr: 800-444-9404
E-mail: wislawyer@wisbar.org
URL: http://www.wisbar.org/wislawmag/

Monthly. $42.00/year for individuals; $24.00/year for law libraries, educational groups, law students. Magazine for Wisconsin legal professionals.

PLACEMENT AND JOB REFERRAL SERVICES

★6334★ African Studies Association (ASA)

Rutgers the State University of New Jersey
132 George St.- Douglass Campus
New Brunswick, NJ 08901-1400
Ph: (732)932-8173

E-mail: callasa@rci.rutgers.edu

Members: Persons specializing in teaching, writing, or research on Africa including political scientists, historians, geographers, anthropologists, economists, librarians, linguists, and government officials; persons who are studying African subjects; institutional members are universities, libraries, government agencies, and others interested in receiving information about Africa. **Purpose:** Seeks to foster communication and to stimulate research among scholars on Africa. **Activities:** Sponsors placement service; conducts panels and discussion groups; presents exhibits and films.

★6335★ American Association of Law Libraries (AALL)

53 W Jackson Blvd., Ste. 940
Chicago, IL 60604
Ph: (312)939-4764   Fax: (312)431-1097
E-mail: aallhq@aall.org
URL: http://www.aallnet.org

Members: Librarians who serve the legal profession in the courts, bar associations, law societies, law schools, private law firms, federal, state, and county governments, and business; associate members are legal publishers and other interested persons. **Purpose:** Seeks to advance the profession of law librarianship. **Activities:** Conducts continuing professional development programs for members; maintains placement service.

★6336★ American Library Association (ALA)

50 E Huron St.
Chicago, IL 60611
Ph: (312)944-7298   Fax: (312)440-9374
Fr: 800-545-2433
E-mail: ala@ala.org
URL: http://www.ala.org

Members: Librarians, libraries, trustees, friends of libraries, and others interested in the responsibilities of libraries in the educational, social, and cultural needs of society. **Purpose:** Promotes and improves library service and librarianship. Establishes standards of service, support, education, and welfare for libraries and library personnel; promotes the adoption of such standards in libraries of all kinds; safeguards the professional status of librarians; encourages the recruiting of competent personnel for professional careers in librarianship; promotes popular understanding and public acceptance of the value of library service and librarianship. **Activities:** Works in liaison with federal agencies to initiate the enactment and administration of legislation that will extend library services. Offers placement services.

★6337★ American Society for Information Science and Technology (ASIST)

1320 Fenwick Ln., No. 510
Silver Spring, MD 20910
Ph: (301)495-0900   Fax: (301)495-0810
E-mail: asis@asis.org
URL: http://www.asis.org

Members: Information specialists, scientists, librarians, administrators, social scientists, and others interested in the use, organization, storage, retrieval, evaluation, and dissemination of recorded specialized information. **Purpose:** Seeks to improve the information transfer process through research, development, application, and education. **Activities:** Provides a forum for the discussion, publication, and critical analysis of work dealing with the theory, practice, research, and development of elements involved in communication of information. Members are engaged in a variety of activities and specialties including classification and coding systems, automatic and associative indexing, machine translation of languages, special librarianship and library systems analysis, and copyright issues. Sponsors National Auxiliary Publications Service, which provides reproduction services and a central depository for all types of information (operated for ASIS by Microfiche Publications). Maintains placement service. Sponsors numerous special interest groups. Conducts continuing education programs and professional development workshops.

★6338★ **Asian/Pacific American Librarians Association (APALA)**
3735 Palomar Ctr., Ste. 150
PMB 26
Lexington, KY 40513
Ph: (859)257-5679   Fax: (859)257-4205
E-mail: webmaster@apalweb.org
URL: http://www.apalaweb.org

Description: Librarians and information specialists of Asian Pacific descent working in the U.S.; interested persons. Provides a forum for discussing problems and concerns; supports and encourages library services to Asian Pacific communities; recruits and supports Asian Pacific Americans in the library and information science professions. Offers placement service; compiles statistics. Conducts fundraising for scholarships.

★6339★ **Association of College and Research Libraries (ACRL)**
50 E Huron St.
Chicago, IL 60611-2795
Ph: (312)280-2523   Fax: (312)280-2520
Fr: 800-545-2433
E-mail: acrl@ala.org
URL: http://www.ala.org/acrl

Description: A division of the American Library Association. **Members:** Academic and research librarians **Purpose:** seeking to improve the quality of service in academic libraries; promotes the professional and career development of academic and research librarians; represent the interests and support the programs of academic and research libraries. **Activities:** Operates placement services; sponsors specialized education and research grants and programs; gathers, compiles, and disseminates statistics. Establishes and adopts standards; maintains publishing program; offers professional development courses.

★6340★ **Association of Jewish Libraries (AJL)**
15 E 26th St., Rm. 1034
New York, NY 10010-1579
Ph: (212)725-5359
E-mail: ajl@jewishbooks.org
URL: http://www.jewishlibraries.org

Description: Works to advance the interests of Jewish libraries and promote publications of Jewish bibliographical interest. Provides placement and library consultant services.

★6341★ **Association of Seventh-Day Adventist Librarians (ASDAL)**
Columbia Union College Library
Takoma Park, MD 20912-7796
Ph: (301)891-4222   Fax: (301)891-4204
E-mail: lwisel@cuc.edu
URL: http://www.asdal.org

Members: Librarians belonging to the Seventh-Day Adventist church. **Purpose:** Works to enhance communication among members; serve as a forum for discussion of mutual problems and professional concerns; promote librarianship and library services to Seventh-Day Adventist institutions. **Activities:** Sponsors D. Glenn Hilts Scholarship for graduate studies. Maintains placement service. Compiles statistics.

★6342★ **Chinese American Librarians Association (CALA)**
California State University, Los Angeles
5151 State University Dr.
Los Angeles, CA 90032
Fax: (949)857-1988
URL: http://www.cala-web.org

Purpose: Promotes better communication among Chinese American librarians in the U.S., serves as a forum for the discussion of mutual problems, and supports the development and promotion of librarianship. **Activities:** Maintains placement referral service.

★6343★ **Health Sciences Communications Association (HESCA)**
39 Wedgewood Dr., Ste. A
Jewett City, CT 06351
Ph: (860)376-5915   Fax: (860)376-6621
E-mail: hesca@hesca.org
URL: http://www.hesca.org/

Description: Media managers, graphic artists, biomedical librarians, producers, faculty members of health science and veterinary medicine schools, health professional organizations, and industry representatives. Acts as a clearinghouse for information used by professionals engaged in health science communications. Coordinates Media Festivals Program which recognizes outstanding media productions in the health sciences. Offers placement service.

★6344★ **Music Library Association (MLA)**
8551 Research Way, Ste. 180
Middleton, WI 53562-3567
Ph: (608)836-5825   Fax: (608)831-8200
E-mail: mla@areditions.com
URL: http://www.musiclibraryassoc.org/

Description: Promotes the establishment, growth, and use of music libraries and collection of music, musical instruments, musical literature, and audiovisual aids. Maintains placement service.

★6345★ **Special Libraries Association (SLA)**
1700 18th St. NW
Washington, DC 20009-2514
Ph: (202)234-4700   Fax: (202)265-9317
E-mail: sla@sla.org
URL: http://www.sla.org/

Description: International association of information professionals who work in special libraries serving business, research, government, universities, newspapers, museums, and institutions that use or produce specialized information. Seeks to advance the leadership role of special librarians. Offers consulting services to organizations that wish to establish or expand a library or information services. Conducts strategic learning and development courses, public relations, and government relations programs. Provides employment services. Operates knowledge exchange on topics pertaining to the development and management of special libraries. Maintains Hall of Fame.

EMPLOYER DIRECTORIES AND NETWORKING LISTS

★6346★ *American Art Directory*
LexisNexis Group
121 Chanlon Rd.
New Providence, NJ 07974
Ph: (908)464-6800   Fax: (908)771-7704
Fr: 800-526-4902
URL: http://nationalregisterpub.com

Biennial. $299.00. Covers over 7,000 museums, art libraries, and art organizations, and 1,700 art schools; also includes lists of state directors and supervisors of art education in schools, traveling exhibition booking agencies, corporations having art holdings for public viewing, newspapers that carry art notes, art scholarships and fellowships; and 190 national, regional, and state open art exhibitions. Entries include: For museums-Name, address, phone, fax, electronic mail address, name of curator; days and hours of operation, collection, budget, publications. For exhibits-Name, address, phone, fax, electronic mail address, name of contact; date, deadline. For schools-Name, address, phone, name of director, names of faculty members, majors or degrees offered, tuition fees; summer school or adult hobby class information. For newspapers-Name, address, phone, name of art editor. Arrangement: Geographical. Indexes: Geographical, collection/subject/name, personal name, institution name.

★6347★ American Library Directory

Information Today Inc.
143 Old Marlton Pke.
Medford, NJ 08055-8750
Ph: (609)654-6266   Fax: (609)654-4309
Fr: 800-300-9848
URL: http://books.infotoday.com/dir/amerlib56.shtml

Annual, latest edition 56th, 2003-2004. $269.10. Covers over 36,000 U.S. and Canadian academic, public, county, provincial, and regional libraries; library systems; medical, law, and other special libraries; and libraries for the blind and physically handicapped. Separate section lists over 350 library networks and consortia and 220 accredited and unaccredited library school programs. Entries include: For libraries-Name, supporting or affiliated institution or firm name, address, phone, fax, email address, Standard Address Number (SANs), names of librarian and department heads, income, collection size, special collections, computer hardware, automated functions, and type of catalog. For library systems-Name, location. For library schools-Name, address, phone, fax, email address, director, type of training and degrees, admission requirements, tuition, faculty size. For networks and consortia-Name, address, phone, names of affiliates, name of director, function. Arrangement: Geographical. Indexes: Institution name.

★6348★ The Basic Business Library: Core Resources

Greenwood Publishing Group Inc.
88 Post Rd. W.
PO Box 5007
Westport, CT 06881-5007
Ph: (203)226-3571   Fax: (203)226-6009
Fr: 800-225-5800

$64.95. Publication includes: Publisher's web site as part of each entry. Principal content of publication is list of 210 entries of suggested resources for business libraries, as well as essays on business references sources and services. Indexes: Alphabetical.

★6349★ Directory of Federal Libraries

Oryx Press
1434 E San Miguel Ave.
Phoenix, AZ 85014-2422
Fr: 800-225-5800
URL: http://www.greenwood.com

Irregular, previous edition March 1987; January 1993; latest edition May 1997. Covers nearly 3,000 libraries serving branches of the federal government. Entries include: Library name, type, address, phone, fax, e-mail, telnet, and websites, name of administrator and selected staff, special collections, database services available, depository status for documents from the Government Printing Office or other organizations, involvement with cooperative library organizations, electronic mail or cataloging networks, whether accessible to the public. Arrangement: Classified by federal establishment. Indexes: Library type, subject, geographical, alphabetical index of libraries by name.

★6350★ Directory of Public School Systems in the U.S.

American Association for Employment in Education
3040 Riverside Dr., Ste. 125
Columbus, OH 43221
Ph: (614)485-1111   Fax: (614)485-9609

Annual, Winter. $80.00. Covers about 14,500 public school systems in the United States and their administrative personnel. Entries include: System name, address, phone, website address, name and title of personnel administrator, levels taught and approx. student population. Arrangement: Geographical by state.

★6351★ Directory of Special Libraries and Information Centers

Thomson Gale
27500 Drake Rd.
Farmington Hills, MI 48331-3535
Ph: (248)699-4253   Fax: (248)699-8065
Fr: 800-877-GALE
E-mail: businessproducts@gale.com
URL: http://www.galegroup.com

Annual. $975.00 for set; $740.00 for set without supplement; $560.00 for indexes. Covers over 34,000 special libraries, information centers, documentation centers, etc.; about 500 networks and consortia; major special libraries abroad also included. Volume 1 part 3 contains 6 other appendices (besides networks and consortia): Regional and Subregional Libraries for the Blind & Physically Handicapped, Patent & Trademark Depository Libraries, Regional Government Depository Libraries, United Nations Depository Libraries, World Bank Depository Libraries, and European Community Depository Libraries. Entries include: Library name, address, phone, fax, e-mail address; contact; year founded; sponsoring organization; special collections; subject interests; names and titles of staff; services (copying, online searches); size of collection; subscriptions; computerized services and automated operations; Internet home page address; publications; special catalogs; special indexes. For consortia and networks-Name, address, phone, contact. Other appendices have varying amounts of directory information. Contents of Volume 1 are available in "Subject Directory of Special Libraries and Information Centers". Arrangement: Libraries are alphabetical by name of sponsoring organization or institution; consortia and networks are geographical. Indexes: Subject. Geographic and personnel indexes constitute volume 2.

★6352★ Fifty State Educational Directories

Career Guidance Foundation
8090 Engineer Rd., Ste. B
San Diego, CA 92111
Ph: (858)560-8051   Fax: (858)278-8960
Fr: 800-854-2670
URL: http://www.cgf.org

Annual, latest edition June 1996. $89.00. Microfiche. Collection consists of reproductions of the state educational directories published by the departments of education of individual 50 states. Directory contents vary, but the majority contain listings of elementary and secondary schools, colleges and universities, and state education officials. Amount of detail in each also varies. Entries include: Usually, institution name, address, and name of one executive.

★6353★ Guide to Employment Sources in the Library & Information Professions

Office for Human Resource Development and Recruitment
50 E Huron St.
Chicago, IL 60611
Ph: (312)280-4282   Fax: (312)280-3256
URL: http://www.ala.org/hrdr/employment_guide.html

Annual, spring. Free. Covers library job sources, such as specialized and state and regional library associations, state library agencies, federal library agencies, and overseas exchange programs. Entries include: Library, company, or organization name, address, phone; contact name, description of services, publications, etc. This is a reprint of a segment of the "Bowker Annual of Library and Book Trade Information," described separately. Arrangement: Classified by type of source.

★6354★ Handbook of Private Schools

Porter Sargent Publishers Inc.
11 Beacon St., Ste. 1400
Boston, MA 02108-3099
Ph: (617)523-1670   Fax: (617)523-1021
Fr: 800-342-7470
E-mail: orders@portersargent.com

Annual, June. $99.00. Covers more than 1,600 elementary and secondary boarding and day schools in the United States. Entries include: School name, address, phone, fax, E-mail, URL, type of school (boarding or day), sex and age range, names and titles of administrators, grades offered, academic orientation, curriculum, new admissions yearly, tests required for admission, enrollment and faculty, graduate record, number of alumni, tuition and scholarship figures, summer session, plant evaluation and endowment, date of establishment, calendar, association membership, description of school's offerings and history, test score averages, uniform requirements, geographical, and demographic date. Arrangement: Geographical. Indexes: Alphabetical by school name, cross indexed by state, region, grade range, sexes accepted, school features and enrollment.

★6355★ Higher Education Directory

Higher Education Publications Inc.
6400 Arlington Blvd., Ste. 648
Falls Church, VA 22042
Ph: (703)532-2300   Fax: (703)532-2305
Fr: 888-349-7715
URL: http://www.hepinc.com

Annual, October. $70.00. Covers over 4,100 degree granting colleges and universities accredited by approved agencies recognized by the U.S. Secretary of Education and by the Council of Higher Education Accreditation (CHEA); 103 systems offices; over 550 related associations and state government agencies; recognized accrediting agencies. Entries include: For institutions-Name, address, congressional district, phone, fax, year established; Carnegie classification; enrollment; type of student body; religious or other affiliation; undergraduate tuition and fees; type of academic calendar; highest degree offered; accreditations; IRS status; names, titles and job classification codes for academic and administrative officers. For associations and state agencies-Name, address, phone, name of chief executive officer. Same content and coverage as the base volume of the Department of Education's publication "Directory of Postsecondary Institutions". Arrangement: Geographical, alphabetical by state. Indexes: Administrator name (with phone and e-mail addresses), accreditation, FICE numbers, college or university name.

★6356★ Independent Schools Association of the Southwest-Membership List

Independent Schools Association of the Southwest
4700 Bryant Irvin Ct., Ste. 204
Fort Worth, TX 76107
Ph: (817)569-9200   Fax: (817)569-9103
Fr: 800-688-5007
URL: http://www.isasw.org

Annual, August. Covers over 75 independent elementary and secondary schools accredited by the association. Entries include: School name, address, phone, chief administrative officer, structure, and enrollment. Arrangement: Geographical. Indexes: Alphabetical.

★6357★ International Directory of Children's Literature

George Kurian Reference Books
Box 519
Baldwin Place, NY 10505
Ph: (914)962-3287   Fax: (914)962-5287

Irregular, previous edition 1990; latest edition 2001. $48.95. Covers about 5,000 children's book and magazine publishers, organizations, children's libraries and special collections, fairs, seminars, and conferences concerned with children's literature; worldwide coverage. Entries include: For book publishers, children's literature organizations, and major children's libraries and special collections-Name, address, purpose of activity. For periodicals, prizes, and events-Name, responsible organization, address, frequency or time period, subject. Arrangement: Geographical.

★6358★ MDR's School Directories

Market Data Retrieval
1 Forest Pkwy.
Shelton, CT 06484
Ph: (203)926-4800   Fax: (203)926-1826
Fr: 800-333-8802
URL: http://www.schooldata.com

Annual, October. $1,349.00 for set. Covers over 90,000 public, 8,000 Catholic, and 15,000 other private schools (grades K-12) in the United States; over 15,000 school district offices, and 76,000 school librarians; and 27,000 media specialists, 33,000 technology coordinators. Includes names of over 165,000 school district administrators and staff members in county and state education administration. Entries include: For districts: District name and address; telephone and fax number; number of schools; number of teachers in the district; district enrollment; special Ed students; limited-english proficient students; minority percentage by race, college bound students; expenditures per student for instructional materials; poverty level; title 1 dollars; site-based management; district open/close dates; construction indicator; technologies and quantities (instructional computer brands, multimedia computers; networks, VCRs, satellite dish, DVD Player/Drive High-Speed Internet Access URL); district-level adminstrators, *new superintendents shaded.* For schools: School name and address-new public shaded; telephone and fax number; principal new principal shaded; librarian, media specialist and technology coordinator; grade span; special programs and school type; student enrollment; technologies and quantities (instructional computer brand noting predominant brand); Multi-Media Computers; internet connection or access; Tech Sophistication Index. Arrangement: Geographical. Indexes: District County; District Personnel; Principal; New Public Schools and Key Personnel; District and School Telephone; District URLs.

★6359★ Midwest Archives Conference-Membership Directory

Midwest Archives Conference
c/o Menzi Behrnd-Klodt
7422 Longmeadow Rd.
Madison, WI 53717
Ph: (608)827-5727
URL: http://www.midwestarchives.org

Annual. Covers more than 1,000 individual and institutional members, largely librarians, archivists, records managers, manuscripts curators, historians, and museum and historical society personnel; about 25 archival associations in the Midwest. Entries include: For institutions-Name of archives, parent organization, address, phone. For individuals-Name, title, business address, phone. Arrangement: Separate alphabetical sections for individuals and institutions.

★6360★ Patterson's American Education

Educational Directories Inc.
PO Box 68097
Schaumburg, IL 60168-0097
Ph: (847)891-1250   Fax: (847)891-0945
Fr: 800-357-6183
URL: http://www.ediusa.com

Annual, October; latest edition 2002. $87.00. Covers over 11,400 school districts in the United States; more than 34,000 public, private, and Catholic high schools, middle schools, and junior high schools; approximately 300 parochial superintendents; 400 state department of education personnel. Entries include: For school districts and schools-District and superintendent name, address, phone, fax, grade ranges, enrollment , school names, addresses, phone numbers, grade ranges, enrollment, names of principals. For postsecondary schools-School name, address, phone number, URL, e-mail, names of administrator or director of admissions. For private and Catholic high schools-Name, address, phone, fax, enrollment, grades offered, name of principal. Postsecondary institutions are covered in 'Patterson's Schools Classified'. Arrangement: Geographical by state, then alphabetical by city.

★6361★ Patterson's Schools Classified

Educational Directories Inc.
PO Box 68097
Schaumburg, IL 60168-0097
Ph: (847)891-1250   Fax: (847)891-0945
Fr: 800-357-6183
URL: http://www.ediusa.com

Annual, April. $15.00. Covers over 7,000 accredited colleges, universities, community colleges, junior colleges, career schools and teaching hospitals. Entries include: School name, address, phone, URL, e-mail, name of administrator or admissions officer, description, professional accreditation (where applicable). Updated from previous year's edition of 'Patterson's American Education'. Arrangement: Classified by area of study, then geographical by state. Indexes: Alphabetical by name.

★6362★ Requirements for Certification of Teachers, Counselors, Librarians, Administrators for Elementary and Secondary Schools

University of Chicago Press
Journals Division
PO Box 37005
Chicago, IL 60637
Ph: (773)753-3347   Fax: (773)753-0811
Fr: 877-705-1878

Annual, June. $44.00. Publication includes: List of state and local departments of education. Entries include: Office name, address, phone. Principal content of publication is summaries of each state's teaching and administrative certification requirements. Arrangement: Geographical.

HANDBOOKS AND MANUALS

★6363★ Career Information Center

Macmillan Publishing Co. Inc.
200 Old Tappan Rd.
Old Tappan, NJ 07675
Fr: 800-428-5331

Visual Education Center Staff. Seventh edition, 1999. $275.00. 2080 pages. This 13-volume set profiles over 600 occupations. Each occupational profile describes job duties, educational requirements, how to get the job, advancement possibilities, employment outlook, working conditions, earnings and benefits, and where to write for more information.

★6364★ Career Opportunities for Writers

Checkmark Books
132 W. 31st St., 17th Fl.
New York, NY 10001-2006
Ph: (212)967-8800   Fax: (212)967-9196
Fr: 800-322-8755
URL: http://www.factsonfile.com

Rosemary Ellen Guiley and Janet Frick. Fourth edition, 2000. $45.00. Part of the Career Opportunities Series. Describes more than 100 jobs in eight major fields, offering such details as duties, salaries, perquisites, employment and advancement opportunities, organizations to join, and opportunities for women and minorities.

★6365★ Careers in Health Care

McGraw-Hill Trade
2 Penn Plaza
New York, NY 10121
Ph: (212)904-2000   Fr: 800-722-4726
E-mail: ntcpub@tribune.com

Barbara M. Swanson. Fourth edition, 2000. $17.95; $13.95 (paper). 320 pages. Describes job duties, work settings, salaries, licensing and certification requirements, educational preparation, and future outlook. Gives ideas on how to secure a job.

★6366★ Careers in Music Librarianship II: Traditions and Transitions

Scarecrow Press, Inc.
4501 Forbes Blvd., Ste. 200
Lanham, MD 20706-4310
Ph: (301)459-3366   Fax: (301)429-5747

January 2004. $29.95 (paper). 168 pages. Explores music librarianship.

★6367★ Extending the Librarian's Domain: A Survey of Emerging Occupational Opportunities for Librarians & Information Professionals

Special Libraries Association
1700 18th St. NW
Washington, DC 20009
Ph: (202)234-4700   Fax: (202)234-2442

1994. $38.00 (paper). 64 pages. Occasional Papers, No. 4.

★6368★ Great Jobs for History Majors

McGraw-Hill Trade
2 Penn Plaza
New York, NY 10121
Ph: (212)904-2000   Fr: 800-722-4726
E-mail: ntcpub@tribune.com

Julie DeGalan and Stephen Lambert. 1994. $11.95 (paper). 442 pages.

★6369★ How to Get a Job in Education

Adams Media Corp.
57 Littlefield St.
Avon, MA 02322
Ph: (508)427-7100   Fax: (508)427-6790
Fr: 800-872-5627
URL: http://www.adamsmedia.com

Joel Levin. Second edition, 1995. $15.95. 320 pages. Out of print. Prepared for recent college graduates, seasoned educators, and career-changing professionals, this publication guides the job-seeker through the necessary steps to obtaining a job in education at the elementary, secondary, and university levels. Offers advice on how to prepare for state and local examinations, how to locate teaching opportunities nationwide, and how to obtain certification. Includes a nationwide salary survey. Covers public, private, summer, and overseas opportunities.

★6370★ Library Employment Within the Law

Neal-Schuman Publishers, Inc.
100 Varick St.
New York, NY 10013
Ph: (212)925-8650   Fax: (212)219-8916

Arlene C. Bielefield and Lawrence G. Cheeseman. 1993. $45.00 (paper). 147 pages.

★6371★ MLA Salary Survey

Medical Library Association, Inc.
65 E. Wacker Pl., Ste. 1900
Chicago, IL 60601-7298
Ph: (312)419-9094   Fax: (312)419-8950
URL: http://www.mlanet.org

1995. $60.00 (paper).

★6372★ Opportunities in Library and Information Science Careers

McGraw-Hill Trade
2 Penn Plaza
New York, NY 10121
Ph: (212)904-2000   Fr: 800-722-4726

Kathleen M. Heim and Margaret Myers. 1993. $10.95 (paper). 160 pages. A guide to planning for and seeking opportunities in this changing field. Includes bibliography and illustrations.

★6373★ Opportunities in State and Local Government Careers

Vgm Career Horizons
1221 Avenue of the Americas
New York, NY 10020
Ph: (212)904-2000   Fr: 800-323-4900
E-mail: ntcpub@tribune.com

Neale J. Baxter. 1994. $14.95; $10.95 (paper). 160 pages. Points out the incentives and drawbacks of a government career. Describes hiring procedures and provides tips on filling out applications, taking physical and aptitude tests, handling interviews, and finding jobs. Describes the jobs in which 75% of all state and local government workers are employed. For each occupation,

covers the nature of the work and the training required.

★6374★ Special Librarianship As a Career: An SLA Information Kit

Special Libraries Association
1700 18th St., NW
Washington, DC 20009
Ph: (202)234-4700   Fax: (202)234-2442

McCauley. 1995. $27.00 (paper). 105 pages.

★6375★ What Else You Can Do with a Library Degree: Career Options for the 90s and Beyond

Neal-Schuman Publishers, Inc.
100 Varick St.
New York, NY 10013
Ph: (212)925-8650   Fax: (212)219-8916

Betty-Carol Sellen. 1997. $32.95 (paper). 337 pages. Discusses job requirements, offers advice, and recommends how to get started. Chapters are arranged according to specialization, such as products and services for libraries, independent librarians, association work, and the corporate world.

★6376★ Writing Resumes That Work: A How-to-Do-It Manual for Librarians

Neal-Schuman Publishers, Inc.
100 Varick St.
New York, NY 10013
Ph: (212)925-8650   Fax: (212)219-8916

Robert R. Newlen. 1998. $39.95 (paper). 151 pages. Provides ideas for alternate library careers in this new edition of a 1980 publication. Most of the 62 contributors have information science, academic, and other adult-focused backgrounds; four come from the fields of children's and elementary school media services and one from the YA ranks.

EMPLOYMENT AGENCIES AND SEARCH FIRMS

★6377★ C. Berger Group Inc.

327 E Gundersen Dr.
Carol Stream, IL 60188-2421
Ph: (630)653-1115   Fax: (630)653-1691
Fr: 800-382-4222

Provides consultation in library services and information and knowledge management. The firm staffs and directs projects which range from organizing, inventorying, and cataloging special collections and files to installing custom PC databases. Personnel services include executive search for information specialists and supplying temporary and contract librarians, support staff, and loose-leaf filers on demand. Serves corporate, not for profit and academic libraries as well as government agencies.

★6378★ Educational Placement Service
1001 Craig Rd., Ste. 170
St. Louis, MO 63146
Ph: (314)991-5855   Fax: (314)991-5295
URL: http://www.educatorjobs.com
Employment agency. Focuses on teaching, administrative, and education-related openings.

★6379★ Gossage Sager Associates LLC
25 W. 43rd St., Ste. 812
New York, NY 10036
Ph: (212)417-9468   Fax: (212)997-1127
E-mail: dsager@g=ossagesager.com
URL: http://www.gossagesager.com
Executive search firm. Concentrates in placement of library and information professionals on permanent basis nationwide.

ONLINE JOB SOURCES AND SERVICES

★6380★ American Library Association Education and Employment
URL: http://www.ala.org/education
Description: Contains links to monthly job and career leads lists posted in *American Libraries* and *College & Research Libraries NewsNet* and other sources, as well as a Conference Placement Service and accreditation information.

★6381★ Library and Information Technology Association Job Listing
URL: http://www.lita.org/jobs/index.html
Description: Contains weekly postings of available library jobs. Searchable by region.

★6382★ Library Job Postings on the Internet
E-mail: sarah@libraryjobpostings.org
URL: http://www.libraryjobpostings.org
Description: Employers may post library position announcements. Also contains links to around 250 library employment sites and links to library-related e-mail lists. Positions are searchable by region and type of library.

TRADESHOWS

★6383★ American Association of School Librarians National Conference and Exhibition
American Association of School Librarians
50 E. Huron St.
Chicago, IL 60611
Ph: (312)280-4386   Fax: (312)664-7459
Fr: 800-545-2433

E-mail: aasl@ala.org
URL: http://www.ala.org/AASL
Biennial. **Primary Exhibits:** Equipment, supplies, and services for school library media centers, including print and nonprint materials and other equipment. **Dates and Locations:** 2005 Oct 05-09; Pittsburgh, PA; Pittsburgh Convention Center.

★6384★ American Library Association Annual Conference
American Library Association
50 E. Huron St.
Chicago, IL 60611-2795
Ph: (312)944-6780   Fax: (312)280-3255
Fr: 800-545-2433
URL: http://www.ala.org
Annual. **Primary Exhibits:** Books, periodicals, reference works, audio-visual equipment, films, data processing services, computer hardware and software, library equipment and supplies.

★6385★ American Library Association Mid-Winter Meeting
American Library Association
50 E. Huron St.
Chicago, IL 60611-2795
Ph: (312)944-6780   Fax: (312)280-3255
Fr: 800-545-2433
URL: http://www.ala.org
Annual. **Primary Exhibits:** Books, periodicals, reference works, audio-visual equipment, films, data processing services, computer hardware and software, library equipment and supplies.

★6386★ Art Libraries Society of North America Annual Conference
Art Libraries Society of North America
4101 Lake Boone Trl., Ste. 201
Raleigh, NC 27607-7506
Ph: (919)787-5181   Fax: (919)787-4916
Fr: 800-89-ARLIS
E-mail: arlisna@mercury.interpath.com
Annual. **Primary Exhibits:** Publications, slides, library supplies, and related services.

★6387★ Association of College and Research Libraries National Conference
Association of College and Research Libraries
50 E. Huron St.
Chicago, IL 60611
Ph: (312)280-2511   Fax: (312)280-2520
Fr: 800-545-2433
E-mail: acrl@ala.org
URL: http://www.ala.org/acrl.html
Biennial. **Primary Exhibits:** Books, Computers, Web Products, furniture, journals, audio-visual publications, library materials, equipment, supplies, and services.

★6388★ Church and Synagogue Library Association Conference
Church and Synagogue Library Association
PO Box 19357
Portland, OR 97280-0357
Ph: (503)244-6919   Fax: (503)977-3734
Fr: 800-542-2752
E-mail: csla@worldaccessnet.com
URL: http://www.worldaccessnet.com/~csla
Annual. **Primary Exhibits:** Books, media, and library equipment, supplies, and services.

★6389★ Idaho Library Association Annual Convention
Idaho Library Association
3577 East Pecan
Boise, ID 83716
Ph: (208)383-0165
URL: http://www.idaholibraries.org
Annual. **Primary Exhibits:** Library equipment, supplies, and services including computers, audiovisual equipment, and books. **Dates and Locations:** 2004 Oct 06-09; Boise, ID • 2005 Oct 05-08; Pocatello, ID.

★6390★ Illinois School Library Media Association Conference
Illinois School Library Media Association
PO Box 598
Canton, IL 61520
Ph: (309)649-0911   Fax: (309)649-0916
E-mail: islma@aol.com
URL: http://www.islma.org
Annual. **Primary Exhibits:** Equipment, supplies, and services for elementary and secondary school library media specialists interested in the general improvement and extension of services for children and young people. **Dates and Locations:** 2004 Nov 3-6; Arlington Park, IL; Sheraton Arlington Park • 2005 Oct 27-29; Decatur, IL; Holiday Inn Decatur • 2006 Nov 2-5; Arlington Park, IL; Sheraton Arlington Park.

★6391★ Indiana Library Federation Conference
Indiana Library Federation
941 E 66th St. Ste. 260
Indianapolis, IN 46240-1853
Ph: (317)257-2040   Fax: (317)257-1393
E-mail: ilf@indy.net
Annual. **Primary Exhibits:** Equipment, supplies, and services for elementary and secondary school library media specialists interested in the general improvement and extension of services for children and young people.

★6392★ Michigan Library Association Annual Conference
Michigan Library Association
6810 S. Cedar, Ste. 6
Lansing, MI 48911
Ph: (517)373-5400
Annual. **Primary Exhibits:** Exhibits pertaining to library and information technology.

Dates and Locations: 2004 Oct 26-29; Traverse City, MI; Grand Traverse Resort.

★6393★ Public Library Association National Conference

Public Library Association
c/o American Library Association
50 E. Huron St.
Chicago, IL 60611
Ph: (312)280-5752   Fax: (312)280-5029
Fr: 800-545-2433
E-mail: pla@ala.org
URL: http://www.pla.org

Biennial. **Primary Exhibits:** Books, software & hardware and other equipment, supplies, and services for libraries.

★6394★ Special Libraries Association Information Revolution

Special Libraries Association
1700 18th St., NW
Washington, DC 20009
Ph: (202)234-4700   Fax: (202)265-9317
E-mail: sla@sla.org
URL: http://www.sla.org

Annual. **Primary Exhibits:** Library equipment, supplies, and services, including computers and software, database information.

★6395★ Tennessee Library Association Annual Convention

Tennessee Library Association
PO Box 241074
Memphis, TN 38184-1074
Ph: (901)485-6952
URL: http://www.tnl.org

Annual. **Primary Exhibits:** Audiovisual materials and library equipment, supplies, and services. **Dates and Locations:** 2005 Apr; Nashville, TN.

★6396★ Texas Library Association Conference

Texas Library Association
3355 Bee Cave Rd., Ste. 401
Austin, TX 78746
Ph: (512)328-1518   Fax: (512)328-8852
E-mail: info@txla.org
URL: http://www.txla.org

Annual. **Primary Exhibits:** Library equipment, supplies, and services, including book-

binding materials, library shelving and furniture, computers, books, audiovisual materials, small press publications, automation, hardware, software, and telecommunications.

★6397★ Wisconsin Library Association Annual Conference

Wisconsin Library Association
5250 E. Terrace Dr., Ste. A1
Madison, WI 53718-8345
Ph: (608)245-3640   Fax: (608)245-3646

Annual. **Primary Exhibits:** Library equipment, supplies, and services, including books. **Dates and Locations:** 2004 Nov 11-15; Lake Geneva, WI; Lake Geneva Resort.

OTHER SOURCES

★6398★ American Almanac of Jobs and Salaries

Morrow Avon
1350 Avenue of the Americas
New York, NY 10019
Ph: (212)261-6788   Fr: 800-242-7737

John W. Wright. Revised edition, 2000. $20.00 (paper). 672 pages. This is a comprehensive guide to the wages of hundreds of occupations in a wide variety of industries and organizations.

★6399★ Association for Library and Information Science Education (ALISE)

1009 Commerce Park Dr., Ste. 150
Oak Ridge, TN 37830
Ph: (865)425-0155   Fax: (865)481-0390
E-mail: contact@alise.org
URL: http://www.alise.org

Description: Graduate schools offering degree programs in library science and their faculties. Seeks to: promote excellence in education for library and information science as a means of increasing the effectiveness of library and information services; provide a forum for the active interchange of ideas and information among library educators; promote research related to teaching and to library and information science; formulate and promulgate positions on matters related

to library education. Offers employment program at annual conference.

★6400★ Education and Training

Cambridge Educational
2572 Brunswick Ave.
Lawrenceville, NJ 08648-4128
Fax: 800-FAX-ON-US   Fr: 800-468-4227
URL: http://www.cambridgeeducational.com

$89.95. 2002. 18 minutes.

★6401★ Librarians

Evon Publishing
832 N 7th Ave.
Iron River, MI 49935
Ph: (906)265-3190

Audiocassette. 1996. $16.95. 32 minutes. Part of the Careers and Vocational Guidance Series. Provides information about the nature of the work, educational requirements, employment outlook, earnings, and work conditions as well as additional related information.

★6402★ North American Serials Interest Group (NASIG)

Trinity University
Coates Library
One Trinity Pl.
San Antonio, TX 78212-7200
E-mail: info@nasig.org
URL: http://www.nasig.org

Members: Librarians; subscription vendors; publishers; serial automation experts; serials binders; library science educators; others involved in serials management. **Purpose:** Promotes educational and social networking among members. Participates in the preliminary organization of standards and guidelines. **Activities:** Disseminates information.

★6403★ Teaching & Related Occupations

Delphi Productions
3160 4th St.
Boulder, CO 80304
Fax: (303)443-4022   Fr: 888-443-2400
URL: http://www.delphivideo.com

$95.00. 50 minutes. Part of the Careers for the 21st Century Video Library.

Library Technicians

SOURCES OF HELP-WANTED ADS

★6404★ AALL Spectrum

American Association of Law Libraries
53 W Jackson Blvd., Ste. 940
Chicago, IL 60604
Ph: (312)939-4764   Fax: (312)431-1097
URL: http://www.aallnet.org

Description: Ten issues/year. Presents news of interest to law libraries. Includes job listings and announcements from the Association's officers, chapters, and committees.

★6405★ Base Line

Map and Geography Round Table
c/o James A. Coombs
SW Missiouri State Univ.
Maps Library
Springfield, MO 65804-0095
Ph: (417)280-3205   Fax: (417)280-3257
Fr: 800-545-2433
URL: http://magert.whoi.edu:8000/

Description: Bimonthly. Provides current information on cartographic materials, publications of interest to map and geography librarians, related government activities, and map librarianship. Recurring features include conference and meeting information, news of research, job listings, and columns by the Division chair and the editor.

★6406★ Book Marks

Elizabeth Fox
Box 2115
S Dakota State University
Brookings, SD 57007-1098
Ph: (605)668-5569   Fax: (605)688-6133

Description: Bimonthly. Carries news by and for South Dakota public, school, academic, and special libraries. Discusses statewide library issues, reviews South Dakota books, and advises members of continuing education opportunities. Recurring features include columns, a calendar of events, news from libraries, and job listings.

★6407★ Computers in Libraries

Information Today Inc.
143 Old Marlton Pke.
Medford, NJ 08055-8750
Ph: (609)654-6266   Fax: (609)654-4309
Fr: 800-300-9848
URL: http://www.infotoday.com

Monthly. $99.95/year for U.S. $114.00/year for Canada and Mexico; $124.00/year for other countries. Library science and computer magazine.

★6408★ Information Today

Information Today Inc.
143 Old Marlton Pke.
Medford, NJ 08055-8750
Ph: (609)654-6266   Fax: (609)654-4309
Fr: 800-300-9848
URL: http://www.infotoday.com

$69.95/year for U.S.; $93.00/year for Canada and Mexico; $102.00/year for other countries. User and producer magazine (tabloid) covering electronic and optical information services.

★6409★ Law Librarians' Bulletin Board

Legal Information Services
6609 Glen Forest Dr.
Chapel Hill, NC 27517
Ph: (919)672-3035   Fax: (919)408-0267

Description: Eight issues/year. Tracks current events in law librarianship. Recurring features include job listings.

★6410★ Library Journal

Reed Business Information
360 Park Ave. S
New York, NY 10010
Ph: (646)746-6400   Fax: (646)746-6734
E-mail: ljinfo@reedbusiness.com

$94.50/year for individuals. Library management and book selection journal.

★6411★ MLA News

Medical Library Association Inc.
65 E Wacker Dr., Ste. 1900
Chicago, IL 60601-7298
Ph: (312)419-9094   Fax: (312)419-8950
URL: http://www.mlanet.org/publications/mlanews

Description: Monthly, except June/July and November/December, which are combined issues. Covers topics about the association, the health sciences information industry, legislation, and international events. Regular features include updates and reviews of new information technology, medical publication trends, classifieds, educational opportunities, and Internet resources.

★6412★ The Outrider

Wyoming State Library
2301 Capitol Ave.
Cheyenne, WY 82002-0060
Ph: (307)777-5915   Fax: (307)777-6289
URL: http://will.state.wy.us/slpub/index.html

Description: Biennial. Provides news about the activities of the Wyoming State Library, its board, other tax-supported libraries in the state, the American Library Association, and the library field in general. Recurring features include job listings, meetings, workshops, and other events; personnel news; reports on consultant activities and acquisitions news; and columns titled News Briefs, Around the State.

★6413★ School Library Journal

Reed Business Information
360 Park Ave. S
New York, NY 10010
Ph: (646)746-6400   Fax: (646)746-6734
E-mail: slj@cahners.com

$87.50/year for individuals; $129.00/year for Canada.

★6414★ SLA Geography & Map Division-Bulletin

Geography & Map Div.
c/o Pat Allen, Physics Library
Physics Bldg., Rm. 1396
Purdue University
West Lafayette, IN 47907
Ph: (317)494-2858 Fax: (317)494-0706

Description: Three issues/year. Provides a medium of exchange of information, news, and research in the field of geographic and cartographic bibliography, literature, and libraries. Recurring features include a letters to the editor, news of research, a calendar of events, reports of meetings, news of educational opportunities, job listings, book reviews, and notices of publications available.

PLACEMENT AND JOB REFERRAL SERVICES

★6415★ American Library Association (ALA)

50 E Huron St.
Chicago, IL 60611
Ph: (312)944-7298 Fax: (312)440-9374
Fr: 800-545-2433
E-mail: ala@ala.org
URL: http://www.ala.org

Members: Librarians, libraries, trustees, friends of libraries, and others interested in the responsibilities of libraries in the educational, social, and cultural needs of society. **Purpose:** Promotes and improves library service and librarianship. Establishes standards of service, support, education, and welfare for libraries and library personnel; promotes the adoption of such standards in libraries of all kinds; safeguards the professional status of librarians; encourages the recruiting of competent personnel for professional careers in librarianship; promotes popular understanding and public acceptance of the value of library service and librarianship. **Activities:** Works in liaison with federal agencies to initiate the enactment and administration of legislation that will extend library services. Offers placement services.

★6416★ American Society for Information Science and Technology (ASIST)

1320 Fenwick Ln., No. 510
Silver Spring, MD 20910
Ph: (301)495-0900 Fax: (301)495-0810
E-mail: asis@asis.org
URL: http://www.asis.org

Members: Information specialists, scientists, librarians, administrators, social scientists, and others interested in the use, organization, storage, retrieval, evaluation, and dissemination of recorded specialized information. **Purpose:** Seeks to improve the information transfer process through research, development, application, and education. **Activities:** Provides a forum for the discussion, publication, and critical analysis of work dealing with the theory, practice, research, and development of elements involved in communication of information. Members are engaged in a variety of activities and specialties including classification and coding systems, automatic and associative indexing, machine translation of languages, special librarianship and library systems analysis, and copyright issues. Sponsors National Auxiliary Publications Service, which provides reproduction services and a central depository for all types of information (operated for ASIS by Microfiche Publications). Maintains placement service. Sponsors numerous special interest groups. Conducts continuing education programs and professional development workshops.

★6417★ Association of College and Research Libraries (ACRL)

50 E Huron St.
Chicago, IL 60611-2795
Ph: (312)280-2523 Fax: (312)280-2520
Fr: 800-545-2433
E-mail: acrl@ala.org
URL: http://www.ala.org/acrl

Description: A division of the American Library Association. **Members:** Academic and research librarians **Purpose:** seeking to improve the quality of service in academic libraries; promotes the professional and career development of academic and research librarians; represent the interests and support the programs of academic and research libraries. **Activities:** Operates placement services; sponsors specialized education and research grants and programs; gathers, compiles, and disseminates statistics. Establishes and adopts standards; maintains publishing program; offers professional development courses.

★6418★ Special Libraries Association (SLA)

1700 18th St. NW
Washington, DC 20009-2514
Ph: (202)234-4700 Fax: (202)265-9317
E-mail: sla@sla.org
URL: http://www.sla.org/

Description: International association of information professionals who work in special libraries serving business, research, government, universities, newspapers, museums, and institutions that use or produce specialized information. Seeks to advance the leadership role of special librarians. Offers consulting services to organizations that wish to establish or expand a library or information services. Conducts strategic learning and development courses, public relations, and government relations programs. Provides employment services. Operates knowledge exchange on topics pertaining to the development and management of special libraries. Maintains Hall of Fame.

EMPLOYER DIRECTORIES AND NETWORKING LISTS

★6419★ American Library Directory

Information Today Inc.
143 Old Marlton Pke.
Medford, NJ 08055-8750
Ph: (609)654-6266 Fax: (609)654-4309
Fr: 800-300-9848
URL: http://books.infotoday.com/dir/amerlib56.shtml

Annual, latest edition 56th, 2003-2004. $269.10. Covers over 36,000 U.S. and Canadian academic, public, county, provincial, and regional libraries; library systems; medical, law, and other special libraries; and libraries for the blind and physically handicapped. Separate section lists over 350 library networks and consortia and 220 accredited and unaccredited library school programs. Entries include: For libraries-Name, supporting or affiliated institution or firm name, address, phone, fax, email address, Standard Address Number (SANs), names of librarian and department heads, income, collection size, special collections, computer hardware, automated functions, and type of catalog. For library systems-Name, location. For library schools-Name, address, phone, fax, email address, director, type of training and degrees, admission requirements, tuition, faculty size. For networks and consortia-Name, address, phone, names of affiliates, name of director, function. Arrangement: Geographical. Indexes: Institution name.

★6420★ The Basic Business Library: Core Resources

Greenwood Publishing Group Inc.
88 Post Rd. W.
PO Box 5007
Westport, CT 06881-5007
Ph: (203)226-3571 Fax: (203)226-6009
Fr: 800-225-5800

$64.95. Publication includes: Publisher's web site as part of each entry. Principal content of publication is list of 210 entries of suggested resources for business libraries, as well as essays on business references sources and services. Indexes: Alphabetical.

★6421★ Directory of Federal Libraries

Oryx Press
1434 E San Miguel Ave.
Phoenix, AZ 85014-2422
Fr: 800-225-5800
URL: http://www.greenwood.com

Irregular, previous edition March 1987; January 1993; latest edition May 1997. Covers nearly 3,000 libraries serving branches of the federal government. Entries include: Library name, type, address, phone, fax, e-mail, telnet, and websites, name of administrator and selected staff, special collections, database services available, depository status for documents from the Government Printing Office or other organizations, involvement with cooperative library organizations, electronic mail or cataloging networks, whether accessible to the public. Arrangement: Classified by federal establishment. Indexes: Library type, subject, geographical, alphabetical index of libraries by name.

★6422★ Directory of Public School Systems in the U.S.

American Association for Employment in Education
3040 Riverside Dr., Ste. 125
Columbus, OH 43221
Ph: (614)485-1111   Fax: (614)485-9609

Annual, Winter. $80.00. Covers about 14,500 public school systems in the United States and their administrative personnel. Entries include: System name, address, phone, website address, name and title of personnel administrator, levels taught and approx. student population. Arrangement: Geographical by state.

★6423★ Directory of Special Libraries and Information Centers

Thomson Gale
27500 Drake Rd.
Farmington Hills, MI 48331-3535
Ph: (248)699-4253   Fax: (248)699-8065
Fr: 800-877-GALE
E-mail: businessproducts@gale.com
URL: http://www.galegroup.com

Annual. $975.00 for set; $740.00 for set without supplement; $560.00 for indexes. Covers over 34,000 special libraries, information centers, documentation centers, etc.; about 500 networks and consortia; major special libraries abroad also included. Volume 1 part 3 contains 6 other appendices (besides networks and consortia): Regional and Subregional Libraries for the Blind & Physically Handicapped, Patent & Trademark Depository Libraries, Regional Government Depository Libraries, United Nations Depository Libraries, World Bank Depository Libraries, and European Community Depository Libraries. Entries include: Library name, address, phone, fax, e-mail address; contact; year founded; sponsoring organization; special collections; subject interests; names and titles of staff; services (copying, online searches); size of collection; subscriptions; computerized services and automated operations; Internet home page address; publications; special catalogs; special indexes. For consortia and networks-Name, address, phone, contact. Other appendices have varying amounts of directory information. Contents of Volume 1 are available in "Subject Directory of Special Libraries and Information Centers". Arrangement: Libraries are alphabetical by name of sponsoring organization or institution; consortia and networks are geographical. Indexes: Subject. Geographic and personnel indexes constitute volume 2.

★6424★ Fifty State Educational Directories

Career Guidance Foundation
8090 Engineer Rd., Ste. B
San Diego, CA 92111
Ph: (858)560-8051   Fax: (858)278-8960
Fr: 800-854-2670
URL: http://www.cgf.org

Annual, latest edition June 1996. $89.00. Microfiche. Collection consists of reproductions of the state educational directories published by the departments of education of individual 50 states. Directory contents vary, but the majority contain listings of elementary and secondary schools, colleges and universities, and state education officials. Amount of detail in each also varies. Entries include: Usually, institution name, address, and name of one executive.

★6425★ Guide to Employment Sources in the Library & Information Professions

Office for Human Resource Development and Recruitment
50 E Huron St.
Chicago, IL 60611
Ph: (312)280-4282   Fax: (312)280-3256
URL: http://www.ala.org/hrdr/employment_guide.html

Annual, spring. Free. Covers library job sources, such as specialized and state and regional library associations, state library agencies, federal library agencies, and overseas exchange programs. Entries include: Library, company, or organization name, address, phone; contact name, description of services, publications, etc. This is a reprint of a segment of the "Bowker Annual of Library and Book Trade Information," described separately. Arrangement: Classified by type of source.

★6426★ Higher Education Directory

Higher Education Publications Inc.
6400 Arlington Blvd., Ste. 648
Falls Church, VA 22042
Ph: (703)532-2300   Fax: (703)532-2305
Fr: 888-349-7715
URL: http://www.hepinc.com

Annual, October. $70.00. Covers over 4,100 degree granting colleges and universities accredited by approved agencies recognized by the U.S. Secretary of Education and by the Council of Higher Education Accreditation (CHEA); 103 systems offices; over 550 related associations and state government agencies; recognized accrediting agencies. Entries include: For institutions-Name, address, congressional district, phone, fax, year established; Carnegie classification; enrollment; type of student body; religious or other affiliation; undergraduate tuition and fees; type of academic calendar; highest degree offered; accreditations; IRS status; names, titles and job classification codes for academic and administrative officers. For associations and state agencies-Name, address, phone, name of chief executive officer. Same content and coverage as the base volume of the Department of Education's publication "Directory of Postsecondary In-

stitutions". Arrangement: Geographical, alphabetical by state. Indexes: Administrator name (with phone and e-mail addresses), accreditation, FICE numbers, college or university name.

★6427★ International Directory of Children's Literature

George Kurian Reference Books
Box 519
Baldwin Place, NY 10505
Ph: (914)962-3287   Fax: (914)962-5287

Irregular, previous edition 1990; latest edition 2001. $48.95. Covers about 5,000 children's book and magazine publishers, organizations, children's libraries and special collections, fairs, seminars, and conferences concerned with children's literature; worldwide coverage. Entries include: For book publishers, children's literature organizations, and major children's libraries and special collections-Name, address, purpose of activity. For periodicals, prizes, and events-Name, responsible organization, address, frequency or time period, subject. Arrangement: Geographical.

★6428★ Midwest Archives Conference-Membership Directory

Midwest Archives Conference
c/o Menzi Behrnd-Klodt
7422 Longmeadow Rd.
Madison, WI 53717
Ph: (608)827-5727
URL: http://www.midwestarchives.org

Annual. Covers more than 1,000 individual and institutional members, largely librarians, archivists, records managers, manuscripts curators, historians, and museum and historical society personnel; about 25 archival associations in the Midwest. Entries include: For institutions-Name of archives, parent organization, address, phone. For individuals-Name, title, business address, phone. Arrangement: Separate alphabetical sections for individuals and institutions.

★6429★ Patterson's American Education

Educational Directories Inc.
PO Box 68097
Schaumburg, IL 60168-0097
Ph: (847)891-1250   Fax: (847)891-0945
Fr: 800-357-6183
URL: http://www.ediusa.com

Annual, October; latest edition 2002. $87.00. Covers over 11,400 school districts in the United States; more than 34,000 public, private, and Catholic high schools, middle schools, and junior high schools; approximately 300 parochial superintendents; 400 state department of education personnel. Entries include: For school districts and schools-District and superintendent name, address, phone, fax, grade ranges, enrollment , school names, addresses, phone numbers, grade ranges, enrollment, names of principals. For postsecondary schools-School name, address, phone number, URL, e-mail, names of administrator or director of admissions. For private and Catholic high schools-Name, address, phone, fax, enrollment, grades offered, name of principal. Postsecondary institutions are covered in 'Patterson's Schools Classified'. Arrangement: Geographical by state, then alphabetical by city.

★6430★ **Patterson's Schools Classified**
Educational Directories Inc.
PO Box 68097
Schaumburg, IL 60168-0097
Ph: (847)891-1250   Fax: (847)891-0945
Fr: 800-357-6183
URL: http://www.ediusa.com

Annual, April. $15.00. Covers over 7,000 accredited colleges, universities, community colleges, junior colleges, career schools and teaching hospitals. Entries include: School name, address, phone, URL, e-mail, name of administrator or admissions officer, description, professional accreditation (where applicable). Updated from previous year's edition of 'Patterson's American Education'. Arrangement: Classified by area of study, then geographical by state. Indexes: Alphabetical by name.

★6431★ **Requirements for Certification of Teachers, Counselors, Librarians, Administrators for Elementary and Secondary Schools**
University of Chicago Press
Journals Division
PO Box 37005
Chicago, IL 60637
Ph: (773)753-3347   Fax: (773)753-0811
Fr: 877-705-1878

Annual, June. $44.00. Publication includes: List of state and local departments of education. Entries include: Office name, address, phone. Principal content of publication is summaries of each state's teaching and administrative certification requirements. Arrangement: Geographical.

HANDBOOKS AND MANUALS

★6432★ **Extending the Librarian's Domain: A Survey of Emerging Occupational Opportunities for Librarians & Information Professionals**
Special Libraries Association
1700 18th St. NW
Washington, DC 20009
Ph: (202)234-4700   Fax: (202)234-2442
1994. $38.00 (paper). 64 pages. Occasional Papers, No. 4.

★6433★ **How to Get a Job in Education**
Adams Media Corp.
57 Littlefield St.
Avon, MA 02322
Ph: (508)427-7100   Fax: (508)427-6790
Fr: 800-872-5627

URL: http://www.adamsmedia.com
Joel Levin. Second edition, 1995. $15.95. 320 pages. Out of print. Prepared for recent college graduates, seasoned educators, and career-changing professionals, this publication guides the job-seeker through the necessary steps to obtaining a job in education at the elementary, secondary, and university levels. Offers advice on how to prepare for state and local examinations, how to locate teaching opportunities nationwide, and how to obtain certification. Includes a nationwide salary survey. Covers public, private, summer, and overseas opportunities.

★6434★ **Library Employment Within the Law**
Neal-Schuman Publishers, Inc.
100 Varick St.
New York, NY 10013
Ph: (212)925-8650   Fax: (212)219-8916
Arlene C. Bielefield and Lawrence G. Cheeseman. 1993. $45.00 (paper). 147 pages.

★6435★ **Opportunities in Library and Information Science Careers**
McGraw-Hill Trade
2 Penn Plaza
New York, NY 10121
Ph: (212)904-2000   Fr: 800-722-4726
Kathleen M. Heim and Margaret Myers. 1993. $10.95 (paper). 160 pages. A guide to planning for and seeking opportunities in this changing field. Includes bibliography and illustrations.

★6436★ **What Else You Can Do with a Library Degree: Career Options for the 90s and Beyond**
Neal-Schuman Publishers, Inc.
100 Varick St.
New York, NY 10013
Ph: (212)925-8650   Fax: (212)219-8916
Betty-Carol Sellen. 1997. $32.95 (paper). 337 pages. Discusses job requirements, offers advice, and recommends how to get started. Chapters are arranged according to specialization, such as products and services for libraries, independent librarians, association work, and the corporate world.

EMPLOYMENT AGENCIES AND SEARCH FIRMS

★6437★ **Gossage Sager Associates LLC**
25 W. 43rd St., Ste. 812
New York, NY 10036
Ph: (212)417-9468   Fax: (212)997-1127
E-mail: dsager@g=ossagesager.com
URL: http://www.gossagesager.com
Executive search firm. Concentrates in

placement of library and information professionals on permanent basis nationwide.

ONLINE JOB SOURCES AND SERVICES

★6438★ **Library Job Postings on the Internet**
E-mail: sarah@libraryjobpostings.org
URL: http://www.libraryjobpostings.org
Description: Employers may post library position announcements. Also contains links to around 250 library employment sites and links to library-related e-mail lists. Positions are searchable by region and type of library.

TRADESHOWS

★6439★ **Illinois School Library Media Association Conference**
Illinois School Library Media Association
PO Box 598
Canton, IL 61520
Ph: (309)649-0911   Fax: (309)649-0916
E-mail: islma@aol.com
URL: http://www.islma.org

Annual. **Primary Exhibits:** Equipment, supplies, and services for elementary and secondary school library media specialists interested in the general improvement and extension of services for children and young people. **Dates and Locations:** 2004 Nov 3-6; Arlington Park, IL; Sheraton Arlington Park • 2005 Oct 27-29; Decatur, IL; Holiday Inn Decatur • 2006 Nov 2-5; Arlington Park, IL; Sheraton Arlington Park.

★6440★ **Indiana Library Federation Conference**
Indiana Library Federation
941 E 66th St. Ste. 260
Indianapolis, IN 46240-1853
Ph: (317)257-2040   Fax: (317)257-1393
E-mail: ilf@indy.net

Annual. **Primary Exhibits:** Equipment, supplies, and services for elementary and secondary school library media specialists interested in the general improvement and extension of services for children and young people.

★6441★ **Public Library Association National Conference**
Public Library Association
c/o American Library Association
50 E. Huron St.
Chicago, IL 60611
Ph: (312)280-5752   Fax: (312)280-5029
Fr: 800-545-2433
E-mail: pla@ala.org
URL: http://www.pla.org

Biennial. **Primary Exhibits:** Books, software & hardware and other equipment, supplies, and services for libraries.

★6442★ **Special Libraries Association Information Revolution**

Special Libraries Association
1700 18th St., NW
Washington, DC 20009
Ph: (202)234-4700   Fax: (202)265-9317
E-mail: sla@sla.org
URL: http://www.sla.org

Annual. **Primary Exhibits:** Library equipment, supplies, and services, including computers and software, database information.

OTHER SOURCES

★6443★ **Association of Jewish Libraries (AJL)**

15 E 26th St., Rm. 1034
New York, NY 10010-1579
Ph: (212)725-5359
E-mail: ajl@jewishbooks.org
URL: http://www.jewishlibraries.org

Description: Works to advance the interests of Jewish libraries and promote publications of Jewish bibliographical interest. Provides placement and library consultant services.

★6444★ **Council on Library-Media Technicians (COLT)**

Daniel Boone Regional Library
100 W Broadway
Columbia, MO 65203
Ph: (573)443-3161   Fax: (573)874-0862
E-mail: pmcquitt@coin.org
URL: http://colt.ucr.edu

Description: Persons involved in two-year associate degree programs for the training of library technical assistants (professional-support workers) and graduates of programs employed as library/media technical assistants (B.A. degree holders without M.L.S. degree). Membership includes junior college deans, librarians, curriculum directors, professors, employers, special libraries, university libraries, library schools, publishers, and library technical assistants. Provides a channel of communication among the institutions and personnel that have developed such training programs; attempts to standardize curriculum offerings; develops educational standards; conducts research on graduates of the programs; represents the interests of library technical assistants and support staff. The council's concerns also include development of clear job descriptions and criteria for employment of technicians and dissemination of information to the public and to prospective students. Sponsors workshops for support staff in areas such as management, supervisory skills, interpersonal communication, business writing, and media center management. Maintains speakers' bureau. Is developing a program for certification of library media technicians and a continuing education program for library support staff.

★6445★ *Education and Training*

Cambridge Educational
2572 Brunswick Ave.
Lawrenceville, NJ 08648-4128
Fax: 800-FAX-ON-US   Fr: 800-468-4227
URL: http://www.cambridgeeducational.com

$89.95. 2002. 18 minutes.

★6446★ *Library Technicians*

Evon Publishing
832 N 7th Ave.
Iron River, MI 49935
Ph: (906)265-3190

Audiocassette. 1996. $16.95. 32 minutes. Part of the Careers and Vocational Guidance Series. Provides information about the nature of the work, educational requirements, employment outlook, earnings, and work conditions as well as additional related information.

★6447★ **Music Library Association (MLA)**

8551 Research Way, Ste. 180
Middleton, WI 53562-3567
Ph: (608)836-5825   Fax: (608)831-8200
E-mail: mla@areditions.com
URL: http://www.musiclibraryassoc.org/

Description: Promotes the establishment, growth, and use of music libraries and collection of music, musical instruments, musical literature, and audiovisual aids. Maintains placement service.

★6448★ **North American Serials Interest Group (NASIG)**

Trinity University
Coates Library
One Trinity Pl.
San Antonio, TX 78212-7200
E-mail: info@nasig.org
URL: http://www.nasig.org

Members: Librarians; subscription vendors; publishers; serial automation experts; serials binders; library science educators; others involved in serials management. **Purpose:** Promotes educational and social networking among members. Participates in the preliminary organization of standards and guidelines. **Activities:** Disseminates information.

★6449★ *Special Librarianship As a Career: An SLA Information Kit*

Special Libraries Association
1700 18th St., NW
Washington, DC 20009
Ph: (202)234-4700   Fax: (202)234-2442

McCauley. 1995. $27.00 (paper). 105 pages.

Licensed Practical Nurses

★6460★ **Clinical Nurse Specialist**
Lippincott Williams & Wilkins
530 Walnut St.
Philadelphia, PA 19106-3621
Ph: (215)521-8300   Fax: (215)521-8483
E-mail: info@nacns.org

Bimonthly. $100.00/year for individuals; $142.00/year for institutions. Nursing journal.

★6461★ **Dialysis & Transplantation**
Creative Age Publications Inc.
7628 Densmore Ave.
Van Nuys, CA 91406-2042
Ph: (818)782-7328   Fax: (818)782-7450
Fr: 800-442-5667
URL: http://www.eneph.com

Monthly. $35.00/year for individuals; $105.00/year for other countries. Multi-disciplinary, peer-reviewed journal on clinical applications in dialysis, transplantation and nephrology for renal-care team.

★6462★ **Health Care Weekly Review**
The Martin Group Inc.
24901 Northwestern Hwy., Ste. 316A
Southfield, MI 48075
Ph: (248)440-6080   Fax: (248)352-4801
E-mail: hcwr@compuserve.com

Weekly. $48.00/year for individuals. Professional newspaper covering the health care industry.

★6463★ **Health Education Reports**
Chester Associates Inc.
4401-A Connecticut Ave. NW, PMB 212
Washington, DC 20008
Ph: (703)960-6859   Fax: (703)960-0189

Description: Biweekly. Focuses on developments relating to public health and wellness programs and government health policy. Covers activities at Centers for Disease Control around the U.S. and subjects such as health promotion, disease prevention, and medical studies. Recurring features include interviews, news of educational opportunities, job listings, book reviews and notices of publications available, reports of meetings, and a calendar of events.

★6464★ **Heart and Lung**
Mosby Inc.
Curtis Ctr., 3rd Fl.
170 S. Independence Mall W
Philadelphia, PA 19106-3399
Ph: (215)238-7800
URL: http://www.mosby.com/hrtlng

Bimonthly. $66.00/year for individuals; $217.00/year for institutions. Journal offering articles prepared by nurse and physician members of the critical care team, recognizing the nurse's role in the care and management of major organ-system conditions in critically ill patients.

★6465★ **Home Healthcare Nurse**
Lippincott Williams & Wilkins
530 Walnut St.
Philadelphia, PA 19106
Ph: (215)521-8300   Fax: (215)521-8902
Fr: 800-638-3030
E-mail: hhnedit@bellsouth.net
URL: http://www.homehealthcarenurseonline.com/

Monthly. $49.95/year for individuals; $198.95/year for institutions; $102.95/year for other countries; $232.95/year for institutions, other countries. Magazine for the practicing professional nurse working in the home health, community health, and public health areas.

★6466★ **HomeCare Magazine**
Miramar Communications Inc.
23805 Stuart Ranch Rd., Ste. 235
PO Box 8987
Malibu, CA 90265-8987
Ph: (310)317-4522   Fax: (310)317-0264
Fr: 800-543-4116
URL: http://www.homecaremag.com

Monthly. Magazine serving home medical equipment suppliers, including independent and chain centers specializing in home care, pharmacies or chain drug stores with home care products, and joint-ventured hospital home health care businesses. Contains industry news and new product launches and marketing strategies.

★6467★ **Hospitals & Health Networks**
Health Forum L.L.C.
One N Franklin
Chicago, IL 60606
Ph: (312)893-6800   Fax: (312)422-4600
Fr: 800-621-6902
E-mail: hhn@healthforum.com
URL: http://www.hhnmag.com

Monthly. Publication covering the health care industry.

★6468★ **Imprint**
National Student Nurses' Association
45 Main St., Ste. 606
Brooklyn, NY 11201
Ph: (718)210-0705   Fax: (718)210-0710
E-mail: nsna@nsna.org

$15.00/year, non-members; $29.00/year for two years, non-members. Magazine for nursing students, focusing on issues and trends in nursing.

★6469★ **The Journal of Continuing Education in Nursing**
SLACK Inc.
6900 Grove Rd.
Thorofare, NJ 08086-9447
Ph: (856)848-1000   Fax: (856)853-5991
Fr: 800-257-8290
E-mail: jcen@slackinc.com

Bimonthly. $69.00/year for individuals; $139.00/year for institutions, add 7% Canada; $40.00/year for other countries. Journal for nurses involved in planning and imple-

menting educational programs for the practitioner and others in patient care.

★6470★ **Journal of Emergency Nursing**
Mosby Inc.
The Curtis Ctr., 3rd Fl.
Independence Sq. W
Philadelphia, PA 19106-3399
Ph: (215)235-7800   Fax: (215)238-7883
Fr: 800-523-1649
URL: http://www.mosby.com/jen

Bimonthly. $66.00/year for individuals; $218.00/year for institutions; $33.00/year for students; $85.00/year for individuals, out of country; $240.00/year for institutions, other countries; $43.00/year for students, other countries. Journal containing peer-reviewed articles on clinical aspects of emergency care by, and for, emergency nurses. Presents information about professional, political, administrative, and educational aspects of emergency nursing and nursing in general.

★6471★ **Journal of Gerontological Nursing**
SLACK Inc.
6900 Grove Rd.
Thorofare, NJ 08086-9447
Ph: (856)848-1000   Fax: (856)853-5991
Fr: 800-257-8290
E-mail: jgn@slackinc.com

Monthly. $59.00/year; $109.00/year for institutions; $19.00/year for single issue. Gerontological nursing journal.

★6472★ **Journal of Nursing Administration (JONA)**
Lippincott Williams & Wilkins
530 Walnut St.
Philadelphia, PA 19106
Ph: (215)521-8300   Fax: (215)521-8902
Fr: 800-638-3030
URL: http://jonajournal.com/

$91.95/year for individuals; $299.95/year for institutions; $161.95/year for other countries; $391.95/year for institutions, other countries. Journal covering developments and advances in nursing administration and management.

★6473★ **Journal of Nursing Scholarship**
Sigma Theta Tau International Honor Society of Nursing
550 W N St.
Indianapolis, IN 46202
Ph: (317)634-8171   Fax: (317)634-8188
Fr: 888-634-7575

Quarterly. $39.00/year for individuals; $20.00 for single issue; $63.00/year for institutions; $81.00/year for out of country. Peer-reviewed journal covering nursing.

★6474★ Journal of Obstetric, Gynecologic and Neonatal Nursing (JOGNN)

Sage Publications Inc.
2455 Teller Rd.
Thousand Oaks, CA 91320
Ph: (805)499-0721 Fax: (805)499-0871
Fr: 800-818-SAGE
E-mail: advertising@sagepub.com
URL: http://jognn.awhonn.org/

Bimonthly. $83.00/year for individuals; $165.00/year for out of country; $546.00/year for institutions; $596.00/year for institutions, other countries. Journal covering trends, policies, and research. Official publication of the Association of Women's Health, Obstetric, and Neonatal Nurses (AWHONN).

★6475★ Journal of Pediatric Health Care

Mosby Inc.
Curtis Ctr., 3rd Fl.
170 Independence Mall W
Philadelphia, PA 19106-3399
Ph: (215)238-7800
URL: http://www.mosby.com/pedhc

Bimonthly. $70.00/year for individuals; $158.00/year for institutions. Official publication of the National Association of Pediatric Nurse Practitioners. Provides current information on pediatric clinical topics as well as research studies, health policy, and legislative issues applicable to pediatric clinical practice.

★6476★ Journal of Practical Nursing

National Association for Practical Nurse Education and Service Inc.
1400 Spring St., Ste. 330
Silver Spring, MD 20910-2735
Ph: (301)588-2491 Fax: (301)588-2839

Quarterly. $15.00/year for U.S.; $30.00/year for other countries; $4.50/year for single issue. Journal providing information on licensed practical nursing for LPNs, PN educators, and students.

★6477★ Journal of Psychosocial Nursing and Mental Health Services

SLACK Inc.
6900 Grove Rd.
Thorofare, NJ 08086-9447
Ph: (856)848-1000 Fax: (856)853-5991
Fr: 800-257-8290
E-mail: jpn@slackinc.com

Monthly. $49.00/year; $74.00/year for institutions; $19.00/year for single issue. Journal presenting original, peer-reviewed articles on psychiatric/mental health nursing.

★6478★ Journal of Trauma Nursing

Nursecom Inc.
1211 Locust St.
Philadelphia, PA 19107-5409
Ph: (215)545-7222 Fax: (215)545-8107
Fr: 800-242-6757

Quarterly. Professional publication covering nursing.

★6479★ McKnight's Long-Term Care News

McKnight's Long-Term Care News
Two Northfield Plz., Ste. 300
Northfield, IL 60093-1219
Ph: (847)784-8706 Fax: (847)441-3701
E-mail: ltcnews@medec.com

Monthly. Free to qualified subscribers in U.S.; $5.00/year for single issue; $9.00 for single back issue; $54.95/year for Canada; $59.95/year, foreign. Professional magazine.

★6480★ MCN, The American Journal of Maternal/Child Nursing

Lippincott Williams & Wilkins
530 Walnut St.
Philadelphia, PA 19106
Ph: (215)521-8300 Fax: (215)521-8902
Fr: 800-638-3030
URL: http://www.mcnjournal.com/

Bimonthly. $41.95/year for individuals; $111.95/year for institutions; $81.95/year for other countries; $131.95/year for institutions, other countries. Journal focusing on maternal/child nursing and health.

★6481★ Military Medicine

Association of Military Surgeons of the U.S. (AMSUS)
9320 Old Georgetown Rd.
Bethesda, MD 20814
Ph: (301)897-8800 Fax: (301)530-5446
Fr: 800-761-9320
E-mail: milmed@amsus.org

Monthly. $65.00/year for individuals; $70.00/year for other countries; $6.00 for single issue. Journal for professional personnel affiliated with the Federal medical services.

★6482★ Minority Nurse Newsletter

Tucker Publications Inc.
PO Box 580
Lisle, IL 60532-0580
Ph: (630)969-3809 Fax: (630)969-3895
E-mail: sallen@tuckerpub.com

Description: Quarterly. Provides health care information of interest to minority nursing faculty.

★6483★ Modern Healthcare

Crain Communications Inc.
360 N Michigan Ave.
Chicago, IL 60601
Ph: (312)649-5200 Fax: (312)280-3174
Fr: 800-678-2724
E-mail: mhcedit@crain.com
URL: http://www.modernhealthcare.com

Weekly. $135.00/year. Weekly Business news magazine for Healthcare Management

★6484★ Nephrology Nursing Journal

American Nephrology Nurses' Association
E Holly Ave.
Box 56
Pitman, NJ 08071-0056
Ph: (856)589-2300 Fax: (856)589-7463

E-mail: anjrnl@mail.ajj.com
Bimonthly. $5.00 for single issue; $28.00/year; $40.00/year. Nursing journal.

★6485★ The Nurse Practitioner

Lippincott Williams & Wilkins
1111 Bethlehem Pke.
PO Box 908
Springhouse, PA 19477
Ph: 800-346-7844 Fax: (215)646-108?
Fr: 800-346-7844
URL: http://www.tnpj.com

Monthly. $50.00/year; $83.00/year for institutions; $67.00/year for Canada; $98.00/year for institutions in Canada; $104.00/year international. Magazine presenting clinical information to nurses in advanced primary care practice. Also covers legal, business, economic, ethical, research, and pharmaceutical issues.

★6486★ Nurse Practitioner Forum

Elsevier Science Inc.
The Curtis Ctr.
170 Independence Mall W, 300F
Philadelphia, PA 19106-3399
Ph: (215)238-7800 Fax: (215)238-7883
Fr: 800-523-1649

Quarterly. $49.00/year for individuals; $42.00/year for students; $76.00/year for institutions; $106.00/year for out of country. Journal for nurse practitioners.

★6487★ Nursing Education Perspectives

National League for Nursing Press
61 Broadway, 33rd Fl.
New York, NY 10006-2701
Ph: (212)363-5555 Fr: 800-669-1656
URL: http://www.nln.org

Free to qualified subscribers; $60.00/year; $90.00/year, libraries and institutions. Professional journal for nurses. Includes articles on health policy, social and economic issues affecting health care, and nursing education and practice.

★6488★ Nursing Management

Spring House
434 W Downer Pl.
Aurora, IL 60506
Ph: (630)844-6911 Fr: 800-950-0879

Monthly. $25.00/year for individuals. Magazine focusing on nursing management.

★6489★ Nursing 96

Lippincott Williams & Wilkins
530 Walnut St.
Philadelphia, PA 19106
Ph: (215)521-8300 Fax: (215)521-8902
Fr: 800-638-3030
E-mail: nursing@springnet.com

Monthly. $42.00/year for individuals; $4.00 for single issue. Practical journal for nurses. Includes special sections for hospital critical-care and home health.

★6490★ Nursing Outlook

Mosby Inc.
10801 Executive Center Dr., Ste. 509
Little Rock, AR 72211
Ph: (501)223-5165   Fax: (501)223-0519
URL: http://www.mosby.com

Bimonthly. $57.00/year for individuals; $106.00/year for institutions. Official journal of the American Academy of Nursing, reporting on trends and issues in nursing.

★6491★ Orthopaedic Nursing

National Association of Orthopaedic Nurses
E Holly Ave. Box 56
Pitman, NJ 08071-0056
Ph: (609)256-2310   Fax: (609)589-7463
E-mail: onjrnl@mail
URL: http://www.inurse.com~naon

Bimonthly. $28.00/year; $40.00/year for institutions; $5.00/year for single issue. Nursing magazine.

★6492★ Pediatric Nursing

Jannetti Publications Inc.
E Holly Ave.
Box 56
Pitman, NJ 08071-0056
Ph: (856)256-2300   Fax: (856)589-7463
E-mail: adver@ajj.com
URL: http://www.pediatricnursing.net

Bimonthly. $38.00/year; $47.00/year for institutions; $6.00/year for single issue. Professional nursing magazine.

★6493★ Provider

American Health Care Association
1201 L St. NW
Washington, DC 20005
Ph: (202)842-4444   Fax: (202)842-3860
Fr: 800-321-4444
E-mail: provider@ahca.org

Monthly. $48.00/year for nonmembers. Provider Magazine.

★6494★ Rehabilitation Nursing

Rehabilitation Nursing
4700 W Lake Ave.
Glenview, IL 60025
Ph: (847)375-4710   Fax: 877-734-9384
Fr: 800-229-7530
E-mail: info@rehabnurse.org

Bimonthly. $95.00/year for individuals; $125.00/year for institutions; $135.00/year for other countries; $18.00 for single issue; $125.00/year for Canada. Magazine focusing on rehabilitation nursing involving clinical practice, research, education, and administration.

★6495★ Research in Healthcare Financial Management

International Society for Research in Healthcare Financial Management Ltd.
305 W Chesapeake Ave.
CSBA Ste. L-096
Towson, MD 21204

Annual. Publication covering issues in the healthcare industry.

★6496★ Research in Nursing & Health

John Wiley and Sons Inc.
111 River St.
Hoboken, NJ 07030
Ph: (201)748-8866   Fax: (201)748-8824

Bimonthly. $115.00/year for U.S.; $115.00/year for Canada and Mexico; $151.00/year for other countries. Journal providing forum for research in the areas of nursing practice, education, and administration. Covers health issues relevant to nursing as well as investigations of the applications of research findings in clinical settings.

★6497★ Seminars in Oncology

Elsevier Science Inc.
The Curtis Ctr.
170 Independence Mall W, 300F
Philadelphia, PA 19106-3399
Ph: (215)238-7800   Fax: (215)238-7883
Fr: 800-523-1649
E-mail: elspcs@elsevier.com

$199.00/year for individuals; $318.00/year for institutions; $295.00/year for other countries; $382.00/year for institutions, other countries; $100.00/year for students, US students and residents; $64.00 for single issue. Journal reviewing current diagnostic and treatment techniques used in oncology patient care.

PLACEMENT AND JOB REFERRAL SERVICES

★6498★ American Association of Occupational Health Nurses (AAOHN)

2920 Brandy Wine Rd., Ste. 100
Atlanta, GA 30341
Ph: (770)455-7757   Fax: (770)455-7271
URL: http://www.aaohn.org

Description: Registered professional nurses employed by business and industrial firms; nurse educators, nurse editors, nurse writers, and others interested in occupational health nursing. Promotes and sets standards for the profession. Provides and approves continuing education; maintains governmental affairs program; offers placement service.

★6499★ American Public Health Association (APHA)

800 I St. NW
Washington, DC 20001-3710
Ph: (202)777-2742   Fax: (202)777-2534

E-mail: comments@apha.org
URL: http://www.apha.org

Members: Professional organization of physicians, nurses, educators, academicians, environmentalists, epidemiologists, new professionals, social workers, health administrators, optometrists, podiatrists, pharmacists, dentists, nutritionists, health planners, other community and mental health specialists, and interested consumers. **Purpose:** Seeks to protect and promote personal, mental, and environmental health. **Activities:** Services include promulgation of standards; establishment of uniform practices and procedures; development of the etiology of communicable diseases; research in public health; exploration of medical care programs and their relationships to public health. Sponsors job placement service.

EMPLOYER DIRECTORIES AND NETWORKING LISTS

★6500★ AHA Guide to the Health Care Field

American Hospital Association (AHA)
1 N. Franklin St., 27th Fl.
Chicago, IL 60606
Ph: (312)422-2050   Fax: (312)422-4700
Fr: 800-424-4301

Annual, August. $295.00. Covers hospitals, networks, multi-health care systems, free-standing ambulatory surgery centers, psychiatric facilities, long-term care facilities, substance abuse programs, and other health-related organizations. Entries include: For hospitals-Facility name, address, phone, administrator's name, number of beds, facilities and services, number of employees, expenses, other statistics. For other organizations-Name, address, phone, fax, name and title of contact. Arrangement: Geographical. Indexes: Hospital name.

★6501★ American Journal of Nursing-Career Guide

American Journal of Nursing
c/o Lippincott, Williams, & Wilkins
530 Walnut St.
Philadelphia, PA 19106-3621
Ph: (215)521-8300   Fax: (215)521-8902
Fr: 800-627-0484
URL: http://www.nursingcenter.com

Annual, April. $13.95. Publication includes: List of nursing organizations and agencies. Entries include: Name, address, names of officers or nursing representative. Arrangement: Classified by type of organization.

★6502★ CriticalCare Choices

Springhouse Office of Lippincott, Williams & Wilkins
PO Box 908
Spring House, PA 19477-0908
Ph: (215)646-8700   Fax: (215)646-4399
Fr: 800-346-7844

URL: http://www.nursingcenter.com
Annual, May. Clinical and career directory for critical care nurses. Covers non-profit and investor-owned hospitals and departments of the United States government that hire critical care nurses. Arrangement: Geographical. Indexes: Geographical.

★6503★ Directory of Hospital Personnel

Thomson Medical Economics
5 Paragon Dr.
Montvale, NJ 07645-1742
Ph: (201)358-7200   Fax: (201)722-2680
Annual, November. $325.00. Covers 200,000 executives at 7,000 U.S. hospitals. Entries include: Name of hospital, address, phone, number of beds, type and JCAHO status of hospital, names and titles of key department heads and staff, medical and nursing school affiliations; number of residents, interns, and nursing students. Arrangement: Geographical. Indexes: Hospital name, personnel, hospital size.

★6504★ Essentials of Internet Use in Nursing

Springer Publishing Co. Inc.
536 Broadway
New York, NY 10012
Ph: (212)431-4370   Fax: (212)941-7842
Fr: 877-687-7476
$32.95. Publication includes: Appendix listing relevant web sites. Principal content of publication is information on Internet usage for clinical nursing practice, for continuing nursing education, for medical research, and for nursing staff recruitment and development. Indexes: Topical.

★6505★ Guide to Careers in the Health Professions

The Princeton Review
1745 Broadway
New York, NY 10019
Ph: (212)829-6928   Fax: (212)940-7400
Fr: 800-733-3000
Published January, 2001. $24.95. Presents advice and information for those searching for satisfying careers in the health professions. Publication includes: Directory of schools and academic programs. Entries include: Name, address, phone, tuition, program details, employment profiles.

★6506★ Hitting the Road: A Guide to Travel Nursing

Lippincott Williams & Wilkins
530 Walnut St.
Philadelphia, PA 19106-3621
Ph: (215)521-8300   Fax: (215)521-8902
Fr: 800-638-3030
$25.95. Publication includes: List of 70 health care staffing agencies. Principal content of publication is discussion of and assistance in entering field of travel nursing.

★6507★ Hospital Blue Book

Billian/Transworld Publishing Inc.
2100 Powers Ferry Rd.
Ste. 300
Atlanta, GA 30339
Ph: (770)955-8484   Fax: (770)955-8485
Fr: 800-533-8484
E-mail: blu-book@billian.com
Annual, January. $285.00 for national edition; $160.00 for southern edition. Covers more than 6,687 hospitals; some listings also appear in a separate southern edition of this publication. Entries include: Name of hospital, accreditation, mailing address, phone, fax, number of beds, type of facility (nonprofit, general, state, etc.); list of administrative personnel and chiefs of medical services, with specific titles. Arrangement: Geographical.

★6508★ How to Survive and Maybe Even Love Nursing School!

F.A. Davis Co.
1915 Arch St.
Philadelphia, PA 19103
Ph: (215)368-2270   Fax: (215)568-5065
Fr: 800-523-4049
$19.95. Publication includes: List of resources for nursing students such as web sites and organizations. Principal content of publication is information about succeeding in nursing school.

★6509★ The JobBank Guide to Health Care Companies

Adams Media Corp.
57 Littlefield St.
Avon, MA 02322
Ph: (508)427-7100   Fax: (508)427-6790
Fr: 800-872-5627
$17.95. Covers Jobs nationwide in health care companies. Entries include: Firm or organization name, address, phone, name and title of contact; description of organization, headquarters location, typical titles for entry- and middle-level positions, educational backgrounds desired, fringe benefits offered, stock exchange listing, training programs, internships, parent company, number of employees, revenues, e-mail and web address, projected number of hires. Indexes: Alphabetical.

★6510★ Medical and Health Information Directory

Thomson Gale
27500 Drake Rd.
Farmington Hills, MI 48331-3535
Ph: (248)699-4253   Fax: (248)699-8065
Fr: 800-877-GALE
E-mail: businessproducts@gale.com
Annual. $285.00 per volume; $675.00 per set. Covers in Volume 1, more than 26,500 medical and health oriented associations, organizations, institutions, and government agencies, including health maintenance organizations (HMOs), preferred provider organizations (PPOs), insurance companies, pharmaceutical companies, research centers, and medical and allied health schools.

In Volume 2, over 12,000 medical book publishers; medical periodicals, directories, audiovisual producers and services, medical libraries and information centers, electronic resources, and health-related internet search engines. In Volume 3, more than 35,500 clinics, treatment centers, care programs, and counseling/diagnostic services for 34 subject areas. Entries include: Institution, service, or firm name, address, phone, fax, email and URL; many include names of key personnel and, when pertinent, descriptive annotation. Volume 3 was formerly listed separately as Health Services Directory. Arrangement: Classified by organization activity, service, etc. Indexes: Each volume has a complete alphabetical name and keyword index.

★6511★ Nurses and Nurses' Registries Directory

infoUSA Inc.
5711 S 86th Cir.
Omaha, NE 68127-0347
Ph: (402)930-3500   Fax: (402)331-0176
Fr: 800-555-6124
URL: http://www.abii.com
Annual. Number of listings: 10,949. Entries include: Name, address, phone (including area code), size of advertisement, year first in "Yellow Pages," name of owner or manager, number of employees. Compiled from telephone company "Yellow Pages," nationwide. Arrangement: Geographical.

★6512★ Nursing Career Directory

Springhouse Office of Lippincott, Williams & Wilkins
PO Box 908
Spring House, PA 19477-0908
Ph: (215)646-8700   Fax: (215)646-4399
Fr: 800-346-7844
URL: http://www.springnet.com
Annual, January. $10.00. Covers nonprofit and investor-owned hospitals and departments of the United States government which hire nurses. Does not report specific positions available. Entries include: Unit name, location, areas of nursing specialization, educational requirements for nurses, licensing, facilities, benefits, etc. Arrangement: Geographical. Indexes: Geographical.

★6513★ The Nursing Job Search Handbook

University of Pennsylvania Press
4200 Pine St.
Philadelphia, PA 19104-4011
Ph: (215)898-6261   Fax: (215)898-0404
Fr: 800-445-9880
$17.95. Publication includes: Appendix listing state licensing boards and nursing organizations. Entries include: Name, address, phone. Principal content of publication is information on obtaining a job in the field of nursing. Indexes: Alphabetical.

★6514★ Peterson's Guide to Nursing Programs

Thomson Peterson's
Princeton Pke. Corporate Ctr., 2000
  Lenox Dr.
PO Box 67005
Lawrenceville, NJ 08648
Ph: (609)896-1800   Fax: (609)896-4531
Fr: 800-338-3282

Annual, latest edition 2002. $26.95. Covers over 700 institutions offering approximately 2,000 accredited nursing programs in the U.S. and Canada. Entries include: Academic information, extracurricular issues, costs, financial aid.

★6515★ Peterson's Job Opportunities for Health and Science Majors

Thomson Peterson's
Princeton Pke. Corporate Ctr., 2000
  Lenox Dr.
PO Box 67005
Lawrenceville, NJ 08648
Ph: (609)896-1800   Fax: (609)896-4531
Fr: 800-338-3282
URL: http://www.petersons.com

Irregular, latest edition 1999. $18.95. Covers approximately 1,300 research, consulting, government, and non-profit and profit service organizations that hire college and university graduates in science and health-related majors. Entries include: Organization name, address, phone, name and title of contact, type of organization, number of employees, Standard Industrial Classification (SIC) code; description of opportunities available including disciplines, level of education required, starting locations and salaries, level of experience accepted, benefits.

HANDBOOKS AND MANUALS

★6516★ Anatomy of a Job Search: A Nurse's Guide to Finding and Landing the Job You Want

Springhouse Corporation
P.O. Box 908
Springhouse, PA 19477-0908
Ph: (215)646-8700   Fax: (215)646-4508
Fr: 800-346-7844

Jeanna Bozell. 1999. $22.95 (paper).

★6517★ Building and Managing a Career in Nursing: Strategies for Advancing Your Career

Sigma Theta Tau International, Center for
  Nursing Press
550 W. North St.
Indianapolis, IN 46202
Ph: (317)634-8171   Fax: (317)634-8188
Fr: 888-634-7575

Terry W. Miller. May 2003. $24.95. Illustrated. 411 pages.

★6518★ Career Opportunities in Health Care (Career Opportunities)

Facts on File
132 W. 31st St., 17th Fl.
New York, NY 10001-2006
Ph: (212)967-8800   Fax: (212)967-8107
Fr: 800-322-8755

Shelly Field. Arthur E. Weintraub. 2002. Reprint. $18.95. 243 pages. Part of the Career Opportunities Series.

★6519★ Careers in Health Care

McGraw-Hill Trade
2 Penn Plaza
New York, NY 10121
Ph: (212)904-2000   Fr: 800-722-4726
E-mail: ntcpub@tribune.com

Barbara M. Swanson. Fourth edition, 2000. $17.95; $13.95 (paper). 320 pages. Describes job duties, work settings, salaries, licensing and certification requirements, educational preparation, and future outlook. Gives ideas on how to secure a job.

★6520★ Careers for Night Owls and Other Insomniacs

McGraw-Hill Trade
2 Penn Plaza
New York, NY 10121
Ph: (212)904-2000   Fr: 800-722-4726
E-mail: ntcpub@tribune.com

Louise Miller. 1995. $14.95; $9.95 (paper). 160 pages.

★6521★ Careers in Nursing

McGraw-Hill Trade
2 Penn Plaza
New York, NY 10121
Ph: (212)904-2000   Fr: 800-722-4726
E-mail: ntcpub@tribune.com

Terence J. Sacks. 1998. $17.95; 13.95 (paper). 278 pages.

★6522★ Comprehensive Review of Practical Nursing for NCLEX-PN

Mosby Inc.
11830 Westline Industrial Dr.
St. Louis, MO 63146
Ph: (314)872-8370   Fax: 800-235-0256
Fr: 800-325-4177

Mary O. Eyles, editor. First edition, 2000. $29.95 (paper). 735 pages.

★6523★ Developing Your Career in Nursing

Sage Publications Inc.
370 Lexington Ave.
New York, NY 10017-6503
Ph: (212)953-5858   Fax: (212)953-5944

Robert Newell, editor. 1996. $90.00.

★6524★ Expert Resumes for Health Care Careers

JIST Publishing
8902 Otis Ave.
Indianapolis, IN 46216-1033
Ph: (317)613-4200   Fax: 800-547-8329

December 2003. $16.95. 288 pages.

★6525★ Federal Jobs in Nursing and Health Sciences

Impact Publications
9104 Manassas Dr., Ste. N
Manassas Park, VA 20111-5211
Ph: (703)361-7300   Fax: (703)335-9486

Russ Smith. 1996. Part of Federal Jobs in...Series. $14.95. 130 pages.

★6526★ Focus on Practical-Vocational Nursing

National League for Nursing Press
61 Broadway, 33rd Fl.
New York, NY 10006-2701
Ph: (978)443-5000   Fax: (212)989-3710
Fr: 800-669-9656

Fitzsimons. 1997. $35.00. 80 pages.

★6527★ Gerontological Nursing Certification Review Guide for the Generalist, Clinical Specialist & Nurse Practitioner

Health Leadership Associates, Inc
PO Box 59153
Potomac, MD 20859
Ph: (301)983-2405   Fax: (301)983-2693
Fr: 800-435-4775

Catharine Kopac and Virginia L. Millonig, editors. Revised, 1996. $26.00 (paper). 541 pages.

★6528★ Health Care Career Starter: Finding and Getting a Great Job

LearningExpress, LLC
900 Broadway, Ste. 604
New York, NY 10003
Ph: (212)995-2566   Fax: (212)995-5512
Fr: 800-295-9556

Cheryl Jean Hancock. Brigit Dermott. Reprint. 2002. $15.95 (paper). 216 pages. Part of the Heath Care Career Starters Series.

★6529★ Health Careers Today

Elsevier-Health Sciences Division
The Curtis Center, Ste. 300E, 3rd Fl.
170 S. Independence Mall W.
Philadelphia, PA 19106
Ph: (215)238-7800   Fax: (215)238-7362
Fr: 800-523-4069

Gerdin. Revised edition. April 2004. $52.95.

★6530★ Healthcare Career Directory-Nurses and Physicians

Thomson Gale
27500 Drake Rd.
Farmington Hills, MI 48331-3535
Ph: (248)699-GALE   Fax: 800-414-5043
Fr: 800-877-GALE
E-mail: galeord@gale.com
URL: http://www.gale.com

Bradley Morgan. Second edition, 1993. $39.00. 300 pages. Out of print. Essays on specific careers provide an insider's perspective. Features extensive listings of contacts and entry-level job opportunities. Provides information on internships and sources of help-wanted ads.

★6531★ Licensed Practical Nurse

Capstone Press
2132 O'Toole Ave.
San Jose, CA 95131-1302
Ronald R. Smith. 1993. $2.50 (paper).

★6532★ Mosby's Assestest: A Practice Exam for RN Licensure

Mosby Inc.
11830 Westline Industrial Dr.
St. Louis, MO 63146
Ph: (314)872-8370   Fax: 800-235-0256
Fr: 800-325-4177

Delores F. Saxton. 1994. $28.95 (paper). 80 pages. Out of print.

★6533★ Mosby's Review Questions for NCLEX-RN

Mosby Inc.
11830 Westline Industrial Dr.
St. Louis, MO 63146
Ph: (314)872-8370   Fax: 800-235-0256
Fr: 800-325-4177

Nugent. Fourth edition, 2001. $31.95 (paper). 650 pages.

★6534★ Mosby's Tour Guide to Nursing School: A Student's Road Survival Guide

Mosby Inc.
11830 Westline Industrial Dr.
St. Louis, MO 63146
Ph: (314)872-8370   Fax: 800-235-0256
Fr: 800-325-4177

Melodie Chenevert. Third edition. 1994. $21.95 (paper). 216 pages.

★6535★ NSNA, NCLEX-RN Review

Thomson Delmar Learning
PO Box 15015
Albany, NY 12212-5015
Ph: (518)348-2300   Fax: (518)464-0393
Fr: 800-998-7498

Alice M. Stein. Third edition. 1996. $32.00 (paper). Out of print.

★6536★ The Nurses' Career Guide: Discovering New Horizons in Health Care

Sovereignty Press
1241 Johnson Ave., No. 353
San Luis Obispo, CA 93401
Ph: (805)543-6100   Fax: (805)543-1085
Fr: 888-201-2501

Zardoya E. Eagles and Marti Kock. 1999. $17.95 (paper). Helps the reader identify work skills and achievements, clarify values and goals, explore career options, develop a personal action plan, prepare cover letters and resumes, and conduct informational and job interviews. Also addresses the dramatic changes that nurses currently face in the workplace. Includes a 65-page resource section which lists references, samples of resumes and letters, professional magazines, organizations, and online resources.

★6537★ Nursing (Career Portraits)

McGraw-Hill Trade
2 Penn Plaza
New York, NY 10121
Ph: (212)904-2000   Fax: (212)755-5645
Fr: 800-722-4726
E-mail: ntcpub@tribune.com

Blythe Camenson. 1995. $13.95. 335 pages.

★6538★ The Nursing Experience: Trends, Challenges & Transitions

McGraw-Hill Professional
PO Box 545
Blacklick, OH 43004-0545
Fax: (614)755-5645   Fr: 800-722-4726

Lucie Y. Kelly. Fourth edition, 2001. $34.95 (paper). 792 pages.

★6539★ Nursing Today: Transition and Trends

W.B. Saunders Co.
150 S. Independence Mall W
The Public Ledger Bldg., Ste. 1250
Philadelphia, PA 19106-3412
Ph: (215)238-5500   Fax: (215)238-8495
Fr: 800-654-2452

JoAnn Zerwekh and Jo C. Claborn, editors. Second edition, 1997.

★6540★ 101 Careers in Nursing

Springer Publishing Company, Inc.
536 Broadway, 11th Fl.
New York, NY 10012-3955
Ph: (212)431-4370   Fax: (212)941-7842

Jeanne M. Novotny, Doris T. Lippman, Nicole K. Sanders, Joyce J. Fitzpatrick. August 2003. $33.95 (paper). Illustrated. 240 pages.

★6541★ Opportunities in Child Care Careers

McGraw-Hill Trade
2 Penn Plaza
New York, NY 10121
Ph: (212)904-2000   Fr: 800-722-4726

Renee Wittenberg. 1998. $14.95; $11.95 (paper). 210 pages. Discusses various job

opportunities and how to secure a position. Illustrated.

★6542★ Opportunities in Environmental Careers

McGraw-Hill Trade
2 Penn Plaza
New York, NY 10121
Ph: (212)904-2000   Fr: 800-722-4726
E-mail: ntcpub@tribune.com

Odom Fanning. Revised, 2002. $12.95 (paper). 160 pages. Describes a broad range of opportunities in fields such as environmental health, recreation, physics, and hygiene, and provides job search advice. Part of Opportunities in...Series.

★6543★ Opportunities in Health and Medical Careers

McGraw-Hill Trade
2 Penn Plaza
New York, NY 10121
Ph: (212)904-2000   Fr: 800-722-4726

I. Donald Snook, Jr. and Leo D'Orazio. 1997. $14.95; $11.95 (paper). 202 pages. Covers the full range of medical and health occupations. Illustrated.

★6544★ Opportunities in Nursing Careers

McGraw-Hill Trade
2 Penn Plaza
New York, NY 10121
Ph: (212)904-2000   Fr: 800-722-4726

Keville Frederickson and Judith A. Ryan. 1995. $14.95; $11.95 (paper). 205 pages. Discusses the employment outlook and job-seeking techniques for LVN's, LPN's, RN's, nurse practitioners, nurse anesthetists, and other nurse members of the medical team. Includes a complete list of state nurses associations, state nursing boards, and specialty nursing organizations. Contains bibliography and illustrations.

★6545★ Opportunities in Physician Assistant Careers

McGraw-Hill Trade
2 Penn Plaza
New York, NY 10121
Ph: (212)904-2000   Fr: 800-722-4726

Terence J. Sacks. 2002. $14.95; $12.95 (paper). 160 pages.

★6546★ Opportunities in State and Local Government Careers

Vgm Career Horizons
1221 Avenue of the Americas
New York, NY 10020
Ph: (212)904-2000   Fr: 800-323-4900
E-mail: ntcpub@tribune.com

Neale J. Baxter. 1994. $14.95; $10.95 (paper). 160 pages. Points out the incentives and drawbacks of a government career. Describes hiring procedures and provides tips on filling out applications, taking physical and aptitude tests, handling interviews, and finding jobs. Describes the jobs in which 75% of all state and local government workers are employed. For each occupation, covers the nature of the work and the training required.

★6547★ Real People Working in Health Care
McGraw-Hill Contemporary Books
1221 Avenue of the Americas
New York, NY 10020
Ph: (212)904-2000   Fr: 800-323-4900
E-mail: ntcpub@tribune.com

Blythe Camenson, Jan Goldberg. 1996. $17.95; $12.95 (paper). Interviews and profiles of working professionals capture a range of opportunities in this field.

★6548★ Real-Resumes for Nursing Jobs: Including Real Resumes Used to Change Careers and Resumes Used to Gain Federal Employment
PREP Publishing
1110 1/2 Hay St., PMB 66
Fayetteville, NC 28305
Ph: (910)483-6611   Fax: (910)483-2439
Fr: 800-533-2814

April 2003. $16.95. 192 pages. Real-Resumes Series.

★6549★ Reinventing Your Nursing Career: A Handbook for Success in the Age of Managed Care
Jones and Bartlett Publishing
200 Orchard Ridge Dr., Ste. 200
Gaithersburg, MD 20878
Ph: (301)417-7500   Fax: (301)695-7931
Fr: 800-638-8437

Michael Newell and Mario Pinardo. 1997. $37.00 (paper). 272 pages. Helps nurses identify career goals and take practical steps to realize them using self-surveys, goal-setting methods, personal action plans, and networking techniques.

★6550★ Resumes for the Health Care Professional
John Wiley & Sons Inc.
111 River Rd.
Hoboken, NJ 07030-5774
Ph: (201)748-6000   Fax: (201)748-6088
Fr: 800-225-5945

Kim Marino. Second edition, 2000. $14.95 (paper). 224 pages.

★6551★ Resumes for Nursing Careers
McGraw-Hill Professional
2 Penn Plaza
New York, NY 10121
Ph: (212)904-2000   Fr: 800-722-4726
E-mail: ntcpub@tribune.com

2001. $10.95 (paper). 160 pages.

★6552★ Vocational & Personal Adjustments in Practical Nursing
Mosby Inc.
11830 Westline Industrial Dr.
St. Louis, MO 63146
Ph: (314)872-8370   Fax: 800-235-0256
Fr: 800-325-4177

Betty G. Becker and Dolores T. Fendler. Seventh edition, 1994. $24.95 (paper). 194 pages.

★6553★ Your Career in Nursing: Manage Your Future in the Changing World of Healthcare
Kaplan Books
1230 Avenue of the Americas, 1st Fl.
New York, NY 10020
Ph: (212)698-7000   Fax: (212)698-7007
Fr: 800-223-2348

Annette Vallano. January 2003. $18.00 (paper). Illustrated. 368 Pages. Vocational guide.

★6554★ Your First Year as a Nurse: Making the Transition from Total Novice to Successful Professional
Prima Publishing
3000 Lava Ridge Ct.
Roseville, CA 95661
Ph: (916)787-7000   Fax: (916)787-7001

2001. $19.95 (paper).

EMPLOYMENT AGENCIES AND SEARCH FIRMS

★6555★ Harper Associates
29870 Middlebelt
Farmington Hills, MI 48334
Ph: (248)932-1170   Fax: (248)932-1214
E-mail: resumes@harperjobs.com
URL: http://www.harperjobs.com

Executive search firm and employment agency.

★6556★ Medical Personnel Services, Inc.
1707 L St. NW, Ste. 760
Washington, DC 20036
Ph: (202)466-2955

Employment agency specializing in permanent health/medical placements.

★6557★ Nursing Technomics
814 Sunset Hollow Rd.
West Chester, PA 19380-1848
Ph: (610)436-4551   Fax: (610)436-0255

Administrative nursing consultants offer expertise in the design and implementation of customized software applications for departments of nursing, organizational design and implementation, and executive nurse search. Also specializes in department staffing,

scheduling and nurse recruitment. Serves private industries as well as government agencies.

★6558★ Professional Placement Associates, Inc.
287 Bowman Ave., Ste. 309
Purchase, NY 10577
Ph: (914)251-1000   Fax: (914)251-1055
E-mail: lschachter@ppasearch.com
URL: http://www.ppasearch.com

Executive search firm specializing in the health and medical field.

★6559★ Team Placement Service, Inc.
5113 Leesburg Pike, Ste. 510
Falls Church, VA 22041-3242
Ph: (703)820-8618   Fax: (703)820-3368
Fr: 800-495-6767
E-mail: 4jobs@teamplace.com
URL: http://www.teamplace.com

Temporary agency that also handles some permanent placements.

★6560★ Travcorps, Inc.
40 Eastern Ave.
Malden, MA 02148
Ph: (781)322-2600   Fax: 800-803-1186
Fr: 800-343-3270
URL: http://www.travcorps.com

Places staff in temporary assignments. Other locations nationwide.

ONLINE JOB SOURCES AND SERVICES

★6561★ Health Care Job Store
395 South End Ave., Ste. 15-D
New York, NY 10280
Ph: (212)912-0175
E-mail: jobs@atshealthcarejobstore.com
URL: http://www.healthcarejobstore.com/adag.html

Description: Job sites include every job title in the healthcare industry,every healthcare industry and every geographic location in the U.S.

★6562★ HealthCareerWeb
URL: http://www.healthcareerweb.com/

Description: Advertises jobs for healthcare professionals. **Main files include:** Jobs, Employers, Resumes, Jobwire. Relocation tools and career guidance resources available.

★6563★ MedExplorer
URL: http://www.medexplorer.com

Description: Employment postings make up one module of this general medical site.

Other sections contain: Newsletter, Classifieds, and Discussion Forum.

★6564★ Medhunters.com
E-mail: info@medhunters.com
URL: http://www.medhunters.com

Description: Career search site for jobs in all health care specialties; educational resources; visa and licensing information for relocation; interesting articles; relocation tools; links to professional organizations and general resources.

★6565★ Monster Healthcare
E-mail: office@atsmedsearch.com
URL: http://myh.monster.com/

Description: H Monster delivers nationwide access to healthcare recruiting. Employers can post job listings or ads. Job seekers can post and code resumes, and search over 150,000 healthcare job listings, healthcare career advice columns, career resources information, and member employer profiles and services.

★6566★ NursesRX.com
E-mail: nursesrx@nursesrx.com
URL: http://www.nursesrx.com

Description: Job board site for travel nursing. In addition to traditional travel nursing, Nurses Rx provides staffing possibilities from temporary-to-permanent, traditional permanent placement, staffing/recruitment outsourcing, new graduate internship programs, and a full Canadian Placement Division.

★6567★ ProHealthJobs
E-mail: sales@prohealthjobs.com
URL: http://www.prohealthjobs.com

Description: Career resources site for the medical and health care field. Lists professional opportunities, product information, continuing education and open positions.

TRADESHOWS

★6568★ American Association of Office Nurses Annual Meeting and Convention
American Association of Office Nurses
109 Kinderkamack Rd.
Montvale, NJ 07645
Ph: (201)391-2600   Fax: (201)573-8543
Fr: 800-457-7504
E-mail: aaonmail@aaon.org
URL: http://www.aaon.org

Annual. **Primary Exhibits:** Exhibits of interest to nurses.

★6569★ AORN World Conference on Surgical Patient Care
Association of Perioperative Registered Nurses (AORN)
2170 S. Parker Rd., Ste. 300
Denver, CO 80231-5711
Ph: (303)755-6300   Fax: (303)752-0299
Fr: 800-755-2676
URL: http://www.aorn.org

Biennial. **Primary Exhibits:** Equipment, supplies, and services used in operating room suites and pre-surgical areas.

★6570★ Conference on Classification of Nursing Diagnosis
North American Nursing Diagnosis Association
1211 Locust St.
Philadelphia, PA 19107
Ph: (215)545-8105   Fax: (215)545-8107
Fr: 800-647-9002
E-mail: nanda@nursecominc.com

Biennial. **Primary Exhibits:** Exhibits relating to the development of a taxonomy of diagnostic terminology for use by professional nurses. Booth publishers, electronic media publishers.

★6571★ Conference of the National Association of Pediatric Nurse Associates and Practitioners
National Association of Pediatric Nurse Associates and Practitioners
20 Brace Rd., Ste. 200
Cherry Hill, NJ 08034-1912
Ph: (856)857-9700   Fax: (856)857-1600
Fr: 877-662-7627
E-mail: info@napnap.org
URL: http://www.napnap.org

Annual. **Primary Exhibits:** Equipment, supplies, and services for pediatric, school, and family nurse practitioners.

★6572★ Emergency Nurses Association Annual Meeting
Emergency Nurses Association
915 Lee St.
Des Plaines, IL 60016-6569
Fax: (847)460-4001   Fr: 800-900-9659
E-mail: enainfo@iqnow.com
URL: http://www.ena.org

Annual. **Primary Exhibits:** Exhibits relating to emergency room care.

★6573★ House of Delegates Meeting
American Nurses Association
600 Maryland Ave. SW, Ste. 100 W
Washington, DC 20024-2571
Ph: (202)651-7203   Fax: (202)651-7003
E-mail: exhibits@ana.org
URL: http://www.nursingworld.org

Biennial. **Primary Exhibits:** Equipment, supplies, and services for nurses, including publications, uniforms and shoes, computers, laboratory services, medical equipment, and nutritional products.

★6574★ International Society of Psychiatric-Mental Health Nurses Annual Conference
International Society of Psychiatric - Mental Health Nurses
1211 Locust St.
Philadelphia, PA 19107
Ph: (215)545-2843   Fax: (215)545-8107
Fr: 800-826-2950
E-mail: ispn@nursecominc.com
URL: http://www.ispn-psych.org

Annual. **Primary Exhibits:** Psychiatric nursing equipment, supplies, and services.

★6575★ NASN Annual Conference
National Association of School Nurses
Lamplighter Ln.
PO Box 1300
Scarborough, ME 04070
Ph: (207)883-2117   Fax: (207)883-2683
E-mail: nasn@aol.com
URL: http://www.VRmedia.com/nurses

Annual. **Primary Exhibits:** School nursing equipment, supplies, and services.

★6576★ National Association of Orthopedic Nurses Annual Congress
Smith, Bucklin and Associates, Inc. (Chicago)
401 N. Michigan Ave.
Chicago, IL 60611-4267
Ph: (312)321-6610   Fax: (312)673-6670
Fr: 800-289-NAON
E-mail: info@smithbucklin.com
URL: http://www.sba.com

Annual. **Primary Exhibits:** Pharmaceuticals, medical equipment, medical instruments, and publications. **Dates and Locations:** 2005 May 14-18; Phoenix, AZ; Phoenix Hyatt Regency and Civic Plaza.

★6577★ National League for Nursing Convention
SLACK, Inc.
6900 Grove Rd.
Thorofare, NJ 08086
Ph: (609)848-1000   Fax: (609)848-3522

Biennial. **Primary Exhibits:** Equipment, supplies, and services for nurses and related healthcare professionals.

★6578★ National Student Nurses' Association Convention
National Student Nurses' Association
45 Main St., Ste. 606
Brooklyn, NY 11201
Ph: (718)210-0705   Fax: (718)210-0710
E-mail: nsna.net@internetmci.com
URL: http://www.nsna.org

Biennial. **Primary Exhibits:** Equipment, supplies, and services for the student nurse. **Dates and Locations:** 2004 Nov 11-14; Daytona Beach, FL • 2005 Apr 06-10; Salt Lake City, UT.

★6579★ North Carolina Nurses Association Convention

North Carolina Nurses Association
103 Enterprise St.
PO Box 12025
Raleigh, NC 27605
Ph: (919)821-4250   Fax: (919)829-5807
Fr: 800-626-2153
E-mail: ncnurses@ncnurses.org
URL: http://www.ncnurses.org

Annual. **Primary Exhibits:** Nursing equipment, supplies, and services, books.

★6580★ Oncology Nursing Society Meeting

Oncology Nursing Society
501 Holiday Dr.
Pittsburgh, PA 15220
Ph: (412)921-7373   Fax: (412)921-6565

Annual. **Primary Exhibits:** Oncology nursing equipment, supplies, and services.

★6581★ Wisconsin Nurses Association Convention

Wisconsin Nurses Association, Inc.
6117 Monona Dr.
Madison, WI 53716
Ph: (608)221-0383   Fax: (608)221-2788
E-mail: wna@execpc.com
URL: http://www.execpc.com/~wna

Annual. **Primary Exhibits:** Nursing equipment, supplies, and services.

OTHER SOURCES

★6582★ American Almanac of Jobs and Salaries

Morrow Avon
1350 Avenue of the Americas
New York, NY 10019
Ph: (212)261-6788   Fr: 800-242-7737

John W. Wright. Revised edition, 2000. $20.00 (paper). 672 pages. This is a comprehensive guide to the wages of hundreds of occupations in a wide variety of industries and organizations.

★6583★ American Health Care Association (AHCA)

1201 L St. NW
Washington, DC 20005
Ph: (202)842-4444   Fax: (202)842-3860
URL: http://www.ahca.org

Description: Federation of state associations of long-term health care facilities. Promotes standards for professionals in long-term health care delivery and quality care for patients and residents in a safe environment. Focuses on issues of availability, quality, affordability, and fair payment. Operates as liaison with governmental agencies, Congress, and professional associations. Compiles statistics.

★6584★ American Hospital Association (AHA)

1 N. Franklin
Chicago, IL 60606-3421
Ph: (312)422-3000   Fax: (312)422-4796
URL: http://www.aha.org

Description: Health care provider organizations. Seeks to advance the health of individuals and communities. Leads, represents, and serves health care provider organizations that are accountable to the community and committed to health improvement.

★6585★ American Licensed Practical Nurses Association (ALPNA)

1090 Vermont Ave. NW, Ste. 800
Washington, DC 20005
Ph: (202)682-9000   Fax: (202)682-0168
E-mail: ptendler@tendler.com

Members: Licensed practical nurses. **Purpose:** Promotes the practical nursing profession; lobbies and maintains relations with the government on issues and legislation that may have an impact on LPNs. **Activities:** Conducts continuing education classes. Facilitates discussion of issues affecting the nursing and health professions.

★6586★ American Organization of Nurse Executives (AONE)

325 Seventh St. NW
Washington, DC 20004
Ph: (202)626-2240   Fax: (202)638-5499
E-mail: aone@aha.org
URL: http://www.aone.org

Description: Provides leadership, professional development, advocacy, and research to advance nursing practice and patient care, promote nursing leadership and excellence, and shape healthcare public policy. Supports and enhances the management, leadership, educational, and professional development of nursing leaders. Offers placement service through Career Development and Referral Center.

★6587★ American School Health Association (ASHA)

PO Box 708
7263 State Route 43
Kent, OH 44240
Ph: (330)678-1601   Fax: (330)678-4526
Fr: 800-445-2742
E-mail: asha@ashaweb.org
URL: http://www.ashaweb.org

Description: School physicians, school nurses, dentist, nurses, nutritionists, health educators, dental hygienist, school-based professionals and public health workers. Promotes coordinated school health programs that include health education, health services, a healthful school environment, physical education, nutrition services, and psycho-social health services offered in schools collaboratively with families and other members of the community. Offers professional reference materials. Conducts pilot programs that inform materials development, provides technical assistance to school professionals, advocates for school health, and complies statistics.

★6588★ EMTs, Nurses, Therapists, and Assistants

Cambridge Educational
2572 Brunswick Ave.
Lawrenceville, NJ 08648-4128
Fax: 800-FAX-ON-US   Fr: 800-468-4227
URL: http://www.cambridgeeducational.com

$79.95. 1999. Part of the series "Exploring Health Occupations."

★6589★ Exploring Health Occupations

Cambridge Educational
2572 Brunswick Ave.
Lawrenceville, NJ 08648-4128
Fax: 800-FAX-ON-US   Fr: 800-468-4227
URL: http://www.cambridgeeducational.com

Two videos. $139.95. 1999.

★6590★ Health Service Occupations

Delphi Productions
3160 4th St.
Boulder, CO 80304
Fax: (303)443-4022   Fr: 888-443-2400
URL: http://www.delphivideo.com

$95.00. 50 minutes. Part of the Careers for the 21st Century Video Library.

★6591★ Health Technologists & Technicians

Delphi Productions
3160 4th St.
Boulder, CO 80304
Fax: (303)443-4022   Fr: 888-443-2400
URL: http://www.delphivideo.com

$95.00. 50 minutes. Part of the Careers for the 21st Century Video Library.

★6592★ Interviewing Skills for Nurses & Other Health Care Professionals: A Structured Approach

Routledge
29 W. 35th St.
New York, NY 10001-2299
Ph: (212)216-7800   Fax: (212)564-7854
Fr: 800-634-7064

Robert Newell. 1994. $24.99 (paper). 208 pages. Out of print.

★6593★ Licensed Practical Nurses

Evon Publishing
832 N 7th Ave.
Iron River, MI 49935
Ph: (906)265-3190

Audiocassette. 1996. $16.95. 32 minutes. Part of the Careers and Vocational Guidance Series. Provides information about the nature of the work, educational requirements, employment outlook, earnings, and work conditions as well as additional related information.

★6594★ Medicine & Related Occupations

Delphi Productions
3160 4th St.
Boulder, CO 80304
Fax: (303)443-4022   Fr: 888-443-2400
URL: http://www.delphivideo.com

$95.00. 45 minutes. Part of the Careers for the 21st Century Video Library.

★6595★ National Association for Practical Nurse Education and Service (NAPNES)

8607 Second Ave., Ste. 404-A
Silver Spring, MD 20910-2745
Ph: (301)588-2491   Fax: (301)588-2839
E-mail: napnes@bellatlantic.net
URL: http://www.napnes.org

Description: Licensed practical/vocational nurses, registered nurses, physicians, hospital and nursing home administrators, and interested others. Provides consultation service to advise schools wishing to develop a practical/vocational nursing program on facilities, equipment, policies, curriculum, and staffing. Promotes recruitment of students through preparation and distribution of recruitment materials. Sponsors seminars for directors and instructors in schools of practical/vocational nursing and continuing education programs for LPNs/LVNs; approves continuing education programs and awards contact hours; holds national certification courses in post licensure specialities such as pharmacology, long term care and gerontics.

★6596★ National Federation of Licensed Practical Nurses (NFLPN)

605 Poole Dr.
Garner, NC 27529
Ph: (919)779-0046   Fax: (919)779-5642
E-mail: cbarbour@mgmt4u.com
URL: http://www.nflpn.org

Description: Federation of state associations of licensed practical and vocational nurses. Aims to: preserve and foster the ideal of comprehensive nursing care for the ill and aged; improve standards of practice; secure recognition and effective utilization of LPNs; further continued improvement in the education of LPNs. Acts as clearinghouse for information on practical nursing and cooperates with other groups concerned with better patient care. Maintains loan program.

★6597★ National League for Nursing (NLN)

61 Broadway 33rd Fl.
New York, NY 10006-2701
Ph: (212)363-5555   Fax: (212)812-0393
Fr: 800-669-1656
E-mail: rcorcor@nln.org
URL: http://www.nln.org

Description: Champions the pursuit of quality nursing education. A professional association of nursing faculty, education agencies, healthcare agencies, allied/public agencies, and public members whose mission is to advance quality nursing education that prepares the nursing workforce to meet the needs of diverse populations in an ever-changing health care environment. Serves as the primary source of information about every type of nursing education, from the LVN and LPN to the EDD and PHD. There are 33 affiliated constituent leagues that provide a local forum for members. The National League for Nursing Accrediting Commission is an independent corporate affiliate of the NLN, responsible for providing accreditation services to all levels of nursing education. NLN's bimonthly update is available free of charge on the website and by email.

★6598★ National Rural Health Association (NRHA)

1 W Armour Blvd., Ste. 203
Kansas City, MO 64111-2087
Ph: (816)756-3140   Fax: (816)756-3144
E-mail: mail@nrharural.org
URL: http://www.nrharural.org

Description: Administrators, physicians, nurses, physician assistants, health planners, academicians, and others interested or involved in rural health care. Creates a better understanding of health care problems unique to rural areas; utilizes a collective approach in finding positive solutions; articulates and represents the health care needs of rural America; supplies current information to rural health care providers; serves as a liaison between rural health care programs throughout the country. Offers continuing education credits for medical, dental, nursing, and management courses.

★6599★ The Patient Care Nursing Team

Cambridge Educational
2572 Brunswick Ave.
Lawrenceville, NJ 08648
Fax: 800-FAX-ON-US   Fr: 800-468-4227
URL: http://www.cambridgeeducational.com

$89.95. 2001. 18 minutes.

★6600★ Visiting Nurse Associations of America (VNAA)

99 Summer St., Ste. 1700
Boston, MA 02110
Ph: (617)737-3200   Fax: (617)737-1144
Fr: 800-426-2547
E-mail: vnaa@vnaa.org
URL: http://www.vnaa.org

Members: Voluntary, nonprofit home health care agencies. **Purpose:** Develops competitive strength among community-based nonprofit visiting nurse organizations; works to strengthen business resources and economic programs through contracting, marketing, governmental affairs and publications.

Loan Officers

SOURCES OF HELP-WANTED ADS

★6601★ *American Banker*
American Banker/Bond Buyer Inc.
1 State St. Plz.
New York, NY 10004
Ph: (212)803-8200   Fax: (212)843-9600
Fr: 800-982-0633
URL: http://www.americanbanker.com

Daily. $775.00/year. Newspaper for senior executives in banking and other financial services industries. Coverage includes trends, analysis, and statistics of the legislative scene in Washington; finance; mortgages; technology; small business; and regional banking.

★6602★ *Mortgage Banking Magazine*
Mortgage Bankers Association of America
1919 Pennsylvania Ave. NW
Washington, DC 20006-3438
Ph: (202)557-2700   Fax: (202)721-0245
Fr: 800-793-MBAA
URL: http://
www.mortgagebankingmagazine.com/

Monthly. $15.00 for single issue; $69.95/year for nonmembers; $110.00/year for two years; $74.95/year for Canada and foreign subscriptions. Magazine of the real estate finance industry.

★6603★ *National Mortgage News*
Thomson Financial
195 Broadway
New York, NY 10007
Ph: (646)822-2000
E-mail: nmnews@aol.com

$198.00/year for individuals. Newspaper for mortgage lenders and investment bankers.

★6604★ *Northwestern Financial Review*
NFR Communications Inc.
4948 Washburn Ave.S.
Minneapolis, MN 55410
Ph: (612)929-8110   Fax: (612)929-8146

E-mail: web@nfrcom.com
URL: http://www.nfrcom.com

Bimonthly. $89.00/year for individuals; $160.00 for two years; $5.00/year for single issue. Trade publication covering commercial banking.

★6605★ *Servicing Management*
LDJ Corp.
70 Edwin Ave.
PO Box 2330
Waterbury, CT 06722
Ph: (203)755-0158   Fax: (203)755-3480
Fr: 800-325-6745

Monthly. $48.00/year for individuals; $8.00 for single issue. Trade magazine for mortgage professionals involved with mortgage loan servicing.

★6606★ *U.S. Banker*
Thomson Financial
195 Broadway
New York, NY 10007
Ph: (646)822-2000
URL: http://www.electronicbanker.com

Monthly. $59.00/year for individuals. Magazine serving the financial services industry.

PLACEMENT AND JOB REFERRAL SERVICES

★6607★ **National Bankers Association (NBA)**
1513 P St. NW
Washington, DC 20005
Ph: (202)588-5432   Fax: (202)588-5443
E-mail: nahart@nationalbankers.org
URL: http://www.nationalbankers.org/

Members: Minority banking institutions owned by minority individuals and institutions. **Purpose:** Serves as an advocate for the minority banking industry. Organizes banking services, government relations, marketing, scholarship, and technical assis-

tance programs. **Activities:** Offers placement services; compiles statistics.

EMPLOYER DIRECTORIES AND NETWORKING LISTS

★6608★ *American Banker-Top Commercial Banks by Assets, Deposits*
American Banker/Bond Buyer Inc.
1 State St. Plz.
New York, NY 10004
Ph: (212)803-8200   Fax: (212)843-9600
Fr: 800-982-0633

Semiannual, March and September. $25.00. Publication includes: List of the top 300 commercial banks. Entries include: Name of bank, headquarters, amount of deposits at the previous quarter, place in rank at quarter. Arrangement: Ranked by deposits and assets. Indexes: Geographical.

★6609★ *American Banker-Top Finance Companies Issue*
American Banker/Bond Buyer Inc.
1 State St. Plz.
New York, NY 10004
Ph: (212)803-8200   Fax: (212)843-9600
Fr: 800-982-0633

Annual, December. $25.00. Publication includes: List of top finance companies with $10 million or more in capital funds. Entries include: Finance company name, headquarters, city; rankings of net receivables by type, business, consumer, and other; total capital funds for two preceding years; capital and surplus, total assets, net receivables, net income, deferred income, receivables acquired, and amount of bank credit at end of the preceding year. Arrangement: Ranked by size of capital funds.

★6610★ American Banker-Top 300 Mortgage Companies Issue

American Banker/Bond Buyer Inc.
1 State St. Plz.
New York, NY 10004
Ph: (212)803-8200   Fax: (212)843-9600
Fr: 800-982-0633

Annual, October. $25.00. Entries include: Company name, headquarters city, rank; dollar value of mortgages serviced for current and prior year; prior year's rank and gain in rank; number of mortgages; number of investors. Arrangement: Ranked by total dollar value of mortgages.

★6611★ American Banker-Top 300 Thrifts by Deposits

American Banker/Bond Buyer Inc.
1 State St. Plz.
New York, NY 10004
Ph: (212)803-8200   Fax: (212)843-9600
Fr: 800-982-0633

Semiannual, May and November. $25.00. Publication includes: List of top 300 thrift institutions. Entries include: Name of institution, city, rank; total assets, deposits, and total capital. Arrangement: Ranked by deposits, assets, and risk-based capital ratios.

★6612★ Branches of Your State: Banks, Savings and Loans, Credit Unions, & Savings Banks

Sheshunoff Information Services
807 Las Cimas Pkwy., Ste. 300
Austin, TX 78746
Ph: (512)472-2244   Fax: (512)305-6575
Fr: 800-456-2340

Annual, February. $475.00. Covers in separate state editions, banks, savings and loan branches, and credit unions. For those states without branch banking, individual banks, savings and loan institutions, and credit unions are listed. Entries include: Institution name, address, institution type, deposit totals, percent change over 12 months, percentage share of parent company's total deposits. Arrangement: Geographical.

★6613★ Corporate Finance Sourcebook

LexisNexis Group
121 Chanlon Rd.
New Providence, NJ 07974
Ph: (908)464-6800   Fax: (908)771-7704
Fr: 800-526-4902
URL: http://www.financesourcebook.com/cfs_info.htm

Annual, November. $689.00. Covers securities research analysts; major private lenders; investment banking firms; commercial banks; United States-based foreign banks; commercial finance firms; leasing companies; foreign investment bankers in the United States; pension managers; banks that offer master trusts; cash managers; business insurance brokers; business real estate specialists; lists about 3,400 firms; 14,500 key financial experts. Entries include: Firm name, address, phone, e-mail, and names

and titles of officers, contacts, or specialists in corporate finance. Additional details are given as appropriate, including names of major clients, number of companies served, services, total assets, branch locations, years in business. Arrangement: Classified by line of business and then alphabetized within that line of business. Indexes: Firm name, personnel name, geographical.

★6614★ Employment Opportunities, USA

Washington Research Associates
1090 Vermont Ave., NW, Ste. 800
Washington, DC 20005
Ph: (202)408-7025

Annual, quarterly updates. $184.00. Publication includes: List of over 1,000 employment contacts in companies and agencies in the banking, arts, telecommunications, education, and 14 other industries and professions, including the federal government. Entries include: Company name, name of representative, address, description of products or services, hiring and recruiting practices, training programs, and year established. Principal content is industry overviews, career news, employment opportunity information on 14 different job markets, and comprehensive guidance to career resources on the Internet. Arrangement: Classified by industry. Indexes: Occupation.

★6615★ Mergent Bank and Finance Manual

Mergent Inc.
5250 77 Center Dr., Ste. 150
Charlotte, NC 28217
Ph: (704)559-7601   Fax: (704)559-6945
Fr: 800-342-5647
URL: http://www.mergent.com

Annual, July; supplements in 'Mergent Bank & Finance News Reports'. $2,095.00. Covers in four volumes, over 12,000 national, state, and private banks, savings and loans, mutual funds, unit investment trusts, and insurance and real estate companies in the United States. Entries include: Company name, headquarters and branch offices, phones, names and titles of principal executives, directors, history, Moody's rating, and extensive financial and statistical data. Arrangement: Classified by type of business. Indexes: Company name.

★6616★ National Bankers Association-Roster of Minority Banking Institutions

National Bankers Association
1513 P St. NW
Washington, DC 20005
Ph: (202)588-5432   Fax: (202)588-5443

Annual, October. $5.00. Covers about 140 banks owned or controlled by minority group persons or women. Entries include: Bank name, address, phone, name of one executive. Arrangement: Geographical.

★6617★ Peterson's Job Opportunities for Business Majors

Thomson Peterson's
Princeton Pke. Corporate Ctr., 2000 Lenox Dr.
PO Box 67005
Lawrenceville, NJ 08648
Ph: (609)896-1800   Fax: (609)896-4531
Fr: 800-338-3282
URL: http://www.petersons.com

Irregular, latest edition 2000 - 16th ed. $18.95. Covers the 2,000 largest U.S. employers hiring in several fields, including financial services, management consulting, consumer products, and media/ entertainment. Entries include: Organization name, address, phone, name and title of contact, number of employees, type of organization. Arrangement: Alphabetical. Indexes: Type of organization.

★6618★ Roster of Minority Financial Institutions

U.S. Department of the Treasury
1500 Pennsylvania Ave. NW
Washington, DC 20220
Ph: (202)622-2000

Biennial. Covers about 170 commercial, minority-owned and controlled financial institutions participating in the Department of the Treasury's Minority Bank Deposit Program. Entries include: Name of institution, name and title of chief officer, address, phone, fax. Arrangement: Geographical.

★6619★ Thomson Bank Directory

Thomson Financial Publishing
4709 W.Golf Rd., Ste. 600
Skokie, IL 60076
Ph: (847)676-9600   Fax: (847)933-8101
Fr: 800-321-3373
URL: http://www.tgbr.com

Semiannual, June and December. $608.00; $509.00 for annual subscription. Covers in three volumes, about 11,000 banks and 50,000 branches of United States banks, and 60,000 foreign banks and branches engaged in foreign banking; Federal Reserve system and other United States government and state government banking agencies; 500 largest North American and International commercial banks; paper and automated clearinghouses. Volumes 1 and 2 contain North American listings; volumes 3 and 4, international listings (also cited as 'Thomson International Bank Directory'); volume 5, Worldwide Correspondents Guide containing key correspondent data to facilitate funds transfer. Entries include: For domestic banks-Bank name, address, phone, telex, cable, date established, routing number, charter type, bank holding company affiliation, memberships in Federal Reserve System and other banking organizations, principal officers by function performed, principal correspondent banks, and key financial data (deposits, etc.). For international banks-Bank name, address, phone, fax, telex, cable, SWIFT address, transit or sort codes within home country, ownership, financial data, names and titles of key personnel, branch locations. For branches-Bank name, address, phone, charter type, ownership and other details comparable to domestic bank listings. Arrangement: Geographical. Indexes: Alphabetical, geographical.

★6620★ **Thomson North American Financial Institutions Directory**

Thomson Financial Publishing
4709 W.Golf Rd., Ste. 600
Skokie, IL 60076
Ph: (847)676-9600   Fax: (847)933-8101
Fr: 800-321-3373

Semiannual. $449.00 for single issue. Covers 15,000 banks and their branches; over 2,000 head offices, and 15,500 branches of savings and loan associations; over 5,500 credit unions with assets over $5 million; Federal Reserve System and other U.S. government and state government banking agencies; bank holding, commercial finance, and leasing companies; coverage includes the United States, Canada, Mexico, and Central America. Entries include: Bank name, address, phone, fax, telex, principal officers and directors, date established, financial data, association memberships, attorney or counsel, correspondent banks, out-of-town branch, holding company affiliation, ABA transit number and routing symbol, MICR number with check digit, credit card(s) issued, trust powers, current par value and dividend of common stock, kind of charter. Arrangement: Geographical. Indexes: Alphabetical.

★6621★ **Who's Who in Finance and Industry**

Marquis Who's Who
121 Chanlon Rd.
New Providence, NJ 07974
Ph: (908)673-1101   Fax: (908)673-1189
Fr: 800-473-7020
URL: http://www.marquiswhoswho.com

Biennial, July of odd years. $292.50. Covers over 21,000 individuals. Entries include: Name, home and office addresses, personal, career, and family data; civic and political activities; memberships, publications, awards. Arrangement: Alphabetical.

HANDBOOKS AND MANUALS

★6622★ **Careers in Banking and Finance**

Rosen Publishing Group, Inc.
29 E. 21st St.
New York, NY 10010
Ph: (212)777-3017   Fax: 888-436-4643
Fr: 800-237-9932

Patricia Haddock. 2001. $16.95 139 pages. Offers advice on job hunting. Describes jobs at all levels in banking and finance. Contains information about the types of financial organizations where the jobs are found, educational requirements, job duties, and salaries.

★6623★ **Opportunities in Banking Careers**

McGraw-Hill Trade
2 Penn Plaza
New York, NY 10121
Ph: (212)904-2000   Fr: 800-722-4726

Philip Perry. 1994. $14.95; $11.95 (paper). 160 pages. Discusses banking opportunities in a variety of settings: commercial banks, savings and loans, finance companies, and mortgage banks.

★6624★ **Opportunities in Financial Careers**

McGraw-Hill Trade
2 Penn Plaza
New York, NY 10121
Ph: (212)904-2000   Fr: 800-722-4726

Michael Sumichrast. 1997. $14.95; $11.95 (paper). 210 pages. A guide to planning for and seeking opportunities in this challenging field.

★6625★ **Opportunities in Real Estate Careers**

McGraw-Hill Professional
2 Penn Plaza
New York, NY 10121
Ph: (212)904-2000   Fr: 800-722-4726
E-mail: ntcpub@tribune.com

Mariwyn Evans. 2002. $15.95; $11.95 (paper). 160 pages.

★6626★ **Resumes for Banking and Financial Careers**

McGraw-Hill Contemporary Books
1221 Avenue of the Americas
New York, NY 10020
Ph: (212)904-2000   Fr: 800-323-4900
E-mail: ntcpub@tribune.com

2001. $10.95 (paper). 468 pages.

★6627★ **Where the Jobs Are: The Hottest Careers for the 90s**

The Career Press, Inc.
3 Tice Rd.
PO Box 687
Franklin Lakes, NJ 07417-1322
Ph: (201)848-0310   Fax: (201)848-1727
Fr: 800-227-3371

Joyce Hadley. Third edition, 2000. $13.99 (paper). 400 pages. Out of print. Describes careers in fifteen general fields, from accounting to travel and hospitality.

EMPLOYMENT AGENCIES AND SEARCH FIRMS

★6628★ **Financial Professionals**

4100 Spring Valley Rd., Ste. 307
Dallas, TX 75244
Ph: (972)991-8999   Fax: (972)702-0776

Executive search consultants with additional offices in Forth Worth and Houston.

★6629★ **J.B. Brown and Associates**

50Public Square, Ste. 820
Cleveland, OH 44113
Ph: (216)696-2525

Employment agency and executive recruiter.

★6630★ **The Murphy Group**

245 W Roosevelt Rd., Bldg.15 Ste.101
Chicago, IL 60185
Ph: (630)639-5110   Fax: (630)639-5113
E-mail: info@murphygroup.com
URL: http://www.murphygroup.com

Employment agency. Places personnel in a variety of positions. Additional offices located in Napierville, Park Ridge, and OakBrook.

★6631★ **Romac International, Inc.**

1001 E Palm Ave
Tampa, FL 33605
Ph: (813)552-5239   Fax: (813)552-2122
URL: http://www.romac.com

Executive search firm. More than 30 locations throughout the United States.

OTHER SOURCES

★6632★ **American Bankers Association (ABA)**

1120 Connecticut Ave. NW
Washington, DC 20036
Ph: (202)663-5000   Fax: (202)663-7543
Fr: 800-BAN-KERS
E-mail: mwhitake@aba.com
URL: http://www.aba.com

Members: Principally commercial banks and trust companies; combined assets of members represent approximately 90% of the U.S. banking industry; approximately 94% of members are community banks with less than $500 million in assets. **Purpose:** Seeks to enhance the role of commerical bankers as preeminent providers of financial services through communications, research, legal action, lobbying of federal legislative and regulatory bodies, and education and training programs. Serves as spokesperson for the banking industry; facilitates exchange of information among members. Maintains the American Institute of Banking, an industry-sponsored adult education program. **Activities:** Conducts educational and training programs for bank employees and officers through a wide range of banking schools and national conferences. Maintains liaison with federal bank regulators; lobbies Congress on issues affecting commercial banks; testifies before congressional committees; represents members in U.S. postal rate proceedings. Serves as secretariat of the International Monetary Conference and the Financial Institutions Committee for the American National Standards Institute. Files briefs and lawsuits in major court cases affecting the industry. Conducts teleconferences with state banking associations on such issues as regulatory compliance; works to build consensus and coordinate activities of leading bank and financial service trade groups. Provides services to members including: public advocacy; news media contact; insurance program providing directors and officers with liability coverage, financial institution bond, and trust errors and omissions coverage; research service operated through ABA Center for Banking Information; fingerprint set processing in conjunction with the Federal Bureau of Investigation; discounts on operational and income-producing projects through the Corporation for American Banking. Conducts conferences, forums, and workshops covering subjects such as small business, consumer credit, agricultural and community banking, trust management, bank operations, and automation. Sponsors ABA Educational Foundation and the Personal Economics Program, which educates schoolchildren and the community on banking, economics, and personal finance.

★6633★ **American League of Financial Institutions (ALFI)**
900 19th St. NW, Ste. 400
Washington, DC 20006
Ph: (202)857-6176   Fax: (202)296-8716
URL: http://www.alfi.org

Members: Federal and state chartered minority savings and loan associations in 25 states and the District of Columbia. **Purpose:** Undertakes programs to increase the income of and savings flow into the associations including a direct solicitation effort; provides counseling and technical assistance for member associations; offers consultant services to assist individual associations and groups wishing to organize new associations or acquire existing associations with development potential; collects, organizes, and distributes materials that will aid member associations. **Activities:** Conducts research to improve investment capability, resolve common management problems, and evaluate statistical data on an industry-wide basis to develop and institute training programs for management personnel. Conducts research programs.

★6634★ **Bank Administration Institute (BAI)**
1 N. Franklin St., Ste. 1000
Chicago, IL 60606
Ph: (312)653-2464   Fax: (312)683-2373
E-mail: info@bai.org
URL: http://www.bai.org

Description: Works to improve the competitive position of banking companies through strategic research and educational offerings.

★6635★ **Financial Managers Society (FMS)**
100 W Monroe, Ste. 810
Chicago, IL 60603
Ph: (312)578-1300   Fax: (312)578-1308
Fr: 800-275-4367
E-mail: info@fmsinc.org
URL: http://www.fmsinc.org

Purpose: Technical information exchange for financial managers of financial institutions.

★6636★ *Financial Occupations*
Delphi Productions
3160 4th St.
Boulder, CO 80304
Fax: (303)443-4022   Fr: 888-443-2400
URL: http://www.delphivideo.com

$95.00. 50 minutes. Part of the Careers for the 21st Century Video Library.

★6637★ **Risk Management Association**
1 Liberty Pl.
1650 Market St., Ste. 2300
Philadelphia, PA 19103-7398
Ph: (215)446-4000   Fax: (215)446-4101
Fr: 800-677-7621
E-mail: member@rmahq.org
URL: http://www.rmahq.org

Members: Commercial and savings banks, and savings and loan, and other financial services companies. **Activities:** Conducts research and professional development activities in areas of loan administration, asset management, and commercial lending and credit to increase professionalism.

Management Analysts and Consultants

SOURCES OF HELP-WANTED ADS

★6638★ Forbes
Forbes Magazine
60 5th Ave.
New York, NY 10011
Ph: (212)620-2200   Fax: (212)206-5174
URL: http://www.forbes.com

Biweekly. $52.00/year; $4.95 for single issue. Magazine reporting on industry, business and finance management.

★6639★ Journal of Staff Development
National Staff Development Council
PO Box 240
Oxford, OH 45056
Ph: (513)523-6029   Fax: (513)523-0638
Fr: 800-727-7288

Quarterly. Professional journal covering administration issues.

★6640★ Organizations and Change
International Registry of Organization
Development Professionals
11234 Walnut Ridge Rd.
Chesterland, OH 44026
Ph: (440)729-7419
URL: http://members.aol.com/odinst

Description: Monthly. Serves organization development professionals, teachers of organizational behavior, management consultants, personnel directors and executives by carrying news items, interest surveys, economic information, and committee reports. Recurring features include announcements of conferences, meetings, publications, consulting opportunities, and employment openings. Subscription includes annual publication titled *The International Registry of Organization Development Professionals and Organization Development Handbook,* and copies of *The Organizational Development Journal.*

★6641★ Supply Chain Management Review
Reed Business Information
275 Washington St.
Newton, MA 02458-1630
Ph: (617)964-3030

Bimonthly. Publication covering business and management.

★6642★ T & D Magazine
American Society for Training &
Development
PO Box 1443
Alexandria, VA 22313-2043
Ph: (703)683-8100   Fax: (703)683-8103
Fr: 800-NAT-ASTD
URL: http://www.astd.org

Monthly. $99.00/year for U.S.; $165.00/year for other countries. Magazine on training and development.

PLACEMENT AND JOB REFERRAL SERVICES

★6643★ Franchise Consultants International Association (FCIA)
5147 S Angela Rd.
Memphis, TN 38117
Ph: (901)368-3361   Fax: (901)368-1144
E-mail: franmark@msn.com

Members: Individuals and corporations involved in franchising including attorneys, consultants, brokers, sales personnel, suppliers, Universities, consultants, advertisers, and developers. **Purpose:** To provide standardized information for the franchise industry. Seeks to coordinate effective and professional franchise consulting and to educate members in franchise law and logistics. Serves as a clearinghouse of approved literature on franchising. **Activities:** Operates archive and hall of fame; compiles statistics. Provides placement service, charitable program, and speakers' bureau. Has extensive library. Expert witness specialists.

EMPLOYER DIRECTORIES AND NETWORKING LISTS

★6644★ ACMF-The Association of Management Consulting Firms-Directory of Members
ACMF
380 Lexington Ave., No. 1699
New York, NY 10168-0002
URL: http://www.acmeworld.org

Biennial, previous edition 1994, latest edition 1996. $50.00. Covers about 50 management consulting firms that are members of ACMF. Entries include: Firm name, address, description of services offered, areas of expertise, locations of branch offices and affiliates. Arrangement: Alphabetical. Indexes: Classified by industry and specialty.

★6645★ Business Management Consultants Directory
infoUSA Inc.
5711 S 86th Cir.
Omaha, NE 68127-0347
Ph: (402)930-3500   Fax: (402)331-0176
Fr: 800-555-6124
URL: http://www.abii.com

Annual. Number of listings: 51,839. Entries include: Name, address, phone (including area code), size of advertisement, year first in "Yellow Pages," name of owner or manager, number of employees. Compiled from telephone company "Yellow Pages," nationwide. Arrangement: Geographical.

★6646★ Business: The Ultimate Resource
Perseus Publishing
Eleven Cambridge Ctr.
Cambridge, MA 02142
Ph: (617)252-5200   Fax: (617)252-5275

$59.95. Covers more than 3,000 business resource web sites, organizations, books, journals, and magazines. Indexes: Alphabetical.

★6647★ Consultants and Consulting Organizations Directory

Thomson Gale
27500 Drake Rd.
Farmington Hills, MI 48331-3535
Ph: (248)699-4253   Fax: (248)699-8065
Fr: 800-877-GALE
E-mail: businessproducts@gale.com
URL: http://www.gale.com

Annual, with inter-edition supplement. $865.00. Covers over 25,000 firms, individuals, and organizations active in consulting. Entries include: Individual or organization name, address, phone, fax, e-mail, URL, specialties, founding date, branch offices, names and titles of key personnel, number of employees, financial data, publications, seminars and workshops. Arrangement: By broad subject categories. Indexes: Subject, geographical, organization name.

★6648★ Consultants in the Midwest

Midwest Society of Professional
   Consultants
640 Camelot Dr.
La Grange, IL 60525
Ph: (630)734-0211   Fax: (630)734-0212
URL: http://www.mspc.org/

Annual. $60.00; Free. Covers members of the Midwest Society of Professional Consultants. Entries include: Individual member profiles, brief descriptions of each member's background, experience, and expertise. Arrangement: Alphabetical. Indexes: Company name and area of specialization.

★6649★ D & B Consultants Directory

Dun & Bradstreet
3 Sylvan Way
Parsippany, NJ 07054-3896
Fax: (973)605-6911   Fr: 800-526-0651
URL: http://www.dnb.com

Annual. $345.00 for public libraries; $425.00 commercially. Covers top 30,000 U.S. consulting firms in more than 200 areas of specialization. Entries include: Firm name, address, phone, sales, number of employees, year established, description of service, other locations, names and titles of key personnel, reference to parent company, D&B DUNS number, trade name, consulting activity, owned companies clientele, territory served, number of accounts, stock exchange symbol and indicator for publicly owned companies. Arrangement: Complete consultants profiles appear in the consultants alphabetical section. Companies are cross-referenced geographically and by activity. Indexes: All companies with a primary or secondary Standard Industrial Classification (SIC) code of 8748 "Business Consulting Services," as well as those companies whose type of business description includes the word "consult." All companies must have a phone number and be either a headquarters or single location.

★6650★ Directory of Certified Business Counselors

Institute of Certified Business Counselors
PO Box 7214
Eugene, OR 97401-0001
Ph: (541)345-8064   Fax: (541)349-0753

Irregular, updated as necessary. Covers 160 member counselors, brokers, and attorneys qualified to act as advisors for persons with business problems. Entries include: Name, address, phone, business specialty. Arrangement: Alphabetical.

★6651★ Directory of Management Consultants

Kennedy Information Inc.
One Phoenix Mill Ln., 5th Fl.
Peterborough, NH 03458
Ph: (603)924-1006   Fax: (603)924-4460
Fr: 800-531-0007

Biennial, latest edition 2003. $295.00. Covers over 2,500 management consulting firms in North America. Entries include: Firm name, address, phone, fax, e-mail, name of principal executive, date founded, staff size and revenue (in range), services offered, SIC numbers of industries served, plus brief description of firm. For commercial use requests, please contact publisher. Arrangement: Alphabetical. Indexes: Geographical, key principals, services, industries.

★6652★ Institute of Management Consultants-Management Consultants Resource Guide

Institute of Management Consultants
2025 M St. NW, Ste. 800
Washington, DC 20036-3309
Ph: (202)367-1134   Fax: (202)367-2134
Fr: 800-221-2557
URL: http://www.imcusa.org

Database covers: 2,800 individuals who practice management consulting as individuals or members of firms worldwide. Database includes: Name, firm, address, phone; fax; email; website; areas of competence for certified management consultants. Arrangement: Classified by alphabetically. Indexes: Geographical, industry specialization, consulting practice areas.

★6653★ Manager's Handbook: Everything You Need to Know about How Business and Management Work

Pearson Learning
135 S. Mount Zion Rd.
PO Box 2500
Lebanon, IN 46052
Ph: 800-526-9907   Fax: 800-393-3156

$24.95. Publication includes: Business directory representing key areas of management in Canada and the United States. Principal content of publication is reference guide for new and experienced managers. Indexes: Alphabetical.

★6654★ MBA Employment Guide Report

Association of MBA Executives Inc.
388 E Main St., Ste. A
Branford, CT 06405-3527
Ph: (203)315-5221   Fax: (203)483-6186

Continuous. Database covers more than 4,000 firms that employ persons with Master of Business Administration degrees. More detailed profiles are given for 100 firms selected on the basis of their on-campus recruitment activity. Custom reports are issued upon request at $10.00 per report. Database includes: For companies covered in detail-Name, headquarters location, description of business, current recruitment objectives, employment policies, benefits offered, name and address of employment representative, financial data. For others-Name, location, contact person and telephone number, parent company (if any), code for primary line of business.

★6655★ Peterson's Job Opportunities for Business Majors

Thomson Peterson's
Princeton Pke. Corporate Ctr., 2000
   Lenox Dr.
PO Box 67005
Lawrenceville, NJ 08648
Ph: (609)896-1800   Fax: (609)896-4531
Fr: 800-338-3282
URL: http://www.petersons.com

Irregular, latest edition 2000 - 16th ed. $18.95. Covers the 2,000 largest U.S. employers hiring in several fields, including financial services, management consulting, consumer products, and media/ entertainment. Entries include: Organization name, address, phone, name and title of contact, number of employees, type of organization. Arrangement: Alphabetical. Indexes: Type of organization.

★6656★ Professional and Technical Consultants Association-Directory of Consultants

Professional and Technical Consultants Association
PO Box 78008
San Francisco, CA 94107-8008
Ph: (408)971-5902   Fax: (408)999-0344
Fr: 800-747-2822
URL: http://www.patca.org

Annual, January. $15.00. Covers more than 350 consultants involved in computer technology, management, marketing, manufacturing, engineering, etc. Entries include: Individual or firm name, address, phone, specialties, degrees held. Arrangement: Alphabetical. Indexes: Specialty, geographical.

★6657★ Project Management Step-by-Step

AMACOM
1601 Broadway, 12th Fl.
New York, NY 10019-7420
Ph: (212)586-8100   Fax: (212)903-8168
Fr: 800-262-9699

$27.95. Publication includes: List of resources for project management. Principal content of publication is information on the theory and practice of project management. Indexes: Alphabetical.

★6658★ *Turning Research into Results: A Guide to Selecting the Right Performance Solutions*
CEP Press
1100 Johnson Ferry Rd., Ste. 150
Atlanta, GA 30342
Ph: (770)458-4080   Fr: 800-558-4CEP
$26.95. Publication includes: Extensive list of references in the management field. Principal content of publication is an explanation of ways to implement change in an organization's structure and operating culture. Indexes: Alphabetical.

HANDBOOKS AND MANUALS

★6659★ *Become a Successful Consultant: Manage & Market Your Skills Effectively*
Atrium Publishers Group
1501 County Hospital Rd.
Nashville, TN 37218
Ph: (615)254-2450   Fax: (615)254-2405
Fr: 800-327-5113
Raymond Hebson. 1995. $15.95. 96 pages.

★6660★ *Developing a Consulting Practice (Survival Skills for Scholars, Vol. 3)*
Sage Publications, Inc.
2455 Teller Rd.
Thousand Oaks, CA 91320-2218
Ph: (805)499-0721   Fax: (805)499-0871
Robert O. Metzger. 1993. Volume 3. Survival Skills for Scholars Series. $37.00; $16.50 (paper). 138 pages. Out of print.

★6661★ *How to Be Your Own Management Consultant: Consultant Tools and Techniques to Improve Your Business*
Kogan Page, Ltd.
22 Broad St., Suite 34
Milford, CT 06460
Calvert Markham. 2002.

★6662★ *Opportunities in Business Management Careers*
McGraw-Hill Contemporary Books
1221 Avenue of the Americas
New York, NY 10020
Ph: (212)904-2000   Fr: 800-323-4900
E-mail: ntcpub@tribune.com
Irene Place and Lewis Baratz. 1997. $14.95; $11.95 (paper). 160 pages. Provides guidance on the most effective channels to management positions.

★6663★ *Rasputin for Hire: An Inside Look at Management Consulting Between Jobs or as a Second Career*
Dialogue Press
155 Roseville Rd.
Westport, CT 06880-2615
Ph: (203)226-8824   Fax: (203)226-1823
Michael A. Goodman. February 2004. $19.95 (paper). 213 pages.

★6664★ *So You Want to Be a Consultant*
Black Forrest Press
914 Nolan Way
Chula Vista, CA 91911-2408
Ph: (619)656-8048   Fax: (619)482-8704
Harry E. Chandler. 1993. $59.95.

★6665★ *The 10 Hottest Consulting Practices: What They Are, How to Get into Them*
John Wiley & Sons, Inc.
111 River St.
Hoboken, NJ 07030-5774
Ph: (201)748-6000   Fax: (201)748-6088
Fr: 800-225-5945
Ron Tepper. 1995. $27.95. 210 pages.

EMPLOYMENT AGENCIES AND SEARCH FIRMS

★6666★ **A-L Associates Inc.**
546 5th Ave., Fl. 6
New York, NY 10036
Ph: (212)878-9000   Fax: (212)878-9096
Executive search firm.

★6667★ **AD Check Associates Inc.**
204 S. Franklin St.
Wilkes-Barre, PA 18701
Ph: (570)829-5066
Executive search firm.

★6668★ **Allerton Heneghan & O'Neill**
1 Tower Ln., Ste. 1700
Oakbrook Terrace, IL 60181
Ph: (630)645-2294   Fax: (630)645-2298
Executive Search firm.

★6669★ **Ashworth Consultants Inc.**
53 Fulton St.
Boston, MA 02109-1401
Ph: (617)720-0350
Executive search firm.

★6670★ **Baker, Nelms & Montgomery**
980 N. Michigan Ave., Ste. 930
Chicago, IL 60611
Ph: (312)397-8833   Fax: (312)397-9631
Executive search firm.

★6671★ **Banister International**
1 Commerce Square
2005 Market St., Ste. 820
Philadelphia, PA 19103
Ph: (267)256-2300   Fax: (267)330-0333
Executive search firm.

★6672★ **Bartram/Taylor Group LLC**
60 E. 42nd St., Ste. 3204
New York, NY 10165
Ph: (212)692-9644   Fax: (212)370-3627
Executive search firm concentrating on finance.

★6673★ **BeechTree Partners LLC**
401 N. Michigan Ave., Ste. 1200
Chicago, IL 60611
Ph: (312)840-8229   Fax: (773)665-8682
Executive search firm.

★6674★ **Boyden**
360 Lexington Ave., Ste. 1300
New York, NY 10532-1217
Ph: (212)949-9850   Fax: (212)949-5905
E-mail: jrice@boyden.com
URL: http://www.boyden.com/newyork
Executive search firm. Affiliate offices across the country and abroad.

★6675★ **Callan Associates Ltd.**
2021 Spring Rd., Ste. 175
Oak Brook, IL 60523
Fax: (630)574-3099
Executive search firm.

★6676★ **Career Consulting International**
550 Brickell Ave., Ste. 502
Miami, FL 33131-2508
Ph: (305)361-2174
Executive search firm.

★6677★ **Chandler Group**
4165 Shoreline Dr., Ste. 220
Spring Park, MN 55384
Ph: (952)471-3000   Fax: (952)471-3021
Executive search firm.

★6678★ **Charleston Partners**
2 Bellevue Ave.
Rumson, NJ 07760
Ph: (732)842-5015   Fax: (732)842-0993
Executive search firm concentrated on human resource services.

★6679★ The Cheyenne Group
60 E. 42nd St., Ste. 2821
New York, NY 10165
Ph: (212)471-5000   Fax: (212)471-5050
Executive search firm.

★6680★ CMSI Consulting LLC
14580 SW 87th Ave., Ste. 1G
Miami, FL 33176
Ph: (305)969-0683   Fax: (212)202-4096
Fr: 800-713-0093
Executive search firm.

★6681★ The Cooke Group Inc.
1001 W. Glen Oaks Lane, Ste. 102
Mequon, WI 53092
Ph: (262)241-9843   Fax: (262)241-1004
Fr: 888-432-7800
Executive search firm.

★6682★ Cowell & Associates Ltd.
819 Keystone Ave.
River Forest, IL 60305-1319
Ph: (708)771-8989   Fax: (708)771-1788
Executive search firm.

★6683★ Custom Research Solutions
5450 Katella, Ste. 104
Los Alamitos, CA 90720
Ph: (562)431-6690
Executive search firm.

★6684★ De Funiak & Edwards
1602 Hidden Hills Trail
Long Beach, IN 46360
Fax: (219)874-5347
Executive search firm.

★6685★ DNPitchon Associates
60 W. Ridgewood Ave.
Ridgewood, NJ 07450
Ph: (201)612-8350
Executive search firm.

★6686★ Drinkwater & Associates
167 West St.
Beverly, MA 01915
Ph: (978)922-3676
Executive search firm.

★6687★ DuVall & Associates
4203 Costa Salada
San Clemente, CA 92673
Ph: (949)488-8790   Fax: (949)488-8793
Executive search firm specializing in management team placement.

★6688★ Executive Search Consultants International Inc.
Empire State Bldg.
3505th Ave., Ste. 5501
New York, NY 10118
Ph: (212)330-1900   Fax: (212)330-1906
Executive search firm.

★6689★ Executive Search Consultants LLC
149 Shortwoods Rd.
New Fairfield, CT 06812
Ph: (203)746-7265   Fax: (203)746-7265
Executive search firm.

★6690★ The Executive Source Inc.
55 5th Ave., Fl. 19
New York, NY 10003-4301
Ph: (212)691-5505   Fax: (212)691-9839
Executive search firm.

★6691★ Explore Company
1054 31st St. NW, Ste. 330
Washington, DC 20007
Ph: (202)333-3473
Executive search firm.

★6692★ The Finnegan Partnerships
PO Box 1183
Palos Verdes Estates, CA 90274-1938
Ph: (310)377-4762
Executive search firm.

★6693★ Foy, Schneid & Daniel Inc.
575 Madison Ave., Ste. 1006
New York, NY 10022
Ph: (212)980-2525
Executive search firm with a second location Ridgefield, CT.

★6694★ Hawkes Peers
224 Fifth Ave., Floor 6
New York, NY 10001
Ph: (212)624-4070   Fax: (212)624-4089
E-mail: info@hawkespeers.com
URL: http://www.hawkespeers.com
Executive search firm specializing in the areas of banking and sales.

★6695★ Heidrick and Struggles, Inc.
233 S. Wacker Dr., Ste. 4200
Sears Tower
Chicago, IL 60606-6303
Ph: (312)496-1200   Fax: (312)496-1290
URL: http://www.heidrick.com
Executive search firm. International organization with a variety of affiliate offices.

★6696★ Hintz Associates, Inc.
196 Prospect Ave.
Valhalla, NY 10595-1831
Ph: (914)761-4227   Fax: (914)948-8630
E-mail: geohintz@aol.com
URL: http://www.hintz.bigstep.com
Executive search firm specializing in cost reduction analysis and internal/external consultants.

★6697★ Intech Summit Group, Inc.
5075 Shoreham Pl., Ste. 280
San Diego, CA 92122
Ph: (858)452-2100   Fax: (858)452-8500
E-mail: isg@isgsearch.com
URL: http://www.isgsearch.com
Employment agency and executive recruiter with a branch in Carlsbad, CA.

★6698★ Kenmore Executives Inc.
2821 Spanish River Rd
Boca Raton, FL 33432
Ph: (561)392-0700   Fax: (561)750-0818
E-mail: inquires@kenmoreexecutives.com
URL: http://www.kenmoreexecutives.com
Executive search firm that works with consultants in a variety of fields.

★6699★ Korn/Ferry International
200 Park Ave., Floor 37
New York, NY 10166
Ph: (212)687-1834   Fax: (212)986-5684
URL: http://www.kornferry.com
Executive search firm. International organization with a variety of affiliate offices.

★6700★ Protocol Agency Inc.
2659 Townsgate Rd., Ste.203
Westlake Village, CA 91361-2774
Ph: (626)449-2214   Fax: (805)371-0048
E-mail: wiv@protocalagency.com
URL: http://www.protocolagency.com
Executive search firm focusing on a variety of placements.

★6701★ Ronald Dukes Associates LLC
20 N. Wacker Dr., Ste. 2010
Chicago, IL 60606
Ph: (312)357-2895   Fax: (312)357-2897
Executive search firm focus on the industrial and automotive industries.

★6702★ Russell Reynolds Associates, Inc.
200 Park Ave., Ste. 2300
New York, NY 10166-0002
Ph: (212)351-2000   Fax: (212)370-0896
E-mail: info@russellreynolds.com
URL: http://www.russelreynolds.com
Executive search firm. Affiliate offices across the country and abroad.

★6703★ Systems Careers
211 Sutter St., Ste. 607
San Francisco, CA 94108
Ph: (415)434-4770
Executive search firm and employment agency.

★6704★ Valerie Fredrickson & Company
800 Menlo Ave., Ste. 220
Menlo Park, CA 94025
Ph: (650)614-0220   Fax: (650)614-0223
Executive search firm.

ONLINE JOB SOURCES AND SERVICES

★6705★ Careers in Business
E-mail: wtunstall@careerselector.com
URL: http://careers-in-business.com
Description: Job search site with concentration in business, finance, consulting, marketing and non-profit related careers. Seekers may search database or post resume, plus review resources list for further information.

TRADESHOWS

★6706★ Association of Career Management Consulting Firms International Annual Conference
Association of Career Management Consulting Firms International
204 E St. NE
Washington, DC 20002
Ph: (202)547-6344   Fax: (202)547-6348
URL: http://www.aocfi.org
Annual. **Primary Exhibits:** Exhibits relating for outplacement consultants, who counsel and assist in job searching, as well as educate about the techniques and practices of choosing a career.

★6707★ Organization Development Network Conference
Organization Development Network
71 Valley St., Ste. 301
South Orange, NJ 07079-2825
Ph: (973)763-7337   Fax: (973)763-7488
URL: http://www.odnet.org
Annual. **Primary Exhibits:** Exhibits related to organization development.

OTHER SOURCES

★6708★ Administration and Management Occupations
Delphi Productions
3160 4th St.
Boulder, CO 80304
Fax: (303)443-4022   Fr: 888-443-2400
URL: http://www.delphivideo.com
$95.00. 50 minutes. Part of the Careers for the 21st Century Video Library.

★6709★ American Almanac of Jobs and Salaries
Morrow Avon
1350 Avenue of the Americas
New York, NY 10019
Ph: (212)261-6788   Fr: 800-242-7737
John W. Wright. Revised edition, 2000. $20.00 (paper). 672 pages. This is a comprehensive guide to the wages of hundreds of occupations in a wide variety of industries and organizations.

★6710★ Association of Management Consulting Firms (AMCF)
380 Lexington Ave., No. 1700
New York, NY 10168-0002
Ph: (218)551-7887   Fax: (212)551-7934
E-mail: info@amcf.org
URL: http://www.amcf.org
Description: Trade association for consulting organizations that provide a broad range of managerial services to commercial, industrial, governmental and other organizations and individuals. Seeks to unite management consulting firms in order to develop and improve professional standards and practice in the field. Offers information and referral services on management consultants; administers public relations program. Conducts research. Monitors regulatory environment.

★6711★ Budget and Management Analyst
Vocational Biographies, Inc.
PO Box 31
Sauk Centre, MN 56378-0031
Ph: (612)352-6516   Fax: (612)352-5546
Fr: 800-255-0752
1992. $5.00. Four-page pamphlet containing a personal narrative about a worker's job, work likes and dislikes, career path from high school to the present. Education and training, the rewards and frustrations, and the effects of the job on the rest of the worker's life. The data file portion of this pamphlet gives a concise occupational summary, including work descriptions, working conditions, places of employment, personal characteristics, education and training, job outlook, and salary range.

★6712★ Management Analysts and Consultants
Evon Publishing
832 N 7th Ave.
Iron River, MI 49935
Ph: (906)265-3190
Audiocassette. 1996. $16.95. 32 minutes. Part of the Careers and Vocational Guidance Series. Provides information about the nature of the work, educational requirements, employment outlook, earnings, and work conditions as well as additional related information.

★6713★ Organization Development Institute
11234 Walnut Ridge Rd.
Chesterland, OH 44026
Ph: (440)729-7419   Fax: (440)729-9319
E-mail: donwcole@aol.com
URL: http://www.odinstitute.org
Description: Professionals, students, and individuals interested in organization development. Disseminates information on and promotes a better understanding of organization development worldwide. Conducts specialized education programs. Has developed the International O.D. Code of Ethics and a competency test for individuals wishing to qualify as a Registered Organization Development Consultant. Has developed a statement on the knowledge and skill necessary to be competent in organization development and criteria for the accreditation of OD/OB academic programs. Maintains job and consultant information service. Sponsors International Registry of Organization Development Professionals and Research/ Study Team on Nonviolent Large Systems Change. Maintains 18 committees including an International Advisory Board.

★6714★ Organization Development Network (ODNetwork)
71 Valley St., Ste. 301
South Orange, NJ 07079-2825
Ph: (973)763-7337   Fax: (973)763-7448
E-mail: odnetwork@odnetwork.org
URL: http://www.odnetwork.org
Description: Practitioners, academics, managers, and students employed or interested in organization development. Works to enhance and provide opportunities for colleagueship and professional development.

★6715★ Professional and Technical Consultants Association (PATCA)
543 Vista Mar Ave.
Pacifica, CA 94044
Ph: (408)971-5902   Fax: (650)359-3089
Fr: 800-74-PATCA
E-mail: info@patca.org
URL: http://www.patca.org
Description: Independent consultants active in the support of business, industry, and government. Serves as a referral service to aid independent consultants in marketing their services as well as to assist those seeking their services.

Manicurists and Nail Technicians

SOURCES OF HELP-WANTED ADS

★6716★ **Global Cosmetic Industry**
Allured Publishing Corp.
362 S Schmale Rd.
Carol Stream, IL 60188-2787
Ph: (630)480-2997   Fax: (630)653-2192
Monthly. Trade publication covering the cosmetics industry worldwide.

★6717★ **Modern Salon**
Vance Publishing Corp.
400 Knightsbridge Pkwy.
Lincolnshire, IL 60069
Ph: (847)634-2600   Fax: (847)634-4343
Fr: 800-621-2845
E-mail: modernsalon.com
Monthly. $20.00/year for individuals; $4.00 for single issue. Magazine focusing on hairstyling salons for men and women.

★6718★ **Nailpro**
Creative Age Publications Inc.
7628 Densmore Ave.
Van Nuys, CA 91406-2042
Ph: (818)782-7328   Fax: (818)782-7450
Fr: 800-442-5667
E-mail: nailpro@creativeage.com
URL: http://www.nailpro.com
Monthly. $24.00/year for individuals; $5.00 for single issue; $20.00/year for students. Salon owners and nail technicians read Nailpro for continuing education in techniques and services, marketing and management tips, product information and industry news.

★6719★ **SalonNews**
Fairchild Publications Inc.
7 W 34th St.
New York, NY 10001
Ph: (212)630-4000
Monthly. Trade publication covering the hair and beauty salon industries.

★6720★ **Soap and Cosmetics**
Chemical Week Associates
110 Williams St., 11th Fl.
New York, NY 10038
Ph: (212)621-4900   Fax: (212)621-4949
Monthly. Trade publication covering the cosmetics industry.

PLACEMENT AND JOB REFERRAL SERVICES

★6721★ **World International Nail and Beauty Association (WINBA)**
1221 N. Lake View Ave.
Anaheim, CA 92807
Ph: (714)779-9892   Fax: (714)779-9971
Fr: 800-541-9838
Members: Professionals in the nail and skin care industries. **Purpose:** Objectives are to represent the manicure and skin care industry; promote the effective use and application of manicuring and skin care products and equipment; provide a means for mutual communication and joint study; represent the industry before state boards, the Food and Drug Administration, and other regulatory agencies. **Activities:** Conducts seminars; secures discounts on supplies; offers special conducts public relations program; sponsors research and educational programs; compiles statistics. Maintains speakers' bureau and placement service.

EMPLOYER DIRECTORIES AND NETWORKING LISTS

★6722★ **Manicuring Salons Directory**
infoUSA Inc.
5711 S 86th Cir.
Omaha, NE 68127-0347
Ph: (402)930-3500   Fax: (402)331-0176
Fr: 800-555-6124

URL: http://www.abii.com
Annual. Number of listings: 52,194. Entries include: Name, address, phone (including area code), size of advertisement, year first in "Yellow Pages," name of owner or manager, number of employees. Regional editions available: Eastern, $645.00; Western, $610.00. Compiled from telephone company "Yellow Pages," nationwide. Arrangement: Geographical.

HANDBOOKS AND MANUALS

★6723★ **The Art and Science of Nail Technology**
Thomson Learning
7625 Empire Dr.
Florence, KY 41042
Ph: (859)525-6620   Fax: (859)525-0978
Fr: 800-347-7707
Second edition, revised, 1997. $52.95. Part of Nails series. 288 pages.

★6724★ **Career After Cosmetology School: Step-by-Step Guide to a Lucrative Career and Salon Ownership**
Step-by-Step Publications
1645 Westmont Ave.
Campbell, CA 95008
Ph: (408)376-0276   Fax: (408)376-0396
Fr: 800-305-2205
Jessica Brooks. 1997. $29.95. 320 pages.

★6725★ **Cosmetology Career Starter**
LearningExpress, LLC
900 Broadway, Ste. 604
New York, NY 10003
Ph: (212)995-2566   Fax: (212)995-5512
Fr: 800-295-9556
Lorraine Korman. Second edition, 2002.

★6726★ Opportunities in Beauty Culture Careers

McGraw-Hill/Contemporary Books
1221 Avenue of the Americas
New York, NY 10020
Ph: (212)904-2000   Fr: 800-323-4900

Susan W. Gearhart. 1996. $14.95. Part of the Opportunities In... Series.

★6727★ Planning Your Cosmetology Career

Prentice Hall PTR
200 Old Tappan Rd.
Old Tappan, NJ 07675
Ph: (201)236-7000   Fr: 800-223-1360

Mary Murphy-Martin. 1993. $12.90 (paper). 108 pages.

★6728★ The Transition, How to Become a Salon Professional

Thomson Learning
7625 Empire Dr.
Florence, KY 41042
Ph: (859)525-6620   Fax: (859)525-0978
Fr: 800-347-7707

Louise Cotter and Frances L. DuBose. 1996. $19.25. Part of the Cosmetology Series. 352 pages.

TRADESHOWS

★6729★ American Association of Cosmetology Schools Annual Conference

American Association of Cosmetology Schools
15825 N 71st St., Ste. 100
Scottsdale, AZ 85254-1521
Fax: (602)404-8900   Fr: 800-831-1086
URL: http://www.beautyschools.org

Annual. **Primary Exhibits:** Beauty supplies and products, and cosmetology services.

★6730★ American Electrology Association Annual Convention

American Electrology Association
106 Oak Ridge Rd.
Trumbull, CT 06611
Ph: (203)374-6667   Fax: (203)372-7134
URL: http://www.electrology.com

Annual. **Primary Exhibits:** Electrology equipment, supplies, and services.

★6731★ IBS - International Beauty Show, New York

Advanstar Communications Inc.
7500 Old Oak Blvd.
Cleveland, OH 44130
Ph: (440)891-2701   Fax: (440)891-2741
Fr: 800-225-4569
E-mail: info@advantstar.com
URL: http://www.advanstar.com

Annual. **Primary Exhibits:** Beauty and health related equipment, supplies, and services.

★6732★ IBS Seattle - International Beauty Show

Advanstar Communications Inc.
7500 Old Oak Blvd.
Cleveland, OH 44130
Ph: (440)891-2701   Fax: (440)891-2741
Fr: 800-225-4569
E-mail: info@advantstar.com
URL: http://www.advanstar.com

Primary Exhibits: Beauty and healthcare exhibition.

★6733★ Midwest Beauty Show

Chicago Cosmetologists Association
401 N. Michigan
Chicago, IL 60611
Ph: (312)321-6809   Fax: (312)245-1080
Fr: 800-648-2505

Annual. **Primary Exhibits:** Goods and services for the beauty trade.

★6734★ NAILS Show

Bobit Publishing
21061 S. Western Ave.
Torrance, CA 90501
Ph: (310)533-2400   Fax: (310)533-2500

Annual. **Primary Exhibits:** Manicure equipment, supplies, and services.

★6735★ National Beauty Show - HAIRWORLD

National Cosmetology Association
401 N. Michigan Ave.
Chicago, IL 60611-4255
Fr: 800-527-1683
E-mail: nca-now@primary.net
URL: http://www.nca-now.com

Annual. **Primary Exhibits:** Hair products, cosmetics, and jewelry.

OTHER SOURCES

★6736★ National Cosmetology Association (NCA)

401 N Michigan Ave.
Chicago, IL 60611-4255
Ph: (312)527-6757   Fax: (312)464-6118
E-mail: nca1@sba.com
URL: http://www.salonprofessionals.org

Members: Owners of cosmetology salons; cosmetologists. **Activities:** Sponsors National Cosmetology Month and National Beauty Show. Provides special sections for estheticians, school owners, salon owners, and nail technicians. Maintains hall of fame. Conducts educational and charitable programs.

★6737★ Personal & Building Service Occupations

Delphi Productions
3160 4th St.
Boulder, CO 80304
Fax: (303)443-4022   Fr: 888-443-2400
URL: http://www.delphivideo.com

$95.00. 48 minutes. Part of the Careers for the 21st Century Video Library.

★6738★ World International Nail and Beauty Association (WINBA)

1221 N. Lake View Ave.
Anaheim, CA 92807
Ph: (714)779-9892   Fax: (714)779-9971
Fr: 800-541-9838

Members: Professionals in the nail and skin care industries. **Purpose:** Objectives are to represent the manicure and skin care industry; promote the effective use and application of manicuring and skin care products and equipment; provide a means for mutual communication and joint study; represent the industry before state boards, the Food and Drug Administration, and other regulatory agencies. **Activities:** Conducts seminars; secures discounts on supplies; offers special conducts public relations program; sponsors research and educational programs; compiles statistics. Maintains speakers' bureau and placement service.

Manufacturer's Sales Representatives

SOURCES OF HELP-WANTED ADS

★6739★ AATCC Review

American Association of Textile Chemists and Colorists
PO Box 12215
Research Triangle Park, NC 27709
Ph: (919)549-8141   Fax: (919)549-8933
URL: http://www.aatcc.org

Monthly. $180.00/year for U.S. and Canada; $210.00/year for other countries. Magazine focusing on dyeing, finishing of fibers and fabrics.

★6740★ Agency Sales Magazine

Manufacturers' Agents National Association
One Spectrum Pointe, Ste. 150
Lake Forest, CA 92630-2283
Ph: (949)859-4040   Fax: (949)855-2973
E-mail: mana@manaonline.org

Monthly. $54.00/year for individuals; $60.50/year for Canada; $66.50/year for other countries. Magazine for manufacturers' agents and manufacturers. Includes tax developments and tips, management aids for manufacturers and agents, legal bulletins, trend-identifying market data, classified ads.

★6741★ BEDTimes

International Sleep Products Association
501 Wythe St.
Alexandria, VA 22314-1917
Ph: (703)683-8371   Fax: (703)683-4503
E-mail: bedtimes@sleepproducts.org

Monthly. $50.00/year; $65.00/year for other countries. Magazine covering trends and developments in the mattress manufacturing industry.

★6742★ Beverage World

Beverage World
770 Broadway
New York, NY 10003-9595
Ph: (646)654-4500   Fax: (646)654-7727
E-mail: bevworld@aol.com
URL: http://www.beverageworld.com

Monthly. $70.00/year for individuals; $110.00 for two years; $125.00/year for other countries; $165.00 for two years, other countries; $8.00 for single issue. Trade magazine for corporate, marketing, distribution, production, and purchasing top and middle management in the multi-product beverage industry.

★6743★ Bobbin Magazine

Bill Communications Inc.
1500 Hampton St., Ste. 150
Columbia, SC 29202
Ph: (803)771-7500   Fax: (803)779-1461
Fr: 800-845-8820
E-mail: bobbin.pubsinfo@mfi.com
URL: http://www.bobbin.com

Monthly. Free to qualified manufacturers; $48.00/year for others. Trade magazine on sewn-products industry management and manufacturing. Reports on industry trends, technology, new products, etc.

★6744★ BtoB Magazine

Crain Communications Inc.
711 Third Ave.
New York, NY 10017-4036
Ph: (212)210-0100   Fax: (212)210-0244
Fr: 800-446-1420
URL: http://www.btobonline.com

Monthly. $59.00/year for individuals. Trade magazine on business-to-business marketing news, strategy, and tactics.

★6745★ Building Supply Home Centers

Reed Business Information
360 Park Ave. S
New York, NY 10014
Ph: (646)746-7764

Monthly. Free to qualified subscribers; $60.00/year for individuals. Magazine for owners, executives, and managers responsible for product selection and purchase, merchandising, marketing, and management within the building supply retail and home center market.

★6746★ Chemical Market Reporter

Schnell Publishing Company Inc.
2 Rector St., 26th Fl.
New York, NY 10006-1819
Ph: (212)791-4200   Fax: (212)791-4313

Weekly. $109.00/year for individuals. International tabloid newspaper for the chemical process industries. Includes analytical reports on developments in the chemical marketplace, plant expansions, new technology, corporate mergers, finance, current chemical prices, and regulatory matters.

★6747★ Concrete Products

Primedia Business
9800 Metcalf Ave.
Overland Park, KS 66212
Ph: (913)341-1300   Fax: (913)967-1898
E-mail: concreteproducts@intertec.com
URL: http://www.concreteproducts.com

Monthly. $54.00/year for U.S.; $74.00/year for other countries. Magazine on concrete products and ready-mixed concrete.

★6748★ Cosmetics & Toiletries

Allured Publishing Corp.
362 S Schmale Rd.
Carol Stream, IL 60188-2787
Ph: (630)480-2997   Fax: (630)653-2192
E-mail: cosmtoil@allured.com

Monthly. $98.00/year for individuals; $137.00/year for Canada; $189.00/year for other countries. Trade magazine on cosmetic and toiletries manufacturing with an emphasis on product research and development issues.

★6749★ CRN

CMP Media L.L.C.
600 Community Dr.
Manhasset, NY 11030
Ph: (516)562-5000
URL: http://www.crn.com

Weekly. Free to qualified subscribers; $209.00/year. Newspaper for value added resellers, retailers, and distributors in the computer market.

★6750★ Dealernews

Advanstar Communications Inc.
201 Sandpointe Ave., Ste. 600
Santa Ana, CA 92707
Ph: (714)513-8400   Fax: (714)513-8414
Fr: 800-854-3112
URL: http://www.dealernews.com

Monthly. $48.00/year. Magazine covering dealers of motorcycles, ATV/off-road vehicles, watercraft, other powersport vehicles, and related aftermarket and apparel products.

★6751★ Earnshaw's Review

Earnshaw Publications Inc.
112 W 34th St. Ste. 1515
New York, NY 10120
Ph: (212)563-2742   Fax: (212)629-3249

Monthly. $24.00/year. Fashion and business magazine for retailers, manufacturers, licensees, and fiber companies in the children's apparel industry.

★6752★ Electrical Wholesaling

Primedia Business
9800 Metcalf Ave.
Overland Park, KS 66212
Ph: (913)341-1300   Fax: (913)967-1898

Monthly. $20.00/year for individuals. Magazine focusing on electrical wholesaling.

★6753★ Feedstuffs

Miller Publishing Co.
12400 Whitewater Dr., Ste. 160
Minnetonka, MN 55343
Ph: (952)930-1832   Fax: (952)938-4390
URL: http://www.feedstuffs.com

Weekly. $135.00/year. Magazine serving the grain and feed industries and animal agriculture.

★6754★ Food Production Management

CTI Publications Inc.
2 Oakway Rd.
Timonium, MD 21093-4247
Ph: (410)308-2080   Fax: (410)308-2079
E-mail: fpmeditorial@ctipubs.com

Monthly. $40.00/year for individuals; $15.00 for single issue. Magazine on food processing and individual packing news for management, sales, and production personnel in the canning, glass packing, aseptic, and frozen food industries.

★6755★ Furniture Today

Reed Business Information
7025 Albert Pick Rd., Ste. 200
Greensboro, NC 27409
Ph: (336)605-1055   Fax: (336)605-1149
Fr: 800-561-5681
URL: http://www.furnituretoday.com

Weekly. $159.97/year for U.S., Canada, and Mexico; $295.00/year for out of country; $550.00/year for airmail to other countries. Furniture retailing and manufacturing magazine (tabloid).

★6756★ Gases & Welding Distributor

Penton Media Inc.
1300 E 9th St.
Cleveland, OH 44114-1503
Ph: (216)696-7000   Fax: (216)931-9799
URL: http://www.penton.com/cgi-bin/super-directory/details.pl?id=3

Bimonthly. $45.00/year for individuals; $76.50 for two years; $49.50/year for Canada; $67.50/year for other countries. Distributor magazine featuring industrial, medical, specialty gases and welding supplies.

★6757★ Health Products Business

Cygnus Business Media Inc.
445 Broad Hollow Rd.
Melville, NY 11747
Ph: (631)845-2700   Fax: (631)845-2798
Fr: 800-308-6397
E-mail: info@healthproductsbusiness.com
URL: http://www.healthproductsbusiness.com

Monthly. Health and nutrition magazine focusing on the natural products industry.

★6758★ Implement & Tractor

Agra USA
2302 W 1st St.
Cedar Falls, IA 50613-1879
Ph: (319)277-3599   Fax: (319)277-3783
Fr: 800-959-3276
E-mail: agrausa@cfu.net
URL: http://www.ag-implement.com

Bimonthly. $36.00/year for U.S. and Canada; $95.00/year for other countries. Magazine on farm and industrial machinery, trends and technology.

★6759★ Industrial Distribution

Reed Business Information
275 Washington St.
Newton, MA 02458-1630
Ph: (617)964-3030
URL: http://www.inddist.com

Monthly. Magazine covering industrial supplies marketing, management, sales, telecommunications, computers, inventory, and warehouse management.

★6760★ Industrial Heating

Business News Publishing Co.
Manor Oak One
1910 Cochran Rd., Ste. 450
Pittsburgh, PA 15220
Ph: (412)531-3370   Fax: (412)531-3375

Monthly. $25.00/year for Canada; $50.00/year for other countries. Magazine.

★6761★ Institutional Distribution

Institutional Distribution
770 Broadway
New York, NY 10003
Ph: (646)654-5000
E-mail: cleibman@bill.com
URL: http://www.billcom.com

Monthly. $66.00/year; $7.00 for single issue.

Trade magazine for foodservice wholesalers and sales force.

★6762★ Kitchen and Bath Business

VNU Business Media
770 Broadway
New York, NY 10003-9595
Ph: (646)654-5000
URL: http://www.kitchen-bath.com

Monthly. $35.00/year for qualified subscribers; $65.00/year for others. Trade magazine on kitchen and bath remodeling and construction.

★6763★ Laser Focus World

PennWell Corp.
98 Spit Brook Rd.
Nashua, NH 03062-5737
Ph: (603)891-0123   Fax: (603)891-0574
URL: http://www.laserfocusworld.com

Monthly. $150.00/year for individuals; $200.00/year for Canada; $15.00 for single issue. Magazine covering advances and applications in optoelectronics and photonics.

★6764★ LDB Interior Textiles

E.W. Williams Publications
2125 Center Ave., Ste. 305
Fort Lee, NJ 07024
Ph: (201)592-7007   Fax: (201)592-7171

Monthly. $72.00/year for individuals; $115.00/year for other countries; $7.00 for single issue; $125.00/year for Canada; $150.00/year for elsewhere. Magazine for buyers of home fashions, including bed, bath and table linens, hard and soft window treatments, home fragrances, decorative pillows and home accessories, accent rugs, and decorative fabrics.

★6765★ Managing Automation

Thomas Publishing Co.
5 Penn Plz.
New York, NY 10001
Ph: (212)695-0500   Fax: (212)290-7362
URL: http://www.managingautomation.com

Monthly. $60.00/year for individuals; $8.00 for single issue. Managing Automation covers advanced manufacturing technology including automation, integrated manufacturing, enterprise applications, and IT and e-business for the manufacturing enterprise.

★6766★ Manufacturers Representatives of America-Newsline

Manufacturers Representatives of America
P O Box 150229
Arlington, TX 76015
Ph: (817)561-7272   Fax: (817)561-7275

Description: Monthly. Published for member independent manufacturers' representatives handling sanitary supplies and paper and plastic disposable products. Carries articles to help improve agent sales skills, market coverage, and customer service, and to help establish more effective agent/principal communications. Recurring features include news of members, a calendar of events, job listings, notices of publications available, news of educational opportunities, and a column titled President's Report.

★6767★ **Meat & Poultry**
Sosland Publishing Co.
4800 Main St., Ste. 100
Kansas City, MO 64112-2513
Ph: (816)756-1000   Fax: (816)756-0494
Fr: 800-338-6201
E-mail: meat&poultry@sosland.com

Monthly. $40.00/year for individuals; $45.00/year for Canada and Mexico; $75.00/year for other countries; $10.00 for single issue. Magazine serving the meat and poultry processing, distributing, and wholesaling industries in the U.S. and Canada.

★6768★ **Med Ad News**
Engel Publishing Partners
820 Bear Tavern Rd., Ste. 300
West Trenton, NJ 08628
Ph: (609)530-0044   Fax: (609)530-0207
E-mail: mwalsh@engelpub.com

Monthly. $150.00/year for U.S.; $270.00/year for other countries. Pharmaceutical business and marketing magazine.

★6769★ **Milling & Baking News**
Sosland Publishing Co.
4800 Main St., Ste. 100
Kansas City, MO 64112-2513
Ph: (816)756-1000   Fax: (816)756-0494
Fr: 800-338-6201
E-mail: mbn@sosland.com

Weekly. $104.00/year for individuals. Trade magazine covering the grain-based food industries.

★6770★ **Modern Grocer**
GC Publishing Company Inc.
1 University Dr., Ste. 200
Hackensack, NJ 07601
Ph: (201)488-1800   Fax: (201)488-7357
URL: http://www.griffcomm.net

Monthly. $45.00/year for individuals. Magazine for food retailers, wholesalers, distributors, brokers, manufacturers, and packers in the metro New York and New Jersey marketing area.

★6771★ **Modern Plastics**
Chemical Week Associates
110 Williams St., 11th Fl.
New York, NY 10038
Ph: (212)621-4900   Fax: (212)621-4949
URL: http://www.modplas.com

Monthly. $59.00/year. Magazine for the plastics industry.

★6772★ **Money Making Opportunities**
Success Publishing International
11071 Ventura Blvd.
Studio City, CA 91604-3548
Ph: (818)765-2344   Fax: (818)980-7829
URL: http://www.moneymakingopps.com

$8.00/year. Magazine Source for small business opportunity seekers.

★6773★ **Multi-Housing News**
VNU Business Media
770 Broadway
New York, NY 10003-9595
Ph: (646)654-5000
E-mail: lvicarro@mfi.com

$65.00/year. Trade magazine (tabloid).

★6774★ **National Home Center News**
Lebhar-Friedman Inc.
425 Park Ave.
New York, NY 10022-3556
Ph: (212)756-5088   Fax: (212)756-5120
Fr: 800-453-2427
URL: http://www.homecenternews.com

$99.00/year for individuals; $119.00/year for Canada; $279.00/year for other countries. Business tabloid serving home center/building material retailers.

★6775★ **Nursery Business Retailer**
Brantwood Publications Inc.
2410 Northside Dr.
Clearwater, FL 33761
Ph: (727)786-9771   Fax: (727)791-4126

Bimonthly. $15.00/year for individuals; $3.00 for single issue. Wholesale and retail nursery operations magazine.

★6776★ **Packaging Digest**
Reed Business Information
360 Park Ave. S
New York, NY 10014
Ph: (646)746-7764
URL: http://www.packagingdigest.com/

Business trade magazine for the packaging field.

★6777★ **Photo Marketing**
Photo Marketing Association International
3000 Picture Pl.
Jackson, MI 49201
Ph: (517)788-8100   Fax: (517)788-8371
URL: http://www.pmai.org

Monthly. $30.00/year for individuals; $35.00/year for Canada; $50.00/year, international. Trade magazine for photo/video dealers and photo finishers.

★6778★ **RV Business**
TL Enterprises Inc.
2575 Vista Del Mar
Ventura, CA 93001
Ph: (805)667-4100   Fax: (805)667-4454
E-mail: rvb@tl.com

Monthly. $48.00/year for individuals; $4.00 for single issue; free to qualified subscribers. Magazine about the business of manufacturing, distributing, and selling travel trailers, conversion vehicles, and motorhomes and related parts, accessories, and services.

★6779★ **Sales & Marketing Management**
Bill Communications Inc.
770 Broadway
New York, NY 10003-9595
Ph: (646)654-4500   Fax: (646)654-7212
E-mail: edit@salesandmarketing.com
URL: http://www.salesandmarketing.com

$48.00/year. Business magazine.

★6780★ **Sporting Goods Dealer**
Bill Communications Inc.
1115 Northmeadow Pkwy.
Roswell, GA 30076
Ph: (770)569-5105   Fax: (770)569-5105
Fr: 800-241-9034
URL: http://www.sgdealer.com

Monthly. Free to qualified subscribers; $100.00/year; $6.00/year for single issue. Magazine which offers expert reporting on trends affecting team dealers and retailers who service schools, colleges, pro and local teams.

★6781★ **Timber Harvesting**
Hatton-Brown Publishers
PO Box 2268
Montgomery, AL 36102
Ph: (334)834-1170   Fax: (334)834-4525
Fr: 800-669-5613
URL: http://www.timberharvesting.com

Free to qualified subscribers; $40.00/year. National magazine for the U.S. logging industry.

★6782★ **Transmission Digest**
MD Publications Inc.
3057 E Cairo
PO Box 2210
Springfield, MO 65801-2210
Ph: (417)866-3917   Fax: (417)866-2781
Fr: 800-274-7890

Monthly. $39.00/year for individuals; $4.75 for single issue.

★6783★ **TWICE**
Reed Business Information
360 Park Ave. S
New York, NY 10010
Ph: (646)746-6400   Fax: (646)746-6734
E-mail: ssmith@cahners.com
URL: http://www.twice.com

Semiweekly. $35.00/year; $150.00/year for Canada; $200.00/year for other countries. Trade tabloid covering consumer electronics, appliance, and camera industries for retailers, manufacturers, and distributors.

★6784★ UAMR Confidential Bulletin

United Association of Manufacturers'
Representatives (UAMR)
PO Box 986
Dana Point, CA 92629
Fax: (714)240-4966

Description: Monthly. Covers product lines offered for representation in all fields. Provides details of the company and product, type of accounts to be serviced, and the areas open for representation. Subscription includes bulletin of lines for representatives, articles on rep business, and trade show listings.

★6785★ Undercar Digest

M D Publications Inc.
PO Box 2210
Springfield, MO 65801-2210
Ph: (417)866-3917   Fax: (417)866-2781
Fr: 800-274-7890

Monthly. $39.00/year; $4.75 for single issue. Magazine for the undercar service and supply industry.

★6786★ Watch & Clock Review

Golden Bell Press
2403 Champa St.
Denver, CO 80205
Ph: (303)296-1600   Fax: (303)295-2159

$19.50/year; $3.00 for single issue. Magazine on watches and clocks.

★6787★ Yard and Garden

Cygnus Business Media
1233 Janesville Ave.
Fort Atkinson, WI 53538
Fr: 800-547-7377
URL: http://www.cygnusexpos.com/PropertyPub.cfm?PropertyID=117

Yard and garden magazine featuring product news and retailer success stories.

PLACEMENT AND JOB REFERRAL SERVICES

★6788★ Sporting Goods Agents Association (SGAA)

PO Box 998
Morton Grove, IL 60053
Ph: (847)296-3670   Fax: (847)827-0196
E-mail: sgaa998@aol.com
URL: http://www.r-sports.com/SGAA/

Members: Manufacturers' agents whose goal is to provide free legal counsel for members and additional product lines from manufacturers, and to improve the image of the independent agent. **Activities:** Maintains Sporting Goods Agents Hall of Fame, Manufacturers Appreciation Award, and Lifetime Sales Achievement Award. Offers placement service.

EMPLOYER DIRECTORIES AND NETWORKING LISTS

★6789★ Agricultural & Industrial Manufacturers Representatives Association-Membership Directory

Agricultural & Industrial Manufacturers
Representatives Association
7500 Flying Cloud Dr., Ste. 900
Eden Prairie, MN 55344-3756
Fax: (952)835-4774   Fr: 800-759-2467

Annual, October. $50.00. Covers 120 members; coverage includes Canada. Entries include: Company name, address, phone, name of principal executive, territory covered. Arrangement: Alphabetical.

★6790★ American Hardware Manufacturers Association-Rep/ Factory Contact Service Directory

American Hardware Manufacturers
Association (AHMA)
801 N Plaza Dr.
Schaumburg, IL 60173
Ph: (847)605-1025   Fax: (847)605-1093

Annual, April. $200.00. Covers over 280 manufacturer representatives in the hardware industry. Entries include: Firm name, address, number of years in business, number of salespeople, territory covered, manufacturers represented, products or service offered, type of accounts currently served, whether firm has a distribution network or warehouses, whether firm provides in-store service. Arrangement: Geographical. Indexes: Product line, firm name.

★6791★ American Manufacturers Directory

infoUSA Inc.
5711 S 86th Cir.
Omaha, NE 68127-0347
Ph: (402)930-3500   Fax: (402)331-0176
Fr: 800-555-6124
URL: http://www.abii.com

Annual, January. $295.00; $595.00 for print and CD-ROM. Covers more than 150,000 manufacturing companies with 20 or more employees. CD-ROM version lists all 531,000 U.S. manufacturers, in all employee size ranges. Entries include: Company name, address, phone, contact name, Standard Industrial Classification (SIC) codes, number of employees, sales volume code, credit rating scores. Arrangement: Entries listed alphabetically, geographically, and by Standard Industrial Classification (SIC) code. Indexes: Geographical.

★6792★ American Salon's Green Book

Advanstar Communications Inc.
7500 Old Oak Blvd.
Cleveland, OH 44130-3369
Ph: (440)243-8100   Fax: (440)891-2777
E-mail: directories@advanstar.com
URL: http://www.advanstar.com

Annual, November. $145.00. Covers about 1,300 manufacturers of supplies and equipment for salons and spas; 130 manufacturers' representatives; 3,200 distributors; employment agencies, show management companies, and related trade organizations. Entries include: For manufacturers and agents-Company name, address, phone, names of principal executives, products available. For distributors-Company name, address, phone, branches, name of owner or president, number of sales representatives, trade association affiliation, Metropolitan Statistical Area (MSA) in which located. For representatives-Company name, address, phone, territory covered. Arrangement: Manufacturers are alphabetical; agents, distributors, representatives are geographical. Indexes: Product, trade name.

★6793★ American Wholesalers and Distributors Directory

Thomson Gale
27500 Drake Rd.
Farmington Hills, MI 48331-3535
Ph: (248)699-4253   Fax: (248)699-8065
Fr: 800-877-GALE
E-mail: businessproducts@gale.com
URL: http://www.gale.com

Annual. $250.00. Covers more than 28,000 wholesalers and distributors of consumer products in the U.S. Entries include: Company name, address, phone, fax, e-mail, URLs, names and titles of key personnel, personal e-mail addresses, number of employees, financial data, product line, Standard Industrial Classification (SIC) code, and date established. Arrangement: Classified by subject, then alphabetical by company name. Indexes: SIC, geographical, alphabetical.

★6794★ Bacon's Radio/TV/Cable Directory, Volume 1

Bacon's Information Inc.
332 S Michigan Ave., Ste. 900
Chicago, IL 60604
Ph: (312)922-2400   Fax: (312)987-9773
Fr: 800-621-0561
URL: http://www.bacons.com/research/radiotvcable.htm

Annual, November. $375.00. Covers over 13,500 radio and television stations, including college radio and public television stations, and cable companies. Entries include: For radio and television stations-Call letters, address, phone, names and titles of key personnel, programs, times broadcast, name of contact, network affiliation, frequency or channel number, target audience data. For cable companies-Name, address, phone, description of activities. Arrangement: Geographical.

★6795★ Electrical Equipment Representatives Association-Membership Directory

Electrical Equipment Representatives
Association (EERA)
PO Box 419264
Kansas City, MO 64141
Ph: (816)561-5323   Fax: (816)561-1249
URL: http://www.eera.org

Annual, October. Covers more than 105 manufacturers' representatives of electrical equipment companies. Entries include: Company name, address, phone, names and titles of key personnel. Arrangement: Alphabetical.

★6796★ **Gift and Decorative Accessories Center Association-Directory**

Gift and Decorative Accessories Center Association
59 Middlesex Tpke.
Bedford, MA 01730
Ph: (781)275-2775   Fax: (781)275-7479
Fr: 800-435-2775
URL: http://www.thegiftcenter.com

Semiannual, January and July. $3.95. Covers about 60 individuals who are giftware manufacturers' representatives in New England; also lists their manufacturers and suppliers. Entries include: For representatives-Name, address, phone, e-mail, manufacturers and products represented. Arrangement: Alphabetical.

★6797★ **Hardware Age Home Improvement Market: Who's Who Verified Directory of Home Improvement Buyers**

Reed Business Information
360 Park Ave. S
New York, NY 10014
Ph: (646)746-7764
E-mail: homeimprmt@aol.com

Biennial, July of even years. $195.00. Covers about 2,500 hardware wholesalers, specialty distributors, manufacturers' representatives, retailers (hardware, home center, building material, general retail, home and auto supply, specialty stores) and export management companies. Entries include: Generally, company name, address, phone, sales volume, territories covered, names of principal executives, area served, buyers of lines handled, special services (drop shipments, warehousing, etc.), if any, type of outlet, number of salesmen. Arrangement: Classified by type of company, then geographical. Indexes: By section, alphabetical by company name.

★6798★ **Incentive-Directory Issue**

Bill Communications Inc.
770 Broadway
New York, NY 10003-9595
Ph: (646)654-4500   Fax: (646)654-7212

Annual, March. $5.00. Publication includes: List of approximately 1,000 suppliers of products used as promotional premiums and incentives, and services needed to conduct a premium or incentive campaign; includes trading stamp services and specialists in various forms of promotion (contests and sweepstakes, financial promotion, etc.), and manufacturers' representatives. Entries include: Company name, address, phone, name of contact, information on product or service. Arrangement: Classified by product or service.

★6799★ **The Locator-The Electronics Representatives Directory/Electronics Industry Calendar**

Electronics Representatives Association
444 N Michigan Ave., Ste. 1960
Chicago, IL 60611
Ph: (312)527-3050   Fax: (312)527-3783
URL: http://www.era.org/

Annual, October. $50.00 for CD-ROM; $75.00 for nonmembers. Covers 1,400 member and approximately 4,000 nonmember firms and 500 electronics industry trade shows; international coverage. Entries include: Firm name, address, phone; names of owners; facilities; states in territory; association divisional memberships; number of employees; branch offices' addresses, phone numbers, fax, and names of managers. Type of product handled is shown in separate tabulation at beginning of each chapter section. Arrangement: Geographical, by chapter. Indexes: Key personnel name, company.

★6800★ **Manufacturers' Agents National Association-Directory of Manufacturers' Sales Agencies**

Manufacturers' Agents National Association
One Spectrum Pointe, Ste. 150
Lake Forest, CA 92630-2283
Ph: (949)859-4040   Fax: (949)855-2973
URL: http://www.MANAonline.org

Online Directory. $199.00. Covers 4,000 independent agents and firms representing manufacturers and other businesses in specified territories on a commission basis, including consultants and associate member firms interested in the manufacturer/agency method of marketing. Entries include: For manufacturers-Company name, address, phone, fax, E-mail, URL, name of contact, product. For agencies-Agency name, address, phone, fax, E-mail, URL, name of contact, warehouse facilities, territory covered, number of field sales representatives, branch office location, year established, date of joining association. Arrangement: Separate alphabetical sections for manufacturers and agencies. Indexes: Geographic, target industries.

★6801★ **Manufacturers Agents & Representatives Directory**

infoUSA Inc.
5711 S 86th Cir.
Omaha, NE 68127-0347
Ph: (402)930-3500   Fax: (402)331-0176
Fr: 800-555-6124
URL: http://www.abii.com

Annual. Number of listings: 23,096. Entries include: Name, address, phone (including area code), size of advertisement, year first in "Yellow Pages," name of owner or manager, number of employees. Compiled from telephone company "Yellow Pages," nationwide. Arrangement: Geographical.

★6802★ **Manufacturers Representatives of America-Yearbook and Directory of Members**

Manufacturers Representatives of America
P O Box 150229
Arlington, TX 76015
Ph: (817)561-7272   Fax: (817)561-7275
URL: http://www.mra-reps.com/lookup.asp

Annual, fall. $250.00. Covers several hundred independent manufacturers' representatives in paper, plastic, packaging, and sanitary supplies. Entries include: Name, address, phone, distributors served, territory, number of persons in sales, branch offices, products handled, marketing services provided, warehouse locations and facilities. Arrangement: Geographical. Indexes: Organization, personal name.

★6803★ **Office Products Representatives Association-Rep Locator**

Office Products Representatives Association
307 N Michigan Ave., Ste. 800
Chicago, IL 60601-5309
Ph: (312)360-0386   Fax: (312)360-0388
Fr: 888-414-OPRA
URL: http://www.oprareps.org

Annual, June. $50.00. Covers about 105 member manufacturers' representative firms in the office products industry. Entries include: Firm name, address, phone, names of contacts, fax, e-mail, website addresses. Arrangement: Geographical. Indexes: Market segment (business products and furniture), districts, firm listing, principal listing.

★6804★ **Pharmaceutical Marketers Directory**

CPS Communications Inc.
7200 W Camino Real, Ste. 215
Boca Raton, FL 33433
Ph: (561)368-9301   Fax: (561)368-7870
Fr: 800-346-2015
E-mail: pmd@cpsnet.com
URL: http://www.pmdcentral.com

Annual, April. $225.00. Covers about 15,000 personnel of pharmaceutical, medical device and equipment manufacturers, and biotechnology companies; advertising agencies with clients in the healthcare field; health care publications; alternative media and healthcare industry suppliers. Entries include: Company name, address, list of personnel by job classification (with titles, phone, internet and e-mail addresses, direct dial and fax numbers). Arrangement: Classified by type of business (health care company, advertising agency, healthcare journals, medical education service, and industry suppliers). Indexes: Personnel, geographical/product or service.

★6805★ **Pharmaceutical Products-Wholesalers Directory**

infoUSA Inc.
5711 S 86th Cir.
Omaha, NE 68127-0347
Ph: (402)930-3500   Fax: (402)331-0176
Fr: 800-555-6124

URL: http://www.abii.com

Annual. Number of listings: 3,250. Entries include: Name, address, phone (including area code), size of advertisement, year first in "Yellow Pages," name of owner or manager, number of employees. Compiled from telephone company "Yellow Pages," nationwide. Arrangement: Geographical.

★6806★ **Thomas Register of American Manufacturers**

Thomas Publishing Co.
5 Penn Plz.
New York, NY 10001
Ph: (212)695-0500   Fax: (212)290-7362
URL: http://www.thomasregister.com

Annual, January. More than 168,000 manufacturing firms are listed in this 34 volume set. Volumes 1-23 list the firms under 68,000 product headings. Thomas Register is enhanced with over 8,000 manufacturers' catalogs and is available in print, CD-ROM, DVD or online. Logistics Guide, a reference manual for freight and shipping sourcing. Arrangement: Volumes 1-23, classified by product or service; Volumes 24-26 alphabetical by company; Volumes 27-34 company catalogs alphabetical by company. Indexes: Product/service, brand/trade name (Volume 22).

★6807★ **The Wholesaler-'The Wholesaling 100' Issue**

TMB Publishing Inc.
1838 Techny Ct.
Northbrook, IL 60062
Ph: (847)564-1127   Fax: (847)564-1264
URL: http://www.technotribe.net/clients/tmb/production/tw_res.htm

Annual, July. $50.00. Publication includes: Ranks 100 leading wholesalers of plumbing, heating, air conditioning, refrigeration equipment, and industrial pipe, valves and fittings. Entries include: Company name, address, phone, fax, names and titles of key personnel, number of employees, business breakdown (percentage). Arrangement: Ranked by sales.

HANDBOOKS AND MANUALS

★6808★ **America's Top Office, Management, & Sales Jobs**

JIST Publishing
8902 Otis Ave.
Indianapolis, IN 46216-1033
Ph: (317)613-4200   Fax: (317)613-4307
Fr: 800-648-5478
E-mail: jistworks@aol.com
URL: http://www.jist.com

Micheal J. Farr. Fifth edition, 2000. $16.95 (paper). 473 pages. Part of America's Top White-Collar Jobs Series.

★6809★ **Careers for Talkative Types and Others with the Gift of Gab**

McGraw-Hill Trade
2 Penn Plaza
New York, NY 10121
Ph: (212)904-2000   Fr: 800-722-4726
E-mail: ntcpub@tribune.com

Marjorie Eberts and Margaret Gisler. 1998. $14.95; $9.95 (paper). 160 pages.

★6810★ **Great Jobs for Business Majors**

McGraw-Hill Trade
2 Penn Plaza
New York, NY 10121
Ph: (212)904-2000   Fr: 800-722-4726
E-mail: ntcpub@tribune.com

Stephen Lambert. 1996. $11.95 (paper). 462 pages.

★6811★ **Loyalty-Based Selling: The Magic Formula for Becoming the No. 1 Sales Rep**

AMACOM
1601 Broadway, 12th Fl.
New York, NY 10019-7420
Ph: (518)891-1500   Fax: (518)903-8168

Tim Smith. 2001. $17.95 (paper).

★6812★ **Opportunities in Marketing Careers**

McGraw-Hill Trade
2 Penn Plaza
New York, NY 10121
Ph: (212)904-2000   Fr: 800-722-4726

Margery Steinberg. 1999. $14.95; $11.95 (paper). 202 pages. Includes guidance on identifying and pursuing job opportunities. Illustrated.

★6813★ **Opportunities in Medical Sales Careers**

McGraw-Hill Trade
2 Penn Plaza
New York, NY 10121
Ph: (212)904-2000   Fr: 800-722-4726

Chad Ellis. 1997. $14.95; $11.95 (paper). 200 pages. Includes index.

★6814★ **Opportunities in Pharmacy Careers**

McGraw-Hill Trade
2 Penn Plaza
New York, NY 10121
Ph: (212)904-2000   Fr: 800-722-4726

Fred B. Gable. 1997. $14.95; $11.95 (paper). 200 pages. Identifies opportunities in a variety of settings, including retail chains, private ownership, clinics, hospitals, and other private, commercial, and industrial operations. Provides information on job-hunting techniques. Illustrated.

★6815★ **Opportunities in Sales Careers**

McGraw-Hill Professional
2 Penn Plaza
New York, NY 10121
Ph: (212)904-2000   Fr: 800-722-4726
E-mail: ntcpub@tribune.com

James Brescoll and Ralph Dahm. 160 pages. 1995. $12.95; $11.95 (paper). Details sales in retail, wholesale and industrial sales, sales of services and intangibles, and sales management. Illustrated.

★6816★ **Resumes for Sales and Marketing Careers**

McGraw-Hill Professional
2 Penn Plaza
New York, NY 10121
Ph: (212)904-2000   Fr: 800-722-4726
E-mail: ntcpub@tribune.com

Chuck Cochran and Donna Peerce. Second edition, 1998. $10.95 (paper). 336 pages. Sample resumes and cover letters from all levels of the sales and marketing field.

★6817★ **Sales Careers: The Ultimate Guide to Getting a High-Paying Sales Job**

JIST Publishing
8902 Otis Ave.
Indianapolis, IN 46216-1033
Ph: (317)613-4200   Fax: 800-547-8329

Edward R. Newill, Louise Kursmark. June 2003. $12.95. 208 pages.

★6818★ **Where the Jobs Are: The Hottest Careers for the 90s**

The Career Press, Inc.
3 Tice Rd.
PO Box 687
Franklin Lakes, NJ 07417-1322
Ph: (201)848-0310   Fax: (201)848-1727
Fr: 800-227-3371

Joyce Hadley. Third edition, 2000. $13.99 (paper). 400 pages. Out of print. Describes careers in fifteen general fields, from accounting to travel and hospitality.

★6819★ **Your Opportunities in Sales**

Energeia Publishing, Inc.
1307 Fairmount Ave., S
Salem, OR 97302-4313
Ph: (503)362-1480   Fax: (503)362-2123
Fr: 800-639-6048

Shawn E. Strahan. 1994. $2.50 (paper). 8 pages.

EMPLOYMENT AGENCIES AND SEARCH FIRMS

★6820★ Adams & Associates International
520 Shorely Dr. 201, PO Box 129
Barrington, IL 60011-0129
Ph: (847)304-5300
Global executive search firm.

★6821★ Advanced Employment Resources
3040 Charlevoix Dr.
Grand Rapids, MI 49546
Ph: (616)942-9950   Fax: (616)942-9950
Executive search firm.

★6822★ Aegis Consulting
633 3rd Ave., Fl. 27
New York, NY 10017
Ph: (212)687-2200   Fax: (212)687-0079
Executive search firm.

★6823★ Amherst Personnel Group Inc.
PO Box 580
Hicksville, NY 11801-7848
Ph: (516)433-7610   Fax: (516)433-7848
E-mail: amherstgroup1@aol.com
Employment agency. Executive search firm. Other offices in Milltown, NJ, and Rochelle Park, NJ.

★6824★ ARI Management Consultants - Executive Search
241 W. 36th St., Fl. 6
New York, NY 10018
Ph: (212)736-9114   Fax: (212)658-9958
Executive firm specializing in American-European searches.

★6825★ BMF Reynolds Inc.
336 Nassau St.
Princeton, NJ 08540
Ph: (609)688-8700
Executive search firm.

★6826★ The Borton Wallace Company
PO Box 8816
Asheville, NC 28814-0989
Ph: (828)258-1831   Fax: (828)251-0989
Executive search firm.

★6827★ The Caler Group
23337 Lago Mar Circle
Boca Raton, FL 33433
Ph: (561)394-8045   Fax: (561)394-4645
Executive search firm.

★6828★ Cendea
13740 Research Blvd., Bldg. O-1
Austin, TX 78750
Ph: (512)219-6000
Executive search firm.

★6829★ Chaitin & Associates Inc.
22543 Ventura Blvd., Ste. 220
Woodland Hills, CA 91364
Ph: (818)225-8655   Fax: (818)225-8660
Executive search firm.

★6830★ Cizek Associates Inc.
2415 E. Camelback Rd., Ste. 700
Camelback Esplanade I
Phoenix, AZ 85016
Ph: (602)553-1066   Fax: (602)553-1166
Executive search firm.

★6831★ Clarey Andrews & Klein Inc.
1200 Shermer Rd., Ste. 108
Northbrook, IL 60062
Ph: (847)498-2870
Executive search firm.

★6832★ Cowell & Associates Ltd.
819 Keystone Ave.
River Forest, IL 60305-1319
Ph: (708)771-8989   Fax: (708)771-1788
Executive search firm.

★6833★ Crowe-Innes & Associates LLC
1120 Mar W., Ste. D
Tiburon, CA 94920
Ph: (415)789-1422   Fax: (415)435-6867
Executive search firm.

★6834★ The Culver Group
1810 Gateway Dr., Ste140
San Mateo, CA 94404
Ph: (650)356-1100   Fax: (650)356-1111
E-mail: gfagin@culvercareers.com
URL: http://www.culvercorp.com
Employment agency specializing in sales positions.

★6835★ Cyntal International Ltd.
405 Lexington Ave., Ste. 2600-19
New York, NY 10174
Ph: (917)368-8181
Executive search firm.

★6836★ The Dalley Hewitt Company
1401 Peachtree St. NE, Ste. 500
Atlanta, GA 30309
Ph: (404)885-6642   Fax: (404)355-6136
Executive search firm.

★6837★ DMR Global Inc.
10230 W. Sample Rd.
Coral Springs, FL 33065
Ph: (954)796-5043   Fax: (954)796-5044
Executive search firm.

★6838★ Don Waldron and Associates, Inc.
450 7th Ave., Ste. 507A
New York, NY 10123
Ph: (212)239-9110   Fax: (212)239-9114
E-mail: salepositions@comcast.net
URL: http://www.salespositions.com
Employment agency.

★6839★ Egan & Associates Inc.
White House Ctr.
128 S. 6th Ave.
West Bend, WI 53095
Ph: (262)335-0707   Fax: (262)335-0625
Executive search firm.

★6840★ Executive Search International
60 Walnut St.
Wellesley, MA 02481
Ph: (781)239-0303   Fax: (781)235-0465
Executive search firm.

★6841★ Fairfield
Trump Tower
721 5th Ave.
New York, NY 10022-2523
Ph: (212)838-0220
Executive search firm specializing in retail and apparel manufacturing.

★6842★ James Drury Partners
875 N. Michigan Ave., Ste. 3805
Chicago, IL 60611
Ph: (312)654-6708   Fax: (312)654-6710
Executive search firm.

★6843★ M.J. Curran & Associates Inc.
304 Newbury St., Ste. 509
Boston, MA 02115
Ph: (617)247-7700   Fax: (617)267-6429
Executive search firm.

★6844★ National Register Columbus, Inc.
2700 E. Dublin Granville Rd., Ste. 555
Columbus, OH 43231-4097
Ph: (614)890-1200   Fax: (614)890-1259
E-mail: sales@nrcols.com
URL: http://www.nrcols.com
Employment agency. Offices in Akron and Toledo, OH.

★6845★ 1 Exec Street

201 Post St., Ste. 401
San Francisco, CA 94108
Ph: (415)982-0555   Fax: (415)982-0550
Executive search firm.

★6846★ Sales Executives Inc.

755 W. Big Beaver Rd., Ste. 2107
Troy, MI 48084
Ph: (248)362-1900
E-mail: dale@salesexecutives.com
URL: http://www.salesexecutives.com
Employment agency. Executive search firm.

★6847★ Selected Executives Inc.

36 Ash Ste., Ste102
Cambridge, MA 02138
Ph: (781)933-1500   Fax: (617)547-7333
E-mail: seilrs@aol.com
Executive search firm and employment agency.

TRADESHOWS

★6848★ International Mass Retail Association Convention and Exhibits

International Mass Retail Association
1700 N. Moore St., Ste. 2250
Arlington, VA 22209
Ph: (703)841-2300   Fax: (703)841-1184
URL: http://www.imra.org
Annual. **Primary Exhibits:** Consumer products.

★6849★ Marketing Seminar Conference

Manufacturers Agents for Food Service
  Industry
2402 Mt. Vernon Rd., Ste. 110
Dunwoody, GA 30338
Ph: (770)698-8994   Fax: (770)698-8043
URL: http://www.mafsi.org
Annual. **Primary Exhibits:** Manufacturers' representative equipment, furnishings, and supplies for dealers and users.

★6850★ National Agri-Marketing Association Conference

National Agri-Marketing Association
11020 King St., Ste. 205
Overland Park, KS 66210
Ph: (913)491-6500   Fax: (913)492-6502
E-mail: agrimktg@nama.org
URL: http://www.nama.org
Annual. **Primary Exhibits:** Marketing and communication suppliers, including trade publications, radio and television broadcast sales organizations, premium/incentive manufacturers, printers, marketing research firms, photographers, and related professionals.

★6851★ Wisconsin Plastics & Manufacturing Expo

Expo Productions Inc.
510 Hartbrook Dr.
Hartland, WI 53029
Ph: (262)367-5500   Fax: (262)367-9956
Fr: 800-367-5520
E-mail: expo@execpc.com
URL: http://www.execpc.com/~expo
Biennial. **Primary Exhibits:** Plastics, manufacturing and precision metalforming pavilions.

OTHER SOURCES

★6852★ American Wholesale Marketers Association (AWMA)

2750 Prosperity Ave., Ste. 530
Fairfax, VA 22031
Ph: (703)208-3358   Fax: (703)573-5738
Fr: 800-482-2962
E-mail: info@awmanet.org
URL: http://www.awmanet.org
Description: Represents the interests of distributors of convenience products. Its members include wholesalers, retailers, manufacturers, brokers and allied organizations from across the U.S. and abroad. AWMA programs include strong legislative representation in Washington and a broad spectrum of targeted education, business and information services. AWMA also sponsors the country's largest show for candy and convenience related products in conjunction with its semiannual convention.

★6853★ Asian American MultiTechnology Association (AAMA)

3300 Zanker Rd., Maildrop SJ2F8
San Jose, CA 95134
Ph: (408)955-4505   Fax: (408)955-4516
E-mail: aama@aamasv.com
URL: http://www.aamasv.com
Description: Asian American manufacturers of technology products, such as computers, microprocessors, semiconductors, biotech, software and electronics equipment. Seeks to enhance members' business opportunities. Sponsors educational programs in management and business operations.

★6854★ Association of Independent Manufacturers'/Representatives (AIM/R)

One Spectrum Pt., Ste. 150
Lake Forest, CA 92630
Ph: (949)859-2884   Fax: (949)855-2973
Fr: (866)729-0975
E-mail: info@aimr.net
URL: http://www.aimr.net
Description: Manufacturers' representative companies in the plumbing-heating-cooling-piping industry promoting the use of independent sales representatives. Conducts educational programs and establishes a code of ethics between members and customers.

★6855★ Automotive Aftermarket Industry Association (AAIA)

4600 East-West Hwy., Ste. 300
Bethesda, MD 20814-3415
Ph: (301)654-6664   Fax: (301)654-3299
E-mail: aaia@aftermarket.org
URL: http://www.aftermarket.org
Members: Automotive parts and accessories retailers, distributors, manufacturers, and manufacturers' representatives. **Activities:** Conducts research and compiles statistics. Conducts seminars and provides specialized education program.

★6856★ Computing Technology Industry Association (CompTIA)

1815 S Meyers Rd., Ste. 300
Oakbrook Terrace, IL 60181
Ph: (630)678-8300   Fax: (630)627-2930
E-mail: info@comptia.org
URL: http://www.comptia.org
Description: Trade association of more than 19,000 companies and professional IT members in the rapidly converging computing and communications market. Has members in more than 89 countries and provides a unified voice for the industry in the areas of e-commerce standards, vendor-neutral certification, service metrics, public policy and workforce development. Serves as information clearinghouse and resource for the industry; sponsors educational programs.

★6857★ Manufacturers' Agents National Association (MANA)

1 Spectrum Pte., Ste. 150
Lake Forest, CA 92630-2283
Ph: (949)859-4040   Fax: (949)855-2973
Fr: 877-626-2766
E-mail: mana@manaonline.org
URL: http://www.manaonline.org
Members: Manufacturers' agents in all fields representing two or more manufacturers on a commission basis; associate members are manufacturers and others interested in improving the agent-principal relationship. **Activities:** Maintains code of ethics and rules of business and professional conduct; issues model standard form of agreement.

★6858★ Manufacturers Sales Workers

Evon Publishing
832 N 7th Ave.
Iron River, MI 49935
Ph: (906)265-3190
Audiocassette. 1996. $16.95. 32 minutes. Part of the Careers and Vocational Guidance Series. Provides information about the nature of the work, educational requirements, employment outlook, earnings, and work conditions as well as additional related information.

★6859★ Marketing & Sales Occupations

Delphi Productions
3160 4th St.
Boulder, CO 80304
Fax: (303)443-4022   Fr: 888-443-2400

URL: http://www.delphivideo.com
$95.00. 50 minutes. Part of the Careers for the 21st Century Video Library.

★6860★ National Association of Chain Drug Stores (NACDS)
413 N Lee St.
PO Box 1417-D49
Alexandria, VA 22313-1480
Ph: (703)549-3001   Fax: (703)836-4869
E-mail: dharrington@nacds.org
URL: http://www.nacds.org

Description: Chain drug members (130); associate members (1400) and (80) international members include manufacturers, suppliers, manufacturer's representatives, publishers, and advertising agencies. Interprets actions by government agencies in such areas as drugs, public health, federal trade, labor, and excise taxes. Sponsors meetings

and pharmacy student recruitment program. Maintains library. Offers insurance and discount services to members.

★6861★ National Electrical Manufacturers Representatives Association (NEMRA)
660 White Plains Rd., Ste. 600
Tarrytown, NY 10591
Ph: (914)524-8650   Fax: (914)524-8655
E-mail: nemra@nemra.org
URL: http://www.nemra.org

Purpose: North American trade association dedicated to promoting continuing education, professionalism, and the use of independent manufacturers representatives in the electrical industry. Offers professional development programs in business management and sales training, and offers a proprietary computer system for independent elec-

trical representatives. Sponsors educational programs; compiles statistics; and holds an annual networking conference for its representative members and their manufacturers.

★6862★ National Marine Representatives Association (NMRA)
PO Box 360
Gurnee, IL 60031
Ph: (847)662-3167   Fax: (847)336-7126
E-mail: info@nmraonline.org
URL: http://www.nmraonline.org

Description: Works to serve the marine industry independent sales reps and the manufacturers selling through reps. Serves as industry voice, networking tool and information source promoting benefits of utilizing independent marine reps for sales. Aims to assist manufacturers find the right marine sales reps for product lines.

Market Research Analysts

SOURCES OF HELP-WANTED ADS

★6863★ *Alert!*
Marketing Research Association
1344 Silas Deane Hwy., Ste. 306
Rocky Hill, CT 06067-0230
Ph: (860)257-4008   Fax: (860)257-3990
URL: http://www.mra-net.org/newsletter/archives

Description: Monthly. Provides information about marketing industry events, trends in marketing research, management techniques, association events, and legislative activities affecting the marketing industry. Recurring features include news of research, a calendar of events, reports of meetings, news of educational opportunities, job listings, notices of publications available, business opportunities, and facilities for sale.

★6864★ *BtoB Magazine*
Crain Communications Inc.
711 Third Ave.
New York, NY 10017-4036
Ph: (212)210-0100   Fax: (212)210-0244
Fr: 800-446-1420
URL: http://www.btobonline.com

Monthly. $59.00/year for individuals. Trade magazine on business-to-business marketing news, strategy, and tactics.

★6865★ *Direct Marketing Magazine*
Hoke Communications Inc.
224 7th St.
Garden City, NY 11530
Ph: (516)746-6700   Fax: (516)294-8141
Fr: 800-229-6700

Monthly. $60.00/year for individuals; $6.00 for single issue. Direct response advertising magazine.

★6866★ *DM News*
DM News
100 6th Ave.of the Americas
New York, NY 10013
Ph: (212)925-7300   Fax: (212)925-8752

E-mail: inquiry@dmnews.com
URL: http://www.dmnews.com

Weekly. $75.00/year. Tabloid newspaper for publishers, fund raisers, financial marketers, catalogers, package goods advertisers and their agencies, and other marketers who use direct mail, mail order advertising, catalogs, or other direct response media to sell their products or services.

★6867★ *Frohlinger's Marketing Report*
Joseph Frohlinger
7 Coppell Dr.
Tenafly, NJ 07670-2903
Ph: (201)567-4447   Fr: 800-962-7538

Description: Four issues/year. Provides information on marketing, advertising, and the media. Recurring features include interviews, news of research, a calendar of events, reports of meetings, job listings, and book reviews.

★6868★ *Marketing News*
American Marketing Association
311 S Wacker Dr., Ste. 5800
Chicago, IL 60606-2266
Ph: (312)542-9000   Fax: (312)542-9001
Fr: 800-262-1150
E-mail: news
URL: http://www.marketingpower.com/pubs

Semimonthly. $100.00/year for nonmembers; $130.00/year, libraries and corporations; $3.00 for single issue, institutions. Business magazine focusing on current marketing trends.

★6869★ *Quirk's Marketing Research Review*
Quirk Enterprises Inc.
PO Box 23536
Minneapolis, MN 55423-0536
Ph: (952)854-5101   Fax: (952)854-8191
URL: http://www.quirks.com

$70.00/year. Trade publication for the marketing research industry.

★6870★ *Sales & Marketing Management*
Bill Communications Inc.
770 Broadway
New York, NY 10003-9595
Ph: (646)654-4500   Fax: (646)654-7212
E-mail: edit@salesandmarketing.com
URL: http://www.salesandmarketing.com

$48.00/year. Business magazine.

PLACEMENT AND JOB REFERRAL SERVICES

★6871★ American Marketing Association (AMA)
311 S Wacker Dr., Ste. 5800
Chicago, IL 60606
Ph: (312)542-9000   Fax: (312)542-9001
Fr: 800-262-1150
E-mail: info@ama.org
URL: http://www.marketingpower.com/

Description: Professional society of marketing and market research executives, sales and promotion managers, advertising specialists, academics, and others interested in marketing. **Activities:** Fosters research; sponsors seminars, conferences, and student marketing clubs; provides educational placement service and doctoral consortium.

EMPLOYER DIRECTORIES AND NETWORKING LISTS

★6872★ *Bradford's International Directory of Marketing Research Agencies*
Business Research Services Inc.
4201 Connecticut Ave. NW, Ste. 610
Washington, DC 20008
Ph: (202)364-6473   Fax: (202)686-3228
Fr: 800-845-8420

Biennial. $95.00. Covers over 1,700 marketing research agencies worldwide. Includes domestic and international demographic data and professional association contacts. Entries include: Company name, address, phone, name and title of contact, date founded, number of employees, description of products or services, e-mail, URL. Arrangement: Geographical. Indexes: Alphabetical by company.

★6873★ GreenBook Worldwide-Directory of Marketing Research Companies and Services

New York AMA-Green Book
Lakewood Business Park
4301 32nd St. W, Ste. E-11
Bradenton, FL 34210
Ph: (941)752-4498   Fax: 800-879-3751
Fr: 800-972-9202
URL: http://www.greenbook.org

Annual, March. $250.00. Covers more than 2,500 marketing research companies worldwide (computer services, interviewing services, etc.) of marketing research needs; international coverage. Includes a list of computer programs for marketing research. Entries include: Company name, address, phone, name of principal executive, products and services, branch offices. Arrangement: Alphabetical. Indexes: Geographical, principal executive name, research services, market/industry served, computer program name, trademark/servicemarks.

★6874★ Market Research and Analysis Directory

infoUSA Inc.
5711 S 86th Cir.
Omaha, NE 68127-0347
Ph: (402)930-3500   Fax: (402)331-0176
Fr: 800-555-6124
URL: http://www.abii.com

Annual. Number of listings: 5,443. Entries include: Name, address, phone (including area code), size of advertisement, year first in "Yellow Pages," name of owner or manager, number of employees. Compiled from telephone company "Yellow Pages," nationwide. Arrangement: Geographical.

★6875★ MRA Blue Book Research Services Directory

Marketing Research Association
1344 Silas Deane Hwy., Ste. 306
Rocky Hill, CT 06067-0230
Ph: (860)257-4008   Fax: (860)257-3990
E-mail: email@mra-net.org
URL: http://www.bluebook.org

Annual, February. $169.95. Covers over 1,200 marketing research companies and field interviewing services. Entries include: Company name, address, phone, names of executives, services, facilities, special interviewing capabilities. Arrangement: Geographical; business type. Indexes: geographic and by specialty.

★6876★ Quirk's Marketing Research Review-Researcher SourceBook Issue

Quirk Enterprises Inc.
8030 Cedar Ave. S.,Ste 229
Minneapolis, MN 55425
Ph: (952)854-5101   Fax: (952)854-8191
URL: http://www.quirks.com

Annual, September. $35.00; $50.00 for international. Covers about 7,300 organizations providing marketing research products and services. Entries include: Name, address, phone, fax, contact, research specialties, URL, e-mail. Arrangement: Geographical. Indexes: Personnel, industry specialization, research specialization, alphabetic.

HANDBOOKS AND MANUALS

★6877★ Careers in Marketing

McGraw-Hill Trade
2 Penn Plaza
New York, NY 10121
Ph: (212)904-2000   Fr: 800-722-4726
E-mail: ntcpub@tribune.com

Lila B. Stair and Leslie Stair. Third edition, 2001. $19.95; $14.95 (paper). 192 pages. Surveys career opportunities in marketing and related areas such as marketing research, product development, and sales promotion. Includes a description of the work, places of employment, employment outlook, trends, and salaries. Offers job hunting advice.

★6878★ Careers for Number Crunchers and Other Quantitative Types

McGraw-Hill Trade
2 Penn Plaza
New York, NY 10121
Ph: (212)904-2000   Fr: 800-722-4726
E-mail: ntcpub@tribune.com

Rebecca Burnett. Second edition, 2002. $15.95; $12.95 (paper). 192 pages. Provides information to math-oriented job hunters on how to become statisticians, field researchers, computer programmers, stock analysts, investment managers, bankers, engineers, accountants, underwriters, economists, market analysts, mathematicians, systems analysts, and more.

★6879★ Great Jobs for History Majors

McGraw-Hill Trade
2 Penn Plaza
New York, NY 10121
Ph: (212)904-2000   Fr: 800-722-4726
E-mail: ntcpub@tribune.com

Julie DeGalan and Stephen Lambert. 1994. $11.95 (paper). 442 pages.

★6880★ How to Get into Marketing and PR

Continuum International Publishing Group, Inc.
15 E. 26th St., Ste. 1703
New York, NY 10010
Ph: (212)953-5858   Fax: (212)953-5944

Annie Gurton. June 2003. $21.95 (paper). 256 pages.

★6881★ Opportunities in Direct Marketing

McGraw-Hill Contemporary Books
1221 Avenue of the Americas
New York, NY 10020
Ph: (212)904-2000   Fr: 800-323-4900
E-mail: ntcpub@tribune.com

Anne Basye. Revised, 2000. $14.95; $11.95 (paper). 160 pages. Examines opportunities with direct marketers, catalog companies, direct marketing agencies, telemarketing firms, mailing list brokers, and database marketing companies. Describes how to prepare for a career in direct marketing and how to break into the field. Includes sources of short-term professional training.

★6882★ Opportunities in Marketing Careers

McGraw-Hill Trade
2 Penn Plaza
New York, NY 10121
Ph: (212)904-2000   Fr: 800-722-4726

Margery Steinberg. 1999. $14.95; $11.95 (paper). 202 pages. Includes guidance on identifying and pursuing job opportunities. Illustrated.

★6883★ Resumes for Sales and Marketing Careers

McGraw-Hill Professional
2 Penn Plaza
New York, NY 10121
Ph: (212)904-2000   Fr: 800-722-4726
E-mail: ntcpub@tribune.com

Chuck Cochran and Donna Peerce. Second edition, 1998. $10.95 (paper). 336 pages. Sample resumes and cover letters from all levels of the sales and marketing field.

OTHER SOURCES

★6884★ Academy of Marketing Science (AMS)

University of Miami
School of Bus. Admin.
PO Box 248012
Coral Gables, FL 33124
Ph: (305)284-6673   Fax: (305)284-3762
E-mail: ams.sba@miami.edu
URL: http://www.ams-web.org

Description: Marketing academicians and practitioners; individuals interested in fostering education in marketing science. Purpose is to promote the advancement of knowledge and the furthering of professional standards in the field of marketing. Explores the special application areas of marketing science and its responsibilities as an economic, ethical, and social force; promotes research and the widespread dissemination of findings. Facilitates exchange of information and experience among members, and the transfer of marketing knowledge and technology to developing countries; promotes marketing science on an international level. Provides a forum for discussion and refinement of concepts, methods and applications, and the opportunity to publish papers in the field. Assists member educators in the development of improved teaching methods, devices, directions, and materials. Offers guidance and direction in marketing practice and reviewer assistance on scholarly works. Contributes to the solution of marketing problems encountered by individual firms, industries, and society as a whole. Encourages members to utilize their marketing talents to the fullest through redirection, reassignment, and relocation. Sponsors competitions.

★6885★ *Financial Occupations*

Delphi Productions
3160 4th St.
Boulder, CO 80304
Fax: (303)443-4022   Fr: 888-443-2400
URL: http://www.delphivideo.com

$95.00. 50 minutes. Part of the Careers for the 21st Century Video Library.

★6886★ Marketing Agencies Association Worldwide (MAA)

1031 US Hwy. 22 West, 3rd Fl.
Bridgewater, NJ 08807
Ph: (908)595-6924   Fax: (908)707-0407
E-mail: vincentsottosanti@maaw.org
URL: http://www.maaw.org

Members: Agencies with a primary interest in promotion marketing. **Purpose:** Seeks to increase understanding, by management, of promotion marketing as a special component of the total marketing management and corporate communication function; will stimulate methods of scientific research and evaluation of marketing promotion effectiveness. Conducts research; maintains speakers' bureau and hall of fame.

★6887★ Marketing Research Association (MRA)

1344 Silas Deane Hwy., Ste. 306
PO Box 230
Rocky Hill, CT 06067-0230
Ph: (860)257-4008   Fax: (860)257-3990
E-mail: email@mra-net.org
URL: http://www.mra-net.org

Members: Companies and individuals involved in any area of opinion and marketing research, such as data collection, research, or as an end-user.

★6888★ Society for Marketing Professional Services (SMPS)

99 Canal Center Plz., Ste. 330
Alexandria, VA 22314
Ph: (703)549-6117   Fax: (703)549-2498
Fr: 800-292-7677
E-mail: info@smps.org
URL: http://www.smps.org

Members: Marketing employees of architectural, engineering, planning, interior design, landscape architectural, and construction management firms who are responsible for the new business development of their companies. **Activities:** Compiles statistics. Offers local and national educational programs; maintains certification program.

★6889★ Women in Direct Marketing International (WDMI)

224 7th St.
Garden City, NY 11530
Ph: (732)469-5000   Fax: (732)469-8414
E-mail: bladden@directmaildepot.com
URL: http://www.wdmi.org

Description: Direct marketing professionals. Seeks to advance the interests and influence of women in the direct response industry; provide for communication and career education; assist in advancement of personal career objectives; serve as professional network to develop business contacts and foster mutual goals. Maintains career talent bank. Distributes information nationally; maintains other chapters in Chicago, IL, Los Angeles, CA, Dallas, TX, Japan, UK, and Belgium.

Marketing, Advertising, and Public Relations Managers

SOURCES OF HELP-WANTED ADS

★6890★ Advertising Age

Crain Communications Inc.
711 Third Ave.
New York, NY 10017-4036
Ph: (212)210-0100   Fax: (212)210-0244
Fr: 800-446-1420

Weekly. $99.00/year; $3.00 for single issue. Advertising trade publication covering agency, media, and advertiser news and trends.

★6891★ Adweek

VNU Business Media USA
770 Broadway
New York, NY 10003
Ph: (646)654-5000
E-mail: info@adweek.com
URL: http://www.adweek.com

Weekly. $149.00/year for individuals; $3.95 for single issue. Advertising news magazine.

★6892★ Adweek/New England

Adweek L.P.
100 Boylston St., Ste. 210
Boston, MA 02116-4610
Ph: (617)482-0876   Fax: (617)482-2921
URL: http://www.adweek.com

Weekly. $145.00/year for individuals. News magazine serving the advertising, marketing, and media industries in New England.

★6893★ Alert!

Marketing Research Association
1344 Silas Deane Hwy., Ste. 306
Rocky Hill, CT 06067-0230
Ph: (860)257-4008   Fax: (860)257-3990
URL: http://www.mra-net.org/newsletter/archives

Description: Monthly. Provides information about marketing industry events, trends in marketing research, management techniques, association events, and legislative activities affecting the marketing industry. Recurring features include news of research,

a calendar of events, reports of meetings, news of educational opportunities, job listings, notices of publications available, business opportunities, and facilities for sale.

★6894★ ANDY Souvenir Journal

Advertising Club of New York
235 Park Ave. S, 6th Fl.
New York, NY 10003
Ph: (212)533-8080   Fax: (212)533-1929

Annual. Professional journal covering issues for advertising and communications executives.

★6895★ BtoB Magazine

Crain Communications Inc.
711 Third Ave.
New York, NY 10017-4036
Ph: (212)210-0100   Fax: (212)210-0244
Fr: 800-446-1420
URL: http://www.btobonline.com

Monthly. $59.00/year for individuals. Trade magazine on business-to-business marketing news, strategy, and tactics.

★6896★ Business Ideas Newsletter

Dan Newman Co.
1051 Bloomfield Ave.
Clifton, NJ 07012

Description: Ten issues/year. Publishes information for advertising and marketing executives to "increase results, returns, and profits." Reports on and interprets developments affecting the business community, including issues such as legislative and regulatory activities and tax reform. Covers new product developments, employment strategies, advertising techniques, and direct marketing potential. Recurring features include news of research, reports of meetings, news of educational opportunities, and book reviews.

★6897★ The Counselor

Advertising Specialty Institute
4800 St. Rd.
Trevose, PA 19053-6698
Ph: (215)942-8600   Fax: (215)953-3107

Monthly. $70.00/year for individuals; $90.00/year for Canada; $185.00/year for other countries. Magazine.

★6898★ Direct Marketing Magazine

Hoke Communications Inc.
224 7th St.
Garden City, NY 11530
Ph: (516)746-6700   Fax: (516)294-8141
Fr: 800-229-6700

Monthly. $60.00/year for individuals; $6.00 for single issue. Direct response advertising magazine.

★6899★ DM News

DM News
100 6th Ave.of the Americas
New York, NY 10013
Ph: (212)925-7300   Fax: (212)925-8752
E-mail: inquiry@dmnews.com
URL: http://www.dmnews.com

Weekly. $75.00/year. Tabloid newspaper for publishers, fund raisers, financial marketers, catalogers, package goods advertisers and their agencies, and other marketers who use direct mail, mail order advertising, catalogs, or other direct response media to sell their products or services.

★6900★ Editor & Publisher

Editor & Publisher Magazine
770 Broadway
New York, NY 10003-9595
Fax: (646)654-5360   Fr: 800-336-4380
URL: http://www.editorandpublisher.com

Weekly. $99.00/year for U.S. and Canada, includes exclusive web access; $130.00/year for other countries; $4.00 for single issue. Magazine focusing on newspaper journalism, advertising, printing equipment, and interactive services.

★6901★ *Electronic Media*

Crain Communications Inc.
1155 Gratiot Ave.
Detroit, MI 48207-2997
Ph: (313)446-6000
E-mail: info@crain.com
URL: http://www.crain.com/

Newspaper covering management, programming, cable and trends in the television and the media industry.

★6902★ *Franchising World*

International Franchise Association
1350 New York Ave. NW, Ste. 900
Washington, DC 20005-4709
Ph: (202)628-8000   Fax: (202)628-0812
Fr: 800-543-1038

$18.00/year for individuals; $3.50 for single issue. Trade magazine covering topics of interest to franchise company executives and the business world.

★6903★ *Frohlinger's Marketing Report*

Joseph Frohlinger
7 Coppell Dr.
Tenafly, NJ 07670-2903
Ph: (201)567-4447   Fr: 800-962-7538

Description: Four issues/year. Provides information on marketing, advertising, and the media. Recurring features include interviews, news of research, a calendar of events, reports of meetings, job listings, and book reviews.

★6904★ *HOW*

F & W Publications Inc.
4700 E Galbraith Rd.
Cincinnati, OH 45236-6708
Ph: (513)531-2690   Fax: (513)531-2902
Fr: 800-289-0963
E-mail: editorial@howdesign.com

Bimonthly. $49.00/year for individuals; $7.95 for single issue, Jan/Feb or May/June; $9.95 for single issue, Mar/April or July/Aug; $11.95/year for single issue, Sept/Oct or Nov/Dec. Instructional trade magazine.

★6905★ *Marketing News*

American Marketing Association
311 S Wacker Dr., Ste. 5800
Chicago, IL 60606-2266
Ph: (312)542-9000   Fax: (312)542-9001
Fr: 800-262-1150
E-mail: news
URL: http://www.marketingpower.com/pubs

Semimonthly. $100.00/year for nonmembers; $130.00/year, libraries and corporations; $3.00 for single issue, institutions. Business magazine focusing on current marketing trends.

★6906★ *PR Marcom Jobs East*

Rachel P.R. Services
208 E 51st St., No. 1600
New York, NY 10022

Description: Biweekly. Provides news of job openings in public relations, marketing, jour-

nalism, communications, public relations agencies and corporations, and freelance and temporary writing positions. Focuses on the New York City, Washington, D.C., Boston, and surrounding states. Recurring features include a calendar of events, job listings, book reviews, and notices of publications available.

★6907★ *Public Relations Career Opportunities*

Public Relations Career Opportunities
101 S Whiting St., No. 305
Alexandria, VA 22304
Ph: (703)823-4094   Fax: (703)823-5352
URL: http://www.careeropps.com

Description: Semimonthly. Provides information about positions available in the fields of public affairs and public relations.

★6908★ *Quirk's Marketing Research Review*

Quirk Enterprises Inc.
PO Box 23536
Minneapolis, MN 55423-0536
Ph: (952)854-5101   Fax: (952)854-8191
URL: http://www.quirks.com

$70.00/year. Trade publication for the marketing research industry.

★6909★ *Sales and Marketing Executive Report*

The Dartnell Corp.
PO Box 980
Horsham, PA 19044-0980
Fr: 800-621-5463

Description: Biweekly. Discusses topics of interest to managers, including motivating and training sales personnel, executive self-improvement, and advertising and public relations strategies. Recurring features include news of research, letters to the editor, book reviews, a calendar of events, and columns titled Sales/Marketing Briefs and Special Report.

★6910★ *Sales & Marketing Management*

Bill Communications Inc.
770 Broadway
New York, NY 10003-9595
Ph: (646)654-4500   Fax: (646)654-7212
E-mail: edit@salesandmarketing.com
URL: http://www.salesandmarketing.com

$48.00/year. Business magazine.

★6911★ *Web Marketing Today*

Wilson Internet Services
PO Box 308
Rocklin, CA 95677-0308

Monthly. Publication covering marketing and advertising.

PLACEMENT AND JOB REFERRAL SERVICES

★6912★ **Advertising Production Club of New York (APC)**

276 Bowery
New York, NY 10012
Ph: (212)334-2018   Fax: (212)431-5786
E-mail: admin@apc-ny.org
URL: http://www.apc-ny.org

Description: Production and traffic department personnel from advertising agencies, corporate or retail advertising departments, and publishing companies; college level graphic arts educators. Meetings include educational programs on graphic arts procedures and plant tours. Maintains employment service for members.

★6913★ **American Marketing Association (AMA)**

311 S Wacker Dr., Ste. 5800
Chicago, IL 60606
Ph: (312)542-9000   Fax: (312)542-9001
Fr: 800-262-1150
E-mail: info@ama.org
URL: http://www.marketingpower.com/

Description: Professional society of marketing and market research executives, sales and promotion managers, advertising specialists, academics, and others interested in marketing. **Activities:** Fosters research; sponsors seminars, conferences, and student marketing clubs; provides educational placement service and doctoral consortium.

★6914★ **Direct Marketing Association (DMA)**

1120 Avenue of the Americas
New York, NY 10036-6700
Ph: (212)768-7277   Fax: (212)302-6714
E-mail: president@the-dma.org
URL: http://www.the-dma.org

Members: Manufacturers, wholesalers, public utilities, retailers, mail order firms, publishers, schools, clubs, insurance companies, financial organizations, business equipment manufacturers, paper and envelope manufacturers, list brokers, compilers, managers, owners, computer service bureaus, advertising agencies, lettershops, research organizations, printers, lithographers, creators, and producers of direct mail and direct response advertising. **Purpose:** Studies consumer and business attitudes toward direct mail and related direct marketing statistics. **Activities:** Offers Mail Preference Service for consumers who wish to receive less mail advertising, Mail Order Action Line to help resolve difficulties with mail order purchases, and Telephone Preference Service for people who wish to receive fewer telephone sales calls. Maintains hall of fame; offers placement service; compiles statistics. Sponsors several three-day Basic Direct Marketing Institutes, Advanced Direct Marketing Institutes, and special interest seminars and workshops. Maintains Government

Affairs office in Washington, DC. Operates Direct Marketing Educational Foundation.

★6915★ Franchise Consultants International Association (FCIA)
5147 S Angela Rd.
Memphis, TN 38117
Ph: (901)368-3361   Fax: (901)368-1144
E-mail: franmark@msn.com

Members: Individuals and corporations involved in franchising including attorneys, consultants, brokers, sales personnel, suppliers, Universities, consultants, advertisers, and developers. **Purpose:** To provide standardized information for the franchise industry. Seeks to coordinate effective and professional franchise consulting and to educate members in franchise law and logistics. Serves as a clearinghouse of approved literature on franchising. **Activities:** Operates archive and hall of fame; compiles statistics. Provides placement service, charitable program, and speakers' bureau. Has extensive library. Expert witness specialists.

EMPLOYER DIRECTORIES AND NETWORKING LISTS

★6916★ Adcrafter-Roster Issue
Adcraft Club of Detroit
3011 W Grand Blvd., Ste. 1715
Detroit, MI 48202
Ph: (313)872-7850   Fax: (313)872-7858

Annual, May. $20.00. Covers 3,000 executives of advertising agencies, advertising media, and advertising companies in the Detroit metropolitan area, and 500 out-of-state members. Entries include: Name, title, company name, office address and phone, business classification, membership code. Arrangement: Alphabetical and classified by line of business; identical information in both sections.

★6917★ Advertiser & Agency Red Books Plus
LexisNexis Group
121 Chanlon Rd.
New Providence, NJ 07974
Ph: (908)464-6800   Fax: (908)771-7704
Fr: 800-526-4902
URL: http://www.redbooks.com

Quarterly. $1,495.00. CD-ROM. Covers 15,750 of the world's top advertisers, their products and what media they use, as well as 13,900 U.S. and international ad agencies and nearly 100,000 key executives worldwide in management, creative, and media positions. Entries include: For advertisers-Company name, job function/title, product/brand name, advertising expenditures by media. For personnel-Name and title.

★6918★ Advertising Age-Advertising Agency Income Report Issue
Crain Communications Inc.
360 N. Michigan Ave.
Chicago, IL 60601-3806
Ph: (312)649-5200   Fax: (312)280-3174
Fr: 800-678-2724
URL: http://www.adage.com

Annual, April. $3.50. Publication includes: Ranked lists of about 650 U.S advertising agencies, 1,600 foreign agencies, the world's Top 50 advertising organizations, top media services companies in the U.S. and worldwide, top U.S. healthcare agencies, and multicultural agencies, which reported billings and gross income, or whose billings and gross incomes were ascertained through research. Entries include: U.S. and foreign agency lists from more than 120 countries include gross income and capitalized billings. Profiles of the World's Top 30 ad organizations include gross income, capitalized billings, and billings for each operating unit, subsidiary, and full service office. Arrangement: Ranked by gross income.

★6919★ The Advertising Age Encyclopedia of Advertising
Fitzroy Dearborn Publishers Inc.
919 N. Michigan Ave., Ste. 760
Chicago, IL 60611
Ph: (312)587-0131   Fax: (312)587-1049
Fr: 800-850-8102

$385.00. Publication includes: Profiles of 120 ad agencies worldwide. Principal content of publication is encyclopedic account of the advertising industry. Indexes: Alphabetical.

★6920★ Advertising-Radio Directory
infoUSA Inc.
5711 S 86th Cir.
Omaha, NE 68127-0347
Ph: (402)930-3500   Fax: (402)331-0176
Fr: 800-555-6124
URL: http://www.abii.com

Updated continuously; printed on request. Number of listings: 2,175. Entries include: Name, address, phone (including area code), size of advertisement, year first in "Yellow Pages," name of owner or manager, number of employees. Compiled from telephone company "Yellow Pages," nationwide. Arrangement: Geographical.

★6921★ The ADWEEK Directory
ADWEEK Magazines
770 Broadway, 7th Fl.
New York, NY 10003
Ph: (646)654-5174   Fax: (646)654-5351
Fr: 800-468-2395
URL: http://www.adweek.com/directories

Annual, August. $700.00. Covers over 6,400 U.S. advertising agencies, public relations firms, media buying services, direct marketing and related organizations. Entries include: Agency name, address, phone, fax/e-mail, URL; names and titles of key personnel; major accounts; Ultimate parent company; headquarters location; major subsidiaries

and other operating units; year founded; number of employees; fee income; billings; percentage of billings by medium. Individual listings for each agency branch. Arrangement: Alphabetical. Indexes: Geographical; parent company, subsidiary, branch; ethnic specialities; organization, name changes, agencies opened/closed.

★6922★ Agri Marketing-The Top 50: Ag's Biggest Agencies Issue
Doane Agricultural Services
11701 Borman Dr., Ste. 300
St. Louis, MO 63146-4193
Ph: (314)569-2700   Fax: (314)569-1083
Fr: 800-535-2342

Annual, April or May. $5.00. Publication includes: List of the top 50 U.S. and Canadian advertising agencies and public relations firms, chosen on the basis of agricultural business income. Entries include: Agency name, location, income for agricultural accounts in most recent year, branch offices, major clients served. Arrangement: Alphabetical.

★6923★ American Marketing Association-The M Guide Directory
American Marketing Association
311 S Wacker Dr., Ste. 5800
Chicago, IL 60606-2266
Ph: (312)542-9000   Fax: (312)542-9001
Fr: 800-262-1150
E-mail: ads@ama.org
URL: http://www.ama.org

Annual, February. $150.00. Covers 24,000 individual members and about 1,000 paid listings for member research and service firms. Entries include: For individuals-Member name, position, home and office address, and phone numbers. For advertisers-Company name, address, phone, names of principal executives.

★6924★ Black Book Photography
Black Book Marketing Group
10 Astor Pl., 6th Fl.
New York, NY 10003
Ph: (212)539-9800   Fax: (212)539-9801
Fr: 800-841-1246
URL: http://www.BlackBook.com

Annual, January. $110.00. Publication includes over 19,000 art directors, creative directors, photographers and photographic services, design firms, advertising agencies, and other firms whose products or services are used in advertising. Entries include: Company name, address, phone. Principal content of publication is 4-color samples from the leading commercial photographers. Arrangement: Classified by product/service.

★6925★ Chicago Creative Directory
Chicago Creative Directory
333 N Michigan, Ste. 810
Chicago, IL 60601
Ph: (312)236-7337   Fax: (312)236-6078
URL: http://www.creativedir.com

Annual, March. $50.00. Covers over 6,000

advertising agencies, photographers, sound studios, talent agencies, audiovisual services, and others offering creative and production services. Entries include: For most listings-Company name, address, phone, list of officers, description of services. For freelance listings-Name, talent, address, phone. Arrangement: Classified by specialty.

★6926★ **Fashion & Print Directory**
Peter Glenn Publications
6040 NW 43rd Ter.
Boca Raton, FL 33496-4043
Ph: (561)999-8930   Fax: (561)999-8931
Fr: 888-332-6700
URL: http://www.pgdirect.com

Annual, November. $59.95. Covers advertising agencies, PR firms, marketing companies, 1000 client brand companies and related services in the U.S. and Canada. Includes photographers, marketing agency, suppliers, sources of props and rentals, fashion houses, beauty services, locations. Entries include: Company name, address, phone; paid listings numbering 5000 include description of products or services, key personnel. Arrangement: Classified by line of business.

★6927★ **4 Data Base**
Hunt-Scanlon Publishing
20 Signal Rd.
Stamford, CT 06902-7907
Ph: (203)352-2920   Fax: (203)352-2930

Annual. $1,350.00 for individuals. Database covers more than 100,000 top and middle management professionals in human resources, finance, sales and marketing, and information technology at over 10,000 companies in the U.S. Entries include: Company name, address, phone, number of employees, SIC codes, revenues, individual name, title, phone number, industry specialization.

★6928★ **International Advertising Association-Membership Directory**
International Advertising Association
521 5th Ave., Ste. 1807
New York, NY 10175
Ph: (212)557-1133   Fax: (212)983-0455

Annual, April. Database covers over 3,600 advertisers, advertising agencies, media, and other firms involved in advertising. Database includes: Company name, address, phone, fax. Arrangement: Geographical. Indexes: By company and last name.

★6929★ **Medical Marketing and Media-Healthcare Agency Profiles Issue**
CPS Communications Inc.
7200 W Camino Real, Ste. 215
Boca Raton, FL 33433
Ph: (561)368-9301   Fax: (561)368-7870
Fr: 800-346-2015
URL: http://www.cpsnet.com/Pubs/mmm.asp

Monthly, July. $10.00. Publication includes: List of about 130 health care advertising agencies. Entries include: Agency name, address, phone, name and title of contact, financial data, percentages of regional markets, market breakdown, current accounts, new accounts and accounts lost, number of employees, year established, special services, divisions, and best ad submissions with creative team information. Arrangement: Alphabetical.

★6930★ **O'Dwyer's Directory of Corporate Communications**
J.R. O'Dwyer Company Inc.
271 Madison Ave.
New York, NY 10016
Ph: (212)679-2471   Fax: (212)683-2750

Annual, latest edition February, 2003. $130. Covers public relations departments of approximately 4,450 major United States companies (listed on the New York Stock Exchange and in the "Fortune" list of 1,000 largest firms); also includes similar information on over 1,300 large trade associations and foreign embassies in the United States. Entries include: Company name, address, phone, sales, type of business; names and duties of principal public relations personnel at headquarters and other major offices, plus name and title of person to whom PR head reports; PR budget. Arrangement: Alphabetical. Indexes: Geographical, product.

★6931★ **O'Dwyer's Directory of Public Relations Firms**
J.R. O'Dwyer Company Inc.
271 Madison Ave.
New York, NY 10016
Ph: (212)679-2471   Fax: (212)683-2750
E-mail: sales@odwyerpr.com
URL: http://www.odwyerpr.com/index.html

Annual, latest edition June, 2002. $175.00. Covers over 2,900 public relations firms; international coverage. Entries include: Firm name, address, phone, principal executives, branch and overseas offices, billings, date founded, and 19,000+ clients are cross-indexed. Arrangement: Geographical by country. Indexes: Specialty (beauty and fashions, finance/investor, etc.), geographical, client.

★6932★ **O'Dwyer's New York Public Relations Directory**
J.R. O'Dwyer Company Inc.
271 Madison Ave.
New York, NY 10016
Ph: (212)679-2471   Fax: (212)683-2750

Annual. $50.00. Covers approximately 600 public relations firms, 750 corporations, 225 trade associations, and 500 public relations service firms; over 50 executive recruiters and employment agencies. Entries include: Contact information.

★6933★ **Peterson's Job Opportunities for Business Majors**
Thomson Peterson's
Princeton Pke. Corporate Ctr., 2000 Lenox Dr.
PO Box 67005
Lawrenceville, NJ 08648
Ph: (609)896-1800   Fax: (609)896-4531
Fr: 800-338-3282
URL: http://www.petersons.com

Irregular, latest edition 2000 - 16th ed. $18.95. Covers the 2,000 largest U.S. employers hiring in several fields, including financial services, management consulting, consumer products, and media/ entertainment. Entries include: Organization name, address, phone, name and title of contact, number of employees, type of organization. Arrangement: Alphabetical. Indexes: Type of organization.

★6934★ **Plunkett's Advertising and Branding Industry Almanac**
Plunkett Research Ltd.
PO Drawer 541737
Houston, TX 77254-1737
Ph: (713)932-0000   Fax: (713)932-7080

$249.99. Covers leading companies in advertising and marketing including the areas of media, direct mail, online advertising, branding, and image-crafting. Entries include: Name, address, phone, fax, and key executives. Also includes analysis and information on trends, technology, and statistics in the field.

★6935★ **Public Relations Tactics-Member Services Directory-The Blue Book**
Public Relations Society of America (PRSA)
33 Irving Pl.
New York, NY 10003-2376
Ph: (212)995-2230   Fax: (212)995-0757
E-mail: 74224.1456@compuserve.com
URL: http://www.prsa.org

Annual, January. $375.00 for nonmembers. Covers PRSA members-headquarters, staff contacts, and chapter, section, and district information. Entries include: Name, professional affiliation and title, address, phone, membership rank. Arrangement: Alphabetical. Indexes: Geographical, organizational.

★6936★ **Quirk's Marketing Research Review-Researcher SourceBook Issue**
Quirk Enterprises Inc.
8030 Cedar Ave. S.,Ste 229
Minneapolis, MN 55425
Ph: (952)854-5101   Fax: (952)854-8191
URL: http://www.quirks.com

Annual, September. $35.00; $50.00 for international. Covers about 7,300 organizations providing marketing research products and services. Entries include: Name, address, phone, fax, contact, research specialties, URL, e-mail. Arrangement: Geographical. Indexes: Personnel, industry specialization, research specialization, alphabetic.

★6937★ **Reed's Worldwide Directory of Public Relations Organizations**

Pigafetta Press
PO Box 39244
Washington, DC 20016
Ph: (202)244-2580   Fax: (202)244-2581
E-mail: 110104.1310@compuserve.com

Annual, October. $95.00. Covers approximately 225 professional public relations associations in 75 countries. Entries include: Association name, address, phone, publications, current officers, activities, and history of the organization. Arrangement: Geographical; separate section for international organizations.

★6938★ **Sports Market Place**

Sportsguide L.L.C.
13901 N 73rd St., Ste. 219
Scottsdale, AZ 85260
Ph: (480)948-8885   Fax: (480)948-7701
Fr: 800-776-7877
E-mail: smp@sportsmarketplace.com
URL: http://www.sportsmarketplace.com

Annual, January. $249.00. Covers manufacturers, organizations, professional sports teams, broadcasting networks, sports arenas, syndicators, publications, trade shows, marketing services, corporate sports sponsors, and other groups concerned with the business and promotional aspects of sports generally and with air sports, arm wrestling, auto sports, badminton, baseball, basketball, biathlon, bowling, boxing, curling, equestrian, exercise, fencing, field hockey, football, golf, gymnastics, ice hockey, lacrosse, martial arts, paddleball, paddle tennis, platform tennis, pentathlon, racquetball, rowing, rugby, running/jogging, skiing, soccer, softball, squash, swimming, table tennis, tennis, track and field, volleyball, water sports, weightlifting, and wrestling. Entries include: Name of company or organization, address, fax, e-mail, URL, name of key personnel with titles, and description of products or services. Arrangement: Classified by type of firm, sport, or activity. Indexes: Alphabetical, single sprt, media, sport sponsors, agencies, manufacturers, brand name, facilities, executive, and Geographical.

★6939★ **Standard Directory of Advertising Agencies**

LexisNexis Group
121 Chanlon Rd.
New Providence, NJ 07974
Ph: (908)464-6800   Fax: (908)771-7704
Fr: 800-526-4902
URL: http://www.redbooks.com

Semiannual, January and July; semiannual supplements, April and October. $799.00 for single copy without supplements. Covers nearly 10,800 advertising agencies. Entries include: Agency name, address, phone, e-mail, website, year founded, number of employees, association memberships, area of specialization, annual billing, breakdown of gross billings by media, clients, executives, special markets, and new agencies. Arrangement: Alphabetical. Indexes: Geographical (includes address), special market, agency responsibilities, and personnel.

★6940★ **Standard Directory of International Advertisers and Agencies**

LexisNexis Group
121 Chanlon Rd.
New Providence, NJ 07974
Ph: (908)464-6800   Fax: (908)771-7704
Fr: 800-526-4902
URL: http://www.lexisnexis.com/

Annual, January. $629.00. Covers nearly 13,500 advertiser companies and advertising agencies; international coverage. Entries include: Company name, address, phone, fax, telex, annual sales or billings, number of employees, Standard Industrial Classification (SIC) code, names and titles of key personnel, line of business, subsidiary and branch office names, address, phone, telex, key officers; advertiser companies include their advertising agency's name, address, and description of advertising budget and strategies; advertising agencies include names of client companies and their lines of business. Arrangement: Separate alphabetical and geographical sections for advertiser companies and advertising agencies. Indexes: Geographical, company name, personal name, trade name, SIC.

★6941★ **The Workbook**

Scott & Daughters Publishing Inc.
940 N Highland Ave., Ste. A
Los Angeles, CA 90038
Ph: (323)856-0008   Fax: (323)856-0443
Fr: 800-547-2688
URL: http://www.workbook.com

Annual, February. $120.00. Covers 49,000 advertising agencies, art directors, photographers, freelance illustrators and designers, artists' representatives, interactive designers, pre-press services, and other graphic arts services in the U.S. Entries include: Company or individual name, address, phone, specialty. National in scope. Arrangement: Classified by product or service.

HANDBOOKS AND MANUALS

★6942★ **The Advertising Age Handbook of Advertising**

McGraw-Hill Contemporary Books
1221 Avenue of the Americas
New York, NY 10020
Ph: (212)904-2000   Fr: 800-323-4900

Herschell Gordon Lewis, Carol Nelson. Contributor: Rance Crain. 1999. $39.95.

★6943★ **Becoming a Public Relations Writer: A Writing Process Workbook for the Profession**

Lawrence Erlbaum Associates Inc.
10 Industrial Ave.
Mahwah, NJ 07430
Ph: (201)236-9500   Fax: (781)942-1117
Fr: 800-447-2226

Ronald D. Smith. 1997. $24.00 (paper). Out of print.

★6944★ **A Big Life in Advertising**

Alfred A. Knopf Incorporated
299 Park Ave.
New York, NY 10171
Ph: (212)751-2600   Fax: (212)572-2593
Fr: 800-726-0600

2002. $26.00.

★6945★ **Breaking into Advertising**

Thomson Peterson's
202 Carnegie Ctr.
Box 67005
Princeton, NJ 08540
Fr: 800-338-3282

Smith. 1998. $14.95 (paper). Explains how to get a job in advertising.

★6946★ **Career Opportunities in Advertising and Public Relations (Career Opportunities Series)**

Checkmark Books, Inc.
132 W. 31st St., 17th Fl.
New York, NY 10001-2006
Ph: (212)967-8800   Fax: (212)967-9196
Fr: 800-322-8755
URL: http://www.factsonfile.com

Shelly Field and Howard J. Rubenstein. Third edition, 2001. $14.95 (paper). 320 pages. Provides the job seeker with information about locating and landing the right position. Includes detailed job descriptions for many specific positions and lists trade associations, recruiting organizations, and major agencies. Contains index and bibliography.

★6947★ **Career Opportunities for Writers**

Checkmark Books
132 W. 31st St., 17th Fl.
New York, NY 10001-2006
Ph: (212)967-8800   Fax: (212)967-9196
Fr: 800-322-8755
URL: http://www.factsonfile.com

Rosemary Ellen Guiley and Janet Frick. Fourth edition, 2000. $45.00. Part of the Career Opportunities Series. Describes more than 100 jobs in eight major fields, offering such details as duties, salaries, perquisites, employment and advancement opportunities, organizations to join, and opportunities for women and minorities.

★6948★ **Career Solutions for Creative People: How to Balance Artistic Goals with Career Security**

Allworth Press
10 E. 23rd St., Suite 510
New York, NY 10010
Ph: (212)777-8395   Fax: (212)777-8261
Fr: 800-491-2808

Ronda Ormont. 2001. $19.95 (paper).

★6949★ *Careers in Advertising*

VGM Career Horizons
1221 Avenue of the Americas
New York, NY 10020
Ph: (212)904-2000   Fr: 800-323-4900
E-mail: ntcpub@tribune.com

S. William Pattis. 1996; Second Edition. $17.95. 144 pages.

★6950★ *Careers in Communications*

VGM Career Horizons
4255 W. Touhy Ave.
Lincolnwood, IL 60646-1975
Ph: (847)679-5500   Fax: (847)679-2494
Fr: 800-323-4900
E-mail: ntcpub@tribune.com

Shonan Noronha. Third edition, 1998. $17.95; $13.95 (paper). 418 pages. Examines the fields of journalism, photography, radio, television, film, public relations, and advertising. Gives concrete details on job locations and how to secure a job. Suggests many resources for job hunting.

★6951★ *Careers in International Business*

McGraw-Hill Trade
2 Penn Plaza
New York, NY 10121
Ph: (212)904-2000   Fr: 800-722-4726
E-mail: ntcpub@tribune.com

Ed Halloran. 1996. $17.95; 13.95 (paper). 160 pages.

★6952★ *Careers in Marketing*

McGraw-Hill Trade
2 Penn Plaza
New York, NY 10121
Ph: (212)904-2000   Fr: 800-722-4726
E-mail: ntcpub@tribune.com

Lila B. Stair and Leslie Stair. Third edition, 2001. $19.95; $14.95 (paper). 192 pages. Surveys career opportunities in marketing and related areas such as marketing research, product development, and sales promotion. Includes a description of the work, places of employment, employment outlook, trends, and salaries. Offers job hunting advice.

★6953★ *Careers in Marketing, Advertising and Public Relations*

Kogan Page, Ltd.
22 Broad St.
Ste. 34
Milford, CT 06460

Adela Stanley. 2003. $14.95 (paper). 128 pages. Part of the Kogan Page Careers Series. Out of print.

★6954★ *Careers in the Visual Arts: A Guide to Jobs, Money, Opportunities, and an Artistic Life*

Watson-Guptill Publications, Inc.
BPI Communications, Inc.
770 Broadway
New York, NY 10003
Ph: (646)654-5400   Fax: (646)654-5486
Fr: 800-323-9432

Dee Ito. 1993. $14.95 (paper). 320 pages. Out of print. Gives a broad overview of each field included, with educational requirements and employment opportunities. Includes ideas on how to get started.

★6955★ *Careers for Writers and Others Who Have a Way with Words*

McGraw-Hill Trade
2 Penn Plaza
New York, NY 10121
Ph: (212)904-2000   Fr: 800-722-4726
E-mail: ntcpub@tribune.com

Robert W. Bly. 1995. $14.95; $9.95 (paper). 295 pages.

★6956★ *Encyclopedia of Advertising*

Fitzroy Dearborn Publishers Inc.
919 N. Michigan Ave., Ste. 760
Chicago, IL 60611
Ph: (312)587-0131   Fax: (312)587-1049
Fr: 800-850-8102

Editor: John McDonough. 2001. $385.00.

★6957★ *Get Noticed!: Self Promotion for Creative Professionals*

F & W Publications Inc.
4700 E Galbraith Rd.
Cincinnati, OH 45236
Ph: (513)531-2690   Fax: (513)531-4082
Fr: 800-289-0963

Sheree Clark, Kristen Lennert. 2000. $29.99 (paper).

★6958★ *Great Jobs for Business Majors*

McGraw-Hill Trade
2 Penn Plaza
New York, NY 10121
Ph: (212)904-2000   Fr: 800-722-4726
E-mail: ntcpub@tribune.com

Stephen Lambert. 1996. $11.95 (paper). 462 pages.

★6959★ *Great Jobs for Communications Majors*

McGraw-Hill Professional
2 Penn Plaza
New York, NY 10121
Ph: (212)904-2000   Fr: 800-722-4726
E-mail: ntcpub@tribune.com

Blythe Camenson. Second edition, 2001. $14.95 (paper). 256 pages.

★6960★ *Great Jobs for English Majors*

McGraw-Hill Trade
2 Penn Plaza
New York, NY 10121
Ph: (212)904-2000   Fr: 800-722-4726
E-mail: ntcpub@tribune.com

Julie DeGalan. Second edition, 2000. $12.95 (paper). 462 pages.

★6961★ *Great Jobs for Liberal Arts Majors*

McGraw-Hill Professional
2 Penn Plaza
New York, NY 10121
Ph: (212)904-2000   Fr: 800-722-4726
E-mail: ntcpub@tribune.com

Blythe Camenson. Second edition, 2001. $14.95 (paper). 256 pages.

★6962★ *Harvard Business School Guide to Careers in Marketing: A Guide to Management Careers in Marketing*

Harvard Business School Press
60 Harvard Way
Boston, MA 02163
Ph: (617)783-7400   Fax: (617)783-7492
Fr: 888-500-1016

Harvard Business School Press Staff. 2000. $22.95 (paper).

★6963★ *How to Become a Marketing Superstar: Unexpected Rules That Ring the Cash Register*

Hyperion Press
77 W. 66th St., 11th Fl.
New York, NY 10023-6298
Ph: (212)456-0100   Fax: (212)456-0108
Fr: 800-759-0190

Jeffrey J. Fox. May 2003. $11.95. E-book.

★6964★ *How to Get into Marketing and PR*

Continuum International Publishing Group, Inc.
15 E. 26th St., Ste. 1703
New York, NY 10010
Ph: (212)953-5858   Fax: (212)953-5944

Annie Gurton. June 2003. $21.95 (paper). 256 pages.

★6965★ *Opportunities in Advertising Careers*

McGraw-Hill Trade
2 Penn Plaza
New York, NY 10121
Ph: (212)904-2000   Fax: (212)755-5645
Fr: 800-722-4726

S. William Pattis and Ruth Wooden. 1995. $14.95; $11.95 (paper). 198 pages. A guide to planning for and seeking opportunities in this growing field. Illustrated.

★6966★ Opportunities in Direct Marketing

McGraw-Hill Contemporary Books
1221 Avenue of the Americas
New York, NY 10020
Ph: (212)904-2000   Fr: 800-323-4900
E-mail: ntcpub@tribune.com

Anne Basye. Revised, 2000. $14.95; $11.95 (paper). 160 pages. Examines opportunities with direct marketers, catalog companies, direct marketing agencies, telemarketing firms, mailing list brokers, and database marketing companies. Describes how to prepare for a career in direct marketing and how to break into the field. Includes sources of short-term professional training.

★6967★ Opportunities in International Business Careers

McGraw-Hill Trade
2 Penn Plaza
New York, NY 10121
Ph: (212)904-2000   Fr: 800-722-4726

Jeffrey Arpan. 1994. $11.95 (paper). 200 pages. Describes what types of jobs exist in international business, where they are located, what challenges and rewards they bring, and how to prepare for and obtain jobs in international business.

★6968★ Opportunities in Journalism Careers

McGraw-Hill/Contemporary Books
1221 Avenue of the Americas
New York, NY 10020
Ph: (212)904-2000   Fr: 800-323-4900
E-mail: ntcpub@tribune.com

Jim Patten and Donald L. Ferguson. 1995. $14.95; $11.95 (paper). 160 pages. Outlines opportunities in every field of journalism, including newspaper reporting and editing, magazine and book publishing, corporate communications, advertising and public relations, freelance writing, and teaching. Covers how to prepare for and enter each field, outlining responsibilities, salaries, benefits, and job outlook for each specialty. Illustrated.

★6969★ Opportunities in Magazine Publishing Careers

McGraw-Hill Trade
2 Penn Plaza
New York, NY 10121
Ph: (212)904-2000   Fr: 800-722-4726
E-mail: ntcpub@tribune.com

S. William Pattis. 1994. $13.95; $12.95 (paper). 160 pages. Covers the scope of magazine publishing and addresses how to identify and pursue available positions. Illustrated.

★6970★ Opportunities in Marketing Careers

McGraw-Hill Trade
2 Penn Plaza
New York, NY 10121
Ph: (212)904-2000   Fr: 800-722-4726

Margery Steinberg. 1999. $14.95; $11.95 (paper). 202 pages. Includes guidance on identifying and pursuing job opportunities. Illustrated.

★6971★ Opportunities in Public Relations Careers

McGraw-Hill Trade
2 Penn Plaza
New York, NY 10121
Ph: (212)904-2000   Fr: 800-722-4726
E-mail: ntcpub@tribune.com

Morris B. Rotman. 1995. $14.95; $11.95 (paper). 200 pages. Tells the reader how to enter the field and how to build a career. Contains bibliography and illustrations.

★6972★ Opportunities in Publishing Careers

McGraw-Hill Professional
2 Penn Plaza
New York, NY 10121
Ph: (212)904-2000   Fr: 800-722-4726
E-mail: ntcpub@tribune.com

Robert A. Carter and S. William Pattis. 1995. $14.95; $11.95 (paper). 160 pages. Covers all positions in book and magazine publishing, including new opportunities in multimedia publishing.

★6973★ Opportunities in Writing Careers

McGraw-Hill Contemporary Books
1221 Avenue of the Americas
New York, NY 10020
Ph: (212)904-2000   Fr: 800-323-4900
E-mail: ntcpub@tribune.com

Elizabeth Foote-Smith. 1999. $14.95; $11.95 (paper). 160 pages. Discusses opportunities in the print media, broadcasting, advertising or publishing. Business writing, public relations, and technical writing are among the careers covered. Contains bibliography and illustrations.

★6974★ Public Relations Career Directory

Thomson Gale
27500 Drake Rd.
Farmington Hills, MI 48331-3535
Ph: (248)699-GALE   Fax: 800-414-5043
Fr: 800-877-GALE
E-mail: galeord@gale.com
URL: http://www.gale.com

Bradley Morgan. Fifth edition, 1993. $39.00. 300 pages. Out of print. Features extensive listings of contacts and entry-level job opportunities at major corporations and public relations agencies nationwide. Includes articles and advice from top public relations practitioners on such areas as corporate communications, international public rela-

tions, community affairs, and media relations.

★6975★ Real People Working in Communications

McGraw-Hill Contemporary Books
1221 Avenue of the Americas
New York, NY 10020
Ph: (212)904-2000   Fr: 800-323-4900
E-mail: ntcpub@tribune.com

Jan Goldberg. 1996. $14.95; $12.95 (paper). Interviews and profiles of working professionals capture a range of opportunities in this field.

★6976★ Resumes for Advertising Careers

McGraw-Hill Contemporary Books
1221 Avenue of the Americas
New York, NY 10020
Ph: (212)904-2000   Fr: 800-323-4900
E-mail: ntcpub@tribune.com

1998. $9.95 (paper). 392 pages. Aimed at job seekers trying to enter or advance in advertising. Provides sample resumes for copywriters, art directors, account managers, ad managers, and media people at all levels of experience. Furnishes sample cover letters.

★6977★ Resumes for Communications Careers

McGraw-Hill Contemporary Books
1221 Avenue of the Americas
New York, NY 10020
Ph: (212)904-2000   Fr: 800-323-4900
E-mail: ntcpub@tribune.com

1998. $9.95 (paper). 464 pages.

★6978★ Resumes for Sales and Marketing Careers

McGraw-Hill Professional
2 Penn Plaza
New York, NY 10121
Ph: (212)904-2000   Fr: 800-722-4726
E-mail: ntcpub@tribune.com

Chuck Cochran and Donna Peerce. Second edition, 1998. $10.95 (paper). 336 pages. Sample resumes and cover letters from all levels of the sales and marketing field.

★6979★ This Business of Music Marketing and Promotion

Watson-Guptill Publications, Incorporated
770 Broadway
New York, NY 10003
Ph: (646)654-5400   Fax: (646)654-5486
Fr: 800-323-9432

Tad Lathrop and Jim Pettigrew, Jr. 1999. $21.95.

★6980★ Vault Career Guide to Advertising

Vault.com
150 W. 22nd St., 5th Fl.
New York, NY 10011
Ph: (212)366-4212   Fax: (212)366-6117
Fr: 888-562-8285

Ira Berkowitz. April 2004. $29.95 (paper). 128 pages.

★6981★ Where the Jobs Are: The Hottest Careers for the 90s

The Career Press, Inc.
3 Tice Rd.
PO Box 687
Franklin Lakes, NJ 07417-1322
Ph: (201)848-0310   Fax: (201)848-1727
Fr: 800-227-3371

Joyce Hadley. Third edition, 2000. $13.99 (paper). 400 pages. Out of print. Describes careers in fifteen general fields, from accounting to travel and hospitality.

★6982★ Working in Public Relations: How to Gain the Skills and Opportunities for a Career in Public Relations

How to Books, Ltd.
311 Bainbridge St.
Philadelphia, PA 19147
Ph: (215)925-5083   Fax: (215)925-1912

Carole Chester. 1998. $21.95 (paper). 144 pages.

EMPLOYMENT AGENCIES AND SEARCH FIRMS

★6983★ Accu Staff Inc.

2350 W River Park Dr.
Tucson, AZ 85705
Ph: (520)690-6630

Services provided include recruiting, temporary help, retained search, outplacement, testing and consulting. Specialties include management, executive, administrative, accounting/bookkeeping, data processing, financial, sales, marketing, technical, manufacturing, industrial and secretarial/office support. Serves private industries as well as government agencies.

★6984★ Adler Management Inc.

66 Witherspoon St., Ste. 315
Princeton, NJ 08542
Ph: (609)443-3300   Fax: (609)443-4439
Executive Search Firm.

★6985★ Advanced Employment Resources

3040 Charlevoix Dr.
Grand Rapids, MI 49546
Ph: (616)942-9950   Fax: (616)942-9950
Executive search firm.

★6986★ Alexander & Company

8308 Barber Oak Dr.
Plano, TX 75025
Ph: 877-495-8300
Executive search firm.

★6987★ Allen Associates

650 Westlake Ctr.
Cincinnati, OH 45242
Ph: (513)563-3040
Executive senior-level search firm.

★6988★ Allen Austin

4543 Post Oak Pl., Ste. 217
Houston, TX 77027
Ph: (713)355-1900   Fax: (713)355-1901
Executive search firm. Branches in North Carolina and Dallas.

★6989★ Ambler Associates

14881 Quorum Dr., Ste. 450
Dallas, TX 75254-7018
Ph: (972)404-8712   Fax: (972)404-8761
Fr: 800-728-8712
Executive search firm.

★6990★ American Executive Management Inc.

30 Federal St.
Salem, MA 01970
Ph: (978)477-5923
Executive search firm. Second location in Boston.

★6991★ Ariel Associates

141 E. 89 St., Ste. 9-H
New York, NY 10128-2330
Ph: (212)348-9600
Executive search firm specializing in media, advertising and publishing.

★6992★ Aubin International Inc.

30 Rowes Wharf
Boston, MA 02110
Ph: (617)443-9922   Fax: (617)443-9955
Executive search firm.

★6993★ Banyan Group ESC Ltd.

411 Theodore Fremd Ave., Fl. 2
Rye, NY 10580
Ph: (914)921-1010   Fax: (914)921-1011
Executive search firm.

★6994★ The Barack Group Inc.

Grand Central Station
PO Box 4407
New York, NY 10163
Ph: (212)867-9700   Fax: (212)681-9555
Executive search firm.

★6995★ Barton Associates Inc.

4314 Yoakum Blvd.
Houston, TX 77006
Ph: (713)961-9111   Fax: (713)993-9399
Executive search firm. Affiliate in Houston, TX.

★6996★ Bender Executive Search Management Consulting

45 N. Station Plaza, Ste. 315
Great Neck, NY 11021
Ph: (516)773-4300   Fax: (516)482-5355
Executive search firm.

★6997★ Bennett Wheelless Group Ltd.

30 S. Wacker Dr., Fl. 22
Chicago, IL 60606
Ph: (312)596-8388   Fax: (801)697-5227
Executive search firm focused on direct marketing positions.

★6998★ Berardi & Associates

1140 Avenue of the Americas, Fl. 8
New York, NY 10036
Ph: (212)403-6180   Fax: (212)764-9690
Executive search firm.

★6999★ Bert Davis Executive Search Inc.

425 Madison Ave., Fl. 14
New York, NY 10017
Ph: (212)838-4000   Fax: (212)888-3823
Executive search firm.

★7000★ Best, Coleman and Partners

1085 Commonwealth Ave., Ste. 325
Boston, MA 02115
Executive search firm. Focused on wholesale and retail industries.

★7001★ Blumenthal-Hart LLC

53 W. Jackson Blvd., Ste. 1307
Chicago, IL 60604
Ph: (312)663-0090   Fax: (312)663-0405
Executive search firm.

★7002★ Buffkin & Associates LLC

730 Cool Springs Blvd., Ste. 120
Franklin, TN 37067
Ph: (615)771-0098   Fax: (615)771-0099
Executive search firm.

★7003★ Byron Leonard International
99 Long Ct., Ste. 201
Thousand Oaks, CA 91360
Ph: (805)373-7500   Fr: (818)222-2744
Executive search firm.

★7004★ Canny, Bowen Inc.
280 Park Ave., Fl. 30 W
New York, NY 10017
Ph: (212)949-6611   Fax: (212)949-5191
Executive search firm.

★7005★ Cantor Executive Search Solutions Inc.
315 W. 57 St., Ste. 207
New York, NY 10019
Ph: (212)333-3000   Fax: (212)245-1012
Executive search firm. Branch in Fairfield, CT.

★7006★ Cardinal Mark Inc.
601 Carlson Pkwy., Ste. 1050
Minnetonka, MN 55305
Ph: (952)449-3005
Executive search firm concentrated on telecommunication industry.

★7007★ Cardwell Enterprises Inc.
PO Box 59418
Chicago, IL 60659
Ph: (773)273-5774   Fr: (847)475-6792
Executive search firm.

★7008★ Carnegie Partners Inc.
3941 Park Dr., Ste. 20-353
El Dorado Hills, CA 95762-4549
Ph: (916)941-9053   Fax: (916)941-9256
Executive search firm. Branches in Glenview IL, Kewadin MI, and Westlake OH.

★7009★ Carpenter, Shackleton & Company
58 Foxwood Ln., Ste. 100
Barrington, IL 60010-1615
Ph: (847)381-2555
Executive search firm. Branch in Chicago.

★7010★ Caruthers & Company LLC
1175 Post Rd. East
Westport, CT 06880
Ph: (203)221-3234   Fax: (203)221-7300
Executive search firm.

★7011★ Century City Partners LLC
PO Box 15747
Beverly Hills, CA 90209
Ph: (310)777-0240
Executive search firm.

★7012★ cFour Partners
100 Wilshire Blvd., Ste. 1840
Santa Monica, CA 90401
Ph: (310)394-2639   Fax: (310)394-2669
Executive search firm.

★7013★ Chaloner Associates
36 Milford St.
Boston, MA 02118
Ph: (617)451-5170   Fax: (617)451-8160
E-mail: info@chaloner.com
URL: http://www.chaloner.com
Executive search firm.

★7014★ Cheryl Alexander & Associates
8588 Shadow Creek Dr.
Maple Grove, MN 55311
Ph: (763)416-4570
Executive search firm.

★7015★ Churchill & Affiliates Inc.
180 E. Elizabeth Ln.
Richboro, PA 18954
Ph: (215)364-8070   Fax: (215)364-0519
Executive search firm focusing on the telecommunications industry.

★7016★ Colton Bernard Inc.
870 Market St., Ste. 822
San Francisco, CA 94102
Ph: (415)399-8700   Fax: (415)399-0750
Executive search firm focused on textiles, apparel and retail industries.

★7017★ Corporate Moves Inc.
PO Box 1638
Buffalo, NY 14231-1638
Ph: (716)633-0234   Fax: (716)626-9147
Executive search & recruitment specialist firm with emphasis on sales and marketing, generally in the $70,000 and above income levels. Offers a total program to develop sales and marketing divisions to high productivity and profit. Program involves planning, searching, training plans, and development of existing people. Industries served: medical, scientific, pharmaceutical, consumer, industrial, business products.

★7018★ Crest Associates Inc.
366 Crest Ave.
Alamo, CA 94507
Ph: (925)945-7374   Fax: (925)935-9170
Executive search firm.

★7019★ Crowe-Innes & Associates LLC
1120 Mar W., Ste. D
Tiburon, CA 94920
Ph: (415)789-1422   Fax: (415)435-6867
Executive search firm.

★7020★ Curry Company
25 Eastfield Rd.
Mount Vernon, NY 10552
Ph: (914)667-5735
Executive search firm.

★7021★ David Allen Associates
PO Box 56
Haddonfield, NJ 08033-0048
Ph: (856)795-6470   Fax: (856)795-0175
Executive search firm.

★7022★ David Blevins & Associates Inc.
2261 Market St., Ste. 105
San Francisco, CA 94114
Ph: (707)495-3714
Executive search firm.

★7023★ David M. Ellner Associates
13 Central Dr.
Port Washington, NY 11050
Ph: (212)279-0665
Executive search firm.

★7024★ Delta Services
PO Box 1294
Sugar Land, TX 77487-1294
Ph: (281)494-9300
Executive search firm.

★7025★ The Dinerstein Group
45 Rockefeller Plaza, Ste. 2000
New York, NY 10111
Ph: (212)332-3224
Executive search firm. Branch in Stamford, CT.

★7026★ Dise & Company Inc.
20600 Chagrin Blvd., Ste. 925
Shaker Heights, OH 44122
Ph: (216)752-1700
Executive search firm.

★7027★ DLB Associates
271 Madison Ave., Ste. 1406
New York, NY 10016
Ph: (212)953-6460   Fax: (212)953-6764
Executive search firm.

★7028★ Doherty International Inc.
899 Skokie Blvd., Ste. 430
Northbrook, IL 60062
Ph: (847)564-1753   Fax: (847)564-1763
Executive search firm.

★7029★ **Dotson & Associates**
412 E. 55th St., Ste. 8A
New York, NY 10022
Ph: (212)593-4274
Executive search firm.

★7030★ **Dussick Management Associates**
54 White Birch Rd.
Madison, CT 06443
Ph: (203)245-9311   Fax: (203)245-9570
E-mail: vince@dussick.com
URL: http://www.dussick.com
Executive search firm.

★7031★ **Edgewood International**
3018 Edgewood Pkwy.
Woodridge, IL 60517-3720
Ph: (630)985-6067   Fax: (630)985-6069
Executive search firm.

★7032★ **The Enfield Company**
1605 Juliet St.
Austin, TX 78704
Ph: (512)444-9921
Executive search firm.

★7033★ **Epsen, Fuller & Associates LLC**
10 Park Place On the Green, Ste. 420
Morristown, NJ 07960
Ph: (973)359-9929   Fax: (973)359-9928
Executive search firm.

★7034★ **The Esquire Staffing Group Ltd.**
1 S. Wacker Dr., Ste. 1616
Chicago, IL 60606-4616
Ph: (312)795-4300   Fax: (312)795-4329
E-mail: s.fischer@esquirestaffing.com
URL: http://www.esquirestaffing.com
Employment agency. Fills permanent as well as temporary openings.

★7035★ **The Executive Roundtable**
PO Box 64421
Souderton, PA 18964
Ph: (215)721-1650   Fax: (215)721-8650
Fr: 888-315-1150
Executive search firm.

★7036★ **Fairfield**
Trump Tower
721 5th Ave.
New York, NY 10022-2523
Ph: (212)838-0220
Executive search firm specializing in retail and apparel manufacturing.

★7037★ **Filcro Media Staffing**
342 Madison Ave., Fl. 7
New York, NY 10017
Ph: (212)599-0909   Fax: (212)599-1023
Executive search firm for the entertainment industry.

★7038★ **Fisher & Associates**
1063 Lenor Way
San Jose, CA 95128
Ph: (408)554-0156   Fax: (408)246-7807
Executive search firm focused on the high technology industry.

★7039★ **Forray Associates Inc.**
2 Penn Plaza, Ste. 1910
New York, NY 10121
Ph: (212)279-0404
Executive search firm.

★7040★ **Franchise Recruiters Ltd.**
Lincolnshire Country Club
3500 Innsbruck
Crete, IL 60417
Ph: (708)757-5595
Executive search firm. Second location in Toronto, Canada.

★7041★ **Frederick William International**
1957 California St., Ste. 10
Mountain View, CA 94040
Ph: (650)968-1503
Executive search firm.

★7042★ **Houser Martin Morris**
110 110th Ave. NE, Ste. 580
PO Box 90015
Bellevue, WA 98004-9015
Ph: (425)453-2700   Fax: (425)453-8726
Focus is in the areas of retained executive search, professional and technical recruiting. Areas of specialization include software engineering, sales and marketing, information technology, legal, human resources, accounting and finance, manufacturing, factory automation, and engineering.

★7043★ **Howard-Sloan Professional Search Inc.**
1140 Ave. of the Americas
New York, NY 10036
Ph: (212)704-0444   Fax: (212)869-7999
Fr: 800-221-1326
E-mail: info@howardsloan.com
URL: http://www.howardsloan.com
Executive search firm.

★7044★ **Joseph A. Davis Consultants Inc.**
104 E. 40th St., Ste. 203
New York, NY 10016
Ph: (212)682-4006   Fax: (212)661-0846
Executive search firm.

★7045★ **Joy Reed Belt Search Consultants Inc.**
5804 Grand Blvd.
PO Box 54410
Oklahoma City, OK 73154
Ph: (405)842-5155   Fax: (405)842-6357
Executive search firm. Branch in Tulsa, OK.

★7046★ **JT Brady & Associates**
10900 Perry Hwy. 12203
Wexford, PA 15090
Ph: (412)934-2228   Fax: (724)935-8059
Executive search firm.

★7047★ **Judith Cushman & Associates**
1275 12th Ave. NW, Ste. 14
Issaquah, WA 98027
Ph: (425)392-8660   Fax: (425)391-9190
Executive search firm.

★7048★ **Karen Dexter & Associates**
1740 Ridge Ave.
Evanston, IL 60201
Ph: (847)733-7103   Fax: (847)733-9254
Training and development consultant offering interpersonal skills training and one-on-one performance counseling for employees of large organizations. Industries served: advertising, banking and finance, consumer products, entertainment, food and beverage, healthcare, legal profession, manufacturing, government agencies, publishing and broadcasting.

★7049★ **Kinser & Baillou L.L.C.**
515 Madison Ave., 36th Fl.
New York, NY 10022
Ph: (212)588-8801   Fax: (212)588-8802
A general executive search firm with specialties in management consulting and communications/marketing communications.

★7050★ **Lamay Associates**
1465 Post Rd. E
Westport, CT 06880
Ph: (203)256-3593   Fax: (203)256-3594
Offers executive search and recruitment specializing in all areas of direct marketing-both to consumers, business-to-business, and non-profit development. Clients include advertising agencies, retailers, manufacturers of consumer goods, cataloguers, publishers, and Internet/e-commerce entities.

★7051★ **LandaJob Advertising Staffing Specialists**
8177 Wornall Rd.
Kansas City, MO 64114
Ph: (816)523-1881   Fax: (816)523-1876
Fr: 800-931-8806
Personnel consultants and recruiters for advertising, marketing, and communications positions. Industries served: advertising,

communications, marketing, graphic arts, printing, and publishing.

★7052★ Max Brown
3208 Q St. NW
Washington, DC 20007
Ph: (202)338-2727   Fax: (202)338-3131

Executive recruiter to the magazine and book publishing industries. Employment placements in all publishing disciplines, including operation and financial management, new product development, marketing, advertising sales, editorial, graphic design, production, manufacturing, circulation, distribution, corporate communications, promotion, and administration. Secondary concentrations include management advising for publishers, providing the following services: marketing and product positioning for new and existing publications, market research and development, business planning and financial projections, publishing models, launch strategies and start-up operations, and acquisitions and mergers counsel.

★7053★ MedSearch Staffing Services Inc.
7271 Engle Rd., Ste. 115
Middleburg Heights, OH 44130
Ph: (440)243-6363   Fax: (440)243-9117

Provides specialized recruitment of sales, marketing and management personnel. Also involved in top-level hospital management consulting and physician recruitment, interim/temporary staffing. Industries served: healthcare manufacturers and institutions in the United States.

★7054★ Neil Frank & Company
PO Box 3570
Redondo Beach, CA 90277-1570
Ph: (310)543-1611   Fax: (310)540-2639

Executive search firm.

★7055★ Personalized Management Associates
1950 Spectrum Cir., Ste. B310
Marietta, GA 30067
Ph: (770)916-1668   Fax: (770)916-1429
Fr: 800-466-7822

Mid-level to executive level management placement firm specializing in retail, restaurant and service management. Industries served: retail, restaurant, finance, sales, marketing, advertising.

★7056★ Sales Executives Inc.
755 W. Big Beaver Rd., Ste. 2107
Troy, MI 48084
Ph: (248)362-1900
E-mail: dale@salesexecutives.com
URL: http://www.salesexecutives.com

Employment agency. Executive search firm.

★7057★ Selected Executives Inc.
36 Ash Ste., Ste102
Cambridge, MA 02138
Ph: (781)933-1500   Fax: (617)547-7333
E-mail: seilrs@aol.com

Executive search firm and employment agency.

★7058★ Toby Clark Associates Inc.
405 E 54th St., Ste. 6C
New York, NY 10022
Ph: (212)752-5670   Fax: (212)752-5674

Executive recruiting firm specializing in marketing communications and public relations.

★7059★ Todd Arro Inc.
3024 Delaware Ave.
PO Box 172
Buffalo, NY 14217
Ph: (716)871-0993   Fax: (716)871-1376

Recruiting and search consultants specializing in sales and marketing management in the industrial, commercial, consumer product, pharmaceutical and medical areas.

★7060★ Wendell L. Johnson Associates Inc.
12 Granview Dr.
Danbury, CT 06811-4321
Ph: (203)743-4112   Fax: (203)778-5377

Executive search firm specializing in areas of workforce diversity, accounting/finance, human resources, marketing/sales, strategic planning, and MIS.

★7061★ Zachary & Sanders Inc.
PO Box 32
East Norwich, NY 11732
Ph: (516)922-5500   Fax: (516)922-2286
Fr: 800-540-7919

An executive recruiting firm exclusively serving the printing, packaging, publishing, advertising, direct marketing, and fulfillment industries.

ONLINE JOB SOURCES AND SERVICES

★7062★ Careers in Business
E-mail: wtunstall@careerselector.com
URL: http://careers-in-business.com

Description: Job search site with concentration in business, finance, consulting, marketing and non-profit related careers. Seekers may search database or post resume, plus review resources list for further information.

★7063★ Omni Search, Inc.
E-mail: omni@the-salesnet.com
URL: http://www.omnisearch.biz/opps.htm

Description: Job search engine for those in the sales and marketing positions in the pharmaceutical, medical and consumer industries.

TRADESHOWS

★7064★ Direct Marketing Association Annual Conference & Exhibition
Direct Marketing Association
1120 Avenue of the Americas
New York, NY 10036-8096
Ph: (212)768-7277   Fax: (212)768-4546
Fr: 800-255-0006

Annual. **Primary Exhibits:** Printers, list brokers, envelope manufacturers, telephone marketing companies, computers and other equipment, supplies, and services for direct marketing.

★7065★ Retail Advertising Conference Expo
Retail Advertising and Marketing Association International
325 7th St. Nw Ste. 1100
Washington, DC 20004-2818
E-mail: mtmrama@aol.com
URL: http://www.ramarac.org

Annual. **Primary Exhibits:** Retail advertising supplies; art materials; audiovisual equipment; catalogues; direct mail marketing; graphics; music; printing; broadcasting; photography; typesetting equipment; signing systems; advertising and sales promotion agencies information.

OTHER SOURCES

★7066★ ABA Marketing Network
1120 Conneticut Ave. NW
Washington, DC 20036
Ph: (202)663-5283   Fax: (202)828-4540
Fr: 800-BAN-KERS
E-mail: marketingnetwork@aba.com
URL: http://www.aba.com/MarketingNetwork/default.htm

Members: Marketing and public relations executives for commercial and savings banks, credit unions, and savings and loans associations, and related groups such as advertising agencies and research firms. **Purpose:** Provides marketing education, information, and services to the financial services industry. **Activities:** Conducts research; cosponsors summer sessions of fundamentals and advanced courses in marketing at the University of Colorado at Boulder; compiles statistics.

★7067★ **Academy of Marketing Science (AMS)**

University of Miami
School of Bus. Admin.
PO Box 248012
Coral Gables, FL 33124
Ph: (305)284-6673   Fax: (305)284-3762
E-mail: ams.sba@miami.edu
URL: http://www.ams-web.org

Description: Marketing academicians and practitioners; individuals interested in fostering education in marketing science. Purpose is to promote the advancement of knowledge and the furthering of professional standards in the field of marketing. Explores the special application areas of marketing science and its responsibilities as an economic, ethical, and social force; promotes research and the widespread dissemination of findings. Facilitates exchange of information and experience among members, and the transfer of marketing knowledge and technology to developing countries; promotes marketing science on an international level. Provides a forum for discussion and refinement of concepts, methods and applications, and the opportunity to publish papers in the field. Assists member educators in the development of improved teaching methods, devices, directions, and materials. Offers guidance and direction in marketing practice and reviewer assistance on scholarly works. Contributes to the solution of marketing problems encountered by individual firms, industries, and society as a whole. Encourages members to utilize their marketing talents to the fullest through redirection, reassignment, and relocation. Sponsors competitions.

★7068★ *Administration and Management Occupations*

Delphi Productions
3160 4th St.
Boulder, CO 80304
Fax: (303)443-4022   Fr: 888-443-2400
URL: http://www.delphivideo.com

$95.00. 50 minutes. Part of the Careers for the 21st Century Video Library.

★7069★ **American Advertising Federation (AAF)**

1101 Vermont Ave. NW, Ste. 500
Washington, DC 20005-6306
Ph: (202)898-0089   Fax: (202)898-0159
E-mail: aaf@aaf.org
URL: http://www.aaf.org

Purpose: Works to advance the business of advertising as a vital and essential part of the American economy and culture through government and public relations; professional development and recognition; community service, social responsibility and high standards; and benefits and services to members. **Activities:** Operates Advertising Hall of Fame, Hall of Achievement, and National Student Advertising Competition. Maintains speakers' bureau.

★7070★ **American Association of Advertising Agencies (AAAA)**

405 Lexington Ave., 18th Fl.
New York, NY 10174-1801
Ph: (212)682-2500   Fax: (212)953-5665
E-mail: obd@aaaa.org
URL: http://www.aaaa.org

Purpose: Fosters development of the advertising industry; assists member agencies to operate more efficiently and profitably. **Activities:** Sponsors member information and international services. Maintains 47 committees. Conducts government relations.

★7071★ **American Society of Association Executives (ASAE)**

1575 I St. NW
Washington, DC 20005-1103
Ph: (202)626-2723   Fax: (202)371-8825
Fr: 888-950-2723
E-mail: pr@asaenet.org
URL: http://www.asaenet.org

Members: Professional society of paid executives of international, national, state, and local trade, professional, and philanthropic associations. **Purpose:** Seeks to educate association executives on effective management, including: the proper objectives, functions, and activities of associations; the basic principles of association management; the legal aspects of association activity; policies relating to association management; efficient methods, procedures, and techniques of association management; the responsibilities and professional standards of association executives. Maintains information resource center. **Activities:** Conducts resume, guidance, and consultation services; compiles statistics in the form of reports, surveys, and studies; carries out research and education. Maintains ASAE Services Corporation to provide special services and ASAE Foundation to do future-oriented research and make grant awards. Offers executive search services and insurance programs. Provides CEO center for chief staff executives. Conducts Certified Association Executive (CAE) program.

★7072★ **American Wholesale Marketers Association (AWMA)**

2750 Prosperity Ave., Ste. 530
Fairfax, VA 22031
Ph: (703)208-3358   Fax: (703)573-5738
Fr: 800-482-2962
E-mail: info@awmanet.org
URL: http://www.awmanet.org

Description: Represents the interests of distributors of convenience products. Its members include wholesalers, retailers, manufacturers, brokers and allied organizations from across the U.S. and abroad. AWMA programs include strong legislative representation in Washington and a broad spectrum of targeted education, business and information services. AWMA also sponsors the country's largest show for candy and convenience related products in conjunction with its semiannual convention.

★7073★ **Association for Women in Communications**

780 Ritchie Hwy., Ste. 28-S
Severna Park, MD 21146
Ph: (410)544-7442   Fax: (410)544-4640
E-mail: pat@womcom.org
URL: http://www.womcom.org

Description: Professional association of journalism and communications.

★7074★ *Marketing, Advertising and Public Relations Managers*

Evon Publishing
832 N 7th Ave.
Iron River, MI 49935
Ph: (906)265-3190

Audiocassette. 1996. $16.95. 32 minutes. Part of the Careers and Vocational Guidance Series. Provides information about the nature of the work, educational requirements, employment outlook, earnings, and work conditions as well as additional related information.

★7075★ **Marketing Agencies Association Worldwide (MAA)**

1031 US Hwy. 22 West, 3rd Fl.
Bridgewater, NJ 08807
Ph: (908)595-6924   Fax: (908)707-0407
E-mail: vincentsottosanti@maaw.org
URL: http://www.maaw.org

Members: Agencies with a primary interest in promotion marketing. **Purpose:** Seeks to increase understanding, by management, of promotion marketing as a special component of the total marketing management and corporate communication function; will stimulate methods of scientific research and evaluation of marketing promotion effectiveness. Conducts research; maintains speakers' bureau and hall of fame.

★7076★ **Marketing Research Association (MRA)**

1344 Silas Deane Hwy., Ste. 306
PO Box 230
Rocky Hill, CT 06067-0230
Ph: (860)257-4008   Fax: (860)257-3990
E-mail: email@mra-net.org
URL: http://www.mra-net.org

Members: Companies and individuals involved in any area of opinion and marketing research, such as data collection, research, or as an end-user.

★7077★ *Marketing & Sales Occupations*

Delphi Productions
3160 4th St.
Boulder, CO 80304
Fax: (303)443-4022   Fr: 888-443-2400
URL: http://www.delphivideo.com

$95.00. 50 minutes. Part of the Careers for the 21st Century Video Library.

★7078★ National Management Association (NMA)

2210 Arbor Blvd.
Dayton, OH 45439
Ph: (937)294-0421   Fax: (937)294-2374
E-mail: nma@nma1.org
URL: http://www.nma1.org

Description: Business and industrial management personnel; membership comes from supervisory level, with the remainder from middle management and above. Seeks to develop and recognize management as a profession and to promote the free enterprise system. Prepares chapter programs on basic management, management policy and practice, communications, human behavior, industrial relations, economics, political education, and liberal education. Maintains speakers' bureau and hall of fame. Maintains educational, charitable, and research programs. Sponsors charitable programs.

★7079★ National School Public Relations Association (NSPRA)

15948 Derwood Rd.
Rockville, MD 20855-2123
Ph: (301)519-0496   Fax: (301)519-0494
E-mail: nspra@nspra.org
URL: http://www.nspra.org/

Description: School system public relations directors, school administrators, and others interested in furthering public understanding of the public schools. Has adopted standards for public relations professionals and programs and an accreditation program.

★7080★ PROMAX

2029 Century Park East, Ste. 555
Los Angeles, CA 90067-2906
Ph: (310)788-7600   Fax: (310)788-7616
E-mail: bonnie@promax.tv
URL: http://www.promax.tv

Members: Advertising, public relations, and promotion managers of cable, radio, and television stations, systems and networks; syndicators. **Purpose:** Seeks to advance the role and increase the effectiveness of promotion and marketing within the industry, related industries, and educational communities. **Activities:** Conducts workshops and

weekly fax service for members. Operates employment service. Maintains speakers' bureau, hall of fame, and resource center with print, audio, and visual materials.

★7081★ Promotion Marketing Association of America (PMAA)

257 Park Ave. S., 11th Fl.
New York, NY 10010-7304
Ph: (212)420-1100   Fax: (212)533-7622
E-mail: pma@pmalink.org
URL: http://www.pmalink.org

Description: Fortune 500 marketer companies, promotion agencies, and companies using promotion programs; supplier members are manufacturers of package goods, cosmetics, and pharmaceuticals, consultants, and advertising agencies. Conducts surveys and studies of industry issues.

★7082★ Public Relations Society of America (PRSA)

33 Irving Pl.
New York, NY 10003-2376
Ph: (212)995-2230   Fax: (212)995-0757
E-mail: exec@prsa.org
URL: http://www.prsa.org

Description: Professional society of public relations practitioners in business and industry, counseling firms, government, associations, hospitals, schools, and nonprofit organizations. Conducts professional development programs. Maintains Professional Resource Center. Offers accreditation program.

★7083★ Society for Marketing Professional Services (SMPS)

99 Canal Center Plz., Ste. 330
Alexandria, VA 22314
Ph: (703)549-6117   Fax: (703)549-2498
Fr: 800-292-7677
E-mail: info@smps.org
URL: http://www.smps.org

Members: Marketing employees of architectural, engineering, planning, interior design, landscape architectural, and construction management firms who are responsible for the new business development of their com-

panies. **Activities:** Compiles statistics. Offers local and national educational programs; maintains certification program.

★7084★ Trade Show Exhibitors Association

2301 S Lake Shore Dr., Ste. 1005
Chicago, IL 60616
Ph: (312)842-8732   Fax: (312)842-8744
E-mail: tsea@tsea.org
URL: http://www.tsea.org

Description: Exhibitors working to improve the effectiveness of trade shows as a marketing tool. Purposes are to promote the progress and development of trade show exhibiting; to collect and disseminate trade show information; conduct studies, surveys, and stated projects designed to improve trade shows; to foster good relations and communications with organizations representing others in the industry; to undertake other activities necessary to promote the welfare of member companies. Sponsors Exhibit Industry Education Foundation and professional exhibiting seminars; the forum series of educational programs on key issues affecting the industry. Maintains placement services; compiles statistics.

★7085★ Women in Direct Marketing International (WDMI)

224 7th St.
Garden City, NY 11530
Ph: (732)469-5000   Fax: (732)469-8414
E-mail: bladden@directmaildepot.com
URL: http://www.wdmi.org

Description: Direct marketing professionals. Seeks to advance the interests and influence of women in the direct response industry; provide for communication and career education; assist in advancement of personal career objectives; serve as professional network to develop business contacts and foster mutual goals. Maintains career talent bank. Distributes information nationally; maintains other chapters in Chicago, IL, Los Angeles, CA, Dallas, TX, Japan, UK, and Belgium.

Marriage and Family Counselors

SOURCES OF HELP-WANTED ADS

★7086★ **APA Monitor**
American Psychological Association
750 1st St. NE
Washington, DC 20002-4242
Ph: (202)336-5500   Fax: (202)336-5620
Fr: 800-374-2721
E-mail: journals@apa.org
URL: http://www.apa.org/monitor/

Monthly. Free to qualified subscribers; $46.00/year for nonmembers; $87.00/year for institutions. Official newspaper of the APA. Reports on the science, profession, and social responsibility of psychology, including latest legislative developments affecting mental health, education, and research support.

★7087★ **Contemporary Family Therapy**
Kluwer Academic/Plenum Publishing Corp.
233 Spring St., 7th Fl.
New York, NY 10013-1522
Ph: (212)620-8000   Fax: (212)463-0742
Fr: 800-221-9369
E-mail: bischoff@plenum.com
URL: http://www.kluweronline.com/issn/0892-2764

Bimonthly. $565.00/year for institutions. Family therapy journal.

★7088★ **Family Relations**
National Council on Family Relations
3989 Central Ave. NE, Ste. 550
Minneapolis, MN 55421
Ph: (763)781-9331   Fax: (763)781-9348
Fr: 888-781-9331
E-mail: fr@iog.wayne.edu
URL: http://www.ncfr.org

Quarterly. $87.00/year for individuals; $117.00/year for institutions; $43.00/year for students, non-US students add $15. Publication for family practitioners and academics on relationships across the life cycle with implications for intervention, education and public policy.

★7089★ **Family Therapy**
Libra Publishers Inc.
3089C Clairemont Dr., PMB 383
San Diego, CA 92117
Ph: (858)571-1414   Fax: (858)571-1414

$85.00/year for institutions; $76.00/year for individuals. Journal covering clinical, family, group, and interactional therapy.

★7090★ **Family Therapy News**
American Association for Marriage and Family Therapy
1133 15th St. NW, Ste. 300
Washington, DC 20005-2710
Ph: (202)452-0109
E-mail: ftn@aamft.org

Bimonthly. $20.00/year for individuals; $35.00/year for institutions, Canada; $10.00/year for out of country. Newspaper for professionals in family therapy and mental health-related issues.

★7091★ **Journal of Counseling and Development**
American Counseling Association
5999 Stevenson Ave.
Alexandria, VA 22304-3300
Ph: (703)823-9800   Fax: (703)823-0252
Fr: 800-347-6647
URL: http://www.counseling.org

Quarterly. $40.00/year for individuals; $175.00/year for institutions. Journal for counseling and human development professionals concerning research, empirical data on current issues, and emerging counseling trends.

★7092★ **Journal of Counseling Psychology**
American Psychological Association
750 1st St. NE
Washington, DC 20002-4242
Ph: (202)336-5500   Fax: (202)336-5620
Fr: 800-374-2721
E-mail: journals@apa.org
URL: http://www.apa.org/journals/cou.html

Quarterly. $41.00/year for members; $23.00/year for students; $81.00/year for nonmembers; $199.00/year for institutions. Journal presenting empirical studies about counseling processes and interventions, theoretical articles about counseling, and studies dealing with evaluation of counseling applications and programs.

★7093★ **Journal of Family Issues**
Sage Publications Inc.
2455 Teller Rd.
Thousand Oaks, CA 91320
Ph: (805)499-0721   Fax: (805)499-0871
Fr: 800-818-SAGE
E-mail: advertising@sagepub.com
URL: http://www.sagepub.com/journal.aspx?pid=163

$109.00/year for individuals; $109.00/year for out of country; $699.00/year for institutions; $699.00/year for institutions, other countries; $19.00/year for single issue, individuals; $97.00 for single issue, institutions. Family studies journal.

★7094★ **Journal of Family Psychology**
American Psychological Association
750 1st St. NE
Washington, DC 20002-4242
Ph: (202)336-5500   Fax: (202)336-5620
Fr: 800-374-2721
E-mail: journals@apa.org
URL: http://www.apa.org/journals/fam.html

Quarterly. $49.00/year for members; $30.00/year for students; $99.00/year for nonmembers; $169.00/year for institutions. Journal reporting on theory, research, and clinical practice in family psychology; including articles on family and marital theory and concepts, research and evaluation, therapeutic frameworks and methods, and policies and legal matters concerning family and marriage.

★7095★ **Journal of Family Psychotherapy**
The Haworth Press Inc.
10 Alice St.
Binghamton, NY 13904-1580
Ph: (607)722-5857   Fax: (607)722-1424
Fr: 800-429-6784
URL: http://www.haworthpress.com

Quarterly. $34.00/year for individuals, USA; $75.00/year for institutions, USA; $175.00/year for libraries, USA; $44.20/year for individuals, Canada; $97.50/year for institutions, Canada; $227.50/year for libraries, Canada; $47.60/year for individuals, other countries; $105.00/year for institutions, other countries; $245.00/year for libraries, other countries. Journal includes case studies, treatment reports, and strategies in clinical practice for psychotherapists.

★7096★ **Journal of Family Social Work**

The Haworth Press Inc.
10 Alice St.
Binghamton, NY 13904-1580
Ph: (607)722-5857   Fax: (607)722-1424
Fr: 800-429-6784
URL: http://www.haworthpress.com

Quarterly. $60.00/year for individuals, USA; $95.00/year for institutions, USA; $175.00/year for libraries, USA; $81.00/year for individuals, Canada; $128.25/year for institutions, Canada; $236.25/year for libraries, Canada; $87.00/year for individuals, other countries; $137.75/year for institutions, other countries; $123.75/year for libraries, other countries. Journal serves as a forum for family practitioners, scholars, and educators in the field of social work.

★7097★ **Journal of Family Violence**

Kluwer Academic/Plenum Publishing Corp.
233 Spring St., 7th
New York, NY 10013-1578
Ph: (212)620-8000   Fax: (212)463-0742
Fr: 800-221-9369

Quarterly. $225.00/year for institutions; $265.00/year for institutions, other countries. Psychology journal.

★7098★ **Journal of Feminist Family Therapy**

The Haworth Press Inc.
10 Alice St.
Binghamton, NY 13904-1580
Ph: (607)722-5857   Fax: (607)722-1424
Fr: 800-429-6784
URL: http://www.haworthpress.com

Quarterly. $24.00/year; $105.00/year for libraries. Journal exploring the relationship between feminist theory and family therapy practice and theory.

★7099★ **Journal of Marital & Family Therapy**

American Association for Marriage and Family Therapy
1133 15th St. NW, Ste. 300
Washington, DC 20005-2710
Ph: (202)452-0109
E-mail: jmft@ssa.uchicago.edu

Quarterly. $45.00/year for individuals; $75.00 for two years; $140.00/year for institutions; $11.25 for single issue. Journal for professional therapists. Covers clinical techniques, research, and theory of marital and family therapy.

★7100★ **Journal of Marriage and Family**

National Council on Family Relations
3989 Central Ave. NE, Ste. 550
Minneapolis, MN 55421
Ph: (763)781-9331   Fax: (763)781-9348
Fr: 888-781-9331
URL: http://www.ncfr.allenpress.com

Quarterly. $86.00/year for individuals; $121.00/year for institutions; $25.00/year for students. Publication in the family field featuring original research and theory, research interpretation, and critical discussion related to marriage and the family.

★7101★ **Marriage and Family Review**

The Haworth Press Inc.
10 Alice St.
Binghamton, NY 13904-1580
Ph: (607)722-5857   Fax: (607)722-1424
Fr: 800-429-6784
URL: http://www.haworthpress.com

Quarterly. $75.00/year for individuals; $250.00/year for institutions; $465.00/year for libraries; $101.25/year for individuals-Canada; $337.50/year for institutions-Canada; $627.75/year for libraries-Canada; $108.75/year for individuals-other countries; $362.50/year for institutions-other countries; $674.25/year for libraries-other countries. Journal for socially oriented and clinically oriented marriage and family specialists in a broad range of research and applied disciplines.

★7102★ **National Council News**

National Council for Community Behavioral Healthcare
12300 Twinbrook Pkwy., Ste. 320
Rockville, MD 20852
Ph: (301)984-6200   Fax: (301)881-7159
URL: http://www.nccbh.org

Description: Monthly. Dedicated to increasing the quality and accessibility of community mental health services. Recurring features include interviews, a calendar of events, news of educational opportunities, book reviews, marketplace news, and job listings.

★7103★ **Sage Family Studies Abstracts**

Sage Publications Inc.
2455 Teller Rd.
Thousand Oaks, CA 91320
Ph: (805)499-0721   Fax: (805)499-0871
Fr: 800-818-SAGE
E-mail: advertising@sagepub.com
URL: http://www.sagepub.com/journal.aspx?pid=141

Quarterly. $157.00/year for individuals; $157.00/year for out of country; $847.00/year for institutions; $847.00/year for institutions, other countries. Journal containing family studies abstracts.

EMPLOYER DIRECTORIES AND NETWORKING LISTS

★7104★ **Counselors Directory-Marriage & Family**

infoUSA Inc.
5711 S 86th Cir.
Omaha, NE 68127-0347
Ph: (402)930-3500   Fax: (402)331-0176
Fr: 800-555-6124
URL: http://www.abii.com

Annual. Number of listings: 55,129. Entries include: Name, address, phone, size of advertisement, name of owner or manager, number of employees, year first in "Yellow Pages." Compiled from telephone company "Yellow Pages," nationwide. Arrangement: Geographical.

★7105★ **Magill's Encyclopedia of Social Science: Psychology**

Salem Press Inc.
Two University Plz., Ste. 121
Hackensack, NJ 07601
Ph: (201)968-9899   Fax: (201)968-1411
Fr: 800-221-1592

$385.00. Publication includes: Lists of Web sites, organizations, and support groups in the field of psychology. Principal content of publication is entries on psychology including specific disorders, diagnosis, and therapies. Indexes: Alphabetical.

★7106★ **Mental Help Net**

CenterSite, LLC
570 Metro Place
Dublin, OH 43017
URL: http://www.mentalhelp.net

Covers resources for finding mental help including local therapists and self-help groups; Services including upcoming conferences, professional education, and universities offering degrees in mental health fields.

★7107★ **National Directory of Children, Youth & Families Services**

Penny K. Spencer, Publisher
14 Inverness Dr. E. Ste. D-144
Englewood, CO 80112
Ph: (303)662-8165   Fax: 800-845-6452
Fr: 800-343-6681
URL: http://www.childrenyouthfamilydir.com/

Annual, July. $159.00. Covers more than 45,000 key contacts in the areas of Social Services, Health & Mental Health Services, Juvenile Justice Agencies, Education Departments, Treatment Centers & Hospitals, Referral Networks, child, youth, and family-oriented social services, health and mental health services, and juvenile/family court and youth advocacy services, educational listings in state and private agencies, major cities, and 3,300 counties; also covers runaway youth centers, child abuse projects, congressional committees, clearinghouses, and national organizations concerned with family health and welfare; buyers' guide to specialized services and products. Entries include: Agency listings include agency name, address, phone, fax, after-hours phone, websites, names of principal executives and staff, description of services. Arrangement: Geographical.

HANDBOOKS AND MANUALS

★7108★ *Careers in Counseling & Human Services*

Taylor and Francis
325 Chestnut St., 8t Fl.
Philadelphia, PA 19106
Ph: (215)625-2919   Fax: (215)269-0363
Fr: 800-821-8312

Brooke B. Collison and Nancy J. Garfield, editors. Second edition, 1995. $19.95 (paper). 153 pages.

★7109★ *Careers in Social and Rehabilitation Services*

McGraw-Hill Trade
2 Penn Plaza
New York, NY 10121
Ph: (212)904-2000   Fr: 800-722-4726
E-mail: ntcpub@tribune.com

Geraldine O. Garner. Second edition, 2001. $19.95; 14.95 (paper). 128 pages.

★7110★ *Great Jobs for Liberal Arts Majors*

McGraw-Hill Professional
2 Penn Plaza
New York, NY 10121
Ph: (212)904-2000   Fr: 800-722-4726
E-mail: ntcpub@tribune.com

Blythe Camenson. Second edition, 2001. $14.95 (paper). 256 pages.

★7111★ *Great Jobs for Psychology Majors*

McGraw-Hill Trade
2 Penn Plaza
New York, NY 10121
Ph: (212)904-2000   Fr: 800-722-4726
E-mail: ntcpub@tribune.com

Julie DeGalan and Stephen Lambert. 1995. $11.95 (paper). 468 pages. Out of print.

★7112★ *Opportunities in Counseling and Development Careers*

McGraw-Hill Contemporary Books
1221 Avenue of the Americas
New York, NY 10020
Ph: (212)904-2000   Fr: 800-323-4900
E-mail: ntcpub@tribune.com

Neale Baxter, Mark U. Toch, and Philip A. Perry. 1997. $14.95; $11.95 (paper). 160 pages. A guide to planning for and seeking opportunities in this challenging field. Illustrated.

TRADESHOWS

★7113★ **American Counseling Association World Conference**

American Counseling Association
5999 Stevenson Ave.
Alexandria, VA 22304-3300
Ph: (703)823-9800   Fax: (703)823-0252
Fr: 800-347-6647
E-mail: meetings@counseling.org
URL: http://www.counseling.org

Annual. **Primary Exhibits:** Books, career development information, college selection, student financial aid, testing and measurement techniques, practice management companies, software, rehabilitation aids, and community agencies and private clinics specializing in substance abuse and mental health.

★7114★ **Association for Counselor Education and Supervision National Conference**

Association for Counselor Education and Supervision
c/o American Counseling Association
5999 Stevenson Ave.
Alexandria, VA 22304
Ph: (703)823-9800   Fax: (703)823-0252
Fr: 800-347-6647

Quadrennial. **Primary Exhibits:** Exhibits relating to the professional preparation of counselors.

OTHER SOURCES

★7115★ **Alliance for Children and Families (ACF)**

11700 W Lake Park Dr.
Milwaukee, WI 53224-3099
Ph: (414)359-1040   Fax: (414)359-1074
Fr: 800-221-3726
E-mail: info@alliance1.org
URL: http://www.alliance1.org

Description: Membership organization of local agencies in more than 1000 communities providing family counseling, family life education and family advocacy services, and other programs to help families with parent-child, marital, mental health, and other problems of family living. Assists member agencies in developing and providing effective family services. Works with the media, government, and corporations to promote strong family life. Compiles statistics; conducts research. Maintains extensive files of unpublished materials from member agencies. Offers career placement services.

★7116★ **American Association for Marriage and Family Therapy (AAMFT)**

112 S Alfred St.
Alexandria, VA 22314
Ph: (703)838-9808   Fax: (703)838-9805

E-mail: exec@aamft.org
URL: http://www.aamft.org

Members: Professional society of marriage and family therapists. **Purpose:** Assumes a major role in developing & maintaining the highest standards of excellence in this field. **Activities:** Has 76 accredited training programs throughout the U.S. Sponsors educational and research programs.

★7117★ **American Psychological Association (APA)**

750 First St. NE
Washington, DC 20002-4242
Ph: (202)336-5500   Fax: (202)336-6069
Fr: 800-374-2721
E-mail: mhonaker@apa.org
URL: http://www.apa.org/

Members: Scientific and professional society of psychologists. Students participate as affiliates. **Purpose:** Works to advance psychology as a science, a profession, and as a means of promoting human welfare.

★7118★ **Association of Family and Conciliation Courts (AFCC)**

6515 Grand Teton Plaza, Ste. 210
Madison, WI 53719-1048
Ph: (608)664-3750   Fax: (608)664-3751
E-mail: afcc@afccnet.org
URL: http://www.afccnet.org

Members: Judges, counselors, family court personnel, attorneys, mediators, researchers, and teachers concerned with the resolution of family disputes as they affect children. **Purpose:** Proposes to develop and improve the practice of dispute resolution procedure as a complement to judicial procedures. Aims to strengthen the family unit and minimize family strife by improving the process of marriage, family, and divorce counseling; and to provide an interdisciplinary forum for the exchange of ideas, for the creation of new approaches to child custody matters and solutions to problems of family discord. Collaborates with the National Council of Juvenile and Family Court Judges, National Judicial College, the National Center for State Courts, the American Bar Association. Several universities, lawschools, and state organizations responsible for providing on-going training for attorneys, judges, and family therapists. **Activities:** Conducts research and offers technical assistance and training to courts, legal associations, judicial organizations, and behavioral science professionals

★7119★ *Human Services Occupations*

Delphi Productions
3160 4th St.
Boulder, CO 80304
Fax: (303)443-4022   Fr: 888-443-2400
URL: http://www.delphivideo.com

$95.00. 50 minutes. Part of the Careers for the 21st Century Video Library.

★7120★ International Association for Marriage and Family Counselors (IAMFC)

5999 Stevenson Ave.
Alexandria, VA 22304
Fax: (703)823-0252   Fr: 800-347-6647
URL: http://www.counseling.org

Description: A division of the American Counseling Association. Individuals working in the areas of marriage counseling, marital therapy, divorce counseling, mediation, and family counseling and therapy; interested others. Promotes ethical practices in marriage and family counseling/therapy. Encour- ages research; provides a forum for dialogue on relevant issues; facilitates the exchange of information. Assists couples and families in coping with life challenges; works to ameliorate problems confronting families and married couples.

★7121★ National Council on Family Relations (NCFR)

3989 Central Ave. NE, Ste. 550
Minneapolis, MN 55421
Ph: (763)781-9331   Fax: (763)781-9348
Fr: 888-781-9331
E-mail: info@ncfr.com
URL: http://www.ncfr.org

Members: Multidisciplinary group of family life professionals, including clergy, counsel- ors, educators, home economists, lawyers, nurses, therapists, librarians, physicians, psychologists, social workers, sociologists, and researchers. **Purpose:** Seeks to provide opportunities for members to plan and act together to advance marriage and family life through consultation, conferences, and the dissemination of information and research.

Mathematicians

SOURCES OF HELP-WANTED ADS

★7122★ Association for Women in Mathematics Newsletter

Association for Women in Mathematics
4114 Computer & Space Sciences Bldg.
University of Maryland
College Park, MD 20742-2461
Ph: (301)405-7892

Description: Six issues/year (Jan, Mar, May, Jul, Sep, Nov). Concerned with the progress of women in professional fields, particularly in mathematics and related careers. Recounts facets of the history of women in mathematics, discusses issues related to education, and highlights women being honored for studies and achievements. Recurring features include letters to the editor and a section on job openings.

★7123★ AWIS Magazine

Association for Women in Science
1200 New York Ave. NW, Ste. 650
Washington, DC 20005
Ph: (202)326-8940   Fax: (202)326-8960
Fr: 800-886-AWIS

Description: Bimonthly. Covers issues, legislation, and trends related to science education for girls, women, and minorities. Includes information on grants and fellowships, job openings, educational programs, events, and notices of publications available.

★7124★ Employment Information in the Mathematical Sciences/Journal

American Mathematical Society
201 Charles St.
Providence, RI 02904-2294
Ph: (401)455-4000   Fax: (401)331-3842
Fr: 800-321-4AMS

Description: Six issues/year. Provides concise listings of open positions (1,400-1,500/ yr.) "suitable for mathematicians with education and experience at every level beyond the Bachelor's degree." Lists positions by state. Computer the Mathematical Associa-

tion of America (MAA) and the Society for Industrial and Applied Mathematics.

★7125★ Notices of the American Mathematical Society

American Mathematical Society
201 Charles St.
Providence, RI 02904-2294
Ph: (401)455-4000   Fax: (401)331-3842
Fr: 800-321-4267
URL: http://www.ams.org/notices

$401.00/year, individual members; $321.00/ year, institutional members. AMS journal publishing programs, meeting reports, new publications announcements, upcoming mathematical meetings, scientific development trends, computer software reviews, and federal funding reports.

PLACEMENT AND JOB REFERRAL SERVICES

★7126★ American Geophysical Union (AGU)

2000 Florida Ave. NW
Washington, DC 20009-1277
Ph: (202)462-6900   Fax: (202)328-0566
Fr: 800-966-AGU1
E-mail: service@agu.org
URL: http://www.agu.org

Members: Individuals professionally associated with the field of geophysics; supporting institutional members are companies and other organizations whose work involves geophysics. **Purpose:** Promotes the study of problems concerned with the figure and physics of the earth; initiates and coordinates research that depends upon national and international cooperation and provides for scientific discussion of research results. **Activities:** Sponsors placement service at semiannual meeting.

★7127★ American Mathematical Society (AMS)

201 Charles St.
Providence, RI 02904-2294
Ph: (401)455-4000   Fax: (401)331-3842
Fr: 800-321-4AMS
E-mail: ams@ams.org
URL: http://www.ams.org/

Description: Professional society of mathematicians and educators. Promotes the interests of mathematical scholarship and research. Holds institutes, seminars, short courses, and symposia to further mathematical research; awards prizes. Offers placement services; compiles statistics.

★7128★ Mathematical Association of America (MAA)

1529 18th St. NW
Washington, DC 20036-1385
Ph: (202)387-5200   Fax: (202)265-2384
Fr: 800-741-9415
E-mail: maahq@maa.org
URL: http://www.maa.org

Description: College mathematics teachers; individuals using mathematics as a tool in a business or profession. Sponsors annual high school mathematics contests and W.L. Putnam Competition for college students. Conducts faculty enhancement workshops and promotes the use of computers through classroom training. Offers college placement test program; operates speakers' bureau.

EMPLOYER DIRECTORIES AND NETWORKING LISTS

★7129★ American Men and Women of Science

Thomson Gale
27500 Drake Rd.
Farmington Hills, MI 48331-3535
Ph: (248)699-4253   Fax: (248)699-8065
Fr: 800-877-GALE
E-mail: amws@galegroup.com

Biennial, latest edition December 2002.

$975.00. Covers over 129,700 U.S. and Canadian scientists active in the physical, biological, mathematical, computer science, and engineering fields; includes references to previous edition for deceased scientists and nonrespondents. Entries include: Name, address, education, personal and career data, memberships, honors and awards, research interest. Arrangement: Alphabetical. Indexes: Discipline (in separate volume).

★7130★ **Assistantships and Graduate Fellowships in the Mathematical Sciences**
American Mathematical Society
201 Charles St.
Providence, RI 02904-2294
Ph: (401)455-4000   Fax: (401)331-3842
Fr: 800-321-4AMS
URL: http://www.ams.org/employment/asst2001-frnt.pdf

Annual, October. $22.00. Publication includes: List of assistantship and graduate fellowship opportunities in math, statistics, computer science and related fields in about 270 colleges and universities in the United States and Canada; sources of fellowship information. Entries include: For assistantships and fellowships-Title, sponsoring organization name, web site address, address, name and title of contact; description of position, including stipend (if any), duties, deadline for application; number and type of degrees awarded for previous year. For fellowship information sources-Name, address. Arrangement: Geographical. Indexes: Type of stipend.

★7131★ **Employment Information in the Mathematical Sciences**
American Mathematical Society
201 Charles St.
Providence, RI 02904-2294
Ph: (401)455-4000   Fax: (401)331-3842
Fr: 800-321-4AMS
E-mail: eims-info@ams.org
URL: http://www.ams.org/eims/

Five times a year. $180.00 for institutions; $108.00 for individuals; $45.00 for students. Covers colleges and universities with departments in the mathematical sciences, and non-academic and foreign organizations with employment openings. Entries include: For departments-Name, address, name and title of contact; job title, job description, salary (if applicable). Arrangement: Classified as academic or nonacademic, then geographical.

★7132★ **Facts on File Geometry Handbook**
Facts On File Inc.
132 W 31st St., 17th Fl.
New York, NY 10001-2006
Ph: (212)967-8800   Fax: 800-678-3633
Fr: 800-322-8755

$45.00. Publication includes: List of web sites to consult for further information on geometry. Principal content of publication is over 3,000 terms covering Euclidean and non-Euclidean geometry as well as other

overlapping mathematical branches. Indexes: Alphabetical.

★7133★ **Mathematical Sciences Professional Directory**
American Mathematical Society
201 Charles St.
Providence, RI 02904-2294
Ph: (401)455-4000   Fax: (401)331-3842
Fr: 800-321-4AMS
URL: http://www.ams.org

Annual. $55.00 for nonmembers; $44.00 for members. Covers 37 professional organizations concerned with mathematics, government agencies, academic institutions with department in the mathematical sciences, nonacademic organizations, and individuals. Entries include: For professional organizations and government agencies-Name, address, names and titles of key personnel. For institutions-Name, address; name, title, and address of department chair. Arrangement: Classified by type of organization; institutions are then geographical; others, alphabetical. Indexes: University or college name.

HANDBOOKS AND MANUALS

★7134★ **Careers for Number Crunchers and Other Quantitative Types**
McGraw-Hill Trade
2 Penn Plaza
New York, NY 10121
Ph: (212)904-2000   Fr: 800-722-4726
E-mail: ntcpub@tribune.com

Rebecca Burnett. Second edition, 2002. $15.95; $12.95 (paper). 192 pages. Provides information to math-oriented job hunters on how to become statisticians, field researchers, computer programmers, stock analysts, investment managers, bankers, engineers, accountants, underwriters, economists, market analysts, mathematicians, systems analysts, and more.

★7135★ **Chronicle Math & Science Occupations Guidebook**
Chronicle Guidance Publications, Inc.
66 Aurora St.
Moravia, NY 13118-3576
Fax: (315)497-3359   Fr: 800-899-0454

Paul Downes, editor. 1994. Revised edition. $109.25. 415 pages.

★7136★ **Great Jobs for Math Majors**
McGraw-Hill Trade
2 Penn Plaza
New York, NY 10121
Ph: (212)904-2000   Fr: 800-722-4726
E-mail: ntcpub@tribune.com

Stephen Lambert and Ruth J. DeCotis. 1998. $11.95 (paper). 488 pages.

★7137★ **Guide to Nontraditional Careers in Science**
Hemisphere Publishing Corp.
325 Chestnut St., 8th Fl.
Philadelphia, PA 19106
Ph: (215)785-5800   Fax: (215)269-0363
Fr: 800-821-8312

Karen Young Kreeger. 1998. $38.95 (paper). 263 pages.

★7138★ **A Mathematician's Survival Guide: Graduate School and Early Career Development**
American Mathematical Society
201 Charles St.
Providence, RI 02904
Ph: (401)455-4157   Fax: (401)331-3842
Fr: 800-321-4267

Steven G. Krantz. April 2003. $28.00 (paper). Illustrated. 240 pages.

★7139★ **101 Careers in Mathematics**
Mathematical Association of America
1529 18th St. NW
Washington, DC 20036
Ph: (301)617-7800   Fax: (301)206-9789
Fr: 800-331-1622

Andrew Sterrett (Editor). December 2002. $34.95. 360 pages. Classroom Resource Materials Series.

★7140★ **Opportunities in Research and Development Careers**
McGraw-Hill/Contemporary Books
1221 Avenue of the Americas
New York, NY 10020
Ph: (212)904-2000   Fr: 800-323-4900
E-mail: ntcpub@tribune.com

Jan Goldberg. 1997. $14.95; $11.95 (paper). 204 pages.

★7141★ **Prentice Hall Guide to Scholarships and Fellowships for Math and Science Students: A Resource for Students Pursuing Careers in Mathematics and Science**
Prentice Hall PTR
200 Old Tappan Rd.
Old Tappan, NJ 07675
Fax: 800-445-6991   Fr: 800-223-1360

Mark Kantrowitz and Joann P. DiGennaro. 1993. First edition. $29.95; $19.95 (paper). 352 pages. Out of print. Acts as a resource guide for those pursuing careers in mathematics, science, and engineering.

★7142★ **Project MASCOT Mathematics & Science Careers of Tomorrow**
American Counseling Association
5999 Stevenson Ave.
Alexandria, VA 22304-3300
Ph: (703)823-9800   Fax: 800-473-2329

1994. $14.99. 160 pages.

★7143★ *Starting Our Careers: A Collection of Essays & Advice on Professional Development from the Young Mathematicians' Network*
American Mathematical Society
201 Charles St.
Providence, RI 02940-6248
Ph: (401)455-4000   Fax: (401)331-3842
Fr: 800-321-4267

Curtis D. Bennett and Annalisa Crannell. 1999. $24.00.

★7144★ *To Boldly Go: A Practical Career Guide for Scientists*
American Geophysical Union
2000 Florida Ave., NW
Washington, DC 20009
Ph: (202)462-6900   Fax: (202)328-0566
Fr: 800-966-2481

Peter S. Fiske. 1996. $19.00 (paper).

OTHER SOURCES

★7145★ **Association for International Practical Training (AIPT)**
10400 Little Patuxent Pky., Ste. 250
Columbia, MD 21044-3519
Ph: (410)997-2200   Fax: (410)992-3924

E-mail: aipt@aipt.org
URL: http://www.aipt.org

Description: Providers worldwide on-the-job training programs for students and professionals seeking international career development and life-changing experiences. Arranges workplace exchanges in hundreds of professional fields, bringing employers and trainees together from around the world. Client list ranges from small farming communities to Fortune 500 companies.

★7146★ **Institute of Mathematical Statistics (IMS)**
PO Box 22718
Beachwood, OH 44122
Ph: (216)295-2340   Fax: (216)295-5661
E-mail: ims@imstat.org
URL: http://www.imstat.org/

Members: Professional society of mathematicians and others interested in mathematical statistics and probability theory. **Purpose:** Seeks to further research in mathematical statistics and probability.

★7147★ *Mathematicians*
Evon Publishing
832 N 7th Ave.
Iron River, MI 49935
Ph: (906)265-3190

Audiocassette. 1996. $16.95. 32 minutes. Part of the Careers and Vocational Guidance Series. Provides information about the nature of the work, educational requirements, employment outlook, earnings, and work conditions as well as additional related information.

★7148★ **National Council of Teachers of Mathematics (NCTM)**
1906 Association Dr.
Reston, VA 20191-1502
Ph: (703)620-9840   Fax: (703)476-2970
Fr: 800-235-7566
E-mail: orders@nctm.org
URL: http://www.nctm.org

Description: Dedicated to improving teaching and learning of mathematics. Toll-free number is for orders only.

★7149★ *Scientific, Engineering, and Technical Services*
Cambridge Educational
2572 Brunswick Ave.
Lawrenceville, NJ 08648-4128
Fax: 800-FAX-ON-US   Fr: 800-468-4227
URL: http://www.cambridgeeducational.com

$89.95. 2002. 18 minutes. Part of the Career Cluster Series.

Mechanical Engineers

SOURCES OF HELP-WANTED ADS

★7150★ Advanced Materials & Processes

ASM International
9639 Kinsman Rd.
Materials Park, OH 44073-0002
Ph: (440)338-5151   Fax: (440)338-4634
Fr: 800-336-5152
URL: http://www.asm.intl.org

Monthly. Free-to members; $250.00/year for nonmembers. Magazine covering advances in metal, materials, testing technology and more.

★7151★ ASME News

American Society of Mechanical
Engineers
3 Park Ave.
New York, NY 10016-5990
Ph: (212)591-7000   Fax: (212)591-7674
Fr: 800-843-2763
URL: http://www.asmenews.org/

Monthly. Engineering tabloid.

★7152★ AWIS Magazine

Association for Women in Science
1200 New York Ave. NW, Ste. 650
Washington, DC 20005
Ph: (202)326-8940   Fax: (202)326-8960
Fr: 800-886-AWIS

Description: Bimonthly. Covers issues, legislation, and trends related to science education for girls, women, and minorities. Includes information on grants and fellowships, job openings, educational programs, events, and notices of publications available.

★7153★ Chemical Equipment

Reed Business Information
301 Gibraltar Dr.
Morris Plains, NJ 07950
Ph: (973)292-5100   Fax: (973)539-3476

Tabloid on the chemical process industry.

★7154★ Consulting-Specifying Engineer

Reed Business Information
360 Park Ave. S
New York, NY 10014
Ph: (646)746-7764
URL: http://www.csemag.com/index.asp?webzine=cse&publication=cse

The integrated engineering magazine of the building construction industry.

★7155★ Engineering Times

National Society of Professional
Engineers
1420 King St.
Alexandria, VA 22314
Ph: (703)684-2875   Fax: (703)836-4875
E-mail: et@nspe.org
URL: http://http//:www.nspc.org/1et.asp

$30.00/year for individuals; $48.00/year for out of country. Magazine (tabloid) covering professional, legislative, and techology issues for an engineering audience.

★7156★ ENR: Engineering News-Record

McGraw-Hill Companies
1221 Avenue of the Americas
New York, NY 10020
Ph: (212)512-2000
URL: http://www.enr.com

Weekly. $74.00/year; $5.00 for single issue. Magazine focusing on engineering and construction.

★7157★ Graduating Engineer & Computer Careers

Career Recruitment Media
211 W. Wacker Dr., No. 900
Chicago, IL 60606
Ph: (312)525-3100
URL: http://www.graduatingengineer.com

$16.00/year for individuals. Magazine focusing on employment, education, and career development for entry-level engineers and computer scientists.

★7158★ High Technology Careers Magazine

HTC
4701 Patrick Henry Dr., No. 1901
Santa Clara, CA 95054-1847
Ph: (408)970-8800   Fax: (408)567-0242
URL: http://www.hightechcareers.com

Bimonthly. $29.00/year; $35.00/year for Canada; $85.00/year for out of country. Magazine (tabloid) containing employment opportunity information for the engineering and technical community.

★7159★ Hydraulics & Pneumatics

Penton Media Inc.
1300 E 9th St.
Cleveland, OH 44114-1503
Ph: (216)696-7000   Fax: (216)931-9799
URL: http://www.fpweb.com/

$60.00/year; $95.00/year for other countries. Magazine of hydraulic and pneumatic systems and engineering.

★7160★ Machine Design

Penton Media Inc.
1300 E 9th St.
Cleveland, OH 44114-1503
Ph: (216)696-7000   Fax: (216)931-9799
E-mail: mdeditor@penton.com
URL: http://www.machinedesign.com

$153.00/year for individuals. Magazine on design engineering function.

★7161★ Mechanical Engineering

American Society of Mechanical
Engineers
3 Park Ave.
New York, NY 10016-5990
Ph: (212)591-7000   Fax: (212)591-7674
Fr: 800-843-2763
E-mail: memag@asme.org
URL: http://www.memagazine.org

Monthly. $25.00 for single issue. Mechanical Engineering featuring technical and industry related technological advancements and news.

★7162★ *Noise Control Engineer Journal*

Institute of Noise Control Engineering
212 Ross Hall
Dept. of Mechanical Engineering
Auburn, AL 36849-3541
Fax: (205)844-3307

Bimonthly. $60.00/year for individuals. Refereed journal containing technical articles for professionals concerned with noise reduction in industry, buildings, transportation, products, and communities.

★7163★ *NSBE Magazine*

NSBE Publications
1454 Duke St.
Alexandria, VA 22314
Ph: (703)549-2207   Fax: (703)683-5312

$10.00/year for individuals; $2.00 for single issue. Journal providing information on engineering careers, self-development, and cultural issues for recent graduates with technical majors.

★7164★ *Plumbing Engineer*

TMB Publishing Inc.
1838 Techny Ct.
Northbrook, IL 60062
Ph: (847)564-1127   Fax: (847)564-1264
E-mail: info@plumbingengineer.com

Free to qualified subscribers; $50.00/year. Trade journal for consulting engineering, mechanical engineering, architecture, and contracting professionals.

★7165★ *Power*

McGraw-Hill Companies
1221 Avenue of the Americas
New York, NY 10020
Ph: (212)512-2000

Monthly. $19.00/year; $5.00 for single issue. Magazine for engineers in electric utilities, process and manufacturing plants, commercial and service establishments, and consulting, design, and construction engineering firms working in the power technology field.

★7166★ *Reeves Journal*

Business News Publishing Co.
23211 S Pointe Dr., Ste. 101
PO Box 30700
Laguna Hills, CA 92653
Ph: (949)830-0881   Fax: (949)859-7845
URL: http://www.reevesjournal.com

Monthly. Free to qualified subscribers. Regional plumbing, heating, and cooling magazine.

★7167★ *SWE*

Society of Women Engineers
230 E Ohio St., No. 400
2135 Lamberton Rd.
Chicago, IL 60611-3265
Ph: (312)596-5223   Fax: (312)596-5252
E-mail: hq@swe.org
URL: http://www.swe.org

Bimonthly. $30.00/year for nonmembers. Magazine for engineering students and for women and men working in the engineering and technology fields. Covers career guidance, continuing development and topical issues.

★7168★ *Technology Review*

Technology Review
201 Vassar St.
Cambridge, MA 02139
Ph: (617)253-8250   Fax: (617)258-5850
E-mail: trcomments@mit.edu

$30.00/year for individuals; $42.00/year for other countries; $4.95/year for single issue. Magazine reviewing new developments in technology with an emphasis on economic, political, and social implications. Not a new product publication.

★7169★ *WEPANEWS*

Women in Engineering Programs & Advocates Network
Castle Point on the Hudson
Hoboken, NJ 07030
Ph: (201)216-5245   Fax: (201)216-5175
URL: http://www.wepan.org/newsletter.html

Description: Two issues/year. Seeks to provide greater access for women to careers in engineering. Includes news of graduate, undergraduate, freshmen, pre-college, and re-entry engineering programs for women. Recurring features include job listings, faculty, grant, and conference news, international engineering program news, action group news, notices of publications available, and a column titled Kudos.

PLACEMENT AND JOB REFERRAL SERVICES

★7170★ **American Indian Science and Engineering Society (AISES)**

PO Box 9828
Albuquerque, NM 87119-9828
Ph: (505)765-1052   Fax: (505)765-5608
E-mail: info@aises.org
URL: http://www.aises.org

Description: American Indian and non-Indian students and professionals in science, technology, and engineering fields; corporations representing energy, mining, aerospace, electronic, and computer fields. Seeks to motivate and encourage students to pursue undergraduate and graduate studies in science, engineering, and technology. Sponsors science fairs in grade schools, teacher training workshops, summer math/science sessions for 8th-12th graders, professional chapters, and student chapters in colleges. Offers scholarships. Adult members serve as role models, advisers, and mentors for students. Operates placement service.

★7171★ **Engineering Society of Detroit (ESD)**

26100 American Dr., Ste. 500
Southfield, MI 48034-6184
Ph: (248)355-2910   Fax: (248)355-1492
E-mail: esd@esd.org
URL: http://esd.org

Description: Engineers from all disciplines; scientists and technologists. Conducts technical programs and engineering refresher courses; sponsors conferences and expositions. Maintains speakers' bureau; offers placement services. Although based in Detroit, MI, society membership is international.

★7172★ **Korean Scientists and Engineers Association in America (KSEA)**

1952 Gallows Rd., Ste. 300
Vienna, VA 22182
Ph: (703)748-1221   Fax: (703)748-1331
E-mail: sejong@ksea.org
URL: http://www.ksea.org

Description: Scientists and engineers holding single or advanced degrees. Goals are to: promote friendship and mutuality among Korean and American scientists and engineers; contribute to Korea's scientific, technological, industrial, and economic developments; strengthen the scientific, technological, and cultural bonds between Korea and the U.S. Sponsors symposium. Maintains speakers' bureau, placement service, and biographical archives. Compiles statistics. Maintains 100 volume library of scientific handbooks and yearbooks in Korean.

★7173★ **Robotics International of the Society of Manufacturing Engineers (RI/SME)**

One SME Dr.
PO Box 930
Dearborn, MI 48121
Ph: (313)271-1500   Fax: (313)271-2861
Fr: 800-733-4763
E-mail: service@sme.org
URL: http://www.sme.org/ri

Description: Engineers, managers, educators, and government officials in 50 countries working or interested in the field of robotics. Promotes efficient and effective use of current and future robot technology. Serves as a clearinghouse for the industry trends and developments. Areas of interest include: aerospace; assembly systems; casting and forging; education and training; human factors and safety; human and food service; material handling; military systems; nontraditional systems; research and development; small shop applications; welding. Offers professional certification. Operates placement service; compiles statistics. Maintains speakers' bureau.

★7174★ **Society of Hispanic Professional Engineers (SHPE)**

5400 E Olympic Blvd., Ste. 210
Los Angeles, CA 90022
Ph: (323)725-3970   Fax: (323)725-0316
E-mail: shpenational@shpe.org

URL: http://www.shpe.org

Description: Engineers, student engineers, and scientists seeking to increase the number of Hispanic engineers by providing motivation and support to students. Sponsors competitions and educational programs. Maintains placement service and speakers' bureau; compiles statistics.

EMPLOYER DIRECTORIES AND NETWORKING LISTS

★7175★   *American Men and Women of Science*

Thomson Gale
27500 Drake Rd.
Farmington Hills, MI 48331-3535
Ph: (248)699-4253   Fax: (248)699-8065
Fr: 800-877-GALE
E-mail: amws@galegroup.com

Biennial, latest edition December 2002. $975.00. Covers over 129,700 U.S. and Canadian scientists active in the physical, biological, mathematical, computer science, and engineering fields; includes references to previous edition for deceased scientists and nonrespondents. Entries include: Name, address, education, personal and career data, memberships, honors and awards, research interest. Arrangement: Alphabetical. Indexes: Discipline (in separate volume).

★7176★   *Directory of Contract Staffing Firms*

C.E. Publications Inc.
PO Box 3006
Bothell, WA 98041-3006
Ph: (425)806-5200   Fax: (425)806-5585
URL: http://www.cjhunter.com/dcsf/overview.html

$15.00. Covers nearly 1,300 contract firms actively engaged in the employment of engineering, IT/IS, and technical personnel for 'temporary' contract assignments throughout the world. Entries include: Company name, address, phone, name of contact, email, web address. Arrangement: Alphabetical. Indexes: Geographical.

★7177★   *Engineers-Mechanical Directory*

infoUSA Inc.
5711 S 86th Cir.
Omaha, NE 68127-0347
Ph: (402)930-3500   Fax: (402)331-0176
Fr: 800-555-6124
URL: http://www.abii.com

Updated continuously; printed on request. Number of listings: 2,635. Entries include: Name, address, phone (including area code), size of advertisement, year first in "Yellow Pages," name of owner or manager, number of employees. Compiled from telephone company "Yellow Pages," nationwide. Arrangement: Geographical.

★7178★   *Indiana Society of Professional Engineers-Directory*

Indiana Society of Professional Engineers
PO Box 20806
Indianapolis, IN 46220
Ph: (317)255-2267   Fax: (317)255-2530

Annual, fall. $55.00. Covers member registered engineers, land surveyors, engineering students, and engineers in training. Entries include: Member name, address, phone, type of membership, business information, specialty. Arrangement: Alpha by chapter area.

★7179★   *International Directory of Engineering Societies and Related Organizations*

American Association of Engineering
  Societies
1828 L St. NW, Ste. 906
Washington, DC 20036
Ph: (202)296-2237   Fax: (202)296-1151
Fr: 888-400-AAES

Irregular, latest edition December 1998. $240.00. Covers about 1,370 national, regional, Canadian, and international organizations concerned with engineering and related fields. Entries include: Name, address, phone, fax, e-mail, key personnel, objectives, publications, activities, mailing lists, federation memberships, meeting and convention dates, and budget data. Arrangement: Alphabetical. Indexes: Acronym, geographical, area of specialization.

★7180★   *Mechanical Contractors Association of America (MCAA)-Membership Directory*

National Certified Pipe Welding Bureau
1385 Piccard Dr.
Rockville, MD 20850
Ph: (301)869-5800   Fax: (301)990-9690

Annual, December. Covers about 600 mechanical contractors regularly engaged in the fabrication or erecting of piping systems, who employ certified pipe welders. Entries include: Firm name, address, phone, telex, fax, name of contact. Arrangement: By each chapter, then by firm name.

★7181★   *Peterson's Job Opportunities in Engineering and Technology*

Thomson Peterson's
PO Box 67005
Lawrenceville, NJ 08648-6105
Fr: 800-338-3282

Compiled by the Peterson's staff. Fourth edition, 1996. $21.95 (paper). 384 pages. Profiles 2,000 high-tech companies looking primarily for technical personnel in such fields as biotechnology, telecommunications, software, computers and peripherals, defense, and aerospace. Contains job-search strategies and career options to help match education and expertise to the job market. Indexed geographically, by industry, and by hiring needs.

HANDBOOKS AND MANUALS

★7182★   *The Best Resumes for Scientists and Engineers*

John Wiley & Sons Inc.
1 Wiley Dr.
Somerset, NJ 08873
Ph: (732)469-4400   Fr: 800-225-5945

Adele Lewis and David J. Moore. Second edition, 1993. $37.50; $19.95 (paper). 224 pages. Presents an extensive collection of scientific and engineering resumes, highlighting the important differences between these and resumes written for other occupations.

★7183★   *Careers in Power Engineering and Boiler Operation: Your Guide to a Secure Future*

Powerplant Press
PO Box 431219
Pontiac, MI 48343

Stanley Douglas Guiling. 1993. $39.95 (paper). 500 pages. Complete reference for those seeking employment in the Power Industry.

★7184★   *Engineering Your Job Search: A Job-Finding Resource for Engineering Professionals*

Professional Publications, Inc.
1250 5th Ave.
Belmont, CA 94002
Ph: (650)593-9119   Fax: (650)592-4519
Fr: 800-426-1178

Compiled by Professional Publications, editors. 1995. $24.95 (paper). 154 pages. Out of print.

★7185★   *Great Jobs for Engineering Majors*

McGraw-Hill Professional
McGraw-Hill Higher Education
2 Penn Plaza
New York, NY 10121
Ph: (212)904-2000   Fr: 800-722-4726
E-mail: ntcpub@tribune.com

Geraldine O. Garner. Second edition, 2002. $14.95. 256 pages. Covers all the career options open to students majoring in engineering.

★7186★   *How to Succeed as an Engineer: A Practical Guide to Enhance Your Career*

Institute of Electrical & Electronics
  Engineers Inc.
PO Box 87204
Vancouver, WA 98687
Ph: (360)253-9532   Fax: (360)253-4084

Todd Yuzuriha. 1999. $29.95 (paper). 367 pages.

★7187★ *The I Hate Selling Book: Business-Building Advice for Consultants, Attorneys, Accountants, Engineers, Architects, and Other Professionals*

Allan Boress & Associates
1500 University Dr., Suite 239
Coral Springs, FL 33071
Ph: (954)345-4666   Fax: (954)344-2453

Allan S. Boress. 2001. $29.95.

★7188★ *Keys to Engineering Success*

Prentice Hall PTR
One Lake St.
Upper Saddle River, NJ 07458
Ph: (201)236-7000

Jill S. Tietjen, Kristy A. Schloss, Carol Carter, Joyce Bishop, and Sarah Lyman. 2000. $32.00 (paper).

★7189★ *Majoring in Engineering: How to Get from Your Freshman Year to Your First Job*

Farrar, Straus & Giroux, Inc.
19 Union Sq., W
New York, NY 10003
Ph: (212)741-6900   Fax: (212)633-9385
Fr: 888-330-8477

John Garcia and Carol Carter, editors. 2000. $20.00; $10.00 (paper). 134 pages.

★7190★ *The New Engineer's Guide to Career Growth & Professional Awareness*

Institute of Electrical & Electronics Engineers Inc.
445 Hoes Ln.
PO Box 1331
Piscataway, NJ 08855-1331
Ph: (732)562-3967   Fax: (732)981-9334
Fr: 800-678-4333

Irving J. Gabelman, editor. 1996. $39.95 (paper). 275 pages.

★7191★ *Opportunities in Engineering Careers*

McGraw-Hill Contemporary Books
1221 Avenue of the Americas
New York, NY 10020
Ph: (212)904-2000   Fr: 800-323-4900
E-mail: ntcpub@tribune.com

Nicholas Basta. Revised, 1995. $14.95; $11.95 (paper). 200 pages. Outlines typical job titles, salaries, career paths, and employment prospects.

★7192★ *Opportunities in High Tech Careers*

McGraw-Hill Trade
2 Penn Plaza
New York, NY 10121
Ph: (212)904-2000   Fr: 800-722-4726

Gary Colter and Deborah Yanuck. 1995. $14.95; $11.95 (paper). 160 pages. Explores high technology careers. Describes job opportunities, how to make a career decision, how to prepare for high technology jobs, job hunting techniques, and future trends.

★7193★ *Opportunities in Research and Development Careers*

McGraw-Hill/Contemporary Books
1221 Avenue of the Americas
New York, NY 10020
Ph: (212)904-2000   Fr: 800-323-4900
E-mail: ntcpub@tribune.com

Jan Goldberg. 1997. $14.95; $11.95 (paper). 204 pages.

★7194★ *Real People Working in Engineering*

McGraw-Hill Contemporary Books
1221 Avenue of the Americas
New York, NY 10020
Ph: (212)904-2000   Fr: 800-323-4900
E-mail: ntcpub@tribune.com

Blythe Camenson, Jan Goldberg. 1997. $14.95; $12.95 (paper). Interviews and profiles of working professionals capture a range of opportunities in this field.

★7195★ *Resumes for Engineering Careers*

McGraw-Hill Trade
2 Penn Plaza
New York, NY 10121
Ph: (212)904-2000   Fr: 800-722-4726
E-mail: ntcpub@tribune.com

2000. $10.95 (paper). 456 pages. Contains sample resumes and cover letters applicable to any engineering field.

★7196★ *Resumes for Scientific and Technical Careers*

McGraw-Hill Contemporary Books
1221 Avenue of the Americas
New York, NY 10020
Ph: (212)904-2000   Fr: 800-323-4900
E-mail: ntcpub@tribune.com

1999. $9.95 (paper). 450 pages. Provides resume advice for individuals interested in working in scientific and technical careers. Includes sample resumes and cover letters.

★7197★ *Where the Jobs Are: The Hottest Careers for the 90s*

The Career Press, Inc.
3 Tice Rd.
PO Box 687
Franklin Lakes, NJ 07417-1322
Ph: (201)848-0310   Fax: (201)848-1727
Fr: 800-227-3371

Joyce Hadley. Third edition, 2000. $13.99 (paper). 400 pages. Out of print. Describes careers in fifteen general fields, from accounting to travel and hospitality.

EMPLOYMENT AGENCIES AND SEARCH FIRMS

★7198★ **The Aspire Group**
52 Second Ave, 1st Fl
Waltham, MA 02451-1129
Fax: (718)890-1810   Fr: 800-546-5675
URL: http://www.bmanet.com

Employment agency.

★7199★ **Bell Oaks Co.**
10 Glenlake Parkway, Ste. 300
Atlanta, GA 30328
Ph: (678)287-2000   Fax: (678)287-2001
E-mail: atlantacareers@belloaks.com
URL: http://www.belloaks.com

Personnel service firm.

★7200★ **The Bradbury Group Inc.**
2112 Vizcaya Way, Ste. 200
Campbell, CA 95008
Ph: (408)377-5400   Fax: (408)377-1112

Executive search firm

★7201★ **Brown Venture Associates Inc.**
3000 Sand Hill Rd., Bldg. 3, Ste. 110
Menlo Park, CA 94025
Ph: (650)233-0205   Fax: (650)233-1902

Executive search firm.

★7202★ **Claremont-Branan, Inc.**
1298 Rockbridge Rd., Ste. B
Stone Mountain, GA 30087
Ph: (770)925-2915   Fax: (770)925-2601

Employment agency. Executive search firm.

★7203★ **Colli Associates**
404 Caboose Ln.
Valrico, FL 33594
Ph: (813)681-2145   Fax: (813)661-5217
E-mail: colli@gte.net

Employment agency. Executive search firm.

★7204★ **The Corporate Source Group Inc.**
280 S. Main St.
Andover, MA 01810
Ph: (987)475-6400   Fax: (987)475-6800

Executive search firm branches in Phoenix, AZ; Tampa, Fl; North Potomac, MD; McMurray, PA.

★7205★ **The Coxe Group Inc.**
1218 3rd Ave., Ste. 1700
Seattle, WA 98101-3021
Ph: (206)467-4040   Fax: (206)467-4038

Executive search firm.

★7206★ Dunlap & Sullivan Associates
29 Pearl St. NW, Ste. 227
Grand Rapids, MI 49503
Ph: (616)458-4142   Fax: (616)458-4203

Executive search firm with second location in Hobe Sound, FL.

★7207★ Engineer One, Inc.
PO Box 23037
Knoxville, TN 37933
Fax: (865)691-0110
E-mail: engineerone@engineerone.com
URL: http://www.engineerone.com

Employment agency.

★7208★ Executive Recruiters Agency
14 Office Park Dr., Ste. 100
PO Box 21810
Little Rock, AR 72221-1810
Ph: (501)224-7000   Fax: (501)224-8534
E-mail: grogers@execrecruit.com
URL: http://www.execrecruit.com

Personnel service firm.

★7209★ High Employee Services Ltd.
525 Greenfield Rd., 2nd Fl.
Lancaster, PA 17601
Ph: (717)396-7701   Fax: (717)396-7779

Personnel consultants serving all industries including business and finance, engineering, sales and marketing, and focusing on manufacturing, industrial, and transportation operations. Conducts full time, contract staffing, and temporary (clerical and skilled) placements. Serves private industries as well as government agencies.

★7210★ Main Line Personnel Service, Inc.
Pagoda Blding.
100 Presidential Blvd. Ste. 200
Bala Cynwyd, PA 19004-0448
Ph: (610)667-1820   Fax: (610)668-5000
URL: http://www.mlpers.com

Employment agency.

★7211★ Modem Engineering Design Associates
1575 Lauzon Rd.
Windsor, ON, Canada N8S 3N4
Ph: (519)944-7221   Fax: (519)944-6862
Fr: 800-999-6332

Engineering consultants offering design services principally to automotive, OEM and components manufacturing industries, including military applications. Major area of expertise is in engine, transmission and chassis design. Also provides technical personnel recruitment. Industries served: automotive, petrochemical, food, brewery, aircraft, ship building, tooling, and environmental companies.

★7212★ Rand Personnel
1200 Truxtun, Ste. 130
Bakersfield, CA 93301
Ph: (805)325-0751   Fax: (805)325-4120

Personnel service firm serving a variety of fields.

★7213★ Search and Recruit International
4455 South Blvd.
Virginia Beach, VA 23452
Ph: (757)490-3151   Fax: (757)497-6503
E-mail: britt@searchandrecruit.com
URL: http://www.searchandrecruit.com

Employment agency. Headquartered in Virginia Beach. Other offices in Bremerton, WA; Charleston, SC; Jacksonville, FL; Memphis, TN; Pensacola, FL; Sacramento, CA; San Bernardino, CA; San Diego, CA.

★7214★ Techtronix Technical Search
PO Box 17713
Milwaukee, WI 53217-0173
Ph: (414)466-3100   Fax: (414)466-3598

Firm specializes in recruiting executives for the engineering, information systems, manufacturing, marketing, finance, and human resources industries.

★7215★ TRC Staffing Services Inc.
2110 15 Mile Rd., Ste. B
Sterling Heights, MI 48310
Ph: (586)939-3210   Fax: (586)978-0572

A full-service executive search company with permanent placements encompassing engineering, industrial sales, financial and computer science positions. Screen, interview, and verify past employment for all candidates prior to referral. Also assist personnel staffs in the attainment of their EEO/AAP goals with the placement of talented individuals in positions which are underutilized with minorities and/or women. In addition, firm has a clerical temporary service division, TRC Temporary Service; and an employment agency, TRC Staffing Services.

★7216★ Tri-Serv Inc.
22 W. Padonia Rd., Ste. C-353
Timonium, MD 21093
Ph: (410)561-1740   Fax: (410)252-7417
E-mail: info@tri-serv.coom
URL: http://www.tri-serv.com

Permanent employment agency.

★7217★ Winters Technical Staffing Services
2025 Sheppard Ave. E, Ste. 4110
Willowdale, ON, Canada M2T 1V7
Ph: (416)495-7422   Fax: (416)495-8479

Technical staffing service for permanent and contract positions in all facets of engineering. Serves government agencies, consulting engineers, and all areas of manufacturing in Canada and northeast U.S.

ONLINE JOB SOURCES AND SERVICES

★7218★ Spherion Workforce Architects
URL: http://www.spherion.com

Description: Recruitment firm specializing in accounting and finance, sales and marketing, interim executives, technology, engineering, retail and human resources.

TRADESHOWS

★7219★ American Society for Engineering Education Annual Conference and Exposition
American Society for Engineering Education
1818 N St., Ste. 600
Washington, DC 20036
Ph: (202)331-3500   Fax: (202)265-8504
URL: http://www.asee.org

Annual. **Primary Exhibits:** Publications, engineering supplies and equipment, computers, software, and research companies all products and services related to engineering education. **Dates and Locations:** 2005 Jun 12-15; Portland, OR • 2006 Jun 18-21; Chicago, IL • 2007 Jun 24-27; Honolulu, HI.

OTHER SOURCES

★7220★ American Almanac of Jobs and Salaries
Morrow Avon
1350 Avenue of the Americas
New York, NY 10019
Ph: (212)261-6788   Fr: 800-242-7737

John W. Wright. Revised edition, 2000. $20.00 (paper). 672 pages. This is a comprehensive guide to the wages of hundreds of occupations in a wide variety of industries and organizations.

★7221★ American Association of Engineering Societies (AAES)
1828 L St. NW, No. 906
Washington, DC 20036
Ph: (202)296-2237   Fax: (202)296-1151
Fr: 888-400-2237
E-mail: tprice@aaes.org
URL: http://www.aaes.org

Description: Coordinates the efforts of the member societies in the provision of reliable and objective information to the general public concerning issues which affect the engineering profession and the field of engineering as a whole; to collect, analyze, document, and disseminate data which will inform the general public of the relationship between engineering and the national welfare; to provide a forum for the engineering societies to exchange and discuss their views on matters of common interest; and to represent the U.S. engineering community aborad through representation in WFEO and UPADI.

★7222★ **American Society of Mechanical Engineers (ASME)**

3 Park Ave.
New York, NY 10016-5990
Ph: (973)882-1167   Fax: (212)591-7674
Fr: 800-THE-ASME
E-mail: infocentral@asme.org
URL: http://www.asme.org

Members: Technical society of mechanical engineers and students. **Purpose:** Conducts research; develops boiler, pressure vessel, and power test codes. Develops safety codes and standards for equipment. Conducts short course programs, and Identifying Research Needs Program. Maintains 19 research committees and 38 divisions.

★7223★ **Association for International Practical Training (AIPT)**

10400 Little Patuxent Pky., Ste. 250
Columbia, MD 21044-3519
Ph: (410)997-2200   Fax: (410)992-3924
E-mail: aipt@aipt.org
URL: http://www.aipt.org

Description: Providers worldwide on-the-job training programs for students and professionals seeking international career development and life-changing experiences. Arranges workplace exchanges in hundreds of professional fields, bringing employers and trainees together from around the world. Client list ranges from small farming communities to Fortune 500 companies.

★7224★ *Engineering Occupations*

Delphi Productions
3160 4th St.
Boulder, CO 80304
Fax: (303)443-4022   Fr: 888-443-2400
URL: http://www.delphivideo.com

$95.00. 50 minutes. Part of the Careers for the 21st Century Video Library.

★7225★ **ISA - Instrumentation, Systems, and Automation Society**

67 Alexander Dr.
PO Box 12277
Research Triangle Park, NC 27709
Ph: (919)549-8411   Fax: (919)549-8288

E-mail: info@isa.org
URL: http://www.isa.org

Purpose: Fosters advancement in the theory, design, manufacture, and use of instruments, computers, and systems for measurement and control.

★7226★ *Mechanical Engineers*

Evon Publishing
832 N 7th Ave.
Iron River, MI 49935
Ph: (906)265-3190

Audiocassette. 1996. $16.95. 32 minutes. Part of the Careers and Vocational Guidance Series. Provides information about the nature of the work, educational requirements, employment outlook, earnings, and work conditions as well as additional related information.

★7227★ **National Action Council for Minorities in Engineering (NACME)**

Empire State Bldg., Ste. 2212
350 Fifth Ave.
New York, NY 10118-2299
Ph: (212)279-2626   Fax: (212)629-5178
E-mail: webmaster@nacme.org
URL: http://www.nacme.org/

Description: Leads the national effort to increase access to careers in engineering and other science-based disciplines. Supported by the nation's leading technology-intensive companies, NACME conducts research and public policy analysis, develops and operates national demonstration programs at precollege and university levels, and disseminates information through publications, conferences, and electronic media. NACME is also the nation's largest privately funded source of scholarships for minority students in engineering.

★7228★ **National Society of Professional Engineers (NSPE)**

1420 King St.
Alexandria, VA 22314
Ph: (703)684-2800   Fax: (703)836-4875
Fr: 888-285-6773
E-mail: custserv@nspe.org
URL: http://www.nspe.org

Description: Professional engineers and engineers-in-training in all fields registered in accordance with the laws of states or territories of the U.S. or provinces of Canada; qualified graduate engineers, student members, and registered land surveyors. Is concerned with social, professional, ethical, and

economic considerations of engineering as a profession; encompasses programs in public relations, employment practices, ethical considerations, education, and career guidance. Monitors legislative and regulatory actions of interest to the engineering profession.

★7229★ *Scientific, Engineering, and Technical Services*

Cambridge Educational
2572 Brunswick Ave.
Lawrenceville, NJ 08648-4128
Fax: 800-FAX-ON-US   Fr: 800-468-4227
URL: http://www.cambridgeeducational.com

$89.95. 2002. 18 minutes. Part of the Career Cluster Series.

★7230★ **Society of Women Engineers (SWE)**

230 E Ohio St., No. 400
Chicago, IL 60611-3265
Ph: (312)596-5223   Fax: (312)596-5252
E-mail: hq@swe.org
URL: http://www.swe.org

Description: Educational and service organization representing both students and professional women in engineering and technical fields.

★7231★ **SPIE - The International Society for Optical Engineering (SPIE)**

PO Box 10
Bellingham, WA 98227-0010
Ph: (360)676-3290   Fax: (360)647-1445
E-mail: spie@spie.org
URL: http://www.spie.org

Description: Dedicated to advancing scientific research and engineering applications of optical, photonic, imaging and optoelectronic technologies through meetings, education programs, and publications.

★7232★ *Women in Engineering*

Her Own Words
PO Box 5264
Madison, WI 53705-0264
Ph: (608)271-7083   Fax: (608)271-0209
URL: http://www.herownwords.com/

Video. Jocelyn Riley. $95.00. 15 minutes. Resource guide also available for $45.00.

Medical Assistants

SOURCES OF HELP-WANTED ADS

★7233★ Ambulatory Outreach
Society for Ambulatory Care Professionals
1 N Franklin, 31st Fl.
Chicago, IL 60606
Fax: (312)422-4577

Quarterly. Subscription included in membership; $95.00/year for nonmembers. Professional journal for ambulatory care personnel.

★7234★ ASRT Scanner
American Society of Radiologic
  Technologists
15000 Central Ave. SE
Albuquerque, NM 87123-3917
Ph: (505)298-4500   Fax: (505)298-5063
Fr: 800-444-2778

Monthly. Subscription included in membership. Professional magazine covering issues in radiology and medical technology. Includes calendar of events, member profiles, state affiliate news, educational opportunities, and research updates.

★7235★ Health Care Weekly Review
The Martin Group Inc.
24901 Northwestern Hwy., Ste. 316A
Southfield, MI 48075
Ph: (248)440-6080   Fax: (248)352-4801
E-mail: hcwr@compuserve.com

Weekly. $48.00/year for individuals. Professional newspaper covering the health care industry.

★7236★ Hospitals & Health Networks
Health Forum L.L.C.
One N Franklin
Chicago, IL 60606
Ph: (312)893-6800   Fax: (312)422-4600
Fr: 800-621-6902
E-mail: hhn@healthforum.com
URL: http://www.hhnmag.com

Monthly. Publication covering the health care industry.

★7237★ Journal of the American Society of Podiatric Medical Assistants
American Society of Podiatric Medical
  Assistants
2124 S Austin Blvd.
Cicero, IL 60804
Ph: (708)863-6303   Fax: (708)863-5375
Fr: 888-88A-SPMA

Quarterly. Subscription included in membership. Professional journal covering issues in podiatry.

★7238★ Journal of Health and Hospital Law
American Health Lawyers Association
1025 Connecticut NW, Ste. 600
Washington, DC 20036
Ph: (202)833-1100   Fax: (202)833-1105

Quarterly. $150.00/year. Professional journal covering healthcare issues and cases and their impact on the health care arena.

★7239★ Medicine and Health
Thomson Financial
195 Broadway
New York, NY 10007
Ph: (646)822-2000

Weekly. Professional publication covering the health care industry.

★7240★ Minority Health Today
Heritage Information Holdings Inc.
1101 Pennsylvania Ave. NW, Ste. 820
Washington, DC 20001

Bimonthly. Publication covering minority issues in health.

★7241★ The PMA
American Association of Medical
  Assistants
20 N Wacker Dr., Ste. 1575
Chicago, IL 60606
Ph: (312)899-1500   Fax: (312)899-1259

Bimonthly. $30.00/year for nonmembers. Professional health journal.

★7242★ Research in Healthcare Financial Management
International Society for Research in
  Healthcare Financial Management Ltd.
305 W Chesapeake Ave.
CSBA Ste. L-096
Towson, MD 21204

Annual. Publication covering issues in the healthcare industry.

★7243★ State Health Monitor
Atlantic Information Services Inc.
1100 17th St. NW, No. 300
Washington, DC 20036
Ph: (202)775-9008   Fax: (202)331-9542
Fr: 800-521-4323
E-mail: customerserv@aispub.com

Monthly. Publication covering health care.

★7244★ Trauma Reports
Thomson Medical Economics
5 Paragon Dr.
Montvale, NJ 07645-1742
Ph: (201)358-7200   Fax: (201)722-2680
URL: http://www.ahcpub.com/ahc_root_
html/products/newsletters/tr.

Bimonthly. $239.00/year for individuals. Professional publication covering health care.

EMPLOYER DIRECTORIES AND NETWORKING LISTS

★7245★ AHA Guide to the Health Care Field
American Hospital Association (AHA)
1 N. Franklin St., 27th Fl.
Chicago, IL 60606
Ph: (312)422-2050   Fax: (312)422-4700
Fr: 800-424-4301

Annual, August. $295.00. Covers hospitals, networks, multi-health care systems, freestanding ambulatory surgery centers, psychiatric facilities, long-term care facilities, substance abuse programs, and other health-related organizations. Entries include: For hospitals-Facility name, address, phone, administrator's name, number of beds, facilities and services, number of employees, expenses, other statistics. For other organizations-Name, address, phone, fax, name and title of contact. Arrangement: Geographical. Indexes: Hospital name.

★7246★ **Guide to Careers in the Health Professions**

The Princeton Review
1745 Broadway
New York, NY 10019
Ph: (212)829-6928   Fax: (212)940-7400
Fr: 800-733-3000

Published January, 2001. $24.95. Presents advice and information for those searching for satisfying careers in the health professions. Publication includes: Directory of schools and academic programs. Entries include: Name, address, phone, tuition, program details, employment profiles.

★7247★ **Hospital Blue Book**

Billian/Transworld Publishing Inc.
2100 Powers Ferry Rd.
Ste. 300
Atlanta, GA 30339
Ph: (770)955-8484   Fax: (770)955-8485
Fr: 800-533-8484
E-mail: blu-book@billian.com

Annual, January. $285.00 for national edition; $160.00 for southern edition. Covers more than 6,687 hospitals; some listings also appear in a separate southern edition of this publication. Entries include: Name of hospital, accreditation, mailing address, phone, fax, number of beds, type of facility (nonprofit, general, state, etc.); list of administrative personnel and chiefs of medical services, with specific titles. Arrangement: Geographical.

★7248★ **Medical and Health Information Directory**

Thomson Gale
27500 Drake Rd.
Farmington Hills, MI 48331-3535
Ph: (248)699-4253   Fax: (248)699-8065
Fr: 800-877-GALE
E-mail: businessproducts@gale.com

Annual. $285.00 per volume; $675.00 per set. Covers in Volume 1, more than 26,500 medical and health oriented associations, organizations, institutions, and government agencies, including health maintenance organizations (HMOs), preferred provider organizations (PPOs), insurance companies, pharmaceutical companies, research centers, and medical and allied health schools. In Volume 2, over 12,000 medical book publishers; medical periodicals, directories, audiovisual producers and services, medical libraries and information centers, electronic resources, and health-related internet search engines. In Volume 3, more than 35,500 clinics, treatment centers, care programs, and counseling/diagnostic services for 34 subject areas. Entries include: Institution, service, or firm name, address, phone,

fax, email and URL; many include names of key personnel and, when pertinent, descriptive annotation. Volume 3 was formerly listed separately as Health Services Directory. Arrangement: Classified by organization activity, service, etc. Indexes: Each volume has a complete alphabetical name and keyword index.

★7249★ **Peterson's Job Opportunities for Health and Science Majors**

Thomson Peterson's
Princeton Pke. Corporate Ctr., 2000
  Lenox Dr.
PO Box 67005
Lawrenceville, NJ 08648
Ph: (609)896-1800   Fax: (609)896-4531
Fr: 800-338-3282
URL: http://www.petersons.com

Irregular, latest edition 1999. $18.95. Covers approximately 1,300 research, consulting, government, and non-profit and profit service organizations that hire college and university graduates in science and health-related majors. Entries include: Organization name, address, phone, name and title of contact, type of organization, number of employees, Standard Industrial Classification (SIC) code; description of opportunities available including disciplines, level of education required, starting locations and salaries, level of experience accepted, benefits.

HANDBOOKS AND MANUALS

★7250★ **America's Fastest Growing Jobs**

JIST Works, Inc.
8902 Otis Ave.
Indianapolis, IN 46216-1033
Ph: (317)613-4200   Fax: (317)613-4307
Fr: 800-648-5478
E-mail: jistworks@aol.com
URL: http://www.jist.com

Seventh edition, 2002. $16.95 (paper). 438 pages. Each job profile explains the nature of the work, skills and abilities required, employment outlook, average earnings, related occupations, education and training requirements, and employment opportunities. Also contains career planning information and job search tips.

★7251★ **Careers in Health Care**

McGraw-Hill Trade
2 Penn Plaza
New York, NY 10121
Ph: (212)904-2000   Fr: 800-722-4726
E-mail: ntcpub@tribune.com

Barbara M. Swanson. Fourth edition, 2000. $17.95; $13.95 (paper). 320 pages. Describes job duties, work settings, salaries, licensing and certification requirements, educational preparation, and future outlook. Gives ideas on how to secure a job.

★7252★ **Chronicle Health Occupations Guidebook**

Chronicle Guidance Publications, Inc.
66 Aurora St.
Moravia, NY 13118-3576
Fax: (315)497-3359   Fr: 800-899-0454
E-mail: customerservice@chronicleguidance.com
URL: http://www.chronicleguidance.com

Paul Downes, editor. Revised edition, 1994. $100.65.

★7253★ **Delmar's Comprehensive Medical Assisting: Administrative and Clinical Competencies**

Thomson Delmar Learning
PO Box 15015
Albany, NY 12212-5015
Ph: (518)348-2300   Fax: (518)373-6345
Fr: 800-988-7498

Wilburta Q. Lindh. Second edition, 2002. $34.95. Illustrated. 758 pages. Explores medical assisting.

★7254★ **Expert Resumes for Health Care Careers**

JIST Publishing
8902 Otis Ave.
Indianapolis, IN 46216-1033
Ph: (317)613-4200   Fax: 800-547-8329

December 2003. $16.95. 288 pages.

★7255★ **Health Care Job Explosion! High Growth Health Care Careers and Job Locator**

Bookhaven Press LLC
PO Box 1243
Moon Township, PA 15108
Ph: (412)494-6926   Fax: (412)494-5749
Fr: 800-782-7424

Dennis V. Damp. Third edition, 2001. 288 pages.

★7256★ **Health Careers Today**

Elsevier-Health Sciences Division
The Curtis Center, Ste. 300E, 3rd Fl.
170 S. Independence Mall W.
Philadelphia, PA 19106
Ph: (215)238-7800   Fax: (215)238-7362
Fr: 800-523-4069

Gerdin. Revised edition. April 2004. $52.95.

★7257★ **Health Careers: Undergraduate Careers in the Health Profession**

Kendall Hunt Publishing Co.
4050 Westmark Dr.
PO Box 1840
Dubuque, IA 52004-1840
Ph: (319)589-1000   Fax: (319)589-1046
Fr: 800-228-0810

Michael Beard and Yasmen Simonian. 1996. $12.54. 80 pages.

★7258★ Hot Health-Care Careers

MasterMedia Publishing Corp.
46585 SE Coalman Rd.
Sandy, OR 97055
Ph: (503)668-0296   Fax: (503)668-0494
Fr: 800-334-8232

Margaret McNally. 1993. $17.95; $10.95 (paper). Out of print.

★7259★ Medical Assisting: Administrative and Clinical Competencies

The McGraw-Hill Companies
860 Taylor Station Rd.
Blacklick, OH 43004-0545
Fax: (614)755-5645   Fr: 800-722-4726

Barbara Prickett-Ramutkowski. 2004. Explores medical assisting and the competencies of it.

★7260★ 150 Careers in Health Care

U.S. Directory Service
121 Chanlon Rd.
New Providence, NJ 07974
Ph: (908)464-6800   Fax: (908)665-3560
Fr: 800-521-8110

Sudjic, contributor. Revised, 1993. $59.95. Book describes the occupation & training requirements of allied health personnel, administrators, assistants, auxiliary workers, technicians, therapists, technologists, & many more.

★7261★ Opportunities in Health and Medical Careers

McGraw-Hill Trade
2 Penn Plaza
New York, NY 10121
Ph: (212)904-2000   Fr: 800-722-4726

I. Donald Snook, Jr. and Leo D'Orazio. 1997. $14.95; $11.95 (paper). 202 pages. Covers the full range of medical and health occupations. Illustrated.

★7262★ Opportunities in Paramedical Careers

McGraw-Hill/Contemporary Books
1221 Avenue of the Americas
New York, NY 10020
Ph: (212)904-2000   Fr: 800-323-4900
E-mail: ntcpub@tribune.com

Alex Kacen. Revised, 1999. $14.95; 11.95 (paper). 200 pages. Discusses a variety of opportunities in this field and how to pursue them. Illustrated.

★7263★ Resumes for the Health Care Professional

John Wiley & Sons Inc.
111 River Rd.
Hoboken, NJ 07030-5774
Ph: (201)748-6000   Fax: (201)748-6088
Fr: 800-225-5945

Kim Marino. Second edition, 2000. $14.95 (paper). 224 pages.

★7264★ Resumes for Health and Medical Careers

McGraw-Hill Trade
2 Penn Plaza
New York, NY 10121
Ph: (212)904-2000   Fr: 800-722-4726
E-mail: ntcpub@tribune.com

1997. $9.95 (paper). 455 pages.

★7265★ VGM's Handbook of Health Care Careers

McGraw-Hill Trade
2 Penn Plaza
New York, NY 10121
Ph: (212)904-2000   Fr: 800-722-4726
E-mail: ntcpub@tribune.com

VGM Career Horizons Staff. Second edition, revised, 1997. $12.95 (paper). 112 pages.

★7266★ Where the Jobs Are: The Hottest Careers for the 90s

The Career Press, Inc.
3 Tice Rd.
PO Box 687
Franklin Lakes, NJ 07417-1322
Ph: (201)848-0310   Fax: (201)848-1727
Fr: 800-227-3371

Joyce Hadley. Third edition, 2000. $13.99 (paper). 400 pages. Out of print. Describes careers in fifteen general fields, from accounting to travel and hospitality.

EMPLOYMENT AGENCIES AND SEARCH FIRMS

★7267★ Davis-Smith, Inc.

27656 Franklin Rd.
Southfield, MI 48034
Ph: (248)354-4100   Fax: (248)354-6702
Fr: 800-541-4672
E-mail: info@davissmith.com
URL: http://www.davissmith.com

Employment agency. Executive search firm.

★7268★ Harper Associates

29870 Middlebelt
Farmington Hills, MI 48334
Ph: (248)932-1170   Fax: (248)932-1214
E-mail: resumes@harperjobs.com
URL: http://www.harperjobs.com

Executive search firm and employment agency.

★7269★ Professional Placement Associates, Inc.

287 Bowman Ave., Ste. 309
Purchase, NY 10577
Ph: (914)251-1000   Fax: (914)251-1055
E-mail: lschachter@ppasearch.com
URL: http://www.ppasearch.com

Executive search firm specializing in the health and medical field.

ONLINE JOB SOURCES AND SERVICES

★7270★ Medhunters.com

E-mail: info@medhunters.com
URL: http://www.medhunters.com

Description: Career search site for jobs in all health care specialties; educational resources; visa and licensing information for relocation; interesting articles; relocation tools; links to professional organizations and general resources.

★7271★ ProHealthJobs

E-mail: sales@prohealthjobs.com
URL: http://www.prohealthjobs.com

Description: Career resources site for the medical and health care field. Lists professional opportunities, product information, continuing education and open positions.

OTHER SOURCES

★7272★ American Association of Medical Assistants (AAMA)

20 N. Wacker Dr., Ste. 1575
Chicago, IL 60606-2963
Ph: (312)899-1500   Fax: (312)899-1259
Fr: 800-228-2262
URL: http://www.aama-ntl.org

Description: Medical assistants are allied health professionals who work primarily in anbilatory (out patient) settings and perform clinical and administrative procedures. Activities include a certification program consisting of study and an examination, passage of which entitles the individual to become credentialed as a Certified Medical Assistant. Conducts accreditation of one- and two-year programs in medical assisting in conjunction with the commission on Accreditation of Allied Health Education Programs. Provides assistance and information to institutions of higher learning desirous of initiating courses for medical assistants. Awards continuing education units for selected educational programs.

★7273★ American Medical Technologists (AMT)

710 Higgins Rd.
Park Ridge, IL 60068-5765
Ph: (847)823-5169   Fax: (847)823-0458
Fr: 800-275-1268
E-mail: mail@amt1.com
URL: http://www.amt1.com

Description: National professional association and certifying body for medical laboratory technologists, technicians, medical assistants, dental assistants, and phlebotomists. Maintains job information service. Sponsors AMT Institute for Education, evaluates and recommends continuing education programs.

★7274★ **American Society of Podiatric Medical Assistants (ASPMA)**

2124 S Austin Blvd.
Cicero, IL 60804
Ph: (708)863-6303   Fax: (708)863-5375
Fr: 888-88A-SPMA
E-mail: mmalone@aspma.org
URL: http://www.aspma.org

Description: Podiatric assistants. Purposes are to hold educational seminars and to administer certification examinations.

★7275★ **Exploring Health Occupations**

Cambridge Educational
2572 Brunswick Ave.
Lawrenceville, NJ 08648-4128
Fax: 800-FAX-ON-US   Fr: 800-468-4227
URL: http://www.cambridgeeducational.com

Two videos. $139.95. 1999.

★7276★ **Health Service Occupations**

Delphi Productions
3160 4th St.
Boulder, CO 80304
Fax: (303)443-4022   Fr: 888-443-2400
URL: http://www.delphivideo.com

$95.00. 50 minutes. Part of the Careers for the 21st Century Video Library.

★7277★ **Medical Assistants**

Evon Publishing
832 N 7th Ave.
Iron River, MI 49935
Ph: (906)265-3190

Audiocassette. 1996. $16.95. 32 minutes. Part of the Careers and Vocational Guidance Series. Provides information about the nature of the work, educational requirements, employment outlook, earnings, and work conditions as well as additional related information.

★7278★ **Medical Technicians and Technologists**

Cambridge Educational
2572 Brunswick Ave.
Lawrenceville, NJ 08648-4128
Fax: 800-FAX-ON-US   Fr: 800-468-4227
URL: http://www.cambridgeeducational.com

$79.95. 15 minutes. Part of the Exploring Health Occupations Series.

★7279★ **Medicine & Related Occupations**

Delphi Productions
3160 4th St.
Boulder, CO 80304
Fax: (303)443-4022   Fr: 888-443-2400
URL: http://www.delphivideo.com

$95.00. 45 minutes. Part of the Careers for the 21st Century Video Library.

Medical Record Technicians

EMPLOYER DIRECTORIES AND NETWORKING LISTS

★7280★ AHA Guide to the Health Care Field

American Hospital Association (AHA)
1 N. Franklin St., 27th Fl.
Chicago, IL 60606
Ph: (312)422-2050   Fax: (312)422-4700
Fr: 800-424-4301

Annual, August. $295.00. Covers hospitals, networks, multi-health care systems, free-standing ambulatory surgery centers, psychiatric facilities, long-term care facilities, substance abuse programs, and other health-related organizations. Entries include: For hospitals-Facility name, address, phone, administrator's name, number of beds, facilities and services, number of employees, expenses, other statistics. For other organizations-Name, address, phone, fax, name and title of contact. Arrangement: Geographical. Indexes: Hospital name.

★7281★ Directory of Hospital Personnel

Thomson Medical Economics
5 Paragon Dr.
Montvale, NJ 07645-1742
Ph: (201)358-7200   Fax: (201)722-2680

Annual, November. $325.00. Covers 200,000 executives at 7,000 U.S. hospitals. Entries include: Name of hospital, address, phone, number of beds, type and JCAHO status of hospital, names and titles of key department heads and staff, medical and nursing school affiliations; number of residents, interns, and nursing students. Arrangement: Geographical. Indexes: Hospital name, personnel, hospital size.

★7282★ Guide to Careers in the Health Professions

The Princeton Review
1745 Broadway
New York, NY 10019
Ph: (212)829-6928   Fax: (212)940-7400
Fr: 800-733-3000

Published January, 2001. $24.95. Presents advice and information for those searching for satisfying careers in the health professions. Publication includes: Directory of schools and academic programs. Entries include: Name, address, phone, tuition, program details, employment profiles.

★7283★ Hospital Blue Book

Billian/Transworld Publishing Inc.
2100 Powers Ferry Rd.
Ste. 300
Atlanta, GA 30339
Ph: (770)955-8484   Fax: (770)955-8485
Fr: 800-533-8484
E-mail: blu-book@billian.com

Annual, January. $285.00 for national edition; $160.00 for southern edition. Covers more than 6,687 hospitals; some listings also appear in a separate southern edition of this publication. Entries include: Name of hospital, accreditation, mailing address, phone, fax, number of beds, type of facility (nonprofit, general, state, etc.); list of administrative personnel and chiefs of medical services, with specific titles. Arrangement: Geographical.

★7284★ The JobBank Guide to Health Care Companies

Adams Media Corp.
57 Littlefield St.
Avon, MA 02322
Ph: (508)427-7100   Fax: (508)427-6790
Fr: 800-872-5627

$17.95. Covers Jobs nationwide in health care companies. Entries include: Firm or organization name, address, phone, name and title of contact; description of organization, headquarters location, typical titles for entry- and middle-level positions, educational backgrounds desired, fringe benefits offered, stock exchange listing, training programs, internships, parent company, number of employees, revenues, e-mail and web address, projected number of hires. Indexes: Alphabetical.

★7285★ Medical and Health Information Directory

Thomson Gale
27500 Drake Rd.
Farmington Hills, MI 48331-3535
Ph: (248)699-4253   Fax: (248)699-8065
Fr: 800-877-GALE
E-mail: businessproducts@gale.com

Annual. $285.00 per volume; $675.00 per set. Covers in Volume 1, more than 26,500 medical and health oriented associations, organizations, institutions, and government agencies, including health maintenance organizations (HMOs), preferred provider organizations (PPOs), insurance companies, pharmaceutical companies, research centers, and medical and allied health schools. In Volume 2, over 12,000 medical book publishers; medical periodicals, directories, audiovisual producers and services, medical libraries and information centers, electronic resources, and health-related internet search engines. In Volume 3, more than 35,500 clinics, treatment centers, care programs, and counseling/diagnostic services for 34 subject areas. Entries include: Institution, service, or firm name, address, phone, fax, email and URL; many include names of key personnel and, when pertinent, descriptive annotation. Volume 3 was formerly listed separately as Health Services Directory. Arrangement: Classified by organization activity, service, etc. Indexes: Each volume has a complete alphabetical name and keyword index.

HANDBOOKS AND MANUALS

★7286★ Careers in Health Care

McGraw-Hill Trade
2 Penn Plaza
New York, NY 10121
Ph: (212)904-2000   Fr: 800-722-4726
E-mail: ntcpub@tribune.com

Barbara M. Swanson. Fourth edition, 2000. $17.95; $13.95 (paper). 320 pages. Describes job duties, work settings, salaries, licensing and certification requirements, educational preparation, and future outlook. Gives ideas on how to secure a job.

★7287★ **Expert Resumes for Health Care Careers**
JIST Publishing
8902 Otis Ave.
Indianapolis, IN 46216-1033
Ph: (317)613-4200   Fax: 800-547-8329

December 2003. $16.95. 288 pages.

★7288★ **Health Careers Today**
Elsevier-Health Sciences Division
The Curtis Center, Ste. 300E, 3rd Fl.
170 S. Independence Mall W.
Philadelphia, PA 19106
Ph: (215)238-7800   Fax: (215)238-7362
Fr: 800-523-4069

Gerdin. Revised edition. April 2004. $52.95.

★7289★ **Health Careers: Undergraduate Careers in the Health Profession**
Kendall Hunt Publishing Co.
4050 Westmark Dr.
PO Box 1840
Dubuque, IA 52004-1840
Ph: (319)589-1000   Fax: (319)589-1046
Fr: 800-228-0810

Michael Beard and Yasmen Simonian. 1996. $12.54. 80 pages.

★7290★ **Hot Health-Care Careers**
MasterMedia Publishing Corp.
46585 SE Coalman Rd.
Sandy, OR 97055
Ph: (503)668-0296   Fax: (503)668-0494
Fr: 800-334-8232

Margaret McNally. 1993. $17.95; $10.95 (paper). Out of print.

★7291★ **Opportunities in Health and Medical Careers**
McGraw-Hill Trade
2 Penn Plaza
New York, NY 10121
Ph: (212)904-2000   Fr: 800-722-4726

I. Donald Snook, Jr. and Leo D'Orazio. 1997. $14.95; $11.95 (paper). 202 pages. Covers the full range of medical and health occupations. Illustrated.

★7292★ **Resumes for Health and Medical Careers**
McGraw-Hill Trade
2 Penn Plaza
New York, NY 10121
Ph: (212)904-2000   Fr: 800-722-4726
E-mail: ntcpub@tribune.com
1997. $9.95 (paper). 455 pages.

★7293★ **Your Career in Administrative Medical Services**
W. B. Saunders Co.
6277 Sea Harbor Dr.
Orlando, FL 32821
Fr: 800-654-2452

Roberta C. Weiss. 1996. $38.00. 384 pages.

EMPLOYMENT AGENCIES AND SEARCH FIRMS

★7294★ **Davis-Smith, Inc.**
27656 Franklin Rd.
Southfield, MI 48034
Ph: (248)354-4100   Fax: (248)354-6702
Fr: 800-541-4672
E-mail: info@davissmith.com
URL: http://www.davissmith.com

Employment agency. Executive search firm.

★7295★ **Harper Associates**
29870 Middlebelt
Farmington Hills, MI 48334
Ph: (248)932-1170   Fax: (248)932-1214
E-mail: resumes@harperjobs.com
URL: http://www.harperjobs.com

Executive search firm and employment agency.

★7296★ **JPM International**
26060 Acero
Mission Viejo, CA 92691
Ph: (949)699-4300   Fax: (949)699-4333
Fr: 800-685-7856
E-mail: leslieo@jpmintl.com
URL: http://www.jpmintl.com

Executive search firm and employment agency.

★7297★ **Professional Placement Associates, Inc.**
287 Bowman Ave., Ste. 309
Purchase, NY 10577
Ph: (914)251-1000   Fax: (914)251-1055
E-mail: lschachter@ppasearch.com
URL: http://www.ppasearch.com

Executive search firm specializing in the health and medical field.

ONLINE JOB SOURCES AND SERVICES

★7298★ **Medbulletin Medical Career Resource Center**
E-mail: medbulletin@atsmedbulletin.com
URL: http://www.medbulletin.com

Description: Offers free specialized update service, resume posting, recruiter directory, varied job listings, and relocation services.

★7299★ **Medhunters.com**
E-mail: info@medhunters.com
URL: http://www.medhunters.com

Description: Career search site for jobs in all health care specialties; educational resources; visa and licensing information for relocation; interesting articles; relocation tools; links to professional organizations and general resources.

★7300★ **ProHealthJobs**
E-mail: sales@prohealthjobs.com
URL: http://www.prohealthjobs.com

Description: Career resources site for the medical and health care field. Lists professional opportunities, product information, continuing education and open positions.

OTHER SOURCES

★7301★ **American Health Information Management Association (AMRA)**
233 N. Michigan Ave., Ste. 2150
Chicago, IL 60601-5800
Ph: (312)233-1100   Fax: (312)233-1090
E-mail: info@ahima.org
URL: http://www.ahima.org

Description: Registered record administrators; accredited record technicians with expertise in health information management, biostatistics, classification systems, and systems analysis. Sponsors Independent Study Programs in Medical Record Technology and coding. Conducts annual qualification examinations to credential medical record personnel as Registered Record Administrators (RRA), Accredited Record Technicians (ART) and Certified Coding Specialists (CCS). Maintains Foundation of Research and Education Library, Scholarships and loans.

★7302★ **ARMA International - The Association of Information Management Professionals**
13725 W 109th St. Ste. 101
Lenexa, KS 66215
Ph: (913)341-3808   Fax: (913)341-3742
Fr: 800-422-2762
E-mail: phermann@arma.org
URL: http://www.arma.org

Description: Provides education, research, and networking opportunities to information professionals, to enble them to use their skills and experience to leverage the value of records, information and knowledge as corporate assets and as contributors to organizational success.

★7303★ Exploring Health Occupations
Cambridge Educational
2572 Brunswick Ave.
Lawrenceville, NJ 08648-4128
Fax: 800-FAX-ON-US   Fr: 800-468-4227
URL: http://www.cambridgeeducational.com
Two videos. $139.95. 1999.

★7304★ Health Service Occupations
Delphi Productions
3160 4th St.
Boulder, CO 80304
Fax: (303)443-4022   Fr: 888-443-2400
URL: http://www.delphivideo.com
$95.00. 50 minutes. Part of the Careers for the 21st Century Video Library.

★7305★ Health Technologists & Technicians
Delphi Productions
3160 4th St.
Boulder, CO 80304
Fax: (303)443-4022   Fr: 888-443-2400
URL: http://www.delphivideo.com
$95.00. 50 minutes. Part of the Careers for the 21st Century Video Library.

★7306★ Medical Record Technicians
Evon Publishing
832 N 7th Ave.
Iron River, MI 49935
Ph: (906)265-3190
Audiocassette. 1996. $16.95. 32 minutes. Part of the Careers and Vocational Guidance Series. Provides information about the nature of the work, educational requirements, employment outlook, earnings, and work conditions as well as additional related information.

★7307★ Medical Technicians and Technologists
Cambridge Educational
2572 Brunswick Ave.
Lawrenceville, NJ 08648-4128
Fax: 800-FAX-ON-US   Fr: 800-468-4227
URL: http://www.cambridgeeducational.com
$79.95. 15 minutes. Part of the Exploring Health Occupations Series.

★7308★ Medicine & Related Occupations
Delphi Productions
3160 4th St.
Boulder, CO 80304
Fax: (303)443-4022   Fr: 888-443-2400

URL: http://www.delphivideo.com
$95.00. 45 minutes. Part of the Careers for the 21st Century Video Library.

★7309★ National Association for Healthcare Quality (NAHQ)
4700 W Lake Ave.
Glenview, IL 60025-1485
Ph: (847)375-4720   Fax: 877-218-7939
Fr: 800-966-9392
E-mail: dsimmons@nahq.com
URL: http://www.nahq.org
Description: Healthcare professionals in quality assessment and improvement, utilization and risk management, case management, infection control, managed care, nursing, and medical records. Objectives are: to encourage, develop, and provide continuing education for all persons involved in health care quality; to give the patient primary consideration in all actions affecting his or her health and welfare; to promote the sharing of knowledge and encourage a high degree of professional ethics in health care quality. Offers accredited certification in the field of healthcare quality, utilization, and risk management. Facilitates communication and cooperation among members, medical staff, and health care government agencies. Conducts educational seminars and conferences.

Metallurgical, Ceramic, and Materials Engineers

SOURCES OF HELP-WANTED ADS

★7310★ Advanced Materials & Processes

ASM International
9639 Kinsman Rd.
Materials Park, OH 44073-0002
Ph: (440)338-5151   Fax: (440)338-4634
Fr: 800-336-5152
URL: http://www.asm.intl.org

Monthly. Free-to members; $250.00/year for nonmembers. Magazine covering advances in metal, materials, testing technology and more.

★7311★ American Machinist

Penton Media Inc.
1300 E 9th St.
Cleveland, OH 44114-1503
Ph: (216)696-7000   Fax: (216)931-9799
URL: http://www.americanmachinist.com/

Monthly. Free for US residents; $81.00/year for Canada; $108.00/year for other countries. Magazine serving the metalworking marketplace, consisting of plants in industries primarily engaged in manufacturing durable goods and other metal products.

★7312★ The Electrochemical Society Interface

Electrochemical Society Inc.
65 S Main St.
Pennington, NJ 08534-2839
Ph: (609)737-1902   Fax: (609)737-2743
E-mail: interface@electrochem.org
URL: http://www.electrochem.org

Quarterly. $40.00/year; $10.00 for single issue. Publication featuring news and articles of interest to members of the Electrochemical Society.

★7313★ Engineering Times

National Society of Professional Engineers
1420 King St.
Alexandria, VA 22314
Ph: (703)684-2875   Fax: (703)836-4875
E-mail: et@nspe.org
URL: http://http//:www.nspc.org/1et.asp

$30.00/year for individuals; $48.00/year for out of country. Magazine (tabloid) covering professional, legislative, and techology issues for an engineering audience.

★7314★ ENR: Engineering News-Record

McGraw-Hill Companies
1221 Avenue of the Americas
New York, NY 10020
Ph: (212)512-2000
URL: http://www.enr.com

Weekly. $74.00/year; $5.00 for single issue. Magazine focusing on engineering and construction.

★7315★ Finishers' Management

Publication Management Inc.
4350 DiPaolo Ctr.
Glenview, IL 60025
Ph: (847)699-1706   Fax: (847)699-1703
E-mail: info@finishers-management.com

$35.00/year for individuals; free to qualified subscribers. Magazine on metal-finishing management.

★7316★ Graduating Engineer & Computer Careers

Career Recruitment Media
211 W. Wacker Dr., No. 900
Chicago, IL 60606
Ph: (312)525-3100
URL: http://www.graduatingengineer.com

$16.00/year for individuals. Magazine focusing on employment, education, and career development for entry-level engineers and computer scientists.

★7317★ High Technology Careers Magazine

HTC
4701 Patrick Henry Dr., No. 1901
Santa Clara, CA 95054-1847
Ph: (408)970-8800   Fax: (408)567-0242
URL: http://www.hightechcareers.com

Bimonthly. $29.00/year; $35.00/year for Canada; $85.00/year for out of country. Magazine (tabloid) containing employment opportunity information for the engineering and technical community.

★7318★ International Journal of Powder Metallurgy

APMI International
105 College Rd. E
Princeton, NJ 08540
Ph: (609)452-7700   Fax: (609)987-8523

$171.00/year for institutions; $80.00/year for individuals; $33.00/year for single issue. Powder metallurgy journal.

★7319★ Light Metal Age

Fellom Publishing Co.
170 S Spruce Ave., Ste. 120
South San Francisco, CA 94080
Ph: (415)588-8832   Fax: (415)588-0901
E-mail: lma@lightmetalage.com

Bimonthly. $40.00/year for individuals. Magazine serving primary and semi-fabrication metal plants that produce, semi-fabricate, process or manufacture the light metals: aluminum, magnesium, titanium, beryllium and their alloys, and/or the non-ferrous metals copper and zinc.

★7320★ Materials Performance

NACE International
1440 S Creek Dr.
Houston, TX 77084-4906
Ph: (281)228-6223   Fax: (281)228-6300
E-mail: pubs@mail.nace.org

Monthly. $115.00/year for individuals, U.S.A.; $130.00/year for out of country; $205.00/year for libraries, U.S.A.; $220.00/year for libraries, foreign. Magazine on performance and protection of materials in a corrosive environment.

★7321★ Metal Finishing

Elsevier Science Inc.
360 Park Ave. S, No. 11
New York, NY 10010-1710
Ph: (212)989-5800   Fax: (212)633-3965
Fr: 888-437-4636
URL: http://www.elsevier.com/inca/publications/store/5/2/2/9/3/1/

Monthly. $110.00/year for institutions, Canada and Mexico; $178.00/year for institutions outside USA, Canada, Mexico, Europe and Japan; $78.00/year for institutions, USA. Magazine informing on the practical and technical aspects of finishing metal and plastic products, including waste treatment and pollution control.

★7322★ Metalforming

Precision Metalforming Association
6363 Oak Tree Blvd.
Independence, OH 44131-2500
Ph: (216)901-8800   Fax: (216)901-9190
E-mail: metalforming@pma.org
URL: http://
www.metalformingmagazine.com

Monthly. $25.00/year for individuals; $175.00/year for other countries; $3.50 for single issue; free to qualified subscribers. Serving those who add value to sheetmetal.

★7323★ Modern Casting Magazine

American Foundrymen's Society
505 State St.
Des Plaines, IL 60016-8399
Ph: (847)824-0181   Fax: (847)824-7848
Fr: 800-537-4237

Monthly. $40.00/year for individuals; $5.00 for single issue; $50.00/year; $75.00/year for by mail. Magazine on metal casting plants and pattern shops.

★7324★ Modern Metals

Trend Publishing
One E Erie, Ste. 401
Chicago, IL 60611
Ph: (312)654-2300   Fax: (312)654-2323
Fr: 800-278-7363
URL: http://www.modernmetals.com

Monthly. $85.00/year for individuals; $14.00 for single issue. Metals fabrication magazine.

★7325★ NSBE Magazine

NSBE Publications
1454 Duke St.
Alexandria, VA 22314
Ph: (703)549-2207   Fax: (703)683-5312

$10.00/year for individuals; $2.00 for single issue. Journal providing information on engineering careers, self-development, and cultural issues for recent graduates with technical majors.

★7326★ Snips Magazine

Snips Magazine
755 W Big Beaver., Ste. 1000
Troy, MI 48084-4903
Ph: (248)362-3700   Fax: (248)362-0317
URL: http://www.snipsmag.com

Monthly. Magazine for the sheet metal, warm-air heating, ventilating, and air conditioning industry.Provides helpful hints for contractors.

★7327★ SWE

Society of Women Engineers
230 E Ohio St., No. 400
2135 Lamberton Rd.
Chicago, IL 60611-3265
Ph: (312)596-5223   Fax: (312)596-5252
E-mail: hq@swe.org
URL: http://www.swe.org

Bimonthly. $30.00/year for nonmembers. Magazine for engineering students and for women and men working in the engineering and technology fields. Covers career guidance, continuing development and topical issues.

★7328★ Technology Review

Technology Review
201 Vassar St.
Cambridge, MA 02139
Ph: (617)253-8250   Fax: (617)258-5850
E-mail: trcomments@mit.edu

$30.00/year for individuals; $42.00/year for other countries; $4.95/year for single issue. Magazine reviewing new developments in technology with an emphasis on economic, political, and social implications. Not a new product publication.

★7329★ 33 Metal Producing

Penton Media Inc.
1300 E 9th St.
Cleveland, OH 44114-1503
Ph: (216)696-7000   Fax: (216)931-9799
E-mail: infor@mdna.com
URL: http://www.33metalproducing.com/default.asp?Section=home

$35.00/year for individuals; $38.00/year for Canada; $48.00/year for other countries. Magazine covering the metalproducing industry.

★7330★ Tooling & Production

Nelson Publishing Inc.
2500 Tamiami Trl. N
Nokomis, FL 34275-3482
Ph: (941)966-9521   Fax: (941)966-2590
Fr: 800-226-6113
URL: http://www.toolingandproduction.com

Monthly. $90.00/year for individuals. Magazine concerning metalworking.

★7331★ WEPANEWS

Women in Engineering Programs &
  Advocates Network
Castle Point on the Hudson
Hoboken, NJ 07030
Ph: (201)216-5245   Fax: (201)216-5175
URL: http://www.wepan.org/newsletter.html

Description: Two issues/year. Seeks to provide greater access for women to careers in engineering. Includes news of graduate, undergraduate, freshmen, pre-college, and re-entry engineering programs for women. Recurring features include job listings, faculty, grant, and conference news, international engineering program news, action group news, notices of publications available, and a column titled Kudos.

PLACEMENT AND JOB REFERRAL SERVICES

★7332★ American Ceramic Society (ACerS)

PO Box 6136
Westerville, OH 43086-6136
Ph: (614)890-4700   Fax: (614)899-6109
E-mail: info@ceramics.org
URL: http://www.acers.org

Description: Professional society of scientists, engineers, educators, plant operators, and others interested in the glass, cements, refractories, nuclear ceramics, whitewares, electronics, engineering, and structural clay products industries. Disseminates scientific and technical information through its publications and technical meetings. Conducts continuing education courses and training such as the Precollege Education Program. Sponsors over 10 meetings yearly; encourages high school and college students' interest in ceramics. Maintains Ross C. Purdy Museum of Ceramics; offers placement service and speakers' bureau.

★7333★ American Indian Science and Engineering Society (AISES)

PO Box 9828
Albuquerque, NM 87119-9828
Ph: (505)765-1052   Fax: (505)765-5608
E-mail: info@aises.org
URL: http://www.aises.org

Description: American Indian and non-Indian students and professionals in science, technology, and engineering fields; corporations representing energy, mining, aerospace, electronic, and computer fields. Seeks to motivate and encourage students to pursue undergraduate and graduate studies in science, engineering, and technology. Sponsors science fairs in grade schools, teacher training workshops, summer math/science sessions for 8th-12th graders, professional chapters, and student chapters in colleges. Offers scholarships. Adult members serve as role models, advisers, and mentors for students. Operates placement service.

★7334★ **APMI International**

105 College Rd. E
Princeton, NJ 08540
Ph: (609)452-7700   Fax: (609)987-8523
E-mail: apmi@mpif.org
URL: http://www.mpif.org

Description: Technical society for powder metallurgists and others interested in powder metallurgy and particulate materials, and their applications. Maintains speakers' bureau and placement service.

★7335★ **Engineering Society of Detroit (ESD)**

26100 American Dr., Ste. 500
Southfield, MI 48034-6184
Ph: (248)355-2910   Fax: (248)355-1492
E-mail: esd@esd.org
URL: http://esd.org

Description: Engineers from all disciplines; scientists and technologists. Conducts technical programs and engineering refresher courses; sponsors conferences and expositions. Maintains speakers' bureau; offers placement services. Although based in Detroit, MI, society membership is international.

★7336★ **Korean Scientists and Engineers Association in America (KSEA)**

1952 Gallows Rd., Ste. 300
Vienna, VA 22182
Ph: (703)748-1221   Fax: (703)748-1331
E-mail: sejong@ksea.org
URL: http://www.ksea.org

Description: Scientists and engineers holding single or advanced degrees. Goals are to: promote friendship and mutuality among Korean and American scientists and engineers; contribute to Korea's scientific, technological, industrial, and economic developments; strengthen the scientific, technological, and cultural bonds between Korea and the U.S. Sponsors symposium. Maintains speakers' bureau, placement service, and biographical archives. Compiles statistics. Maintains 100 volume library of scientific handbooks and yearbooks in Korean.

★7337★ **Metal Powder Industries Federation (MPIF)**

105 College Rd. E.
Princeton, NJ 08540-6692
Ph: (609)452-7700   Fax: (609)987-8523
E-mail: info@mpif.org
URL: http://www.mpif.org

Members: Manufacturers of metal powders, powder metallurgy processing equipment and tools, powder metallurgy products, and refractory and reactive metals. Member associations are: Metal Injection Molding Association; Metal Powder Producers Association; Advanced Particulate Materials Association; Powder Metallurgy Equipment Association; Powder Metallurgy Parts Association; Refractory Metals Association. **Purpose:** Promotes the science and industry of powder metallurgy and metal powder application through: sponsorship of technical meetings, seminars, and exhibits; establishment of

standards; compilation of statistics; public relations; publications. **Activities:** Maintains speakers' bureau and placement service; conducts research.

★7338★ **National Institute of Ceramic Engineers (NICE)**

Virginia Polytechnic Institute & State University
Dept. of Materials Science & Eng.
213 Holden Hall
Roanoke, VA 24040-0237
Ph: (540)231-3897   Fax: (540)231-8919
E-mail: dfolz@mse.vt.edu
URL: http://www.ceramics.org/membership/sdc_pages/sdcdisplay.asp?ItemID=4

Purpose: Promotes the profession of ceramic engineering, accreditation of educational programs in ceramic and glass engineering and science, and in materials science and engineering and high ethical engineering standards and practices. **Activities:** Sponsors continuing education courses. Offers employment service and promotes professional engineer registration. Responsible for Professional Engineering exams in Ceramic Engineering.

★7339★ **Society for the Advancement of Material and Process Engineering (SAMPE)**

PO Box 2459
Covina, CA 91722-8459
Ph: (626)331-0616   Fax: (626)332-8929
Fr: 800-562-7360
E-mail: officemanager@sampe.org
URL: http://www.sampe.org

Description: Material and process engineers, scientists, and other professionals engaged in development of advanced materials and processing technology in airframe, missile, aerospace, propulsion, electronics, life sciences, management, and related industries. International and local chapters sponsor scholarships for science students seeking financial assistance. Provides placement service for members.

★7340★ **Society of Hispanic Professional Engineers (SHPE)**

5400 E Olympic Blvd., Ste. 210
Los Angeles, CA 90022
Ph: (323)725-3970   Fax: (323)725-0316
E-mail: shpenational@shpe.org
URL: http://www.shpe.org

Description: Engineers, student engineers, and scientists seeking to increase the number of Hispanic engineers by providing motivation and support to students. Sponsors competitions and educational programs. Maintains placement service and speakers' bureau; compiles statistics.

★7341★ **Society for Mining, Metallurgy, and Exploration (SME)**

8307 Shaffer Pky.
PO Box 277002
Littleton, CO 80127-7002
Ph: (303)973-9550   Fax: (303)973-3845
Fr: 800-763-3132

E-mail: sme@smenet.org
URL: http://www.smenet.org

Description: A member society of the American Institute of Mining, Metallurgical and Petroleum Engineers. Persons engaged in the finding, exploitation, treatment, and marketing of all classes of minerals (metal ores, industrial minerals, and solid fuels) except petroleum. Promotes the arts and sciences connected with the production of useful minerals and metals. Offers specialized education programs; compiles enrollment and graduation statistics from schools offering engineering degrees in mining, mineral, mineral processing/metallurgical, geological, geophysical, and mining technology. Provides placement service and sponsors charitable programs.

EMPLOYER DIRECTORIES AND NETWORKING LISTS

★7342★ *American Men and Women of Science*

Thomson Gale
27500 Drake Rd.
Farmington Hills, MI 48331-3535
Ph: (248)699-4253   Fax: (248)699-8065
Fr: 800-877-GALE
E-mail: amws@galegroup.com

Biennial, latest edition December 2002. $975.00. Covers over 129,700 U.S. and Canadian scientists active in the physical, biological, mathematical, computer science, and engineering fields; includes references to previous edition for deceased scientists and nonrespondents. Entries include: Name, address, education, personal and career data, memberships, honors and awards, research interest. Arrangement: Alphabetical. Indexes: Discipline (in separate volume).

★7343★ *Careers in Focus: Engineering*

Ferguson Publishing Co.
200 W Jackson Blvd.
Chicago, IL 60606
Ph: (312)692-0109

2nd edition, 2002. $22.95. Publication includes: List of resources to consult for more information. Principal content of publication is job descriptions, advancement opportunities, educational requirements, employment outlook, salary information, and working conditions for careers in the field of engineering. Indexes: Alphabetical.

★7344★ *Directory of Contract Staffing Firms*

C.E. Publications Inc.
PO Box 3006
Bothell, WA 98041-3006
Ph: (425)806-5200   Fax: (425)806-5585
URL: http://www.cjhunter.com/dcsf/overview.html

$15.00. Covers nearly 1,300 contract firms actively engaged in the employment of engineering, IT/IS, and technical personnel for 'temporary' contract assignments throughout the world. Entries include: Company name, address, phone, name of contact, email, web address. Arrangement: Alphabetical. Indexes: Geographical.

★7345★ International Directory of Engineering Societies and Related Organizations

American Association of Engineering Societies
1828 L St. NW, Ste. 906
Washington, DC 20036
Ph: (202)296-2237   Fax: (202)296-1151
Fr: 888-400-AAES

Irregular, latest edition December 1998. $240.00. Covers about 1,370 national, regional, Canadian, and international organizations concerned with engineering and related fields. Entries include: Name, address, phone, fax, e-mail, key personnel, objectives, publications, activities, mailing lists, federation memberships, meeting and convention dates, and budget data. Arrangement: Alphabetical. Indexes: Acronym, geographical, area of specialization.

★7346★ The Minerals, Metals & Materials Society Membership Directory

American Institute of Mining, Metallurgical and Petroleum Engineers
184 Thorn Hill Rd.
Warrendale, PA 15086
Ph: (724)776-9000   Fax: (724)776-3770
Fr: 800-759-4867
E-mail: csc@tms.org

Annual, July. Covers 8,300 metallurgists, metallurgical engineers, and materials scientists, worldwide. Entries include: Name, office address, career data, telephone number. Arrangement: Alphabetical; geographical. Indexes: Geographical.

★7347★ Peterson's Job Opportunities in Engineering and Technology

Thomson Peterson's
PO Box 67005
Lawrenceville, NJ 08648-6105
Fr: 800-338-3282

Compiled by the Peterson's staff. Fourth edition, 1996. $21.95 (paper). 384 pages. Profiles 2,000 high-tech companies looking primarily for technical personnel in such fields as biotechnology, telecommunications, software, computers and peripherals, defense, and aerospace. Contains job-search strategies and career options to help match education and expertise to the job market. Indexed geographically, by industry, and by hiring needs.

HANDBOOKS AND MANUALS

★7348★ The Best Resumes for Scientists and Engineers

John Wiley & Sons Inc.
1 Wiley Dr.
Somerset, NJ 08873
Ph: (732)469-4400   Fr: 800-225-5945

Adele Lewis and David J. Moore. Second edition, 1993. $37.50; $19.95 (paper). 224 pages. Presents an extensive collection of scientific and engineering resumes, highlighting the important differences between these and resumes written for other occupations.

★7349★ Great Jobs for Engineering Majors

McGraw-Hill Professional
McGraw-Hill Higher Education
2 Penn Plaza
New York, NY 10121
Ph: (212)904-2000   Fr: 800-722-4726
E-mail: ntcpub@tribune.com

Geraldine O. Garner. Second edition, 2002. $14.95. 256 pages. Covers all the career options open to students majoring in engineering.

★7350★ The I Hate Selling Book: Business-Building Advice for Consultants, Attorneys, Accountants, Engineers, Architects, and Other Professionals

Allan Boress & Associates
1500 University Dr., Suite 239
Coral Springs, FL 33071
Ph: (954)345-4666   Fax: (954)344-2453

Allan S. Boress. 2001. $29.95.

★7351★ Keys to Engineering Success

Prentice Hall PTR
One Lake St.
Upper Saddle River, NJ 07458
Ph: (201)236-7000

Jill S. Tietjen, Kristy A. Schloss, Carol Carter, Joyce Bishop, and Sarah Lyman. 2000. $32.00 (paper).

★7352★ Opportunities in Engineering Careers

McGraw-Hill Contemporary Books
1221 Avenue of the Americas
New York, NY 10020
Ph: (212)904-2000   Fr: 800-323-4900
E-mail: ntcpub@tribune.com

Nicholas Basta. Revised, 1995. $14.95; $11.95 (paper). 200 pages. Outlines typical job titles, salaries, career paths, and employment prospects.

★7353★ Opportunities in High Tech Careers

McGraw-Hill Trade
2 Penn Plaza
New York, NY 10121
Ph: (212)904-2000   Fr: 800-722-4726

Gary Colter and Deborah Yanuck. 1995. $14.95; $11.95 (paper). 160 pages. Explores high technology careers. Describes job opportunities, how to make a career decision, how to prepare for high technology jobs, job hunting techniques, and future trends.

★7354★ Real People Working in Engineering

McGraw-Hill Contemporary Books
1221 Avenue of the Americas
New York, NY 10020
Ph: (212)904-2000   Fr: 800-323-4900
E-mail: ntcpub@tribune.com

Blythe Camenson, Jan Goldberg. 1997. $14.95; $12.95 (paper). Interviews and profiles of working professionals capture a range of opportunities in this field.

★7355★ Resumes for Engineering Careers

McGraw-Hill Trade
2 Penn Plaza
New York, NY 10121
Ph: (212)904-2000   Fr: 800-722-4726
E-mail: ntcpub@tribune.com

2000. $10.95 (paper). 456 pages. Contains sample resumes and cover letters applicable to any engineering field.

★7356★ Resumes for Scientific and Technical Careers

McGraw-Hill Contemporary Books
1221 Avenue of the Americas
New York, NY 10020
Ph: (212)904-2000   Fr: 800-323-4900
E-mail: ntcpub@tribune.com

1999. $9.95 (paper). 450 pages. Provides resume advice for individuals interested in working in scientific and technical careers. Includes sample resumes and cover letters.

EMPLOYMENT AGENCIES AND SEARCH FIRMS

★7357★ Colli Associates

404 Caboose Ln.
Valrico, FL 33594
Ph: (813)681-2145   Fax: (813)661-5217
E-mail: colli@gte.net

Employment agency. Executive search firm.

★7358★ Edgewood International
3018 Edgewood Pkwy.
Woodridge, IL 60517-3720
Ph: (630)985-6067   Fax: (630)985-6069
Executive search firm.

★7359★ Elite Resources Group
PO Box 13113
Fairlawn, OH 44334
Ph: (330)867-9412   Fax: (330)867-0468
Executive search firm.

★7360★ Empire International
1147 Lancaster Ave.
Berwyn, PA 19312
Ph: (610)647-7976   Fax: (610)647-8488
Executive search firm.

★7361★ Engineer One, Inc.
PO Box 23037
Knoxville, TN 37933
Fax: (865)691-0110
E-mail: engineerone@engineerone.com
URL: http://www.engineerone.com
Employment agency.

★7362★ Evenium
520 Marquette Ave., Ste. 800
Minneapolis, MN 55402
Ph: (612)436-3200   Fax: (612)436-3157
Executive search firm.

★7363★ Executive Directions
9701 Cleveland Ave. NW
PO Box 3006
North Canton, OH 44720
Ph: (330)499-1001   Fax: (330)499-2579
Executive search firm.

★7364★ Executive Resource Group Inc.
2470 Windy Hill Rd., Ste. 300
Marietta, GA 30067
Ph: (770)955-1811
Executive search firm.

★7365★ Executives Unlimited Inc.
6475 E. Pacific Coast Hwy., Ste. 369
Long Beach, CA 90803
Ph: (562)597-4466   Fr: (866)957-4466
Executive search firm. Branches in Western Springs, IL; Scotch Plains, NJ; Long Beach, CA.

★7366★ Eyler Associates Inc.
400 Locust St., Ste. 170
Des Moines, IA 50309
Ph: (515)245-4244
Executive search firm.

★7367★ First Choice Search
PO Box 31324
Seattle, WA 98103-1324
Ph: (206)632-0050
Executive search firm.

★7368★ Fischer Group International Inc.
296 Country Club Dr., Bldg A
Avon, CT 06001
Ph: (860)404-7700   Fax: (860)404-7799
Executive search firm.

★7369★ International Staffing Consultants
2901 W Coast Hwy.,Ste. 200
Newport Beach, CA 92663
Ph: (949)263-5933   Fax: (949)767-5959
E-mail: iscinc@iscworld.com
URL: http://www.iscworld.com
Employment agency. Provides placement on regular or temporary basis. Affiliate office in London.

★7370★ Main Line Personnel Service, Inc.
Pagoda Blding.
100 Presidential Blvd. Ste. 200
Bala Cynwyd, PA 19004-0448
Ph: (610)667-1820   Fax: (610)668-5000
URL: http://www.mlpers.com
Employment agency.

★7371★ National Recruiting Service
1832 Hart St.
PO Box 218
Dyer, IN 46311
Ph: (219)865-2373   Fax: (219)865-2375
A privately held midwestern human resource firm which specializes in the identification and screening of personnel. In addition to the recruiting function the firm also offers a comprehensive outplacement and employee termination service, which can be used for all levels of management. Through executive search, psychological evaluations, contingency methods, consulting and outplacement services, firm helps organizations to fully utilize client personnel as a cost effective asset. Industries served: metals.

★7372★ Search and Recruit International
4455 South Blvd.
Virginia Beach, VA 23452
Ph: (757)490-3151   Fax: (757)497-6503
E-mail: britt@searchandrecruit.com
URL: http://www.searchandrecruit.com
Employment agency. Headquartered in Virginia Beach. Other offices in Bremerton, WA; Charleston, SC; Jacksonville, FL; Memphis, TN; Pensacola, FL; Sacramento, CA; San Bernardino, CA; San Diego, CA.

ONLINE JOB SOURCES AND SERVICES

★7373★ Spherion Workforce Architects
URL: http://www.spherion.com
Description: Recruitment firm specializing in accounting and finance, sales and marketing, interim executives, technology, engineering, retail and human resources.

TRADESHOWS

★7374★ American Ceramic Society Annual Meeting and Exposition
American Ceramic Society
735 Ceramic Place
Westerville, OH 43081
Ph: (614)794-5884   Fax: (614)794-5882
Annual. **Primary Exhibits:** Manufacturing equipment, supplies, raw materials, and advanced products.

★7375★ METALFORM
Precision Metalforming Association
6363 Oak Tree Blvd.
Independence, OH 44131
Ph: (216)901-8800   Fax: (216)901-9190
URL: http://www.metalforming.com
Annual. **Primary Exhibits:** Presses and stamping equipment, tooling and fabricating machines, management aids, and related materials.

★7376★ The NGA Show: America's Glass Expo
National Glass Association
8200 Greensboro Dr., 3rd Fl.
McLean, VA 22102-3881
Ph: (703)442-4890   Fax: (703)442-0630
E-mail: nga@glass.org
URL: http://www.glass.org
Annual. **Primary Exhibits:** Glass and glass-related products, supplies, equipment, tools, and machinery, automotive glazing, equipment/machinery, curtain wall, store front systems, doors/hardware, windows, mirrors, shower/tub enclosures, and tools.

★7377★ TMS Annual Meeting and Exhibition
TMS - Minerals, Metals and Materials Society
184 Thorn Hill Rd.
Warrendale, PA 15086-7528
Ph: (724)776-9000   Fax: (724)776-3770
Fr: 800-966-4867
E-mail: tmsgeneral@tms.org
URL: http://www.tms.org
Annual. **Primary Exhibits:** Equipment, supplies, and services for those involved in the scientific and technological aspects of the minerals, metals, and materials industries.

Dates and Locations: 2005 Feb 13-17; San Francisco, CA; Moscone West Convention Center • 2006 Mar 12-16; San Antonio, TX.

★7378★ WELDEX - International Welding, Cutting, and Metal Fabrication Exhibition

Reed Exhibitions (North American Headquarters)
383 Main Ave.
PO Box 6059
Norwalk, CT 06851
Ph: (203)840-5402   Fax: (203)840-9402
E-mail: inquiry@reedexpo.com
URL: http://www.reedexpo.com

Quadrennial. **Primary Exhibits:** Plant, equipment, and consumables for welding, brazing, soldering, and surfacing; equipment for safety and fume extraction, gases and gas, industrial robots and automated welding, metal working and machinery, and inspection; fasteners, and hand and power tools.

★7379★ Western Plastics Expo

Advanstar Communications Inc.
7500 Old Oak Blvd.
Cleveland, OH 44130
Ph: (440)891-2701   Fax: (440)891-2741
Fr: 800-225-4569
E-mail: info@advanstar.com
URL: http://www.advanstar.com

Triennial. **Primary Exhibits:** Plastics machinery, equipment, materials, supplies, and related services.

OTHER SOURCES

★7380★ American Almanac of Jobs and Salaries

Morrow Avon
1350 Avenue of the Americas
New York, NY 10019
Ph: (212)261-6788   Fr: 800-242-7737

John W. Wright. Revised edition, 2000. $20.00 (paper). 672 pages. This is a comprehensive guide to the wages of hundreds of occupations in a wide variety of industries and organizations.

★7381★ American Association of Engineering Societies (AAES)

1828 L St. NW, No. 906
Washington, DC 20036
Ph: (202)296-2237   Fax: (202)296-1151
Fr: 888-400-2237
E-mail: tprice@aaes.org
URL: http://www.aaes.org

Description: Coordinates the efforts of the member societies in the provision of reliable and objective information to the general public concerning issues which affect the engineering profession and the field of engineering as a whole; to collect, analyze, document, and disseminate data which will inform the general public of the relationship between engineering and the national welfare; to provide a forum for the engineering societies to exchange and discuss their views on matters of common interest; and to represent the U.S. engineering community aborad through representation in WFEO and UPADI.

★7382★ ASM International (ASM)

9639 Kinsman Rd.
Materials Park, OH 44073-0002
Ph: (440)338-5151   Fax: (440)338-4634
Fr: 800-336-5152
E-mail: cust-srv@asminternational.org
URL: http://www.asminternational.org

Description: Metallurgists, materials engineers, executives in materials producing and consuming industries; teachers and students. Disseminates technical information about the manufacture, use, and treatment of engineered materials. Offers in-plant, home study, and intensive courses through Materials Engineering Institute. Conducts career development program. Established ASM Foundation for Education and Research. Maintains library of 10,000 volumes on metals and other materials.

★7383★ Association for International Practical Training (AIPT)

10400 Little Patuxent Pky., Ste. 250
Columbia, MD 21044-3519
Ph: (410)997-2200   Fax: (410)992-3924
E-mail: aipt@aipt.org
URL: http://www.aipt.org

Description: Providers worldwide on-the-job training programs for students and professionals seeking international career development and life-changing experiences. Arranges workplace exchanges in hundreds of professional fields, bringing employers and trainees together from around the world. Client list ranges from small farming communities to Fortune 500 companies.

★7384★ Engineering Occupations

Delphi Productions
3160 4th St.
Boulder, CO 80304
Fax: (303)443-4022   Fr: 888-443-2400
URL: http://www.delphivideo.com

$95.00. 50 minutes. Part of the Careers for the 21st Century Video Library.

★7385★ ISA - Instrumentation, Systems, and Automation Society

67 Alexander Dr.
PO Box 12277
Research Triangle Park, NC 27709
Ph: (919)549-8411   Fax: (919)549-8288
E-mail: info@isa.org
URL: http://www.isa.org

Purpose: Fosters advancement in the theory, design, manufacture, and use of instruments, computers, and systems for measurement and control.

★7386★ Metallurgical, Ceramic, and Material Engineers

Evon Publishing
832 N 7th Ave.
Iron River, MI 49935
Ph: (906)265-3190

Audiocassette. 1996. $16.95. 32 minutes. Part of the Careers and Vocational Guidance Series. Provides information about the nature of the work, educational requirements, employment outlook, earnings, and work conditions as well as additional related information.

★7387★ National Action Council for Minorities in Engineering (NACME)

Empire State Bldg., Ste. 2212
350 Fifth Ave.
New York, NY 10118-2299
Ph: (212)279-2626   Fax: (212)629-5178
E-mail: webmaster@nacme.org
URL: http://www.nacme.org/

Description: Leads the national effort to increase access to careers in engineering and other science-based disciplines. Supported by the nation's leading technology-intensive companies, NACME conducts research and public policy analysis, develops and operates national demonstration programs at precollege and university levels, and disseminates information through publications, conferences, and electronic media. NACME is also the nation's largest privately funded source of scholarships for minority students in engineering.

★7388★ National Society of Professional Engineers (NSPE)

1420 King St.
Alexandria, VA 22314
Ph: (703)684-2800   Fax: (703)836-4875
Fr: 888-285-6773
E-mail: custserv@nspe.org
URL: http://www.nspe.org

Description: Professional engineers and engineers-in-training in all fields registered in accordance with the laws of states or territories of the U.S. or provinces of Canada; qualified graduate engineers, student members, and registered land surveyors. Is concerned with social, professional, ethical, and economic considerations of engineering as a profession; encompasses programs in public relations, employment practices, ethical considerations, education, and career guidance. Monitors legislative and regulatory actions of interest to the engineering profession.

★7389★ Scientific, Engineering, and Technical Services

Cambridge Educational
2572 Brunswick Ave.
Lawrenceville, NJ 08648-4128
Fax: 800-FAX-ON-US   Fr: 800-468-4227
URL: http://www.cambrigeeducational.com

$89.95. 2002. 18 minutes. Part of the Career Cluster Series.

★7390★ **Society of Women Engineers (SWE)**
230 E Ohio St., No. 400
Chicago, IL 60611-3265
Ph: (312)596-5223   Fax: (312)596-5252
E-mail: hq@swe.org
URL: http://www.swe.org
Description: Educational and service organization representing both students and professional women in engineering and technical fields.

★7391★ *Women in Engineering*
Her Own Words
PO Box 5264
Madison, WI 53705-0264
Ph: (608)271-7083   Fax: (608)271-0209
URL: http://www.herownwords.com/

Video. Jocelyn Riley. $95.00. 15 minutes. Resource guide also available for $45.00.

Meteorologists

SOURCES OF HELP-WANTED ADS

★7392★ **National Weather Association Newsletter**

National Weather Association
1697 Capri Way
Charlottesville, VA 22911-3534
Ph: (434)296-9966   Fax: (434)296-9966
URL: http://www.nwas.org

Description: Monthly. Provides information about operational meteorology and related activities. Recurring features include letters to the editor, interviews, news of research, a calendar of events, reports of meetings, news of educational opportunities, job listings, notices of publications available, and columns titled President's Message, Member News, and Local Chapter News.

★7393★ **Nature International Weekly Journal of Science**

Nature Publishing Group
345 Park Ave. S
New York, NY 10010-1707
Ph: (212)726-9200   Fax: (212)689-9711
Fr: 888-331-6288
E-mail: nature@natureny.com
URL: http://www.nature.com

Weekly. $145.00/year for individuals; $495.00/year for institutions. Magazine covering science and technology, including the fields of biology, biochemistry, genetics, medicine, earth sciences, physics, pharmacology, and behavioral sciences.

★7394★ **PE & RS Photogrammetric Engineering & Remote Sensing**

The Imaging and Geospatial Information Society
5410 Grosvenor Ln., Ste. 210
Bethesda, MD 20814
Ph: (301)493-0290   Fax: (301)493-0208
E-mail: asprs@asprs.org

Monthly. $130.00/year. Journal covering photogrammetry, remote sensing, geographic information systems, cartography, and surveying, global positioning systems, digital photogrammetry.

★7395★ **The Scientist**

The Scientist Inc.
3535 Market St., Ste. 200
Philadelphia, PA 19104-2645
Ph: (215)386-9601   Fax: (215)386-7542
Fr: 800-258-6008
E-mail: info@the-scientist.com
URL: http://www.the-scientist.com

Biweekly. $49.00/year for individuals; $149.00/year for institutions; $24.00/year for students; $82.00/year for other countries; $49.00/year for students, other countries; $174.00/year for institutions, other countries. News journal (tabloid) for life scientists featuring news, opinions, research, and professional section.

★7396★ **Weatherwise**

Heldref Publications
1319 18th St. NW
Washington, DC 20036-1802
Ph: (202)296-6267   Fax: (202)296-5149
Fr: 800-365-9753
URL: http://www.heldref.org/html/body_ ww.html

Bimonthly. $35.00/year for individuals; $74.00/year for institutions, other countries. Popular weather magazine for students, teachers, and professionals.

PLACEMENT AND JOB REFERRAL SERVICES

★7397★ **Korean Scientists and Engineers Association in America (KSEA)**

1952 Gallows Rd., Ste. 300
Vienna, VA 22182
Ph: (703)748-1221   Fax: (703)748-1331
E-mail: sejong@ksea.org
URL: http://www.ksea.org

Description: Scientists and engineers holding single or advanced degrees. Goals are to: promote friendship and mutuality among Korean and American scientists and engineers; contribute to Korea's scientific, technological, industrial, and economic developments; strengthen the scientific, technological, and cultural bonds between Korea and the U.S. Sponsors symposium. Maintains speakers' bureau, placement service, and biographical archives. Compiles statistics. Maintains 100 volume library of scientific handbooks and yearbooks in Korean.

EMPLOYER DIRECTORIES AND NETWORKING LISTS

★7398★ **American Men and Women of Science**

Thomson Gale
27500 Drake Rd.
Farmington Hills, MI 48331-3535
Ph: (248)699-4253   Fax: (248)699-8065
Fr: 800-877-GALE
E-mail: amws@galegroup.com

Biennial, latest edition December 2002. $975.00. Covers over 129,700 U.S. and Canadian scientists active in the physical, biological, mathematical, computer science, and engineering fields; includes references to previous edition for deceased scientists and nonrespondents. Entries include: Name, address, education, personal and career data, memberships, honors and awards, research interest. Arrangement: Alphabetical. Indexes: Discipline (in separate volume).

★7399★ **American Weather Observer Supplemental Observation Network Directory of Stations**

American Weather Observer Supplemental Observation Network
401 Whitney Blvd.
Belvidere, IL 61008-3772
Fax: (815)544-6334

On demand. $6.00. Publication includes: List of member weather observers in North America. Entries include: Personal or organization name, address, phone. Arrangement: Geographical.

★7400★ **National Weather Service Offices and Stations**

U.S. National Weather Service
1325 East-West Hwy.
Silver Spring, MD 20910
Ph: (301)713-1698

Annual, September. Covers offices and stations operated by or under the supervision of the National Weather Service in the United States, Mexico, the Caribbean, Central and South America, and Oceania. Entries include: Station and airport name, type of station, call letters, International Index Number, latitude, longitude, elevation; and number, type, and frequency of weather observations. Arrangement: Geographical.

★7401★ **Peterson's Job Opportunities in Engineering and Technology**

Thomson Peterson's
PO Box 67005
Lawrenceville, NJ 08648-6105
Fr: 800-338-3282

Compiled by the Peterson's staff. Fourth edition, 1996. $21.95 (paper). 384 pages. Profiles 2,000 high-tech companies looking primarily for technical personnel in such fields as biotechnology, telecommunications, software, computers and peripherals, defense, and aerospace. Contains job-search strategies and career options to help match education and expertise to the job market. Indexed geographically, by industry, and by hiring needs.

HANDBOOKS AND MANUALS

★7402★ **The Best Resumes for Scientists and Engineers**

John Wiley & Sons Inc.
1 Wiley Dr.
Somerset, NJ 08873
Ph: (732)469-4400   Fr: 800-225-5945

Adele Lewis and David J. Moore. Second edition, 1993. $37.50; $19.95 (paper). 224 pages. Presents an extensive collection of scientific and engineering resumes, highlighting the important differences between these and resumes written for other occupations.

★7403★ **Career Information Center**

Macmillan Publishing Co. Inc.
200 Old Tappan Rd.
Old Tappan, NJ 07675
Fr: 800-428-5331

Visual Education Center Staff. Seventh edition, 1999. $275.00. 2080 pages. This 13-volume set profiles over 600 occupations. Each occupational profile describes job duties, educational requirements, how to get the job, advancement possibilities, employ-

ment outlook, working conditions, earnings and benefits, and where to write for more information.

★7404★ **Opportunities in Research and Development Careers**

McGraw-Hill/Contemporary Books
1221 Avenue of the Americas
New York, NY 10020
Ph: (212)904-2000   Fr: 800-323-4900
E-mail: ntcpub@tribune.com

Jan Goldberg. 1997. $14.95; $11.95 (paper). 204 pages.

OTHER SOURCES

★7405★ **American Almanac of Jobs and Salaries**

Morrow Avon
1350 Avenue of the Americas
New York, NY 10019
Ph: (212)261-6788   Fr: 800-242-7737

John W. Wright. Revised edition, 2000. $20.00 (paper). 672 pages. This is a comprehensive guide to the wages of hundreds of occupations in a wide variety of industries and organizations.

★7406★ **American Meteorological Society (AMS)**

45 Beacon St.
Boston, MA 02108-3693
Ph: (617)227-2425   Fax: (617)742-8718
E-mail: amsinfo@ametsoc.org
URL: http://www.ametsoc.org/AMS

Description: Professional meteorologists, oceanographers, and hydrologists; interested students and nonprofessionals. Develops and disseminates information on the atmospheric and related oceanic and hydrospheric sciences; seeks to advance professional applications. Activities include guidance service, scholarship programs, career information, certification of consulting meteorologists, and a seal of approval program to recognize competence in radio and television weathercasting. Issues statements of policy to assist public understanding on subjects such as weather modification, forecasting, tornadoes, hurricanes, flash floods, and meteorological satellites. Provides abstracting services. Has prepared educational films, filmstrips, and slides for a new curriculum in meteorology at the ninth grade level. Issues monthly announcements of job openings for meteorologists.

★7407★ **ASPRS - The Imaging and Geospatial Information Society**

5410 Grosvenor Ln., Ste. 210
Bethesda, MD 20814-2160
Ph: (301)493-0290   Fax: (301)493-0208
E-mail: asprs@asprs.org
URL: http://www.asprs.org

Members: Firms, individuals, government

employees, and academicians engaged in photogrammetry, photointerpretation, remote sensing, and geographic information systems and their application to such fields as archaeology, geographic information systems, military reconnaissance, urban planning, engineering, traffic surveys, meteorological observations, medicine, geology, forestry, agriculture, construction, and topographic mapping. Mission is to advance knowledge and improve understanding of these sciences and to promote responsible applications. **Activities:** Offers voluntary certification program open to persons associated with one or more functional area of photogrammetry, remote sensing, and GIS. Surveys the profession of private firms in photogrammetry and remote sensing in the areas of productsand services

★7408★ **Association for International Practical Training (AIPT)**

10400 Little Patuxent Pky., Ste. 250
Columbia, MD 21044-3519
Ph: (410)997-2200   Fax: (410)992-3924
E-mail: aipt@aipt.org
URL: http://www.aipt.org

Description: Providers worldwide on-the-job training programs for students and professionals seeking international career development and life-changing experiences. Arranges workplace exchanges in hundreds of professional fields, bringing employers and trainees together from around the world. Client list ranges from small farming communities to Fortune 500 companies.

★7409★ **Meteorologists**

Evon Publishing
832 N 7th Ave.
Iron River, MI 49935
Ph: (906)265-3190

Audiocassette. 1996. $16.95. 32 minutes. Part of the Careers and Vocational Guidance Series. Provides information about the nature of the work, educational requirements, employment outlook, earnings, and work conditions as well as additional related information.

★7410★ **Minority Women In Science (MWIS)**

Directorate for Education and Human Resources Programs
1200 New York Ave. NW
Washington, DC 20005
Ph: (202)326-7019   Fax: (202)371-9849
E-mail: sassefa@aaas.org

Description: A national network group of the American association for the Advancement of Science (AAAS), Education and Human Resources Directorate. The objectives of this group are: to identify and share information on resources and programs that could help in mentoring young women and minorities interested in science and engineering careers, and to strengthen communication among women and minorities in science and education.

★7411★ *Scientific, Engineering, and Technical Services*
Cambridge Educational
2572 Brunswick Ave.
Lawrenceville, NJ 08648-4128
Fax: 800-FAX-ON-US   Fr: 800-468-4227
URL: http://www.cambridgeeducational.com

$89.95. 2002. 18 minutes. Part of the Career Cluster Series.

★7412★ *Scientific Occupations*
Delphi Productions
3160 4th St.
Boulder, CO 80304
Fax: (303)443-4022   Fr: 888-443-2400
URL: http://www.delphivideo.com

$95.00. 60 minutes. Part of the Careers for the 21st Century Video Library.

Mining Engineers

SOURCES OF HELP-WANTED ADS

★7413★ AEG News
Association of Engineering Geologists
PO Box 460518
Denver, CO 80246
Ph: (303)757-2926   Fax: (303)757-2969
Description: Bimonthly. Covers news of the engineering geology profession and the Association, whose members are engineering geologists and geological engineers worldwide. Recurring features include letters to the editor, a calendar of events, news of research, and short articles of technical interest.

★7414★ Coal Age
Primedia Business
9800 Metcalf Ave.
Overland Park, KS 66212
Ph: (913)341-1300   Fax: (913)967-1898
URL: http://www.coolage.com

Monthly. $62.50/year for Canada; $100.00/year for other countries. Coal production magazine.

★7415★ Energy User News
BNP Media, Inc.
2401 W Big Beaver Rd., Ste. 700
Troy, MI 48084
Ph: (248)362-3700   Fax: (248)362-0317
URL: http://www.energyusernews.com

Monthly. Magazine exreporting on the energy management market as it relates to commercial, industrial, and institutional facilites.

★7416★ Engineering Economist
Institute of Industrial Engineers
3577 Pkwy. Ln., Ste. 200
Norcross, GA 30092
Ph: (770)449-0461   Fax: (770)263-8532
Fr: 800-494-0460

Quarterly. Publication covering business issues in the energy, petroleum and mining industries.

★7417★ Engineering and Mining Journal
Primedia Business
9800 Metcalf Ave.
Overland Park, KS 66212
Ph: (913)341-1300   Fax: (913)967-1898
URL: http://www.e-mj.com

Monthly. $79.00/year, Canada and U.S.; $129.00/year for other countries. Provides professionals in metallic and nonmetallic ores and minerals industries with news and technical economic information.

★7418★ Engineering Times
National Society of Professional
    Engineers
1420 King St.
Alexandria, VA 22314
Ph: (703)684-2875   Fax: (703)836-4875
E-mail: et@nspe.org
URL: http://http//:www.nspc.org/1et.asp

$30.00/year for individuals; $48.00/year for out of country. Magazine (tabloid) covering professional, legislative, and techology issues for an engineering audience.

★7419★ ENR: Engineering News-Record
McGraw-Hill Companies
1221 Avenue of the Americas
New York, NY 10020
Ph: (212)512-2000
URL: http://www.enr.com

Weekly. $74.00/year; $5.00 for single issue. Magazine focusing on engineering and construction.

★7420★ Graduating Engineer & Computer Careers
Career Recruitment Media
211 W. Wacker Dr., No. 900
Chicago, IL 60606
Ph: (312)525-3100
URL: http://www.graduatingengineer.com

$16.00/year for individuals. Magazine focusing on employment, education, and career development for entry-level engineers and computer scientists.

★7421★ High Technology Careers Magazine
HTC
4701 Patrick Henry Dr., No. 1901
Santa Clara, CA 95054-1847
Ph: (408)970-8800   Fax: (408)567-0242
URL: http://www.hightechcareers.com

Bimonthly. $29.00/year; $35.00/year for Canada; $85.00/year for out of country. Magazine (tabloid) containing employment opportunity information for the engineering and technical community.

★7422★ International California Mining Journal
International California Mining Journal
PO Box 2260
Aptos, CA 95001
Ph: (831)479-1500   Fax: (831)479-4385

Monthly. $25.95/year for individuals; $3.25 for single issue; $38.95/year for other countries. Mining trade magazine covering prospecting and mining throughout the world.

★7423★ The Mining Record
Howell International Enterprises
PO Box 370510
Denver, CO 80237
Ph: (303)663-7820   Fax: (303)663-7823
Fr: 800-441-4748
URL: http://www.miningrecord.com

Monthly. $45.00/year for individuals. International mining industry newspaper. Features reporting on exploration, discovery, development, production, joint ventures, acquisitions, operating results, legislation, government reports, and metals prices.

★7424★ Monthly Energy Review

Superintendent of Documents
PO Box 371954
MS4004-MIB
Pittsburgh, PA 15250-7954
Ph: (202)512-1800

Monthly. Publication covering the petroleum, energy and mining industries.

★7425★ National Engineer

National Association of Power Engineers
One Springfield St.
Chicopee, MA 01013-2624
Ph: (413)592-6273   Fax: (413)592-1998

Bimonthly. $25.00/year for individuals; $3.00 for single issue.

★7426★ NSBE Magazine

NSBE Publications
1454 Duke St.
Alexandria, VA 22314
Ph: (703)549-2207   Fax: (703)683-5312

$10.00/year for individuals; $2.00 for single issue. Journal providing information on engineering careers, self-development, and cultural issues for recent graduates with technical majors.

★7427★ Oil and Gas Interests

PBI Media L.L.C.
1201 Seven Locks Rd., Ste. 300
Potomac, MD 20854
Ph: (301)354-2000

Monthly. Trade publication covering the petroleum, energy and mining industries.

★7428★ Pay Dirt Magazine

Copper Queen Publishing Company Inc.
Drawer 48
Bisbee, AZ 85603
Ph: (520)432-2244   Fax: (520)432-2247
E-mail: paydirt@theriver.com
URL: http://www.voiceofmining.com

Monthly. $30.00/year for individuals; $3.00 for single issue. Magazine bringing mining developments, government mining policies, environmental issues, and mining heritage to the U.S. and around the world.

★7429★ SWE

Society of Women Engineers
230 E Ohio St., No. 400
2135 Lamberton Rd.
Chicago, IL 60611-3265
Ph: (312)596-5223   Fax: (312)596-5252
E-mail: hq@swe.org
URL: http://www.swe.org

Bimonthly. $30.00/year for nonmembers. Magazine for engineering students and for women and men working in the engineering and technology fields. Covers career guidance, continuing development and topical issues.

★7430★ Technology Review

Technology Review
201 Vassar St.
Cambridge, MA 02139
Ph: (617)253-8250   Fax: (617)258-5850
E-mail: trcomments@mit.edu

$30.00/year for individuals; $42.00/year for other countries; $4.95/year for single issue. Magazine reviewing new developments in technology with an emphasis on economic, political, and social implications. Not a new product publication.

★7431★ WEPANEWS

Women in Engineering Programs & Advocates Network
Castle Point on the Hudson
Hoboken, NJ 07030
Ph: (201)216-5245   Fax: (201)216-5175
URL: http://www.wepan.org/newsletter.html

Description: Two issues/year. Seeks to provide greater access for women to careers in engineering. Includes news of graduate, undergraduate, freshmen, pre-college, and re-entry engineering programs for women. Recurring features include job listings, faculty, grant, and conference news, international engineering program news, action group news, notices of publications available, and a column titled Kudos.

★7432★ World Mining Equipment

World Mining Equipment
1250 Broadway, 26th Fl.
New York, NY 10001
Ph: (212)213-6202   Fax: (212)213-1870
Fr: 800-MET-AL25

Monthly. Trade publication covering mining equipment worldwide.

PLACEMENT AND JOB REFERRAL SERVICES

★7433★ American Indian Science and Engineering Society (AISES)

PO Box 9828
Albuquerque, NM 87119-9828
Ph: (505)765-1052   Fax: (505)765-5608
E-mail: info@aises.org
URL: http://www.aises.org

Description: American Indian and non-Indian students and professionals in science, technology, and engineering fields; corporations representing energy, mining, aerospace, electronic, and computer fields. Seeks to motivate and encourage students to pursue undergraduate and graduate studies in science, engineering, and technology. Sponsors science fairs in grade schools, teacher training workshops, summer math/science sessions for 8th-12th graders, professional chapters, and student chapters in colleges. Offers scholarships. Adult members serve as role models, advisers, and mentors for students. Operates placement service.

★7434★ Engineering Society of Detroit (ESD)

26100 American Dr., Ste. 500
Southfield, MI 48034-6184
Ph: (248)355-2910   Fax: (248)355-1492
E-mail: esd@esd.org
URL: http://esd.org

Description: Engineers from all disciplines; scientists and technologists. Conducts technical programs and engineering refresher courses; sponsors conferences and expositions. Maintains speakers' bureau; offers placement services. Although based in Detroit, MI, society membership is international.

★7435★ Korean Scientists and Engineers Association in America (KSEA)

1952 Gallows Rd., Ste. 300
Vienna, VA 22182
Ph: (703)748-1221   Fax: (703)748-1331
E-mail: sejong@ksea.org
URL: http://www.ksea.org

Description: Scientists and engineers holding single or advanced degrees. Goals are to: promote friendship and mutuality among Korean and American scientists and engineers; contribute to Korea's scientific, technological, industrial, and economic developments; strengthen the scientific, technological, and cultural bonds between Korea and the U.S. Sponsors symposium. Maintains speakers' bureau, placement service, and biographical archives. Compiles statistics. Maintains 100 volume library of scientific handbooks and yearbooks in Korean.

★7436★ Society of Hispanic Professional Engineers (SHPE)

5400 E Olympic Blvd., Ste. 210
Los Angeles, CA 90022
Ph: (323)725-3970   Fax: (323)725-0316
E-mail: shpenational@shpe.org
URL: http://www.shpe.org

Description: Engineers, student engineers, and scientists seeking to increase the number of Hispanic engineers by providing motivation and support to students. Sponsors competitions and educational programs. Maintains placement service and speakers' bureau; compiles statistics.

★7437★ Society for Mining, Metallurgy, and Exploration (SME)

8307 Shaffer Pky.
PO Box 277002
Littleton, CO 80127-7002
Ph: (303)973-9550   Fax: (303)973-3845
Fr: 800-763-3132
E-mail: sme@smenet.org
URL: http://www.smenet.org

Description: A member society of the American Institute of Mining, Metallurgical and Petroleum Engineers. Persons engaged in the finding, exploitation, treatment, and marketing of all classes of minerals (metal ores, industrial minerals, and solid fuels) except petroleum. Promotes the arts and sciences connected with the production of useful minerals and metals. Offers specialized education programs; compiles enrollment and graduation statistics from schools offering engineering degrees in mining, mineral, mineral processing/metallurgical, geological, geophysical, and mining technology. Provides placement service and sponsors charitable programs.

EMPLOYER DIRECTORIES AND NETWORKING LISTS

★7438★ American Men and Women of Science

Thomson Gale
27500 Drake Rd.
Farmington Hills, MI 48331-3535
Ph: (248)699-4253   Fax: (248)699-8065
Fr: 800-877-GALE
E-mail: amws@galegroup.com

Biennial, latest edition December 2002. $975.00. Covers over 129,700 U.S. and Canadian scientists active in the physical, biological, mathematical, computer science, and engineering fields; includes references to previous edition for deceased scientists and nonrespondents. Entries include: Name, address, education, personal and career data, memberships, honors and awards, research interest. Arrangement: Alphabetical. Indexes: Discipline (in separate volume).

★7439★ Careers in Focus: Engineering

Ferguson Publishing Co.
200 W Jackson Blvd.
Chicago, IL 60606
Ph: (312)692-0109

2nd edition, 2002. $22.95. Publication includes: List of resources to consult for more information. Principal content of publication is job descriptions, advancement opportunities, educational requirements, employment outlook, salary information, and working conditions for careers in the field of engineering. Indexes: Alphabetical.

★7440★ Directory of Contract Staffing Firms

C.E. Publications Inc.
PO Box 3006
Bothell, WA 98041-3006
Ph: (425)806-5200   Fax: (425)806-5585
URL: http://www.cjhunter.com/dcsf/overview.html

$15.00. Covers nearly 1,300 contract firms actively engaged in the employment of engineering, IT/IS, and technical personnel for 'temporary' contract assignments throughout the world. Entries include: Company name, address, phone, name of contact, email, web address. Arrangement: Alphabetical. Indexes: Geographical.

★7441★ The Geophysical Directory

Geophysical Directory Inc.
PO Box 130508
Houston, TX 77219
Ph: (713)529-8789   Fax: (713)529-3646
Fr: 800-929-2462
E-mail: info@geophysicaldirectory.com

Annual, March. $125.00 within USA; $140.00 outside USA. Covers about 4,000 companies that provide geophysical equipment, supplies, or services, and mining and petroleum companies that use geophysical techniques; international coverage. Entries include: Company name, address, phone, fax, names of principal executives, operations, and sales personnel; similar information for branch locations. Arrangement: Classified by product or service. Indexes: Company name, personal name.

★7442★ Indiana Society of Professional Engineers-Directory

Indiana Society of Professional Engineers
PO Box 20806
Indianapolis, IN 46220
Ph: (317)255-2267   Fax: (317)255-2530

Annual, fall. $55.00. Covers member registered engineers, land surveyors, engineering students, and engineers in training. Entries include: Member name, address, phone, type of membership, business information, specialty. Arrangement: Alpha by chapter area.

★7443★ International Directory of Engineering Societies and Related Organizations

American Association of Engineering Societies
1828 L St. NW, Ste. 906
Washington, DC 20036
Ph: (202)296-2237   Fax: (202)296-1151
Fr: 888-400-AAES

Irregular, latest edition December 1998. $240.00. Covers about 1,370 national, regional, Canadian, and international organizations concerned with engineering and related fields. Entries include: Name, address, phone, fax, e-mail, key personnel, objectives, publications, activities, mailing lists, federation memberships, meeting and convention dates, and budget data. Arrangement: Alphabetical. Indexes: Acronym, geographical, area of specialization.

★7444★ Peterson's Job Opportunities in Engineering and Technology

Thomson Peterson's
PO Box 67005
Lawrenceville, NJ 08648-6105
Fr: 800-338-3282

Compiled by the Peterson's staff. Fourth edition, 1996. $21.95 (paper). 384 pages. Profiles 2,000 high-tech companies looking primarily for technical personnel in such fields as biotechnology, telecommunications, software, computers and peripherals, defense, and aerospace. Contains job-search strategies and career options to help match education and expertise to the job market.

Indexed geographically, by industry, and by hiring needs.

★7445★ SME Mining Reference Handbook

Society for Mining, Metallurgy, and Exploration Inc.
8307 Shaffer Pkwy.
Littleton, CO 80127
Ph: (303)973-9550   Fax: (303)948-4265
Fr: 800-763-3132

$129.00. Publication includes: List of web sites for further mining information. Principal content of publication is detailed information helpful for mining engineers working in the field. Indexes: Alphabetical.

★7446★ Western Mining Directory

Howell International Enterprises
P.O. Box 1630
Castle Rock, CO 80104-6130
Ph: (303)663-7820   Fax: (303)663-7823
Fr: 800-441-4748
URL: http://www.miningrecord.com/product_information

Annual, March. $49.00. Covers about 300 mining firms and organizations in the mining industry of the western United States, including active hardrock and coal mines, uranium and vanadium mines; mining firms, consultants, contractors-developers, suppliers of equipment and services, exploration and drilling companies; educational institutions; mining associations; related government agencies; mining exhibitions and conferences. Entries include: For mining companies-Name, corporate, regional, and exploration office addresses; information regarding companies that are privately or publicly held; stock exchange information; trading symbol. For mines-Names of managers, location, open pit, underground, type of recovery, product, operator, reserves, grade, mining rates, number of employees. Arrangement: Alphabetical and geographical. Indexes: Mining location.

HANDBOOKS AND MANUALS

★7447★ The Best Resumes for Scientists and Engineers

John Wiley & Sons Inc.
1 Wiley Dr.
Somerset, NJ 08873
Ph: (732)469-4400   Fr: 800-225-5945

Adele Lewis and David J. Moore. Second edition, 1993. $37.50; $19.95 (paper). 224 pages. Presents an extensive collection of scientific and engineering resumes, highlighting the important differences between these and resumes written for other occupations.

★7448★ Career Information Center

Macmillan Publishing Co. Inc.
200 Old Tappan Rd.
Old Tappan, NJ 07675
Fr: 800-428-5331

Visual Education Center Staff. Seventh edition, 1999. $275.00. 2080 pages. This 13-volume set profiles over 600 occupations. Each occupational profile describes job duties, educational requirements, how to get the job, advancement possibilities, employment outlook, working conditions, earnings and benefits, and where to write for more information.

★7449★ Engineering Your Job Search: A Job-Finding Resource for Engineering Professionals

Professional Publications, Inc.
1250 5th Ave.
Belmont, CA 94002
Ph: (650)593-9119   Fax: (650)592-4519
Fr: 800-426-1178

Compiled by Professional Publications, editors. 1995. $24.95 (paper). 154 pages. Out of print.

★7450★ The I Hate Selling Book: Business-Building Advice for Consultants, Attorneys, Accountants, Engineers, Architects, and Other Professionals

Allan Boress & Associates
1500 University Dr., Suite 239
Coral Springs, FL 33071
Ph: (954)345-4666   Fax: (954)344-2453

Allan S. Boress. 2001. $29.95.

★7451★ Majoring in Engineering: How to Get from Your Freshman Year to Your First Job

Farrar, Straus & Giroux, Inc.
19 Union Sq., W
New York, NY 10003
Ph: (212)741-6900   Fax: (212)633-9385
Fr: 888-330-8477

John Garcia and Carol Carter, editors. 2000. $20.00; $10.00 (paper). 134 pages.

★7452★ Opportunities in Engineering Careers

McGraw-Hill Contemporary Books
1221 Avenue of the Americas
New York, NY 10020
Ph: (212)904-2000   Fr: 800-323-4900
E-mail: ntcpub@tribune.com

Nicholas Basta. Revised, 1995. $14.95; $11.95 (paper). 200 pages. Outlines typical job titles, salaries, career paths, and employment prospects.

★7453★ Real People Working in Engineering

McGraw-Hill Contemporary Books
1221 Avenue of the Americas
New York, NY 10020
Ph: (212)904-2000   Fr: 800-323-4900

E-mail: ntcpub@tribune.com

Blythe Camenson, Jan Goldberg. 1997. $14.95; $12.95 (paper). Interviews and profiles of working professionals capture a range of opportunities in this field.

★7454★ Resumes for Engineering Careers

McGraw-Hill Trade
2 Penn Plaza
New York, NY 10121
Ph: (212)904-2000   Fr: 800-722-4726
E-mail: ntcpub@tribune.com

2000. $10.95 (paper). 456 pages. Contains sample resumes and cover letters applicable to any engineering field.

★7455★ Resumes for Scientific and Technical Careers

McGraw-Hill Contemporary Books
1221 Avenue of the Americas
New York, NY 10020
Ph: (212)904-2000   Fr: 800-323-4900
E-mail: ntcpub@tribune.com

1999. $9.95 (paper). 450 pages. Provides resume advice for individuals interested in working in scientific and technical careers. Includes sample resumes and cover letters.

★7456★ Study Guide for the Professional Registration of Mining/Mineral Engineers

Society for Mining, and Metallurgy Exploration, Inc.
PO Box 625002
Littleton, CO 80162-5002
Ph: (303)973-9550   Fax: (303)973-3845
Fr: 800-763-3132

Fifth edition. 1996. $25.00 (paper). 120 pages.

EMPLOYMENT AGENCIES AND SEARCH FIRMS

★7457★ Engineer One, Inc.

PO Box 23037
Knoxville, TN 37933
Fax: (865)691-0110
E-mail: engineerone@engineerone.com
URL: http://www.engineerone.com

Employment agency.

★7458★ Main Line Personnel Service, Inc.

Pagoda Blding.
100 Presidential Blvd. Ste. 200
Bala Cynwyd, PA 19004-0448
Ph: (610)667-1820   Fax: (610)668-5000
URL: http://www.mlpers.com

Employment agency.

★7459★ Search and Recruit International

4455 South Blvd.
Virginia Beach, VA 23452
Ph: (757)490-3151   Fax: (757)497-6503
E-mail: britt@searchandrecruit.com
URL: http://www.searchandrecruit.com

Employment agency. Headquartered in Virginia Beach. Other offices in Bremerton, WA; Charleston, SC; Jacksonville, FL; Memphis, TN; Pensacola, FL; Sacramento, CA; San Bernardino, CA; San Diego, CA.

ONLINE JOB SOURCES AND SERVICES

★7460★ Spherion Workforce Architects
URL: http://www.spherion.com

Description: Recruitment firm specializing in accounting and finance, sales and marketing, interim executives, technology, engineering, retail and human resources.

TRADESHOWS

★7461★ American Society of Mining and Reclamation

American Society of Mining and Reclamation
3134 Montevesta Rd.
Lexington, KY 40502
Ph: (606)257-8627   Fax: (606)257-2185
URL: http://www.ca.uky.edu/assmr

Annual. **Primary Exhibits:** Exhibits relating to the protection and enhancement of land disturbed by mining.

★7462★ Rapid Excavation & Tunneling Conference

Society for Mining, Metallurgy, and Exploration, Inc.
PO Box 625002
Littleton, CO 80162
Ph: (303)973-9550   Fax: (303)979-3461
Fr: 800-763-3132
E-mail: smenet@aol.com
URL: http://www.smenet.org

Biennial. **Primary Exhibits:** Excavation equipment.

OTHER SOURCES

★7463★ **American Almanac of Jobs and Salaries**
Morrow Avon
1350 Avenue of the Americas
New York, NY 10019
Ph: (212)261-6788   Fr: 800-242-7737
John W. Wright. Revised edition, 2000. $20.00 (paper). 672 pages. This is a comprehensive guide to the wages of hundreds of occupations in a wide variety of industries and organizations.

★7464★ **American Association of Blacks in Energy (AABE)**
927 15th St. NW, Ste. 200
Washington, DC 20005
Ph: (202)371-9530   Fax: (202)371-9218
Fr: 800-466-0204
E-mail: aabe@aabe.org
URL: http://www.aabe.org
Description: Blacks in energy-related professions, including engineers, scientists, consultants, academicians, and entrepreneurs; government officials and public policymakers; interested students. Represents blacks and other minorities in matters involving energy use and research, the formulation of energy policy, the ownership of energy resources, and the development of energy technologies. Seeks to increase the knowledge, understanding, and awareness of the minority community in energy issues by serving as an energy information source for policymakers, recommending blacks and other minorities to appropriate energy officials and executives, encouraging students to pursue professional careers in the energy industry, and advocating the participation of blacks and other minorities in energy programsand policymaking activities. Updates members on key legislation and regulations being developed by the Department of Energy, the Department of Interior, the Department of Commerce, the Small Business Administration, and other federal and state agencies. Offers information on current job openings

★7465★ **American Association of Engineering Societies (AAES)**
1828 L St. NW, No. 906
Washington, DC 20036
Ph: (202)296-2237   Fax: (202)296-1151
Fr: 888-400-2237
E-mail: tprice@aaes.org
URL: http://www.aaes.org
Description: Coordinates the efforts of the member societies in the provision of reliable and objective information to the general public concerning issues which affect the engineering profession and the field of engineering as a whole; to collect, analyze, document, and disseminate data which will inform the general public of the relationship between engineering and the national welfare; to provide a forum for the engineering societies to exchange and discuss their views on matters of common interest; and to represent the U.S. engineering community aborad through representation in WFEO and UPADI.

★7466★ **Association for International Practical Training (AIPT)**
10400 Little Patuxent Pky., Ste. 250
Columbia, MD 21044-3519
Ph: (410)997-2200   Fax: (410)992-3924
E-mail: aipt@aipt.org
URL: http://www.aipt.org
Description: Providers worldwide on-the-job training programs for students and professionals seeking international career development and life-changing experiences. Arranges workplace exchanges in hundreds of professional fields, bringing employers and trainees together from around the world. Client list ranges from small farming communities to Fortune 500 companies.

★7467★ **Engineering Occupations**
Delphi Productions
3160 4th St.
Boulder, CO 80304
Fax: (303)443-4022   Fr: 888-443-2400
URL: http://www.delphivideo.com
$95.00. 50 minutes. Part of the Careers for the 21st Century Video Library.

★7468★ **Mining Engineers**
Evon Publishing
832 N 7th Ave.
Iron River, MI 49935
Ph: (906)265-3190
Audiocassette. 1996. $16.95. 32 minutes. Part of the Careers and Vocational Guidance Series. Provides information about the nature of the work, educational requirements, employment outlook, earnings, and work conditions as well as additional related information.

★7469★ **National Action Council for Minorities in Engineering (NACME)**
Empire State Bldg., Ste. 2212
350 Fifth Ave.
New York, NY 10118-2299
Ph: (212)279-2626   Fax: (212)629-5178
E-mail: webmaster@nacme.org
URL: http://www.nacme.org/
Description: Leads the national effort to increase access to careers in engineering and other science-based disciplines. Supported by the nation's leading technology-intensive companies, NACME conducts research and public policy analysis, develops and operates national demonstration programs at precollege and university levels, and disseminates information through publications, conferences, and electronic media. NACME is also the nation's largest privately funded source of scholarships for minority students in engineering.

★7470★ **National Society of Professional Engineers (NSPE)**
1420 King St.
Alexandria, VA 22314
Ph: (703)684-2800   Fax: (703)836-4875
Fr: 888-285-6773
E-mail: custserv@nspe.org
URL: http://www.nspe.org
Description: Professional engineers and engineers-in-training in all fields registered in accordance with the laws of states or territories of the U.S. or provinces of Canada; qualified graduate engineers, student members, and registered land surveyors. Is concerned with social, professional, ethical, and economic considerations of engineering as a profession; encompasses programs in public relations, employment practices, ethical considerations, education, and career guidance. Monitors legislative and regulatory actions of interest to the engineering profession.

★7471★ **Scientific, Engineering, and Technical Services**
Cambridge Educational
2572 Brunswick Ave.
Lawrenceville, NJ 08648-4128
Fax: 800-FAX-ON-US   Fr: 800-468-4227
URL: http://www.cambridgeeducational.com
$89.95. 2002. 18 minutes. Part of the Career Cluster Series.

★7472★ **Society of Women Engineers (SWE)**
230 E Ohio St., No. 400
Chicago, IL 60611-3265
Ph: (312)596-5223   Fax: (312)596-5252
E-mail: hq@swe.org
URL: http://www.swe.org
Description: Educational and service organization representing both students and professional women in engineering and technical fields.

★7473★ **Women in Engineering**
Her Own Words
PO Box 5264
Madison, WI 53705-0264
Ph: (608)271-7083   Fax: (608)271-0209
URL: http://www.herownwords.com/
Video. Jocelyn Riley. $95.00. 15 minutes. Resource guide also available for $45.00.

Ministers and Christian Religious Professionals

SOURCES OF HELP-WANTED ADS

★7474★ The Lutheran

Augsburg Fortress, Publishers
100 S Fifth St., Ste. 700
Minneapolis, MN 55402
Ph: (612)330-3300   Fax: (612)330-3521
Fr: 800-426-0115
E-mail: lutheran@elca.org
URL: http://www.thelutheran.org

Monthly. $15.95/year for individuals; $1.50 for single issue. Magazine of the Evangelical Lutheran Church in America.

★7475★ Panorama

Pittsburgh Theological Seminary
616 N Highland Ave.
Pittsburgh, PA 15206
Ph: (412)362-5610   Fax: (412)363-3260

Provides news for Semimary faculty, staff. Recurring features include Interviews, news of research, calendar of events, news of educational opportunities, job listings, book reviews, notices of publications available.

★7476★ Sojourners

Sojourners
2401 15th St. NW
Washington, DC 20009
Ph: (202)328-8842   Fax: (202)328-8757
Fr: 800-714-7474
URL: http://www.sojo.net

Bimonthly. $4.95 for single issue; $30.00/year. Independent, ecumenical Christian magazine which analyzes faith, politics, and culture from a progressive, justice-oriented perspective.

★7477★ United Church News

United Church of Christ
Proclamation, Identity, and
  Communications
700 Prospect Ave.
Cleveland, OH 44115-1100
Ph: (216)736-2177   Fax: (216)736-2223

URL: http://www.ucc.org/ucnews.htm

Description: Ten issues/year. Concerned with the programs and activities of the United Church of Christ. Reports news of the UCC's 39 regional groupings and carries notices of pastoral changes within the UCC. Recurring features include letters to the editor, interviews, reports of meetings, news of resources and educational opportunities, and job listings. Also includes columns titled Focus on Faith, Heart Warmers, As I See It, and Current Comment.

★7478★ Vision

National Association of Catholic Chaplains
3501 S Lake Dr.
PO Box 070473
Milwaukee, WI 53207-0473
Ph: (414)483-4898   Fax: (414)483-6712

Description: Ten issues/year. Serves Catholic lay persons, priests, and religious personnel in professional health care, related institutional ministries and parishes. Recurring features include book reviews of publications on pastoral care, employment opportunities, and notices of conferences and meetings.

PLACEMENT AND JOB REFERRAL SERVICES

★7479★ American Association of Christian Schools (AACS)

PO Box 1097
Independence, MO 64051-0597
Ph: (816)252-9900   Fax: (816)252-6700
E-mail: national@aacs.org
URL: http://www.aacs.org

Description: Maintains teacher/administrator certification program and placement service. Participates in school accreditation program. Sponsors National Academic Tournament. Maintains American Christian Honor Society. Compiles statistics; maintains speakers' bureau and placement service.

★7480★ American Association of Pastoral Counselors (AAPC)

9504A Lee Hwy.
Fairfax, VA 22031-2303
Ph: (703)385-6967   Fax: (703)352-7725
E-mail: info@aapc.org
URL: http://www.aapc.org

Description: Pastoral counseling is a form of psychotherapy which uses spiritual resources as well as psychological understanding for healing and growth. Counselors are certified mental health professionals who have had in-depth religious and/or theological training. Represents and sets standards for the profession around the world. Certifies counselors, accredits pastoral counseling centers and approves training programs. Members may join through a process of consultation and review of academic and clinical education. Offers members continuing education opportunities, encourages networks of members for professional support and enrichment, facilitates growth and innovation in the ministry of pastoral counseling and provides both specialized in-service training and supervision in pastoral counseling.

★7481★ Association of North American Missions (ANAM)

PO Box 8667
Longview, TX 75607
Ph: (903)234-2075
E-mail: delthea@aol.com
URL: http://www.anamissions.org

Description: Missions of more than five missionaries operating in North America. To make missions more credible and visible; to promote unity and cooperation among members; to collect, organize, and disseminate information relating to missionary work to the public and to act as clearinghouse for members. Offers referral and placement service to qualified missionaries not serving with member missions. Provides information about missions to pastors and schools. Offers workshops and in-depth seminars for mission leaders and missionaries.

★7482★ Association of Southern Baptist Campus Ministers (ASBCM)

Box 25118
Baton Rouge, LA 70894-5118
Ph: (225)343-0408   Fax: (225)343-0424
E-mail: lsubcm@eatel.net

Description: Full-time campus ministers with a graduate degree or five years experience in ministry (125); part-time and volunteer ministers, students, and interested individuals are affiliate members (25). Purposes are to: strengthen the individual's commitment and expertise in the ministry through fellowship and programs; enhance the minister's view of campus and church; promote professional competence among campus ministers; develop and encourage fellowship among members; act as a liaison between campus ministers seeking employment or reassignment and employers seeking campus ministers; share knowledge, personnel, and material resources. Cooperates with seminaries in continuing education. Maintains collection of records available at the Dargan-Carver Library in Nashville, TN. Maintains placement registry for Southern Baptist campus ministers and applicants.

★7483★ Association of Unity Churches

401 SW Oldham Pkwy.
Lee's Summit, MO 64081
Ph: (816)524-7414   Fax: (816)525-4020
E-mail: info@unity.org
URL: http://www.unity.org

Description: Ministers and interested members of Unity Churches and study groups. Serves and supports member ministries by providing human resources, administrative and educational programs, and consultation in accordance with the teachings of the Unity School of Christianity founded by Charles and Myrtle Fillmore. Trains and licenses teachers, ministers, and youth advisors; offers continuing education programs and minister employment service. Holds skills development seminars and workshops; sponsors retreats. Offers media service consultation. Assists with the development of local groups.

★7484★ Catholic Campus Ministry Association (CCMA)

1118 Pendleton St., Ste. 300
Cincinnati, OH 45202
Ph: (513)842-0167   Fax: (513)842-0171
Fr: 888-714-6631
E-mail: craig@ccmanet.org
URL: http://www.ccmanet.org

Purpose: Works to form a strong and coordinated voice for the church's ministry in higher education; to provide continuing education programs for members; to provide liaison with other individuals and agencies of the church interested in campus ministry and the role of the church in higher education; to advance ecumenical and interfaith understanding and cooperation; to provide guidelines for, and assistance in, developing effective campus ministries. Maintains placement service and speakers' bureau; offers colleague consultation service.

★7485★ Catholic Press Association (CPA)

3555 Veterans Memorial Hwy., Unit 0
Ronkonkoma, NY 11779
Ph: (631)471-4730   Fax: (631)471-4804
E-mail: rosep@catholicpress.org
URL: http://www.catholicpress.org

Description: Publishers of Catholic newspapers, magazines, pamphlets, and books; Catholic writers, illustrators, and teachers. Sponsors research and specialized education programs. Maintains placement service. Maintains 25 committees, including Freedom of Information, News Service Liaison, and Research.

★7486★ Chinese Christian Mission (CCM)

PO Box 750759
Petaluma, CA 94975
Ph: (707)762-1314   Fax: (707)762-1713
E-mail: ccm@ccmusa.org
URL: http://www.ccmusa.org

Purpose: Serves as an evangelical faith mission dedicated to reaching Chinese people around the world with the gospel of Jesus Christ. Broadcasts radio programs to foster Christianity in China. **Activities:** Operates placement service providing ministers with churches. Sponsors short-term mission trips to Latin America and East Asia.

★7487★ Christian Chiropractors Association (CCA)

2550 Stover, No. B-102
PO Box 9715
Fort Collins, CO 80525
Ph: (970)482-1404   Fax: (970)482-1538
Fr: 800-999-1970
E-mail: carlas@frii.com
URL: http://www.christianchiropractors.org

Description: Works to spread the Gospel of Christ throughout the U.S. and abroad. Offers Christian fellowship and works to unify Christian chiropractors around the essentials of the fail, "leaving minor points of doctrine to the conscience of the individual believer." Focus is on world missions; seeks to expand the variety of mission fields; aids in placement of Christian chiropractors as missionaries.

★7488★ Christian Management Association (CMA)

PO Box 4090
San Clemente, CA 92674-4090
Ph: (949)487-0900   Fax: (949)487-0927
Fr: 800-727-4CMA
E-mail: CMA@cmaonline.org
URL: http://www.christianity.com/cma

Description: CEO's, key leaders and managers who serve Christian organizations and churches. Provides management information, leadership training and strategic networking. management through its annual national conference, the Christian Management Institute. Holds bimonthly fellowship meeting for training and information reports. Provides job referral and professional refer-

ral service to assist Christian managment personnel.

★7489★ Christian Schools International (CSI)

3350 E Paris Ave. SE
Grand Rapids, MI 49512-3054
Ph: (616)957-1070   Fax: (616)957-5022
Fr: 800-635-8288
E-mail: info@csionline.org
URL: http://community.gospelcom.net/Brix?pageID=2831

Description: Christian elementary and secondary schools enrolling 100,000 pupils and employing 7800 teachers. Purposes are: to provide a medium for a united witness regarding the role of Christian schools in contemporary society; to promote the establishment of Christian schools; to help members function more effectively in areas of promotion, organization, administration, and curriculum; to help establish standards and criteria to guide the operation of its members; to foster high professional ideals and economic well-being among Christian school personnel; to establish and maintain communication with member schools, colleges, churches, government agencies, and the public. Encourages study, research, and writing that embodies Christian theories of education; conducts salary studies, research, andsurveys on operating costs; offers expert and confidential analysis of member school programs and operation. Sponsors meetings, workshops, and seminars; offers placement service. Administers the Christian School Pension and Trust Funds, Group Insurance Plans, and Life and Insurance Plans and Trust Funds.

★7490★ Conservative Baptist Association of America

1501 W Mineral Ave., Ste. B
Littleton, CO 80120-5612
Ph: (720)283-3030   Fax: (720)283-3333
Fr: 888-627-1995
E-mail: info@cbamerica.org
URL: http://www.cbamerica.org

Description: Provides leadership, fellowship, counseling services, and specialized support ministries to 1,200 member churches in an effort "to advance the cause of Christ through worship, evangelism, instruction, and service throughout the world." Conducts charitable program; offers placement service, chaplaincy endorsement.

★7491★ Council for Health and Human Services Ministries, United Church of Christ (CHHSM)

700 Prospect Ave.
Cleveland, OH 44115
Ph: (216)736-2253   Fax: (216)736-2251
E-mail: sickbert@chhsm.org
URL: http://www.chhsm.org

Members: Health and human service institutions related to the United Church of Christ. **Purpose:** Seeks to study, plan, and implement a program in health and human services; assist members in developing and providing quality services and in financing institutional and noninstitutional health and human service ministries; stimulate awareness of and support for these programs; inform the UCC of policies that affect the needs, problems, and conditions of patients; cooperate with interdenominational agencies and others in the field. **Activities:** Maintains placement service and hall of fame. Compiles statistics; provides specialized education programs.

★7492★ International Catholic Stewardship Council

1275 K St. NW, Ste. 980
Washington, DC 20005-4006
Ph: (202)289-1093   Fax: (202)682-9018
E-mail: icsc@catholicstewardship.org
URL: http://www.catholicstewardship.org

Description: Committed to promoting the right use of God's gifts of time, talent, and treasure through diocesan and parish leadership. Encourages the adoption of the wholistic stewardship concept which stresses that everything is a gift from God, and that gratitude for gifts received is best expressed in right management and ministry to others. Fosters the exchange of ideas and materials among dioceses, parishes, and other church organizations. Maintains speakers' bureau and placement service. Compiles statistics.

★7493★ International Council of Community Churches (ICCC)

21116 Washington Pkwy.
Frankfort, IL 60423-3112
Ph: (815)464-5690   Fax: (815)464-5692
E-mail: icccml@sbcglobal.net
URL: http://iccc.i-go.to

Purpose: Promotes the fellowship of community churches internationally and provides an instrument through which community-minded and freedom-loving churches can cooperate in making a contribution toward a united church. **Activities:** Maintains placement bureau for ministers.

★7494★ Jesuit Association of Student Personnel Administrators (JASPA)

1 DuPont Cir., Ste. 405
Washington, DC 20036
Ph: (202)862-9893   Fax: (202)862-8523
E-mail: treynold@regis.edu
URL: http://jaspa.creighton.edu

Description: Administrators of student personnel programs in 28 Jesuit colleges and universities in the United States. Sponsors institutes and seminars for personnel in Jesuit colleges. Bestows Rev. Victor R. Yanitelli Award; compiles statistics. Cooperates with Catholic and non-Catholic educational associations in various projects. Maintains placement service; conducts workshops. Operates organizational archives; compiles statistics.

★7495★ National Association of Church Business Administration (NACBA)

100 N Central Expressway, Ste. 914
Richardson, TX 75080-5326
Ph: (972)699-7555   Fax: (972)699-7617
Fr: 800-898-8085
E-mail: info@nacba.net
URL: http://www.nacba.net

Members: Business administrators and managers employed by local churches or institutions of the Christian church. **Purpose:** Provides a program of certification, study, service, fellowship, training, information exchange, and problem discussion. **Activities:** Offers placement service; conducts research programs; compiles statistics. Maintains hall of fame.

★7496★ National Association of Congregational Christian Churches (NACCC)

8473 S Howell Ave.
PO Box 288
Oak Creek, WI 53154
Ph: (414)764-1620   Fax: (414)764-0319
Fr: 800-262-1620
E-mail: naccc@naccc.org
URL: http://www.naccc.org/

Purpose: Aims to provide a means whereby Congregational Christian churches may consult and exchange advise on spiritual and temporal matters of common concern; and to encourage the continuance of Christian purposes and practices that have been the historic and accepted characteristics of Congregational Christian churches. **Activities:** Supports the education of ministers through its Congregational Foundation for Theological Studies. Compiles statistics. Operates placement service and mission program. Provides a variety of financial services. Supports youth programming from coast to coast and hosts annual meeting.

★7497★ National Association of Pastoral Musicians (NPM)

962 Wayne Ave., Ste. 210
Silver Spring, MD 20910-4461
Ph: (240)247-3000   Fax: (240)247-3001
E-mail: npmsing@npm.org
URL: http://www.npm.org

Description: Parish clergy, parish musicians, music teachers, and others engaged or interested in Catholic church music. Goal is to improve music in an ordinary parish situation. Reviews current music; assists in parish music celebrations. Conducts research and specialized education programs. Maintains speakers' bureau and placement service.

★7498★ National Lutheran Outdoors Ministry Association (NLOMA)

PO Box 2109
Pottsboro, TX 75076
Ph: (979)247-4128   Fax: (979)247-4120
Fr: 877-397-2401
E-mail: nloma@nloma.org
URL: http://www.nloma.org

Description: Individuals (100) and camps (20) joined to aid in the mission of the Lutheran church and to promote Christian camping and related experience. Provides support for all areas of outdoor ministry. Serves as resource base for camps in the areas of personnel development, site evaluation, program development, and staff recruitment. Conducts seminars and training sessions. Maintains placement service for individuals seeking employment at a member camp.

★7499★ North American Maritime Ministry Association (NAMMA)

3257 Post Rd.
Warwick, RI 02886
Ph: (401)739-5257   Fax: (401)737-4148
E-mail: peter.michaelson@ecunet.org
URL: http://www.namma.org

Description: Spiritual and social welfare agencies from the U.S., Canada, and the Caribbean providing facilities and services for merchant seafarers. Sponsors Chaplain Training School; operates placement service. Maintains archives; conducts research programs.

★7500★ Presbyterian Association of Musicians (PAM)

100 Witherspoon St.
Louisville, KY 40202-1396
Ph: (502)569-5288   Fax: (502)569-8465
Fr: 888-728-7228
E-mail: abarthel@ctr.pcusa.org
URL: http://www.pam.pcusa.org

Description: Organists, choir directors, singers, churches, clergy, directors of Christian education, and interested persons of all denominations. Objective is to develop use of music and the arts in the life and worship of individual congregations. Offers assistance in the areas of worship, music, and the arts. Conducts continuing education. Acts as a clearinghouse for job referrals; promotes the professional status of church musicians and recommends salaries and benefits to churches; certifies church musicians.

★7501★ Presbyterians for Renewal

8134 New LaGrange Rd.
Louisville, KY 40222-4679
Ph: (502)425-4630   Fax: (502)423-8329
E-mail: joe@pfrenewal.org
URL: http://www.pfrenewal.org

Description: Supporters are individuals, congregations, and foundations. Trains church officers. Conducts renewal weekends, officer retreats, and marriage enrichment programs. Provides placement service; bestows awards; compiles statistics. Operates charitable program and speakers' bureau.

★7502★ Society of Biblical Literature (SBL)

825 Houston Mill Rd., Ste. 350
Atlanta, GA 30329
Ph: (404)727-3100   Fax: (404)727-3101

E-mail: sbl@sbl-site.org
URL: http://www.sbl-site.org

Members: Professors and persons interested in biblical studies, ancient world and religious studies. **Purpose:** Seeks to "stimulate the critical investigation of classical biblical literature, together with other related literature, by the exchange of scholarly research both in published form and in public forum." Endeavors to support those disciplines and subdisciplines pertinent to the illumination of the literatures and religions of the ancient Near Eastern and Mediterranean regions, including the study of ancient languages, textual criticism, history, and archaeology. **Activities:** Supports and cooperates with several national and international groups. Conducts research programs; offers placement services.

★7503★ **Teen Missions International (TMI)**

885 E Hall Rd.
Merritt Island, FL 32953
Ph: (321)453-0350   Fax: (321)452-7988
E-mail: info@teenmissions.org
URL: http://www.teenmissions.org

Description: Organizes interdenominational evangelical missionary work projects in areas such as agriculture and community development; programs have operated in 60 countries, including Australia, Brazil, Mongolia, India, Indonesia, Mexico, South Africa, and Zimbabwe. Trains teen and adult missionaries through camps and conferences; operates placement service. Promotes the Christian gospel through the production of films, videos, printed materials, and media presentations. Assists in establishing local teen mission clubs in an effort to encourage evangelical outreach.

★7504★ **Youth for Christ/U.S.A. (YFC/USA)**

PO Box 228822
Denver, CO 80222
Ph: (303)843-9000   Fax: (303)843-9002
E-mail: info@yfc.net
URL: http://community.gospelcom.net/Brix/yfcusa/public

Description: Interdenominational organization for the evangelization and discipling of teenagers. Fights juvenile delinquency through counseling and Youth Guidance programs for youth penal institutions. Carries on projects in 110 countries through Youth for Christ International. Maintains placement service. Programs for staff: Area refreshers; college training; intern training; summer training. Programs for youth: Camps; Campus Life Clubs; counseling; short-term missions and work projects overseas; Youth Guidance work with troubled teenagers. Sponsors "Lighten Up!" radio, which airs on over 1,000 radio stations and satellites.

EMPLOYER DIRECTORIES AND NETWORKING LISTS

★7505★ **Christian Schools International-Directory**

Christian Schools International
3350 E Paris Ave. SE
Grand Rapids, MI 49512-3054
Ph: (616)957-1070   Fax: (616)957-5022
Fr: 800-635-8288
URL: http://www.gospelcom.net/csi

Annual, November. $52.00 for nonmembers. Covers nearly 450 Reformed Christian elementary and secondary schools; related associations; societies without schools. Entries include: For schools-School name, address, phone; name, title, and address of officers; names of faculty members. Arrangement: Geographical.

★7506★ **Directory of Catholic Charities USA Directories**

Catholic Charities USA
1731 King St.
Alexandria, VA 22314
Ph: (703)549-1390   Fax: (703)549-1656
URL: http://www.catholiccharitiesusa.org

Annual. $25.00 for members; $40.00 for nonmembers. Covers nearly 1,200 Catholic community and social service agencies. Listings include diocesan agencies, state Catholic conferences. Entries include: Organization name, address, name and title of director, phone, fax. Arrangement: Geographical by state, then classified by diocese.

★7507★ **Ganley's Catholic Schools in America-Elementary/Secondary/College & University**

Fisher Publishing Co.
PO Box 15070
Scottsdale, AZ 85267
Ph: (480)657-9422   Fax: (480)657-9422
Fr: 800-759-7615
URL: http://www.ganleyscatholicschools.com

Annual, summer; latest edition 2003. $51.50. Covers over 8,400 Catholic K-12 Schools. Arrangement: Geographical by state, then alphabetical by Diocese name.

★7508★ **New Catholic Encyclopedia**

Thomson Gale
27500 Drake Rd.
Farmington Hills, MI 48331-3535
Ph: (248)699-4253   Fax: (248)699-8065
Fr: 800-877-GALE
URL: http://www.gale.com

Second edition September 2002; first edition 1967. $1,195.00. Publication includes: Listing of contemporary religious figures. Entries include: Biographical data. Principal content of publication is approximately 12,000 articles presenting persons and subjects related to Catholicism and the humanities. Indexes: Cumulative.

HANDBOOKS AND MANUALS

★7509★ **Becoming a Minister**

Baker Books
PO Box 6287
Grand Rapids, MI 49516-6287
Ph: (616)676-9185   Fax: (616)676-9573
Fr: 800-877-2665

Thomas C. Oden. Reprint, 2000. $16.99 (paper). 192 pages. Part of Classical Pastoral Care Series Volume One. Out of print.

★7510★ **Careers in Social and Rehabilitation Services**

McGraw-Hill Trade
2 Penn Plaza
New York, NY 10121
Ph: (212)904-2000   Fr: 800-722-4726
E-mail: ntcpub@tribune.com

Geraldine O. Garner. Second edition, 2001. $19.95; 14.95 (paper). 128 pages.

★7511★ **The National Business Employment Weekly Jobs Rated Almanac**

John Wiley & Sons Inc.
1 Wiley Dr.
Somerset, NJ 08873
Ph: (732)469-4400   Fr: 800-225-5945

Les Krantz. First edition, 1995. $16.95. 340 pages. Ranks 250 jobs by environment, salary, outlook, physical demands, stress, security, travel opportunities, and geographic location.

★7512★ **Non-Profits and Education Job Finder**

Planning Communications
7215 Oak Ave.
River Forest, IL 60305-1935
Ph: (708)366-5200   Fax: (708)366-5280
Fr: 888-366-5200
URL: http://jobfinderonline.com

Daniel Lauber. 1997. $32.95; $16.95 (paper). 336 pages. Covers 1600 sources. Discusses how to use sources of non-profit sector job vacancies in a number of specialties and state-by-state, including job-matching services, job hotlines, specialty periodicals with job ads, salary surveys, and directories. Covers a variety of fields from education to religion. Includes chapters on resume and cover letter preparation and interviewing.

★7513★ **Opportunities in Religious Service Careers**

McGraw-Hill Trade
2 Penn Plaza
New York, NY 10121
Ph: (212)904-2000   Fr: 800-722-4726
E-mail: ntcpub@tribune.com

John Oliver Nelson. 1998. $14.95; $11.95 (paper). 160 pages.

★7514★ What Shall I Say? Discerning God's Call to Ministry

Evangelical Lutheran Church in America
Division For Ministry
8765 W. Higgins Rd.
Chicago, IL 60631
Ph: (773)380-2874   Fax: (773)380-2829
Fr: 800-638-3522

Walter R. Bouman and Sue M. Setzer. 1998. $6.95 (paper).

★7515★ Who Will Go for Us?: An Invitation to Ordained Ministry

Abingdon Press
PO Box 801
Nashville, TN 37202
Ph: (615)749-6409   Fax: (615)749-6056
Fr: 800-251-3320

Dennis M. Campbell. 1994. $8.00 (paper). 128 pages.

TRADESHOWS

★7516★ Society for the Scientific Study of Religion Annual Meeting

Exhibit Promotions Plus
11620 Vixens Path
Ellicott City, MD 21043-1539
Ph: (410)997-0763   Fax: (410)997-0764
E-mail: exhibit@erols.com
URL: http://www.epponline.com

Annual. **Primary Exhibits:** Publications and films and other resources in the fields of religion, philosophy, sociology, psychology and anthropology. **Dates and Locations:** 2004 Oct 20-24; Kansas City, MO; Marriott Country Club Plaza • 2005 Nov 2-7; Rochester, NY; Hyatt • 2006 Oct 18-23; Portland, OR; Marriott.

OTHER SOURCES

★7517★ American Orff-Schulwerk Association (AOSA)

PO Box 391089
Cleveland, OH 44139-8089
Ph: (440)543-5366   Fax: (440)543-2687
E-mail: info@aosa.org
URL: http://www.aosa.org

Description: Music and movement educators, music therapists, and church choir directors united to promote and encourage the philosophy of Carl Orff's (1895-1982, German composer) Schulwerk (Music for Children) in America. Distributes information on the activities and growth of Orff Schulwerk in America. Conducts research; offers information on teacher training. Operates clearinghouse.

★7518★ Association of Christian Schools International (ACSI)

731 Chapel Hills Dr.
Colorado Springs, CO 80920-1027
Ph: (719)528-6906   Fax: (719)531-0631
Fr: 800-367-0798
E-mail: info@acsi.org
URL: http://www.acsi.org

Description: Seeks to enable Christian educators and schools worldwide to effectively prepare students for life.

★7519★ Baptist Women in Ministry/Folio (BWIM/FOLIO)

714 N 31st St.
Kansas City, KS 66102
Ph: (913)321-6864
E-mail: bwim@bwim.org
URL: http://www.bwim.org

Members: Ordained and unordained female Baptist ministers; students of the Baptist ministry; interested individuals. **Purpose:** Promotes the image of women as ministers. Fosters support and communication among members. **Activities:** Conducts educational and research programs.

★7520★ A Christian Ministry in the National Parks (ACMNP)

10 Justins Way
Freeport, ME 04032
Ph: (207)865-6436   Fax: (207)865-6852
Fr: 800-786-3450
E-mail: info@acmnp.com
URL: http://www.acmnp.com

Description: Recommends employment for seminary and college students with private concessionaires operating lodges, inns, restaurants, and stores within national parks; aims to offer students the opportunity to conduct interdenominational worship services and Bible studies for park employees and visitors.

★7521★ Division of Higher Education, Christian Church-Disciples of Christ

11477 Olde Cabin Rd., Ste. 310
St. Louis, MO 63141-7130
Ph: (314)991-3000   Fax: (314)991-2957
E-mail: dhe@dhedisciples.org
URL: http://dhedisciples.org

Description: Elected administrative board working to advance the concerns of the Christian Church - Disciples of Christ in higher education and interpret issues in higher education to CCDC leadership. Maintains affiliation with 17 liberal arts colleges and 7 theological seminaries throughout the U.S.

★7522★ Evangelical Press Association (EPA)

PO Box 28129
Crystal, MN 55428
Ph: (763)535-4793   Fax: (763)535-4794
E-mail: director@epassoc.org
URL: http://www.gospelcom.net/epa

Members: Editors and publishers of Christian periodicals. **Activities:** Maintains placement service.

★7523★ Forward in Faith North America

2905 Lackland Rd., Ste. D
Fort Worth, TX 76116
Ph: (817)735-1675   Fax: (817)735-1351
Fr: 800-225-3661
E-mail: fif.northamerica@forwardinfaith.com
URL: http://www.forwardinfaith.com/about/contact.html

Description: Dioceses, parishes, institutions, and societies of Anglican laity and clergy in North America, Central America, South America and the Caribbean who "embrace the Gospel of Jesus Christ and uphold evangelical faith and order, laboring with zeal for the reform and renewal of the church." Promotes the establishment and implementation of cooperative programs.

★7524★ Human Services Occupations

Delphi Productions
3160 4th St.
Boulder, CO 80304
Fax: (303)443-4022   Fr: 888-443-2400
URL: http://www.delphivideo.com

$95.00. 50 minutes. Part of the Careers for the 21st Century Video Library.

★7525★ IFCA International

PO Box 810
Grandville, MI 49468-0810
Fax: (616)531-1814   Fr: 800-347-1840
E-mail: office@ifca.org
URL: http://www.ifca.org

Members: Ministers, missionaries, youth leaders, musicians, and ministerial students (1248); churches and organizations (712). **Purpose:** Seeks to offer independent churches the benefits of unity, while allowing them to keep their autonomy. **Activities:** Supports active evangelism; encourages churches to extend their ministry into neighboring communities, the military, and other Christian churches, which the IFCA believes are in harmony with the Word of God. Serves to reinforce members' doctrinal beliefs; provides interchurch fellowship and the sharing of ministers; trains pastors and lay workers.

★7526★ Intercristo

19303 Fremont Ave. N
Seattle, WA 98133
Ph: (206)546-7330   Fax: (206)546-7375
Fr: 800-251-7740
E-mail: careerhelp@intercristo.com
URL: http://www.jobsinaflash.org

Members: Division of CRISTA Ministries. **Purpose:** Provides job exploration and job information service with computerized referrals on current openings with Christian organizations. Career counseling also available using The Birkman Method Assessment Tool.

★7527★ Lutheran Deaconess Conference (LDC)

1304 La Porte Ave.
Valparaiso, IN 46383
Ph: (219)464-6925   Fax: (219)464-6928
E-mail: deacserv@valpo.edu
URL: http://www.valpo.edu/lda

Members: Consecrated deaconesses having completed the educational requirements of the Lutheran Deaconess Association; students in training. **Purpose:** Seeks to develop sisterhood and community among deaconesses; present an opportunity for renewed inspiration and personal and professional growth; encourage women in the church to use their full potential and to shape, promote, and support the total deaconess program.

★7528★ National Association of Episcopal Schools (NAES)

815 2nd Ave., Ste. 313
New York, NY 10017-4594
Ph: (212)716-6134   Fax: (212)286-9366
Fr: 800-334-7626
E-mail: info@episcopalschools.org
URL: http://www.naes.org

Description: Episcopal day and boarding schools and preschools. Promotes the educational ministry of the Episcopal Church. Provides publications, consultation services and conference focusing on Episcopal identity of schools, worship, religious education, spirituality, leadership development and governance for heads/directors, administrators, chaplains and teachers of religion, trustees, rectors and other church and school leaders.

★7529★ National Association of Parish Catechetical Directors (NPCD)

1077 30th St. NW, Ste. 100
Washington, DC 20007-3852
Ph: (202)337-6232   Fax: (202)333-6706
E-mail: npcd@ncea.org
URL: http://www.ncea.org/departments/npcd

Members: A subdivision of the National Catholic Educational Association. Directors, coordinators and administrators of religious education/catechesis in Roman Catholic parishes; students considering careers as catechetical leaders; clergy, laity, and others involved in the religious community. **Purpose:** Works to act as a representative and advocate for professionals who administer parish catechetical programs; foster cooperation and communication among organizations serving parish catechesis including other NCEA groups and independent associations; promote the spiritual, personal, and professional growth of parish DREs and encourage careers in catechetical ministry. **Activities:** Supports and develops the practice of family catechesis and encourages efforts in adult religious education; urges cooperation among parish leadership, especially parish staff members; promotes competency standards. Provides guidelines for members' contracts, salaries, benefits, and job descriptions. Disseminates information on members' jobs, educational background, salaries, and benefits; reports on parish program activities and surveys. Conducts research.

★7530★ National Conference for Catechetical Leadership

3021 4th St. NE
Washington, DC 20017-1102
Ph: (202)636-3826   Fax: (202)832-2712
E-mail: nccl@nccl.org
URL: http://nccl.org

Members: Diocesan directors of religious education and their staff; publishers, academics, Diocesan religious education, Associations, and individuals interested in religious education. **Purpose:** Fosters communication and unity among members. Addresses the special responsibility to provide lifelong religious education within the Catholic church; assists members with increasing religious education needs; coordinates religious education and helps to supply needed materials. **Activities:** Aids in formal religious education for children, adults, and handicapped persons. Compiles statistics; provides placement service; operates research programs; conducts charitable program; maintains speakers' bureau.

★7531★ North American Association of Christians in Social Work (NACSW)

PO Box 121
Botsford, CT 06404-0121
Ph: (203)270-8780   Fax: (203)270-8780
Fr: 888-426-4712
E-mail: info@nacsw.org
URL: http://www.nacsw.org

Description: Professional social workers and related professionals, students, interested individuals. Supports the integration of Christian faith and professional social work practice in the lives of its members, the profession and the church, promoting love and justice in social service and social reform. Provides opportunities for Christian fellowship, education and service opportunities; articulates informed Christian voice on social welfare practice and policy to the social work profession; provides professional understanding and help for the social ministry of the church; and promotes social welfare services and policies in society which bring about greater justice and meet basic human needs.

★7532★ OMF International - USA

10 W Dry Creek Cir.
Littleton, CO 80120-4413
Ph: (303)730-4160   Fax: (303)730-4165
Fr: 800-422-5330
E-mail: pnelson@omf.org
URL: http://www.us.omf.org

Description: Protestant missionaries. American office of international missionary society which originated in England in 1865 for work in inland China. Activities now carried out in 13 countries of East Asia. Through its publications, the group seeks to recruit new missionaries and supporters, and educate the public.

★7533★ Presbyterian-Reformed Ministries International (PRMI)

PO Box 429
Black Mountain, NC 28711-0429
Ph: (828)669-7373   Fax: (828)669-4880
E-mail: prmi@prmi.org
URL: http://www.prmi.org

Purpose: Strives to "ignite the church in the power of the Holy Spirit through prayer," leadership development, congregational renewal, and mission outreach. Seeks to call the church to prayer and teach the work of prayer, equip clergy and laity for Holy Spirit-empowered ministry, assist congregations in their renewal process and promote "the Holy Spirit for the advancement of the Kingdom of God."

★7534★ *Protestant Ministers*

Evon Publishing
832 N 7th Ave.
Iron River, MI 49935
Ph: (906)265-3190

Audiocassette. 1996. $16.95. 32 minutes. Part of the Careers and Vocational Guidance Series. Provides information about the nature of the work, educational requirements, employment outlook, earnings, and work conditions as well as additional related information.

★7535★ *Religion*

Evon Publishing
832 N 7th Ave.
Iron River, MI 49935
Ph: (906)265-3190

Audiocassette. 1996. $16.95. 32 minutes. Part of the Careers and Vocational Guidance Series. Provides information about the nature of the work, educational requirements, employment outlook, earnings, and work conditions as well as additional related information.

★7536★ United Church of Christ Justice and Witness Ministries

700 Prospect Ave.
Cleveland, OH 44115-1110
Ph: (216)736-3704   Fax: (216)736-3703
E-mail: fordjond@ucc.org
URL: http://www.ucc.org/justice/index.html

Description: Ministers of United Church of Christ who work to maximize the impact of African American and other people of color constituencies within the UCC.

Musicians

SOURCES OF HELP-WANTED ADS

★7537★ ArtSEARCH
Theatre Communications Group
520 Eighth Ave., 24th Fl.
New York, NY 10018-4156
Ph: (212)609-5900   Fax: (212)609-5901
E-mail: custserv@tcg.org
URL: http://www.tcg.org

Description: Biweekly. Publishes classified listings for job opportunities in the arts, especially theatre, dance, music, and educational institutions. Listings include opportunities in administration, artistic, education, production, and career development.

★7538★ Country Airplay Monitor
VNU Business Media USA
770 Broadway
New York, NY 10003
Ph: (646)654-5000
URL: http://www.vnubusinessmedia.com/box/bp/div_ent_music_airm.ht

Weekly. $295.00/year for individuals. Trade publication covering the radio and music industry.

★7539★ Daily Variety
Reed Business Information
5700 Wilshire Blvd., Ste. 120
Los Angeles, CA 90036
Ph: (323)857-6600   Fax: (323)965-2475

Daily. Global entertainment newspaper (tabloid).

★7540★ The DIAPASON
Scranton Gillette Communications Inc.
380 E NW Hwy., Ste. 200
Des Plaines, IL 60016-2282
Ph: (847)298-6622   Fax: (847)390-0408

Monthly. $25.00/year for individuals; $6.00 for single issue. Magazine devoted to pipe organ building, organ and church music performance, and repertoire.

★7541★ Down Beat
Maher Publications Inc.
102 N Haven Rd.
Elmhurst, IL 60126
Ph: (630)941-2030   Fax: (630)941-3210
Fr: 800-535-7496

Monthly. $26.00/year for individuals; $2.50 for single issue. Magazine edited for the learning musician.

★7542★ Electronic Musician
Primedia Business
6400 Hollis St., Ste. 12
Emeryville, CA 94608
Ph: (510)653-3307   Fax: (510)653-5142
Fr: 800-541-7706
URL: http://www.emusician.com

Monthly. $27.95/year for individuals. Magazine on music and home or personal recording industry technology.

★7543★ IAWM Journal
International Alliance for Women in Music
Department of Music
Indiana University of Pennsylvania
422. 11th St., No. 209
Indiana, PA 15705-1070
Ph: (724)357-7918   Fax: (724)357-9570
URL: http://music.acu.edu/www/iawm/home.html

Description: Three issues/year (Feb, Jun, Oct). Concerned with women in music. Features scholarly articles, reviews, reports, announcements, press releases and member activities. Recurring features include letters to the editor, interviews, news of research, news of educational opportunities, job listings, and notices of publications available.

★7544★ International Musician
American Federation of Musicians
1501 Broadway, Ste. 600
New York, NY 10036
Ph: (212)869-1330   Fax: (212)302-4374
E-mail: info@afm.org

Monthly. Tabloid for labor union musicians.

★7545★ Journal of the AMIS
American Musical Instrument Society
126 Darlington Ave.
Ramsey, NJ 07446
Ph: (201)327-8426

Annual. Subscription included in membership. Journal covering all aspects of musical instruments.

★7546★ Music Educators Journal
MENC: The National Association for Music Education
1806 Robert Fulton Dr.
Reston, VA 20191
Ph: (703)860-4000   Fr: 800-336-3768

Bimonthly. Journal covering all levels of music education. Published on alternate months with Teaching Music.

★7547★ Music and Media
VNU Business Media USA
770 Broadway
New York, NY 10003
Ph: (646)654-5000
URL: http://www.vnubusinessmedia.com/box/bp/div_ent_music_musicm.

Weekly. $175.00/year. Publication covering the music and entertainment industries.

★7548★ The Music Paper
The Music Paper
PO Box 5167
Bay Shore, NY 11706
Fax: (516)666-7445

Monthly. Consumer magazine covering music for amateurs and professionals.

★7549★ Music Trades
Music Trades Corp.
80 W St.
Englewood, NJ 07631
Ph: (201)871-1965   Fax: (201)871-0455
Fr: 800-423-6530

Monthly. $12.00/year; $3.00 for single issue. Music trade magazine.

★7550★ Rock Airplay Monitor

VNU Business Media USA
770 Broadway
New York, NY 10003
Ph: (646)654-5000
URL: http://www.vnubusinessmedia.com/box/bp/div_ent_music_airm.ht

Weekly. $295.00/year for individuals. Trade publication covering the music and radio industries.

★7551★ SYMPHONY

American Symphony Orchestra League
33 W 60th St., 5th Fl.
New York, NY 10023-7905
Ph: (212)262-5161   Fax: (212)262-5198
E-mail: editor@symphony.org

Bimonthly. $35.00/year for individuals. Magazine with news and articles for symphony orchestra managers, trustees, conductors, volunteers, and musicians.

★7552★ Variety

Reed Business Information
5700 Wilshire Blvd., Ste. 120
Los Angeles, CA 90036
Ph: (323)857-6600   Fax: (323)965-2475

Weekly. $129.00/year. Newspaper (tabloid) reporting on theatre, television, radio, music, records, and movies.

PLACEMENT AND JOB REFERRAL SERVICES

★7553★ American Symphony Orchestra League

33 W 60th St., 5th Fl.
New York, NY 10023
Ph: (212)262-5161   Fax: (212)262-5198
E-mail: league@symphony.org
URL: http://www.symphony.org

Members: Symphony orchestras; associate members include educational institutions, arts councils, public libraries, business firms, orchestra professionals, and individuals interested in symphony orchestras. **Purpose:** Engages in extensive research on diverse facets of symphony orchestra operations and development. Provides consulting services for orchestras, their boards, and volunteer organizations. **Activities:** Sponsors management seminars and workshops for professional symphony orchestra administrative and artistic staff, volunteers, and prospective management personnel. Maintains employment services; collects and distributes resource materials, financial data, and statistical reports on many aspects of orchestra operations. Compiles statistics; sponsors educational programs; maintains resource center.

★7554★ Association of Anglican Musicians (AAM)

28 Ashton Rd.
Fort Mitchell, KY 41017
Ph: (859)344-9308   Fax: (859)344-9308
E-mail: cr273@aol.com
URL: http://www.anglicanmusicians.org

Description: Church musicians (laypersons or clergy) serving Episcopal and Anglican churches. Seeks to promote excellence in church music by: fostering a relationship of mutual respect and trust between clergy and musicians actively encouraging and supporting composers and other artists to create works for the church; maintaining communication with and supporting the work of the Standing Commission on Liturgy and Church. Encourages equitable compensation and benefits for professional church musicians. Works closely with seminaries toward the establishment and continuation of courses in music and the allied arts as they relate to worship and theology. Maintains placement service.

★7555★ Jazz World Society (JWS)

PO Box 777
New York, NY 10108-0777
Ph: (212)253-4160   Fax: (212)253-4160
E-mail: jwd@jazzworlddatabase.com
URL: http://www.jazzsociety.com/

Description: Professionals involved in jazz, including musicians, composers, record producers, distributors, collectors, and journalists; individuals actively supporting jazz music. Promotes the development of jazz music in its various interpretations and fosters communication among jazz participants. Operates library of records, publications, books, and photographs. Organizes competitions; offers specialized education programs, seminars, and placement service. Maintains hall of fame and biographical archives.

★7556★ National Association of Pastoral Musicians (NPM)

962 Wayne Ave., Ste. 210
Silver Spring, MD 20910-4461
Ph: (240)247-3000   Fax: (240)247-3001
E-mail: npmsing@npm.org
URL: http://www.npm.org

Description: Parish clergy, parish musicians, music teachers, and others engaged or interested in Catholic church music. Goal is to improve music in an ordinary parish situation. Reviews current music; assists in parish music celebrations. Conducts research and specialized education programs. Maintains speakers' bureau and placement service.

★7557★ National Traditional Country Music Association (NTCMA)

PO Box 492
Anita, IA 50020
Ph: (712)762-4363
E-mail: bobeverhart@yahoo.com
URL: http://www.oldtimemusic.bigstep.com/

Description: Individuals interested in the preservation, presentation, and perpetuation of traditional acoustic country, folk, honky-tonk, ragtime, mountain, and bluegrass music celebrating contributions of U.S. settlers and pioneers; country music associations. Supports what the association views as related, traditional values. Holds jam sessions; sponsors booths and offers hands-on music and craft experiences; operates charitable program; offers children's services; maintains placement service. Sponsors championship contests in numerous categories, including: Great Plains Story Telling; Hank Williams Songwriting; International Country Singer; Jimmie Rodgers Yodeling; National Bluegrass Band; National Harmonica Playing. Programs are taped and televised by various local, national, and international stations. Established the "Old-Time Music Hour" radio program at the Walnut Country Opera House, Pioneer Music Museum, America Old-Time Fiddlers Hall of Fame, and America Country Music Hall of Fame.

★7558★ Presbyterian Association of Musicians (PAM)

100 Witherspoon St.
Louisville, KY 40202-1396
Ph: (502)569-5288   Fax: (502)569-8465
Fr: 888-728-7228
E-mail: abarthel@ctr.pcusa.org
URL: http://www.pam.pcusa.org

Description: Organists, choir directors, singers, churches, clergy, directors of Christian education, and interested persons of all denominations. Objective is to develop use of music and the arts in the life and worship of individual congregations. Offers assistance in the areas of worship, music, and the arts. Conducts continuing education. Acts as a clearinghouse for job referrals; promotes the professional status of church musicians and recommends salaries and benefits to churches; certifies church musicians.

★7559★ Texas International Theatrical Arts Society (TITAS)

3101 N Fitzhugh, Ste. 301
Dallas, TX 75204
Ph: (214)528-6112   Fax: (214)528-2617
E-mail: csantos@titas.org
URL: http://www.titas.org

Description: Theatrical agencies working to book entertainers and international acts into all live music venues. Provides placement service; conducts educational seminars.

EMPLOYER DIRECTORIES AND NETWORKING LISTS

★7560★ AMG's All Music Guide

All Media Guide
301 E Liberty, Ste. 400
Ann Arbor, MI 48104
Ph: (734)887-5600   Fax: (734)827-2492

Database covers: Information on musical artists. Entries include: Birth year, biography, list of recordings, genre, years in the business, instruments played, tone, labels, and where to buy sheet music.

★7561★ Chamber Music America-Membership Directory

Chamber Music America
305 7th Ave., 5th Fl.
New York, NY 10001
Ph: (212)242-2022   Fax: (212)242-7955

Annual, in the September/October issue of Chamber Music Magazine. $65.00. Covers over 800 member ensembles, presenters, festivals, and training programs; over 4,000 associate members, including managers, publishers, arts organizations, instrument manufacturers, libraries and individuals. Entries include: For members-Name, address, phone, name of contact, activities, awards, year established. For associates-Name, address, phone. Arrangement: Separate geographical sections for ensembles, presenters, festivals and training programs; associate members are classified by type of organization, then alphabetical. Indexes: General, subject.

★7562★ Chicago Creative Directory

Chicago Creative Directory
333 N Michigan, Ste. 810
Chicago, IL 60601
Ph: (312)236-7337   Fax: (312)236-6078
URL: http://www.creativedir.com

Annual, March. $50.00. Covers over 6,000 advertising agencies, photographers, sound studios, talent agencies, audiovisual services, and others offering creative and production services. Entries include: For most listings-Company name, address, phone, list of officers, description of services. For freelance listings-Name, talent, address, phone. Arrangement: Classified by specialty.

★7563★ Directory of Festivals and Workshops

Chamber Music America
305 7th Ave., 5th Fl.
New York, NY 10001
Ph: (212)242-2022   Fax: (212)242-7955
URL: http://www.chamber-music.org/summerdir/summerdir1.asp

Annual, in the March/April issue of Chamber Music Magazine. $3.95. Covers over 150 chamber music workshops and schools for students, young professionals, and adult amateurs; international listings. Entries include: Name, location or address, description of program and participants sought, procedure for auditions, type of accommodations and recreational facilities, dates, age requirements, and fees as of spring 2000. Arrangement: Geographical. Indexes: Alphabetical by state, alphabetical by program.

★7564★ Employment Opportunities, USA

Washington Research Associates
1090 Vermont Ave., NW, Ste. 800
Washington, DC 20005
Ph: (202)408-7025

Annual, quarterly updates. $184.00. Publication includes: List of over 1,000 employment contacts in companies and agencies in the banking, arts, telecommunications, education, and 14 other industries and professions, including the federal government. Entries include: Company name, name of representative, address, description of products or services, hiring and recruiting practices, training programs, and year established. Principal content is industry overviews, career news, employment opportunity information on 14 different job markets, and comprehensive guidance to career resources on the Internet. Arrangement: Classified by industry. Indexes: Occupation.

★7565★ GMA'S Online Christian Music Networking Guide

Gospel Music Association
1205 Division St.
Nashville, TN 37203
Ph: (615)242-0303   Fax: (615)254-9755
E-mail: info@gospelmusic.org
URL: http://www.gospelmusic.org

Continuous, January. $39.95 for nonmembers; $19.95 for members. Covers gospel musicians, composers, and artists; recording companies, studios, and production companies; booking agencies; publishers; performing rights organizations; television and radio broadcasting stations; book stores, Bible supply stores, and other retailers/managers; publications; ministry organizations, artist managers, industry related services, christian clubs, concert promoters, distributors. Entries include: Name, contact address, phone, fax, E-mail. Broadcasting station listings include contact, program title, format. Arrangement: Search engine is flexible.

★7566★ Instrumentalist-Directory of Summer Music Camps, Clinics, and Workshops Issue

Instrumentalist Co.
200 Northfield Rd.
Northfield, IL 60093
Ph: 888-446-6888   Fax: (847)446-6263

Annual, March. $2.50. Publication includes: List of nearly 250 summer music camps, clinics, and workshops in the United States; limited Canadian and foreign coverage. Entries include: Camp name, location, name of director, opening and closing dates, tuition fees, courses offered. Arrangement: Geographical.

★7567★ Musical America International Directory of the Performing Arts

Commonwealth Business Media
400 Windsor Corporate Park
50 Millstone Rd., Ste. 200
East Windsor, NJ 08520-1415
Ph: (609)371-7700   Fax: (609)371-7883
Fr: 800-221-5488
E-mail: info@musicalamerican.com
URL: http://www.musicalamerica.com

Annual, December. $115.00. Covers U.S., Canadian, and international orchestras, musicians, singers, performing arts series, dance and opera companies, festivals, contests, foundations and awards, publishers of music, artist managers, booking agents, music magazines, and service and professional music organizations. Section for U.S. and Canada also includes listings of choral groups, music schools and departments, and newspaper music critics; international directory section also lists concert managers. Entries include: Name of organization, institution, address, phone, fax, URL, e-mail addressess, key personnel; most entries include name of contact, manager, conductor, etc. For schools-Number of students and faculty. For orchestras-Number of concerts and seats. Other entries show similar details as appropriate. Arrangement: Geographical. Indexes: Alphabetical and by category.

★7568★ National Directory of Arts Internships

National Network for Artist Placement
935 W. Ave. 37
Los Angeles, CA 90065
Ph: (323)222-4035   Fax: (323)225-5711
URL: http://www.artistplacement.com/intern.htm

Biennial, odd years. $85.00. Covers over 5,000 internship opportunities in dance, music, theater, art, design, film, and video & over 1,250 host organizations Entries include: Name of sponsoring organization, address, name of contact; description of positions available, eligibility requirements, stipend or salary (if any), application procedures. Arrangement: Classified by discipline, then geographical.

★7569★ The R & R Directory

Radio and Records Inc.
10100 Santa Monica Blvd., 3rd Fl.
Los Angeles, CA 90067-4004
Ph: (310)553-4330   Fax: (310)203-8727
E-mail: moreinfo@rronline.com
URL: http://www.radioandrecords.com

Semiannual, Spring and Fall. $75.00. Covers more than 3,000 radio group owners, equipment manufacturers, jingle producers, TV production houses and spot producers, record companies, representative firms, research companies, consulting firms, media brokers, networks, program suppliers, trade associations, and other organizations involved in the radio and record industry. Entries include: Organization name, address, phone, fax, E-mail, name and title of contacts, branch offices or subsidiary names and locations. Arrangement: Alphabetical; classified by subject. Indexes: Company.

★7570★ Regional Theater Directory

American Theatre Works Inc.
PO Box 510
Dorset, VT 05251
Ph: (802)867-2223   Fax: (802)867-0144
URL: http://www.theatredirectories.com

Annual, May. $20.95. Covers regional theater companies and dinner theatres with employment opportunities in acting, design, production, and management. Entries include: Company name, address, phone, name and title of contact; type of company, activities, and size of house; whether union affiliated, whether nonprofit or commercial; year established; hiring procedure and number of positions hired annually, season; description of stage; internships, description of artistic policy and audience. Arrangement: Geographical. Indexes: Company name, type of plays produced.

★7571★ *Songwriter's Market*

Writer's Digest Books
4700 E Galbraith Rd.
Cincinnati, OH 45236
Ph: (513)531-2690   Fr: 800-289-0963
E-mail: songmarket@fwpubs.com

Annual, September. $23.99. Covers 2,000 music publishers, jingle writers, advertising agencies, audiovisual firms, radio and television stations, booking agents, and other buyers of musical compositions and lyrics; also lists contests, competitions, and workshops. Entries include: Buyer's name and address, phone, payment rates, submission requirements, etc. Arrangement: Classified by type of market. Indexes: Geographical.

★7572★ *Summer Theater Directory*

American Theatre Works Inc.
PO Box 510
Dorset, VT 05251
Ph: (802)867-2223   Fax: (802)867-0144
URL: http://www.theatredirectories.com

Annual, December. $20.95. Covers summer theater companies, theme parks and cruise lines that offer employment opportunities in acting, design, production, and management; summer theater training programs. Entries include: Company name, address, phone, name and title of contact; type of company, activities and size of house; whether union affiliated, whether nonprofit or commercial; year established; hiring procedure and number of positions hired annually, season; description of stage; internships; description of company's artistic goals and audience. Arrangement: Geographical. Indexes: Company name.

★7573★ *Women and Music in America Since 1900: An Encyclopedia*

Oryx Press
1434 E San Miguel Ave.
Phoenix, AZ 85014-2422
Fr: 800-225-5800

$150.00. Publication includes: Women's organizations, women's subcommittees in other organizations, and groups in which women have historically been underrepresented. Principal content of publication is entries on issues and individuals highlighting women's impact on music. Arrangement: Alphabetical. Indexes: Alphabetical.

HANDBOOKS AND MANUALS

★7574★ *All You Need to Know About the Music Business*

Simon & Schuster Inc.
1230 Ave. of the Americas
New York, NY 10020
Ph: (212)698-7000   Fax: (212)698-7007
Fr: 800-897-7650

Donald S. Passman. 2000. $30.00. 448 pages.

★7575★ *Breakin' into the Music Business*

Fireside
10 Midland Ave.
PO Box 430
Port Chester, NY 10573
Ph: (914)937-8601   Fax: (914)937-9139
Fr: 800-354-4004

Alan H. Siegel. 1993. $19.95. 276 pages. Describes the record deal; the artist-manager relationship; working with copyrights, demos, and the terminology used in the industry.

★7576★ *Build and Manage Your Music Career*

artistpro.com, LLC
236 Georgia St., Suite 100
Vallejo, CA 94590
Ph: (707)554-1935   Fax: (707)554-9751

Maurice Johnson. 1999.

★7577★ *The Business of Getting More Gigs as a Professional Musician*

Hal Leonard Corporation
7777 W. Bluemound Rd.
Milwaukee, WI 53213
Ph: (414)774-3630   Fax: (414)774-3259
Fr: 800-524-4425

Bob Popyk. June 2003. $14.95. 144 pages. Music Business Series.

★7578★ *A Career Handbook for TV, Radio, Film, Video and Interactive Media*

A & C Black
37 Soho Sq.
London W1D 3QZ, United Kingdom
Ph: 020 7758 0200

Shiona Llewellyn.

★7579★ *Career Information Center*

Macmillan Publishing Co. Inc.
200 Old Tappan Rd.
Old Tappan, NJ 07675
Fr: 800-428-5331

Visual Education Center Staff. Seventh edition, 1999. $275.00. 2080 pages. This 13-volume set profiles over 600 occupations. Each occupational profile describes job duties, educational requirements, how to get the job, advancement possibilities, employ-

ment outlook, working conditions, earnings and benefits, and where to write for more information.

★7580★ *Career Opportunities in the Music Industry*

Facts on File, Inc.
132 W. 31st St., 17th Fl.
New York, NY 10001-2006
Ph: (212)967-8800   Fax: (212)967-9196
Fr: 800-322-8755
URL: http://www.factsonfile.com

Shelly Field. Fourth edition, 2000. $45.00.

★7581★ *Career Opportunities in Theater and the Performing Arts*

Facts on File, Inc.
132 W. 31st St., 17th Fl.
New York, NY 10001-2006
Ph: (212)967-8800   Fax: (212)967-9196
Fr: 800-322-8755
URL: http://www.factsonfile.com

Shelly Field. Second edition, 1999. $29.95; $18.95 (paper). 256 pages. Offers a complete range of information about job opportunities in the performing arts. Part of Career Opportunities Series.

★7582★ *Careers for Culture Lovers and Other Artsy Types*

VGM Career Horizons
1221 Avenue of the Americas
New York, NY 10020
Ph: (212)904-2000   Fr: 800-323-4900
E-mail: ntcpub@tribune.com

Marjorie Eberts and Margaret Gisler. Second edition, 1999. $14.95; $9.95 (paper). 234 pages. Describes how to get work in a variety of fields related to art and culture. Opportunities include picture framer, curator, art restorer, symphony manager, disk jockey, music reviewer, dance teacher, choreographer, costume designer, theater manager, light designer, drama teacher, bookstore owner, interior decorator, antique store owner, and others.

★7583★ *Careers for Music Lovers and Other Tuneful Types*

McGraw-Hill Contemporary Books
N T C Publishing Group
1221 Avenue of the Americas
New York, NY 10020
Ph: (212)904-2000   Fr: 800-323-4900
E-mail: ntcpub@tribune.com

Jeff Johnson. 1996. $14.95; $9.95 (paper). 160 pages. Describes hundreds of music industry jobs and careers.

★7584★ *Careers for Night Owls and Other Insomniacs*

McGraw-Hill Trade
2 Penn Plaza
New York, NY 10121
Ph: (212)904-2000   Fr: 800-722-4726
E-mail: ntcpub@tribune.com

Louise Miller. 1995. $14.95; $9.95 (paper). 160 pages.

★7585★ Careers Without College: Music

Thomson Peterson's
PO Box 67005
Lawrenceville, NJ 08648
Fr: 800-338-3282

Ted Greenwald. 1997. $7.95 (paper).

★7586★ The Essential Songwriter's Contract Handbook

Nashville Songwriters Association
  International
15 Music Sq. W
Nashville, TN 37203
Ph: (615)256-3354   Fax: (615)256-0034
Fr: 800-321-6008

Compiled by NSAI Equity Committee staff. 1994. $12.95 (paper). Examines a typical songwriter agreement point by point in layman's terms with an index for easy reference.

★7587★ The Garage Band Cookbook: How to Operate a Band for Success and Profit

Juice Gallery Multimedia
2042 Big Oak Ave.
Chino Hills, CA 91709
Ph: (909)597-0791   Fr: 800-710-0163

$34.95. Part of the VM business Series.

★7588★ Getting Radio Airplay: The Guide to Getting Your Music Played on College, Public and Commercial

Rockpress Publishing
107 Norfolk St.
New York, NY 10002
Ph: (212)473-9530   Fax: (212)473-9735

Gary Hustwit. Third edition, 1997. $19.95 (paper).

★7589★ The Gigs Handbook: A Beginner's Guide to Playing Professionally

Benny Publishing
9403 Lincolnwood Dr.
Evanston, IL 60203
Ph: (847)673-2039

Sharon Black. 2000. $18.95 (paper). "The Gigs Handbook" is for music students who want to earn money through performing, amateurs who want to play professionally, or anyone who can say gig gag giggle 10 times really fast. "The Gigs Handbook" is a beginners guide to playing professionally. The book will help readers learn how to get gigs & become professional musicians, make contacts & promote themselves, deal with problems on the job, play weddings & other special events & begin playing by ear. "The Gigs Handbook" is sure to be enjoyed by anyone interested in music as a career, bettering their musician skills, expanding

their repertoire, adding to their styles & private music teaching. Author, pianist & educator Sharon Black is a seasoned "gigger" who has taught music to all grade levels & holds a Master of Music Degree from Northwestern University. She has written & performed for WBBM & WGN television & is the author/composer of the Halloween musical "Samhain."

★7590★ Great Jobs for Music Majors

McGraw-Hill Companies
1221 Avenue of the Americas
New York, NY 10020
Ph: (212)904-2000   Fr: 800-323-4900
E-mail: ntcpub@tribune.com

Jan Goldberg, Stephen Lambert, Julie DeGalan. 1997. $11.95 (paper). 365 pages.

★7591★ How to Be Your Own Booking Agent and Save Thousands of Dollars: A Performing Artist's Guide to a Successful Touring Career

New Music Times, Inc.
PO Box 1105
Charlottesville, VA 22902-1105
Ph: (804)977-8979   Fax: (804)977-6914

Jeri Goldstein. 2000. $29.97 (paper).

★7592★ How to Make It in the New Music Business: Lessons, Tips and Inspiration from Music's Biggest and Best

Watson-Guptill Publications, Inc.
770 Broadway
New York, NY 10003
Ph: (732)363-4511   Fax: 877-227-6564

Robert Wolff. May 2004. $19.95 (paper). Illustrated. 288 pages.

★7593★ How to Make a Living as a Musician: So You Never Have to Have a Day Job Again

Sonata Publishing
1277 S. Adams St.
Glendale, CA 91205
Ph: (818)380-7155   Fax: (818)242-5551
Fr: 800-924-2200

Marty Buttwinick. 1994. $29.95 (paper). 272 pages. This book covers the day-to-day activities, truths & myths of how to actually make a living, directly answers the thousands of questions asked of the author over the past twenty-five years, & emphasizes professionalism & goal achievement.

★7594★ In Concert: The Freelance Musician's Keys to Financial Success

Preludes Nouveaux, Ltd.
1506 E. Fox. Ln.
Milwaukee, WI 53217-2853
Ph: (414)241-9711

Gail Nelson and Pamela Fourd. 1994. $16.95 (paper). 96 pages.

★7595★ The Lost Soul Companion: Comfort & Constructive Advice for Struggling Actors, Musicians, Artists, Writers & Other Free Spirits

Puckitt Press, Incorporated
P.O. Box 3248
Bloomington, IN 47402-3248
Ph: (812)331-4337

Susan M. Brackney. 2000. $10.00

★7596★ Making Money Teaching Music

Writer's Digest Books
F & W Publications, Inc.
1507 Dana Ave.
Cincinnati, OH 45207
Ph: (513)531-2690   Fax: (513)531-4082
Fr: 800-289-0963

Barbara Newsam and David Newsam. 1995. $18.99 (paper). 240 pages.

★7597★ Making Music Your Business

Backbeat Books
600 Harrison St.
San Francisco, CA 94107
Ph: (408)848-5294   Fax: (408)848-5784
Fr: (866)222-5232

David Ellefson. 1997. $14.95. 144 pages. Covers many aspects of the music business.

★7598★ Making Your Living As a String Player: Career Guidance from the Experts at Strings Magazine

Hal Leonard Corporation
7777 W. Bluemound Rd.
Milwaukee, WI 53213
Ph: (414)774-3630   Fax: (414)774-3259
Fr: 800-524-4425

Greg Cahill. January 2004. $12.95. 96 pages.

★7599★ Monsters and Angels: Surviving a Career in Music

Hal Leonard Corporation
7777 W. Bluemound Rd.
Milwaukee, WI 53213
Ph: (414)774-3630   Fax: (414)774-3259
Fr: 800-524-4425

Seymour Bernstein. March 2004. $22.95. 507 pages.

★7600★ More About This Business of Music

Watson-Guptill Publications, Inc.
770 Broadway
New York, NY 10003
Ph: (646)654-5400   Fax: (646)654-5486
Fr: 800-323-9432

M. William Krasilovsky and Sidney Shemel. Fifth edition, 1994. $18.95. 224 pages.

★7601★ Moving up in the Music Business

Allworth Press
10 E. 23rd St., Suite 510
New York, NY 10010
Ph: (212)777-8395   Fax: (212)777-8261
Fr: 800-491-2808

Jodi Summers. 2000. $18.95 (paper).

★7602★ Music Business Made Simple: A Guide to Becoming a Recording Artist

Music Sales Corporation
257 Park Ave., S., 20th Fl.
New York, NY 10010
Ph: (212)254-2100   Fax: (212)254-2103

J. Scott Rudsenke. January 2004. $14.95. Illustrated. 144 pages. Music Business Made Simpler Series.

★7603★ Music Business Primer

Prentice Hall PTR
240 Frisch Ct.
Paramus, NJ 07652-5240
Fax: 800-835-5327   Fr: 800-282-0693

Diane Sward Rapaport. September 2002. $29.95 (paper). 329 pages. Illustrated.

★7604★ The Musician's Guide to Making and Selling Your Own CDs and Cassettes

F & W Publications, Inc.
4700 Galbraith Rd.
Cincinnati, OH 45236
Ph: (513)531-2690   Fax: (513)531-4082
Fr: 800-289-0963

Jana Stanfield. 1997. $18.99 (paper).

★7605★ Opportunities in Entertainment Careers

McGraw-Hill Trade
2 Penn Plaza
New York, NY 10121
Ph: (212)904-2000   Fr: 800-722-4726
E-mail: ntcpub@tribune.com

Jan Goldberg. 1999. $14.95; $11.95 (paper). 160 pages.

★7606★ Opportunities in Music Careers

McGraw-Hill Professional
2 Penn Plaza
New York, NY 10121
Ph: (212)904-2000   Fr: 800-722-4726

Robert Gerardi. Fourth edition, revised, 2002. $15.95; $11.95 (paper). 160 pages. Describes the job market and where to find work. Covers careers in performing, writing, musical directing, management, and technical areas. Illustrated.

★7607★ Resumes for Performing Arts Careers

Vgm Career Horizons
1221 Avenue of the Americas
New York, NY 10020
Ph: (212)904-2000   Fr: 800-323-4900
E-mail: ntcpub@tribune.com

1997. $9.95 (paper). 462 pages.

★7608★ The Rock Band Handbook: Everything You Need to Know to Get a Band Together and Take It on the Road

Berkley Publishing Group
375 Hudson St.
New York, NY 10014
Ph: (212)366-2000   Fax: (212)366-2385
Fr: 800-788-6262

Kathryn Lineberger. 1996. $10.00 (paper).

★7609★ Ruthless Self-Promotion in the Music Industry

artistpro.com, LLC
236 Georgia St., Suite 100
Vallejo, CA 94590
Ph: (707)554-1935   Fax: (707)554-9751

Jeffrey P. Fisher. 1999.

★7610★ Secrets of Negotiating a Record Contract: The Musician's Guide to Understanding & Avoiding Sneaky Lawyer Tricks

Backbeat Books
600 Harrison St.
San Francisco, CA 94107
Ph: (408)848-5294   Fax: (408)848-5784
Fr: (866)222-5232

Moses Avalon. 2001. $19.95 (paper).

★7611★ Songwriting Success: How to Write Songs for Fun and (Maybe) Profit

Routledge
29 W. 35th St.
New York, NY 10001-2299
Ph: (212)216-7800   Fax: (212)564-7845
Fr: 800-634-7064

Michael Lydon. May 2004. $19.95 (paper). Illustrated. 208 pages.

★7612★ Stage Writers Handbook: A Complete Business Guide for Playwrights, Composers, Lyricists, and Librettists

Theatre Communications Group
520 Eighth Ave., 24th Fl.
New York, NY 10018-4156
Ph: (212)609-5900   Fax: (212)609-5901

Dana Singer. 1996. $18.95 (paper). 192 pages.

★7613★ Star Tracks: Principles for Success in the Music and Entertainment Business

Thumbs Up Publishing
1700 Falcon Ct.
Mount Juliet, TN 37122-7425
Ph: (615)269-7412

Larry E. Wacholtz. 1996. $21.95 (paper). Discusses copyright law, music publishing, songwriting, record labels, recording studios, studio musicians, recording artists, audio engineers, record producers, marketing, radio promotion, artist management, concert promotion, distribution, budgets, and music business economics.

★7614★ This Business of Music Marketing and Promotion

Watson-Guptill Publications, Incorporated
770 Broadway
New York, NY 10003
Ph: (646)654-5400   Fax: (646)654-5486
Fr: 800-323-9432

Tad Lathrop and Jim Pettigrew, Jr. 1999. $21.95.

★7615★ What's up Dawg: How to Become a Superstar in the Music Business

Hyperion Press
77 W. 66th St., 11th Fl.
New York, NY 10023-6298
Ph: (212)456-0100   Fax: (212)456-0108
Fr: 800-759-0190

Randy Jackson. January 2004. $14.70 (paper). 288 pages.

TRADESHOWS

★7616★ American Harp Society National Conference

American Harp Society
1900 S. Broadway
Denver, CO 80210
Ph: (303)722-6081   Fax: (303)722-3996
E-mail: kmc1930@aol.com
URL: http://www.harpsociety.org

Annual. **Primary Exhibits:** Harps and related materials.

★7617★ American Orff-Schulwerk Association National Conference

American Orff-Schulwerk Association Inc.
PO Box 391089
Cleveland, OH 44139-8089
Ph: (440)543-5366   Fax: (440)543-2687
E-mail: info@aosa.org
URL: http://www.aosa.org

Annual. **Primary Exhibits:** Music, music books, instruments. pitched and unpitched percussion, early music instruments, records and music gifts, computer music software. **Dates and Locations:** 2004 Nov 10-14; Long Beach, CA; Convention Center • 2005

Nov 9-13; Birmingham, AL; Sheraton & Convention Center • 2006 Nov 8-12; Omaha, NE; Convention Center.

★7618★ The Midwest Clinic An International Band and Orchestra Conference

The Midwest Clinic
828 Davis St., Ste. 100
Evanston, IL 60201
Ph: (847)474-4163   Fax: (847)424-5185
E-mail: info@midwestclinic.org
URL: http://www.midwestclinic.org

Annual. **Primary Exhibits:** Music instruments and publications, supplies, and services, universities, military org., fund raisers, music publishers. **Dates and Locations:** 2004 Dec 15-19; Chicago, IL; Hilton Chicago.

★7619★ National Association of Pastoral Musicians National Convention

National Association of Pastoral Musicians
225 Sheridan St. NW
Washington, DC 20011
Ph: (202)723-5800   Fax: (202)723-2262
E-mail: npmsing@npm.org
URL: http://npm.org

Annual. **Primary Exhibits:** Music, musical instruments, books, church furnishings and art.

★7620★ National Opera Association Conference

National Opera Association
c/o Robert Hansen
PO Box 60869
Canyon, TX 79016-0869
Ph: (806)651-2857   Fax: (806)651-2958
URL: http://www.noa.org

Annual. **Primary Exhibits:** Opera-related music, cds and equipment, supplies, and services.

★7621★ Violin Society of America Convention

Violin Society of America
c/o Edward Campbell
614 Lerew Rd.
Boiling Springs, PA 17007
Ph: (717)258-3203   Fax: (717)258-3201
E-mail: edwardcampbell@sprintmail.com

Annual. **Primary Exhibits:** Violins, violas, cellos, and their bows, strings, and other accessories; books; tone and bow woods.

★7622★ Western Division Choral Directors Association Convention

American Choral Directors Association
PO Box 6310
Lawton, OK 73506
Ph: (580)355-8161   Fax: (580)248-1465
E-mail: acda@acdaonline.org
URL: http://www.acdaonline.org

Biennial. **Primary Exhibits:** Exhibits of interest to choral directors.

OTHER SOURCES

★7623★ American Almanac of Jobs and Salaries

Morrow Avon
1350 Avenue of the Americas
New York, NY 10019
Ph: (212)261-6788   Fr: 800-242-7737

John W. Wright. Revised edition, 2000. $20.00 (paper). 672 pages. This is a comprehensive guide to the wages of hundreds of occupations in a wide variety of industries and organizations.

★7624★ American Federation of Musicians of the United States and Canada (AFM)

1501 Broadway, Ste. 600
New York, NY 10036
Ph: (212)869-1330   Fax: (212)764-6134
E-mail: info@afm.org
URL: http://www.afm.org

Description: Union representing the interests of professional musicians through collective bargaining, bebefits, and services.

★7625★ American Guild of Musical Artists (AGMA)

1430 Broadway, 14th Fl.
New York, NY 10018
Ph: (212)265-3687   Fax: (212)262-9088
E-mail: agma@musicalartists.org
URL: http://www.musicalartists.org

Description: AFL-CIO. Opera and classical concert singers, classical ballet and modern dance performers, and affiliated stage directors, stage managers and choreographers.

★7626★ American Guild of Organists (AGO)

475 Riverside Dr., Ste. 1260
New York, NY 10115
Ph: (212)870-2310   Fax: (212)870-2163
Fr: 800-AGO-5115
E-mail: info@agohq.org
URL: http://www.agohq.org

Purpose: Educational and service organization organized to advance the cause of organ and choral music and to maintain standards of artistic excellence of organists and choral conductors. **Activities:** Offers professional certification in organ playing, choral and instrumental training, and theory and general knowledge of music.

★7627★ Band Director

Cambridge Educational
2572 Brunswick Ave.
Lawrenceville, NJ 08648-4128
Fax: 800-FAX-ON-US   Fr: 800-468-4227
URL: http://www.cambridgeeducational.com

$39.95. 15 minutes. Part of the Vocational Visions Career series.

★7628★ Country Music Showcase International (CMSI)

PO Box 368
Carlisle, IA 50047
Ph: (515)989-3748   Fax: (515)989-0235
E-mail: haroldl@cmshowcase.org
URL: http://www.cmshowcase.org

Purpose: Helps songwriters and entertainers learn more about songwriting and the general music industry. **Activities:** Sponsors Song Evaluation and Critiques Service, songwriting seminars and workshops and songwriter showcases. Also operates a BMI Music Publishing Company for the benefit of members whose songs qualify for publishing. Also configures specially made computers for songwriters, musicians, and entertainers to use.

★7629★ Media and the Arts Occupations

Delphi Productions
3160 4th St.
Boulder, CO 80304
Fax: (303)443-4022   Fr: 888-443-2400
URL: http://www.delphivideo.com

$95.00. 50 minutes. Part of the Careers for the 21st Century Video Library.

★7630★ MENC: The National Association for Music Education (MENC)

1806 Robert Fulton Dr.
Reston, VA 20191
Ph: (703)860-4000   Fax: (703)860-1531
Fr: 800-336-3768
URL: http://www.menc.org

Description: Professional organization of music educators, administrators, supervisors, consultants, and music education majors in colleges. Publishes materials for music educators, presents conferences, compiles statistics.

★7631★ Music Teachers National Association (MTNA)

441 Vine St., Ste. 505
Cincinnati, OH 45202-2811
Ph: (513)421-1420   Fax: (513)421-2503
Fr: 888-512-5278
E-mail: mtnanet@mtna.org
URL: http://www.mtna.org

Description: Professional society of independent and collegiate music teachers committed to furthering the art of music through programs that encourage and support teaching, performance, composition, and scholarly research.

★7632★ Nashville Music Consultants Inc.

10840 Chapman Hwy.
Seymour, TN 37865
Ph: (865)577-5597   Fax: (865)259-0199

Consults aspiring country music singers and songwriters by listening to their works prior to submission to record labels and publishing companies. Singers and songwriters who the firm feels are not ready will be given the opportunity to resubmit material after six months at no additional charge.

★7633★ **National Association of Teachers of Singing (NATS)**
4745 Sutton Park Ct., Ste. 201
Jacksonville, FL 32224-0249
Ph: (904)992-9101   Fax: (904)992-9236
E-mail: info@nats.org
URL: http://www.nats.org

Description: Professional society of teachers of singing. Encourages the highest standards of the vocal art and of ethical principles in the teaching of singing. Promotes vocal education and research at all levels, both for the enrichment of the general public and for the professional advancement of the talented.

★7634★ **Organization of American Kodaly Educators (OAKE)**
1612 29th Ave. S
Moorhead, MN 56560
Ph: (218)227-6253   Fax: (218)277-6254
E-mail: oakeoffice@nbinternet.com
URL: http://www.oake.org

Description: Music educators, students, organizations, schools, and libraries interested in the Kodaly concept of music education. Zoltan Kodaly (1882-1967), Hungarian composer and educator, originated a concept of music education that seeks to develop the sensibilities, intellectual facilities, and skills of children, with the intention of creating a musically educated public. Objectives are: to encourage communication and cooperation among Kodaly educators; to encourage musical and human growth; to provide a forum for comment on the impact of the Kodaly concept; to recognize, identify, and convey the multicultural musical heritage of American society; to contribute to and encourage the aesthetic education of the child. Conducts clinics and other small unit activities.

★7635★ **Professional Women Singers Association (PWSA)**
PO Box 884, Planetarium Sta.
New York, NY 10024
Ph: (212)969-0590   Fax: (928)395-2560
E-mail: info@womensingers.org
URL: http://www.womensingers.org

Members: Professional women singers. **Purpose:** Promotes career advancement of women singers. **Activities:** Serves as a network for singers looking for career support.

Nuclear Engineers

SOURCES OF HELP-WANTED ADS

★7636★ AWIS Magazine
Association for Women in Science
1200 New York Ave. NW, Ste. 650
Washington, DC 20005
Ph: (202)326-8940   Fax: (202)326-8960
Fr: 800-886-AWIS

Description: Bimonthly. Covers issues, legislation, and trends related to science education for girls, women, and minorities. Includes information on grants and fellowships, job openings, educational programs, events, and notices of publications available.

★7637★ Energy User News
BNP Media, Inc.
2401 W Big Beaver Rd., Ste. 700
Troy, MI 48084
Ph: (248)362-3700   Fax: (248)362-0317
URL: http://www.energyusernews.com

Monthly. Magazine exreporting on the energy management market as it relates to commercial, industrial, and institutional facilites.

★7638★ Engineering Economist
Institute of Industrial Engineers
3577 Pkwy. Ln., Ste. 200
Norcross, GA 30092
Ph: (770)449-0461   Fax: (770)263-8532
Fr: 800-494-0460

Quarterly. Publication covering business issues in the energy, petroleum and mining industries.

★7639★ Engineering Times
National Society of Professional
  Engineers
1420 King St.
Alexandria, VA 22314
Ph: (703)684-2875   Fax: (703)836-4875
E-mail: et@nspe.org
URL: http://http//:www.nspc.org/1et.asp

$30.00/year for individuals; $48.00/year for out of country. Magazine (tabloid) covering professional, legislative, and techology issues for an engineering audience.

★7640★ ENR: Engineering News-Record
McGraw-Hill Companies
1221 Avenue of the Americas
New York, NY 10020
Ph: (212)512-2000
URL: http://www.enr.com

Weekly. $74.00/year; $5.00 for single issue. Magazine focusing on engineering and construction.

★7641★ Graduating Engineer & Computer Careers
Career Recruitment Media
211 W. Wacker Dr., No. 900
Chicago, IL 60606
Ph: (312)525-3100
URL: http://www.graduatingengineer.com

$16.00/year for individuals. Magazine focusing on employment, education, and career development for entry-level engineers and computer scientists.

★7642★ High Technology Careers Magazine
HTC
4701 Patrick Henry Dr., No. 1901
Santa Clara, CA 95054-1847
Ph: (408)970-8800   Fax: (408)567-0242
URL: http://www.hightechcareers.com

Bimonthly. $29.00/year; $35.00/year for Canada; $85.00/year for out of country. Magazine (tabloid) containing employment opportunity information for the engineering and technical community.

★7643★ National Engineer
National Association of Power Engineers
One Springfield St.
Chicopee, MA 01013-2624
Ph: (413)592-6273   Fax: (413)592-1998

Bimonthly. $25.00/year for individuals; $3.00 for single issue.

★7644★ NSBE Magazine
NSBE Publications
1454 Duke St.
Alexandria, VA 22314
Ph: (703)549-2207   Fax: (703)683-5312

$10.00/year for individuals; $2.00 for single issue. Journal providing information on engineering careers, self-development, and cultural issues for recent graduates with technical majors.

★7645★ Nuclear Plant Journal
Nuclear Plant Journal
799 Roosevelt Rd., Bldg. 6, Ste. 208
Glen Ellyn, IL 60137
Ph: (630)858-6161   Fax: (630)858-8787
E-mail: npj@goinfo.com
URL: http://www.NPJOnline.com

$130.00/year for individuals; $165.00/year for other countries; $25.00 for single issue. Magazine focusing on nuclear power plants.

★7646★ Power
McGraw-Hill Companies
1221 Avenue of the Americas
New York, NY 10020
Ph: (212)512-2000

Monthly. $19.00/year; $5.00 for single issue. Magazine for engineers in electric utilities, process and manufacturing plants, commercial and service establishments, and consulting, design, and construction engineering firms working in the power technology field.

★7647★ Power Engineering
PennWell Corp.
1421 S Sheridan Rd.
Tulsa, OK 74112
Ph: (918)835-3161   Fax: (918)832-9201
Fr: 800-331-4463
E-mail: pe@pennwell.com
URL: http://www.power-eng.com

Monthly. $74.00/year for individuals. Magazine focusing on power generation.

★7648★ SWE

Society of Women Engineers
230 E Ohio St., No. 400
2135 Lamberton Rd.
Chicago, IL 60611-3265
Ph: (312)596-5223   Fax: (312)596-5252
E-mail: hq@swe.org
URL: http://www.swe.org

Bimonthly. $30.00/year for nonmembers. Magazine for engineering students and for women and men working in the engineering and technology fields. Covers career guidance, continuing development and topical issues.

★7649★ Technology Review

Technology Review
201 Vassar St.
Cambridge, MA 02139
Ph: (617)253-8250   Fax: (617)258-5850
E-mail: trcomments@mit.edu

$30.00/year for individuals; $42.00/year for other countries; $4.95/year for single issue. Magazine reviewing new developments in technology with an emphasis on economic, political, and social implications. Not a new product publication.

★7650★ Weapons Complex Monitor

Exchange/Monitor Publications
1725 K St. NW, Ste. 1203
Washington, DC 20006
Ph: (202)296-2814   Fax: (202)296-2805
Fr: 800-776-1314
URL: http://www.exchangemonitor.com

Description: Weekly. Devoted exclusively to providing intelligence and inside information on the largest environmental program in the world. Includes special bi-weekly report Post-Soviet States & Eastern Europe Monitor, which covers radioactive waste management and nuclear facilities cleanup in Russia and the post-Soviet States.

★7651★ WEPANEWS

Women in Engineering Programs & Advocates Network
Castle Point on the Hudson
Hoboken, NJ 07030
Ph: (201)216-5245   Fax: (201)216-5175
URL: http://www.wepan.org/newsletter.html

Description: Two issues/year. Seeks to provide greater access for women to careers in engineering. Includes news of graduate, undergraduate, freshmen, pre-college, and re-entry engineering programs for women. Recurring features include job listings, faculty, grant, and conference news, international engineering program news, action group news, notices of publications available, and a column titled Kudos.

PLACEMENT AND JOB REFERRAL SERVICES

★7652★ American Indian Science and Engineering Society (AISES)

PO Box 9828
Albuquerque, NM 87119-9828
Ph: (505)765-1052   Fax: (505)765-5608
E-mail: info@aises.org
URL: http://www.aises.org

Description: American Indian and non-Indian students and professionals in science, technology, and engineering fields; corporations representing energy, mining, aerospace, electronic, and computer fields. Seeks to motivate and encourage students to pursue undergraduate and graduate studies in science, engineering, and technology. Sponsors science fairs in grade schools, teacher training workshops, summer math/science sessions for 8th-12th graders, professional chapters, and student chapters in colleges. Offers scholarships. Adult members serve as role models, advisers, and mentors for students. Operates placement service.

★7653★ Engineering Society of Detroit (ESD)

26100 American Dr., Ste. 500
Southfield, MI 48034-6184
Ph: (248)355-2910   Fax: (248)355-1492
E-mail: esd@esd.org
URL: http://esd.org

Description: Engineers from all disciplines; scientists and technologists. Conducts technical programs and engineering refresher courses; sponsors conferences and expositions. Maintains speakers' bureau; offers placement services. Although based in Detroit, MI, society membership is international.

★7654★ Korean Scientists and Engineers Association in America (KSEA)

1952 Gallows Rd., Ste. 300
Vienna, VA 22182
Ph: (703)748-1221   Fax: (703)748-1331
E-mail: sejong@ksea.org
URL: http://www.ksea.org

Description: Scientists and engineers holding single or advanced degrees. Goals are to: promote friendship and mutuality among Korean and American scientists and engineers; contribute to Korea's scientific, technological, industrial, and economic developments; strengthen the scientific, technological, and cultural bonds between Korea and the U.S. Sponsors symposium. Maintains speakers' bureau, placement service, and biographical archives. Compiles statistics. Maintains 100 volume library of scientific handbooks and yearbooks in Korean.

★7655★ Society of Hispanic Professional Engineers (SHPE)

5400 E Olympic Blvd., Ste. 210
Los Angeles, CA 90022
Ph: (323)725-3970   Fax: (323)725-0316

E-mail: shpenational@shpe.org
URL: http://www.shpe.org

Description: Engineers, student engineers, and scientists seeking to increase the number of Hispanic engineers by providing motivation and support to students. Sponsors competitions and educational programs. Maintains placement service and speakers' bureau; compiles statistics.

EMPLOYER DIRECTORIES AND NETWORKING LISTS

★7656★ American Men and Women of Science

Thomson Gale
27500 Drake Rd.
Farmington Hills, MI 48331-3535
Ph: (248)699-4253   Fax: (248)699-8065
Fr: 800-877-GALE
E-mail: amws@galegroup.com

Biennial, latest edition December 2002. $975.00. Covers over 129,700 U.S. and Canadian scientists active in the physical, biological, mathematical, computer science, and engineering fields; includes references to previous edition for deceased scientists and nonrespondents. Entries include: Name, address, education, personal and career data, memberships, honors and awards, research interest. Arrangement: Alphabetical. Indexes: Discipline (in separate volume).

★7657★ Careers in Focus: Engineering

Ferguson Publishing Co.
200 W Jackson Blvd.
Chicago, IL 60606
Ph: (312)692-0109

2nd edition, 2002. $22.95. Publication includes: List of resources to consult for more information. Principal content of publication is job descriptions, advancement opportunities, educational requirements, employment outlook, salary information, and working conditions for careers in the field of engineering. Indexes: Alphabetical.

★7658★ Directory of Contract Staffing Firms

C.E. Publications Inc.
PO Box 3006
Bothell, WA 98041-3006
Ph: (425)806-5200   Fax: (425)806-5585
URL: http://www.cjhunter.com/dcsf/overview.html

$15.00. Covers nearly 1,300 contract firms actively engaged in the employment of engineering, IT/IS, and technical personnel for 'temporary' contract assignments throughout the world. Entries include: Company name, address, phone, name of contact, email, web address. Arrangement: Alphabetical. Indexes: Geographical.

★7659★ Indiana Society of Professional Engineers-Directory

Indiana Society of Professional Engineers
PO Box 20806
Indianapolis, IN 46220
Ph: (317)255-2267   Fax: (317)255-2530

Annual, fall. $55.00. Covers member registered engineers, land surveyors, engineering students, and engineers in training. Entries include: Member name, address, phone, type of membership, business information, specialty. Arrangement: Alpha by chapter area.

★7660★ International Directory of Engineering Societies and Related Organizations

American Association of Engineering Societies
1828 L St. NW, Ste. 906
Washington, DC 20036
Ph: (202)296-2237   Fax: (202)296-1151
Fr: 888-400-AAES

Irregular, latest edition December 1998. $240.00. Covers about 1,370 national, regional, Canadian, and international organizations concerned with engineering and related fields. Entries include: Name, address, phone, fax, e-mail, key personnel, objectives, publications, activities, mailing lists, federation memberships, meeting and convention dates, and budget data. Arrangement: Alphabetical. Indexes: Acronym, geographical, area of specialization.

★7661★ Peterson's Job Opportunities in Engineering and Technology

Thomson Peterson's
PO Box 67005
Lawrenceville, NJ 08648-6105
Fr: 800-338-3282

Compiled by the Peterson's staff. Fourth edition, 1996. $21.95 (paper). 384 pages. Profiles 2,000 high-tech companies looking primarily for technical personnel in such fields as biotechnology, telecommunications, software, computers and peripherals, defense, and aerospace. Contains job-search strategies and career options to help match education and expertise to the job market. Indexed geographically, by industry, and by hiring needs.

HANDBOOKS AND MANUALS

★7662★ The Best Resumes for Scientists and Engineers

John Wiley & Sons Inc.
1 Wiley Dr.
Somerset, NJ 08873
Ph: (732)469-4400   Fr: 800-225-5945

Adele Lewis and David J. Moore. Second edition, 1993. $37.50; $19.95 (paper). 224 pages. Presents an extensive collection of scientific and engineering resumes, highlighting the important differences between these and resumes written for other occupations.

★7663★ Engineering Your Job Search: A Job-Finding Resource for Engineering Professionals

Professional Publications, Inc.
1250 5th Ave.
Belmont, CA 94002
Ph: (650)593-9119   Fax: (650)592-4519
Fr: 800-426-1178

Compiled by Professional Publications, editors. 1995. $24.95 (paper). 154 pages. Out of print.

★7664★ Great Jobs for Engineering Majors

McGraw-Hill Professional
McGraw-Hill Higher Education
2 Penn Plaza
New York, NY 10121
Ph: (212)904-2000   Fr: 800-722-4726
E-mail: ntcpub@tribune.com

Geraldine O. Garner. Second edition, 2002. $14.95. 256 pages. Covers all the career options open to students majoring in engineering.

★7665★ How to Succeed as an Engineer: A Practical Guide to Enhance Your Career

Institute of Electrical & Electronics Engineers Inc.
PO Box 87204
Vancouver, WA 98687
Ph: (360)253-9532   Fax: (360)253-4084

Todd Yuzuriha. 1999. $29.95 (paper). 367 pages.

★7666★ The I Hate Selling Book: Business-Building Advice for Consultants, Attorneys, Accountants, Engineers, Architects, and Other Professionals

Allan Boress & Associates
1500 University Dr., Suite 239
Coral Springs, FL 33071
Ph: (954)345-4666   Fax: (954)344-2453

Allan S. Boress. 2001. $29.95.

★7667★ Keys to Engineering Success

Prentice Hall PTR
One Lake St.
Upper Saddle River, NJ 07458
Ph: (201)236-7000

Jill S. Tietjen, Kristy A. Schloss, Carol Carter, Joyce Bishop, and Sarah Lyman. 2000. $32.00 (paper).

★7668★ Majoring in Engineering: How to Get from Your Freshman Year to Your First Job

Farrar, Straus & Giroux, Inc.
19 Union Sq., W
New York, NY 10003
Ph: (212)741-6900   Fax: (212)633-9385
Fr: 888-330-8477

John Garcia and Carol Carter, editors. 2000. $20.00; $10.00 (paper). 134 pages.

★7669★ The New Engineer's Guide to Career Growth & Professional Awareness

Institute of Electrical & Electronics Engineers Inc.
445 Hoes Ln.
PO Box 1331
Piscataway, NJ 08855-1331
Ph: (732)562-3967   Fax: (732)981-9334
Fr: 800-678-4333

Irving J. Gabelman, editor. 1996. $39.95 (paper). 275 pages.

★7670★ Opportunities in Energy Careers

McGraw-Hill Trade
2 Penn Plaza
New York, NY 10121
Ph: (212)904-2000   Fr: 800-722-4726
E-mail: ntcpub@tribune.com

Nicholas Basta. 1995. $13.95; $10.95 (paper). 160 pages. Discusses opportunities in a variety of fields, including petroleum, nuclear, and thermal energy, and how to pursue employment. Illustrated. Out of print.

★7671★ Opportunities in Engineering Careers

McGraw-Hill Contemporary Books
1221 Avenue of the Americas
New York, NY 10020
Ph: (212)904-2000   Fr: 800-323-4900
E-mail: ntcpub@tribune.com

Nicholas Basta. Revised, 1995. $14.95; $11.95 (paper). 200 pages. Outlines typical job titles, salaries, career paths, and employment prospects.

★7672★ Opportunities in High Tech Careers

McGraw-Hill Trade
2 Penn Plaza
New York, NY 10121
Ph: (212)904-2000   Fr: 800-722-4726

Gary Colter and Deborah Yanuck. 1995. $14.95; $11.95 (paper). 160 pages. Explores high technology careers. Describes job opportunities, how to make a career decision, how to prepare for high technology jobs, job hunting techniques, and future trends.

★7673★ Opportunities in Research and Development Careers

McGraw-Hill/Contemporary Books
1221 Avenue of the Americas
New York, NY 10020
Ph: (212)904-2000   Fr: 800-323-4900
E-mail: ntcpub@tribune.com

Jan Goldberg. 1997. $14.95; $11.95 (paper). 204 pages.

★7674★ Real People Working in Engineering

McGraw-Hill Contemporary Books
1221 Avenue of the Americas
New York, NY 10020
Ph: (212)904-2000   Fr: 800-323-4900
E-mail: ntcpub@tribune.com

Blythe Camenson, Jan Goldberg. 1997. $14.95; $12.95 (paper). Interviews and profiles of working professionals capture a range of opportunities in this field.

★7675★ Resumes for Engineering Careers

McGraw-Hill Trade
2 Penn Plaza
New York, NY 10121
Ph: (212)904-2000   Fr: 800-722-4726
E-mail: ntcpub@tribune.com

2000. $10.95 (paper). 456 pages. Contains sample resumes and cover letters applicable to any engineering field.

★7676★ Resumes for Scientific and Technical Careers

McGraw-Hill Contemporary Books
1221 Avenue of the Americas
New York, NY 10020
Ph: (212)904-2000   Fr: 800-323-4900
E-mail: ntcpub@tribune.com

1999. $9.95 (paper). 450 pages. Provides resume advice for individuals interested in working in scientific and technical careers. Includes sample resumes and cover letters.

EMPLOYMENT AGENCIES AND SEARCH FIRMS

★7677★ Engineer One, Inc.

PO Box 23037
Knoxville, TN 37933
Fax: (865)691-0110
E-mail: engineerone@engineerone.com
URL: http://www.engineerone.com

Employment agency.

★7678★ International Staffing Consultants

2901 W Coast Hwy.,Ste. 200
Newport Beach, CA 92663
Ph: (949)263-5933   Fax: (949)767-5959
E-mail: iscinc@iscworld.com

URL: http://www.iscworld.com

Employment agency. Provides placement on regular or temporary basis. Affiliate office in London.

★7679★ Main Line Personnel Service, Inc.

Pagoda Blding.
100 Presidential Blvd. Ste. 200
Bala Cynwyd, PA 19004-0448
Ph: (610)667-1820   Fax: (610)668-5000
URL: http://www.mlpers.com

Employment agency.

★7680★ Search and Recruit International

4455 South Blvd.
Virginia Beach, VA 23452
Ph: (757)490-3151   Fax: (757)497-6503
E-mail: britt@searchandrecruit.com
URL: http://www.searchandrecruit.com

Employment agency. Headquartered in Virginia Beach. Other offices in Bremerton, WA; Charleston, SC; Jacksonville, FL; Memphis, TN; Pensacola, FL; Sacramento, CA; San Bernardino, CA; San Diego, CA.

★7681★ Techtronix Technical Search

PO Box 17713
Milwaukee, WI 53217-0173
Ph: (414)466-3100   Fax: (414)466-3598

Firm specializes in recruiting executives for the engineering, information systems, manufacturing, marketing, finance, and human resources industries.

★7682★ Winters Technical Staffing Services

2025 Sheppard Ave. E, Ste. 4110
Willowdale, ON, Canada M2T 1V7
Ph: (416)495-7422   Fax: (416)495-8479

Technical staffing service for permanent and contract positions in all facets of engineering. Serves government agencies, consulting engineers, and all areas of manufacturing in Canada and northeast U.S.

ONLINE JOB SOURCES AND SERVICES

★7683★ NuclearMarket.com
E-mail: info@nuclearmarket.com
URL: http://www.nuclearmarket.com

Description: Nuclear Market's Career Centre allows seekers to search a database of Nuclear Jobs in the United States, Europe and beyond. Candidates also have the option of registering their profile in database in order to receive email notification of any relevant vacancies.

★7684★ Spherion Workforce Architects
URL: http://www.spherion.com

Description: Recruitment firm specializing in accounting and finance, sales and marketing, interim executives, technology, engineering, retail and human resources.

TRADESHOWS

★7685★ American Society for Engineering Education Annual Conference and Exposition

American Society for Engineering Education
1818 N St., Ste. 600
Washington, DC 20036
Ph: (202)331-3500   Fax: (202)265-8504
URL: http://www.asee.org

Annual. **Primary Exhibits:** Publications, engineering supplies and equipment, computers, software, and research companies all products and services related to engineering education. **Dates and Locations:** 2005 Jun 12-15; Portland, OR • 2006 Jun 18-21; Chicago, IL • 2007 Jun 24-27; Honolulu, HI.

OTHER SOURCES

★7686★ American Almanac of Jobs and Salaries

Morrow Avon
1350 Avenue of the Americas
New York, NY 10019
Ph: (212)261-6788   Fr: 800-242-7737

John W. Wright. Revised edition, 2000. $20.00 (paper). 672 pages. This is a comprehensive guide to the wages of hundreds of occupations in a wide variety of industries and organizations.

★7687★ American Association of Blacks in Energy (AABE)

927 15th St. NW, Ste. 200
Washington, DC 20005
Ph: (202)371-9530   Fax: (202)371-9218
Fr: 800-466-0204
E-mail: aabe@aabe.org
URL: http://www.aabe.org

Description: Blacks in energy-related professions, including engineers, scientists, consultants, academicians, and entrepreneurs; government officials and public policymakers; interested students. Represents blacks and other minorities in matters involving energy use and research, the formulation of energy policy, the ownership of energy resources, and the development of energy technologies. Seeks to increase the knowledge, understanding, and awareness of the minority community in energy issues by serving as an energy information source for policymakers, recommending blacks and other minorities to appropriate energy officials and executives, encouraging students to pursue professional careers in the energy industry, and advocating the participation of blacks and other minorities in energy programsand policymaking activities. Updates members on key legislation and regulations being developed by the Department of Energy, the Department of Interior, the Department of Commerce, the Small Business Administration, and other federal and state agencies. Offers information on current job openings

★7688★ American Association of Engineering Societies (AAES)

1828 L St. NW, No. 906
Washington, DC 20036
Ph: (202)296-2237   Fax: (202)296-1151
Fr: 888-400-2237
E-mail: tprice@aaes.org
URL: http://www.aaes.org

Description: Coordinates the efforts of the member societies in the provision of reliable and objective information to the general public concerning issues which affect the engineering profession and the field of engineering as a whole; to collect, analyze, document, and disseminate data which will inform the general public of the relationship between engineering and the national welfare; to provide a forum for the engineering societies to exchange and discuss their views on matters of common interest; and to represent the U.S. engineering community aborad through representation in WFEO and UPADI.

★7689★ American Nuclear Society (ANS)

555 N. Kensington Ave.
La Grange Park, IL 60526
Ph: (708)352-6611   Fax: (708)352-0499
URL: http://www.ans.org

Description: Physicists, chemists, educators, mathematicians, life scientists, engineers, metallurgists, managers, and administrators with professional experience in nuclear science or nuclear engineering. Works to advance science and engineering in the nuclear industry. Disseminates information; promotes research; conducts meetings devoted to scientific and technical papers; works with government agencies, educational institutions, and other organizations dealing with nuclear issues.

★7690★ Association for International Practical Training (AIPT)

10400 Little Patuxent Pky., Ste. 250
Columbia, MD 21044-3519
Ph: (410)997-2200   Fax: (410)992-3924
E-mail: aipt@aipt.org
URL: http://www.aipt.org

Description: Providers worldwide on-the-job training programs for students and professionals seeking international career development and life-changing experiences. Arranges workplace exchanges in hundreds of professional fields, bringing employers and trainees together from around the world. Client list ranges from small farming communities to Fortune 500 companies.

★7691★ Engineering Occupations

Delphi Productions
3160 4th St.
Boulder, CO 80304
Fax: (303)443-4022   Fr: 888-443-2400
URL: http://www.delphivideo.com

$95.00. 50 minutes. Part of the Careers for the 21st Century Video Library.

★7692★ National Action Council for Minorities in Engineering (NACME)

Empire State Bldg., Ste. 2212
350 Fifth Ave.
New York, NY 10118-2299
Ph: (212)279-2626   Fax: (212)629-5178
E-mail: webmaster@nacme.org
URL: http://www.nacme.org/

Description: Leads the national effort to increase access to careers in engineering and other science-based disciplines. Supported by the nation's leading technology-intensive companies, NACME conducts research and public policy analysis, develops and operates national demonstration programs at precollege and university levels, and disseminates information through publications, conferences, and electronic media. NACME is also the nation's largest privately funded source of scholarships for minority students in engineering.

★7693★ National Society of Professional Engineers (NSPE)

1420 King St.
Alexandria, VA 22314
Ph: (703)684-2800   Fax: (703)836-4875
Fr: 888-285-6773
E-mail: custserv@nspe.org
URL: http://www.nspe.org

Description: Professional engineers and engineers-in-training in all fields registered in

accordance with the laws of states or territories of the U.S. or provinces of Canada; qualified graduate engineers, student members, and registered land surveyors. Is concerned with social, professional, ethical, and economic considerations of engineering as a profession; encompasses programs in public relations, employment practices, ethical considerations, education, and career guidance. Monitors legislative and regulatory actions of interest to the engineering profession.

★7694★ Nuclear Engineers

Evon Publishing
832 N 7th Ave.
Iron River, MI 49935
Ph: (906)265-3190

Audiocassette. 1996. $16.95. 32 minutes. Part of the Careers and Vocational Guidance Series. Provides information about the nature of the work, educational requirements, employment outlook, earnings, and work conditions as well as additional related information.

★7695★ Scientific, Engineering, and Technical Services

Cambridge Educational
2572 Brunswick Ave.
Lawrenceville, NJ 08648-4128
Fax: 800-FAX-ON-US   Fr: 800-468-4227
URL: http://www.cambridgeeducational.com

$89.95. 2002. 18 minutes. Part of the Career Cluster Series.

★7696★ Society of Women Engineers (SWE)

230 E Ohio St., No. 400
Chicago, IL 60611-3265
Ph: (312)596-5223   Fax: (312)596-5252
E-mail: hq@swe.org
URL: http://www.swe.org

Description: Educational and service organization representing both students and professional women in engineering and technical fields.

★7697★ Women in Engineering

Her Own Words
PO Box 5264
Madison, WI 53705-0264
Ph: (608)271-7083   Fax: (608)271-0209
URL: http://www.herownwords.com/

Video. Jocelyn Riley. $95.00. 15 minutes. Resource guide also available for $45.00.

Nuclear Medicine Technologists

SOURCES OF HELP-WANTED ADS

★7698★ ASRT Scanner

American Society of Radiologic
  Technologists
15000 Central Ave. SE
Albuquerque, NM 87123-3917
Ph: (505)298-4500   Fax: (505)298-5063
Fr: 800-444-2778

Monthly. Subscription included in membership. Professional magazine covering issues in radiology and medical technology. Includes calendar of events, member profiles, state affiliate news, educational opportunities, and research updates.

★7699★ ASTRO News

American Society for Therapeutic
  Radiology and Oncology
12500 Fair Lakes Cir., Ste. 375
Fairfax, VA 22033-3882
Ph: (703)502-1550   Fax: (703)502-7852
Fr: 800-962-7876

Quarterly. Subscription included in membership. Professional magazine covering radiology.

★7700★ Clinical Nuclear Medicine

Lippincott Williams & Wilkins
530 Walnut St.
Philadelphia, PA 19106
Ph: (215)521-8300   Fax: (215)521-8902
Fr: 800-638-3030
E-mail: cnm@pond.com
URL: http://www.nuclearmed.com/

Monthly. $257.00/year for individuals; $447.00/year for institutions; $333.00/year for other countries, current and back issues; $509.00/year for institutions, other countries. Journal publishing original manuscripts about scanning, imaging, and related subjects.

★7701★ Diagnostic Imaging

CMP Media L.L.C.
600 Community Dr.
Manhasset, NY 11030
Ph: (516)562-5000
E-mail: mtoledo@cmp.com
URL: http://www.mfi.com

Monthly. $109.00/year for individuals; $125.00/year for other countries. News and analysis on clinical and economic developments in medical imaging.

★7702★ Journal of Nuclear Medicine Technology

Society of Nuclear Medicine Inc.
1850 Samuel Morse Dr.
Reston, VA 20190-5316
Ph: (703)708-9000   Fax: (703)708-9018
URL: http://tech.snmjournals.org

Quarterly. Peer-reviewed scientific journal for technologists presenting original research, clinical reports, continuing education articles, and commentary on scientific trends and discoveries in nuclear medicine.

★7703★ Radiologic Technology

American Society of Radiologic
  Technologists
15000 Central Ave. SE
Albuquerque, NM 87123-3917
Ph: (505)298-4500   Fax: (505)298-5063
Fr: 800-444-2778
E-mail: pubsdept@asrt.org

Bimonthly. $49.00/year; $75.00/year for other countries; $29.50/year for students; $9.50 for single issue. Medical imaging technology. Includes annual index.

EMPLOYER DIRECTORIES AND NETWORKING LISTS

★7704★ AHA Guide to the Health Care Field

American Hospital Association (AHA)
1 N. Franklin St., 27th Fl.
Chicago, IL 60606
Ph: (312)422-2050   Fax: (312)422-4700
Fr: 800-424-4301

Annual, August. $295.00. Covers hospitals, networks, multi-health care systems, freestanding ambulatory surgery centers, psychiatric facilities, long-term care facilities, substance abuse programs, and other health-related organizations. Entries include: For hospitals-Facility name, address, phone, administrator's name, number of beds, facilities and services, number of employees, expenses, other statistics. For other organizations-Name, address, phone, fax, name and title of contact. Arrangement: Geographical. Indexes: Hospital name.

★7705★ Directory of Hospital Personnel

Thomson Medical Economics
5 Paragon Dr.
Montvale, NJ 07645-1742
Ph: (201)358-7200   Fax: (201)722-2680

Annual, November. $325.00. Covers 200,000 executives at 7,000 U.S. hospitals. Entries include: Name of hospital, address, phone, number of beds, type and JCAHO status of hospital, names and titles of key department heads and staff, medical and nursing school affiliations; number of residents, interns, and nursing students. Arrangement: Geographical. Indexes: Hospital name, personnel, hospital size.

★7706★ Guide to Careers in the Health Professions

The Princeton Review
1745 Broadway
New York, NY 10019
Ph: (212)829-6928   Fax: (212)940-7400
Fr: 800-733-3000

Published January, 2001. $24.95. Presents advice and information for those searching for satisfying careers in the health professions. Publication includes: Directory of schools and academic programs. Entries include: Name, address, phone, tuition, program details, employment profiles.

★7707★ Hospital Blue Book

Billian/Transworld Publishing Inc.
2100 Powers Ferry Rd.
Ste. 300
Atlanta, GA 30339
Ph: (770)955-8484   Fax: (770)955-8485
Fr: 800-533-8484
E-mail: blu-book@billian.com

Annual, January. $285.00 for national edition; $160.00 for southern edition. Covers more than 6,687 hospitals; some listings also appear in a separate southern edition of this publication. Entries include: Name of hospital, accreditation, mailing address, phone, fax, number of beds, type of facility (nonprofit, general, state, etc.); list of administrative personnel and chiefs of medical services, with specific titles. Arrangement: Geographical.

★7708★ The JobBank Guide to Health Care Companies

Adams Media Corp.
57 Littlefield St.
Avon, MA 02322
Ph: (508)427-7100   Fax: (508)427-6790
Fr: 800-872-5627

$17.95. Covers Jobs nationwide in health care companies. Entries include: Firm or organization name, address, phone, name and title of contact; description of organization, headquarters location, typical titles for entry- and middle-level positions, educational backgrounds desired, fringe benefits offered, stock exchange listing, training programs, internships, parent company, number of employees, revenues, e-mail and web address, projected number of hires. Indexes: Alphabetical.

★7709★ Medical and Health Information Directory

Thomson Gale
27500 Drake Rd.
Farmington Hills, MI 48331-3535
Ph: (248)699-4253   Fax: (248)699-8065
Fr: 800-877-GALE
E-mail: businessproducts@gale.com

Annual. $285.00 per volume; $675.00 per set. Covers in Volume 1, more than 26,500 medical and health oriented associations, organizations, institutions, and government agencies, including health maintenance organizations (HMOs), preferred provider organizations (PPOs), insurance companies, pharmaceutical companies, research centers, and medical and allied health schools. In Volume 2, over 12,000 medical book publishers; medical periodicals, directories, audiovisual producers and services, medical libraries and information centers, electronic resources, and health-related internet search engines. In Volume 3, more than 35,500 clinics, treatment centers, care programs, and counseling/diagnostic services for 34 subject areas. Entries include: Institution, service, or firm name, address, phone, fax, email and URL; many include names of key personnel and, when pertinent, descriptive annotation. Volume 3 was formerly listed separately as Health Services Directory. Arrangement: Classified by organization activity, service, etc. Indexes: Each volume has a complete alphabetical name and keyword index.

HANDBOOKS AND MANUALS

★7710★ Cardiac Nuclear Medicine

McGraw-Hill Professional
PO Box 545
Blacklick, OH 43004-0545
Fax: (614)755-5645   Fr: 800-722-4726

Myron C. Gerson, editor. Third edition, 1996. $155.00. 830 pages.

★7711★ Careers in Health Care

McGraw-Hill Trade
2 Penn Plaza
New York, NY 10121
Ph: (212)904-2000   Fr: 800-722-4726
E-mail: ntcpub@tribune.com

Barbara M. Swanson. Fourth edition, 2000. $17.95; $13.95 (paper). 320 pages. Describes job duties, work settings, salaries, licensing and certification requirements, educational preparation, and future outlook. Gives ideas on how to secure a job.

★7712★ Expert Resumes for Health Care Careers

JIST Publishing
8902 Otis Ave.
Indianapolis, IN 46216-1033
Ph: (317)613-4200   Fax: 800-547-8329

December 2003. $16.95. 288 pages.

★7713★ Health Careers Today

Elsevier-Health Sciences Division
The Curtis Center, Ste. 300E, 3rd Fl.
170 S. Independence Mall W.
Philadelphia, PA 19106
Ph: (215)238-7800   Fax: (215)238-7362
Fr: 800-523-4069

Gerdin. Revised edition. April 2004. $52.95.

★7714★ Opportunities in Health and Medical Careers

McGraw-Hill Trade
2 Penn Plaza
New York, NY 10121
Ph: (212)904-2000   Fr: 800-722-4726

I. Donald Snook, Jr. and Leo D'Orazio. 1997. $14.95; $11.95 (paper). 202 pages. Covers the full range of medical and health occupations. Illustrated.

★7715★ Opportunities in High Tech Careers

McGraw-Hill Trade
2 Penn Plaza
New York, NY 10121
Ph: (212)904-2000   Fr: 800-722-4726

Gary Colter and Deborah Yanuck. 1995. $14.95; $11.95 (paper). 160 pages. Explores high technology careers. Describes job opportunities, how to make a career decision, how to prepare for high technology jobs, job hunting techniques, and future trends.

★7716★ Opportunities in Medical Technology Careers

McGraw-Hill/Contemporary Books
1221 Avenue of the Americas
New York, NY 10020
Ph: (212)904-2000   Fr: 800-323-4900
E-mail: ntcpub@tribune.com

Karen R. Karni. Revised, 1996. $14.95; $11.95 (paper). 205 pages. Details opportunities for various technical medical personnel and supplies up-to-date information on salary levels and employment outlook. Appendices list associations and unions in each field. Illustrated.

★7717★ Resumes for Health and Medical Careers

McGraw-Hill Trade
2 Penn Plaza
New York, NY 10121
Ph: (212)904-2000   Fr: 800-722-4726
E-mail: ntcpub@tribune.com

1997. $9.95 (paper). 455 pages.

EMPLOYMENT AGENCIES AND SEARCH FIRMS

★7718★ JPM International

26060 Acero
Mission Viejo, CA 92691
Ph: (949)699-4300   Fax: (949)699-4333
Fr: 800-685-7856
E-mail: leslieo@jpmintl.com
URL: http://www.jpmintl.com

Executive search firm and employment agency.

ONLINE JOB SOURCES AND SERVICES

★7719★ Medbulletin Medical Career Resource Center
E-mail: medbulletin@atsmedbulletin.com
URL: http://www.medbulletin.com

Description: Offers free specialized update service, resume posting, recruiter directory, varied job listings, and relocation services.

★7720★ Medhunters.com
E-mail: info@medhunters.com
URL: http://www.medhunters.com

Description: Career search site for jobs in all health care specialties; educational resources; visa and licensing information for relocation; interesting articles; relocation tools; links to professional organizations and general resources.

★7721★ ProHealthJobs
E-mail: sales@prohealthjobs.com
URL: http://www.prohealthjobs.com

Description: Career resources site for the medical and health care field. Lists professional opportunities, product information, continuing education and open positions.

TRADESHOWS

★7722★ American Association of Physicists in Medicine Annual Meeting
American Association of Physicists in Medicine
1 Physics Ellipse
College Park, MD 20740-3846
Ph: (301)209-3350   Fax: (301)209-0862
E-mail: aapm@aapm.org
URL: http://www.aapm.org

Annual. **Primary Exhibits:** Radiation therapy, diagnostic radiology, radiation protection, hyperthermia, nuclear medicine, and magnetic resonance imaging.

★7723★ Society of Nuclear Medicine Annual Meeting
Society of Nuclear Medicine Inc.
1850 Samuel Morse Dr.
Reston, VA 20190-5316
Ph: (703)326-1184   Fax: (703)709-9274
E-mail: meetinginfo@snm.org
URL: http://www.snm.org

Biennial. **Primary Exhibits:** Nuclear medicine equipment, supplies, and services and radiopharmaceuticals.

★7724★ Southwestern Chapter - Society of Nuclear Medicine Exhibition
Southwestern Chapter - Society of Nuclear Medicine
910 Pecan St.
Kerrville, TX 78028
Ph: (830)257-0112   Fax: (830)257-0119
E-mail: cmetzger@swcnm.org
URL: http://www.swcsnm.org

Annual. **Primary Exhibits:** Industry related technology and pharmaceuticals.

OTHER SOURCES

★7725★ American Registry of Radiologic Technologists (ARRT)
1255 Northland Dr.
St. Paul, MN 55120-1155
Ph: (651)687-0048
URL: http://www.arrt.org

Description: Radiologic technologist certification board that administers examinations, issues certificates of registration to radiographers, nuclear medicine technologists, and radiation therapists, and investigates the qualifications of practicing radiologic technologists. Governed by trustees appointed from American College of Radiology and American Society of Radiologic Technologists.

★7726★ American Society of Radiologic Technologists (ASRT)
15000 Central Ave. SE
Albuquerque, NM 87123
Ph: (505)298-4500   Fax: (505)298-5063
Fr: 800-444-2778
E-mail: asrtbod@asrt.org
URL: http://www.asrt.org

Description: Professional society of diagnostic radiography, radiation therapy, ultrasound, and nuclear medicine technologists. Advances the science of radiologic technology; establishes and maintains high standards of education; evaluates the quality of patient care; improves the welfare and socioeconomics of radiologic technologists. Operates ASRT Education and Research Foundation, which provides educational materials to radiologic technologists.

★7727★ Exploring Health Occupations
Cambridge Educational
2572 Brunswick Ave.
Lawrenceville, NJ 08648-4128
Fax: 800-FAX-ON-US   Fr: 800-468-4227
URL: http://www.cambridgeeducational.com

Two videos. $139.95. 1999.

★7728★ Health Service Occupations
Delphi Productions
3160 4th St.
Boulder, CO 80304
Fax: (303)443-4022   Fr: 888-443-2400
URL: http://www.delphivideo.com

$95.00. 50 minutes. Part of the Careers for the 21st Century Video Library.

★7729★ Health Technologists & Technicians
Delphi Productions
3160 4th St.
Boulder, CO 80304
Fax: (303)443-4022   Fr: 888-443-2400
URL: http://www.delphivideo.com

$95.00. 50 minutes. Part of the Careers for the 21st Century Video Library.

★7730★ Medical Technicians and Technologists
Cambridge Educational
2572 Brunswick Ave.
Lawrenceville, NJ 08648-4128
Fax: 800-FAX-ON-US   Fr: 800-468-4227
URL: http://www.cambridgeeducational.com

$79.95. 15 minutes. Part of the Exploring Health Occupations Series.

★7731★ Medicine & Related Occupations
Delphi Productions
3160 4th St.
Boulder, CO 80304
Fax: (303)443-4022   Fr: 888-443-2400
URL: http://www.delphivideo.com

$95.00. 45 minutes. Part of the Careers for the 21st Century Video Library.

★7732★ Nuclear Medicine Technologists
Evon Publishing
832 N 7th Ave.
Iron River, MI 49935
Ph: (906)265-3190

Audiocassette. 1996. $16.95. 32 minutes. Part of the Careers and Vocational Guidance Series. Provides information about the nature of the work, educational requirements, employment outlook, earnings, and work conditions as well as additional related information.

★7733★ Nuclear Medicine Technology Certification Board (NMTCB)
2970 Clairmont Rd., Ste. 935
Atlanta, GA 30329
Ph: (404)315-1739   Fax: (404)315-6502
E-mail: board@nmtcb.org
URL: http://www.nmtcb.org

Description: Purposes are to provide for the certification of nuclear medical technologists and to develop, assess, and administer an examination relevant to nuclear medicine technology. Compiles statistics.

★7734★ Society of Nuclear Medicine (SNM)
1850 Samuel Morse Dr.
Reston, VA 20190-5316
Ph: (703)708-9000   Fax: (703)708-9020

E-mail: vpappas@snm.org
URL: http://www.snm.org

Description: Professional society of physicians, physicists, chemists, radiopharmacists, nuclear medicine technologists, and others interested in nuclear medicine, nuclear magnetic resonance, and the use of radioactive isotopes in clinical practice, research, and teaching. Disseminates information concerning the utilization of nuclear phenomena in the diagnosis and treatment of disease. Oversees the Technologist Section of the Society of Nuclear Medicine.

Nursing Aides and Psychiatric Aides

★7735★ AANA Journal

AANA Publishing Inc.
222 S Prospect Ave.
Park Ridge, IL 60068
Ph: (847)692-7050   Fax: (847)692-7137

Bimonthly. $45.00/year; $10.00 for single issue. Nursing and anesthesia journal.

★7736★ AAOHN Journal

SLACK Inc.
6900 Grove Rd.
Thorofare, NJ 08086-9447
Ph: (856)848-1000   Fax: (856)853-5991
Fr: 800-257-8290
E-mail: aaohn@slackinc.com

Monthly. $79.00/year; $179.00/year for institutions; $19.00/year for single issue. Official journal of the American Association of Occupational Health Nurses.

★7737★ ADVANCE for Nurse Practitioners

Merion Publications Inc.
2900 Horizon Dr.
PO Box 61556
King of Prussia, PA 19406-0956
Ph: (610)278-1400
URL: http://www.advancefornp.com

Monthly. Free to qualified subscribers. For practicing nurse practitioner students with senior status.

★7738★ Advances in Nursing Science

Aspen Publishers Inc.
1185 Avenue of the Americas
New York, NY 10036
Ph: (212)597-0200   Fax: (212)597-0338
Fr: 800-234-1660
URL: http://www.lww.com

Quarterly. $81.95/year for individuals; $201.95/year for institutions; $101.95/year for other countries; $231.95/year for institutions, other countries. Academic medical

journal focusing on nursing research and education.

★7739★ Ambulatory Outreach

Society for Ambulatory Care Professionals
1 N Franklin, 31st Fl.
Chicago, IL 60606
Fax: (312)422-4577

Quarterly. Subscription included in membership; $95.00/year for nonmembers. Professional journal for ambulatory care personnel.

★7740★ American Journal of Nursing

American Journal of Nursing
c/o Lippincott, Williams, & Wilkins
530 Walnut
Philadelphia, PA 19106
Fr: 800-627-0484
URL: http://www.nursingcenter.com

Monthly. $29.95/year. Journal for staff nurses, nurse managers, and clinical nurse specialists. Focuses on patient care in hospitals, hospital ICUs and homes. Provides news coverage of health care from the nursing perspective.

★7741★ American Journal of Psychology

University of Illinois Press
1325 S Oak St.
Champaign, IL 61820-6903
Ph: (217)333-0950   Fax: (217)244-8082
Fr: 800-537-5487
E-mail: ajp@s.psych.uiuc.edu

Quarterly. $133.00/year for institutions; $143.00/year, foreign. Journal dealing with experimental psychology and basic principles of psychology.

★7742★ The American Nurse

American Nurses Association
600 Maryland Ave. SW, Ste. 100 W
Washington, DC 20024-2571
Ph: (202)651-7000   Fax: (202)651-7000
Fr: 800-284-2378
E-mail: adsales@anan.org

$10.00/year for students; $20.00/year for

nonmembers; $30.00/year for other countries. Newspaper (tabloid) for the nursing profession.

★7743★ Annals of the American Psychotherapy Association

American Psychotherapy Association
2750 E Sunshine Rd.
Springfield, MO 65804
Ph: (417)823-0173

Bimonthly. Publication covering the field of psychology and mental health for professionals.

★7744★ Annals of Behavioral Medicine

Society of Behavioral Medicine
7611 Elmwood Ave., Ste. 201
Middleton, WI 53562
Ph: (608)827-7267   Fax: (608)831-5122

Quarterly. $135.00/year; $160.00/year for other countries. Journal describing the interactions of behavior and health.

★7745★ Annual Review of Psychology

Annual Reviews Inc.
PO Box 10139
Palo Alto, CA 94303-0139
Ph: (650)493-4400   Fax: (650)855-9815
Fr: 800-523-8635

Annual. Publication covering psychology and mental health issues.

★7746★ APA Monitor

American Psychological Association
750 1st St. NE
Washington, DC 20002-4242
Ph: (202)336-5500   Fax: (202)336-5620
Fr: 800-374-2721
E-mail: journals@apa.org
URL: http://www.apa.org/monitor/

Monthly. Free to qualified subscribers; $46.00/year for nonmembers; $87.00/year for institutions. Official newspaper of the APA. Reports on the science, profession, and social responsibility of psychology, including latest legislative developments affecting mental health, education, and research support.

★7747★ **Cancer Nursing**
Lippincott Williams & Wilkins
530 Walnut St.
Philadelphia, PA 19106
Ph: (215)521-8300   Fax: (215)521-8902
Fr: 800-638-3030
E-mail: ashcr@nursing.ufl.edu
URL: http://www.cancernursingonline.com/

Bimonthly. $82.95/year for individuals; $122.95/year for other countries; $192.95/year for institutions; $222.95/year for institutions, other countries. Medical journal covering problems arising in the care and support of cancer patients.

★7748★ **Clinical Nurse Specialist**
Lippincott Williams & Wilkins
530 Walnut St.
Philadelphia, PA 19106-3621
Ph: (215)521-8300   Fax: (215)521-8483
E-mail: info@nacns.org

Bimonthly. $100.00/year for individuals; $142.00/year for institutions. Nursing journal.

★7749★ **Clinical Psychiatry News**
International Medical News Group
60 Columbia Rd., Bldg. B
Morristown, NJ 07960
Ph: (973)290-8200   Fax: (973)290-8245
E-mail: cpnews@imng.com

Monthly. $60.00/year. Medical and psychiatry tabloid.

★7750★ **Health Care Weekly Review**
The Martin Group Inc.
24901 Northwestern Hwy., Ste. 316A
Southfield, MI 48075
Ph: (248)440-6080   Fax: (248)352-4801
E-mail: hcwr@compuserve.com

Weekly. $48.00/year for individuals. Professional newspaper covering the health care industry.

★7751★ **Home Healthcare Nurse**
Lippincott Williams & Wilkins
530 Walnut St.
Philadelphia, PA 19106
Ph: (215)521-8300   Fax: (215)521-8902
Fr: 800-638-3030
E-mail: hhnedit@bellsouth.net
URL: http://www.homehealthcarenurseonline.com/

Monthly. $49.95/year for individuals; $198.95/year for institutions; $102.95/year for other countries; $232.95/year for institutions, other countries. Magazine for the practicing professional nurse working in the home health, community health, and public health areas.

★7752★ **HomeCare Magazine**
Miramar Communications Inc.
23805 Stuart Ranch Rd., Ste. 235
PO Box 8987
Malibu, CA 90265-8987
Ph: (310)317-4522   Fax: (310)317-0264
Fr: 800-543-4116
URL: http://www.homecaremag.com

Monthly. Magazine serving home medical equipment suppliers, including independent and chain centers specializing in home care, pharmacies or chain drug stores with home care products, and joint-ventured hospital home health care businesses. Contains industry news and new product launches and marketing strategies.

★7753★ **Hospitals & Health Networks**
Health Forum L.L.C.
One N Franklin
Chicago, IL 60606
Ph: (312)893-6800   Fax: (312)422-4600
Fr: 800-621-6902
E-mail: hhn@healthforum.com
URL: http://www.hhnmag.com

Monthly. Publication covering the health care industry.

★7754★ **The Journal of Continuing Education in Nursing**
SLACK Inc.
6900 Grove Rd.
Thorofare, NJ 08086-9447
Ph: (856)848-1000   Fax: (856)853-5991
Fr: 800-257-8290
E-mail: jcen@slackinc.com

Bimonthly. $69.00/year for individuals; $139.00/year for institutions, add 7% Canada; $40.00/year for other countries. Journal for nurses involved in planning and implementing educational programs for the practitioner and others in patient care.

★7755★ **Journal of Gerontological Nursing**
SLACK Inc.
6900 Grove Rd.
Thorofare, NJ 08086-9447
Ph: (856)848-1000   Fax: (856)853-5991
Fr: 800-257-8290
E-mail: jgn@slackinc.com

Monthly. $59.00/year; $109.00/year for institutions; $19.00/year for single issue. Gerontological nursing journal.

★7756★ **Journal of Nursing Administration (JONA)**
Lippincott Williams & Wilkins
530 Walnut St.
Philadelphia, PA 19106
Ph: (215)521-8300   Fax: (215)521-8902
Fr: 800-638-3030
URL: http://jonajournal.com/

$91.95/year for individuals; $299.95/year for institutions; $161.95/year for other countries; $391.95/year for institutions, other countries. Journal covering developments and ad-

vances in nursing administration and management.

★7757★ **Journal of Nursing Scholarship**
Sigma Theta Tau International Honor Society of Nursing
550 W N St.
Indianapolis, IN 46202
Ph: (317)634-8171   Fax: (317)634-8188
Fr: 888-634-7575

Quarterly. $39.00/year for individuals; $20.00 for single issue; $63.00/year for institutions; $81.00/year for out of country. Peer-reviewed journal covering nursing.

★7758★ **Journal of Obstetric, Gynecologic and Neonatal Nursing (JOGNN)**
Sage Publications Inc.
2455 Teller Rd.
Thousand Oaks, CA 91320
Ph: (805)499-0721   Fax: (805)499-0871
Fr: 800-818-SAGE
E-mail: advertising@sagepub.com
URL: http://jognn.awhonn.org/

Bimonthly. $83.00/year for individuals; $165.00/year for out of country; $546.00/year for institutions; $596.00/year for institutions, other countries. Journal covering trends, policies, and research. Official publication of the Association of Women's Health, Obstetric, and Neonatal Nurses (AWHONN).

★7759★ **Journal of Positive Behavior Interventions**
PRO-ED Inc.
8700 Shoal Creek Blvd.
Austin, TX 78757-6897
Ph: (512)451-3246   Fax: (512)451-8542
Fr: 800-897-3202

Quarterly. Journal covering issues in mental health and psychology.

★7760★ **Journal of Psychosocial Nursing and Mental Health Services**
SLACK Inc.
6900 Grove Rd.
Thorofare, NJ 08086-9447
Ph: (856)848-1000   Fax: (856)853-5991
Fr: 800-257-8290
E-mail: jpn@slackinc.com

Monthly. $49.00/year; $74.00/year for institutions; $19.00/year for single issue. Journal presenting original, peer-reviewed articles on psychiatric/mental health nursing.

★7761★ **Journal of Trauma Nursing**
Nursecom Inc.
1211 Locust St.
Philadelphia, PA 19107-5409
Ph: (215)545-7222   Fax: (215)545-8107
Fr: 800-242-6757

Quarterly. Professional publication covering nursing.

★7762★ McKnight's Long-Term Care News

McKnight's Long-Term Care News
Two Northfield Plz., Ste. 300
Northfield, IL 60093-1219
Ph: (847)784-8706   Fax: (847)441-3701
E-mail: ltcnews@medec.com

Monthly. Free to qualified subscribers in U.S.; $5.00/year for single issue; $9.00 for single back issue; $54.95/year for Canada; $59.95/year, foreign. Professional magazine.

★7763★ MCN, The American Journal of Maternal/Child Nursing

Lippincott Williams & Wilkins
530 Walnut St.
Philadelphia, PA 19106
Ph: (215)521-8300   Fax: (215)521-8902
Fr: 800-638-3030
URL: http://www.mcnjournal.com/

Bimonthly. $41.95/year for individuals; $111.95/year for institutions; $81.95/year for other countries; $131.95/year for institutions, other countries. Journal focusing on maternal/child nursing and health.

★7764★ Minority Nurse Newsletter

Tucker Publications Inc.
PO Box 580
Lisle, IL 60532-0580
Ph: (630)969-3809   Fax: (630)969-3895
E-mail: sallen@tuckerpub.com

Description: Quarterly. Provides health care information of interest to minority nursing faculty.

★7765★ Modern Healthcare

Crain Communications Inc.
360 N Michigan Ave.
Chicago, IL 60601
Ph: (312)649-5200   Fax: (312)280-3174
Fr: 800-678-2724
E-mail: mhcedit@crain.com
URL: http://www.modernhealthcare.com

Weekly. $135.00/year. Weekly Business news magazine for Healthcare Management

★7766★ Nurse Practitioner Forum

Elsevier Science Inc.
The Curtis Ctr.
170 Independence Mall W, 300F
Philadelphia, PA 19106-3399
Ph: (215)238-7800   Fax: (215)238-7883
Fr: 800-523-1649

Quarterly. $49.00/year for individuals; $42.00/year for students; $76.00/year for institutions; $106.00/year for out of country. Journal for nurse practitioners.

★7767★ Nursing Education Perspectives

National League for Nursing Press
61 Broadway, 33rd Fl.
New York, NY 10006-2701
Ph: (212)363-5555   Fr: 800-669-1656
URL: http://www.nln.org

Free to qualified subscribers; $60.00/year; $90.00/year, libraries and institutions. Professional journal for nurses. Includes articles on health policy, social and economic issues affecting health care, and nursing education and practice.

★7768★ Nursing Management

Spring House
434 W Downer Pl.
Aurora, IL 60506
Ph: (630)844-6911   Fr: 800-950-0879

Monthly. $25.00/year for individuals. Magazine focusing on nursing management.

★7769★ Nursing 96

Lippincott Williams & Wilkins
530 Walnut St.
Philadelphia, PA 19106
Ph: (215)521-8300   Fax: (215)521-8902
Fr: 800-638-3030
E-mail: nursing@springnet.com

Monthly. $42.00/year for individuals; $4.00 for single issue. Practical journal for nurses. Includes special sections for hospital critical-care and home health.

★7770★ Nursing Outlook

Mosby Inc.
10801 Executive Center Dr., Ste. 509
Little Rock, AR 72211
Ph: (501)223-5165   Fax: (501)223-0519
URL: http://www.mosby.com

Bimonthly. $57.00/year for individuals; $106.00/year for institutions. Official journal of the American Academy of Nursing, reporting on trends and issues in nursing.

★7771★ Provider

American Health Care Association
1201 L St. NW
Washington, DC 20005
Ph: (202)842-4444   Fax: (202)842-3860
Fr: 800-321-4444
E-mail: provider@ahca.org

Monthly. $48.00/year for nonmembers. Provider Magazine.

★7772★ Psychiatric Annals

SLACK Inc.
6900 Grove Rd.
Thorofare, NJ 08086-9447
Ph: (856)848-1000   Fax: (856)853-5991
Fr: 800-257-8290
E-mail: idn@slackinc.com
URL: http://www.slackinc.com/general/psyann/psyahome.htm

Monthly. $129.00/year for individuals; $289.00/year for institutions. Journal analyzing concepts and practices in every area of psychiatry.

★7773★ Psychiatric News

American Psychiatric Publishing Inc.
1000 Wilson Blvd., Ste. 1825
Arlington, VA 22209
Ph: (703)907-7300   Fax: (703)907-1091
Fr: 800-368-5777
E-mail: pnews@psych.org
URL: http://www.psch.org/pnews/

Semimonthly. $40.00/year for individuals. Professional magazine of the American Psychiatric Assn.

★7774★ Psychiatric Services

Association of Partners for Public Lands
2401 Blueridge Ave., Ste. 303
Wheaton, MD 20902-4517
Ph: (301)946-9475   Fax: (301)946-9478
URL: http://www.appl.org/psjournal

Monthly. Interdisciplinary mental health journal covering clinical, legal, and public policy issues.

★7775★ Psychological Bulletin

American Psychological Association
750 1st St. NE
Washington, DC 20002-4242
Ph: (202)336-5500   Fax: (202)336-5620
Fr: 800-374-2721
URL: http://www.apa.org/journals/bul.html

Bimonthly. $81.00/year for members; $164.00/year for nonmembers; $398.00/year for institutions; $93.00/year for members, other countries; $184.00/year for other countries; $442.00/year for institutions, other countries; $49.00/year for students; $61.00/year for students, other countries. Journal presenting comprehensive and integrative reviews and interpretations of critical substantive and methodological issues and practical problems from all the diverse areas of psychology.

★7776★ Rehabilitation Nursing

Rehabilitation Nursing
4700 W Lake Ave.
Glenview, IL 60025
Ph: (847)375-4710   Fax: 877-734-9384
Fr: 800-229-7530
E-mail: info@rehabnurse.org

Bimonthly. $95.00/year for individuals; $125.00/year for institutions; $135.00/year for other countries; $18.00 for single issue; $125.00/year for Canada. Magazine focusing on rehabilitation nursing involving clinical practice, research, education, and administration.

★7777★ Research in Healthcare Financial Management

International Society for Research in Healthcare Financial Management Ltd.
305 W Chesapeake Ave.
CSBA Ste. L-096
Towson, MD 21204

Annual. Publication covering issues in the healthcare industry.

★7778★ Research in Nursing & Health

John Wiley and Sons Inc.
111 River St.
Hoboken, NJ 07030
Ph: (201)748-8866   Fax: (201)748-8824

Bimonthly. $115.00/year for U.S.; $115.00/year for Canada and Mexico; $151.00/year for other countries. Journal providing forum for research in the areas of nursing practice, education, and administration. Covers health issues relevant to nursing as well as investigations of the applications of research findings in clinical settings.

★7779★ Seminars in Oncology

Elsevier Science Inc.
The Curtis Ctr.
170 Independence Mall W, 300F
Philadelphia, PA 19106-3399
Ph: (215)238-7800   Fax: (215)238-7883
Fr: 800-523-1649
E-mail: elspcs@elsevier.com

$199.00/year for individuals; $318.00/year for institutions; $295.00/year for other countries; $382.00/year for institutions, other countries; $100.00/year for students, US students and residents; $64.00 for single issue. Journal reviewing current diagnostic and treatment techniques used in oncology patient care.

PLACEMENT AND JOB REFERRAL SERVICES

★7780★ American Association of Psychiatric Technicians (AAPT)

2000 "O" St., Ste. 250
Sacramento, CA 95814-5286
Ph: (916)443-1701   Fax: (916)329-9145
Fr: 800-391-7589
E-mail: hearn@psychtechs.org
URL: http://www.psychtechs.org

Description: Administers the Nationally Certified Psychiatric Technician examination to non-licensed direct-care workers in the fields of mental illness, developmental disabilities and substance abuse.

★7781★ American Public Health Association (APHA)

800 I St. NW
Washington, DC 20001-3710
Ph: (202)777-2742   Fax: (202)777-2534
E-mail: comments@apha.org
URL: http://www.apha.org

Members: Professional organization of physicians, nurses, educators, academicians, environmentalists, epidemiologists, new professionals, social workers, health administrators, optometrists, podiatrists, pharmacists, dentists, nutritionists, health planners, other community and mental health specialists, and interested consumers. **Purpose:** Seeks to protect and promote personal, mental, and environmental health. **Activities:** Services include promulgation of standards;

establishment of uniform practices and procedures; development of the etiology of communicable diseases; research in public health; exploration of medical care programs and their relationships to public health. Sponsors job placement service.

EMPLOYER DIRECTORIES AND NETWORKING LISTS

★7782★ AHA Guide to the Health Care Field

American Hospital Association (AHA)
1 N. Franklin St., 27th Fl.
Chicago, IL 60606
Ph: (312)422-2050   Fax: (312)422-4700
Fr: 800-424-4301

Annual, August. $295.00. Covers hospitals, networks, multi-health care systems, free-standing ambulatory surgery centers, psychiatric facilities, long-term care facilities, substance abuse programs, and other health-related organizations. Entries include: For hospitals-Facility name, address, phone, administrator's name, number of beds, facilities and services, number of employees, expenses, other statistics. For other organizations-Name, address, phone, fax, name and title of contact. Arrangement: Geographical. Indexes: Hospital name.

★7783★ American Journal of Nursing-Career Guide

American Journal of Nursing
c/o Lippincott, Williams, & Wilkins
530 Walnut St.
Philadelphia, PA 19106-3621
Ph: (215)521-8300   Fax: (215)521-8902
Fr: 800-627-0484
URL: http://www.nursingcenter.com

Annual, April. $13.95. Publication includes: List of nursing organizations and agencies. Entries include: Name, address, names of officers or nursing representative. Arrangement: Classified by type of organization.

★7784★ Careers in Focus: Geriatric Care

Ferguson Publishing Co.
200 W Jackson Blvd.
Chicago, IL 60606
Ph: (312)692-0109

$22.95. Publication includes: List of resources to consult for more information. Principal content of publication is job descriptions, advancement opportunities, educational requirements, employment outlook, salary information, and working conditions for careers in the field of geriatric care. Indexes: Alphabetical.

★7785★ Directory of Hospital Personnel

Thomson Medical Economics
5 Paragon Dr.
Montvale, NJ 07645-1742
Ph: (201)358-7200   Fax: (201)722-2680

Annual, November. $325.00. Covers 200,000 executives at 7,000 U.S. hospitals. Entries include: Name of hospital, address, phone, number of beds, type and JCAHO status of hospital, names and titles of key department heads and staff, medical and nursing school affiliations; number of residents, interns, and nursing students. Arrangement: Geographical. Indexes: Hospital name, personnel, hospital size.

★7786★ Hospital Blue Book

Billian/Transworld Publishing Inc.
2100 Powers Ferry Rd.
Ste. 300
Atlanta, GA 30339
Ph: (770)955-8484   Fax: (770)955-8485
Fr: 800-533-8484
E-mail: blu-book@billian.com

Annual, January. $285.00 for national edition; $160.00 for southern edition. Covers more than 6,687 hospitals; some listings also appear in a separate southern edition of this publication. Entries include: Name of hospital, accreditation, mailing address, phone, fax, number of beds, type of facility (nonprofit, general, state, etc.); list of administrative personnel and chiefs of medical services, with specific titles. Arrangement: Geographical.

★7787★ How to Survive and Maybe Even Love Nursing School!

F.A. Davis Co.
1915 Arch St.
Philadelphia, PA 19103
Ph: (215)368-2270   Fax: (215)568-5065
Fr: 800-523-4049

$19.95. Publication includes: List of resources for nursing students such as web sites and organizations. Principal content of publication is information about succeeding in nursing school.

★7788★ The JobBank Guide to Health Care Companies

Adams Media Corp.
57 Littlefield St.
Avon, MA 02322
Ph: (508)427-7100   Fax: (508)427-6790
Fr: 800-872-5627

$17.95. Covers Jobs nationwide in health care companies. Entries include: Firm or organization name, address, phone, name and title of contact; description of organization, headquarters location, typical titles for entry- and middle-level positions, educational backgrounds desired, fringe benefits offered, stock exchange listing, training programs, internships, parent company, number of employees, revenues, e-mail and web address, projected number of hires. Indexes: Alphabetical.

★7789★ Legal and Ethical Dictionary for Mental Health Professionals

University Press of America
4501 Forbes Blvd., Ste. 200
Lanham, MD 20706
Ph: (301)459-3366   Fax: (301)429-5748
Fr: 800-462-6420

$65.00. Publication includes: Lists of state licensure boards and web sites for mental health organizations. Principal content of publication is a dictionary of legal and ethical responsibilities for mental health professionals.

★7790★ Medical and Health Information Directory

Thomson Gale
27500 Drake Rd.
Farmington Hills, MI 48331-3535
Ph: (248)699-4253   Fax: (248)699-8065
Fr: 800-877-GALE
E-mail: businessproducts@gale.com

Annual. $285.00 per volume; $675.00 per set. Covers in Volume 1, more than 26,500 medical and health oriented associations, organizations, institutions, and government agencies, including health maintenance organizations (HMOs), preferred provider organizations (PPOs), insurance companies, pharmaceutical companies, research centers, and medical and allied health schools. In Volume 2, over 12,000 medical book publishers; medical periodicals, directories, audiovisual producers and services, medical libraries and information centers, electronic resources, and health-related internet search engines. In Volume 3, more than 35,500 clinics, treatment centers, care programs, and counseling/diagnostic services for 34 subject areas. Entries include: Institution, service, or firm name, address, phone, fax, email and URL; many include names of key personnel and, when pertinent, descriptive annotation. Volume 3 was formerly listed separately as Health Services Directory. Arrangement: Classified by organization activity, service, etc. Indexes: Each volume has a complete alphabetical name and keyword index.

★7791★ Mental Health Directory

Office of Consumer, Family & Public Information
Parklawn Bldg.
5600 Fishers Ln.
Rockville, MD 20857
Ph: (301)443-4795   Fax: (301)443-0284

Irregular, previous edition 1990; latest edition 1995. $23.00. Covers hospitals, treatment centers, outpatient clinics, day/night facilities, residential treatment centers for emotionally disturbed children, residential supportive programs such as halfway houses, and mental health centers offering mental health assistance; not included are substance abuse programs, Veteran's Administration programs, nursing homes, programs for the developmentally disabled, and organizations in which fees are retained by individual members. Entries include: Name, address, phone. Arrangement: Geographical.

★7792★ Mental Health Services Directory

infoUSA Inc.
5711 S 86th Cir.
Omaha, NE 68127-0347
Ph: (402)930-3500   Fax: (402)331-0176
Fr: 800-555-6124
URL: http://www.abii.com

Annual. Number of listings: 18,282. Entries include: Name, address, phone (including area code), size of advertisement, year first in "Yellow Pages," name of owner or manager, number of employees. Compiled from telephone company "Yellow Pages," nationwide. Arrangement: Geographical.

★7793★ Nurses and Nurses' Registries Directory

infoUSA Inc.
5711 S 86th Cir.
Omaha, NE 68127-0347
Ph: (402)930-3500   Fax: (402)331-0176
Fr: 800-555-6124
URL: http://www.abii.com

Annual. Number of listings: 10,949. Entries include: Name, address, phone (including area code), size of advertisement, year first in "Yellow Pages," name of owner or manager, number of employees. Compiled from telephone company "Yellow Pages," nationwide. Arrangement: Geographical.

★7794★ Nursing Career Directory

Springhouse Office of Lippincott, Williams & Wilkins
PO Box 908
Spring House, PA 19477-0908
Ph: (215)646-8700   Fax: (215)646-4399
Fr: 800-346-7844
URL: http://www.springnet.com

Annual, January. $10.00. Covers nonprofit and investor-owned hospitals and departments of the United States government which hire nurses. Does not report specific positions available. Entries include: Unit name, location, areas of nursing specialization, educational requirements for nurses, licensing, facilities, benefits, etc. Arrangement: Geographical. Indexes: Geographical.

★7795★ Online Resources for Senior Citizens

McFarland & Company Inc., Publishers
PO Box 611
Jefferson, NC 28640-0611
Ph: (336)246-4460   Fax: (336)246-5018
Fr: 800-253-2187

$32.00. Covers Federal government resources, general resources, and resources listed by topic such as caregivers, death and dying, volunteering, employment, grandparenting, health care, and travel.

★7796★ Peterson's Job Opportunities for Health and Science Majors

Thomson Peterson's
Princeton Pke. Corporate Ctr., 2000 Lenox Dr.
PO Box 67005
Lawrenceville, NJ 08648
Ph: (609)896-1800   Fax: (609)896-4531
Fr: 800-338-3282
URL: http://www.petersons.com

Irregular, latest edition 1999. $18.95. Covers approximately 1,300 research, consulting, government, and non-profit and profit service organizations that hire college and university graduates in science and health-related majors. Entries include: Organization name, address, phone, name and title of contact, type of organization, number of employees, Standard Industrial Classification (SIC) code; description of opportunities available including disciplines, level of education required, starting locations and salaries, level of experience accepted, benefits.

HANDBOOKS AND MANUALS

★7797★ America's Fastest Growing Jobs

JIST Works, Inc.
8902 Otis Ave.
Indianapolis, IN 46216-1033
Ph: (317)613-4200   Fax: (317)613-4307
Fr: 800-648-5478
E-mail: jistworks@aol.com
URL: http://www.jist.com

Seventh edition, 2002. $16.95 (paper). 438 pages. Each job profile explains the nature of the work, skills and abilities required, employment outlook, average earnings, related occupations, education and training requirements, and employment opportunities. Also contains career planning information and job search tips.

★7798★ Being a Long-Term Care Nursing Assistant

Prentice Hall PTR
200 Old Tappan Rd.
Old Tappan, NJ 07675
Ph: (201)236-7000   Fr: 800-223-1360

Connie Will-Black and Judith B. Eighmy. Fifth edition, 2001. $48.00 (paper). 560 pages.

★7799★ Being a Nursing Assistant

Prentice Hall PTR
200 Old Tappan Rd.
Old Tappan, NJ 07675
Ph: (201)236-7000   Fr: 800-223-1360

Eighth edition, 1999. $26.60 (paper).

★7800★ Careers for Caring People and Other Sensitive Types

VGM Career Horizons
1221 Avenue of the Americas
New York, NY 10020
Ph: (212)904-2000   Fr: 800-323-4900
E-mail: ntcpub@tribune.com

Adrian Paradis. 1995. $14.95; $9.95 (paper). 205 pages.

★7801★ Careers in Health Care

McGraw-Hill Trade
2 Penn Plaza
New York, NY 10121
Ph: (212)904-2000   Fr: 800-722-4726
E-mail: ntcpub@tribune.com

Barbara M. Swanson. Fourth edition, 2000. $17.95; $13.95 (paper). 320 pages. Describes job duties, work settings, salaries, licensing and certification requirements, educational preparation, and future outlook. Gives ideas on how to secure a job.

★7802★ Developing Your Career in Nursing

Sage Publications Inc.
370 Lexington Ave.
New York, NY 10017-6503
Ph: (212)953-5858   Fax: (212)953-5944

Robert Newell, editor. 1996. $90.00.

★7803★ Expert Resumes for Health Care Careers

JIST Publishing
8902 Otis Ave.
Indianapolis, IN 46216-1033
Ph: (317)613-4200   Fax: 800-547-8329

December 2003. $16.95. 288 pages.

★7804★ Federal Jobs in Nursing and Health Sciences

Impact Publications
9104 Manassas Dr., Ste. N
Manassas Park, VA 20111-5211
Ph: (703)361-7300   Fax: (703)335-9486

Russ Smith. 1996. Part of Federal Jobs in...Series. $14.95. 130 pages.

★7805★ From Nursing Assistant to Clinical Care Associate

Pearson Allyn & Bacon
1230 Ave. of the Americas
New York, NY 10020
Ph: (212)782-3300   Fr: 800-922-0579

Carole Miele. 1998. $47.00 (paper). 512 pages.

★7806★ From Nursing Assistant to Patient Care Technician: New Roles, New Knowledge, New Skills

W. B. Saunders Co.
6277 Sea Harbor Dr.
Orlando, FL 32887
Fr: 800-654-2452

Donna J. Brust and Joyce A. Foster. 1997.

★7807★ Gerontological Nursing Certification Review Guide for the Generalist, Clinical Specialist & Nurse Practitioner

Health Leadership Associates, Inc
PO Box 59153
Potomac, MD 20859
Ph: (301)983-2405   Fax: (301)983-2693
Fr: 800-435-4775

Catharine Kopac and Virginia L. Millonig, editors. Revised, 1996. $26.00 (paper). 541 pages.

★7808★ Health Careers Today

Elsevier-Health Sciences Division
The Curtis Center, Ste. 300E, 3rd Fl.
170 S. Independence Mall W.
Philadelphia, PA 19106
Ph: (215)238-7800   Fax: (215)238-7362
Fr: 800-523-4069

Gerdin. Revised edition. April 2004. $52.95.

★7809★ How to Be a Nurse Assistant: Career Training in Long Term Care

American Health Care Association
1201 L St. NW
Washington, DC 20005
Ph: (202)842-4444   Fax: (202)842-3860
Fr: 800-325-4177

Margaret Casey, editor. 1994. $23.95 (paper). 480 pages. Out of print.

★7810★ The Long-Term Care Nursing Assistant Training Manual

Health Professions Press
PO Box 10624
Baltimore, MD 21285-0624
Ph: (410)337-9585   Fax: (410)337-8539
Fr: 888-337-8808

Mary A. Anderson, Karen W. Beaver and Kathleen R. Culliton, editors. Second edition, 1996. $29.95 (paper). 352 pages.

★7811★ Nurse Assistant Test Preparation

Prentice Hall PTR
200 Old Tappan Rd.
Old Tappan, NJ 07675
Ph: (201)236-7000   Fr: 800-567-3800

Wanda Smith. 1994. $31.80 (paper). 192 pages.

★7812★ The Nurses' Career Guide: Discovering New Horizons in Health Care

Sovereignty Press
1241 Johnson Ave., No. 353
San Luis Obispo, CA 93401
Ph: (805)543-6100   Fax: (805)543-1085
Fr: 888-201-2501

Zardoya E. Eagles and Marti Kock. 1999. $17.95 (paper). Helps the reader identify work skills and achievements, clarify values and goals, explore career options, develop a personal action plan, prepare cover letters and resumes, and conduct informational and job interviews. Also addresses the dramatic changes that nurses currently face in the workplace. Includes a 65-page resource section which lists references, samples of resumes and letters, professional magazines, organizations, and online resources.

★7813★ Nursing Assistant: A Nursing Process Approach

Thomson Delmar Learning
PO Box 15015
Albany, NY 12212-5015
Ph: (518)348-2300   Fax: (518)464-0393
Fr: 800-998-7498

Barbara Hegner, Joan F. Needham and Esther Caldwell. Eighth edition, 1999. $35.95 (paper).

★7814★ Nursing Assistants: A Basic Study Guide

First Class Books, Inc.
113 E. Magnesium Rd., Ste. C
Spokane, WA 99208
Ph: (509)466-6847   Fax: (509)466-6896
Fr: 800-524-6911

Beverly Robertson. Fifth edition, revised, 1998. $13.95 (paper).

★7815★ Nursing (Career Portraits)

McGraw-Hill Trade
2 Penn Plaza
New York, NY 10121
Ph: (212)904-2000   Fax: (212)755-5645
Fr: 800-722-4726
E-mail: ntcpub@tribune.com

Blythe Camenson. 1995. $13.95. 335 pages.

★7816★ The Nursing Experience: Trends, Challenges & Transitions

McGraw-Hill Professional
PO Box 545
Blacklick, OH 43004-0545
Fax: (614)755-5645   Fr: 800-722-4726

Lucie Y. Kelly. Fourth edition, 2001. $34.95 (paper). 792 pages.

★7817★ Nursing Today: Transition and Trends

W.B. Saunders Co.
150 S. Independence Mall W
The Public Ledger Bldg., Ste. 1250
Philadelphia, PA 19106-3412
Ph: (215)238-5500   Fax: (215)238-8495
Fr: 800-654-2452

JoAnn Zerwekh and Jo C. Claborn, editors. Second edition, 1997.

★7818★ Opportunities in Health and Medical Careers

McGraw-Hill Trade
2 Penn Plaza
New York, NY 10121
Ph: (212)904-2000   Fr: 800-722-4726

I. Donald Snook, Jr. and Leo D'Orazio. 1997. $14.95; $11.95 (paper). 202 pages. Covers

the full range of medical and health occupations. Illustrated.

★7819★ **Opportunities in Mental Health Careers**
McGraw-Hill Trade
2 Penn Plaza
New York, NY 10121
Ph: (212)904-2000   Fr: 800-722-4726
Philip A. Perry and George Blake. 1996. $14.95; $11.95 (paper). 160 pages.

★7820★ **Opportunities in Nursing Careers**
McGraw-Hill Trade
2 Penn Plaza
New York, NY 10121
Ph: (212)904-2000   Fr: 800-722-4726
Keville Frederickson and Judith A. Ryan. 1995. $14.95; $11.95 (paper). 205 pages. Discusses the employment outlook and job-seeking techniques for LVN's, LPN's, RN's, nurse practitioners, nurse anesthetists, and other nurse members of the medical team. Includes a complete list of state nurses associations, state nursing boards, and specialty nursing organizations. Contains bibliography and illustrations.

★7821★ **Psychiatric Therapy Aide**
National Learning Corp.
212 Michael Dr.
Syosset, NY 11791
Ph: (516)921-8888   Fax: (516)921-8743
Fr: 800-645-6337
Jack Rudman. 1994. $27.95 (paper). Part of the Career Examination Series.

★7822★ **Real People Working in Health Care**
McGraw-Hill Contemporary Books
1221 Avenue of the Americas
New York, NY 10020
Ph: (212)904-2000   Fr: 800-323-4900
E-mail: ntcpub@tribune.com
Blythe Camenson, Jan Goldberg. 1996. $17.95; $12.95 (paper). Interviews and profiles of working professionals capture a range of opportunities in this field.

★7823★ **Real People Working in the Helping Professions**
McGraw-Hill Contemporary Books
1221 Avenue of the Americas
New York, NY 10020
Ph: (212)904-2000   Fr: 800-323-4900
E-mail: ntcpub@tribune.com
Blythe Camenson, Jan Goldberg. 1997. $17.95; $12.95 (paper). Interviews and profiles of working professionals capture a range of opportunities in this field.

★7824★ **Reinventing Your Nursing Career: A Handbook for Success in the Age of Managed Care**
Jones and Bartlett Publishing
200 Orchard Ridge Dr., Ste. 200
Gaithersburg, MD 20878
Ph: (301)417-7500   Fax: (301)695-7931
Fr: 800-638-8437
Michael Newell and Mario Pinardo. 1997. $37.00 (paper). 272 pages. Helps nurses identify career goals and take practical steps to realize them using self-surveys, goal-setting methods, personal action plans, and networking techniques.

★7825★ **Resumes for Health and Medical Careers**
McGraw-Hill Trade
2 Penn Plaza
New York, NY 10121
Ph: (212)904-2000   Fr: 800-722-4726
E-mail: ntcpub@tribune.com
1997. $9.95 (paper). 455 pages.

EMPLOYMENT AGENCIES AND SEARCH FIRMS

★7826★ **Daudlin, De Beaupre & Company Inc.**
18530 Mack Ave., Ste. 315
Grosse Pointe Farms, MI 48236
Ph: (313)885-1235   Fax: (313)885-1247
Executive search firm focused on the healthcare industry.

★7827★ **Davis-Smith, Inc.**
27656 Franklin Rd.
Southfield, MI 48034
Ph: (248)354-4100   Fax: (248)354-6702
Fr: 800-541-4672
E-mail: info@davissmith.com
URL: http://www.davissmith.com
Employment agency. Executive search firm.

★7828★ **Harper Associates**
29870 Middlebelt
Farmington Hills, MI 48334
Ph: (248)932-1170   Fax: (248)932-1214
E-mail: resumes@harperjobs.com
URL: http://www.harperjobs.com
Executive search firm and employment agency.

★7829★ **Medical Personnel Services, Inc.**
1707 L St. NW, Ste. 760
Washington, DC 20036
Ph: (202)466-2955
Employment agency specializing in permanent health/medical placements.

★7830★ **Professional Placement Associates, Inc.**
287 Bowman Ave., Ste. 309
Purchase, NY 10577
Ph: (914)251-1000   Fax: (914)251-1055
E-mail: lschachter@ppasearch.com
URL: http://www.ppasearch.com
Executive search firm specializing in the health and medical field.

★7831★ **Travcorps, Inc.**
40 Eastern Ave.
Malden, MA 02148
Ph: (781)322-2600   Fax: 800-803-1186
Fr: 800-343-3270
URL: http://www.travcorps.com
Places staff in temporary assignments. Other locations nationwide.

ONLINE JOB SOURCES AND SERVICES

★7832★ **Delta T Group**
E-mail: staffing@sdelta-tgroup.com
URL: http://www.delta-tgroup.com
Description: Specialized contract temporary staffing source for healthcare professionals in the fields of social service, psychiatry, mental health, and substance abuse. Organizations may request services and staffing; job seekers may view services provided, submit a resume, or peruse jobs available.

★7833★ **Medhunters.com**
E-mail: info@medhunters.com
URL: http://www.medhunters.com
Description: Career search site for jobs in all health care specialties; educational resources; visa and licensing information for relocation; interesting articles; relocation tools; links to professional organizations and general resources.

★7834★ **Medzilla**
URL: http://www.medzilla.com
Description: General medical website which matches employers and job hunters to their ideal employees and jobs through search capabilities. **Main files include:** Post Jobs, Search Resumes, Post Resumes, Search Jobs, Head Hunters, Articles, Salary Survey.

★7835★ **ProHealthJobs**
E-mail: sales@prohealthjobs.com
URL: http://www.prohealthjobs.com
Description: Career resources site for the medical and health care field. Lists professional opportunities, product information, continuing education and open positions.

TRADESHOWS

★7836★ American Association of Office Nurses Annual Meeting and Convention

American Association of Office Nurses
109 Kinderkamack Rd.
Montvale, NJ 07645
Ph: (201)391-2600   Fax: (201)573-8543
Fr: 800-457-7504
E-mail: aaonmail@aaon.org
URL: http://www.aaon.org

Annual. **Primary Exhibits:** Exhibits of interest to nurses.

★7837★ American Psychiatric Association Annual Meeting

American Psychiatric Association
1000 Wilson Blvd., Ste. 1825
Arlington, VA 22209-1825
Ph: (703)907-7300   Fax: (202)682-6132
E-mail: apa@psych.org
URL: http://www.psych.org

Annual. **Primary Exhibits:** Computer software online service, media product, criminal justice, diagnostic tool, ECT educational, insurance, market research, professional/support organizations, publishers, recruitment, store/federal and pharmaceuticals.

★7838★ Association for Gerontology in Higher Education Annual Meeting

Association for Gerontology in Higher Education
1030 15th St. NW, Ste. 240
Washington, DC 20005-1505
Ph: (202)289-9806   Fax: (202)289-9824
E-mail: aghetemp@aghe.org
URL: http://www.aghe.org

Annual. **Primary Exhibits:** Publications and education programs related to gerontology.

★7839★ International Association for Suicide Prevention Convention

International Association for Suicide Prevention
Rush Center for Suicide Research and Prevention
1725 W. Harrison St., Ste. 955
Chicago, IL 60612
Ph: (312)942-7208   Fax: (312)942-2177
E-mail: IASP@aol.com

Biennial. **Primary Exhibits:** Suicide prevention related articles.

★7840★ International Society of Psychiatric-Mental Health Nurses Annual Conference

International Society of Psychiatric - Mental Health Nurses
1211 Locust St.
Philadelphia, PA 19107
Ph: (215)545-2843   Fax: (215)545-8107
Fr: 800-826-2950
E-mail: ispn@nursecominc.com
URL: http://www.ispn-psych.org

Annual. **Primary Exhibits:** Psychiatric nursing equipment, supplies, and services.

OTHER SOURCES

★7841★ American Academy of Addiction Psychiatry (AAAP)

7301 Mission Rd., Ste. 252
Prairie Village, KS 66208
Ph: (913)262-6161   Fax: (913)262-4311
E-mail: info@aaap.org
URL: http://www.aaap.org

Members: Psychiatrists and other health care and mental health professionals treating people with addictive behaviors. **Purpose:** Promotes accessibility to highest quality treatment for all who need it; promotes excellence in clinical practice in addiction psychiatry; educates the public to influence public policy regarding addictive illness; provides continuing education for addiction professionals; disseminates new information in the field of addiction psychiatry; and encourages research on the etiology, prevention, identification, and treatment of the addictions.

★7842★ American Association for Geriatric Psychiatry (AAGP)

7910 Woodmont Ave., Ste. 1050
Bethesda, MD 20814-3004
Ph: (301)654-7850   Fax: (301)654-4137
E-mail: main@aagponline.org
URL: http://www.aagpgpa.org

Description: Psychiatrists interested in promoting better mental health care for the elderly. Maintains placement service and speakers' bureau.

★7843★ American Health Care Association (AHCA)

1201 L St. NW
Washington, DC 20005
Ph: (202)842-4444   Fax: (202)842-3860
URL: http://www.ahca.org

Description: Federation of state associations of long-term health care facilities. Promotes standards for professionals in long-term health care delivery and quality care for patients and residents in a safe environment. Focuses on issues of availability, quality, affordability, and fair payment. Operates as liaison with governmental agencies, Congress, and professional associations. Compiles statistics.

★7844★ American Hospital Association (AHA)

1 N. Franklin
Chicago, IL 60606-3421
Ph: (312)422-3000   Fax: (312)422-4796
URL: http://www.aha.org

Description: Health care provider organizations. Seeks to advance the health of individuals and communities. Leads, represents, and serves health care provider organizations that are accountable to the community and committed to health improvement.

★7845★ American School Health Association (ASHA)

PO Box 708
7263 State Route 43
Kent, OH 44240
Ph: (330)678-1601   Fax: (330)678-4526
Fr: 800-445-2742
E-mail: asha@ashaweb.org
URL: http://www.ashaweb.org

Description: School physicians, school nurses, dentist, nurses, nutritionists, health educators, dental hygienist, school-based professionals and public health workers. Promotes coordinated school health programs that include health education, health services, a healthful school environment, physical education, nutrition services, and psycho-social health services offered in schools collaboratively with families and other members of the community. Offers professional reference materials. Conducts pilot programs that inform materials development, provides technical assistance to school professionals, advocates for school health, and complies statistics.

★7846★ Exploring Health Occupations

Cambridge Educational
2572 Brunswick Ave.
Lawrenceville, NJ 08648-4128
Fax: 800-FAX-ON-US   Fr: 800-468-4227
URL: http://www.cambridgeeducational.com

Two videos. $139.95. 1999.

★7847★ Health Service Occupations

Delphi Productions
3160 4th St.
Boulder, CO 80304
Fax: (303)443-4022   Fr: 888-443-2400
URL: http://www.delphivideo.com

$95.00. 50 minutes. Part of the Careers for the 21st Century Video Library.

★7848★ Institute on Psychiatric Services/American Psychiatric Association

1000 Wilson Blvd., Ste. 1825
Arlington, VA 22209-3901
Fax: (703)907-1090   Fr: 888-357-7924
E-mail: apa@psych.org
URL: http://www.psych.org

Description: Annual meeting sponsored by the American Psychiatric Association. Open to employees of all psychiatric and related health and educational facilities. Includes lectures by experts in the field and workshops and accredited courses on problems, programs, and trends. Offers on-site Job Bank, which lists opportunities for mental health professionals. Organized scientific exhibits.

★7849★ *Medical Assistants*

Evon Publishing
832 N 7th Ave.
Iron River, MI 49935
Ph: (906)265-3190

Audiocassette. 1996. $16.95. 32 minutes. Part of the Careers and Vocational Guidance Series. Provides information about the nature of the work, educational requirements, employment outlook, earnings, and work conditions as well as additional related information.

★7850★ *Medicine & Related Occupations*

Delphi Productions
3160 4th St.
Boulder, CO 80304
Fax: (303)443-4022   Fr: 888-443-2400
URL: http://www.delphivideo.com

$95.00. 45 minutes. Part of the Careers for the 21st Century Video Library.

★7851★ **National League for Nursing (NLN)**

61 Broadway 33rd Fl.
New York, NY 10006-2701
Ph: (212)363-5555   Fax: (212)812-0393
Fr: 800-669-1656
E-mail: rcorcor@nln.org
URL: http://www.nln.org

Description: Champions the pursuit of quality nursing education. A professional association of nursing faculty, education agencies, healthcare agencies, allied/public agencies, and public members whose mission is to advance quality nursing education that prepares the nursing workforce to meet the needs of diverse populations in an ever-changing health care environment. Serves as the primary source of information about every type of nursing education, from the LVN and LPN to the EDD and PHD. There are 33 affiliated constituent leagues that provide a local forum for members. The National League for Nursing Accrediting Commission is an independent corporate affiliate of the NLN, responsible for providing accreditation services to all levels of nursing education. NLN's bimonthly update is available free of charge on the website and by email.

★7852★ **National Rural Health Association (NRHA)**

1 W Armour Blvd., Ste. 203
Kansas City, MO 64111-2087
Ph: (816)756-3140   Fax: (816)756-3144
E-mail: mail@nrharural.org
URL: http://www.nrharural.org

Description: Administrators, physicians, nurses, physician assistants, health planners, academicians, and others interested or involved in rural health care. Creates a better understanding of health care problems unique to rural areas; utilizes a collective approach in finding positive solutions; articulates and represents the health care needs of rural America; supplies current information to rural health care providers; serves as a liaison between rural health care programs throughout the country. Offers continuing education credits for medical, dental, nursing, and management courses.

★7853★ *Nursing Aides and Psychiatric Aides*

Evon Publishing
832 N 7th Ave.
Iron River, MI 49935
Ph: (906)265-3190

Audiocassette. 1996. $16.95. 32 minutes. Part of the Careers and Vocational Guidance Series. Provides information about the nature of the work, educational requirements, employment outlook, earnings, and work conditions as well as additional related information.

★7854★ **Visiting Nurse Associations of America (VNAA)**

99 Summer St., Ste. 1700
Boston, MA 02110
Ph: (617)737-3200   Fax: (617)737-1144
Fr: 800-426-2547
E-mail: vnaa@vnaa.org
URL: http://www.vnaa.org

Members: Voluntary, nonprofit home health care agencies. **Purpose:** Develops competitive strength among community-based non-profit visiting nurse organizations; works to strengthen business resources and economic programs through contracting, marketing, governmental affairs and publications.

Occupational Health and Safety Specialists and Technicians

SOURCES OF HELP-WANTED ADS

★7855★ BNA's SafetyNet
Bureau of National Affairs Inc.
1231 25th St. NW
Washington, DC 20037
Ph: (202)452-4200   Fax: (202)452-4644
Fr: 800-372-1033

Description: Biweekly. Designed to help employers deal with occupational safety and health regulations, policies, standards, and practices, and to understand the effects of compliance on employee relations. Covers the establishment, management, evaluation, maintenance, and administration of health and safety programs. Carries information on recordkeeping, inspections, enforcement, employer defenses, and training.

★7856★ Cal-OSHA Reporter
Commanon Corp.
PO Box 1100
Grass Valley, CA 95945-1100
Ph: (530)470-7500   Fax: (530)470-7600

Description: Fifty/year. Reports on laws, regulations, court cases, and other issues of interest to occupational safety and health professionals. Recurring features include a calendar of events, reports of meetings, news of educational opportunities, job listings, and notices of publications available. Reviews all Cal-OSHA cases.

★7857★ Construction Division Newsletter
NSC Press
1121 Spring Lake Dr.
Itasca, IL 60143-3201
Ph: (630)285-1121   Fax: (630)285-1315
Fr: 800-621-7615
URL: http://www.nsc.org

Description: Bimonthly. Focuses on industrial and occupational safety in the construction industry. Carries items on such topics as safe work practices and products; accident prevention; and successful industrial safety programs and policies. Available online only.

★7858★ CTD News
LRP Publications
747 Dresher Rd., Ste. 500
PO Box 980
Horsham, PA 19044
Ph: (215)784-0910   Fax: (215)784-0870
Fr: 800-341-7874

Description: Monthly. Concerned with occupational health hazards that result in Cumulative Trauma Disorders (CTD) such as carpal tunnel syndrome, RSI, stress, and back discomfort. Covers prevention, treatment, litigation, and worker's compensation related to CTD.

★7859★ Inside OSHA
Inside Washington Publishers
PO Box 7167
Ben Franklin Sta.
Washington, DC 20044-7167
Ph: (703)416-8500   Fax: (703)416-8543
Fr: 800-424-9068

Description: Biweekly, every other Monday. Reports on news of the Occupational Safety and Health Administration.

★7860★ Job Safety and Health Quarterly
Occupational Safety and Health Administration
200 Constitution Ave. NW, N 3647
Washington, DC 20210
Ph: (202)693-1999   Fax: (202)693-1634
URL: http://www.osha.gov

Description: Quarterly. Informs readers of changes, developments, and new rulings made by the Occupational Safety and Health Administration (OSHA).

★7861★ Keller's Industrial Safety Report
J.J. Keller & Associates Inc.
PO Box 368
Neenah, WI 54957-0368
Ph: (920)722-2848   Fax: 800-727-7516
Fr: 800-327-6868

Description: Monthly. Concerned with activities of the Occupational Safety and Health Administration (OSHA) and all aspects of safety in an industrial setting. Recurring features include includes sections titles OSHA Activity, Safety Issues, and State Activity.

★7862★ Labor Division Newsletter
NSC Press
1121 Spring Lake Dr.
Itasca, IL 60143-3201
Ph: (630)285-1121   Fax: (630)285-1315
Fr: 800-621-7615
URL: http://www.nsc.org

Description: Bimonthly. Concerned with industrial and occupational safety, safe work practices, and products. Covers industrial safety programs and relevant legislation and regulations. Reports on conferences and seminars centered on safety. Available online only.

★7863★ Occupational Safety & Health Reporter
Bureau of National Affairs Inc.
1231 25th St. NW
Washington, DC 20037
Ph: (202)452-4200   Fax: (202)452-4644
Fr: 800-372-1033
URL: http://www.bna.com

Description: Weekly. Provides a notification and reference service covering federal and state regulation of occupational safety and health, standards, legislation, enforcement activities, research, and legal decisions. Recurring features include a calendar of meetings and seminars and the full text of selected administrative rulings, proposed standards, criteria documents, variance notices, and compliance manuals.

★7864★ Safety Focus
NSC Press
1121 Spring Lake Dr.
Itasca, IL 60143-3201
Ph: (630)285-1121   Fax: (630)285-1315
Fr: 800-621-7615
URL: http://www.nsc.org

Description: Bimonthly. Concerned with occupational safety, safety products, hazard control, and accident prevention in the following industries and sectors: chemical, metals, heath care, marine, air transport, public employment, rubber/plastics, laboratories/emerging technology, and retail trades and services. Recurring features include news of research and announcements of related conferences.

★7865★ **Safety Management**
Bureau of Business Practice
125 Eugene O'Neill Dr., Ste. 103
New London, CT 06320
Ph: (860)442-4365   Fax: (860)437-3150
Fr: 800-876-9105
URL: http://www.bbpnews.com

Description: Monthly. Discusses successful safety programs and legal issues pertinent to safety management.

EMPLOYER DIRECTORIES AND NETWORKING LISTS

★7866★ **The JobBank Guide to Health Care Companies**
Adams Media Corp.
57 Littlefield St.
Avon, MA 02322
Ph: (508)427-7100   Fax: (508)427-6790
Fr: 800-872-5627

$17.95. Covers Jobs nationwide in health care companies. Entries include: Firm or organization name, address, phone, name and title of contact; description of organization, headquarters location, typical titles for entry- and middle-level positions, educational backgrounds desired, fringe benefits offered, stock exchange listing, training programs, internships, parent company, number of employees, revenues, e-mail and web address, projected number of hires. Indexes: Alphabetical.

HANDBOOKS AND MANUALS

★7867★ **Career Guide to the Safety Profession**
American Society of Safety Engineers
1800 E. Oakton St.
Des Plaines, IL 60018-2187
Ph: (847)699-2929   Fax: (847)768-3434
1997. 68 pages.

★7868★ **Labor Safety Technician**
National Learning Corporation
212 Michael Dr.
Syosset, NY 11791
Ph: (516)921-8888   Fax: (516)921-8743
Fr: 800-645-6337
Rudman, Jack. 1994. $29.95 (Trade paper).

★7869★ **Principal Safety Coordinator**
National Learning Corporation
212 Michael Dr.
Syosset, NY 11791
Ph: (516)921-8888   Fax: (516)921-8743
Fr: 800-645-6337
Rudman, Jack. 1994. $39.95 (Trade paper).

★7870★ **Safety Consultant**
National Learning Corporation
212 Michael Dr.
Syosset, NY 11791
Ph: (516)921-8888   Fax: (516)921-8743
Fr: 800-645-6337
Rudman, Jack. 1994. $34.95 (Trade paper).

Occupational Therapists

PLACEMENT AND JOB REFERRAL SERVICES

★7881★ American Public Health Association (APHA)
800 I St. NW
Washington, DC 20001-3710
Ph: (202)777-2742   Fax: (202)777-2534
E-mail: comments@apha.org
URL: http://www.apha.org

Members: Professional organization of physicians, nurses, educators, academicians, environmentalists, epidemiologists, new professionals, social workers, health administrators, optometrists, podiatrists, pharmacists, dentists, nutritionists, health planners, other community and mental health specialists, and interested consumers. **Purpose:** Seeks to protect and promote personal, mental, and environmental health. **Activities:** Services include promulgation of standards; establishment of uniform practices and procedures; development of the etiology of communicable diseases; research in public health; exploration of medical care programs and their relationships to public health. Sponsors job placement service.

EMPLOYER DIRECTORIES AND NETWORKING LISTS

★7882★ AHA Guide to the Health Care Field
American Hospital Association (AHA)
1 N. Franklin St., 27th Fl.
Chicago, IL 60606
Ph: (312)422-2050   Fax: (312)422-4700
Fr: 800-424-4301

Annual, August. $295.00. Covers hospitals, networks, multi-health care systems, free-standing ambulatory surgery centers, psychiatric facilities, long-term care facilities, substance abuse programs, and other health-related organizations. Entries include: For hospitals-Facility name, address, phone, administrator's name, number of beds, facilities and services, number of employees, expenses, other statistics. For other organizations-Name, address, phone, fax, name and title of contact. Arrangement: Geographical. Indexes: Hospital name.

★7883★ Directory of Hospital Personnel
Thomson Medical Economics
5 Paragon Dr.
Montvale, NJ 07645-1742
Ph: (201)358-7200   Fax: (201)722-2680

Annual, November. $325.00. Covers 200,000 executives at 7,000 U.S. hospitals. Entries include: Name of hospital, address, phone, number of beds, type and JCAHO status of hospital, names and titles of key department heads and staff, medical and nursing school affiliations; number of resi-

dents, interns, and nursing students. Arrangement: Geographical. Indexes: Hospital name, personnel, hospital size.

★7884★ Home Health Service Directory
infoUSA Inc.
5711 S 86th Cir.
Omaha, NE 68127-0347
Ph: (402)930-3500   Fax: (402)331-0176
Fr: 800-555-6124
URL: http://www.abii.com

Annual. Number of listings: 21,158. Entries include: Name, address, phone (including area code), size of advertisement, year first in "Yellow Pages," name of owl her or manager, number of employees. Compiled from telephone company "Yellow Pages," nationwide. Arrangement: Geographical.

★7885★ Hospital Blue Book
Billian/Transworld Publishing Inc.
2100 Powers Ferry Rd.
Ste. 300
Atlanta, GA 30339
Ph: (770)955-8484   Fax: (770)955-8485
Fr: 800-533-8484
E-mail: blu-book@billian.com

Annual, January. $285.00 for national edition; $160.00 for southern edition. Covers more than 6,687 hospitals; some listings also appear in a separate southern edition of this publication. Entries include: Name of hospital, accreditation, mailing address, phone, fax, number of beds, type of facility (nonprofit, general, state, etc.); list of administrative personnel and chiefs of medical services, with specific titles. Arrangement: Geographical.

★7886★ The JobBank Guide to Health Care Companies
Adams Media Corp.
57 Littlefield St.
Avon, MA 02322
Ph: (508)427-7100   Fax: (508)427-6790
Fr: 800-872-5627

$17.95. Covers Jobs nationwide in health care companies. Entries include: Firm or organization name, address, phone, name and title of contact; description of organization, headquarters location, typical titles for entry- and middle-level positions, educational backgrounds desired, fringe benefits offered, stock exchange listing, training programs, internships, parent company, number of employees, revenues, e-mail and web address, projected number of hires. Indexes: Alphabetical.

★7887★ Medical and Health Information Directory
Thomson Gale
27500 Drake Rd.
Farmington Hills, MI 48331-3535
Ph: (248)699-4253   Fax: (248)699-8065
Fr: 800-877-GALE
E-mail: businessproducts@gale.com

Annual. $285.00 per volume; $675.00 per

set. Covers in Volume 1, more than 26,500 medical and health oriented associations, organizations, institutions, and government agencies, including health maintenance organizations (HMOs), preferred provider organizations (PPOs), insurance companies, pharmaceutical companies, research centers, and medical and allied health schools. In Volume 2, over 12,000 medical book publishers; medical periodicals, directories, audiovisual producers and services, medical libraries and information centers, electronic resources, and health-related internet search engines. In Volume 3, more than 35,500 clinics, treatment centers, care programs, and counseling/diagnostic services for 34 subject areas. Entries include: Institution, service, or firm name, address, phone, fax, email and URL; many include names of key personnel and, when pertinent, descriptive annotation. Volume 3 was formerly listed separately as Health Services Directory. Arrangement: Classified by organization activity, service, etc. Indexes: Each volume has a complete alphabetical name and keyword index.

★7888★ Occupational Therapists Directory
infoUSA Inc.
5711 S 86th Cir.
Omaha, NE 68127-0347
Ph: (402)930-3500   Fax: (402)331-0176
Fr: 800-555-6124
URL: http://www.abii.com

Updated continuously; printed on request. Number of listings: 3,419. Entries include: Name, address, phone, size of advertisement, name of owner or manager, number of employees, year first in "Yellow Pages." Compiled from telephone company "Yellow Pages," nationwide. Arrangement: Geographical.

HANDBOOKS AND MANUALS

★7889★ Careers in Health Care
McGraw-Hill Trade
2 Penn Plaza
New York, NY 10121
Ph: (212)904-2000   Fr: 800-722-4726
E-mail: ntcpub@tribune.com

Barbara M. Swanson. Fourth edition, 2000. $17.95; $13.95 (paper). 320 pages. Describes job duties, work settings, salaries, licensing and certification requirements, educational preparation, and future outlook. Gives ideas on how to secure a job.

★7890★ Careers for Health Nuts and Others Who Like to Stay Fit
McGraw-Hill Trade
2 Penn Plaza
New York, NY 10121
Ph: (212)904-2000   Fr: 800-722-4726
E-mail: ntcpub@tribune.com

Blythe Camenson. 1996. $14.95; $9.95 (paper). 160 pages.

★7891★ Careers in Social and Rehabilitation Services

McGraw-Hill Trade
2 Penn Plaza
New York, NY 10121
Ph: (212)904-2000   Fr: 800-722-4726
E-mail: ntcpub@tribune.com

Geraldine O. Garner. Second edition, 2001. $19.95; 14.95 (paper). 128 pages.

★7892★ Developmental Disabilities Program Specialist

National Learning Corp.
212 Michael Dr.
Syosset, NY 11791
Ph: (516)921-8888   Fax: (516)921-8743
Fr: 800-645-6337

Jack Rudman. 1994. $27.95 (paper). Part of Career Examination Series.

★7893★ Opportunities in Fitness Careers

McGraw-Hill Contemporary Books
1221 Avenue of the Americas
New York, NY 10020
Ph: (212)904-2000   Fr: 800-323-4900
E-mail: ntcpub@tribune.com

Mary Miller. 1998. $14.95; $11.95 (paper). 160 pages. Surveys fitness related careers. Describes career opportunities, education and experience needed, how to get into entry-level jobs and what income to expect. Schools are listed in the appendix.

★7894★ Opportunities in Health and Medical Careers

McGraw-Hill Trade
2 Penn Plaza
New York, NY 10121
Ph: (212)904-2000   Fr: 800-722-4726

I. Donald Snook, Jr. and Leo D'Orazio. 1997. $14.95; $11.95 (paper). 202 pages. Covers the full range of medical and health occupations. Illustrated.

★7895★ Opportunities in Occupational Therapy Careers

McGraw-Hill Trade
2 Penn Plaza
New York, NY 10121
Ph: (212)904-2000   Fr: 800-722-4726

Zona R. Weeks, Marie Louise Franciscus, and Marguerite Abbott. 2000. $14.95; $11.95 (paper). 146 pages. Provides an overview of opportunities in clinical positions, government and nonprofit agencies, rehabilitation centers, hospices, and other areas, and provides job-hunting guidance. Illustrated.

★7896★ Opportunities in Paramedical Careers

McGraw-Hill/Contemporary Books
1221 Avenue of the Americas
New York, NY 10020
Ph: (212)904-2000   Fr: 800-323-4900
E-mail: ntcpub@tribune.com

Alex Kacen. Revised, 1999. $14.95; 11.95 (paper). 200 pages. Discusses a variety of opportunities in this field and how to pursue them. Illustrated.

★7897★ Real People Working in Health Care

McGraw-Hill Contemporary Books
1221 Avenue of the Americas
New York, NY 10020
Ph: (212)904-2000   Fr: 800-323-4900
E-mail: ntcpub@tribune.com

Blythe Camenson, Jan Goldberg. 1996. $17.95; $12.95 (paper). Interviews and profiles of working professionals capture a range of opportunities in this field.

★7898★ Real People Working in the Helping Professions

McGraw-Hill Contemporary Books
1221 Avenue of the Americas
New York, NY 10020
Ph: (212)904-2000   Fr: 800-323-4900
E-mail: ntcpub@tribune.com

Blythe Camenson, Jan Goldberg. 1997. $17.95; $12.95 (paper). Interviews and profiles of working professionals capture a range of opportunities in this field.

★7899★ Where the Jobs Are: The Hottest Careers for the 90s

The Career Press, Inc.
3 Tice Rd.
PO Box 687
Franklin Lakes, NJ 07417-1322
Ph: (201)848-0310   Fax: (201)848-1727
Fr: 800-227-3371

Joyce Hadley. Third edition, 2000. $13.99 (paper). 400 pages. Out of print. Describes careers in fifteen general fields, from accounting to travel and hospitality.

EMPLOYMENT AGENCIES AND SEARCH FIRMS

★7900★ Harper Associates

29870 Middlebelt
Farmington Hills, MI 48334
Ph: (248)932-1170   Fax: (248)932-1214
E-mail: resumes@harperjobs.com
URL: http://www.harperjobs.com

Executive search firm and employment agency.

★7901★ J.B. Brown and Associates

50Public Square, Ste. 820
Cleveland, OH 44113
Ph: (216)696-2525

Employment agency and executive recruiter.

★7902★ JPM International

26060 Acero
Mission Viejo, CA 92691
Ph: (949)699-4300   Fax: (949)699-4333
Fr: 800-685-7856
E-mail: leslieo@jpmintl.com
URL: http://www.jpmintl.com

Executive search firm and employment agency.

★7903★ Professional Placement Associates, Inc.

287 Bowman Ave., Ste. 309
Purchase, NY 10577
Ph: (914)251-1000   Fax: (914)251-1055
E-mail: lschachter@ppasearch.com
URL: http://www.ppasearch.com

Executive search firm specializing in the health and medical field.

★7904★ Travcorps, Inc.

40 Eastern Ave.
Malden, MA 02148
Ph: (781)322-2600   Fax: 800-803-1186
Fr: 800-343-3270
URL: http://www.travcorps.com

Places staff in temporary assignments. Other locations nationwide.

ONLINE JOB SOURCES AND SERVICES

★7905★ Medhunters.com
E-mail: info@medhunters.com
URL: http://www.medhunters.com

Description: Career search site for jobs in all health care specialties; educational resources; visa and licensing information for relocation; interesting articles; relocation tools; links to professional organizations and general resources.

★7906★ Medzilla
URL: http://www.medzilla.com

Description: General medical website which matches employers and job hunters to their ideal employees and jobs through search capabilities. **Main files include:** Post Jobs, Search Resumes, Post Resumes, Search Jobs, Head Hunters, Articles, Salary Survey.

★7907★ ProHealthJobs
E-mail: sales@prohealthjobs.com
URL: http://www.prohealthjobs.com

Description: Career resources site for the medical and health care field. Lists professional opportunities, product information, continuing education and open positions.

★7908★ **RehabJobs Online**
PO Box 480536
Los Angeles, CA 90048
Ph: (213)938-7718   Fax: (213)938-9609
Fr: 800-43-REHAB
E-mail: support@atsrehabjobs.com
URL: http://www.rehabjobs.com

Description: @dq1On-line resource center for the professional therapist.@dq2 **Main files include:** Therapists Only, Therapy Forums, Nationwide Job Search (database), Therapy Job Outlook, Therapy Job Search Utilities, Therapy Links, Information for Employers and Recruiters.

★7909★ **RehabWorld**
URL: http://www.rehabworld.com
Description: Site for rehabilitation professionals to learn about the profession and locate jobs. Includes user groups, salary surveys, and chat capabilities. **Main files include:** Physical Therapy, Occupational Therapy, Speech Therapy, Mental Health, Employer World, Student World, International World, Forum.

TRADESHOWS

★7910★ **American Occupational Health Conference & Exhibits**
SLACK, Inc.
6900 Grove Rd.
Thorofare, NJ 08086
Ph: (609)848-1000   Fax: (609)848-3522
Annual. **Primary Exhibits:** Pharmaceuticals, medical equipment, computer software packages for medical offices, lab services, diagnostic testing, and EAP's., ergonomics, environmental products and services.

★7911★ **American Society of Hand Therapists Annual Meeting**
Smith, Bucklin and Associates, Inc. (Chicago)
401 N. Michigan Ave.
Chicago, IL 60611-4267
Ph: (312)321-6610   Fax: (312)673-6670
Fr: 800-289-NAON
E-mail: info@smithbucklin.com
URL: http://www.sba.com
Annual. **Primary Exhibits:** Hand therapy equipment and products. **Dates and Locations:** 2004 Oct 21-24; Charlotte, NC • 2005 Dates not set; San Antonio, TX.

★7912★ **National Rehabilitation Association Annual Training Conference and Exhibit**
National Rehabilitation Association
633 S. Washington St.
Alexandria, VA 22314-4109
Ph: (703)836-0850   Fax: (703)836-0848
E-mail: info@nationalrehab.org
URL: http://www.nationalrehab.org
Annual. **Primary Exhibits:** Rehabilitation equipment, supplies, and services; educational computer systems for the disabled; cars and vans featuring accessible equipment.

★7913★ **Occupational Therapy Association of California Conference**
Occupational Therapy Association of California
1401 El Camino Ave. Ste. 230
Sacramento, CA 95815
Ph: (916)567-7000   Fax: (916)567-7001
E-mail: OtofCA@aol.com
URL: http://www.healthcaresource.com/otac
Primary Exhibits: Occupational therapy equipment, supplies, and services.

OTHER SOURCES

★7914★ *American Almanac of Jobs and Salaries*
Morrow Avon
1350 Avenue of the Americas
New York, NY 10019
Ph: (212)261-6788   Fr: 800-242-7737
John W. Wright. Revised edition, 2000. $20.00 (paper). 672 pages. This is a comprehensive guide to the wages of hundreds of occupations in a wide variety of industries and organizations.

★7915★ **American Health Care Association (AHCA)**
1201 L St. NW
Washington, DC 20005
Ph: (202)842-4444   Fax: (202)842-3860
URL: http://www.ahca.org
Description: Federation of state associations of long-term health care facilities. Promotes standards for professionals in long-term health care delivery and quality care for patients and residents in a safe environment. Focuses on issues of availability, quality, affordability, and fair payment. Operates as liaison with governmental agencies, Congress, and professional associations. Compiles statistics.

★7916★ **American Kinesiotherapy Association (AKTA)**
PO Box 1390
Hines, IL 60141-1390
Fr: 800-296-AKTA
E-mail: ccbkt@aol.com
URL: http://www.AKTA.org

Members: Professional society of kinesiotherapists, and associate and student members with interest in physical and mental rehabilitation and adapted physical education. (Kinesiology therapy is the application of scientifically-based exercise principles adapted to enhance the strength, endurance and mobility of individuals with functional limitations of those requiring extended physical reconditioning.) **Purpose:** Seeks to serve the interest of members and represent the profession to the public. Works to enhance the standard of care provided by kinesiotherapists through the promotion and provision of educational opportunities.

★7917★ **American Occupational Therapy Association (AOTA)**
4720 Montgomery Ln.
PO Box 31220
Bethesda, MD 20824-1220
Ph: (301)652-2682   Fax: (301)652-7711
Fr: 800-377-8555
E-mail: aotapresident@aol.com
URL: http://www.aota.org
Members: Occupational therapists and occupational therapy assistants who **Purpose:** provide services to people whose lives have been disrupted by physical injury or illness, developmental problems, the aging process, or social or psychological difficulties. Occupational therapy focuses on the active involvement of the patient in specially designed therapeutic tasks and activities to improve function, performance capacity, and the ability to cope with demands of daily living.

★7918★ **American Society of Hand Therapists (ASHT)**
401 N Michigan Ave.
Chicago, IL 60611-4267
Ph: (312)321-6866   Fax: (312)673-6670
E-mail: asht@sba.com
URL: http://www.asht.org
Members: Registered and licensed occupational and physical therapists specializing in hand therapy and committed to excellence and professionalism in hand rehabilitation. **Purpose:** Works to promote research, publish information, improve treatment techniques, and standardize hand evaluation and care. Fosters education and communication between therapists in the U.S. and abroad. **Activities:** Compiles statistics; conducts research and education programs and continuing education seminars.

★7919★ **Association on Higher Education and Disability (AHEAD)**
PO Box 540666
Waltham, MA 02454
Ph: (781)788-0003   Fax: (781)788-0033
E-mail: ahead@ahead.org
URL: http://www.ahead.org.
Description: Individuals interested in promoting the equal rights and opportunities of disabled postsecondary students, staff, faculty, and graduates. Provides an exchange of communication for those professionally

involved with disabled students; collects, evaluates, and disseminates information; encourages and supports legislation for the benefit of disabled students. Conducts surveys on issues pertinent to college students with disabilities; offers resource referral system and employment exchange for positions in disability student services. Conducts research programs; compiles statistics.

★7920★ Association for Pediatric Therapists (APT)
2784 Lantz Ave.
San Jose, CA 95124
Ph: (408)377-3345

Members: Occupational, physical, and speech therapists, certified assistants, and students. **Purpose:** Promotes continuing professional development of members. **Activities:** Functions as a communication network linking members. Cooperates with other organizations representing professionals in related fields. Conducts continuing professional education programs.

★7921★ EMTs, Nurses, Therapists, and Assistants
Cambridge Educational
2572 Brunswick Ave.
Lawrenceville, NJ 08648-4128
Fax: 800-FAX-ON-US   Fr: 800-468-4227
URL: http://www.cambridgeeducational.com
$79.95. 1999. Part of the series "Exploring Health Occupations."

★7922★ Exploring Health Occupations
Cambridge Educational
2572 Brunswick Ave.
Lawrenceville, NJ 08648-4128
Fax: 800-FAX-ON-US   Fr: 800-468-4227
URL: http://www.cambridgeeducational.com
Two videos. $139.95. 1999.

★7923★ Health Assessment & Treating Occupations
Delphi Productions
3160 4th St.
Boulder, CO 80304
Fax: (303)443-4022   Fr: 888-443-2400

URL: http://www.delphivideo.com
$95.00. 50 minutes. Part of the Careers for the 21st Century Video Library.

★7924★ Health Service Occupations
Delphi Productions
3160 4th St.
Boulder, CO 80304
Fax: (303)443-4022   Fr: 888-443-2400
URL: http://www.delphivideo.com
$95.00. 50 minutes. Part of the Careers for the 21st Century Video Library.

★7925★ Medicine & Related Occupations
Delphi Productions
3160 4th St.
Boulder, CO 80304
Fax: (303)443-4022   Fr: 888-443-2400
URL: http://www.delphivideo.com
$95.00. 45 minutes. Part of the Careers for the 21st Century Video Library.

★7926★ National Board for Certification in Occupational Therapy (NBCOT)
The Eugene B. Casey Bldg. 800 S Frederick Ave. Ste 200
Gaithersburg, MD 20877-4150
Ph: (301)990-7979   Fax: (301)869-8492
URL: http://www.nbcot.org

Members: Participants are occupational therapists and occupational therapy assistants. **Activities:** Administers certification program and maintains certification records of certificants; operates disciplinary mechanisms.

★7927★ National Rehabilitation Association (NRA)
633 S Washington St.
Alexandria, VA 22314
Ph: (703)836-0850   Fax: (703)836-0848
E-mail: info@nationalrehab.org
URL: http://www.nationalrehab.org/website/index.html

Description: Providing opportunities through knowledge and diversity for profes-

sionals in the fields of rehabilitation of people with disabilities.

★7928★ Neuro-Developmental Treatment Association (NDTA)
1540 S Coast Hwy., Ste. 203
Laguna Beach, CA 92651
Fax: (949)376-3456   Fr: 800-869-9295
E-mail: membership@ndta.org
URL: http://www.ndta.org

Members: Physical and occupational therapists, speech pathologists, special educators, physicians, parents, and others interested in neurodevelopmental treatment. (NDT is a form of therapy for individuals who suffer from central nervous system disorders resulting in abnormal movement. Treatment attempts to initiate or refine normal stages and processes in the development of movement.) **Purpose:** Informs members of new developments in the field and with ideas that will eventually improve fundamental independence. **Activities:** Locates articles related to NDT.

★7929★ Project Magic (PM)
Kansas Rehabilitation Hospital
1504 SW 8 St.
Topeka, KS 66606
Ph: (785)235-6600   Fax: (785)232-8545
Fr: 888-221-8199
URL: http://www.dcopperfield.com

Description: Provides information and facilitates communication between magicians, occupational therapists, and patients with physical, psychosocial, and developmental disabilities. Created by television magician David Copperfield, the project works to rehabilitate patients by teaching them magic tricks instead of, or in addition to, traditional therapy techniques. Seeks to motivate patients to develop new skills and improve their self-image by demonstrating magical tricks. Tricks such as sleight-of-hand teach physical dexterity and mental puzzles help people to improve memory, concentration, and the ability to think sequentially. Provides interested magicians and occupational therapists with information and written material on the therapeutic value of magic for disabled persons. Sponsors educational seminars and workshops for rehabilitation facilities and health professionals.

Occupational Therapy Assistants and Aides

★7930★ ADVANCE for Occupational Therapy Practitioners

Merion Publications Inc.
2900 Horizon Dr.
PO Box 61556
King of Prussia, PA 19406-0956
Ph: (610)278-1400
E-mail: advance@merion.com
URL: http://www.advanceweb.com

Biweekly. Free. Serves licensed and registered occupational therapists, ceritified occupational therapy assistants, and senior OT students nationwide.

★7931★ The American Journal of Occupational Therapy

American Occupational Therapy
 Association Inc.
PO Box 31220
Bethesda, MD 20824-1220
Ph: (301)652-2682   Fax: (301)652-7711
Fr: 800-877-1383
E-mail: ajotsis@aota.org
URL: http://www.aota.org

Bimonthly. $60.00/year for individuals; $250.00/year for other countries; $15.00 for single issue. Journal providing a forum for occupational therapy personnel to share research, case studies, and new theory.

★7932★ American Journal of Physical Medicine and Rehabilitation

Lippincott Williams & Wilkins
530 Walnut St.
Philadelphia, PA 19106
Ph: (215)521-8300   Fax: (215)521-8902
Fr: 800-638-3030
E-mail: jmulliga@lww.com
URL: http://www.amjphysmedrehab.com/

Monthly. $182.00/year for individuals; $247.00/year for other countries; $309.00/year for institutions; $374.00/year for institutions. Medical journal.

★7933★ Journal of Occupational Rehabilitation

Kluwer Academic/Plenum Publishing Corp.
233 Spring St., 7th Fl.
New York, NY 10013-1578
Ph: (212)620-8000   Fax: (212)463-0742
Fr: 800-221-9369

Quarterly. $255.00/year for institutions; $300.00/year for institutions, other countries.

★7934★ Occupational Therapy in Health Care

The Haworth Press Inc.
10 Alice St.
Binghamton, NY 13904-1580
Ph: (607)722-5857   Fax: (607)722-1424
Fr: 800-429-6784
URL: http://www.haworthpress.com

Quarterly. $40.00/year for individuals; $75.00/year for institutions; $105.00/year for libraries. Journal for occupational therapists.

★7935★ Occupational Therapy in Mental Health

The Haworth Press Inc.
10 Alice St.
Binghamton, NY 13904-1580
Ph: (607)722-5857   Fax: (607)722-1424
Fr: 800-429-6784
E-mail: info@haworthpress.com
URL: http://www.haworthpress.com

Quarterly. $60.00/year for individuals, USA; $150.00/year for institutions, USA; $365.00/year for libraries, USA; $81.00/year for individuals, Canada; $202.50/year for institutions, Canada; $492.75/year for libraries, Canada; $87.00/year for individuals, other countries; $217.50/year for institutions, other countries; $529.25/year for libraries, other countries. Journal for occupational therapists working in the mental health field.

★7936★ OT Practice

American Occupational Therapy
 Association Inc.
PO Box 31220
Bethesda, MD 20824-1220
Ph: (301)652-2682   Fax: (301)652-7711
Fr: 800-877-1383

Professional magazine for occupational therapy practitioners.

★7937★ Physical & Occupational Therapy in Geriatrics

The Haworth Press Inc.
10 Alice St.
Binghamton, NY 13904-1580
Ph: (607)722-5857   Fax: (607)722-1424
Fr: 800-429-6784
URL: http://www.haworthpress.com

Quarterly. $40.00/year for individuals, USA; $160.00/year for institutions, USA; $225.00/year for libraries, USA; $52.00/year for individuals, Canada; $208.00/year for institutions, Canada; $292.52/year for libraries, Canada; $56.00/year for individuals, other countries; $224.00/year for institutions, other countries; $315.00/year for libraries, other countries. Journal for allied health professionals focusing on current practice and emerging issues in the health care of and rehabilitation of the older client.

★7938★ Physical and Occupational Therapy in Pediatrics

The Haworth Press Inc.
10 Alice St.
Binghamton, NY 13904-1580
Ph: (607)722-5857   Fax: (607)722-1424
Fr: 800-429-6784
URL: http://www.haworthpress.com

Quarterly. $75.00/year for individuals; $150.00/year for institutions; $465.00/year for libraries; $101.25/year for individuals, Canada; $202.50/year for institutions, Canada; $627.75/year for libraries, Canada; $108.75/year for individuals, other countries; $217.50/year for institutions, other countries; $674.25/year for libraries, other countries. Journal for therapists involved in developmental and physical rehabilitation of infants and children.

★7939★ Portable Practitioner: Opportunities in the Healing Arts

Monica Gruler & Co.
PO Box 2095
Petoskey, MI 49770
Ph: (616)347-8591   Fax: (616)347-8591
Fr: 800-968-2877
E-mail: portprac@freeway.net
URL: http://www.cybersytes.com/portprac

Description: Quarterly. Features marketing and practice-growing suggestions for massage therapists and bodyworkers. Recurring features include interviews, a calendar of events, news of educational opportunities, job listings, and notices of publications available.

EMPLOYER DIRECTORIES AND NETWORKING LISTS

★7940★ Health Professions Career and Education Directory

American Medical Association Alliance
515 N. State St.
Chicago, IL 60610
Ph: (312)464-5000   Fax: (312)464-5020
Fr: 800-621-8335
E-mail: dorothy-grant@ama-assn.org
URL: http://ama-assn.org/hpe-letter

Annual, January. $55.00 for members; $65.00 for nonmembers. Covers more than 6,500 health career educational programs in over 64 health occupations at 2,800 sponsoring institutions. Entries include: Occupational descriptions, employment characteristics, and information on education programs, such as length, curriculum, and prerequisites. Arrangement: Classified by occupation, then geographical. Indexes: Institution name, program name.

★7941★ The JobBank Guide to Health Care Companies

Adams Media Corp.
57 Littlefield St.
Avon, MA 02322
Ph: (508)427-7100   Fax: (508)427-6790
Fr: 800-872-5627

$17.95. Covers Jobs nationwide in health care companies. Entries include: Firm or organization name, address, phone, name and title of contact; description of organization, headquarters location, typical titles for entry- and middle-level positions, educational backgrounds desired, fringe benefits offered, stock exchange listing, training programs, internships, parent company, number of employees, revenues, e-mail and web address, projected number of hires. Indexes: Alphabetical.

★7942★ Occupational Therapists Directory

infoUSA Inc.
5711 S 86th Cir.
Omaha, NE 68127-0347
Ph: (402)930-3500   Fax: (402)331-0176
Fr: 800-555-6124
URL: http://www.abii.com

Updated continuously; printed on request. Number of listings: 3,419. Entries include: Name, address, phone, size of advertisement, name of owner or manager, number of employees, year first in "Yellow Pages." Compiled from telephone company "Yellow Pages," nationwide. Arrangement: Geographical.

★7943★ Occupational Therapy Educational Programs List

American Occupational Therapy Association Inc.
PO Box 31220
Bethesda, MD 20824-1220
Ph: (301)652-2682   Fax: (301)652-7711
Fr: 800-877-1383
E-mail: accred@aota.org
URL: http://www.aota.org

Database covers: Approximately 150 accredited, developing, and applicant programs in occupational therapy and 149 accredited, developing, and applicant occupational therapy assistant programs. Database includes: Institution name, address, phone, URL, level of program. Telecommunications Device for the Deaf, 800-377-8555. Arrangement: Geographical, then classified by educational institution. Separate listings for accredited, developing, and applicant OT and OTA programs.

HANDBOOKS AND MANUALS

★7944★ Careers for Health Nuts and Others Who Like to Stay Fit

McGraw-Hill Trade
2 Penn Plaza
New York, NY 10121
Ph: (212)904-2000   Fr: 800-722-4726
E-mail: ntcpub@tribune.com

Blythe Camenson. 1996. $14.95; $9.95 (paper). 160 pages.

★7945★ Careers Inside the World of Health Care

Rosen Publishing Group Inc.
29 E. 21st. St.
New York, NY 10010
Ph: (212)777-3017   Fax: 888-436-4643
Fr: 800-237-9932

Beth Wilkinson. 1999. $17.95. 64 pages.

★7946★ Careers in Social and Rehabilitation Services

McGraw-Hill Trade
2 Penn Plaza
New York, NY 10121
Ph: (212)904-2000   Fr: 800-722-4726
E-mail: ntcpub@tribune.com

Geraldine O. Garner. Second edition, 2001. $19.95; 14.95 (paper). 128 pages.

★7947★ Opportunities in Health and Medical Careers

McGraw-Hill Trade
2 Penn Plaza
New York, NY 10121
Ph: (212)904-2000   Fr: 800-722-4726

I. Donald Snook, Jr. and Leo D'Orazio. 1997. $14.95; $11.95 (paper). 202 pages. Covers the full range of medical and health occupations. Illustrated.

★7948★ Opportunities in Occupational Therapy Careers

McGraw-Hill Trade
2 Penn Plaza
New York, NY 10121
Ph: (212)904-2000   Fr: 800-722-4726

Zona R. Weeks, Marie Louise Franciscus, and Marguerite Abbott. 2000. $14.95; $11.95 (paper). 146 pages. Provides an overview of opportunities in clinical positions, government and nonprofit agencies, rehabilitation centers, hospices, and other areas, and provides job-hunting guidance. Illustrated.

★7949★ Real People Working in Health Care

McGraw-Hill Contemporary Books
1221 Avenue of the Americas
New York, NY 10020
Ph: (212)904-2000   Fr: 800-323-4900
E-mail: ntcpub@tribune.com

Blythe Camenson, Jan Goldberg. 1996. $17.95; $12.95 (paper). Interviews and profiles of working professionals capture a range of opportunities in this field.

★7950★ Real People Working in the Helping Professions

McGraw-Hill Contemporary Books
1221 Avenue of the Americas
New York, NY 10020
Ph: (212)904-2000   Fr: 800-323-4900
E-mail: ntcpub@tribune.com

Blythe Camenson, Jan Goldberg. 1997. $17.95; $12.95 (paper). Interviews and profiles of working professionals capture a range of opportunities in this field.

★7951★ Resumes for the Health Care Professional
John Wiley & Sons Inc.
111 River Rd.
Hoboken, NJ 07030-5774
Ph: (201)748-6000   Fax: (201)748-6088
Fr: 800-225-5945

Kim Marino. Second edition, 2000. $14.95 (paper). 224 pages.

EMPLOYMENT AGENCIES AND SEARCH FIRMS

★7952★ Team Placement Service, Inc.
5113 Leesburg Pike, Ste. 510
Falls Church, VA 22041-3242
Ph: (703)820-8618   Fax: (703)820-3368
Fr: 800-495-6767
E-mail: 4jobs@teamplace.com
URL: http://www.teamplace.com

Temporary agency that also handles some permanent placements.

★7953★ Travcorps, Inc.
40 Eastern Ave.
Malden, MA 02148
Ph: (781)322-2600   Fax: 800-803-1186
Fr: 800-343-3270
URL: http://www.travcorps.com

Places staff in temporary assignments. Other locations nationwide.

ONLINE JOB SOURCES AND SERVICES

★7954★ RehabJobs Online
PO Box 480536
Los Angeles, CA 90048
Ph: (213)938-7718   Fax: (213)938-9609
Fr: 800-43-REHAB
E-mail: support@atsrehabjobs.com
URL: http://www.rehabjobs.com

Description: @dq1On-line resource center for the professional therapist.@dq2 **Main files include:** Therapists Only, Therapy Forums, Nationwide Job Search (database), Therapy Job Outlook, Therapy Job Search Utilities, Therapy Links, Information for Employers and Recruiters.

★7955★ RehabWorld
URL: http://www.rehabworld.com
Description: Site for rehabilitation professionals to learn about the profession and locate jobs. Includes user groups, salary surveys, and chat capabilities. **Main files include:** Physical Therapy, Occupational Therapy, Speech Therapy, Mental Health, Employer World, Student World, International World, Forum.

TRADESHOWS

★7956★ American Society of Hand Therapists Annual Meeting
Smith, Bucklin and Associates, Inc. (Chicago)
401 N. Michigan Ave.
Chicago, IL 60611-4267
Ph: (312)321-6610   Fax: (312)673-6670
Fr: 800-289-NAON
E-mail: info@smithbucklin.com
URL: http://www.sba.com

Annual. **Primary Exhibits:** Hand therapy equipment and products. **Dates and Locations:** 2004 Oct 21-24; Charlotte, NC • 2005 Dates not set; San Antonio, TX.

★7957★ Occupational Therapy Association of California Conference
Occupational Therapy Association of California
1401 El Camino Ave. Ste. 230
Sacramento, CA 95815
Ph: (916)567-7000   Fax: (916)567-7001
E-mail: OtofCA@aol.com
URL: http://www.healthcaresource.com/otac

Primary Exhibits: Occupational therapy equipment, supplies, and services.

OTHER SOURCES

★7958★ American Occupational Therapy Association (AOTA)
4720 Montgomery Ln.
PO Box 31220
Bethesda, MD 20824-1220
Ph: (301)652-2682   Fax: (301)652-7711
Fr: 800-377-8555
E-mail: aotapresident@aol.com
URL: http://www.aota.org

Members: Occupational therapists and occupational therapy assistants who **Purpose:** provide services to people whose lives have been disrupted by physical injury or illness, developmental problems, the aging process, or social or psychological difficulties. Occupational therapy focuses on the active involvement of the patient in specially designed therapeutic tasks and activities to improve function, performance capacity, and the ability to cope with demands of daily living.

★7959★ EMTs, Nurses, Therapists, and Assistants
Cambridge Educational
2572 Brunswick Ave.
Lawrenceville, NJ 08648-4128
Fax: 800-FAX-ON-US   Fr: 800-468-4227
URL: http://www.cambridgeeducational.com

$79.95. 1999. Part of the series "Exploring Health Occupations."

★7960★ Exploring Health Occupations
Cambridge Educational
2572 Brunswick Ave.
Lawrenceville, NJ 08648-4128
Fax: 800-FAX-ON-US   Fr: 800-468-4227
URL: http://www.cambridgeeducational.com

Two videos. $139.95. 1999.

★7961★ Health Assessment & Treating Occupations
Delphi Productions
3160 4th St.
Boulder, CO 80304
Fax: (303)443-4022   Fr: 888-443-2400
URL: http://www.delphivideo.com

$95.00. 50 minutes. Part of the Careers for the 21st Century Video Library.

★7962★ Health Service Occupations
Delphi Productions
3160 4th St.
Boulder, CO 80304
Fax: (303)443-4022   Fr: 888-443-2400
URL: http://www.delphivideo.com

$95.00. 50 minutes. Part of the Careers for the 21st Century Video Library.

★7963★ Medical Assistants
Evon Publishing
832 N 7th Ave.
Iron River, MI 49935
Ph: (906)265-3190

Audiocassette. 1996. $16.95. 32 minutes. Part of the Careers and Vocational Guidance Series. Provides information about the nature of the work, educational requirements, employment outlook, earnings, and work conditions as well as additional related information.

★7964★ Medicine & Related Occupations
Delphi Productions
3160 4th St.
Boulder, CO 80304
Fax: (303)443-4022   Fr: 888-443-2400
URL: http://www.delphivideo.com

$95.00. 45 minutes. Part of the Careers for the 21st Century Video Library.

★7965★ National Board for Certification in Occupational Therapy (NBCOT)
The Eugene B. Casey Bldg. 800 S Frederick Ave. Ste 200
Gaithersburg, MD 20877-4150
Ph: (301)990-7979   Fax: (301)869-8492
URL: http://www.nbcot.org

Members: Participants are occupational therapists and occupational therapy assistants. **Activities:** Administers certification program and maintains certification records of certificants; operates disciplinary mechanisms.

★7966★ Neuro-Developmental Treatment Association (NDTA)
1540 S Coast Hwy., Ste. 203
Laguna Beach, CA 92651
Fax: (949)376-3456   Fr: 800-869-9295
E-mail: membership@ndta.org
URL: http://www.ndta.org

Members: Physical and occupational therapists, speech pathologists, special educators, physicians, parents, and others interested in neurodevelopmental treatment. (NDT is a form of therapy for individuals who suffer from central nervous system disorders resulting in abnormal movement. Treatment attempts to initiate or refine normal stages and processes in the development of movement.) **Purpose:** Informs members of new developments in the field and with ideas that will eventually improve fundamental independence. **Activities:** Locates articles related to NDT.

★7967★ Project Magic (PM)
Kansas Rehabilitation Hospital
1504 SW 8 St.
Topeka, KS 66606
Ph: (785)235-6600   Fax: (785)232-8545
Fr: 888-221-8199
URL: http://www.dcopperfield.com

Description: Provides information and facilitates communication between magicians, occupational therapists, and patients with physical, psychosocial, and developmental disabilities. Created by television magician David Copperfield, the project works to rehabilitate patients by teaching them magic tricks instead of, or in addition to, traditional therapy techniques. Seeks to motivate patients to develop new skills and improve their self-image by demonstrating magical tricks. Tricks such as sleight-of-hand teach physical dexterity and mental puzzles help people to improve memory, concentration, and the ability to think sequentially. Provides interested magicians and occupational therapists with information and written material on the therapeutic value of magic for disabled persons. Sponsors educational seminars and workshops for rehabilitation facilities and health professionals.

Office and Administrative Support Worker Supervisors and Managers

SOURCES OF HELP-WANTED ADS

★7968★ **Industry Focus**
Association of Business Support Services
International Inc.
5852 Oak Meadow Dr.
Yorba Linda, CA 92886-5930
Ph: (714)695-9398   Fax: (714)779-8106
Fr: 800-237-1462
E-mail: abssi4you@aol.com

Description: Monthly. Deals with every facet of business-support-service and virtual-assistant operations: pricing, successful new sales techniques for adding clients, dealing with clients and employees, work scheduling, forms and contracts, financial management, equipment and technology. Contains input from ABSSI members.

★7969★ **Journal of Staff Development**
National Staff Development Council
PO Box 240
Oxford, OH 45056
Ph: (513)523-6029   Fax: (513)523-0638
Fr: 800-727-7288

Quarterly. Professional journal covering administration issues.

★7970★ **OfficePRO**
Stratton Publishing and Marketing Inc.
5501 Backlick Rd., Ste. 240
Springfield, VA 22151
Ph: (703)914-9200   Fax: (703)914-6777
E-mail: officepromag@strattonpub.com

$25.00/year for individuals. Magazine for administrative assistants, office managers, and secretaries featuring information on trends in business, technology, career development, and management.

★7971★ **Supply Chain Management Review**
Reed Business Information
275 Washington St.
Newton, MA 02458-1630
Ph: (617)964-3030

Bimonthly. Publication covering business and management.

HANDBOOKS AND MANUALS

★7972★ **Administrative Manager**
National Learning Corporation
212 Michael Dr.
Syosset, NY 11791
Ph: (516)921-8888   Fax: (516)921-8743
Fr: 800-645-6337

Rudman, Jack. 1994. $34.95 (Trade paper).

★7973★ **Real-Resumes for Administrative Support, Office and Secretarial Jobs**
PREP Publishing
1110 1/2 Hay St., PMB 66
Fayetteville, NC 28305
Ph: (910)483-6611   Fax: (910)483-2439
Fr: 800-533-2814

Anne McKinney (Editor). March 2004. $25.95. Illustrated. 192 pages. Part of the Real-Resumes Series.

★7974★ **Supervising for Success: A Guide for Supervisors**
Crisp Publications, Inc.
1200 Hamilton Ct.
Menlo Park, CA 94025
Ph: (650)323-6100   Fax: (650)323-5800
Fr: 800-442-7477

Tony Moglia. 1997. $12.95.

EMPLOYMENT AGENCIES AND SEARCH FIRMS

★7975★ **Churchill & Affiliates Inc.**
180 E. Elizabeth Ln.
Richboro, PA 18954
Ph: (215)364-8070   Fax: (215)364-0519

Executive search firm focusing on the telecommunications industry.

★7976★ **Metropolitan Personnel Inc.**
PO Box 641
Valley Forge, PA 19482
Ph: (610)933-4000   Fax: (610)933-4670

Offers permanent placement services and specializes in office support, medical and technological staffing. Industries served: multi-industry oriented including government agencies. Firm also provides temporary staffing services and is a PEO.

ONLINE JOB SOURCES AND SERVICES

★7977★ **Admin Exchange**
E-mail: info@adminexchange.com
URL: http://www.adminexchange.com

Description: Career resources for administrative support staff. Contains resume posting and job databank. Also discussion forum and client list for recruitment purposes.

★7978★ **Career One Stop**
Ph: 877-348-0501   Fax: 877-348-0499
URL: http://www.careeronestop.org

Description: Career resources for administrative staff. Job seekers can post their resume and search for job openings.

★7979★ **Office Team**
URL: http://www.officeteam.com

Description: Job search site for administrative support staff. Contains resume submission and job databank, plus resources and e-mail notification of available jobs.

OTHER SOURCES

★7980★ *Administration and Management Occupations*
Delphi Productions
3160 4th St.
Boulder, CO 80304
Fax: (303)443-4022   Fr: 888-443-2400
URL: http://www.delphivideo.com

$95.00. 50 minutes. Part of the Careers for the 21st Century Video Library.

★7981★ *Business and Administration Support Occupations*
Delphi Productions
3160 4th St.
Boulder, CO 80304
Fax: (303)443-4022   Fr: 888-443-2400
URL: http://www.delphivideo.com

$95.00. 42 minutes. Part of the Careers for the 21st Century Video Library.

★7982★ **Clerical & Administrative Support**
Careers, Inc.
PO Box 135
Largo, FL 33779
Ph: (813)584-7333

26 mins. $79.95. Part of the Video Career Library covering 165 occupations.

★7983★ **International Association of Administrative Professionals (IAAP)**
10502 NW Ambassador Dr.
Kansas City, MO 64195-0404
Ph: (816)891-6600   Fax: (816)891-9118
URL: http://www.iaap-hq.org/

Description: IAAP is the world's largest association of administrative support staff, with over 600 chapters and 40,000 members and affiliates worldwide. Provides up-to-date research on office trends, publications, seminars and conferences, and resources to help administrative professionals enhance their skills and become more effective contributors to their employers.

Operations Research Analysts

HANDBOOKS AND MANUALS

★7984★ Career Information Center
Macmillan Publishing Co. Inc.
200 Old Tappan Rd.
Old Tappan, NJ 07675
Fr: 800-428-5331

Visual Education Center Staff. Seventh edition, 1999. $275.00. 2080 pages. This 13-volume set profiles over 600 occupations. Each occupational profile describes job duties, educational requirements, how to get the job, advancement possibilities, employment outlook, working conditions, earnings and benefits, and where to write for more information.

★7985★ Great Jobs for Computer Science Majors
McGraw-Hill Companies
1221 Avenue of the Americas
New York, NY 10020
Ph: (212)904-2000   Fr: 800-323-4900
E-mail: ntcpub@tribune.com

Jan Goldberg, Stephen Lambert, Julie De-Galan. 1997. $11.95 (paper). 365 pages.

★7986★ The Information System Consultant's Handbook: Systems Analysis and Design
CRC Press LLC
2000 NW Corporate Blvd.
Boca Raton, FL 33431
Fr: 800-272-7737

William S. Davis and David C. Yen. 1998. $139.95. 800 pages. This book familiarizes systems analysts, systems designers, and information systems consultants with underlying principles, specific documentation, and methodologies.

★7987★ Next Generation Product Development: How to Increase Productivity, Cut Costs, and Reduce Cycle Times
McGraw-Hill Companies
2 Penn Plaza
New York, NY 10121
Ph: (212)904-2000   Fr: 800-722-4729

Michael E. McGrath. 2004. $39.95. 379 pages. A guide to making the most of today's product development breakthroughs.

★7988★ Opportunities in Research and Development Careers
McGraw-Hill/Contemporary Books
1221 Avenue of the Americas
New York, NY 10020
Ph: (212)904-2000   Fr: 800-323-4900
E-mail: ntcpub@tribune.com

Jan Goldberg. 1997. $14.95; $11.95 (paper). 204 pages.

EMPLOYMENT AGENCIES AND SEARCH FIRMS

★7989★ Analytic Recruiting, Inc.
12 E. 41st St., 9th Fl.
New York, NY 10017
Ph: (212)545-8511   Fax: (212)545-8520
E-mail: email@analyticrecruiting.com
URL: http://www.analyticrecruiting.com

Executive search firm.

★7990★ The Aspire Group
52 Second Ave, 1st Fl
Waltham, MA 02451-1129
Fax: (718)890-1810   Fr: 800-546-5675
URL: http://www.bmanet.com

Employment agency.

★7991★ Colli Associates
404 Caboose Ln.
Valrico, FL 33594
Ph: (813)681-2145   Fax: (813)661-5217
E-mail: colli@gte.net

Employment agency. Executive search firm.

★7992★ Data Systems Search Consultants
1615 Bonanza St., Ste.205
Walnut Creek, CA 94596
Ph: (925)256-0635   Fax: (925)256-9099
E-mail: dsscinfo@dssc.com
URL: http://www.dssc.com

Employment agency. Executive search firm.

★7993★ Mfg/Search, Inc.
431 E Colfax Ave., Ste.120
South Bend, IN 46617
Ph: (574)282-2547   Fr: 800-782-7976
E-mail: mfg@mfgsearch.com
URL: http://www.mfgsearch.com

Executive search firm. Offices in GA, IL, MI, NY.

★7994★ Placemart Personnel Service
766 Shrewsbury Ave E Office Fl. 5
Tinton Falls, NJ 07724
Ph: (732)212-0144   Fax: (732)212-0145
Fr: 800-394-7522
E-mail: info@placemart.com
URL: http://www.placemart.com

Executive search firm focusing on the field of clinical research.

★7995★ Tri-Serv Inc.
22 W. Padonia Rd., Ste. C-353
Timonium, MD 21093
Ph: (410)561-1740   Fax: (410)252-7417
E-mail: info@tri-serv.coom
URL: http://www.tri-serv.com

Permanent employment agency.

★7996★ **Werbin Associates Executive Search, Inc.**
140 Riverside Dr., Ste. 10N
New York, NY 10024-2605
Ph: (212)799-6111
E-mail: swerb@bellatlantic.net

Employment agency. Executive search firm.

TRADESHOWS

★7997★ **Organization Development Network Conference**
Organization Development Network
71 Valley St., Ste. 301
South Orange, NJ 07079-2825
Ph: (973)763-7337   Fax: (973)763-7488
URL: http://www.odnet.org

Annual. **Primary Exhibits:** Exhibits related to organization development.

OTHER SOURCES

★7998★ **American Supplier Institute (ASI)**
4050 Legato Rd.
Fairfax, VA 22033
Ph: (734)464-1395   Fax: (734)464-1399
Fr: 800-462-4500
E-mail: asi@asiusa.com
URL: http://www.amsup.com

Description: Seeks to encourage change in U.S. industry through development and implementation of advanced manufacturing and engineering technologies such as Taguchi Methods, Quality Function Deployment, Statistical Process Control, and Total Quality Management. Offers educational courses, training seminars, and workshops to improve quality, reduce cost, and enhance competitive position of U.S. products. Maintains international network of affiliates for developing training specialists and technologies curriculum. Has government contract to provide training services to government supplier companies.

★7999★ **Military Operations Research Society (MORS)**
1703 N Beauregard St., No. 450
Alexandria, VA 22311-1717
Ph: (703)933-9070   Fax: (703)933-9066
E-mail: morsoffice@mors.org
URL: http://www.mors.org

Description: Works to improve the quality and effectiveness of military operations research. Sponsors colloquia; facilitates exchange of information and peer criticism among students, theoreticians, practitioners, and users of military operations research. Does not make or advocate official policy nor does it attempt to influence policy formulation.

Ophthalmic Laboratory Technicians

SOURCES OF HELP-WANTED ADS

★8000★ American Optician
Opticians Association of America
PO Box 6600
Springfield, VA 22150-6600
Ph: (703)916-8856   Fax: (703)916-7966
Fr: 800-443-8997

Quarterly. Subscription included in membership. Professional journal covering optometry.

★8001★ Archives of Ophthalmology
American Medical Association
515 N State St.
Chicago, IL 60610
Ph: (312)464-4470   Fax: (312)464-5020

Monthly. $190.00/year for individuals; $170.00 for single issue. Educational/clinical journal for ophthalmologists.

★8002★ EyeNet
American Academy of Ophthalmology
655 Beach St.
PO Box 7424
San Francisco, CA 94120
Ph: (415)561-8500
E-mail: eyenet@aao.org
URL: http://206.14.84.3/eyenet_mag/

Monthly. $128.00/year for individuals. Professional magazine of the American Academy of Ophthalmology covering clinical, socioeconomic and political trends affecting their practice for members.

★8003★ Ophthalmology Journal
American Academy of Ophthalmology
655 Beach St.
PO Box 7424
San Francisco, CA 94120
Ph: (415)561-8500
URL: http://www.aaojournal.org

Monthly. $161.00/year for individuals; $275.00/year for institutions; $30.00 for sin-

gle issue, current and back issues. Medical journal for clinicians.

★8004★ Optometry
American Optometric Association
243 N Lindbergh Blvd.
St. Louis, MO 63141-7881
Ph: (314)991-4100   Fax: (314)991-4101
E-mail: jdkopp@aoa.org

Monthly. Subscription included in membership; $101.00/year for nonmembers; $5.00/year for nonmembers, single issue. Clinical journal for members of the American Optometric Association.

★8005★ Review of Optometry
Jobson Professional Publications Group
11 Campus Blvd., Ste. 100
Newtown Square, PA 19073
Ph: (610)492-1000   Fax: (610)492-1039
E-mail: reviewofoptometry@jobson.com
URL: http://http:www.revoptom.com

Monthly. $46.00/year for individuals. Journal for the optometric profession and optical industry.

EMPLOYER DIRECTORIES AND NETWORKING LISTS

★8006★ Eye Care Sourcebook
Omnigraphics Inc.
615 Griswold St., Ste. 1400
Detroit, MI 48226
Ph: (313)961-1340   Fax: (313)961-1383
Fr: 800-234-1340

$78.00. Publication includes: List of eye care organizations. Principal content of publication is information on various eye-related problems and solutions. Indexes: Alphabetical.

★8007★ Optometry: A Career with Vision
American Optometric Association
243 N Lindbergh Blvd.
St. Louis, MO 63141-7881
Ph: (314)991-4100   Fax: (314)991-4101
URL: http://www.aoanet.org

Free. Covers 17 optometry schools. Entries include: School name, address, phone; name of contact; admission requirements; statistical profile of students in program. Arrangement: Alphabetical.

HANDBOOKS AND MANUALS

★8008★ Careers in Health Care
McGraw-Hill Trade
2 Penn Plaza
New York, NY 10121
Ph: (212)904-2000   Fr: 800-722-4726
E-mail: ntcpub@tribune.com

Barbara M. Swanson. Fourth edition, 2000. $17.95; $13.95 (paper). 320 pages. Describes job duties, work settings, salaries, licensing and certification requirements, educational preparation, and future outlook. Gives ideas on how to secure a job.

★8009★ Certified Ophthalmic Technician Exam Review Manual
SLACK, Inc.
6900 Grove Rd.
Thorofare, NJ 08086-9447
Ph: (856)848-1000   Fax: (856)853-5991
Fr: 800-257-8290

Janice K. Ledford. 1997. $33.00 (paper). 256 pages. Part of the Basic Bookshelf for Eyecare Professionals Series.

★8010★ Expert Resumes for Health Care Careers

JIST Publishing
8902 Otis Ave.
Indianapolis, IN 46216-1033
Ph: (317)613-4200   Fax: 800-547-8329

December 2003. $16.95. 288 pages.

★8011★ Health Careers Today

Elsevier-Health Sciences Division
The Curtis Center, Ste. 300E, 3rd Fl.
170 S. Independence Mall W.
Philadelphia, PA 19106
Ph: (215)238-7800   Fax: (215)238-7362
Fr: 800-523-4069

Gerdin. Revised edition. April 2004. $52.95.

★8012★ Home Study for Optometric Assisting

Butterworth-Heinemann
225 Wildwood Ave., Unit B
Woburn, MA 01801
Ph: (781)904-2500   Fax: (781)904-2640
Fr: 800-366-2665

Mary Jameson, editor. Second edition, 1996. $255.00. 432 pages. Out of print.

★8013★ Ophthalmology: Pretest Self-Assessment and Review

McGraw-Hill Education Group
PO Box 545
Blacklick, OH 43004-0545
Fax: (614)755-5645   Fr: 800-722-4726

H. Jay Wisnicki. 1996. $47.00 (paper). 242 pages. Out of print. Part of the Pretest Specialty Level Series.

★8014★ Opportunities in Eye Care Careers

McGraw-Hill Trade
2 Penn Plaza
New York, NY 10121
Ph: (212)904-2000   Fr: 800-722-4726

Kathleen Belkoff. 1998. $14.95; $11.95 (paper). 206 pages. Explores careers in ophthalmology, optometry, and support positions. Describes the work, salary, and employment outlook and opportunities.

★8015★ Resumes for Health and Medical Careers

McGraw-Hill Trade
2 Penn Plaza
New York, NY 10121
Ph: (212)904-2000   Fr: 800-722-4726
E-mail: ntcpub@tribune.com

1997. $9.95 (paper). 455 pages.

EMPLOYMENT AGENCIES AND SEARCH FIRMS

★8016★ Retail Recruiters/Spectrum Consultants, Inc.

10 E Athens Ave., Ste.200
Ardmore, PA 19003
Ph: (610)645-9520
E-mail: rrspectrum@erols.com

Employment agency. Affiliate offices in many locations across the country.

ONLINE JOB SOURCES AND SERVICES

★8017★ American Academy of Ophthalmology Professional Choices Career Center

American Academy of Ophthalmology
655 Beach St.
PO Box 7424
San Francisco, CA 94120-7424
Ph: (415)561-8500   Fax: (415)561-8595
E-mail: pchoices@atsaao.org
URL: http://secure3.aao.org/professional-choices/index.cfm

Description: A site providing regularly updated ophthalmology positions. Applicants for jobs contact the AAO with resume, cover letter, and listing reference number. Job hunters may also join the Applicant Database which allows access to a greater number of employers. **Fee:** $70 for nonmembers, $60 for members to subscribe to the Applicant Database.

★8018★ Medhunters.com

E-mail: info@medhunters.com
URL: http://www.medhunters.com

Description: Career search site for jobs in all health care specialties; educational resources; visa and licensing information for relocation; interesting articles; relocation tools; links to professional organizations and general resources.

★8019★ ProHealthJobs

E-mail: sales@prohealthjobs.com
URL: http://www.prohealthjobs.com

Description: Career resources site for the medical and health care field. Lists professional opportunities, product information, continuing education and open positions.

TRADESHOWS

★8020★ The OLA

Optical Laboratories Association
PO Box 2000
Merrifield, VA 22116-2000
Ph: (703)359-2830   Fax: (703)359-283
URL: http://www.OLA-labs.org

Annual. **Primary Exhibits:** Ophthalmic laboratory equipment, supplies, and services. **Dates and Locations:** 2004 Nov 11-13 Nashville, TN; Opryland Hotel.

★8021★ Pan-American Congress of Ophthalmology

Pan-American Association of Ophthalmology
1301 S Bowen Rd., Ste. 365
Arlington, TX 76013
Ph: (817)275-7553   Fax: (817)275-3961
E-mail: info@paao.org
URL: http://www.paao.org

Biennial. **Primary Exhibits:** Ophthalmology equipment, supplies, and services. **Dates and Locations:** 2005 Mar 18-21; Santiago, Chile; Casa Piedra Convention Center.

★8022★ Symposium of the New Orleans Academy of Ophthalmology

New Orleans Academy of Ophthalmology
924 Valmont St., Ste. 301B
New Orleans, LA 70115
Ph: (504)899-9955   Fax: (504)899-4948
URL: http://www.noao.org

Annual. **Primary Exhibits:** Medical instruments, drug companies, and medical publishers.

★8023★ Washington Academy of Eye Physicians and Surgeons Trade Show

Washington Academy of Eye Physicians and Surgeons
2033 6th Ave., Ste. 1100
Seattle, WA 98121
Ph: (206)441-9762   Fax: (206)441-5863
Fr: 800-552-0612

Annual. **Primary Exhibits:** Ophthalmic, technical, and scientific equipment, supplies, and services.

★8024★ Wills Eye Hospital Annual Conference

Wills Eye Society of Ex-Residents
1621 Norristown Rd.
Maple Glen, PA 19002
Ph: (215)641-9569

Annual. **Primary Exhibits:** Ophthalmic equipment, supplies, and services.

OTHER SOURCES

★8025★ **American Academy of Optometry (AAO)**
6110 Executive Blvd., Ste. 506
Rockville, MD 20852
Ph: (301)984-1441   Fax: (301)984-4737
E-mail: aaoptom@aol.com
URL: http://www.aaopt.org

Description: Optometrists, educators, and scientists interested in optometric education, and standards of care in visual problems. Conducts continuing education for optometrists and visual scientists. Sponsors 4-day annual meeting.

★8026★ **Association of Technical Personnel in Ophthalmology (ATPO)**
2025 Woodlane Dr.
St. Paul, MN 55125-2995
Ph: (651)731-7239   Fax: (651)731-0410
Fr: 800-482-4858
E-mail: atppresident@yahoo.com
URL: http://www.atpo.org

Members: Ophthalmic assistants, technicians, technologists, surgical and keratorefractive techs, photographers, nurses, and orthoptists. **Purpose:** Promotes high standards and professional ethics dedicated to quality ophthalmic medical care under the direction of an ophthalmologist. Recognizes the utilization of ophthalmalic medical personnel to perform certain non-medical procedures or tests as a means of enhancing the productivity of ophthalmologists and thereby increasing the availability of ophthalmologists to provide the highest level of medical service and comprehensive vision care to their patients.

★8027★ **Association of University Professors of Ophthalmology (AUPO)**
PO Box 420369
San Francisco, CA 94142-0369
Ph: (415)561-8548   Fax: (415)561-8531
E-mail: aupo@aao.org

Members: Heads of departments or divisions of ophthalmology in accredited medical schools throughout the U.S. and Canada; directors of ophthalmology residency programs in institutions not connected to medical schools. **Purpose:** Promotes medical education, research, and patient care relating to ophthalmology. **Activities:** Operates Ophthalmology Matching Program and faculty placement service, which aids ophthalmologists interested in being associated with university ophthalmology programs to locate such programs.

★8028★ **Exploring Health Occupations**
Cambridge Educational
2572 Brunswick Ave.
Lawrenceville, NJ 08648-4128
Fax: 800-FAX-ON-US   Fr: 800-468-4227
URL: http://www.cambridgeeducational.com

Two videos. $139.95. 1999.

★8029★ **Health Service Occupations**
Delphi Productions
3160 4th St.
Boulder, CO 80304
Fax: (303)443-4022   Fr: 888-443-2400
URL: http://www.delphivideo.com

$95.00. 50 minutes. Part of the Careers for the 21st Century Video Library.

★8030★ **Health Technologists & Technicians**
Delphi Productions
3160 4th St.
Boulder, CO 80304
Fax: (303)443-4022   Fr: 888-443-2400
URL: http://www.delphivideo.com

$95.00. 50 minutes. Part of the Careers for the 21st Century Video Library.

★8031★ **International Vision Expo and Conference/East**
Association Expositions and Services
383 Main Ave.
Norwalk, CT 06851
Ph: (203)840-5600   Fax: (203)840-9600

E-mail: inquiry@shot.reedexpo.com
Annual. **Primary Exhibits:** Equipment, supplies and services for the vision industry.

★8032★ **Medical Technicians and Technologists**
Cambridge Educational
2572 Brunswick Ave.
Lawrenceville, NJ 08648-4128
Fax: 800-FAX-ON-US   Fr: 800-468-4227
URL: http://www.cambridgeeducational.com

$79.95. 15 minutes. Part of the Exploring Health Occupations Series.

★8033★ **Medicine & Related Occupations**
Delphi Productions
3160 4th St.
Boulder, CO 80304
Fax: (303)443-4022   Fr: 888-443-2400
URL: http://www.delphivideo.com

$95.00. 45 minutes. Part of the Careers for the 21st Century Video Library.

★8034★ **Production Occupations**
Delphi Productions
3160 4th St.
Boulder, CO 80304
Fax: (303)443-4022   Fr: 888-443-2400
URL: http://www.delphivideo.com

$95.00. 49 minutes. Part of the Careers for the 21st Century Video Library.

★8035★ **Technical & Related Occupations**
Delphi Productions
3160 4th St.
Boulder, CO 80304
Fax: (303)443-4022   Fr: 888-443-2400
URL: http://www.delphivideo.com

$95.00. 49 minutes. Part of the Careers for the 21st Century Video Library.

Optometrists

SOURCES OF HELP-WANTED ADS

★8036★ American Optician

Opticians Association of America
PO Box 6600
Springfield, VA 22150-6600
Ph: (703)916-8856   Fax: (703)916-7966
Fr: 800-443-8997

Quarterly. Subscription included in membership. Professional journal covering optometry.

★8037★ Archives of Ophthalmology

American Medical Association
515 N State St.
Chicago, IL 60610
Ph: (312)464-4470   Fax: (312)464-5020

Monthly. $190.00/year for individuals; $170.00 for single issue. Educational/clinical journal for ophthalmologists.

★8038★ EyeNet

American Academy of Ophthalmology
655 Beach St.
PO Box 7424
San Francisco, CA 94120
Ph: (415)561-8500
E-mail: eyenet@aao.org
URL: http://206.14.84.3/eyenet_mag/

Monthly. $128.00/year for individuals. Professional magazine of the American Academy of Ophthalmology covering clinical, socioeconomic and political trends affecting their practice for members.

★8039★ oemagazine

SPIE - International Society for Optical Engineering
1000 20th St.
Bellingham, WA 98225
Ph: (360)676-3290   Fax: (360)647-1445
E-mail: info@oemagazine.com
URL: http://oemagazine.com

Monthly. Subscription included in membership. Magazine publishing technical articles

and interviews with recognized leaders in optical and optoelectronic applied science and engineering. Includes information about the industry, technological advances, upcoming symposia, and other news. Official magazine of SPIE—The International Society for Optical Engineering.

★8040★ Ophthalmology Journal

American Academy of Ophthalmology
655 Beach St.
PO Box 7424
San Francisco, CA 94120
Ph: (415)561-8500
URL: http://www.aaojournal.org

Monthly. $161.00/year for individuals; $275.00/year for institutions; $30.00 for single issue, current and back issues. Medical journal for clinicians.

★8041★ Optometric Management

Boucher Communications Inc.
1300 Virginia Dr., Ste. 400
Fort Washington, PA 19034-3221
Ph: (215)643-8000   Fax: (215)643-8099
E-mail: om@boucher1.com

Monthly. $37.00/year for individuals; $59.00 for two years; $48.00/year for Canada; $72.00 for two years-Canada; $85.00/year for elsewhere. Medical professional journal.

★8042★ Optometry

American Optometric Association
243 N Lindbergh Blvd.
St. Louis, MO 63141-7881
Ph: (314)991-4100   Fax: (314)991-4101
E-mail: jdkopp@aoa.org

Monthly. Subscription included in membership; $101.00/year for nonmembers; $5.00/year for nonmembers, single issue. Clinical journal for members of the American Optometric Association.

★8043★ RETINA

Lippincott Williams & Wilkins
530 Walnut St.
Philadelphia, PA 19106-3621
Ph: (215)521-8300   Fax: (215)521-8483

URL: http://www.retinajournal.com

Bimonthly. $159.00/year for individuals; $307.00/year for institutions; $60.00 for single issue, current and back issues. Journal publishing clinically oriented articles for the general ophthalmologist and vitreoretinal specialist.

★8044★ Review of Optometry

Jobson Professional Publications Group
11 Campus Blvd., Ste. 100
Newtown Square, PA 19073
Ph: (610)492-1000   Fax: (610)492-1039
E-mail: reviewofoptometry@jobson.com
URL: http://http:www.revoptom.com

Monthly. $46.00/year for individuals. Journal for the optometric profession and optical industry.

PLACEMENT AND JOB REFERRAL SERVICES

★8045★ American Optometric Association (AOA)

243 N Lindbergh Blvd.
St. Louis, MO 63141
Ph: (314)991-4100   Fax: (314)991-4101
URL: http://www.aoanet.org/

Members: Professional association of optometrists, students of optometry, and paraoptometric assistants and technicians. **Purpose:** Purposes are to improve the quality, availability, and accessibility of eye and vision care; to represent the optometric profession; to help members conduct their practices; to promote the highest standards of patient care. **Activities:** Monitors and promotes legislation concerning the scope of optometric practice, alternate health care delivery systems, health care cost containment, Medicare, and other issues relevant to eye/vision care. Supports the International Library, Archives and Museum of Optometry which includes references on ophthalmic and related sciences with emphasis on the history and socioeconomic aspects of optometry. Operates Vision U.S.A. program, which provides free eye care to the working poor. Conducts specialized education programs; operates placement service; compiles statistics. Maintains museum. Conducts Seal of Certification and Acceptance Program.

★8046★ American Public Health Association (APHA)

800 I St. NW
Washington, DC 20001-3710
Ph: (202)777-2742   Fax: (202)777-2534
E-mail: comments@apha.org
URL: http://www.apha.org

Members: Professional organization of physicians, nurses, educators, academicians, environmentalists, epidemiologists, new professionals, social workers, health administrators, optometrists, podiatrists, pharmacists, dentists, nutritionists, health planners, other community and mental health specialists, and interested consumers. **Purpose:** Seeks to protect and promote personal, mental, and environmental health. **Activities:** Services include promulgation of standards; establishment of uniform practices and procedures; development of the etiology of communicable diseases; research in public health; exploration of medical care programs and their relationships to public health. Sponsors job placement service.

★8047★ National Optometric Association (NOA)

3723 Main St.
PO Box F
East Chicago, IN 46312
Ph: (219)398-1832   Fax: (219)398-1077
Fr: 877-394-2020
E-mail: marshall@indiana.edu
URL: http://www.natoptassoc.org

Description: Optometrists dedicated to increasing awareness of the status of eye/vision health in the minority community and the national community at-large; and strives to make known the impact of the eye/vision dysfunction on the effectiveness and productivity of citizens and the academic proficiency of students. Conducts national minority recruiting programs, job placement, assistance programs for graduates, practitioners, and optometric organizations, and the promotion of delivery of care. Maintains speakers' bureau. Offers specialized education program.

EMPLOYER DIRECTORIES AND NETWORKING LISTS

★8048★ College of Optometrists in Vision Development-Membership Directory

College of Optometrists in Vision Development
243 N Lindbergh Blvd., Ste. 310
St. Louis, MO 63141
Ph: (314)991-4007   Fax: (314)991-1167
Fr: 888-268-3770

Annual, April. $3.50 for nonmembers. Covers about 1500 members. Entries include: Name, address, phone, fax, e-mail. Arrangement: Geographical.

★8049★ Eye Care Sourcebook

Omnigraphics Inc.
615 Griswold St., Ste. 1400
Detroit, MI 48226
Ph: (313)961-1340   Fax: (313)961-1383
Fr: 800-234-1340

$78.00. Publication includes: List of eye care organizations. Principal content of publication is information on various eye-related problems and solutions. Indexes: Alphabetical.

★8050★ HMO/PPO Directory

Thomson Medical Economics
5 Paragon Dr.
Montvale, NJ 07645-1742
Ph: (201)358-7200   Fax: (201)722-2680

Annual, November. $215.00. Covers over 600 health maintenance organizations (HMOs) and more than 1,000 preferred provider organizations (PPOs). Entries include: Name of organization, address, phone, number of members, names of officers, employer references, geographical area served, parent company, average fees and copayments, financial data, and cost control procedures. Arrangement: Geographical. Indexes: Organization name, personnel name, HMOs and PPOs by state, and number of members enrolled.

★8051★ Medical and Health Information Directory

Thomson Gale
27500 Drake Rd.
Farmington Hills, MI 48331-3535
Ph: (248)699-4253   Fax: (248)699-8065
Fr: 800-877-GALE
E-mail: businessproducts@gale.com

Annual. $285.00 per volume; $675.00 per set. Covers in Volume 1, more than 26,500 medical and health oriented associations, organizations, institutions, and government agencies, including health maintenance organizations (HMOs), preferred provider organizations (PPOs), insurance companies, pharmaceutical companies, research centers, and medical and allied health schools. In Volume 2, over 12,000 medical book publishers; medical periodicals, directories,

audiovisual producers and services, medical libraries and information centers, electronic resources, and health-related internet search engines. In Volume 3, more than 35,500 clinics, treatment centers, care programs, and counseling/diagnostic services for 34 subject areas. Entries include: Institution, service, or firm name, address, phone, fax, email and URL; many include names of key personnel and, when pertinent, descriptive annotation. Volume 3 was formerly listed separately as Health Services Directory. Arrangement: Classified by organization activity, service, etc. Indexes: Each volume has a complete alphabetical name and keyword index.

★8052★ Optometrists OD Directory

infoUSA Inc.
5711 S 86th Cir.
Omaha, NE 68127-0347
Ph: (402)930-3500   Fax: (402)331-0176
Fr: 800-555-6124
URL: http://www.abii.com

Annual. Number of listings: 37,423. Entries include: Name, address, phone (including area code), size of advertisement, year first in "Yellow Pages," name of owner or manager, number of employees. Regional editions available: Eastern, $725.00; Western, $555.00. Compiled from telephone company "Yellow Pages," nationwide. Arrangement: Geographical.

★8053★ Optometry: A Career with Vision

American Optometric Association
243 N Lindbergh Blvd.
St. Louis, MO 63141-7881
Ph: (314)991-4100   Fax: (314)991-4101
URL: http://www.aoanet.org

Free. Covers 17 optometry schools. Entries include: School name, address, phone; name of contact; admission requirements; statistical profile of students in program. Arrangement: Alphabetical.

★8054★ Optometry and Vision Science-Geographical Directory, American Academy of Optometry Issue

American Academy of Optometry
6110 Executive Blvd., Ste. 506
Rockville, MD 20852
Ph: (301)984-1441   Fax: (301)984-4737
URL: http://www.aaopt.org

Biennial, odd years. $25.00. Publication includes: List of 3,400 members; international coverage. Entries include: Name, title, affiliation; office address, phone, fax, email. Arrangement: Geographical and alphabetical. Indexes: Name, specialty.

HANDBOOKS AND MANUALS

★8055★ Business Awareness for Optometrists: A Primer

Butterworth-Heinemann
225 Wildwood Ave., Unit B
Woburn, MA 01801
Ph: (781)904-2500   Fax: (781)904-2640
Fr: 800-366-2665

Nizar K. Hirji. 1999. $55.00.

★8056★ Expert Resumes for Health Care Careers

JIST Publishing
8902 Otis Ave.
Indianapolis, IN 46216-1033
Ph: (317)613-4200   Fax: 800-547-8329

December 2003. $16.95. 288 pages.

★8057★ Health Careers Today

Elsevier-Health Sciences Division
The Curtis Center, Ste. 300E, 3rd Fl.
170 S. Independence Mall W.
Philadelphia, PA 19106
Ph: (215)238-7800   Fax: (215)238-7362
Fr: 800-523-4069

Gerdin. Revised edition. April 2004. $52.95.

★8058★ Home Study for Optometric Assisting

Butterworth-Heinemann
225 Wildwood Ave., Unit B
Woburn, MA 01801
Ph: (781)904-2500   Fax: (781)904-2640
Fr: 800-366-2665

Mary Jameson, editor. Second edition, 1996. $255.00. 432 pages. Out of print.

★8059★ Opportunities in Eye Care Careers

McGraw-Hill Trade
2 Penn Plaza
New York, NY 10121
Ph: (212)904-2000   Fr: 800-722-4726

Kathleen Belkoff. 1998. $14.95; $11.95 (paper). 206 pages. Explores careers in ophthalmology, optometry, and support positions. Describes the work, salary, and employment outlook and opportunities.

★8060★ Opportunities in Paramedical Careers

McGraw-Hill/Contemporary Books
1221 Avenue of the Americas
New York, NY 10020
Ph: (212)904-2000   Fr: 800-323-4900
E-mail: ntcpub@tribune.com

Alex Kacen. Revised, 1999. $14.95; 11.95 (paper). 200 pages. Discusses a variety of opportunities in this field and how to pursue them. Illustrated.

★8061★ Resumes for Health and Medical Careers

McGraw-Hill Trade
2 Penn Plaza
New York, NY 10121
Ph: (212)904-2000   Fr: 800-722-4726
E-mail: ntcpub@tribune.com

1997. $9.95 (paper). 455 pages.

EMPLOYMENT AGENCIES AND SEARCH FIRMS

★8062★ Retail Recruiters/Spectrum Consultants, Inc.

10 E Athens Ave., Ste.200
Ardmore, PA 19003
Ph: (610)645-9520
E-mail: rrspectrum@erols.com

Employment agency. Affiliate offices in many locations across the country.

ONLINE JOB SOURCES AND SERVICES

★8063★ American Academy of Ophthalmology Professional Choices Career Center

American Academy of Ophthalmology
655 Beach St.
PO Box 7424
San Francisco, CA 94120-7424
Ph: (415)561-8500   Fax: (415)561-8595
E-mail: pchoices@atsaao.org
URL: http://secure3.aao.org/professional-choices/index.cfm

Description: A site providing regularly updated ophthalmology positions. Applicants for jobs contact the AAO with resume, cover letter, and listing reference number. Job hunters may also join the Applicant Database which allows access to a greater number of employers. **Fee:** $70 for nonmembers, $60 for members to subscribe to the Applicant Database.

★8064★ Medhunters.com

E-mail: info@medhunters.com
URL: http://www.medhunters.com

Description: Career search site for jobs in all health care specialties; educational resources; visa and licensing information for relocation; interesting articles; relocation tools; links to professional organizations and general resources.

★8065★ ProHealthJobs

E-mail: sales@prohealthjobs.com
URL: http://www.prohealthjobs.com

Description: Career resources site for the medical and health care field. Lists professional opportunities, product information, continuing education and open positions.

TRADESHOWS

★8066★ American Academy of Optometry

American Academy of Optometry
6110 Executive Blvd., Ste. 506
Rockville, MD 20852
Ph: (301)984-1441   Fax: (301)984-4737
E-mail: aaoptom@aol.com

Annual. **Primary Exhibits:** Exhibits focusing on the latest research and patient treatments relating to clinical practice standards, optometric education, and experimental research in visual problems. **Dates and Locations:** 2004 Dec 09-13; Tampa, FL; Convention Center.

★8067★ American Optometric Association Congress

American Optometric Association
243 N. Lindbergh Blvd.
St. Louis, MO 63141
Ph: (314)991-4100   Fax: (314)991-4101
Fr: 800-365-2219
URL: http://www.aoa.org

Annual. **Primary Exhibits:** Optometry equipment, supplies, and services. **Dates and Locations:** 2005 Jun 22-26; Dallas, TX; Gaylord Palms.

★8068★ American Optometric Student Association Annual Meeting

American Optometric Student Association
243 N. Lindbergh
St. Louis, MO 63141
Ph: (314)991-4100   Fax: (314)991-4101

Annual. **Primary Exhibits:** Optometry equipment, supplies, and services.

★8069★ College of Optometrists in Vision Development Annual Meeting

College of Optometrists in Vision Development
243 N. Lindbergh Blvd., No. 310
St. Louis, MO 63141
Ph: (314)991-4007   Fax: (314)991-1167
E-mail: smillod@aol.com
URL: http://www.covd.org

Annual. **Primary Exhibits:** Exhibits relating to orthoptics and optometric vision therapy with emphasis on visual information processing in visually related learning problems.

★8070★ International Vision Expo and Conference/East

Association Expositions and Services
383 Main Ave.
Norwalk, CT 06851
Ph: (203)840-5600   Fax: (203)840-9600
E-mail: inquiry@shot.reedexpo.com

Annual. **Primary Exhibits:** Equipment, supplies and services for the vision industry.

★8071★ Pan-American Congress of Ophthalmology

Pan-American Association of
Ophthalmology
1301 S Bowen Rd., Ste. 365
Arlington, TX 76013
Ph: (817)275-7553   Fax: (817)275-3961
E-mail: info@paao.org
URL: http://www.paao.org

Biennial. **Primary Exhibits:** Ophthalmology equipment, supplies, and services. **Dates and Locations:** 2005 Mar 18-21; Santiago, Chile; Casa Piedra Convention Center.

★8072★ SECO International (Southern Council of Optometrists)

Southern Council of Optometrists
4661 N. Shallowford Rd.
Atlanta, GA 30338
Ph: (404)451-8206   Fax: (404)451-3156
URL: http://www.optcom.com

Annual. **Primary Exhibits:** Ophthalmic supplies, diagnostic equipment, reference books, frames for glasses, office equipment, computers, contact lenses, and ophthalmic pharmaceuticals.

OTHER SOURCES

★8073★ American Academy of Optometry (AAO)

6110 Executive Blvd., Ste. 506
Rockville, MD 20852
Ph: (301)984-1441   Fax: (301)984-4737
E-mail: aaoptom@aol.com
URL: http://www.aaopt.org

Description: Optometrists, educators, and scientists interested in optometric education, and standards of care in visual problems.

Conducts continuing education for optometrists and visual scientists. Sponsors 4-day annual meeting.

★8074★ American Almanac of Jobs and Salaries

Morrow Avon
1350 Avenue of the Americas
New York, NY 10019
Ph: (212)261-6788   Fr: 800-242-7737

John W. Wright. Revised edition, 2000. $20.00 (paper). 672 pages. This is a comprehensive guide to the wages of hundreds of occupations in a wide variety of industries and organizations.

★8075★ American Optometric Student Association (AOSA)

243 N Lindbergh
St. Louis, MO 63141
Ph: (314)991-4100   Fax: (314)991-4101
E-mail: president@theaosa.org
URL: http://www.theaosa.org/frameset2.htm

Members: Optometric students, state optometric associations, and family members of optometric students. **Activities:** Collects updated information on progress in the optometry field. Provides members with opportunities to work in areas of health care need such as local community health projects, school curriculum changes, and health manpower legislation. Works to improve optometric education and health care for the general population. Maintains active liaison with other optometric associations. Conducts communications program.

★8076★ Exploring Health Occupations

Cambridge Educational
2572 Brunswick Ave.
Lawrenceville, NJ 08648-4128
Fax: 800-FAX-ON-US   Fr: 800-468-4227
URL: http://www.cambridgeeducational.com

Two videos. $139.95. 1999.

★8077★ Health Service Occupations

Delphi Productions
3160 4th St.
Boulder, CO 80304
Fax: (303)443-4022   Fr: 888-443-2400
URL: http://www.delphivideo.com

$95.00. 50 minutes. Part of the Careers for the 21st Century Video Library.

★8078★ Medicine & Related Occupations

Delphi Productions
3160 4th St.
Boulder, CO 80304
Fax: (303)443-4022   Fr: 888-443-2400
URL: http://www.delphivideo.com

$95.00. 45 minutes. Part of the Careers for the 21st Century Video Library.

★8079★ National Association of Optometrists and Opticians (NAOO)

PO Box 459
Marblehead, OH 43440
Ph: (419)798-2031   Fax: (419)798-8548
E-mail: fdrozak@cros.net

Description: Licensed optometrists, opticians, and corporations. Conducts public affairs programs of mutual importance to members; serves as an organizational center for special purpose programs; acts as a clearinghouse for information affecting the retail optical industry.

★8080★ Optometrists

Evon Publishing
832 N 7th Ave.
Iron River, MI 49935
Ph: (906)265-3190

Audiocassette. 1996. $16.95. 32 minutes. Part of the Careers and Vocational Guidance Series. Provides information about the nature of the work, educational requirements, employment outlook, earnings, and work conditions as well as additional related information.

PC Network Administrators

SOURCES OF HELP-WANTED ADS

★8081★ PC Computing

Ziff-Davis Media Inc.
28 E 28th St.
New York, NY 10016-7930
Ph: (212)503-3500

Monthly. Magazine on personal computers.

★8082★ PC Magazine

Ziff-Davis Media Inc.
28 E 28th St.
New York, NY 10016-7930
Ph: (212)503-3500

Semimonthly. Consumer magazine focusing on the personal computer industry.

★8083★ PC Today

Sandhills Publishing
120 W Harvest Dr.
PO Box 85310
Lincoln, NE 68501-5310
Ph: (402)479-2141   Fax: (402)479-2120
Fr: 800-247-4880

Monthly. $24.00/year; $32.00/year for other countries; $2.95/year for single issue; $3.50/year. Magazine for personal computer users.

★8084★ PC Week

Ziff-Davis Media Inc.
28 E 28th St.
New York, NY 10016-7930
Ph: (212)503-3500
URL: http://www.pcweek.com

Weekly. Free to qualified subscribers; $195.00/year for individuals; $250.00/year for Canada and Mexico; $395.00/year for other countries; $6.00 for single issue. Tabloid featuring microcomputer products and developments.

★8085★ PC WORLD

101 Communications
9121 Oakdale Ave.
Chatsworth, CA 91311
Ph: (818)734-1520   Fax: (818)734-1522
URL: http://www.pcworld.com

Monthly. $29.90/year for individuals; $5.95 for single issue.

EMPLOYER DIRECTORIES AND NETWORKING LISTS

★8086★ Computer Directory

Computer Directories Inc.
23815 Nichols Sawmill Rd.
Hockley, TX 77447
Ph: (281)259-5959   Fax: (281)356-7980
Fr: 800-234-4353
URL: http://www.compdirinc.com

Annual, fall. Covers approximately 130,000 computer installations; 19 separate volumes for Alaska/Hawaii, Connecticut/New Jersey, Dallas/Ft. Worth, Eastern Seaboard, Far Midwest, Houston, Illinois, Midatlantic, Midcentral, Mideast, Minnesota/Wisconsin, North Central, New England, New York Metro, Northwest, Ohio, Pennsylvania/West Virginia, Southeast, and Southwest Texas. Entries include: Company name, address, phone, fax, email, name and title of contact, hardware used, software application, operating system, programming language, computer graphics, networking system. Arrangement: Geographical. Indexes: Alphabetical, industry, hardware.

★8087★ Peterson's Job Opportunities for Engineering and Computer Science Majors

Thomson Thomson Peterson's
Princeton Pke. Corporate Ctr., 2000 Lenox Dr.
PO Box 67005
Lawrenceville, NJ 08648
Ph: (609)896-1800   Fax: (609)896-4531
Fr: 800-338-3282

Annual, latest edition 1999. $18.95. Covers approximately 2,000 research, consulting, manufacturing, government, and technical services organizations hiring colleges graduates in the fields of engineering, telecommunications, biotechnology, software, and consumer electronics. Entries include: Organization name, address, phone, name and title of contact, type of organization, number of employees, Standard Industrial Classification (SIC) code, description of opportunities available, level of education required, starting salary, location, level of experience accepted, benefits.

HANDBOOKS AND MANUALS

★8088★ The Digital Frontier Job & Opportunity Finder

Moon Lake Media
PO Box 251466
Los Angeles, CA 90025
Ph: (310)535-2453

Don B. Altman. 1996. $19.95 (paper). 256 pages.

★8089★ Great Jobs for Computer Science Majors

McGraw-Hill Companies
1221 Avenue of the Americas
New York, NY 10020
Ph: (212)904-2000   Fr: 800-323-4900
E-mail: ntcpub@tribune.com

Jan Goldberg, Stephen Lambert, Julie De-Galan. 1997. $11.95 (paper). 365 pages.

★8090★ Job Seekers Guide to Silicon Valley Recruiters

John Wily and Sons, Inc.
605 Third Ave., 4th Fl.
New York, NY 10158-0012
Ph: (212)850-6276   Fax: (212)850-8641

Christopher W. Hunt, Scott A. Scanlon. First edition, 1998. $19.95 (paper). 371 pages. Includes a list of 2,400 recruiters specializing in high technology positions and explains how to work with them.

★8091★ The JobBank Guide to Computer and High-Tech Companies

Adams Media Corp.
57 Littlefield St.
Avon, MA 02322
Ph: (508)427-7100   Fax: (508)427-6790
Fr: 800-872-5627
URL: http://www.adamsmedia.com

Second edition, 1999. $17.95 (paper). 704 pages. Contains profiles of more than 4,500 high-tech employers.

★8092★ Opportunities in Computer Systems Careers

McGraw-Hill Contemporary Books
1221 Avenue of the Americas
New York, NY 10020
Ph: (212)904-2000   Fr: 800-323-4900
E-mail: ntcpub@tribune.com

Julie King Burns. 1996. $14.95; $11.95 (paper). 160 pages.

★8093★ Opportunities in High Tech Careers

McGraw-Hill Trade
2 Penn Plaza
New York, NY 10121
Ph: (212)904-2000   Fr: 800-722-4726

Gary Colter and Deborah Yanuck. 1995. $14.95; $11.95 (paper). 160 pages. Explores high technology careers. Describes job opportunities, how to make a career decision, how to prepare for high technology jobs, job hunting techniques, and future trends.

★8094★ Opportunities in Telecommunications Careers

Vgm Career Horizons
1221 Avenue of the Americas
New York, NY 10020
Ph: (212)904-2000   Fr: 800-323-4900
E-mail: ntcpub@tribune.com

Jan Bone, Suzanne Nagle. 1995. $12.95; $11.95 (paper).

★8095★ Winning Resumes for Computer Personnel

Barron's Educational Series, Inc.
250 Wireless Blvd.
Hauppauge, NY 11788-3917
Ph: (631)434-3311   Fax: (631)434-3723
Fr: 800-645-3476

Anne Hart. Second edition, 1998. $12.95 (paper). 320 pages.

★8096★ Your Opportunities in Computers

Energeia Publishing, Inc.
1307 Fairmount Ave., S
Salem, OR 97302-4313
Ph: (503)362-1480   Fax: (503)362-2123
Fr: 800-639-6048

John Tribbett. 1994. $2.50 (paper). 8 pages.

EMPLOYMENT AGENCIES AND SEARCH FIRMS

★8097★ Data Systems Search Consultants

1615 Bonanza St., Ste.205
Walnut Creek, CA 94596
Ph: (925)256-0635   Fax: (925)256-9099
E-mail: dsscinfo@dssc.com
URL: http://www.dssc.com

Employment agency. Executive search firm.

★8098★ Huntington Personnel Consultants, Inc.

PO Box 1077
Huntington, NY 11743-0640
Ph: (516)549-8888

Executive search firm and employment agency.

★8099★ Intech Summit Group, Inc.

5075 Shoreham Pl., Ste. 280
San Diego, CA 92122
Ph: (858)452-2100   Fax: (858)452-8500
E-mail: isg@isgsearch.com
URL: http://www.isgsearch.com

Employment agency and executive recruiter with a branch in Carlsbad, CA.

★8100★ O'Keefe and Associates

PO Box 1092
Southport, CT 06890-2092
Ph: (203)254-2544   Fax: (203)254-2126
E-mail: jokeefe@okeefeinc.com
URL: http://www.okeefeinc.com

Executive search firm.

★8101★ Sullivan and Cogliano

230 2nd Ave
Waltham, MA 02451
Ph: (781)890-7890   Fr: 888-785-2641
E-mail: contact@sullivansogliano.com
URL: http://www.sullivancogliano.com

Executive search firm.

★8102★ Technical Talent Locators Ltd.

5570 Sterrett Place, Ste.208
Columbia, MD 21044
Ph: (410)740-0091
URL: http://www.ttlgroup.com

Permanent employment agency working

within the following fields: software and database engineering; computer, communication, and telecommunication system engineering; and other computer-related disciplines.

★8103★ Worlco Computer Resources, Inc.

997 Old Eagle School Rd., Ste. 219
Wayne, PA 19087-1706
Ph: (610)293-9070   Fax: (610)293-1027
E-mail: parisi@worlco.com
URL: http://www.worlco.com

Employment agency and executive search firm. Second location in Cherry Hill, New Jersey.

ONLINE JOB SOURCES AND SERVICES

★8104★ ComputerJobs.com
URL: http://www.computerjobs.com

Description: The site is an employment tool for technology professionals. Information on positions is updated hourly for seekers. Jobs may be searched by skill, or by location nationally or in a specific state or city job market. Contains thousands of job postings. National jobs may be posted for free. Also career resources for IT professionals.

★8105★ Computerwork.com
E-mail: candidate_support@computerwork.com
URL: http://computerwork.com/

Description: Job search and resume submission service for professionals in information technology.

★8106★ Computerworld Careers
URL: http://www.computerworld.com/cwi/careers/

Description: Offers career opportunities for IT (information technology) professionals. Job seekers may search the jobs database, register at the site, and read about job surveys and employment trends. Employers may post jobs.

★8107★ Computing Research Association Job Announcements
URL: http://www.cra.org/main/cra.jobs.html

Description: Contains dated links to national college and university computer technology positions.

★8108★ Dice.com
URL: http://www.dice.com

Description: Job search database for computer consultants and high-tech professionals, listing thousands of high tech permanent contract and consulting jobs for programmers, software engineers, systems administrators, web developers, and hardware engineers. Also free career advice e-mail newsletter and job posting e-alerts.

★8109★ **Ittalent.com**
E-mail: ewsmith@ITtalent.com
URL: http://www.ittalent.com
Description: Job search and resume submission service for professionals in information technology.

★8110★ **ZDNet Tech Jobs**
URL: http://www.zdnet.com/special/filters/techjobs/

Description: Site houses a listing of national employment opportunities for professionals in high tech fields. Also contains resume building tips and relocation resources. Powered by Dice.com

OTHER SOURCES

★8111★ *Computer Occupations*
Delphi Productions
3160 4th St.
Boulder, CO 80304
Fax: (303)443-4022   Fr: 888-443-2400

URL: http://www.delphivideo.com
$95.00. 50 minutes. Part of the Careers for the 21st Century Video Library.

★8112★ *Information Technology Occupations*
Delphi Productions
3160 4th St.
Boulder, CO 80304
Fax: (303)443-4022   Fr: 888-443-2400
URL: http://www.delphivideo.com
$95.00. 52 minutes. Part of the Emerging Careers Video Library.

Personal Service Providers

HANDBOOKS AND MANUALS

★8113★ Career Information Center: Consumer, Homemaking, and Personal Services

Thomson Delmar Learning
5 Maxwell Dr.
PO Box 8007
Clifton Park, NY 12065

Darryl Kestler. January 2002. 58 pages.

★8114★ Household Careers: Nannies, Butlers, Maids and More: The Complete Guide for Finding Household Employment or 'If the Dog Likes You, You're Hired!'

Five Star Publications, Inc.
PO Box 6698
Chandler, AZ 85246-6698
Ph: (602)940-8182   Fax: (602)940-8787
Fr: 800-545-7827

Linda F. Radke. 2001. 102 pages.

★8115★ How to Start and Operate an Errand Service

Legacy Marketing
403 Hobart Dr.
Laurel Springs, NJ 08021
Ph: (609)346-0276   Fax: (609)346-2994
Fr: 888-725-2639

Robin C. Spina. 1996. $29.95. 67 pages.

TRADESHOWS

★8116★ IEHA Convention & Trade Show

International Executive Housekeepers Association Inc.
1001 Eastwind Dr., Ste. 301
Westerville, OH 43081-3361
Ph: (614)895-7166   Fax: (614)895-1248
Fr: 800-200-6342
E-mail: excel@ieha.org

URL: http://www.ieha.org

Biennial. **Primary Exhibits:** Cleaning, maintenance, and sterilization supplies and equipment, including chemicals, cleaners, paper products, linens, and amenities.

OTHER SOURCES

★8117★ Association of Residential Cleaning Professionals

PO Box 2051
Meridian, MS 39302
Ph: (601)914-0270
URL: http://www.arcp.us

Description: Assists residential cleaning service owners and professionals in starting, promoting, building, and expanding their businesses.

★8118★ International Nanny Association (INA)

191 Clarksville Rd.
Princeton Junction, NJ 08550-3111
Ph: (609)799-7527   Fax: (856)858-2519
Fr: 888-878-1477
E-mail: ina@nanny.org
URL: http://www.nanny.org

Description: An educational association for nannies and those who educate, place, employ, and support professional in-home child care. Membership is open to those who are directly involved with the in-home child care profession, including nannies, nanny employers, nanny placement agency owners (and staff), nanny educators, and providers of special services related to the nanny profession.

★8119★ National Association of Nannies

PMB 2004, 25 Rte. 31 S., Ste. C
Pennington, NJ 08534
Fr: 800-344-6266
URL: http://www.nannyassociation.com

Description: Promotes the nanny as a legitimate career choice.

★8120★ National Association of Professional Organizers (NAPO)

4700 W. Lake Ave.
Glenview, IL 60025
Ph: (847)375-4746   Fax: 877-734-8668
URL: http://www.napo.net/

Description: Educational association whose members include organizing consultants, speakers, trainers, authors, and manufacturers of organizing people.

★8121★ National Association of Professional Pet Sitters (NAPPS)

17000 Commerce Pkwy., Ste. C
Mount Laurel, NJ 08054
Ph: (856)439-0324   Fax: (856)439-0525
Fr: 800-296-PETS
E-mail: napps@ahint.com
URL: http://www.petsitters.org

Description: Owners or employees of pet-sitting services; professionals or businesses in related fields. Promotes professional and ethical standards in pet sitting and fosters cooperation among members of the pet-care industry. Serves as a network for the exchange of ideas and information on pet sitting and current industry practices. Disseminates information educating the pet-owning public on the advantages of leaving pets in a home environment and how to choose a reliable sitter.

★8122★ Personal & Building Service Occupations

Delphi Productions
3160 4th St.
Boulder, CO 80304
Fax: (303)443-4022   Fr: 888-443-2400
URL: http://www.delphivideo.com

$95.00. 48 minutes. Part of the Careers for the 21st Century Video Library.

★8123★ Pet Sitters International
201 E King St.
King, NC 27021-9161
Ph: (336)983-9222   Fax: (336)983-5266
E-mail: info@petsit.com
URL: http://www.petsit.com

Members: Professional pet sitters. Educational organization for professional pet sitters and advocates of at-home pet care. PSI promotes, recognizes and supports excellence in pet sitting. **Purpose:** Provides a forum of communication for members who share a common vision of excellence in at-home pet care.

★8124★ United States Personal Chef Association
481 Rio Rancho Boulevard NE
Rio Rancho, NM 87124
Fr: 800-995-2138
URL: http://www.uspca.com

Description: The largest organization dedicated to the personal service industry.

Personnel, Training, and Labor Relations Specialists and Managers

SOURCES OF HELP-WANTED ADS

★8125★ **Business Insurance**
Crain Communications Inc.
711 Third Ave.
New York, NY 10017-4036
Ph: (212)210-0100   Fax: (212)210-0244
Fr: 800-446-1420
URL: http://www.businessinsurance.com

Weekly. $97.00/year for individuals. International newsweekly reporting on corporate risk and employee benefit management news.

★8126★ **Checkpoint**
Russell Staffing Resources
PO Box 6279
San Rafael, CA 94903-0279
Fax: (415)986-6003

Description: Quarterly. Designed to meet the needs of persons responsible for hiring and employment. Includes updates on hot trends, technologies, laws, new human resource tools, techniques, advice, and columns titled You Heard It Here First and It's Enough to Drive You Batty.

★8127★ **Government Training News**
Ronald G. Rago
PO Box 1036
Harpers Ferry, WV 25425
Ph: (304)535-2355   Fax: (304)535-9914

Description: Monthly. Reports on the latest training trends and opportunities, best practices, and overall learning and training policy. Serves as a source of information and ideas about training techniques and career development programs among training professionals at the federal, state, and local levels. Reviews new training tools. Recurring features include a calendar of events, view from inside, news, book reviews, best practices, resources, etc.

★8128★ **Human Resource Executive**
LRP Publications
360 Hiatt Dr.
Palm Beach Gardens, FL 33418
Fr: 800-341-7874
E-mail: bmckenna@lrp.com
URL: http://www.hrexecutive.com

$89.95/year for individuals; $101.95/year for Canada and Mexico; $133.95/year for other countries; $8.95 for single issue. Business magazine (tabloid) for human resource executives in corporations, non-profit organizations, and government agencies.

★8129★ **Labor Studies Forum**
University & College Labor Education Association (UCLEA)
Center for Labor Research & Studies (CLRS)
Florida International University
Miami, FL 33199
Ph: (305)348-2371   Fax: (305)348-2241

Description: Quarterly. Addresses labor and union issues. Recurring features include letters to the editor, news of research, a calendar of events, reports of meetings, news of educational opportunities, job listings, notices of publications available, notices of audio-visual material, research activities, calls for papers, and funding opportunities.

★8130★ **Organizations and Change**
International Registry of Organization Development Professionals
11234 Walnut Ridge Rd.
Chesterland, OH 44026
Ph: (440)729-7419
URL: http://members.aol.com/odinst

Description: Monthly. Serves organization development professionals, teachers of organizational behavior, management consultants, personnel directors and executives by carrying news items, interest surveys, economic information, and committee reports. Recurring features include announcements of conferences, meetings, publications, consulting opportunities, and employment openings. Subscription includes annual publication titled *The International Registry of Organization Development Professionals and Or-*

ganization Development Handbook, and copies of *The Organizational Development Journal*.

★8131★ **PENSION Management**
Primedia Business
6151 Powers Ferry Rd.
Atlanta, GA 30339
Ph: (770)955-2500   Fax: (770)618-0348

Monthly. $68.00/year for individuals. Magazine on pension investment and fund administration.

★8132★ **Pensions & Investments**
Crain Communications Inc.
711 Third Ave.
New York, NY 10017-4036
Ph: (212)210-0100   Fax: (212)210-0244
Fr: 800-446-1420

Biweekly. $205.00/year. Magazine containing news and features on investment management, pension management, corporate finance, and cash management.

★8133★ **T & D Magazine**
American Society for Training & Development
PO Box 1443
Alexandria, VA 22313-2043
Ph: (703)683-8100   Fax: (703)683-8103
Fr: 800-NAT-ASTD
URL: http://www.astd.org

Monthly. $99.00/year for U.S.; $165.00/year for other countries. Magazine on training and development.

★8134★ **Workforce**
ACC Communications Inc.
245 Fischer Ave., B-2
Costa Mesa, CA 92626
Ph: (714)751-1883   Fax: (714)751-4106
E-mail: mailroom@workforcemag.com
URL: http://www.workforceonline.com

Monthly. $59.00/year for individuals; $99.00/year for Canada. A Business magazine for human resources management leaders.

PLACEMENT AND JOB REFERRAL SERVICES

★8135★ International Registry of Organization Development Professionals (IRODP)
11234 Walnut Ridge Rd.
Chesterland, OH 44026
Ph: (440)729-7419   Fax: (440)729-9319
E-mail: donwcole@aol.com
URL: http://members.aol.com/odinst

Description: Educational subsidiary of the Organization Development Institute. **Members:** Organization development professionals, students, and persons interested in improving the way organizations function. **Purpose:** Promotes a better understanding of and disseminates information about organization development. **Activities:** Maintains placement service. Conducts specialized education.

EMPLOYER DIRECTORIES AND NETWORKING LISTS

★8136★ College and University Professional Association-Membership Directory
College and University Professional
 Association for Human Resources
Tyson Pl.
2607 Kingston Pk., Ste. 250
Knoxville, TN 37919
Ph: (865)637-7673   Fax: (865)637-7674
E-mail: arothstein@cupahr.org
URL: http://cupahr.org/membersonly.html

Online continually updated; access restricted to members. $150.00. Covers more than 7,000 members interested in college and university human resource administration; over 1,700 institutions. Entries include: For members-Personal name, title, affiliation, address, fax, e-mail, phone. For institutions-Organization name, address, phone, and names/titles of representatives. Arrangement: Members are alphabetical; institutions are geographical.

★8137★ Executive Search Consultants Directory
infoUSA Inc.
5711 S 86th Cir.
Omaha, NE 68127-0347
Ph: (402)930-3500   Fax: (402)331-0176
Fr: 800-555-6124
URL: http://www.abii.com

Annual. Number of listings: 8,320. Entries include: Name, address, phone (including area code), size of advertisement, year first in "Yellow Pages," name of owner or manager, number of employees. Compiled from telephone company "Yellow Pages," nationwide. Arrangement: Geographical.

★8138★ 4 Data Base
Hunt-Scanlon Publishing
20 Signal Rd.
Stamford, CT 06902-7907
Ph: (203)352-2920   Fax: (203)352-2930

Annual. $1,350.00 for individuals. Database covers more than 100,000 top and middle management professionals in human resources, finance, sales and marketing, and information technology at over 10,000 companies in the U.S. Entries include: Company name, address, phone, number of employees, SIC codes, revenues, individual name, title, phone number, industry specialization.

★8139★ Peterson's Job Opportunities for Business Majors
Thomson Peterson's
Princeton Pke. Corporate Ctr., 2000
 Lenox Dr.
PO Box 67005
Lawrenceville, NJ 08648
Ph: (609)896-1800   Fax: (609)896-4531
Fr: 800-338-3282
URL: http://www.petersons.com

Irregular, latest edition 2000 - 16th ed. $18.95. Covers the 2,000 largest U.S. employers hiring in several fields, including financial services, management consulting, consumer products, and media/ entertainment. Entries include: Organization name, address, phone, name and title of contact, number of employees, type of organization. Arrangement: Alphabetical. Indexes: Type of organization.

★8140★ Skills and Training Directory: A Complete Sourcebook of Best Practice and Training Providers
World View Forum
55 W 17th St.
New York, NY 10011-5513
Ph: (212)255-0352   Fax: (212)675-7869

Latest edition 4th, 2003. Covers over 1000 occupational training and business education providers for professionals in human resource development. Entries include: Name, address, phone.

HANDBOOKS AND MANUALS

★8141★ Great Jobs for Psychology Majors
McGraw-Hill Trade
2 Penn Plaza
New York, NY 10121
Ph: (212)904-2000   Fr: 800-722-4726
E-mail: ntcpub@tribune.com

Julie DeGalan and Stephen Lambert. 1995. $11.95 (paper). 468 pages. Out of print.

★8142★ How to Succeed in Employee Development: Moving from Vision to Results
The McGraw-Hill Companies
860 Taylor Station Rd.
Blacklick, OH 43004-0545
Fr: 800-722-4726

Edward Moorby. Third edition, 1998. 183 pages. Part of the Training Series.

★8143★ Management Development: Strategy and Practice
Blackwell Publishing
350 Main St.
Malden, MA 02148
Ph: (781)388-8200   Fax: (781)388-8210
Fr: 800-759-6102

Jean Woodall and Diana Winstanley. 1998. $49.95 (paper). 288 pages.

★8144★ 96 Great Interview Questions to Ask Before You Hire
AMACOM
1601 Broadway, 12th Fl.
New York, NY 10019-7420
Ph: (518)891-1500   Fax: (518)903-8168

Paul Falcone. 2000. $10.95.

★8145★ Opportunities in Hospital Administration Careers
McGraw-Hill/Contemporary Books
1221 Avenue of the Americas
New York, NY 10020
Ph: (212)904-2000   Fr: 800-323-4900
E-mail: ntcpub@tribune.com

I. Donald Snook. 1997. $14.95; $11.95 (paper). 160 pages. Discusses opportunities for administrators in a variety of management settings: hospital, department, clinic, group practice, HMO, mental health, and extended care facilities.

★8146★ Opportunities in Insurance Careers
McGraw-Hill/Contemporary Books
1221 Avenue of the Americas
New York, NY 10020
Ph: (212)904-2000   Fr: 800-323-4900
E-mail: ntcpub@tribune.com

Robert Schrayer. Revised, 1999. $14.95; $11.95 (paper). 148 pages. A guide to planning for and seeking opportunities in the field. Contains bibliography and illustrations.

★8147★ Opportunities in International Business Careers
McGraw-Hill Trade
2 Penn Plaza
New York, NY 10121
Ph: (212)904-2000   Fr: 800-722-4726

Jeffrey Arpan. 1994. $11.95 (paper). 200 pages. Describes what types of jobs exist in international business, where they are located, what challenges and rewards they bring, and how to prepare for and obtain jobs in international business.

★8148★ **Real-Resumes for Human-Resources and Personnel Jobs: Including Real Resumes Used to Change Careers and Transfer Skills to Other Industries**
PREP Publishing
1110 1/2 Hay St., PMB 66
Fayetteville, NC 28305
Ph: (910)483-6611   Fax: (910)483-2439
Fr: 800-533-2814

Anne McKinney. September 2002. $16.95.

★8149★ **Up Is Not the Only Way: A Guide to Developing Workforce Talent**
Davies-Black Publishers, Inc.
3803 E. Bayshore Rd.
Palo Alto, CA 94303
Ph: (650)969-8901   Fax: (650)969-8608
Fr: 800-624-1765

Beverly L. Kaye. Second Edition. 2002. $22.95. 320 pages.

★8150★ **Where the Jobs Are: The Hottest Careers for the 90s**
The Career Press, Inc.
3 Tice Rd.
PO Box 687
Franklin Lakes, NJ 07417-1322
Ph: (201)848-0310   Fax: (201)848-1727
Fr: 800-227-3371

Joyce Hadley. Third edition, 2000. $13.99 (paper). 400 pages. Out of print. Describes careers in fifteen general fields, from accounting to travel and hospitality.

EMPLOYMENT AGENCIES AND SEARCH FIRMS

★8151★ **Abbott Smith Associates, Inc.**
PO Box 318
3290 Franklin Ave.
Millbrook, NY 12545
Ph: (845)677-5300   Fax: (845)677-3315
E-mail: abbottsmith@prodigy.net

Executive search firm. Affiliate offices in Chicago and London.

★8152★ **The Alexander Group**
2700 Post Oak Blvd., Ste. 2400
Houston, TX 77056
Ph: (713)993-7900   Fax: (713)993-7979

Executive search firm. Second location in San Francisco.

★8153★ **The Aspire Group**
52 Second Ave, 1st Fl
Waltham, MA 02451-1129
Fax: (718)890-1810   Fr: 800-546-5675
URL: http://www.bmanet.com

Employment agency.

★8154★ **Boettcher Associates**
120 Bishops Way, Ste. 126
Brookfield, WI 53005
Ph: (262)782-2205

Executive search firm.

★8155★ **Brindisi Search**
10751 Falls Rd., Ste. 250
Lutherville, MD 21093
Ph: (410)339-7673   Fax: (410)823-0146

Provides professional human resource recruitment services.

★8156★ **Charleston Partners**
2 Bellevue Ave.
Rumson, NJ 07760
Ph: (732)842-5015   Fax: (732)842-0993

Executive search firm concentrated on human resource services.

★8157★ **CJA Executive Search**
17852 17th St., Ste. 209
Tustin, CA 92780
Ph: (714)573-1820   Fax: (714)731-3952
Fr: 800-559-2559

Executive search firm. Second location in Los Angeles.

★8158★ **Dankowski and Associates, Inc.**
6479 Stoney Ridge Rd.NE, Ste. 200
PO Box 39478
North Ridgeville, OH 44039-0478
Ph: (440)327-8717   Fax: (440)327-1853
E-mail: dankowski@aol.com
URL: http://www.samkowskiassociates.com

Executive search firm.

★8159★ **Daubenspeck and Associates Ltd.**
401 N. Michigan Ave., Ste. 1200
Chicago, IL 60611
Ph: (312)453-9410

Executive search firm specializes in team building.

★8160★ **Elinvar**
1804 Hillsborough St.
Raleigh, NC 27605
Ph: (919)878-4454

Executive search firm.

★8161★ **The Esquire Staffing Group Ltd.**
1 S. Wacker Dr., Ste. 1616
Chicago, IL 60606-4616
Ph: (312)795-4300   Fax: (312)795-4329
E-mail: s.fischer@esquirestaffing.com
URL: http://www.esquirestaffing.com

Employment agency. Fills permanent as well as temporary openings.

★8162★ **ExecuGroup Inc.**
142 S. Main St.
PO Box 5040
Grenada, MS 38901
Ph: (662)226-9025   Fax: (662)226-9090

Executive search firm. Second location in Bethlehem, PA.

★8163★ **The Executive Management Consulting Organization (TEMCO)**
PO Box 303
Oconomowoc, WI 53066-0303
Ph: (262)567-2069

Executive search firm.

★8164★ **HRD Consultants Inc.**
60 Walnut Ave., Ste. 100
Clark, NJ 07066
Ph: (732)815-7825   Fax: (732)815-7810

A retainer executive search firm that focuses on human resources.

★8165★ **James Farris Associates**
909 NW 63rd St.
Oklahoma City, OK 73116
Ph: (405)525-5061   Fax: (405)525-5069

Executive search firm.

★8166★ **Karras Personnel, Inc.**
2 Central Ave.
Madison, NJ 07940
Ph: (973)966-6800
E-mail: karraspersonnel@mindspring.com
URL: http://www.karraspersonnel.home.mindspring.com

Executive search firm specializing in human resources recruiting.

★8167★ **Protocol Agency Inc.**
2659 Townsgate Rd., Ste.203
Westlake Village, CA 91361-2774
Ph: (626)449-2214   Fax: (805)371-0048
E-mail: wiv@protocalagency.com
URL: http://www.protocolagency.com

Executive search firm focusing on a variety of placements.

★8168★ **R.A. Clark Consulting Ltd.**
3400 Peachtree Rd. NE, Ste. 645
Atlanta, GA 30326
Ph: (404)231-0005   Fax: (404)231-1030
Fr: 800-251-0041

National and international executive search focusing exclusively in the Human Resource field. Also contract HR executives for temporary assignments.

★8169★ Shannon Management Group

415 Walnut St.
PO Box 702
Coshocton, OH 43812
Ph: (740)622-2600   Fax: (740)622-9638

Serving broad range of industries and public sector organizations and foundations. Specializing in human resources recruiting and outplacement counseling on international scale for businesses of all sizes. Offers expertise in human resources policies and procedures, supervisor development, manager leadership style development, interview training, etc. Provides consulting to small business in human resources, advertising, marketing, sales, public relations and community relations.

★8170★ Willmott and Associates

922 Waltham St., Ste. 103
Lexington, MA 02421-8019
Ph: (781)863-5400   Fax: (781)863-8000
E-mail: willmont@willmont.com
URL: http://www.willmott.com

Executive search firm and permanent employment agency. Also fills some temporary placements.

TRADESHOWS

★8171★ Annual Employee Benefits Conference

International Foundation of Employee Benefit Plans
18700 W. Bluemound Rd.
PO Box 69
Brookfield, WI 53008
Ph: (262)786-6700   Fax: (262)786-8670
Fr: 888-33-IFEBP
E-mail: pr@ifebp.org

Annual. **Primary Exhibits:** Products and services relating to accounting services, alternative medicine, banking/financial, communication, computer software, consulting services, health services, insurance, investments, legal services, preretirement planning. **Dates and Locations:** 2005 Nov 11-16; Honolulu, HI.

★8172★ EAPA Annual Conference

Employee Assistance Professionals Association
2101 Wilson Blvd., Ste. 500
Arlington, VA 22201-3062
Ph: (703)387-1000   Fax: (703)522-4585
E-mail: eapamain@aol.com
URL: http://www.eap-association.com

Annual. **Primary Exhibits:** Exhibits geared toward persons employed full-time in the development or operation of employee assistance programs (EAPs) as administrators, consultants, or motivational counselors.

★8173★ Education Technology

Society for Applied Learning Technology
50 Culpeper St.
Warrenton, VA 20186
Ph: (540)347-0055   Fax: (540)349-3169
E-mail: info@lti.org
URL: http://www.salt.org

Annual. **Primary Exhibits:** Distance learning, web-based training systems, knowledge management systems, instructional systems design, and e-learning technology.

★8174★ Media Human Resources Association Conference

Media Human Resources Association
1800 Duke St.
Alexandria, VA 22314-1943
Ph: (703)548-3440   Fax: (703)739-0399
Fr: 800-283-7476
URL: http://www.shrm.org

Annual. **Primary Exhibits:** Exhibits related to human resources and labor relations at newspapers.

★8175★ Society for Human Resource Management-The HRM Marketplace Exposition

Society for Human Resource Management
1800 Duke St.
Alexandria, VA 22314
Ph: (703)535-6111   Fax: (703)535-6477
Fr: 800-283-SHRM
URL: http://www.shrm.org

Annual. **Primary Exhibits:** Human resource management products and services; including relocation human resource information systems, recruitment, executive search, temporary/contact personnel employee compensation and benefits, incentive program information, childcare/eldercare, and drug testing information.

★8176★ Training Conference and Expo

VNU Expositions
14685 Avion Parkway
Ste. 400
Chantilly, VA 20151
Ph: (703)488-2700   Fax: (703)488-2800
Fr: 800-765-7615
URL: http://www.vnuexpo.com

Annual. **Primary Exhibits:** Training and personnel materials, equipment, and services.

OTHER SOURCES

★8177★ Administration and Management Occupations

Delphi Productions
3160 4th St.
Boulder, CO 80304
Fax: (303)443-4022   Fr: 888-443-2400
URL: http://www.delphivideo.com

$95.00. 50 minutes. Part of the Careers for the 21st Century Video Library.

★8178★ American Almanac of Jobs and Salaries

Morrow Avon
1350 Avenue of the Americas
New York, NY 10019
Ph: (212)261-6788   Fr: 800-242-7737

John W. Wright. Revised edition, 2000. $20.00 (paper). 672 pages. This is a comprehensive guide to the wages of hundreds of occupations in a wide variety of industries and organizations.

★8179★ American Society for Healthcare Human Resources Administration (ASHHRA)

1 N Franklin, 31st Fl.
Chicago, IL 60606
Ph: (312)422-3725   Fax: (312)422-4577
E-mail: ashhra@aha.org
URL: http://www.ashhra.org

Description: Purposes are to provide effective and continuous leadership in the field of health care human resources administration; to promote cooperation with hospitals and allied associations in matters pertaining to hospital human resources administration; to further the professional and educational development of members; to encourage and promote research; to encourage and assist local groups in chapter formation through regular programs and institutes on health care human resources issues. Offers placement service.

★8180★ American Society of Pension Actuaries (ASPA)

4245 N Fairfax Dr., Ste. 750
Arlington, VA 22203
Ph: (703)516-9300   Fax: (703)516-9308
E-mail: aspa@aspa.org
URL: http://www.aspa.org

Members: Individuals involved in the consulting, administrative, and design aspects of the employee benefit business. **Purpose:** Promotes high standards in the profession; provides nine-part educational program.

★8181★ American Staffing Association (ASA)

277 S. Washington St., Ste. 200
Alexandria, VA 22314-3646
Ph: (703)253-2020   Fax: (703)253-2053
E-mail: asa@staffingtoday.net
URL: http://www.staffingtoday.net

Description: Promotes and represents the staffing industry through legal and legislative advocacy, public relations, education, and the establishment of high standards of ethical conduct.

★8182★ Association for Quality and Participation (AQP)
PO Box 2055
Milwaukee, WI 53201-2055
Ph: (414)765-7219   Fax: (414)272-2145
Fr: 800-733-3310
E-mail: aqp@aqp.org
URL: http://www.aqp.org

Description: A non-for-profit educational association and learning resource for individuals, teams, and organizations dedicated to promoting the ideas of involvement, empowerment and workplace democracy. AQP has been in operation for 20 years and disseminates information to members through the internet, publications, conferences and educational events.

★8183★ ASTD
Box 1443
1640 King St.
Alexandria, VA 22313-2043
Ph: (703)683-8100   Fax: (703)683-1523
Fr: 800-628-2783
URL: http://www.astd.org

Description: Professional association for persons engaged in the training and development of business, industry, education, and government employees. Undertakes special research projects and acts as clearinghouse. Operates information center on human resource development.

★8184★ College and University Professional Association for Human Resources (CUPA-HR)
2607 Kingston Pke., Ste. 250
Knoxville, TN 37919
Ph: (865)637-7673
E-mail: sotzenberger@cupahr.org
URL: http://www.cupahr.org

Members: Professional organization made up of colleges and universities interested in the improvement of campus Human Resource administration. **Activities:** Carries out special research projects and surveys, including annual administrative compensation survey for higher education. Sponsors training seminars to meet members' technical, professional, and developmental needs in human resource management. Disseminates information to members regarding federal legislation and regulations affecting higher education institutions. Compiles statistics.

★8185★ Employee Assistance Society of North America (EASNA)
230 E Ohio St., Ste. 400
Chicago, IL 60611-3265
Ph: (312)644-0828   Fax: (312)644-8557
E-mail: easna@bostrom.com
URL: http://www.easna.org

Description: Individuals in the field of employee assistance, including psychiatrists, psychologists, and managers. Facilitates communication among members; provides resource information; serves as a network for employee assistance programs nationwide. Conducts research.

★8186★ Human Resource Certification Institute (HRCI)
1800 Duke St.
Alexandria, VA 22314
Ph: (703)548-3440   Fax: (703)535-6490
Fr: (866)898-4724
E-mail: info@hrci.org
URL: http://www.shrm.org/hrci

Description: Promotes the establishment of standards for the profession. Recognizes human resource professionals who have met, through demonstrated professional experience and the passing of a comprehensive written examination, the Institute's requirements for mastering the codified HR body of knowledge. Offers two professional certifications: Professional in Human Resources (PHR) and Senior Professional in Human Resources (SPHR).

★8187★ Human Resource Planning Society (HRPS)
317 Madison Ave., Ste. 1509
New York, NY 10017
Ph: (212)490-6387   Fax: (212)682-6851
E-mail: info@hrps.org
URL: http://www.hrps.org

Members: Human resource planning professionals representing 160 corporations and 3000 individual members, including strategic human resources planning and development specialists, staffing analysts, business planners, line managers, and others who function as business partners in the application of strategic human resource management practices. **Purpose:** Seeks to increase the impact of human resource planning and management on business and organizational performance. **Activities:** Sponsors program of professional development in human resource planning concepts, techniques, and practices. Offers networking opportunities.

★8188★ Industrial Relations Research Association (IRRA)
University of Illinois
121 LIR
504 E. Armory Ave.
Champaign, IL 61820
Ph: (217)333-0072   Fax: (217)265-5130
E-mail: irra@uiuc.edu
URL: http://www.irra.uiuc.edu

Description: Businesspersons, union leaders, government officials, lawyers, arbitrators, academics, and others interested in research and exchange of ideas on social, political, economic, legal, and psychological aspects of labor, including employer and employee organization, labor relations, personnel administration, social security, and labor legislation. Disseminates research results.

★8189★ International Association for Human Resource Information Management (IHRIM)
PO Box 1086
Burlington, MA 01803-1086
Ph: (512)453-6363   Fax: (781)998-8011
Fr: 800-846-6363

E-mail: moreinfo@ihrim.org
URL: http://www.ihrim.org

Description: Human resource, payroll, and data processing professionals; others concerned with the development, maintenance, and operation of automated human resource systems. Provides a forum for exchanging experiences, acquiring information, and discussing common needs and problems relating to human resource systems. Works to enhance capabilities for effective and efficient human resource management. Conducts activities on the local, national, and international level. Offers programs and job posting services. Operates resource center, member referral network, and vendor fairs.

★8190★ International Personnel Management Association (IPMA)
1617 Duke St.
Alexandria, VA 22314
Ph: (703)549-7100   Fax: (703)684-0948
E-mail: ipma@ipma-hr.org
URL: http://www.ipma-hr.org

Members: Public (1700); individuals, including human resource workers, consultants, and professors (4400). **Purpose:** Seeks to improve human resource practices in government through provision of testing services, advisory service, conferences, professional development programs, research, and publications. Sponsors seminars, conferences, and workshops on various phases of public personnel administration. Compiles statistics.

★8191★ Organization Development Institute
11234 Walnut Ridge Rd.
Chesterland, OH 44026
Ph: (440)729-7419   Fax: (440)729-9319
E-mail: donwcole@aol.com
URL: http://www.odinstitute.org

Description: Professionals, students, and individuals interested in organization development. Disseminates information on and promotes a better understanding of organization development worldwide. Conducts specialized education programs. Has developed the International O.D. Code of Ethics and a competency test for individuals wishing to qualify as a Registered Organization Development Consultant. Has developed a statement on the knowledge and skill necessary to be competent in organization development and criteria for the accreditation of OD/OB academic programs. Maintains job and consultant information service. Sponsors International Registry of Organization Development Professionals and Research/Study Team on Nonviolent Large Systems Change. Maintains 18 committees including an International Advisory Board.

★8192★ Organization Development Network (ODNetwork)
71 Valley St., Ste. 301
South Orange, NJ 07079-2825
Ph: (973)763-7337   Fax: (973)763-7448
E-mail: odnetwork@odnetwork.org
URL: http://www.odnetwork.org

Description: Practitioners, academics, managers, and students employed or interested in organization development. Works to enhance and provide opportunities for colleagueship and professional development.

★8193★ Personnel, Training and Labor Relations Specialists and Managers
Evon Publishing
832 N 7th Ave.
Iron River, MI 49935
Ph: (906)265-3190

Audiocassette. 1996. $16.95. 32 minutes. Part of the Careers and Vocational Guidance Series. Provides information about the nature of the work, educational requirements, employment outlook, earnings, and work conditions as well as additional related information.

★8194★ Society for Human Resource Management (SHRM)
1800 Duke St.
Alexandria, VA 22314-3499
Ph: (703)548-3440   Fax: (703)535-6497
Fr: 800-283-7476
E-mail: shrm@shrm.org
URL: http://www.shrm.org

Members: Professional organization of human resource, personnel, and industrial relations professionals and executives. **Purpose:** Promotes the advancement of human resource management. **Activities:** Sponsors SHRM Foundation. Offers certification through the Human Resource Certification Institute.

★8195★ WorldatWork
14040 N Northsight Blvd.
Scottsdale, AZ 85260
Ph: (480)951-9191   Fax: (480)483-8352
Fr: 877-951-9191
E-mail: customerrelations@worldatwork.org
URL: http://www.worldatwork.org

Description: Dedicated to knowledge leadership in compensation, benefits and total rewards, focusing on disciplines associated with attracting, retaining and motivating employees. Offers CCP, CBP, and GRP certification and education programs, conducts surveys, research and provides networking opportunities.

Pest Control Workers

SOURCES OF HELP-WANTED ADS

★8196★ Common Sense Pest Control

Bio-Integral Resource Center
PO Box 7414
Berkeley, CA 94707
Ph: (510)524-2567   Fax: (510)524-1758
Quarterly. Features descriptions of the latest research, products, resources, and book reviews.

★8197★ Pest Control

Advanstar Communications Inc.
One Park Ave.
New York, NY 10016
Ph: (212)951-6600   Fax: (212)951-6793
Covers issues affecting residential, commercial, and industrial pest management professionals.

★8198★ Pest Control Technology

GIE Media
4012 Bridge Ave.
Cleveland, OH 44113
Fr: 800-456-0707
Industry news.

EMPLOYER DIRECTORIES AND NETWORKING LISTS

★8199★ Directory of Mosquito Control Agencies

American Mosquito Control Association Inc.
White House
681 US 1
North Brunswick, NJ 08902
Ph: (732)214-8899   Fax: (732)214-0110
Biennial. $5.00. Covers about 740 mosquito control agencies in the United States and Canada, of which about 150 control other disease carriers as well. Entries include: Company name, address, phone, geographic area covered, methods used. Arrangement: Geographical.

★8200★ Pest Control Companies Directory

infoUSA Inc.
5711 S 86th Cir.
Omaha, NE 68127-0347
Ph: (402)930-3500   Fax: (402)331-0176
Fr: 800-555-6124
URL: http://www.abii.com
Latest edition September 1988. Number of listings: 24,491. Entries include: Name, address, phone (including area code), size of advertisement, year first in "Yellow Pages," name of owner or manager, number of employees. Compiled from telephone company "Yellow Pages," nationwide. Arrangement: Geographical.

★8201★ Pest Control Supplies & Equipment Directory

infoUSA Inc.
5711 S 86th Cir.
Omaha, NE 68127-0347
Ph: (402)930-3500   Fax: (402)331-0176
Fr: 800-555-6124
URL: http://www.abii.com
Updated continuously; printed on request. Number of listings: 934. Entries include: Name, address, phone, size of advertisement, name of owner or manager, number of employees, year first in "Yellow Pages." Compiled from telephone company "Yellow Pages," nationwide. Arrangement: Geographical.

★8202★ United Products Formulators and Distributor-Roster

United Products Formulators and Distributors
2034 Beaver Ruin Rd.
Norcross, GA 30071
Ph: (770)417-1418   Fax: (770)417-1419
Annual, February. Covers nearly 100 suppliers to the pest control industry in United States, Canada, and Spain. Entries include: Company name, address, name and title of contact, products or services. Arrangement: Alphabetical. Indexes: Product/service, contact name.

HANDBOOKS AND MANUALS

★8203★ Ecological Theory and Integrated Pest Management Practice

John Wiley & Sons Inc.
111 River St.
Hoboken, NJ 07030-5774
Ph: (201)748-6000   Fax: (201)748-6088
Fr: 800-225-5945
Marcos Kogan. 1996. $89.95. 362 pages. Presents and develops ecological theory as a foundation for integrated pest management practices, with the aim of improving those practices.

★8204★ Insect Pest Management: Field and Protected Crops

Springer-Verlag New York, Inc.
175 Fifth Ave.
New York, NY 10010
Ph: (212)460-1500   Fax: (212)473-6272
A. Rami Horowitz, I. Ishaaya. May 2004. $29.00. Illustrated. 340 pages.

★8205★ Introduction to Insect Pest Management

John Wiley & Sons Inc.
111 River St.
Hoboken, NJ 07030-5774
Ph: (201)748-6000   Fax: (201)748-6088
Fr: 800-225-5945
Robert L. Metcalf and William H. Luckmann. Third edition. 1994. $210.00. 672 pages. Presents the philosophy and practice, ecological and economic background, as well as strategies and techniques of pest management, including the use of chemical pesticides. Also addresses biological, genetic and cultural methods to manage the harm done by insect pests.

★8206★ Pests of Landscape Trees and Shrubs: An Integrated Pest Management Guide

UC Regents University of California
One Shields Ave.
Davis, CA 95616
Ph: (530)752-8350   Fax: (530)752-6004

Steve H. Dreistadt. 2004. $42.00. Compiled by scientists at the University of California's Statewide Integrated Pest Management Project, this guide is aimed at homeowners and gardeners as well as landscape and pest management professionals.

TRADESHOWS

★8207★ American Mosquito Control Association Convention

American Mosquito Control Association Inc.
White House
681 US 1
North Brunswick, NJ 08902
Ph: (732)214-8899   Fax: (732)214-0110
E-mail: amca@mosquito.org
URL: http://www.mosquito.org

Annual. **Primary Exhibits:** Equipment, supplies, and services related to mosquito control, including chemicals.

★8208★ Florida Pest Management Association Convention and Exposition

Florida Pest Management Association
6882 Edgewater Commerce Pkwy.
Orlando, FL 32810
Ph: (407)293-8627   Fax: (407)292-0918
Fr: 800-426-4829

Annual. **Primary Exhibits:** Equipment, services, and supplies for the chemical industry.

★8209★ Pest Control Operators of California Convention

Pest Control Operators of California
3031 Beacon Blvd.
West Sacramento, CA 95691
Ph: (916)372-4363   Fax: (916)372-5437
E-mail: hlogan1@ix.netcom.com

Annual. **Primary Exhibits:** Equipment, supplies, and services for owners and operators of structural pest control companies in California.

OTHER SOURCES

★8210★ American Mosquito Control Association (AMCA)

PO Box 234
Eatontown, NJ 07724-0234
Ph: (732)544-4645   Fax: (732)542-3267
E-mail: amca@mosquito.org

URL: http://www.mosquito.org

Members: Entomologists, biologists, medical personnel, engineers, public health officials, military personnel, and others interested in mosquito control and related work.

★8211★ Association of American Pesticide Control Officials (AAPCO)

Office of the Sec.
PO Box 1249
Hardwick, VT 05843
Ph: (802)472-6956   Fax: (802)472-6957
E-mail: aapco@vtlink.net
URL: http://aapco.ceris.purdue.edu

Description: State agencies controlling the sale, use, and distribution of pesticides. Promotes uniform laws, regulations, and policies of enforcement.

★8212★ Association of Applied IPM Ecologists (AAIE)

PO Box 10880
Napa, CA 94581
Ph: (707)265-9349   Fax: (707)265-9349
E-mail: director@aaie.net
URL: http://www.aaie.net

Description: Professional agricultural pest management consultants, entomologists, and field personnel. Promotes the implementation of integrated pest management in agricultural and urban environments. Provides a forum for the exchange of technical information on pest control. Offers placement service.

★8213★ Bio-Integral Resource Center (BIRC)

PO Box 7414
Berkeley, CA 94707
Ph: (510)524-2567   Fax: (510)524-1758
E-mail: birc@igc.org
URL: http://www.birc.org

Purpose: Provides publications and consultations for pest management professionals, farmers, foresters, park service resource managers, environmentalists, and interested individuals. Provides practical information on methods of managing pests and land resource problems. Evaluates and disseminates information on the least toxic method of managing weed, vertebrate, insect, and microbe pests in urban, agricultural, forestall, and veterinary environments. Develops integrated pest management programs for community groups, public agencies, and private institutions. (IPM involves integrating biological, horticultural, mechanical, and chemical strategies to suppress pest populations below levels causing economic, medical, or aesthetic damage.) **Activities:** Areas of technical assistance include consultation of community pest problems; identification of pests and their natural enemies; pest control program evaluation; development of contract specifications; landscape design and design plan review; integration of IPM methods and sustainable agriculture. Reports on educational opportunities; sponsors workshops and lectures.

★8214★ Interstate Professional Applicators Association (IPAA)

PO Box 13262
Salem, OR 97309
Ph: (503)363-7205   Fax: (503)378-0864

Description: Companies engaged in the application of horticultural spraying. Goal is to insure a healthy and safe environment through proper pesticide usage. Works to acquire and disseminate technological information regarding the safe application of pesticides. Contributes to state research facilities. Sponsors seminars on entomology, pathology, safety, soils, business management, and employee relations.

★8215★ National Animal Damage Control Association (NADCA)

PO Box 2180
Ardmore, OK 73402

Description: Vertebrate pest controllers; nuisance wildlife control operators; trappers; federal, state, and local directors, managers, and employees concerned with wildlife management; individuals concerned with creating a more favorable attitude toward vertebrate pest management. Strives to increase public awareness and understanding of the purposes and principles of animal damage control. Supports the use of vertebrate pest management programs as a wildlife management tool. Promotes the animal damage control profession as it relates to the agribusiness community, wildlife resource management, and various government and private entities. Conducts educational and informational programs designed to aid in public and private decision-making concerning animal damage control. Maintains information center on animal damage control problems; sponsors seminars and workshops on vertebrate pest management.

★8216★ National Pest Management Association International (NPMA)

8100 Oak St.
Dunn Loring, VA 22027
Ph: (703)573-8330   Fax: (703)573-4116
Fr: 800-678-NPCA
E-mail: lederer@pestworld.org
URL: http://www.pestworld.org

Description: Firms engaged in control of insects, rodents, birds, and other pests, in or around structures, through use of insecticides, rodenticides, miticides, fumigants, and non-chemical methods. Provides advisory services on control procedures, new products, and safety and business administration practices. Promotes June as National Pest Control Month. Sponsors research, periodic technical and management seminars.

★8217★ Pesticide Action Network North America (PANNA)

49 Powell St., Ste. 500
San Francisco, CA 94102
Ph: (415)981-1771   Fax: (415)981-1991
E-mail: panna@panna.org
URL: http://www.panna.org/

Description: One of five PAN Regional

Centers worldwide. Works to replace pesticide use with ecologically sound and socially just alternatives; links local and international consumer, labor, health, environment and agriculture groups as an international citizens' action group challenging proliferation of pesticides, defends basic rights to health and environmental quality.

★8218★ **Pesticide Applicators Professional Association (PAPA)**
PO Box 80095
Salinas, CA 93912-0095
Ph: (831)442-3536   Fax: (831)442-2351
E-mail: stephanie@papaseminars.com
URL: http://www.papaseminars.com

Purpose: Seeks to provide continuing education for members to be able to renew state licenses.

★8219★ **Responsible Industry for a Sound Environment (RISE)**
1156 15th St. NW, Ste. 400
Washington, DC 20005
Ph: (202)872-3860   Fax: (202)463-0474
Fr: 888-295-1585
E-mail: margulies@bluepumpkingroup.com
URL: http://www.pestfacts.org

Members: Manufacturers, formulators, distributors, and representatives of the specialty pesticides industry. **Purpose:** Promotes the environmental, health, and safety benefits of the proper use of specialty pesticides.

★8220★ **Safer Pest Control Project**
25 E. Washington, Ste. 1515
Chicago, IL 60602
Ph: (312)641-5575   Fax: (312)641-5454
URL: http://spcpweb.org/

Description: Non-profit organization dedicated to reducing the public health risks and environmental impacts of pesticide use and promoting safer alternatives.

★8221★ **The Structural Pest Control Board**
1418 Howe Avenue Ste. 18
Sacramento, CA 95825
Fax: (916)263-2469
E-mail: pestboard@dca.ca.gov
URL: http://www.pestboard.ca.gov/

Description: Strives to be the national leader in creating an environment where the public is fully protected and well informed, and where structural pest control industry operates without unreasonable restraint.

Petroleum Engineers

★8222★ AEG News

Association of Engineering Geologists
PO Box 460518
Denver, CO 80246
Ph: (303)757-2926   Fax: (303)757-2969

Description: Bimonthly. Covers news of the engineering geology profession and the Association, whose members are engineering geologists and geological engineers worldwide. Recurring features include letters to the editor, a calendar of events, news of research, and short articles of technical interest.

★8223★ Diesel & Gas Turbine Worldwide

Diesel & Gas Turbine Publications
20855 Watertown Rd.
Waukesha, WI 53186
Ph: (262)832-5000   Fax: (262)832-5075
Fr: 800-558-4322

Monthly. $65.00/year; free to qualified subscribers. International magazine covering the design, application, and operation of diesel, natural gas, and gas turbine engine systems.

★8224★ Energy User News

BNP Media, Inc.
2401 W Big Beaver Rd., Ste. 700
Troy, MI 48084
Ph: (248)362-3700   Fax: (248)362-0317
URL: http://www.energyusernews.com

Monthly. Magazine exreporting on the energy management market as it relates to commercial, industrial, and institutional facilites.

★8225★ Engineering Economist

Institute of Industrial Engineers
3577 Pkwy. Ln., Ste. 200
Norcross, GA 30092
Ph: (770)449-0461   Fax: (770)263-8532
Fr: 800-494-0460

Quarterly. Publication covering business issues in the energy, petroleum and mining industries.

★8226★ Engineering Times

National Society of Professional Engineers
1420 King St.
Alexandria, VA 22314
Ph: (703)684-2875   Fax: (703)836-4875
E-mail: et@nspe.org
URL: http://http//:www.nspc.org/1et.asp

$30.00/year for individuals; $48.00/year for out of country. Magazine (tabloid) covering professional, legislative, and techology issues for an engineering audience.

★8227★ ENR: Engineering News-Record

McGraw-Hill Companies
1221 Avenue of the Americas
New York, NY 10020
Ph: (212)512-2000
URL: http://www.enr.com

Weekly. $74.00/year; $5.00 for single issue. Magazine focusing on engineering and construction.

★8228★ Gas Turbine World

Pequot Publishing Inc.
PO Box 447
Southport, CT 06490-0447
Ph: (203)259-1812

Bimonthly. $90.00/year for individuals; $135.00/year for other countries. Magazine containing technical and business information on the design application, operation, and maintenance of power plants for electrical generation, mechanical drive, oil and gas production and transmission, industrial process, CHP, and DHC applications.

★8229★ Graduating Engineer & Computer Careers

Career Recruitment Media
211 W. Wacker Dr., No. 900
Chicago, IL 60606
Ph: (312)525-3100
URL: http://www.graduatingengineer.com

$16.00/year for individuals. Magazine focusing on employment, education, and career development for entry-level engineers and computer scientists.

★8230★ High Technology Careers Magazine

HTC
4701 Patrick Henry Dr., No. 1901
Santa Clara, CA 95054-1847
Ph: (408)970-8800   Fax: (408)567-0242
URL: http://www.hightechcareers.com

Bimonthly. $29.00/year; $35.00/year for Canada; $85.00/year for out of country. Magazine (tabloid) containing employment opportunity information for the engineering and technical community.

★8231★ Monthly Energy Review

Superintendent of Documents
PO Box 371954
MS4004-MIB
Pittsburgh, PA 15250-7954
Ph: (202)512-1800

Monthly. Publication covering the petroleum, energy and mining industries.

★8232★ National Engineer

National Association of Power Engineers
One Springfield St.
Chicopee, MA 01013-2624
Ph: (413)592-6273   Fax: (413)592-1998
Bimonthly. $25.00/year for individuals; $3.00 for single issue.

★8233★ NSBE Magazine
NSBE Publications
1454 Duke St.
Alexandria, VA 22314
Ph: (703)549-2207   Fax: (703)683-5312

$10.00/year for individuals; $2.00 for single issue. Journal providing information on engineering careers, self-development, and cultural issues for recent graduates with technical majors.

★8234★ Offshore
PennWell Corp.
1700 W Loop S, Ste. 1000
Houston, TX 77027
Ph: (713)621-9720   Fax: (713)963-6296
Fr: 800-736-6935
URL: http://www.offshore-mag.com

Monthly. $62.00/year; $82.00/year for other countries, surface mail; $145.00/year for other countries, airmail. Magazine for petroleum industry covering offshore operations, engineering, and technology.

★8235★ Oil and Gas Interests
PBI Media L.L.C.
1201 Seven Locks Rd., Ste. 300
Potomac, MD 20854
Ph: (301)354-2000

Monthly. Trade publication covering the petroleum, energy and mining industries.

★8236★ Oil & Gas Journal
PennWell Corp.
1700 W Loop S, Ste. 1000
Houston, TX 77027
Ph: (713)621-9720   Fax: (713)963-6296
Fr: 800-736-6935
URL: http://www.ogjonline.com

Weekly. $79.00/year for individuals. Trade magazine serving engineers and managers in international petroleum operations.

★8237★ SWE
Society of Women Engineers
230 E Ohio St., No. 400
2135 Lamberton Rd.
Chicago, IL 60611-3265
Ph: (312)596-5223   Fax: (312)596-5252
E-mail: hq@swe.org
URL: http://www.swe.org

Bimonthly. $30.00/year for nonmembers. Magazine for engineering students and for women and men working in the engineering and technology fields. Covers career guidance, continuing development and topical issues.

★8238★ Technology Review
Technology Review
201 Vassar St.
Cambridge, MA 02139
Ph: (617)253-8250   Fax: (617)258-5850
E-mail: trcomments@mit.edu

$30.00/year for individuals; $42.00/year for other countries; $4.95/year for single issue.

Magazine reviewing new developments in technology with an emphasis on economic, political, and social implications. Not a new product publication.

★8239★ WEPANEWS
Women in Engineering Programs & Advocates Network
Castle Point on the Hudson
Hoboken, NJ 07030
Ph: (201)216-5245   Fax: (201)216-5175
URL: http://www.wepan.org/newsletter.html

Description: Two issues/year. Seeks to provide greater access for women to careers in engineering. Includes news of graduate, undergraduate, freshmen, pre-college, and re-entry engineering programs for women. Recurring features include job listings, faculty, grant, and conference news, international engineering program news, action group news, notices of publications available, and a column titled Kudos.

★8240★ World Oil
Gulf Publishing Co.
3 Greenway Plz., 9th Fl.
Houston, TX 77252-2608
Ph: (713)529-4301   Fax: (713)520-4433
Fr: 800-231-6275
E-mail: editorial@worldoil.com
URL: http://www.worldoil.com

Monthly. $34.00/year, U.S. and Canada; $41.00/year, countries outside North America. Trade magazine on oil and gas exploration, drilling, and production.

PLACEMENT AND JOB REFERRAL SERVICES

★8241★ American Indian Science and Engineering Society (AISES)
PO Box 9828
Albuquerque, NM 87119-9828
Ph: (505)765-1052   Fax: (505)765-5608
E-mail: info@aises.org
URL: http://www.aises.org

Description: American Indian and non-Indian students and professionals in science, technology, and engineering fields; corporations representing energy, mining, aerospace, electronic, and computer fields. Seeks to motivate and encourage students to pursue undergraduate and graduate studies in science, engineering, and technology. Sponsors science fairs in grade schools, teacher training workshops, summer math/science sessions for 8th-12th graders, professional chapters, and student chapters in colleges. Offers scholarships. Adult members serve as role models, advisers, and mentors for students. Operates placement service.

★8242★ Engineering Society of Detroit (ESD)
26100 American Dr., Ste. 500
Southfield, MI 48034-6184
Ph: (248)355-2910   Fax: (248)355-1492
E-mail: esd@esd.org
URL: http://esd.org

Description: Engineers from all disciplines; scientists and technologists. Conducts technical programs and engineering refresher courses; sponsors conferences and expositions. Maintains speakers' bureau; offers placement services. Although based in Detroit, MI, society membership is international.

★8243★ Korean Scientists and Engineers Association in America (KSEA)
1952 Gallows Rd., Ste. 300
Vienna, VA 22182
Ph: (703)748-1221   Fax: (703)748-1331
E-mail: sejong@ksea.org
URL: http://www.ksea.org

Description: Scientists and engineers holding single or advanced degrees. Goals are to: promote friendship and mutuality among Korean and American scientists and engineers; contribute to Korea's scientific, technological, industrial, and economic developments; strengthen the scientific, technological, and cultural bonds between Korea and the U.S. Sponsors symposium. Maintains speakers' bureau, placement service, and biographical archives. Compiles statistics. Maintains 100 volume library of scientific handbooks and yearbooks in Korean.

★8244★ Society of Hispanic Professional Engineers (SHPE)
5400 E Olympic Blvd., Ste. 210
Los Angeles, CA 90022
Ph: (323)725-3970   Fax: (323)725-0316
E-mail: shpenational@shpe.org
URL: http://www.shpe.org

Description: Engineers, student engineers, and scientists seeking to increase the number of Hispanic engineers by providing motivation and support to students. Sponsors competitions and educational programs. Maintains placement service and speakers' bureau; compiles statistics.

★8245★ Society of Petroleum Engineers (SPE)
222 Palisades Creek Dr.
PO Box 833836
Richardson, TX 75083-3836
Ph: (972)952-9393   Fax: (972)952-9435
Fr: 800-456-6863
E-mail: spedal@spe.org
URL: http://www.spe.org

Members: Worldwide technical society of engineers, scientists, managers, and operating personnel in the upstream petroleum industry **Activities:** Offers distance learning, continuing education short courses, and distinguished lecturer program; sponsors contests; offers placement service and Internet Career Center.

EMPLOYER DIRECTORIES AND NETWORKING LISTS

★8246★ *American Men and Women of Science*

Thomson Gale
27500 Drake Rd.
Farmington Hills, MI 48331-3535
Ph: (248)699-4253   Fax: (248)699-8065
Fr: 800-877-GALE
E-mail: amws@galegroup.com

Biennial, latest edition December 2002. $975.00. Covers over 129,700 U.S. and Canadian scientists active in the physical, biological, mathematical, computer science, and engineering fields; includes references to previous edition for deceased scientists and nonrespondents. Entries include: Name, address, education, personal and career data, memberships, honors and awards, research interest. Arrangement: Alphabetical. Indexes: Discipline (in separate volume).

★8247★ *Careers in Focus: Engineering*

Ferguson Publishing Co.
200 W Jackson Blvd.
Chicago, IL 60606
Ph: (312)692-0109

2nd edition, 2002. $22.95. Publication includes: List of resources to consult for more information. Principal content of publication is job descriptions, advancement opportunities, educational requirements, employment outlook, salary information, and working conditions for careers in the field of engineering. Indexes: Alphabetical.

★8248★ *Directory of Certified Petroleum Geologists*

American Association of Petroleum Geologists
1444 S Boulder
PO Box 979
Tulsa, OK 74101-0979
Ph: (918)584-2555   Fax: (918)560-2636
Fr: 800-364-AAPG

Covers about 3,400 members of the association. Entries include: Name, address; education and career data; whether available for consulting. Arrangement: Alphabetical. Indexes: Geographical.

★8249★ *Directory of Contract Staffing Firms*

C.E. Publications Inc.
PO Box 3006
Bothell, WA 98041-3006
Ph: (425)806-5200   Fax: (425)806-5585
URL: http://www.cjhunter.com/dcsf/overview.html

$15.00. Covers nearly 1,300 contract firms actively engaged in the employment of engineering, IT/IS, and technical personnel for 'temporary' contract assignments throughout the world. Entries include: Company name, address, phone, name of contact, email, web address. Arrangement: Alphabetical. Indexes: Geographical.

★8250★ *The Geophysical Directory*

Geophysical Directory Inc.
PO Box 130508
Houston, TX 77219
Ph: (713)529-8789   Fax: (713)529-3646
Fr: 800-929-2462
E-mail: info@geophysicaldirectory.com

Annual, March. $125.00 within USA; $140.00 outside USA. Covers about 4,000 companies that provide geophysical equipment, supplies, or services, and mining and petroleum companies that use geophysical techniques; international coverage. Entries include: Company name, address, phone, fax, names of principal executives, operations, and sales personnel; similar information for branch locations. Arrangement: Classified by product or service. Indexes: Company name, personal name.

★8251★ *Indiana Society of Professional Engineers-Directory*

Indiana Society of Professional Engineers
PO Box 20806
Indianapolis, IN 46220
Ph: (317)255-2267   Fax: (317)255-2530

Annual, fall. $55.00. Covers member registered engineers, land surveyors, engineering students, and engineers in training. Entries include: Member name, address, phone, type of membership, business information, specialty. Arrangement: Alpha by chapter area.

★8252★ *International Directory of Engineering Societies and Related Organizations*

American Association of Engineering Societies
1828 L St. NW, Ste. 906
Washington, DC 20036
Ph: (202)296-2237   Fax: (202)296-1151
Fr: 888-400-AAES

Irregular, latest edition December 1998. $240.00. Covers about 1,370 national, regional, Canadian, and international organizations concerned with engineering and related fields. Entries include: Name, address, phone, fax, e-mail, key personnel, objectives, publications, activities, mailing lists, federation memberships, meeting and convention dates, and budget data. Arrangement: Alphabetical. Indexes: Acronym, geographical, area of specialization.

★8253★ *The Oil & Gas Directory*

Geophysical Directory Inc.
PO Box 130508
Houston, TX 77219
Ph: (713)529-8789   Fax: (713)529-3646
Fr: 800-929-2462
E-mail: info@theoilandandgasdirectory.com

Annual, October. $105.00 within USA; $120.00 outside USA. Covers about 9,000 companies worldwide involved in petroleum exploration, drilling, and production, and suppliers to the industry. Entries include: Company name, address, phone, fax, names of principal personnel, branch office addresses, phone numbers, and key personnel. Arrangement: Classified by activity. Indexes: Company name, personal name.

★8254★ *Peterson's Job Opportunities in Engineering and Technology*

Thomson Peterson's
PO Box 67005
Lawrenceville, NJ 08648-6105
Fr: 800-338-3282

Compiled by the Peterson's staff. Fourth edition, 1996. $21.95 (paper). 384 pages. Profiles 2,000 high-tech companies looking primarily for technical personnel in such fields as biotechnology, telecommunications, software, computers and peripherals, defense, and aerospace. Contains job-search strategies and career options to help match education and expertise to the job market. Indexed geographically, by industry, and by hiring needs.

HANDBOOKS AND MANUALS

★8255★ *The Best Resumes for Scientists and Engineers*

John Wiley & Sons Inc.
1 Wiley Dr.
Somerset, NJ 08873
Ph: (732)469-4400   Fr: 800-225-5945

Adele Lewis and David J. Moore. Second edition, 1993. $37.50; $19.95 (paper). 224 pages. Presents an extensive collection of scientific and engineering resumes, highlighting the important differences between these and resumes written for other occupations.

★8256★ *Career Information Center*

Macmillan Publishing Co. Inc.
200 Old Tappan Rd.
Old Tappan, NJ 07675
Fr: 800-428-5331

Visual Education Center Staff. Seventh edition, 1999. $275.00. 2080 pages. This 13-volume set profiles over 600 occupations. Each occupational profile describes job duties, educational requirements, how to get the job, advancement possibilities, employment outlook, working conditions, earnings and benefits, and where to write for more information.

★8257★ *Careers in Environmental Geoscience*

American Association of Petroleum Geologists
PO Box 979
Tulsa, OK 74101-0979
Ph: (918)584-2555   Fax: (918)560-2652
Fr: 800-364-2274

Robert R. Jordan, Rima Petrossian, and

William J. Murphy. 1996. $5.00 (paper). DEP Publications Series. 54 pages.

★8258★ **Engineering Your Job Search: A Job-Finding Resource for Engineering Professionals**

Professional Publications, Inc.
1250 5th Ave.
Belmont, CA 94002
Ph: (650)593-9119   Fax: (650)592-4519
Fr: 800-426-1178

Compiled by Professional Publications, editors. 1995. $24.95 (paper). 154 pages. Out of print.

★8259★ **How to Succeed as an Engineer: A Practical Guide to Enhance Your Career**

Institute of Electrical & Electronics Engineers Inc.
PO Box 87204
Vancouver, WA 98687
Ph: (360)253-9532   Fax: (360)253-4084

Todd Yuzuriha. 1999. $29.95 (paper). 367 pages.

★8260★ **The I Hate Selling Book: Business-Building Advice for Consultants, Attorneys, Accountants, Engineers, Architects, and Other Professionals**

Allan Boress & Associates
1500 University Dr., Suite 239
Coral Springs, FL 33071
Ph: (954)345-4666   Fax: (954)344-2453

Allan S. Boress. 2001. $29.95.

★8261★ **Majoring in Engineering: How to Get from Your Freshman Year to Your First Job**

Farrar, Straus & Giroux, Inc.
19 Union Sq., W
New York, NY 10003
Ph: (212)741-6900   Fax: (212)633-9385
Fr: 888-330-8477

John Garcia and Carol Carter, editors. 2000. $20.00; $10.00 (paper). 134 pages.

★8262★ **The New Engineer's Guide to Career Growth & Professional Awareness**

Institute of Electrical & Electronics Engineers Inc.
445 Hoes Ln.
PO Box 1331
Piscataway, NJ 08855-1331
Ph: (732)562-3967   Fax: (732)981-9334
Fr: 800-678-4333

Irving J. Gabelman, editor. 1996. $39.95 (paper). 275 pages.

★8263★ **Opportunities in Energy Careers**

McGraw-Hill Trade
2 Penn Plaza
New York, NY 10121
Ph: (212)904-2000   Fr: 800-722-4726
E-mail: ntcpub@tribune.com

Nicholas Basta. 1995. $13.95; $10.95 (paper). 160 pages. Discusses opportunities in a variety of fields, including petroleum, nuclear, and thermal energy, and how to pursue employment. Illustrated. Out of print.

★8264★ **Opportunities in Engineering Careers**

McGraw-Hill Contemporary Books
1221 Avenue of the Americas
New York, NY 10020
Ph: (212)904-2000   Fr: 800-323-4900
E-mail: ntcpub@tribune.com

Nicholas Basta. Revised, 1995. $14.95; $11.95 (paper). 200 pages. Outlines typical job titles, salaries, career paths, and employment prospects.

★8265★ **Opportunities in Petroleum Careers**

McGraw-Hill Contemporary Books
1221 Avenue of the Americas
New York, NY 10020
Ph: (212)904-2000   Fr: 800-323-4900
E-mail: ntcpub@tribune.com

Gretchen Krueger. 1998. $14.95; $11.95 (paper). 200 pages. Outlines jobs in looking for oil; drilling and producing oil; and transporting, refining, and marketing oil. Discusses job seeking, opportunities for advancement, and employment outlook.

★8266★ **Real People Working in Engineering**

McGraw-Hill Contemporary Books
1221 Avenue of the Americas
New York, NY 10020
Ph: (212)904-2000   Fr: 800-323-4900
E-mail: ntcpub@tribune.com

Blythe Camenson, Jan Goldberg. 1997. $14.95; $12.95 (paper). Interviews and profiles of working professionals capture a range of opportunities in this field.

★8267★ **Resumes for Engineering Careers**

McGraw-Hill Trade
2 Penn Plaza
New York, NY 10121
Ph: (212)904-2000   Fr: 800-722-4726
E-mail: ntcpub@tribune.com

2000. $10.95 (paper). 456 pages. Contains sample resumes and cover letters applicable to any engineering field.

★8268★ **Resumes for Scientific and Technical Careers**

McGraw-Hill Contemporary Books
1221 Avenue of the Americas
New York, NY 10020
Ph: (212)904-2000   Fr: 800-323-4900
E-mail: ntcpub@tribune.com

1999. $9.95 (paper). 450 pages. Provides resume advice for individuals interested in working in scientific and technical careers. Includes sample resumes and cover letters.

EMPLOYMENT AGENCIES AND SEARCH FIRMS

★8269★ **Anderson Bradshaw Associates Inc.**
PO Box 924045
Houston, TX 77292-4045
Ph: (713)869-6789

Domestic and international search firm.

★8270★ **Dunn Associates**
229 Limberline Dr.
Greensburg, PA 15601
Ph: (724)832-9822   Fax: (724)832-9836
Fr: 877-586-2538

Executive search firm.

★8271★ **Engineer One, Inc.**
PO Box 23037
Knoxville, TN 37933
Fax: (865)691-0110
E-mail: engineerone@engineerone.com
URL: http://www.engineerone.com

Employment agency.

★8272★ **First Choice Search**
PO Box 31324
Seattle, WA 98103-1324
Ph: (206)632-0050

Executive search firm.

★8273★ **International Staffing Consultants**
2901 W Coast Hwy.,Ste. 200
Newport Beach, CA 92663
Ph: (949)263-5933   Fax: (949)767-5959
E-mail: iscinc@iscworld.com
URL: http://www.iscworld.com

Employment agency. Provides placement on regular or temporary basis. Affiliate office in London.

★8274★ **Main Line Personnel Service, Inc.**
Pagoda Blding.
100 Presidential Blvd. Ste. 200
Bala Cynwyd, PA 19004-0448
Ph: (610)667-1820   Fax: (610)668-5000

URL: http://www.mlpers.com
Employment agency.

★8275★ Search and Recruit International

4455 South Blvd.
Virginia Beach, VA 23452
Ph: (757)490-3151   Fax: (757)497-6503
E-mail: britt@searchandrecruit.com
URL: http://www.searchandrecruit.com

Employment agency. Headquartered in Virginia Beach. Other offices in Bremerton, WA; Charleston, SC; Jacksonville, FL; Memphis, TN; Pensacola, FL; Sacramento, CA; San Bernardino, CA; San Diego, CA.

★8276★ Techtronix Technical Search

PO Box 17713
Milwaukee, WI 53217-0173
Ph: (414)466-3100   Fax: (414)466-3598

Firm specializes in recruiting executives for the engineering, information systems, manufacturing, marketing, finance, and human resources industries.

TRADESHOWS

★8277★ American Society for Engineering Education Annual Conference and Exposition

American Society for Engineering Education
1818 N St., Ste. 600
Washington, DC 20036
Ph: (202)331-3500   Fax: (202)265-8504
URL: http://www.asee.org

Annual. **Primary Exhibits:** Publications, engineering supplies and equipment, computers, software, and research companies all products and services related to engineering education. **Dates and Locations:** 2005 Jun 12-15; Portland, OR • 2006 Jun 18-21; Chicago, IL • 2007 Jun 24-27; Honolulu, HI.

★8278★ International Thermal and Heavy Oil Symposium

Society of Petroleum Engineers (Texas)
222 Palisades Creek Dr.
PO Box 833836
Richardson, TX 75083-3836
Ph: (972)952-9494   Fax: (972)952-9435
E-mail: spedal@spe.org
URL: http://www.otcnet.org

Biennial. **Primary Exhibits:** Equipment, supplies, and services for thermal operations, new recovery techniques, cold pumping, and application of horizontal drilling.

★8279★ SPE Production and Operations Symposium

Society of Petroleum Engineers (Texas)
222 Palisades Creek Dr.
PO Box 833836
Richardson, TX 75083-3836
Ph: (972)952-9494   Fax: (972)952-9435
E-mail: spedal@spe.org
URL: http://www.otcnet.org

Biennial. **Primary Exhibits:** Devoted exclusively to the discussion and display of practical solutions for oil and gas production problems including drilling and completion, mud and sand control, automated controls, fracturing and acidizing, and well site safety.

OTHER SOURCES

★8280★ American Association of Blacks in Energy (AABE)

927 15th St. NW, Ste. 200
Washington, DC 20005
Ph: (202)371-9530   Fax: (202)371-9218
Fr: 800-466-0204
E-mail: aabe@aabe.org
URL: http://www.aabe.org

Description: Blacks in energy-related professions, including engineers, scientists, consultants, academicians, and entrepreneurs; government officials and public policymakers; interested students. Represents blacks and other minorities in matters involving energy use and research, the formulation of energy policy, the ownership of energy resources, and the development of energy technologies. Seeks to increase the knowledge, understanding, and awareness of the minority community in energy issues by serving as an energy information source for policymakers, recommending blacks and other minorities to appropriate energy officials and executives, encouraging students to pursue professional careers in the energy industry, and advocating the participation of blacks and other minorities in energy programsand policymaking activities. Updates members on key legislation and regulations being developed by the Department of Energy, the Department of Interior, the Department of Commerce, the Small Business Administration, and other federal and state agencies. Offers information on current job openings

★8281★ American Association of Engineering Societies (AAES)

1828 L St. NW, No. 906
Washington, DC 20036
Ph: (202)296-2237   Fax: (202)296-1151
Fr: 888-400-2237
E-mail: tprice@aaes.org
URL: http://www.aaes.org

Description: Coordinates the efforts of the member societies in the provision of reliable and objective information to the general public concerning issues which affect the engineering profession and the field of engineering as a whole; to collect, analyze, document, and disseminate data which will inform the general public of the relationship between engineering and the national welfare; to provide a forum for the engineering societies to exchange and discuss their views on matters of common interest; and to represent the U.S. engineering community aborad through representation in WFEO and UPADI.

★8282★ Association for International Practical Training (AIPT)

10400 Little Patuxent Pky., Ste. 250
Columbia, MD 21044-3519
Ph: (410)997-2200   Fax: (410)992-3924
E-mail: aipt@aipt.org
URL: http://www.aipt.org

Description: Providers worldwide on-the-job training programs for students and professionals seeking international career development and life-changing experiences. Arranges workplace exchanges in hundreds of professional fields, bringing employers and trainees together from around the world. Client list ranges from small farming communities to Fortune 500 companies.

★8283★ Association for Women Geoscientists (AWG)

PO Box 30645
Lincoln, NE 68503-0645
Fax: (402)489-8122
E-mail: office@awg.org
URL: http://www.awg.org

Members: Men and women geologists, geophysicists, petroleum engineers, geological engineers, hydrogeologists, paleontologists, geochemists, and other geoscientists. **Purpose:** Aims to: encourage the participation of women in the geosciences; exchange educational, technical, and professional information; enhance the professional growth and advancement of women in the geosciences. Provides information through web site on opportunities and careers available to women in the geosciences. **Activities:** Sponsors educational booths and programs at geological society conventions. Operates charitable program. Maintains speakers' bureau, and Association for Women Geoscientists Foundation (educational arm).

★8284★ Engineering Occupations

Delphi Productions
3160 4th St.
Boulder, CO 80304
Fax: (303)443-4022   Fr: 888-443-2400
URL: http://www.delphivideo.com

$95.00. 50 minutes. Part of the Careers for the 21st Century Video Library.

★8285★ National Action Council for Minorities in Engineering (NACME)

Empire State Bldg., Ste. 2212
350 Fifth Ave.
New York, NY 10118-2299
Ph: (212)279-2626   Fax: (212)629-5178
E-mail: webmaster@nacme.org
URL: http://www.nacme.org/

Description: Leads the national effort to increase access to careers in engineering and other science-based disciplines. Supported by the nation's leading technology-intensive companies, NACME conducts research and public policy analysis, develops and operates national demonstration programs at precollege and university levels, and disseminates information through publications, conferences, and electronic media. NACME is also the nation's largest privately funded source of scholarships for minority students in engineering.

★8286★ **National Society of Professional Engineers (NSPE)**
1420 King St.
Alexandria, VA 22314
Ph: (703)684-2800   Fax: (703)836-4875
Fr: 888-285-6773
E-mail: custserv@nspe.org
URL: http://www.nspe.org

Description: Professional engineers and engineers-in-training in all fields registered in accordance with the laws of states or territories of the U.S. or provinces of Canada; qualified graduate engineers, student members, and registered land surveyors. Is concerned with social, professional, ethical, and economic considerations of engineering as a profession; encompasses programs in public relations, employment practices, ethical con-

siderations, education, and career guidance. Monitors legislative and regulatory actions of interest to the engineering profession.

★8287★ *Petroleum Engineers*
Evon Publishing
832 N 7th Ave.
Iron River, MI 49935
Ph: (906)265-3190

Audiocassette. 1996. $16.95. 32 minutes. Part of the Careers and Vocational Guidance Series. Provides information about the nature of the work, educational requirements, employment outlook, earnings, and work conditions as well as additional related information.

★8288★ *The Petroleum Industry*
Evon Publishing
832 N 7th Ave.
Iron River, MI 49935
Ph: (906)265-3190

Audiocassette. 1996. $16.95. 32 minutes. Part of the Careers and Vocational Guidance Series. Provides information about the nature of the work, educational requirements, employment outlook, earnings, and work conditions as well as additional related information.

★8289★ *Scientific, Engineering, and Technical Services*
Cambridge Educational
2572 Brunswick Ave.
Lawrenceville, NJ 08648-4128
Fax: 800-FAX-ON-US   Fr: 800-468-4227
URL: http://www.cambridgeeducational.com

$89.95. 2002. 18 minutes. Part of the Career Cluster Series.

★8290★ **Society of Women Engineers (SWE)**
230 E Ohio St., No. 400
Chicago, IL 60611-3265
Ph: (312)596-5223   Fax: (312)596-5252
E-mail: hq@swe.org
URL: http://www.swe.org

Description: Educational and service organization representing both students and professional women in engineering and technical fields.

★8291★ *Women in Engineering*
Her Own Words
PO Box 5264
Madison, WI 53705-0264
Ph: (608)271-7083   Fax: (608)271-0209
URL: http://www.herownwords.com/

Video. Jocelyn Riley. $95.00. 15 minutes. Resource guide also available for $45.00.

Pharmacists

SOURCES OF HELP-WANTED ADS

★8292★ AACP News
American Association of Colleges of
  Pharmacy
1426 Prince St.
Alexandria, VA 22314
Ph: (703)739-2330   Fax: (703)836-8982
Fr: 800-510-2227
E-mail: pthompson@aacp.org

Description: Monthly. Discusses issues relating to pharmaceutical education. Carries legislative information, feature stories on award winners, and Association news. Recurring features include news of research, notices of continuing education and employment opportunities, and listings of publications.

★8293★ American Journal of Health-System Pharmacy
American Society of Health-System
  Pharmacists
7272 Wisconsin Ave.
Bethesda, MD 20814
Ph: (301)657-3000   Fax: (301)657-8857
E-mail: ajhp@ashp.org
URL: http://www.ashp.org

Bimonthly. $195.00/year for individuals; $225.00/year for nonmembers, U.S. and Canada. Journal for pharmacists practicing in health-systems (acute care, ambulatory care, homecare, long term care, HMO's, PPOs, & PBMs).

★8294★ The Annals of Pharmacotherapy
Harvey Whitney Books Co.
Box 42696
Cincinnati, OH 45242
Ph: (513)793-3555   Fax: (513)793-3600
Fr: 877-742-7631
E-mail: customerserv@theannals.com
URL: http://www.theannals.com

Monthly. $261.00/year for institutions. Journal covering drug therapy, new drugs, and pharmacotherapy.

★8295★ ASP Newsletter
American Society of Pharmacognosy
Temple University
3307 N Broad St.
Philadelphia, PA 19140
Ph: (215)707-4946   Fax: (215)707-3678

Description: Quarterly. Features information on natural products and news of the Society. Recurring features include a calendar of events, reports of meetings, job listings, and notices of publications available.

★8296★ Clinical Pharmacology and Therapeutics
Mosby Inc.
11830 Westline Industrial Dr.
St. Louis, MO 63146
Ph: (314)872-8370   Fax: (314)432-1380
Fr: 800-325-4177
URL: http://www.mosby.com/cpt

Monthly. $200.00/year for individuals; $422.00/year for institutions; $100.00/year for students; $238.00/year for individuals, other countries; $460.00/year for institutions, other countries; $120.00/year for students, other countries. Pharmacology journal devoted to the study of the nature, action, efficacy, and total evaluation of drugs as they are used in humans.

★8297★ Community Pharmacist
ELF Publications Inc.
5285 W Louisiana Ave.
Lakewood, CO 80232-5976
Ph: (303)975-0075   Fr: 800-922-8513
E-mail: elfedit@qwest.net
URL: http://www.elfpublications.com

Bimonthly. $12.00/year; $5.00 for single issue. National magazine addressing the professional and business needs, concerns and continuing education of retail pharmacists practicing in independent, chain and supermarket pharmacies.

★8298★ Drug Store News
Lebhar-Friedman Inc.
425 Park Ave.
New York, NY 10022-3556
Ph: (212)756-5088   Fax: (212)756-5120
Fr: 800-453-2427

Semimonthly. $19.50/year. Drug store industry tabloid.

★8299★ Drug Topics
Thomson Medical Economics
5 Paragon Dr.
Montvale, NJ 07645-1742
Ph: (201)358-7200   Fax: (201)722-2680
URL: http://www.medec.com/html/products/productdetail/dt_mag.html

Bimonthly. $61.00/year for individuals; $109.00/year for other countries; $109.00/year for Canada. Newsmagazine for pharmacists.

★8300★ Hospital Pharmacist Report
Thomson Medical Economics
5 Paragon Dr.
Montvale, NJ 07645-1742
Ph: (201)358-7200   Fax: (201)722-2680
URL: http://www.medec.com/html/products/productdetail/hpr_mag.htm

Monthly. $39.00/year for individuals; $55.00/year for other countries; $55.00/year for Canada. Trade periodical for hospital pharmacists.

★8301★ Journal of the American Pharmaceutical Association
American Pharmaceutical Association
2215 Constitution Ave. NW
Washington, DC 20037-2985
Ph: (202)628-4410   Fax: (202)783-2351
Fr: 800-237-2742
E-mail: japha@mail.aphanet.org
URL: http://www.aphanet.org

Bimonthly. $30.00/year, subscription included in membership; $175.00/year for individuals; $200.00/year for out of country; $35.00 for single issue. Journal for pharmacy professionals.

★8302★ McKnight's Long-Term Care News

McKnight's Long-Term Care News
Two Northfield Plz., Ste. 300
Northfield, IL 60093-1219
Ph: (847)784-8706   Fax: (847)441-3701
E-mail: ltcnews@medec.com

Monthly. Free to qualified subscribers in U.S.; $5.00/year for single issue; $9.00 for single back issue; $54.95/year for Canada; $59.95/year, foreign. Professional magazine.

★8303★ Med Ad News

Engel Publishing Partners
820 Bear Tavern Rd., Ste. 300
West Trenton, NJ 08628
Ph: (609)530-0044   Fax: (609)530-0207
E-mail: mwalsh@engelpub.com

Monthly. $150.00/year for U.S.; $270.00/year for other countries. Pharmaceutical business and marketing magazine.

★8304★ The Nurse Practitioner

Lippincott Williams & Wilkins
1111 Bethlehem Pke.
PO Box 908
Springhouse, PA 19477
Ph: 800-346-7844   Fax: (215)646-1083
Fr: 800-346-7844
URL: http://www.tnpj.com

Monthly. $50.00/year; $83.00/year for institutions; $67.00/year for Canada; $98.00/year for institutions in Canada; $104.00/year, international. Magazine presenting clinical information to nurses in advanced primary care practice. Also covers legal, business, economic, ethical, research, and pharmaceutical issues.

★8305★ The PDA Journal of Pharmaceutical Science & Technology

PDA
3 Bethesda Metro Ctr., Ste. 1500
Bethesda, MD 20814
Ph: (301)656-5900   Fax: (301)986-0296
E-mail: pda-journal@uiowa.edu

Bimonthly. $135.00/year for individuals; $30.00 for single issue. Professional journal covering pharmaceutical science.

★8306★ Pharmaceutical Engineering

International Society for Pharmaceutical Engineering Inc.
3109 W Dr. Martin Luther King Jr. Blvd., Ste. 250
Tampa, FL 33607-6260
Ph: (813)960-2105   Fax: (813)264-2816
URL: http://ispe.org

Bimonthly. Subscription included in membership. Magazine on the health care manufacturing industry.

★8307★ Pharmaceutical Executive

Advanstar Communications Inc.
Raritan Plz. III
101 Fieldcrest Ave.
Edison, NJ 08837
Ph: (732)225-9500   Fax: (732)225-0211
E-mail: pehome@pharmaportal.com
URL: http://www.pharmexec.com

Monthly. $64.00/year for individuals; $12.00 for single issue; $84.00/year for Canada; $124.00/year for other countries. Pharmaceutical industry journal.

★8308★ Pharmaceutical Laboratory

Reed Business Information
301 Gibraltar Dr.
Morris Plains, NJ 07950
Ph: (973)292-5100   Fax: (973)539-3476
E-mail: gbyam@cahners.com
URL: http://www.biotechmedia.com/y2001-ed-cahners-pharmlab.html

Trade publication covering the pharmaceutical industry.

★8309★ Pharmaceutical Technology

Advanstar Communications Inc.
Raritan Plz. III
101 Fieldcrest Ave.
Edison, NJ 08837
Ph: (732)225-9500   Fax: (732)225-0211
E-mail: ptpress@advanstar.com

Monthly. Free to qualified subscribers; $54.00/year. Magazine on applied technology for pharmaceutical firms.

★8310★ Pharmacy Times

Romaine Pierson Publishers Inc.
241 Forsgate Dr.
Jamesburg, NJ 08831
Ph: (732)656-0200   Fax: (732)656-1142
E-mail: pharmtimes@aol.com
URL: http://www.pharmacytimes.com

Monthly. $38.00/year. Journal providing information on health items (including prescription and over-the-counter drugs and surgical supplies) to independent, chain, and hospital pharmacists.

★8311★ Pharmacy Today

American Pharmaceutical Association
2215 Constitution Ave. NW
Washington, DC 20037-2985
Ph: (202)628-4410   Fax: (202)783-2351
Fr: 800-237-2742
E-mail: pt@aphanet.org

Monthly. Reports on current news and opinions for pharmacists.

PLACEMENT AND JOB REFERRAL SERVICES

★8312★ American Association of Pharmaceutical Scientists (AAPS)

2107 Wilson Blvd., No. 700
Arlington, VA 22201-3042
Ph: (703)243-2800   Fax: (703)243-9650
E-mail: aaps@aaps.org
URL: http://www.aapspharmaceutica.com

Description: Pharmaceutical scientists. Provides a forum for exchange of scientific information; serves as a resource in forming public policies to regulate pharmaceutical sciences and related issues of public concern. Promotes pharmaceutical sciences and provides for recognition of individual achievement; works to foster career growth and the development of members. Offers placement service.

★8313★ American College of Clinical Pharmacy (ACCP)

3101 Broadway, Ste. 650
Kansas City, MO 64111
Ph: (816)531-2177   Fax: (816)531-4990
E-mail: accp@accp.com
URL: http://www.accp.com

Description: Clinical pharmacists dedicated to: promoting rational use of drugs in society; advancing the practice of clinical pharmacy and interdisciplinary health care; assuring high quality clinical pharmacy by establishing and maintaining standards in education and training at advanced levels. Encourages research and recognizes excellence in clinical pharmacy. Offers educational programs, symposia, research forums, fellowship training, and college-funded grants through competitions. Maintains placement service.

★8314★ American Public Health Association (APHA)

800 I St. NW
Washington, DC 20001-3710
Ph: (202)777-2742   Fax: (202)777-2534
E-mail: comments@apha.org
URL: http://www.apha.org

Members: Professional organization of physicians, nurses, educators, academicians, environmentalists, epidemiologists, new professionals, social workers, health administrators, optometrists, podiatrists, pharmacists, dentists, nutritionists, health planners, other community and mental health specialists, and interested consumers. **Purpose:** Seeks to protect and promote personal, mental, and environmental health. **Activities:** Services include promulgation of standards; establishment of uniform practices and procedures; development of the etiology of communicable diseases; research in public health; exploration of medical care programs and their relationships to public health. Sponsors job placement service.

★8315★ American Society of Consultant Pharmacists (ASCP)

1321 Duke St.
Alexandria, VA 22314-3563
Ph: (703)739-1300   Fax: (703)739-1321
Fr: 800-355-2727
E-mail: info@ascp.com
URL: http://www.ascp.com

Description: Provides leadership, education, advocacy, and resources to advance the practice of senior care pharmacy practice. **Activities:** Conducts surveys of long-term care pharmacy operations. Sponsors educational and research programs. Maintains information center, hall of fame, and speakers' bureau; operates placement service; compiles statistics.

★8316★ American Society of Health System Pharmacists (ASHP)

7272 Wisconsin Ave.
Bethesda, MD 20814
Ph: (301)657-3000   Fax: (301)664-8867
E-mail: evp@ashp.org
URL: http://www.ashp.org

Description: Professional society of pharmacists employed by hospitals, HMOs, clinics, and other health systems. Provides personnel placement service for members; sponsors professional and personal liability program. Conducts educational and exhibit programs. Has 30 practice interest areas, special sections for home care practitioners and clinical specialists, and research and education foundation.

EMPLOYER DIRECTORIES AND NETWORKING LISTS

★8317★ AHA Guide to the Health Care Field

American Hospital Association (AHA)
1 N. Franklin St., 27th Fl.
Chicago, IL 60606
Ph: (312)422-2050   Fax: (312)422-4700
Fr: 800-424-4301

Annual, August. $295.00. Covers hospitals, networks, multi-health care systems, free-standing ambulatory surgery centers, psychiatric facilities, long-term care facilities, substance abuse programs, and other health-related organizations. Entries include: For hospitals-Facility name, address, phone, administrator's name, number of beds, facilities and services, number of employees, expenses, other statistics. For other organizations-Name, address, phone, fax, name and title of contact. Arrangement: Geographical. Indexes: Hospital name.

★8318★ Directory of Drug Store & HBC Chains

Chain Store Guide
3922 Coconut Palm Dr.
Tampa, FL 33619
Ph: (813)627-6800   Fax: (813)627-6882
Fr: 800-927-9292

URL: http://www.csgis.com

Annual, May. $335.00. Covers 1,600 drug store chains operation two or more units, including mass merchants and grocers with pharmacies; 215 wholesale drug companies in the United States and Canada. Entries include: For retailers-company name; phone and fax numbers; physical and mailing addresses; company e-mail and web addresses; listing type; number of stores; product lines; percentage of sales by product line; total sales; prescription drug sales; percentage of prescriptions filled with generic drugs; number of prescriptions filled daily; percentage of prescriptions filled with private third party, cash, and Medicaid; number of stores by type; mail order pharmacy indicator; managed care division indicator; projected openings and remodelings; store prototype sizes; total selling square footage; trading area; franchise group headquarter's name and location; distribution center and primary wholesaler names and locations; number of specialty departments; packaged liquor indicators; private label indicators; computerized pharmacy indicator; average number of checkouts; year founded; public company indicator; parent company name and location; regional and divisional office locations; headquarters personnel with titles. For wholesalers-company name, address, phone, and fax; e-mail and web addresses; listing type; product lines; percentage of sales by product line; total sales; percentage of sales by customer type; total stores served; number of member and non-member stores served; trading area; group store trading names; wholesaler type; distribution center locations; private label indicator; year founded; public company indicator; headquarters personnel with titles. Arrangement: Separate geographical sections for retailers and wholesalers. Indexes: Alphabetical, exclusions.

★8319★ Directory of Hospital Personnel

Thomson Medical Economics
5 Paragon Dr.
Montvale, NJ 07645-1742
Ph: (201)358-7200   Fax: (201)722-2680

Annual, November. $325.00. Covers 200,000 executives at 7,000 U.S. hospitals. Entries include: Name of hospital, address, phone, number of beds, type and JCAHO status of hospital, names and titles of key department heads and staff, medical and nursing school affiliations; number of residents, interns, and nursing students. Arrangement: Geographical. Indexes: Hospital name, personnel, hospital size.

★8320★ Federation of American Societies for Experimental Biology-Directory of Members

Federation of American Societies for Experimental Biology
9650 Rockville Pke.
Bethesda, MD 20814-3998
Ph: (301)634-7100   Fax: (301)634-7809
Fr: 800-43F-ASEB
URL: http://www.faseb.org/

Annual, Fall. $68.00 for nonmembers; $34.00 for members. Covers about 61,000 members of The American Physiological Society, American Society for Biochemistry and Molecular Biology, American Society for Pharmacology and Experimental Therapeutics, American Society for Investigative Pathology, American Society for Nutritional Sciences, The American Association of Immunologists, Biophysical Society, American Association of Anatomists, The Protein Society, The American Society for Bone and Mineral Research, American Society for Clinical Investigation, The Endocrine Society, The American Society of Human Genetics, Society for Developmental Biology, American Peptide Society, Society for the Study of Reproduction and Radiation Research Society. Entries include: Name, address, title, affiliation, memberships in federation societies, highest degree, year elected to membership, phone, fax and email address. Membership directories of the Biophysical Society, The Protein Society, The American Society for Bone and Mineral Research, and American Society for Clinical Investigation are also available separately. Arrangement: Alphabetical. Indexes: Geographical.

★8321★ Hospital Blue Book

Billian/Transworld Publishing Inc.
2100 Powers Ferry Rd.
Ste. 300
Atlanta, GA 30339
Ph: (770)955-8484   Fax: (770)955-8485
Fr: 800-533-8484
E-mail: blu-book@billian.com

Annual, January. $285.00 for national edition; $160.00 for southern edition. Covers more than 6,687 hospitals; some listings also appear in a separate southern edition of this publication. Entries include: Name of hospital, accreditation, mailing address, phone, fax, number of beds, type of facility (nonprofit, general, state, etc.); list of administrative personnel and chiefs of medical services, with specific titles. Arrangement: Geographical.

★8322★ Medical and Health Information Directory

Thomson Gale
27500 Drake Rd.
Farmington Hills, MI 48331-3535
Ph: (248)699-4253   Fax: (248)699-8065
Fr: 800-877-GALE
E-mail: businessproducts@gale.com

Annual. $285.00 per volume; $675.00 per set. Covers in Volume 1, more than 26,500 medical and health oriented associations, organizations, institutions, and government agencies, including health maintenance organizations (HMOs), preferred provider organizations (PPOs), insurance companies, pharmaceutical companies, research centers, and medical and allied health schools. In Volume 2, over 12,000 medical book publishers; medical periodicals, directories, audiovisual producers and services, medical libraries and information centers, electronic resources, and health-related internet search engines. In Volume 3, more than 35,500 clinics, treatment centers, care programs, and counseling/diagnostic services for 34 subject areas. Entries include: Institution, service, or firm name, address, phone, fax, email and URL; many include names of key personnel and, when pertinent, descriptive annotation. Volume 3 was formerly listed separately as Health Services Directory. Arrangement: Classified by organization activity, service, etc. Indexes: Each volume has a complete alphabetical name and keyword index.

★8323★ **NWDA Directory**
National Wholesale Druggists' Association
1821 Michael Faraday Dr., Ste. 400
Reston, VA 20190
Ph: (703)787-0000   Fax: (703)787-6930
E-mail: member@nwda.org
URL: http://www.nwda.org

Annual, January. $295.00. Covers wholesalers, manufacturers, national drug-trade associations, and colleges of pharmacy. Entries include: For industry-Company name, address, phone, fax, names, of principal executives. For colleges-Institution name, address. Arrangement: Classified by type of membership.

★8324★ **Peterson's Job Opportunities for Health and Science Majors**
Thomson Peterson's
Princeton Pke. Corporate Ctr., 2000 Lenox Dr.
PO Box 67005
Lawrenceville, NJ 08648
Ph: (609)896-1800   Fax: (609)896-4531
Fr: 800-338-3282
URL: http://www.petersons.com

Irregular, latest edition 1999. $18.95. Covers approximately 1,300 research, consulting, government, and non-profit and profit service organizations that hire college and university graduates in science and health-related majors. Entries include: Organization name, address, phone, name and title of contact, type of organization, number of employees, Standard Industrial Classification (SIC) code; description of opportunities available including disciplines, level of education required, starting locations and salaries, level of experience accepted, benefits.

★8325★ **Pharmaceutical Products-Wholesalers Directory**
infoUSA Inc.
5711 S 86th Cir.
Omaha, NE 68127-0347
Ph: (402)930-3500   Fax: (402)331-0176
Fr: 800-555-6124
URL: http://www.abii.com

Annual. Number of listings: 3,250. Entries include: Name, address, phone (including area code), size of advertisement, year first in "Yellow Pages," name of owner or manager, number of employees. Compiled from telephone company "Yellow Pages," nationwide. Arrangement: Geographical.

★8326★ **Pharmacies Directory**
infoUSA Inc.
5711 S 86th Cir.
Omaha, NE 68127-0347
Ph: (402)930-3500   Fax: (402)331-0176
Fr: 800-555-6124
URL: http://www.abii.com

Annual. Number of listings: 54,430. Entries include: Name, address, phone, size of advertisement, name of owner or manager, number of employees, year first in "Yellow Pages." Compiled from telephone company "Yellow Pages," nationwide. Available in regional editions; please inquire. Arrangement: Geographical.

HANDBOOKS AND MANUALS

★8327★ **Careers in Health Care**
McGraw-Hill Trade
2 Penn Plaza
New York, NY 10121
Ph: (212)904-2000   Fr: 800-722-4726
E-mail: ntcpub@tribune.com

Barbara M. Swanson. Fourth edition, 2000. $17.95; $13.95 (paper). 320 pages. Describes job duties, work settings, salaries, licensing and certification requirements, educational preparation, and future outlook. Gives ideas on how to secure a job.

★8328★ **Discovering New Medicines: Careers in Pharmaceutical Research & Development**
John Wiley & Sons Inc.
111 River St.
Hoboken, NJ 07030-5774
Ph: (201)748-6000   Fax: (201)748-6088
Fr: 800-225-5945

Peter D. Stonier, editor. 1995. $65.00 (paper). 406 pages.

★8329★ **Expert Resumes for Health Care Careers**
JIST Publishing
8902 Otis Ave.
Indianapolis, IN 46216-1033
Ph: (317)613-4200   Fax: 800-547-8329

December 2003. $16.95. 288 pages.

★8330★ **Health Careers Today**
Elsevier-Health Sciences Division
The Curtis Center, Ste. 300E, 3rd Fl.
170 S. Independence Mall W.
Philadelphia, PA 19106
Ph: (215)238-7800   Fax: (215)238-7362
Fr: 800-523-4069

Gerdin. Revised edition. April 2004. $52.95.

★8331★ **Inside Pharmacy: The Anatomy of a Profession**
CRC Press LLC
2000 NW Corporate Blvd.
Boca Raton, FL 33431
Ph: (561)994-0555   Fax: (561)989-8732
Fr: 800-272-7737

Raymond A. Gosselin and Jack Robbins. 1998. $41.95. 134 pages.

★8332★ **Opportunities in Health and Medical Careers**
McGraw-Hill Trade
2 Penn Plaza
New York, NY 10121
Ph: (212)904-2000   Fr: 800-722-4726

I. Donald Snook, Jr. and Leo D'Orazio. 1997. $14.95; $11.95 (paper). 202 pages. Covers the full range of medical and health occupations. Illustrated.

★8333★ **Opportunities in Pharmacy Careers**
McGraw-Hill Trade
2 Penn Plaza
New York, NY 10121
Ph: (212)904-2000   Fr: 800-722-4726

Fred B. Gable. 1997. $14.95; $11.95 (paper). 200 pages. Identifies opportunities in a variety of settings, including retail chains, private ownership, clinics, hospitals, and other private, commercial, and industrial operations. Provides information on job-hunting techniques. Illustrated.

★8334★ **The Pharmacy Student Companion: Your Road Map to Pharmacy Education and Careers**
American Pharmaceutical Association
2215 Constitution Ave., NW
Washington, DC 20037
Ph: (202)628-4410   Fax: (202)783-2351
Fr: 800-878-0729

Daniel H. Albrant and Linda R. Harteker, authors. Vicki L. Meade, editor. Third edition, revised, 1999. $20.00 (paper).

★8335★ **Resumes for Health and Medical Careers**
McGraw-Hill Trade
2 Penn Plaza
New York, NY 10121
Ph: (212)904-2000   Fr: 800-722-4726
E-mail: ntcpub@tribune.com

1997. $9.95 (paper). 455 pages.

★8336★ **Road Map to a Profession's Future: The Millis Study Commission on Pharmacy**
Gordon & Breach Publishing Group
29 W. 35th St.
New York, NY 10001
Ph: (212)216-7800   Fax: (212)564-7854

Dennis B. Worthen. 1999. $39.00.

EMPLOYMENT AGENCIES AND SEARCH FIRMS

★8337★ Allerton Heneghan & O'Neill
1 Tower Ln., Ste. 1700
Oakbrook Terrace, IL 60181
Ph: (630)645-2294   Fax: (630)645-2298
Executive Search firm.

★8338★ BioQuest
100 Spear St., Ste. 1125
San Francisco, CA 94105
Ph: (415)777-2422
Executive search firm focused in healthcare and life sciences.

★8339★ Brandywine Consulting Group
5 Great Valley Pkwy., Ste. 322
Malvern, PA 19355
Ph: (610)407-4600
Executive search firm. An Affiliate of Brandywine Management Group in Berlin, MD.

★8340★ Caplan Associates Inc.
77 Bull Path
PO Box 4227
East Hampton, NY 11937
Ph: (631)907-9700   Fax: (631)907-0444
Executive search firm.

★8341★ Carlyle & Conlan Inc.
630 Davis Dr., Ste. 260
Morrisville, NC 27560
Ph: (919)474-0771   Fax: (919)474-0682
Executive search firm.

★8342★ Clark Executive Search Inc.
135 N. Ferry Rd.
PO Box 560
Shelter Island, NY 11964
Ph: (631)749-3540
Executive search firm.

★8343★ CNR Search
4535 Saddlehorn Dr.
Reno, NV 89511
Ph: (775)851-2829   Fax: (775)851-4514
Provides staffing services of permanent and temporary employees. Works primarily on a retained basis. Contingency on a limited basis. Active in providing human resources consulting services. Also active in mergers and acquisitions in high technology firms. Industries served: computer; information services; insurance, pharmaceutical and health care.

★8344★ Colucci, Blendow & Johnson
643 Main St., Ste. 8
Half Moon Bay, CA 94019-1988
Ph: (650)712-0103   Fax: (650)712-0105
Executive search consultants in the medical technology area that includes pharmaceuticals, medical equipment and device manufacturers, biotechnology, therapeutic supplies, diagnostic laboratory equipment and supplies, diagnostic imaging equipment and supplies, medical services, chemicals, cosmetic and toiletries, dental, veterinarian, and agricultural genetics companies.

★8345★ Conyngham Partners LLC
PO Box 94
Ridgewood, NJ 07451
Ph: (201)652-3444   Fax: (201)652-6357
Executive search firm.

★8346★ Courtright & Associates Inc.
PO Box 503
Clarks Summit, PA 18411-0503
Ph: (570)586-0735   Fax: (570)586-3969
Executive search firm.

★8347★ Cromwell Partners Inc.
305 Madison Ave.
New York, NY 10165
Ph: (212)953-3220   Fax: (212)953-4688
Executive search firm.

★8348★ Day & Associates
577 Airport Blvd., Ste. 130
Burlingame, CA 94010
Executive search firm.

★8349★ Doleman Enterprises Ln.
1151 Water Pointe
Reston, VA 20194-1035
Ph: (703)742-5454   Fax: (703)708-6992
Human resources firm specializes in recruiting for the high-tech, data and computer engineering, and pharmaceutical industries.

★8350★ Emerging Medical Technologies Inc.
7784 S. Addison Way
Aurora, CO 80016
Ph: (303)699-1990
Executive search firm focused on the medical devices industry.

★8351★ Franklin Allen Consultants Ltd.
1205 Franklin Ave., Ste. 350
Garden City, NY 11530
Ph: (516)248-4511   Fax: (516)294-6646
Executive search firm.

★8352★ J. Blakeslee International Inc.
645 E. Blithedale Ave.
Mill Valley, CA 94941
Ph: (415)389-7300   Fax: (415)389-7302
Executive search firm.

★8353★ J. Burkey Associates
900 Laurel Ave.
River Edge, NJ 07661
Ph: (201)262-7990   Fax: (201)262-7955
Executive search firm.

★8354★ JPM International
26060 Acero
Mission Viejo, CA 92691
Ph: (949)699-4300   Fax: (949)699-4333
Fr: 800-685-7856
E-mail: leslieo@jpmintl.com
URL: http://www.jpmintl.com
Executive search firm and employment agency.

★8355★ Ken Clark International
2000 Lenox Dr., Ste. 200
Lawrenceville, NJ 08648
Ph: (609)308-5200   Fax: (609)308-5250
Executive search firm. Branches in Newport Beach, CA; Deerfield, IL; Waltham, MA; and Wayne, PA.

★8356★ Rosemary Cass Ltd.
175 Post Rd. W
Westport, CT 06880
Ph: (203)454-2920   Fax: (203)454-4643
Executive search firm.

ONLINE JOB SOURCES AND SERVICES

★8357★ BioView.com
URL: http://www.bioview.com
Description: Provides information on biopharmaceutical jobs, news, and resources. Job hunters may search jobs by keyword, state, and job title or discipline. **Main files include:** Submit Company Summary, CareerView, CompanyView, NewsView, InvestorView, MarketView. **Fee:** Single Job Posting - $225/60 days Unlimited Job Postings $2,000/month. Posting packages also available.

★8358★ MedExplorer
URL: http://www.medexplorer.com
Description: Employment postings make up one module of this general medical site. Other sections contain: Newsletter, Classifieds, and Discussion Forum.

★8359★ **Medhunters.com**
E-mail: info@medhunters.com
URL: http://www.medhunters.com

Description: Career search site for jobs in all health care specialties; educational resources; visa and licensing information for relocation; interesting articles; relocation tools; links to professional organizations and general resources.

★8360★ **ProHealthJobs**
E-mail: sales@prohealthjobs.com
URL: http://www.prohealthjobs.com

Description: Career resources site for the medical and health care field. Lists professional opportunities, product information, continuing education and open positions.

TRADESHOWS

★8361★ **American Association of Pharmaceutical Scientists Annual Meeting and Exposition**
American Association of Pharmaceutical Scientists
2107 Wilson Blvd., No. 700
Arlington, VA 22201-3042
Ph: (703)243-2800   Fax: (703)243-5582
E-mail: aaps@aaps.org
URL: http://www.aapspharmaceutica.com

Annual. **Primary Exhibits:** Raw materials, supplies, equipment, contract research & contract service labs, computer software, packaging, and other suppliers to pharmaceutical scientists. **Dates and Locations:** 2004 Nov 7-11; Baltimore, MD; Baltimore Convention Ctr. • 2005 Nov 6-10; Nashville, TN; Opryland Hotel • 2006 Oct 29 - Nov 2; San Antonio, TX; San Antonio Conv. Center • 2007 Nov 12-16; San Diego, CA; San Diego Convention Center • 2008 Nov 16-20; Atlanta, GA; Georgia World Congress Center • 2009 Nov 8-12; Los Angeles, CA; Los Angeles Convention Center.

★8362★ **American Society of Consultant Pharmacists Annual Meeting and Exhibition**
American Society of Consultant Pharmacists
1321 Duke St.
Alexandria, VA 22314-3563
Ph: (703)739-1300   Fax: (703)739-1500
Fr: 800-355-2727
E-mail: info@ascp.com
URL: http://www.ascp.com

Annual. **Primary Exhibits:** Pharmaceuticals, drug distribution systems, packaging equipment, computers, durable medical equipment, and medical supplies. **Dates and Locations:** 2004 Nov 04-06; San Francisco, CA; Moscone Convention Center • 2005 Nov 09-12; Boston, MA; Hynes Convention Center • 2006 Nov 15-18; Phoenix, AZ; Phoenix Civic Plaza • 2007 Nov 14-17; Philadelphia, PA; Pennsylvania Convention Center • 2008

Nov 09-12; New Orleans, LA; Ernest E. Morial Convention Center.

★8363★ **Georgia Pharmacy Association Convention**
Georgia Pharmacy Association
50 Lenox Pointe, NE-30324
PO Box 95527
Atlanta, GA 30347
Ph: (404)231-5074   Fax: (404)237-8435

Annual. **Primary Exhibits:** Pharmaceutical equipment, supplies, and services.

★8364★ **Pharmacists Society of the State of New York Annual Meeting**
Pharmacists Society of the State of New York
210 Washington Ave. Ext.
Albany, NY 12203
Ph: (518)869-6595   Fax: (518)464-0618

Annual. **Primary Exhibits:** Pharmaceuticals.

★8365★ **RX Expo - An Educational Forum and Buying Show**
National Community Pharmacists Association
205 Daingerfield Rd.
Alexandria, VA 22314
Ph: (703)683-8200   Fax: (703)683-3619

Annual. **Primary Exhibits:** General gifts, sundries, and seasonal items; over the counter products; health and beauty aids; electronic products; prescription drug products, personal care products, home health care products, IV products, and related products.

★8366★ **Texas Pharmacy Association Annual Meeting and Exhibit**
Texas Pharmacy Association
1624 E. Anderson Ln.
PO Box 14709
Austin, TX 78761-4079
Ph: (512)836-8350   Fax: (512)836-0308
Fr: 800-505-5463
URL: http://www.txpharmacy.com

Annual. **Primary Exhibits:** Pharmaceuticals and various services provided to pharmacists.

★8367★ **Western Pharmacy Education Fair**
California Pharmacists Association
1112 I St., Ste. 300
Sacramento, CA 95814
Ph: (916)444-7811   Fax: (916)444-7929
E-mail: cpha@cpha.com
URL: http://www.cpha.com

Annual. **Primary Exhibits:** Pharmaceutical equipment, supplies, and services.

OTHER SOURCES

★8368★ **American Academy of Clinical Toxicology (AACT)**
777 E Park Dr.
PO Box 8820
Harrisburg, PA 17105-8820
Ph: (717)558-7847   Fax: (717)558-7845
Fr: 888-633-5784
E-mail: jreisinger@pamedsoc.org
URL: http://www.clintox.org

Members: Physicians, veterinarians, pharmacists, nurses research scientists, and analytical chemists. **Purpose:** Works to unite medical scientists and facilitate the exchange of information; encourage the development of therapeutic methods and technology. **Activities:** Conducts professional training in poison information and emergency service personnel.

★8369★ *American Almanac of Jobs and Salaries*
Morrow Avon
1350 Avenue of the Americas
New York, NY 10019
Ph: (212)261-6788   Fr: 800-242-7737

John W. Wright. Revised edition, 2000. $20.00 (paper). 672 pages. This is a comprehensive guide to the wages of hundreds of occupations in a wide variety of industries and organizations.

★8370★ **American Hospital Association (AHA)**
1 N. Franklin
Chicago, IL 60606-3421
Ph: (312)422-3000   Fax: (312)422-4796
URL: http://www.aha.org

Description: Health care provider organizations. Seeks to advance the health of individuals and communities. Leads, represents, and serves health care provider organizations that are accountable to the community and committed to health improvement.

★8371★ **American Pharmacists Association - Academy of Pharmacy Practice and Management (APhA-APPM)**
2215 Constitution Ave. NW
Washington, DC 20037-2985
Ph: (202)628-4410   Fax: (202)783-2351
Fr: 800-237-APHA
E-mail: apha-appm@aphanet.org
URL: http://www.aphanet.org

Description: Pharmacists concerned with rendering professional services directly to the public, without regard for status of employment or environment of practice. Purposes are to provide a forum and mechanism whereby pharmacists may meet to discuss and implement programs and activities relevant and helpful to the practitioner of pharmacy; to recommend programs and courses of action which should be undertaken or implemented by the profession; to coordinate academy efforts so as to be an asset to the progress of the profession. Provides and cosponsors continuing education meetings, seminars, and workshops; produces audiovisual materials.

★8372★ Exploring Health Occupations
Cambridge Educational
2572 Brunswick Ave.
Lawrenceville, NJ 08648-4128
Fax: 800-FAX-ON-US   Fr: 800-468-4227
URL: http://www.cambridgeeducational.com

Two videos. $139.95. 1999.

★8373★ Health Assessment & Treating Occupations
Delphi Productions
3160 4th St.
Boulder, CO 80304
Fax: (303)443-4022   Fr: 888-443-2400
URL: http://www.delphivideo.com

$95.00. 50 minutes. Part of the Careers for the 21st Century Video Library.

★8374★ Health Service Occupations
Delphi Productions
3160 4th St.
Boulder, CO 80304
Fax: (303)443-4022   Fr: 888-443-2400
URL: http://www.delphivideo.com

$95.00. 50 minutes. Part of the Careers for the 21st Century Video Library.

★8375★ Medicine & Related Occupations
Delphi Productions
3160 4th St.
Boulder, CO 80304
Fax: (303)443-4022   Fr: 888-443-2400
URL: http://www.delphivideo.com

$95.00. 45 minutes. Part of the Careers for the 21st Century Video Library.

★8376★ National Association of Boards of Pharmacy (NABP)
700 Busse Hwy.
Park Ridge, IL 60068
Ph: (847)698-6227   Fax: (847)698-0124
E-mail: custserv@nabp.net
URL: http://www.nabp.net

Members: Pharmacy boards of several states, District of Columbia, Puerto Rico, Virgin Islands, several Canadian provinces, the states of Victoria, Australia, and New South Wales, the Pharmaceutical Society of New Zealand, and the South African Pharmacy Council. **Purpose:** Provides for interstate reciprocity in pharmaceutic licensure based upon a uniform minimum standard of pharmaceutic education and uniform legislation; improves the standards of pharmaceutical education licensure and practice. **Activities:** Provides legislative information; sponsors uniform licensure examination; also provides information on accredited school and college requirements. Maintains pharmacy and drug law statistics.

★8377★ National Association of Chain Drug Stores (NACDS)
413 N Lee St.
PO Box 1417-D49
Alexandria, VA 22313-1480
Ph: (703)549-3001   Fax: (703)836-4869
E-mail: dharrington@nacds.org
URL: http://www.nacds.org

Description: Chain drug members (130); associate members (1400) and (80) international members include manufacturers, suppliers, manufacturer's representatives, publishers, and advertising agencies. Interprets actions by government agencies in such areas as drugs, public health, federal trade, labor, and excise taxes. Sponsors meetings and pharmacy student recruitment program. Maintains library. Offers insurance and discount services to members.

★8378★ National Pharmaceutical Association (NPhA)
107 Kilmayne Dr., Ste. C
Cary, NC 27511
Fax: (919)469-5870   Fr: 800-944-NPH
E-mail: npha@npha.net
URL: http://www.npha.net/

Description: State and local associations of professional minority pharmacists. To provide a means whereby members may "contribute to their common improvement, share their experiences, and contribute to the public good."

★8379★ Pharmaceutical Care Management Association (PCMA)
601 Pennsylvania Ave. NW, No. 740
Washington, DC 20004
Ph: (202)207-3610   Fax: (202)207-362
URL: http://www.pcmanet.org

Description: Represents managed care pharmacy, pharmaceutical benefits management companies (PBMs) and their health care partners in pharmaceutical care. Promotes education, legislation, practice standards, and research to foster quality, affordable pharmaceutical care.

★8380★ Pharmacists
Evon Publishing
832 N 7th Ave.
Iron River, MI 49935
Ph: (906)265-3190

Audiocassette. 1996. $16.95. 32 minutes. Part of the Careers and Vocational Guidance Series. Provides information about the nature of the work, educational requirements, employment outlook, earnings, and work conditions as well as additional related information.

Pharmacy Assistants

★8381★ AACP News

American Association of Colleges of
   Pharmacy
1426 Prince St.
Alexandria, VA 22314
Ph: (703)739-2330   Fax: (703)836-8982
Fr: 800-510-2227
E-mail: pthompson@aacp.org

Description: Monthly. Discusses issues relating to pharmaceutical education. Carries legislative information, feature stories on award winners, and Association news. Recurring features include news of research, notices of continuing education and employment opportunities, and listings of publications.

★8382★ American Journal of Health-System Pharmacy

American Society of Health-System
   Pharmacists
7272 Wisconsin Ave.
Bethesda, MD 20814
Ph: (301)657-3000   Fax: (301)657-8857
E-mail: ajhp@ashp.org
URL: http://www.ashp.org

Bimonthly. $195.00/year for individuals; $225.00/year for nonmembers, U.S. and Canada. Journal for pharmacists practicing in health-systems (acute care, ambulatory care, homecare, long term care, HMO's, PPOs, & PBMs).

★8383★ The Annals of Pharmacotherapy

Harvey Whitney Books Co.
Box 42696
Cincinnati, OH 45242
Ph: (513)793-3555   Fax: (513)793-3600
Fr: 877-742-7631
E-mail: customerserv@theannals.com
URL: http://www.theannals.com

Monthly. $261.00/year for institutions. Journal covering drug therapy, new drugs, and pharmacotherapy.

★8384★ Clinical Pharmacology and Therapeutics

Mosby Inc.
11830 Westline Industrial Dr.
St. Louis, MO 63146
Ph: (314)872-8370   Fax: (314)432-1380
Fr: 800-325-4177
URL: http://www.mosby.com/cpt

Monthly. $200.00/year for individuals; $422.00/year for institutions; $100.00/year for students; $238.00/year for individuals, other countries; $460.00/year for institutions, other countries; $120.00/year for students, other countries. Pharmacology journal devoted to the study of the nature, action, efficacy, and total evaluation of drugs as they are used in humans.

★8385★ Community Pharmacist

ELF Publications Inc.
5285 W Louisiana Ave.
Lakewood, CO 80232-5976
Ph: (303)975-0075   Fr: 800-922-8513
E-mail: elfedit@qwest.net
URL: http://www.elfpublications.com

Bimonthly. $12.00/year; $5.00 for single issue. National magazine addressing the professional and business needs, concerns and continuing education of retail pharmacists practicing in independent, chain and supermarket pharmacies.

★8386★ Drug Store News

Lebhar-Friedman Inc.
425 Park Ave.
New York, NY 10022-3556
Ph: (212)756-5088   Fax: (212)756-5120
Fr: 800-453-2427

Semimonthly. $19.50/year. Drug store industry tabloid.

★8387★ Journal of the American Pharmaceutical Association

American Pharmaceutical Association
2215 Constitution Ave. NW
Washington, DC 20037-2985
Ph: (202)628-4410   Fax: (202)783-2351
Fr: 800-237-2742
E-mail: japha@mail.aphanet.org

URL: http://www.aphanet.org

Bimonthly. $30.00/year, subscription included in membership; $175.00/year for individuals; $200.00/year for out of country; $35.00 for single issue. Journal for pharmacy professionals.

★8388★ Med Ad News

Engel Publishing Partners
820 Bear Tavern Rd., Ste. 300
West Trenton, NJ 08628
Ph: (609)530-0044   Fax: (609)530-0207
E-mail: mwalsh@engelpub.com

Monthly. $150.00/year for U.S.; $270.00/year for other countries. Pharmaceutical business and marketing magazine.

★8389★ The PDA Journal of Pharmaceutical Science & Technology

PDA
3 Bethesda Metro Ctr., Ste. 1500
Bethesda, MD 20814
Ph: (301)656-5900   Fax: (301)986-0296
E-mail: pda-journal@uiowa.edu

Bimonthly. $135.00/year for individuals; $30.00 for single issue. Professional journal covering pharmaceutical science.

★8390★ Pharmaceutical Engineering

International Society for Pharmaceutical
   Engineering Inc.
3109 W Dr. Martin Luther King Jr. Blvd.,
   Ste. 250
Tampa, FL 33607-6260
Ph: (813)960-2105   Fax: (813)264-2816
URL: http://ispe.org

Bimonthly. Subscription included in membership. Magazine on the health care manufacturing industry.

★8391★ Pharmaceutical Laboratory

Reed Business Information
301 Gibraltar Dr.
Morris Plains, NJ 07950
Ph: (973)292-5100   Fax: (973)539-3476
E-mail: gbyam@cahners.com
URL: http://www.biotechmedia.com/y2001-

ed-cahners-pharmlab.html

Trade publication covering the pharmaceutical industry.

★8392★ Pharmacy Times

Romaine Pierson Publishers Inc.
241 Forsgate Dr.
Jamesburg, NJ 08831
Ph: (732)656-0200   Fax: (732)656-1142
E-mail: pharmtimes@aol.com
URL: http://www.pharmacytimes.com

Monthly. $38.00/year. Journal providing information on health items (including prescription and over-the-counter drugs and surgical supplies) to independent, chain, and hospital pharmacists.

★8393★ Pharmacy Today

American Pharmaceutical Association
2215 Constitution Ave. NW
Washington, DC 20037-2985
Ph: (202)628-4410   Fax: (202)783-2351
Fr: 800-237-2742
E-mail: pt@aphanet.org

Monthly. Reports on current news and opinions for pharmacists.

PLACEMENT AND JOB REFERRAL SERVICES

★8394★ American Public Health Association (APHA)

800 I St. NW
Washington, DC 20001-3710
Ph: (202)777-2742   Fax: (202)777-2534
E-mail: comments@apha.org
URL: http://www.apha.org

Members: Professional organization of physicians, nurses, educators, academicians, environmentalists, epidemiologists, new professionals, social workers, health administrators, optometrists, podiatrists, pharmacists, dentists, nutritionists, health planners, other community and mental health specialists, and interested consumers. **Purpose:** Seeks to protect and promote personal, mental, and environmental health. **Activities:** Services include promulgation of standards; establishment of uniform practices and procedures; development of the etiology of communicable diseases; research in public health; exploration of medical care programs and their relationships to public health. Sponsors job placement service.

EMPLOYER DIRECTORIES AND NETWORKING LISTS

★8395★ AHA Guide to the Health Care Field

American Hospital Association (AHA)
1 N. Franklin St., 27th Fl.
Chicago, IL 60606
Ph: (312)422-2050   Fax: (312)422-4700
Fr: 800-424-4301

Annual, August. $295.00. Covers hospitals, networks, multi-health care systems, free-standing ambulatory surgery centers, psychiatric facilities, long-term care facilities, substance abuse programs, and other health-related organizations. Entries include: For hospitals-Facility name, address, phone, administrator's name, number of beds, facilities and services, number of employees, expenses, other statistics. For other organizations-Name, address, phone, fax, name and title of contact. Arrangement: Geographical. Indexes: Hospital name.

★8396★ Directory of Drug Store & HBC Chains

Chain Store Guide
3922 Coconut Palm Dr.
Tampa, FL 33619
Ph: (813)627-6800   Fax: (813)627-6882
Fr: 800-927-9292
URL: http://www.csgis.com

Annual, May. $335.00. Covers 1,600 drug store chains operation two or more units, including mass merchants and grocers with pharmacies; 215 wholesale drug companies in the United States and Canada. Entries include: For retailers-company name; phone and fax numbers; physical and mailing addresses; company e-mail and web addresses; listing type; number of stores; product lines; percentage of sales by product line; total sales; prescription drug sales; percentage of prescriptions filled with generic drugs; number of prescriptions filled daily; percentage of prescriptions filled with private third party, cash, and Medicaid; number of stores by type; mail order pharmacy indicator; managed care division indicator; projected openings and remodelings; store prototype sizes; total selling square footage; trading area; franchise group headquarter's name and location; distribution center and primary wholesaler names and locations; number of specialty departments; packaged liquor indicators; private label indicators; computerized pharmacy indicator; average number of checkouts; year founded; public company indicator; parent company name and location; regional and divisional office locations; headquarters personnel with titles. For wholesalers-company name, address, phone, and fax; e-mail and web addresses; listing type; product lines; percentage of sales by product line; total sales; percentage of sales by customer type; total stores served; number of member and non-member stores served; trading area; group store trading names; wholesaler type; distribution center locations; private label indicator; year founded; public company indicator; head-

quarters personnel with titles. Arrangement: Separate geographical sections for retailers and wholesalers. Indexes: Alphabetical, exclusions.

★8397★ Directory of Hospital Personnel

Thomson Medical Economics
5 Paragon Dr.
Montvale, NJ 07645-1742
Ph: (201)358-7200   Fax: (201)722-2680

Annual, November. $325.00. Covers 200,000 executives at 7,000 U.S. hospitals. Entries include: Name of hospital, address, phone, number of beds, type and JCAHO status of hospital, names and titles of key department heads and staff, medical and nursing school affiliations; number of residents, interns, and nursing students. Arrangement: Geographical. Indexes: Hospital name, personnel, hospital size.

★8398★ Hospital Blue Book

Billian/Transworld Publishing Inc.
2100 Powers Ferry Rd.
Ste. 300
Atlanta, GA 30339
Ph: (770)955-8484   Fax: (770)955-8485
Fr: 800-533-8484
E-mail: blu-book@billian.com

Annual, January. $285.00 for national edition; $160.00 for southern edition. Covers more than 6,687 hospitals; some listings also appear in a separate southern edition of this publication. Entries include: Name of hospital, accreditation, mailing address, phone, fax, number of beds, type of facility (nonprofit, general, state, etc.); list of administrative personnel and chiefs of medical services, with specific titles. Arrangement: Geographical.

★8399★ Medical and Health Information Directory

Thomson Gale
27500 Drake Rd.
Farmington Hills, MI 48331-3535
Ph: (248)699-4253   Fax: (248)699-8065
Fr: 800-877-GALE
E-mail: businessproducts@gale.com

Annual. $285.00 per volume; $675.00 per set. Covers in Volume 1, more than 26,500 medical and health oriented associations, organizations, institutions, and government agencies, including health maintenance organizations (HMOs), preferred provider organizations (PPOs), insurance companies, pharmaceutical companies, research centers, and medical and allied health schools. In Volume 2, over 12,000 medical book publishers; medical periodicals, directories, audiovisual producers and services, medical libraries and information centers, electronic resources, and health-related internet search engines. In Volume 3, more than 35,500 clinics, treatment centers, care programs, and counseling/diagnostic services for 34 subject areas. Entries include: Institution, service, or firm name, address, phone, fax, email and URL; many include names of key personnel and, when pertinent, descriptive annotation. Volume 3 was formerly listed separately as Health Services Directory. Arrangement: Classified by organization activity, service, etc. Indexes: Each volume has a complete alphabetical name and keyword index.

★8400★ **NWDA Directory**
National Wholesale Druggists' Association
1821 Michael Faraday Dr., Ste. 400
Reston, VA 20190
Ph: (703)787-0000   Fax: (703)787-6930
E-mail: member@nwda.org
URL: http://www.nwda.org
Annual, January. $295.00. Covers wholesalers, manufacturers, national drug-trade associations, and colleges of pharmacy. Entries include: For industry-Company name, address, phone, fax, names, of principal executives. For colleges-Institution name, address. Arrangement: Classified by type of membership.

★8401★ **Peterson's Job Opportunities for Health and Science Majors**
Thomson Peterson's
Princeton Pke. Corporate Ctr., 2000
  Lenox Dr.
PO Box 67005
Lawrenceville, NJ 08648
Ph: (609)896-1800   Fax: (609)896-4531
Fr: 800-338-3282
URL: http://www.petersons.com
Irregular, latest edition 1999. $18.95. Covers approximately 1,300 research, consulting, government, and non-profit and profit service organizations that hire college and university graduates in science and health-related majors. Entries include: Organization name, address, phone, name and title of contact, type of organization, number of employees, Standard Industrial Classification (SIC) code; description of opportunities available including disciplines, level of education required, starting locations and salaries, level of experience accepted, benefits.

★8402★ **Pharmaceutical Products-Wholesalers Directory**
infoUSA Inc.
5711 S 86th Cir.
Omaha, NE 68127-0347
Ph: (402)930-3500   Fax: (402)331-0176
Fr: 800-555-6124
URL: http://www.abii.com
Annual. Number of listings: 3,250. Entries include: Name, address, phone (including area code), size of advertisement, year first in "Yellow Pages," name of owner or manager, number of employees. Compiled from telephone company "Yellow Pages," nationwide. Arrangement: Geographical.

HANDBOOKS AND MANUALS

★8403★ **Discovering New Medicines: Careers in Pharmaceutical Research & Development**
John Wiley & Sons Inc.
111 River St.
Hoboken, NJ 07030-5774
Ph: (201)748-6000   Fax: (201)748-6088
Fr: 800-225-5945
Peter D. Stonier, editor. 1995. $65.00 (paper). 406 pages.

★8404★ **Expert Resumes for Health Care Careers**
JIST Publishing
8902 Otis Ave.
Indianapolis, IN 46216-1033
Ph: (317)613-4200   Fax: 800-547-8329
December 2003. $16.95. 288 pages.

★8405★ **Health Careers Today**
Elsevier-Health Sciences Division
The Curtis Center, Ste. 300E, 3rd Fl.
170 S. Independence Mall W.
Philadelphia, PA 19106
Ph: (215)238-7800   Fax: (215)238-7362
Fr: 800-523-4069
Gerdin. Revised edition. April 2004. $52.95.

★8406★ **Inside Pharmacy: The Anatomy of a Profession**
CRC Press LLC
2000 NW Corporate Blvd.
Boca Raton, FL 33431
Ph: (561)994-0555   Fax: (561)989-8732
Fr: 800-272-7737
Raymond A. Gosselin and Jack Robbins. 1998. $41.95. 134 pages.

★8407★ **Opportunities in Pharmacy Careers**
McGraw-Hill Trade
2 Penn Plaza
New York, NY 10121
Ph: (212)904-2000   Fr: 800-722-4726
Fred B. Gable. 1997. $14.95; $11.95 (paper). 200 pages. Identifies opportunities in a variety of settings, including retail chains, private ownership, clinics, hospitals, and other private, commercial, and industrial operations. Provides information on job-hunting techniques. Illustrated.

★8408★ **The Pharmacy Student Companion: Your Road Map to Pharmacy Education and Careers**
American Pharmaceutical Association
2215 Constitution Ave., NW
Washington, DC 20037
Ph: (202)628-4410   Fax: (202)783-2351
Fr: 800-878-0729
Daniel H. Albrant and Linda R. Harteker,

authors. Vicki L. Meade, editor. Third edition, revised, 1999. $20.00 (paper).

★8409★ **Resumes for Health and Medical Careers**
McGraw-Hill Trade
2 Penn Plaza
New York, NY 10121
Ph: (212)904-2000   Fr: 800-722-4726
E-mail: ntcpub@tribune.com
1997. $9.95 (paper). 455 pages.

★8410★ **Resumes for Science Careers**
McGraw-Hill Professional
1221 Avenue of the Americas
New York, NY 10020
Ph: (212)904-2000   Fr: 800-323-4900
E-mail: ntcpub@tribune.com
1997. $9.95 (paper). 466 pages.

EMPLOYMENT AGENCIES AND SEARCH FIRMS

★8411★ **CNR Search**
4535 Saddlehorn Dr.
Reno, NV 89511
Ph: (775)851-2829   Fax: (775)851-4514
Provides staffing services of permanent and temporary employees. Works primarily on a retained basis. Contingency on a limited basis. Active in providing human resources consulting services. Also active in mergers and acquisitions in high technology firms. Industries served: computer; information services; insurance, pharmaceutical and health care.

★8412★ **Colucci, Blendow & Johnson**
643 Main St., Ste. 8
Half Moon Bay, CA 94019-1988
Ph: (650)712-0103   Fax: (650)712-0105
Executive search consultants in the medical technology area that includes pharmaceuticals, medical equipment and device manufacturers, biotechnology, therapeutic supplies, diagnostic laboratory equipment and supplies, diagnostic imaging equipment and supplies, medical services, chemicals, cosmetic and toiletries, dental, veterinarian, and agricultural genetics companies.

TRADESHOWS

★8413★ Georgia Pharmacy Association Convention

Georgia Pharmacy Association
50 Lenox Pointe, NE-30324
PO Box 95527
Atlanta, GA 30347
Ph: (404)231-5074   Fax: (404)237-8435

Annual. **Primary Exhibits:** Pharmaceutical equipment, supplies, and services.

OTHER SOURCES

★8414★ American Society of Consultant Pharmacists (ASCP)

1321 Duke St.
Alexandria, VA 22314-3563
Ph: (703)739-1300   Fax: (703)739-1321
Fr: 800-355-2727
E-mail: info@ascp.com
URL: http://www.ascp.com

Description: Provides leadership, education, advocacy, and resources to advance the practice of senior care pharmacy practice. **Activities:** Conducts surveys of long-term care pharmacy operations. Sponsors educational and research programs. Maintains information center, hall of fame, and speakers' bureau; operates placement service; compiles statistics.

★8415★ Exploring Health Occupations

Cambridge Educational
2572 Brunswick Ave.
Lawrenceville, NJ 08648-4128
Fax: 800-FAX-ON-US   Fr: 800-468-4227
URL: http://www.cambridgeeducational.com

Two videos. $139.95. 1999.

★8416★ Health Service Occupations

Delphi Productions
3160 4th St.
Boulder, CO 80304
Fax: (303)443-4022   Fr: 888-443-2400
URL: http://www.delphivideo.com

$95.00. 50 minutes. Part of the Careers for the 21st Century Video Library.

★8417★ Medical Assistants

Evon Publishing
832 N 7th Ave.
Iron River, MI 49935
Ph: (906)265-3190

Audiocassette. 1996. $16.95. 32 minutes. Part of the Careers and Vocational Guidance Series. Provides information about the nature of the work, educational requirements, employment outlook, earnings, and work conditions as well as additional related information.

★8418★ Medicine & Related Occupations

Delphi Productions
3160 4th St.
Boulder, CO 80304
Fax: (303)443-4022   Fr: 888-443-2400
URL: http://www.delphivideo.com

$95.00. 45 minutes. Part of the Careers for the 21st Century Video Library.

★8419★ National Association of Boards of Pharmacy (NABP)

700 Busse Hwy.
Park Ridge, IL 60068
Ph: (847)698-6227   Fax: (847)698-0124
E-mail: custserv@nabp.net
URL: http://www.nabp.net

Members: Pharmacy boards of several states, District of Columbia, Puerto Rico, Virgin Islands, several Canadian provinces, the states of Victoria, Australia, and New South Wales, the Pharmaceutical Society of New Zealand, and the South African Pharmacy Council. **Purpose:** Provides for interstate reciprocity in pharmaceutic licensure based upon a uniform minimum standard of pharmaceutic education and uniform legislation; improves the standards of pharmaceutical education licensure and practice. **Activities:** Provides legislative information; sponsors uniform licensure examination; also provides information on accredited school and college requirements. Maintains pharmacy and drug law statistics.

★8420★ National Association of Chain Drug Stores (NACDS)

413 N Lee St.
PO Box 1417-D49
Alexandria, VA 22313-1480
Ph: (703)549-3001   Fax: (703)836-4869

E-mail: dharrington@nacds.org
URL: http://www.nacds.org

Description: Chain drug members (130); associate members (1400) and (80) international members include manufacturers, suppliers, manufacturer's representatives, publishers, and advertising agencies. Interprets actions by government agencies in such areas as drugs, public health, federal trade, labor, and excise taxes. Sponsors meetings and pharmacy student recruitment program. Maintains library. Offers insurance and discount services to members.

★8421★ National Pharmaceutical Association (NPhA)

107 Kilmayne Dr., Ste. C
Cary, NC 27511
Fax: (919)469-5870   Fr: 800-944-NPHA
E-mail: npha@npha.net
URL: http://www.npha.net/

Description: State and local associations of professional minority pharmacists. To provide a means whereby members may "contribute to their common improvement, share their experiences, and contribute to the public good."

★8422★ Pharmaceutical Care Management Association (PCMA)

601 Pennsylvania Ave. NW, No. 740
Washington, DC 20004
Ph: (202)207-3610   Fax: (202)207-3623
URL: http://www.pcmanet.org

Description: Represents managed care pharmacy, pharmaceutical benefits management companies (PBMs) and their healthcare partners in pharmaceutical care. Promotes education, legislation, practice standards, and research to foster quality, affordable pharmaceutical care.

★8423★ Pharmacy Technician

Cambridge Educational
2572 Brunswick Ave.
Lawrenceville, NJ 08648-4128
Fax: 800-FAX-ON-US   Fr: 800-468-4227
URL: http://www.cambridgeeducational.com

$89.95. 2001. 18 minutes. Part of the series "Working in Health Care: Opportunities for Life."

Photographers and Camera Operators

★8435★ The Hollywood Reporter

The Hollywood Reporter
5055 Wilshire Blvd.
Los Angeles, CA 90036-4396
Ph: (323)525-2000   Fax: (323)525-2377
E-mail: special-is-
sues@hollywoodreporter.com
URL: http://www.hollywoodreporter.com

Daily. Film, TV, and entertainment trade newspaper.

★8436★ HOW

F & W Publications Inc.
4700 E Galbraith Rd.
Cincinnati, OH 45236-6708
Ph: (513)531-2690   Fax: (513)531-2902
Fr: 800-289-0963
E-mail: editorial@howdesign.com

Bimonthly. $49.00/year for individuals; $7.95 for single issue, Jan/Feb or May/June; $9.95 for single issue, Mar/April or July/Aug; $11.95/year for single issue, Sept/Oct or Nov/Dec. Instructional trade magazine.

★8437★ News Photographer

National Press Photographers Association
3200 Croasdaile Dr., No. 306
Durham, NC 27705
Ph: (919)383-7246   Fax: (919)383-7261

Monthly. $38.00/year for individuals. Magazine featuring still and television photojournalism.

★8438★ Photo Trade News

Cygnus Business Media Inc.
445 Broad Hollow Rd.
Melville, NY 11747
Ph: (631)845-2700   Fax: (631)845-2798
Fr: 800-308-6397

Monthly. Trade publication covering the photography business.

★8439★ Producers Masterguide

Producers Masterguide
60 E 8th St., 34th Fl.
New York, NY 10003-6514
Ph: (212)777-4002   Fax: (212)777-4101
URL: http://
www.producers.masterguide.com

Annual. $145.00/year for U.S.; $155.00/year for Canada; $175.00/year for other countries. An international film and TV production directory and guide for the professional motion picture, broadcast television, feature film, TV commercial, cable/satellite, digital and videotape industries in the U.S., Canada, the UK, the Caribbean Islands, Mexico, Australia, New Zealand, Europe, Israel, Morocco, the Far East, and South America.

★8440★ Professional Photographer Storytellers

Professional Photographers of America Inc.
229 Peachtree St. NE, Ste. 2200
Atlanta, GA 30303
Ph: (404)522-8600   Fax: (404)614-6405
Fr: 800-786-6277
E-mail: ppaeditor@aol.com
URL: http://www.ppa-world.org

Monthly. $27.00/year for individuals; $45.00/year for Canada; $66.00/year for other countries.

★8441★ The RangeFinder

The RangeFinder Publishing Company Inc.
1312 Lincoln Blvd.
PO Box 1703
Santa Monica, CA 90406
Ph: (310)451-8506   Fax: (310)395-9058
E-mail: jketts@earthlink.net

Monthly. $18.00/year for individuals. Trade publication for portrait, commercial and wedding photographers.

★8442★ SHOOT

BPI Communications Inc.
575 Prospect Ave.
Lakewood, NJ 08701
Ph: (732)363-5679   Fax: (732)363-0338
Fr: 888-463-6110
E-mail: shoot@inch.com

Weekly. $79.00/year for individuals. Trade magazine covering all aspects of the commercial production industry, including creative and post-production elements.

★8443★ SMPTE Journal

Society of Motion Picture and Television Engineers
595 W Hartsdale Ave.
White Plains, NY 10607
Ph: (914)761-1100   Fax: (914)761-3115
URL: http://www.smpte.org

Monthly. $90.00/year; $100.00/year for out of country. Journal containing articles pertaining to new developments in motion picture and television technology; standards and recommended practices; general news of the industry.

★8444★ Video Systems

Primedia Business
9800 Metcalf Ave.
Overland Park, KS 66212
Ph: (913)341-1300   Fax: (913)967-1898
E-mail: vs@intertec.com
URL: http://www.videosystems.com

Monthly. $60.00/year for individuals; $10.00 for single issue; for other countries; $135.00/year for by mail. Magazine for users of professional video equipment.

PLACEMENT AND JOB REFERRAL SERVICES

★8445★ BDA

2029 Century Park East, Ste. 555
Los Angeles, CA 90067-2906
Ph: (310)789-1509   Fax: (310)712-0039
E-mail: bonnie@promax.tv
URL: http://www.bda.tv

Members: Designers, artists, art directors, illustrators, photographers, animators, and other motion graphic professionals in the electronic media industry; educators and students; commercial and industrial companies that manufacture products related to design. **Purpose:** Objectives are to promote understanding between designers, clients, and management; to stimulate innovative ideas and techniques; to encourage and provide a resource for young talent; and to provide a forum for discussion on industry issues and concerns. **Activities:** Maintains placement service; conducts surveys and compiles statistics.

★8446★ Health Sciences Communications Association (HESCA)

39 Wedgewood Dr., Ste. A
Jewett City, CT 06351
Ph: (860)376-5915   Fax: (860)376-6621
E-mail: hesca@hesca.org
URL: http://www.hesca.org/

Description: Media managers, graphic artists, biomedical librarians, producers, faculty members of health science and veterinary medicine schools, health professional organizations, and industry representatives. Acts as a clearinghouse for information used by professionals engaged in health science communications. Coordinates Media Festivals Program which recognizes outstanding media productions in the health sciences. Offers placement service.

★8447★ Institute of American Indian Arts (IAIA)

83 Avan Nu Po Rd.
Santa Fe, NM 87505
Ph: (505)424-2300   Fax: (505)424-4500
Fr: 800-804-6423
E-mail: webmaster@iaiancad.org
URL: http://www.iaiancad.org

Description: Federally chartered private institution. Offers learning opportunities in the arts and crafts to Native American youth (Indian, Eskimo, or Aleut). Emphasis is placed upon Indian traditions as the basis for creative expression in fine arts including painting, sculpture, museum studies, creative writing, printmaking, photography, communications, design, and dance, as well as training in metal crafts, jewelry, ceramics, textiles, and various traditional crafts. Students are encouraged to identify with their heritage and to be aware of themselves as members of a race rich in architecture, the fine arts, music, pageantry, and the humanities. All programs are based on elements of the Native American cultural heritage that emphasize differences between Native American and non-Native Americancultures. Sponsors Indian arts-oriented junior college offering Associate of Fine Arts degrees in various fields as well as seminars, an exhibition program, and traveling exhibits. Maintains extensive library, museum, and biographical archives. Provides placement service

★8448★ National Association of Broadcasters (NAB)

1771 N St. NW
Washington, DC 20036
Ph: (202)429-5300   Fax: (202)429-4199
E-mail: nab@nab.org
URL: http://www.nab.org

Description: Representatives of radio and television stations and networks; associate members include producers of equipment and programs. Seeks to ensure the viability, strength, and success of free, over-the-air broadcasters; serves as an information resource to the industry. Monitors and reports on events regarding radio and television broadcasting. Maintains Broadcasting Hall of Fame. Offers minority placement service and employment clearinghouse.

★8449★ University Photographers Association of America (UPAA)

SUNY Brockport
350 New Campus Dr.
Brockport, NY 14420-2931
Ph: (585)395-2133   Fax: (585)395-2733
E-mail: jdusen@brockport.edu
URL: http://www.upaa.org/

Description: College and university personnel engaged professionally in photography, audiovisual work, or journalism for universities. Seeks to advance applied photography and the profession through the exchange of thoughts and opinions among its members. Awards fellowship for exceptional work in the advancement of photography. Provides a medium for exchange of ideas and technical information on photography, especially university photographic work. Sponsors exhibits. Provides placement service for members.

EMPLOYER DIRECTORIES AND NETWORKING LISTS

★8450★ American Society of Media Photographers-Membership Directory

American Society of Media Photographers
150 N Second St.
Philadelphia, PA 19106
Ph: (215)451-2767   Fax: (215)451-0880
URL: http://www.asmp.org

Covers 5,000 professional photographers for publications. Entries include: Name, address, phone, fax, e-mail address, specialty.

★8451★ Artist's & Graphic Designer's Market

Writer's Digest Books
4700 E Galbraith Rd.
Cincinnati, OH 45236
Ph: (513)531-2690   Fr: 800-289-0963
E-mail: artdesign@fwpubs.com

Annual, September. $24.99. Covers 2,500 buyers of free-lance art work, including ad agencies, art studios, galleries, clip art firms, audiovisual firms, television film producers, periodicals, record companies, book publishers; coverage includes Canada. Entries include: Name of buyer, address, phone, payment rates, special submission requirements, reporting time, how to break in. Arrangement: Classified by type of market.

★8452★ Below-the-Line Guide

IFILM Publishing
1024 N Orange Dr.
Hollywood, CA 90038
Ph: (323)308-3490   Fax: (323)308-3493
E-mail: lrossini@ifilm.com
URL: http://www.loneeagle.com

Annual, latest edition 9th. $49.95. Covers approximately 2,500 motion picture and television cinematographers, editors, production designers, and costume designers, now includes set decorators. Entries include: Personal name; name, address, phone of agent or contact; chronological list of films or shows. Arrangement: Classified by line of business. Indexes: Film/show title, contact name, agents and managers.

★8453★ Black Book Photography

Black Book Marketing Group
10 Astor Pl., 6th Fl.
New York, NY 10003
Ph: (212)539-9800   Fax: (212)539-9801
Fr: 800-841-1246
URL: http://www.BlackBook.com

Annual, January. $110.00. Publication includes over 19,000 art directors, creative directors, photographers and photographic services, design firms, advertising agencies, and other firms whose products or services are used in advertising. Entries include: Company name, address, phone. Principal content of publication is 4-color samples from the leading commercial photographers. Arrangement: Classified by product/service.

★8454★ Broadcasting & Cable Yearbook

R.R. Bowker L.L.C.
630 Central Ave.
New Providence, NJ 07974
Ph: (908)286-1090   Fax: (908)219-0098
Fr: 888-269-5372

Annual, March, latest edition 2003-2004. $179.95. Covers over 17,000 television and radio stations in the United States, its territories, and Canada; cable MSOs and their individual systems; television and radio networks, broadcast and cable group owners, station representatives, satellite networks and services, film companies, advertising agencies, government agencies, trade asso-

ciations, schools, and suppliers of professional and technical services, including books, serials, and videos; communications lawyers. Entries include: Company name, address, phone, fax, names of executives. Station listings include broadcast power, other operating details. Arrangement: Stations and systems are geographical, others are alphabetical. Indexes: Alphabetical.

★8455★ Burrelle's New York Media Directory

Burrelle's Information Services
75 E. Northfield Rd.
Livingston, NJ 07039
Ph: (973)992-6600   Fax: (973)992-7675
Fr: 800-631-1160
URL: http://www.burrellesluce.com/media-data/regional.html

Annual. $200.00. Covers Print and electronic media in New York. Entries include: Name, address, phone, fax, names and titles of key personnel, geographical area served, subsidiary and branch names and locations, description. Arrangement: Geographical; magazines are arranged by subject. Indexes: Name, subject, geographical.

★8456★ Chicago Creative Directory

Chicago Creative Directory
333 N Michigan, Ste. 810
Chicago, IL 60601
Ph: (312)236-7337   Fax: (312)236-6078
URL: http://www.creativedir.com

Annual, March. $50.00. Covers over 6,000 advertising agencies, photographers, sound studios, talent agencies, audiovisual services, and others offering creative and production services. Entries include: For most listings-Company name, address, phone, list of officers, description of services. For freelance listings-Name, talent, address, phone. Arrangement: Classified by specialty.

★8457★ Chicago Sourcebook

Black Book Marketing Group
10 Astor Pl., 6th Fl.
New York, NY 10003-6935
Ph: (212)539-9800   Fax: (212)539-9801

Annual, November. Covers commercial artists and photographers and graphic designers in Chicago, Illinois area. Entries include: Firm name, address, phone; other details as provided by firm. Arrangement: Alphabetical.

★8458★ CPB Public Broadcasting Directory

Corporation for Public Broadcasting
901 E St. NW
Washington, DC 20004-2037
Ph: (202)879-9600   Fax: (202)783-9700
URL: http://www.cpb.org/directory/home.html

Annual. $15.00. Covers public television and radio stations, national and regional public broadcasting organizations and networks, state government agencies and commissions, and other related organizations. Entries include: For radio and television stations-Station call letters, frequency or channel, address, phone, licensee name, licensee type, date on air, antenna height, area covered, names and titles of key personnel. For organizations-Name, address, phone, name and title of key personnel. Arrangement: National and regional listings are alphabetical; state groups and the public radio and television stations are each geographical; other organizations and agencies are alphabetical. Indexes: Geographical, personnel, call letter, licensee type (all in separate indexes for radio and television).

★8459★ Fashion & Print Directory

Peter Glenn Publications
6040 NW 43rd Ter.
Boca Raton, FL 33496-4043
Ph: (561)999-8930   Fax: (561)999-8931
Fr: 888-332-6700
URL: http://www.pgdirect.com

Annual, November. $59.95. Covers advertising agencies, PR firms, marketing companies, 1000 client brand companies and related services in the U.S. and Canada. Includes photographers, marketing agency, suppliers, sources of props and rentals, fashion houses, beauty services, locations. Entries include: Company name, address, phone; paid listings numbering 5000 include description of products or services, key personnel. Arrangement: Classified by line of business.

★8460★ International Television and Video Almanac

Quigley Publishing Company Inc.
64 Wintergreen Ln.
Groton, MA 01450-4129
Fr: 800-231-8239
URL: http://hometown.aol.com/quigleypub/mp.html

Annual, January. $130.00. Covers "Who's Who in Motion Pictures and Television and Home Video," television networks, major program producers, major group station owners, cable television companies, distributors, firms serving the television and home video industry, equipment manufacturers, casting agencies, literary agencies, advertising and publicity representatives, television stations, associations, list of feature films produced for television; statistics, industry's year in review, award winners, satellite & wireless cable provider, primtime programming, video producers, distributors, wholesalers. Entries include: Generally, company name, address, phone; manufacturer and service listings may include description of products and services and name of contact; producing, distributing, and station listings include additional detail, and contacts for cable and broadcast networks. Arrangement: Classified by service or activity. Indexes: Full.

★8461★ Klik! Showcase Photography

American Showcase Inc.
915 Broadway, 14th Fl.
New York, NY 10010
Ph: (212)673-6600   Fax: (212)673-9795
Fr: 800-894-7469

URL: http://www.americanshowcase.com/pages/k9_branding.html

Annual. $55.00. Covers 9,500 photographers, and related companies. Entries include: Name, address, phone, sample of work. Illustrators and graphic designers are described in 'American Showcase Illustration'. Arrangement: Geographical. Indexes: Specialty.

★8462★ National Directory of Arts Internships

National Network for Artist Placement
935 W. Ave. 37
Los Angeles, CA 90065
Ph: (323)222-4035   Fax: (323)225-5711
URL: http://www.artistplacement.com/intern.htm

Biennial, odd years. $85.00. Covers over 5,000 internship opportunities in dance, music, theater, art, design, film, and video & over 1,250 host organizations Entries include: Name of sponsoring organization, address, name of contact; description of positions available, eligibility requirements, stipend or salary (if any), application procedures. Arrangement: Classified by discipline, then geographical.

★8463★ National Directory of Magazines

Oxbridge Communications Inc.
186 5th Ave., 6th Fl.
New York, NY 10010
Ph: (212)741-0231   Fax: (212)633-2938
Fr: 800-955-0231
E-mail: custserv@oxbridge.com
URL: http://www.mediafinder.com

October. $895.00. Covers over 20,000 magazines; coverage includes Canada. Entries include: Title, publisher name, address, phone, fax number, names and titles of contact and key personnel, financial data, editorial and advertising information, circulation. Arrangement: Classified by subject. Indexes: Title, geographical, publisher.

★8464★ Photographers-Aerial Directory

infoUSA Inc.
5711 S 86th Cir.
Omaha, NE 68127-0347
Ph: (402)930-3500   Fax: (402)331-0176
Fr: 800-555-6124
URL: http://www.abii.com

Updated continuously; printed on request. Number of listings: 1,772. Entries include: Name, address, phone (including area code), size of advertisement, year first in "Yellow Pages," name of owner or manager, number of employees. Compiled from telephone company "Yellow Pages," nationwide. Arrangement: Geographical.

★8465★ Photographers-Commercial Directory

infoUSA Inc.
5711 S 86th Cir.
Omaha, NE 68127-0347
Ph: (402)930-3500   Fax: (402)331-0176
Fr: 800-555-6124
URL: http://www.abii.com

Annual. Number of listings: 19,476. Entries include: Name, address, phone (including area code), size of advertisement, year first in "Yellow Pages," name of owner or manager, number of employees. Compiled from telephone company "Yellow Pages," nationwide. Arrangement: Geographical.

★8466★ Photographer's Market

Writer's Digest Books
4700 E Galbraith Rd.
Cincinnati, OH 45236
Ph: (513)531-2690   Fr: 800-289-0963
E-mail: photomarket@fwpubs.com

Annual, September. $24.99. Covers 2,000 companies and publications that purchase original photographs, including advertising agencies, public relations agencies, book and periodical publishers, stock photo agencies, photographic workshops, galleries, and competitions. Entries include: Name of buyer, address, phone, payment rates, requirements, reporting time, how to break in. Arrangement: Classified by type of market. Indexes: Digital markets, subject.

★8467★ Photographers-Passport Directory

infoUSA Inc.
5711 S 86th Cir.
Omaha, NE 68127-0347
Ph: (402)930-3500   Fax: (402)331-0176
Fr: 800-555-6124
URL: http://www.abii.com

Annual. Number of listings: 5,397. Entries include: Name, address, phone (including area code), size of advertisement, year first in "Yellow Pages," name of owner or manager, number of employees. Compiled from telephone company "Yellow pages," nationwide. Arrangement: Geographical.

★8468★ Photographers-Portrait Directory

infoUSA Inc.
5711 S 86th Cir.
Omaha, NE 68127-0347
Ph: (402)930-3500   Fax: (402)331-0176
Fr: 800-555-6124
URL: http://www.abii.com

Annual. Number of listings: 31,739. Entries include: Name, address, phone (including area code), size of advertisement, year first in "Yellow Pages," name of owner or manager, number of employees. Regional editions available: Eastern, $645.00; Western, $475.00. Compiled from telephone company "Yellow Pages," nationwide. Arrangement: Geographical.

★8469★ PhotoSource Book

PhotoSource International
Pine Lake Farm
1910 35th Rd.
Osceola, WI 54020
Ph: (715)248-3800   Fax: (715)248-7394
Fr: 800-624-0266
E-mail: web@photosource.com
URL: http://www.photosource.com

Bimonthly, and weekly. $365.00. Covers magazine and book publishers, public relations firms, advertising and government agencies currently soliciting photographs for publication; 6-12 listings per issue. Entries include: Company name, name of contact, address, phone, project title, and nature of photos sought. Indexes: CD-ROM editors.

★8470★ Registry of Freelance Photographers

Publishers Network Inc.
PO Box 3190
Vista, CA 92085
Ph: (619)941-2235   Fax: (619)941-0773

Semiannual, January and June. $15.00. Covers approximately 1,000 photographers available for assignment in the cities in which they reside; coverage is mostly U.S. and Canada, with a few in Europe and Asia. Entries include: Name, geographical area served, phone, biographical data, qualifications, interests and experience. Arrangement: Geographical by ZIP code.

★8471★ Self-Employed Writers and Artists Network-Directory

Self-Employed Writers and Artists Network Inc.
PO Box 440
Paramus, NJ 07653
Ph: (201)967-1313
URL: http://www.swan-net.com

Annual, spring. Covers over 135 freelance writers, graphic designers, illustrators, photographers, and other graphic arts professionals in northern New Jersey and New York city providing services in advertising, marketing, sales promotion, public relations, and telecommunications. Entries include: Name, address, phone, biographical data, description of services provided. Arrangement: Alphabetical. Indexes: Line of business.

★8472★ Television & Cable Factbook

Warren Communications News
2115 Ward Ct. NW
Washington, DC 20037
Ph: (202)872-9202   Fax: (202)293-3435
Fr: 800-771-9202
URL: http://www.warren-news.com/factbook.htm

Annual, March. Weekly updates available. $795.00. Covers commercial and noncommercial television stations and networks, including educational, low-power and instructional TV stations, and translators; United States cable television systems; cable and television group owners; program and service suppliers; and brokerage and financ-

ing companies. Entries include: For stations-Call letters, licensee name and address, studio address and phone; identification of owners, sales and legal representatives and chief station personnel; rates, technical data, map of service area, and Nielsen circulation data. For cable systems-Name, address, basic and pay subscribers, programming and fees, physical plant; names of personnel and ownership. ownership. Arrangement: Geographical by state, province, city, county, or country. Indexes: Call letters, product/service, name, general subject.

★8473★ Who's Who in Photographic Management

Photo Marketing Association International
3000 Picture Pl.
Jackson, MI 49201
Ph: (517)788-8100   Fax: (517)788-8371

Annual. $75.00. Covers over 15,500 members of the association and manufacturers and suppliers of photographic equipment; also members of the National Association of Photo Equipment Technicians and of the Professional School Photographers of America. Entries include: Name of firm, address, phone, name of contact. Arrangement: Separate alphabetical sections for each association and for the companies. Indexes: Geographical, product.

★8474★ Who's Who in Professional Imaging

Professional Photographers of America Inc.
229 Peachtree St. NE, Ste. 2200
Atlanta, GA 30303
Ph: (404)522-8600   Fax: (404)614-6405
Fr: 800-786-6277
URL: http://www.ppa-world.org

Annual, April. $110.00. Covers over 18,000 members, including portrait, commercial, wedding, and industrial photographers; also includes guide to photographic equipment and supply manufacturers and distributors. Entries include: For members-Name, office address, phone, show specialties; listings for members available for assignments. For suppliers-Company name, address, phone, product/service. Arrangement: Geographical.

★8475★ The Workbook

Scott & Daughters Publishing Inc.
940 N Highland Ave., Ste. A
Los Angeles, CA 90038
Ph: (323)856-0008   Fax: (323)856-0443
Fr: 800-547-2688
URL: http://www.workbook.com

Annual, February. $120.00. Covers 49,000 advertising agencies, art directors, photographers, freelance illustrators and designers, artists' representatives, interactive designers, pre-press services, and other graphic arts services in the U.S. Entries include: Company or individual name, address, phone, specialty. National in scope. Arrangement: Classified by product or service.

★8476★ Working Press of the Nation

R.R. Bowker L.L.C.
630 Central Ave.
New Providence, NJ 07974
Ph: (908)286-1090   Fax: (908)219-0098
Fr: 888-269-5372
E-mail: wpn@bowker.com

Annual, September. $530.00 for set; $295.00 each volume. Covers in three separate volumes, syndicates and over 8,500 daily and weekly newspapers; 1,750 newsletters; over 16,800 radio and television stations; 5,500 magazines; 1,000 internal publications. Entries include: Name of publication or station, address, phone, fax, e-mail and URL, names of executives, editors, writers, etc., as appropriate. Broadcasting and magazine volumes include data on kinds of material accepted. Technical and mechanical requirements for publications are given. Arrangement: Magazines are classified by subject; newspapers and broadcasting stations are geographical. Indexes: Newspaper department/editor by interest, metro area, feature syndicate subject; magazine subject, publication title; television director/personnel by subject, radio personnel and director by subject.

HANDBOOKS AND MANUALS

★8477★ ASMP Professional Business Practices in Photography

Allworth Press
10 E. 23rd St., Ste. 510
New York, NY 10010
Ph: (212)777-8395   Fax: (212)777-8261
Fr: 800-491-2808

Sixth edition, 2001. 416 pages.

★8478★ Breaking into Film

Thomson Peterson's
202 Carnegie Ctr.
Box 67005
Princeton, NJ 08540
Fr: 800-338-3282

Kenna Mchugh. 1998. $14.95 (paper). Provides insight into jobs dealing with film and video and explains how to get a job in the film industry, with a list of key employers. Also offers advice from industry insiders and internship information.

★8479★ Breaking into Television

Thomson Peterson's
202 Carnegie Ctr.
Box 67005
Princeton, NJ 08540
Fr: 800-338-3282

Weaver. 1998. $14.95 (paper). Explains how to get a job in the television industry, with a list of internship opportunities.

★8480★ Business of Wedding Photography

Watson-Guptill Publications, Inc.
770 Broadway
New York, NY 10003
Ph: (646)654-5400   Fax: (646)654-5486
Fr: 800-323-9432

Ann Monteith. 1996. $35.00 (paper). 192 pages. Subtitled, "A Professional's Guide to Marketing and Managing a Successful Studio With Profiles of 30 Top Portrait Photographers."

★8481★ Career Information Center

Macmillan Publishing Co. Inc.
200 Old Tappan Rd.
Old Tappan, NJ 07675
Fr: 800-428-5331

Visual Education Center Staff. Seventh edition, 1999. $275.00. 2080 pages. This 13-volume set profiles over 600 occupations. Each occupational profile describes job duties, educational requirements, how to get the job, advancement possibilities, employment outlook, working conditions, earnings and benefits, and where to write for more information.

★8482★ Careers in Communications

VGM Career Horizons
4255 W. Touhy Ave.
Lincolnwood, IL 60646-1975
Ph: (847)679-5500   Fax: (847)679-2494
Fr: 800-323-4900
E-mail: ntcpub@tribune.com

Shonan Noronha. Third edition, 1998. $17.95; $13.95 (paper). 418 pages. Examines the fields of journalism, photography, radio, television, film, public relations, and advertising. Gives concrete details on job locations and how to secure a job. Suggests many resources for job hunting.

★8483★ Careers for Film Buffs and Other Hollywood Types

VGM Career Horizons
1221 Avenue of the Americas
New York, NY 10020
Ph: (212)904-2000   Fr: 800-323-4900
E-mail: ntcpub@tribune.com

Jaq Greenspon. 1994. $14.95; $9.95 (paper). 250 pages. Describes job descriptions in production, camera, sound, special effects, grips, electrical, makeup, costumes, etc.

★8484★ Careers in Health Care

McGraw-Hill Trade
2 Penn Plaza
New York, NY 10121
Ph: (212)904-2000   Fr: 800-722-4726
E-mail: ntcpub@tribune.com

Barbara M. Swanson. Fourth edition, 2000. $17.95; $13.95 (paper). 320 pages. Describes job duties, work settings, salaries, licensing and certification requirements, educational preparation, and future outlook. Gives ideas on how to secure a job.

★8485★ Careers for Night Owls and Other Insomniacs

McGraw-Hill Trade
2 Penn Plaza
New York, NY 10121
Ph: (212)904-2000   Fr: 800-722-4726
E-mail: ntcpub@tribune.com

Louise Miller. 1995. $14.95; $9.95 (paper). 160 pages.

★8486★ Careers for Shutterbugs: And Other Candid Types

McGraw-Hill Contemporary Books
1221 Avenue of the Americas
New York, NY 10020
Ph: (212)904-2000   Fr: 800-323-4900
E-mail: ntcpub@tribune.com

Cheryl McLean. 1995. $14.95 (paper).

★8487★ International Directory of Film, Photography, Video and Television

Penrose Press
PO Box 470925
San Francisco, CA 94147
Ph: (415)567-4157   Fax: (415)567-4165

Raymond Lavzzana and Denise Penrose, editors. Fifth edition, 1998. $77.00 (paper). 200 pages. Part of the International Directory of Design Series. Includes references for educational programs, professional organizations and periodical publications. The subjects covered span the range of subjects of interest to photographers, cinematographers & videographers practicing in entertainment & documentation industries, including photography, cinematography, filmaking, videography & electronic imaging. Contact information includes street addresses, telephone & fax numbers, e-mail addresses & URL links to home pages. This directory is one of ten supplemental directories that are domain-specific guides to educational programs; professional societies, trade organizations, scholarly journals, & trade magazines throughout the world.

★8488★ Magazines Career Directory

Thomson Gale
27500 Drake Rd.
Farmington Hills, MI 48331-3535
Ph: (248)699-GALE   Fax: (248)699-8069
Fr: 800-877-GALE
E-mail: galeord@gale.com
URL: http://www.galegroup.com

Bradley Morgan. Fifth edition, 1993. $39.00. Features extensive listings of contacts and entry-level job opportunities at many magazine publishing organizations. Includes articles by top professionals in the field on some of the industry's varied career paths: art, editorial, sales, and business management. Part of Career Advisor series.

★8489★ Make Money with Your Camera

Amherst Media, Incorporated
P.O. Box 586
Buffalo, NY 14226
Ph: (716)874-4450   Fax: (716)874-4508

David Neil Arndt. 1999. $29.95 (paper).

★8490★ Newspapers Career Directory

Thomson Gale
27500 Drake Rd.
Farmington Hills, MI 48331-3535
Ph: (248)699-GALE   Fax: 800-414-5043
Fr: 800-877-GALE
E-mail: galeord@gale.com
URL: http://www.gale.com

Bradley Morgan. Fourth edition, 1993. $39.00. 300 pages. Out of print. Features extensive listings of contacts and entry-level job opportunities at many newspaper organizations. Focuses on each area of the business, from reporting and editorial to sales and marketing to promotion and production.

★8491★ On Being a Photographer: A Practical Guide

Lenswork Publishing
909 Third St.
Anacortes, OR 98221-1502
Fax: (503)905-6111   Fr: 800-659-2130

David Hurn and Bill Jay. 1997. $12.95 (paper). 96 pages.

★8492★ Opportunities in Cable Television Careers

McGraw-Hill Trade
2 Penn Plaza
New York, NY 10121
Ph: (212)904-2000   Fr: 800-722-4726

Jan Bone. 1994. $14.95; $11.95 (paper). 160 pages. Focuses on what the jobs are, where they are, and how to get them. Illustrated.

★8493★ Opportunities in Film Careers

McGraw-Hill Trade
2 Penn Plaza
New York, NY 10121
Ph: (212)904-2000   Fr: 800-722-4726

Jan Bone. 1998. $14.95; $11.95 (paper). 160 pages. Provides advice on obtaining a job in film and in corporate non-broadcast film/video production. Illustrated.

★8494★ Opportunities in Journalism Careers

McGraw-Hill/Contemporary Books
1221 Avenue of the Americas
New York, NY 10020
Ph: (212)904-2000   Fr: 800-323-4900
E-mail: ntcpub@tribune.com

Jim Patten and Donald L. Ferguson. 1995. $14.95; $11.95 (paper). 160 pages. Outlines opportunities in every field of journalism, including newspaper reporting and editing, magazine and book publishing, corporate communications, advertising and public relations, freelance writing, and teaching. Covers how to prepare for and enter each field, outlining responsibilities, salaries, benefits, and job outlook for each specialty. Illustrated.

★8495★ **Opportunities in Magazine Publishing Careers**
McGraw-Hill Trade
2 Penn Plaza
New York, NY 10121
Ph: (212)904-2000   Fr: 800-722-4726
E-mail: ntcpub@tribune.com
S. William Pattis. 1994. $13.95; $12.95 (paper). 160 pages. Covers the scope of magazine publishing and addresses how to identify and pursue available positions. Illustrated.

★8496★ **Opportunities in Photography Careers**
McGraw-Hill Trade
2 Penn Plaza
New York, NY 10121
Ph: (212)904-2000   Fr: 800-722-4726
Bervin Johnson, Robert Mayer, and Fred Schmidt. 1994. $14.95; $11.95 (paper). Details opportunities in the field, including technical processing and sales, and how to pursue them. Contains bibliography and illustrations. Out of print.

★8497★ **Opportunities in Publishing Careers**
McGraw-Hill Professional
2 Penn Plaza
New York, NY 10121
Ph: (212)904-2000   Fr: 800-722-4726
E-mail: ntcpub@tribune.com
Robert A. Carter and S. William Pattis. 1995. $14.95; $11.95 (paper). 160 pages. Covers all positions in book and magazine publishing, including new opportunities in multimedia publishing.

★8498★ **Opportunities in Sports and Athletics Careers**
McGraw-Hill Trade
2 Penn Plaza
New York, NY 10121
Ph: (212)904-2000   Fr: 800-722-4726
E-mail: ntcpub@tribune.com
William Ray Heitzmann. 1994. 160 pages. $14.95; $11.95 (paper). A guide to planning for and seeking opportunities in this growing field. Illustrated.

★8499★ **Opportunities in Television and Video Careers**
McGraw-Hill Trade
2 Penn Plaza
New York, NY 10121
Ph: (212)904-2000   Fr: 800-722-4726
E-mail: ntcpub@tribune.com
Shonan Noronha. 1998. $14.95; $11.95 (paper). 206 pages. Details the employment

opportunities open in television, cable, corporate video, institutional and government media, including independent production, and discusses how to land a job. Illustrated.

★8500★ **Opportunities in Visual Arts Careers**
McGraw-Hill Trade
2 Penn Plaza
New York, NY 10121
Ph: (212)904-2000   Fr: 800-722-4726
E-mail: ntcpub@tribune.com
Mark Salmon. 1994. $14.95; $11.95 (paper). 160 pages. Points the way to a career in the visual arts, examining opportunities for designers, painters, sculptors, illustrators, animators, photographers, art therapists, educators, and others. Offers a view of the pros and cons of working for an art or design company or on your own.

★8501★ **The Photographer's Market Guide to Photo Submission and Portfolio Formats**
F & W Publications, Inc.
4700 E Galbraith Rd.
Cincinnati, OH 45236
Ph: (513)531-2690   Fax: (513)531-4082
Fr: 800-289-0963
Michael Willins. 1997. $18.99 (paper). 160 pages. Includes steps for amateur and professional photographers to successfully market their work.

★8502★ **Photography Your Way: A Career Guide to Satisfaction and Success**
Allworth Press
10 E. 23rd St., Ste. 510
New York, NY 10010
Ph: (212)777-8395   Fax: (212)777-8261
Fr: 800-491-2808
Chuck Delaney. 1999. $18.95 (paper). 256 pages.

★8503★ **Photos That Sell: The Art of Successful Freelance Photography**
Watson-Guptill Publications, Incorporated
770 Broadway
New York, NY 10003
Ph: (646)654-5400   Fax: (646)654-5486
Fr: 800-323-9432
Lee Frost. 2001. $24.95 (paper).

★8504★ **Radio and Television Career Directory**
Thomson Gale
27500 Drake Rd.
Farmington Hills, MI 48331-3535
Ph: (248)699-GALE   Fax: 800-414-5043
Fr: 800-877-GALE
E-mail: galeord@gale.com
URL: http://www.gale.com
Bradley Morgan. Second edition, 1993. $39.00. 300 pages. Features extensive listings of contacts and entry-level job opportu-

nities. Provides information on internships and sources of help-wanted ads.

★8505★ **2001 Photographer's Market**
Writer's Digest Books
F & W Publications, Inc.
1507 Dana Ave.
Cincinnati, OH 45207
Ph: (513)531-2690   Fax: (513)531-4082
Fr: 800-289-0963
Donna Poehner, editor. 2000. $24.99 (paper). 640 pages.

TRADESHOWS

★8506★ **Mid East States Regional Print Competition and Exhibition and Trade Show**
Professional Photographers of Ohio
37 W. Broad St., Ste. 480
Columbus, OH 43215
Ph: (614)228-6703   Fax: (614)228-1216
E-mail: PPofOH@aol.com
URL: http://www.PPofOhio.org
Annual. **Primary Exhibits:** Photographic equipment, supplies, and services; to include office equipment, computers and phone systems.

★8507★ **Photohistory**
Photographic Historical Society
PO Box 39563
Rochester, NY 14604
Ph: (585)671-0298
E-mail: tphs@rochester.rr.com
URL: http://www.tphs.org
Triennial. **Primary Exhibits:** Cameras and photographic images.

★8508★ **PMA - Photo Marketing Association International Annual Convention and Trade Show**
Photo Marketing Association International
3000 Picture Place
Jackson, MI 49201
Ph: (517)788-8100   Fax: (517)788-8371
E-mail: PMA_Trade_Exhibits@pmai.org
URL: http://www.pmai.org
Annual. **Primary Exhibits:** Film, cameras and photo accessory manufacturers and distributors; photo processing equipment and materials suppliers; digital imaging hardware and software marketers; studio imaging equipment distributors; and original equipment manufacturers (OEMs).

★8509★ **PMAI Imaging Conference & Mini-Trade Show**
Photo Marketing Association International
3000 Picture Place
Jackson, MI 49201
Ph: (517)788-8100   Fax: (517)788-8371
E-mail: PMA_Trade_Exhibits@pmai.org

URL: http://www.pmai.org

Annual. **Primary Exhibits:** People-oriented, educational event for photo-imaging industry executives and their suppliers. Manufacturers and distributors of consumer photo, video, optics, and digital picture products; photoprocessing equipment and supplies; professional photo services; and digital imaging systems and supplies.

★8510★ **Professional Photography of America - Imaging USA**

Professional Photographers of America
229 Peachtree St., NE, Ste. 2200
Atlanta, GA 30303-2206
Ph: (404)522-8600   Fax: (404)614-6405
Fr: 800-786-6277
URL: http://www.ppa.com

Annual. **Primary Exhibits:** Photographic equipment, supplies, and services.

★8511★ **Virginia Professional Photographers Association Annual Convention**

Virginia Professional Photographers Association
9909 Chancellor Pl.
Richmond, VA 23235
Ph: (804)272-0119
URL: http://www.vppa.com

Annual. **Primary Exhibits:** Color laboratory equipment, photographic equipment, frames, and related supplies.

OTHER SOURCES

★8512★ *American Almanac of Jobs and Salaries*

Morrow Avon
1350 Avenue of the Americas
New York, NY 10019
Ph: (212)261-6788   Fr: 800-242-7737

John W. Wright. Revised edition, 2000. $20.00 (paper). 672 pages. This is a comprehensive guide to the wages of hundreds of occupations in a wide variety of industries and organizations.

★8513★ **American Society of Media Photographers (ASMP)**

150 N 2nd St.
Philadelphia, PA 19106
Ph: (215)451-2767   Fax: (215)451-0880
E-mail: mopsik@asmp.org
URL: http://www.asmp.org

Members: Professional society of freelance photographers. **Purpose:** Works to evolve trade practices for photographers in communications fields. Provides business information to photographers and their potential clients; promotes ethics and rights of members. **Activities:** Holds educational programs and seminars. Compiles statistics.

★8514★ **Art Directors Club (ADC)**

106 W 29th St.
New York, NY 10001
Ph: (212)643-1440   Fax: (212)643-4266
E-mail: info@adcny.org
URL: http://www.adcny.org

Members: Art directors of advertising magazines and agencies, visual information specialists, and graphic designers; associate members are artists, cinematographers, photographers, copywriters, educators, journalists, and critics. **Purpose:** Promotes and stimulates interest in the practice of art direction. **Activities:** Sponsors Annual Exhibition of Advertising, Editorial and Television Art and Design; International Traveling Exhibition; Hall of Fame. Provides educational, professional, and entertainment programs; on-premise art exhibitions; portfolio review program. Conducts panels for students and faculty.

★8515★ **BioCommunications Association (BCA)**

220 Southwind Ln.
Hillsborough, NC 27278
Ph: (919)245-0906   Fax: (919)245-0906
E-mail: bcaoffice@aol.com
URL: http://bca.org

Description: Photographers, technicians, doctors, scientists, educators, and others concerned with photography in the health sciences and related fields. Seeks to advance the techniques of biophotography and biomedical communications through meetings, seminars, and workshops. Has established Board of Registry to offer qualifying examinations for Registered Biological Photographer.

★8516★ **Corporation for Public Broadcasting (CPB)**

401 9th St. NW
Washington, DC 20004-2129
Ph: (202)879-9600   Fax: (202)879-9700
Fr: 800-272-2190
E-mail: comments@cpb.org
URL: http://www.cpb.org

Description: A private, nonprofit corporation authorized under Public Broadcasting Act of 1967. Funded by U.S. government. Works to promote and finance the growth and development of noncommercial radio and television. Makes grants to local public television and radio stations, program producers, and regional networks; studies emerging technologies; works to provide adequate long-range financing from the U.S. government and other sources for public broadcasting. Supports children's services; compiles statistics; sponsors training programs. Presents awards annually for outstanding local television and radio programs.

★8517★ **Media Alliance (MA)**

814 Mission St., Ste. 205
San Francisco, CA 94103
Ph: (415)546-6334   Fax: (415)546-6218
E-mail: info@media-alliance.org
URL: http://www.media-alliance.org

Description: Writers, photographers, editors, broadcast workers, public relations practioners, videographers, filmmakers, commercial artists and other media workers and aspiring media workers. Supports free press and independent, alternative journalism that services progressive politics and social justice.

★8518★ *Media and the Arts Occupations*

Delphi Productions
3160 4th St.
Boulder, CO 80304
Fax: (303)443-4022   Fr: 888-443-2400
URL: http://www.delphivideo.com

$95.00. 50 minutes. Part of the Careers for the 21st Century Video Library.

★8519★ **National Press Photographers Association (NPPA)**

3200 Croasdaile Dr., Ste. 306
Durham, NC 27705
Ph: (919)383-7246   Fax: (919)383-7261
E-mail: info@nppa.org
URL: http://www.nppa.org

Purpose: Professional news photographers and others whose occupation has a direct professional relationship with photojournalism, the art of news communication by photographic image through publication, television film, or theater screen. **Activities:** Sponsors annual television-newsfilm workshop and annual cross-country (five locations) short course. Conducts annual competition for newsphotos and for television-newsfilm, and monthly contest for still clipping and television-newsfilm.

★8520★ *Photographers and Camera Operators*

Evon Publishing
832 N 7th Ave.
Iron River, MI 49935
Ph: (906)265-3190

Audiocassette. 1996. $16.95. 32 minutes. Part of the Careers and Vocational Guidance Series. Provides information about the nature of the work, educational requirements, employment outlook, earnings, and work conditions as well as additional related information.

★8521★ **Professional Photographers of America (PP of A)**

229 Peachtree St. NE, Ste. 2200
Atlanta, GA 30303
Ph: (404)522-8600   Fax: (404)614-6404
Fr: 800-786-6277
E-mail: csc@ppa.com
URL: http://ppa.com

Members: Creating a global perspective that promotes business first, creativity foremost and excellence always. To be the leader in the dissemination of knowledge in the areas of professional business practices and creative image-making, and to define and maintain the industry's standards of excellence.

Professional society of portrait, wedding, commercial, and industrial, and specialized photographers. **Activities:** Sponsors PPA International School of Professional Photography, Maintains speakers' bureau.

★8522★ **Professional School Photographers Association International (PSPA)**

3000 Picture Pl.
Jackson, MI 49201
Ph: (517)788-8100   Fax: (517)788-8371
URL: http://pspa.pmai.org

Description: A section of the Photo Marketing Association International. Firms engaged in the photographing and/or processing of school photographs. Purposes are: to encourage the exchange of production ideas and economies; to cooperate in the overall promotion of photography; to work for better relations and understanding with schools; to act as a group in making manufacturers of sensitized goods and photographic equipment aware of the specialized needs of school photography; to maintain a close watch on any legislation that may affect school photography; to promote career possibilities and personnel training and recruitment for school photography; to foster the well-being of the member firms by providing some of the advantages of a large-scale operation.

★8523★ **Wedding and Portrait Photographers International (WPPI)**

1312 Lincoln Blvd.
PO Box 2003
Santa Monica, CA 90406-2003
Ph: (310)451-0090   Fax: (310)395-9058
URL: http://www.wppinow.com/index2.tml

Description: Wedding portrait and digital photographers and photographers employed at general photography studios. Promotes high artistic and technical standards in wedding photography. Serves as a forum for the exchange of technical knowledge and experience; makes available the expertise of top professionals in the field of photographic arts and technology, advertising, sales promotion, marketing, public relations, accounting, business management, tax, and profit planning. Members are offered the opportunity to purchase special products and services.

★8524★ **Women in Cable and Telecommunications (WIT)**

14555 Avion Pkwy., Ste. 250
Chantilly, VA 20151
Ph: (703)234-9810   Fax: (703)817-1595
URL: http://www.wict.org

Description: Empowers and educate women to achieve their professional goals by providing opportunities for leadership, networking and advocacy.

Physical Therapists

Merion Publications Inc.
2900 Horizon Dr.
PO Box 61556
King of Prussia, PA 19406-0956
Ph: (610)278-1400
URL: http://www.advanceforpt.com

Biweekly. Free to qualified subscribers. Reaches active, qualified physical therapists, physical therapist assistants, and senior students in PT and PTA programs.

★8526★ The American Journal of Orthopedics

Quadrant HealthCom Inc.
26 Main St.
Chatham, NJ 07928-2402
Ph: (973)701-8900   Fax: (973)701-8894
URL: http://www.quadranthealth.com

Monthly. $85.00/year for individuals; $135.00/year for institutions; $190.00/year for out of country, air mail; $128.00/year for out of country, surface mail. Medical journal.

★8527★ American Journal of Physical Medicine and Rehabilitation

Lippincott Williams & Wilkins
530 Walnut St.
Philadelphia, PA 19106
Ph: (215)521-8300   Fax: (215)521-8902
Fr: 800-638-3030
E-mail: jmulliga@lww.com
URL: http://www.amjphysmedrehab.com/

Monthly. $182.00/year for individuals; $247.00/year for other countries; $309.00/year for institutions; $374.00/year for institutions. Medical journal.

★8528★ Critical Care Medicine

Lippincott Williams & Wilkins
530 Walnut St.
Philadelphia, PA 19106
Ph: (215)521-8300   Fax: (215)521-8902
Fr: 800-638-3030
E-mail: jewers@lww.com
URL: http://www.ccmjournal.com/

Monthly. $244.00/year for individuals; $379.00/year for institutions; $451.00/year for institutions, other countries; $315.00/year for out of country. Interdisciplinary journal for ICU and CCU specialists.

★8529★ Journal of Applied Physiology

The American Physiological Society
9650 Rockville Pke.
Bethesda, MD 20814-3991
Ph: (301)634-7164
URL: http://jap.physiology.com

Monthly. Journal covering respiratory, environmental, and exercise physiology.

★8530★ Journal of Learning Disabilities

PRO-ED Inc.
8700 Shoal Creek Blvd.
Austin, TX 78757-6897
Ph: (512)451-3246   Fax: (512)451-8542
Fr: 800-897-3202

$49.00/year for individuals; $105.00/year for institutions; $115.00/year for other countries. Special education journal.

★8531★ The Journal of Orthopaedic and Sports Physical Therapy (JOSPT)

Lippincott Williams & Wilkins
530 Walnut St.
Philadelphia, PA 19106
Ph: (215)521-8300   Fax: (215)521-8902
Fr: 800-638-3030

Monthly. Medical journal.

★8532★ Massage Therapy Journal

American Massage Therapy Association
820 Davis St., Ste. 100
Evanston, IL 60201-4444
Ph: (847)864-0123   Fax: (847)864-1178
E-mail: adsales@amtamassage.org
URL: http://www.amtamassage.org

Quarterly. $25.00/year for individuals. Magazine focusing on professional massage therapy benefits, techniques, research, news, and practitioners.

★8533★ Pediatric Physical Therapy

Lippincott Williams & Wilkins
530 Walnut St.
Philadelphia, PA 19106
Ph: (215)521-8300   Fax: (215)521-8902
Fr: 800-638-3030
URL: http://www.pedpt.com/

Quarterly. $119.00/year for individuals; $157.00/year for other countries; $189.00/year for institutions; $230.00/year for institutions, other countries. Journal reporting on new clinical care for pediatric patients.

★8534★ Physical & Occupational Therapy in Geriatrics

The Haworth Press Inc.
10 Alice St.
Binghamton, NY 13904-1580
Ph: (607)722-5857   Fax: (607)722-1424
Fr: 800-429-6784
URL: http://www.haworthpress.com

Quarterly. $40.00/year for individuals, USA; $160.00/year for institutions, USA; $225.00/year for libraries, USA; $52.00/year for individuals, Canada; $208.00/year for institutions, Canada; $292.52/year for libraries, Canada; $56.00/year for individuals, other countries; $224.00/year for institutions, other countries; $315.00/year for libraries, other countries. Journal for allied health professionals focusing on current practice and emerging issues in the health care of and rehabilitation of the older client.

★8535★ Physical and Occupational Therapy in Pediatrics

The Haworth Press Inc.
10 Alice St.
Binghamton, NY 13904-1580
Ph: (607)722-5857   Fax: (607)722-1424
Fr: 800-429-6784
URL: http://www.haworthpress.com

Quarterly. $75.00/year for individuals; $150.00/year for institutions; $465.00/year for libraries; $101.25/year for individuals, Canada; $202.50/year for institutions, Canada; $627.75/year for libraries, Canada; $108.75/year for individuals, other countries; $217.50/year for institutions, other countries; $674.25/year for libraries, other countries. Journal for therapists involved in developmental and physical rehabilitation of infants and children.

★8536★ Physical Therapy

American Physical Therapy Association
1111 N Fairfax St.
Alexandria, VA 22314-1488
Ph: (703)706-3171   Fax: (703)706-3396
Fr: 800-999-2782
E-mail: ptjourn@apta.org
URL: http://www.apta.org/pt_journal/index.html

Monthly. $70.00/year for nonmembers; $10.00 for single issue. Journal of the American Physical Therapy Association.

★8537★ Physical Therapy Products

Novicom Inc.
6701 Center Dr. W, Ste. 450
Los Angeles, CA 90045
Ph: (310)642-4400   Fax: (310)641-4444
URL: http://www.alliedhealthjournals.com

$12.00/year; $2.00 for single issue. Magazine featuring new products and services available in the physical therapy field.

★8538★ PT, Magazine of Physical Therapy

American Physical Therapy Association
1111 N Fairfax St.
Alexandria, VA 22314-1488
Ph: (703)706-3171   Fax: (703)706-3396
Fr: 800-999-2782
URL: http://www.apta.org

Monthly. $60.00/year for individuals. Magazine for physical therapy professionals.

★8539★ Teaching Exceptional Children

Council for Exceptional Children
1110 N Glebe Rd., Ste. 300
Arlington, VA 22201
Ph: (703)620-3660   Fax: (703)264-9494
Fr: 888-232-7733
E-mail: tec@bc.edu

$58.00/year for individuals; $66.00/year for other countries by surface mail; $95.00/year for other countries by airmail; $10.50 for single issue. Journal exploring practical methods for teaching students who have exceptionalities and those who are gifted and talented.

PLACEMENT AND JOB REFERRAL SERVICES

★8540★ American Physical Therapy Association (APTA)

1111 N Fairfax St.
Alexandria, VA 22314-1488
Ph: (703)684-2782   Fax: (703)684-7343
Fr: 800-999-2782
E-mail: kathygiancoli@apta.org
URL: http://www.apta.org

Members: Professional organization of physical therapists and physical therapist assistants and students. **Purpose:** Fosters the development and improvement of physical therapy service, education, and research; evaluates the organization and administration of curricula; directs the maintenance of standards and promotes scientific research. Acts as an accrediting body for educational programs in physical therapy and is responsible for establishing standards. **Activities:** Offers advisory and consultation services to schools of physical therapy and facilities offering physical therapy services; provides placement services at conference.

★8541★ American Public Health Association (APHA)

800 I St. NW
Washington, DC 20001-3710
Ph: (202)777-2742   Fax: (202)777-2534
E-mail: comments@apha.org
URL: http://www.apha.org

Members: Professional organization of physicians, nurses, educators, academicians, environmentalists, epidemiologists, new professionals, social workers, health administrators, optometrists, podiatrists, pharmacists, dentists, nutritionists, health planners, other community and mental health specialists, and interested consumers. **Purpose:** Seeks to protect and promote personal, mental, and environmental health. **Activities:** Services include promulgation of standards; establishment of uniform practices and procedures; development of the etiology of communicable diseases; research in public health; exploration of medical care programs and their relationships to public health. Sponsors job placement service.

EMPLOYER DIRECTORIES AND NETWORKING LISTS

★8542★ AHA Guide to the Health Care Field

American Hospital Association (AHA)
1 N. Franklin St., 27th Fl.
Chicago, IL 60606
Ph: (312)422-2050   Fax: (312)422-4700
Fr: 800-424-4301

Annual, August. $295.00. Covers hospitals, networks, multi-health care systems, free-standing ambulatory surgery centers, psychiatric facilities, long-term care facilities, substance abuse programs, and other health-related organizations. Entries include: For hospitals-Facility name, address, phone, administrator's name, number of beds, facilities and services, number of employees, expenses, other statistics. For other organizations-Name, address, phone, fax, name and title of contact. Arrangement: Geographical. Indexes: Hospital name.

★8543★ Directory of Hospital Personnel

Thomson Medical Economics
5 Paragon Dr.
Montvale, NJ 07645-1742
Ph: (201)358-7200   Fax: (201)722-2680

Annual, November. $325.00. Covers 200,000 executives at 7,000 U.S. hospitals. Entries include: Name of hospital, address, phone, number of beds, type and JCAHO status of hospital, names and titles of key department heads and staff, medical and nursing school affiliations; number of residents, interns, and nursing students. Arrangement: Geographical. Indexes: Hospital name, personnel, hospital size.

★8544★ Home Health Service Directory

infoUSA Inc.
5711 S 86th Cir.
Omaha, NE 68127-0347
Ph: (402)930-3500   Fax: (402)331-0176
Fr: 800-555-6124
URL: http://www.abii.com

Annual. Number of listings: 21,158. Entries include: Name, address, phone (including area code), size of advertisement, year first in "Yellow Pages," name of owl her or manager, number of employees. Compiled from telephone company "Yellow Pages," nationwide. Arrangement: Geographical.

★8545★ Hospital Blue Book

Billian/Transworld Publishing Inc.
2100 Powers Ferry Rd.
Ste. 300
Atlanta, GA 30339
Ph: (770)955-8484   Fax: (770)955-8485
Fr: 800-533-8484
E-mail: blu-book@billian.com

Annual, January. $285.00 for national edition; $160.00 for southern edition. Covers more than 6,687 hospitals; some listings also appear in a separate southern edition of this publication. Entries include: Name of hospital, accreditation, mailing address, phone, fax, number of beds, type of facility (nonprofit, general, state, etc.); list of administrative personnel and chiefs of medical services, with specific titles. Arrangement: Geographical.

★8546★ The JobBank Guide to Health Care Companies

Adams Media Corp.
57 Littlefield St.
Avon, MA 02322
Ph: (508)427-7100   Fax: (508)427-6790
Fr: 800-872-5627

$17.95. Covers Jobs nationwide in health care companies. Entries include: Firm or organization name, address, phone, name and title of contact; description of organization, headquarters location, typical titles for entry- and middle-level positions, educational backgrounds desired, fringe benefits offered, stock exchange listing, training programs, internships, parent company, number of employees, revenues, e-mail and web address, projected number of hires. Indexes: Alphabetical.

★8547★ Medical and Health Information Directory

Thomson Gale
27500 Drake Rd.
Farmington Hills, MI 48331-3535
Ph: (248)699-4253   Fax: (248)699-8065
Fr: 800-877-GALE
E-mail: businessproducts@gale.com

Annual. $285.00 per volume; $675.00 per set. Covers in Volume 1, more than 26,500 medical and health oriented associations, organizations, institutions, and government agencies, including health maintenance organizations (HMOs), preferred provider organizations (PPOs), insurance companies, pharmaceutical companies, research centers, and medical and allied health schools. In Volume 2, over 12,000 medical book publishers; medical periodicals, directories, audiovisual producers and services, medical libraries and information centers, electronic resources, and health-related internet search engines. In Volume 3, more than 35,500 clinics, treatment centers, care programs, and counseling/diagnostic services for 34 subject areas. Entries include: Institution, service, or firm name, address, phone, fax, email and URL; many include names of key personnel and, when pertinent, descriptive annotation. Volume 3 was formerly listed separately as Health Services Directory. Arrangement: Classified by organization activity, service, etc. Indexes: Each volume has a complete alphabetical name and keyword index.

★8548★ Physical Therapists Directory

infoUSA Inc.
5711 S 86th Cir.
Omaha, NE 68127-0347
Ph: (402)930-3500   Fax: (402)331-0176
Fr: 800-555-6124
URL: http://www.abii.com

Annual. Number of listings: 26,318. Entries include: Name, address, phone (including area code), size of advertisement, year first in "Yellow Pages," name of owner or manager, number of employees. Compiled from telephone company "Yellow Pages," nationwide. Arrangement: Geographical.

★8549★ Private Practice Section of the American Physical Therapy Association-Membership Directory

American Physical Therapy Association
1055 N. Fairfax St., Ste. 100
Alexandria, VA 22314
Ph: (703)299-2410   Fax: (703)299-2411
URL: http://www.ppsapta.org

Biennial, fall of even years. $250.00. Covers about 4,700 member physical therapists in private practice. Entries include: Firm name, home address, business address and phone, fax, names and titles of key personnel, specialty, type of practice, congressional district. Arrangement: Same information is listed alphabetically and geographically. Indexes: Geographical, personal name.

HANDBOOKS AND MANUALS

★8550★ Careers in Health Care

McGraw-Hill Trade
2 Penn Plaza
New York, NY 10121
Ph: (212)904-2000   Fr: 800-722-4726
E-mail: ntcpub@tribune.com

Barbara M. Swanson. Fourth edition, 2000. $17.95; $13.95 (paper). 320 pages. Describes job duties, work settings, salaries, licensing and certification requirements, educational preparation, and future outlook. Gives ideas on how to secure a job.

★8551★ Careers for Health Nuts and Others Who Like to Stay Fit

McGraw-Hill Trade
2 Penn Plaza
New York, NY 10121
Ph: (212)904-2000   Fr: 800-722-4726
E-mail: ntcpub@tribune.com

Blythe Camenson. 1996. $14.95; $9.95 (paper). 160 pages.

★8552★ Careers in Social and Rehabilitation Services

McGraw-Hill Trade
2 Penn Plaza
New York, NY 10121
Ph: (212)904-2000   Fr: 800-722-4726
E-mail: ntcpub@tribune.com

Geraldine O. Garner. Second edition, 2001. $19.95; 14.95 (paper). 128 pages.

★8553★ Expert Resumes for Health Care Careers

JIST Publishing
8902 Otis Ave.
Indianapolis, IN 46216-1033
Ph: (317)613-4200   Fax: 800-547-8329

December 2003. $16.95. 288 pages.

★8554★ Handbook of Teaching for Physical Therapists

Butterworth-Heinemann
225 Wildwood Ave., Unit B
Woburn, MA 01801
Ph: (781)904-2500   Fax: (781)904-2640
Fr: 800-366-2665

Katherine F. Shepard and Gail M. Jensen. Second edition, 2001. $39.99 (paper). 432 pages.

★8555★ Health Care Career Starter: Finding and Getting a Great Job

LearningExpress, LLC
900 Broadway, Ste. 604
New York, NY 10003
Ph: (212)995-2566   Fax: (212)995-5512
Fr: 800-295-9556

Cheryl Jean Hancock. Brigit Dermott. Reprint. 2002. $15.95 (paper). 216 pages. Part of the Heath Care Career Starters Series.

★8556★ Health Careers Today

Elsevier-Health Sciences Division
The Curtis Center, Ste. 300E, 3rd Fl.
170 S. Independence Mall W.
Philadelphia, PA 19106
Ph: (215)238-7800   Fax: (215)238-7362
Fr: 800-523-4069

Gerdin. Revised edition. April 2004. $52.95.

★8557★ How to Become a Physical Therapist

Skip Hunter
PO Box 61
Clemson, SC 29633
Ph: (803)654-3800   Fax: (803)654-4006

Skip Hunter and Lori Whitlow. 1996. $19.95 (paper). 115 pages.

★8558★ Opportunities in Fitness Careers

McGraw-Hill Contemporary Books
1221 Avenue of the Americas
New York, NY 10020
Ph: (212)904-2000   Fr: 800-323-4900
E-mail: ntcpub@tribune.com

Mary Miller. 1998. $14.95; $11.95 (paper). 160 pages. Surveys fitness related careers. Describes career opportunities, education and experience needed, how to get into entry-level jobs and what income to expect. Schools are listed in the appendix.

★8559★ Opportunities in Health and Medical Careers

McGraw-Hill Trade
2 Penn Plaza
New York, NY 10121
Ph: (212)904-2000   Fr: 800-722-4726

I. Donald Snook, Jr. and Leo D'Orazio. 1997. $14.95; $11.95 (paper). 202 pages. Covers the full range of medical and health occupations. Illustrated.

★8560★ Opportunities in Paramedical Careers

McGraw-Hill/Contemporary Books
1221 Avenue of the Americas
New York, NY 10020
Ph: (212)904-2000   Fr: 800-323-4900
E-mail: ntcpub@tribune.com

Alex Kacen. Revised, 1999. $14.95; 11.95 (paper). 200 pages. Discusses a variety of opportunities in this field and how to pursue them. Illustrated.

★8561★ Opportunities in Physical Therapy Careers

McGraw-Hill/Contemporary Books
1221 Avenue of the Americas
New York, NY 10020
Ph: (212)904-2000   Fr: 800-323-4900
E-mail: ntcpub@tribune.com

Bernice R. Krumhansl. 1999. $14.95; $11.95 (paper). 160 pages. Defines what the jobs are, where they are, and how to pursue them. Contains bibliography and illustrations.

★8562★ Opportunities in Sports and Athletics Careers

McGraw-Hill Trade
2 Penn Plaza
New York, NY 10121
Ph: (212)904-2000   Fr: 800-722-4726
E-mail: ntcpub@tribune.com

William Ray Heitzmann. 1994. 160 pages. $14.95; $11.95 (paper). A guide to planning for and seeking opportunities in this growing field. Illustrated.

★8563★ Opportunities in Sports Medicine Careers

McGraw-Hill Trade
2 Penn Plaza
New York, NY 10121
Ph: (212)904-2000   Fr: 800-722-4726
E-mail: ntcpub@tribune.com

William Ray Heitzmann. 1995. $14.95; $11.95 (paper). 160 pages. Discusses a variety of opportunities in this field and how to pursue them. Contains bibliography and illustrations.

★8564★ Real People Working in Health Care

McGraw-Hill Contemporary Books
1221 Avenue of the Americas
New York, NY 10020
Ph: (212)904-2000   Fr: 800-323-4900
E-mail: ntcpub@tribune.com

Blythe Camenson, Jan Goldberg. 1996. $17.95; $12.95 (paper). Interviews and profiles of working professionals capture a range of opportunities in this field.

★8565★ Real People Working in the Helping Professions

McGraw-Hill Contemporary Books
1221 Avenue of the Americas
New York, NY 10020
Ph: (212)904-2000   Fr: 800-323-4900
E-mail: ntcpub@tribune.com

Blythe Camenson, Jan Goldberg. 1997. $17.95; $12.95 (paper). Interviews and profiles of working professionals capture a range of opportunities in this field.

★8566★ Resumes for Health and Medical Careers

McGraw-Hill Trade
2 Penn Plaza
New York, NY 10121
Ph: (212)904-2000   Fr: 800-722-4726
E-mail: ntcpub@tribune.com

1997. $9.95 (paper). 455 pages.

★8567★ Where the Jobs Are: The Hottest Careers for the 90s

The Career Press, Inc.
3 Tice Rd.
PO Box 687
Franklin Lakes, NJ 07417-1322
Ph: (201)848-0310   Fax: (201)848-1727
Fr: 800-227-3371

Joyce Hadley. Third edition, 2000. $13.99 (paper). 400 pages. Out of print. Describes careers in fifteen general fields, from accounting to travel and hospitality.

EMPLOYMENT AGENCIES AND SEARCH FIRMS

★8568★ Harper Associates

29870 Middlebelt
Farmington Hills, MI 48334
Ph: (248)932-1170   Fax: (248)932-1214
E-mail: resumes@harperjobs.com
URL: http://www.harperjobs.com

Executive search firm and employment agency.

★8569★ J.B. Brown and Associates

50 Public Square, Ste. 820
Cleveland, OH 44113
Ph: (216)696-2525

Employment agency and executive recruiter.

★8570★ JPM International

26060 Acero
Mission Viejo, CA 92691
Ph: (949)699-4300   Fax: (949)699-4333
Fr: 800-685-7856
E-mail: leslieo@jpmintl.com
URL: http://www.jpmintl.com

Executive search firm and employment agency.

★8571★ Professional Placement Associates, Inc.

287 Bowman Ave., Ste. 309
Purchase, NY 10577
Ph: (914)251-1000   Fax: (914)251-1055
E-mail: lschachter@ppasearch.com
URL: http://www.ppasearch.com

Executive search firm specializing in the health and medical field.

★8572★ Team Placement Service, Inc.

5113 Leesburg Pike, Ste. 510
Falls Church, VA 22041-3242
Ph: (703)820-8618   Fax: (703)820-3368
Fr: 800-495-6767
E-mail: 4jobs@teamplace.com
URL: http://www.teamplace.com

Temporary agency that also handles some permanent placements.

★8573★ Travcorps, Inc.

40 Eastern Ave.
Malden, MA 02148
Ph: (781)322-2600   Fax: 800-803-1186
Fr: 800-343-3270
URL: http://www.travcorps.com

Places staff in temporary assignments. Other locations nationwide.

ONLINE JOB SOURCES AND SERVICES

★8574★ Medhunters.com
E-mail: info@medhunters.com
URL: http://www.medhunters.com

Description: Career search site for jobs in all health care specialties; educational resources; visa and licensing information for relocation; interesting articles; relocation tools; links to professional organizations and general resources.

★8575★ ProHealthJobs
E-mail: sales@prohealthjobs.com
URL: http://www.prohealthjobs.com

Description: Career resources site for the medical and health care field. Lists professional opportunities, product information, continuing education and open positions.

★8576★ RehabJobs Online
PO Box 480536
Los Angeles, CA 90048
Ph: (213)938-7718   Fax: (213)938-9609
Fr: 800-43-REHAB
E-mail: support@atsrehabjobs.com
URL: http://www.rehabjobs.com

Description: @dq1On-line resource center for the professional therapist.@dq2 **Main files include:** Therapists Only, Therapy Forums, Nationwide Job Search (database), Therapy Job Outlook, Therapy Job Search

Utilities, Therapy Links, Information for Employers and Recruiters.

★8577★ RehabWorld

URL: http://www.rehabworld.com

Description: Site for rehabilitation professionals to learn about the profession and locate jobs. Includes user groups, salary surveys, and chat capabilities. **Main files include:** Physical Therapy, Occupational Therapy, Speech Therapy, Mental Health, Employer World, Student World, International World, Forum.

TRADESHOWS

★8578★ American Physical Therapy Association Annual Conference

American Physical Therapy Association
1111 N Fairfax St.
Alexandria, VA 22314
Ph: (703)706-3225   Fax: (703)706-8501
Fr: 800-999-2782
URL: http://www.apta.org

Annual. **Primary Exhibits:** Physical therapy products, equipment, and services.

★8579★ American Physical Therapy Association Private Practice Session

American Physical Therapy Association
1111 N Fairfax St.
Alexandria, VA 22314
Ph: (703)706-3225   Fax: (703)706-8501
Fr: 800-999-2782
URL: http://www.apta.org

Annual. **Primary Exhibits:** Physical therapy and rehabilitation equipment, supplies, and physical therapy software.

★8580★ American Society of Hand Therapists Annual Meeting

Smith, Bucklin and Associates, Inc.
 (Chicago)
401 N. Michigan Ave.
Chicago, IL 60611-4267
Ph: (312)321-6610   Fax: (312)673-6670
Fr: 800-289-NAON
E-mail: info@smithbucklin.com
URL: http://www.sba.com

Annual. **Primary Exhibits:** Hand therapy equipment and products. **Dates and Locations:** 2004 Oct 21-24; Charlotte, NC • 2005 Dates not set; San Antonio, TX.

OTHER SOURCES

★8581★ American Almanac of Jobs and Salaries

Morrow Avon
1350 Avenue of the Americas
New York, NY 10019
Ph: (212)261-6788   Fr: 800-242-7737

John W. Wright. Revised edition, 2000. $20.00 (paper). 672 pages. This is a comprehensive guide to the wages of hundreds of occupations in a wide variety of industries and organizations.

★8582★ American Health Care Association (AHCA)

1201 L St. NW
Washington, DC 20005
Ph: (202)842-4444   Fax: (202)842-3860
URL: http://www.ahca.org

Description: Federation of state associations of long-term health care facilities. Promotes standards for professionals in long-term health care delivery and quality care for patients and residents in a safe environment. Focuses on issues of availability, quality, affordability, and fair payment. Operates as liaison with governmental agencies, Congress, and professional associations. Compiles statistics.

★8583★ American Kinesiotherapy Association (AKTA)

PO Box 1390
Hines, IL 60141-1390
Fr: 800-296-AKTA
E-mail: ccbkt@aol.com
URL: http://www.AKTA.org

Members: Professional society of kinesiotherapists, and associate and student members with interest in physical and mental rehabilitation and adapted physical education. (Kinesiology therapy is the application of scientifically-based exercise principles adapted to enhance the strength, endurance and mobility of individuals with functional limitations of those requiring extended physical reconditioning.) **Purpose:** Seeks to serve the interest of members and represent the profession to the public. Works to enhance the standard of care provided by kinesiotherapists through the promotion and provision of educational opportunities.

★8584★ American Society of Hand Therapists (ASHT)

401 N Michigan Ave.
Chicago, IL 60611-4267
Ph: (312)321-6866   Fax: (312)673-6670
E-mail: asht@sba.com
URL: http://www.asht.org

Members: Registered and licensed occupational and physical therapists specializing in hand therapy and committed to excellence and professionalism in hand rehabilitation. **Purpose:** Works to promote research, publish information, improve treatment techniques, and standardize hand evaluation and

care. Fosters education and communicatio between therapists in the U.S. and abroac **Activities:** Compiles statistics; conducts re search and education programs and continu ing education seminars.

★8585★ Association on Higher Education and Disability (AHEAD)

PO Box 540666
Waltham, MA 02454
Ph: (781)788-0003   Fax: (781)788-003
E-mail: ahead@ahead.org
URL: http://www.ahead.org.

Description: Individuals interested in pro moting the equal rights and opportunities c disabled postsecondary students, staff, fac ulty, and graduates. Provides an exchang of communication for those professionall involved with disabled students; collects evaluates, and disseminates information; er courages and supports legislation for the benefit of disabled students. Conducts sur veys on issues pertinent to college student with disabilities; offers resource referral sys tem and employment exchange for position in disability student services. Conducts re search programs; compiles statistics.

★8586★ Association for Pediatric Therapists (APT)

2784 Lantz Ave.
San Jose, CA 95124
Ph: (408)377-3345

Members: Occupational, physical, anc speech therapists, certified assistants, anc students. **Purpose:** Promotes continuing professional development of members. **Ac tivities:** Functions as a communication net work linking members. Cooperates with oth er organizations representing professionals in related fields. Conducts continuing profes sional education programs.

★8587★ EMTs, Nurses, Therapists, anc Assistants

Cambridge Educational
2572 Brunswick Ave.
Lawrenceville, NJ 08648-4128
Fax: 800-FAX-ON-US   Fr: 800-468-4227
URL: http://www.cambridgeeducational.com

$79.95. 1999. Part of the series "Exploring Health Occupations."

★8588★ Exploring Health Occupations

Cambridge Educational
2572 Brunswick Ave.
Lawrenceville, NJ 08648-4128
Fax: 800-FAX-ON-US   Fr: 800-468-4227
URL: http://www.cambridgeeducational.com

Two videos. $139.95. 1999.

★8589★ Health Assessment & Treating Occupations

Delphi Productions
3160 4th St.
Boulder, CO 80304
Fax: (303)443-4022   Fr: 888-443-2400

URL: http://www.delphivideo.com

$95.00. 50 minutes. Part of the Careers for the 21st Century Video Library.

★8590★ Health Service Occupations

Delphi Productions
3160 4th St.
Boulder, CO 80304
Fax: (303)443-4022   Fr: 888-443-2400
URL: http://www.delphivideo.com

$95.00. 50 minutes. Part of the Careers for the 21st Century Video Library.

★8591★ Holistic Dental Association (HDA)

PO Box 5007
Durango, CO 81301
Ph: (970)259-1091   Fax: (970)259-1091
E-mail: info@holisticdental.org
URL: http://www.holisticdental.org

Description: Dentists, chiropractors, dental hygienists, physical therapists, and medical doctors. Goals are: to provide a holistic approach to better dental care for patients; to expand techniques, medications, and philosophies that pertain to extractions, anesthetics, fillings, crowns, and orthodontics. Encourages use of homeopathic medications, acupuncture, cranial osteopathy, nutritional techniques, and physical therapy in treating patients in addition to conventional treatments. Sponsors training and educational seminars.

★8592★ Medicine & Related Occupations

Delphi Productions
3160 4th St.
Boulder, CO 80304
Fax: (303)443-4022   Fr: 888-443-2400
URL: http://www.delphivideo.com

$95.00. 45 minutes. Part of the Careers for the 21st Century Video Library.

★8593★ National Rehabilitation Association (NRA)

633 S Washington St.
Alexandria, VA 22314
Ph: (703)836-0850   Fax: (703)836-0848
E-mail: info@nationalrehab.org
URL: http://www.nationalrehab.org/website/index.html

Description: Providing opportunities through knowledge and diversity for professionals in the fields of rehabilitation of people with disabilities.

★8594★ National Strength and Conditioning Association (NSCA)

PO Box 9908
Colorado Springs, CO 80932-0908
Ph: (719)632-6722   Fax: (719)632-6367
Fr: 800-815-6826
E-mail: nsca@nsca-lift.org
URL: http://www.nsca-lift.org

Description: Professionals in the sports science, athletic, and fitness industries. Promotes the total conditioning of athletes to a level of optimum performance, with the belief that a better conditioned athlete not only performs better but is less prone to injury. Gathers and disseminates information on strength and conditioning techniques and benefits. Conducts national, regional, state, and local clinics and workshops. Operates professional certification program.

★8595★ Physical Therapist

Cambridge Educational
2572 Brunswick Ave.
Lawrenceville, NJ 08648-4128
Fax: 800-FAX-ON-US   Fr: 800-468-4227
URL: http://www.cambridgeeducational.com

$39.95. 15 minutes. Part of the Vocational Visions Career Series.

Physical Therapy Assistants and Aides

SOURCES OF HELP-WANTED ADS

★8596★ ADVANCE for Physical Therapists and PT Assistants
Merion Publications Inc.
2900 Horizon Dr.
PO Box 61556
King of Prussia, PA 19406-0956
Ph: (610)278-1400
URL: http://www.advanceforpt.com

Biweekly. Free to qualified subscribers. Reaches active, qualified physical therapists, physical therapist assistants, and senior students in PT and PTA programs.

★8597★ American Journal of Physical Medicine and Rehabilitation
Lippincott Williams & Wilkins
530 Walnut St.
Philadelphia, PA 19106
Ph: (215)521-8300   Fax: (215)521-8902
Fr: 800-638-3030
E-mail: jmulliga@lww.com
URL: http://www.amjphysmedrehab.com/

Monthly. $182.00/year for individuals; $247.00/year for other countries; $309.00/year for institutions; $374.00/year for institutions. Medical journal.

★8598★ The Journal of Orthopaedic and Sports Physical Therapy (JOSPT)
Lippincott Williams & Wilkins
530 Walnut St.
Philadelphia, PA 19106
Ph: (215)521-8300   Fax: (215)521-8902
Fr: 800-638-3030

Monthly. Medical journal.

★8599★ Massage Therapy Journal
American Massage Therapy Association
820 Davis St., Ste. 100
Evanston, IL 60201-4444
Ph: (847)864-0123   Fax: (847)864-1178
E-mail: adsales@amtamassage.org
URL: http://www.amtamassage.org

Quarterly. $25.00/year for individuals. Magazine focusing on professional massage therapy benefits, techniques, research, news, and practitioners.

★8600★ Pediatric Physical Therapy
Lippincott Williams & Wilkins
530 Walnut St.
Philadelphia, PA 19106
Ph: (215)521-8300   Fax: (215)521-8902
Fr: 800-638-3030
URL: http://www.pedpt.com/

Quarterly. $119.00/year for individuals; $157.00/year for other countries; $189.00/year for institutions; $230.00/year for institutions, other countries. Journal reporting on new clinical care for pediatric patients.

★8601★ Physical & Occupational Therapy in Geriatrics
The Haworth Press Inc.
10 Alice St.
Binghamton, NY 13904-1580
Ph: (607)722-5857   Fax: (607)722-1424
Fr: 800-429-6784
URL: http://www.haworthpress.com

Quarterly. $40.00/year for individuals, USA; $160.00/year for institutions, USA; $225.00/year for libraries, USA; $52.00/year for individuals, Canada; $208.00/year for institutions, Canada; $292.52/year for libraries, Canada; $56.00/year for individuals, other countries; $224.00/year for institutions, other countries; $315.00/year for libraries, other countries. Journal for allied health professionals focusing on current practice and emerging issues in the health care of and rehabilitation of the older client.

★8602★ Physical and Occupational Therapy in Pediatrics
The Haworth Press Inc.
10 Alice St.
Binghamton, NY 13904-1580
Ph: (607)722-5857   Fax: (607)722-1424
Fr: 800-429-6784
URL: http://www.haworthpress.com

Quarterly. $75.00/year for individuals; $150.00/year for institutions; $465.00/year for libraries; $101.25/year for individuals, Canada; $202.50/year for institutions, Canada; $627.75/year for libraries, Canada; $108.75/year for individuals, other countries; $217.50/year for institutions, other countries; $674.25/year for libraries, other countries. Journal for therapists involved in developmental and physical rehabilitation of infants and children.

★8603★ Physical Therapy
American Physical Therapy Association
1111 N Fairfax St.
Alexandria, VA 22314-1488
Ph: (703)706-3171   Fax: (703)706-3396
Fr: 800-999-2782
E-mail: ptjourn@apta.org
URL: http://www.apta.org/pt_journal/index.html

Monthly. $70.00/year for nonmembers; $10.00 for single issue. Journal of the American Physical Therapy Association.

★8604★ Physical Therapy Products
Novicom Inc.
6701 Center Dr. W, Ste. 450
Los Angeles, CA 90045
Ph: (310)642-4400   Fax: (310)641-4444
URL: http://www.alliedhealthjournals.com

$12.00/year; $2.00 for single issue. Magazine featuring new products and services available in the physical therapy field.

★8605★ Portable Practitioner: Opportunities in the Healing Arts
Monica Gruler & Co.
PO Box 2095
Petoskey, MI 49770
Ph: (616)347-8591   Fax: (616)347-8591
Fr: 800-968-2877
E-mail: portprac@freeway.net
URL: http://www.cybersytes.com/portprac

Description: Quarterly. Features marketing and practice-growing suggestions for massage therapists and bodyworkers. Recurring features include interviews, a calendar of events, news of educational opportunities, job listings, and notices of publications available.

★8606★ **PT, Magazine of Physical Therapy**

American Physical Therapy Association
1111 N Fairfax St.
Alexandria, VA 22314-1488
Ph: (703)706-3171   Fax: (703)706-3396
Fr: 800-999-2782
URL: http://www.apta.org

Monthly. $60.00/year for individuals. Magazine for physical therapy professionals.

PLACEMENT AND JOB REFERRAL SERVICES

★8607★ **American Physical Therapy Association (APTA)**

1111 N Fairfax St.
Alexandria, VA 22314-1488
Ph: (703)684-2782   Fax: (703)684-7343
Fr: 800-999-2782
E-mail: kathygiancoli@apta.org
URL: http://www.apta.org

Members: Professional organization of physical therapists and physical therapist assistants and students. **Purpose:** Fosters the development and improvement of physical therapy service, education, and research; evaluates the organization and administration of curricula; directs the maintenance of standards and promotes scientific research. Acts as an accrediting body for educational programs in physical therapy and is responsible for establishing standards. **Activities:** Offers advisory and consultation services to schools of physical therapy and facilities offering physical therapy services; provides placement services at conference.

EMPLOYER DIRECTORIES AND NETWORKING LISTS

★8608★ **The JobBank Guide to Health Care Companies**

Adams Media Corp.
57 Littlefield St.
Avon, MA 02322
Ph: (508)427-7100   Fax: (508)427-6790
Fr: 800-872-5627

$17.95. Covers Jobs nationwide in health care companies. Entries include: Firm or organization name, address, phone, name and title of contact; description of organization, headquarters location, typical titles for entry- and middle-level positions, educational backgrounds desired, fringe benefits offered, stock exchange listing, training programs, internships, parent company, number of employees, revenues, e-mail and web address, projected number of hires. Indexes: Alphabetical.

★8609★ **Physical Therapists Directory**

infoUSA Inc.
5711 S 86th Cir.
Omaha, NE 68127-0347
Ph: (402)930-3500   Fax: (402)331-0176
Fr: 800-555-6124
URL: http://www.abii.com

Annual. Number of listings: 26,318. Entries include: Name, address, phone (including area code), size of advertisement, year first in "Yellow Pages," name of owner or manager, number of employees. Compiled from telephone company "Yellow Pages," nationwide. Arrangement: Geographical.

HANDBOOKS AND MANUALS

★8610★ **Careers for Health Nuts and Others Who Like to Stay Fit**

McGraw-Hill Trade
2 Penn Plaza
New York, NY 10121
Ph: (212)904-2000   Fr: 800-722-4726
E-mail: ntcpub@tribune.com

Blythe Camenson. 1996. $14.95; $9.95 (paper). 160 pages.

★8611★ **Careers Inside the World of Health Care**

Rosen Publishing Group Inc.
29 E. 21st. St.
New York, NY 10010
Ph: (212)777-3017   Fax: 888-436-4643
Fr: 800-237-9932

Beth Wilkinson. 1999. $17.95. 64 pages.

★8612★ **Careers in Social and Rehabilitation Services**

McGraw-Hill Trade
2 Penn Plaza
New York, NY 10121
Ph: (212)904-2000   Fr: 800-722-4726
E-mail: ntcpub@tribune.com

Geraldine O. Garner. Second edition, 2001. $19.95; 14.95 (paper). 128 pages.

★8613★ **Expert Resumes for Health Care Careers**

JIST Publishing
8902 Otis Ave.
Indianapolis, IN 46216-1033
Ph: (317)613-4200   Fax: 800-547-8329

December 2003. $16.95. 288 pages.

★8614★ **Handbook of Teaching for Physical Therapists**

Butterworth-Heinemann
225 Wildwood Ave., Unit B
Woburn, MA 01801
Ph: (781)904-2500   Fax: (781)904-2640
Fr: 800-366-2665

Katherine F. Shepard and Gail M. Jensen.

Second edition, 2001. $39.99 (paper). 432 pages.

★8615★ **Health Care Career Starter: Finding and Getting a Great Job**

LearningExpress, LLC
900 Broadway, Ste. 604
New York, NY 10003
Ph: (212)995-2566   Fax: (212)995-5512
Fr: 800-295-9556

Cheryl Jean Hancock. Brigit Dermott. Reprint. 2002. $15.95 (paper). 216 pages. Part of the Heath Care Career Starters Series.

★8616★ **Health Careers Today**

Elsevier-Health Sciences Division
The Curtis Center, Ste. 300E, 3rd Fl.
170 S. Independence Mall W.
Philadelphia, PA 19106
Ph: (215)238-7800   Fax: (215)238-7362
Fr: 800-523-4069

Gerdin. Revised edition. April 2004. $52.95.

★8617★ **How to Become a Physical Therapist**

Skip Hunter
PO Box 61
Clemson, SC 29633
Ph: (803)654-3800   Fax: (803)654-4006

Skip Hunter and Lori Whitlow. 1996. $19.95 (paper). 115 pages.

★8618★ **Opportunities in Health and Medical Careers**

McGraw-Hill Trade
2 Penn Plaza
New York, NY 10121
Ph: (212)904-2000   Fr: 800-722-4726

I. Donald Snook, Jr. and Leo D'Orazio. 1997. $14.95; $11.95 (paper). 202 pages. Covers the full range of medical and health occupations. Illustrated.

★8619★ **Opportunities in Physical Therapy Careers**

McGraw-Hill/Contemporary Books
1221 Avenue of the Americas
New York, NY 10020
Ph: (212)904-2000   Fr: 800-323-4900
E-mail: ntcpub@tribune.com

Bernice R. Krumhansl. 1999. $14.95; $11.95 (paper). 160 pages. Defines what the jobs are, where they are, and how to pursue them. Contains bibliography and illustrations.

★8620★ **Pediatric Physical Therapy for the Physical Therapist Assistant**

Mosby Inc.
11830 Westline Industrial Dr.
St. Louis, MO 63146
Ph: (314)872-8370   Fax: 800-235-0256
Fr: 800-325-4177

Ratliffe. 1997. $39.00. 464 pages.

★8621★ Real People Working in Health Care

McGraw-Hill Contemporary Books
1221 Avenue of the Americas
New York, NY 10020
Ph: (212)904-2000   Fr: 800-323-4900
E-mail: ntcpub@tribune.com

Blythe Camenson, Jan Goldberg. 1996. $17.95; $12.95 (paper). Interviews and profiles of working professionals capture a range of opportunities in this field.

★8622★ Real People Working in the Helping Professions

McGraw-Hill Contemporary Books
1221 Avenue of the Americas
New York, NY 10020
Ph: (212)904-2000   Fr: 800-323-4900
E-mail: ntcpub@tribune.com

Blythe Camenson, Jan Goldberg. 1997. $17.95; $12.95 (paper). Interviews and profiles of working professionals capture a range of opportunities in this field.

★8623★ Resumes for the Health Care Professional

John Wiley & Sons Inc.
111 River Rd.
Hoboken, NJ 07030-5774
Ph: (201)748-6000   Fax: (201)748-6088
Fr: 800-225-5945

Kim Marino. Second edition, 2000. $14.95 (paper). 224 pages.

EMPLOYMENT AGENCIES AND SEARCH FIRMS

★8624★ Team Placement Service, Inc.

5113 Leesburg Pike, Ste. 510
Falls Church, VA 22041-3242
Ph: (703)820-8618   Fax: (703)820-3368
Fr: 800-495-6767
E-mail: 4jobs@teamplace.com
URL: http://www.teamplace.com

Temporary agency that also handles some permanent placements.

★8625★ Travcorps, Inc.

40 Eastern Ave.
Malden, MA 02148
Ph: (781)322-2600   Fax: 800-803-1186
Fr: 800-343-3270
URL: http://www.travcorps.com

Places staff in temporary assignments. Other locations nationwide.

ONLINE JOB SOURCES AND SERVICES

★8626★ Medhunters.com

E-mail: info@medhunters.com
URL: http://www.medhunters.com

Description: Career search site for jobs in all health care specialties; educational resources; visa and licensing information for relocation; interesting articles; relocation tools; links to professional organizations and general resources.

★8627★ ProHealthJobs

E-mail: sales@prohealthjobs.com
URL: http://www.prohealthjobs.com

Description: Career resources site for the medical and health care field. Lists professional opportunities, product information, continuing education and open positions.

★8628★ RehabJobs Online

PO Box 480536
Los Angeles, CA 90048
Ph: (213)938-7718   Fax: (213)938-9609
Fr: 800-43-REHAB
E-mail: support@atsrehabjobs.com
URL: http://www.rehabjobs.com

Description: @dq1On-line resource center for the professional therapist.@dq2 **Main files include:** Therapists Only, Therapy Forums, Nationwide Job Search (database), Therapy Job Outlook, Therapy Job Search Utilities, Therapy Links, Information for Employers and Recruiters.

★8629★ RehabWorld

URL: http://www.rehabworld.com

Description: Site for rehabilitation professionals to learn about the profession and locate jobs. Includes user groups, salary surveys, and chat capabilities. **Main files include:** Physical Therapy, Occupational Therapy, Speech Therapy, Mental Health, Employer World, Student World, International World, Forum.

TRADESHOWS

★8630★ American Physical Therapy Association Annual Conference

American Physical Therapy Association
1111 N Fairfax St.
Alexandria, VA 22314
Ph: (703)706-3225   Fax: (703)706-8501
Fr: 800-999-2782
URL: http://www.apta.org

Annual. **Primary Exhibits:** Physical therapy products, equipment, and services.

★8631★ American Physical Therapy Association Private Practice Session

American Physical Therapy Association
1111 N Fairfax St.
Alexandria, VA 22314
Ph: (703)706-3225   Fax: (703)706-8501
Fr: 800-999-2782
URL: http://www.apta.org

Annual. **Primary Exhibits:** Physical therapy and rehabilitation equipment, supplies, and physical therapy software.

★8632★ American Society of Hand Therapists Annual Meeting

Smith, Bucklin and Associates, Inc. (Chicago)
401 N. Michigan Ave.
Chicago, IL 60611-4267
Ph: (312)321-6610   Fax: (312)673-6670
Fr: 800-289-NAON
E-mail: info@smithbucklin.com
URL: http://www.sba.com

Annual. **Primary Exhibits:** Hand therapy equipment and products. **Dates and Locations:** 2004 Oct 21-24; Charlotte, NC • 2005 Dates not set; San Antonio, TX.

OTHER SOURCES

★8633★ Association for Pediatric Therapists (APT)

2784 Lantz Ave.
San Jose, CA 95124
Ph: (408)377-3345

Members: Occupational, physical, and speech therapists, certified assistants, and students. **Purpose:** Promotes continuing professional development of members. **Activities:** Functions as a communication network linking members. Cooperates with other organizations representing professionals in related fields. Conducts continuing professional education programs.

★8634★ EMTs, Nurses, Therapists, and Assistants

Cambridge Educational
2572 Brunswick Ave.
Lawrenceville, NJ 08648-4128
Fax: 800-FAX-ON-US   Fr: 800-468-4227
URL: http://www.cambridgeeducational.com

$79.95. 1999. Part of the series "Exploring Health Occupations."

★8635★ Exploring Health Occupations

Cambridge Educational
2572 Brunswick Ave.
Lawrenceville, NJ 08648-4128
Fax: 800-FAX-ON-US   Fr: 800-468-4227
URL: http://www.cambridgeeducational.com

Two videos. $139.95. 1999.

★8636★ Foundation for Physical Therapy (FPT)
1111 Fairfax St.
Alexandria, VA 22314-1488
Ph: (703)683-6743   Fax: (703)684-7343
Fr: 800-999-2782
E-mail: foundation@apta.org
URL: http://www.apta.org/Foundation

Description: Supports the physical therapy profession's research needs by funding scientific and clinically-relevant physical therapy research.

★8637★ Health Assessment & Treating Occupations
Delphi Productions
3160 4th St.
Boulder, CO 80304
Fax: (303)443-4022   Fr: 888-443-2400
URL: http://www.delphivideo.com

$95.00. 50 minutes. Part of the Careers for the 21st Century Video Library.

★8638★ Health Service Occupations
Delphi Productions
3160 4th St.
Boulder, CO 80304
Fax: (303)443-4022   Fr: 888-443-2400
URL: http://www.delphivideo.com

$95.00. 50 minutes. Part of the Careers for the 21st Century Video Library.

★8639★ Medical Assistants
Evon Publishing
832 N 7th Ave.
Iron River, MI 49935
Ph: (906)265-3190

Audiocassette. 1996. $16.95. 32 minutes. Part of the Careers and Vocational Guidance Series. Provides information about the nature of the work, educational requirements, employment outlook, earnings, and work conditions as well as additional related information.

★8640★ Medicine & Related Occupations
Delphi Productions
3160 4th St.
Boulder, CO 80304
Fax: (303)443-4022   Fr: 888-443-2400
URL: http://www.delphivideo.com

$95.00. 45 minutes. Part of the Careers for the 21st Century Video Library.

★8641★ National Association of Rehabilitation Providers and Agencies
12100 Sunset Hills Rd., Ste. 130
Reston, VA 20190-5202
Ph: (703)437-4377   Fax: (703)435-4390
E-mail: nara@naranet.org
URL: http://www.naranet.org

Members: Rehabilitation companies servicing patients (including Medicare recipients) with physical therapy, occupational therapy and speech pathology services in outpatient and long-term care settings. Associate members are rehabilitation vendors.

Physician Assistants

SOURCES OF HELP-WANTED ADS

★8642★ ADVANCE for Physician Assistants
Merion Publications Inc.
2900 Horizon Dr.
PO Box 61556
King of Prussia, PA 19406-0956
Ph: (610)278-1400
URL: http://www.advanceforpa.com

Monthly. Free to qualified subscribers. Targets practicing physician assistants and physician assistant students with senior status.

★8643★ Ambulatory Outreach
Society for Ambulatory Care Professionals
1 N Franklin, 31st Fl.
Chicago, IL 60606
Fax: (312)422-4577

Quarterly. Subscription included in membership; $95.00/year for nonmembers. Professional journal for ambulatory care personnel.

★8644★ American Family Physician
American Academy of Family Physicians
11400 Tomahawk Creek Pkwy.
Leawood, KS 66211
Ph: (913)906-6000   Fax: (913)906-6080
Fr: 800-274-2237
E-mail: afpedit@aafp.org
URL: http://www.aafp.org/afp

Semimonthly. $95.00/year for individuals; $9.00 for single issue. Peer reviewed clinical journal for family physicians and others in primary care. Review articles detail the latest diagnostic and therapeutic techniques in the medical field. Department features in each issue include "Tips from other Journals," CME credit opportunities and course calendar.

★8645★ ASRT Scanner
American Society of Radiologic Technologists
15000 Central Ave. SE
Albuquerque, NM 87123-3917
Ph: (505)298-4500   Fax: (505)298-5063
Fr: 800-444-2778

Monthly. Subscription included in membership. Professional magazine covering issues in radiology and medical technology. Includes calendar of events, member profiles, state affiliate news, educational opportunities, and research updates.

★8646★ Health Care Weekly Review
The Martin Group Inc.
24901 Northwestern Hwy., Ste. 316A
Southfield, MI 48075
Ph: (248)440-6080   Fax: (248)352-4801
E-mail: hcwr@compuserve.com

Weekly. $48.00/year for individuals. Professional newspaper covering the health care industry.

★8647★ Hospitals & Health Networks
Health Forum L.L.C.
One N Franklin
Chicago, IL 60606
Ph: (312)893-6800   Fax: (312)422-4600
Fr: 800-621-6902
E-mail: hhn@healthforum.com
URL: http://www.hhnmag.com

Monthly. Publication covering the health care industry.

★8648★ Journal of the American Society of Podiatric Medical Assistants
American Society of Podiatric Medical Assistants
2124 S Austin Blvd.
Cicero, IL 60804
Ph: (708)863-6303   Fax: (708)863-5375
Fr: 888-88A-SPMA

Quarterly. Subscription included in membership. Professional journal covering issues in podiatry.

★8649★ Journal of Health and Hospital Law
American Health Lawyers Association
1025 Connecticut NW, Ste. 600
Washington, DC 20036
Ph: (202)833-1100   Fax: (202)833-1105

Quarterly. $150.00/year. Professional journal covering healthcare issues and cases and their impact on the health care arena.

★8650★ Laboratory Medicine
American Society of Clinical Pathologists
2100 W Harrison St.
Chicago, IL 60612
Ph: (312)738-1336   Fax: (312)738-0101
URL: http://www.asep.org

Monthly. $50.00/year for individuals; $8.00 for single issue. Professional journal covering medical technology and pathology.

★8651★ Medicine and Health
Thomson Financial
195 Broadway
New York, NY 10007
Ph: (646)822-2000

Weekly. Professional publication covering the health care industry.

★8652★ Minnesota Medicine
Minnesota Medical Association
1300 Godward St. NE, Ste. 2500
Minneapolis, MN 55413
Ph: (612)378-1875   Fax: (612)378-3875
Fr: 800-DIAL-MMA
E-mail: mm@mnmed.org

Monthly. $45.00/year for individuals; $5.00 for single issue; $80.00/year for out of country. Magazine on medical, socioeconomic, public health, medical-legal, and biomedical ethics issues of interest to physicians.

★8653★ Minority Health Today

Heritage Information Holdings Inc.
1101 Pennsylvania Ave. NW, Ste. 820
Washington, DC 20001

Bimonthly. Publication covering minority issues in health.

★8654★ Physician Assistant

Smith Publications
105 Raider Blvd.
Belle Mead, NJ 08502
Ph: (908)874-8550   Fax: (908)874-0700

Monthly. $50.00/year; $60.00/year for institutions; $28.00/year for students; $75.00/year for other countries. Medical journal covering primary care, clinical medicine, and other professional and medical topics.

★8655★ The PMA

American Association of Medical
  Assistants
20 N Wacker Dr., Ste. 1575
Chicago, IL 60606
Ph: (312)899-1500   Fax: (312)899-1259

Bimonthly. $30.00/year for nonmembers. Professional health journal.

★8656★ Research in Healthcare Financial Management

International Society for Research in
  Healthcare Financial Management Ltd.
305 W Chesapeake Ave.
CSBA Ste. L-096
Towson, MD 21204

Annual. Publication covering issues in the healthcare industry.

★8657★ State Health Monitor

Atlantic Information Services Inc.
1100 17th St. NW, No. 300
Washington, DC 20036
Ph: (202)775-9008   Fax: (202)331-9542
Fr: 800-521-4323
E-mail: customerserv@aispub.com

Monthly. Publication covering health care.

★8658★ Trauma Reports

Thomson Medical Economics
5 Paragon Dr.
Montvale, NJ 07645-1742
Ph: (201)358-7200   Fax: (201)722-2680
URL: http://www.ahcpub.com/ahc_root_
html/products/newsletters/tr.

Bimonthly. $239.00/year for individuals. Professional publication covering health care.

PLACEMENT AND JOB REFERRAL SERVICES

★8659★ American Association of Pathologists' Assistants (AAPA)

Rosewood Office Plaza
1711 W County Rd. B, Ste. 300 N.
Roseville, MN 55113-4036
Ph: (651)697-9264   Fax: (651)635-0307
Fr: 800-532-AAPA
E-mail: oei@assocmgmt.org
URL: http://www.pathologistsassistants.org

Members: Pathologists' assistants and individuals qualified by academic and practical training to provide service in anatomic pathology under the direction of a qualified pathologist who is responsible for the performance of the assistant. **Purpose:** Promotes the mutual association of trained pathologists' assistants and informs the public and the medical profession concerning the goals of this profession. **Activities:** Compiles statistics on salaries, geographic distribution, and duties of pathologists' assistants. Sponsors a continuing medical education program; offers a job hotline for members only.

★8660★ Association of Physician Assistant Programs (APAP)

950 N. Washington St.
Alexandria, VA 22314-1552
Ph: (703)548-5538   Fax: (703)684-1924
E-mail: apap@aapa.org
URL: http://www.apap.org

Description: Represents physician assistant (PA) educational programs in the United States. Assists PA educational programs-institutions with training programs for physician assistants to primary care and surgical physicians. Assists in the development and organization of educational curricula for PA programs to assure the public of competent PAs. Contributes to defining the roles of PAs in the field of medicine to maximize their benefit to the public; serves as a public information center on the profession; coordinates program logistics such as admissions and career placements; and is currently initiating a centralized application service for PA applicants. Sponsors the Annual Survey of Physician Assistant Educational Programs in the United States. Conducts and sponsors research projects; compiles statistics; offers ongoing training for PA leadership and faculty.

EMPLOYER DIRECTORIES AND NETWORKING LISTS

★8661★ AHA Guide to the Health Care Field

American Hospital Association (AHA)
1 N. Franklin St., 27th Fl.
Chicago, IL 60606
Ph: (312)422-2050   Fax: (312)422-4700
Fr: 800-424-4301

Annual, August. $295.00. Covers hospitals, networks, multi-health care systems, free-standing ambulatory surgery centers, psychiatric facilities, long-term care facilities, substance abuse programs, and other health-related organizations. Entries include: For hospitals-Facility name, address, phone, administrator's name, number of beds, facilities and services, number of employees, expenses, other statistics. For other organizations-Name, address, phone, fax, name and title of contact. Arrangement: Geographical. Indexes: Hospital name.

★8662★ Association of Physician's Assistants in Cardiovascular Surgery-Membership Directory

Association of Physician's Assistants in
  Cardiovascular Surgery
PO Box 4834
Englewood, CA 80155
Ph: (303)221-5651

Annual. Covers about 800 physician's assistants who work with cardiovascular surgeons. Entries include: Name, address, phone. Arrangement: Alphabetical.

★8663★ Directory of Hospital Personnel

Thomson Medical Economics
5 Paragon Dr.
Montvale, NJ 07645-1742
Ph: (201)358-7200   Fax: (201)722-2680

Annual, November. $325.00. Covers 200,000 executives at 7,000 U.S. hospitals. Entries include: Name of hospital, address, phone, number of beds, type and JCAHO status of hospital, names and titles of key department heads and staff, medical and nursing school affiliations; number of residents, interns, and nursing students. Arrangement: Geographical. Indexes: Hospital name, personnel, hospital size.

★8664★ Guide to Careers in the Health Professions

The Princeton Review
1745 Broadway
New York, NY 10019
Ph: (212)829-6928   Fax: (212)940-7400
Fr: 800-733-3000

Published January, 2001. $24.95. Presents advice and information for those searching for satisfying careers in the health professions. Publication includes: Directory of schools and academic programs. Entries include: Name, address, phone, tuition, program details, employment profiles.

★8665★ Hospital Blue Book

Billian/Transworld Publishing Inc.
2100 Powers Ferry Rd.
Ste. 300
Atlanta, GA 30339
Ph: (770)955-8484　　Fax: (770)955-8485
Fr: 800-533-8484
E-mail: blu-book@billian.com

Annual, January. $285.00 for national edition; $160.00 for southern edition. Covers more than 6,687 hospitals; some listings also appear in a separate southern edition of this publication. Entries include: Name of hospital, accreditation, mailing address, phone, fax, number of beds, type of facility (nonprofit, general, state, etc.); list of administrative personnel and chiefs of medical services, with specific titles. Arrangement: Geographical.

★8666★ The JobBank Guide to Health Care Companies

Adams Media Corp.
57 Littlefield St.
Avon, MA 02322
Ph: (508)427-7100　　Fax: (508)427-6790
Fr: 800-872-5627

$17.95. Covers Jobs nationwide in health care companies. Entries include: Firm or organization name, address, phone, name and title of contact; description of organization, headquarters location, typical titles for entry- and middle-level positions, educational backgrounds desired, fringe benefits offered, stock exchange listing, training programs, internships, parent company, number of employees, revenues, e-mail and web address, projected number of hires. Indexes: Alphabetical.

★8667★ Medical and Health Information Directory

Thomson Gale
27500 Drake Rd.
Farmington Hills, MI 48331-3535
Ph: (248)699-4253　　Fax: (248)699-8065
Fr: 800-877-GALE
E-mail: businessproducts@gale.com

Annual. $285.00 per volume; $675.00 per set. Covers in Volume 1, more than 26,500 medical and health oriented associations, organizations, institutions, and government agencies, including health maintenance organizations (HMOs), preferred provider organizations (PPOs), insurance companies, pharmaceutical companies, research centers, and medical and allied health schools. In Volume 2, over 12,000 medical book publishers; medical periodicals, directories, audiovisual producers and services, medical libraries and information centers, electronic resources, and health-related internet search engines. In Volume 3, more than 35,500 clinics, treatment centers, care programs, and counseling/diagnostic services for 34 subject areas. Entries include: Institution, service, or firm name, address, phone, fax, email and URL; many include names of

key personnel and, when pertinent, descriptive annotation. Volume 3 was formerly listed separately as Health Services Directory. Arrangement: Classified by organization activity, service, etc. Indexes: Each volume has a complete alphabetical name and keyword index.

★8668★ Peterson's Job Opportunities for Health and Science Majors

Thomson Peterson's
Princeton Pke. Corporate Ctr., 2000 Lenox Dr.
PO Box 67005
Lawrenceville, NJ 08648
Ph: (609)896-1800　　Fax: (609)896-4531
Fr: 800-338-3282
URL: http://www.petersons.com

Irregular, latest edition 1999. $18.95. Covers approximately 1,300 research, consulting, government, and non-profit and profit service organizations that hire college and university graduates in science and health-related majors. Entries include: Organization name, address, phone, name and title of contact, type of organization, number of employees, Standard Industrial Classification (SIC) code; description of opportunities available including disciplines, level of education required, starting locations and salaries, level of experience accepted, benefits.

★8669★ Physician Assistant Directory

Association of Physician Assistant Programs
950 N Washington St.
Alexandria, VA 22314-1552
Ph: (703)548-5538　　Fax: (703)684-1924
URL: http://www.apap.org

Annual. $35.00. Covers over 100 accredited programs that educate physician assistants. Entries include: Program name, institution name, address, phone; description of program, including curriculum, selection criteria, degrees of certificates offered. Arrangement: Geographical.

HANDBOOKS AND MANUALS

★8670★ Career Opportunities in Health Care (Career Opportunities)

Facts on File
132 W. 31st St., 17th Fl.
New York, NY 10001-2006
Ph: (212)967-8800　　Fax: (212)967-8107
Fr: 800-322-8755

Shelly Field. Arthur E. Weintraub. 2002. Reprint. $18.95. 243 pages. Part of the Career Opportunities Series.

★8671★ Careers in Health Care

McGraw-Hill Trade
2 Penn Plaza
New York, NY 10121
Ph: (212)904-2000　　Fr: 800-722-4726

E-mail: ntcpub@tribune.com

Barbara M. Swanson. Fourth edition, 2000. $17.95; $13.95 (paper). 320 pages. Describes job duties, work settings, salaries, licensing and certification requirements, educational preparation, and future outlook. Gives ideas on how to secure a job.

★8672★ Careers for Night Owls and Other Insomniacs

McGraw-Hill Trade
2 Penn Plaza
New York, NY 10121
Ph: (212)904-2000　　Fr: 800-722-4726
E-mail: ntcpub@tribune.com

Louise Miller. 1995. $14.95; $9.95 (paper). 160 pages.

★8673★ Expert Resumes for Health Care Careers

JIST Publishing
8902 Otis Ave.
Indianapolis, IN 46216-1033
Ph: (317)613-4200　　Fax: 800-547-8329

December 2003. $16.95. 288 pages.

★8674★ Federal Jobs in Nursing and Health Sciences

Impact Publications
9104 Manassas Dr., Ste. N
Manassas Park, VA 20111-5211
Ph: (703)361-7300　　Fax: (703)335-9486

Russ Smith. 1996. Part of Federal Jobs in...Series. $14.95. 130 pages.

★8675★ Health Care Career Starter: Finding and Getting a Great Job

LearningExpress, LLC
900 Broadway, Ste. 604
New York, NY 10003
Ph: (212)995-2566　　Fax: (212)995-5512
Fr: 800-295-9556

Cheryl Jean Hancock. Brigit Dermott. Reprint. 2002. $15.95 (paper). 216 pages. Part of the Heath Care Career Starters Series.

★8676★ Health Careers Today

Elsevier-Health Sciences Division
The Curtis Center, Ste. 300E, 3rd Fl.
170 S. Independence Mall W.
Philadelphia, PA 19106
Ph: (215)238-7800　　Fax: (215)238-7362
Fr: 800-523-4069

Gerdin. Revised edition. April 2004. $52.95.

★8677★ Healthcare Career Directory-Nurses and Physicians

Thomson Gale
27500 Drake Rd.
Farmington Hills, MI 48331-3535
Ph: (248)699-GALE　　Fax: 800-414-5043
Fr: 800-877-GALE
E-mail: galeord@gale.com
URL: http://www.gale.com

Bradley Morgan. Second edition, 1993. $39.00. 300 pages. Out of print. Essays on specific careers provide an insider's perspective. Features extensive listings of contacts and entry-level job opportunities. Provides information on internships and sources of help-wanted ads.

★8678★ **Opportunities in Health and Medical Careers**

McGraw-Hill Trade
2 Penn Plaza
New York, NY 10121
Ph: (212)904-2000   Fr: 800-722-4726
I. Donald Snook, Jr. and Leo D'Orazio. 1997. $14.95; $11.95 (paper). 202 pages. Covers the full range of medical and health occupations. Illustrated.

★8679★ **Opportunities in Paramedical Careers**

McGraw-Hill/Contemporary Books
1221 Avenue of the Americas
New York, NY 10020
Ph: (212)904-2000   Fr: 800-323-4900
E-mail: ntcpub@tribune.com
Alex Kacen. Revised, 1999. $14.95; 11.95 (paper). 200 pages. Discusses a variety of opportunities in this field and how to pursue them. Illustrated.

★8680★ **Opportunities in Physician Assistant Careers**

McGraw-Hill Trade
2 Penn Plaza
New York, NY 10121
Ph: (212)904-2000   Fr: 800-722-4726
Terence J. Sacks. 2002. $14.95; $12.95 (paper). 160 pages.

★8681★ **Physician Assistant: A Guide to Clinical Practice**

W.B. Saunders
6277 Sea Harbor Dr.
Orlando, FL 32887
Fax: 800-235-0256   Fr: 800-543-1918
Ruth Ballweg and Sherry Stolberg. Second edition, 1999. $71.00. 860 pages.

★8682★ **Physician Assistants in American Medicine**

W B Saunders Co.
6277 Sea Harbor Dr.
Orlando, FL 32887
Fr: 800-654-2452
Roderick S. Hooker, D. B. Ferguson, A. Shuttleworth, D. K. Whittaker and James F. Cawley. 1997. $29.95 (paper).

★8683★ **Real People Working in Health Care**

McGraw-Hill Contemporary Books
1221 Avenue of the Americas
New York, NY 10020
Ph: (212)904-2000   Fr: 800-323-4900

E-mail: ntcpub@tribune.com
Blythe Camenson, Jan Goldberg. 1996. $17.95; $12.95 (paper). Interviews and profiles of working professionals capture a range of opportunities in this field.

★8684★ **Resumes for the Health Care Professional**

John Wiley & Sons Inc.
111 River Rd.
Hoboken, NJ 07030-5774
Ph: (201)748-6000   Fax: (201)748-6088
Fr: 800-225-5945
Kim Marino. Second edition, 2000. $14.95 (paper). 224 pages.

★8685★ **Resumes for Health and Medical Careers**

McGraw-Hill Trade
2 Penn Plaza
New York, NY 10121
Ph: (212)904-2000   Fr: 800-722-4726
E-mail: ntcpub@tribune.com
1997. $9.95 (paper). 455 pages.

★8686★ **Where the Jobs Are: The Hottest Careers for the 90s**

The Career Press, Inc.
3 Tice Rd.
PO Box 687
Franklin Lakes, NJ 07417-1322
Ph: (201)848-0310   Fax: (201)848-1727
Fr: 800-227-3371
Joyce Hadley. Third edition, 2000. $13.99 (paper). 400 pages. Out of print. Describes careers in fifteen general fields, from accounting to travel and hospitality.

EMPLOYMENT AGENCIES AND SEARCH FIRMS

★8687★ **Davis-Smith, Inc.**

27656 Franklin Rd.
Southfield, MI 48034
Ph: (248)354-4100   Fax: (248)354-6702
Fr: 800-541-4672
E-mail: info@davissmith.com
URL: http://www.davissmith.com
Employment agency. Executive search firm.

★8688★ **P.J. Murphy & Associates Inc.**

735 N Water St., Ste. 915
Milwaukee, WI 53202
Ph: (414)277-9777   Fax: (414)277-7626
Management consulting firm which specializes in retained executive search. Industries served: all industries, to include healthcare and physician recruiting.

★8689★ **Professional Placement Associates, Inc.**

287 Bowman Ave., Ste. 309
Purchase, NY 10577
Ph: (914)251-1000   Fax: (914)251-1055
E-mail: lschachter@ppasearch.com
URL: http://www.ppasearch.com
Executive search firm specializing in the health and medical field.

ONLINE JOB SOURCES AND SERVICES

★8690★ **American Academy of Physician Assistants Career Opportunities**

URL: http://www.medical-admart.com/aapa
Description: Online newsletter of the AAPA. Job opportunities may be searched by state or type. Members may also post position wanted on AAPA website.

★8691★ **Medhunters.com**

E-mail: info@medhunters.com
URL: http://www.medhunters.com
Description: Career search site for jobs in all health care specialties; educational resources; visa and licensing information for relocation; interesting articles; relocation tools; links to professional organizations and general resources.

★8692★ **ProHealthJobs**

E-mail: sales@prohealthjobs.com
URL: http://www.prohealthjobs.com
Description: Career resources site for the medical and health care field. Lists professional opportunities, product information, continuing education and open positions.

TRADESHOWS

★8693★ **Annual Academy of Physician Assistants Conference**

American Academy of Physician Assistants
950 N. Washington St.
Alexandria, VA 22314-1552
Ph: (703)836-2272   Fax: (703)684-1924
E-mail: aapa@aapa.org
URL: http://www.aapa.org
Primary Exhibits: Pharmaceuticals, medical equipment and supplies, medical books, and medical software. **Dates and Locations:** 2005 May 28-2; Orlando, FL; Orange County Convention Center.

★8694★ California Academy of Physician Assistants Convention

California Academy of Physician Assistants
3100 W. Warner Ave., Ste. 3
Santa Ana, CA 92704-5331
Ph: (714)427-0321   Fax: (714)427-0324

Annual. **Primary Exhibits:** Medical equipment, supplies, and services, including pharmaceuticals and employment recruitment services. **Dates and Locations:** 2004 Oct 22-24; Palm Springs, CA; Palm Springs Convention Ctr. and Wyndham Palm Springs.

★8695★ Washington State Academy of Physician Assistants Convention

Washington State Academy of Physician Assistants
2033 6th Ave. Ste. 1100
Seattle, WA 98121-2590
Ph: (206)575-4633   Fax: (206)575-4657
E-mail: wapa123@aol.com

Semiannual. **Primary Exhibits:** Medical equipment, supplies, and services.

OTHER SOURCES

★8696★ American Academy of Physician Assistants (AAPA)

950 N Washington St.
Alexandria, VA 22314-1552
Ph: (703)836-2272   Fax: (703)684-1924
E-mail: aapa@aapa.org
URL: http://www.aapa.org

Description: Physician assistants and other interested parties. Seeks to promote quality, cost-effective, and accessible healthcare, and the professional and personal development of PAs. Provide services for members. **Activities:** Organizes annual National PA Day. Develops research and education programs; compiles statistics.

★8697★ American Academy of Tropical Medicine (AATM)

PO Box 24224
Detroit, MI 48224
Ph: (313)882-0641   Fax: (313)882-0979

Members: Physicians and allied health professionals interested in tropical medicine. **Purpose:** Provides postgraduate continuing medical education; confers certificates and diplomas. **Activities:** Maintains speakers' bureau; provides placement service. Conducts research and compiles statistics. Conducts educational programs; offers children's services.

★8698★ American Almanac of Jobs and Salaries

Morrow Avon
1350 Avenue of the Americas
New York, NY 10019
Ph: (212)261-6788   Fr: 800-242-7737

John W. Wright. Revised edition, 2000. $20.00 (paper). 672 pages. This is a comprehensive guide to the wages of hundreds of occupations in a wide variety of industries and organizations.

★8699★ Association of Physician Assistants in Cardiovascular Surgery (APACVS)

PO Box 4834
Englewood, CO 80155
Ph: (303)221-5651   Fax: (303)771-2550
Fr: 877-221-5651
E-mail: carol@goddardassociates.com
URL: http://www.apacvs.org

Description: Physician assistants who work with cardiovascular surgeons. Objective is to assist in defining the role of physician assistants in the field of cardiovascular surgery through educational forums.

★8700★ Commission on Accreditation of Allied Health Education Programs (CAAHEP)

35 E. Wacker Dr., Ste. 1970
Chicago, IL 60601-2208
Ph: (312)553-9355   Fax: (312)553-9616
E-mail: caahep@caahep.org
URL: http://www.caahep.org

Description: Serves as a nationally recognized accrediting agency for allied health programs in 18 occupational areas.

★8701★ EMTs, Nurses, Therapists, and Assistants

Cambridge Educational
2572 Brunswick Ave.
Lawrenceville, NJ 08648-4128
Fax: 800-FAX-ON-US   Fr: 800-468-4227
URL: http://www.cambridgeeducational.com

$79.95. 1999. Part of the series "Exploring Health Occupations."

★8702★ Exploring Health Occupations

Cambridge Educational
2572 Brunswick Ave.
Lawrenceville, NJ 08648-4128
Fax: 800-FAX-ON-US   Fr: 800-468-4227
URL: http://www.cambridgeeducational.com

Two videos. $139.95. 1999.

★8703★ Health Service Occupations

Delphi Productions
3160 4th St.
Boulder, CO 80304
Fax: (303)443-4022   Fr: 888-443-2400
URL: http://www.delphivideo.com

$95.00. 50 minutes. Part of the Careers for the 21st Century Video Library.

★8704★ Joint Council of Allergy, Asthma and Immunology (JCAAI)

50 N Brockway, Ste. 3-3
Palatine, IL 60067
Ph: (847)934-1918   Fax: (847)934-1820
E-mail: info@jcaai.org
URL: http://www.jcaai.org

Description: Physicians specializing in allergy or clinical immunology. Members must belong to the American Academy of Allergy and Immunology or the American College of Allergy and Immunology. Serves as political and socioeconomic arm for these sponsoring organizations.

★8705★ Medical Assistants

Evon Publishing
832 N 7th Ave.
Iron River, MI 49935
Ph: (906)265-3190

Audiocassette. 1996. $16.95. 32 minutes. Part of the Careers and Vocational Guidance Series. Provides information about the nature of the work, educational requirements, employment outlook, earnings, and work conditions as well as additional related information.

★8706★ Medicine & Related Occupations

Delphi Productions
3160 4th St.
Boulder, CO 80304
Fax: (303)443-4022   Fr: 888-443-2400
URL: http://www.delphivideo.com

$95.00. 45 minutes. Part of the Careers for the 21st Century Video Library.

★8707★ National Commission on Certification of Physician Assistants (NCCPA)

157 Technology Pkwy., Ste. 800
Norcross, GA 30092-2913
Ph: (770)734-4500
E-mail: heatherr@nccpa.net
URL: http://www.nccpa.net

Description: Certifies physician assistants at the entry level and for continued competence. Has certified 22,750 physician assistants.

★8708★ National Rural Health Association (NRHA)

1 W Armour Blvd., Ste. 203
Kansas City, MO 64111-2087
Ph: (816)756-3140   Fax: (816)756-314
E-mail: mail@nrharural.org
URL: http://www.nrharural.org

Description: Administrators, physicians, nurses, physician assistants, health planners, academicians, and others interested or involved in rural health care. Creates a better understanding of health care problems unique to rural areas; utilizes a collective approach in finding positive solutions; articulates and represents the health care needs of rural America; supplies current information to rural health care providers; serves as a liaison between rural health care programs throughout the country. Offers continuing education credits for medical, dental, nursing, and management courses.

★8709★ *Physician Assistants*
Evon Publishing
832 N 7th Ave.
Iron River, MI 49935
Ph: (906)265-3190

Audiocassette. 1996. $16.95. 32 minutes. Part of the Careers and Vocational Guidance Series. Provides information about the nature of the work, educational requirements, employment outlook, earnings, and work conditions as well as additional related information.

★8710★ **Visiting Nurse Associations of America (VNAA)**
99 Summer St., Ste. 1700
Boston, MA 02110
Ph: (617)737-3200   Fax: (617)737-1144
Fr: 800-426-2547
E-mail: vnaa@vnaa.org

URL: http://www.vnaa.org

Members: Voluntary, nonprofit home health care agencies. **Purpose:** Develops competitive strength among community-based nonprofit visiting nurse organizations; works to strengthen business resources and economic programs through contracting, marketing, governmental affairs and publications.

Physicians

★8711★ AACAP News

American Academy of Child and
  Adolescent Psychiatry (AACAP)
3615 Wisconsin Ave. NW
Washington, DC 20016
Ph: (202)966-7300   Fax: (202)363-0582

Description: Six issues/year. Publishes news of the Academy, child and adolescent psychiatrists, and AACAP members. Focuses on the practice of child and adolescent psychiatry. Recurring features include letters to the editor, legislative updates, news of research, statistics, announcements of open positions, and columns titled Ethics, Clinical Vignettes, Forensic Corner, and Clinical Marketing.

★8712★ AARC Times

Daedalus Enterprises Inc.
PO Box 29686
Dallas, TX 75229
Ph: (972)243-2272   Fax: (972)484-6010
URL: http://aarc.org

Monthly. $90.00/year; $10.00 for single issue. Professional magazine for respiratory therapists and other cardiopulmonary specialists.

★8713★ ACP Observer

American College of Physicians
190 N Independence Mall W
Philadelphia, PA 19106-1572
Ph: (215)351-2400   Fax: (215)351-2799
Fr: 800-523-1546
URL: http://www.acponline.org

Monthly. $12.00/year; $1.50 for single issue. Official membership tabloid of the American College of Physicians.

★8714★ Ambulatory Outreach

Society for Ambulatory Care Professionals
1 N Franklin, 31st Fl.
Chicago, IL 60606
Fax: (312)422-4577

Quarterly. Subscription included in membership; $95.00/year for nonmembers. Professional journal for ambulatory care personnel.

★8715★ American Family Physician

American Academy of Family Physicians
11400 Tomahawk Creek Pkwy.
Leawood, KS 66211
Ph: (913)906-6000   Fax: (913)906-6080
Fr: 800-274-2237
E-mail: afpedit@aafp.org
URL: http://www.aafp.org/afp

Semimonthly. $95.00/year for individuals; $9.00 for single issue. Peer reviewed clinical journal for family physicians and others in primary care. Review articles detail the latest diagnostic and therapeutic techniques in the medical field. Department features in each issue include "Tips from other Journals," CME credit opportunities and course calendar.

★8716★ American Heart Journal

Mosby Inc.
The Curtis Ctr., 3rd Fl.
Independence Sq. W
Philadelphia, PA 19106-3399
Ph: (215)235-7800   Fax: (215)238-7883
Fr: 800-523-1649
URL: http://www.mosby.com/ahs

Monthly. $190.00/year for individuals; $406.00/year for institutions; $95.00/year for students; $238.00/year for individuals, other countries; $454.00/year for institutions, other countries; $119.00/year for students, other countries. Medical journal serving practicing cardiologists, university-affiliated clinicians, and physicians keeping abreast of developments in the diagnosis and management of cardiovascular disease.

★8717★ The American Journal of Cardiology

Excerpta Medica Inc.
655 Avenue of the Americas
New York, NY 10010
Ph: (212)989-5800

Semimonthly. $66.00/year. Journal for heart specialists.

★8718★ American Journal of Clinical Nutrition

The American Society for Clinical Nutrition
9650 Rockville Pke.
Bethesda, MD 20814-3998
Ph: (301)530-7110   Fax: (301)571-1863
E-mail: ajcn@ucdavis.edu
URL: http://www.ajcn.org

Monthly. $60.00/year for members; $120.00/year for nonmembers; $190.00/year for institutions; $50.00/year for students. Journal of basic and clinical studies relevant to human nutrition.

★8719★ American Journal of Epidemiology

Oxford University Press Inc.
111 Market Pl. Ste. 840
Baltimore, MD 21202-6709
Ph: (410)223-1600   Fax: (410)223-1620
URL: http://11phweb.5ph.jhu.edu/pubs/jepi

Semimonthly. $250.00/year for other countries; $258.00/year for other countries; $15.00 for single issue. Science research and medicine journal.

★8720★ American Journal of Medical Genetics

John Wiley and Sons Inc.
111 River St.
Hoboken, NJ 07030
Ph: (201)748-8866   Fax: (201)748-8824

$645.00/year for U.S.; $645.00/year for Canada and Mexico; $885.00/year for other countries. Medical research journal.

★8721★ American Journal of Medicine
Excerpta Medica Inc.
655 Avenue of the Americas
New York, NY 10010
Ph: (212)989-5800

Monthly. $66.00/year. Medical journal.

★8722★ American Journal of Obstetrics and Gynecology
Mosby Inc.
11830 Westline Industrial Dr.
St. Louis, MO 63146
Ph: (314)872-8370   Fax: (314)432-1380
Fr: 800-325-4177
URL: http://www.mosby.com/ajog

Monthly. $195.00/year for individuals; $420.00/year for institutions; $98.00/year for students; $240.00/year for individuals, other countries; $466.00/year for institutions, other countries; $120.00/year for students, other countries. Journal for specialists in obstetrics and gynecology and for general practitioners. Official Journal of the American Gynecological and Obstetrical Society, American Board of Obstetrics and Gynecology, Society of Gynecologic Surgeons, and Society of Maternal-Fetal Medicine.

★8723★ American Journal of Ophthalmology
Elsevier Science Inc.
360 Park Ave. S, No. 11
New York, NY 10010-1710
Ph: (212)989-5800   Fax: (212)633-3965
Fr: 888-437-4636
URL: http://www.elsevier.com/inca/publications/store/6/0/1/0/2/8/

Monthly. $103.00/year for individuals, USA and Canada; $203.00/year for individuals, except Europe and Japan; $477.00/year for institutions, except Europe and Japan; $369.00/year for institutions, USA and Canada; $139.00/year for students, except Europe and Japan. Ophthalmology magazine describing clinical investigations, clinical observations, and clinically relevant laboratory investigations related to ophthalmology.

★8724★ The American Journal of Orthopedics
Quadrant HealthCom Inc.
26 Main St.
Chatham, NJ 07928-2402
Ph: (973)701-8900   Fax: (973)701-8894
URL: http://www.quadranthealth.com

Monthly. $85.00/year for individuals; $135.00/year for institutions; $190.00/year for out of country, air mail; $128.00/year for out of country, surface mail. Medical journal.

★8725★ The American Journal of Pathology
The American Journal of Pathology
9650 Rockville Pke.
Bethesda, MD 20814-3993
Ph: (301)634-7959   Fax: (301)634-7961
E-mail: ajp@pathol.faseb.org
URL: http://www.edoc.com/pathology

Monthly. $195.00/year for individuals; $350.00/year for institutions; $30.00 for single issue; $75.00/year for Canada; $95.00/year for Mexico. Journal publishing original experimental and clinical studies in diagnostic and experimental pathology.

★8726★ American Journal of Psychiatry
American Psychiatric Publishing Inc.
1000 Wilson Blvd., Ste. 1825
Arlington, VA 22209
Ph: (703)907-7300   Fax: (703)907-1091
Fr: 800-368-5777
E-mail: ajp@psych.org

Monthly. $70.00/year for individuals; $100.00/year for institutions; $35.00/year for students. Psychiatry journal.

★8727★ The American Journal of Sports Medicine
The American Orthopaedic Society for Sports Medicine
6300 N River Rd.
Rosemont, IL 60018
Ph: (847)292-4900   Fax: (847)292-4905
URL: http://www.ajsm.org

Bimonthly. $125.00/year for individuals; $145.00/year for out of country; $160.00/year for institutions; $25.00/year for single issue. Medical journal.

★8728★ American Journal of Surgery
Excerpta Medica Inc.
655 Avenue of the Americas
New York, NY 10010
Ph: (212)989-5800

Monthly. $69.00/year. Surgical journal.

★8729★ The American Journal of Surgical Pathology (AJSP)
Lippincott Williams & Wilkins
351 W Camden St.
Baltimore, MD 21201
Ph: (410)528-8517   Fax: (410)528-4312
Fr: 800-638-3030
URL: http://www.ajsp.com/

Monthly. $357.00/year for individuals; $750.00/year for institutions; $457.00/year for other countries; $812.00/year for institutions, other countries. Medical journal covering issues concerning diagnostic problems.

★8730★ American Review of Respiratory Disease
American Lung Association
61 Broadway
New York, NY 10019
Ph: (212)315-8700   Fax: (212)265-5642
E-mail: alahr@lungusa.org

Monthly. $130.00/year; $170.00/year. Medical journal focusing on lung diseases.

★8731★ Anesthesia & Analgesia
Lippincott Williams & Wilkins
530 Walnut St.
Philadelphia, PA 19106
Ph: (215)521-8300   Fax: (215)521-8902
Fr: 800-638-3030
URL: http://www.anesthesia-analgesia.org/

$372.00/year for individuals; $461.00/year for other countries; $526.00/year for institutions; $615.00/year for institutions, other countries. Medical journal.

★8732★ Anesthesiology
Lippincott Williams & Wilkins
530 Walnut St.
Philadelphia, PA 19106
Ph: (215)521-8300   Fax: (215)521-8902
Fr: 800-638-3030
E-mail: jderrico@lww.com
URL: http://www.anesthesiology.org

Monthly. $268.00/year for individuals; $491.00/year for institutions; $355.00/year for other countries; $551.00/year for institutions, other countries. Medical journal publishing original manuscripts and brief abstracts from current literature on anesthesiology.

★8733★ Annals of Behavioral Medicine
Society of Behavioral Medicine
7611 Elmwood Ave., Ste. 201
Middleton, WI 53562
Ph: (608)827-7267   Fax: (608)831-5122

Quarterly. $135.00/year; $160.00/year for other countries. Journal describing the interactions of behavior and health.

★8734★ Annals of Emergency Medicine
Mosby Inc.
11830 Westline Industrial Dr.
St. Louis, MO 63146
Ph: (314)872-8370   Fax: (314)432-1380
Fr: 800-325-4177

Monthly. $149.00/year for individuals; $195.00/year for other countries; $260.00/year for institutions; $306.00/year for institutions, other countries; $23.00/year for single issue. Medical journal for emergency physicians.

★8735★ Annals of Neurology
John Wiley and Sons Inc.
111 River St.
Hoboken, NJ 07030
Ph: (201)748-8866   Fax: (201)748-8824

Monthly. $194.00/year for individuals; $300.00/year for institutions; $38.00 for single issue, current and back issues. Articles of scientific and clinical merit for neurologists.

★8736★ Annals of Plastic Surgery

Lippincott Williams & Wilkins
530 Walnut St.
Philadelphia, PA 19106
Ph: (215)521-8300   Fax: (215)521-8902
Fr: 800-638-3030
E-mail: anplsurg@grm.net
URL: http://www.annalsplasticsurgery.com/

Monthly. $329.00/year for individuals; $530.00/year for institutions; $425.00/year for other countries, current and back issues; $612.00/year for institutions, other countries. Medical journal for the plastic surgeon.

★8737★ Annals of Surgery

Lippincott Williams & Wilkins
530 Walnut St.
Philadelphia, PA 19106
Ph: (215)521-8300   Fax: (215)521-8902
Fr: 800-638-3030
E-mail: bmorrill@lww.com
URL: http://www.annalsofsurgery.com/

Monthly. $190.00/year for individuals; $475.00/year for institutions; $290.00/year for other countries, including current and back issues; $602.00/year for institutions, other countries. Medical journal publishing original manuscripts promoting the advancement of surgical knowledge and practice.

★8738★ Applied Radiology

Anderson Publishing Ltd.
1301 W Park Ave.
Ocean, NJ 07712
Ph: (732)695-0600   Fax: (732)695-9501
E-mail: andersonpub@compuserve.com

Monthly. Free to qualified subscribers; $85.00/year for individuals; $10.00 for single issue. Magazine for radiologists, chief radiologic technologists, radiology department administrators, and key managers in HMOs. Presents articles written by radiologic professionals on all aspects of general diagnostic radiology, the diagnostic radiologic subspecialties, radiation therapy, and the socioeconomics of imaging.

★8739★ Archives of Dermatology

American Medical Association
515 N State St.
Chicago, IL 60610
Ph: (312)464-4470   Fax: (312)464-5020
E-mail: http://www.archdematol.com

Monthly. $155.00/year for other countries; $12.00/year for single issue. Educational/clinical journal for dermatologists.

★8740★ Archives of General Psychiatry

American Medical Association
515 N State St.
PO Box 10946
Chicago, IL 60610
Ph: (312)670-7827   Fr: 800-262-2350
E-mail: ama-subs@ama-assn.org
URL: http://archpsyc.ama-assn.org/

Educational/clinical journal for psychiatrists.

★8741★ Archives of Neurology

American Medical Association
515 N State St.
Chicago, IL 60610
Ph: (312)464-4470   Fax: (312)464-5020
E-mail: archneurol@mednet.swmed.edu
URL: http://archneur.ama-assn.org

Monthly. $168.00/year for individuals. Educational/clinical journal for neurologists.

★8742★ Archives of Ophthalmology

American Medical Association
515 N State St.
Chicago, IL 60610
Ph: (312)464-4470   Fax: (312)464-5020

Monthly. $190.00/year for individuals; $170.00 for single issue. Educational/clinical journal for ophthalmologists.

★8743★ Archives of Otolaryngology-Head & Neck Surgery

American Medical Association
515 N State St.
Chicago, IL 60610
Ph: (312)464-4470   Fax: (312)464-5020
URL: http://www.ama-assn.org

Monthly. $210.00/year for individuals; $155.00/year. Educational/clinical journal for otolaryngologists.

★8744★ Archives of Pathology & Laboratory Medicine

American Medical Association
515 N State St.
Chicago, IL 60610
Ph: (312)464-4470   Fax: (312)464-5020
URL: http://www.ama-assn.org

Monthly. Educational/clinical journal for pathologists. Published in cooperation with the College of American Pathologists.

★8745★ Archives of Surgery

American Medical Association
515 N State St.
Chicago, IL 60610
Ph: (312)464-4470   Fax: (312)464-5020
URL: http://www.archsurg.com

Monthly. $175.00/year for individuals; $155.00/year for other countries. Educational/clinical journal for general surgeons and surgical specialists.

★8746★ ASRT Scanner

American Society of Radiologic Technologists
15000 Central Ave. SE
Albuquerque, NM 87123-3917
Ph: (505)298-4500   Fax: (505)298-5063
Fr: 800-444-2778

Monthly. Subscription included in membership. Professional magazine covering issues in radiology and medical technology. Includes calendar of events, member profiles, state affiliate news, educational opportunities, and research updates.

★8747★ Chinese American Medical Society Newsletter

Chinese American Medical Society
281 Edgewood Ave.
Teaneck, NJ 07666
Ph: (201)833-1506   Fax: (201)833-8252
URL: http://www.camsociety.org

Description: Three to Four issues/year. Publishes Society news for Chinese-American physicians, Recurring features include editorials, news of research letters to the editor, news of members, job listings, and a calendar of events.

★8748★ Clinical Cardiology

Clinical Cardiology Publishing Company Inc.
PO Box 832
Mahwah, NJ 07430-0832
Ph: (201)818-1010   Fax: (201)818-0086
Fr: 800-443-0263
E-mail: clinicalcardiology@fams.org
URL: http://www.clinicalcardiology.org

Monthly. $80.00/year; $126.50/year for other countries. Peer-reviewed indexed medical journal.

★8749★ Clinical Pediatrics

Westminster Publications Inc.
708 Glen Cove Ave.
Glen Head, NY 11545
Ph: (516)759-0025   Fax: (516)759-5524
URL: http://www.westminsterpublications.com

$171.00/year for individuals; $196.00/year for other countries; $297.00/year for institutions; $325.00/year for institutions, other countries. Professional journal for pediatric practitioners.

★8750★ Clinical Psychiatry News

International Medical News Group
60 Columbia Rd., Bldg. B
Morristown, NJ 07960
Ph: (973)290-8200   Fax: (973)290-8245
E-mail: cpnews@imng.com

Monthly. $60.00/year. Medical and psychiatry tabloid.

★8751★ Contemporary OB/GYN

Thomson Medical Economics
5 Paragon Dr.
Montvale, NJ 07645-1742
Ph: (201)358-7200   Fax: (201)722-2680
URL: http://www.medec.com/html/products/productdetail/obgyn_mag.h

$99.00/year for individuals; $127.00/year for other countries; $127.00/year for Canada Magazine covering clinical, investigative, and socioeconomic aspects of obstetrics and gynecology for specialists.

★8752★ Contemporary Pediatrics

Thomson Medical Economics
5 Paragon Dr.
Montvale, NJ 07645-1742
Ph: (201)358-7200   Fax: (201)722-2680

URL: http://www.medec.com/html/products/productdetail/cp_mag.html

Monthly. $89.00/year for individuals; $105.00/year for other countries; $105.00/year for Canada. Journal to help pediatricians diagnose, treat, and prevent illness in infants, children, adolescents, and young adults.

★8753★ **Contemporary Urology**
Thomson Medical Economics
5 Paragon Dr.
Montvale, NJ 07645-1742
Ph: (201)358-7200   Fax: (201)722-2680
URL: http://www.medec.com/html/products/productdetail/urology.htm

$99.00/year for individuals; $126.00/year for other countries; $126.00/year for Canada. Clinical magazine for urologists.

★8754★ **Critical Care Medicine**
Lippincott Williams & Wilkins
530 Walnut St.
Philadelphia, PA 19106
Ph: (215)521-8300   Fax: (215)521-8902
Fr: 800-638-3030
E-mail: jewers@lww.com
URL: http://www.ccmjournal.com/

Monthly. $244.00/year for individuals; $379.00/year for institutions; $451.00/year for institutions, other countries; $315.00/year for out of country. Interdisciplinary journal for ICU and CCU specialists.

★8755★ **Current Surgery**
Lippincott Williams & Wilkins
530 Walnut St.
Philadelphia, PA 19106
Ph: (215)521-8300   Fax: (215)521-8902
Fr: 800-638-3030

Professional journal covering continuing education for surgical residents and general surgeons.

★8756★ **Diabetes**
Washington University School of Medicine
660 S Euclid Ave.
PO Box 8127
St. Louis, MO 63110
Ph: (314)454-8702

Monthly. $100.00/year for individuals. Magazine containing original research about diabetes.

★8757★ **Diagnostic Imaging**
CMP Media L.L.C.
600 Community Dr.
Manhasset, NY 11030
Ph: (516)562-5000
E-mail: mtoledo@cmp.com
URL: http://www.mfi.com

Monthly. $109.00/year for individuals; $125.00/year for other countries. News and analysis on clinical and economic developments in medical imaging.

★8758★ **Dialysis & Transplantation**
Creative Age Publications Inc.
7628 Densmore Ave.
Van Nuys, CA 91406-2042
Ph: (818)782-7328   Fax: (818)782-7450
Fr: 800-442-5667
URL: http://www.eneph.com

Monthly. $35.00/year for individuals; $105.00/year for other countries. Multi-disciplinary, peer-reviewed journal on clinical applications in dialysis, transplantation and nephrology for renal-care team.

★8759★ **Diseases of the Colon and Rectum**
Lippincott Williams & Wilkins
530 Walnut St.
Philadelphia, PA 19106
Ph: (215)521-8300   Fax: (215)521-8902
Fr: 800-638-3030
E-mail: oldenburg.patricia@mayo.edu
URL: http://www.discolrect.com/

Monthly. $294.00/year for individuals; $351.00/year for other countries; $429.00/year for institutions; $487.00/year for institutions, other countries. Medical journal.

★8760★ **The DO**
American Osteopathic Association
142 E Ontario St.
Chicago, IL 60611
Ph: (312)202-8000   Fax: (312)202-8200
Fr: 800-621-1773

Monthly. $65.00/year by mail. Osteopathic medical magazine.

★8761★ **Ear, Nose & Throat Journal**
MEDQUEST Communications L.L.C.
3800 Lakeside Ave. E, Ste. 201
Cleveland, OH 44114-3857
Ph: (216)522-9700   Fax: (216)391-9200
URL: http://www.entjournal.com

Monthly. $175.00/year for individuals; $88.00/year for students; $200.00/year for Canada and Mexico; $210.00/year for other countries; $210.00/year for institutions; $225.00/year for institutions, Canada and Mexico; $253.00/year for institutions, other countries; $20.00 for single issue. Journal on otorhinolaryugology, head and neck surgery, and allergies.

★8762★ **Emergency Medical Services**
Summer Communications Inc.
7626 Densmore Ave.
Van Nuys, CA 91406-2042
Ph: (818)786-4367   Fax: (818)786-9246
Fr: 800-224-4367
E-mail: emsmag@earthlink.net
URL: http://www.emsmagazine.com

Monthly. $19.95/year for individuals. Magazine covering emergency care, rescue and transportation.

★8763★ **Family Practice Management**
American Academy of Family Physicians
11400 Tomahawk Creek Pkwy.
Leawood, KS 66211
Ph: (913)906-6000   Fax: (913)906-6080
Fr: 800-274-2237
E-mail: fpmedit@aafp.org
URL: http://www.aafp.org/fpm

$48.00/year for individuals; $68.00/year for other countries; $6.00/year for single issue; $8.00/year for single issue, other countries. Magazine covering socio-economic and management topics concerning family physicians.

★8764★ **Family Practice News**
International Medical News Group
60 Columbia Rd., Bldg. B
Morristown, NJ 07960
Ph: (973)290-8200   Fax: (973)290-8245
E-mail: fpnews@imng.com
URL: http://www.efamilypracticenews.com

$105.00/year. Family physician medical tabloid.

★8765★ **The Federal Physician**
Federal Physicians Association
PO Box 45150
Washington, DC 20026
Ph: (703)426-8100   Fax: (703)426-8400
Fr: 800-403-3374

Description: Bimonthly. Covers issues affecting physicians in the federal government. Recurring features include news of research, reports of meetings, and job listings.

★8766★ **Fertility and Sterility**
The American Society for Productive Medicine
1209 Montgomery Hwy.
Birmingham, AL 35216
Ph: (205)978-5000   Fax: (205)978-5005

Monthly. $110.00/year for individuals; $175.00/year for institutions. Medical journal covering all aspects of reproductive medicine.

★8767★ **Gynecologic Oncology**
Academic Press
525 B St., Ste. 1900
San Diego, CA 92101-4495
Ph: (619)231-6616   Fax: (619)699-6715
Fr: 800-321-5068
E-mail: usinfo-f@elsevier.com

$2,010.00/year for institutions; $351.00/year for individuals; $57.00/year for students. Journal dedicated to publishing clinical and investigative articles concerning tumors of the female reproductive tract.

★8768★ **Head & Neck Surgery**
John Wiley and Sons Inc.
111 River St.
Hoboken, NJ 07030
Ph: (201)748-8866   Fax: (201)748-8824

Monthly. $995.00/year for U.S.; $1,115.00/year for Canada and Mexico; $1,217.00/year for other countries. International, multidisciplinary publication of original contributions concerning diagnosis and surgical management of diseases of the head and neck. Publishes articles of interest to several medical and surgical specialists including general surgeons, neurosurgeons, otolaryngologists, and plastic surgeons.

★8769★ Health Care Weekly Review

The Martin Group Inc.
24901 Northwestern Hwy., Ste. 316A
Southfield, MI 48075
Ph: (248)440-6080   Fax: (248)352-4801
E-mail: hcwr@compuserve.com

Weekly. $48.00/year for individuals. Professional newspaper covering the health care industry.

★8770★ Heart and Lung

Mosby Inc.
Curtis Ctr., 3rd Fl.
170 S. Independence Mall W
Philadelphia, PA 19106-3399
Ph: (215)238-7800
URL: http://www.mosby.com/hrtlng

Bimonthly. $66.00/year for individuals; $217.00/year for institutions. Journal offering articles prepared by nurse and physician members of the critical care team, recognizing the nurse's role in the care and management of major organ-system conditions in critically ill patients.

★8771★ Hospitals & Health Networks

Health Forum L.L.C.
One N Franklin
Chicago, IL 60606
Ph: (312)893-6800   Fax: (312)422-4600
Fr: 800-621-6902
E-mail: hhn@healthforum.com
URL: http://www.hhnmag.com

Monthly. Publication covering the health care industry.

★8772★ Infectious Disease News

SLACK Inc.
6900 Grove Rd.
Thorofare, NJ 08086-9447
Ph: (856)848-1000   Fax: (856)853-5991
Fr: 800-257-8290
E-mail: idn@slackinc.com
URL: http://www.slackinc.com/ssl/idn/idnsub.asp

Monthly. $179.00/year for individuals; $339.00/year for institutions. Newspaper for infectious disease specialists.

★8773★ Infectious Diseases in Children

SLACK Inc.
6900 Grove Rd.
Thorofare, NJ 08086-9447
Ph: (856)848-1000   Fax: (856)853-5991
Fr: 800-257-8290
E-mail: idc@slackinc.com
URL: http://www.idinchildren.com/

Monthly. $179.00/year for individuals; $339.00/year for institutions. Newspapers for physician.

★8774★ The Journal of Allergy and Clinical Immunology

Mosby Inc.
11830 Westline Industrial Dr.
St. Louis, MO 63146
Ph: (314)872-8370   Fax: (314)432-1380
Fr: 800-325-4177
URL: http://www.mosby.com/jaci

Monthly. $195.00/year for individuals; $414.00/year for institutions; $97.00/year for students; $250.00/year for individuals, out of country; $470.00/year for institutions, other countries; $126.00/year for students, other countries. Journal for clinical allergists and immunologists, as well as dermatologists, internists, general practitioners, pediatricians, and otolaryngologists (ENT physicians) concerned with clinical manifestations of allergies in their practice.

★8775★ Journal of the American Academy of Child and Adolescent Psychiatry

Lippincott Williams & Wilkins
530 Walnut St.
Philadelphia, PA 19106
Ph: (215)521-8300   Fax: (215)521-8902
Fr: 800-638-3030
E-mail: swilloughby@jaacap.org
URL: http://www.jaacap.com/

Monthly. $151.00/year for individuals; $195.00/year for out of country; $260.00/year for institutions; $304.00/year for institutions. Child psychiatry journal.

★8776★ Journal of the American Academy of Dermatology

Mosby Inc.
11830 Westline Industrial Dr.
St. Louis, MO 63146
Ph: (314)872-8370   Fax: (314)432-1380
Fr: 800-325-4177
URL: http://www.elsevier.com

Monthly. $222.00/year for individuals; $432.00/year for institutions; $112.00/year for students; $270.00/year for individuals, other countries; $480.00/year for institutions, other countries; $134.00/year for students, other countries. Journal for dermatologists and for family practitioners, pediatricians, and internists who are concerned with clinical manifestations of skin disease in their practice.

★8777★ Journal of the American College of Surgeons

Elsevier Science Inc.
360 Park Ave. S, No. 11
New York, NY 10010-1710
Ph: (212)989-5800   Fax: (212)633-3965
Fr: 888-437-4636
URL: http://www.elsevier.com/inca/publications/store/6/0/0/6/2/3/

Monthly. $55.00/year for members, USA residents; $144.00/year for nonmembers, residents for all countries except Europe and Japan; $165.00/year for institutions, U.S. and Canada; $436.00/year for institutions, all countries except USA, Europe and Japan; $241.00/year for institutions, USA; $243.00/year for individuals, all countries except USA, Europe and Japan; $149.00/year for individuals, USA. Journal covering general surgery, surgical specialties, and experimental surgery.

★8778★ Journal of the American Medical Women's Association

American Medical Women's Association
Eastern Virginia Medical School
825 Fairfax Ave.
Norfolk, VA 23507-1912
Ph: (757)446-7468   Fax: (757)446-7442
E-mail: jamwa@amwa-doc.org
URL: http://www.jamwa.org

Quarterly. $70.00/year; $80.00/year for out of country; $20.00 for single issue. Medical journal.

★8779★ Journal of the American Osteopathic Association

American Osteopathic Association
142 E Ontario St.
Chicago, IL 60611
Ph: (312)202-8000   Fax: (312)202-8200
Fr: 800-621-1773
URL: http://www.aoa-net.org

Monthly. Free to qualified subscribers; $50.00/year for institutions. Osteopathic clinical journal.

★8780★ Journal of the American Society of Echocardiography

Mosby
The Curtis Ctr., 3rd Fl.
Independence Sq. W
Philadelphia, PA 19106-3399
Ph: (215)235-7800   Fax: (215)238-7883
Fr: 800-523-1649
URL: http://www.mosby.com/echo

Monthly. $180.00/year for individuals; $253.00/year for institutions; $90.00/year for students; $228.00/year for individuals, out of country; $301.00/year for institutions, out of country; $114.00/year for students, out of country. Official journal of the American Society of Echocardiography serving as a source of information on the technical basis and clinical application of echocardiography. Peer-reviewed publication featuring research, reviews, and case studies.

★8781★ Journal of the American Society of Podiatric Medical Assistants

American Society of Podiatric Medical Assistants
2124 S Austin Blvd.
Cicero, IL 60804
Ph: (708)863-6303   Fax: (708)863-5375
Fr: 888-88A-SPMA

Quarterly. Subscription included in membership. Professional journal covering issues in podiatry.

★8782★ Journal of Clinical Psychiatry
Physicians Postgraduate Press Inc.
PO Box 752870
Memphis, TN 38175
Fax: (901)751-3444   Fr: 800-489-1001
E-mail: jclinpsych@aol.com
URL: http://www.psychiatrist.com

Monthly. $89.00/year. Journal containing original papers about practical and clinical psychiatry.

★8783★ Journal of Health and Hospital Law
American Health Lawyers Association
1025 Connecticut NW, Ste. 600
Washington, DC 20036
Ph: (202)833-1100   Fax: (202)833-1105

Quarterly. $150.00/year. Professional journal covering healthcare issues and cases and their impact on the health care arena.

★8784★ Journal of Intensive Care Medicine
Sage Publications Inc.
2455 Teller Rd.
Thousand Oaks, CA 91320
Ph: (805)499-0721   Fax: (805)499-0871
Fr: 800-818-SAGE
E-mail: advertising@sagepub.com
URL: http://www.sagepub.com/journal.aspx?pid=340

Bimonthly. $198.00/year for individuals; $198.00/year for out of country; $520.00/year for institutions; $520.00/year for institutions, other countries. Medical journal for specialists working in intensive care units.

★8785★ Journal of the National Medical Association
National Medical Association
1012 10th St. NW
Washington, DC 20001
Ph: (202)347-1895   Fax: (202)207-1555
URL: http://www.nmanet.org

Monthly. $116.00/year for individuals; $155.00/year for institutions; $16.00 for single issue. Journal on specialized clinical research related to the health problems of African-Americans and other minorities. Recognizes significant contributions by black physicians and others involved with minority health issues and health disparities.

★8786★ Journal of Occupational and Environmental Medicine
Lippincott Williams & Wilkins
530 Walnut St.
Philadelphia, PA 19106
Ph: (215)521-8300   Fax: (215)521-8902
Fr: 800-638-3030
URL: http://www.joem.org

Monthly. $250.00/year for individuals; $318.00/year for institutions; $32.00 for single issue; $319.00/year for other countries;

$387.00/year for institutions, other countries; $32.00 for single issue, other countries. Occupational and environmental medicine journal.

★8787★ Journal of Pediatric Hematology/Oncology
Lippincott Williams & Wilkins
351 W Camden St.
Baltimore, MD 21201
Ph: (410)528-8517   Fax: (410)528-4312
Fr: 800-638-3030
URL: http://www.jpho-online.com/

Monthly. $312.00/year for individuals; $509.00/year for institutions; $372.00/year for other countries; $589.00/year for institutions, other countries. Journal containing reports on major advances in the diagnosis and treatment of cancer and blood diseases in children.

★8788★ The Journal of Pediatrics
Mosby Inc.
11830 Westline Industrial Dr.
St. Louis, MO 63146
Ph: (314)872-8370   Fax: (314)432-1380
Fr: 800-325-4177

Monthly. $160.00/year for individuals; $197.00/year for other countries; $406.00/year for institutions; $442.00/year for institutions, other countries. Journal for physicians who diagnose and treat disorders in infants and children.

★8789★ Journal of Trauma
Lippincott Williams & Wilkins
530 Walnut St.
Philadelphia, PA 19106
Ph: (215)521-8300   Fax: (215)521-8902
Fr: 800-638-3030
E-mail: jtrauma@uthscsa.edu
URL: http://www.jtrauma.com

Monthly. $296.00/year for individuals; $377.00/year for other countries; $391.00/year for institutions; $472.00/year for institutions, other countries. Surgery journal.

★8790★ Journal of Urology
Lippincott Williams & Wilkins
530 Walnut St.
Philadelphia, PA 19106
Ph: (215)521-8300   Fax: (215)521-8902
Fr: 800-638-3030
E-mail: mguire@lww.com
URL: http://www.jurology.com/

$504.00/year for individuals; $556.00/year for institutions; $726.00/year for institutions, other countries. Medical journal.

★8791★ Journal of Vascular Surgery
Mosby Inc.
360 Park Ave. S
New York, NY 10010
Fax: (212)633-3913
URL: http://www.mosby.com

Monthly. $224.00/year for individuals; $432.00/year for institutions; $112.00/year

for students; $268.00/year for individuals, out of country; $478.00/year for institutions, other countries; $134.00/year for students, other countries. Journal providing a forum for the advances in knowledge of the peripheral vascular system. Publishes peer-reviewed original articles on all aspects of disease and injury to the arterial and venous systems.

★8792★ Laboratory Medicine
American Society of Clinical Pathologists
2100 W Harrison St.
Chicago, IL 60612
Ph: (312)738-1336   Fax: (312)738-0101
URL: http://www.asep.org

Monthly. $50.00/year for individuals; $8.00 for single issue. Professional journal covering medical technology and pathology.

★8793★ The Lancet (North American Edition)
Lippincott Williams & Wilkins
530 Walnut St.
Philadelphia, PA 19106
Ph: (215)521-8300   Fax: (215)521-8902
Fr: 800-638-3030

Weekly. $98.00/year for individuals. Medical journal. Contents identical to British edition.

★8794★ Medical Economics
Thomson Medical Economics
5 Paragon Dr.
Montvale, NJ 07645-1742
Ph: (201)358-7200   Fax: (201)722-2680
URL: http://www.medec.com/html/products/productdetail/me_mag.html

Semimonthly. $89.00/year for individuals; $175.00/year for Canada; $109.00/year for individuals outside the medical field. Magazine covering physicians practice management, professional relations, and financial affairs.

★8795★ Medical Society of Milwaukee County-Membership Newsletter
Medical Society of Milwaukee County
1126 S 70th St., Ste. S507
Milwaukee, WI 53214
Ph: (414)475-4750   Fax: (414)475-4799
URL: http://www.district-1.org

Description: Monthly. Serves as an informational newsletter for physicians. Contains IOCU medical business notes and practice announcements. Recurring features include letters to the editor, a calendar of events, reports of meetings, news of educational opportunities, job listings, and columns titled President's Letter.

★8796★ Medicine and Health
Thomson Financial
195 Broadway
New York, NY 10007
Ph: (646)822-2000

Weekly. Professional publication covering the health care industry.

★8797★ Military Medicine

Association of Military Surgeons of the
U.S. (AMSUS)
9320 Old Georgetown Rd.
Bethesda, MD 20814
Ph: (301)897-8800   Fax: (301)530-5446
Fr: 800-761-9320
E-mail: milmed@amsus.org

Monthly. $65.00/year for individuals; $70.00/
year for other countries; $6.00 for single
issue. Journal for professional personnel
affiliated with the Federal medical services.

★8798★ Minnesota Medicine

Minnesota Medical Association
1300 Godward St. NE, Ste. 2500
Minneapolis, MN 55413
Ph: (612)378-1875   Fax: (612)378-3875
Fr: 800-DIAL-MMA
E-mail: mm@mnmed.org

Monthly. $45.00/year for individuals; $5.00
for single issue; $80.00/year for out of
country. Magazine on medical, socioeconomic, public health, medical-legal, and biomedical ethics issues of interest to physicians.

★8799★ Minority Health Today

Heritage Information Holdings Inc.
1101 Pennsylvania Ave. NW, Ste. 820
Washington, DC 20001
Bimonthly. Publication covering minority issues in health.

★8800★ Neonatal Intensive Care

Goldstein & Associates
1150 Yale St., Ste. 12
Santa Monica, CA 90403
Ph: (310)828-1309

Bimonthly.

★8801★ Neuroscience Newsletter

Society for Neuroscience
11 Dupont Cir. NW, Ste. 500
Washington, DC 20036
Ph: (202)462-6688   Fax: (202)462-1574
URL: http://www.sfn.org/NL/current

Description: Bimonthly. Covers developments in neuroscience, with attention to
research findings and funding, education,
and interdisciplinary programs. Carries summaries or text of talks, papers, and of the
prepared testimony of the Society's representatives before congressional committees.
Recurring features include announcements
of meetings and symposia, reports of foreign
neuroscience societies, and Society news.

**★8802★ The New England Journal of
Medicine**

The New England Journal of Medicine
860 Winter St.
Waltham Woods Corporate Ctr.
Waltham, MA 02451-1441
Ph: (781)893-4610
E-mail: nejmcust@mms.org

URL: http://www.nejm.org
Weekly. $135.00/year for individuals. Jour-
nal for the medical profession.

★8803★ Ob Gyn News

International Medical News Group
60 Columbia Rd., Bldg. B
Morristown, NJ 07960
Ph: (973)290-8200   Fax: (973)290-8245
E-mail: obnews@imng.com

Semimonthly. Obstetrics and gynecology
tabloid distributed to obstetricians and gynecologists.

★8804★ Ocular Surgery News

SLACK Inc.
6900 Grove Rd.
Thorofare, NJ 08086-9447
Ph: (856)848-1000   Fax: (856)853-5991
Fr: 800-257-8290
E-mail: osn@slackinc.com
URL: http://www.osnsupersite.com

Semimonthly. $339.00/year for individuals;
$419.00/year for institutions; $29.00 for single issue. Medical newspaper for ophthalmologists. Covering scientific meetings and
events, with emphasis on cataract/IOL, glau-
coma treatment, refractive therapy, general
ophthalmic topics, and legislative/ regulatory
developments, and industry news.

★8805★ Oncology

S. Karger Publishers Inc.
26 W Avon Rd.
PO Box 529
Farmington, CT 06085
Ph: (860)675-7834   Fax: (860)675-7302
Fr: 800-828-5479

$1328.00/year for institutions, add $50.40
post/handling for foreign; $1434.00/year for
institutions, print and online combined;
$664.00/year for individuals, add $40.40
post/handling for foreign; $724.00/year for
individuals, print and online combined. Medical journal presenting experimental and clinical findings.

**★8806★ Ophthalmic Surgery Lasers
and Imaging**

SLACK Inc.
6900 Grove Rd.
Thorofare, NJ 08086-9447
Ph: (856)848-1000   Fax: (856)853-5991
Fr: 800-257-8290
E-mail: osl@opal.tufts.edu
URL: http://www.osli.com

Monthly. $66.00/year for individuals; $96.00/
year for institutions; $15.00/year for single
issue. Journal publishing articles on ophthalmic surgery, lasers, research, and clinical
approaches.

★8807★ Optometric Management

Boucher Communications Inc.
1300 Virginia Dr., Ste. 400
Fort Washington, PA 19034-3221
Ph: (215)643-8000   Fax: (215)643-8099

E-mail: om@boucher1.com

Monthly. $37.00/year for individuals; $59.00
for two years; $48.00/year for Canada;
$72.00 for two years-Canada; $85.00/year
for elsewhere. Medical professional journal.

★8808★ Orthopedics Today

SLACK Inc.
6900 Grove Rd.
Thorofare, NJ 08086-9447
Ph: (856)848-1000   Fax: (856)853-5991
Fr: 800-257-8290
E-mail: ortoday@slackinc.com
URL: http://www.slackinc.com/bone/orto-
day/othome.asp

Monthly. $179.00/year; $339.00/year for institutions. Newspaper covering orthopedic
meetings, courses, and symposia.

**★8809★ Otolaryngology-Head and
Neck Surgery**

Mosby Inc.
360 Park Ave. S
New York, NY 10010
Fax: (212)633-3913
URL: http://www.mosby.com

Monthly. $216.00/year for individuals;
$384.00/year for institutions; $108.00/year
for students; $258.00/year for individuals,
other countries; $426.00/year for institutions,
other countries; $130.00/year for students,
other countries. Medical journal comprising
peer-reviewed papers presented at the annual meeting of the American Academy of
Otolaryngolgy-Head and Neck Surgery.
Subjects covered include head and neck
surgical oncology, otologic surgery and neu-
ro-otology, rhinology, and rhinoplastic surgery.

★8810★ Patient Care

Thomson Medical Economics
5 Paragon Dr.
Montvale, NJ 07645-1742
Ph: (201)358-7200   Fax: (201)722-2680
URL: http://www.medec.com/html/products/
productdetail/pc_mag.html

$99.00/year for individuals; $124.00/year for
Canada; $124.00/year for other countries;
$46.00/year for students. Medical journal.

★8811★ Pediatric Annals

SLACK Inc.
6900 Grove Rd.
Thorofare, NJ 08086-9447
Ph: (856)848-1000   Fax: (856)853-5991
Fr: 800-257-8290
E-mail: customerservice@slackinc.com
URL: http://www.slackinc.com/child/pedann/
pedahome.htm

Monthly. $129.00/year; $189.00/year for institutions; $145.00/year. Scholarly journal.

★8812★ *Pediatric News*

International Medical News Group
60 Columbia Rd., Bldg. B
Morristown, NJ 07960
Ph: (973)290-8200   Fax: (973)290-8245
E-mail: pdnews@imng.com
URL: http://www.epediatricnews.com

Monthly. $80.00/year for U.S.; $110.00/year other countries. Tabloid covering pediatric medicine and distributed to pediatric ians.

★8813★ *Pediatrics*

American Academy of Pediatrics
141 NW Point Blvd.
Elk Grove Village, IL 60007-1098
Ph: (847)434-4000   Fax: (847)434-8000
Fr: 800-433-9016
E-mail: journals@aap.org

Monthly. $149.00/year for individuals; $169.00/year for other countries. Medical journal reporting on pediatrics.

★8814★ *Psychiatric Annals*

SLACK Inc.
6900 Grove Rd.
Thorofare, NJ 08086-9447
Ph: (856)848-1000   Fax: (856)853-5991
Fr: 800-257-8290
E-mail: idn@slackinc.com
URL: http://www.slackinc.com/general/psyann/psyahome.htm

Monthly. $129.00/year for individuals; $289.00/year for institutions. Journal analyzing concepts and practices in every area of psychiatry.

★8815★ *Psychiatric News*

American Psychiatric Publishing Inc.
1000 Wilson Blvd., Ste. 1825
Arlington, VA 22209
Ph: (703)907-7300   Fax: (703)907-1091
Fr: 800-368-5777
E-mail: pnews@psych.org
URL: http://www.psch.org/pnews/

Semimonthly. $40.00/year for individuals. Professional magazine of the American Psychiatric Assn.

★8816★ *Psychiatric Services*

Association of Partners for Public Lands
2401 Blueridge Ave., Ste. 303
Wheaton, MD 20902-4517
Ph: (301)946-9475   Fax: (301)946-9478
URL: http://www.appl.org/psjournal

Monthly. Interdisciplinary mental health journal covering clinical, legal, and public policy issues.

★8817★ *The Psychiatric Times*

CME Inc.
2801 McGaw Ave.
Irvine, CA 92614-5835
Ph: (949)250-1008   Fr: 800-933-2632
URL: http://www.psychiatrictimes.com/

Monthly. Newspaper (tabloid) on psychiatric disorders and issues.

★8818★ *Research in Healthcare Financial Management*

International Society for Research in Healthcare Financial Management Ltd.
305 W Chesapeake Ave.
CSBA Ste. L-096
Towson, MD 21204

Annual. Publication covering issues in the healthcare industry.

★8819★ *Resident & Staff Physician*

Romaine Pierson Publishers Inc.
241 Forsgate Dr.
Jamesburg, NJ 08831
Ph: (732)656-0200   Fax: (732)656-1142

Monthly. $62.00/year for individuals. Medical journal.

★8820★ *RETINA*

Lippincott Williams & Wilkins
530 Walnut St.
Philadelphia, PA 19106-3621
Ph: (215)521-8300   Fax: (215)521-8483
URL: http://www.retinajournal.com

Bimonthly. $159.00/year for individuals; $307.00/year for institutions; $60.00 for single issue, current and back issues. Journal publishing clinically oriented articles for the general ophthalmologist and vitreoretinal specialist.

★8821★ *Seminars in Oncology*

Elsevier Science Inc.
The Curtis Ctr.
170 Independence Mall W, 300F
Philadelphia, PA 19106-3399
Ph: (215)238-7800   Fax: (215)238-7883
Fr: 800-523-1649
E-mail: elspcs@elsevier.com

$199.00/year for individuals; $318.00/year for institutions; $295.00/year for other countries; $382.00/year for institutions, other countries; $100.00/year for students, US students and residents; $64.00 for single issue. Journal reviewing current diagnostic and treatment techniques used in oncology patient care.

★8822★ *Skin & Allergy News*

International Medical News Group
60 Columbia Rd., Bldg. B
Morristown, NJ 07960
Ph: (973)290-8200   Fax: (973)290-8245
E-mail: sknews@imng.com

Monthly. $70.00/year. Dermatology/allergy tabloid.

★8823★ *Southern Medical Journal*

Southern Medical Association
35 Lakeshore Dr.
PO Box 190088
Birmingham, AL 35219-0088
Ph: (205)945-1840   Fax: (205)945-1830
Fr: 800-423-4992
E-mail: smj@sma.org

URL: http://www.sma.org/smj/index.cfm
Monthly. Multispecialty medical journal.

★8824★ *State Health Monitor*

Atlantic Information Services Inc.
1100 17th St. NW, No. 300
Washington, DC 20036
Ph: (202)775-9008   Fax: (202)331-9542
Fr: 800-521-4323
E-mail: customerserv@aispub.com

Monthly. Publication covering health care.

★8825★ *Stethoscope*

National Association of Residents and Interns (NARI)
Hillsboro Executive Ctr. N
350 Fairway Dr., Ste. 200
Deerfield Beach, FL 33441-1834
Ph: (954)571-1877   Fax: (954)571-8582

Description: Semiannual. Provides current information on the financial and practice management aspects of medical and dental practices. "Focuses on the economic, tax, investment, and career concerns of the young doctor." Recurring features include Association news and news of research.

★8826★ *Surgical Rounds*

Romaine Pierson Publishers Inc.
241 Forsgate Dr.
Jamesburg, NJ 08831
Ph: (732)656-0200   Fax: (732)656-1142

Monthly. Free to qualified subscribers; $76.00/year for individuals. Journal featuring clinical articles of interest to office-based and hospital-based surgeons, including residents, full-time staff, and surgical faculty.

★8827★ *Trauma Reports*

Thomson Medical Economics
5 Paragon Dr.
Montvale, NJ 07645-1742
Ph: (201)358-7200   Fax: (201)722-2680
URL: http://www.ahcpub.com/ahc_root_html/products/newsletters/tr.

Bimonthly. $239.00/year for individuals. Professional publication covering health care.

PLACEMENT AND JOB REFERRAL SERVICES

★8828★ **American Academy of Dermatology (AAD)**

PO Box 4014
Schaumburg, IL 60168-4014
Ph: (847)330-0230   Fax: (847)330-0050
Fr: 888-462-DERM
E-mail: memsrv@aad.org
URL: http://www.aad.org

Description: Professional society of medical doctors specializing in skin diseases. Provides educational opportunities through meetings and publications. Provides support to members' practices. Promotes dermatologists as experts in treating skin, hair, and nail conditions. Maintains liaison with Congress, Federal agencies, State legislatures and State agencies.

★8829★ American Academy of Neurology (AAN)

1080 Montreal Ave.
St. Paul, MN 55116-2325
Ph: (651)695-2717   Fax: (651)695-2791
Fr: 800-879-1960
E-mail: memberservices@aan.com
URL: http://www.aan.com

Description: Professional society of medical doctors specializing in brain and nervous system diseases. Maintains placement service. Sponsors research and educational programs. Compiles statistics. Publishes scientific journal.

★8830★ American Academy of Tropical Medicine (AATM)

PO Box 24224
Detroit, MI 48224
Ph: (313)882-0641   Fax: (313)882-0979

Members: Physicians and allied health professionals interested in tropical medicine. **Purpose:** Provides postgraduate continuing medical education; confers certificates and diplomas. **Activities:** Maintains speakers' bureau; provides placement service. Conducts research and compiles statistics. Conducts educational programs; offers children's services.

★8831★ American Association of Certified Orthoptists (AACO)

5733 Toronto Dr.
Sterling Heights, MI 48314
Ph: (586)739-2062   Fax: (319)384-9831
E-mail: orthoptics@att.net
URL: http://www.orthoptics.org

Members: Orthoptists certified by the American Orthoptic Council, after completing a minimum of 24 months' special training, to treat defects in binocular function. **Activities:** Assists in postgraduate instruction courses; conducts programs and courses at international, national, and regional meetings; helps individual orthoptists with special or unusual problem cases; trains new orthoptists. Operates a placement listing.

★8832★ American Association for Geriatric Psychiatry (AAGP)

7910 Woodmont Ave., Ste. 1050
Bethesda, MD 20814-3004
Ph: (301)654-7850   Fax: (301)654-4137
E-mail: main@aagponline.org
URL: http://www.aagpgpa.org

Description: Psychiatrists interested in promoting better mental health care for the elderly. Maintains placement service and speakers' bureau.

★8833★ American Association of Neuropathologists (AANP)

Institute of Pathology
Case Western Reserve University
2095 Adelbert Rd.
Cleveland, OH 44106
Ph: (216)368-2488   Fax: (216)368-8964
E-mail: aanp@cwru.edu
URL: http://www.aanp-jnen.com

Description: Promotes neuropathology, especially the study of diverse aspects of diseases of the nervous system including changes at tissue, cellular, subcellular, and molecular levels with consideration of etiology and pathophysiology, genetics, epidemiology and clinical manifestations of such diseases.

★8834★ American College of Chest Physicians (ACCP)

3300 Dundee Rd.
Northbrook, IL 60062
Ph: (847)498-1400   Fax: (847)498-5460
Fr: 800-343-ACCP
E-mail: accp@chestnet.org
URL: http://www.chestnet.org

Description: Professional society of physicians and surgeons specializing in diseases of the chest (heart and lungs). Promotes undergraduate and postgraduate medical education and research in the field. Sponsors forums. Maintains placement service; conducts educational programs.

★8835★ American College Health Association (ACHA)

PO Box 28937
Baltimore, MD 21240-8937
Ph: (410)859-1500   Fax: (410)859-1510
E-mail: pcrone@acha.org
URL: http://www.acha.org

Members: Institutions (930) and individuals (2500). **Purpose:** Provides an organization in which institutions of higher education and interested individuals may work together to promote health in its broadest aspects for students and all other members of the college community. **Activities:** Offers continuing education programs for health professionals. Maintains placement listings for physicians and other personnel seeking positions in college health. Compiles statistics. Conducts seminars and training programs.

★8836★ American College of Medical Quality (ACMQ)

4334 Montgomery Ave.
Bethesda, MD 20814
Ph: (301)913-9149   Fax: (301)913-9142
Fr: 800-924-2149
E-mail: ACMQ@acmq.org
URL: http://www.acmq.org

Members: Physicians, affiliates, and institutions. **Purpose:** Seeks to educate and set standards of competence in the field of quality improvement and management. Offers a core curriculum in quality. Maintains speakers' bureau.

★8837★ American College of Occupational and Environmental Medicine (ACOEM)

1114 N Arlington Hts. Rd.
Arlington Heights, IL 60004-4770
Ph: (847)818-1800   Fax: (847)818-9266
E-mail: acoeminfo@acoem.org
URL: http://www.acoem.org

Description: Physicians specializing in occupational and environmental medicine. Promotes maintenance and improvement of the health of workers; works to increase awareness of occupational medicine as a medical specialty. Sponsors educational programs; maintains placement service.

★8838★ American College of Osteopathic Internists (ACOI)

3 Bethesda Metro Ctr., Ste.508
Bethesda, MD 20814
Ph: (301)656-8877   Fax: (301)656-7133
Fr: 800-327-5183
E-mail: bjd@acoi.org
URL: http://www.acoi.org

Description: Osteopathic doctors who limit their practice to internal medicine and various subspecialties and who intend, through postdoctoral education, to qualify as certified specialists in the field. Aims to provide educational programs and to improve educational standards in the field of osteopathic internal medicine. Sponsors competitions. Compiles statistics; offers placement service.

★8839★ American College of Osteopathic Surgeons (ACOS)

123 N Henry St.
Alexandria, VA 22314-2903
Ph: (703)684-0416   Fax: (703)684-3280
E-mail: info@theacos.org
URL: http://www.facos.org

Members: Professional society of osteopathic physicians specializing in surgery and surgical specialties. **Purpose:** Maintains placement service; conducts seminars in continuing surgical education.

★8840★ American College of Physician Executives (ACPE)

4890 W Kennedy Blvd., Ste. 200
Tampa, FL 33609
Ph: (813)287-2000   Fax: (813)287-8993
Fr: 800-562-8088
E-mail: acpe@acpe.org
URL: http://www.acpe.org

Description: Physicians whose primary professional responsibility is the management of health care organizations. Provides for continuing education and certification of the physician executive and the advancement and recognition of the physician executive and the profession. Offers specialized career planning, counseling, recruitment and placement services, and research and information data on physician managers.

★8841★ American Gastroenterological Association (AGA)

4930 Del Ray Ave.
Bethesda, MD 20814
Ph: (301)654-2055   Fax: (301)654-5920
E-mail: info@gastro.org
URL: http://www.gastro.org

Description: Physicians of internal medicine certified in gastroenterology; radiologists, pathologists, surgeons, and physiologists with special interest and competency in gastroenterology. Studies normal and abnormal conditions of the digestive organs and problems connected with their metabolism; conducts scientific research; offers placement services.

★8842★ American Health Quality Association (AHQA)

1140 Conneticut Ave. NW, Ste. 1050
Washington, DC 20036
Ph: (202)331-5790   Fax: (202)331-9334
E-mail: info@ahqa.org
URL: http://www.ahqa.org

Description: Institutions and individuals. Purpose is to develop communications programs for physicians, institutions, and others interested in peer review organizations (PROs). Provides a national forum for the interchange of ideas, techniques, and information relating to medical quality assessment. Conducts courses and on-site educational programs to increase physicians' involvement and leadership in PROs, improve practice patterns through review, understand and use PRO data to improve service delivery, pre-admission review, profile analysis, retrospective review, and organizational development. Sponsors placement service; maintains a speakers' bureau and a library.

★8843★ American Medical Association (AMA)

515 N State St.
Chicago, IL 60610
Ph: (312)464-5000   Fax: (312)464-4184
Fr: 800-621-8335
URL: http://www.ama-assn.org/

Description: County medical societies and physicians. Disseminates scientific information to members and the public. Informs members on significant medical and health legislation on state and national levels and represents the profession before Congress and governmental agencies. Cooperates in setting standards for medical schools, hospitals, residency programs, and continuing medical education courses. Offers physician placement service and counseling on practice management problems. Operates library which lends material and provides specific medical information to physicians. Ad-hoc committees are formed for such topics as health care planning and principles of medical ethics.

★8844★ American Osteopathic Association (AOA)

142 E. Ontario St.
Chicago, IL 60611
Ph: (312)202-8000   Fax: (312)202-8200
Fr: 800-621-1773
E-mail: info@aoa-net.org
URL: http://www.aoa-net.org

Description: Osteopathic physicians, surgeons, and graduates of approved colleges of osteopathic medicine. Associate members include teaching, research, administrative, and executive employees of approved colleges, hospitals, divisional societies, and affiliated organizations. Forms (with its affiliates) an officially recognized structure of the osteopathic profession. Promotes the public health, to encourage scientific research, and to maintain and improve high standards of medical education in osteopathic colleges. Inspects and accredits colleges and hospitals; conducts a specialty certification program; sponsors a national examining board satisfactory to state licensing agencies; maintains mandatory program of continuing medical education for members. Compiles statistics on location and type of practice of osteopathic physicians. Sponsors research activities through Bureau of Research in osteopathic colleges and hospitals. Maintains Physician Placement Service. Produces public service radio and television programs; maintains 2000 item library and biographical archives on osteopathic medicine and history. Offers speakers' bureau.

★8845★ American Public Health Association (APHA)

800 I St. NW
Washington, DC 20001-3710
Ph: (202)777-2742   Fax: (202)777-2534
E-mail: comments@apha.org
URL: http://www.apha.org

Members: Professional organization of physicians, nurses, educators, academicians, environmentalists, epidemiologists, new professionals, social workers, health administrators, optometrists, podiatrists, pharmacists, dentists, nutritionists, health planners, other community and mental health specialists, and interested consumers. **Purpose:** Seeks to protect and promote personal, mental, and environmental health. **Activities:** Services include promulgation of standards; establishment of uniform practices and procedures; development of the etiology of communicable diseases; research in public health; exploration of medical care programs and their relationships to public health. Sponsors job placement service.

★8846★ American Society of Anesthesiologists (ASA)

520 N Northwest Hwy.
Park Ridge, IL 60068-2573
Ph: (847)825-5586   Fax: (847)825-1692
E-mail: mail@asahq.org
URL: http://www.asahq.org

Members: Professional society of physicians specializing or interested in anesthesiology. **Purpose:** Seeks "to develop and further the specialty of anesthesiology for the general elevation of the standards of medical practice." Encourages education, research, and scientific progress in anesthesiology. **Activities:** Conducts refresher courses and other postgraduate educational activities. Maintains placement service.

★8847★ American Society of Colon and Rectal Surgeons (ASCRS)

85 W Alqonquin Rd., Ste. 550
Arlington Heights, IL 60005
Ph: (847)290-9184   Fax: (847)290-9203
E-mail: ascrs@ascrs.org
URL: http://www.fascrs.org/

Description: Professional society of surgeons specializing in the diagnosis and treatment of diseases of the colon, rectum, and anus. Offers placement service; conducts research programs.

★8848★ American Society of Handicapped Physicians (ASHP)

PO Box S. Culpepper Ct.
Springfield, MO 65804
Fax: (417)887-9830

Description: Handicapped physicians and others concerned with the problems faced by handicapped physicians. Acts as a forum to address the needs of physically disabled physicians. Works against discrimination of the handicapped and serves as a support group and legal and career counselor. Disseminates information about resources for handicapped physicians. Plans to offer rehabilitation services. Maintains speakers' bureau and placement service; compiles statistics; offers specialized education. Founded by the late Spencer B. Lewis, M.D. and Terry Winkler, M.D.

★8849★ American Society for Histocompatibility and Immunogenetics (ASHI)

17000 Commerce Pky., Ste. C
Mount Laurel, NJ 08054
Ph: (856)638-0428   Fax: (856)439-0525
E-mail: info@ashi-hla.org
URL: http://www.ashi-hla.org

Members: Scientists, physicians, and technologists involved in research and clinical activities related to histocompatibility testing (a state of mutual tolerance that allows some tissues to be grafted effectively to others). **Activities:** Conducts proficiency testing and educational programs. Maintains liaison with regulatory agencies; offers placement services and laboratory accreditation. Has co-sponsored development of histocompatability specialist and laboratory certification program.

★8850★ American Society of Nephrology (ASN)

1725 I St. NW, Ste. 510
Washington, DC 20006
Ph: (202)659-0599   Fax: (202)659-0709
E-mail: email@asn-online.org
URL: http://www.asn-online.org/

Members: Nephrologists united for the exchange of scientific information. **Purpose:** Seeks to contribute to the education of members and to improve the quality of patient care. **Activities:** Conducts educational courses. Maintains placement service.

★8851★ American Society for Reproductive Medicine (ASRM)

1209 Montgomery Hwy.
Birmingham, AL 35216-2809
Ph: (205)978-5000   Fax: (205)978-5005
E-mail: asrm@asrm.org
URL: http://www.asrm.com/

Description: Gynecologists, obstetricians, urologists, reproductive endocrinologists, veterinarians, research workers, and others interested in reproductive health in humans and animals. Seeks to extend knowledge of all aspects of fertility and problems of infertility and mammalian reproduction; provides a rostrum for the presentation of scientific studies dealing with these subjects. Offers patient resource information and placement service.

★8852★ Association for Academic Surgery (AAS)

60 Revere Dr., Ste. 500
Northbrook, IL 60062
Ph: (847)509-1945   Fax: (847)480-9282
E-mail: lfeyn@aasurg.org
URL: http://www.aasurg.org

Description: Active (700) and senior (1250) surgeons with backgrounds in all surgical specialties in academic surgical centers at chief resident level or above. Encourages young surgeons to pursue careers in academic surgery; supports them in establishing themselves as investigators and educators by providing a forum in which senior surgical residents and junior faculty members may present papers on subjects of clinical or laboratory investigations; promotes interchange of ideas between senior surgical residents, junior faculty, and established academic surgeons; facilitates communication among academic surgeons in all surgical fields. Maintains placement service. service. service.

★8853★ Association for the Advancement of Medical Instrumentation (AAMI)

1110 N Glebe Rd., No. 220
Arlington, VA 22201-4795
Ph: (703)525-4890   Fax: (703)525-1424
Fr: 800-332-2264
URL: http://www.aami.org

Description: Clinical engineers, biomedical equipment technicians, physicians, hospital administrators, consultants, engineers, manufacturers of medical devices, nurses researchers and others interested in medical instrumentation. Purpose is to improve the quality of medical care through the application, development, and management of technology. Maintains placement service. Offers certification programs for biomedical equipment technicians and clinical engineers. Produces numerous standards and recom-

mended practices on medical devices and procedures. Offers educational programs.

★8854★ Association for Research in Vision and Ophthalmology (ARVO)

12300 Twinbrook Pkwy., Ste. 250
Rockville, MD 20852-1606
Ph: (240)221-2900   Fax: (240)221-0370
E-mail: arvo@arvo.org
URL: http://www.arvo.org

Members: Professional society of researchers in vision and ophthalmology. **Purpose:** To encourage ophthalmic research in the field of blinding eye disease. **Activities:** Operates placement service. Maintains 13 scientific sections.

★8855★ Chinese American Medical Society (CAMS)

281 Edgewood Ave.
Teaneck, NJ 07666
Ph: (201)833-1506   Fax: (201)833-8252
E-mail: hw5@columbia.edu
URL: http://www.camsociety.org

Members: Physicians of Chinese origin residing in the U.S. and Canada. **Purpose:** Seeks to advance medical knowledge, scientific research, and interchange of information among members and to promote the health status of Chinese Americans. **Activities:** Conducts educational meetings; supports research. Maintains placement service. Sponsors limited charitable program.

★8856★ Clinical Ligand Assay Society (CLAS)

3139 S Wayne Rd.
Wayne, MI 48184
Ph: (734)722-6290   Fax: (734)722-7006
E-mail: clas@clas.org
URL: http://www.clas.org

Description: Seeks to establish and promote high standards in the science and application of ligand assay technology by encouraging research, education practitioners, and fostering communication and cooperation among individuals in laboratories in medicine, academia, and industry. Sponsors job placement service.

★8857★ College of American Pathologists (CAP)

325 Waukegan Rd.
Northfield, IL 60093-2750
Ph: (847)832-7000   Fax: (847)832-8000
Fr: 800-323-4040
URL: http://www.cap.org

Description: Physicians practicing the specialty of pathology (diagnosis, treatment, observation, and understanding of the progress of disease or medical condition) obtained by morphologic, microscopic, chemical, microbiologic, serologic, or any other type of laboratory examination made on the patient. Fosters improvement of education, research, and medical laboratory service to physicians, hospitals, and the public. Provides job placement information for members. Conducts laboratory accreditation pro-

gram and laboratory proficiency testing surveys. Maintains spokespersons network; provides free health information to the public; compiles statistics; sponsors educational programs.

★8858★ Congress of Neurological Surgeons (CNS)

10 N Martingale Rd., Ste. 190
Schaumburg, IL 60173
Ph: (847)240-2500   Fax: (847)240-0804
Fr: 877-517-1267
E-mail: info@1cns.org
URL: http://www.neurosurgeon.org

Description: Professional society of neurological surgeons in the United States and 55 other countries who meet annually to express their views on various aspects of the principles and practice of neurological surgery; to exchange technical information and experience; to join study of the developments in scientific fields allied to neurological surgery. Promotes interest of neurological surgeons in their practice; provides placement service; honors a living leader in the field of neurological surgery annually.

★8859★ Endocrine Society (ES)

8401 Connecticut Ave., Ste. 900
Chevy Chase, MD 20815-5817
Ph: (301)941-0200   Fax: (301)941-0259
E-mail: endostaff@endo-society.org
URL: http://www.endo-society.org

Purpose: Promotes excellence in research, education, and clinical practice in endocrinology and related disciplines. **Activities:** Maintains placement service.

★8860★ Islamic Medical Association of North America (IMANA)

950 75th St.
Downers Grove, IL 60516
Ph: (630)852-2122   Fax: (630)435-1429
E-mail: hq@imana.org
URL: http://www.imana.org

Members: Muslim physicians and allied health professionals. **Purpose:** Unites Muslim physicians and allied health professionals in the U.S. and Canada for the improvement of professional and social contact; provides assistance to Muslim communities worldwide. Charitable programs include: donation of books, journals, and educational and research materials to medical institutions; donation of medical supplies and equipment to charity medical institutions in Muslim countries. **Activities:** Maintains speakers' bureau to present Islamic viewpoints on medical topics; sponsors placement service; offers assistance in orientation.

★8861★ National Association of Managed Care Physicians (NAMCP)

4435 Waterfront Dr., Ste. 101
PO Box 4765
Glen Allen, VA 23058-4765
Ph: (804)527-1905   Fax: (804)747-5316
Fr: 800-722-0376

E-mail: info@namcp.com
URL: http://www.namcp.com

Members: Licensed physicians and allied health professionals working in managed health care programs; medical residents and students interested in managed health care; corporations or agencies providing services or goods to the industry; interested others. **Purpose:** Enhances the ability of practicing physicians to proactively participate within the managed health care arena through research, communication, and education. Provides a forum for members to communicate their concerns about the changing health care environment, integrate into managed health care delivery systems, and assure continuous improvement in the quality of health care services provided. Develops practice criteria, quality assurance measures, and appropriate utilization management criteria. **Activities:** Offers educational programs; maintains speakers' bureau and placement services; conducts research programs; developing informational clearinghouse.

★8862★ **Ruth Jackson Orthopaedic Society (RJOS)**

6300 N River Rd., Ste. 727
Rosemont, IL 60018
Ph: (847)698-1637 Fax: (847)823-0536
E-mail: gebhardt@aaos.org
URL: http://www.rjos.org

Members: Women orthopaedic surgeons, residents, fellows, and medical students. **Purpose:** Seeks to advance the science of orthopaedic surgery and to provide support for women orthopaedic surgeons. Named for practicing orthopaedic surgeon Dr. Ruth Jackson (1902-94), the first woman certified by the American Board of Orthopaedic Surgery and the first female member of the American Academy of Orthopaedic Surgeons. **Activities:** Conducts educational programs; operates placement service and speakers' bureau, holds biennial meeting, sponsors mentoring program, offers traveling fellowship and resident research award.

★8863★ **Ukrainian Medical Association of North America (UMANA)**

2247 W. Chicago Ave., 2nd Fl.
Chicago, IL 60622
Ph: (773)278-6262 Fax: (773)278-6962
Fr: 888-RXU-MANA
E-mail: umana@umana.org
URL: http://www.umana.org

Description: Physicians, surgeons, dentists, and persons in related professions who are of Ukrainian descent. Provides assistance to members; sponsors lectures. Maintains placement service, museum, biographical and medical archives, and library of 1800 medical books and journals in Ukrainian.

EMPLOYER DIRECTORIES AND NETWORKING LISTS

★8864★ **AHA Guide to the Health Care Field**

American Hospital Association (AHA)
1 N. Franklin St., 27th Fl.
Chicago, IL 60606
Ph: (312)422-2050 Fax: (312)422-4700
Fr: 800-424-4301

Annual, August. $295.00. Covers hospitals, networks, multi-health care systems, free-standing ambulatory surgery centers, psychiatric facilities, long-term care facilities, substance abuse programs, and other health-related organizations. Entries include: For hospitals-Facility name, address, phone, administrator's name, number of beds, facilities and services, number of employees, expenses, other statistics. For other organizations-Name, address, phone, fax, name and title of contact. Arrangement: Geographical. Indexes: Hospital name.

★8865★ **American Association of Public Health Physicians-Membership Roster**

American Association of Public Health Physicians
LSU Medical Ctr.
Dept. of PM and PH
1600 Canal St., Rm. 801
New Orleans, LA 70112
Ph: (504)568-6935 Fax: (504)568-6905

Annual. Covers 200 physicians. Entries include: Name, address, professional affiliation. Arrangement: Available in alphabetical or geographical arrangement.

★8866★ **American Group Psychotherapy Association-Membership Directory**

American Group Psychotherapy Association Inc.
25 E 21st St., 6th Fl.
New York, NY 10023
Ph: (212)477-2677 Fax: (212)979-6627
Fr: 877-668-AGPA

Biennial, fall. $90.00. Covers 4,500 physicians, psychologists, clinical social workers, psychiatric nurses, and other mental health professionals interested in treatment of emotional problems by group methods. Entries include: Name, office or home address, highest degree held, office or home phone number. Arrangement: Alphabetical. Indexes: Geographical.

★8867★ **American Holistic Medical Association-National Referral Directory**

American Holistic Medical Association
12101 Menaul Blvd., NE, Ste. C
Albuquerque, MN 87112-2460
URL: http://www.holisticmedicine.org

Annual, spring. $10.00. Covers medical doctors, doctors of osteopathy, and health prac-

titioners who are certified, registered, or licensed by their state and are interested in or practice holistic medicine. Entries include: Name, address, specialty, description of practice Arrangement: Geographical. Indexes: Geographical.

★8868★ **American Osteopathic Association-Yearbook and Directory of Osteopathic Physicians**

American Osteopathic Association
142 E Ontario St.
Chicago, IL 60611
Ph: (312)202-8000 Fax: (312)202-8200
Fr: 800-621-1773
URL: http://www.aoa-net.org

Last print edition June 2000. Covers member and nonmember osteopathic physicians; includes associate members. Entries include: Name, office or home address, specialty, type of practice, age, date and institution granting degree and board certifications. Arrangement: Alphabetical. Indexes: Geographical, certifying board, field.

★8869★ **Directory of Child Life Programs**

Child Life Council Inc.
11820 Parklawn Dr., Ste. 202
Rockville, MD 20852-2529
Ph: (301)881-7090 Fax: (301)881-7092
URL: http://www.childlife.org/

Biennial. $15.00 for members; $20.00 for nonmembers. Covers over 400 child life programs. Entries include: Facility name, address, phone, name of child life department and director, reporting structure, staff statistics, educational requirements for employment, and internship or educational opportunities. Arrangement: Geographical. Indexes: Speciality areas, internship sessions, program size, fellowships.

★8870★ **Directory of Hospital Personnel**

Thomson Medical Economics
5 Paragon Dr.
Montvale, NJ 07645-1742
Ph: (201)358-7200 Fax: (201)722-2680

Annual, November. $325.00. Covers 200,000 executives at 7,000 U.S. hospitals. Entries include: Name of hospital, address, phone, number of beds, type and JCAHO status of hospital, names and titles of key department heads and staff, medical and nursing school affiliations; number of residents, interns, and nursing students. Arrangement: Geographical. Indexes: Hospital name, personnel, hospital size.

★8871★ **Directory of Physicians in the United States**

American Medical Association Alliance
515 N. State St.
Chicago, IL 60610
Ph: (312)464-5000 Fax: (312)464-5020
Fr: 800-621-8335
URL: http://www.directoryofphysicians.org

Biennial, November of even years. $750.00.

Covers in four volume set, more than 850,000 physicians in the United States, Puerto Rico, Virgin Islands, and certain Pacific Islands. Entries include: Name, address, year licensed in mailing address state, medical school, type of practice, primary and secondary specialties, board certifications, and Physician's Recognition award status. Both print and CD-ROM versions are available. Arrangement: Geographical by city; federal service separate section. Indexes: Alphabetical (constitutes Volume 1 of set); geographical.

★8872★ Guide to Careers in the Health Professions

The Princeton Review
1745 Broadway
New York, NY 10019
Ph: (212)829-6928   Fax: (212)940-7400
Fr: 800-733-3000

Published January, 2001. $24.95. Presents advice and information for those searching for satisfying careers in the health professions. Publication includes: Directory of schools and academic programs. Entries include: Name, address, phone, tuition, program details, employment profiles.

★8873★ Health & Medical Industry Directory

infoUSA Inc.
5711 S 86th Cir.
Omaha, NE 68127-0347
Ph: (402)930-3500   Fax: (402)331-0176
Fr: 800-555-6124
URL: http://www.abii.com

Released 1993. CD-ROM. Lists over 1.1 million physicians and surgeons, dentists, clinics, health clubs, and other health-related businesses in the U.S. and Canada. Entries include: Name, address, phone. IBM-compatible equipment required.

★8874★ Health & Wellness Resource Center

Thomson Gale
27500 Drake Rd.
Farmington Hills, MI 48331-3535
Ph: (248)699-4253   Fax: (248)699-8065
Fr: 800-877-GALE
URL: http://www.gale.com

Database includes: Located in the Health Organization Directory component: Listings of agencies, schools and organizations; journals, newsletters, and publishers websites; hospitals, health care facilities, programs and special care. Data is derived from the Medical and Health Information Directory. Entries include: Contact information. Principal content of database is a medical encyclopedia, drug and herb locator, health assessment tools, medical dictionary, links to other sites, and health news. Indexes: Searchable by key term along with city and state.

★8875★ Health & Wellness Resource Center-Alternative Health Module

Thomson Gale
27500 Drake Rd.
Farmington Hills, MI 48331-3535
Ph: (248)699-4253   Fax: (248)699-8065
Fr: 800-877-GALE
URL: http://www.gale.com

Database includes: Focused upon alternative medicine topics this information is located in the Health Organization Directory component: listings of agencies, schools and organizations; journals, newsletters, and publishers websites; hospitals, health care facilities, programs and special care. Data is derived from the Medical and Health Information Directory. Entries include: Contact information. Principal content of database is a medical encyclopedia, drug and herb locator, health assessment tools, medical dictionary, links to other sites, and health news and includes references to homeopathic treatments, yoga, massage therapy, etc.

★8876★ HMO/PPO Directory

Thomson Medical Economics
5 Paragon Dr.
Montvale, NJ 07645-1742
Ph: (201)358-7200   Fax: (201)722-2680

Annual, November. $215.00. Covers over 600 health maintenance organizations (HMOs) and more than 1,000 preferred provider organizations (PPOs). Entries include: Name of organization, address, phone, number of members, names of officers, employer references, geographical area served, parent company, average fees and copayments, financial data, and cost control procedures. Arrangement: Geographical. Indexes: Organization name, personnel name, HMOs and PPOs by state, and number of members enrolled.

★8877★ Hospital Blue Book

Billian/Transworld Publishing Inc.
2100 Powers Ferry Rd.
Ste. 300
Atlanta, GA 30339
Ph: (770)955-8484   Fax: (770)955-8485
Fr: 800-533-8484
E-mail: blu-book@billian.com

Annual, January. $285.00 for national edition; $160.00 for southern edition. Covers more than 6,687 hospitals; some listings also appear in a separate southern edition of this publication. Entries include: Name of hospital, accreditation, mailing address, phone, fax, number of beds, type of facility (nonprofit, general, state, etc.); list of administrative personnel and chiefs of medical services, with specific titles. Arrangement: Geographical.

★8878★ The JobBank Guide to Health Care Companies

Adams Media Corp.
57 Littlefield St.
Avon, MA 02322
Ph: (508)427-7100   Fax: (508)427-6790
Fr: 800-872-5627

$17.95. Covers Jobs nationwide in health care companies. Entries include: Firm or organization name, address, phone, name and title of contact; description of organization, headquarters location, typical titles for entry- and middle-level positions, educational backgrounds desired, fringe benefits offered, stock exchange listing, training programs, internships, parent company, number of employees, revenues, e-mail and web address, projected number of hires. Indexes: Alphabetical.

★8879★ Journal of the American Medical Association-Physician Service Opportunities Overseas Section

American Medical Association Alliance
515 N. State St.
Chicago, IL 60610
Ph: (312)464-5000   Fax: (312)464-5020
Fr: 800-621-8335

Irregular, latest edition August 2002. Publication includes: List of more than 60 organizations that provide assignments overseas for physicians from the United States. Entries include: Organization name, address, phone, contact person, countries served, and medical specialties sought. Arrangement: Alphabetical.

★8880★ Medical and Health Information Directory

Thomson Gale
27500 Drake Rd.
Farmington Hills, MI 48331-3535
Ph: (248)699-4253   Fax: (248)699-8065
Fr: 800-877-GALE
E-mail: businessproducts@gale.com

Annual. $285.00 per volume; $675.00 per set. Covers in Volume 1, more than 26,500 medical and health oriented associations, organizations, institutions, and government agencies, including health maintenance organizations (HMOs), preferred provider organizations (PPOs), insurance companies, pharmaceutical companies, research centers, and medical and allied health schools. In Volume 2, over 12,000 medical book publishers; medical periodicals, directories, audiovisual producers and services, medical libraries and information centers, electronic resources, and health-related internet search engines. In Volume 3, more than 35,500 clinics, treatment centers, care programs, and counseling/diagnostic services for 34 subject areas. Entries include: Institution, service, or firm name, address, phone, fax, email and URL; many include names of key personnel and, when pertinent, descriptive annotation. Volume 3 was formerly listed separately as Health Services Directory. Arrangement: Classified by organization activity, service, etc. Indexes: Each volume has a complete alphabetical name and keyword index.

★8881★ The Official ABMS Directory of Board Certified Medical Specialists

Marquis Who's Who
121 Chanlon Rd.
New Providence, NJ 07974
Ph: (908)673-1101   Fax: (908)673-1189
Fr: 800-473-7020

URL: http://www.marquiswhoswho.com

Annual, October. $399.00; $795.00 for CD-ROM. Covers more than 565,000 board-certified specialists in 25 areas of medical practice from allergy to urology. Prior to 1997, all 25 areas were covered in separate publications. Entries include: Name, certifications, office address, phone, date and place of birth, education, career data, date certified, type of practice, professional memberships. Arrangement: Classified by specialty, then geographical. Indexes: Alphabetical within each speciality, and one alpha index of all physicians listed in the directory.

★8882★ **Physicians and Dentists Database**
Firstmark Inc.
25 Vintinner Rd.
PO Box 1270
Campton, NH 03223-1270
Ph: (603)726-4800   Fax: (603)726-4840
Fr: 800-729-2600
URL: http://www.firstmark.com/fmkcat/docs+3.htm

Updated continuously; printed on request. Database covers: Over 500,000 physicians and 160,000 dentists nationwide. Entries include: Individual name, address, phone, medical specialty, whether in single or group practice.

★8883★ **Physicians & Surgeons Directory**
infoUSA Inc.
5711 S 86th Cir.
Omaha, NE 68127-0347
Ph: (402)930-3500   Fax: (402)331-0176
Fr: 800-555-6124
URL: http://www.abii.com

Annual. Number of listings: 536,808. Entries include: Name, address, phone, size of advertisement, year first in "Yellow Pages," name of owner or manager, number of employees. Compiled from telephone company "Yellow Pages" nationwide. Arrangement: Geographical.

★8884★ **Physicians & Surgeons Information Bureaus Directory**
infoUSA Inc.
5711 S 86th Cir.
Omaha, NE 68127-0347
Ph: (402)930-3500   Fax: (402)331-0176
Fr: 800-555-6124
URL: http://www.abii.com

Updated continuously; printed on request. Number of listings: 1,920. Entries include: Name, address, phone (including area code), size of advertisement, year first in "Yellow Pages," name of owner or manager, number of employees. Compiled from telephone company "Yellow Pages," nationwide. Arrangement: Geographical.

★8885★ **Principles and Practice of Clinical Research**
Academic Press
525 B St., Ste. 1900
San Diego, CA 92101-4495
Ph: (619)231-0926

$99.95. Publication includes: List of web sites for further information about review processes and process changes for grants. Principal content of publication is a comprehensive review of clinical research including history, ethics, regulations, biostatistics, protocol development, and funding. Indexes: Alphabetical.

★8886★ **Student Resource Center-Health Module**
Thomson Gale
27500 Drake Rd.
Farmington Hills, MI 48331-3535
Ph: (248)699-4253   Fax: (248)699-8065
Fr: 800-877-GALE
URL: http://www.gale.com

Database includes: Listing of individuals who have "made significant contributions to the world of health." Entries include: Biographical data. Principal content of database is approximately 1,200 essays on all aspects of major health issues along with events, definitions, pamphlets and links to reviewed websites.

★8887★ **Transplantation Sourcebook**
Omnigraphics Inc.
615 Griswold St., Ste. 1400
Detroit, MI 48226
Ph: (313)961-1340   Fax: (313)961-1383
Fr: 800-234-1340

$78.00. Publication includes: List of transplant organizations, donor centers, and major transplant hospitals in the United States. Principal content of publication is a detailed discussion of the issues surrounding transplantation. Indexes: Alphabetical.

HANDBOOKS AND MANUALS

★8888★ **Barron's Guide to Medical and Dental Schools**
Barron's Educational Series, Inc.
250 Wireless Blvd.
Hauppauge, NY 11788-3917
Ph: (631)434-3311   Fax: (631)434-3723
Fr: 800-645-3476

Saul Wischnitzer and Edith Wischnitzer. Eighth edition, 1997. $16.95. 384 pages. Out of print.

★8889★ **Cardiac Nuclear Medicine**
McGraw-Hill Professional
PO Box 545
Blacklick, OH 43004-0545
Fax: (614)755-5645   Fr: 800-722-4726

Myron C. Gerson, editor. Third edition, 1996. $155.00. 830 pages.

★8890★ **Career Guide in Pathology**
A S C P Press
2100 W. Harrison St.
Chicago, IL 60612
Ph: (312)738-1336   Fax: (312)738-1619
Fr: 800-621-4142

Ellis S. Benson, Barbara F. Atkinson, and Martin Flax. 1999.

★8891★ **Career Opportunities in Health Care (Career Opportunities)**
Facts on File
132 W. 31st St., 17th Fl.
New York, NY 10001-2006
Ph: (212)967-8800   Fax: (212)967-8107
Fr: 800-322-8755

Shelly Field. Arthur E. Weintraub. 2002. Reprint. $18.95. 243 pages. Part of the Career Opportunities Series.

★8892★ **Careers in Health Care**
McGraw-Hill Trade
2 Penn Plaza
New York, NY 10121
Ph: (212)904-2000   Fr: 800-722-4726
E-mail: ntcpub@tribune.com

Barbara M. Swanson. Fourth edition, 2000. $17.95; $13.95 (paper). 320 pages. Describes job duties, work settings, salaries, licensing and certification requirements, educational preparation, and future outlook. Gives ideas on how to secure a job.

★8893★ **Careers in Medicine**
McGraw-Hill Contemporary Books
1221 Avenue of the Americas
New York, NY 10020
Ph: (212)904-2000   Fr: 800-323-4900
E-mail: ntcpub@tribune.com

Terence J. Sacks. Second edition, 1996. $17.95; $13.95 (paper). 144 pages. Examines the many paths open to M.D.s, D.O.s, and M.D./Ph.D.s, including clinical private or group practice, hospitals, public health organizations, the armed forces, emergency rooms, research institutions, medical schools, pharmaceutical companies and private industry, and research/advocacy groups like the World Health Organization. A special chapter on osteopathy and chiropractic explores this branch of medicine.

★8894★ **Careers in Medicine, Dentistry and Mental Health**
Kogan Page, Ltd.
22 Broad St., Ste. 34
Milford, CT 06460

Judith Humphries and Loulou Brown. Seventh edition, 1996. $14.95 (paper). Part of the Kogan Page Careers Series. Out of print.

★8895★ **Careers for Night Owls and Other Insomniacs**
McGraw-Hill Trade
2 Penn Plaza
New York, NY 10121
Ph: (212)904-2000   Fr: 800-722-4726

E-mail: ntcpub@tribune.com
Louise Miller. 1995. $14.95; $9.95 (paper).
160 pages.

★8896★ **Chronicle Health Occupations Guidebook**
Chronicle Guidance Publications, Inc.
66 Aurora St.
Moravia, NY 13118-3576
Fax: (315)497-3359   Fr: 800-899-0454
E-mail: customerservice@chronicleguidance.com
URL: http://www.chronicleguidance.com

Paul Downes, editor. Revised edition, 1994.
$100.65.

★8897★ **The Complete Medical Marketing Handbook: A Guide for Physicians & Managers**
Professional Medical Management Corp.
4727 Wilshire Blvd., Ste. 300
Los Angeles, CA 90010
Ph: (323)954-0224   Fax: (323)954-0253
Fr: 800-633-4215

Maryann Szotstak-Ricardo. 1994. $49.95.
112 pages.

★8898★ **Evaluating and Negotiating Compensation Arrangements: Understanding the Process and Ensuring Your Future**
American Medical Association
515 N. State St.
Chicago, IL 60610
Ph: (312)464-5000   Fax: (312)464-5226
Fr: 800-621-8335

American Medical Association Staff, authors.
1998. $39.95. 69 pages. Part of the Career
Development Series.

★8899★ **Expert Resumes for Health Care Careers**
JIST Publishing
8902 Otis Ave.
Indianapolis, IN 46216-1033
Ph: (317)613-4200   Fax: 800-547-8329

December 2003. $16.95. 288 pages.

★8900★ **Health Care Career Starter: Finding and Getting a Great Job**
LearningExpress, LLC
900 Broadway, Ste. 604
New York, NY 10003
Ph: (212)995-2566   Fax: (212)995-5512
Fr: 800-295-9556

Cheryl Jean Hancock. Brigit Dermott. Reprint. 2002. $15.95 (paper). 216 pages. Part
of the Heath Care Career Starters Series.

★8901★ **Health Care Job Explosion! High Growth Health Care Careers and Job Locator**
Bookhaven Press LLC
PO Box 1243
Moon Township, PA 15108
Ph: (412)494-6926   Fax: (412)494-5749
Fr: 800-782-7424

Dennis V. Damp. Third edition, 2001. 288
pages.

★8902★ **Health Careers Today**
Elsevier-Health Sciences Division
The Curtis Center, Ste. 300E, 3rd Fl.
170 S. Independence Mall W.
Philadelphia, PA 19106
Ph: (215)238-7800   Fax: (215)238-7362
Fr: 800-523-4069

Gerdin. Revised edition. April 2004. $52.95.

★8903★ **Healthcare Career Directory-Nurses and Physicians**
Thomson Gale
27500 Drake Rd.
Farmington Hills, MI 48331-3535
Ph: (248)699-GALE   Fax: 800-414-5043
Fr: 800-877-GALE
E-mail: galeord@gale.com
URL: http://www.gale.com

Bradley Morgan. Second edition, 1993.
$39.00. 300 pages. Out of print. Essays on
specific careers provide an insider's perspective. Features extensive listings of contacts and entry-level job opportunities. Provides information on internships and sources
of help-wanted ads.

★8904★ **Hot Health-Care Careers**
MasterMedia Publishing Corp.
46585 SE Coalman Rd.
Sandy, OR 97055
Ph: (503)668-0296   Fax: (503)668-0494
Fr: 800-334-8232

Margaret McNally. 1993. $17.95; $10.95
(paper). Out of print.

★8905★ **How to Start a Private Practice**
Yvonne Mart Fox
9454 Wilshire Blvd., Suite 650
Beverly Hills, CA 90212
Ph: (323)934-9949   Fax: (323)935-7954

Yvonne Mart Fox. 2000. $36.00 (paper).

★8906★ **The Medical Job Interview**
Blackwell Science, Incorporated
Commerce Pl.
350 Main St.
Malden, MA 02148-5018
Ph: (617)388-8250   Fax: (781)388-8255
Fr: 800-759-6102

Colin Mumford. 2000. $23.95 (paper).

★8907★ **The New Practice Handbook: A Guide to Establishing a Successful Medical Practice**
McGraw-Hill Companies
1221 Avenue of the Americas
New York, NY 10020
Ph: (212)904-2000   Fax: (212)954-0253
Fr: 800-633-4215

Maryann Szostak-Ricardo. 1994. $49.95.
155 pages.

★8908★ **Opportunities in Health and Medical Careers**
McGraw-Hill Trade
2 Penn Plaza
New York, NY 10121
Ph: (212)904-2000   Fr: 800-722-4726

I. Donald Snook, Jr. and Leo D'Orazio. 1997.
$14.95; $11.95 (paper). 202 pages. Covers
the full range of medical and health occupations. Illustrated.

★8909★ **Opportunities in Sports and Athletics Careers**
McGraw-Hill Trade
2 Penn Plaza
New York, NY 10121
Ph: (212)904-2000   Fr: 800-722-4726
E-mail: ntcpub@tribune.com

William Ray Heitzmann. 1994. 160 pages.
$14.95; $11.95 (paper). A guide to planning
for and seeking opportunities in this growing
field. Illustrated.

★8910★ **Opportunities in Sports Medicine Careers**
McGraw-Hill Trade
2 Penn Plaza
New York, NY 10121
Ph: (212)904-2000   Fr: 800-722-4726
E-mail: ntcpub@tribune.com

William Ray Heitzmann. 1995. $14.95;
$11.95 (paper). 160 pages. Discusses a
variety of opportunities in this field and how
to pursue them. Contains bibliography and
illustrations.

★8911★ **Preparing to Tack: When Physicians Change Careers**
Vantage Press, Inc.
516 W. 34th St.
New York, NY 10001
Ph: (212)736-1767   Fax: (212)736-2273
Fr: 800-882-3273

Jack Kushner. 1996. $13.95. Out of print.

★8912★ **Real People Working in Health Care**
McGraw-Hill Contemporary Books
1221 Avenue of the Americas
New York, NY 10020
Ph: (212)904-2000   Fr: 800-323-4900
E-mail: ntcpub@tribune.com

Blythe Camenson, Jan Goldberg. 1996.
$17.95; $12.95 (paper). Interviews and pro-

files of working professionals capture a range of opportunities in this field.

★8913★ **Resumes for Health and Medical Careers**
McGraw-Hill Trade
2 Penn Plaza
New York, NY 10121
Ph: (212)904-2000   Fr: 800-722-4726
E-mail: ntcpub@tribune.com

1997. $9.95 (paper). 455 pages.

★8914★ **Resumes & Personal Statements for Health Professionals**
Galen Press, Ltd.
PO Box 64400
Tucson, AZ 85728-4400
Ph: (520)577-8363   Fax: (520)529-6459
Fr: 800-442-5369

James W. Tysinger. Second edition, 1998. $18.95 (paper).

★8915★ **Where the Jobs Are: The Hottest Careers for the 90s**
The Career Press, Inc.
3 Tice Rd.
PO Box 687
Franklin Lakes, NJ 07417-1322
Ph: (201)848-0310   Fax: (201)848-1727
Fr: 800-227-3371

Joyce Hadley. Third edition, 2000. $13.99 (paper). 400 pages. Out of print. Describes careers in fifteen general fields, from accounting to travel and hospitality.

★8916★ **Your Career in Physical Medicine**
W. B. Saunders Co.
6277 Sea Harbor Dr.
Orlando, FL 32887
Fr: 800-654-2452

Roberta C. Weiss. 1997. $42.00 (paper). 475 pages.

EMPLOYMENT AGENCIES AND SEARCH FIRMS

★8917★ **Alan Darling Consulting**
374 Dover Rd., Ste. 18
South Newfane, VT 05351
Ph: (802)348-6365

Executive search firm focused on the healthcare industry.

★8918★ **The Bauman Group**
220 Main St., Ste. 200
Los Altos, CA 94022
Ph: (650)941-0800   Fax: (650)941-1729
Executive search firm.

★8919★ **BeechTree Partners LLC**
401 N. Michigan Ave., Ste. 1200
Chicago, IL 60611
Ph: (312)840-8229   Fax: (773)665-8682
Executive search firm.

★8920★ **Breitner Clark & Hall Inc.**
1017 Turnpike St., Ste. 22A
Canton, MA 02021
Ph: (781)828-6411   Fax: (781)828-6431
Fr: 800-331-7004
Executive search firm focused on the healthcare industry.

★8921★ **Carson Kolb Healthcare Group Inc.**
20301 Birch St., Ste. 101
Newport Beach, CA 92660-1754
Ph: (949)476-2988   Fax: (949)476-2155
Fr: 800-606-9439
Executive search firm focused on the healthcare industry.

★8922★ **Cejka Search**
222 S. Central, Ste. 400
St. Louis, MO 63105
Ph: (314)727-6650   Fax: (314)863-1705
Fr: 800-678-7858
Executive search firm for the healthcare industry. Branch in Norcross, GA.

★8923★ **DPSI Medical One**
5105 Clinton St., Ste. 2
Erie, PA 16509
Ph: (814)868-0961
Executive search firm.

★8924★ **Drew Associates International**
25 Pompton Ave., Ste. 305
Verona, NJ 07044
Ph: (973)571-9735
Executive search firm focused on the healthcare industry.

★8925★ **The Energists**
10260 Westheimer Blvd., Ste. 300
Houston, TX 77042
Ph: (713)781-6881   Fax: (713)781-2998
E-mail: search@energists.com
URL: http://www.energists.com
Executive search firm.

★8926★ **Foley Proctor Yoskowitz LLC**
1 Cattano Ave.
Morristown, NJ 07960-6820
Ph: (973)605-1000   Fax: (973)605-1020
Fr: 800-238-1123
Executive search firm for the healthcare industry. Second location in New York, NY.

★8927★ **Forager**
1516 Sudeenew Dr.
McHenry, IL 60050
Ph: (815)344-0006

Executive search firm. Branches in Alta Loma, CA; Littleton, CO; and North Barrington, IL.

★8928★ **Harper Associates**
29870 Middlebelt
Farmington Hills, MI 48334
Ph: (248)932-1170   Fax: (248)932-1214
E-mail: resumes@harperjobs.com
URL: http://www.harperjobs.com

Executive search firm and employment agency.

★8929★ **Lee Calhoon & Company Inc.**
1621 Birchrun Rd.
PO Box 201
Birchrunville, PA 19421
Ph: (610)469-9000   Fax: (610)469-0398
Fr: 800-469-0896
Executive search firm.

★8930★ **MedSearch Staffing Services Inc.**
7271 Engle Rd., Ste. 115
Middleburg Heights, OH 44130
Ph: (440)243-6363   Fax: (440)243-9117

Provides specialized recruitment of sales, marketing and management personnel. Also involved in top-level hospital management consulting and physician recruitment, interim/temporary staffing. Industries served: healthcare manufacturers and institutions in the United States.

★8931★ **Merritt Hawkins & Associates**
5001 Statesman Dr.
Irving, TX 75063
Ph: (469)524-1400   Fax: (469)524-1421
Fr: 800-876-0500

Physician recruitment firm. Industries served: healthcare.

★8932★ **Pate Resources Group Inc.**
595 Orleans, Ste. 707
Beaumont, TX 77701
Ph: (409)833-4514   Fax: (409)833-4646
Fr: 800-669-4514

Offers executive search and recruiting services to professionals who include physicians, healthcare administrators, engineers, accounting and financial disciplines, legal, outplacement, sales and marketing. Industries served: healthcare, petrochemicals, accounting, utility, legal, and municipalities.

★8933★ **Phyllis Hawkins and Associates**
105 E Northern Ave.
Phoenix, AZ 85020
Ph: (602)263-0248   Fax: (602)678-1564

E-mail: phassoc@qweat.com
URL: http://www.azlawsearch.com

Executive search firm focusing on attorney searches.

★8934★ **Physicians Search, Inc.**
5581 E. Stetson Ct.
Anaheim, CA 92807-4650
Ph: (714)685-1047   Fax: (714)685-1143
Fr: 800-748-6320
E-mail: info@physicianssearch.com
URL: http://www.physicianssearch.com

Executive search firm. Affiliate office in Spokane, WA.

★8935★ **P.J. Murphy & Associates Inc.**
735 N Water St., Ste. 915
Milwaukee, WI 53202
Ph: (414)277-9777   Fax: (414)277-7626

Management consulting firm which specializes in retained executive search. Industries served: all industries, to include healthcare and physician recruiting.

★8936★ **Professional Placement Associates, Inc.**
287 Bowman Ave., Ste. 309
Purchase, NY 10577
Ph: (914)251-1000   Fax: (914)251-1055
E-mail: lschachter@ppasearch.com
URL: http://www.ppasearch.com

Executive search firm specializing in the health and medical field.

★8937★ **Shiloh Careers International, Inc.**
7105 Peach Ct., Ste102
PO Box 831
Brentwood, TN 37024-0831
Ph: (615)373-3090   Fax: (615)373-3480
E-mail: maryann@shilohcareers.com
URL: http://www.shilohcareers.com

Employment agency serving the industry field.

★8938★ **Team Placement Service, Inc.**
5113 Leesburg Pike, Ste. 510
Falls Church, VA 22041-3242
Ph: (703)820-8618   Fax: (703)820-3368
Fr: 800-495-6767
E-mail: 4jobs@teamplace.com
URL: http://www.teamplace.com

Temporary agency that also handles some permanent placements.

★8939★ **Weatherby Locum**
6451 N Federal Hwy. , Ste. 80
Fort Lauderdale, FL 33308
Ph: (203)866-1144   Fax: 800-463-2985
Fr: 800-365-8900
E-mail: info@weatherbylocums.com
URL: http://www.weatherbylocums.com

Executive search firm for physicians. Branch office in Fairfax, VA.

ONLINE JOB SOURCES AND SERVICES

★8940★ **American Association of Anatomists Career Center**
URL: http://www.anatomy.org/public/pages/index.cfm?pageid=117

Description: Job advertisers include academic sites in the U.S. and Canada. Job seekers may review these posted jobs through "Positions Offered" or post their own needs under "Positions Wanted." Offerings for Postdoctoral Positions also available. Contains Career Resources sections and links to online career resources.

★8941★ **EmployMED: Healthcare Job Listings**
E-mail: ashrafn@aol.com
URL: http://www.employmed.com/

Description: Lists practice opportunities throughout North America for all medical specialties. Contains job listings directory. Posting option is available for those who wish to advertise jobs. **Fee:** $25 per month per posting for minimum of 2 months.

★8942★ **FCS - The 1st Choice in Psychiatric Recruitment**
1711 Ashley Cir., Ste. 6
Bowling Green, KY 42104-5801
Fax: (502)782-1055   Fr: 800-783-9152
E-mail: fcsinfo@atsfcspsy.com
URL: http://www.fcspsy.com

Description: Physician search firm specializing in the recruitment of psychiatrists. After the applicant fills out an interest survey, a tailored search is run on the jobs database. Confidential and free.

★8943★ **Health Care Job Store**
395 South End Ave., Ste. 15-D
New York, NY 10280
Ph: (212)912-0175
E-mail: jobs@atshealthcarejobstore.com
URL: http://www.healthcarejobstore.com/adag.html

Description: Job sites include every job title in the healthcare industry,every healthcare industry and every geographic location in the U.S.

★8944★ **Health Search USA**
E-mail: info@atshealthsearchusa.com
URL: http://www.healthsearchusa.com

Description: A site for national physician recruitment. Offers job postings classified by region and salary comparison.

★8945★ **MDJobsite.com**
E-mail: contact@mdjobsite.com
URL: http://www.mdjobsite.com/

Description: Career search site for physicians. Physicians can search thousands of physician employment opportunities, register

for email notifications of new jobs listed in their specialty and post a CV searchable by facilities and healthcare firms nationwide.

★8946★ **Med Source Consultants**
20 Summer Ct.
Stamford, CT 06901
Ph: (203)324-0388   Fax: (203)324-0551
Fr: 800-575-2880
URL: http://www.psychiatricresources.com

Description: Site houses a physician search and consulting company for psychiatrists. Consultants attempt to match job seekers to positions according to the individual's personal and professional needs. This page also aids institutions looking to recruit psychiatrists.

★8947★ **Medbulletin Medical Career Resource Center**
E-mail: medbulletin@atsmedbulletin.com
URL: http://www.medbulletin.com

Description: Offers free specialized update service, resume posting, recruiter directory, varied job listings, and relocation services.

★8948★ **MedExplorer**
URL: http://www.medexplorer.com

Description: Employment postings make up one module of this general medical site. Other sections contain: Newsletter, Classifieds, and Discussion Forum.

★8949★ **Medhunters.com**
E-mail: info@medhunters.com
URL: http://www.medhunters.com

Description: Career search site for jobs in all health care specialties; educational resources; visa and licensing information for relocation; interesting articles; relocation tools; links to professional organizations and general resources.

★8950★ **Medzilla**
URL: http://www.medzilla.com

Description: General medical website which matches employers and job hunters to their ideal employees and jobs through search capabilities. **Main files include:** Post Jobs, Search Resumes, Post Resumes, Search Jobs, Head Hunters, Articles, Salary Survey.

★8951★ **Monster Healthcare**
E-mail: office@atsmedsearch.com
URL: http://myh.monster.com/

Description: H Monster delivers nationwide access to healthcare recruiting. Employers can post job listings or ads. Job seekers can post and code resumes, and search over 150,000 healthcare job listings, healthcare career advice columns, career resources information, and member employer profiles and services.

TRADESHOWS

★8952★ American Academy of Pediatrics National Conference and Exhibition

American Academy of Pediatrics
141 Northwest Point Blvd.
PO Box 927
Elk Grove Village, IL 60009-0927
Ph: (847)228-5005   Fax: (847)228-5059
Fr: 800-433-9016
E-mail: kidsdocs@aap.org
URL: http://www.aap.org

Annual. **Primary Exhibits:** Prescription and over-the-counter drugs, infant formulas and baby foods, medical equipment, developmental toys, and publications.

★8953★ American Academy of Physical Medicine and Rehabilitation Annual Meeting

American Academy of Physical Medicine and Rehabilitation
One IBM Plaza, Ste. 2500
Chicago, IL 60611-3514
Ph: (312)464-9700   Fax: (312)464-0227
E-mail: info@aapmr.org
URL: http://www.aapmr.org

Annual. **Primary Exhibits:** Pharmaceuticals, electrodiagnostic equipment, wheelchairs, and related equipment, supplies, and services. **Dates and Locations:** 2004 Oct 7-10; Phoenix, AZ; Hyatt Convention Center • 2005 Oct 27-30; Philadelphia, PA; Philadelphia Marriott.

★8954★ American College of Osteopathic Obstetricians and Gynecologists Annual Convention

American College of Osteopathic Obstetricians and Gynecologists
900 Auburn Rd.
Pontiac, MI 48342
Ph: (248)332-6360   Fax: (248)332-4607
Fr: 800-875-6360
E-mail: acoog@acoog.com
URL: http://www.acoog.com

Annual. **Primary Exhibits:** Pharmaceuticals and medical supplies pertaining to Ob/Gyn. Clothing, vitamins, personal toiletries (all relating to healthcare for women).

★8955★ American College of Sports Medicine Annual Meeting

American College of Sports Medicine
401 W. Michigan St.
Indianapolis, IN 46202
Ph: (317)637-9200   Fax: (317)634-7817
URL: http://www.acsm.org

Annual. **Primary Exhibits:** Exercise equipment, physiological monitoring equipment, ergometers, treadmills, scientific publications, sports medicine monitoring software, and pharmaceuticals. **Dates and Locations:** 2005 Jun 1-4; Nashville, TN; Opryland • 2006 May 31 - Jun 03; Denver, CO • 2007 May 30 - Jun 02; New Orleans, LA.

★8956★ American College of Surgeons Annual Clinical Congress

American College of Surgeons
633 N. Saint Clair St.
Chicago, IL 60611-3211
Ph: (312)202-5000   Fax: (312)202-5001
E-mail: postmaster@facs.org
URL: http://www.facs.org

Annual. **Primary Exhibits:** Medical products, patient care, practice management and educational services and products.

★8957★ American Heart Association Scientific Sessions

American Heart Association
7272 Greenville Ave.
Dallas, TX 75231-4596
Ph: (214)706-1425   Fax: (214)706-1517

Annual. **Primary Exhibits:** Equipment, books, pharmaceuticals, exercise equipment, heart healthy food, and services relevant to cardiological research or physician practice. **Dates and Locations:** 2005 Nov 13-16; New Orleans, LA; Convention Center.

★8958★ American Medical Women's Association Annual Meeting

American Medical Women's Association
801 N. Fairfax St., Ste. 400
Alexandria, VA 22314
Ph: (703)838-0500   Fax: (703)549-3864

Annual. **Primary Exhibits:** Medical equipment, supplies, pharmaceuticals, and services.

★8959★ American Pain Society Scientific Meeting

American Pain Society
4700 W. Lake Ave.
Glenview, IL 60025
Ph: (847)375-4715   Fax: 877-734-8758
E-mail: info@ampainsoc.org
URL: http://www.ampainsoc.org

Annual. **Primary Exhibits:** Pharmaceutical and medical instruments, medical equipment, products, supplies, services and alternative delivery systems (homecare, hospice).

★8960★ American Society for Laser Medicine and Surgery Conference

American Society for Laser Medicine and Surgery
2404 Stewart Ave.
Wausau, WI 54401
Ph: (715)845-9283   Fax: (715)848-2493
E-mail: information@aslms.org
URL: http://www.aslms.org

Annual. **Primary Exhibits:** Laser medicine equipment, supplies, and services.

★8961★ Annual Meeting of the American Academy of Ophthalmology

American Academy of Ophthalmology
655 Beach St.
PO Box 7424
San Francisco, CA 94109
Ph: (415)561-8500   Fax: (415)561-8576
E-mail: meetings@aao.org
URL: http://www.aao.org

Annual. **Primary Exhibits:** Ophthalmic equipment and instruments. **Dates and Locations:** 2004 Oct 23-26; New Orleans, LA; Ernest N. Morial Convention Center.

★8962★ International College of Surgeons North American Federation Congress

International College of Surgeons - US
1516 N. Lake Shore Dr.
Chicago, IL 60610-1694
Ph: (312)787-6274   Fax: (312)787-9289
Fr: 800-766-FICS

Annual. **Primary Exhibits:** Medical equipment, including pharmaceuticals, surgery books, surgical equipment, new hospital devices, and anatomy models.

★8963★ International Medical and Dental Hypnotherapy Association (IMDHA)

International Medical and Dental Hypnotherapy Association (IMDHA)
4110 Edgeland, Ste. 800
Royal Oak, MI 48073-2285
Ph: (248)549-5594   Fax: (248)549-5421
E-mail: aspencer@infinityinst.com
URL: http://www.infinityinst.com

Annual. **Primary Exhibits:** Hypnotherapy and Holistic Health.

★8964★ National Medical Association Annual Convention and Scientific Assembly

National Medical Association
1012 10th St. NW
Washington, DC 20001
Ph: (202)347-1895   Fax: (202)842-3293

Annual. **Primary Exhibits:** Medical equipment, supplies, and services.

OTHER SOURCES

★8965★ American Academy of Clinical Toxicology (AACT)

777 E Park Dr.
PO Box 8820
Harrisburg, PA 17105-8820
Ph: (717)558-7847   Fax: (717)558-7845
Fr: 888-633-5784
E-mail: jreisinger@pamedsoc.org
URL: http://www.clintox.org

Members: Physicians, veterinarians, pharmacists, nurses research scientists, and analytical chemists. **Purpose:** Works to unite medical scientists and facilitate the exchange of information; encourage the development of therapeutic methods and technology. **Activities:** Conducts professional training in poison information and emergency service personnel.

★8966★ American Academy of Craniofacial Pain (AACP)

516 W. Pipeline Rd.
Hurst, TX 76053-4924
Ph: (817)282-1501   Fax: (817)282-8012
Fr: 800-322-8651
E-mail: central@aacfp.org
URL: http://www.aacfp.org

Members: Health Care Practitioners who treat head, facial, and neck pain. **Purpose:** Functions as a referral service for patients suffering from head, facial, and neck pain worldwide. Plans to establish computerized medical procedures and insurance database.

★8967★ American Academy of Family Physicians (AAFP)

11400 Tomahawk Creek Pkwy.
Leawood, KS 66211-2672
Ph: (913)906-6000   Fax: (913)906-6077
Fr: 800-274-2237
E-mail: fp@aafp.org
URL: http://www.aafp.org

Description: Professional society of family physicians who provide continuing comprehensive care to patients.

★8968★ American Academy of Medical Acupuncture

4929 Wilshire Blvd., Ste. 428
Los Angeles, CA 90010
Ph: (323)937-5514   Fax: (323)937-0959
E-mail: jdowden@prodigy.net
URL: http://www.medicalacupuncture.org

Members: Professional society of physicians and osteopaths who utilize acupuncture in their practices. **Purpose:** Provides ongoing training and information related to the Chinese practice of puncturing the body at specific points to cure disease or relieve pain. **Activities:** Offers educational and research programs.

★8969★ American Academy of Otolaryngology - Head and Neck Surgery (AAO-HNS)

1 Prince St.
Alexandria, VA 22314-3357
Ph: (703)836-4444   Fax: (703)683-5100
E-mail: webmaster@entnet.org
URL: http://www.entnet.org

Description: Professional society of medical doctors specializing in otolaryngology (diseases of the ear, nose, and throat) and head and neck surgery. Represents otolaryngology in governmental and socioeconomic areas and provides high-quality medical education for otolaryngologists. Coordinates Combined Otolaryngological Spring Meetings for ten national otolaryngological socie-

ties. Operates job information exchange service and museum.

★8970★ American Academy of Sports Physicians (AASP)

17445 Oak Creek Court
Encino, CA 91316
Ph: (818)501-4433   Fax: (818)501-8855

Description: Clinical physicians engaged in the practice of sports medicine who have made contributions in research, academics, or related fields. Objectives are to educate and inform physicians whose practices comprise mainly sports medicine and to register and recognize physicians who have expertise in sports medicine. Sponsors seminars.

★8971★ American Association of Immunologists (AAI)

9650 Rockville Pike
Bethesda, MD 20814-3994
Ph: (301)634-7178   Fax: (301)571-1816
E-mail: infoaai@aai.faseb.org
URL: http://mercury.faseb.org/aai/default.asp

Description: Scientists engaged in immunological research including aspects of virology, bacteriology, biochemistry, genetics, and related disciplines. Goals are to advance knowledge of immunology and related disciplines and to facilitate the interchange of information among investigators in various fields. Promotes interaction between laboratory investigators and clinicians. Conducts training courses, symposia, workshop, and lectures. Compiles statistics.

★8972★ American Association of Physician Specialists (AAPS)

2296 Henderson Mill Rd., Ste. 206
Atlanta, GA 30345
Ph: (770)939-8555   Fax: (770)939-8559
Fr: 800-447-9397
E-mail: wcarbone@aapsga.org
URL: http://www.aapsga.org

Description: Represents twelve major specialties and twelve sub-specialties of medicine. Accepts qualified physicians into membership with either an allopathic (M.D.) or osteopathic (D.O.) degree. Official headquarters for 12 academies of medicine and boards of certification in the following specialties: anesthesiology, dermatology, emergency medicine, family practice, internal medicine, geriatric medicine, neurology/psychiatry, obstetrics/gynecology, orthopedic surgery, plastic/reconstructive surgery, radiology, surgery.

★8973★ American College of Radiology (ACR)

1891 Preston White Dr.
Reston, VA 20191-4397
Ph: (703)648-8900   Fax: (703)295-6773
Fr: 800-ACR-LINE
E-mail: info@acr.org
URL: http://www.acr.org

Description: Principal organization serving radiologists with programs which focus on

the practice of radiology and the delivery of comprehensive radiological health services. These programs in medical sciences, education, and in practice management, serve the public interest and the interests of the medical community in which radiologists serve in both diagnostic and therapeutic roles. Seeks to "advance the science of radiology, improve radiologic service to the patient, study the economic aspects of the practice of radiology, and encourage imroved and continuing education for radiologists and allied professional fields".

★8974★ American College of Sports Medicine (ACSM)

401 W Michigan St.
Indianapolis, IN 46202-3233
Ph: (317)637-9200   Fax: (317)634-7817
E-mail: publicinfo@acsm.org
URL: http://www.acsm.org

Purpose: Promotes and integrates scientific research, education, and practical applications of sports medicine and exercise science to maintain and enhance physical performance, fitness, health, and quality of life. **Activities:** Certifies fitness leaders, fitness instructors, exercise test technologists, exercise specialists, health/fitness program directors, and U.S. military fitness personnel. Grants continuing medical education (CME) and continuing education credits (CEC). Operates more than 50 committees.

★8975★ American Hospital Association (AHA)

1 N. Franklin
Chicago, IL 60606-3421
Ph: (312)422-3000   Fax: (312)422-4796
URL: http://www.aha.org

Description: Health care provider organizations. Seeks to advance the health of individuals and communities. Leads, represents, and serves health care provider organizations that are accountable to the community and committed to health improvement.

★8976★ American Medical Group Association (AMGA)

1422 Duke St.
Alexandria, VA 22314-3430
Ph: (703)838-0033   Fax: (703)548-1890
E-mail: roconnor@amga.org
URL: http://www.amga.org

Description: Trade association for medical groups and integrated delivery systems and IPAS representing more than 65,000 physicians. Provides public policy advocacy, compiles statistics on group practice, sponsors research, patient education, insurance programs.

★8977★ American School Health Association (ASHA)

PO Box 708
7263 State Route 43
Kent, OH 44240
Ph: (330)678-1601   Fax: (330)678-4526
Fr: 800-445-2742

E-mail: asha@ashaweb.org
URL: http://www.ashaweb.org

Description: School physicians, school nurses, dentist, nurses, nutritionists, health educators, dental hygienist, school-based professionals and public health workers. Promotes coordinated school health programs that include health education, health services, a healthful school environment, physical education, nutrition services, and psycho-social health services offered in schools collaboratively with families and other members of the community. Offers professional reference materials. Conducts pilot programs that inform materials development, provides technical assistance to school professionals, advocates for school health, and complies statistics.

★8978★ **American Society of Extra-Corporeal Technology (AmSECT)**

503 Carlisle Dr. No. 125
Herndon, VA 20170-4838
Ph: (703)435-8556   Fax: (703)435-0056
E-mail: gcate@amsect.org
URL: http://www.amsect.org

Description: Perfusionists, technologists, doctors, nurses, and others actively employed and using the applied skills relating to the practice of extracorporeal technology (involving heart-lung machines); student members. Disseminates information necessary to the proper practice of the technology. Conducts programs in continuing education and professional-public liaison and hands-on workshops. Maintains placement service.

★8979★ **American Society of Psychopathology of Expression (ASPE)**

74 Lawton St.
Brookline, MA 02446
Ph: (617)738-9821   Fax: (617)975-0411

Description: Psychiatrists, psychologists, art therapists, sociologists, art critics, artists, social workers, linguists, educators, criminologists, writers, and historians. At least two-thirds of the members must be physicians. Fosters collaboration among specialists in the United States who are interested in the problems of expression and in the artistic activities connected with psychiatric, sociological, and psychological research. Disseminates information about research and clinical applications in the field of psychopathology of expression. Sponsors consultations, seminars, and lectures on art therapy.

★8980★ **American Urological Association (AUA)**

1000 Corporate Blvd.
Linthicum, MD 21090
Ph: (410)689-3700   Fax: (410)689-3800
Fr: (866)746-4282
E-mail: aua@auanet.org
URL: http://www.auanet.org

Description: Professional society of physicians specializing in urology. Provides education and formulation of health casre policy for urologists.

★8981★ **Emergency Medicine Residents' Association (EMRA)**

1125 Executive Cir.
Irving, TX 75038-2522
Ph: (972)550-0920   Fax: (972)580-2829
Fr: 800-798-1822
E-mail: lmcdonald@emra.org
URL: http://www.emra.org

Description: Physicians enrolled in emergency medicine residency training programs; medical students. Purposes are to provide a unified voice for emergency medicine residents and encourage high standards in training and education for emergency physicians. Encourages research to improve emergency medicine education; promotes community, state, and national representation for emergency medicine in organized and academic medicine.

★8982★ **Exploring Health Occupations**

Cambridge Educational
2572 Brunswick Ave.
Lawrenceville, NJ 08648-4128
Fax: 800-FAX-ON-US   Fr: 800-468-4227
URL: http://www.cambridgeeducational.com

Two videos. $139.95. 1999.

★8983★ **Health Service Occupations**

Delphi Productions
3160 4th St.
Boulder, CO 80304
Fax: (303)443-4022   Fr: 888-443-2400
URL: http://www.delphivideo.com

$95.00. 50 minutes. Part of the Careers for the 21st Century Video Library.

★8984★ **Holistic Dental Association (HDA)**

PO Box 5007
Durango, CO 81301
Ph: (970)259-1091   Fax: (970)259-1091
E-mail: info@holisticdental.org
URL: http://www.holisticdental.org

Description: Dentists, chiropractors, dental hygienists, physical therapists, and medical doctors. Goals are: to provide a holistic approach to better dental care for patients; to expand techniques, medications, and philosophies that pertain to extractions, anesthetics, fillings, crowns, and orthodontics. Encourages use of homeopathic medications, acupuncture, cranial osteopathy, nutritional techniques, and physical therapy in treating patients in addition to conventional treatments. Sponsors training and educational seminars.

★8985★ **Institute on Psychiatric Services/American Psychiatric Association**

1000 Wilson Blvd., Ste. 1825
Arlington, VA 22209-3901
Fax: (703)907-1090   Fr: 888-357-7924
E-mail: apa@psych.org
URL: http://www.psych.org

Description: Annual meeting sponsored by the American Psychiatric Association. Open

to employees of all psychiatric and related health and educational facilities. Includes lectures by experts in the field and workshops and accredited courses on problems, programs, and trends. Offers on-site Job Bank, which lists opportunities for mental health professionals. Organized scientific exhibits.

★8986★ **International Association of Hygienic Physicians (IAHP)**

4620 Euclid Blvd.
Youngstown, OH 44512
Ph: (330)788-0526   Fax: (330)788-0093
E-mail: boar_mah@access-k12.org
URL: http://free.freespeech.org/nhn/iahp/

Members: Doctors of medicine, osteopathy, chiropractic, and naturopathy who specialize in the supervision of therapeutic fasting as part of a natural hygiene regimen. **Purpose:** Promotes clinical advancement and ethical responsibility. Works for the health freedom of members. **Activities:** Provides certification for professionals and accreditation for schools and training programs; offers internship programs. Funds research.

★8987★ **International Society of Stress Analysts (ISSA)**

9 Westchester Dr.
Kissimmee, FL 34744
Ph: (407)933-4839   Fax: (407)935-0911
E-mail: diogenesfl@aol.com

Members: Jurists, attorneys, physicians, private detectives, law enforcement personnel, security personnel, scholar/researchers, and individuals interested in stress analysis for lie detection/truth verification. **Purpose:** Works to promote the science of psychological stress evaluation and the efficient administration of justice; aid indigent persons, without cost, who may be wrongfully accused; develop and maintain high educational standards; observe and evaluate training programs for the purpose of accreditation and endorsement. **Activities:** Sponsors and certifies schools; offers workshops and research and educational programs; conducts forums. Offers expertise, consultation, and advice; invites inquiries.

★8988★ **Joint Council of Allergy, Asthma and Immunology (JCAAI)**

50 N Brockway, Ste. 3-3
Palatine, IL 60067
Ph: (847)934-1918   Fax: (847)934-1820
E-mail: info@jcaai.org
URL: http://www.jcaai.org

Description: Physicians specializing in allergy or clinical immunology. Members must belong to the American Academy of Allergy and Immunology or the American College of Allergy and Immunology. Serves as political and socioeconomic arm for these sponsoring organizations.

★8989★ Medicine & Related Occupations

Delphi Productions
3160 4th St.
Boulder, CO 80304
Fax: (303)443-4022   Fr: 888-443-2400
URL: http://www.delphivideo.com

$95.00. 45 minutes. Part of the Careers for the 21st Century Video Library.

★8990★ National Medical Association (NMA)

1012 10th St. NW
Washington, DC 20001
Ph: (202)347-1895   Fax: (202)371-1162
E-mail: president@nmanet.org
URL: http://www.nmanet.org

Description: Professional society of minority physicians.

★8991★ National Rehabilitation Association (NRA)

633 S Washington St.
Alexandria, VA 22314
Ph: (703)836-0850   Fax: (703)836-0848
E-mail: info@nationalrehab.org
URL: http://www.nationalrehab.org/website/index.html

Description: Providing   opportunities through knowledge and diversity for professionals in the fields of rehabilitation of people with disabilities.

★8992★ National Rural Health Association (NRHA)

1 W Armour Blvd., Ste. 203
Kansas City, MO 64111-2087
Ph: (816)756-3140   Fax: (816)756-3144
E-mail: mail@nrharural.org
URL: http://www.nrharural.org

Description: Administrators, physicians, nurses, physician assistants, health planners, academicians, and others interested or involved in rural health care. Creates a better understanding of health care problems unique to rural areas; utilizes a collective approach in finding positive solutions; articulates and represents the health care needs of rural America; supplies current information to rural health care providers; serves as a liaison between rural health care programs throughout the country. Offers continuing education credits for medical, dental, nursing, and management courses.

★8993★ Neuro-Developmental Treatment Association (NDTA)

1540 S Coast Hwy., Ste. 203
Laguna Beach, CA 92651
Fax: (949)376-3456   Fr: 800-869-9295
E-mail: membership@ndta.org
URL: http://www.ndta.org

Members: Physical and occupational therapists, speech pathologists, special educators, physicians, parents, and others interested in neurodevelopmental treatment. (NDT is a form of therapy for individuals who suffer from central nervous system disorders resulting in abnormal movement. Treatment attempts to initiate or refine normal stages and processes in the development of movement.) **Purpose:** Informs members of new developments in the field and with ideas that will eventually improve fundamental independence. **Activities:** Locates articles related to NDT.

★8994★ Physicians

Evon Publishing
832 N 7th Ave.
Iron River, MI 49935
Ph: (906)265-3190

Audiocassette. 1996. $16.95. 32 minutes. Part of the Careers and Vocational Guidance Series. Provides information about the nature of the work, educational requirements, employment outlook, earnings, and work conditions as well as additional related information.

Physicists and Astronomers

SOURCES OF HELP-WANTED ADS

★8995★ *AACG Newsletter*
American Association for Crystal Growth
25 Fourth St.
Somerville, NJ 08876
Ph: (908)575-0649   Fax: (908)575-0794
Description: Three issues/year. Contains news and features on developments in crystal growth and characterization, international research, and historical retrospectives. Recurring features include news from local AACG chapters, employment notices, coverage of meetings and conferences, letters to the editor, a calendar of events, and columns titled Crystal Growth News, Historical Perspectives, and The President's Corner.

★8996★ *Astronomy*
Kalmbach Publishing Co.
PO Box 1612
Waukesha, WI 53187-1612
Ph: (262)796-8776   Fax: (262)796-1615
Fr: 800-533-6644
URL: http://www.astronomy.com

Monthly. $39.95/year for individuals; $50.00/year for other countries; $4.95 for single issue. Magazine for the "star gazing public."

★8997★ *AWIS Magazine*
Association for Women in Science
1200 New York Ave. NW, Ste. 650
Washington, DC 20005
Ph: (202)326-8940   Fax: (202)326-8960
Fr: 800-886-AWIS
Description: Bimonthly. Covers issues, legislation, and trends related to science education for girls, women, and minorities. Includes information on grants and fellowships, job openings, educational programs, events, and notices of publications available.

★8998★ *The Electrochemical Society Interface*
Electrochemical Society Inc.
65 S Main St.
Pennington, NJ 08534-2839
Ph: (609)737-1902   Fax: (609)737-2743
E-mail: interface@electrochem.org
URL: http://www.electrochem.org

Quarterly. $40.00/year; $10.00 for single issue. Publication featuring news and articles of interest to members of the Electrochemical Society.

★8999★ *Journal of Vacuum Science and Technology A & B*
American Institute of Physics
1 Physics Ellipse
College Park, MD 20740-3843
Ph: (301)209-3000   Fax: (301)209-0842
E-mail: jvst@mcnc.org

Monthly. $670.00/year for individuals. Journal containing research review articles in all areas of vacuum science.

★9000★ *Laser Focus World*
PennWell Corp.
98 Spit Brook Rd.
Nashua, NH 03062-5737
Ph: (603)891-0123   Fax: (603)891-0574
URL: http://www.laserfocusworld.com

Monthly. $150.00/year for individuals; $200.00/year for Canada; $15.00 for single issue. Magazine covering advances and applications in optoelectronics and photonics.

★9001★ *Lasers & Optronics*
Reed Business Information
301 Gibraltar Dr.
Morris Plains, NJ 07950
Ph: (973)292-5100   Fax: (973)539-3476
URL: http://www.laseroptmag.com

Monthly. $55.00/year for individuals. Magazine serving the laser and optoelectronic market.

★9002★ *Nature International Weekly Journal of Science*
Nature Publishing Group
345 Park Ave. S
New York, NY 10010-1707
Ph: (212)726-9200   Fax: (212)689-9711
Fr: 888-331-6288
E-mail: nature@natureny.com
URL: http://www.nature.com

Weekly. $145.00/year for individuals; $495.00/year for institutions. Magazine covering science and technology, including the fields of biology, biochemistry, genetics, medicine, earth sciences, physics, pharmacology, and behavioral sciences.

★9003★ *PE & RS Photogrammetric Engineering & Remote Sensing*
The Imaging and Geospatial Information Society
5410 Grosvenor Ln., Ste. 210
Bethesda, MD 20814
Ph: (301)493-0290   Fax: (301)493-0208
E-mail: asprs@asprs.org

Monthly. $130.00/year. Journal covering photogrammetry, remote sensing, geographic information systems, cartography, and surveying, global positioning systems, digital photogrammetry.

★9004★ *The Physics Teacher*
American Association of Physics Teachers
One Physics Ellipse
College Park, MD 20740-3845
Ph: (301)209-3350   Fax: (301)209-0845
E-mail: tpt@appstate.edu
URL: http:///www.aapt.org/tpt

$94.00/year for individuals; $47.00/year. Scientific education magazine.

★9005★ *Physics Today*
American Institute of Physics
1 Physics Ellipse
College Park, MD 20740-3843
Ph: (301)209-3000   Fax: (301)209-0842
URL: http://www.physicstoday.org

Monthly. $2.25/year for members; $49.00/year for members of affiliated societies;

$69.00/year for nonmembers; $165.00/year for institutions; $15.00/year for shipping/handling via surface mail; $30.00/year for international airmail delivery; $20.00 for single issue. Journal covering news of physics research and activities that affect physics.

★9006★ *The Scientist*

The Scientist Inc.
3535 Market St., Ste. 200
Philadelphia, PA 19104-2645
Ph: (215)386-9601   Fax: (215)386-7542
Fr: 800-258-6008
E-mail: info@the-scientist.com
URL: http://www.the-scientist.com

Biweekly. $49.00/year for individuals; $149.00/year for institutions; $24.00/year for students; $82.00/year for other countries; $49.00/year for students, other countries; $174.00/year for institutions, other countries. News journal (tabloid) for life scientists featuring news, opinions, research, and professional section.

★9007★ *Sky & Telescope*

Sky Publishing Corp.
49 Bay State Rd.
Cambridge, MA 02138
Ph: (617)864-7360   Fax: (617)864-6117
Fr: 800-253-0245
URL: http://www.skypub.com

Monthly. $39.95/year for individuals; $29.95/year for students; $4.99/year for single issue. Magazine on astronomy and space science.

★9008★ *SPS Newsletter*

Society of Physics Students
One Physics Ellipse
College Park, MD 20740
Ph: (301)209-3007   Fax: (301)209-0839

Description: Four issues/year. Carries material of interest to undergraduate and graduate-level physics students, including articles on employment, available fellowships, meetings, and Society news.

PLACEMENT AND JOB REFERRAL SERVICES

★9009★ **American Association of Physicists in Medicine (AAPM)**

One Physics Ellipse
College Park, MD 20740-3846
Ph: (301)209-3350   Fax: (301)209-0862
E-mail: aapm@aapm.org
URL: http://www.aapm.org

Members: Persons professionally engaged in application of physics to medicine and biology in medical research and educational institutions; **Purpose:** Encourages interest and training in medical physics and related fields; promotes high professional standards; disseminates technical information. **Activi-**

ties: Maintains placement service. Conducts research programs. Member society of American Institute of Physics.

★9010★ **American Astronomical Society (AAS)**

2000 Florida Ave. NW, Ste. 400
Washington, DC 20009-1231
Ph: (202)328-2010   Fax: (202)234-2560
E-mail: aas@aas.org
URL: http://www.aas.org

Description: Astronomers, physicists, and scientists in related fields. Conducts Visiting Professor in Astronomy Program.

★9011★ **American Institute of Physics (AIP)**

1 Physics Ellipse
College Park, MD 20740-3843
Ph: (301)209-3100   Fax: (301)209-0843
E-mail: aipinfo@aip.org
URL: http://www.aip.org

Description: Corporation of ten national societies in the fields of physics, astronomy and related disciplines with a total of 100,000 members, 17 affiliated societies, 47 corporate associates, and 7500 student members. Seeks to assist in the advancement and diffusion of the knowledge of physics and its application to human welfare. To this end the institute publishes scientific journals devoted to physics and related sciences; provides secondary information services; provides online electronic journals serves the public by making available to the press and other channels of public information reliable communications on physics and its progress; carries on extensive career services activities; maintains projects directed toward providing information about physics education to students, physics teachers, and physics departments; encourages and assists in the documentation and study of the history of recent physics; cooperates with local, national, and international organizations devoted to physics; and fosters the relations of the science of physics to other sciences and to the arts and industry. Provides placement service; compiles statistics; maintains biographical archives and Niels Bohr Library of History of Physics.

★9012★ **Health Physics Society (HPS)**

1313 Dolley Madison Blvd., Ste. 402
McLean, VA 22101-3926
Ph: (703)790-1745   Fax: (703)790-2672
E-mail: hps@burkinc.com
URL: http://www.hps.org/

Description: Persons engaged in some form of activity in the field of health physics (the profession devoted to radiation protection). Works to improve public understanding of the problems and needs in radiation protection; to promote health physics as a profession. Maintains Elda E. Anderson Memorial Fund to be used for teachers, researchers, and others. Provides placement service at annual meeting. Co-sponsors American Board of Health Physics for certification of health physicists.

★9013★ **International Planetarium Society (IPS)**

PO Box 1812
Greenville, NC 27835
Ph: (252)328-6139   Fax: (252)328-621
E-mail: 102424.1032@compuserve.com
URL: http://www.ips-planetarium.org

Description: Planetarium staff members planetarium equipment suppliers; students in planetarium education and astronomy. Encourages exchange of ideas relating to planetariums and the profession. Operates placement service.

★9014★ **Korean Scientists and Engineers Association in America (KSEA)**

1952 Gallows Rd., Ste. 300
Vienna, VA 22182
Ph: (703)748-1221   Fax: (703)748-133
E-mail: sejong@ksea.org
URL: http://www.ksea.org

Description: Scientists and engineers holding single or advanced degrees. Goals are to: promote friendship and mutuality among Korean and American scientists and engineers; contribute to Korea's scientific, technological, industrial, and economic developments; strengthen the scientific, technological, and cultural bonds between Korea and the U.S. Sponsors symposium. Maintains speakers' bureau, placement service, and biographical archives. Compiles statistics Maintains 100 volume library of scientific handbooks and yearbooks in Korean.

★9015★ **Society for In Vitro Biology (SIVB)**

9315 Largo Dr., Ste. 255
Largo, MD 20774
Ph: (301)324-5054   Fax: (301)324-505?
Fr: 800-741-7476
E-mail: sivb@sivb.org
URL: http://www.sivb.org

Description: Professional society of individuals using mammalian, invertebrate, plant cell tissue, and organ cultures as research tools in chemistry, physics, radiation, medicine, physiology, nutrition, and cytogenetics Aims are to foster collection and dissemination of information concerning the maintenance and experimental use of tissue cells in vitro and to establish evaluation and development procedures. Operates placement service.

EMPLOYER DIRECTORIES AND NETWORKING LISTS

★9016★ *American Men and Women of Science*

Thomson Gale
27500 Drake Rd.
Farmington Hills, MI 48331-3535
Ph: (248)699-4253   Fax: (248)699-8065
Fr: 800-877-GALE

E-mail: amws@galegroup.com

Biennial, latest edition December 2002. $975.00. Covers over 129,700 U.S. and Canadian scientists active in the physical, biological, mathematical, computer science, and engineering fields; includes references to previous edition for deceased scientists and nonrespondents. Entries include: Name, address, education, personal and career data, memberships, honors and awards, research interest. Arrangement: Alphabetical. Indexes: Discipline (in separate volume).

★9017★ **Directory of Physics, Astronomy, and Geophysics Staff**

American Institute of Physics
1 Physics Ellipse
College Park, MD 20740-3843
Ph: (301)209-3100   Fax: (301)209-0843
URL: http://www.aip.org/catalog/books/dpags.html

Biennial. $65.00. Covers 31,000 staff members at 2,300 colleges, universities, and laboratories throughout North America that employ physicists and astronomers; list of foreign organizations. Entries include: Name, address, phone, fax, email address. Arrangement: Separate alphabetical sections for individuals, academic institutions, and laboratories. Indexes: Academic institution location, type of laboratory.

★9018★ **Peterson's Job Opportunities in Engineering and Technology**

Thomson Peterson's
PO Box 67005
Lawrenceville, NJ 08648-6105
Fr: 800-338-3282

Compiled by the Peterson's staff. Fourth edition, 1996. $21.95 (paper). 384 pages. Profiles 2,000 high-tech companies looking primarily for technical personnel in such fields as biotechnology, telecommunications, software, computers and peripherals, defense, and aerospace. Contains job-search strategies and career options to help match education and expertise to the job market. Indexed geographically, by industry, and by hiring needs.

HANDBOOKS AND MANUALS

★9019★ **The Best Resumes for Scientists and Engineers**

John Wiley & Sons Inc.
1 Wiley Dr.
Somerset, NJ 08873
Ph: (732)469-4400   Fr: 800-225-5945

Adele Lewis and David J. Moore. Second edition, 1993. $37.50; $19.95 (paper). 224 pages. Presents an extensive collection of scientific and engineering resumes, highlighting the important differences between these and resumes written for other occupations.

★9020★ **A Career in Theoretical Physics**

World Scientific Publishing Co. Inc.
1060 Main St.
River Edge, NJ 07661
Ph: (201)487-9655   Fax: (201)487-9656
Fr: 800-227-7562

Philip W. Anderson. 1994. $96.00; $51.00 (paper). 696 pages. Part of the Series in Twentieth Century Physics.

★9021★ **Guide to Nontraditional Careers in Science**

Hemisphere Publishing Corp.
325 Chestnut St., 8th Fl.
Philadelphia, PA 19106
Ph: (215)785-5800   Fax: (215)269-0363
Fr: 800-821-8312

Karen Young Kreeger. 1998. $38.95 (paper). 263 pages.

★9022★ **Opportunities in Environmental Careers**

McGraw-Hill Trade
2 Penn Plaza
New York, NY 10121
Ph: (212)904-2000   Fr: 800-722-4726
E-mail: ntcpub@tribune.com

Odom Fanning. Revised, 2002. $12.95 (paper). 160 pages. Describes a broad range of opportunities in fields such as environmental health, recreation, physics, and hygiene, and provides job search advice. Part of Opportunities in...Series.

★9023★ **Opportunities in High Tech Careers**

McGraw-Hill Trade
2 Penn Plaza
New York, NY 10121
Ph: (212)904-2000   Fr: 800-722-4726

Gary Colter and Deborah Yanuck. 1995. $14.95; $11.95 (paper). 160 pages. Explores high technology careers. Describes job opportunities, how to make a career decision, how to prepare for high technology jobs, job hunting techniques, and future trends.

★9024★ **Opportunities in Research and Development Careers**

McGraw-Hill/Contemporary Books
1221 Avenue of the Americas
New York, NY 10020
Ph: (212)904-2000   Fr: 800-323-4900
E-mail: ntcpub@tribune.com

Jan Goldberg. 1997. $14.95; $11.95 (paper). 204 pages.

★9025★ **Resumes for Scientific and Technical Careers**

McGraw-Hill Contemporary Books
1221 Avenue of the Americas
New York, NY 10020
Ph: (212)904-2000   Fr: 800-323-4900
E-mail: ntcpub@tribune.com

1999. $9.95 (paper). 450 pages. Provides

resume advice for individuals interested in working in scientific and technical careers. Includes sample resumes and cover letters.

★9026★ **To Boldly Go: A Practical Career Guide for Scientists**

American Geophysical Union
2000 Florida Ave., NW
Washington, DC 20009
Ph: (202)462-6900   Fax: (202)328-0566
Fr: 800-966-2481

Peter S. Fiske. 1996. $19.00 (paper).

EMPLOYMENT AGENCIES AND SEARCH FIRMS

★9027★ **Erspamer Associates**

4010 W. 65th St., Ste. 100
Edina, MN 55435
Ph: (952)925-3747   Fax: (952)925-4022
E-mail: hdhuntrel@aol.com

Executive search firm specializing in technical management.

★9028★ **International Staffing Consultants**

2901 W Coast Hwy.,Ste. 200
Newport Beach, CA 92663
Ph: (949)263-5933   Fax: (949)767-5959
E-mail: iscinc@iscworld.com
URL: http://www.iscworld.com

Employment agency. Provides placement on regular or temporary basis. Affiliate office in London.

TRADESHOWS

★9029★ **March Meeting of the American Physical Society**

American Physical Society
1 Physics Ellipse
College Park, MD 20740-3844
Ph: (301)209-3200   Fax: (301)209-0865
E-mail: exoffice@aps.org
URL: http://www.aps.org

Annual. **Primary Exhibits:** Physics equipment.

OTHER SOURCES

★9030★ American Almanac of Jobs and Salaries

Morrow Avon
1350 Avenue of the Americas
New York, NY 10019
Ph: (212)261-6788   Fr: 800-242-7737

John W. Wright. Revised edition, 2000. $20.00 (paper). 672 pages. This is a comprehensive guide to the wages of hundreds of occupations in a wide variety of industries and organizations.

★9031★ American Crystallographic Association (ACA)

PO Box 96, Ellicott Sta.
Buffalo, NY 14205-0096
Ph: (716)856-9600   Fax: (716)852-4846
E-mail: aca@hwi.buffalo.edu
URL: http://www.hwi.buffalo.edu/aca/

Members: Chemists, biochemists, physicists, mineralogists, and metallurgists interested in crystallography and in the application of X-ray, electron, and neutron diffraction. **Purpose:** Promotes the study of the arrangement of atoms in matter, its causes, its nature, and its consequences, and of the tools and methods used in such studies. **Activities:** Maintains employment clearinghouse for members and employers.

★9032★ American Physical Society (APS)

1 Physics Ellipse
College Park, MD 20740-3844
Ph: (301)209-3200   Fax: (301)209-0865
E-mail: exoffice@aps.org
URL: http://www.aps.org

Description: Scientists worldwide, dedicated to the advancement and the diffusion of the knowledge of physics. Publishes some of the leading international physics journals, organizes major scientific meetings, and provides strong outreach programs in physics education and in international and public affairs.

★9033★ ASPRS - The Imaging and Geospatial Information Society

5410 Grosvenor Ln., Ste. 210
Bethesda, MD 20814-2160
Ph: (301)493-0290   Fax: (301)493-0208
E-mail: asprs@asprs.org
URL: http://www.asprs.org

Members: Firms, individuals, government employees, and academicians engaged in photogrammetry, photointerpretation, remote sensing, and geographic information systems and their application to such fields as archaeology, geographic information systems, military reconnaissance, urban planning, engineering, traffic surveys, meteorological observations, medicine, geology, forestry, agriculture, construction, and topographic mapping. Mission is to advance knowledge and improve understanding of these sciences and to promote responsible applications. **Activities:** Offers voluntary certification program open to persons associated with one or more functional area of photogrammetry, remote sensing, and GIS. Surveys the profession of private firms in photogrammetry and remote sensing in the areas of productsand services

★9034★ Association for International Practical Training (AIPT)

10400 Little Patuxent Pky., Ste. 250
Columbia, MD 21044-3519
Ph: (410)997-2200   Fax: (410)992-3924
E-mail: aipt@aipt.org
URL: http://www.aipt.org

Description: Providers worldwide on-the-job training programs for students and professionals seeking international career development and life-changing experiences. Arranges workplace exchanges in hundreds of professional fields, bringing employers and trainees together from around the world. Client list ranges from small farming communities to Fortune 500 companies.

★9035★ Astronomical League

11305 King St.
Overland Park, KS 66210-3421
Ph: (913)469-0135
E-mail: m31@everestkc.net
URL: http://www.astroleague.org/

Description: Members of 250 astronomical societies and other interested individuals. Promotes the science of astronomy; encourages and coordinates activities of amateur astronomical societies; fosters observational and computational work and craftsmanship in various fields of astronomy; correlates amateur activities with professional research. Sponsors educational programs.

★9036★ Minority Women In Science (MWIS)

Directorate for Education and Human Resources Programs
1200 New York Ave. NW
Washington, DC 20005
Ph: (202)326-7019   Fax: (202)371-9849
E-mail: sassefa@aaas.org

Description: A national network group of the American association for the Advancement of Science (AAAS), Education and Human Resources Directorate. The objectives of this group are: to identify and share information on resources and programs that could help in mentoring young women and minorities interested in science and engineering careers, and to strengthen communication among women and minorities in science and education.

★9037★ Physicists and Astronomers

Evon Publishing
832 N 7th Ave.
Iron River, MI 49935
Ph: (906)265-3190

Audiocassette. 1996. $16.95. 32 minutes. Part of the Careers and Vocational Guidance Series. Provides information about the nature of the work, educational requirements, employment outlook, earnings, and work conditions as well as additional related information.

★9038★ Radiation Research Society (RRS)

10105 Cottesmore Ct.
Great Falls, VA 22066-3540
Ph: (703)757-4585   Fax: (703)757-0454
E-mail: info@radres.org
URL: http://www.radres.org

Description: Professional society of biologists, physicists, chemists, and physicians contributing to knowledge of radiation and its effects. Promotes original research in the natural sciences relating to radiation; facilitates integration of different disciplines in the study of radiation effects.

★9039★ Scientific, Engineering, and Technical Services

Cambridge Educational
2572 Brunswick Ave.
Lawrenceville, NJ 08648-4128
Fax: 800-FAX-ON-US   Fr: 800-468-4227
URL: http://www.cambridgeeducational.com

$89.95. 2002. 18 minutes. Part of the Career Cluster Series.

★9040★ Scientific Occupations

Delphi Productions
3160 4th St.
Boulder, CO 80304
Fax: (303)443-4022   Fr: 888-443-2400
URL: http://www.delphivideo.com

$95.00. 60 minutes. Part of the Careers for the 21st Century Video Library.

Plumbers

SOURCES OF HELP-WANTED ADS

★9041★ Builder
Hanley-Wood L.L.C.
1 Thomas Cir., Ste. 600
Washington, DC 20005
Ph: (202)452-0800   Fax: (202)785-1974
URL: http://www.builderonline.com

Monthly. $29.95/year for individuals. Magazine covering housing and construction industry.

★9042★ Construction Digest
Construction Digest
5804 W 74th St.
Indianapolis, IN 46278
Ph: (317)293-6860   Fax: (317)293-7840
Fr: 888-893-6860

Semimonthly. $3.00 for single issue. Magazine for the public works and construction engineering industries.

★9043★ CONSTRUCTOR
Associated General Contractors
  Information
333 John Carlyle St., Ste. 200
Alexandria, VA 22314
Ph: (703)837-5355   Fax: (703)837-5402
URL: http://www.agc.org

Monthly. $15.00/year for members; $250.00/year for nonmembers; $4.00/year for single issue except July, November, and December; $25.00/year for single issue-November, December; $325.00 for single issue-July. Management magazine for the Construction Industry.

★9044★ Contractor Magazine
Penton Media Inc.
2700 S River Rd., Ste. 109
Des Plaines, IL 60018
Ph: (847)299-3101   Fax: (847)299-3018
URL: http://www.contractormag.com

Industry news and management how-to magazine for heating, plumbing, piping, fire sprinkler, and other mechanical specialties contracting firms.

★9045★ Plumbing Engineer
TMB Publishing Inc.
1838 Techny Ct.
Northbrook, IL 60062
Ph: (847)564-1127   Fax: (847)564-1264
E-mail: info@plumbingengineer.com

Free to qualified subscribers; $50.00/year. Trade journal for consulting engineering, mechanical engineering, architecture, and contracting professionals.

★9046★ Professional Builder
Reed Business Information
360 Park Ave. S
New York, NY 10014
Ph: (646)746-7764
URL: http://www.probuilder.com

Monthly. $10.00 for single issue; $139.95/year for by mail.

★9047★ Reeves Journal
Business News Publishing Co.
23211 S Pointe Dr., Ste. 101
PO Box 30700
Laguna Hills, CA 92653
Ph: (949)830-0881   Fax: (949)859-7845
URL: http://www.reevesjournal.com

Monthly. Free to qualified subscribers. Regional plumbing, heating, and cooling magazine.

★9048★ Southern PHC Magazine
Southern Trade Publications Inc.
Box 7344
Greensboro, NC 27417
Ph: (336)454-3516   Fax: (336)454-3649

Bimonthly. Free to qualified subscribers; $10.00/year for others. Trade magazine covering plumbing, heating, and air conditioning, targeted to contractors and wholesalers in 14 southern states.

★9049★ WIT
Northern New England Tradeswomen
189 N Main St., Ste. 9
Barre, VT 05641-4173
Ph: (802)476-4040   Fax: (802)476-3346

Description: Three issues/year. Provides a network of support, information, and skill sharing for women in skilled trades professions.

EMPLOYER DIRECTORIES AND NETWORKING LISTS

★9050★ ABC Today-Associated Builders and Contractors National Membership Directory Issue
Associated Builders & Contractors Inc.
4250 N Fairfax Dr., 9th Fl.
Arlington, VA 22203
Ph: (703)812-2000   Fax: (703)812-8203

Annual, December. $150.00. Publication includes: List of approximately 19,000 member construction contractors and suppliers. Entries include: Company name, address, phone, name of principal executive, code to volume of business, business specialty. Arrangement: Classified by chapter, then by work specialty.

★9051★ Constructor-AGC Directory of Membership and Services Issue
AGC Information Inc.
333 John Carlyle St., Ste. 200
Alexandria, VA 22314
Ph: (703)548-3118   Fax: (703)548-3119
URL: http://www.agc.org

Annual, July. $250.00 for nonmembers; $15.00 for members; $250.00 for other countries. Publication includes: List of over 8,500 member firms and 24,000 national associate member firms engaged in building, highway, heavy, industrial, municipal utilities, and railroad construction (SIC 1541, 1542, 1611, 1622, 1623, 1629); listing of state and local chapter officers. Entries include: For firms-Company name, address, phone, fax, names of principal executives, and code indicating type of construction undertaken. For officers-Name, title, address. Arrangement: Geographical, Alphabetical. Indexes: Company name.

★9052★ **ENR-Top 400 Construction Contractors Issue**

McGraw-Hill Companies
1221 Ave. of the Americas
New York, NY 10020
Ph: (212)512-2000   Fax: (212)512-3840

Annual, May issue of "Engineering News Record". $10.00. Publication includes: List of 400 United States contractors receiving largest dollar volumes of contracts in preceding calendar year. Separate lists of 50 largest design/construct management firms; 50 largest program and construction managers; 25 building contractors; 25 heavy contractors. Entries include: Company name, headquarters location, total value of contracts received in preceding year, value of foreign contracts, countries in which operated, construction specialities. Arrangement: By total value of contracts received.

★9053★ **Mechanical Contractors Directory**

infoUSA Inc.
5711 S 86th Cir.
Omaha, NE 68127-0347
Ph: (402)930-3500   Fax: (402)331-0176
Fr: 800-555-6124
URL: http://www.abii.com

Annual. Number of listings: 6,849. Entries include: Name, address, phone (including area code), size of advertisement, year first in "Yellow Pages," name of owner or manager, number of employees. Compiled from telephone company "Yellow Pages," nationwide. Arrangement: Geographical.

★9054★ **Michigan Plumbing and Mechanical Contractors Association-Membership Directory**

Michigan Plumbing and Mechanical Contractors Association (MPMCA)
400 N Walnut St.
Lansing, MI 48933
Ph: (517)484-5500   Fax: (517)484-5225

Annual. Covers member firms, industry and auxiliary associations, legislative and regulatory agencies in the plumbing and heating industry of Michigan. Entries include: Organization name, address, phone, names and titles of key personnel. Arrangement: Separate sections for members, industry associations, legislative and regulatory, and auxiliaries; members are geographical. Indexes: Company name (members), president name (members).

★9055★ **Minnesota P-H-C Contractor-Membership Directory Issue**

Minnesota Association of Plumbing-Heating-Cooling Contractors
6300 Shingle Creek Pkwy., No. 275
Brooklyn Center, MN 55430-2183

Annual, July. Publication includes: List of 450 member firms and associates. Entries include: Name of company, address, phone, fax, code indicating type of work, local association affiliation (chapter memberships and other), name and title of owner or officer. Arrangement: Alphabetical. Indexes: Alphabetical by business.

★9056★ **Plumbing Contractors Directory**

infoUSA Inc.
5711 S 86th Cir.
Omaha, NE 68127-0347
Ph: (402)930-3500   Fax: (402)331-0176
Fr: 800-555-6124
URL: http://www.abii.com

Annual. Number of listings: 59,897. Entries include: Name, address, phone (including area code), size of advertisement, year first in "Yellow Pages," name of owner or manager, number of employees. Regional editions available. Compiled from telephone company "Yellow Pages," nationwide. Arrangement: Geographical.

★9057★ **Who's Who in the Plumbing-Heating-Cooling Contracting Business**

National Association of Plumbing, Heating, Cooling Contractors
180 S Washington St.
PO Box 6808
Falls Church, VA 22040
Ph: (703)237-8100   Fax: (703)237-7442
Fr: 800-533-7694

Annual. $75.00. Covers 4,000 professional plumbing/heating/cooling contractors and member firms. Entries include: Name, address, phone, fax, contact. Arrangement: Geographical. Indexes: Individual member.

HANDBOOKS AND MANUALS

★9058★ **Exploring Careers in the Construction Industry**

Rosen Publishing Group Inc.
29 E. 21st St.
New York, NY 10010
Ph: (212)777-3017   Fax: 888-436-4643
Fr: 800-237-9932

Elizabeth Stewart Lytle. Revised edition, 1994. $16.95; $9.95 (paper). Out of print.

★9059★ **Journeyman Plumber's Licensing Exam Guide**

The McGraw-Hill Companies
2 Penn Plaza, 20th Fl.
New York, NY 10121-2298
Ph: (212)904-4509   Fr: 800-338-3987

R. Dodge Woodson. 1995. $34.95; $24.95 (paper). Out of print.

★9060★ **Opportunities in Building Construction Trades**

McGraw-Hill Trade
2 Penn Plaza
New York, NY 10121
Ph: (212)904-2000   Fr: 800-722-4726

Michael Sumichrast. Second edition, 1998. $14.95; $11.95 (paper). 202 pages. From custom builder to rehabber, the many kinds of companies that employ craftspeople and contractors are explored. Includes job descriptions, requirements, and salaries for dozens of specialties within the construction industry. Contains a complete list of Bureau of Apprenticeship and Training state and area offices. Illustrated.

★9061★ **Opportunities in Plumbing and Pipefitting Careers**

McGraw-Hill Trade
2 Penn Plaza
New York, NY 10121
Ph: (212)904-2000   Fr: 800-722-4726

Patrick J. Galvin. 1993. $14.95; $10.95 (paper). 160 pages. Provides information on getting into the trade, apprenticeship programs, and how to build a career in a variety of settings. Illustrated.

★9062★ **Plumber's Licensing Study Guide**

McGraw-Hill Professional
Two Penn Plaza, 20th Flr.
New York, NY 10121-2298
Fr: 800-338-3987

R. Woodson. 2001. $39.95 (paper).

TRADESHOWS

★9063★ **American Society of Plumbing Engineers Convention**

American Society of Plumbing Engineers
8614 W. Catalpa Ave., No. 1007
Chicago, IL 60656-1116
Ph: (773)693-2773   Fax: (773)695-9007
E-mail: aspehq@aol.com
URL: http://www.aspe.org

Biennial. **Primary Exhibits:** Exhibits for the plumbing engineering industry. **Dates and Locations:** 2004 Oct 23-27; Cleveland, OH; Cleveland Convention Center.

★9064★ International Association of Plumbing and Mechanical Officials Conference

International Association of Plumbing and
  Mechanical Officials
c/o R and T International
5001 E Philadelphia St.
Ontario, CA 91761-2816
Ph: (909)595-8449   Fax: (909)594-3690
E-mail: iapmo@earthlink.net
URL: http://www.iapmo.org

Annual. **Primary Exhibits:** Plumbing equipment, supplies, and services.

★9065★ Massachusetts Association of Plumbing/Heating/Cooling Contractors Convention and Tradeshow

Massachusetts Association of Plumbing/
  Heating/Cooling Contractors
178 Forbes Rd., Ste. 218
Braintree, MA 02184
Ph: (617)843-3800   Fax: (781)843-1178
Fr: 800-542-7422
E-mail: phcc@shore.net

Annual. **Primary Exhibits:** Plumbing, heating and cooling equipment, supplies, and services.

★9066★ Michigan Plumbing and Mechanical Contractors Association Conference

Michigan Plumbing and Mechanical
  Contractors Association
400 N. Walnut St.
Lansing, MI 48933-1125
Ph: (517)484-5500   Fax: (517)484-5225
Fr: 800-292-1044

Annual. **Primary Exhibits:** Plumbing equipment, heating and cooling equipment, computers, insurance, and related products.

★9067★ National Plumbing-Heating-Cooling Piping Producers Exposition

National Association of Plumbing,
  Heating, Cooling Contractors
180 S. Washington St.
PO Box 6808
Falls Church, VA 22046
Ph: (703)237-8100   Fax: (703)237-7442
Fr: 800-533-7694
E-mail: naphcc@naphcc.org
URL: http://www.naphcc.org

Annual. **Primary Exhibits:** Equipment, supplies, and services for plumbing, heating, and cooling.

★9068★ The Ohio Plumbing Heating Cooling Expo

Ohio Association of Plumbing-Heating-
  Cooling Contractors
18961 Rivers Edge Dr.
Chagrin Falls, OH 44023
Ph: (440)543-4011   Fax: (440)543-1699
E-mail: ohiophcc@aol.com

Annual. **Primary Exhibits:** Products, tools, and services used by plumbing and heating contractors.

OTHER SOURCES

★9069★ American Society of Plumbing Engineers (ASPE)

8614 W Catalpa Ave., No. 1007
Chicago, IL 60656-1116
Ph: (773)693-2773   Fax: (773)695-9007
E-mail: info@aspe.org
URL: http://www.aspe.org

Description: Engineers and designers involved in the design and specification of plumbing systems; manufacturers, governmental officials, and contractors related to the industry may become members on a limited basis. Seeks to resolve professional problems in plumbing engineering; advocates greater cooperation among members and plumbing officials, contractors, laborers, and the public. Code committees examine regulatory codes pertaining to the industry and submit proposed revisions to code writing authorities to simplify, standardize, and modernize all codes. Sponsors American Society of Plumbing Engineers Research Foundation; operates certification program.

★9070★ American Society of Sanitary Engineering (ASSE)

901 Canterbury, Ste. A
Westlake, OH 44145
Ph: (440)835-3040   Fax: (440)835-3488
E-mail: info@asse-plumbing.org
URL: http://www.asse-plumbing.org/

Description: Plumbing officials, sanitary engineers, plumbers, plumbing contractors, building officials, architects, engineers, designing engineers, physicians, and others interested in health. Conducts research on plumbing and sanitation and develops performance standards for components of the plumbing system. Sponsors disease research program and other studies of waterborne epidemics.

★9071★ Associated Builders and Contractors (ABC)

1300 N. 17th St., Ste. 800
Rosslyn, VA 22209
Ph: (703)812-2000   Fax: (703)812-8201
E-mail: info@abc.org
URL: http://www.abc.org

Description: Construction contractors, subcontractors, suppliers, and associates. Aim is to foster and perpetuate the principles of rewarding construction workers and management on the basis of merit. Sponsors management education programs and craft training; also sponsors apprenticeship and skill training programs. Disseminates technological and labor relations information.

★9072★ Associated General Contractors of America (AGC)

333 John Carlyle St., Ste. 200
Alexandria, VA 22314
Ph: (703)548-3118   Fax: (703)548-3119
E-mail: sandhers@agc.org
URL: http://www.agc.org

Description: General construction contractors; subcontractors; industry suppliers; service firms. Provides market services through its divisions. Conducts special conferences and seminars designed specifically for construction firms. Compiles statistics on job accidents reported by member firms. ors. Maintains 65 committees, including joint cooperative committees with other associations and liaison committees with federal agencies.

★9073★ Associated Specialty Contractors (ASC)

3 Bethesda Metro Ctr., Ste. 1100
Bethesda, MD 20814
Ph: (301)657-3110   Fax: (301)215-4500
E-mail: dgw@necanet.org
URL: http://www.assoc-spec-con.org

Description: Subcontractor associations with a total of 25,000 members representing electrical, heating, piping, mechanical, air conditioning, sheet metal, plumbing, ventilating, painting and decorating, and roofing and insulation contractors. Promotes liaison with general contractors, architects, and engineers on inter-industry matters, codes, bidding, and contracting procedures. Coordinates governmental affairs, research, and educational matters.

★9074★ Building Trades

Delphi Productions
3160 4th St.
Boulder, CO 80304
Fax: (303)443-4022   Fr: 888-443-2400
URL: http://www.delphivideo.com

$95.00. 46 minutes. Part of the Careers for the 21st Century Video Library.

★9075★ COIN Career Guidance System

COIN Educational Products
3361 Executive Pky., Ste. 302
Toledo, OH 43606
Ph: (419)536-5353   Fax: (419)536-7056
Fr: 800-274-8515
URL: http://www.coin3.com/highschool/
guidance.asp

CD-ROM. Provides career information through seven cross-referenced files covering postsecondary schools, college majors, vocational programs, military service, apprenticeship programs, financial aid, and scholarships. Apprenticeship file describes national apprenticeship training programs, including information on how to apply, contact agencies, and program content. Military file describes more than 200 military occupations and training opportunities related to civilian employment.

★9076★ Mechanical Contractors Association of America (MCAA)

1385 Piccard Dr.
Rockville, MD 20850-4329
Ph: (301)869-5800   Fax: (301)990-9690
Fr: 800-556-3653
E-mail: jgentille@mcaa.org

URL: http://www.mcaa.org

Members: Contractors who furnish, install, and service piping systems and related equipment for heating, cooling, refrigeration, ventilating, and air conditioning systems. **Purpose:** Works to standardize materials and methods used in the industry. Conducts business overhead, labor wage, and statistical surveys. Maintains dialogue with key officials in building trade unions. Promotes apprenticeship training programs. Conducts seminars on contracts, labor estimating, job cost control, project management, marketing, collective bargaining, contractor insurance, and other management topics. Promotes methods to conserve energy in new and existing buildings. Sponsors Industrial Relations Council for the Plumbing and Pipe Fitting Industry.

★9077★ **National Association of Home Builders (NAHB)**
1201 15th St. NW
Washington, DC 20005
Ph: (202)266-8200   Fax: (202)822-0586
Fr: 800-368-5242
E-mail: info@nahb.com
URL: http://www.nahb.org

Description: Single and multifamily home builders, commercial builders, and others associated with the building industry. Lobbies on behalf of the housing industry and conducts public affairs activities to increase public understanding of housing and the economy. Collects and disseminates data on current developments in home building and home builders' plans through its Economics Department and nationwide Metropolitan Housing Forecast. Maintains NAHB Research Center, which functions as the research arm of the home building industry. Sponsors seminars and workshops on construction, mortgage credit, labor relations,

cost reduction, land use, remodeling, and business management. Compiles statistics; offers charitable program, spokesman training, and placement service; maintains speakers' bureau, and Hall of Fame. Subsidiaries include the National Council of the Housing Industry. Maintains over 50 committees in many areas of construction; operates National Commercial Builders Council, National Council of the Multifamily Housing Industry, National Remodelers Council, and National Sales and Marketing Council.

★9078★ **National Association of Women in Construction (NAWIC)**
327 S Adams St.
Fort Worth, TX 76104
Ph: (817)877-5551   Fax: (817)877-0324
Fr: 800-552-3506
E-mail: nawic@nawic.org
URL: http://www.nawic.org

Description: Seeks to enhance the success of women in the construction industry.

★9079★ *Plumber*
Cambridge Educational
2572 Brunswick Ave.
Lawrenceville, NJ 08648-4128
Fax: 800-FAX-ON-US   Fr: 800-468-4227
URL: http://www.cambridgeeducational.com

$39.95. 1993. Part of the Career Connections Series.

★9080★ *Plumbers and Pipefitters*
Evon Publishing
832 N 7th Ave.
Iron River, MI 49935
Ph: (906)265-3190

Audiocassette. 1996. $16.95. 32 minutes. Part of the Careers and Vocational Guidance

Series. Provides information about the nature of the work, educational requirements, employment outlook, earnings, and work conditions as well as additional related information.

★9081★ **Plumbing-Heating-Cooling Contractors Association (APHCC)**
180 S Washington St.
PO Box 6808
Falls Church, VA 22046
Ph: (703)237-8100   Fax: (703)237-7442
Fr: 800-533-7694
E-mail: naphcc@naphcc.org
URL: http://www.phccweb.org

Members: Federation of state and local associations of plumbing, heating, and cooling contractors. **Purpose:** Seeks to advance sanitation, encourage sanitary laws, and generally improve the plumbing, heating, ventilating, and air conditioning industries. **Activities:** Conducts apprenticeship training programs, workshops, and seminars; political action committee. Conducts educational and research programs.

★9082★ *Women in Building Construction*
Her Own Words
PO Box 5264
Madison, WI 53705-0264
Ph: (608)271-7083   Fax: (608)271-0209
URL: http://www.herownwords.com/

Video. Jocelyn Riley. $95.00. 15 minutes. Resource guide also available for $45.00.

Podiatrists

SOURCES OF HELP-WANTED ADS

★9083★ APMA News

American Podiatric Medical Association
9312 Old Georgetown Rd.
Bethesda, MD 20814
Ph: (301)581-9200   Fax: (301)530-2752
Fr: 800-ASK-APMA

Monthly. $65.00/year for individuals. Non-scientific news for member podiatrists.

★9084★ Journal of the Academy of Ambulatory Foot Surgery

Academy of Ambulatory Foot and Ankle Surgery
1601 Walnut, Ste. 1005
Philadelphia, PA 19102
Ph: (215)569-3303   Fax: (215)569-3310
Fr: 800-433-4892

Periodic. Professional journal covering issues in podiatry.

★9085★ Journal of the American Medical Women's Association

American Medical Women's Association
Eastern Virginia Medical School
825 Fairfax Ave.
Norfolk, VA 23507-1912
Ph: (757)446-7468   Fax: (757)446-7442
E-mail: jamwa@amwa-doc.org
URL: http://www.jamwa.org

Quarterly. $70.00/year; $80.00/year for out of country; $20.00 for single issue. Medical journal.

★9086★ Journal of the American Podiatric Medical Association

American Podiatric Medical Association
9312 Old Georgetown Rd.
Bethesda, MD 20814
Ph: (301)581-9200   Fax: (301)530-2752
Fr: 800-ASK-APMA
URL: http://www.japmaonline.org

Bimonthly. $125.00/year for nonmembers, U.S., Canada, Mexico; $156.00/year for non-members, other countries; $20.00 for single issue. Professional journal for podiatrists.

★9087★ Journal of the American Society of Podiatric Medical Assistants

American Society of Podiatric Medical Assistants
2124 S Austin Blvd.
Cicero, IL 60804
Ph: (708)863-6303   Fax: (708)863-5375
Fr: 888-88A-SPMA

Quarterly. Subscription included in membership. Professional journal covering issues in podiatry.

★9088★ The New England Journal of Medicine

The New England Journal of Medicine
860 Winter St.
Waltham Woods Corporate Ctr.
Waltham, MA 02451-1441
Ph: (781)893-4610
E-mail: nejmcust@mms.org
URL: http://www.nejm.org

Weekly. $135.00/year for individuals. Journal for the medical profession.

★9089★ Podiatry Management Magazine

Kane Communications Inc.
10 E Athens Ave., Ste. 208
Ardmore, PA 19003
Ph: (610)645-6940   Fax: (610)645-6943
E-mail: podiatrym@kanec.com

$30.00/year; $48.00 for two years. Magazine serving as a medical and surgical management guide for podiatrists.

★9090★ Southern Medical Journal

Southern Medical Association
35 Lakeshore Dr.
PO Box 190088
Birmingham, AL 35219-0088
Ph: (205)945-1840   Fax: (205)945-1830
Fr: 800-423-4992
E-mail: smj@sma.org
URL: http://www.sma.org/smj/index.cfm

Monthly. Multispecialty medical journal.

PLACEMENT AND JOB REFERRAL SERVICES

★9091★ American Association of Podiatric Physicians and Surgeons (AAPPS)

1328 Southern Ave. SE, Ste. 200
Washington, DC 20032
Ph: (202)562-2777   Fax: (202)562-5351
E-mail: rsbenjamin@aol.com

Members: Podiatrists. Seeks to represent members' interests and educate podiatrists and the public. **Purpose:** Provides training and certification for podiatry and podiatric surgery. Offers accreditation to agencies providing podiatric services, education, or training; also provides podiatric peer review. **Activities:** Operates speakers' bureau and placement service; compiles statistics.

★9092★ American Medical Association (AMA)

515 N State St.
Chicago, IL 60610
Ph: (312)464-5000   Fax: (312)464-4184
Fr: 800-621-8335
URL: http://www.ama-assn.org/

Description: County medical societies and physicians. Disseminates scientific information to members and the public. Informs members on significant medical and health legislation on state and national levels and represents the profession before Congress and governmental agencies. Cooperates in setting standards for medical schools, hospitals, residency programs, and continuing medical education courses. Offers physician placement service and counseling on practice management problems. Operates library which lends material and provides specific medical information to physicians. Ad-hoc committees are formed for such topics as health care planning and principles of medical ethics.

★9093★ American Public Health Association (APHA)
800 I St. NW
Washington, DC 20001-3710
Ph: (202)777-2742   Fax: (202)777-2534
E-mail: comments@apha.org
URL: http://www.apha.org

Members: Professional organization of physicians, nurses, educators, academicians, environmentalists, epidemiologists, new professionals, social workers, health administrators, optometrists, podiatrists, pharmacists, dentists, nutritionists, health planners, other community and mental health specialists, and interested consumers. **Purpose:** Seeks to protect and promote personal, mental, and environmental health. **Activities:** Services include promulgation of standards; establishment of uniform practices and procedures; development of the etiology of communicable diseases; research in public health; exploration of medical care programs and their relationships to public health. Sponsors job placement service.

EMPLOYER DIRECTORIES AND NETWORKING LISTS

★9094★ AHA Guide to the Health Care Field
American Hospital Association (AHA)
1 N. Franklin St., 27th Fl.
Chicago, IL 60606
Ph: (312)422-2050   Fax: (312)422-4700
Fr: 800-424-4301

Annual, August. $295.00. Covers hospitals, networks, multi-health care systems, freestanding ambulatory surgery centers, psychiatric facilities, long-term care facilities, substance abuse programs, and other health-related organizations. Entries include: For hospitals-Facility name, address, phone, administrator's name, number of beds, facilities and services, number of employees, expenses, other statistics. For other organizations-Name, address, phone, fax, name and title of contact. Arrangement: Geographical. Indexes: Hospital name.

★9095★ Directory of Hospital Personnel
Thomson Medical Economics
5 Paragon Dr.
Montvale, NJ 07645-1742
Ph: (201)358-7200   Fax: (201)722-2680

Annual, November. $325.00. Covers 200,000 executives at 7,000 U.S. hospitals. Entries include: Name of hospital, address, phone, number of beds, type and JCAHO status of hospital, names and titles of key department heads and staff, medical and nursing school affiliations; number of residents, interns, and nursing students. Arrangement: Geographical. Indexes: Hospital name, personnel, hospital size.

★9096★ HMO/PPO Directory
Thomson Medical Economics
5 Paragon Dr.
Montvale, NJ 07645-1742
Ph: (201)358-7200   Fax: (201)722-2680

Annual, November. $215.00. Covers over 600 health maintenance organizations (HMOs) and more than 1,000 preferred provider organizations (PPOs). Entries include: Name of organization, address, phone, number of members, names of officers, employer references, geographical area served, parent company, average fees and copayments, financial data, and cost control procedures. Arrangement: Geographical. Indexes: Organization name, personnel name, HMOs and PPOs by state, and number of members enrolled.

★9097★ Hospital Blue Book
Billian/Transworld Publishing Inc.
2100 Powers Ferry Rd.
Ste. 300
Atlanta, GA 30339
Ph: (770)955-8484   Fax: (770)955-8485
Fr: 800-533-8484
E-mail: blu-book@billian.com

Annual, January. $285.00 for national edition; $160.00 for southern edition. Covers more than 6,687 hospitals; some listings also appear in a separate southern edition of this publication. Entries include: Name of hospital, accreditation, mailing address, phone, fax, number of beds, type of facility (nonprofit, general, state, etc.); list of administrative personnel and chiefs of medical services, with specific titles. Arrangement: Geographical.

★9098★ Journal of the American Medical Association-Physician Service Opportunities Overseas Section
American Medical Association Alliance
515 N. State St.
Chicago, IL 60610
Ph: (312)464-5000   Fax: (312)464-5020
Fr: 800-621-8335

Irregular, latest edition August 2002. Publication includes: List of more than 60 organizations that provide assignments overseas for physicians from the United States. Entries include: Organization name, address, phone, contact person, countries served, and medical specialties sought. Arrangement: Alphabetical.

★9099★ Medical and Health Information Directory
Thomson Gale
27500 Drake Rd.
Farmington Hills, MI 48331-3535
Ph: (248)699-4253   Fax: (248)699-8065
Fr: 800-877-GALE
E-mail: businessproducts@gale.com

Annual. $285.00 per volume; $675.00 per set. Covers in Volume 1, more than 26,500 medical and health oriented associations, organizations, institutions, and government agencies, including health maintenance organizations (HMOs), preferred provider or-

ganizations (PPOs), insurance companies, pharmaceutical companies, research centers, and medical and allied health schools. In Volume 2, over 12,000 medical book publishers; medical periodicals, directories, audiovisual producers and services, medical libraries and information centers, electronic resources, and health-related internet search engines. In Volume 3, more than 35,500 clinics, treatment centers, care programs, and counseling/diagnostic services for 34 subject areas. Entries include: Institution, service, or firm name, address, phone, fax, email and URL; many include names of key personnel and, when pertinent, descriptive annotation. Volume 3 was formerly listed separately as Health Services Directory. Arrangement: Classified by organization activity, service, etc. Indexes: Each volume has a complete alphabetical name and keyword index.

★9100★ Podiatrists Directory
infoUSA Inc.
5711 S 86th Cir.
Omaha, NE 68127-0347
Ph: (402)930-3500   Fax: (402)331-0176
Fr: 800-555-6124
URL: http://www.abii.com

Annual. Number of listings: 21,010. Entries include: Name, address, phone (including area code), size of advertisement, year first in "Yellow Pages," name of owner or manager, number of employees. Compiled from telephone company "Yellow Pages," nationwide. Arrangement: Geographical.

HANDBOOKS AND MANUALS

★9101★ Expert Resumes for Health Care Careers
JIST Publishing
8902 Otis Ave.
Indianapolis, IN 46216-1033
Ph: (317)613-4200   Fax: 800-547-8329

December 2003. $16.95. 288 pages.

★9102★ Health Careers Today
Elsevier-Health Sciences Division
The Curtis Center, Ste. 300E, 3rd Fl.
170 S. Independence Mall W.
Philadelphia, PA 19106
Ph: (215)238-7800   Fax: (215)238-7362
Fr: 800-523-4069

Gerdin. Revised edition. April 2004. $52.95.

★9103★ Opportunities in Health and Medical Careers
McGraw-Hill Trade
2 Penn Plaza
New York, NY 10121
Ph: (212)904-2000   Fr: 800-722-4726

I. Donald Snook, Jr. and Leo D'Orazio. 1997. $14.95; $11.95 (paper). 202 pages. Covers

the full range of medical and health occupations. Illustrated.

★9104★ *Opportunities in Paramedical Careers*

McGraw-Hill/Contemporary Books
1221 Avenue of the Americas
New York, NY 10020
Ph: (212)904-2000   Fr: 800-323-4900
E-mail: ntcpub@tribune.com

Alex Kacen. Revised, 1999. $14.95; 11.95 (paper). 200 pages. Discusses a variety of opportunities in this field and how to pursue them. Illustrated.

★9105★ *Opportunities in Sports Medicine Careers*

McGraw-Hill Trade
2 Penn Plaza
New York, NY 10121
Ph: (212)904-2000   Fr: 800-722-4726
E-mail: ntcpub@tribune.com

William Ray Heitzmann. 1995. $14.95; $11.95 (paper). 160 pages. Discusses a variety of opportunities in this field and how to pursue them. Contains bibliography and illustrations.

★9106★ *Resumes for Health and Medical Careers*

McGraw-Hill Trade
2 Penn Plaza
New York, NY 10121
Ph: (212)904-2000   Fr: 800-722-4726
E-mail: ntcpub@tribune.com

1997. $9.95 (paper). 455 pages.

EMPLOYMENT AGENCIES AND SEARCH FIRMS

★9107★ Harper Associates

29870 Middlebelt
Farmington Hills, MI 48334
Ph: (248)932-1170   Fax: (248)932-1214
E-mail: resumes@harperjobs.com
URL: http://www.harperjobs.com

Executive search firm and employment agency.

★9108★ Phyllis Hawkins and Associates

105 E Northern Ave.
Phoenix, AZ 85020
Ph: (602)263-0248   Fax: (602)678-1564
E-mail: phassoc@qweat.com
URL: http://www.azlawsearch.com

Executive search firm focusing on attorney searches.

★9109★ Physicians Search, Inc.

5581 E. Stetson Ct.
Anaheim, CA 92807-4650
Ph: (714)685-1047   Fax: (714)685-1143
Fr: 800-748-6320
E-mail: info@physicianssearch.com
URL: http://www.physicianssearch.com

Executive search firm. Affiliate office in Spokane, WA.

★9110★ Professional Placement Associates, Inc.

287 Bowman Ave., Ste. 309
Purchase, NY 10577
Ph: (914)251-1000   Fax: (914)251-1055
E-mail: lschachter@ppasearch.com
URL: http://www.ppasearch.com

Executive search firm specializing in the health and medical field.

★9111★ Shiloh Careers International, Inc.

7105 Peach Ct., Ste102
PO Box 831
Brentwood, TN 37024-0831
Ph: (615)373-3090   Fax: (615)373-3480
E-mail: maryann@shilohcareers.com
URL: http://www.shilohcareers.com

Employment agency serving the industry field.

★9112★ Team Placement Service, Inc.

5113 Leesburg Pike, Ste. 510
Falls Church, VA 22041-3242
Ph: (703)820-8618   Fax: (703)820-3368
Fr: 800-495-6767
E-mail: 4jobs@teamplace.com
URL: http://www.teamplace.com

Temporary agency that also handles some permanent placements.

★9113★ Weatherby Locum

6451 N Federal Hwy. , Ste. 80
Fort Lauderdale, FL 33308
Ph: (203)866-1144   Fax: 800-463-2985
Fr: 800-365-8900
E-mail: info@weatherbylocums.com
URL: http://www.weatherbylocums.com

Executive search firm for physicians. Branch office in Fairfax, VA.

ONLINE JOB SOURCES AND SERVICES

★9114★ MDJobsite.com

E-mail: contact@mdjobsite.com
URL: http://www.mdjobsite.com/

Description: Career search site for physicians. Physicians can search thousands of physician employment opportunities, register for email notifications of new jobs listed in

their specialty and post a CV searchable by facilities and healthcare firms nationwide.

★9115★ Medhunters.com

E-mail: info@medhunters.com
URL: http://www.medhunters.com

Description: Career search site for jobs in all health care specialties; educational resources; visa and licensing information for relocation; interesting articles; relocation tools; links to professional organizations and general resources.

★9116★ ProHealthJobs

E-mail: sales@prohealthjobs.com
URL: http://www.prohealthjobs.com

Description: Career resources site for the medical and health care field. Lists professional opportunities, product information, continuing education and open positions.

TRADESHOWS

★9117★ American College of Foot and Ankle Surgeons Annual Meeting and Scientific Seminar

American College of Foot and Ankle Surgeons
515 Busse Hwy.
Park Ridge, IL 60068
Ph: (847)292-2237   Fax: (847)292-2022
Fr: 800-421-2237
E-mail: mail@acfas.org
URL: http://www.acfas.org

Annual. **Primary Exhibits:** Surgical and podiatric products.

★9118★ American Podiatric Medical Association Annual Meeting

American Podiatric Medical Association
9312 Old Georgetown Rd.
Bethesda, MD 20814-1698
Ph: (301)571-9200   Fax: (301)530-2752

Annual. **Primary Exhibits:** Podiatric supplies and services.

★9119★ Western Podiatric Medical Congress

California Podiatric Medical Association
2430 K St., Ste. 200
Sacramento, CA 95816
Ph: (916)448-0248   Fax: (916)448-0258

Annual. **Primary Exhibits:** Surgical supplies, X-ray equipment, computers, pharmaceuticals and general medical supplies and equipment.

OTHER SOURCES

★9120★ *American Almanac of Jobs and Salaries*

Morrow Avon
1350 Avenue of the Americas
New York, NY 10019
Ph: (212)261-6788   Fr: 800-242-7737

John W. Wright. Revised edition, 2000. $20.00 (paper). 672 pages. This is a comprehensive guide to the wages of hundreds of occupations in a wide variety of industries and organizations.

★9121★ **American Association of Hospital Podiatrists (AAHP)**

8508 18th Ave.
Brooklyn, NY 11214
Ph: (718)259-1822   Fax: (718)259-4002

Description: A general specialty group of the American Podiatric Medical Association. Podiatrists (trained and certified persons dealing in the care and diseases of the foot) who are affiliated with hospitals. Seeks to: elevate the standards of podiatry practices in hospitals and health institutions; standardize hospital podiatry procedures, charting, recording forms, and methods; promote understanding among personnel in podiatry, medicine, and allied health professions; aid podiatrists in attaining institutional affiliations; assist in the educational and teaching programs of health institutions and hospitals; foster the development of podiatric internships and residencies in hospitals and institutions. Compiles statistics.

★9122★ **American Board of Podiatric Orthopedics and Primary Podiatric Medicine (ABPOPPM)**

22910 Crenshaw Blvd., Ste. B
Torrance, CA 90505
Ph: (310)891-0100   Fax: (310)891-0500
E-mail: admin@abpoppm.org
URL: http://www.abpoppm.org/

Description: Podiatrists who have taken a competency exam prepared by the board. Offers certifying examinations in podiatric orthopedics and primary podiatric medicine aims at improving public health by encouraging and elevating standards for practicing podiatrics.

★9123★ **American Board of Podiatric Surgery (ABPS)**

445 Fillmore St.
San Francisco, CA 94117-3404
Ph: (415)553-7800   Fax: (415)553-7801
E-mail: info@abps.org
URL: http://www.abps.org

Description: Podiatrists certified as diplomates. Objectives are to protect and improve public health by advancing the science of foot surgery and by encouraging the study and evaluation of standards of foot surgery; to act upon application for certification of legally licensed podiatrists to ascertain their competency in foot surgery; to grant certificates to candidates who have met all qualifications.

★9124★ **American Hospital Association (AHA)**

1 N. Franklin
Chicago, IL 60606-3421
Ph: (312)422-3000   Fax: (312)422-4796
URL: http://www.aha.org

Description: Health care provider organizations. Seeks to advance the health of individuals and communities. Leads, represents, and serves health care provider organizations that are accountable to the community and committed to health improvement.

★9125★ **American Podiatric Medical Association (APMA)**

9312 Old Georgetown Rd.
Bethesda, MD 20814-1621
Ph: (301)581-9200   Fax: (301)530-2752
Fr: 800-ASK-APMA
E-mail: askapma@apma.org

URL: http://www.apma.org

Description: Professional society of doctors of podiatric medicine.

★9126★ *Exploring Health Occupations*

Cambridge Educational
2572 Brunswick Ave.
Lawrenceville, NJ 08648-4128
Fax: 800-FAX-ON-US   Fr: 800-468-422
URL: http://www.cambridgeeducational.com

Two videos. $139.95. 1999.

★9127★ *Health Service Occupations*

Delphi Productions
3160 4th St.
Boulder, CO 80304
Fax: (303)443-4022   Fr: 888-443-240
URL: http://www.delphivideo.com

$95.00. 50 minutes. Part of the Careers for the 21st Century Video Library.

★9128★ *Medicine & Related Occupations*

Delphi Productions
3160 4th St.
Boulder, CO 80304
Fax: (303)443-4022   Fr: 888-443-240
URL: http://www.delphivideo.com

$95.00. 45 minutes. Part of the Careers for the 21st Century Video Library.

★9129★ *Podiatrists*

Evon Publishing
832 N 7th Ave.
Iron River, MI 49935
Ph: (906)265-3190

Audiocassette. 1996. $16.95. 32 minutes. Part of the Careers and Vocational Guidance Series. Provides information about the nature of the work, educational requirements, employment outlook, earnings, and work conditions as well as additional related information.

Political and Legislative Aides

SOURCES OF HELP-WANTED ADS

★9130★ Civil Rights Journal
U.S. Commission on Civil Rights
624 Ninth St. NW
Washington, DC 20425
Annual. Publication covering civil rights and political science.

★9131★ In These Times
Institute for Public Affairs Inc.
2040 N Milwaukee Ave., 2nd Fl.
Chicago, IL 60647-4002
Ph: (773)772-0100   Fax: (773)772-4180
Fr: 888-READ-ITT
E-mail: itt@inthesetimes.com
URL: http://www.inthesetimes.com
Biweekly. $36.95/year for individuals. National political newsmagazine.

★9132★ Presidential Studies Quarterly
Blackwell Publishing
350 Main St.
Malden, MA 02148
Ph: (781)388-8200   Fax: (781)388-8210
Fr: 800-759-6102
E-mail: center@thepresidency.org
URL: http://www.blackwell-synergy.com
Quarterly. Publication covering political science and history.

PLACEMENT AND JOB REFERRAL SERVICES

★9133★ American Political Science Association (APSA)
527 New Hampshire Ave. NW
Washington, DC 20036-1206
Ph: (202)483-2512   Fax: (202)483-2657
E-mail: apsa@apsanet.org
URL: http://www.apsanet.org

Description: College and university teachers of political science, public officials, research workers, and businessmen. "Encourages the impartial study and promotes the development of the art and science of government." Develops research projects of public interest and educational programs for political scientists and journalists; seeks to improve the knowledge of and increase citizen participation in political and governmental affairs. Serves as clearinghouse for teaching and research positions in colleges, universities, and research bureaus in the U.S. and abroad and for positions open to political scientists in government and private business; conducts Congressional Fellowship Program, which enables political scientists and journalists to spend a year working with members of Congress and congressional committees; conducts the Committee on Professional Ethic, Rights and Freedom which is concerned with the professional ethics, human rights, and academic freedom of political scientists. Gives cash awards and citations for best books and theses of the year in various phases of political science at annual convention. Offers placement service.

EMPLOYER DIRECTORIES AND NETWORKING LISTS

★9134★ Carroll's Federal Directory
Carroll Publishing
145 Taylor St., NE
Washington, DC 20017
Ph: (202)281-2410   Fax: (202)281-2408
Fr: 800-336-4240
URL: http://www.carrollpub.com
Bimonthly. $395.00. Covers about 40,000 executive managers in federal government offices in Washington, DC, including executive, congressional and judicial branches; members of Congress and Congressional committees and staff. Entries include: Agency names, titles, office address (including room numbers), e-mail addresses, and telephone and fax numbers. Also available as part of a "library edition" titled "Federal Directory Annual". Arrangement: By cabinet department or administrative agency. Indexes: Keyword, personal name (with phone) and e-mail addresses.

★9135★ Congressional Directory
Capitol Advantage
PO Box 2018
Order Department
Merrifield, VA 22116
Ph: (703)550-9500   Fax: (703)550-0406
Fr: 877-827-3321
URL: http://congress.nw.dc.us
Annual. $14.95. Covers 100 current senators and 440 House of Representative members. Entries include: Name, district office address, phone, fax; names and titles of key staff; committee and subcommittee assignments; biographical data, percentage of votes won, photo. Arrangement: Available in separate alphabetical, geographical, or condensed editions. Indexes: Name.

★9136★ Congressional Yellow Book
Leadership Directories Inc.
104 5th Ave.
New York, NY 10011
Ph: (212)627-4140   Fax: (212)645-0931
E-mail: congressional@leadershipdirectories.com
URL: http://www.leadershipdirectories.com
Quarterly. $356.00. Covers members of Congress and their principal aides, Congressional committees, leadership, and congressional support arms. Entries include: For members of Congress-Name, Washington office address, party affiliation, state or district represented, year began service, reelection year; names, titles, and legislative responsibilities of principal aides, member's committee assignments and other responsibilities; photograph, biographical data, fax, and map of district; state and district office addresses and phone; ZIP codes by congressional district. For committees-Committee name, office address, phone, members' names and parties, description of committee jurisdiction, fax, key staff for full and subcommittees. Arrangement: Alphabetical by member of Congress or committee name. Indexes: Name, subject, organization.

★9137★ United States Government Manual
Office of the Federal Register
National Archives and Records
  Administration
Washington, DC 20408
Ph: (202)741-6040   Fax: (202)741-6012
URL: http://www.access.gpo.gov/su_docs/

Annual, September; latest edition 2002-2003. $40.00. The "Manual" is the official handbook of the United States government, and includes descriptions and lists of principal personnel of agencies and other bodies in the legislative, judicial, and executive branches; the executive branch is covered in greatest depth. (The "Manual" devotes roughly 40 of 700 pages to the legislative branch and 20 to the judicial; the "Congressional Directory," described in a separate listing, devotes roughly 260 of 1,200 pages to the executive branch and 60 to the judicial.) Text of the listings is primarily concerned with programs and activities rather than administrative structure, but general organization charts are given. The "Congressional Directory" and the "Manual" comprise the "database" for principal federal government organizations and personnel. Entries include: For each cabinet department and independent agency or other unit, titles of major administrative posts and the names of incumbents are given, along with a description of the unit's responsibilities. Additional listings of subordinate offices and bureaus give similar information. Addresses and phone numbers are provided for units at most levels, as well as for obtaining detailed information on consumer activities, contracts and grants, employment, publications, and other areas of public interest. Arrangement: Classified by department and agency. Indexes: Personal name, agency/subject.

★9138★ Washington: A Comprehensive Directory of the Key Institutions and Leaders in the National Capital Area
Columbia Books Inc.
1825 Connecticut Ave., Ste. 625
Washington, DC 20009
Ph: (202)464-1662   Fax: (202)464-1775
Fr: 888-265-0600
URL: http://www.columbiabooks.com

Annual, May. $149.00. Covers over 5,000 federal and district government offices, businesses, associations, publications, radio and television stations, labor organizations, religious and cultural institutions, health care facilities and community organizations in the District of Columbia area. Entries include: Name, address, phone, names and titles of key personnel and board of directors. Arrangement: Classified by subject. Indexes: Individuals, organizations.

★9139★ Washington Information Directory
CQ Press
1255 22nd St. NW, Ste. 400
Washington, DC 20037
Ph: (202)729-1800   Fax: 800-380-3810
Fr: (866)427-7737

URL: http://www.cqpress.com

Annual, latest edition 2003. $120.00. Covers 5,000 governmental agencies, congressional committees, and non-governmental associations considered competent sources of specialized information. Entries include: Name of agency, committee, or association; address, phone, fax, and internet; annotation concerning function or activities of the office; and name of contact. Arrangement: Classified by activity or competence (economics and business, housing and urban affairs, etc.). Indexes: Subject, agency/organization name, contact name.

HANDBOOKS AND MANUALS

★9140★ The Book of US Government Jobs: Where They Are, What's Available and How to Get One
Bookhaven Press LLC
PO Box 1243
Moon Township, PA 15108
Ph: (412)494-6926

Dennis Damp. Eighth edition. May 2002. 288 pages.

★9141★ Career Opportunities in Politics, Government, and Activism
Checkmark Books
132 West 31st St., 17th Fl.
New York, NY 10001

Joan Axelrod-Contrada and John Kerry. May 2003. 274 pages.

★9142★ Great Jobs for Political Science Majors
McGraw-Hill Companies
1221 Avenue of the Americas
New York, NY 10020
Ph: (212)904-2000   Fr: 800-323-4900
E-mail: ntcpub@tribune.com

Mark Rowh. 1998. $11.95 (paper). 340 pages. Includes index.

★9143★ The Insider's Guide to Political Internships: What to Do Once You're in the Door
Westview Press
5500 Central Ave.
Boulder, CO 80301

Grant Reeher, Mack Mariani. September 2002. 240 pages.

★9144★ Politico's Guide to Careers in Politics and Government
Methuen
215 Vauxhall Bridge Rd.
London SW1V 1EJ, United Kingdom
Sally Gillman. March 2002. 217 pages.

★9145★ Washington Job Source
Benjamin Scott Publishing
20 E. Colorado Blvd., No. 202
Pasadena, CA 91105
Ph: (626)449-1339   Fax: (626)449-138
Fr: 800-448-4959

Fifth edition, 2002.

ONLINE JOB SOURCES AND SERVICES

★9146★ Political and Government Career Resources
URL: http://www.politixgroup.com
Description: Job listings.

OTHER SOURCES

★9147★ Congressional Black Caucus (CBC)
1720 Massachusetts Ave. NW
Washington, DC 20036
Ph: (202)263-2800   Fax: (202)775-077
Fr: 800-784-2577
E-mail: info@cbcfinc.org
URL: http://www.cbcfonline.org/

Members: Black members of the U.S House of Representatives. **Purpose:** T address the legislative concerns of black an other underrepresented citizens and to fo malize and strengthen the efforts of it members. Works to implement these objectives through personal contact with othe House members, through the disseminatio of information to individual black constitu ents, and by working closely with blac elected officials in other levels of goverr ment. **Activities:** Establishes a yearly legis lative agenda setting forth the issues which supports: full employment, national healt development, welfare reform, and interna tional affairs.

★9148★ Local and State Government Service
Evon Publishing
832 N 7th Ave.
Iron River, MI 49935
Ph: (906)265-3190

Audiocassette. 1996. $16.95. 32 minutes Part of the Careers and Vocational Guidanc Series. Provides information about the na ture of the work, educational requirements employment outlook, earnings, and worl conditions as well as additional related infor mation.

Political Scientists

SOURCES OF HELP-WANTED ADS

★9149★ Civil Rights Journal

U.S. Commission on Civil Rights
624 Ninth St. NW
Washington, DC 20425
Annual. Publication covering civil rights and political science.

★9150★ Federal Times

Army Times Publishing Co.
6883 Commercial Dr.
Springfield, VA 22159-0001
Ph: (703)750-9000   Fax: (703)750-8767
E-mail: mcofed@aol.com
URL: http://www.armytimes.com

Weekly. $52.00/year for individuals; $2.00 for single issue. Federal bureaucracy; technology in government.

★9151★ In These Times

Institute for Public Affairs Inc.
2040 N Milwaukee Ave., 2nd Fl.
Chicago, IL 60647-4002
Ph: (773)772-0100   Fax: (773)772-4180
Fr: 888-READ-ITT
E-mail: itt@inthesetimes.com
URL: http://www.inthesetimes.com

Biweekly. $36.95/year for individuals. National political newsmagazine.

★9152★ Presidential Studies Quarterly

Blackwell Publishing
350 Main St.
Malden, MA 02148
Ph: (781)388-8200   Fax: (781)388-8210
Fr: 800-759-6102
E-mail: center@thepresidency.org
URL: http://www.blackwell-synergy.com

Quarterly. Publication covering political science and history.

★9153★ State Politics & Policy Quarterly

University of Illinois Press
1325 S Oak St.
Champaign, IL 61820-6903
Ph: (217)333-0950   Fax: (217)244-8082
Fr: 800-537-5487
URL: http://www.press.uillinois.edu/journals/sppq.html

Quarterly. $95.00/year for institutions; $135.00/year for institutions, out of country; $40.00/year for individuals; $80.00/year for individuals, out of country; $48.00 for single issue, institutions; $12.00/year for single issue, individuals. Official journal of the State Politics and Policy section of the American Political Science Association covering studies that develop general hypotheses of the political behavior and policymaking and test those hypotheses using methodological advantages of the states.

★9154★ White House Studies

Nova Science Publishers Inc.
400 Oser Ave., Ste. 1600
Hauppauge, NY 11788-3619
Ph: (631)231-7269   Fax: (631)231-8175
Annual. Publication covering political science and history.

PLACEMENT AND JOB REFERRAL SERVICES

★9155★ African Studies Association (ASA)

Rutgers the State University of New Jersey
132 George St.- Douglass Campus
New Brunswick, NJ 08901-1400
Ph: (732)932-8173
E-mail: callasa@rci.rutgers.edu

Members: Persons specializing in teaching, writing, or research on Africa including political scientists, historians, geographers, anthropologists, economists, librarians, linguists, and government officials; persons who are studying African subjects; institutional members are universities, libraries, government agencies, and others interested in receiving information about Africa. **Purpose:** Seeks to foster communication and to stimulate research among scholars on Africa. **Activities:** Sponsors placement service; conducts panels and discussion groups; presents exhibits and films.

★9156★ American Political Science Association (APSA)

1527 New Hampshire Ave. NW
Washington, DC 20036-1206
Ph: (202)483-2512   Fax: (202)483-2657
E-mail: apsa@apsanet.org
URL: http://www.apsanet.org

Description: College and university teachers of political science, public officials, research workers, and businessmen. "Encourages the impartial study and promotes the development of the art and science of government." Develops research projects of public interest and educational programs for political scientists and journalists; seeks to improve the knowledge of and increase citizen participation in political and governmental affairs. Serves as clearinghouse for teaching and research positions in colleges, universities, and research bureaus in the U.S. and abroad and for positions open to political scientists in government and private business; conducts Congressional Fellowship Program, which enables political scientists and journalists to spend a year working with members of Congress and congressional committees; conducts the Committee on Professional Ethic, Rights and Freedom which is concerned with the professional ethics, human rights, and academic freedom of political scientists. Gives cash awards and citations for best books and theses of the year in various phases of political science at annual convention. Offers placement service.

EMPLOYER DIRECTORIES AND NETWORKING LISTS

★9157★ American Political Science Association-Centennial Biographical Directory of Members

American Political Science Association
1527 New Hampshire Ave. NW
Washington, DC 20036-1206
Ph: (202)483-2512   Fax: (202)483-2657

Irregular, latest edition January 2001. $95.00. Number of listings: 13,500. Entries include: Name, address, affiliation, highest degree, fields of interest, phone, e-mail, URL, honors, employment history, publications. Arrangement: Alphabetical. Indexes: Women members, African American members, Asian American members, Latino/members, Native American members, fields of interest, geographical.

★9158★ Carroll's Federal Directory

Carroll Publishing
145 Taylor St., NE
Washington, DC 20017
Ph: (202)281-2410   Fax: (202)281-2408
Fr: 800-336-4240
URL: http://www.carrollpub.com

Bimonthly. $395.00. Covers about 40,000 executive managers in federal government offices in Washington, DC, including executive, congressional and judicial branches; members of Congress and Congressional committees and staff. Entries include: Agency names, titles, office address (including room numbers), e-mail addresses, and telephone and fax numbers. Also available as part of a "library edition" titled "Federal Directory Annual". Arrangement: By cabinet department or administrative agency. Indexes: Keyword, personal name (with phone) and e-mail addresses.

★9159★ Complete Guide to Public Employment

Impact Publications
9104 Manassas Dr., Ste. N
Manassas Park, VA 20111-5211
Ph: (703)361-7300   Fax: (703)335-9486

Triennial, latest edition 1994. $34.95 for cloth copy; $19.95 for paper copy. Publication includes: List of federal, state, and local government agencies and departments, trade and professional associations, contracting and consulting firms, nonprofit organizations, foundations, research organizations, political support groups, and other organizations offering public service career opportunities. Entries include: Organization name, address, phone, name and title of contact. Complete title is "Complete Guide to Public Employment: Opportunities and Strategies with Federal, State, and Local Government; Trade and Professional Associations; Contracting and and Consulting Firms; Foundations; Research Organizations; and Political Support Groups." Arrangement: Classified by type of service. Indexes: Subject.

★9160★ Encyclopedia of Governmental Advisory Organizations

Thomson Gale
27500 Drake Rd.
Farmington Hills, MI 48331-3535
Ph: (248)699-4253   Fax: (248)699-8065
Fr: 800-877-GALE
E-mail: businessproducts@gale.com

Annual. $685.00. Covers more than 7,300 boards, panels, commissions, committees, presidential conferences, and other groups that advise the President, Congress, and departments and agencies of federal government; includes interagency committees and federally sponsored conferences. Also includes historically significant organizations. Entries include: Unit name, address, phone, URL and email (if active), name of principal executive, legal basis for the unit, purpose, reports and publications, findings and recommendations, description of activities, members. Arrangement: Classified by general subject. Indexes: Alphabetical/keyword, personnel, publication, federal department/agency, presidential administration.

★9161★ Federal Yellow Book

Leadership Directories Inc.
104 5th Ave.
New York, NY 10011
Ph: (212)627-4140   Fax: (212)645-0931
E-mail: federal@leadershipdirectories.com
URL: http://www.leadershipdirectories.com/fyb.htm

Quarterly. $375.00 for first annual subscription; $262.00 for each additional subscription. Covers federal departments, including the Executive Office of the President, the Office of the Vice President, the Office of Management and Budget, the Cabinet, and the National Security Council, and over 40,000 key personnel; over 70 independent federal agencies. Entries include: For personnel-Name, address, phone, fax, e-mails, titles. For departments and agencies-Office, or branch name and address; names and titles of principal personnel, with their room numbers, direct-dial phone numbers, and E-mails. Arrangement: Classified by department or agency. Indexes: Subject, organization, individuals' names.

★9162★ International Directory for Youth Internships

Council on International & Public Affairs
777 United Nations Plz., No.3C
New York, NY 10017
Ph: (212)972-9877   Fax: 800-316-2739
Fr: 800-316-2739

Latest edition 1993. $7.50. Covers United Nations agencies and nongovernmental organizations offering intern and volunteer opportunities. Entries include: Agency, organization, or office name, address, description of internship. Arrangement: Classified by type of organization.

★9163★ Jewish Americans and Political Participation

ABC-CLIO
130 Cremona Dr.
Santa Barbara, CA 93117
Ph: (805)968-1911   Fax: (805)685-9685
Fr: 800-368-6868

$55.00. Publication includes: List of American Jewish historical and political organizations. Entries include: Name, address, phone, and Web site address. Principal content of publication is a historical and current look at the participation of Jews in American politics. Indexes: Alphabetical.

★9164★ Personnel Service Newsletter

American Political Science Association
1527 New Hampshire Ave. NW
Washington, DC 20036-1206
Ph: (202)483-2512   Fax: (202)483-2657
E-mail: psn@apsanet.org
URL: http://www.apsanet.org

Monthly. Covers academic, governmental, and other positions currently open for political scientists, and opportunities for graduate research, study, travel, scholarly exchange abroad. Entries include: For professional openings-Employer name, address, name of contact, description of position; some listings include phone. For fellowships-Name of sponsoring institution, contact name, address, phone, description of award, goals, requirements, deadline. Arrangement: Classified by type of position (administrative, academic, fellowship, late notice); academic positions are by subject area.

★9165★ United States Government Manual

Office of the Federal Register
National Archives and Records Administration
Washington, DC 20408
Ph: (202)741-6040   Fax: (202)741-6012
URL: http://www.access.gpo.gov/su_docs/

Annual, September; latest edition 2002-2003. $40.00. The "Manual" is the official handbook of the United States government, and includes descriptions and lists of principal personnel of agencies and other bodies in the legislative, judicial, and executive branches; the executive branch is covered in greatest depth. (The "Manual" devotes roughly 40 of 700 pages to the legislative branch and 20 to the judicial; the "Congressional Directory," described in a separate listing, devotes roughly 260 of 1,200 pages to the executive branch and 60 to the judicial.) Text of the listings is primarily concerned with programs and activities rather than administrative structure, but general organization charts are given. The "Congressional Directory" and the "Manual" comprise the "database" for principal federal government organizations and personnel. Entries include: For each cabinet department and independent agency or other unit, titles of major administrative posts and the names of incumbents are given, along with a description of the unit's responsibilities. Additional listings of subordinate offices and bureaus give similar information. Addresses and phone numbers are provided for units at most levels, as well as for obtaining detailed information on consumer activities, contracts and grants, employment, publications, and other areas of public interest. Arrangement: Classified by department and agency. Indexes: Personal name, agency/subject.

★9166★ **Washington: A Comprehensive Directory of the Key Institutions and Leaders in the National Capital Area**
Columbia Books Inc.
1825 Connecticut Ave., Ste. 625
Washington, DC 20009
Ph: (202)464-1662   Fax: (202)464-1775
Fr: 888-265-0600
URL: http://www.columbiabooks.com

Annual, May. $149.00. Covers over 5,000 federal and district government offices, businesses, associations, publications, radio and television stations, labor organizations, religious and cultural institutions, health care facilities and community organizations in the District of Columbia area. Entries include: Name, address, phone, names and titles of key personnel and board of directors. Arrangement: Classified by subject. Indexes: Individuals, organizations.

★9167★ **Washington Information Directory**
CQ Press
1255 22nd St. NW, Ste. 400
Washington, DC 20037
Ph: (202)729-1800   Fax: 800-380-3810
Fr: (866)427-7737
URL: http://www.cqpress.com

Annual, latest edition 2003. $120.00. Covers 5,000 governmental agencies, congressional committees, and non-governmental associations considered competent sources of specialized information. Entries include: Name of agency, committee, or association; address, phone, fax, and internet; annotation concerning function or activities of the office; and name of contact. Arrangement: Classified by activity or competence (economics and business, housing and urban affairs, etc.). Indexes: Subject, agency/organization name, contact name.

HANDBOOKS AND MANUALS

★9168★ **The Book of US Government Jobs: Where They Are, What's Available and How to Get One**
Bookhaven Press LLC
PO Box 1243
Moon Township, PA 15108
Ph: (412)494-6926

Dennis Damp. Eighth edition. May 2002. 288 pages.

★9169★ **Career Opportunities in Politics, Government, and Activism**
Checkmark Books
132 West 31st St., 17th Fl.
New York, NY 10001

Joan Axelrod-Contrada and John Kerry. May 2003. 274 pages.

★9170★ **Careers in International Affairs**
Georgetown University Press
3600 O St. NW
Washington, DC 20007-0866
Ph: (202)687-5889   Fr: 800-246-9606

School of Foreign Service, Georgetown University Staff. Sixth edition, 1996. $17.95 (paper). 320 pages. Includes index and bibliography.

★9171★ **Careers & the Study of Political Science: A Guide for Undergraduates**
American Political Science Association
1527 New Hampshire Ave., NW
Washington, DC 20036-1206
Ph: (202)483-2512   Fax: (202)483-2657

Sixth edition, 2001. $6.00 (paper).

★9172★ **Great Jobs for Political Science Majors**
McGraw-Hill Companies
1221 Avenue of the Americas
New York, NY 10020
Ph: (212)904-2000   Fr: 800-323-4900
E-mail: ntcpub@tribune.com

Mark Rowh. 1998. $11.95 (paper). 340 pages. Includes index.

★9173★ **Guide to Careers in World Affairs**
Impact Publications
9104-N Manassas Dr., Ste. N
Manassas Park, VA 20111-5211
Ph: (703)361-7300   Fax: (703)335-9486

Foreign Affairs Association Staff and Pamela Gerard. Third edition. 1993. $14.95. 331 pages. Out of print. Describes jobs in business, government, and nonprofit organizations. Explains the methods and credentials required to secure a job in many fields, including international law and journalism. Contains sections on internships and graduate programs.

★9174★ **The Insider's Guide to Political Internships: What to Do Once You're in the Door**
Westview Press
5500 Central Ave.
Boulder, CO 80301

Grant Reeher, Mack Mariani. September 2002. 240 pages.

★9175★ **Opportunities in Social Science Careers**
McGraw-Hill Companies
860 Taylor Station Rd.
Blacklick, OH 43004-0545
Fax: (614)755-5645   Fr: 800-722-4726

Rosanne J. Marek. March 2004. $22.95. 160 Pages. VGM Opportunities Series.

★9176★ **Politico's Guide to Careers in Politics and Government**
Methuen
215 Vauxhall Bridge Rd.
London SW1V 1EJ, United Kingdom

Sally Gillman. March 2002. 217 pages.

TRADESHOWS

★9177★ **American Political Science Association Meeting**
American Political Science Association
1527 New Hampshire Ave., NW
Washington, DC 20036-1206
Ph: (202)483-2512   Fax: (202)483-2657
E-mail: apsa@apsanet.org

Primary Exhibits: Publications and computer software.

OTHER SOURCES

★9178★ **Academy of Political Science (APS)**
475 Riverside Dr., Ste. 1274
New York, NY 10115-1274
Ph: (212)870-2500   Fax: (212)870-2202
E-mail: aps@psqonline.org
URL: http://www.psqonline.org

Members: Individual members, libraries and institutions. **Purpose:** Promotes the cultivation of political science and its application to the solution of political, social, and economic problems.

★9179★ **American Academy of Political and Social Science (AAPSS)**
3814 Walnut St.
Philadelphia, PA 19104-6197
Ph: (215)746-6500   Fax: (215)898-1202
E-mail: rwpearso@sas.upenn.edu
URL: http://www.aapss.org

Members: Professionals and laymen concerned with the political and social sciences and related fields. **Purpose:** Promotes the progress of political and social science through publications and meetings. The academy does not take sides in controversial issues, but seeks to gather and present reliable information to assist the public in forming an intelligent and accurate judgment.

★9180★ American Association of Political Consultants (AAPC)

600 Pennsylvania Ave., SE, Ste. 330
Washington, DC 20003
Ph: (202)544-9815   Fax: (202)544-9816
E-mail: info@theaapc.org
URL: http://www.theaapc.org

Description: Regular members are corporations and individuals who devote a major portion of their time to or earn a major portion of their livelihood from political counseling and related activities; associate members are persons who devote part of their time to or earn part of their living from political counseling, have an interest in the political process, are teachers of political science, or intend to become actively involved in political activities. Provides a vehicle for the exchange of information, resources, and ideas among persons involved in political activity. Arranges seminars and holds biennial updates on campaign techniques and professional advances.

★9181★ Congressional Black Caucus (CBC)

1720 Massachusetts Ave. NW
Washington, DC 20036
Ph: (202)263-2800   Fax: (202)775-0773
Fr: 800-784-2577
E-mail: info@cbcfinc.org
URL: http://www.cbcfonline.org/

Members: Black members of the U.S. House of Representatives. **Purpose:** To address the legislative concerns of black and other underrepresented citizens and to formalize and strengthen the efforts of its members. Works to implement these objectives through personal contact with other House members, through the dissemination of information to individual black constituents, and by working closely with black elected officials in other levels of government. **Activities:** Establishes a yearly legislative agenda setting forth the issues which it supports: full employment, national health development, welfare reform, and international affairs.

★9182★ International Studies Association (ISA)

324 Social Sciences Bldg.
University of Arizona
Tucson, AZ 85721
Ph: (520)621-7715   Fax: (520)621-5780
E-mail: isa@u.arizona.edu
URL: http://www.isanet.org

Members: Social scientists and other scholars from a wide variety of disciplines who are specialists in international affairs and cross-cultural studies; academicians; government officials; officials in international organizations; business executives; students. **Purpose:** Promotes research, improved teaching, and the orderly growth of knowledge in the field of international studies; emphasizes a multidisciplinary approach to problems. **Activities:** Conducts conventions, workshops and discussion groups.

★9183★ *Storming Washington: An Intern's Guide to National Government*

American Political Science Association
1527 New Hampshire Ave., NW
Washington, DC 20036-1206
Ph: (202)483-2512   Fax: (202)483-2657

Stephen E. Frantzich. Fourth edition, 1994. $6.00 (paper). 63 pages.

★9184★ U.S. Public Interest Research Group (U.S.PIRG)

218 D. St. SE
Washington, DC 20003
Ph: (202)546-9707   Fax: (202)546-2461
E-mail: uspirg@pirg.org
URL: http://www.pirg.org

Description: Individuals who contribute time, effort, or funds toward public interest research and advocacy. Conducts research, monitors corporate and government actions, and lobbies for reforms on consumer, environmental, energy, and governmental issues. Current efforts include support for: laws to protect consumers from unsafe products and unfair banking practices; laws to reduce the use of toxic chemicals; strengthening clean air laws; efforts to reduce global warming and ozone depletion; energy conservation and use of safe, renewable energy sources. Sponsors internships for college students; provides opportunities for students to receive academic credit for activities such as legislative research, lobbying, and public education and organizing. Offers summer jobs.

★9185★ Women's Caucus for Political Science (WCPS)

Center for Urban Affairs of Policy
   Research
Northwestern University
Evanston, IL 60201
Ph: (847)491-8726   Fax: (847)491-9116
E-mail: mansbridge@nwu.edu
URL: http://www.uwm.edu/Org/WCPS/

Members: Women professionally trained in political science. **Purpose:** Purposes are to: upgrade the status of women in the profession of political science; promote equal opportunities for women political scientists for graduate admission, financial assistance in such schools, and in employment, promotion, and tenure. **Activities:** Advances candidates for consideration for APSA offices and committees.

Postal Service Workers

SOURCES OF HELP-WANTED ADS

★9186★ The American Postal Worker
American Postal Workers Union, AFL-CIO
1300 L St. NW
Washington, DC 20005
Ph: (202)842-4200   Fax: (202)842-4297
Monthly. $3.00/year for individuals. AFL-CIO postal labor union.

★9187★ Postal Bulletin
Superintendent of Documents
PO Box 371954
MS4004-MIB
Pittsburgh, PA 15250-7954
Ph: (202)512-1800
Biweekly. $118.00/year for individuals; $147.50/year for other countries; $7.00 for single issue; $9.38 for single issue, other countries. Bulletin reporting U.S. Postal Service news.

★9188★ Postal Record
National Association of Letter Carriers
100 Indiana Ave. NW
Washington, DC 20001-2144
Ph: (202)393-4695
Monthly. Subscription included in membership. Magazine for active and retired letter carriers.

★9189★ Postmasters Gazette
National Association of Postmasters of the United States
8 Herbert St.
Alexandria, VA 22305-2600
Ph: (703)683-9027   Fax: (703)683-6820
Monthly. $10.00/year for individuals. Postal magazine.

EMPLOYER DIRECTORIES AND NETWORKING LISTS

★9190★ National Five-Digit Zip Code and Post Offices Directory
U.S. Postal Service
6060 Primacy Pkwy., Ste. 201
Memphis, TN 38188-0001
Fax: (901)767-8853   Fr: 800-238-3150
Annual, January. $18.00. Covers post offices, named stations, named branches, community post offices, and place names of former post offices frequently used as delivery addresses. Also includes Postal Service regional offices, bulk mail centers, etc. Zip codes are given for cities, for buildings having their own zip codes, and for streets and blocks within zip code areas. Entries include: For post offices–Post office name, county, states, and zip code. For Postal Service installations–Office name, mailing address, areas served. Arrangement: Post offices are listed alphabetically and by zip code. Cities which have more than one zip code are listed separately by state, then city, with buildings and other installations with their own zip code listed first. Discontinued post offices and military installation zip code lists are also provided separately.

★9191★ Who's Who-The MFSA Buyer's Guide to Blue Ribbon Mailing Services
Mail & Fulfillment Service Association
1421 Prince St., No. 410
Alexandria, VA 22314-2806
Ph: (703)836-9200   Fax: (703)548-8204
URL: http://www.mfsanet.org
Annual, December. Covers 750 member firms that provide printing, addressing, inserting, sorting, and other mailing services, and mailing list brokers. Entries include: Firm name; MFSA representative name and title, address, phone, coded list of services, gross business volume for latest year. Arrangement: Geographical. Indexes: Company name, personal name, geographical, product/service.

HANDBOOKS AND MANUALS

★9192★ Post Office Jobs: How to Get a Job With the U.S. Postal Service
Bookhaven Press LLC
PO Box 1243
Moon Township, PA 15108
Ph: (412)494-6926   Fax: (412)494-5749
Dennis V. Damp. Third edition. 2003. 256 pages. Includes tips on how to identify job openings, preparing for interviews, and a study guide for exams.

ONLINE JOB SOURCES AND SERVICES

★9193★ Mailman Stuff
URL: http://www.mailmanstuff.com
Description: Shared resources for letter carriers.

★9194★ Postmasters Online
URL: http://ourworld-top.cs.com/rupzip/home.htm
Description: Provides current news and links to other postal sites.

TRADESHOWS

★9195★ National Association of Postmasters of the United States Convention
National Association of Postmasters of the United States
8 Herbert St.
Alexandria, VA 22305-2600
Ph: (703)683-9027   Fax: (703)683-6820
E-mail: napus1@napus.org

Annual. **Primary Exhibits:** Office supplies and materials for the postal service.

OTHER SOURCES

★9196★ Association of Mailing, Shipping, and Office Automation Specialists (AIMED)
949 Winding Brook Ln.
Walnut, CA 91789-1119
Fax: (909)594-9743   Fr: 888-750-6245
E-mail: barbara@aimedweb.org
URL: http://www.aimedweb.org

Members: Independent dealers of mail-related products and services; manufacturers of mailing equipment. **Purpose:** Works to keep members informed about industry changes and new products. **Activities:** Maintains speakers' bureau, hall of fame; conducts educational programs.

★9197★ Association for Postal Commerce (PostCom)
1901 N Fort Myer Dr., Ste. 401
Arlington, VA 22209-1609
Ph: (703)524-0096   Fax: (703)524-1871
E-mail: info@postcom.org
URL: http://www.postcom.org

Members: Represents supporters and users of mail as an advertising, marketing, and fundraising medium. Seeks to protect interests of members with respect to postal rates and services before Congress, the U.S. Postal Service, and the Postal Rate Commission.

★9198★ Mail Systems Management Association (MSMA)
JAF Bldg.
Box 2155
New York, NY 10116-2155
Fr: 800-955-6762
URL: http://www.msmanational.org/

Description: Mail management executives. Provides training, through the development of management skills, in reducing costs, improving services, and reducing employee turnover. Organizes meetings to discuss topics such as presort discounts, scheduling, and recruiting and training personnel. Conducts certification program, training programs for mail distribution clerks, and management programs for mail managers and supervisors. Maintains placement service. Conducts research; operates speakers' bureau and consulting service.

★9199★ National Association of Letter Carriers
100 Indiana Ave., NW
Washington, DC 20001
URL: http://www.nalc.org

Description: Union.

★9200★ National Association of Postmasters of the United States (NAPUS)
8 Herbert St.
Alexandria, VA 22305-2600
Ph: (703)683-9027   Fax: (703)683-6820
E-mail: napusinfo@napus.org
URL: http://www.napus.org/

Purpose: Serves the professional interests of postmasters and promotes cooperation and interchange of ideas between members and officials of the U.S. Postal Service.

★9201★ National League of Postmasters
1023 N. Royal St.
Alexandria, VA 22314
Ph: (703)548-5922
URL: http://www.postmasters.org/contact.asp

Description: Organized to encourage contact among members, to advance the proficiency of personnel, and to improve working conditions.

★9202★ National Postal Forum (NPF)
50 W Corporate Center
3998 Fair Ridge Dr., Ste. 300
Fairfax, VA 22033-2907
Ph: (703)218-5015   Fax: (703)218-5020
E-mail: info@npf.org
URL: http://www.npf.org

Members: Postal authorities and businesses making use of the postal service.

Purpose: Seeks to ensure the most efficient use of postal services by businesses. **Activities:** Serves as a clearinghouse on products and services offered by the U.S. Postal Service; conducts educational and training programs for business mailers.

★9203★ National Postal Mail Handlers Union
1101 Connecticut Ave., NW, Ste. 500
Washington, DC 20036
Ph: (202)833-9095
URL: http://www.npmhu.org

Description: Negotiates contracts and protects workers' rights.

★9204★ National Rural Letter Carriers Association
1630 Duke St., Fourth Fl.
Alexandria, VA 22314
Ph: (703)684-5545
URL: http://home.nrlca.org

Description: Seeks to improve the methods used by rural letter carriers, to benefit their conditions of labor, and to promote a fraternal spirit.

★9205★ National Star Route Mail Contractors Association (NSRMCA)
324 E. Capitol St.
Washington, DC 20003-3897
Ph: (202)543-1661   Fax: (202)543-8863
E-mail: info@starroutecontractors.org
URL: http://www.starroutecontractors.org

Description: Highway mail contractors with the U.S. Postal Service transporting mail over the highway on authorized schedules.

★9206★ Parcel Shippers Association (PSA)
1211 Connecticut Ave. NW, Ste. 610
Washington, DC 20036-2701
Ph: (202)296-3690   Fax: (202)296-0343
E-mail: psa@parcelshippers.org
URL: http://www.parcelshippers.org

Members: Wholesalers, retailers, mail order houses, and other firms using parcel post service for distribution of products. **Purpose:** Promotes the efficient and economical distribution of small package shipments.

Preschool Teachers

SOURCES OF HELP-WANTED ADS

★9207★ AAEE Connections
American Association for Employment in Education
3040 Riverside Dr., Ste. 125
Columbus, OH 43221
Ph: (614)485-1111   Fax: (614)485-9609
Description: Quarterly. Publishes news of the Association, whose aim is "to enhance and promote the concept of career planning and placement as an integral part of the educational process and to undertake activities designed to help schools, colleges, and universities meet their educational staffing needs." Also concerned with teacher education and the supply of/demand for teachers. Recurring features include news of members, state and regional news, and announcements of upcoming conferences and meetings.

★9208★ Academic Exchange Quarterly
Rapid Intellect Group Inc.
PO Box 131
Stuyvesant Falls, NY 12174
Ph: (518)372-1347
E-mail: AEQ@rapidintellect.com
URL: http://rapidintellect.com/AEQweb/
Quarterly. $156.00/year for individuals; $116.00/year, professional rate; $39.00 for single issue. Periodical covering issues in education.

★9209★ Journal of Language, Identity, and Education
Lawrence Erlbaum Associates Inc.
10 Industrial Ave.
Mahwah, NJ 07430-2262
Ph: (201)236-9500   Fax: (201)236-0072
Fr: 800-9-BOOKS-9
E-mail: journals@erlbaum.com
URL: http://www.erlbaum.com/shop/tek9.asp?pg=products&specific=1
Quarterly. $40.00/year for individuals; $70.00/year for out of country; $225.00/year for institutions; $255.00/year for institutions,

other countries. Scholarly, interdisciplinary journal covering issues in language, identity and education worldwide for academics, educators and policy specialists in a variety of disciplines, and others.

★9210★ Journal of Latinos and Education
Lawrence Erlbaum Associates Inc.
10 Industrial Ave.
Mahwah, NJ 07430-2262
Ph: (201)236-9500   Fax: (201)236-0072
Fr: 800-9-BOOKS-9
E-mail: journals@erlbaum.com
URL: http://www.erlbaum.com/shop/tek9.asp?pg=products&specific=1
Quarterly. $40.00/year for individuals; $70.00/year for out of country; $195.00/year for institutions; $225.00/year for institutions, other countries. Scholarly, multidisciplinary journal covering educational issues that impact Latinos for researchers, teaching professionals, academics, scholars, institutions, and others.

★9211★ Journal of Teacher Education
Boston College
McElroy Commons, No. 113
Chestnut Hill, MA 02467
Ph: (617)552-4820   Fax: (617)552-4823
Magazine of interest to educators.

★9212★ Matrix: The Magazine for Leaders in Higher Education
Professional Media Group L.L.C.
36 Clipper Ct., Ste. B
Mystic, CT 06355-2138
Bimonthly. Trade publication covering issues for higher education professionals.

★9213★ NJEA Review
New Jersey Education Association
180 W State St.
PO Box 1211
Trenton, NJ 08607
Ph: (609)599-4561   Fax: (609)392-6321
E-mail: lgalley@mgea.org

$25.00/year. Educational journal for public school employees.

★9214★ Teaching/K-8
Teaching/K-8
40 Richards Ave.
Norwalk, CT 06854-2509
Ph: (203)855-2650   Fax: (203)855-2656
Fr: 800-249-9363
E-mail: teachingk8@aol.com
URL: http://www.teachingk-8.com
$14.99/year for individuals. Magazine for elementary teachers.

★9215★ Today's OEA
Oregon Education Association
6900 SW Atlanta St.
Portland, OR 97223-2513
Ph: (503)684-3300   Fax: (503)684-8063
Bimonthly. Free to qualified subscribers; $10.00/year for nonmembers. Membership magazine covering educational issues statewide and nationally.

PLACEMENT AND JOB REFERRAL SERVICES

★9216★ American Montessori Society (AMS)
281 Park Ave. S, 6th Fl.
New York, NY 10010
Ph: (212)358-1250   Fax: (212)358-1256
E-mail: east@amshq.org
URL: http://www.amshq.org
Description: School affiliates and teacher training affiliates; heads of schools, teachers, parents, non-Montessori educators, and other interested individuals dedicated to stimulating the use of the Montessori teaching approach and promoting better education for all children. Formed to meet demands of growing interest in the Montessori approach to early learning. Developed in Italy in 1907 by Dr. Maria Montessori, the system "is based on the young child's instinctive love

and need for purposeful work realized in an environment prepared with auto-educative, multi-sensory, manipulative learning devices for language, math, science, and practical life. Freedom within limits and individual growth fostered in classes with three year age mix and peer stimulation. Teacher's role is that of observer and catalyst." Assists in establishing schools; supplies information and limited services to member schools in other countries. Maintains school consultation and accreditation service; provides information service; assists research and gathers statistical data; offers placement service. Maintains Montessori and related materials exhibit.

★9217★ Association for Direct Instruction (ADI)
PO Box 10252
Eugene, OR 97440
Ph: (541)485-1293   Fax: (541)683-7543
Fr: 800-995-2464
E-mail: info@adihome.org
URL: http://www.adihome.org

Members: Public school regular and special education teachers and university instructors. **Purpose:** Encourages, promotes, and engages in research aimed at improving educational methods. Promotes dissemination of developmental information and skills that facilitate the education of adults and children. **Activities:** Administers a preschool for developmentally delayed children. Offers educational training workshops for instructors. Maintains speakers' bureau, and placement service.

EMPLOYER DIRECTORIES AND NETWORKING LISTS

★9218★ Independent School Guide for Washington DC and Surrounding Area
Lift Hill Press Inc.
4930-A Eisenhower Ave.
Alexandria, VA 22304
Ph: (703)212-9113   Fax: (703)212-9114
Fr: 800-699-9113
URL: http://www.washingtonbk.com

Biennial. $15.95. Covers over 475 independent schools (including parochial schools) in the Washington, DC area, including Maryland and Virginia. Entries include: School name, address, phone, name and title of contact, number of faculty, geographical area served, tuition, courses, admission procedures, summer programs, LD/ED programs, scholarships available. Arrangement: Alphabetical. Indexes: Geographical.

★9219★ National Directory of Alternative Schools
National Coalition of Alternative Community Schools
1289 Jewett St.
Ann Arbor, MI 48104-6201
Ph: (734)668-9171   Fax: (734)769-9629
Fr: 888-771-9171

Biennial, odd years. $18.00. Covers over 500 alternative education programs, including home schools, and state and regional coalitions of alternative schools and colleges; also lists organizations and networks offering services and resources to those working with children; international coverage. Entries include: Name, address, phone, name of contact; many also include descriptions of programs. Arrangement: Schools are geographical. Indexes: Complete index of entries.

★9220★ Nursery Schools & Kindergartens Directory
infoUSA Inc.
5711 S 86th Cir.
Omaha, NE 68127-0347
Ph: (402)930-3500   Fax: (402)331-0176
Fr: 800-555-6124
URL: http://www.abii.com

Annual. Number of listings: 44,016. Entries include: Name, address, phone (including area code), size of advertisement, year first in "Yellow Pages," name of owner or manager, number of employees. Regional editions available. Compiled from telephone company "Yellow Pages," nationwide. Arrangement: Geographical.

HANDBOOKS AND MANUALS

★9221★ Career Information Center
Macmillan Publishing Co. Inc.
200 Old Tappan Rd.
Old Tappan, NJ 07675
Fr: 800-428-5331

Visual Education Center Staff. Seventh edition, 1999. $275.00. 2080 pages. This 13-volume set profiles over 600 occupations. Each occupational profile describes job duties, educational requirements, how to get the job, advancement possibilities, employment outlook, working conditions, earnings and benefits, and where to write for more information.

★9222★ Early Childhood Development/ Preschool Teacher Career Starter
Thomson Delmar Learning
P.O. Box 15015
Albany, NY 12212-5015
Ph: (518)348-2300   Fax: (518)464-0393
Fr: 800-998-7498

2002. $15.95 (paper).

★9223★ How to Get the Teaching Position You Want: Teacher Candidate Guide
Educational Enterprises
PO Box 1836
Spring Valley, CA 91979
Ph: (619)660-7720

Phyllis Murton. Second edition, revised, 1996. $9.95 (paper). 110 pages. This book provides a comprehensive guide for the teacher candidate's job search, as the format offers information that includes: interview questions most often asked in the teaching interview (grade-level & subject-matter specific); sample forms for applications, cover letters, & resumes that will impact principals & district personnel; strategies on preparing for the teaching interview; interview follow-up techniques; inside tips from a superintendent, a principal & a counselor.

★9224★ Opportunities in Child Care Careers
McGraw-Hill Trade
2 Penn Plaza
New York, NY 10121
Ph: (212)904-2000   Fr: 800-722-4726

Renee Wittenberg. 1998. $14.95; $11.95 (paper). 210 pages. Discusses various job opportunities and how to secure a position. Illustrated.

★9225★ Real People Working in Education
McGraw-Hill Contemporary Books
1221 Avenue of the Americas
New York, NY 10020
Ph: (212)904-2000   Fr: 800-323-4900
E-mail: ntcpub@tribune.com

Blythe Camenson, Jan Goldberg. 1997. $17.95; $12.95 (paper). Interviews and profiles of working professionals capture a range of opportunities in this field.

★9226★ Skills for Preschool Teachers
Prentice Hall PTR
200 Old Tappan Rd.
Old Tappan, NJ 07675
Ph: (201)236-7000   Fr: 800-223-1360

Sixth edition, 2000. Publication cancelled.

★9227★ Teaching (Career Portraits)
Vgm Career Horizons
1221 Avenue of the Americas
New York, NY 10020
Ph: (212)904-2000   Fr: 800-323-4900
E-mail: ntcpub@tribune.com

Marjorie Eberts and Margaret Gisler. 1994. $13.95. 320 pages.

★9228★ Where the Jobs Are: The Hottest Careers for the 90s
The Career Press, Inc.
3 Tice Rd.
PO Box 687
Franklin Lakes, NJ 07417-1322
Ph: (201)848-0310   Fax: (201)848-1727
Fr: 800-227-3371

Joyce Hadley. Third edition, 2000. $13.99 (paper). 400 pages. Out of print. Describes careers in fifteen general fields, from accounting to travel and hospitality.

EMPLOYMENT AGENCIES AND SEARCH FIRMS

★9229★ Educational Placement Service
1001 Craig Rd., Ste. 170
St. Louis, MO 63146
Ph: (314)991-5855   Fax: (314)991-5295
URL: http://www.educatorjobs.com

Employment agency. Focuses on teaching, administrative, and education-related openings.

TRADESHOWS

★9230★ Association for Childhood Education International Annual International Conference & Exhibition
Association for Childhood Education International
17904 Georgia Ave., Ste. 215
Olney, MD 20832
Ph: (301)570-2111   Fax: (301)570-2212
Fr: 800-423-3563
E-mail: aceimc@aol.com
URL: http://www.acei.org

Annual. **Primary Exhibits:** Commercial and educational exhibits of interest to teachers, teacher educators, college students, day care personnel and other care givers.

★9231★ National Art Education Association Convention
National Art Education Association
1916 Association Dr.
Reston, VA 20191
Ph: (703)860-8000   Fax: (703)860-2960

E-mail: naea@dgs.dgsys.com
URL: http://www.naea-reston.org

Annual. **Primary Exhibits:** Art materials; art-related books and magazines; art career education information; arts and crafts supplies. **Dates and Locations:** 2005 Mar 04-08; Boston, MA • 2006 Mar 22-26; Chicago, IL • 2004 Mar 14-18; New York, NY.

★9232★ National Association for the Education of Young Children Annual Conference
National Association for the Education of Young Children
1509 16th St., NW
Washington, DC 20036
Ph: (202)232-8777   Fax: (202)328-1846
Fr: 800-424-2460
E-mail: conference@naevc.org
URL: http://www.naevc.org

Annual. **Primary Exhibits:** Educational materials and equipment designed for children ages birth through eight years old. **Dates and Locations:** 2004 Nov 10-13; Anaheim, CA; Anaheim Convention Center.

OTHER SOURCES

★9233★ American Federation of Teachers (AFT)
555 New Jersey Ave. NW
Washington, DC 20001
Ph: (202)879-4400   Fax: (202)879-4545
Fr: 800-238-1133
E-mail: online@aft.org
URL: http://www.aft.org

Description: Affiliated with the AFL-CIO. Works with teachers and other educational employees at the state and local level in organizing, collective bargaining, research, educational issues, and public relations. Conducts research in areas such as educational reform, teacher certification, and national assessments and standards. Represents members' concerns through legislative action; offers technical assistance. Also serves professionals with concerns similar to those of teachers, including state employees, healthcare workers, and paraprofessionals.

★9234★ Education and Training
Cambridge Educational
2572 Brunswick Ave.
Lawrenceville, NJ 08648-4128
Fax: 800-FAX-ON-US   Fr: 800-468-4227
URL: http://www.cambridgeeducational.com
$89.95. 2002. 18 minutes.

★9235★ National Association for the Education of Young Children (NAEYC)
1509 16th St. NW
Washington, DC 20036
Ph: (202)232-8777   Fax: (202)328-1846
Fr: 800-424-2460
E-mail: naeyc@naeyc.org
URL: http://www.naeyc.org

Description: Teachers and directors of preschool and primary schools, kindergartens, child care centers, and early other learning programs for young childhood; early childhood education and child development educators, trainers, and researchers and other professionals dedicated to young children's healthy development.

★9236★ Overseas Employment Opportunities for Educators: Department of Defense Dependents Schools
DIANE Publishing Co.
PO Box 1428
Collingdale, PA 19023-8428
Ph: (610)461-6200   Fax: (610)461-6130
Fr: 800-782-3833

Barry Leonard, editor. 1999. $20.00. 44 pages. An introduction to teachings positions in the Dept. of Defense Dependents Schools (DoDDS), a worldwide school system, operated by the DoD in 14 countries.

★9237★ Teaching & Related Occupations
Delphi Productions
3160 4th St.
Boulder, CO 80304
Fax: (303)443-4022   Fr: 888-443-2400
URL: http://www.delphivideo.com

$95.00. 50 minutes. Part of the Careers for the 21st Century Video Library.

Printers and Bookbinders

★9238★ American Printer

Primedia Business
9800 Metcalf Ave.
Overland Park, KS 66212
Ph: (913)341-1300   Fax: (913)967-1898

Monthly. $60.00/year for individuals. Magazine covering the printing and publishing market.

★9239★ Economic Edge

National Association for Printing Leadership
75 W Century Rd.
Paramus, NJ 07652
Ph: (201)634-9600   Fax: (201)634-0324
Fr: 800-642-6275
E-mail: perc@napl.org

Description: Quarterly. Provides current economic data for the printing industry. Also covers sales growth projections, capital spending, and employment.

★9240★ FLEXO

Foundation of Flexographic Technical Association
900 Marconi Ave.
Ronkonkoma, NY 11779-7212
Ph: (631)737-6020   Fax: (631)737-6813
E-mail: flexo@vax.fta-ftta.org
URL: http://www.fta-ffta.org

Monthly. $55.00/year; $76.00/year for other countries. Magazine covering the flexographic printing method.

★9241★ Graphic Arts Monthly

Reed Business Information
360 Park Ave. S
New York, NY 10010
Ph: (646)746-7395   Fax: (646)746-7434
URL: http://www.gammag.com

Monthly. $99.90/year for U.S. and territories; $176.90/year for Canada; $154.90/year for Mexico; $212.90/year for foreign, surface mail; $260.90/year for foreign, air mail. Magazine featuring commercial printing and graphic arts, including digital technologies.

★9242★ Guild of Book Workers Newsletter

Guild of Book Workers Inc.
521 5th Ave.
New York, NY 10175-0038
Ph: (212)292-4444

Description: Every two months. Covers issues in book arts, binding, book conservation, calligraphy, and printing. Recurring features include letters to the editor, interviews, news of research, a calendar of events, reports of meetings, news of educational opportunities, job listings, book reviews, and notices of publications available.

★9243★ High Volume Printing

Innes Publishing Co.
28100 N Ashley
PO Box 7280
Libertyville, IL 60048-7280
Ph: (847)816-7900   Fax: (847)247-8855

Bimonthly. $75.00/year; free to qualified subscribers; $25.00/year for single issue. Magazine for printers, trade binderies, and color tradehouses with more than 20 employees.

★9244★ In-Plant Printer & Electronic Publisher

Innes Publishing Co.
28100 N Ashley
PO Box 7280
Libertyville, IL 60048-7280
Ph: (847)816-7900   Fax: (847)247-8855
URL: http://innespub.com

Bimonthly. $75.00/year; free to qualified subscribers; $20.00/year for single issue. Magazine serving printing, graphics, typesetting facilities, educational, government, and non-profit organizations.

★9245★ Instant and Small Commercial Printer

Innes Publishing Co.
28100 N Ashley
PO Box 7280
Libertyville, IL 60048-7280
Ph: (847)816-7900   Fax: (847)247-8855
E-mail: iscpmag@innespub.com

Monthly. $85.00/year; free to qualified subscribers; $25.00/year for single issue. Magazine serving the field of instant/quick printers, copy shops, small commercial printers, industry suppliers and others allied to the field, including typesetters and thermographers.

★9246★ PaperTronix, Document Management Merging Paper & Electronics

IADT - The International Association for Document & Technologics
100 Daingerfield Rd.
Alexandria, VA 22314
Ph: (703)684-9606   Fax: (703)684-9675
Fr: 888-999-4234
E-mail: news@the-iadt.org

Bimonthly. $45.00/year for individuals; $55.00/year for Canada and Mexico; $65.00/year, elsewhere. Magazine for forms, document and technologics management CEOS; sales/marketing executives, production/plant managers and suppliers.

★9247★ Printing Impressions

North American Publishing Co.
Pierce Financial Corp.
837 Villa Ridge Rd.
Falls Church, VA 22046-3665
Fr: 800-627-2689
URL: http://www.piworld.com

Monthly. Free. Trade magazine.

★9248★ Quick Printing

Cygnus Business Media Inc.
445 Broad Hollow Rd.
Melville, NY 11747
Ph: (631)845-2700   Fax: (631)845-2798
Fr: 800-308-6397
E-mail: kelley.campbell@quickprinting.com

URL: http://www.quickprinting.com

Monthly. $30.00/year for individuals; $10.00 for single issue. For Quick and Small Commercial Printers.

PLACEMENT AND JOB REFERRAL SERVICES

★9249★ **Women in Production (WIP)**
276 Bowery
New York, NY 10012
Ph: (212)334-2108   Fax: (212)431-5786
E-mail: admin@p3-ny.org
URL: http://www.wip.org

Description: Persons involved in all production phases of print and graphics, web and multimedia, including those working in magazine, book, and Web publishing, agency production, conventional and digital print manufacturing, print-related vending and buying, advertising production, catalogs, direct mail; seeks to improve job performance by sharing information with members and suppliers. Sponsors placement service.

EMPLOYER DIRECTORIES AND NETWORKING LISTS

★9250★ *Graphic Arts Blue Book*
Reed Business Information
360 Park Ave. S
New York, NY 10010
Ph: (646)746-7395   Fax: (646)746-7434
E-mail: bluebook@reedbusiness.com
URL: http://www.gabb.com

Annual. $95.00. Covers printing plants, bookbinders, imagesetters, platemakers, paper merchants, paper manufacturers, printing machinery manufacturers and dealers, and others serving the graphic arts industry (Standard Industrial Classification (SIC) code 2600, 2700). Eight editions: New York edition (7,000 establishments) covers metropolitan New York and the state of New Jersey; Southeastern edition (10,500 establishments) covers Kentucky, Tennessee, Alabama, Mississippi, Virginia (except Washington suburbs), North Carolina, South Carolina, Georgia, and Florida; Northeastern edition (6,000 establishments) covers Connecticut, Maine, Massachusetts, New Hampshire, New York (upstate only), Rhode Island, and Vermont and the eastern Canadian provinces; Delaware Valley-Ohio edition (8,500 establishments) covers Pennsylvania, Maryland, Delaware, District of Columbia and its Virginia suburbs, and Ohio; Midwestern edition (13,000 establishments) covers Illinois, Indiana, Iowa, Michigan, Minnesota, Missouri, Wisconsin, North and South Dakota; Southwestern edition (5,500 establishments) covers Arizona, southern California, Hawaii, southern Nevada; Pacific Northwestern edition (5,500 establishments), covers northern California, northern Nevada, Oregon, Washington, Montana, Idaho, Wyoming, Utah, Alaska, and the western provinces of Canada. Texas central edition (8000 establishments) covering Texas, Colorado, New Mexico, Oklahoma, Louisiana, Kansas, Missouri, and Nebraska. Entries include: Company name, address, phone, names and titles of executives, name of buyer, list of products or services, year established. Arrangement: Same information given geographically, classified by product/service, and classified by paper brand name/watermark. Indexes: Alphabetical.

★9251★ *International Directory of Children's Literature*
George Kurian Reference Books
Box 519
Baldwin Place, NY 10505
Ph: (914)962-3287   Fax: (914)962-5287

Irregular, previous edition 1990; latest edition 2001. $48.95. Covers about 5,000 children's book and magazine publishers, organizations, children's libraries and special collections, fairs, seminars, and conferences concerned with children's literature; worldwide coverage. Entries include: For book publishers, children's literature organizations, and major children's libraries and special collections-Name, address, purpose of activity. For periodicals, prizes, and events-Name, responsible organization, address, frequency or time period, subject. Arrangement: Geographical.

★9252★ *International Directory of Private Presses*
Educators Research Service
2443 Fair Oaks Blvd., Ste. 316
Sacramento, CA 95825
Ph: (916)924-1151   Fax: (916)924-9618

Annual, April. $50.00. Covers about 1,200 private presses and hobbyist printers worldwide who use the letterpress process of reproduction. Entries include: Press name, address, phone, information on press and types, kinds of work produced, whether samples will be exchanged, brief statement on goals, printing philosophy, etc. Arrangement: Alphabetical. Indexes: Proprietor name, geographical.

★9253★ *International Literary Market Place*
Information Today Inc.
143 Old Marlton Pke.
Medford, NJ 08055-8750
Ph: (609)654-6266   Fax: (609)654-4309
Fr: 800-300-9848
URL: http://www.literarymarketplace.com

Annual, September, latest edition 2004. $239.00. Covers over 10,799 publishers in over 180 countries outside the United States and Canada, and about 1,499 trade and professional organizations related to publishing abroad; includes major printers, binders, typesetters, book manufacturers, book dealers, libraries, literary agencies, translators, book clubs, reference books and journals, periodicals, prizes, and international reference section. Entries include: For publishers-Name, address, phone, fax, telex, names and titles of key personnel, branches, type of publications, subjects, ISBN prefix. Listings for others include similar information but less detail. Arrangement: Classified by business activities, then geographical. Indexes: Company name, subject, type of publication.

★9254★ *Literary Market Place*
Information Today Inc.
143 Old Marlton Pke.
Medford, NJ 08055-8750
Ph: (609)654-6266   Fax: (609)654-4309
Fr: 800-300-9848
URL: http://www.literarymarketplace.com

Annual, Octber, latest edition 2002. $299.00. Covers over 14,500 firms or organizations offering services related to the publishing industry, including book publishers in the United States and Canada who issued three or more books during the preceding year, plus a small press section of publishers who publish less than three titles per year or those who are self-published. Also included: book printers and binders; book clubs; book trade and literary associations; selected syndicates, newspapers, periodicals, and radio and TV programs that use book reviews or book publishing news; translators and literary agents. Entries include: For publishers-Company name, address, phone, address for orders, principal executives, editorial directors, and managers, date founded, number of titles in previous year, number of backlist titles in print, types of books published, ISBN prefixes, representatives, imprints, and affiliations. For suppliers, etc. - Listings usually show firm name, address, phone, executives, services, etc. Arrangement: Classified by line of business. Indexes: Principal index is 35,000-item combined index of publishers, publications, and personnel; several sections have geographical and/or subject indexes; translators are indexed by source and target language.

★9255★ *Printers Directory*
infoUSA Inc.
5711 S 86th Cir.
Omaha, NE 68127-0347
Ph: (402)930-3500   Fax: (402)331-0176
Fr: 800-555-6124
URL: http://www.abii.com

Annual. Number of listings: 53,081. Entries include: Name, address, phone (including area code), size of advertisement, year first in "Yellow Pages," coding indicates brands carried, specialties, or franchises held. Regional editions available. Compiled from telephone company "Yellow Pages," nationwide. Arrangement: Geographical.

★9256★ *Publishers Directory*
Thomson Gale
27500 Drake Rd.
Farmington Hills, MI 48331-3535
Ph: (248)699-4253   Fax: (248)699-8065
Fr: 800-877-GALE
E-mail: businessproducts@gale.com

URL: http://www.gale.com

Annual. $450.00. Covers over 20,000 new and established, commercial and nonprofit, private and alternative, corporate and association, government and institution publishing programs and their distributors; includes producers of books, classroom materials, prints, reports, and databases. Entries include: Firm name, address, phone, fax, company e-mail address, URL, year founded, ISBN prefix, Standard Address Number, whether firm participates in the Cataloging in Publication program of the Library of Congress, names of principal executives, personal e-mail addresses, number of titles in print, description of firm and its main subject interests, discount and returns policies, affiliated and parent companies, mergers and amalgamations, principal markets, imprints and divisions, alternate formats products are offered; distributors also list firms for which they distribute, special services, terms to publishers and regional offices. Arrangement: Alphabetical; distributors listed separately. Indexes: Subject, geographical, publisher, imprints, and distributor.

★9257★ Who's Who in SGIA
Screenprinting and Graphic Imaging
  Association International
10015 Main St.
Fairfax, VA 22031
Ph: (703)385-1335   Fax: (703)273-0456
Fr: 888-385-3588

Annual, August. Covers about 3,800 screen printers and graphic imaging companies, suppliers of screen printing equipment and graphic imaging materials, and investors in the Screen Printing Technical Foundation; international coverage. Entries include: Company name, address, phone, fax, e-mail, name of contact, products or services. Arrangement: Classified by type of business, then geographical. Indexes: Alphabetical by company, within state or country.

★9258★ The Workbook
Scott & Daughters Publishing Inc.
940 N Highland Ave., Ste. A
Los Angeles, CA 90038
Ph: (323)856-0008   Fax: (323)856-0443
Fr: 800-547-2688
URL: http://www.workbook.com

Annual, February. $120.00. Covers 49,000 advertising agencies, art directors, photographers, freelance illustrators and designers, artists' representatives, interactive designers, pre-press services, and other graphic arts services in the U.S. Entries include: Company or individual name, address, phone, specialty. National in scope. Arrangement: Classified by product or service.

HANDBOOKS AND MANUALS

★9259★ Degree of Mastery: A Journey Through Book Arts Apprenticeship
Penguin Putnam, Incorporated
375 Hudson St.
New York, NY 10014
Ph: (212)366-2000   Fr: (212)366-2666

Annie Tremmel Wilcox. 2000. $12.95 (paper).

★9260★ Opportunities in Printing Careers
McGraw-Hill Trade
2 Penn Plaza
New York, NY 10121
Ph: (212)904-2000   Fr: 800-722-4726
E-mail: ntcpub@tribune.com

Irvin Borowsky. 1998. $14.95; $11.95 (paper). 160 pages. Offers detailed information on the variety of pre-press, press, and post-press jobs available. Covers apprenticeships, unions, salaries, and how to get ahead. Illustrated.

EMPLOYMENT AGENCIES AND SEARCH FIRMS

★9261★ Burton & Grove Inc.
1600 Golf Rd., Ste. 1200
Rolling Meadows, IL 60008
Ph: (847)981-7690

Executive search firm.

★9262★ Core Management Search LLC
5130 Saratoga Ln. N., Ste. 201
Minneapolis, MN 55442
Ph: (763)559-0977   Fax: (763)559-1664

Executive search firm.

★9263★ Executive Resource Group Inc.
29 Oakhurst Rd.
Cape Elizabeth, ME 04107
Ph: (207)871-5527   Fax: (207)799-8624

Executive search firm focused on publishing, new media and broadcast industries.

★9264★ Graphic Arts Employment Service, Inc.
409 N Pacific Coast Hwy., Ste.455
Redondo Beach, CA 90277
Ph: (310)316-1246   Fax: (310)937-3760
Fr: 800-499-9722
E-mail: info@gaes.com
URL: http://www.gaes.com

Employment agency specializing in the publishing and packaging industries.

★9265★ Graphic Search Associates Inc.
PO Box 373
Newtown Square, PA 19073
Ph: (610)359-1234   Fax: (610)353-8120
Fr: 800-342-1777
E-mail: info@graphsrch.com
URL: http://www.graphsrch.com

Executive search firm for the graphic arts industry.

★9266★ Stewart Associates
181 Windover Turn
Lancaster, PA 17601
Ph: (717)299-9242   Fax: (717)299-4879
E-mail: waltp@redrose.net

Executive search firm for the manufacturing industry.

ONLINE JOB SOURCES AND SERVICES

★9267★ PrintJobs.com
PO Box 135
Bowmansville, NY 14026
Ph: (716)686-9251   Fax: (716)686-9258
E-mail: newhouse@atsprintjobs.com
URL: http://www.printjobs.com

Description: Aims to find suitable graphic arts jobs for qualified candidates. Over a hundred jobs are maintained and updated on the site. **Fee:** Must be paid by employers using the site; no registration charge for job hunters.

OTHER SOURCES

★9268★ Amalgamated Printers' Association (APA)
6 Ryan Ct.
Nanuet, NY 10954
E-mail: twoempress@aol.com
URL: http://www.apa-letterpress.org

Description: Active printers interested in the furtherance of the art and craft of printing. Encourages excellence of printing content, design, and techniques among members. Sponsors competitions.

★9269★ American Institute of Graphic Arts (AIGA)
164 5th Ave.
New York, NY 10010
Ph: (212)807-1990   Fax: (212)807-1799
Fr: 800-548-1634
E-mail: comments@aiga.org
URL: http://www.aiga.org

Description: Graphic designers, art directors, art directors, illustrators, packaging designers. Sponsors exhibits and projects in the public interest. Sponsors traveling exhibitions. Operates gallery. Maintains library of design books and periodicals; offers slide archives.

★9270★ *Behind the Scenes: Printing*
Cambridge Educational
2572 Brunswick Ave.
Lawrenceville, NJ 08648-4128
Fax: 800-FAX-ON-US   Fr: 800-468-4227
URL: http://www.cambridgeeducational.com
$89.95. 20 minutes. Part of the series "Behind the Scenes: Industrial Field Trips."

★9271★ **Binding Industries Association International (BIA)**
70 E. Lake St., No. 300
Chicago, IL 60601
Ph: (312)372-7606   Fax: (312)704-5025
E-mail: info@bindingindustries.org
URL: http://www.gain.net/PIA_GATF/BIA/main.html
Members: Trade binders and loose-leaf manufacturers united to conduct seminars, hold conventions, and formulate and maintain standards.

★9272★ **COIN Career Guidance System**
COIN Educational Products
3361 Executive Pky., Ste. 302
Toledo, OH 43606
Ph: (419)536-5353   Fax: (419)536-7056
Fr: 800-274-8515
URL: http://www.coin3.com/highschool/guidance.asp
CD-ROM. Provides career information through seven cross-referenced files covering postsecondary schools, college majors, vocational programs, military service, apprenticeship programs, financial aid, and scholarships. Apprenticeship file describes national apprenticeship training programs, including information on how to apply, contact agencies, and program content. Military file describes more than 200 military occupations and training opportunities related to civilian employment.

★9273★ **Graphic Arts Technical Foundation (GATF)**
200 Deer Run Rd.
Sewickley, PA 15143-2600
Ph: (412)741-6860   Fax: (412)741-2311
Fr: 800-910-GATF
E-mail: info@gatf.org
URL: http://www.gatf.org

Description: Scientific, research, technical, and educational organization serving the international graphic communications industries. Conducts research in all graphic processes and their commercial applications. Conducts seminars, workshops, and forums on graphic arts and environmental subjects. Conducts educational programs, including the publishing of graphic arts textbooks and learning modules, videotapes and CD-ROMs and broadcast video seminars. Conducts the GATF training and certification program in sheet-fed offset press operating, Web Offset press operating, Image Assembly, and desktop publishing. Produces test images and quality control devices for the industry. Performs technical services for the graphic arts industry, including problem-solving, material evaluation, and plant audits. A partner of the Printing Industries of America (PIA).

★9274★ **Master Printers of America (MPA)**
100 Daingerfield Rd.
Alexandria, VA 22314
Fax: (703)548-0129   Fr: 800-742-2666
E-mail: erp@printing.org
URL: http://www.gain.net/PIA_GATF/erp-form.doc
Description: Open-shop establishments in the commercial printing industry. A division of Printing Industries of America. Supports pro-business labor law reform and modern industrial relations in plants. Conducts seminars for industrial relations directors and managers of local associations. Sponsors ongoing employee recognition program.

★9275★ **National Association for Printing Leadership (NAPL)**
75 W. Century Rd.
Paramus, NJ 07652-1408
Ph: (201)634-9600   Fax: (201)634-0325
Fr: 800-642-NAPL
E-mail: info@napl.org
URL: http://www.napl.org
Description: Commercial printers and suppliers to the commercial printing industry. Enables those in the industry to operate their businesses for maximum profitability. Offers following management products and services: sales and marketing, customer service, financial, human resources, operations, economic. **Activities:** Maintains Management Institute, which conducts Executive Certification Program. Compiles extensive economic statistics.

★9276★ **Printing Brokerage/Buyers Association (PB/BAI)**
PO Box 744
Palm Beach, FL 33480
Ph: (561)586-9391   Fax: (561)845-7130
Fr: (866)586-9391
E-mail: Info@pbbai.net
URL: http://www.pbbai.net
Description: Printing buyers/brokers/distributors, printers, typographers, binders, envelope and book manufacturers, packagers, color separation houses, pre-press service organizations, and related companies in the graphic arts industry. Promotes understanding, cooperation, and interaction among members while obtaining the highest standard of professionalism in the graphic arts industry. Gathers information on current technology in the graphic communications industry. Sponsors seminars for members to learn how to work with buyers, brokers and printers; also conducts technical and management seminars. Maintains referral service; compiles statistics. Conducts charitable programs.

★9277★ **Printing Industries of America (PIA)**
100 Daingerfield Rd.
Alexandria, VA 22314-2888
Ph: (703)519-8100   Fax: (703)548-3227
Fr: 800-742-2666
E-mail: gain@printing.org
URL: http://www.gain.net
Description: Commercial printing firms (lithography, letterpress, gravure, platemakers, typographic houses); allied firms in the graphic arts. Provides extensive management services for member companies, including government relations, industry research and statistical information, technology information and assistance, and management education and publications. Compiles statistical and economic data, including annual ratio study which provides a benchmark for printers to compare profits as a basis for improving individual member company and industry profits. Provides reporting system on provisions, rates, and other matters relating to union contracts in effect throughout the industry. Sponsors annual Premier Print Awards Competition.

★9278★ **Typophiles**
35 Schermerhorn St.
Brooklyn, NY 11201-4826
Description: Designers, printers, book collectors, artists, calligraphers, private press owners, wood engravers, and others interested in graphic arts.

Private Detectives and Investigators

SOURCES OF HELP-WANTED ADS

★9279★ The Legal Investigator
National Association of Legal Investigators Inc.
55 S NW Hwy.
Palatine, IL 60074
Ph: (312)226-6300   Fax: (312)432-9300
Description: Quarterly. Focuses on concerns of the legal investigator, especially on professionalization of the career through a certification program. Discusses issues and legal developments relating to the investigation of personal injury matters for the plaintiff and criminal defense.

★9280★ Private Investigators Connection
Thomas Publications Inc.
PO Box 33244
Austin, TX 78764
Ph: (512)719-3595   Fax: (512)719-3594
Description: Bimonthly. Provides information for private investigators.

PLACEMENT AND JOB REFERRAL SERVICES

★9281★ National Association of Investigative Specialists (NAIS)
PO Box 33244
Austin, TX 78764
Ph: (512)719-3595   Fax: (512)719-3594
E-mail: rthomas007@aol.com
URL: http://www.pimall.com/nais
Members: Private investigators, automobile repossessors, bounty hunters, and law enforcement officers. **Purpose:** Promotes professionalism and provides for information exchange among private investigators. Lobbies for investigative regulations. Offers training programs and issues certificates of completion. **Activities:** Sponsors charitable programs; compiles statistics; maintains speakers' bureau and placement service. Operates Investigators' Hall of Fame of Private Investigators. Offers seminars on cassette tape.

EMPLOYER DIRECTORIES AND NETWORKING LISTS

★9282★ Detective Agencies Directory
infoUSA Inc.
5711 S 86th Cir.
Omaha, NE 68127-0347
Ph: (402)930-3500   Fax: (402)331-0176
Fr: 800-555-6124
URL: http://www.abii.com
Annual. Number of listings: 2,025. Entries include: Name, address, phone (including area code), size of advertisement, year first in "Yellow Pages," name of owner or manager, number of employees. Compiled from telephone company "Yellow Pages," nationwide. Arrangement: Geographical.

★9283★ Investigators Directory
infoUSA Inc.
5711 S 86th Cir.
Omaha, NE 68127-0347
Ph: (402)930-3500   Fax: (402)331-0176
Fr: 800-555-6124
URL: http://www.abii.com
Annual. Number of listings: 8,292. Entries include: Name, address, phone (including area code), size of advertisement, year first in "Yellow Pages," name of owner or manager, number of employees. Compiled from telephone company "Yellow Pages," nationwide. Arrangement: Geographical.

★9284★ Investigator's International All-In-One Directory
National Association of Investigative Specialists
PO Box 82148
Austin, TX 78708
Ph: (512)719-3595   Fax: (512)719-3594

URL: http://www.pimall.com/nais
Annual. $30.00. Covers approximately 1,800 NAIS members; national, state, and foreign private investigative and related associations; online networks for private investigators; security associations; publications; information services; training programs and seminars; equipment sources; state investigative licensing agencies. Entries include: Company name or individual name, address, contact, investigative specialty, services provided, geographic area covered. Arrangement: Geographical.

★9285★ Naked in Cyberspace
Information Today Inc.
143 Old Marlton Pke.
Medford, NJ 08055-8750
Ph: (609)654-6266   Fax: (609)654-4309
Fr: 800-300-9848
$29.95. Publication includes: Web sites for finding people via the Internet. Principal content of publication is information on how to investigate people, find genealogical information, find prospective customers, and access public records. Indexes: Alphabetical.

HANDBOOKS AND MANUALS

★9286★ Careers for Legal Eagles and Other Law-and-Order Types
McGraw-Hill Trade
2 Penn Plaza
New York, NY 10121
Ph: (212)904-2000   Fr: 800-722-4726
E-mail: ntcpub@tribune.com
Blythe Camenson. 1998. $14.95; $9.95 (paper). 220 pages.

★9287★ Careers for Mystery Buffs and Other Snoops and Sleuths
McGraw-Hill Trade
2 Penn Plaza
New York, NY 10121
Ph: (212)904-2000   Fr: 800-722-4726

E-mail: ntcpub@tribune.com

Blythe Camenson. 1996. $14.95; $9.95 (paper). 210 pages.

★9288★ **Find Out Fast: The Instant Guide to Private Investigation**
Thomas Investigative Publications, Inc.
PO Box 33244
Austin, TX 78764-3864
Ph: (512)719-3595   Fax: (512)719-3594

Kelly Riddle. 1997. $15.00 (paper).

★9289★ **How to Make One Hundred Thousand Dollars a Year as a Private Investigator**
Paladin Press
7077 Winchester Circle
Boulder, CO 80301
Ph: (303)443-7250   Fax: (303)442-8741

Edmond J. Pankau. 1993. $22.00. 128 pages.

★9290★ **Introduction to Private Investigation: Essential Knowledge and Procedures for the Private Investigator**
Charles C Thomas Publisher, Ltd.
2600 S. 1st St.
PO Box 19265
Springfield, IL 62794-9265
Ph: (217)789-8980   Fax: (217)789-9130
Fr: 800-258-8980

Joseph A. Travers. 1995. $33.95. 256 pages.

★9291★ **An Introduction to Public and Private Investigations**
Thomson Wadsworth
10 Davis Dr.
Belmont, CA 94002
Ph: (650)595-2350

John S. Dempsey. 1996. $88.95 (paper). 415 pages.

★9292★ **100 Best Careers in Crimefighting**
Thomson Peterson's
P.O. Box 67005
Lawrenceville, NJ 08648-6105
Fr: 800-338-3282

Mary P. Lee. 1997. $15.95 (paper). 200 pages. Covers private security careers, government law enforcement positions, and more, with information on employment opportunities.

★9293★ **Primer on Success in the Private Investigative Profession**
Thomas Investigative Publications, Inc.
PO Box 33244
Austin, TX 78764-3864
Ph: (512)719-3595   Fax: (512)719-3594

Irv Baggett. 1996. $25.00 (paper). 65 pages. Subtitled, "A Business and Investigative Manual for Establishing a Successful Investigative Agency and Working the Most In-Demand Types of Cases." 65 pages.

★9294★ **Private Investigative Agency Start-Up Manual**
Thomas Investigative Publications, Inc.
PO Box 33244
Austin, TX 78764-3864
Ph: (512)719-3595   Fax: (512)719-3594

Jody Ball. 1998. $45.00 (paper).

★9295★ **Real People Working in Law**
McGraw-Hill Contemporary Books
1221 Avenue of the Americas
New York, NY 10020
Ph: (212)904-2000   Fr: 800-323-4900
E-mail: ntcpub@tribune.com

Blythe Camenson, Jan Goldberg. 1997. $14.95; $12.95 (paper). 405 pages. Interviews and profiles of working professionals capture a range of opportunities in this field.

OTHER SOURCES

★9296★ **Council of International Investigators (CII)**
2150 North 107th St., No. 205
Seattle, WA 98133-9009
Ph: (206)361-8869   Fax: (206)367-8777
Fr: 888-759-8884
E-mail: information@cii2.org
URL: http://www.cii2.org

Description: Licensed and accredited professional private investigators and detectives in 28 countries. Conducts seminars on investigation, security work, criminology, and lie detection.

★9297★ **International Security and Detective Alliance (ISDA)**
PO Box 6303
Corpus Christi, TX 78466-6303
Fax: (361)888-8060

Members: Private investigators and security professionals, investigative reporters and writers, researchers, military personnel, and some interested laypersons. **Purpose:** Seeks to maintain an international registry of investigators for purpose of referral; support a more positive and accurate media image of P.I.s and security officers; provide a professional association for freelance operators; provide continuing education courses and materials. **Activities:** Provides professional certification in numerous specialty areas of investigation and security.

★9298★ **International Society of Stress Analysts (ISSA)**
9 Westchester Dr.
Kissimmee, FL 34744
Ph: (407)933-4839   Fax: (407)935-0911
E-mail: diogenesfl@aol.com

Members: Jurists, attorneys, physicians, private detectives, law enforcement personnel, security personnel, scholar/researchers, and individuals interested in stress analysis for lie detection/truth verification. **Purpose:** Works to promote the science of psychological stress evaluation and the efficient administration of justice; aid indigent persons, without cost, who may be wrongfully accused; develop and maintain high educational standards; observe and evaluate training programs for the purpose of accreditation and endorsement. **Activities:** Sponsors and certifies schools; offers workshops and research and educational programs; conducts forums. Offers expertise, consultation, and advice; invites inquiries.

★9299★ **National Association of Traffic Accident Reconstructionists and Investigators (NATARI)**
PO Box 398
Chadds Ford, PA 19317
Ph: (610)558-5176   Fax: (610)558-5176
E-mail: lizgurn@aol.com
URL: http://www.actar.org/natari.htm

Description: Engineers, attorneys, police officers, private investigators, medical examiners, and other individuals involved in the analysis of motor vehicle traffic accidents. Gathers and disseminates information on techniques and equipment of potential use to members; reviews literature in the field. Participating Organization of the Accreditation Commission for Traffic Accident Reconstruction.

Property and Real Estate Managers

SOURCES OF HELP-WANTED ADS

★9300★ Buildings
Stamats Communications Inc.
615 5th St. SE
PO Box 1888
Cedar Rapids, IA 52401
Ph: (319)364-6167   Fax: (319)369-0029
Fr: 800-553-8878
E-mail: tom-leaverton@buildings.com
URL: http://www.buildings.com

Monthly. $70.00/year for individuals; $85.00/year for Canada; $8.00/year for single issue. The facilities construction and management magazine covering news, concepts and technologies related to commercial building ownership and facilities management.

★9301★ The Caretaker Gazette
Gary C. Dunn
PO Box 540
River Falls, WI 54022-0540
Ph: (715)426-5500
URL: http://www.caretaker.org

Description: Bimonthly. Covers the property caretaking field. Recurring features include rent-free living opportunities, job listings, letters to the editor, interviews, and a column titled Caretaker Profile. Offers mailing labels.

★9302★ Clayton-Fillmore Report
Clayton-Fillmore Ltd.
125 Dorset Ct.
Castle Rock, CO 80104-9285
Ph: (303)663-0606   Fax: (303)663-1616
Monthly. Periodical covering real estate and business.

★9303★ Journal of Property Management
Institute of Real Estate Management
430 N Michigan Ave.
Chicago, IL 60611-4090
Ph: (312)329-6000   Fax: (312)661-0217
Fr: 800-837-0706

URL: http://www.irem.org
Bimonthly. $43.95/year for individuals; $43.95/year for members. Magazine serving real estate managers.

★9304★ Journal of Real Estate Portfolio Management
American Real Estate Society
c/o Donna Cooper
College Business, MacArthur Campus
Florida Atlantic University
5353 Parkside Dr.
Jupiter, FL 33458
Ph: (561)799-8664   Fax: (561)799-8535
Quarterly. Journal for real estate professionals.

★9305★ New England Real Estate Journal
East Coast Publications
PO Box 55
Accord, MA 02018
Ph: (617)878-4540   Fax: (617)871-1853
Fr: 800-654-4993
E-mail: nerej@ix.net.com

Weekly. $139.00/year for individuals. Newspaper publishing commercial, industrial, and investment real estate news.

★9306★ Property Management Association-Bulletin
Property Management Association
7900 Wisconsin Ave., Ste. 204
Bethesda, MD 20814
Ph: (301)654-9200   Fax: (301)907-9326
URL: http://www.reji.com/reji/associations/pma/non-member/data

Description: Monthly. Reports market trends and other information related to property management. Contains information on the Association and tips for members. Recurring features include news of research, a calendar of events, reports of meetings, news of educational opportunities, job listings, book reviews, and notices of publications available.

★9307★ Real Estate Issues
The Counselors of Real Estate
430 N Michigan Ave.
Chicago, IL 60611
Ph: (312)329-8427   Fax: (312)329-8881
E-mail: info@cre.org

Quarterly. Trade publication covering the real estate industry.

★9308★ REALTOR Magazine
National Association of Realtors
430 N Michigan Ave.
Chicago, IL 60611-4087
Ph: (312)329-8200   Fax: (312)329-5978
URL: http://www.realtormag.com

Monthly. Real estate magazine

PLACEMENT AND JOB REFERRAL SERVICES

★9309★ National Property Management Association (NPMA)
1108 Pinehurst Rd.
Dunedin, FL 34698
Ph: (727)736-3788   Fax: (727)736-6707
E-mail: hq@npma.org
URL: http://www.npma.org

Description: Individuals interested in professional asset management, primarily working with assets provided by government entities to contractors. Objective is to provide a continuing forum for discussion, problem solving, standardized application of government regulations, and design and implementation of effective, efficient property systems. Provides educational methods, programs, materials and opportunities that enable members to learn and apply the principles and techniques of effective contractor property and facilities management and related subjects. Awards designations of Certified Professional Property Administrator, Certified Professional Property Managers, Certified Professional Property Specialist, and Consulting Fellows to qualified individuals. Offers placement services; sponsors educational programs; maintains hall of fame; operates speakers' bureau.

EMPLOYER DIRECTORIES AND NETWORKING LISTS

★9310★ **Executive Guide to Specialists in Industrial and Office Real Estate**
Society of Industrial and Office Realtors
1201 New York Ave., NW, Ste. 350
Washington, DC 20005
Ph: (202)449-8200   Fax: (202)449-8201
Fr: 888-891-7467
URL: http://www.sior.com

Annual, July. $70.00 for nonmembers; $80.00 for out of country. Serves as a guide to the most qualified industrial and office real estate practitioners: the Society's 2,700 designees, affiliates, associates, and candidates. Updated annually, the Guide lists SIOR designees and affiliates geographically. Associate members are listed alphabetically by company for easy reference to leading corporate users, developers, public utilities, universities, and more. Arrangement: Geographical. Indexes: Personal name.

★9311★ **National Association of Real Estate Companies-Membership Directory**
National Association of Real Estate
  Companies
Box 958
Columbia, MD 21044
Ph: (410)992-6476   Fax: (410)992-6363
E-mail: cindy@narec.org
URL: http://www.narec.org

Quarterly. Covers about 200 real estate development companies. Entries include: Company name, address, phone, name of contact.

★9312★ **National Real Estate Investor Sourcebook**
Primedia Business
6151 Powers Ferry Rd., Ste. 200
Atlanta, GA 30339
Ph: (770)995-2500   Fax: (770)618-0204
URL: http://www.nreionline.com

Annual, November. $79.95. Publication includes: List of about 7,000 companies and individuals in 18 real estate fields, including appraisers; asset managers; builders, contractors, and developers; communication services; corporate real estate managers; environmental consultants; equity investors; financial services; hospitality services; institutional advisors; pension funds; property managers; real estate brokers, agents, consultants, and counselors; software products and services; title insurance companies; related associations; and others. Entries include: Company or agency name, address, phone, fax, and, in some cases, names of executives and additional information. Ar-

rangement: Classified by field or type of activity, then geographical.

★9313★ **Real Estate Consultants Directory**
infoUSA Inc.
5711 S 86th Cir.
Omaha, NE 68127-0347
Ph: (402)930-3500   Fax: (402)331-0176
Fr: 800-555-6124
URL: http://www.abii.com

Annual. Number of listings: 10,551. Entries include: Name, address, phone (including area code), size of advertisement, year first in "Yellow Pages," name of owner or manager, number of employees. Compiled from telephone company "Yellow Pages," nationwide. Arrangement: Geographical.

HANDBOOKS AND MANUALS

★9314★ **Becoming a Real Estate Professional**
Vantage Press, Inc.
516 W. 34th St.
New York, NY 10001
Ph: (212)736-1767   Fax: (212)736-2273
Fr: 800-882-3273

Shawn J. Murphy. 1995. $19.95 (paper). Out of print.

★9315★ **How About a Career in Real Estate?**
Noteworthy Publishing Co.
1070 Idylwood Dr. SW
Issaquah, WA 98027
Ph: (425)392-6914   Fax: (425)392-6414
Fr: 800-296-2599

Carla Cross. Second edition, 1996. $14.95 (paper). 175 pages.

★9316★ **How to Become an Apartment Manager (Fast and Live Rent Free)**
Pro Guides Professional Guides
PO Box 2071
Davis, CA 95617-2071

R. Robert Stuart, editor. Third edition, 1997. $18.95 (paper). 112 pages.

★9317★ **The Landlord's Handbook: A Complete Guide to Managing Small Residential Properties**
Dearborn Trade Publishing
155 N. Wacker Dr.
Chicago, IL 60606-1719
Ph: (312)836-4400   Fax: (312)836-1021
Fr: 800-621-9621

Daniel Goodwin and Richard Rusdorf. Second edition, 1997. $29.95 (paper). 250 pages.

★9318★ **Real Estate Blues: A Jump Start Guide to Your Real Estate Career**
PublishAmerica, Incorporated
230 E. Patrick St.
Frederick, MD 21701
Ph: (240)529-1030   Fax: (301)631-9073

David H. Lawrence. May 2004. $19.95 (paper). 138 pages.

★9319★ **Real Estate Careers: Twenty-Five Growing Opportunities**
John Wiley & Sons, Inc.
111 River St.
Hoboken, NJ 07030-5774
Ph: (201)748-6000   Fax: (201)748-6088
Fr: 800-225-5945

Carolyn Janik and Ruth Rejnis. 1994. $55.00; $22.95 (paper). 224 pages.

EMPLOYMENT AGENCIES AND SEARCH FIRMS

★9320★ **The Alfus Group Inc.**
353 Lexington Ave., Fl. 8
New York, NY 10016
Ph: (212)599-1000   Fax: (212)599-1523

Executive search firm. Specializes in the hospitality industry.

★9321★ **Arlene Clapp Ltd.**
4250 Park Glen Rd.
Minneapolis, MN 55416
Ph: (952)928-7474   Fax: (952)928-7475

Executive search firm.

★9322★ **The Barack Group Inc.**
Grand Central Station
PO Box 4407
New York, NY 10163
Ph: (212)867-9700   Fax: (212)681-9555

Executive search firm.

★9323★ **Bennett Search & Consulting Company Inc.**
285-1 W. Naomi Dr.
Naples, FL 34104
Ph: (239)352-0219   Fax: (239)353-7719

Executive search firm.

★9324★ **Caruso & Associates Inc.**
1509 N. Military Trail, Ste. 216
West Palm Beach, FL 33409
Ph: (561)683-2336

Executive search firm.

★9325★ ChaseAmerica Inc.
7100-39 Fairway Dr., Ste. 223
Palm Beach Gardens, FL 33418
Ph: (561)622-1120
Executive search firm.

★9326★ Commonwealth Resources Inc.
262 Washington St., Ste. 800
Boston, MA 02108
Ph: (617)250-1100   Fax: (617)250-1199
Executive search firm.

★9327★ Contractor Marketing
7600 Dayton Rd.
Fairborn, OH 45324-1904
Ph: (937)864-5854   Fax: (937)865-7017
Executive search firm.

★9328★ Crown Advisors Inc.
800 E. Northwest Hwy., Ste. 612
Palatine, IL 60074
Ph: (847)221-2213   Fax: (847)221-2219
Fr: (847)830-6998
Executive search firm.

★9329★ Cullen International Executive Search Inc.
50 Northcrest Dr.
Newnan, GA 30265-1200
Ph: (678)423-1556   Fax: (678)423-1718
Executive search firm.

★9330★ Dean M. Coe Associates
32 Pine St.
Sandwich, MA 02563
Ph: (508)888-8029
Executive search firm focused on real estate and non-profit industries.

★9331★ DLG Associates Inc.
1515 Mockingbird Ln., Ste. 560
Charlotte, NC 28209
Ph: (704)522-9993   Fax: (704)522-7730
Executive search firm.

★9332★ Edward Dellon Associates Inc.
1801 Avenue of the Stars, Ste. 640
Los Angeles, CA 90067
Ph: (310)286-0625   Fax: (310)277-3069
Executive search firm.

★9333★ Eggleston Consulting International
4067 Audubon Dr.
Marietta, GA 30068
Ph: (770)579-2344   Fax: (770)579-1706
Executive search firm.

★9334★ Franchise Recruiters Ltd.
Lincolnshire Country Club
3500 Innsbruck
Crete, IL 60417
Ph: (708)757-5595
Executive search firm. Second location in Toronto, Canada.

★9335★ Real Estate Executive Search, Inc.
PO Box 387
San Francisco, CA 94104-0387
Ph: (415)398-4116
E-mail: jhavrees@aol.com
Executive search firm for the real estate and finance fields.

TRADESHOWS

★9336★ Building Owners and Managers Association International Annual Convention and The Office Building Show
Building Owners and Managers Association International
1201 New York Ave., NW, Ste. 300
Washington, DC 20005
Ph: (202)408-2662   Fax: (202)371-0181
E-mail: webmaster@boma.org
URL: http://www.boma.org
Annual. **Primary Exhibits:** Products, supplies and equipment for the office building industry, including architectural and building hardware, asbestos abatement, building automation, carpeting, control systems, doors, elevators and elevator maintenance, electrical and lighting, environmental services, financial services, fire protection, flooring and floor machines, hazardous waste removal, interior design, landscaping, locks, paper products, parking, pest control, plumbing and fixtures, recycling, renovation and restoration, roofing, security, signage, water treatment, windows.

★9337★ Milwaukee Boma Expo
Expo Group
1125 Parkway Dr.
Brookfield, WI 53005
Ph: (414)641-0255   Fax: (414)641-0259
E-mail: expo_group@pol.com
Annual. **Primary Exhibits:** Products for building owners and managers, including security, plumbing, moving and storage, acoustical products, signage, building supplies, hardware, landscaping, flooring, roofing, windows, doors, lighting, appliances, and environmental services.

★9338★ Nacore Symposium and Exposition
NACORE International
260 Peachtree St. NW, Ste. 1500
Atlanta, GA 30303-1237
Annual. **Primary Exhibits:** Real estate developers, title companies, architects, designers, engineers, property tax consultants, and government, industrial, and economic developers.

★9339★ World Congress of the World Federation of Building Service Contractors
World Federation of Building Service Contractors
10201 Lee Hwy., Ste. 225
Fairfax, VA 22030
Ph: (703)359-7090   Fax: (703)352-0493
Fr: 800-368-3414
Biennial. **Primary Exhibits:** Floor care and carpet care equipment, building service contracting equipment, supplies, and services. **Dates and Locations:** 2004 Dates not set; Montreal, QC, Canada • 2006 Dates not set; Buenos Aires, Argentina.

OTHER SOURCES

★9340★ Administration and Management Occupations
Delphi Productions
3160 4th St.
Boulder, CO 80304
Fax: (303)443-4022   Fr: 888-443-2400
URL: http://www.delphivideo.com
$95.00. 50 minutes. Part of the Careers for the 21st Century Video Library.

★9341★ Building Owners and Managers Association International (BOMA)
1201 New York Ave. NW, Ste. 300
Washington, DC 20005
Ph: (202)408-2662   Fax: (202)371-0181
E-mail: info@boma.org
URL: http://www.boma.org
Description: Building owners, managers, developers, leasing professionals, facility managers, asset managers and the providers of goods and services. Represents all facets of the commercial real estate industry.

★9342★ CoreNet Global
260 Peachtree St. NW
Atlanta, GA 30303-1237
Ph: (404)589-3200   Fax: (404)589-3201
Fr: 800-726-8111
E-mail: corenet@corenetglobal.org
URL: http://www.corenetglobal.org
Description: Executives, attorneys, real estate department heads, architects, engineers, analysts, researchers, and anyone responsible for the management, administra-

tion, and operation of national and regional real estate departments of national and international corporations. Provides a meeting ground for the exchange of ideas, experience, and problems among members; encourages professionalism within corporate real estate through education and communication; protects the interests of corporate realty in dealing with adversaries, public or private; maintains contact with other real estate organizations; publicizes the availability of fully qualified members to the job market. Maintains Institute for Corporate Real Estate as educational arm. Conducts seminars, including concentrated workshops on the corporate real estate field. Compiles statistics; sponsors competitions; maintains biographical archives and placement service.

★9343★ **Institute of Real Estate Management (IREM)**
430 N Michigan Ave.
Chicago, IL 60611-4090
Ph: (312)329-6000   Fax: 800-338-4736
Fr: 800-837-0706
E-mail: custserv@irem.org
URL: http://www.irem.org

Description: Professional organization of real property and asset managers. Awards professional designation Certified Property Manager (CPM) to qualifying individuals and Accredited Management Organization (AMO) to qualifying management firms. Also awards Accredited Residential Manager (ARM) service award which recognizes outstanding residential site managers. Monitors legislation affecting real estate management. Maintains software vendor certification program. Offers management courses and seminars; conducts research and educational

programs; maintains formal code of ethics; compiles statistics; maintains speakers' bureau and job referral service. safety awareness and crime prevention program.

★9344★ **National Apartment Association (NAA)**
201 N Union St., Ste. 200
Alexandria, VA 22314
Ph: (703)518-6141   Fax: (703)518-6191
E-mail: doug@naahq.com
URL: http://www.naahq.org

Members: Federation of 155 state and local associations of industry professionals engaged in all aspects of the multifamily housing industry, including owners, builders, investors, developers, managers, and allied service representatives. **Purpose:** Provides education and certification for property management executives, on-site property managers, maintenance personnel, property supervisors, and leasing agents. Offers a nationwide legislative network concerned with governmental decisions at the federal, state, and local levels.

★9345★ **National Association of Realtors (NAR)**
430 N Michigan Ave.
Chicago, IL 60611
Fax: (312)329-5962   Fr: 800-874-6500
E-mail: infocentral@realtors.org
URL: http://www.realtor.org

Description: Federation of 54 state and territory associations and 1860 local real estate boards whose members are real estate brokers and agents. Terms are registered by the association in the U.S. Patent and Trademark Office and in the states.

Promotes education, high professional standards, and modern techniques in specialized real estate work such as brokerage, appraisal, property management, land development, industrial real estate, farm brokerage, and counseling. Conducts research programs.

★9346★ *Property and Real Estate Managers*
Evon Publishing
832 N 7th Ave.
Iron River, MI 49935
Ph: (906)265-3190

Audiocassette. 1996. $16.95. 32 minutes. Part of the Careers and Vocational Guidance Series. Provides information about the nature of the work, educational requirements, employment outlook, earnings, and work conditions as well as additional related information.

★9347★ **Realtors Land Institute (RLI)**
430 N. Michigan Ave.
Chicago, IL 60611
Fax: (312)329-8633   Fr: 800-441-LAND
E-mail: rli@realtors.org
URL: http://www.rliland.com

Members: Real estate brokers and salespersons selling, managing, appraising, or developing all types of land. **Purpose:** Maintains educational programs for real estate brokers; promotes competence and accredits members. **Activities:** Sponsors courses for realtors and others seeking professional excellence on Land Brokerage, Agricultural Land Brokerage, Exchanging Properties, Estate Planning, Subdivision Development, and Financial Analysis of Land Investment.

Psychologists

SOURCES OF HELP-WANTED ADS

★9348★ AACAP News

American Academy of Child and
Adolescent Psychiatry (AACAP)
3615 Wisconsin Ave. NW
Washington, DC 20016
Ph: (202)966-7300   Fax: (202)363-0582

Description: Six issues/year. Publishes
news of the Academy, child and adolescent
psychiatrists, and AACAP members. Focuses on the practice of child and adolescent
psychiatry. Recurring features include letters
to the editor, legislative updates, news of
research, statistics, announcements of open
positions, and columns titled Ethics, Clinical
Vignettes, Forensic Corner, and Clinical
Marketing.

★9349★ The ABA Newsletter

Association for Behavior Analysis (ABA)
213 W Hall
Western Michigan University
Kalamazoo, MI 49008-5052
Ph: (616)387-8341   Fax: (616)387-8354

Description: Three issues/year. Covers Association activities, with reports of committees and special interest groups, and news
from regional, state, and local associations
for behavior analysis. Recurring features
include convention details and overview,
news of research, and positions-available
notices.

**★9350★ Alcoholism: Clinical and
Experimental Research**

Lippincott Williams & Wilkins
530 Walnut St.
Philadelphia, PA 19106
Ph: (215)521-8300   Fax: (215)521-8902
Fr: 800-638-3030
E-mail: jewers@lww.com
URL: http://www.alcoholism-cer.com/

Monthly. $337.00/year for individuals;
$645.00/year for institutions; $411.00/year
for other countries; $736.00/year for institu-
tions, other countries. Publishing original

clinical and research studies on alcoholism
and alcohol-induced organ damage.

**★9351★ American Journal of
Psychology**

University of Illinois Press
1325 S Oak St.
Champaign, IL 61820-6903
Ph: (217)333-0950   Fax: (217)244-8082
Fr: 800-537-5487
E-mail: ajp@s.psych.uiuc.edu

Quarterly. $133.00/year for institutions;
$143.00/year, foreign. Journal dealing with
experimental psychology and basic principles of psychology.

★9352★ American Psychologist

American Psychological Association
750 1st St. NE
Washington, DC 20002-4242
Ph: (202)336-5500   Fax: (202)336-5620
Fr: 800-374-2721
E-mail: journals@apa.org
URL: http://www.apa.org/journals/amp.html

Monthly. $12.00/year for members; $206.00/
year for nonmembers; $491.00/year for insti-
tutions; $12.00/year for students. Official
journal of the Association. Publishes empirical, theoretical, and professional articles.

**★9353★ Annals of the American
Psychotherapy Association**

American Psychotherapy Association
2750 E Sunshine Rd.
Springfield, MO 65804
Ph: (417)823-0173

Bimonthly. Publication covering the field of
psychology and mental health for professionals.

★9354★ Annals of Behavioral Medicine

Society of Behavioral Medicine
7611 Elmwood Ave., Ste. 201
Middleton, WI 53562
Ph: (608)827-7267   Fax: (608)831-5122

Quarterly. $135.00/year; $160.00/year for
other countries. Journal describing the interactions of behavior and health.

★9355★ Annual Review of Psychology

Annual Reviews Inc.
PO Box 10139
Palo Alto, CA 94303-0139
Ph: (650)493-4400   Fax: (650)855-9815
Fr: 800-523-8635

Annual. Publication covering psychology and
mental health issues.

★9356★ APA Monitor

American Psychological Association
750 1st St. NE
Washington, DC 20002-4242
Ph: (202)336-5500   Fax: (202)336-5620
Fr: 800-374-2721
E-mail: journals@apa.org
URL: http://www.apa.org/monitor/

Monthly. Free to qualified subscribers;
$46.00/year for nonmembers; $87.00/year
for institutions. Official newspaper of the
APA. Reports on the science, profession,
and social responsibility of psychology, including latest legislative developments affecting mental health, education, and research support.

★9357★ APS Observer

American Psychological Society
1010 Vermont Ave. NW, Ste. 1100
Washington, DC 20005-4907
Ph: (202)783-2077   Fax: (202)783-2083
E-mail: apsobserver@aps.washington.dc.us

Description: Ten issues/year. Provides information on issues of interest to members.
Offers a monthly employment listing for
academic and scientific psychologists.

**★9358★ Archives of General
Psychiatry**

American Medical Association
515 N State St.
PO Box 10946
Chicago, IL 60610
Ph: (312)670-7827   Fr: 800-262-2350
E-mail: ama-subs@ama-assn.org
URL: http://archpsyc.ama-assn.org/

Educational/clinical journal for psychiatrists.

★9359★ Clinical Psychiatry News
International Medical News Group
60 Columbia Rd., Bldg. B
Morristown, NJ 07960
Ph: (973)290-8200   Fax: (973)290-8245
E-mail: cpnews@imng.com

Monthly. $60.00/year. Medical and psychiatry tabloid.

★9360★ Contemporary Psychology
American Psychological Association
750 1st St. NE
Washington, DC 20002-4242
Ph: (202)336-5500   Fax: (202)336-5620
Fr: 800-374-2721
E-mail: journals@apa.org
URL: http://www.apa.org/journals/cnt.html

Monthly. $53.00/year for members; $40.00/year for students; $134.00/year for nonmembers; $355.00/year for institutions. Journal presenting critical reviews of books, films, tapes, and other media representing a cross section of psychological literature.

★9361★ EAP Digest
Performance Resource Press Inc.
1270 Rankin Dr., Ste. F
Troy, MI 48083-2843
Ph: (248)588-7733   Fax: (248)588-6633
Fr: 800-453-7733

Quarterly. $10.00 for single issue; $36.00/year, U.S.; $45.00/year, Canada, Hawaii, and Alaska; $55.00/year for other countries; $65.00/year for air mail, other countries. Magazine covering planning, development, and administration of employee assistance programs.

★9362★ Family Therapy News
American Association for Marriage and Family Therapy
1133 15th St. NW, Ste. 300
Washington, DC 20005-2710
Ph: (202)452-0109
E-mail: ftn@aamft.org

Bimonthly. $20.00/year for individuals; $35.00/year for institutions, Canada; $10.00/year for out of country. Newspaper for professionals in family therapy and mental health-related issues.

★9363★ Journal of Behavioral Medicine
Kluwer Academic/Plenum Publishing Corp.
233 Spring St., 7th Fl.
New York, NY 10013-1578
Ph: (212)620-8000   Fax: (212)463-0742
Fr: 800-221-9369

Bimonthly. $265.00/year; $310.00/year for other countries. Journal focusing on behavioral science.

★9364★ Journal of Counseling Psychology
American Psychological Association
750 1st St. NE
Washington, DC 20002-4242
Ph: (202)336-5500   Fax: (202)336-5620
Fr: 800-374-2721
E-mail: journals@apa.org
URL: http://www.apa.org/journals/cou.html

Quarterly. $41.00/year for members; $23.00/year for students; $81.00/year for nonmembers; $199.00/year for institutions. Journal presenting empirical studies about counseling processes and interventions, theoretical articles about counseling, and studies dealing with evaluation of counseling applications and programs.

★9365★ Journal of Family Psychotherapy
The Haworth Press Inc.
10 Alice St.
Binghamton, NY 13904-1580
Ph: (607)722-5857   Fax: (607)722-1424
Fr: 800-429-6784
URL: http://www.haworthpress.com

Quarterly. $34.00/year for individuals, USA; $75.00/year for institutions, USA; $175.00/year for libraries, USA; $44.20/year for individuals, Canada; $97.50/year for institutions, Canada; $227.50/year for libraries, Canada; $47.60/year for individuals, other countries; $105.00/year for institutions, other countries; $245.00/year for libraries, other countries. Journal includes case studies, treatment reports, and strategies in clinical practice for psychotherapists.

★9366★ Journal of Family Violence
Kluwer Academic/Plenum Publishing Corp.
233 Spring St., 7th
New York, NY 10013-1578
Ph: (212)620-8000   Fax: (212)463-0742
Fr: 800-221-9369

Quarterly. $225.00/year for institutions; $265.00/year for institutions, other countries. Psychology journal.

★9367★ Journal of Positive Behavior Interventions
PRO-ED Inc.
8700 Shoal Creek Blvd.
Austin, TX 78757-6897
Ph: (512)451-3246   Fax: (512)451-8542
Fr: 800-897-3202

Quarterly. Journal covering issues in mental health and psychology.

★9368★ The Journal of Psychology
Heldref Publications
1319 18th St. NW
Washington, DC 20036-1802
Ph: (202)296-6267   Fax: (202)296-5149
Fr: 800-365-9753
URL: http://www.heldref.org/html/body_jrl.html

Bimonthly. $166.00/year for individuals and institutions; $166.00/year for institutions, add

$16 for out of country. Psychology journal which publishes a variety of research and theoretical articles.

★9369★ Medical Economics
Thomson Medical Economics
5 Paragon Dr.
Montvale, NJ 07645-1742
Ph: (201)358-7200   Fax: (201)722-2680
URL: http://www.medec.com/html/products/productdetail/me_mag.html

Semimonthly. $89.00/year for individuals; $175.00/year for Canada; $109.00/year for individuals outside the medical field. Magazine covering physicians practice management, professional relations, and financial affairs.

★9370★ Mental Retardation
American Association on Mental Retardation
444 N Capitol St. NW, Ste. 846
Washington, DC 20001-1512
Ph: (202)387-1968   Fax: (202)387-2193
Fr: 800-424-3688
E-mail: staylo01@mailbox.syr.edu

Bimonthly. $115.00/year for nonmembers. Magazine featuring articles on mental retardation for professionals and parents.

★9371★ North American Society of Adlerian Psychology Newsletter
North American Society of Adlerian Psychology
65 E Wacker Pl., Ste. 1710
Chicago, IL 60601-7298
Ph: (312)629-8801   Fax: (312)629-8859
URL: http://www.alfredadler.org

Description: Bimonthly. Relates news and events of the North American Society of Adlerian Psychology and regional news of affiliated associations. Recurring features include lists of courses and workshops offered by affiliated associations, reviews of new publications in the field, professional employment opportunities, a calendar of events, and a column titled President's Message.

★9372★ Pediatrics
American Academy of Pediatrics
141 NW Point Blvd.
Elk Grove Village, IL 60007-1098
Ph: (847)434-4000   Fax: (847)434-8000
Fr: 800-433-9016
E-mail: journals@aap.org

Monthly. $149.00/year for individuals; $169.00/year for other countries. Medical journal reporting on pediatrics.

★9373★ Psychiatric Annals
SLACK Inc.
6900 Grove Rd.
Thorofare, NJ 08086-9447
Ph: (856)848-1000   Fax: (856)853-5991
Fr: 800-257-8290
E-mail: idn@slackinc.com

URL: http://www.slackinc.com/general/psyann/psyahome.htm

Monthly. $129.00/year for individuals; $289.00/year for institutions. Journal analyzing concepts and practices in every area of psychiatry.

★9374★ *Psychiatric News*

American Psychiatric Publishing Inc.
1000 Wilson Blvd., Ste. 1825
Arlington, VA 22209
Ph: (703)907-7300   Fax: (703)907-1091
Fr: 800-368-5777
E-mail: pnews@psych.org
URL: http://www.psch.org/pnews/

Semimonthly. $40.00/year for individuals. Professional magazine of the American Psychiatric Assn.

★9375★ *Psychiatric Services*

Association of Partners for Public Lands
2401 Blueridge Ave., Ste. 303
Wheaton, MD 20902-4517
Ph: (301)946-9475   Fax: (301)946-9478
URL: http://www.appl.org/psjournal

Monthly. Interdisciplinary mental health journal covering clinical, legal, and public policy issues.

★9376★ *Psychological Bulletin*

American Psychological Association
750 1st St. NE
Washington, DC 20002-4242
Ph: (202)336-5500   Fax: (202)336-5620
Fr: 800-374-2721
URL: http://www.apa.org/journals/bul.html

Bimonthly. $81.00/year for members; $164.00/year for nonmembers; $398.00/year for institutions; $93.00/year for members, other countries; $184.00/year for other countries; $442.00/year for institutions, other countries; $49.00/year for students; $61.00/year for students, other countries. Journal presenting comprehensive and integrative reviews and interpretations of critical substantive and methodological issues and practical problems from all the diverse areas of psychology.

★9377★ *Teaching Exceptional Children*

Council for Exceptional Children
1110 N Glebe Rd., Ste. 300
Arlington, VA 22201
Ph: (703)620-3660   Fax: (703)264-9494
Fr: 888-232-7733
E-mail: tec@bc.edu

$58.00/year for individuals; $66.00/year for other countries by surface mail; $95.00/year for other countries by airmail; $10.50 for single issue. Journal exploring practical methods for teaching students who have exceptionalities and those who are gifted and talented.

PLACEMENT AND JOB REFERRAL SERVICES

★9378★ **American Association of Psychiatric Technicians (AAPT)**

2000 "O" St., Ste. 250
Sacramento, CA 95814-5286
Ph: (916)443-1701   Fax: (916)329-9145
Fr: 800-391-7589
E-mail: hearn@psychtechs.org
URL: http://www.psychtechs.org

Description: Administers the Nationally Certified Psychiatric Technician examination to non-licensed direct-care workers in the fields of mental illness, developmental disabilities and substance abuse.

★9379★ **American Public Health Association (APHA)**

800 I St. NW
Washington, DC 20001-3710
Ph: (202)777-2742   Fax: (202)777-2534
E-mail: comments@apha.org
URL: http://www.apha.org

Members: Professional organization of physicians, nurses, educators, academicians, environmentalists, epidemiologists, new professionals, social workers, health administrators, optometrists, podiatrists, pharmacists, dentists, nutritionists, health planners, other community and mental health specialists, and interested consumers. **Purpose:** Seeks to protect and promote personal, mental, and environmental health. **Activities:** Services include promulgation of standards; establishment of uniform practices and procedures; development of the etiology of communicable diseases; research in public health; exploration of medical care programs and their relationships to public health. Sponsors job placement service.

★9380★ **American Society of Criminology (ASC)**

1314 Kinnear Rd., Ste. 212
Columbus, OH 43212-1156
Ph: (614)292-9207   Fax: (614)292-6767
E-mail: ceskridge@unl.edu
URL: http://www.asc41.com

Description: Professional and academic criminologists; students of criminology in accredited universities; psychiatrists, psychologists, and sociologists. Works to develop criminology as a science and academic discipline; to aid in the construction of criminological curricula in accredited universities; to upgrade the practitioner in criminological fields (police, prisons, probation, parole, delinquency workers). Conducts research programs; sponsors three student paper competitions. Provides placement service at annual convention.

★9381★ **Association for Behavior Analysis (ABA)**

1219 S Park St.
Kalamazoo, MI 49001-5607
Ph: (269)492-9310   Fax: (269)492-9316

E-mail: mail@abainternational.org
URL: http://www.abainternational.org

Description: Professionals, paraprofessionals, and students interested in the applied, experimental, and theoretical analysis of behavior. Promotes the development of behavior analysis as a profession and science. Provides a forum for the discussion of issues; disseminates information on behavior analysis. Conducts workshops and seminars in 16 specialty areas including: Behavioral Pharmacology and Toxicology; Developmental Disabilities; Organizational Behavior Analysis. Offers continuing education credits for psychologists. Maintains archives of the association's publications; offers placement service.

★9382★ **Association of Psychology Postdoctoral and Internship Centers (APPIC)**

10 G St., NW Ste. 750
Washington, DC 20002
Ph: (202)589-0600   Fax: (202)589-0603
E-mail: appic@aol.com
URL: http://www.appic.org

Description: Veterans Administration hospitals, medical centers, state hospitals, university counseling centers, and other facilities that provide internship and postdoctoral programs in professional psychology. Promotes activities that assist in the development of professional psychology training programs. Serves as a clearinghouse to provide Ph.D. candidates with internship placement assistance at member facilities. Conducts workshops and seminars on training procedures in clinical psychology at the Ph.D. level.

★9383★ **International Association of Counselors and Therapists (IACT)**

10915 Bonita Beach Rd., Ste. 1101
Bonita Springs, FL 34135-9049
Ph: (239)498-9710   Fax: (239)498-1215
E-mail: iactnow@aol.com
URL: http://www.iact.org

Description: Mental health professionals, medical professionals, social workers, clergy, educators, hypnotherapists, counselors, and individuals interested in the helping professions. Promotes enhanced professional image and prestige for complementary therapy. Provides a forum for exchange of information and ideas among practitioners of traditional and nontraditional therapies and methodologies; fosters unity among "grassroots" practitioners and those with advanced academic credentials. Facilitates the development of new therapy programs. Conducts educational, research, and charitable programs. Awards credits for continuing education. Maintains speakers' bureau and library; operates referral and placement services; compiles statistics. Assists in the development of local chapters.

EMPLOYER DIRECTORIES AND NETWORKING LISTS

★9384★ AHA Guide to the Health Care Field

American Hospital Association (AHA)
1 N. Franklin St., 27th Fl.
Chicago, IL 60606
Ph: (312)422-2050   Fax: (312)422-4700
Fr: 800-424-4301

Annual, August. $295.00. Covers hospitals, networks, multi-health care systems, free-standing ambulatory surgery centers, psychiatric facilities, long-term care facilities, substance abuse programs, and other health-related organizations. Entries include: For hospitals-Facility name, address, phone, administrator's name, number of beds, facilities and services, number of employees, expenses, other statistics. For other organizations-Name, address, phone, fax, name and title of contact. Arrangement: Geographical. Indexes: Hospital name.

★9385★ American Association for Correctional Psychology-Directory

American Association for Correctional Psychology
c/o Robert Smith, Ed.D.
Marshall University Graduate College
100 Angus E Peyton Dr.
South Charleston, WV 25303-1600
Ph: (304)746-1929   Fax: (304)746-1942

Continuously updated. Covers 400 mental health professionals engaged in correctional and rehabilitative work in prisons, reformatories, juvenile institutions, probation and parole agencies, and in other aspects of criminal justice. Entries include: Name, affiliation, address, phone. Arrangement: Alphabetical.

★9386★ American Board of Forensic Psychology-Directory of Diplomates

American Board of Forensic Psychology
638 Popular Ct.
Pittsburgh, PA 15238
Ph: (412)828-9685   Fax: (412)826-8279
URL: http://www.abfp.com/diplomate_search.asp

Biennial. $10.00. Covers approximately 200 forensic psychologists. Entries include: Personal name, home and office addresses and phone numbers, biographical data, services. Arrangement: Alphabetical. Indexes: Geographical, specialty field.

★9387★ American Board of Professional Psychology-Directory of Diplomates

American Board of Professional Psychology
300 Drayton St., 3rd Fl.
Savannah, GA 31401
Fax: (912)644-5655   Fr: 800-255-7792
URL: http://www.abpp.org/directory/

Biennial, odd years. $25.00. Covers 3,200 psychologists who have passed the board's

examination. Entries include: Name, office address, highest degree held, date of certification, practice areas. Arrangement: Alphabetical. Indexes: Geographical; speciality.

★9388★ American Group Psychotherapy Association-Membership Directory

American Group Psychotherapy Association Inc.
25 E 21st St., 6th Fl.
New York, NY 10023
Ph: (212)477-2677   Fax: (212)979-6627
Fr: 877-668-AGPA

Biennial, fall. $90.00. Covers 4,500 physicians, psychologists, clinical social workers, psychiatric nurses, and other mental health professionals interested in treatment of emotional problems by group methods. Entries include: Name, office or home address, highest degree held, office or home phone number. Arrangement: Alphabetical. Indexes: Geographical.

★9389★ American Psychological Association-APA Membership Register

American Psychological Association
750 1st St. NE
Washington, DC 20002-4242
Ph: (202)336-5510   Fax: (202)336-5620
Fr: 800-374-2721
E-mail: regdir@apa.org

Annual, April; except when APA-Directory is. $39.95. Covers over 83,000 members in the United States, Canada, and abroad; also includes membership rosters of American Board of Professional Psychology and American Board of Psychological Hypnosis. Entries include: Name, office or home address, phone, fax, degrees and universities where obtained, election date, membership and divisional affiliations. Arrangement: Alphabetical. Indexes: Association division.

★9390★ American Society for Adolescent Psychiatry-Membership Directory

American Society for Adolescent Psychiatry
PO Box 570218
Dallas, TX 75357-0218
Ph: (972)686-6166   Fax: (972)613-5532

Annual, spring. $15.00. Covers 1,500 members. Entries include: Name, office address and phone, fax, home address and phone (when given). Arrangement: Alphabetical. Indexes: Geographical, chapter.

★9391★ Christian Association for Psychological Studies International-Membership Directory

Christian Association for Psychological Studies
PO Box 310400
New Braunfels, TX 78131-0400
Ph: (830)629-2277   Fax: (830)629-2342
URL: http://www.caps.net/dircoup.htm

Annual, June. $12.00 for other countries. Covers 2,300 Christians involved in psychol-

ogy, psychiatry, counseling, sociology, social work, ministry, and nursing. Entries include: Name, office address and phone number, highest degree held, area of occupational specialization, and career data. Arrangement: Geographical. Indexes: Alphabetical.

★9392★ Directory of the American Psychological Association

American Psychological Association
750 1st St. NE
Washington, DC 20002-4242
Ph: (202)336-5510   Fax: (202)336-5620
Fr: 800-374-2721

Quadrennial. $70.00. Covers over 87,000 members, fellows, associate members, and international affiliates in the United States, Canada, and abroad. Entries include: Name, office or home address, office and/or home phone, fax, e-mail address, major field of study, areas of specialization, highest academic degree (year, field, and institution), present position(s) and immediate past positions, state licensure/certification as a psychologist, U.S. state and Canadian provincial association memberships, and membership and divisional affiliations. Arrangement: Alphabetical. Indexes: Geographical, divisional.

★9393★ Directory of Child Life Programs

Child Life Council Inc.
11820 Parklawn Dr., Ste. 202
Rockville, MD 20852-2529
Ph: (301)881-7090   Fax: (301)881-7092
URL: http://www.childlife.org/

Biennial. $15.00 for members; $20.00 for nonmembers. Covers over 400 child life programs. Entries include: Facility name, address, phone, name of child life department and director, reporting structure, staff statistics, educational requirements for employment, and internship or educational opportunities. Arrangement: Geographical. Indexes: Speciality areas, internship sessions, program size, fellowships.

★9394★ Directory of Counseling Services

International Association of Counseling Services
101 S Whiting St., Ste. 211
Alexandria, VA 22304-3416
Ph: (703)823-9840   Fax: (703)823-9843

Annual, September. $50.00. Covers about 200 accredited services in the United States and Canada concerned with psychological, educational, and vocational counseling, including those at colleges and universities, and public and private agencies. Entries include: Name, address, phone, hours of operation, director's name, service, clientele served. Arrangement: Geographical.

★9395★ Directory of Hospital Personnel

Thomson Medical Economics
5 Paragon Dr.
Montvale, NJ 07645-1742
Ph: (201)358-7200   Fax: (201)722-2680

Annual, November. $325.00. Covers 200,000 executives at 7,000 U.S. hospitals. Entries include: Name of hospital, address, phone, number of beds, type and JCAHO status of hospital, names and titles of key department heads and staff, medical and nursing school affiliations; number of residents, interns, and nursing students. Arrangement: Geographical. Indexes: Hospital name, personnel, hospital size.

★9396★ Directory of Nationally Certified School Psychologists

National Association of School Psychologists
4340 East-West Hwy., Ste. 402
Bethesda, MD 20814
Ph: (301)657-0270   Fax: (301)657-0275

Triennial, latest edition July 1995. Covers nearly 10,000 psychologists who have been accredited by the NASP's National School Psychology Certification System and have been awarded the certificate of Nationally Certified School Psychologist (NCSP); limited international coverage. Entries include: Name, address, phone, position/title, employer, degree level, state certificates and licenses held, language fluency. Arrangement: Alphabetical. Indexes: Geographical.

★9397★ Directory of Refugee Mental Health Professionals and Paraprofessionals

Refugee Assistance Program–Mental Health Technical Assistance Center
University of Minnesota
Mayo Mail Code 85
420 Delaware St. SE
Minneapolis, MN 55455
Ph: (612)638-0700   Fax: (612)627-4205

$18.00. Covers professionals who specialize in refugee mental health. Entries include: Name, address, phone, geographical area served and area of specialty. Arrangement: Geographical.

★9398★ Encyclopedia of Psychology

Jacksonville State University
700 Pelham Rd.
Jacksonville, AL 36265
Ph: (256)782-5402

Free. Database covers: Links to scientific aspects of psychology, including organizations related to the field.

★9399★ The Encyclopedia of Suicide

Facts On File Inc.
132 W 31st St., 17th Fl.
New York, NY 10001-2006
Ph: (212)967-8800   Fax: 800-678-3633
Fr: 800-322-8755

$65.00. Publication includes: List of national organizations and suicide prevention/crisis intervention groups in the United States and Canada. Principal content of publication is detailed information about the problem and history of suicide. Indexes: Alphabetical.

★9400★ Hospital Blue Book

Billian/Transworld Publishing Inc.
2100 Powers Ferry Rd.
Ste. 300
Atlanta, GA 30339
Ph: (770)955-8484   Fax: (770)955-8485
Fr: 800-533-8484
E-mail: blu-book@billian.com

Annual, January. $285.00 for national edition; $160.00 for southern edition. Covers more than 6,687 hospitals; some listings also appear in a separate southern edition of this publication. Entries include: Name of hospital, accreditation, mailing address, phone, fax, number of beds, type of facility (nonprofit, general, state, etc.); list of administrative personnel and chiefs of medical services, with specific titles. Arrangement: Geographical.

★9401★ International Council of Psychologists-Yearbook

International Council of Psychologists
SW Texas State University
Dept. of Psychology
601 University Dr.
San Marcos, TX 78666
Ph: (512)245-2111

Biennial, November of even years. Covers about 1,800 psychologists and related mental health professionals. Entries include: Name, office and home address, career data, languages spoken and written, highest degree, fields of interest. Arrangement: Alphabetical. Indexes: Geographical, major field of interest.

★9402★ Internship Programs in Professional Psychology, Including Post-Doctoral Training Programs

Association of Psychology Postdoctoral and Internship Centers
10 G St. NE, Ste. 750
Washington, DC 20002
Ph: (202)589-0600   Fax: (202)589-0603
URL: http://www.aapic.org

Annual, September. $70.00. Covers institutions offering PhD internship programs in professional psychology. Entries include: Institution name, name and address of contact, description of program, theoretical orientation, number of interns, stipend, admission requirements. Arrangement: Geographical.

★9403★ Legal and Ethical Dictionary for Mental Health Professionals

University Press of America
4501 Forbes Blvd., Ste. 200
Lanham, MD 20706
Ph: (301)459-3366   Fax: (301)429-5748
Fr: 800-462-6420

$65.00. Publication includes: Lists of state licensure boards and web sites for mental health organizations. Principal content of publication is a dictionary of legal and ethical responsibilities for mental health professionals.

★9404★ Magill's Encyclopedia of Social Science: Psychology

Salem Press Inc.
Two University Plz., Ste. 121
Hackensack, NJ 07601
Ph: (201)968-9899   Fax: (201)968-1411
Fr: 800-221-1592

$385.00. Publication includes: Lists of Web sites, organizations, and support groups in the field of psychology. Principal content of publication is entries on psychology including specific disorders, diagnosis, and therapies. Indexes: Alphabetical.

★9405★ Medical and Health Information Directory

Thomson Gale
27500 Drake Rd.
Farmington Hills, MI 48331-3535
Ph: (248)699-4253   Fax: (248)699-8065
Fr: 800-877-GALE
E-mail: businessproducts@gale.com

Annual. $285.00 per volume; $675.00 per set. Covers in Volume 1, more than 26,500 medical and health oriented associations, organizations, institutions, and government agencies, including health maintenance organizations (HMOs), preferred provider organizations (PPOs), insurance companies, pharmaceutical companies, research centers, and medical and allied health schools. In Volume 2, over 12,000 medical book publishers; medical periodicals, directories, audiovisual producers and services, medical libraries and information centers, electronic resources, and health-related internet search engines. In Volume 3, more than 35,500 clinics, treatment centers, care programs, and counseling/diagnostic services for 34 subject areas. Entries include: Institution, service, or firm name, address, phone, fax, email and URL; many include names of key personnel and, when pertinent, descriptive annotation. Volume 3 was formerly listed separately as Health Services Directory. Arrangement: Classified by organization activity, service, etc. Indexes: Each volume has a complete alphabetical name and keyword index.

★9406★ Mental Health Directory

Office of Consumer, Family & Public Information
Parklawn Bldg.
5600 Fishers Ln.
Rockville, MD 20857
Ph: (301)443-4795   Fax: (301)443-0284

Irregular, previous edition 1990; latest edition 1995. $23.00. Covers hospitals, treatment centers, outpatient clinics, day/night facilities, residential treatment centers for emotionally disturbed children, residential supportive programs such as halfway houses, and mental health centers offering mental health assistance; not included are substance abuse programs, Veteran's Administration programs, nursing homes, programs for the developmentally disabled, and organizations in which fees are retained by individual members. Entries include: Name, address, phone. Arrangement: Geographical.

★9407★ **Mental Health Services Directory**

infoUSA Inc.
5711 S 86th Cir.
Omaha, NE 68127-0347
Ph: (402)930-3500   Fax: (402)331-0176
Fr: 800-555-6124
URL: http://www.abii.com

Annual. Number of listings: 18,282. Entries include: Name, address, phone (including area code), size of advertisement, year first in "Yellow Pages," name of owner or manager, number of employees. Compiled from telephone company "Yellow Pages," nationwide. Arrangement: Geographical.

★9408★ **Mental Help Net**

CenterSite, LLC
570 Metro Place
Dublin, OH 43017
URL: http://www.mentalhelp.net

Covers resources for finding mental help including local therapists and self-help groups; Services including upcoming conferences, professional education, and universities offering degrees in mental health fields.

★9409★ **Mental Measurements Yearbook**

University of Nebraska Press
233 N 8th St.
Lincoln, NE 68588-0255
Ph: (402)472-3581   Fax: (402)472-6214
Fr: 800-755-1105

Latest edition 15th, 2003. $195.00. Publication includes: List of publishers of the tests featured in the book. Principal content of publication is description of over 200 new or revised tests used in testing for education, psychology, business law, health care, counseling, and management. Entries include: For tests–Purpose, target population, scores, administration, price, author, and publisher. Indexes: Title, subject, name, acronym, score.

★9410★ **National Directory of Children, Youth & Families Services**

Penny K. Spencer, Publisher
14 Inverness Dr. E. Ste. D-144
Englewood, CO 80112
Ph: (303)662-8165   Fax: 800-845-6452
Fr: 800-343-6681
URL: http://
www.childrenyouthfamilydir.com/

Annual, July. $159.00. Covers more than 45,000 key contacts in the areas of Social Services, Health & Mental Health Services, Juvenile Justice Agencies, Education Departments, Treatment Centers & Hospitals, Referral Networks, child, youth, and family-

oriented social services, health and mental health services, and juvenile/family court and youth advocacy services, educational listings in state and private agencies, major cities, and 3,300 counties; also covers runaway youth centers, child abuse projects, congressional committees, clearinghouses, and national organizations concerned with family health and welfare; buyers' guide to specialized services and products. Entries include: Agency listings include agency name, address, phone, fax, after-hours phone, websites, names of principal executives and staff, description of services. Arrangement: Geographical.

★9411★ **National Directory of Private Social Agencies**

Croner Publications Inc.
10951 Sorrento Valley Rd., Ste. 1D
San Diego, CA 92121-1616
Ph: (619)546-1894   Fax: (858)546-1955
Fr: 800-441-4033
URL: http://www.sdic.net/croner

Base edition supplied upon order; monthly updates. $100.00. Number of listings: Over 10,000. Entries include: Agency name, address, phone, name and title of contact, description of services. Arrangement: Geographical. Indexes: Service, agency type.

★9412★ **Psychologists Directory**

infoUSA Inc.
5711 S 86th Cir.
Omaha, NE 68127-0347
Ph: (402)930-3500   Fax: (402)331-0176
Fr: 800-555-6124
URL: http://www.abii.com

Annual. Number of listings: 41,340. Entries include: Name, address, phone (including area code), size of advertisement, year first in "Yellow Pages," name of owner or manager, number of employees. Regional editions available: Eastern, $920.00; Western, $610.00. Compiled from telephone company "Yellow Pages," nationwide. Arrangement: Geographical.

★9413★ **Psychotherapists Directory**

infoUSA Inc.
5711 S 86th Cir.
Omaha, NE 68127-0347
Ph: (402)930-3500   Fax: (402)331-0176
Fr: 800-555-6124
URL: http://www.abii.com

Annual. Number of listings: 13,570. Entries include: Name, address, phone (including area code), size of advertisement, year first in "Yellow Pages," name of owner or manager, number of employees. Compiled from telephone company "Yellow Pages," nationwide. Arrangement: Geographical.

HANDBOOKS AND MANUALS

★9414★ **Becoming a Complementary Therapist: How to Start a Career in the New Caring Professions**

How To Books
3 Newtec Pl., Magdalen Rd.
Oxford OX4 1RE, United Kingdom

Linda Wilson. 2001.

★9415★ **Career Paths in Psychology: Where Your Degree Can Take You**

American Psychological Association
750 1st St. NE
Washington, DC 20002-4242
Ph: (202)336-5500   Fax: (202)336-5620
Fr: 800-374-2721

Robert J. Sternberg. 1997. $19.95 (paper). 297 pages.

★9416★ **Careers in Medicine, Dentistry and Mental Health**

Kogan Page, Ltd.
22 Broad St., Ste. 34
Milford, CT 06460

Judith Humphries and Loulou Brown. Seventh edition, 1996. $14.95 (paper). Part of the Kogan Page Careers Series. Out of print.

★9417★ **Careers for Mystery Buffs and Other Snoops and Sleuths**

McGraw-Hill Trade
2 Penn Plaza
New York, NY 10121
Ph: (212)904-2000   Fr: 800-722-4726
E-mail: ntcpub@tribune.com

Blythe Camenson. 1996. $14.95; $9.95 (paper). 210 pages.

★9418★ **Careers in Social and Rehabilitation Services**

McGraw-Hill Trade
2 Penn Plaza
New York, NY 10121
Ph: (212)904-2000   Fr: 800-722-4726
E-mail: ntcpub@tribune.com

Geraldine O. Garner. Second edition, 2001. $19.95; 14.95 (paper). 128 pages.

★9419★ **Eighty Dots: Creating a Career in Psychology**

Academic Wine Press
905 Bloomfield Ave.
Glen Ridge, NJ 07028
Ph: (973)743-7916

Thomas E. Heinzen. 2004. College audience.

★9420★ Employment in Community Psychology: The Diversity of Opportunity

Haworth Press, Incorporated
10 Alice St.
Binghamton, NY 13904-1580
Ph: (607)722-5857   Fax: (607)722-6362
Fr: 800-429-6784

Clifford R. O'Donnell and Joseph R. Ferrari. 2000. $24.95 (paper).

★9421★ Everything You Need to Get a Psychology Internship

Windmill Lane Press
1009 S. Bedford St.
Los Angeles, CA 90035-2101
Fax: (310)815-9865   Fr: 800-566-3659

Carl Levinger and Itzchack Schefres. 1996. $24.95 (paper). 153 pages.

★9422★ Great Jobs for Liberal Arts Majors

McGraw-Hill Professional
2 Penn Plaza
New York, NY 10121
Ph: (212)904-2000   Fr: 800-722-4726
E-mail: ntcpub@tribune.com

Blythe Camenson. Second edition, 2001. $14.95 (paper). 256 pages.

★9423★ Great Jobs for Psychology Majors

McGraw-Hill Trade
2 Penn Plaza
New York, NY 10121
Ph: (212)904-2000   Fr: 800-722-4726
E-mail: ntcpub@tribune.com

Julie DeGalan and Stephen Lambert. 1995. $11.95 (paper). 468 pages. Out of print.

★9424★ Independent Practice for the Mental Health Professional: Growing a Private Practice for the 21st Century

Brunner-Routledge
325 Chestnut St., 8th Fl.
Philadelphia, PA 19106
Ph: (215)625-8900   Fax: (215)625-2940

Ralph Earle. 1999. $24.95.

★9425★ Megargee's Guide to Obtaining a Psychological Internship

Hemisphere Publishing Corp.
325 Chestnut St., 8th Fl.
Philadelphia, PA 19106
Fax: (215)269-0363   Fr: 800-821-8312

Edwin I. Megaree. Third edition, 1997. $21.95 (paper). 255 pages.

★9426★ Opportunities in Child Care Careers

McGraw-Hill Trade
2 Penn Plaza
New York, NY 10121
Ph: (212)904-2000   Fr: 800-722-4726

Renee Wittenberg. 1998. $14.95; $11.95 (paper). 210 pages. Discusses various job opportunities and how to secure a position. Illustrated.

★9427★ Opportunities in Health and Medical Careers

McGraw-Hill Trade
2 Penn Plaza
New York, NY 10121
Ph: (212)904-2000   Fr: 800-722-4726

I. Donald Snook, Jr. and Leo D'Orazio. 1997. $14.95; $11.95 (paper). 202 pages. Covers the full range of medical and health occupations. Illustrated.

★9428★ Opportunities in Mental Health Careers

McGraw-Hill Trade
2 Penn Plaza
New York, NY 10121
Ph: (212)904-2000   Fr: 800-722-4726

Philip A. Perry. 1996. $14.95. 160 pages. Part of the Opportunities In... Series.

★9429★ Opportunities in Psychology Careers

McGraw-Hill Trade
2 Penn Plaza
New York, NY 10121
Ph: (212)904-2000   Fr: 800-722-4726
E-mail: ntcpub@tribune.com

Donald E. Super and Charles McAfee Super. 1994. $14.95; $11.95 (paper). A guide to planning for and building a career in the field. Includes bibliography and illustrations. Out of print.

★9430★ Opportunities in Research and Development Careers

McGraw-Hill/Contemporary Books
1221 Avenue of the Americas
New York, NY 10020
Ph: (212)904-2000   Fr: 800-323-4900
E-mail: ntcpub@tribune.com

Jan Goldberg. 1997. $14.95; $11.95 (paper). 204 pages.

★9431★ Opportunities in Social Science Careers

McGraw-Hill Companies
860 Taylor Station Rd.
Blacklick, OH 43004-0545
Fax: (614)755-5645   Fr: 800-722-4726

Rosanne J. Marek. March 2004. $22.95. 160 Pages. VGM Opportunities Series.

★9432★ Opportunities in Sports and Athletics Careers

McGraw-Hill Trade
2 Penn Plaza
New York, NY 10121
Ph: (212)904-2000   Fr: 800-722-4726
E-mail: ntcpub@tribune.com

William Ray Heitzmann. 1994. 160 pages. $14.95; $11.95 (paper). A guide to planning for and seeking opportunities in this growing field. Illustrated.

★9433★ Opportunities in Sports Medicine Careers

McGraw-Hill Trade
2 Penn Plaza
New York, NY 10121
Ph: (212)904-2000   Fr: 800-722-4726
E-mail: ntcpub@tribune.com

William Ray Heitzmann. 1995. $14.95; $11.95 (paper). 160 pages. Discusses a variety of opportunities in this field and how to pursue them. Contains bibliography and illustrations.

★9434★ Real People Working in Education

McGraw-Hill Contemporary Books
1221 Avenue of the Americas
New York, NY 10020
Ph: (212)904-2000   Fr: 800-323-4900
E-mail: ntcpub@tribune.com

Blythe Camenson, Jan Goldberg. 1997. $17.95; $12.95 (paper). Interviews and profiles of working professionals capture a range of opportunities in this field.

★9435★ The Role of Work in People's Lives: Applied Career Counseling & Vocational Psychology

Thomson Wadsworth
10 Davis Dr.
Belmont, CA 94002
Ph: (650)598-9757   Fr: 800-354-9706

Nadine Peterson and Roberto Cortez Gonzalez. 1999. $43.25. 620 pages.

ONLINE JOB SOURCES AND SERVICES

★9436★ Delta T Group
E-mail: staffing@sdelta-tgroup.com
URL: http://www.delta-tgroup.com

Description: Specialized contract temporary staffing source for healthcare professionals in the fields of social service, psychiatry, mental health, and substance abuse. Organizations may request services and staffing; job seekers may view services provided, submit a resume, or peruse jobs available.

★9437★ **Med Source Consultants**
20 Summer Ct.
Stamford, CT 06901
Ph: (203)324-0388   Fax: (203)324-0551
Fr: 800-575-2880
URL: http://www.psychiatricresources.com

Description: Site houses a physician search and consulting company for psychiatrists. Consultants attempt to match job seekers to positions according to the individual's personal and professional needs. This page also aids institutions looking to recruit psychiatrists.

★9438★ **RehabWorld**
URL: http://www.rehabworld.com

Description: Site for rehabilitation professionals to learn about the profession and locate jobs. Includes user groups, salary surveys, and chat capabilities. **Main files include:** Physical Therapy, Occupational Therapy, Speech Therapy, Mental Health, Employer World, Student World, International World, Forum.

TRADESHOWS

★9439★ **American Academy of Psychoanalysis and Dynamic Psychiatry Annual Meeting**
American Academy of Psychoanalysis and Dynamic Psychiatry
PO Box 30
Bloomfield, CT 06002-0030
Ph: (860)243-0437   Fax: (860)286-0787
Fr: 888-691-8281
E-mail: info@aapsa.org
URL: http://www.aapsa.org

Annual. **Primary Exhibits:** Psychoanalysis equipment, supplies, and services.

★9440★ **American Psychological Association Convention**
American Psychological Association
750 1st St., NE
Washington, DC 20002-4242
Ph: (202)336-6020   Fax: (202)336-5568
URL: http://www.apa.org

Annual. **Primary Exhibits:** Computers, publications, and related government services. **Dates and Locations:** 2005 Jul 28-Aug 01; Honolulu, HI • 2006 Aug 10-13; Washington, DC • 2007 Aug 16-19; San Francisco, CA • 2008 Aug 14-17; Boston, MA.

★9441★ **International Association for Suicide Prevention Convention**
International Association for Suicide Prevention
Rush Center for Suicide Research and Prevention
1725 W. Harrison St., Ste. 955
Chicago, IL 60612
Ph: (312)942-7208   Fax: (312)942-2177
E-mail: IASP@aol.com

Biennial. **Primary Exhibits:** Suicide prevention related articles.

★9442★ **Southwestern Psychological Association Annual Meeting**
Southwestern Psychological Association
Tarleton State University
PO Box T-0820
Dr. Bob Newby
Stephenville, TX 76401
Ph: (254)968-9813   Fax: (254)968-9947
E-mail: newby@tarleton.edu

Annual. **Primary Exhibits:** Publications, films, and health products.

OTHER SOURCES

★9443★ **American Almanac of Jobs and Salaries**
Morrow Avon
1350 Avenue of the Americas
New York, NY 10019
Ph: (212)261-6788   Fr: 800-242-7737

John W. Wright. Revised edition, 2000. $20.00 (paper). 672 pages. This is a comprehensive guide to the wages of hundreds of occupations in a wide variety of industries and organizations.

★9444★ **American Association of Mental Health Professionals in Corrections (AAMHPC)**
PO Box 160208
Sacramento, CA 95816-0208
Fax: (916)649-1080
E-mail: corrmentalhealth@aol.com

Description: Psychiatrists, psychologists, social workers, nurses, and other mental health professionals; individuals working in correctional settings. Fosters the progress of behavioral sciences related to corrections. Goals are: to improve the treatment, rehabilitation, and care of the mentally ill, mentally retarded, and emotionally disturbed; to promote research and professional education in psychiatry and allied fields in corrections; to advance standards of correctional services and facilities; to foster cooperation between individuals concerned with the medical, psychological, social, and legal aspects of corrections; to share knowledge with other medical practitioners, scientists, and the public. Conducts scientific meetings to contribute to the advancement of the therapeutic community in all its institutional settings, including correctional institutions, hospitals, churches, schools, industry, and the family.

★9445★ **American Psychological Association (APA)**
750 First St. NE
Washington, DC 20002-4242
Ph: (202)336-5500   Fax: (202)336-6069
Fr: 800-374-2721
E-mail: mhonaker@apa.org

URL: http://www.apa.org/

Members: Scientific and professional society of psychologists. Students participate as affiliates. **Purpose:** Works to advance psychology as a science, a profession, and as a means of promoting human welfare.

★9446★ **American Society of Psychopathology of Expression (ASPE)**
74 Lawton St.
Brookline, MA 02446
Ph: (617)738-9821   Fax: (617)975-0411

Description: Psychiatrists, psychologists, art therapists, sociologists, art critics, artists, social workers, linguists, educators, criminologists, writers, and historians. At least two-thirds of the members must be physicians. Fosters collaboration among specialists in the United States who are interested in the problems of expression and in the artistic activities connected with psychiatric, sociological, and psychological research. Disseminates information about research and clinical applications in the field of psychopathology of expression. Sponsors consultations, seminars, and lectures on art therapy.

★9447★ **Association of Black Psychologists (ABPsi)**
PO Box 55999
Washington, DC 20040-5999
Ph: (202)722-0808   Fax: (202)722-5941
E-mail: admin@abpsi.org
URL: http://www.abpsi.org

Members: Professional psychologists and others in associated disciplines. **Purpose:** Aims to: enhance the psychological well-being of black people in America; define mental health in consonance with newly established psychological concepts and standards; develop policies for local, state, and national decision-making that have impact on the mental health of the black community; support established black sister organizations and aid in the development of new, independent black institutions to enhance the psychological, educational, cultural, and economic situation. **Activities:** Offers training and information on AIDS. Conducts seminars, workshops, and research.

★9448★ **Counseling Association for Humanistic Education and Development (C-AHEAD)**
5999 Stevenson Ave.
Alexandria, VA 22304
Ph: (703)823-9800   Fax: 800-473-2329
Fr: 800-347-6647
E-mail: membership@counseling.org
URL: http://www.counseling.org

Description: A division of the American Counseling Association. Teachers, educational administrators, community agency workers, counselors, school social workers, and psychologists; others interested in the area of human development. Aims to assist individuals in improving their quality of life. Provides forum for the exchange of information about humanistically-oriented administrative and instructional practices. Supports humanistic practices and research on instructional and organizational methods for facilitating humanistic education; encourages cooperation among related professional groups.

★9449★ Employee Assistance Society of North America (EASNA)
230 E Ohio St., Ste. 400
Chicago, IL 60611-3265
Ph: (312)644-0828   Fax: (312)644-8557
E-mail: easna@bostrom.com
URL: http://www.easna.org

Description: Individuals in the field of employee assistance, including psychiatrists, psychologists, and managers. Facilitates communication among members; provides resource information; serves as a network for employee assistance programs nationwide. Conducts research.

★9450★ Internship Selection in Professional Psychology: A Comprehensive Guide for Students, Faculty, and Training Directors
Charles C. Thomas Publisher, Ltd.
2600 S. 1st St.
PO Box 19265
Springfield, IL 62794-9265
Ph: (217)789-8980   Fax: (217)789-9130
Fr: 800-258-8980

Mary E. Oehlert, Scott Sumerall and Shane J. Lopez. 1998. $44.95. 172 pages.

★9451★ National Association of School Psychologists (NASP)
4340 East West Hwy., Ste. 402
Bethesda, MD 20814
Ph: (301)657-0270   Fax: (301)657-0275
E-mail: membership@naspweb.org
URL: http://www.nasponline.org

Members: School psychologists. **Purpose:** Serves to meet the mental health and educational needs of all children and youth. Encourages and provides opportunities for professional growth of individual members. Informs the public on the services and practice of school psychology, and advances the standards of the profession. **Activities:** Operates national school psychologist certification system. Sponsors children's services.

★9452★ Professional Specialty Occupations
Delphi Productions
3160 4th St.
Boulder, CO 80304
Fax: (303)443-4022   Fr: 888-443-2400
URL: http://www.delphivideo.com

$95.00. 53 minutes. Part of the Careers for the 21st Century Video Library.

★9453★ Psychologists
Evon Publishing
832 N 7th Ave.
Iron River, MI 49935
Ph: (906)265-3190

Audiocassette. 1996. $16.95. 32 minutes. Part of the Careers and Vocational Guidance Series. Provides information about the nature of the work, educational requirements, employment outlook, earnings, and work conditions as well as additional related information.

★9454★ Psychology Society (PS)
100 Beekman St.
New York, NY 10038-1810
Ph: (212)285-1872   Fax: (212)285-1872

Description: Professional membership is limited to psychologists who have a doctorate and are certified/licensed as such in the state where they practice. Associate membership is intended for teachers and researchers as well as persons who will attain professional status shortly. Seeks to further the use of psychology in therapy, family and social problems, behavior modification, and treatment of drug abusers and prisoners. Encourages the use of psychology in the solution of social and political conflicts. Operates an information bureau to answer inquiries of authors and media. Sponsors biennial overseas trip to enable members and their spouses to observe other programs and institutions. Collaborates with other associations. Evaluates programs in the use of psychology. Recommends legislation; appears in court cases where issues of mental health occur as expert and impartial witness.

Public Relations Specialists

SOURCES OF HELP-WANTED ADS

★9455★ Editor & Publisher

Editor & Publisher Magazine
770 Broadway
New York, NY 10003-9595
Fax: (646)654-5360   Fr: 800-336-4380
URL: http://www.editorandpublisher.com

Weekly. $99.00/year for U.S. and Canada, includes exclusive web access; $130.00/year for other countries; $4.00 for single issue. Magazine focusing on newspaper journalism, advertising, printing equipment, and interactive services.

★9456★ PR Marcom Jobs East

Rachel P.R. Services
208 E 51st St., No. 1600
New York, NY 10022

Description: Biweekly. Provides news of job openings in public relations, marketing, journalism, communications, public relations agencies and corporations, and freelance and temporary writing positions. Focuses on the New York City, Washington, D.C., Boston, and surrounding states. Recurring features include a calendar of events, job listings, book reviews, and notices of publications available.

★9457★ Public Relations Career Opportunities

Public Relations Career Opportunities
101 S Whiting St., No. 305
Alexandria, VA 22304
Ph: (703)823-4094   Fax: (703)823-5352
URL: http://www.careeropps.com

Description: Semimonthly. Provides information about positions available in the fields of public affairs and public relations.

PLACEMENT AND JOB REFERRAL SERVICES

★9458★ Agricultural Relations Council (ARC)

11020 King St., Ste. 205
Overland Park, KS 66210
Ph: (913)491-6500   Fax: (913)491-6502
E-mail: jennyp@nama.org
URL: http://www.nama.org/arc

Description: Professional society of agricultural public relations executives employed by private business firms, associations, publications, and government agencies. Operates placement service.

EMPLOYER DIRECTORIES AND NETWORKING LISTS

★9459★ The ADWEEK Directory

ADWEEK Magazines
770 Broadway, 7th Fl.
New York, NY 10003
Ph: (646)654-5174   Fax: (646)654-5351
Fr: 800-468-2395
URL: http://www.adweek.com/directories

Annual, August. $700.00. Covers over 6,400 U.S. advertising agencies, public relations firms, media buying services, direct marketing and related organizations. Entries include: Agency name, address, phone, fax/e-mail, URL; names and titles of key personnel; major accounts; Ultimate parent company; headquarters location; major subsidiaries and other operating units; year founded; number of employees; fee income; billings; percentage of billings by medium. Individual listings for each agency branch. Arrangement: Alphabetical. Indexes: Geographical; parent company, subsidiary, branch; ethnic specialities; organization, name changes, agencies opened/closed.

★9460★ Communications Consultants Directory

infoUSA Inc.
5711 S 86th Cir.
Omaha, NE 68127-0347
Ph: (402)930-3500   Fax: (402)331-0176
Fr: 800-555-6124
URL: http://www.abii.com

Annual. Number of listings: 5,302. Entries include: Name, address, phone (including area code), size of advertisement, year first in "Yellow Pages," name of owner or manager, number of employees. Compiled from telephone company "Yellow Pages," nationwide. Arrangement: Geographical.

★9461★ National School Public Relations Association-Directory

National School Public Relations Association
15948 Derwood Rd.
Rockville, MD 20855-2123
Ph: (301)519-0496   Fax: (301)519-0494

Annual, January. Covers approximately 2,000 school system public relations directors, school administrators, principals, and others who are members of the National School Public Relations Association. Entries include: Name, affiliation, address, phone. Arrangement: Geographical.

★9462★ O'Dwyer's Directory of Corporate Communications

J.R. O'Dwyer Company Inc.
271 Madison Ave.
New York, NY 10016
Ph: (212)679-2471   Fax: (212)683-2750

Annual, latest edition February, 2003. $130. Covers public relations departments of approximately 4,450 major United States companies (listed on the New York Stock Exchange and in the "Fortune" list of 1,000 largest firms); also includes similar information on over 1,300 large trade associations and foreign embassies in the United States. Entries include: Company name, address, phone, sales, type of business; names and duties of principal public relations personnel at headquarters and other major offices, plus name and title of person to whom PR head reports; PR budget. Arrangement: Alphabetical. Indexes: Geographical, product.

★9463★ O'Dwyer's Directory of Public Relations Firms

J.R. O'Dwyer Company Inc.
271 Madison Ave.
New York, NY 10016
Ph: (212)679-2471   Fax: (212)683-2750
E-mail: sales@odwyerpr.com
URL: http://www.odwyerpr.com/index.html

Annual, latest edition June, 2002. $175.00. Covers over 2,900 public relations firms; international coverage. Entries include: Firm name, address, phone, principal executives, branch and overseas offices, billings, date founded, and 19,000+ clients are cross-indexed. Arrangement: Geographical by country. Indexes: Specialty (beauty and fashions, finance/investor, etc.), geographical, client.

★9464★ Public Relations Counselors Directory

infoUSA Inc.
5711 S 86th Cir.
Omaha, NE 68127-0347
Ph: (402)930-3500   Fax: (402)331-0176
Fr: 800-555-6124
URL: http://www.abii.com

Number of listings: 8,271. Entries include: Name, address, phone (including area code). Compiled from telephone company "Yellow Pages," nationwide. Arrangement: Geographical.

★9465★ Public Relations Society of America, Chicago Chapter-Membership Directory

Public Relations Society of America, Chicago Chapter
1000 N Rand Rd., Ste. 214
Wauconda, IL 60084
Ph: (847)526-2010   Fax: (847)526-3993

Annual, October. $50.00. Covers about 550 individuals engaged in public relations and related occupations in Chicago. Entries include: Name, title, affiliation, address, phone, type of membership, year joined, employment history. Arrangement: Alphabetical. Indexes: Firm name.

★9466★ Public Relations Tactics-Member Services Directory-The Blue Book

Public Relations Society of America (PRSA)
33 Irving Pl.
New York, NY 10003-2376
Ph: (212)995-2230   Fax: (212)995-0757
E-mail: 74224.1456@compuserve.com
URL: http://www.prsa.org

Annual, January. $375.00 for nonmembers. Covers PRSA members-headquarters, staff contacts, and chapter, section, and district information. Entries include: Name, professional affiliation and title, address, phone, membership rank. Arrangement: Alphabetical. Indexes: Geographical, organizational.

★9467★ Reed's Worldwide Directory of Public Relations Organizations

Pigafetta Press
PO Box 39244
Washington, DC 20016
Ph: (202)244-2580   Fax: (202)244-2581
E-mail: 110104.1310@compuserve.com

Annual, October. $95.00. Covers approximately 225 professional public relations associations in 75 countries. Entries include: Association name, address, phone, publications, current officers, activities, and history of the organization. Arrangement: Geographical; separate section for international organizations.

★9468★ Sports Market Place

Sportsguide L.L.C.
13901 N 73rd St., Ste. 219
Scottsdale, AZ 85260
Ph: (480)948-8885   Fax: (480)948-7701
Fr: 800-776-7877
E-mail: smp@sportsmarketplace.com
URL: http://www.sportsmarketplace.com

Annual, January. $249.00. Covers manufacturers, organizations, professional sports teams, broadcasting networks, sports arenas, syndicators, publications, trade shows, marketing services, corporate sports sponsors, and other groups concerned with the business and promotional aspects of sports generally and with air sports, arm wrestling, auto sports, badminton, baseball, basketball, biathlon, bowling, boxing, curling, equestrian, exercise, fencing, field hockey, football, golf, gymnastics, ice hockey, lacrosse, martial arts, paddleball, paddle tennis, platform tennis, pentathlon, racquetball, rowing, rugby, running/jogging, skiing, soccer, softball, squash, swimming, table tennis, tennis, track and field, volleyball, water sports, weightlifting, and wrestling. Entries include: Name of company or organization, address, fax, e-mail, URL, name of key personnel with titles, and description of products or services. Arrangement: Classified by type of firm, sport, or activity. Indexes: Alphabetical, single sprt, media, sport sponsors, agencies, manufacturers, brand name, facilities, executive, and Geographical.

HANDBOOKS AND MANUALS

★9469★ Becoming a Public Relations Writer: A Writing Process Workbook for the Profession

Lawrence Erlbaum Associates Inc.
10 Industrial Ave.
Mahwah, NJ 07430
Ph: (201)236-9500   Fax: (781)942-1117
Fr: 800-447-2226

Ronald D. Smith. 1997. $24.00 (paper). Out of print.

★9470★ Career Information Center

Macmillan Publishing Co. Inc.
200 Old Tappan Rd.
Old Tappan, NJ 07675
Fr: 800-428-5331

Visual Education Center Staff. Seventh edition, 1999. $275.00. 2080 pages. This 13-volume set profiles over 600 occupations. Each occupational profile describes job duties, educational requirements, how to get the job, advancement possibilities, employment outlook, working conditions, earnings and benefits, and where to write for more information.

★9471★ Career Opportunities in Advertising and Public Relations (Career Opportunities Series)

Checkmark Books, Inc.
132 W. 31st St., 17th Fl.
New York, NY 10001-2006
Ph: (212)967-8800   Fax: (212)967-9196
Fr: 800-322-8755
URL: http://www.factsonfile.com

Shelly Field and Howard J. Rubenstein. Third edition, 2001. $14.95 (paper). 320 pages. Provides the job seeker with information about locating and landing the right position. Includes detailed job descriptions for many specific positions and lists trade associations, recruiting organizations, and major agencies. Contains index and bibliography.

★9472★ Career Opportunities for Writers

Checkmark Books
132 W. 31st St., 17th Fl.
New York, NY 10001-2006
Ph: (212)967-8800   Fax: (212)967-9196
Fr: 800-322-8755
URL: http://www.factsonfile.com

Rosemary Ellen Guiley and Janet Frick. Fourth edition, 2000. $45.00. Part of the Career Opportunities Series. Describes more than 100 jobs in eight major fields, offering such details as duties, salaries, perquisites, employment and advancement opportunities, organizations to join, and opportunities for women and minorities.

★9473★ Careers in Communications

VGM Career Horizons
4255 W. Touhy Ave.
Lincolnwood, IL 60646-1975
Ph: (847)679-5500   Fax: (847)679-2494
Fr: 800-323-4900
E-mail: ntcpub@tribune.com

Shonan Noronha. Third edition, 1998. $17.95; $13.95 (paper). 418 pages. Examines the fields of journalism, photography, radio, television, film, public relations, and advertising. Gives concrete details on job locations and how to secure a job. Suggests many resources for job hunting.

★9474★ Careers in Marketing, Advertising and Public Relations

Kogan Page, Ltd.
22 Broad St.
Ste. 34
Milford, CT 06460

Adela Stanley. 2003. $14.95 (paper). 128 pages. Part of the Kogan Page Careers Series. Out of print.

★9475★ Careers for Writers and Others Who Have a Way with Words

McGraw-Hill Trade
2 Penn Plaza
New York, NY 10121
Ph: (212)904-2000   Fr: 800-722-4726
E-mail: ntcpub@tribune.com

Robert W. Bly. 1995. $14.95; $9.95 (paper). 295 pages.

★9476★ How to Get into Marketing and PR

Continuum International Publishing Group, Inc.
15 E. 26th St., Ste. 1703
New York, NY 10010
Ph: (212)953-5858   Fax: (212)953-5944

Annie Gurton. June 2003. $21.95 (paper). 256 pages.

★9477★ Opportunities in Insurance Careers

McGraw-Hill/Contemporary Books
1221 Avenue of the Americas
New York, NY 10020
Ph: (212)904-2000   Fr: 800-323-4900
E-mail: ntcpub@tribune.com

Robert Schrayer. Revised, 1999. $14.95; $11.95 (paper). 148 pages. A guide to planning for and seeking opportunities in the field. Contains bibliography and illustrations.

★9478★ Opportunities in Journalism Careers

McGraw-Hill/Contemporary Books
1221 Avenue of the Americas
New York, NY 10020
Ph: (212)904-2000   Fr: 800-323-4900
E-mail: ntcpub@tribune.com

Jim Patten and Donald L. Ferguson. 1995. $14.95; $11.95 (paper). 160 pages. Outlines opportunities in every field of journalism, including newspaper reporting and editing, magazine and book publishing, corporate communications, advertising and public relations, freelance writing, and teaching. Covers how to prepare for and enter each field, outlining responsibilities, salaries, benefits, and job outlook for each specialty. Illustrated.

★9479★ Opportunities in Marketing Careers

McGraw-Hill Trade
2 Penn Plaza
New York, NY 10121
Ph: (212)904-2000   Fr: 800-722-4726

Margery Steinberg. 1999. $14.95; $11.95 (paper). 202 pages. Includes guidance on identifying and pursuing job opportunities. Illustrated.

★9480★ Opportunities in Public Relations Careers

McGraw-Hill Trade
2 Penn Plaza
New York, NY 10121
Ph: (212)904-2000   Fr: 800-722-4726
E-mail: ntcpub@tribune.com

Morris B. Rotman. 1995. $14.95; $11.95 (paper). 200 pages. Tells the reader how to enter the field and how to build a career. Contains bibliography and illustrations.

★9481★ Opportunities in Sports and Athletics Careers

McGraw-Hill Trade
2 Penn Plaza
New York, NY 10121
Ph: (212)904-2000   Fr: 800-722-4726
E-mail: ntcpub@tribune.com

William Ray Heitzmann. 1994. 160 pages. $14.95; $11.95 (paper). A guide to planning for and seeking opportunities in this growing field. Illustrated.

★9482★ Opportunities in Writing Careers

McGraw-Hill Contemporary Books
1221 Avenue of the Americas
New York, NY 10020
Ph: (212)904-2000   Fr: 800-323-4900
E-mail: ntcpub@tribune.com

Elizabeth Foote-Smith. 1999. $14.95; $11.95 (paper). 160 pages. Discusses opportunities in the print media, broadcasting, advertising or publishing. Business writing, public relations, and technical writing are among the careers covered. Contains bibliography and illustrations.

★9483★ Public Relations Career Directory

Thomson Gale
27500 Drake Rd.
Farmington Hills, MI 48331-3535
Ph: (248)699-GALE   Fax: 800-414-5043
Fr: 800-877-GALE
E-mail: galeord@gale.com
URL: http://www.gale.com

Bradley Morgan. Fifth edition, 1993. $39.00. 300 pages. Out of print. Features extensive listings of contacts and entry-level job opportunities at major corporations and public relations agencies nationwide. Includes articles and advice from top public relations practitioners on such areas as corporate communications, international public rela-

tions, community affairs, and media relations.

★9484★ Real People Working in Communications

McGraw-Hill Contemporary Books
1221 Avenue of the Americas
New York, NY 10020
Ph: (212)904-2000   Fr: 800-323-4900
E-mail: ntcpub@tribune.com

Jan Goldberg. 1996. $14.95; $12.95 (paper). Interviews and profiles of working professionals capture a range of opportunities in this field.

★9485★ Running a Public Relations Consultancy

Kogan Page, Ltd.
22 Broad St., Ste. 34
Milford, CT 06460

Peter Hehir. 1997. $16.95 (paper). Out of print. Part of the PR in Practice Series.

★9486★ Where the Jobs Are: The Hottest Careers for the 90s

The Career Press, Inc.
3 Tice Rd.
PO Box 687
Franklin Lakes, NJ 07417-1322
Ph: (201)848-0310   Fax: (201)848-1727
Fr: 800-227-3371

Joyce Hadley. Third edition, 2000. $13.99 (paper). 400 pages. Out of print. Describes careers in fifteen general fields, from accounting to travel and hospitality.

★9487★ Working in Public Relations: How to Gain the Skills and Opportunities for a Career in Public Relations

How to Books, Ltd.
311 Bainbridge St.
Philadelphia, PA 19147
Ph: (215)925-5083   Fax: (215)925-1912

Carole Chester. 1998. $21.95 (paper). 144 pages.

★9488★ Writing for Results: Keys to Success for the Public Relations Writer

Alta Villa Publishing, Incorporated
P.O. Box 17684
Indianapolis, IN 46217-0684
Ph: (317)885-1918

Ray Begovich. 2001. $12.00 (paper).

EMPLOYMENT AGENCIES AND SEARCH FIRMS

★9489★ Chaloner Associates
36 Milford St.
Boston, MA 02118
Ph: (617)451-5170   Fax: (617)451-8160
E-mail: info@chaloner.com
URL: http://www.chaloner.com

Executive search firm.

★9490★ The Esquire Staffing Group Ltd.
1 S. Wacker Dr., Ste. 1616
Chicago, IL 60606-4616
Ph: (312)795-4300   Fax: (312)795-4329
E-mail: s.fischer@esquirestaffing.com
URL: http://www.esquirestaffing.com

Employment agency. Fills permanent as well as temporary openings.

★9491★ Howard-Sloan Professional Search Inc.
1140 Ave. of the Americas
New York, NY 10036
Ph: (212)704-0444   Fax: (212)869-7999
Fr: 800-221-1326
E-mail: info@howardsloan.com
URL: http://www.howardsloan.com

Executive search firm.

★9492★ Robert E. Larson and Associates Inc.
N25 W24069 River Park Dr.
Pewaukee, WI 53072
Ph: (262)523-1644   Fax: (414)695-9597

Provides assistance to client companies who seek upper and middle management personnel, in the areas of data processing, manufacturing and engineering, all phases of accounting and finance, sales and marketing, and industrial and public relations.

★9493★ Toby Clark Associates Inc.
405 E 54th St., Ste. 6C
New York, NY 10022
Ph: (212)752-5670   Fax: (212)752-5674

Executive recruiting firm specializing in marketing communications and public relations.

OTHER SOURCES

★9494★ ABA Marketing Network
1120 Conneticut Ave. NW
Washington, DC 20036
Ph: (202)663-5283   Fax: (202)828-4540
Fr: 800-BAN-KERS
E-mail: marketingnetwork@aba.com
URL: http://www.aba.com/MarketingNetwork/default.htm

Members: Marketing and public relations executives for commercial and savings banks, credit unions, and savings and loans associations, and related groups such as advertising agencies and research firms. **Purpose:** Provides marketing education, information, and services to the financial services industry. **Activities:** Conducts research; cosponsors summer sessions of fundamentals and advanced courses in marketing at the University of Colorado at Boulder; compiles statistics.

★9495★ American Almanac of Jobs and Salaries
Morrow Avon
1350 Avenue of the Americas
New York, NY 10019
Ph: (212)261-6788   Fr: 800-242-7737

John W. Wright. Revised edition, 2000. $20.00 (paper). 672 pages. This is a comprehensive guide to the wages of hundreds of occupations in a wide variety of industries and organizations.

★9496★ American Marketing Association (AMA)
311 S Wacker Dr., Ste. 5800
Chicago, IL 60606
Ph: (312)542-9000   Fax: (312)542-9001
Fr: 800-262-1150
E-mail: info@ama.org
URL: http://www.marketingpower.com/

Description: Professional society of marketing and market research executives, sales and promotion managers, advertising specialists, academics, and others interested in marketing. **Activities:** Fosters research; sponsors seminars, conferences, and student marketing clubs; provides educational placement service and doctoral consortium.

★9497★ Association for Women in Communications
780 Ritchie Hwy., Ste. 28-S
Severna Park, MD 21146
Ph: (410)544-7442   Fax: (410)544-4640
E-mail: pat@womcom.org
URL: http://www.womcom.org

Description: Professional association of journalism and communications.

★9498★ Media Alliance (MA)
814 Mission St., Ste. 205
San Francisco, CA 94103
Ph: (415)546-6334   Fax: (415)546-6218
E-mail: info@media-alliance.org
URL: http://www.media-alliance.org

Description: Writers, photographers, editors, broadcast workers, public relations practioners, videographers, filmmakers, commercial artists and other media workers and aspiring media workers. Supports free press and independent, alternative journalism that services progressive politics and social justice.

★9499★ National School Public Relations Association (NSPRA)
15948 Derwood Rd.
Rockville, MD 20855-2123
Ph: (301)519-0496   Fax: (301)519-0494
E-mail: nspra@nspra.org
URL: http://www.nspra.org/

Description: School system public relations directors, school administrators, and others interested in furthering public understanding of the public schools. Has adopted standards for public relations professionals and programs and an accreditation program.

★9500★ PROMAX
2029 Century Park East, Ste. 555
Los Angeles, CA 90067-2906
Ph: (310)788-7600   Fax: (310)788-7616
E-mail: bonnie@promax.tv
URL: http://www.promax.tv

Members: Advertising, public relations, and promotion managers of cable, radio, and television stations, systems and networks; syndicators. **Purpose:** Seeks to advance the role and increase the effectiveness of promotion and marketing within the industry, related industries, and educational communities. **Activities:** Conducts workshops and weekly fax service for members. Operates employment service. Maintains speakers' bureau, hall of fame, and resource center with print, audio, and visual materials.

★9501★ Public Relations Society of America (PRSA)
33 Irving Pl.
New York, NY 10003-2376
Ph: (212)995-2230   Fax: (212)995-0757
E-mail: exec@prsa.org
URL: http://www.prsa.org

Description: Professional society of public relations practitioners in business and industry, counseling firms, government, associations, hospitals, schools, and nonprofit organizations. Conducts professional development programs. Maintains Professional Resource Center. Offers accreditation program.

★9502★ Public Relations Specialists
Evon Publishing
832 N 7th Ave.
Iron River, MI 49935
Ph: (906)265-3190

Audiocassette. 1996. $16.95. 32 minutes. Part of the Careers and Vocational Guidance Series. Provides information about the nature of the work, educational requirements, employment outlook, earnings, and work conditions as well as additional related information.

Purchasing Agents and Managers

SOURCES OF HELP-WANTED ADS

★9503★ **Benchmarking Purchasing**
American Purchasing Society
8 E Galena Blvd., Ste. 203
Aurora, IL 60506-5035
Ph: (630)859-0250   Fax: (630)859-0270
Annual. Professional journal covering issues in purchasing.

★9504★ **Electronic Business**
Reed Business Information
275 Washington St.
Newton, MA 02458
Ph: (617)558-4900   Fax: (617)630-3830
Fr: 800-357-4745
URL: http://www.eb-mag.com
Monthly. Free to qualified readers; $83.90/year, nonqualified; $115.90/year for Canada; $104.90/year for Mexico. Magazine for purchasing managers and buyers of electronic components and materials used in end product manufacture.

★9505★ **Healthcare Purchasing News**
Nelson Publishing Inc.
2500 Tamiami Trl. N
Nokomis, FL 34275-3482
Ph: (941)966-9521   Fax: (941)966-2590
Fr: 800-226-6113
E-mail: hpn@hpnonline.com
URL: http://www.hpnonline.com
Monthly. $44.95/year for U.S.; $54.95/year for Canada; $59.95/year, foreign; $5.00 for single issue; $9.00 for single back issue. Magazine for healthcare material management, central services, operating room and infection control professionals, and others involved in supply chain issues with hospitals and outpatient settings.

★9506★ **NAEB Bulletin**
National Association of Educational
  Buyers Inc.
450 Wireless Blvd.
Hauppauge, NY 11788
Ph: (631)273-2600   Fax: (631)952-3660
E-mail: jfox@naeb.org
Description: Monthly, except May and April. Features information on institutional purchasing and news of the Association. Recurring features include a calendar of events, reports of meetings, news of educational opportunities, job listings, book reviews, notices of publications available, and columns titled Professional Perspective, Market Index, and Roamin' With Yeoman.

★9507★ **Professional Purchasing**
American Purchasing Society
8 E Galena Blvd., Ste. 203
Aurora, IL 60506-5035
Ph: (630)859-0250   Fax: (630)859-0270
E-mail: propurch@mgci.com
URL: http://www.american_purchasing.com
Description: Monthly. Provides information on policies, procedures, methods, and prices of purchasing. Features price indexes. Recurring features include letters to the editor, news of research, reports of meetings, news of educational opportunities, job listings, book reviews, and notices of publications available.

★9508★ **Purchasing Magazine**
Reed Business Information
275 Washington St.
Newton, MA 02458-1630
Ph: (617)964-3030
URL: http://www.purchasing.com
Semimonthly. $99.00/year. Magazine for buying professionals.

PLACEMENT AND JOB REFERRAL SERVICES

★9509★ **American Purchasing Society**
N. Island Ctr., Ste. 203
8 E Galena Blvd.
Aurora, IL 60506
Ph: (630)859-0250   Fax: (630)859-0270
E-mail: propurch@mgci.com
URL: http://www.american-purchasing.com
Description: Seeks to certify qualified purchasing personnel. Maintains speakers' bureau and placement service. Conducts research programs; compiles statistics including salary surveys. Provides consulting service for purchasing, materials management, and marketing. Conducts seminars and online courses.

★9510★ **National Contract Management Association (NCMA)**
8260 Greensboro Dr., Ste. 200
McLean, VA 22102
Ph: (571)382-0082   Fax: (703)448-0939
Fr: 800-344-8096
E-mail: memberservices@ncmahq.org
URL: http://www.ncmahq.org
Description: Professional individuals concerned with administration, procurement, acquisition, negotiation, and management of contracts and subcontracts. Works for the education, improvement, and professional development of members and nonmembers through national and chapter programs, symposia, and educational materials. Offers certification in Contract Management (CPCM, CFCM, and CCCM) designations as well as a credential program. Operates speakers' bureau.

EMPLOYER DIRECTORIES AND NETWORKING LISTS

★9511★ Multi-Hospital Systems and Group Purchasing Organizations Report & Directory

SMG Marketing Group Inc.
875 N Michigan Ave., Ste. 3100
Chicago, IL 60611
Ph: (312)642-3026   Fax: (312)642-9729
Fr: 800-678-3026
URL: http://www.smg.com

Quarterly. $525.00 for single issue; $995.00 for annual subscription. Covers over 750 multi-hospital systems and group purchasing organizations. Entries include: Company name, address, phone; hospital name, address, phone, type of hospital service, licensed number of beds, number of staffed beds, annual admission data, annual surgical information, status of hospital, activity in recent quarter, date and length of management contract with the hospital. Arrangement: Geographical. Indexes: Company name.

HANDBOOKS AND MANUALS

★9512★ Opportunities in Hospital Administration Careers

McGraw-Hill/Contemporary Books
1221 Avenue of the Americas
New York, NY 10020
Ph: (212)904-2000   Fr: 800-323-4900
E-mail: ntcpub@tribune.com

I. Donald Snook. 1997. $14.95; $11.95 (paper). 160 pages. Discusses opportunities for administrators in a variety of management settings: hospital, department, clinic, group practice, HMO, mental health, and extended care facilities.

★9513★ Opportunities in International Business Careers

McGraw-Hill Trade
2 Penn Plaza
New York, NY 10121
Ph: (212)904-2000   Fr: 800-722-4726

Jeffrey Arpan. 1994. $11.95 (paper). 200 pages. Describes what types of jobs exist in international business, where they are located, what challenges and rewards they bring, and how to prepare for and obtain jobs in international business.

EMPLOYMENT AGENCIES AND SEARCH FIRMS

★9514★ The Aspire Group

52 Second Ave, 1st Fl
Waltham, MA 02451-1129
Fax: (718)890-1810   Fr: 800-546-5675
URL: http://www.bmanet.com

Employment agency.

★9515★ Britt Associates Inc.

3533 Lake Shore Dr.
Joliet, IL 60431-8820
Ph: (815)436-8300   Fax: (815)436-9617
E-mail: brittassoc@aol.com

Employment agency.

★9516★ Colli Associates

404 Caboose Ln.
Valrico, FL 33594
Ph: (813)681-2145   Fax: (813)661-5217
E-mail: colli@gte.net

Employment agency. Executive search firm.

★9517★ The Esquire Staffing Group Ltd.

1 S. Wacker Dr., Ste. 1616
Chicago, IL 60606-4616
Ph: (312)795-4300   Fax: (312)795-4329
E-mail: s.fischer@esquirestaffing.com
URL: http://www.esquirestaffing.com

Employment agency. Fills permanent as well as temporary openings.

★9518★ Rocky Mountain Recruiters, Inc.

2000 S Colorado Blvd., Ste. 200
The Annex Bldg.
Denver, CO 80222
Ph: (303)296-2000   Fax: (303)296-2223
E-mail: miket@rmrecruiters.com
URL: http://www.rmrecruiters.com

Accounting, financial, and executive search firm.

★9519★ Romac International, Inc.

1001 E Palm Ave
Tampa, FL 33605
Ph: (813)552-5239   Fax: (813)552-2122
URL: http://www.romac.com

Executive search firm. More than 30 locations throughout the United States.

TRADESHOWS

★9520★ Great Lakes Industrial Show

North American Exposition Co.
33 Rutherford Ave.
Charlestown, MA 02129
Ph: (617)242-6092   Fax: (617)242-1817
Fr: 800-225-1577
E-mail: naexpo@hotmail.com

Annual. **Primary Exhibits:** Industrial products, machine tools, hand tools, pneumatics, hydraulics, plant engineering, and maintenance, paper and packaging, plastics, rubber products, material handling equipment, and dies and stampings.

★9521★ International Mass Retail Association Convention and Exhibits

International Mass Retail Association
1700 N. Moore St., Ste. 2250
Arlington, VA 22209
Ph: (703)841-2300   Fax: (703)841-1184
URL: http://www.imra.org

Annual. **Primary Exhibits:** Consumer products.

★9522★ The NAMSB Show

NSI
309 5th Ave., Ste. 303
New York, NY 10016-6509
Ph: (212)685-4550   Fax: (212)685-4688
Fr: 800-936-2672
E-mail: info@nsi-shows.com
URL: http://www.nsi-shows.com

Semiannual. **Primary Exhibits:** Product lines include mens' and boy's clothing, sportswear, footwear, streetwear, unisex, and accessories.

★9523★ Supermarket Industry Convention and Educational Exposition

Food Marketing Institute
655 15th St., NW
Washington, DC 20005
Ph: (202)452-8444   Fax: (202)429-4519
E-mail: fmi@fmi.org
URL: http://www.fmi.org

Annual. **Primary Exhibits:** Products, equipment, supplies, and services available to and through the supermarket industry, including grocery products, perishables, general merchandise, health and beauty aids, food service equipment, store design services, data processing equipment, advertising, and warehouse services. **Dates and Locations:** 2005 May 01-03; Chicago, IL.

OTHER SOURCES

★9524★ *Administration and Management Occupations*

Delphi Productions
3160 4th St.
Boulder, CO 80304
Fax: (303)443-4022   Fr: 888-443-2400
URL: http://www.delphivideo.com

$95.00. 50 minutes. Part of the Careers for the 21st Century Video Library.

★9525★ *American Almanac of Jobs and Salaries*

Morrow Avon
1350 Avenue of the Americas
New York, NY 10019
Ph: (212)261-6788   Fr: 800-242-7737

John W. Wright. Revised edition, 2000. $20.00 (paper). 672 pages. This is a comprehensive guide to the wages of hundreds of occupations in a wide variety of industries and organizations.

★9526★ **Institute for Supply Management (ISM)**

2055 E. Centennial Cir.
PO Box 22160
Tempe, AZ 85285-2160
Ph: (480)752-6276   Fax: (480)752-7890
Fr: 800-888-6276
URL: http://www.ism.ws

Members: Supply management for industrial, commercial, and utility firms; educational institutions and government agencies. **Pur-**pose: Disseminates information on procurement. Works to develop more efficient supply management methods. **Activities:** Conducts program for certification as a supply manager. Cosponsors executive purchasing management institutes at Michigan State University and Arizona State University. Provides in-company training. Maintains speakers' bureau and reference service.

★9527★ **National Institute of Governmental Purchasing (NIGP)**

151 Spring St.
Herndon, VA 20170
Ph: (703)736-8900   Fax: (703)736-9644
Fr: 800-FOR-NIGP
E-mail: membership@nigp.org
URL: http://www.nigp.org

Description: Federal, state, provincial, county, and local government buying agencies; hospital, school, prison, and public utility purchasing agencies in the U.S. and Canada. Also provides services to the International procurement community. Develops standards and specifications for governmental buying; promotes uniform purchasing laws and procedures; conducts specialized education and research programs. Administers certification program for the Universal Public Purchasing Certification Council (UPPCC) for Certified Professional Public Buyer (CPPB) and Certified Public Purchasing Officer (CPPO); offers audit consulting services and cost saving programs and tools for governmental agencies, including product commodity code to online specifications library. Maintains speakers' bureau; compiles statistics, web based products and services.

★9528★ **National Management Association (NMA)**

2210 Arbor Blvd.
Dayton, OH 45439
Ph: (937)294-0421   Fax: (937)294-2374
E-mail: nma@nma1.org
URL: http://www.nma1.org

Description: Business and industrial management personnel; membership comes from supervisory level, with the remainder from middle management and above. Seeks to develop and recognize management as a profession and to promote the free enterprise system. Prepares chapter programs on basic management, management policy and practice, communications, human behavior, industrial relations, economics, political education, and liberal education. Maintains speakers' bureau and hall of fame. Maintains educational, charitable, and research programs. Sponsors charitable programs.

★9529★ *Purchasing Agents and Managers*

Evon Publishing
832 N 7th Ave.
Iron River, MI 49935
Ph: (906)265-3190

Audiocassette. 1996. $16.95. 32 minutes. Part of the Careers and Vocational Guidance Series. Provides information about the nature of the work, educational requirements, employment outlook, earnings, and work conditions as well as additional related information.

Rabbis and Jewish Religious Professionals

Jewish Communal Service Association
3084 State Hwy. 27, Ste. 9
Kendall Park, NJ 08824-1657
Ph: (732)821-1871   Fax: (732)821-5335

Quarterly. $30.00/year for individuals. Journal covering Jewish communal service and social work.

PLACEMENT AND JOB REFERRAL SERVICES

★9531★ Central Conference of American Rabbis (CCAR)

355 Lexington Ave Fl 18
New York, NY 10017-6603
Ph: (212)972-3636
E-mail: info@ccarnet.org
URL: http://www.ccarnet.org

Description: National organization of Reform rabbis. Offers placement service; compiles statistics. Maintains 38 committees.

★9532★ Council for Jewish Education (CJE)

11 Olympia Ln.
Monsey, NY 10952
Ph: (845)368-8657   Fax: (845)369-6538
E-mail: mjscje@aol.com

Description: Teachers of Hebrew in universities; heads of Bureaus of Jewish Education and their administrative departments; faculty members of Jewish teacher training schools. Seeks to: further the cause of Jewish education in America; raise professional standards and practices; promote the welfare and growth of Jewish educational workers; improve and strengthen Jewish life. Conducts educational programs; cosponsors a Per-

sonnel Placement Committee with Jewish Education Service of North America.

★9533★ Jewish Community Centers Association of North America (JCCANA)

15 E 26th St.
New York, NY 10010
Ph: (212)532-4958   Fax: (212)481-4174
Fr: 877-452-2237
E-mail: info@jcca.org
URL: http://www.jcca.org

Description: Promotes the Jewish community center movement; aims to provide educational, cultural, social, Jewish identity building and recreational programs; fosters connections between North American Jews and Israel and world Jewry. Jewish military personnel and their dependents in the U.S. Armed Forces and Veterans Administration Hospitals through the JWB Jewish Chaplains Council. Operates research center; compiles statistics; maintains placement services for professional Jewish community center and YM and YWHA workers. Jewish military personnel and their dependents in the U.S. Armed Forces and Veterans Administration Hospitals through the JWB Jewish Chaplains Council. Operates research center; compiles statistics; maintains placement services for professional Jewish community center and YM andYWHA workers

★9534★ Jewish Educators Assembly (JEA)

300 Forest Dr.
East Hills, NY 11548
Ph: (516)484-9585   Fax: (516)484-9586
E-mail: jewisheducators@aol.com
URL: http://www.jewisheducators.org/

Members: Educational and supervisory personnel serving Jewish educational institutions. **Purpose:** Seeks to advance the development of Jewish education in the congregation on all levels in consonance with the philosophy of the Conservative Movement; cooperate with the United Synagogue of America Commission on Jewish Education as the policy-making body of the educational enterprise; join in cooperative effort with other Jewish educational institutions and

organizations; establish and maintain professional standards for Jewish educators; serve as a forum for the exchange of ideas; promote the values of Jewish education as a basis for the creative continuity of the Jewish people. **Activities:** Maintains placement service and speakers' bureau.

★9535★ Jewish Reconstructionist Federation (JRF)

7804 Montgomery Ave, Ste. 9
Elkins Park, PA 19027-2649
Ph: (215)782-8500   Fax: (215)782-8805
E-mail: info@jrf.org
URL: http://www.jrf.org

Description: Federation of synagogues and fellowships committed to the philosophy and program of the Jewish Reconstructionist Movement. Maintains placement service and consulting services. Organize services to affiliates.

★9536★ National Association of Temple Administrators (NATA)

6114 La Salle Ave. Box 731
Oakland, CA 94611
Fr: 800-966-NATA
E-mail: nataorg@hotmail.com
URL: http://rj.org/nata/

Description: Full-time administrators of Jewish synagogues affiliated with the Union of American Hebrew Congregations. Conducts educational programs; has established code of standards and ethics. Offers congregational survey service and compiles synagogue research reports and salary reports. Conducts placement service; maintains speakers' bureau.

★9537★ National Association of Temple Educators (NATE)

633 Third Ave. 7th Fl.
New York, NY 10017-6778
Ph: (212)452-6510   Fax: (212)452-6512
E-mail: nateoff@aol.com
URL: http://rj.org/nate/

Members: Directors of education in Reform Jewish religious schools, principals, heads of departments, supervisors, educational consultants, students, and authors. **Purpose:** Purposes are to: assist in the growth and development of Jewish religious education consistent with the aims of Reform Judaism; stimulate communal interest in Jewish religious education; represent and encourage the profession of temple educator. **Activities:** Conducts surveys on personnel practices, confirmation practices, religious school organization and administration, curricular practices, and other aspects of religious education. Sponsors institutes for principals and educational directors; maintains placement service.

★**9538**★ **Rabbinical Alliance of America (RAA)**

3 W. 16th St., 4th Fl.
New York, NY 10011
Ph: (212)242-6420   Fax: (212)255-8313

Description: Orthodox rabbis who serve in pulpits and as principals of Jewish day schools and Hebrew schools throughout the world. Supervises Hebrew Schools Program for Adult Studies. Provides placement service aid for indigent Torah scholars; contributes to Jewish charitable causes. Maintains the Rabbinical Court which handles orthodox Jewish divorces, court of arbitration, Dinei Torahs, and family and marriage counselling.

★**9539**★ **Rabbinical Assembly (RA)**

3080 Broadway
New York, NY 10027
Ph: (212)280-6000   Fax: (212)749-9166
E-mail: rabassembly@jtsa.edu
URL: http://www.rabassembly.org/

Description: Rabbis serving Conservative Jewish congregations; chaplains in the Armed Forces and in educational or communal organizations. Promotes Conservative Judaism; to cooperate with the Jewish Theological Seminary of America; Advances the cause of Jewish learning; Promotes the welfare of the members; fosters the spirit of fellowship and cooperation among the rabbis and other Jewish scholars. Offers placement service.

★**9540**★ **Solomon Schecher Day School Association (SSDSA)**

155 5th Ave.
New York, NY 10010-6802
Ph: (212)533-7800   Fax: (212)353-9439
E-mail: info@uscj.org
URL: http://www.uscj.org

Description: A division of the United Synagogue of Conservative Judaism Commission on Jewish Education. Jewish elementary day schools and high schools with a total of over 21,500 students. Named for Solomon Schecher (1850-1915), scholar of Talmud and rabbinical literature at Cambridge and founder of the United Synagogue of America and the Jewish Theological Seminary. Provides visitations and consultations regarding education, governance and administration; publication of advisories and position papers, biennial conferences for lay leaders, annual conferences of the principals council,

Shibboley Schechter newsletter, listserves for presidents, School heads, Business managers, and development directors. Also provides dissemination of demographics and statistics, chartering and accreditation of schools, seminars and board training for lay leaders, Schechter website, SHAR"R, 7th and 8th grade trips to Israel, placement service, MaToK-TaNaKH curriculum development project for Solomon Schecter Day schools, residency fellowship program to prepare professional leadership (SREL) and a listing of consultants.

★**9541**★ **Young Israel Council of Rabbis (YICR)**

3 W. 16th St.
New York, NY 10011
Ph: (212)929-1525   Fax: (212)727-9526
E-mail: rabbis@youngisrael.org
URL: http://www.youngisrael.org

Description: Rabbis serving 200 Young Israel congregations in the U.S., Canada, and Israel. Encourages study and observance of Judaism and provides spiritual leadership to the Young Israel Movement. Adjudicates issues relating to the Young Israel Synagogues. Maintains speakers' bureau; conducts research and educational programs; provides placement service. Is concerned with welfare of rabbis.

EMPLOYER DIRECTORIES AND NETWORKING LISTS

★**9542**★ **Directory of Day Schools in the United States and Canada**

Torah Umesorah National Society for Hebrew Day Schools
5723 18th Ave.
Brooklyn, NY 11204
Ph: (718)259-1223   Fax: (718)259-1795
E-mail: mail@tupublications.com

Annual, latest edition 2003. $15.00. Covers over 700 elementary and secondary Hebrew day schools in the U.S. and Canada. Entries include: School name, address, phone, names of administrative personnel, grades taught, language of instruction, year established (fax numbers and e-mail addresses when available). Arrangement: Geographical. Indexes: Schools & personnel.

HANDBOOKS AND MANUALS

★**9543**★ **The National Business Employment Weekly Jobs Rated Almanac**

John Wiley & Sons Inc.
1 Wiley Dr.
Somerset, NJ 08873
Ph: (732)469-4400   Fr: 800-225-5945

Les Krantz. First edition, 1995. $16.95. 340 pages. Ranks 250 jobs by environment, salary, outlook, physical demands, stress, security, travel opportunities, and geographic location.

★**9544**★ **Non-Profits and Education Job Finder**

Planning Communications
7215 Oak Ave.
River Forest, IL 60305-1935
Ph: (708)366-5200   Fax: (708)366-5280
Fr: 888-366-5200
URL: http://jobfindersonline.com

Daniel Lauber. 1997. $32.95; $16.95 (paper). 336 pages. Covers 1600 sources. Discusses how to use sources of non-profit sector job vacancies in a number of specialties and state-by-state, including job-matching services, job hotlines, specialty periodicals with job ads, salary surveys, and directories. Covers a variety of fields from education to religion. Includes chapters on resume and cover letter preparation and interviewing.

★**9545**★ **Opportunities in Religious Service Careers**

McGraw-Hill Trade
2 Penn Plaza
New York, NY 10121
Ph: (212)904-2000   Fr: 800-722-4726
E-mail: ntcpub@tribune.com

John Oliver Nelson. 1998. $14.95; $11.95 (paper). 160 pages.

OTHER SOURCES

★**9546**★ **Human Services Occupations**

Delphi Productions
3160 4th St.
Boulder, CO 80304
Fax: (303)443-4022   Fr: 888-443-2400
URL: http://www.delphivideo.com

$95.00. 50 minutes. Part of the Careers for the 21st Century Video Library.

★**9547**★ **Jewish Education Service of North America (JESNA)**

111 8th Ave., 11th Fl.
New York, NY 10011-5201
Ph: (212)284-6950   Fax: (212)284-6951
E-mail: jwoocher@jesna.org

URL: http://www.jesna.org

Description: Widely recognized leader in the areas of research and program evaluation, organizational change and innovative program design and dissemination. Operates the Mandell J. Berman Jewish Heritage Center for Research and Evaluation. Supports the Convenant Foundation, a joint venture with the Crown Family, which makes awards and grants for creativity in Jewish education.

★9548★ National Council of Young Israel (NCYI b1)

3 W 16th St.
New York, NY 10011
Ph: (212)929-1525   Fax: (212)727-9526
Fr: 800-617-NCYI
E-mail: ncyi@youngisrael.org
URL: http://www.youngisrael.org/

Members: Families of traditional Jewish faith in the U.S., Canada, and Israel. **Purpose:** Seeks "to perpetuate traditional Judaism; instill a love for Americanism and the principles of democracy; bring Jewish youth back to the synagogue; educate the youth

and adults in the heritage and culture of the Jewish people." Benevolent Association in the New York City area; conducts programs nationwide for adults and youths. **Activities:** Sponsors Institute for Jewish Studies, which provides specialized programs in Jewish education. The Institute maintains the Torah Tape Library of cassette tapes on Jewish philosophy, law, the Talmud, and related topics. Sponsors children's services, charitable program, and competitions. Maintains speakers' bureau; compiles statistics.

★9549★ Rabbis

Evon Publishing
832 N 7th Ave.
Iron River, MI 49935
Ph: (906)265-3190

Audiocassette. 1996. $16.95. 32 minutes. Part of the Careers and Vocational Guidance Series. Provides information about the nature of the work, educational requirements, employment outlook, earnings, and work conditions as well as additional related information.

★9550★ Religion

Evon Publishing
832 N 7th Ave.
Iron River, MI 49935
Ph: (906)265-3190

Audiocassette. 1996. $16.95. 32 minutes. Part of the Careers and Vocational Guidance Series. Provides information about the nature of the work, educational requirements, employment outlook, earnings, and work conditions as well as additional related information.

★9551★ Union of Sephardic Congregations (USC)

8 W 70th St.
New York, NY 10023
Ph: (212)873-0300   Fax: (212)724-6165
E-mail: office@sshcgrithisrael.org

Description: Affiliated congregations practicing Sephardic (Spanish, Portuguese, or Middle Eastern) Judaism. Publishes and distributes Sephardic prayer books.

Radio and Television Announcers and Newscasters

SOURCES OF HELP-WANTED ADS

★9552★ AFTRA Magazine
American Federation of Television and
  Radio Artists
260 Madison Ave.
New York, NY 10016-2402
Ph: (212)532-0800   Fax: (212)532-2242
Membership magazine covering issues in
television and radio broadcasting.

★9553★ Broadcasting & Cable
Reed Business Information
360 Park Ave. S
New York, NY 10010
Ph: (646)746-6400   Fax: (646)746-6734
URL: http://www.broadcastingcable.com
Weekly. $179.00/year for U.S.; $239.00/year
for Canada. News magazine covering The
Fifth Estate (radio, TV, cable, and satellite),
and the regulatory commissions involved.

★9554★ Country Airplay Monitor
VNU Business Media USA
770 Broadway
New York, NY 10003
Ph: (646)654-5000
URL: http://www.vnubusinessmedia.com/
box/bp/div_ent_music_airm.ht
Weekly. $295.00/year for individuals. Trade
publication covering the radio and music
industry.

★9555★ Current
Heldref Publications
1319 18th St. NW
Washington, DC 20036-1802
Ph: (202)296-6267   Fax: (202)296-5149
Fr: 800-365-9753
URL: http://www.heldref.org/html/curr.html
Monthly. $38.00/year for individuals; $77.00/
year for institutions, add $18 for postage
outside the United States. Journal that re-
prints articles on education, politics, and
other social issues.

★9556★ Daily Variety
Reed Business Information
5700 Wilshire Blvd., Ste. 120
Los Angeles, CA 90036
Ph: (323)857-6600   Fax: (323)965-2475
Daily. Global entertainment newspaper (tab-
loid).

★9557★ Editor & Publisher
Editor & Publisher Magazine
770 Broadway
New York, NY 10003-9595
Fax: (646)654-5360   Fr: 800-336-4380
URL: http://www.editorandpublisher.com
Weekly. $99.00/year for U.S. and Canada,
includes exclusive web access; $130.00/
year for other countries; $4.00 for single
issue. Magazine focusing on newspaper
journalism, advertising, printing equipment,
and interactive services.

★9558★ Electronic Media
Crain Communications Inc.
1155 Gratiot Ave.
Detroit, MI 48207-2997
Ph: (313)446-6000
E-mail: info@crain.com
URL: http://www.crain.com/
Newspaper covering management, program-
ming, cable and trends in the television and
the media industry.

★9559★ FMedia!
FM Atlas Publishing
PO Box 336
Esko, MN 55733-0336
Ph: (218)879-7676   Fr: 800-605-2219
Description: Monthly. Lists information on
the facilities and formats of FM radio, including new station grants and applications. Also
provides official and unofficial news and
comments, as well as FM Dxing and FM
reception concerns. Recurring features include letters to the editor, news of research,
job listings, and notices of publications available.

★9560★ The Hollywood Reporter
The Hollywood Reporter
5055 Wilshire Blvd.
Los Angeles, CA 90036-4396
Ph: (323)525-2000   Fax: (323)525-2377
E-mail: special-is-
sues@hollywoodreporter.com
URL: http://www.hollywoodreporter.com
Daily. Film, TV, and entertainment trade
newspaper.

★9561★ Insiders Sportsletter
American Sportscasters Association Inc.
225 Broadway
New York, NY 10007
Ph: (212)227-8080   Fax: (212)571-0556
E-mail: assassn@juno.com
URL: http://
www.americansportscasters.com/home.html
Description: Quarterly. Highlights Association programs promoting excellence and
recognition in the field of sportscasting.
Carries profiles of award winners and interviews with sportscasting professionals. Recurring features include news of research,
employment opportunities, and a calendar of
events.

★9562★ Journal of Radio Studies
Broadcast Education Association
1771 N St. NW
Washington, DC 20036
Ph: (202)429-5355   Fax: (202)775-2981
Quarterly. Journal covering issues in broad-
casting.

★9563★ QST
American Radio Relay League Inc.
225 Main St.
Newington, CT 06111
Ph: (860)594-0200   Fax: (860)594-0303
Fr: 888-277-5289
E-mail: qst@arrl.org
Monthly. $34.00/year for individuals. Amat-
eur radio magazine.

★9564★ R&B Airplay Monitor

VNU Business Media USA
770 Broadway
New York, NY 10003
Ph: (646)654-5000
URL: http://www.vnubusinessmedia.com/
box/bp/div_ent_music_airm.ht

Weekly. $295.00/year for individuals. Trade publication covering the radio and telecommunications industries.

★9565★ Rock Airplay Monitor

VNU Business Media USA
770 Broadway
New York, NY 10003
Ph: (646)654-5000
URL: http://www.vnubusinessmedia.com/
box/bp/div_ent_music_airm.ht

Weekly. $295.00/year for individuals. Trade publication covering the music and radio industries.

★9566★ SCRIBE

Scribe Media
5606 Medical Cir.
Madison, WI 53719
Ph: (608)271-1025   Fax: (608)271-1150
Fr: 800-373-9692
URL: http://www.msn.fullfeed.com/~scribe/

Description: Quarterly. Concerned about informational programming in religious broadcasting and broadcast journalism. Recurring features include letters to the editor, interviews, news of research, reports of meetings, news of educational opportunities, job listings, and book reviews.

★9567★ SHOOT

BPI Communications Inc.
575 Prospect Ave.
Lakewood, NJ 08701
Ph: (732)363-5679   Fax: (732)363-0338
Fr: 888-463-6110
E-mail: shoot@inch.com

Weekly. $79.00/year for individuals. Trade magazine covering all aspects of the commercial production industry, including creative and post-production elements.

★9568★ SMPTE Journal

Society of Motion Picture and Television
  Engineers
595 W Hartsdale Ave.
White Plains, NY 10607
Ph: (914)761-1100   Fax: (914)761-3115
URL: http://www.smpte.org

Monthly. $90.00/year; $100.00/year for out of country. Journal containing articles pertaining to new developments in motion picture and television technology; standards and recommended practices; general news of the industry.

★9569★ Weatherwise

Heldref Publications
1319 18th St. NW
Washington, DC 20036-1802
Ph: (202)296-6267   Fax: (202)296-5149
Fr: 800-365-9753
URL: http://www.heldref.org/html/body_
ww.html

Bimonthly. $35.00/year for individuals; $74.00/year for institutions, other countries. Popular weather magazine for students, teachers, and professionals.

PLACEMENT AND JOB REFERRAL SERVICES

★9570★ American Sportscasters Association (ASA)

225 Broadway, Ste. 2030
New York, NY 10009
Ph: (212)227-8080   Fax: (212)571-0556
E-mail: lschwa8918@aol.com
URL: http://
www.americansportscasters.com

Members: Radio and television sportscasters. **Purpose:** Sponsors seminars, clinics, and symposia for aspiring announcers and sportscasters. **Activities:** Compiles statistics. Operates speakers' bureau, placement service, hall of fame, and biographical archives. Maintains American Sportscaster Hall of Fame Trust. Is currently implementing Hall of Fame Museum, Community Programs.

★9571★ Broadcast Education Association (BEA)

1771 N St. NW
Washington, DC 20036-2891
Ph: (202)429-3935   Fax: (202)775-2981
Fr: 888-380-7222
E-mail: beainfo@beaweb.org
URL: http://www.beaweb.org/

Description: Universities and colleges; faculty and students; promotes improvement of curriculum and teaching methods, broadcasting research, television and radio production, and programming teaching on the college level.

★9572★ Broadcast Foundation of College/University Students (BROADCAST)

89 Longview Rd.
Port Washington, NY 11050
Ph: (516)883-2897   Fax: (516)883-0159
E-mail: rstarleton@aol.com

Members: College students interested in broadcasting and professional broadcasters interested in encouraging practical broadcasting experience in colleges and universities. **Activities:** Conducts annual survey of all professional broadcasting stations for part-time and summer employment for college students. Sponsors job advisory and placement service.

★9573★ National Association of Broadcasters (NAB)

1771 N St. NW
Washington, DC 20036
Ph: (202)429-5300   Fax: (202)429-4199
E-mail: nab@nab.org
URL: http://www.nab.org

Description: Representatives of radio and television stations and networks; associate members include producers of equipment and programs. Seeks to ensure the viability, strength, and success of free, over-the-air broadcasters; serves as an information resource to the industry. Monitors and reports on events regarding radio and television broadcasting. Maintains Broadcasting Hall of Fame. Offers minority placement service and employment clearinghouse.

★9574★ National Association of Farm Broadcasters (NAFB)

PO Box 500
Platte City, MO 64079
Ph: (816)431-4032   Fax: (816)431-4087
E-mail: info@nafb.com
URL: http://www.nafb.com

Description: Radio and television farm directors (200) actively engaged in broadcasting or telecasting farm news and information; associate members (479) are persons with agricultural interests who are affiliated with advertising agencies, government agencies, farm organizations, and commercial firms. Works to improve quantity and quality of farm programming and serve as a clearinghouse for new ideas in farm broadcasting. Provides placement information.

★9575★ Radio-Television News Directors Association (RTNDA)

1600 K St. NW, Ste. 700
Washington, DC 20006-2838
Ph: (202)659-6510   Fax: (202)223-4007
Fr: 800-80-RTNDA
E-mail: rtnda@rtnda.org
URL: http://rtnda.org

Description: Professional society of heads of news departments for broadcast and cable stations and networks; associate members are journalists engaged in the preparation and presentation of broadcast news and teachers of electronic journalism; other members represent industry services, public relations departments of business firms, public relations firms, and networks. Works to improve standards of electronic journalism; defends rights of journalists to access news; promotes journalism training to meet specific needs of the industry. Operates placement service and speakers' bureau.

EMPLOYER DIRECTORIES AND NETWORKING LISTS

★9576★ Advertising-Radio Directory
infoUSA Inc.
5711 S 86th Cir.
Omaha, NE 68127-0347
Ph: (402)930-3500   Fax: (402)331-0176
Fr: 800-555-6124
URL: http://www.abii.com

Updated continuously; printed on request. Number of listings: 2,175. Entries include: Name, address, phone (including area code), size of advertisement, year first in "Yellow Pages," name of owner or manager, number of employees. Compiled from telephone company "Yellow Pages," nationwide. Arrangement: Geographical.

★9577★ ADWEEK Marketer's Guide to Media
ADWEEK Magazines
770 Broadway, 7th Fl.
New York, NY 10003
Ph: (646)654-5174   Fax: (646)654-5351
Fr: 800-468-2395
URL: http://www.vnubusinessmedia.com/box/bp/div_mma_dir_marketerg

Annual, April. $100.00. Covers television, radio, cable, magazines, newspapers, out-of-home, interactive, Hispanic, and promotion media. Entries include: Current rates, audience demographics, industry trends, market data for all areas of media. Arrangement: Classified by type of media.

★9578★ Bacon's Metro California Media
Bacon's Information Inc.
332 S Michigan Ave., Ste. 900
Chicago, IL 60604
Ph: (312)922-2400   Fax: (312)987-9773
Fr: 800-621-0561
URL: http://www.bacons.com

Annual, November. $250.00. Covers consumer media in the state of California including newspapers, radio television & cable stations, magazines, broadcast programs, ethnic media, news services & syndicates. Entries include: Name, address, phone, names of editors and creative staff, with titles or indication of assignments. Arrangement: Geographical, classified by type of outlet. Indexes: Alphabetical.

★9579★ Bacon's Radio/TV/Cable Directory, Volume 1
Bacon's Information Inc.
332 S Michigan Ave., Ste. 900
Chicago, IL 60604
Ph: (312)922-2400   Fax: (312)987-9773
Fr: 800-621-0561
URL: http://www.bacons.com/research/radiotvcable.htm

Annual, November. $375.00. Covers over 13,500 radio and television stations, including college radio and public television sta-

tions, and cable companies. Entries include: For radio and television stations-Call letters, address, phone, names and titles of key personnel, programs, times broadcast, name of contact, network affiliation, frequency or channel number, target audience data. For cable companies-Name, address, phone, description of activities. Arrangement: Geographical.

★9580★ BIA's Television Yearbook
BIA Financial Network Inc.
15120 Enterprise Ct.
Chantilly, VA 20151
Ph: (703)818-2425   Fax: (703)803-3299
Fr: 800-331-5086
URL: http://www.bia.com

Annual, March. $99.00. Covers U.S. television markets and their inclusive stations, television equipment manufacturers, and related service providers and trade associations. Entries include: For stations-Call letters, address; name and phone of general manager, owner, and other key personnel; technical attributes, rep firm, network affiliation, last acquistion date and price and ratings for total day and prime time. For others-Company or organization name, address, phone, description. Arrangement: Classified by market. Indexes: Numerical by market rank; call letters.

★9581★ Broadcasting & Cable Yearbook
R.R. Bowker L.L.C.
630 Central Ave.
New Providence, NJ 07974
Ph: (908)286-1090   Fax: (908)219-0098
Fr: 888-269-5372

Annual, March, latest edition 2003-2004. $179.95. Covers over 17,000 television and radio stations in the United States, its territories, and Canada; cable MSOs and their individual systems; television and radio networks, broadcast and cable group owners, station representatives, satellite networks and services, film companies, advertising agencies, government agencies, trade associations, schools, and suppliers of professional and technical services, including books, serials, and videos; communications lawyers. Entries include: Company name, address, phone, fax, names of executives. Station listings include broadcast power, other operating details. Arrangement: Stations and systems are geographical, others are alphabetical. Indexes: Alphabetical.

★9582★ Burrelle's New York Media Directory
Burrelle's Information Services
75 E. Northfield Rd.
Livingston, NJ 07039
Ph: (973)992-6600   Fax: (973)992-7675
Fr: 800-631-1160
URL: http://www.burrellesluce.com/mediadata/regional.html

Annual. $200.00. Covers Print and electronic media in New York. Entries include: Name, address, phone, fax, names and titles of key personnel, geographical area served, sub-

sidiary and branch names and locations, description. Arrangement: Geographical; magazines are arranged by subject. Indexes: Name, subject, geographical.

★9583★ CPB Public Broadcasting Directory
Corporation for Public Broadcasting
901 E St. NW
Washington, DC 20004-2037
Ph: (202)879-9600   Fax: (202)783-9700
URL: http://www.cpb.org/directory/home.html

Annual. $15.00. Covers public television and radio stations, national and regional public broadcasting organizations and networks, state government agencies and commissions, and other related organizations. Entries include: For radio and television stations-Station call letters, frequency or channel, address, phone, licensee name, licensee type, date on air, antenna height, area covered, names and titles of key personnel. For organizations-Name, address, phone, name and title of key personnel. Arrangement: National and regional listings are alphabetical; state groups and the public radio and television stations are each geographical; other organizations and agencies are alphabetical. Indexes: Geographical, personnel, call letter, licensee type (all in separate indexes for radio and television).

★9584★ FM Atlas
FM Atlas Publishing
PO Box 336
Esko, MN 55733-0336
Ph: (218)879-7676   Fr: 800-605-2219
URL: http://members.aol.com/fmatlas/home.html

Irregular, latest edition 2003; Previous edition 1999. $21.00; $19.00 each for two books. Covers approximately 10,500 FM stations located in North America. Entries include: Call letters, location, musical format, transmitting radius in kilometers, whether stereo or monaural, FM subcarriers, etc. Arrangement: Geographical, then by frequency.

★9585★ Gebbie Press All-in-One Directory
Gebbie Press Inc.
PO Box 1000
New Paltz, NY 12561
Ph: (845)255-7560   Fax: (845)256-1239
URL: http://www.gebbieinc.com

Annual, November. $125.00. Covers 1,577 daily newspapers, 5,970 weekly newspapers, 7,600 radio stations, 1,260 television stations, 268 general-consumer magazines, 430 professional business publications, 3,100 trade magazines, 320 farm publications, list of the Black press and radio, Hispanic press and radio, and a list of news syndicates. Entries include: For periodicals-Name, address, phone, fax, frequency, editor, circulation, readership. For newspapers-Name, address, phone, fax, circulation. For radio and television stations-Call letters, address, phone, format. Arrangement: Classified by type of media.

★9586★ **International Television and Video Almanac**

Quigley Publishing Company Inc.
64 Wintergreen Ln.
Groton, MA 01450-4129
Fr: 800-231-8239
URL: http://hometown.aol.com/quigleypub/mp.html

Annual, January. $130.00. Covers "Who's Who in Motion Pictures and Television and Home Video," television networks, major program producers, major group station owners, cable television companies, distributors, firms serving the television and home video industry, equipment manufacturers, casting agencies, literary agencies, advertising and publicity representatives, television stations, associations, list of feature films produced for television; statistics, industry's year in review, award winners, satellite & wireless cable provider, primtime programming, video producers, distributors, wholesalers. Entries include: Generally, company name, address, phone; manufacturer and service listings may include description of products and services and name of contact; producing, distributing, and station listings include additional detail, and contacts for cable and broadcast networks. Arrangement: Classified by service or activity. Indexes: Full.

★9587★ **M Street Radio Directory**

M Street Corp.
PO Box 442
Littleton, NH 03561
Ph: (603)444-5720   Fax: (603)444-2872
Fr: 800-248-4242

Annual. $79.00. Covers approximately 14,000 AM and FM radio stations in the U.S. and Canada. Entries include: Company name, address, phone, fax, personnel, geographical area served, format, audience ratings, markets served, technical and market information. Arrangement: Geographical. Indexes: Geographical, call letters, station frequency.

★9588★ **The News Media**

Lucent Books Inc.
10911 Technology Pl.
San Diego, CA 92127-1811
Ph: (858)485-7424   Fax: (858)485-8019
Fr: 800-877-4253

$27.45. Publication includes: List of organizations to contact for further information about careers in the news media. Principal content of publication is an examination of a variety of careers in the news media. Indexes: Alphabetical.

★9589★ **North Carolina News Media Directory**

Brian Highberger Publisher
PO Box 316
Mount Dora, FL 32756
Fax: (866)586-7020   Fr: 800-749-6399

Annual, April. $60.00. Covers about 730 newspapers, periodicals, radio and television broadcasting stations, and press services operating in North Carolina. Entries include: Publisher or company name, address, phone, names and titles of key personnel, publication title, call letters, hours of operation, and frequency. Arrangement: Classified by type of media. Indexes: Title, call letters, county index.

★9590★ **Pocket Media Guide**

Media Distribution Services
307 W. 36th St., Dept. P
New York, NY 10018-6496
Ph: (212)279-4800   Fax: (212)714-9092
Fr: 800-MDS-DATA
URL: http://www.mdsconnect.com/news_release/1_03.htm

Annual, November. Covers about 700 major market newspapers, radio and television stations and networks, foreign and national wire services, and trade and general interest publications in major United States cities and Canada. Entries include: Publication or call name, address, phone. Arrangement: Classified by line of business.

★9591★ **Programming Radio**

Mid-South Management Inc.
PO Box 1051
Vicksburg, MS 39181-1051
Ph: (601)922-8395   Fax: (601)922-2856
URL: http://www.nbpc.com

Irregular, previous edition March 1991; latest edition November 1993. $20.00. Covers approximately 40,000 radio broadcasting companies in the United States. Entries include: Company name, address, phone; names, titles, and biographical data for key personnel. Arrangement: Classified by type of programming.

★9592★ **The R & R Directory**

Radio and Records Inc.
10100 Santa Monica Blvd., 3rd Fl.
Los Angeles, CA 90067-4004
Ph: (310)553-4330   Fax: (310)203-8727
E-mail: moreinfo@rronline.com
URL: http://www.radioandrecords.com

Semiannual, Spring and Fall. $75.00. Covers more than 3,000 radio group owners, equipment manufacturers, jingle producers, TV production houses and spot producers, record companies, representative firms, research companies, consulting firms, media brokers, networks, program suppliers, trade associations, and other organizations involved in the radio and record industry. Entries include: Organization name, address, phone, fax, E-mail, name and title of contacts, branch offices or subsidiary names and locations. Arrangement: Alphabetical; classified by subject. Indexes: Company.

★9593★ **Radio Advertising Source**

SRDS
1700 .E Higgins Rd.
Des Plaines, IL 60018-5605
Ph: (847)375-5000   Fax: (847)375-5001
Fr: 800-851-7737
URL: http://www.srds.com

Quarterly. $534.00. Covers over 10,500 AM and FM stations, networks, syndicators, group owners, and representative firms. Entries include: Call letters, name of owning company, address, phone; names of representatives and station personnel; demostration detail, station format, signal strength, programming opportunities, special features. Arrangement: Geographical by state, then Arbitron metro and nonmetro area.

★9594★ **Radio Programming Profile**

BF/Communication Services Inc.
311 Martling Ave.
Tarrytown, NY 10591-4709
Ph: (516)364-2593

Three times yearly. $250.00. Covers about 3,000 AM and FM radio stations in top 200 markets, with hour-by-hour format information (type of music, news, etc.) for each. Entries include: Station call letters, address, phone, names of executives, hour-by-hour format information. Arrangement: Alphabetical by market and call letters. Volume 1 has top 70 ranking markets; Volume 2 has markets 71-200.

★9595★ **Radio Stations and Broadcasting Companies Directory**

infoUSA Inc.
5711 S 86th Cir.
Omaha, NE 68127-0347
Ph: (402)930-3500   Fax: (402)331-0176
Fr: 800-555-6124
URL: http://www.abii.com

Annual. Number of listings: 13,087. Entries include: Name, address, phone (including area code), size of advertisement, year first in "Yellow Pages," name of owner or manager, number of employees. Available by sinal type. Compiled from telephone company "Yellow Pages," nationwide. Arrangement: Geographical.

★9596★ **RTNDA Communicator-Directory Issues**

Radio-Television News Directors Association
1600 K St. NW, No. 700
Washington, DC 20006
Ph: (202)659-6510   Fax: (202)223-4007
Fr: 800-807-8632

Semiannual, January and July. Number of listings: 3,000; membership includes Canada and some foreign countries. Entries include: Member name, address, phone; and name of radio or television station, network, or other news organization with which affiliated. Arrangement: Same information given in alphabetical and geographical arrangements.

★9597★ **Sports Market Place**
Sportsguide L.L.C.
13901 N 73rd St., Ste. 219
Scottsdale, AZ 85260
Ph: (480)948-8885   Fax: (480)948-7701
Fr: 800-776-7877
E-mail: smp@sportsmarketplace.com
URL: http://www.sportsmarketplace.com

Annual, January. $249.00. Covers manufacturers, organizations, professional sports teams, broadcasting networks, sports arenas, syndicators, publications, trade shows, marketing services, corporate sports sponsors, and other groups concerned with the business and promotional aspects of sports generally and with air sports, arm wrestling, auto sports, badminton, baseball, basketball, biathlon, bowling, boxing, curling, equestrian, exercise, fencing, field hockey, football, golf, gymnastics, ice hockey, lacrosse, martial arts, paddleball, paddle tennis, platform tennis, pentathlon, racquetball, rowing, rugby, running/jogging, skiing, soccer, softball, squash, swimming, table tennis, tennis, track and field, volleyball, water sports, weightlifting, and wrestling. Entries include: Name of company or organization, address, fax, e-mail, URL, name of key personnel with titles, and description of products or services. Arrangement: Classified by type of firm, sport, or activity. Indexes: Alphabetical, single sprt, media, sport sponsors, agencies, manufacturers, brand name, facilities, executive, and Geographical.

★9598★ **Television & Cable Factbook**
Warren Communications News
2115 Ward Ct. NW
Washington, DC 20037
Ph: (202)872-9202   Fax: (202)293-3435
Fr: 800-771-9202
URL: http://www.warren-news.com/factbook.htm

Annual, March. Weekly updates available. $795.00. Covers commercial and noncommercial television stations and networks, including educational, low-power and instructional TV stations, and translators; United States cable television systems; cable and television group owners; program and service suppliers; and brokerage and financing companies. Entries include: For stations-Call letters, licensee name and address, studio address and phone; identification of owners, sales and legal representatives and chief station personnel; rates, technical data, map of service area, and Nielsen circulation data. For cable systems-Name, address, basic and pay subscribers, programming and fees, physical plant; names of personnel and ownership. ownership. Arrangement: Geographical by state, province, city, county, or country. Indexes: Call letters, product/service, name, general subject.

★9599★ **Television Stations & Broadcasting Companies Directory**
infoUSA Inc.
5711 S 86th Cir.
Omaha, NE 68127-0347
Ph: (402)930-3500   Fax: (402)331-0176
Fr: 800-555-6124

URL: http://www.abii.com

Updated continuously; printed on request. Number of listings: 4,158. Entries include: Name, address, phone (including area code), size of advertisement, year first in "Yellow Pages," name of owner or manager, number of employees. Compiled from telephone company "Yellow Pages," nationwide. Arrangement: Geographical.

★9600★ **TV and Cable Source**
SRDS
1700 .E Higgins Rd.
Des Plaines, IL 60018-5605
Ph: (847)375-5000   Fax: (847)375-5001
Fr: 800-851-7737
URL: http://www.srds.com

Quarterly. $520.00. Covers all domestic & international commercial television stations and networks; public television stations, cable networks, systems, interconnects, rep firms, and group owners. Includes separate section showing production specifications of stations and systems. Entries include: Call letters, parent company, address, phone, representative, personnel, facilities, special features, programming. Production specifications section shows call letters or system name, address, and preferred specifications for ad copy. Arrangement: Classified by DMA ranking, then by call letters.

★9601★ **Working Press of the Nation**
R.R. Bowker L.L.C.
630 Central Ave.
New Providence, NJ 07974
Ph: (908)286-1090   Fax: (908)219-0098
Fr: 888-269-5372
E-mail: wpn@bowker.com

Annual, September. $530.00 for set; $295.00 each volume. Covers in three separate volumes, syndicates and over 8,500 daily and weekly newspapers; 1,750 newsletters; over 16,800 radio and television stations; 5,500 magazines; 1,000 internal publications. Entries include: Name of publication or station, address, phone, fax, e-mail and URL, names of executives, editors, writers, etc., as appropriate. Broadcasting and magazine volumes include data on kinds of material accepted. Technical and mechanical requirements for publications are given. Arrangement: Magazines are classified by subject; newspapers and broadcasting stations are geographical. Indexes: Newspaper department/editor by interest, metro area, feature syndicate subject; magazine subject, publication title; television director/personnel by subject, radio personnel and director by subject.

HANDBOOKS AND MANUALS

★9602★ **Breaking into Television**
Thomson Peterson's
202 Carnegie Ctr.
Box 67005
Princeton, NJ 08540
Fr: 800-338-3282

Weaver. 1998. $14.95 (paper). Explains how to get a job in the television industry, with a list of internship opportunities.

★9603★ **A Career Handbook for TV, Radio, Film, Video and Interactive Media**
A & C Black
37 Soho Sq.
London W1D 3QZ, United Kingdom
Ph: 020 7758 0200

Shiona Llewellyn.

★9604★ **Career Information Center**
Macmillan Publishing Co. Inc.
200 Old Tappan Rd.
Old Tappan, NJ 07675
Fr: 800-428-5331

Visual Education Center Staff. Seventh edition, 1999. $275.00. 2080 pages. This 13-volume set profiles over 600 occupations. Each occupational profile describes job duties, educational requirements, how to get the job, advancement possibilities, employment outlook, working conditions, earnings and benefits, and where to write for more information.

★9605★ **Career Opportunities in Radio**
Facts on File Inc.
132 W. 31st St., 17th Fl.
New York, NY 10001-2006
Ph: (212)967-8800   Fax: (212)967-9196
Fr: 800-322-8755

Shelly Field. April 2004. $18.95 (paper). Illustrated. 288 pages.

★9606★ **Careers in Communications**
VGM Career Horizons
4255 W. Touhy Ave.
Lincolnwood, IL 60646-1975
Ph: (847)679-5500   Fax: (847)679-2494
Fr: 800-323-4900
E-mail: ntcpub@tribune.com

Shonan Noronha. Third edition, 1998. $17.95; $13.95 (paper). 418 pages. Examines the fields of journalism, photography, radio, television, film, public relations, and advertising. Gives concrete details on job locations and how to secure a job. Suggests many resources for job hunting.

★9607★ Careers in Television and Radio

Kogan Page, Ltd.
22 Broad St., Ste. 34
Milford, CT 06460

Michael Selby. Sixth edition, 1996. $14.95 (paper). Out of print. Part of the Kogan Page Careers Series.

★9608★ How to Launch Your Career in TV News

McGraw-Hill Trade
2 Penn Plaza
New York, NY 10121
Ph: (212)904-2000   Fr: 800-722-4726
E-mail: ntcpub@tribune.com

Jeff Leshay. 1994. $14.95 (paper). 144 pages.

★9609★ Lights, Camera, Action!: Careers in Film, Television, & Video

Indiana University Press
601 N. Morton St.
Bloomington, IN 47404-3797
Ph: (812)855-4203   Fax: (812)855-7931
Fr: 800-842-6796

Josephine Langham. Second edition, 1996. $19.95 (paper).

★9610★ Making It in Broadcasting: An Insider's Guide to Career Opportunities

Macmillan Publishing Co. Inc.
200 Old Tappan Rd.
Old Tappan, NJ 07675
Fr: 800-428-5331

Leonard Mogel. 1994. $15.00 (paper). 320 pages.

★9611★ The Media Jungle: A Survival Guide

Media Masters
872 Franklin Trace
Zionsville, IN 46077-1169
Ph: (317)733-9440   Fax: (317)873-4493

Carrie Van Dyke. 1996. $15.00. 92 pages.

★9612★ 100 Best Careers in Entertainment

Macmillan Publishing Co. Inc.
200 Old Tappan Rd.
Old Tappan, NJ 07675
Fr: 800-428-5331

Shelly Field. 1995. $14.95 (paper). 352 pages.

★9613★ Opportunities in Broadcasting Careers

McGraw-Hill Trade
2 Penn Plaza
New York, NY 10121
Ph: (212)904-2000   Fr: 800-722-4726

Elmo I. Ellis. 1998. $14.95; $11.95 (paper). Discusses opportunities and job search techniques in broadcasting, television, and radio. Illustrated.

★9614★ Opportunities in Cable Television Careers

McGraw-Hill Trade
2 Penn Plaza
New York, NY 10121
Ph: (212)904-2000   Fr: 800-722-4726

Jan Bone. 1994. $14.95; $11.95 (paper). 160 pages. Focuses on what the jobs are, where they are, and how to get them. Illustrated.

★9615★ Opportunities in Journalism Careers

McGraw-Hill/Contemporary Books
1221 Avenue of the Americas
New York, NY 10020
Ph: (212)904-2000   Fr: 800-323-4900
E-mail: ntcpub@tribune.com

Jim Patten and Donald L. Ferguson. 1995. $14.95; $11.95 (paper). 160 pages. Outlines opportunities in every field of journalism, including newspaper reporting and editing, magazine and book publishing, corporate communications, advertising and public relations, freelance writing, and teaching. Covers how to prepare for and enter each field, outlining responsibilities, salaries, benefits, and job outlook for each specialty. Illustrated.

★9616★ Opportunities in Sports and Athletics Careers

McGraw-Hill Trade
2 Penn Plaza
New York, NY 10121
Ph: (212)904-2000   Fr: 800-722-4726
E-mail: ntcpub@tribune.com

William Ray Heitzmann. 1994. 160 pages. $14.95; $11.95 (paper). A guide to planning for and seeking opportunities in this growing field. Illustrated.

★9617★ Opportunities in Television and Video Careers

McGraw-Hill Trade
2 Penn Plaza
New York, NY 10121
Ph: (212)904-2000   Fr: 800-722-4726
E-mail: ntcpub@tribune.com

Shonan Noronha. 1998. $14.95; $11.95 (paper). 206 pages. Details the employment opportunities open in television, cable, corporate video, institutional and government media, including independent production, and discusses how to land a job. Illustrated.

★9618★ Opportunities in Writing Careers

McGraw-Hill Contemporary Books
1221 Avenue of the Americas
New York, NY 10020
Ph: (212)904-2000   Fr: 800-323-4900
E-mail: ntcpub@tribune.com

Elizabeth Foote-Smith. 1999. $14.95; $11.95 (paper). 160 pages. Discusses opportunities in the print media, broadcasting, advertising or publishing. Business writing, public relations, and technical writing are among the careers covered. Contains bibliography and illustrations.

★9619★ Radio and Television Career Directory

Thomson Gale
27500 Drake Rd.
Farmington Hills, MI 48331-3535
Ph: (248)699-GALE   Fax: 800-414-5043
Fr: 800-877-GALE
E-mail: galeord@gale.com
URL: http://www.gale.com

Bradley Morgan. Second edition, 1993. $39.00. 300 pages. Features extensive listings of contacts and entry-level job opportunities. Provides information on internships and sources of help-wanted ads.

★9620★ Real People Working in Communications

McGraw-Hill Contemporary Books
1221 Avenue of the Americas
New York, NY 10020
Ph: (212)904-2000   Fr: 800-323-4900
E-mail: ntcpub@tribune.com

Jan Goldberg. 1996. $14.95; $12.95 (paper). Interviews and profiles of working professionals capture a range of opportunities in this field.

★9621★ Real-Resumes for Media, Newspaper, Broadcasting and Public Affairs Jobs

PREP Publishing
1110 1/2 Hay St., PMB 66
Fayetteville, NC 28305
Ph: (910)483-6611   Fax: (910)483-2439
Fr: 800-533-2814

Anne McKinney (Editor). October 2002. $16.95. Part of the Real-Resumes Series.

★9622★ Resumes for Communications Careers

McGraw-Hill Contemporary Books
1221 Avenue of the Americas
New York, NY 10020
Ph: (212)904-2000   Fr: 800-323-4900
E-mail: ntcpub@tribune.com

1998. $9.95 (paper). 464 pages.

★9623★ What's up Dawg: How to Become a Superstar in the Music Business

Hyperion Press
77 W. 66th St., 11th Fl.
New York, NY 10023-6298
Ph: (212)456-0100   Fax: (212)456-0108
Fr: 800-759-0190

Randy Jackson. January 2004. $14.70 (paper). 288 pages.

★9624★ Working in TV News: The Insider's Guide
Mustang Publishing
PO Box 770426
Memphis, TN 38177
Ph: (901)684-1200   Fax: (901)684-1256
Fr: 800-250-8713

Carl Filoreto. 1993. $12.95 (paper). 192 pages.

EMPLOYMENT AGENCIES AND SEARCH FIRMS

★9625★ Adler Management Inc.
66 Witherspoon St., Ste. 315
Princeton, NJ 08542
Ph: (609)443-3300   Fax: (609)443-4439
Executive Search Firm.

★9626★ Joe Sullivan and Associates, Inc.
1202 Lexington Ave
PO Box 178
New York, NY 10028
Ph: (212)734-7890
E-mail: jsa612@aol.com
URL: http://www.joesullivanassociates.com

Executive search firm. Recruits for the broadcasting, media, and entertainment industries.

ONLINE JOB SOURCES AND SERVICES

★9627★ JournalismJobs.com
E-mail: contact@journalismjobs.com
URL: http://www.journalismjobs.com

Description: Career-related site for journalists and other media professionals. Seekers can search for jobs, post a resume online, and manage the search online with the Job Seeker Folder feature. They also can receive free job announcements by e-mail.

TRADESHOWS

★9628★ NAB Radio Show and World Media Expo
National Association of Broadcasters
1771 N. St. NW
Washington, DC 20036-2891
Ph: (202)429-5300   Fax: (202)429-5343
Fr: 800-342-2460
URL: http://www.nab.org

Annual. **Primary Exhibits:** Radio and television broadcasting equipment, supplies, and services; supplies and services for production, post-production, computing, multimedia, telecommunications and corporate communications.

★9629★ NATPE Annual Conference
National Association Television Program Executives (NATPE)
2425 W. Olympic Blvd., Ste. 600 East
Santa Monica, CA 90404
Ph: (310)453-4440   Fax: (310)453-5258
Fr: 800-NATPE-GO
URL: http://www.natpe.com

Annual. **Primary Exhibits:** Equipment, supplies, and services for media content production, development, distribution, marketing, advertising, licensing and technology.

★9630★ Radio-Television News Directors Association International Conference & Exhibition
Radio-Television News Directors Association
1600 K St. NW, No. 700
Washington, DC 20006-2838
Ph: (202)659-6510   Fax: (202)223-4007
Fr: 800-807-8632
E-mail: rtnda@rtnda.org
URL: http://www.rtnda.org/

Annual. **Primary Exhibits:** Equipment, supplies, and services for the radio and television news industries, including cameras, recorders, weather equipment, computers, and software. **Dates and Locations:** 2004 Sep 29 - Oct 2; Denver, CO; Denver Convention Center.

OTHER SOURCES

★9631★ American Almanac of Jobs and Salaries
Morrow Avon
1350 Avenue of the Americas
New York, NY 10019
Ph: (212)261-6788   Fr: 800-242-7737

John W. Wright. Revised edition, 2000. $20.00 (paper). 672 pages. This is a comprehensive guide to the wages of hundreds of occupations in a wide variety of industries and organizations.

★9632★ Association for Women in Communications
780 Ritchie Hwy., Ste. 28-S
Severna Park, MD 21146
Ph: (410)544-7442   Fax: (410)544-4640
E-mail: pat@womcom.org
URL: http://www.womcom.org

Description: Professional association of journalism and communications.

★9633★ Corporation for Public Broadcasting (CPB)
401 9th St. NW
Washington, DC 20004-2129
Ph: (202)879-9600   Fax: (202)879-9700
Fr: 800-272-2190
E-mail: comments@cpb.org
URL: http://www.cpb.org

Description: A private, nonprofit corporation authorized under Public Broadcasting Act of 1967. Funded by U.S. government. Works to promote and finance the growth and development of noncommercial radio and television. Makes grants to local public television and radio stations, program producers, and regional networks; studies emerging technologies; works to provide adequate long-range financing from the U.S. government and other sources for public broadcasting. Supports children's services; compiles statistics; sponsors training programs. Presents awards annually for outstanding local television and radio programs.

★9634★ Country Radio Broadcasters (CRB)
819 18th Ave. South
Nashville, TN 37203
Ph: (615)327-4487   Fax: (615)329-4492
E-mail: ed_salamon@crb.org
URL: http://www.crb.org/

Description: Seeks to advance and promote the study of the science of broadcasting through the mutual exchange of ideas by conducting seminars and workshops, as well as providing scholarships to broadcasting students.

★9635★ Media and the Arts Occupations
Delphi Productions
3160 4th St.
Boulder, CO 80304
Fax: (303)443-4022   Fr: 888-443-2400
URL: http://www.delphivideo.com

$95.00. 50 minutes. Part of the Careers for the 21st Century Video Library.

★9636★ National Association of African-American Sportswriters and Broadcasters
308 Deer Park Ave.
Dix Hills, NY 11746
Ph: (631)462-3933
E-mail: clydesports@aol.com

Members: African-American men and women involved in the sports industry. **Purpose:** Provides job information in the areas of sports medicine, sports law, and sports management. **Activities:** Offers children's services; sponsors research and educational programs.

★9637★ National Association of Black Owned Broadcasters (NABOB)
1155 Connecticut Ave. NW, 6th Fl.
Washington, DC 20036
Ph: (202)463-8970   Fax: (202)429-0657

E-mail: info@nabob.org
URL: http://www.nabob.org

Description: Black broadcast station owners; black formatted stations not owned or controlled by blacks; organizations having an interest in the black consumer market or black broadcast industry; individuals interested in becoming owners; and communications schools, departments, and professional groups and associations. Represents the interests of existing and potential black radio and television stations. Is currently working with the Office of Federal Procurement Policy to determine which government contracting major advertisers and advertising agencies are complying with government initiatives to increase the amount of advertising dollars received by minority-owned firms. Conducts lobbying activities; provides legal representation for the protection of minority ownership policies. Sponsors annual Communications Awards Dinner each March. Conducts workshops; compiles statistics.

★9638★ **National Religious Broadcasters (NRB)**
9510 Technology Dr.
Manassas, VA 20110
Ph: (703)330-7000   Fax: (703)330-7100
E-mail: adunlap@nrb.org
URL: http://www.nrb.org

Description: Christian communicators. Fosters electronic media access for the Gospel; promotes standards of excellence; integrity and accountability; and provides networking and fellowship opportunities for its members.

★9639★ *Radio and Television Announcers and Newscasters*
Evon Publishing
832 N 7th Ave.
Iron River, MI 49935
Ph: (906)265-3190

Audiocassette. 1996. $16.95. 32 minutes. Part of the Careers and Vocational Guidance Series. Provides information about the nature of the work, educational requirements, employment outlook, earnings, and work conditions as well as additional related information.

★9640★ *Radio and Television Broadcasting*
Evon Publishing
832 N 7th Ave.
Iron River, MI 49935
Ph: (906)265-3190

Audiocassette. 1996. $16.95. 32 minutes. Part of the Careers and Vocational Guidance Series. Provides information about the nature of the work, educational requirements, employment outlook, earnings, and work conditions as well as additional related information.

★9641★ **Women in Cable and Telecommunications (WIT)**
14555 Avion Pkwy., Ste. 250
Chantilly, VA 20151
Ph: (703)234-9810   Fax: (703)817-1595
URL: http://www.wict.org

Description: Empowers and educate women to achieve their professional goals by providing opportunities for leadership, networking and advocacy.

Radiologic Technologists

★9642★ *ADVANCE for Imaging and Radiation Therapy Professionals*

Merion Publications Inc.
2900 Horizon Dr.
PO Box 61556
King of Prussia, PA 19406-0956
Ph: (610)278-1400
URL: http://advanceforirt.com

Biweekly. Free to qualified subscribers. Professional medical magazine reaching radiology managers, technologists, and therapists.

★9643★ *Applied Radiology*

Anderson Publishing Ltd.
1301 W Park Ave.
Ocean, NJ 07712
Ph: (732)695-0600   Fax: (732)695-9501
E-mail: andersonpub@compuserve.com

Monthly. Free to qualified subscribers; $85.00/year for individuals; $10.00 for single issue. Magazine for radiologists, chief radiologic technologists, radiology department administrators, and key managers in HMOs. Presents articles written by radiologic professionals on all aspects of general diagnostic radiology, the diagnostic radiologic subspecialties, radiation therapy, and the socioeconomics of imaging.

★9644★ *ASRT Scanner*

American Society of Radiologic
 Technologists
15000 Central Ave. SE
Albuquerque, NM 87123-3917
Ph: (505)298-4500   Fax: (505)298-5063
Fr: 800-444-2778

Monthly. Subscription included in membership. Professional magazine covering issues in radiology and medical technology. Includes calendar of events, member profiles, state affiliate news, educational opportunities, and research updates.

★9645★ *ASTRO News*

American Society for Therapeutic
 Radiology and Oncology
12500 Fair Lakes Cir., Ste. 375
Fairfax, VA 22033-3882
Ph: (703)502-1550   Fax: (703)502-7852
Fr: 800-962-7876

Quarterly. Subscription included in membership. Professional magazine covering radiology.

★9646★ *Diagnostic Imaging*

CMP Media L.L.C.
600 Community Dr.
Manhasset, NY 11030
Ph: (516)562-5000
E-mail: mtoledo@cmp.com
URL: http://www.mfi.com

Monthly. $109.00/year for individuals; $125.00/year for other countries. News and analysis on clinical and economic developments in medical imaging.

★9647★ *Investigative Radiology*

Lippincott Williams & Wilkins
530 Walnut St.
Philadelphia, PA 19106
Ph: (215)521-8300   Fax: (215)521-8902
Fr: 800-638-3030
URL: http://www.investigativeradiology.com/

Monthly. $313.00/year for individuals; $729.00/year for institutions; $400.00/year for other countries, current and back issues; $872.00/year for institutions, other countries. Journal covering clinical and laboratory investigations in diagnostic imaging.

★9648★ *Journal of Clinical Ultrasound*

John Wiley and Sons Inc.
111 River St.
Hoboken, NJ 07030
Ph: (201)748-8866   Fax: (201)748-8824

$250.00/year for U.S. $250.00/year for Canada and Mexico; $304.00/year for other countries. International journal devoted to the clinical applications of ultrasound in medicine. Features include scholarly, peer-reviewed articles on research procedures and techniques encompassing all phases of diagnostic ultrasound.

★9649★ *Journal of Computer-Assisted Tomography*

Lippincott Williams & Wilkins
351 W Camden St.
Baltimore, MD 21201
Ph: (410)528-8517   Fax: (410)528-4312
Fr: 800-638-3030
URL: http://www.jcat.org/

Bimonthly. $286.00/year for individuals; $771.00/year for institutions; $346.00/year for other countries; $771.00/year for institutions, other countries. Radiology journal.

★9650★ *RadioGraphics*

Radiological Society of North America
820 Jorie Blvd.
Oak Brook, IL 60523-2251
Ph: (630)571-2670   Fax: (630)571-7837
E-mail: rarnold@rsna.org
URL: http://www.rsna.org

Bimonthly. $135.00/year for individuals; $170.00/year for other countries; $110.00/year, online only. Scientific publication for radiologists.

★9651★ *Radiologic Technology*

American Society of Radiologic
 Technologists
15000 Central Ave. SE
Albuquerque, NM 87123-3917
Ph: (505)298-4500   Fax: (505)298-5063
Fr: 800-444-2778
E-mail: pubsdept@asrt.org

Bimonthly. $49.00/year; $75.00/year for other countries; $29.50/year for students; $9.50 for single issue. Medical imaging technology. Includes annual index.

PLACEMENT AND JOB REFERRAL SERVICES

★9652★ American Institute of Ultrasound in Medicine (AIUM)
14750 Sweitzer Ln., Ste. 100
Laurel, MD 20707-5906
Ph: (301)498-4100   Fax: (301)498-4450
Fr: 800-638-5352
E-mail: admin@aium.org
URL: http://www.aium.org

Description: A multidisciplinary organization dedicated to advancing the art and science of ultrasound in medicine through its educational, scientific, literary and professional activities. Membership comprises professionals from many medical specialties, as well as basic scientists, engineers, manufacturers, nurses, physicists, radiologic technologists, sonographers and veterinarians involved with diagnostic medical ultrasound.

EMPLOYER DIRECTORIES AND NETWORKING LISTS

★9653★ AHA Guide to the Health Care Field
American Hospital Association (AHA)
1 N. Franklin St., 27th Fl.
Chicago, IL 60606
Ph: (312)422-2050   Fax: (312)422-4700
Fr: 800-424-4301

Annual, August. $295.00. Covers hospitals, networks, multi-health care systems, freestanding ambulatory surgery centers, psychiatric facilities, long-term care facilities, substance abuse programs, and other health-related organizations. Entries include: For hospitals-Facility name, address, phone, administrator's name, number of beds, facilities and services, number of employees, expenses, other statistics. For other organizations-Name, address, phone, fax, name and title of contact. Arrangement: Geographical. Indexes: Hospital name.

★9654★ Directory of Hospital Personnel
Thomson Medical Economics
5 Paragon Dr.
Montvale, NJ 07645-1742
Ph: (201)358-7200   Fax: (201)722-2680

Annual, November. $325.00. Covers 200,000 executives at 7,000 U.S. hospitals. Entries include: Name of hospital, address, phone, number of beds, type and JCAHO status of hospital, names and titles of key department heads and staff, medical and nursing school affiliations; number of residents, interns, and nursing students. Arrangement: Geographical. Indexes: Hospital name, personnel, hospital size.

★9655★ Directory of Personnel Responsible for Radiological Health Programs
Conference of Radiation Control Program Directors Inc.
205 Capital Ave.
Frankfort, KY 40601-2832
Ph: (502)227-4543   Fax: (502)227-7862
URL: http://www.crcpd.org

Annual, January. $45.00. Covers about 350 individuals who conduct radiological health program activities in federal, state, and local government agencies; members of the conferences. Entries include: For directors-Name and title, name of agency address, phone; office hours listed with state heading. For members-name, address, phone, affiliation, department, and title. Arrangement: Directors are by level of agency and geographical. Indexes: Personal name, agency, state.

★9656★ Hospital Blue Book
Billian/Transworld Publishing Inc.
2100 Powers Ferry Rd.
Ste. 300
Atlanta, GA 30339
Ph: (770)955-8484   Fax: (770)955-8485
Fr: 800-533-8484
E-mail: blu-book@billian.com

Annual, January. $285.00 for national edition; $160.00 for southern edition. Covers more than 6,687 hospitals; some listings also appear in a separate southern edition of this publication. Entries include: Name of hospital, accreditation, mailing address, phone, fax, number of beds, type of facility (nonprofit, general, state, etc.); list of administrative personnel and chiefs of medical services, with specific titles. Arrangement: Geographical.

★9657★ Medical and Health Information Directory
Thomson Gale
27500 Drake Rd.
Farmington Hills, MI 48331-3535
Ph: (248)699-4253   Fax: (248)699-8065
Fr: 800-877-GALE
E-mail: businessproducts@gale.com

Annual. $285.00 per volume; $675.00 per set. Covers in Volume 1, more than 26,500 medical and health oriented associations, organizations, institutions, and government agencies, including health maintenance organizations (HMOs), preferred provider organizations (PPOs), insurance companies, pharmaceutical companies, research centers, and medical and allied health schools. In Volume 2, over 12,000 medical book publishers; medical periodicals, directories, audiovisual producers and services, medical libraries and information centers, electronic resources, and health-related internet search engines. In Volume 3, more than 35,500 clinics, treatment centers, care programs, and counseling/diagnostic services for 34 subject areas. Entries include: Institution, service, or firm name, address, phone, fax, email and URL; many include names of key personnel and, when pertinent, descriptive annotation. Volume 3 was formerly listed

separately as Health Services Directory. Arrangement: Classified by organization activity, service, etc. Indexes: Each volume has a complete alphabetical name and keyword index.

★9658★ X-Ray Laboratories Medical Directory
infoUSA Inc.
5711 S 86th Cir.
Omaha, NE 68127-0347
Ph: (402)930-3500   Fax: (402)331-0176
Fr: 800-555-6124
URL: http://www.abii.com

Updated continuously; printed on request. Number of listings: 2,147. Entries include: Name, address, phone, size of advertisement, name of owner or manager, number of employees, year first in "Yellow Pages." Compiled from telephone company "Yellow Pages," nationwide. Arrangement: Geographical.

HANDBOOKS AND MANUALS

★9659★ Careers in Health Care
McGraw-Hill Trade
2 Penn Plaza
New York, NY 10121
Ph: (212)904-2000   Fr: 800-722-4726
E-mail: ntcpub@tribune.com

Barbara M. Swanson. Fourth edition, 2000. $17.95; $13.95 (paper). 320 pages. Describes job duties, work settings, salaries, licensing and certification requirements, educational preparation, and future outlook. Gives ideas on how to secure a job.

★9660★ Expert Resumes for Health Care Careers
JIST Publishing
8902 Otis Ave.
Indianapolis, IN 46216-1033
Ph: (317)613-4200   Fax: 800-547-8329

December 2003. $16.95. 288 pages.

★9661★ Health Careers Today
Elsevier-Health Sciences Division
The Curtis Center, Ste. 300E, 3rd Fl.
170 S. Independence Mall W.
Philadelphia, PA 19106
Ph: (215)238-7800   Fax: (215)238-7362
Fr: 800-523-4069

Gerdin. Revised edition. April 2004. $52.95.

★9662★ Opportunities in Health and Medical Careers
McGraw-Hill Trade
2 Penn Plaza
New York, NY 10121
Ph: (212)904-2000   Fr: 800-722-4726

I. Donald Snook, Jr. and Leo D'Orazio. 1997. $14.95; $11.95 (paper). 202 pages. Covers

the full range of medical and health occupations. Illustrated.

★9663★ **Opportunities in Medical Imaging Careers**

McGraw-Hill/Contemporary Books
1221 Ave Of The Americas
New York, NY 10020
Ph: (212)904-2000   Fax: (973)302-2300
Fr: 800-225-5945

Clifford J. Sherry. 1993. $14.95. 160 pages.

★9664★ **Opportunities in Medical Technology Careers**

McGraw-Hill/Contemporary Books
1221 Avenue of the Americas
New York, NY 10020
Ph: (212)904-2000   Fr: 800-323-4900
E-mail: ntcpub@tribune.com

Karen R. Karni. Revised, 1996. $14.95; $11.95 (paper). 205 pages. Details opportunities for various technical medical personnel and supplies up-to-date information on salary levels and employment outlook. Appendices list associations and unions in each field. Illustrated.

EMPLOYMENT AGENCIES AND SEARCH FIRMS

★9665★ **Harper Associates**

29870 Middlebelt
Farmington Hills, MI 48334
Ph: (248)932-1170   Fax: (248)932-1214
E-mail: resumes@harperjobs.com
URL: http://www.harperjobs.com

Executive search firm and employment agency.

★9666★ **JPM International**

26060 Acero
Mission Viejo, CA 92691
Ph: (949)699-4300   Fax: (949)699-4333
Fr: 800-685-7856
E-mail: leslieo@jpmintl.com
URL: http://www.jpmintl.com

Executive search firm and employment agency.

★9667★ **Professional Placement Associates, Inc.**

287 Bowman Ave., Ste. 309
Purchase, NY 10577
Ph: (914)251-1000   Fax: (914)251-1055
E-mail: lschachter@ppasearch.com
URL: http://www.ppasearch.com

Executive search firm specializing in the health and medical field.

★9668★ **Shiloh Careers International, Inc.**

7105 Peach Ct., Ste102
PO Box 831
Brentwood, TN 37024-0831
Ph: (615)373-3090   Fax: (615)373-3480
E-mail: maryann@shilohcareers.com
URL: http://www.shilohcareers.com

Employment agency serving the industry field.

★9669★ **Travcorps, Inc.**

40 Eastern Ave.
Malden, MA 02148
Ph: (781)322-2600   Fax: 800-803-1186
Fr: 800-343-3270
URL: http://www.travcorps.com

Places staff in temporary assignments. Other locations nationwide.

ONLINE JOB SOURCES AND SERVICES

★9670★ **Medhunters.com**
E-mail: info@medhunters.com
URL: http://www.medhunters.com

Description: Career search site for jobs in all health care specialties; educational resources; visa and licensing information for relocation; interesting articles; relocation tools; links to professional organizations and general resources.

★9671★ **ProHealthJobs**
E-mail: sales@prohealthjobs.com
URL: http://www.prohealthjobs.com

Description: Career resources site for the medical and health care field. Lists professional opportunities, product information, continuing education and open positions.

★9672★ **RadWorking.com**
E-mail: info@atsradworking.com
URL: http://www.RadWorking.com

Description: Employment resource dedicated to the profession of radiology. Site is divided into various job-search sections based on job type or nature of support position.

TRADESHOWS

★9673★ **Radiological Society of North America Scientific Assembly and Annual Meeting**

Radiological Society of North America
820 Jorie Blvd.
Oak Brook, IL 60523-2247
Ph: (630)368-3760   Fax: (630)571-7837

E-mail: exhibits@rsna.org
URL: http://www.rsna.org

Annual. **Primary Exhibits:** Radiologic equipment, supplies, services, and publications. **Dates and Locations:** 2004 Nov 28 - Dec 03; Chicago, IL; McCormick Place • 2005 Nov 27 - Dec 02; Chicago, IL; McCormick Place.

★9674★ **SDMS Annual Conference**

Society of Diagnostic Medical Sonographers
2745 Dallas Pkwy. Ste. 350
Plano, TX 75093-4706
E-mail: sdms@sdms.org
URL: http://www.sdms.org

Annual. **Primary Exhibits:** Exhibits related to the science of diagnostic medical sonography.

★9675★ **Ultrasound/Women's Imaging**

Brigham and Women's Hospital
Department of Radiology
75 Francis St.
Boston, MA 02115
Ph: (617)732-5530   Fax: (617)732-6458
URL: http://www.radcme.harvard.edu

Primary Exhibits: Ultrasound scanners, gels, and related equipment; mammography equipment and supplies.

OTHER SOURCES

★9676★ **American Registry of Diagnostic Medical Sonographers (ARDMS)**

51 Monroe St., Plz. East One
Rockville, MD 20850-2400
Ph: (301)738-8401   Fax: (301)738-0312
Fr: 800-541-9754
E-mail: administration@ardms.org
URL: http://www.ardms.org

Members: Administers examinations in the field of diagnostic medical sonography and vascular technology throughout the U.S. and Canada and registers candidates passing those exams in the specialties of their expertise. **Activities:** Maintains central office for administering examination plans and schedules and assisting registered candidates and those interested in becoming registered.

★9677★ **American Registry of Radiologic Technologists (ARRT)**

1255 Northland Dr.
St. Paul, MN 55120-1155
Ph: (651)687-0048
URL: http://www.arrt.org

Description: Radiologic technologist certification board that administers examinations, issues certificates of registration to radiographers, nuclear medicine technologists, and radiation therapists, and investigates the qualifications of practicing radiologic technologists. Governed by trustees appointed from

American College of Radiology and American Society of Radiologic Technologists.

★9678★ **American Society of Radiologic Technologists (ASRT)**
15000 Central Ave. SE
Albuquerque, NM 87123
Ph: (505)298-4500   Fax: (505)298-5063
Fr: 800-444-2778
E-mail: asrtbod@asrt.org
URL: http://www.asrt.org

Description: Professional society of diagnostic radiography, radiation therapy, ultrasound, and nuclear medicine technologists. Advances the science of radiologic technology; establishes and maintains high standards of education; evaluates the quality of patient care; improves the welfare and socioeconomics of radiologic technologists. Operates ASRT Education and Research Foundation, which provides educational materials to radiologic technologists.

★9679★ *Exploring Health Occupations*
Cambridge Educational
2572 Brunswick Ave.
Lawrenceville, NJ 08648-4128
Fax: 800-FAX-ON-US   Fr: 800-468-4227
URL: http://www.cambridgeeducational.com
Two videos. $139.95. 1999.

★9680★ *Health Service Occupations*
Delphi Productions
3160 4th St.
Boulder, CO 80304
Fax: (303)443-4022   Fr: 888-443-2400
URL: http://www.delphivideo.com
$95.00. 50 minutes. Part of the Careers for the 21st Century Video Library.

★9681★ *Health Technologists & Technicians*
Delphi Productions
3160 4th St.
Boulder, CO 80304
Fax: (303)443-4022   Fr: 888-443-2400
URL: http://www.delphivideo.com
$95.00. 50 minutes. Part of the Careers for the 21st Century Video Library.

★9682★ *Medical Technicians and Technologists*
Cambridge Educational
2572 Brunswick Ave.
Lawrenceville, NJ 08648-4128
Fax: 800-FAX-ON-US   Fr: 800-468-4227
URL: http://www.cambridgeeducational.com
$79.95. 15 minutes. Part of the Exploring Health Occupations Series.

★9683★ *Medicine & Related Occupations*
Delphi Productions
3160 4th St.
Boulder, CO 80304
Fax: (303)443-4022   Fr: 888-443-2400
URL: http://www.delphivideo.com
$95.00. 45 minutes. Part of the Careers for the 21st Century Video Library.

★9684★ *Radiologic Technologists*
Evon Publishing
832 N 7th Ave.
Iron River, MI 49935
Ph: (906)265-3190
Audiocassette. 1996. $16.95. 32 minutes. Part of the Careers and Vocational Guidance Series. Provides information about the nature of the work, educational requirements, employment outlook, earnings, and work conditions as well as additional related information.

★9685★ **Society of Diagnostic Medical Sonography (SDMS)**
2745 N Dallas Pky., Ste. 350
Plano, TX 75093-4706
Ph: (214)473-8057   Fax: (214)473-8563
E-mail: dsanchez@sdms.org
URL: http://www.sdms.org

Description: Promotes quality patient care through the advancement of sonology and the practice of diagnostic medical sonography.

Real Estate Agents

SOURCES OF HELP-WANTED ADS

★9686★ Clayton-Fillmore Report
Clayton-Fillmore Ltd.
125 Dorset Ct.
Castle Rock, CO 80104-9285
Ph: (303)663-0606   Fax: (303)663-1616
Monthly. Periodical covering real estate and business.

★9687★ Journal of Property Management
Institute of Real Estate Management
430 N Michigan Ave.
Chicago, IL 60611-4090
Ph: (312)329-6000   Fax: (312)661-0217
Fr: 800-837-0706
URL: http://www.irem.org
Bimonthly. $43.95/year for individuals; $43.95/year for members. Magazine serving real estate managers.

★9688★ Journal of Real Estate Portfolio Management
American Real Estate Society
c/o Donna Cooper
College Business, MacArthur Campus
Florida Atlantic University
5353 Parkside Dr.
Jupiter, FL 33458
Ph: (561)799-8664   Fax: (561)799-8535
Quarterly. Journal for real estate professionals.

★9689★ New England Real Estate Journal
East Coast Publications
PO Box 55
Accord, MA 02018
Ph: (617)878-4540   Fax: (617)871-1853
Fr: 800-654-4993
E-mail: nerej@ix.net.com
Weekly. $139.00/year for individuals. Newspaper publishing commercial, industrial, and investment real estate news.

★9690★ Real Estate Issues
The Counselors of Real Estate
430 N Michigan Ave.
Chicago, IL 60611
Ph: (312)329-8427   Fax: (312)329-8881
E-mail: info@cre.org
Quarterly. Trade publication covering the real estate industry.

★9691★ REALTOR Magazine
National Association of Realtors
430 N Michigan Ave.
Chicago, IL 60611-4087
Ph: (312)329-8200   Fax: (312)329-5978
URL: http://www.realtormag.com
Monthly. Real estate magazine

★9692★ WCR Communique
Women's Council of Realtors
430 N Michigan Ave.
Chicago, IL 60611
Ph: (312)329-8483   Fax: (312)329-3290
Fr: 800-245-8512
Description: Eight issues/year. Carries articles on personal and career growth topics relating to women in real estate. Includes council news.

EMPLOYER DIRECTORIES AND NETWORKING LISTS

★9693★ CRS Referral Directory
Council of Residential Specialists
430 N Michigan Ave., Ste. 300
Chicago, IL 60611-4092
Ph: (312)321-4400   Fax: (312)329-8882
Fr: 800-462-8841
E-mail: crsdirectory@crs.com
URL: http://www.crs.com
Annual, November. Free. Covers 35,000 Certified Residential Specialists (CRS). Entries include: Member name, firm name, address, phone, fax; designations held, areas of specialization, e-mail; web page ad-

dress; years of experience, voicemail; 2nd business phone. Arrangement: Geographical. Indexes: Alphabetical.

★9694★ Directory of Real Estate Development & Related Education Programs
Urban Land Institute
1025 Thomas Jefferson NW, Ste. 500 W
Washington, DC 20007
Ph: (202)624-7000   Fax: (202)624-7140
Fr: 800-321-5011
Biennial, May of even years. $19.00. Covers over 60 real estate development education programs currently being offered at colleges and universities. Entries include: College or university name, address, list of faculty members, curriculum, tuition, length of program, degrees offered, financial aid information, job placement services, international programs, e-mail addresses. Indexes: Faculty, Programs by degree type, Programs by geographical.

★9695★ ERC Directory of Real Estate Appraisers and Brokers
Employee Relocation Council (ERC)
1717 Pennsylvania Ave. NW, Ste. 800
Washington, DC 20006
Ph: (202)857-0857   Fax: (202)659-8631
E-mail: membership@erc.org
URL: http://www.erc.org
Annual, March. $35.00. Covers about 9,000 member brokers and appraisers worldwide, equipped to handle the relocation of employees. Entries include: For brokers-Firm name, address, phone, e-mail, number of offices, median price, code indicating services offered, list of corporations served, code indicating means of working with other brokers. For appraisers-Name, firm affiliation (if any), address, phone, e-mail, code indicating professional designations, names of corporations served. Arrangement: Appraisers and brokers are geographical.

★9696★ Executive Guide to Specialists in Industrial and Office Real Estate

Society of Industrial and Office Realtors
1201 New York Ave., NW, Ste. 350
Washington, DC 20005
Ph: (202)449-8200   Fax: (202)449-8201
Fr: 888-891-7467
URL: http://www.sior.com

Annual, July. $70.00 for nonmembers; $80.00 for out of country. Serves as a guide to the most qualified industrial and office real estate practitioners: the Society's 2,700 designees, affiliates, associates, and candidates. Updated annually, the Guide lists SIOR designees and affiliates geographically. Associate members are listed alphabetically by company for easy reference to leading corporate users, developers, public utilities, universities, and more. Arrangement: Geographical. Indexes: Personal name.

★9697★ National Association of Real Estate Companies-Membership Directory

National Association of Real Estate Companies
Box 958
Columbia, MD 21044
Ph: (410)992-6476   Fax: (410)992-6363
E-mail: cindy@narec.org
URL: http://www.narec.org

Quarterly. Covers about 200 real estate development companies. Entries include: Company name, address, phone, name of contact.

★9698★ National Real Estate Investor Sourcebook

Primedia Business
6151 Powers Ferry Rd., Ste. 200
Atlanta, GA 30339
Ph: (770)995-2500   Fax: (770)618-0204
URL: http://www.nreionline.com

Annual, November. $79.95. Publication includes: List of about 7,000 companies and individuals in 18 real estate fields, including appraisers; asset managers; builders, contractors, and developers; communication services; corporate real estate managers; environmental consultants; equity investors; financial services; hospitality services; institutional advisors; pension funds; property managers; real estate brokers, agents, consultants, and counselors; software products and services; title insurance companies; related associations; and others. Entries include: Company or agency name, address, phone, fax, and, in some cases, names of executives and additional information. Arrangement: Classified by field or type of activity, then geographical.

★9699★ National Referral Roster

Stamats Communications Inc.
615 5th St. SE
PO Box 1888
Cedar Rapids, IA 52401
Ph: (319)364-6167   Fax: (319)369-0029
Fr: 800-553-8878

E-mail: real-estate@roster.com
URL: http://www.roster.com

Annual, May. $175.00; $95.00. Covers 90,000 real estate firms nationwide. Entries include: Regualr firm name, address, phone, fax, contact name, e-mail, URL are included with our advertisers. Arrangement: Geographical.

★9700★ Nelson Information's Directory of Institutional Real Estate

Nelson Information
c/o Thomson Financial
195 Broadway
New York, NY 10007
Ph: (646)822-2000   Fax: (914)937-9490
Fr: 800-333-6357
URL: http://www.nelsoninformation.com

Annual, August. $400.00. Covers 300 real estate investment managers, 1,700 plan sponsor investors in real estate, 1,400 real estate service firms and consultants, 1,000 insurance companies with real estate investments, 2,000 corporations with active real estate operations and 280 real estate investment trusts. Arrangement: Separate sections for real estate investment managers, plan sponsors, corporations, insurance companies, real estate service providers, and REITs. Indexes: Geographical, product/service.

★9701★ Real Estate Consultants Directory

infoUSA Inc.
5711 S 86th Cir.
Omaha, NE 68127-0347
Ph: (402)930-3500   Fax: (402)331-0176
Fr: 800-555-6124
URL: http://www.abii.com

Annual. Number of listings: 10,551. Entries include: Name, address, phone (including area code), size of advertisement, year first in "Yellow Pages," name of owner or manager, number of employees. Compiled from telephone company "Yellow Pages," nationwide. Arrangement: Geographical.

★9702★ Real Estate Schools Directory

infoUSA Inc.
5711 S 86th Cir.
Omaha, NE 68127-0347
Ph: (402)930-3500   Fax: (402)331-0176
Fr: 800-555-6124
URL: http://www.abii.com

Updated continuously; printed on request. Number of listings: 1,116. Entries include: Name, address, phone, size of advertisement, name of owner or manager, number of employees, year first in "Yellow Pages." Compiled from telephone company "Yellow Pages," nationwide. Arrangement: Geographical.

★9703★ U.S. Real Estate Register

Barry Inc.
PO Box 551
Wilmington, MA 01887-0551
Ph: (978)658-0442   Fax: (978)657-8691

URL: http://www.usrealestateregister.com

Annual, October. $95.00. Covers real estate departments of large national companies, industrial economic/development organizations, utilities, real estate brokers, and railroads involved in commercial and industrial real estate development. Entries include: Company or organization name, address; many listings include name of contact. Arrangement: Companies are alphabetical; others are geographical.

★9704★ Who's Who in Luxury Real Estate

JBL Inc.
2110 Western Ave.
Seattle, WA 98121
Ph: (206)441-7900   Fax: (206)695-4837
Fr: 800-488-4066
URL: http://luxuryrealestate.com/euroabout.html

Annual, January. $25.00 for out of area. Covers approximately 500 international luxury real estate brokers. Entries include: Company name, address, phone, names and titles of key personnel, description, number of employees, geographical area served, number of offices, area price range, referral, logo. Arrangement: Geographical. Indexes: Geographical, trade name.

HANDBOOKS AND MANUALS

★9705★ Agent's Guide to Real Estate: Power Your Career to Financial Success and Personal Happiness

Realty Research Group
46879 Willowood Pl.
Potomac Falls, VA 20165
Ph: (571)434-9071

Third edition, 2001. 138 pages.

★9706★ Becoming a Real Estate Professional

Vantage Press, Inc.
516 W. 34th St.
New York, NY 10001
Ph: (212)736-1767   Fax: (212)736-2273
Fr: 800-882-3273

Shawn J. Murphy. 1995. $19.95 (paper). Out of print.

★9707★ How About a Career in Real Estate?

Noteworthy Publishing Co.
1070 Idylwood Dr. SW
Issaquah, WA 98027
Ph: (425)392-6914   Fax: (425)392-6414
Fr: 800-296-2599

Carla Cross. Second edition, 1996. $14.95 (paper). 175 pages.

★9708★ *On Track to Success in 30 Days*

Dearborn Trade, A Kaplan Professional Co.
155 N. Wacker Dr.
Chicago, IL 60606-1719
Ph: (312)836-4400   Fax: (312)836-1021
Fr: 800-621-9621

Carla Cross. 1996. $24.95 (paper). 160 pages.

★9709★ *Opportunities in Real Estate Careers*

McGraw-Hill Professional
2 Penn Plaza
New York, NY 10121
Ph: (212)904-2000   Fr: 800-722-4726
E-mail: ntcpub@tribune.com

Mariwyn Evans. 2002. $15.95; $11.95 (paper). 160 pages.

★9710★ *Real Estate Blues: A Jump Start Guide to Your Real Estate Career*

PublishAmerica, Incorporated
230 E. Patrick St.
Frederick, MD 21701
Ph: (240)529-1030   Fax: (301)631-9073

David H. Lawrence. May 2004. $19.95 (paper). 138 pages.

★9711★ *Real Estate Careers: Twenty-Five Growing Opportunities*

John Wiley & Sons, Inc.
111 River St.
Hoboken, NJ 07030-5774
Ph: (201)748-6000   Fax: (201)748-6088
Fr: 800-225-5945

Carolyn Janik and Ruth Rejnis. 1994. $55.00; $22.95 (paper). 224 pages.

★9712★ *Where the Jobs Are: The Hottest Careers for the 90s*

The Career Press, Inc.
3 Tice Rd.
PO Box 687
Franklin Lakes, NJ 07417-1322
Ph: (201)848-0310   Fax: (201)848-1727
Fr: 800-227-3371

Joyce Hadley. Third edition, 2000. $13.99 (paper). 400 pages. Out of print. Describes careers in fifteen general fields, from accounting to travel and hospitality.

EMPLOYMENT AGENCIES AND SEARCH FIRMS

★9713★ **AET Advisors LLC**
3495 Piedmont Rd., NE Bldg 11, Ste. 824
Atlanta, GA 30305
Ph: (404)237-8208   Fax: (404)261-6961
Executive search and consultant firm. Focuses on the real estate industry.

★9714★ **Ahrensdorf & Associates**
PO Box 7494
St. Davids, PA 19087-7494
Ph: (610)971-0500   Fax: (610)971-9530
Executive search firm.

★9715★ **American Human Resources Associates Ltd. (AHRA)**
PO Box 18269
Cleveland, OH 44118-0269
Ph: (440)995-7120   Fr: 877-342-5833
Executive search firm. Focused on real estate, banking and credit & collection.

★9716★ **Crown Advisors Inc.**
800 E. Northwest Hwy., Ste. 612
Palatine, IL 60074
Ph: (847)221-2213   Fax: (847)221-2219
Fr: (847)830-6998
Executive search firm.

★9717★ **Dudley & Associates**
PO Box 1835
Addison, TX 75001
Ph: (214)560-2222   Fax: (972)818-1069
Executive search firm focused on construction and real estate industries.

★9718★ **Eggleston Consulting International**
4067 Audubon Dr.
Marietta, GA 30068
Ph: (770)579-2344   Fax: (770)579-1706
Executive search firm.

★9719★ **G Adams Partners**
205 W. Wacker Dr., Ste. 810
Chicago, IL 60606
Ph: (312)673-0390   Fax: (312)673-0390
Executive search firm.

★9720★ **John Dickerman and Associates**
9030 Bronson Dr.
Potomac, MD 20854
Ph: (301)983-2546
Specializes in construction, real estate and housing; marketing of manufactured building

materials and products; financing of homes, apartments, and related community elements. Involved in Federal government programs in housing and urban affairs. The firm has done numerous corporate acquisition and investment analyses, management studies, and executive search assignments in the field of building and manufacturing.

★9721★ **Liberty Screening Services**
7500 San Felipe St.
Houston, TX 77063
Ph: (713)961-7666   Fax: (713)961-3140

Real estate specialists conducting retainer and contingency executive searches. Contract, temporary and permanent placement capability. Merger and acquisition expertise. National employment screening services and drug testing. Offers market research, policy manual and job description development, candidate search, contract negotiations, interview assistance, post-placement assistance and outplacement. Also offers career path guidance, creation of opportunities, resume critique, interview guidance, contract negotiation, relocation guidance and post placement assistance follow-up.

★9722★ **Peter R. Taylor Associates Inc.**
43 Orchard Dr.
Williston Park, NY 11596
Ph: (516)742-9292   Fax: (516)742-9296

Executive search consultants specializing in corporate real estate. Industries served: retail, real estate, shopping center developers, and financial institutions.

★9723★ **Real Estate Executive Search, Inc.**
PO Box 387
San Francisco, CA 94104-0387
Ph: (415)398-4116
E-mail: jhavrees@aol.com

Executive search firm for the real estate and finance fields.

★9724★ **20-20 Foresight Executive Search Inc.**
One Lincoln Centre
18 W. 140 Butterfield Rd., Fl. 15
Oakbrook Terrace, IL 60181
Ph: (708)246-2100

Executive search firm. Affiliate offices in CA and Washington DC.

TRADESHOWS

★9725★ American Real Estate Society Annual Meeting
American Real Estate Society
c/o James R. Webb
Cleveland State University
College of Business
Department of Finance, UC513
Cleveland, OH 44114
Ph: (216)687-4732   Fax: (216)687-9331
URL: http://www.aresnet.org

Annual. **Primary Exhibits:** Exhibits relating to decision-making within real estate finance, real estate market analysis, investment, valuation, development, and other areas related to real estate in the private sector. Data providers, book publishers, etc.

★9726★ International Conference on Appraising
International Society of Appraisers
16040 Christensen Rd., Ste. 102
Seattle, WA 98188-2965
Ph: (206)241-0359   Fax: (206)241-0436
Fr: 888-472-5762
E-mail: isa_hq@compuserve.com
URL: http://www.isa-appraisers.org

Annual. **Primary Exhibits:** Exhibits for personal property appraisers.

★9727★ NAIFA National Convention
National Association of Independent Fee Appraisers
7501 Murdoch Ave.
St. Louis, MO 63119
Ph: (314)781-6688   Fax: (314)781-2872
E-mail: info@naifa.com
URL: http://www.naifa.com

Annual. **Primary Exhibits:** Equipment, supplies, and services directed to appraisers for real estate groups, savings and loan associations, title insurance groups, and governmental agencies.

★9728★ National Association of Realtors Trade Exposition
National Association of Realtors
430 N. Michigan Ave.
Chicago, IL 60611
Ph: (312)329-8491   Fax: (312)329-8873
Fr: 800-628-6338
URL: http://www.realtor.com

Annual. **Primary Exhibits:** Real estate industry equipment, supplies, and services, including hardware and software, marketing programs, office products, mortgage and financial services, and insurance.

★9729★ National Association of Review Appraisers and Mortgage Underwriters Convention
National Association of Review Appraisers and Mortgage Underwriters
1224 North Nokomis NE
Alexandria, MN 56308-5072
Ph: (320)763-6870   Fax: (320)763-9290

E-mail: naramu@iami.org
Annual. **Primary Exhibits:** Real estate-related information and services.

★9730★ National Real Estate Environmental Conference
National Society of Environmental Consultants
PO Box 12528
San Antonio, TX 78212-0528
Ph: (210)271-0781   Fax: (210)225-8450
Fr: 800-486-3676

Annual. **Primary Exhibits:** Exhibits related to the environmentally responsible use of real estate.

★9731★ ND/SD Realtors Convention
South Dakota Association of Realtors
120 N. Euclid
Pierre, SD 57501
Ph: (605)224-0554   Fax: (605)224-8975

Annual. **Primary Exhibits:** Realty equipment, supplies, and services.

★9732★ New York State Association of Realtors Annual Conference and Trade Exposition
New York State Association of Realtors
130 Washington Ave.
Albany, NY 12210-2298
Ph: (518)463-0300   Fax: (518)462-5474
Fr: 800-239-4432
E-mail: educate@nysar.com
URL: http://www.nysar.com

Annual. **Primary Exhibits:** Office equipment, publications, and real estate support services and technology.

★9733★ Realtor Annual Convention and Trade Expo
National Association of Realtors
430 N. Michigan Ave.
Chicago, IL 60611
Ph: (312)329-8491   Fax: (312)329-8873
Fr: 800-628-6338
URL: http://www.realtor.com

Annual. **Primary Exhibits:** Products and services related to the real estate business.

OTHER SOURCES

★9734★ Counselors of Real Estate
430 N Michigan Ave.
Chicago, IL 60611-4089
Ph: (312)329-8427   Fax: (312)329-8881
E-mail: info@cre.org
URL: http://www.cre.org

Description: Professional society of individuals with extensive experience in all phases of real estate who provide a counseling service. Members are entitled to use the professional designation CRE (Counselor of

Real Estate). Conducts educational programs during three national meetings.

★9735★ Marketing & Sales Occupations
Delphi Productions
3160 4th St.
Boulder, CO 80304
Fax: (303)443-4022   Fr: 888-443-2400
URL: http://www.delphivideo.com

$95.00. 50 minutes. Part of the Careers for the 21st Century Video Library.

★9736★ National Apartment Association (NAA)
201 N Union St., Ste. 200
Alexandria, VA 22314
Ph: (703)518-6141   Fax: (703)518-6191
E-mail: doug@naahq.com
URL: http://www.naahq.org

Members: Federation of 155 state and local associations of industry professionals engaged in all aspects of the multifamily housing industry, including owners, builders, investors, developers, managers, and allied service representatives. **Purpose:** Provides education and certification for property management executives, on-site property managers, maintenance personnel, property supervisors, and leasing agents. Offers a nationwide legislative network concerned with governmental decisions at the federal, state, and local levels.

★9737★ National Association of Realtors (NAR)
430 N Michigan Ave.
Chicago, IL 60611
Fax: (312)329-5962   Fr: 800-874-6500
E-mail: infocentral@realtors.org
URL: http://www.realtor.org

Description: Federation of 54 state and territory associations and 1860 local real estate boards whose members are real estate brokers and agents. Terms are registered by the association in the U.S. Patent and Trademark Office and in the states. Promotes education, high professional standards, and modern techniques in specialized real estate work such as brokerage, appraisal, property management, land development, industrial real estate, farm brokerage, and counseling. Conducts research programs.

★9738★ Real Estate Agents and Brokers
Evon Publishing
832 N 7th Ave.
Iron River, MI 49935
Ph: (906)265-3190

Audiocassette. 1996. $16.95. 32 minutes. Part of the Careers and Vocational Guidance Series. Provides information about the nature of the work, educational requirements, employment outlook, earnings, and work conditions as well as additional related information.

★9739★ **Realtors Land Institute (RLI)**
430 N. Michigan Ave.
Chicago, IL 60611
Fax: (312)329-8633   Fr: 800-441-LAND
E-mail: rli@realtors.org
URL: http://www.rliland.com

Members: Real estate brokers and sales-persons selling, managing, appraising, or developing all types of land. **Purpose:** Maintains educational programs for real estate brokers; promotes competence and accredits members. **Activities:** Sponsors courses for realtors and others seeking professional excellence on Land Brokerage, Agricultural Land Brokerage, Exchanging Properties, Estate Planning, Subdivision Development, and Financial Analysis of Land Investment.

★9740★ **Women's Council of Realtors (WCR)**
430 N Michigan Ave.
Chicago, IL 60611
Ph: (312)329-8483   Fax: (312)329-3290
Fr: 800-245-8512
E-mail: wcr@wcr.org
URL: http://www.wcr.org

Description: Women and men real estate brokers and salespeople. Provides opportunity for real estate professionals to participate at local, state, and national levels. Makes programs available for personal and career growth. Offers courses in leadership training, and referral and relocation business. Members may earn the Leadership Training Graduate (LTG) designation.

Real Estate Appraisers

SOURCES OF HELP-WANTED ADS

★9741★ Clayton-Fillmore Report
Clayton-Fillmore Ltd.
125 Dorset Ct.
Castle Rock, CO 80104-9285
Ph: (303)663-0606   Fax: (303)663-1616
Monthly. Periodical covering real estate and business.

★9742★ Journal of Property Management
Institute of Real Estate Management
430 N Michigan Ave.
Chicago, IL 60611-4090
Ph: (312)329-6000   Fax: (312)661-0217
Fr: 800-837-0706
URL: http://www.irem.org
Bimonthly. $43.95/year for individuals; $43.95/year for members. Magazine serving real estate managers.

★9743★ Journal of Real Estate Portfolio Management
American Real Estate Society
c/o Donna Cooper
College Business, MacArthur Campus
Florida Atlantic University
5353 Parkside Dr.
Jupiter, FL 33458
Ph: (561)799-8664   Fax: (561)799-8535
Quarterly. Journal for real estate professionals.

★9744★ New England Real Estate Journal
East Coast Publications
PO Box 55
Accord, MA 02018
Ph: (617)878-4540   Fax: (617)871-1853
Fr: 800-654-4993
E-mail: nerej@ix.net.com
Weekly. $139.00/year for individuals. Newspaper publishing commercial, industrial, and investment real estate news.

★9745★ Real Estate Issues
The Counselors of Real Estate
430 N Michigan Ave.
Chicago, IL 60611
Ph: (312)329-8427   Fax: (312)329-8881
E-mail: info@cre.org
Quarterly. Trade publication covering the real estate industry.

★9746★ REALTOR Magazine
National Association of Realtors
430 N Michigan Ave.
Chicago, IL 60611-4087
Ph: (312)329-8200   Fax: (312)329-5978
URL: http://www.realtormag.com
Monthly. Real estate magazine

PLACEMENT AND JOB REFERRAL SERVICES

★9747★ American Society of Farm Managers and Rural Appraisers (ASFMRA)
950 S Cherry St., Ste. 508
Denver, CO 80246-2664
Ph: (303)758-3513   Fax: (303)758-0190
E-mail: asfmra@agri-associations.org
URL: http://www.asfmra.org
Description: Professional farm managers, appraisers, lenders, consultants, educators and researchers in farm and ranch management and/or rural appraisal. Bestows registered ARA (Accredited Rural Appraiser), Accredited Agricultural Consultant (ACC), AFM (Accredited Farm Manager) and RPRA (Real Property Review Appraiser) designations. Operates management and appraisal schools, Internet course offerings. Maintains placement service.

★9748★ International Real Estate Institute (IREI)
1224 N. Nokomis NE
Alexandria, MN 56308-5072
Ph: (320)763-4648   Fax: (320)763-9290
E-mail: irei@iami.org
URL: http://www.iami.org/irei
Description: Professionals in 120 countries specializing in the development, finance, investment, and valuation of real estate. Conducts educational seminars and regional programs; operates speakers' bureau and placement service. Compiles statistics, consults United Nations on property issues.

★9749★ National Association of Review Appraisers and Mortgage Underwriters (NARA/MU)
1224 N Nokomis NE
Alexandria, MN 56308-5072
Ph: (320)763-6870   Fax: (320)763-9290
E-mail: nara@iami.org
URL: http://www.iami.org/nara
Description: Real estate professionals and mortgage underwriters who aid in determining value of property. Acts as umbrella group for real estate appraisers. Conducts educational seminars; maintains speakers' bureau; operates placement service.

EMPLOYER DIRECTORIES AND NETWORKING LISTS

★9750★ Appraisal Institute-Directory of Designated Members
Appraisal Institute
550 W Van Buren St., Ste. 1000
Chicago, IL 60607
Ph: (312)335-4100   Fax: (312)335-4400
E-mail: directory@appraisalinstitute.org
URL: http://p://www.appraisalinstitute.org
Annual, March. Covers over 16,000 real estate appraisers of all types of real property in the United States and Canada who hold the MAI, SRPA, or SREA general appraisal, and/or SRA or RM residential appraisal membership designations of the Appraisal Institute; includes limited overseas listings. Entries include: Name of individual member, company name, address, phone, fax, and email address. Arrangement: Geographical.

★9751★ CRS Referral Directory
Council of Residential Specialists
430 N Michigan Ave., Ste. 300
Chicago, IL 60611-4092
Ph: (312)321-4400   Fax: (312)329-8882
Fr: 800-462-8841
E-mail: crsdirectory@crs.com
URL: http://www.crs.com

Annual, November. Free. Covers 35,000 Certified Residential Specialists (CRS). Entries include: Member name, firm name, address, phone, fax; designations held, areas of specialization, e-mail; web page address; years of experience, voicemail; 2nd business phone. Arrangement: Geographical. Indexes: Alphabetical.

★9752★ Directory of Professional Appraisers
American Society of Appraisers
555 Herndon Pkwy., Ste. 125
Herndon, VA 20170
Ph: (703)478-2228   Fax: (703)742-8471
URL: http://www.appraisers.org

Annual, July. $12.95. Covers approximately 3,000 appraisers of businesses, real property, personal property, machinery, equipment, gems and jewelry, and all other types of property; limited international coverage. Entries include: Personal and company name, address, phone, fax, e-mail, URL, specialty. Arrangement: Geographical.

★9753★ ERC Directory of Real Estate Appraisers and Brokers
Employee Relocation Council (ERC)
1717 Pennsylvania Ave. NW, Ste. 800
Washington, DC 20006
Ph: (202)857-0857   Fax: (202)659-8631
E-mail: membership@erc.org
URL: http://www.erc.org

Annual, March. $35.00. Covers about 9,000 member brokers and appraisers worldwide, equipped to handle the relocation of employees. Entries include: For brokers-Firm name, address, phone, e-mail, number of offices, median price, code indicating services offered, list of corporations served, code indicating means of working with other brokers. For appraisers-Name, firm affiliation (if any), address, phone, e-mail, code indicating professional designations, names of corporations served. Arrangement: Appraisers and brokers are geographical.

★9754★ Executive Guide to Specialists in Industrial and Office Real Estate
Society of Industrial and Office Realtors
1201 New York Ave., NW, Ste. 350
Washington, DC 20005
Ph: (202)449-8200   Fax: (202)449-8201
Fr: 888-891-7467
URL: http://www.sior.com

Annual, July. $70.00 for nonmembers; $80.00 for out of country. Serves as a guide to the most qualified industrial and office real estate practitioners: the Society's 2,700 designees, affiliates, associates, and candidates. Updated annually, the Guide lists SIOR designees and affiliates geographical-

ly. Associate members are listed alphabetically by company for easy reference to leading corporate users, developers, public utilities, universities, and more. Arrangement: Geographical. Indexes: Personal name.

★9755★ National Association of Independent Fee Appraisers-National Membership Directory
National Association of Independent Fee Appraisers
7501 Murdoch Ave.
St. Louis, MO 63119
Ph: (314)781-6688   Fax: (314)781-2872
URL: http://www.naifa.com

Annual, January. Covers 4,300 independent real estate appraisers. Entries include: Name, address, phone, level of membership. Arrangement: Geographical.

★9756★ National Association of Master Appraisers-Membership Directory
National Association of Master Appraisers (NAMA)
303 W Cypress St.
San Antonio, TX 78212
Ph: (512)271-0781   Fax: (512)225-8450
Fr: 800-229-6262
URL: http://www.masterappraisers.com

Annual, January-March. Covers approximately 2,400 real estate appraisers. Entries include: Personal name, address, phone, field of specialty. Arrangement: Geographical. Indexes: Name.

★9757★ National Association of Real Estate Companies-Membership Directory
National Association of Real Estate Companies
Box 958
Columbia, MD 21044
Ph: (410)992-6476   Fax: (410)992-6363
E-mail: cindy@narec.org
URL: http://www.narec.org

Quarterly. Covers about 200 real estate development companies. Entries include: Company name, address, phone, name of contact.

★9758★ National Real Estate Investor Sourcebook
Primedia Business
6151 Powers Ferry Rd., Ste. 200
Atlanta, GA 30339
Ph: (770)995-2500   Fax: (770)618-0204
URL: http://www.nreionline.com

Annual, November. $79.95. Publication includes: List of about 7,000 companies and individuals in 18 real estate fields, including appraisers; asset managers; builders, contractors, and developers; communication services; corporate real estate managers; environmental consultants; equity investors; financial services; hospitality services; institutional advisors; pension funds; property managers; real estate brokers, agents, con-

sultants, and counselors; software products and services; title insurance companies; related associations; and others. Entries include: Company or agency name, address, phone, fax, and, in some cases, names of executives and additional information. Arrangement: Classified by field or type of activity, then geographical.

★9759★ National Referral Roster
Stamats Communications Inc.
615 5th St. SE
PO Box 1888
Cedar Rapids, IA 52401
Ph: (319)364-6167   Fax: (319)369-0029
Fr: 800-553-8878
E-mail: real-estate@roster.com
URL: http://www.roster.com

Annual, May. $175.00; $95.00. Covers 90,000 real estate firms nationwide. Entries include: Regualr firm name, address, phone, fax, contact name, e-mail, URL are included with our advertisers. Arrangement: Geographical.

★9760★ Real Estate Appraisers Directory
infoUSA Inc.
5711 S 86th Cir.
Omaha, NE 68127-0347
Ph: (402)930-3500   Fax: (402)331-0176
Fr: 800-555-6124
URL: http://www.abii.com

Annual. Number of listings: 26,379. Entries include: Name, address, phone (including area code), size of advertisement, year first in "Yellow Pages," name of owner or manager, number of employees. Regional editions available: Eastern, $685.00; Western, $460.00. Compiled from telephone company "Yellow Pages," nationwide. Arrangement: Geographical.

★9761★ Real Estate Consultants Directory
infoUSA Inc.
5711 S 86th Cir.
Omaha, NE 68127-0347
Ph: (402)930-3500   Fax: (402)331-0176
Fr: 800-555-6124
URL: http://www.abii.com

Annual. Number of listings: 10,551. Entries include: Name, address, phone (including area code), size of advertisement, year first in "Yellow Pages," name of owner or manager, number of employees. Compiled from telephone company "Yellow Pages," nationwide. Arrangement: Geographical.

★9762★ Real Estate Schools Directory
infoUSA Inc.
5711 S 86th Cir.
Omaha, NE 68127-0347
Ph: (402)930-3500   Fax: (402)331-0176
Fr: 800-555-6124
URL: http://www.abii.com

Updated continuously; printed on request. Number of listings: 1,116. Entries include: Name, address, phone, size of advertisement, name of owner or manager, number of employees, year first in "Yellow Pages." Compiled from telephone company "Yellow Pages," nationwide. Arrangement: Geographical.

★9763★ **U.S. Real Estate Register**
Barry Inc.
PO Box 551
Wilmington, MA 01887-0551
Ph: (978)658-0442   Fax: (978)657-8691
URL: http://www.usrealestateregister.com

Annual, October. $95.00. Covers real estate departments of large national companies, industrial economic/development organizations, utilities, real estate brokers, and railroads involved in commercial and industrial real estate development. Entries include: Company or organization name, address; many listings include name of contact. Arrangement: Companies are alphabetical; others are geographical.

HANDBOOKS AND MANUALS

★9764★ **Becoming a Real Estate Professional**
Vantage Press, Inc.
516 W. 34th St.
New York, NY 10001
Ph: (212)736-1767   Fax: (212)736-2273
Fr: 800-882-3273

Shawn J. Murphy. 1995. $19.95 (paper). Out of print.

★9765★ **Best Websites for Financial Professionals, Business Appraisers, & Accountants**
John Wiley & Sons Inc.
111 River St.
Hoboken, NJ 07030-5774
Ph: (201)748-6000   Fax: (201)748-5774

Eva M. Lang. 2001. $39.95 (paper).

★9766★ **How About a Career in Real Estate?**
Noteworthy Publishing Co.
1070 Idylwood Dr. SW
Issaquah, WA 98027
Ph: (425)392-6914   Fax: (425)392-6414
Fr: 800-296-2599

Carla Cross. Second edition, 1996. $14.95 (paper). 175 pages.

★9767★ **Opportunities in Real Estate Careers**
McGraw-Hill Professional
2 Penn Plaza
New York, NY 10121
Ph: (212)904-2000   Fr: 800-722-4726
E-mail: ntcpub@tribune.com

Mariwyn Evans. 2002. $15.95; $11.95 (paper). 160 pages.

★9768★ **Real Estate Careers: Twenty-Five Growing Opportunities**
John Wiley & Sons, Inc.
111 River St.
Hoboken, NJ 07030-5774
Ph: (201)748-6000   Fax: (201)748-6088
Fr: 800-225-5945

Carolyn Janik and Ruth Rejnis. 1994. $55.00; $22.95 (paper). 224 pages.

EMPLOYMENT AGENCIES AND SEARCH FIRMS

★9769★ **John Dickerman and Associates**
9030 Bronson Dr.
Potomac, MD 20854
Ph: (301)983-2546

Specializes in construction, real estate and housing; marketing of manufactured building materials and products; financing of homes, apartments, and related community elements. Involved in Federal government programs in housing and urban affairs. The firm has done numerous corporate acquisition and investment analyses, management studies, and executive search assignments in the field of building and manufacturing.

★9770★ **Liberty Screening Services**
7500 San Felipe St.
Houston, TX 77063
Ph: (713)961-7666   Fax: (713)961-3140

Real estate specialists conducting retainer and contingency executive searches. Contract, temporary and permanent placement capability. Merger and acquisition expertise. National employment screening services and drug testing. Offers market research, policy manual and job description development, candidate search, contract negotiations, interview assistance, post-placement assistance and outplacement. Also offers career path guidance, creation of opportunities, resume critique, interview guidance, contract negotiation, relocation guidance and post placement assistance follow-up.

★9771★ **Peter R. Taylor Associates Inc.**
43 Orchard Dr.
Williston Park, NY 11596
Ph: (516)742-9292   Fax: (516)742-9296

Executive search consultants specializing in corporate real estate. Industries served: retail, real estate, shopping center developers, and financial institutions.

★9772★ **Real Estate Executive Search, Inc.**
PO Box 387
San Francisco, CA 94104-0387
Ph: (415)398-4116
E-mail: jhavrees@aol.com

Executive search firm for the real estate and finance fields.

OTHER SOURCES

★9773★ **American Society of Agricultural Appraisers (ASAA)**
1126 Eastland Dr. N
PO Box 186
Twin Falls, ID 83303-0186
Ph: (208)733-2323   Fax: (208)733-2326
Fr: 800-488-7570
E-mail: ag@amagappraisers.com
URL: http://www.amagappraisers.com

Members: Appraisers of livestock, farm equipment, and other agricultural properties, supplies, and products. **Purpose:** Promotes adherence to high standards of ethics and practice in the field of agricultural appraising. **Activities:** Sponsors educational programs.

★9774★ **Appraisal Institute (AI)**
550 W Van Buren St., Ste. 1000
Chicago, IL 60607
Ph: (312)335-4100   Fax: (312)335-4400
E-mail: info@appraisalinstitute.org
URL: http://www.appraisalinstitute.org

Members: General appraisers who hold the MAI designation, and residential members who hold the SRA designation. **Purpose:** Enforces Code of Professional Ethics and Standards of Professional Appraisal Practice. Confers one general designation, the MAI, and one residential designation, the SRA. Provides training in valuation of residential and income properties, market analysis, and standards of professional appraisal practice. Sponsors courses in preparation for state certification and licensing; offers continuing education programs for designated members.

★9775★ **Counselors of Real Estate**
430 N Michigan Ave.
Chicago, IL 60611-4089
Ph: (312)329-8427   Fax: (312)329-8881
E-mail: info@cre.org
URL: http://www.cre.org

Description: Professional society of individuals with extensive experience in all phases of real estate who provide a counseling service. Members are entitled to use the professional designation CRE (Counselor of Real Estate). Conducts educational programs during three national meetings.

★9776★ **National Association of Master Appraisers (NAMA)**
303 W. Cypress St.
PO Box 12617
San Antonio, TX 78212-0617
Ph: (210)271-0781   Fax: (210)225-8450
Fr: 800-229-6262
E-mail: djd@masterappraisers.org
URL: http://www.masterappraisers.org

Members: Appraisers, analysts, assessors, brokers, salespersons, and others involved in real estate appraisal. **Purpose:** Works to enhance competency in the appraisal industry through education. Provides basic and advanced courses and educational meetings in techniques, management practices, and marketing strategies. Offers certification. Areas of interest include: residential, commercial, and rural property; review appraisal; condemnation proceedings; tax assessing. Keeps members apprised of new legislation and legal changes in policy. **Activities:** Sponsors Lender Awareness Program to increase awareness among banks and savings association officers. Provides referral services and speakers' bureau.

★9777★ **National Association of Real Estate Appraisers (NAREA)**
1224 N Nokomis NE
Alexandria, MN 56308-5072
Ph: (320)763-7626   Fax: (320)763-9290

E-mail: narea@iami.org
URL: http://www.iami.org/narea

Description: Real estate appraisers. Strives to "make available the services of the most highly qualified real estate appraisers." Offers certification to members.

★9778★ **National Association of Realtors (NAR)**
430 N Michigan Ave.
Chicago, IL 60611
Fax: (312)329-5962   Fr: 800-874-6500
E-mail: infocentral@realtors.org
URL: http://www.realtor.org

Description: Federation of 54 state and territory associations and 1860 local real estate boards whose members are real estate brokers and agents. Terms are registered by the association in the U.S. Patent and Trademark Office and in the states. Promotes education, high professional standards, and modern techniques in specialized real estate work such as brokerage, appraisal, property management, land development, industrial real estate, farm brokerage, and counseling. Conducts research programs.

★9779★ **Realtors Land Institute (RLI)**
430 N. Michigan Ave.
Chicago, IL 60611
Fax: (312)329-8633   Fr: 800-441-LAND
E-mail: rli@realtors.org
URL: http://www.rliland.com

Members: Real estate brokers and salespersons selling, managing, appraising, or developing all types of land. **Purpose:** Maintains educational programs for real estate brokers; promotes competence and accredits members. **Activities:** Sponsors courses for realtors and others seeking professional excellence on Land Brokerage, Agricultural Land Brokerage, Exchanging Properties, Estate Planning, Subdivision Development, and Financial Analysis of Land Investment.

Recreation Workers

★9780★ American City and County

Primedia Business
6151 Powers Ferry Rd.
Atlanta, GA 30339
Ph: (770)955-2500   Fax: (770)618-0348

Monthly. $67.00/year for individuals. Municipal and county administration magazine.

★9781★ Amusement Business

VNU Business Publications
770 Broadway
New York, NY 10003
Ph: (646)654-5000   Fax: (646)654-4977
URL: http://www.amusementbusiness.com

Weekly. $129.00/year for individuals; $5.00 for single issue. Trade newspaper covering amusement and theme parks, fairs, festivals, carnivals, and touring shows. Live entertainment, merchandise, and food and drink are also covered.

★9782★ Camping Magazine

American Camping Association
5000 State Rd. 67 N
Martinsville, IN 46151-7902
Ph: (765)342-8456   Fax: (765)349-2065
Fr: 800-428-CAMP
E-mail: magazine@ACA-camps.org
URL: http://www.acacamps.org

Bimonthly. $24.95/year for individuals; $32.50/year for institutions; $4.50 for single issue. Magazine on organized camp management.

★9783★ Earth Work

Student Conservation Association
PO Box 550
Charlestown, NH 03603
Ph: (603)543-1700   Fax: (603)543-1828
E-mail: earthwork@sca-inc.org
URL: http://www.sca-inc.org

Description: Eleven issues/year. Contains listings of environmental positions, ranging from internships and administrative assistants for environmental groups to camp directors, state natural resource managers, and biologists.

★9784★ Job Line...and News from CPRS

California Park & Recreation Society Inc.
7971 Freeport Blvd.
Sacramento, CA 95832-9701
Ph: (916)665-2777   Fax: (916)665-9149

Description: Monthly. Discusses parks and recreation news of interest.

★9785★ The Municipality

League of Wisconsin Municipalities
202 State St., Ste. 300
Madison, WI 53703-2215
Ph: (608)267-2380   Fax: (608)267-0645
Fr: 800-991-5502

Monthly. $12.00/year. Magazine for officials of Wisconsin's local municipal governments.

★9786★ NRPA Job Bulletin

National Recreation and Park Association, Professional Services Div.
22377 Belmont Ridge Rd.
Ashburn, VA 20148
Ph: (703)858-0784   Fax: (703)858-0707
Fr: 800-626-6772
URL: http://www.nrpa.org

Description: Semimonthly. Provides listings of employment opportunities in the park, recreation, and leisure services field.

★9787★ Sailing World

Miller Sports Group L.L.C.
79 Madison Ave.
New York, NY 10016-7802
Ph: (212)636-2700   Fr: 800-634-1953
E-mail: 70672.2725@compuserve.com
URL: http://www.sailingworld.com

$28.00/year for individuals. Magazine on performance sailing.

★9788★ Ski Area Management

Beardsley Publishing Corp.
45 Main St. N
PO Box 644
Woodbury, CT 06798
Ph: (203)263-0888   Fax: (203)266-0452
E-mail: sam@saminfo.com
URL: http://www.saminfo.com

Bimonthly. $42.00/year; $7.00 for single issue. Trade magazine.

★9789★ Skiing Trade News

Time4 Media Inc.
2 Park Ave., 10th Fl.
New York, NY 10016
Ph: (212)779-5493   Fax: (212)779-5118
URL: http://www.skinet.com

$15.00/year for individuals. Trade newspaper for the ski industry. Includes trade show previews, company news, retail trends, personnel changes, and miscellaneous news.

★9790★ Strategies

American Alliance for Health, Physical Education, Recreation & Dance
1900 Association Dr.
Reston, VA 20191
Ph: (703)476-3400   Fax: (703)476-9527
Fr: 800-213-7193
E-mail: strategies@aahperd.org

$25.00/year for members; $40.00/year for individuals; $63.00/year for businesses, institutions, and libraries. Journal providing practical, hands-on information to physical educators and coaches.

★9791★ Tourist Attractions & Parks Magazine

Kane Communications Inc.
10 E Athens Ave., Ste. 208
Ardmore, PA 19003
Ph: (610)645-6940   Fax: (610)645-6943
E-mail: tapmag@kanec.com
URL: http://www.tapmag.com

$30.00/year for U.S.; $36.00/year for other countries. Magazine on the management of amusement parks, carnivals, arcades, museums, zoos, campgrounds, fun centers, arenas, minature golf, and watersports.

★9792★ Western City

League of California Cities
1400 K St., 4th Fl.
Sacramento, CA 95814
Ph: (916)658-8223   Fax: (916)658-8289
Fr: 800-262-1801
URL: http://www.westerncity.com

Monthly. $39.00/year for individuals; $63.00
for two years. Municipal interest magazine.

★9793★ WOODALL's Campground Management

Woodall Publications Corp.
2575 Vista Del Mar Dr.
Ventura, CA 93001
Ph: (805)667-4100   Fax: (805)667-4468
Fr: 800-323-9076
E-mail: wcm@kconline.com

Monthly. $24.95/year for individuals; $34.95/
year for Canada. Magazine focusing on
operating and maintaining recreation vehicle
parks.

PLACEMENT AND JOB REFERRAL SERVICES

★9794★ American Alliance for Health, Physical Education, Recreation and Dance (AAHPERD)

1900 Association Dr.
Reston, VA 20191-1598
Ph: (703)476-3400   Fax: (703)476-9527
Fr: 800-213-7193
URL: http://www.aahperd.org

Members: Students and educators in physical education, dance, health, athletics, safety
education, recreation, and outdoor education. **Purpose:** Works to improve its fields of
education at all levels through such services
as consultation, periodicals and special publications, leadership development, determination of standards, and research. Sponsors
placement service.

★9795★ American Sail Training Association (ASTA)

PO Box 1459
Newport, RI 02840
Ph: (401)846-1775   Fax: (401)849-5400
E-mail: asta@sailtraining.org
URL: http://tallships.sailtraining.org

Members: Organizations operating sail
training programs; corporations and educational institutions supporting sail training;
private citizens with an interest in sailing and
sail training. **Purpose:** Promotes sail training
as an educational and character-building
experience for youth of all ages. Seeks to
bring together the sail training ships of the
world in a spirit of friendship and international goodwill. **Activities:** Sponsors Tall Ships
events including sail training rallies. Maintains billet bank/placement service; compiles
statistics.

★9796★ Exercise Safety Association (ESA)

PO Box 547916
Orlando, FL 32854-9716
Ph: (407)246-5090   Fax: (407)246-5090
E-mail: askesa@aol.com
URL: http://www.exercisesafety.com

Description: Fitness instructors, personal
trainers, health spas, YMCAs, community
recreation departments, and hospital
wellness programs. Purposes are: to improve the qualifications of exercise instructors; to train instructors to develop safe
exercise programs that will help people
avoid injury while exercising; to prepare
instructors for national certification. Offers
training in aerobics and exercise and on the
physiological aspects of exercise. Conducts
exercise safety and research programs.
Sponsors charitable program; maintains
speakers' bureau. Offers instructor placement services.

★9797★ Horsemanship Safety Association (HSA)

PO Box 2710
Lake Placid, FL 33862-2710
Ph: (863)465-0289   Fax: (863)699-5577
Fr: 800-798-8106
E-mail: hsanews@juno.com

Description: Schools of horsemanship;
equine programs at colleges and technical
schools; riding instructors and students;
medical personnel. Works to educate eques-
trians and instructors in safe horsemanship
practices. Trains instructors in leadership
techniques; conducts group and private lessons for children and adults; sponsors seminars and speaking engagements by certified
clinicians. Conducts riding instructor clinics
for adults. Certifies instructors at 4 levels:
assistant riding instructor, horsemanship
safety instructor, associate instructor, and
clinic instructor. Certified instructors must
renew certification every 3 years. Provides
on-site consultation. Offers Expert Witness
service. Compiles statistics; maintains library
of instructor training manuals, speakers'
bureau, and placement service. Operates job
placement services

★9798★ Jackie Robinson Foundation (JRF)

3 W 35th St., 11th Fl.
New York, NY 10001-2204
Ph: (212)290-8600   Fax: (212)290-8081
E-mail: general@jackierobinson.org
URL: http://www.jackierobinson.org

Description: Seeks to develop the leadership and achievement potential of minority
and urban youth. Founded by the friends and
family of Jackie Robinson (1919-72), the first
black athlete to play major league baseball.
Trains minority and poor youths for sports
management careers. Provides counseling,
support, and placement services. Awards full
college scholarships to promising minority
students. Maintains collection of Jackie Robinson memorabilia; has produced a national
touring exhibit of archival materials pertaining to Robinson.

★9799★ Resort and Commercial Recreation Association (RCRA)

PO Box 2437
Aurora, IL 60507
Ph: (630)892-2175   Fax: (630)801-4202
E-mail: info@r-c-r-a.org
URL: http://www.r-c-r-a.org

Members: Professionals, agencies, vendors, educators, and students involved in the
resort and commercial recreation field. **Purpose:** Seeks to advance the resort and
commercial recreation industries; increase
the profitability of commercial recreation
enterprises; foster communication among
members; promote professionalism within
the industry; provide opportunities for continuing education. **Activities:** Acts as a vehicle
for networking; offers program exchange and
job placement services. Holds specialized
educational presentations; operates student
chapters; encourages and facilitates internships. Provides car rental discount program.

★9800★ Society of Recreation Executives (SRE)

Box 520
Gonzalez, FL 32560-0520
Ph: (850)937-8354   Fax: (850)937-8356
Fr: 800-281-9186
E-mail: rltresoource@spydee.net

Description: Corporate executives in the
recreation, leisure, and travel industry. To
obtain individual and collective recognition
for recreation executives. Works to: provide
a perspective on needs, trends, and
changes within the industry; provide opportunities for the exchange of ideas and expertise among members; inform, train, and
instruct members in industry principles and
practices. Supports favorable legislation.
Sponsors continuing education and selfhelp
programs. Operates placement service and
speakers' bureau.

★9801★ YMCA International Camp Counselor Program (ICCP)

5 W 63rd St., 2nd Fl.
New York, NY 10010
Ph: (212)727-8800   Fax: (212)727-8814
Fr: 888-477-9622
E-mail: ips@ymcanyc.org
URL: http://www.ymcaiccp.org

Description: A work-travel program designed to introduce international university
students and teachers and social workers
aged 19-30 to life in America. The students
spend 8 to 9 weeks counseling in children's
camps across the country, followed by a
period of independent or group travel. Also
sponsors ICCP-Abroad placement service
for American university students aged 18-25
wishing to serve as camp counselors in
Africa, Asia, Australia, Hungary, New Zealand, and South America.

EMPLOYER DIRECTORIES AND NETWORKING LISTS

★9802★ Camps Directory
infoUSA Inc.
5711 S 86th Cir.
Omaha, NE 68127-0347
Ph: (402)930-3500   Fax: (402)331-0176
Fr: 800-555-6124
URL: http://www.abii.com

Annual. Number of listings: 8,795. Entries include: Name, address, phone (including area code), size of advertisement, year first in "Yellow Pages," name of owner or manager, number of employees. Compiled from telephone company "Yellow Pages," nationwide. Arrangement: Geographical.

★9803★ Directory of Public Garden Internships
American Association of Botanical Gardens and Arboreta (AABGA)
100 W 10th St., Ste. 614
Wilmington, DE 19801-6604
Ph: (302)655-7100   Fax: (302)655-8100
E-mail: bvincent@aabga.org

Annual, November. $10.00 for members; $15.00 for nonmembers. Covers 700 student internships and summer jobs at public gardens throughout North America. Entries include: Name of institution, address, name of contact, deadline for application, number of students hired, whether internships are available, employment period, hours, rate of pay, whether housing is available, other comments. Arrangement: Alphabetical. Indexes: By position, by state/province.

★9804★ Exercise and Physical Fitness Programs Directory
infoUSA Inc.
5711 S 86th Cir.
Omaha, NE 68127-0347
Ph: (402)930-3500   Fax: (402)331-0176
Fr: 800-555-6124
URL: http://www.abii.com

Annual. Number of listings: 8,412. Entries include: Name, address, phone (including area code), size of advertisement, year first in "Yellow Pages," name of owner or manager, number of employees. Compiled from telephone company "Yellow Pages," nationwide. Arrangement: Geographical.

★9805★ Guide to ACA-Accredited Camps
American Camping Association
5000 State Rd. 67 N
Martinsville, IN 46151-7902
Ph: (765)342-8456   Fax: (765)349-2065
Fr: 800-428-CAMP
URL: http://www.ACAcamps.org

Annual, January. $12.95. Covers over 2,400 summer camps. Entries include: Name of camp, address, phone, fax, email addresses, age and sex of children accepted, rates, season, capacity, facilities, programs, activi-

ties offered and camp philosophy. Arrangement: Geographical, then by day or resident camp. Indexes: Activity, special clientele, camp name, specific disabilities.

★9806★ Health Clubs Studios & Gymnasiums Directory
infoUSA Inc.
5711 S 86th Cir.
Omaha, NE 68127-0347
Ph: (402)930-3500   Fax: (402)331-0176
Fr: 800-555-6124
URL: http://www.abii.com

Updated continuously; printed on request. Number of listings: 17,012. Entries include: Name, address, phone (including area code). Compiled from telephone company "Yellow Pages," nationwide. Arrangement: Geographical.

★9807★ Health & Fitness Program Consultants Directory
infoUSA Inc.
5711 S 86th Cir.
Omaha, NE 68127-0347
Ph: (402)930-3500   Fax: (402)331-0176
Fr: 800-555-6124
URL: http://www.abii.com

Annual. Number of listings: 4,627. Entries include: Name, address, phone (including area code), size of advertisement, year first in "Yellow Pages," name of owner or manager, number of employees. Compiled from telephone company "Yellow Pages," nationwide. Arrangement: Geographical.

★9808★ Membership and Peer Network Directory
ESM Association
2211 York Rd., Ste. 207
Oak Brook, IL 60523-2371
Ph: (630)368-1280   Fax: (630)368-1286

Annual, April. Covers over 4,500 personnel managers, recreation directors, suppliers, and certified administrators in employee recreation, fitness, and services. Entries include: Name, address, phone, fax and e-mail. Arrangement: Alphabetical.

★9809★ National Parks: Index
U.S. National Park Service
Harpers Ferry Center
PO Box 50
Harpers Ferry, WV 25425-0050
Ph: (202)208-4747   Fax: (304)535-6144
URL: http://www.nps.gov/

Biennial, odd years. $6.50. Covers over 379 areas administered by the National Park Service, including parks, shores, historic sites, 80 national trails, and wild and scenic rivers. Entries include: Name, location, address, acreage (federal, non-federal, and gross), federal facilities, brief description. Arrangement: Most areas are alphabetical by state; geographical and historical by state; wild and scenic rivers and national trails are alphabetical by state. Indexes: Alphabetical by state.

★9810★ National Sports and Fitness Association-Fitness Directory
National Sports & Fitness Association
1945 Palo Verde, Ste. 202
Long Beach, CA 90815-3445
Ph: (562)682-3559   Fax: (562)799-3355

Annual, summer. Entries include: Name, address, phone, products or services, geographical area covered, sports and fitness interests. Arrangement: Alphabetical.

★9811★ Peterson's Summer Jobs for Students
Thomson Peterson's
Princeton Pke. Corporate Ctr., 2000 Lenox Dr.
PO Box 67005
Lawrenceville, NJ 08648
Ph: (609)896-1800   Fax: (609)896-4531
Fr: 800-338-3282

Annual, latest edition 2002. $18.95. Covers over 650 camps, resorts, amusement parks, hotels, businesses, national parks, conference and training centers, ranches, and restaurants offering about 45,000 temporary summer jobs; listings are paid. Entries include: Name and address, length of employment, pay rate, fringe benefits, duties, qualifications, application deadline and procedure. Arrangement: Geographical, then type of job. Indexes: Job title.

★9812★ Recreation Centers Directory
infoUSA Inc.
5711 S 86th Cir.
Omaha, NE 68127-0347
Ph: (402)930-3500   Fax: (402)331-0176
Fr: 800-555-6124
URL: http://www.abii.com

Annual. Number of listings: 6,654. Entries include: Name, address, phone (including area code), size of advertisement, year first in "Yellow Pages," name of owner or manager, number of employees. Compiled from telephone company "Yellow Pages," nationwide. Arrangement: Geographical.

★9813★ Recreational Sports Directory
National Intramural-Recreational Sports Association
4185 SW Research Way
Corvallis, OR 97333-1067
Ph: (541)766-8211   Fax: (541)766-8284
URL: http://www.nirsa.org

Annual, December. $150.00 to corporate members; $40.00 to student members. Covers recreational sports programs in approximately 2,500 four-year colleges and universities, nearly 700 junior and community colleges, Canadian colleges and universities, and over 350 military installations. Entries include: Institution name and address; institution enrollment; name of president; names, phone numbers, fax numbers, Internet access, and job titles of recreational directors and staff; existing sports clubs; degrees offered in physical education and recreation; whether graduate assistantships or internships are available. A Buyer's Guide is included with supplier addresses and descriptions of products and services. Arrangement: Classified by institution type, then alphabetical. Indexes: Alphabetical, geographical, personal name, recreational sports program.

★9814★ **Seasonal Employment**
U.S. National Park Service
Harpers Ferry Center
PO Box 50
Harpers Ferry, WV 25425-0050
Ph: (202)208-4747   Fax: (304)535-6144
URL: http://www.nps.gov

Updated as needed; go to "InfoZone" to access. Publication includes: List of 10 regional offices and branches of the National Park Service that accept applications for seasonal jobs. Entries include: Name, address, phone, geographical area served. Principal content of publication is information on seasonal jobs offered by the National Park Services, with description of duties, qualifications, and application procedures for each type of job offered. Arrangement: Geographical.

★9815★ **Skiing USA: Where to Ski, Where to Stay, Where to Eat in the 30 Best U.S. Ski Resorts**
Fodor's Travel Publications Inc.
1745 Broadway
New York, NY 10019
Ph: (212)782-9000   Fax: (212)782-9054
Fr: 800-733-3000

Biennial, even years. $17.00. Covers 30 top ski resorts in the U.S. Entries include: Resort name, address, phone; type of lifts, number of trails, snowmaking capabilities, length of season, hotels, restaurants, available transportation, other activities, and recommendations on the best trails for all levels. Arrangement: Geographical. Indexes: Resort name.

★9816★ **White Book of Ski Areas: U.S., Canada**
Inter-Ski Services Inc.
PO Box 3775
Washington, DC 20007
Ph: (202)342-0886   Fax: (202)338-1940
URL: http://www.inter-ski.com

Annual, latest edition 28th, 2004. $19.95. Covers about 500 lift-equipped ski areas and resorts. Entries include: Name of ski area, location, phone; snow condition phone numbers; ski statistics (elevation, lift capacity, etc.); season and rates; equipment and schooling available; lodging availability and phone, restaurants, apres-ski, and other recreational facilities in vicinity; shops; travel instructions. Special industry edition available with more comprehensive information; $395.00. Arrangement: Geographical within four regions-West, North Central, South, and Northeast. Indexes: Geographical.

★9817★ **Who's Who in Sports & Fitness**
National Sports & Fitness Association
1945 Palo Verde, Ste. 202
Long Beach, CA 90815-3445
Ph: (562)682-3559   Fax: (562)799-3355

Annual, January. Entries include: Name, address, phone, biographical data, products or services, geographical area covered. Arrangement: Alphabetical. Indexes: Geographical.

★9818★ **YMCA Resident Camp Directory**
Camping Programs
101 N Wacker Dr.
Chicago, IL 60606
Ph: (312)269-1123   Fax: (312)977-9063
URL: http://www.ymca.com

Updated weekly. $6.00. Database covers: Over 235 resident camps and conference and retreat centers operated by local YMCA associations in the United States. Entries include: Association name, camp name, address and phone of winter office, camp location and summer address and phone, name of director, seasons of operation, capacity; whether coed or restricted to boys or girls, or available for family and adult camping; special programs offered. Arrangement: Classified by type of camp (resident, family, conference centers).

HANDBOOKS AND MANUALS

★9819★ **Athlete's Guide to Career Planning**
Human Kinetics Publishers
PO Box 5076
Champaign, IL 61825-5076
Ph: (217)351-5076   Fax: (217)351-2674
Fr: 800-747-4457

Al Petitpas, Delight Champagne, Judy Chartrand, Shane Murphy and Steven Danish. 1997. $17.95 (paper). 240 pages.

★9820★ **Careers for Health Nuts and Others Who Like to Stay Fit**
McGraw-Hill Trade
2 Penn Plaza
New York, NY 10121
Ph: (212)904-2000   Fr: 800-722-4726
E-mail: ntcpub@tribune.com

Blythe Camenson. 1996. $14.95; $9.95 (paper). 160 pages.

★9821★ **Careers Inside the World of Sports and Entertainment**
Rosen Publishing Group, Inc.
29 E. 21st St.
New York, NY 10010
Ph: (212)777-3017   Fax: 888-436-4643
Fr: 800-237-9932

Bruce McGothlin. 1995. $15.95. 64 pages. Out of print.

★9822★ **Careers in Travel, Tourism, and Hospitality**
McGraw-Hill Contemporary Books
1221 Avenue of the Americas
New York, NY 10020
Ph: (212)904-2000   Fr: 800-323-4900
E-mail: ntcpub@tribune.com

Marjorie Eberts, Linda Brothers, and Ann Gisler. 1997. $17.95; 13.95 (paper). 192 pages.

★9823★ **Careers Without College: Fitness**
Thomson Peterson's
PO Box 67005
Lawrenceville, NJ 08648-6105
Fr: 800-338-3282

Maura R. Curless. 1992. $7.95 (paper).

★9824★ **Great Careers for People Who Like Being Outdoors**
Thomson Gale
27500 Drake Rd.
Farmington Hills, MI 48331-3535
Ph: (248)699-GALE   Fax: (248)699-8069
Fr: 800-877-GALE
E-mail: galeord@gale.com
URL: http://www.galegroup.com

Helen Mason. Volume 6. 1993. $25.00. 48 pages. Part of Career Connections Series 1 Series.

★9825★ **Guiding Your Entry into the Hospitality, Recreation and Tourism Mega-Profession**
Prentice Hall PTR
200 Old Tappan Rd.
Old Tappan, NJ 07675
Fr: 800-223-1360

Jack B. Samuels and Reginald Foucar-Szocki. 1998. $47.00. 296 pages.

★9826★ **How to Get a Job with a Cruise Line**
Ticket to Adventure, Inc.
PO Box 41005
St. Petersburg, FL 33743-1005
Ph: (727)822-5029   Fax: (727)821-3409
Fr: 800-929-7447

Mary Fallon Miller. Fifth edition, 2001. $16.95 (paper). 336 pages. Explores jobs with cruise ships, describing duties, responsibilities, benefits, and training. Lists cruise ship lines and schools offering cruise line training. Offers job hunting advice.

★9827★ **It's More Than Just Making Them Sweat: A Career Training Guide for Personal Fitness Trainers**
Robert D. Reed Publishers
750 La Playa St., Suite 647
San Francisco, CA 94121-3262
Ph: (650)994-6570   Fax: (650)994-6579
Fr: 800-774-7336

Ed Thornton. 2001 (paper).

★9828★ Opportunities in Child Care Careers

McGraw-Hill Trade
2 Penn Plaza
New York, NY 10121
Ph: (212)904-2000   Fr: 800-722-4726
Renee Wittenberg. 1998. $14.95; $11.95 (paper). 210 pages. Discusses various job opportunities and how to secure a position. Illustrated.

★9829★ Opportunities in Sports and Fitness Careers

McGraw-Hill Professional
2 Penn Plaza
New York, NY 10121
Ph: (212)904-2000   Fr: 800-722-4726
William Ray Heitzmann. $12.95. E-book, netLibrary.

★9830★ Opportunities in Travel Careers

McGraw-Hill Contemporary Books
1221 Avenue of the Americas
New York, NY 10020
Ph: (212)904-2000   Fr: 800-323-4900
E-mail: ntcpub@tribune.com
Robert Scott Milne. 1996. $14.95; $11.95 (paper). 198 pages. Discusses what the jobs are and where to find them in airlines, shipping lines, and railroads. Discusses related opportunities in hotels, motels, resorts, travel agencies, public relation firms, and recreation departments. Illustrated.

TRADESHOWS

★9831★ IDEA World Fitness & Personal Trainer Convention

IDEA, The International Association for Fitness Professionals
69190 Cornerstone Ct., E., Ste. 204
San Diego, CA 92121
Ph: (619)535-8979   Fax: (619)535-8234
Fr: 800-999-4332
URL: http://www.ideafit.com
Annual. **Primary Exhibits:** Aerobic clothing and footwear; exercise products; equipment companies; related services.

★9832★ North Carolina Recreation and Park Society Conference

North Carolina Recreation and Park Society
883 Washington St.
Raleigh, NC 27605
Ph: (919)832-5868   Fax: (919)832-3323
E-mail: ncrps@bellsouth.net
Annual. **Primary Exhibits:** Parks and recreation equipment, supplies, and services.

OTHER SOURCES

★9833★ American Association for Leisure and Recreation (AALR)

1900 Association Dr.
Reston, VA 20191-1598
Ph: (703)476-3472   Fax: (703)476-9527
Fr: 800-213-7193
E-mail: aalr@aahperd.org
URL: http://www.aahperd.org/aalr
Description: Mission is to promote and support education, leisure and recreation by developing quality programming and professional training; providing leadership opportunities; disseminating guidelines and standards; enhancing public understanding of the importance of leisure and recreation in maintaining a creative and healthy lifestyle. Goals and objectives are to serve as a forum for professionals, students and organizations to educate and exchange information and ideas on leisure and recreation services; develop and promote professional standards for education, leisure and recreation services; increase public awareness, understanding, appreciation, and support for lifelong education, leisure and recreation services; encourage professional training for all with an interest in education, leisure and recreation services; advance, encourage, conduct and publish scientific knowledge and research in the field of education, leisure, and recreation services.

★9834★ American Camping Association (ACA)

5000 State Rd. 67 N.
Martinsville, IN 46151-7902
Ph: (765)349-3310   Fax: (765)349-0301
E-mail: psmith@acacamps.org
URL: http://www.acacamps.org
Description: Camp owners, directors, program directors, businesses, and students interested in resident and daycamp programming for youth and adults. Conducts camp standards. Offers educational programs in areas of administration, staffing, child development, promotion, and programming.

★9835★ American Council on Exercise (ACE)

4851 Paramount Dr.
San Diego, CA 92123
Ph: (858)279-8227   Fax: (858)279-8064
Fr: 800-825-3636
E-mail: kristiep@acefitness.org
URL: http://www.acefitness.org
Members: Certifies fitness professionals and non-profit organizations. **Purpose:** Keeps them aware of new information in the health and fitness industry. **Activities:** Offers continuing education programs. Sponsors children's services. Provides consumers with health and fitness research and information.

★9836★ Employee Services Management Association

2211 York Rd., Ste. 207
Oak Brook, IL 60523-2371
Ph: (630)368-1280   Fax: (630)368-1286
E-mail: esmahq@esmassn.org
URL: http://www.esmassn.org
Description: Corporations and governmental agencies that sponsor recreation, fitness, and service programs for their employees; associate members are manufacturers and suppliers in the employee recreation market and distributors of consumer products and services. Serves as an information resource network for over 3,000 members nationwide. These members are responsible for implementing and maintaining a diverse range of employee services; believes that employee services, as practical solutions to work/life issues, are essential to sound business management. These programs improve relations between employees and management, increase overall productivity, boost morale, and reduce absenteeism and turnover. The association covers the 10 Components of a Well-Rounded Employee Services Program such as employee stores, convenience services, recognition programs, recreation programs, travel services, and special events. National Associate Members are manufacturers and suppliers in the employee services market and distributors of consumer products and services.

★9837★ Human Services Occupations

Delphi Productions
3160 4th St.
Boulder, CO 80304
Fax: (303)443-4022   Fr: 888-443-2400
URL: http://www.delphivideo.com
$95.00. 50 minutes. Part of the Careers for the 21st Century Video Library.

★9838★ IDEA Health and Fitness Association

6190 Cornerstone Ct. E., Ste. 204
San Diego, CA 92121-3773
Ph: (858)535-8979   Fax: (858)535-8234
Fr: 800-999-IDEA
E-mail: member@ideafit.com
URL: http://www.ideafit.com
Purpose: Provides continuing education for fitness professionals including; fitness instructors, personal trainers, program directors, and club/studio owners. **Activities:** Offers workshops for continuing education credits.

★9839★ International Council of Cruise Lines (ICCL)

2111 Wilson Blvd., 8th Fl.
Arlington, VA 22201
Ph: (703)522-8463   Fax: (703)522-3811
Fr: 800-595-9338
E-mail: info@iccl.org
URL: http://www.iccl.org/
Members: Cruise ship operators. **Purpose:** Seeks to improve the safety and profitability of cruise lines. **Activities:** Represents members' interests before technology, environ-

mental protection, and safety organizations; conducts lobbying and advocacy campaigns to secure legislation favorable to the cruise industry.

★9840★ National Association for Girls and Women in Sport (NAGWS)
1900 Association Dr.
Reston, VA 20191-1598
Ph: (703)476-3450   Fax: (703)476-9527
Fr: 800-213-7193
E-mail: nagws@aahperd.org
URL: http://www.aahperd.org/nagws/template.cfm?template=main.html

Members: An Association of the American Alliance for Health, Physical Education, Recreation, and Dance. Teachers, coaches, athletic trainers, officials, athletic administrators, and students. NAGWS has 8 main structures: Advocacy Coaching Enhancement; Minority Representation; Professional Development Publications, and Student Representation. Purpose: Supports and fosters the development of quality sports programs that will enrich the lives of all participants. Activities: Holds training sessions for leadership development. Maintains speakers' bureau. Conducts research programs; bestows awards.

★9841★ National Association of Underwater Instructors (NAUI)
1232 Tech Blvd.
Tampa, FL 33619-7832
Ph: (813)628-6284   Fax: (813)628-8253
Fr: 800-553-6284
E-mail: nauihq@nauiww.org
URL: http://www.naui.org/index-side.html

Members: Certified instructors of basic, advanced, and specialized courses in underwater diving. Activities: Offers instructor certification programs and training programs. Conducts seminars, workshops, and symposia. Sells diving education books. Sponsors competitions; maintains speakers' bureau and placement service; conducts charitable programs.

★9842★ Recreation Workers
Evon Publishing
832 N 7th Ave.
Iron River, MI 49935
Ph: (906)265-3190

Audiocassette. 1996. $16.95. 32 minutes. Part of the Careers and Vocational Guidance Series. Provides information about the nature of the work, educational requirements, employment outlook, earnings, and work conditions as well as additional related information.

Recreational Therapists

PLACEMENT AND JOB REFERRAL SERVICES

★9843★ Special Recreation for disABLED International (SRDI)
362 Koser Ave.
Iowa City, IA 52246-3938
Ph: (319)337-7578
E-mail: john-nesbitt@uiowa.edu
URL: http://www.jccniowa.org/~recdsabl/SDRI.htm

Description: Seeks to serve and advocate special and therapeutic play and recreation for infants, children, youth, adults, and seniors throughout the world. Services include advisory and consultation, awards, employment information, professional education, public education, publishing, research, resource information and referral, technical assistance on programs and management methods, and an international library. Does international service work to: collect and disseminate international information on special recreation services for disabled persons, special recreation programs, and personnel training; conduct, provide, and support international exchange of technical, professional, and general information on special recreation for the disabled; cooperate with both governmental and voluntary organizations on national and international levels. Offers career guidance and placement service. Maintains speakers' bureau; compiles statistics.

EMPLOYER DIRECTORIES AND NETWORKING LISTS

★9844★ AHA Guide to the Health Care Field
American Hospital Association (AHA)
1 N. Franklin St., 27th Fl.
Chicago, IL 60606
Ph: (312)422-2050   Fax: (312)422-4700
Fr: 800-424-4301

Annual, August. $295.00. Covers hospitals, networks, multi-health care systems, free-standing ambulatory surgery centers, psychiatric facilities, long-term care facilities, substance abuse programs, and other health-related organizations. Entries include: For hospitals-Facility name, address, phone, administrator's name, number of beds, facilities and services, number of employees, expenses, other statistics. For other organizations-Name, address, phone, fax, name and title of contact. Arrangement: Geographical. Indexes: Hospital name.

★9845★ Directory of Hospital Personnel
Thomson Medical Economics
5 Paragon Dr.
Montvale, NJ 07645-1742
Ph: (201)358-7200   Fax: (201)722-2680

Annual, November. $325.00. Covers 200,000 executives at 7,000 U.S. hospitals. Entries include: Name of hospital, address, phone, number of beds, type and JCAHO status of hospital, names and titles of key department heads and staff, medical and nursing school affiliations; number of residents, interns, and nursing students. Arrangement: Geographical. Indexes: Hospital name, personnel, hospital size.

★9846★ Hospital Blue Book
Billian/Transworld Publishing Inc.
2100 Powers Ferry Rd.
Ste. 300
Atlanta, GA 30339
Ph: (770)955-8484   Fax: (770)955-8485
Fr: 800-533-8484
E-mail: blu-book@billian.com

Annual, January. $285.00 for national edition; $160.00 for southern edition. Covers more than 6,687 hospitals; some listings also appear in a separate southern edition of this publication. Entries include: Name of hospital, accreditation, mailing address, phone, fax, number of beds, type of facility (nonprofit, general, state, etc.); list of administrative personnel and chiefs of medical services, with specific titles. Arrangement: Geographical.

★9847★ Medical and Health Information Directory
Thomson Gale
27500 Drake Rd.
Farmington Hills, MI 48331-3535
Ph: (248)699-4253   Fax: (248)699-8065
Fr: 800-877-GALE
E-mail: businessproducts@gale.com

Annual. $285.00 per volume; $675.00 per set. Covers in Volume 1, more than 26,500 medical and health oriented associations, organizations, institutions, and government agencies, including health maintenance organizations (HMOs), preferred provider organizations (PPOs), insurance companies, pharmaceutical companies, research centers, and medical and allied health schools. In Volume 2, over 12,000 medical book publishers; medical periodicals, directories, audiovisual producers and services, medical libraries and information centers, electronic resources, and health-related internet search engines. In Volume 3, more than 35,500 clinics, treatment centers, care programs, and counseling/diagnostic services for 34 subject areas. Entries include: Institution, service, or firm name, address, phone, fax, email and URL; many include names of key personnel and, when pertinent, descriptive annotation. Volume 3 was formerly listed separately as Health Services Directory. Arrangement: Classified by organization activity, service, etc. Indexes: Each volume has a complete alphabetical name and keyword index.

HANDBOOKS AND MANUALS

★9848★ Careers in Health Care
McGraw-Hill Trade
2 Penn Plaza
New York, NY 10121
Ph: (212)904-2000   Fr: 800-722-4726
E-mail: ntcpub@tribune.com

Barbara M. Swanson. Fourth edition, 2000. $17.95; $13.95 (paper). 320 pages. Describes job duties, work settings, salaries, licensing and certification requirements, educational preparation, and future outlook. Gives ideas on how to secure a job.

★9849★ *Careers in Social and Rehabilitation Services*

McGraw-Hill Trade
2 Penn Plaza
New York, NY 10121
Ph: (212)904-2000   Fr: 800-722-4726
E-mail: ntcpub@tribune.com

Geraldine O. Garner. Second edition, 2001. $19.95; 14.95 (paper). 128 pages.

★9850★ *Great Jobs for Psychology Majors*

McGraw-Hill Trade
2 Penn Plaza
New York, NY 10121
Ph: (212)904-2000   Fr: 800-722-4726
E-mail: ntcpub@tribune.com

Julie DeGalan and Stephen Lambert. 1995. $11.95 (paper). 468 pages. Out of print.

★9851★ *Opportunities in Gerontology and Aging Services Careers*

McGraw-Hill Trade
2 Penn Plaza
New York, NY 10121
Ph: (212)904-2000   Fr: 800-722-4726

Ellen Williams. 1995. $14.95; $11.95 (paper). 200 pages. Covers jobs in community, health and medical programs, financial, legal, residential, travel and tourism, and counseling, and how to go after them. Includes bibliography and illustrations.

★9852★ *Opportunities in Health and Medical Careers*

McGraw-Hill Trade
2 Penn Plaza
New York, NY 10121
Ph: (212)904-2000   Fr: 800-722-4726

I. Donald Snook, Jr. and Leo D'Orazio. 1997. $14.95; $11.95 (paper). 202 pages. Covers the full range of medical and health occupations. Illustrated.

★9853★ *Real People Working in the Helping Professions*

McGraw-Hill Contemporary Books
1221 Avenue of the Americas
New York, NY 10020
Ph: (212)904-2000   Fr: 800-323-4900
E-mail: ntcpub@tribune.com

Blythe Camenson, Jan Goldberg. 1997. $17.95; $12.95 (paper). Interviews and profiles of working professionals capture a range of opportunities in this field.

★9854★ *Resumes for Health and Medical Careers*

McGraw-Hill Trade
2 Penn Plaza
New York, NY 10121
Ph: (212)904-2000   Fr: 800-722-4726

E-mail: ntcpub@tribune.com

1997. $9.95 (paper). 455 pages.

EMPLOYMENT AGENCIES AND SEARCH FIRMS

★9855★ **Harper Associates**

29870 Middlebelt
Farmington Hills, MI 48334
Ph: (248)932-1170   Fax: (248)932-1214
E-mail: resumes@harperjobs.com
URL: http://www.harperjobs.com

Executive search firm and employment agency.

★9856★ **Professional Placement Associates, Inc.**

287 Bowman Ave., Ste. 309
Purchase, NY 10577
Ph: (914)251-1000   Fax: (914)251-1055
E-mail: lschachter@ppasearch.com
URL: http://www.ppasearch.com

Executive search firm specializing in the health and medical field.

★9857★ **Travcorps, Inc.**

40 Eastern Ave.
Malden, MA 02148
Ph: (781)322-2600   Fax: 800-803-1186
Fr: 800-343-3270
URL: http://www.travcorps.com

Places staff in temporary assignments. Other locations nationwide.

ONLINE JOB SOURCES AND SERVICES

★9858★ **Medhunters.com**
E-mail: info@medhunters.com
URL: http://www.medhunters.com

Description: Career search site for jobs in all health care specialties; educational resources; visa and licensing information for relocation; interesting articles; relocation tools; links to professional organizations and general resources.

★9859★ **ProHealthJobs**
E-mail: sales@prohealthjobs.com
URL: http://www.prohealthjobs.com

Description: Career resources site for the medical and health care field. Lists professional opportunities, product information, continuing education and open positions.

OTHER SOURCES

★9860★ **American Association for Leisure and Recreation (AALR)**

1900 Association Dr.
Reston, VA 20191-1598
Ph: (703)476-3472   Fax: (703)476-9527
Fr: 800-213-7193
E-mail: aalr@aahperd.org
URL: http://www.aahperd.org/aalr

Description: Mission is to promote and support education, leisure and recreation by developing quality programming and professional training; providing leadership opportunities; disseminating guidelines and standards; enhancing public understanding of the importance of leisure and recreation in maintaining a creative and healthy lifestyle. Goals and objectives are to serve as a forum for professionals, students and organizations to educate and exchange information and ideas on leisure and recreation services; develop and promote professional standards for education, leisure and recreation services; increase public awareness, understanding, appreciation, and support for lifelong education, leisure and recreation services; encourage professional training for all with an interest in education, leisure and recreation services; advance, encourage, conduct and publish scientific knowledge and research in the field of education, leisure, and recreation services.

★9861★ **American Health Care Association (AHCA)**

1201 L St. NW
Washington, DC 20005
Ph: (202)842-4444   Fax: (202)842-3860
URL: http://www.ahca.org

Description: Federation of state associations of long-term health care facilities. Promotes standards for professionals in long-term health care delivery and quality care for patients and residents in a safe environment. Focuses on issues of availability, quality, affordability, and fair payment. Operates as liaison with governmental agencies, Congress, and professional associations. Compiles statistics.

★9862★ **American Kinesiotherapy Association (AKTA)**

PO Box 1390
Hines, IL 60141-1390
Fr: 800-296-AKTA
E-mail: ccbkt@aol.com
URL: http://www.AKTA.org

Members: Professional society of kinesiotherapists, and associate and student members with interest in physical and mental rehabilitation and adapted physical education. (Kinesiology therapy is the application of scientifically-based exercise principles adapted to enhance the strength, endurance and mobility of individuals with functional limitations of those requiring extended physical reconditioning.) **Purpose:** Seeks to serve the interest of members and represent the profession to the public. Works to enhance the standard of care provided by kinesiotherapists through the promotion and provision of educational opportunities.

★9863★ American Therapeutic Recreation Association (ATRA)

1414 Prince St., Ste. 204
Alexandria, VA 22314
Ph: (703)683-9420   Fax: (703)683-9431
E-mail: atra@atra-tr.org
URL: http://www.atra-tr.org/atra.htm

Members: Therapeutic recreation professionals and students; interested others. (Therapeutic recreation is often referred to as recreational therapy and uses treatment modalities to improve the physical, mental, and emotional functions of persons with illnesses or disabling conditions.) **Purpose:** Promotes the use of therapeutic recreation in hospitals, mental rehabilitation centers, physical rehabilitation centers, senior citizen treatment centers, and other public health facilities. **Activities:** Conducts discussions on certification and legislative and regulatory concerns that affect the industry. Sponsors seminars and workshops; conducts research.

★9864★ Association on Higher Education and Disability (AHEAD)

PO Box 540666
Waltham, MA 02454
Ph: (781)788-0003   Fax: (781)788-0033
E-mail: ahead@ahead.org
URL: http://www.ahead.org.

Description: Individuals interested in promoting the equal rights and opportunities of disabled postsecondary students, staff, faculty, and graduates. Provides an exchange of communication for those professionally involved with disabled students; collects, evaluates, and disseminates information; encourages and supports legislation for the benefit of disabled students. Conducts surveys on issues pertinent to college students with disabilities; offers resource referral system and employment exchange for positions in disability student services. Conducts research programs; compiles statistics.

★9865★ Child Life Council (CLC)

11820 Parklawn Dr., Ste. 202
Rockville, MD 20852-2529
Ph: (301)881-7090   Fax: (301)881-7092
Fr: 800-CLC-4515

E-mail: clcstaff@childlife.org
URL: http://www.childlife.org

Members: Professional organization representing child life personnel, patient activities specialists, and students in the field. **Purpose:** Promotes psychological well-being and optimum development of children, adolescents, and their families in health care settings. **Activities:** Works to minimize the stress and anxiety of illness and hospitalization. Addresses professional issues such as program standards, competencies, and core curriculum. Provides resources and conducts research and educational programs. Offers a Job Bank Service listing employment openings.

★9866★ Exploring Health Occupations

Cambridge Educational
2572 Brunswick Ave.
Lawrenceville, NJ 08648-4128
Fax: 800-FAX-ON-US   Fr: 800-468-4227
URL: http://www.cambridgeeducational.com

Two videos. $139.95. 1999.

★9867★ Health Assessment & Treating Occupations

Delphi Productions
3160 4th St.
Boulder, CO 80304
Fax: (303)443-4022   Fr: 888-443-2400
URL: http://www.delphivideo.com

$95.00. 50 minutes. Part of the Careers for the 21st Century Video Library.

★9868★ Health Service Occupations

Delphi Productions
3160 4th St.
Boulder, CO 80304
Fax: (303)443-4022   Fr: 888-443-2400
URL: http://www.delphivideo.com

$95.00. 50 minutes. Part of the Careers for the 21st Century Video Library.

★9869★ Medicine & Related Occupations

Delphi Productions
3160 4th St.
Boulder, CO 80304
Fax: (303)443-4022   Fr: 888-443-2400
URL: http://www.delphivideo.com

$95.00. 45 minutes. Part of the Careers for the 21st Century Video Library.

★9870★ National Council for Therapeutic Recreation Certification (NCTRC)

7 Elmwood Dr.
New City, NY 10956
Ph: (845)639-1439   Fax: (845)639-1471
E-mail: nctrc@nctrc.org
URL: http://www.nctrc.org

Description: Objectives are to establish standards for certification and recertification of individuals who work in the therapeutic recreation field; grant recognition to individuals who voluntarily apply and meet established standards; monitor adherence to standards by certified personnel.

★9871★ National Rehabilitation Association (NRA)

633 S Washington St.
Alexandria, VA 22314
Ph: (703)836-0850   Fax: (703)836-0848
E-mail: info@nationalrehab.org
URL: http://www.nationalrehab.org/website/index.html

Description: Providing opportunities through knowledge and diversity for professionals in the fields of rehabilitation of people with disabilities.

★9872★ National Therapeutic Recreation Society (NTRS)

22377 Belmont Ridge Rd.
Ashburn, VA 20148-4501
Ph: (703)858-0784   Fax: (703)858-0794
Fr: 800-626-6772
E-mail: ntrsnrpa@nrpa.org
URL: http://www.nrpa.org/index.cfm?publicationid=21

Description: A branch of the National Recreation and Park Association. **Members:** Professionals, educators, and students involved in the provision of therapeutic recreation services for persons with disabilities in clinical and residential facilities and in the community. **Purpose:** Offers technical assistance services to agencies, institutions, and individuals.

Registered Nurses

★9873★ *AANA Journal*

AANA Publishing Inc.
222 S Prospect Ave.
Park Ridge, IL 60068
Ph: (847)692-7050   Fax: (847)692-7137

Bimonthly. $45.00/year; $10.00 for single issue. Nursing and anesthesia journal.

★9874★ *AAOHN Journal*

SLACK Inc.
6900 Grove Rd.
Thorofare, NJ 08086-9447
Ph: (856)848-1000   Fax: (856)853-5991
Fr: 800-257-8290
E-mail: aaohn@slackinc.com

Monthly. $79.00/year; $179.00/year for institutions; $19.00/year for single issue. Official journal of the American Association of Occupational Health Nurses.

★9875★ *AAOHN News*

American Association of Occupational
  Health Nurses Inc.
2920 Brandywine Rd., Ste. 100
Atlanta, GA 30341
Ph: (770)455-7757   Fax: (770)455-7271

Description: Monthly. Covers Association events as well as trends and legislation affecting occupational and enivornmental health nursing. Recurring features include news of research, a calendar of events, reports of meetings, news of educational opportunities, job listings, notices of publications available, resources for career-building, briefs on governmental issues concerning occupational and environment health, and a President's column.

★9876★ *ADVANCE for Nurse Practitioners*

Merion Publications Inc.
2900 Horizon Dr.
PO Box 61556
King of Prussia, PA 19406-0956
Ph: (610)278-1400
URL: http://www.advancefornp.com

Monthly. Free to qualified subscribers. For practicing nurse practitioner students with senior status.

★9877★ *Advances in Nursing Science*

Aspen Publishers Inc.
1185 Avenue of the Americas
New York, NY 10036
Ph: (212)597-0200   Fax: (212)597-0338
Fr: 800-234-1660
URL: http://www.lww.com

Quarterly. $81.95/year for individuals; $201.95/year for institutions; $101.95/year for other countries; $231.95/year for institutions, other countries. Academic medical journal focusing on nursing research and education.

★9878★ *Ambulatory Outreach*

Society for Ambulatory Care Professionals
1 N Franklin, 31st Fl.
Chicago, IL 60606
Fax: (312)422-4577

Quarterly. Subscription included in membership; $95.00/year for nonmembers. Professional journal for ambulatory care personnel.

★9879★ *American Family Physician*

American Academy of Family Physicians
11400 Tomahawk Creek Pkwy.
Leawood, KS 66211
Ph: (913)906-6000   Fax: (913)906-6080
Fr: 800-274-2237
E-mail: afpedit@aafp.org
URL: http://www.aafp.org/afp

Semimonthly. $95.00/year for individuals; $9.00 for single issue. Peer reviewed clinical journal for family physicians and others in primary care. Review articles detail the latest diagnostic and therapeutic techniques in the medical field. Department features in each

issue include "Tips from other Journals," CME credit opportunities and course calendar.

★9880★ *American Journal of Medicine*

Excerpta Medica Inc.
655 Avenue of the Americas
New York, NY 10010
Ph: (212)989-5800

Monthly. $66.00/year. Medical journal.

★9881★ *American Journal of Nursing*

American Journal of Nursing
c/o Lippincott, Williams, & Wilkins
530 Walnut
Philadelphia, PA 19106
Fr: 800-627-0484
URL: http://www.nursingcenter.com

Monthly. $29.95/year. Journal for staff nurses, nurse managers, and clinical nurse specialists. Focuses on patient care in hospitals, hospital ICUs and homes. Provides news coverage of health care from the nursing perspective.

★9882★ *The American Nurse*

American Nurses Association
600 Maryland Ave. SW, Ste. 100 W
Washington, DC 20024-2571
Ph: (202)651-7000   Fax: (202)651-7000
Fr: 800-284-2378
E-mail: adsales@anan.org

$10.00/year for students; $20.00/year for nonmembers; $30.00/year for other countries. Newspaper (tabloid) for the nursing profession.

★9883★ *AORN Journal*

AORN Inc.
2170 S Parker Rd., Ste. 300
Denver, CO 80231-5711
Ph: (303)755-6300   Fax: (303)750-3441
Fr: 800-755-AORN
E-mail: nkuehl@aorn.org
URL: http://www.aorn.org

Monthly. $80.00/year for nonmembers. Journal for perioperative nurses.

★9884★ Cancer Nursing
Lippincott Williams & Wilkins
530 Walnut St.
Philadelphia, PA 19106
Ph: (215)521-8300   Fax: (215)521-8902
Fr: 800-638-3030
E-mail: ashcr@nursing.ufl.edu
URL: http://www.cancernursingonline.com/

Bimonthly. $82.95/year for individuals; $122.95/year for other countries; $192.95/year for institutions; $222.95/year for institutions, other countries. Medical journal covering problems arising in the care and support of cancer patients.

★9885★ Clinical Nurse Specialist
Lippincott Williams & Wilkins
530 Walnut St.
Philadelphia, PA 19106-3621
Ph: (215)521-8300   Fax: (215)521-8483
E-mail: info@nacns.org

Bimonthly. $100.00/year for individuals; $142.00/year for institutions. Nursing journal.

★9886★ Critical Care Medicine
Lippincott Williams & Wilkins
530 Walnut St.
Philadelphia, PA 19106
Ph: (215)521-8300   Fax: (215)521-8902
Fr: 800-638-3030
E-mail: jewers@lww.com
URL: http://www.ccmjournal.com/

Monthly. $244.00/year for individuals; $379.00/year for institutions; $451.00/year for institutions, other countries; $315.00/year for out of country. Interdisciplinary journal for ICU and CCU specialists.

★9887★ Critical Care Nurse
Critical Care Nurse
101 Columbia
Aliso Viejo, CA 92656
Ph: (949)362-2000   Fax: (949)362-2049
Fr: 800-899-1712
E-mail: cntnurse@aol.com

Bimonthly. $30.00/year; $8.00 for single issue. Nursing journal.

★9888★ Dialysis & Transplantation
Creative Age Publications Inc.
7628 Densmore Ave.
Van Nuys, CA 91406-2042
Ph: (818)782-7328   Fax: (818)782-7450
Fr: 800-442-5667
URL: http://www.eneph.com

Monthly. $35.00/year for individuals; $105.00/year for other countries. Multi-disciplinary, peer-reviewed journal on clinical applications in dialysis, transplantation and nephrology for renal-care team.

★9889★ Emergency Medical Services
Summer Communications Inc.
7626 Densmore Ave.
Van Nuys, CA 91406-2042
Ph: (818)786-4367   Fax: (818)786-9246
Fr: 800-224-4367

E-mail: emsmag@earthlink.net
URL: http://www.emsmagazine.com

Monthly. $19.95/year for individuals. Magazine covering emergency care, rescue and transportation.

★9890★ Fertility and Sterility
The American Society for Productive Medicine
1209 Montgomery Hwy.
Birmingham, AL 35216
Ph: (205)978-5000   Fax: (205)978-5005

Monthly. $110.00/year for individuals; $175.00/year for institutions. Medical journal covering all aspects of reproductive medicine.

★9891★ Geriatric Nursing
Mosby Inc.
10801 Executive Center Dr., Ste. 509
Little Rock, AR 72211
Ph: (501)223-5165   Fax: (501)223-0519
URL: http://www.mosby.com/gerinurs

Bimonthly. $54.00/year for individuals; $105.00/year for institutions. Magazine for nurses in geriatric and gerontologic nursing practice, the primary professional providers of care for the aging. Provides news on issues affecting elders and clinical information on techniques and procedures.

★9892★ Health Care Weekly Review
The Martin Group Inc.
24901 Northwestern Hwy., Ste. 316A
Southfield, MI 48075
Ph: (248)440-6080   Fax: (248)352-4801
E-mail: hcwr@compuserve.com

Weekly. $48.00/year for individuals. Professional newspaper covering the health care industry.

★9893★ Health Education Reports
Chester Associates Inc.
4401-A Connecticut Ave. NW, PMB 212
Washington, DC 20008
Ph: (703)960-6859   Fax: (703)960-0189

Description: Biweekly. Focuses on developments relating to public health and wellness programs and government health policy. Covers activities at Centers for Disease Control around the U.S. and subjects such as health promotion, disease prevention, and medical studies. Recurring features include interviews, news of educational opportunities, job listings, book reviews and notices of publications available, reports of meetings, and a calendar of events.

★9894★ Health Progress
Catholic Health Association of the United States
4455 Woodson Rd.
St. Louis, MO 63134-3797
Ph: (314)427-2500   Fax: (314)253-3540
E-mail: hpeditor@chausa.org
URL: http://www.chausa.org

Free to qualified subscribers; free to subscribers from CHA; $50.00/year for individuals; $60.00/year for other countries; $10.00 for single issue. Magazine for administrative-level and other managerial personnel in Catholic healthcare and related organizations. Featured are articles on management concepts, legislative and regulatory trends, and theological, sociological, ethical, legal, and technical issues.

★9895★ Heart and Lung
Mosby Inc.
Curtis Ctr., 3rd Fl.
170 S. Independence Mall W
Philadelphia, PA 19106-3399
Ph: (215)238-7800
URL: http://www.mosby.com/hrtlng

Bimonthly. $66.00/year for individuals; $217.00/year for institutions. Journal offering articles prepared by nurse and physician members of the critical care team, recognizing the nurse's role in the care and management of major organ-system conditions in critically ill patients.

★9896★ Home Healthcare Nurse
Lippincott Williams & Wilkins
530 Walnut St.
Philadelphia, PA 19106
Ph: (215)521-8300   Fax: (215)521-8902
Fr: 800-638-3030
E-mail: hhnedit@bellsouth.net
URL: http://www.homehealthcarenurseonline.com/

Monthly. $49.95/year for individuals; $198.95/year for institutions; $102.95/year for other countries; $232.95/year for institutions, other countries. Magazine for the practicing professional nurse working in the home health, community health, and public health areas.

★9897★ HomeCare Magazine
Miramar Communications Inc.
23805 Stuart Ranch Rd., Ste. 235
PO Box 8987
Malibu, CA 90265-8987
Ph: (310)317-4522   Fax: (310)317-0264
Fr: 800-543-4116
URL: http://www.homecaremag.com

Monthly. Magazine serving home medical equipment suppliers, including independent and chain centers specializing in home care, pharmacies or chain drug stores with home care products, and joint-ventured hospital home health care businesses. Contains industry news and new product launches and marketing strategies.

★9898★ Hospitals & Health Networks
Health Forum L.L.C.
One N Franklin
Chicago, IL 60606
Ph: (312)893-6800   Fax: (312)422-4600
Fr: 800-621-6902
E-mail: hhn@healthforum.com
URL: http://www.hhnmag.com

Monthly. Publication covering the health care industry.

★9899★ *Imprint*

National Student Nurses' Association
45 Main St., Ste. 606
Brooklyn, NY 11201
Ph: (718)210-0705   Fax: (718)210-0710
E-mail: nsna@nsna.org

$15.00/year, non-members; $29.00/year for two years, non-members. Magazine for nursing students, focusing on issues and trends in nursing.

★9900★ *The Journal of Continuing Education in Nursing*

SLACK Inc.
6900 Grove Rd.
Thorofare, NJ 08086-9447
Ph: (856)848-1000   Fax: (856)853-5991
Fr: 800-257-8290
E-mail: jcen@slackinc.com

Bimonthly. $69.00/year for individuals; $139.00/year for institutions, add 7% Canada; $40.00/year for other countries. Journal for nurses involved in planning and implementing educational programs for the practitioner and others in patient care.

★9901★ *Journal of Emergency Nursing*

Mosby Inc.
The Curtis Ctr., 3rd Fl.
Independence Sq. W
Philadelphia, PA 19106-3399
Ph: (215)235-7800   Fax: (215)238-7883
Fr: 800-523-1649
URL: http://www.mosby.com/jen

Bimonthly. $66.00/year for individuals; $218.00/year for institutions; $33.00/year for students; $85.00/year for individuals, out of country; $240.00/year for institutions, other countries; $43.00/year for students, other countries. Journal containing peer-reviewed articles on clinical aspects of emergency care by, and for, emergency nurses. Presents information about professional, political, administrative, and educational aspects of emergency nursing and nursing in general.

★9902★ *Journal of Gerontological Nursing*

SLACK Inc.
6900 Grove Rd.
Thorofare, NJ 08086-9447
Ph: (856)848-1000   Fax: (856)853-5991
Fr: 800-257-8290
E-mail: jgn@slackinc.com

Monthly. $59.00/year; $109.00/year for institutions; $19.00/year for single issue. Gerontological nursing journal.

★9903★ *Journal of Intensive Care Medicine*

Sage Publications Inc.
2455 Teller Rd.
Thousand Oaks, CA 91320
Ph: (805)499-0721   Fax: (805)499-0871
Fr: 800-818-SAGE
E-mail: advertising@sagepub.com
URL: http://www.sagepub.com/journal.aspx?pid=340

Bimonthly. $198.00/year for individuals; $198.00/year for out of country; $520.00/year for institutions; $520.00/year for institutions, other countries. Medical journal for specialists working in intensive care units.

★9904★ *Journal of Intravenous Nursing*

Lippincott Williams & Wilkins
530 Walnut St.
Philadelphia, PA 19106
Ph: (215)521-8300   Fax: (215)521-8902
Fr: 800-638-3030
URL: http://www.lww.com

Bimonthly. $103.00/year for individuals; $160.00/year for institutions. Journal publishing I.V.-related articles, studies, reports, and reviews fro the continuing education of professionals in I.V. therapy. Includes correspondence, book reviews, and news of the Intravenous Nurse Society.

★9905★ *Journal of the National Medical Association*

National Medical Association
1012 10th St. NW
Washington, DC 20001
Ph: (202)347-1895   Fax: (202)207-1555
URL: http://www.nmanet.org

Monthly. $116.00/year for individuals; $155.00/year for institutions; $16.00 for single issue. Journal on specialized clinical research related to the health problems of African-Americans and other minorities. Recognizes significant contributions by black physicians and others involved with minority health issues and health disparities.

★9906★ *Journal of Nursing Administration (JONA)*

Lippincott Williams & Wilkins
530 Walnut St.
Philadelphia, PA 19106
Ph: (215)521-8300   Fax: (215)521-8902
Fr: 800-638-3030
URL: http://jonajournal.com/

$91.95/year for individuals; $299.95/year for institutions; $161.95/year for other countries; $391.95/year for institutions, other countries. Journal covering developments and advances in nursing administration and management.

★9907★ *Journal of Nursing Scholarship*

Sigma Theta Tau International Honor Society of Nursing
550 W N St.
Indianapolis, IN 46202
Ph: (317)634-8171   Fax: (317)634-8188
Fr: 888-634-7575

Quarterly. $39.00/year for individuals; $20.00 for single issue; $63.00/year for institutions; $81.00/year for out of country. Peer-reviewed journal covering nursing.

★9908★ *Journal of Obstetric, Gynecologic and Neonatal Nursing (JOGNN)*

Sage Publications Inc.
2455 Teller Rd.
Thousand Oaks, CA 91320
Ph: (805)499-0721   Fax: (805)499-0871
Fr: 800-818-SAGE
E-mail: advertising@sagepub.com
URL: http://jognn.awhonn.org/

Bimonthly. $83.00/year for individuals; $165.00/year for out of country; $546.00/year for institutions; $596.00/year for institutions, other countries. Journal covering trends, policies, and research. Official publication of the Association of Women's Health, Obstetric, and Neonatal Nurses (AWHONN).

★9909★ *Journal of Pediatric Health Care*

Mosby Inc.
Curtis Ctr., 3rd Fl.
170 Independence Mall W
Philadelphia, PA 19106-3399
Ph: (215)238-7800
URL: http://www.mosby.com/pedhc

Bimonthly. $70.00/year for individuals; $158.00/year for institutions. Official publication of the National Association of Pediatric Nurse Practitioners. Provides current information on pediatric clinical topics as well as research studies, health policy, and legislative issues applicable to pediatric clinical practice.

★9910★ *Journal of Psychosocial Nursing and Mental Health Services*

SLACK Inc.
6900 Grove Rd.
Thorofare, NJ 08086-9447
Ph: (856)848-1000   Fax: (856)853-5991
Fr: 800-257-8290
E-mail: jpn@slackinc.com

Monthly. $49.00/year; $74.00/year for institutions; $19.00/year for single issue. Journal presenting original, peer-reviewed articles on psychiatric/mental health nursing.

★9911★ *Journal of Trauma Nursing*

Nursecom Inc.
1211 Locust St.
Philadelphia, PA 19107-5409
Ph: (215)545-7222   Fax: (215)545-8107
Fr: 800-242-6757

Quarterly. Professional publication covering nursing.

★9912★ McKnight's Long-Term Care News

McKnight's Long-Term Care News
Two Northfield Plz., Ste. 300
Northfield, IL 60093-1219
Ph: (847)784-8706   Fax: (847)441-3701
E-mail: ltcnews@medec.com

Monthly. Free to qualified subscribers in
U.S.; $5.00/year for single issue; $9.00 for
single back issue; $54.95/year for Canada;
$59.95/year, foreign. Professional magazine.

★9913★ MCN, The American Journal of Maternal/Child Nursing

Lippincott Williams & Wilkins
530 Walnut St.
Philadelphia, PA 19106
Ph: (215)521-8300   Fax: (215)521-8902
Fr: 800-638-3030
URL: http://www.mcnjournal.com/

Bimonthly. $41.95/year for individuals;
$111.95/year for institutions; $81.95/year for
other countries; $131.95/year for institutions,
other countries. Journal focusing on mater-
nal/child nursing and health.

★9914★ Military Medicine

Association of Military Surgeons of the
 U.S. (AMSUS)
9320 Old Georgetown Rd.
Bethesda, MD 20814
Ph: (301)897-8800   Fax: (301)530-5446
Fr: 800-761-9320
E-mail: milmed@amsus.org

Monthly. $65.00/year for individuals; $70.00/
year for other countries; $6.00 for single
issue. Journal for professional personnel
affiliated with the Federal medical services.

★9915★ Minority Nurse Newsletter

Tucker Publications Inc.
PO Box 580
Lisle, IL 60532-0580
Ph: (630)969-3809   Fax: (630)969-3895
E-mail: sallen@tuckerpub.com

Description: Quarterly. Provides health
care information of interest to minority nursing faculty.

★9916★ Modern Healthcare

Crain Communications Inc.
360 N Michigan Ave.
Chicago, IL 60601
Ph: (312)649-5200   Fax: (312)280-3174
Fr: 800-678-2724
E-mail: mhcedit@crain.com
URL: http://www.modernhealthcare.com

Weekly. $135.00/year. Weekly Business
news magazine for Healthcare Management

★9917★ Nephrology Nursing Journal

American Nephrology Nurses' Association
E Holly Ave.
Box 56
Pitman, NJ 08071-0056
Ph: (856)589-2300   Fax: (856)589-7463

E-mail: anjrnl@mail.ajj.com

Bimonthly. $5.00 for single issue; $28.00/
year; $40.00/year. Nursing journal.

★9918★ The New England Journal of Medicine

The New England Journal of Medicine
860 Winter St.
Waltham Woods Corporate Ctr.
Waltham, MA 02451-1441
Ph: (781)893-4610
E-mail: nejmcust@mms.org
URL: http://www.nejm.org

Weekly. $135.00/year for individuals. Jour-
nal for the medical profession.

★9919★ Nurse Educator

Lippincott Williams & Wilkins
530 Walnut St.
Philadelphia, PA 19106
Ph: (215)521-8300   Fax: (215)521-8902
Fr: 800-638-3030
URL: http://www.nurseeducatoronline.com/

Bimonthly. $87.95/year for individuals;
$201.95/year for institutions; $151.95/year
for other countries; $261.95/year for institu-
tions, other countries. Journal for nursing
educators.

★9920★ The Nurse Practitioner

Lippincott Williams & Wilkins
1111 Bethlehem Pke.
PO Box 908
Springhouse, PA 19477
Ph: 800-346-7844   Fax: (215)646-1083
Fr: 800-346-7844
URL: http://www.tnpj.com

Monthly. $50.00/year; $83.00/year for institutions; $67.00/year for Canada; $98.00/year
for institutions in Canada; $104.00/year,
international. Magazine presenting clinical
information to nurses in advanced primary
care practice. Also covers legal, business,
economic, ethical, research, and pharmaceutical issues.

★9921★ Nurse Practitioner Forum

Elsevier Science Inc.
The Curtis Ctr.
170 Independence Mall W, 300F
Philadelphia, PA 19106-3399
Ph: (215)238-7800   Fax: (215)238-7883
Fr: 800-523-1649

Quarterly. $49.00/year for individuals;
$42.00/year for students; $76.00/year for
institutions; $106.00/year for out of country.
Journal for nurse practitioners.

★9922★ Nursing Economics

Jannetti Publications Inc.
E Holly Ave.
Box 56
Pitman, NJ 08071-0056
Ph: (856)256-2300   Fax: (856)589-7463
E-mail: nejrnl@ajj.com

Bimonthly. $49.00/year; $85.00/year for in-

stitutions; $10.00/year for single issue. Busi-
ness magazine for nursing administrators.

★9923★ Nursing Education Perspectives

National League for Nursing Press
61 Broadway, 33rd Fl.
New York, NY 10006-2701
Ph: (212)363-5555   Fr: 800-669-1656
URL: http://www.nln.org

Free to qualified subscribers; $60.00/year
$90.00/year, libraries and institutions. Pro-
fessional journal for nurses. Includes articles
on health policy, social and economic issues
affecting health care, and nursing education
and practice.

★9924★ Nursing Management

Spring House
434 W Downer Pl.
Aurora, IL 60506
Ph: (630)844-6911   Fr: 800-950-0879

Monthly. $25.00/year for individuals. Maga-
zine focusing on nursing management.

★9925★ Nursing 96

Lippincott Williams & Wilkins
530 Walnut St.
Philadelphia, PA 19106
Ph: (215)521-8300   Fax: (215)521-8902
Fr: 800-638-3030
E-mail: nursing@springnet.com

Monthly. $42.00/year for individuals; $4.00
for single issue. Practical journal for nurses.
Includes special sections for hospital critical-
care and home health.

★9926★ Nursing Outlook

Mosby Inc.
10801 Executive Center Dr., Ste. 509
Little Rock, AR 72211
Ph: (501)223-5165   Fax: (501)223-0519
URL: http://www.mosby.com

Bimonthly. $57.00/year for individuals;
$106.00/year for institutions. Official journal
of the American Academy of Nursing, reporting on trends and issues in nursing.

★9927★ Ob Gyn News

International Medical News Group
60 Columbia Rd., Bldg. B
Morristown, NJ 07960
Ph: (973)290-8200   Fax: (973)290-8245
E-mail: obnews@imng.com

Semimonthly. Obstetrics and gynecology
tabloid distributed to obstetricians and gynecologists.

★9928★ Oncology
S. Karger Publishers Inc.
26 W Avon Rd.
PO Box 529
Farmington, CT 06085
Ph: (860)675-7834   Fax: (860)675-7302
Fr: 800-828-5479

$1328.00/year for institutions, add $50.40 post/handling for foreign; $1434.00/year for institutions, print and online combined; $664.00/year for individuals, add $40.40 post/handling for foreign; $724.00/year for individuals, print and online combined. Medical journal presenting experimental and clinical findings.

★9929★ Orthopaedic Nursing
National Association of Orthopaedic Nurses
E Holly Ave. Box 56
Pitman, NJ 08071-0056
Ph: (609)256-2310   Fax: (609)589-7463
E-mail: onjrnl@mail
URL: http://www.inurse.com~naon

Bimonthly. $28.00/year; $40.00/year for institutions; $5.00/year for single issue. Nursing magazine.

★9930★ Pediatric Nursing
Jannetti Publications Inc.
E Holly Ave.
Box 56
Pitman, NJ 08071-0056
Ph: (856)256-2300   Fax: (856)589-7463
E-mail: adver@ajj.com
URL: http://www.pediatricnursing.net

Bimonthly. $38.00/year; $47.00/year for institutions; $6.00/year for single issue. Professional nursing magazine.

★9931★ Physician Assistant
Smith Publications
105 Raider Blvd.
Belle Mead, NJ 08502
Ph: (908)874-8550   Fax: (908)874-0700

Monthly. $50.00/year; $60.00/year for institutions; $28.00/year for students; $75.00/year for other countries. Medical journal covering primary care, clinical medicine, and other professional and medical topics.

★9932★ Provider
American Health Care Association
1201 L St. NW
Washington, DC 20005
Ph: (202)842-4444   Fax: (202)842-3860
Fr: 800-321-4444
E-mail: provider@ahca.org

Monthly. $48.00/year for nonmembers. Provider Magazine.

★9933★ Rehabilitation Nursing
Rehabilitation Nursing
4700 W Lake Ave.
Glenview, IL 60025
Ph: (847)375-4710   Fax: 877-734-9384
Fr: 800-229-7530

E-mail: info@rehabnurse.org

Bimonthly. $95.00/year for individuals; $125.00/year for institutions; $135.00/year for other countries; $18.00 for single issue; $125.00/year for Canada. Magazine focusing on rehabilitation nursing involving clinical practice, research, education, and administration.

★9934★ Research in Healthcare Financial Management
International Society for Research in Healthcare Financial Management Ltd.
305 W Chesapeake Ave.
CSBA Ste. L-096
Towson, MD 21204

Annual. Publication covering issues in the healthcare industry.

★9935★ Research in Nursing & Health
John Wiley and Sons Inc.
111 River St.
Hoboken, NJ 07030
Ph: (201)748-8866   Fax: (201)748-8824

Bimonthly. $115.00/year for U.S.; $115.00/year for Canada and Mexico; $151.00/year for other countries. Journal providing forum for research in the areas of nursing practice, education, and administration. Covers health issues relevant to nursing as well as investigations of the applications of research findings in clinical settings.

★9936★ RN
Thomson Medical Economics
5 Paragon Dr.
Montvale, NJ 07645-1742
Ph: (201)358-7200   Fax: (201)722-2680
URL: http://www.medec.com/html/products/productdetail/rn_mag.html

Monthly. $35.00/year for individuals; $50.00/year for Canada; $50.00/year for other countries. Clinical journal for registered nurses.

★9937★ Seminars in Oncology
Elsevier Science Inc.
The Curtis Ctr.
170 Independence Mall W, 300F
Philadelphia, PA 19106-3399
Ph: (215)238-7800   Fax: (215)238-7883
Fr: 800-523-1649
E-mail: elspcs@elsevier.com

$199.00/year for individuals; $318.00/year for institutions; $295.00/year for other countries; $382.00/year for institutions, other countries; $100.00/year for students, US students and residents; $64.00 for single issue. Journal reviewing current diagnostic and treatment techniques used in oncology patient care.

PLACEMENT AND JOB REFERRAL SERVICES

★9938★ American Association of Occupational Health Nurses (AAOHN)
2920 Brandy Wine Rd., Ste. 100
Atlanta, GA 30341
Ph: (770)455-7757   Fax: (770)455-7271
URL: http://www.aaohn.org

Description: Registered professional nurses employed by business and industrial firms; nurse educators, nurse editors, nurse writers, and others interested in occupational health nursing. Promotes and sets standards for the profession. Provides and approves continuing education; maintains governmental affairs program; offers placement service.

★9939★ American College of Nurse-Midwives (ACNM)
818 Connecticut Ave. NW, Ste. 900
Washington, DC 20006
Ph: (202)728-9860   Fax: (202)728-9897
E-mail: info@acnm.org
URL: http://www.midwife.org

Description: Seeks to develop and support the profession of certified nurse-midwives in order to promote the health and well-being of women and infants within their families and communities. A CNM is a licensed health care practitioner educated in the two disciplines of nursing and midwifery. Provides gynecological services and care of mothers and babies throughout the maternity cycle; members have completed an ACNM accredited program of study and clinical experience in midwifery and passed a national certification exam. Cooperates with allied groups to enable nurse-midwives to concentrate their efforts in the improvement of services for mothers and newborn babies. Seeks to identify areas of nurse-midwifery practices as they relate to the total service and educational aspects of maternal and newborn care. Studies and evaluates activities of nurse-midwives in order to establish qualifications; cooperates in planning and developing educational programs. conducts research and continuing education workshops. sponsors research. Compiles statistics. Maintains speakers' bureau and archives; offers placement service.

★9940★ American Organization of Nurse Executives (AONE)
325 Seventh St. NW
Washington, DC 20004
Ph: (202)626-2240   Fax: (202)638-5499
E-mail: aone@aha.org
URL: http://www.aone.org

Description: Provides leadership, professional development, advocacy, and research to advance nursing practice and patient care, promote nursing leadership and excellence, and shape healthcare public policy. Supports and enhances the management, leadership, educational, and professional development of nursing leaders. Offers placement service through Career Development and Referral Center.

★9941★ American Public Health Association (APHA)

800 I St. NW
Washington, DC 20001-3710
Ph: (202)777-2742   Fax: (202)777-2534
E-mail: comments@apha.org
URL: http://www.apha.org

Members: Professional organization of physicians, nurses, educators, academicians, environmentalists, epidemiologists, new professionals, social workers, health administrators, optometrists, podiatrists, pharmacists, dentists, nutritionists, health planners, other community and mental health specialists, and interested consumers. **Purpose:** Seeks to protect and promote personal, mental, and environmental health. **Activities:** Services include promulgation of standards; establishment of uniform practices and procedures; development of the etiology of communicable diseases; research in public health; exploration of medical care programs and their relationships to public health. Sponsors job placement service.

★9942★ Association of Black Nursing Faculty (ABNF)

5823 Queens Cove
Lisle, IL 60532
Ph: (630)969-3809   Fax: (630)969-3895
E-mail: stewarth@wt.net

Members: Black nursing faculty teaching in nursing programs accredited by the National League for Nursing. **Purpose:** Works to promote health-related issues and educational concerns of interest to the black community and ABNF. **Activities:** Serves as a forum for communication and the exchange of information among members; develops strategies for expressing concerns to other individuals, institutions, and communities. Assists members in professional development; develops and sponsors continuing education activities; fosters networking and guidance in employment and recruitment activities. Promotes health-related issues of legislation, government programs, and community activities. Supports black consumer advocacy issues. Encourages research. Maintains speakers' bureau and hall of fame. Offers charitable program and placement services. Compiles statistics. Is establishing a computer-assisted job bank; plans to develop bibliographies related to research groups.

EMPLOYER DIRECTORIES AND NETWORKING LISTS

★9943★ AHA Guide to the Health Care Field

American Hospital Association (AHA)
1 N. Franklin St., 27th Fl.
Chicago, IL 60606
Ph: (312)422-2050   Fax: (312)422-4700
Fr: 800-424-4301

Annual, August. $295.00. Covers hospitals, networks, multi-health care systems, free-standing ambulatory surgery centers, psychiatric facilities, long-term care facilities, substance abuse programs, and other health-related organizations. Entries include: For hospitals-Facility name, address, phone, administrator's name, number of beds, facilities and services, number of employees, expenses, other statistics. For other organizations-Name, address, phone, fax, name and title of contact. Arrangement: Geographical. Indexes: Hospital name.

★9944★ American Group Psychotherapy Association-Membership Directory

American Group Psychotherapy Association Inc.
25 E 21st St., 6th Fl.
New York, NY 10023
Ph: (212)477-2677   Fax: (212)979-6627
Fr: 877-668-AGPA

Biennial, fall. $90.00. Covers 4,500 physicians, psychologists, clinical social workers, psychiatric nurses, and other mental health professionals interested in treatment of emotional problems by group methods. Entries include: Name, office or home address, highest degree held, office or home phone number. Arrangement: Alphabetical. Indexes: Geographical.

★9945★ American Journal of Nursing-Career Guide

American Journal of Nursing
c/o Lippincott, Williams, & Wilkins
530 Walnut St.
Philadelphia, PA 19106-3621
Ph: (215)521-8300   Fax: (215)521-8902
Fr: 800-627-0484
URL: http://www.nursingcenter.com

Annual, April. $13.95. Publication includes: List of nursing organizations and agencies. Entries include: Name, address, names of officers or nursing representative. Arrangement: Classified by type of organization.

★9946★ CriticalCare Choices

Springhouse Office of Lippincott, Williams & Wilkins
PO Box 908
Spring House, PA 19477-0908
Ph: (215)646-8700   Fax: (215)646-4399
Fr: 800-346-7844
URL: http://www.nursingcenter.com

Annual, May. Clinical and career directory

for critical care nurses. Covers non-profit and investor-owned hospitals and departments of the United States government that hire critical care nurses. Arrangement: Geographical. Indexes: Geographical.

★9947★ Directory of Child Life Programs

Child Life Council Inc.
11820 Parklawn Dr., Ste. 202
Rockville, MD 20852-2529
Ph: (301)881-7090   Fax: (301)881-7092
URL: http://www.childlife.org/

Biennial. $15.00 for members; $20.00 for nonmembers. Covers over 400 child life programs. Entries include: Facility name, address, phone, name of child life department and director, reporting structure, staff statistics, educational requirements for employment, and internship or educational opportunities. Arrangement: Geographical. Indexes: Speciality areas, internship sessions, program size, fellowships.

★9948★ Directory of Hospital Personnel

Thomson Medical Economics
5 Paragon Dr.
Montvale, NJ 07645-1742
Ph: (201)358-7200   Fax: (201)722-2680

Annual, November. $325.00. Covers 200,000 executives at 7,000 U.S. hospitals. Entries include: Name of hospital, address, phone, number of beds, type and JCAHO status of hospital, names and titles of key department heads and staff, medical and nursing school affiliations; number of residents, interns, and nursing students. Arrangement: Geographical. Indexes: Hospital name, personnel, hospital size.

★9949★ Essentials of Internet Use in Nursing

Springer Publishing Co. Inc.
536 Broadway
New York, NY 10012
Ph: (212)431-4370   Fax: (212)941-7842
Fr: 877-687-7476

$32.95. Publication includes: Appendix listing relevant web sites. Principal content of publication is information on Internet usage for clinical nursing practice, for continuing nursing education, for medical research, and for nursing staff recruitment and development. Indexes: Topical.

★9950★ Hitting the Road: A Guide to Travel Nursing

Lippincott Williams & Wilkins
530 Walnut St.
Philadelphia, PA 19106-3621
Ph: (215)521-8300   Fax: (215)521-8902
Fr: 800-638-3030

$25.95. Publication includes: List of 70 health care staffing agencies. Principal content of publication is discussion of and assistance in entering field of travel nursing.

★9951★ **Hospital Blue Book**
Billian/Transworld Publishing Inc.
2100 Powers Ferry Rd.
Ste. 300
Atlanta, GA 30339
Ph: (770)955-8484   Fax: (770)955-8485
Fr: 800-533-8484
E-mail: blu-book@billian.com

Annual, January. $285.00 for national edition; $160.00 for southern edition. Covers more than 6,687 hospitals; some listings also appear in a separate southern edition of this publication. Entries include: Name of hospital, accreditation, mailing address, phone, fax, number of beds, type of facility (nonprofit, general, state, etc.); list of administrative personnel and chiefs of medical services, with specific titles. Arrangement: Geographical.

★9952★ **How to Survive and Maybe Even Love Nursing School!**
F.A. Davis Co.
1915 Arch St.
Philadelphia, PA 19103
Ph: (215)368-2270   Fax: (215)568-5065
Fr: 800-523-4049

$19.95. Publication includes: List of resources for nursing students such as web sites and organizations. Principal content of publication is information about succeeding in nursing school.

★9953★ **The JobBank Guide to Health Care Companies**
Adams Media Corp.
57 Littlefield St.
Avon, MA 02322
Ph: (508)427-7100   Fax: (508)427-6790
Fr: 800-872-5627

$17.95. Covers Jobs nationwide in health care companies. Entries include: Firm or organization name, address, phone, name and title of contact; description of organization, headquarters location, typical titles for entry- and middle-level positions, educational backgrounds desired, fringe benefits offered, stock exchange listing, training programs, internships, parent company, number of employees, revenues, e-mail and web address, projected number of hires. Indexes: Alphabetical.

★9954★ **Medical and Health Information Directory**
Thomson Gale
27500 Drake Rd.
Farmington Hills, MI 48331-3535
Ph: (248)699-4253   Fax: (248)699-8065
Fr: 800-877-GALE
E-mail: businessproducts@gale.com

Annual. $285.00 per volume; $675.00 per set. Covers in Volume 1, more than 26,500 medical and health oriented associations, organizations, institutions, and government agencies, including health maintenance organizations (HMOs), preferred provider organizations (PPOs), insurance companies, pharmaceutical companies, research centers, and medical and allied health schools.

In Volume 2, over 12,000 medical book publishers; medical periodicals, directories, audiovisual producers and services, medical libraries and information centers, electronic resources, and health-related internet search engines. In Volume 3, more than 35,500 clinics, treatment centers, care programs, and counseling/diagnostic services for 34 subject areas. Entries include: Institution, service, or firm name, address, phone, fax, email and URL; many include names of key personnel and, when pertinent, descriptive annotation. Volume 3 was formerly listed separately as Health Services Directory. Arrangement: Classified by organization activity, service, etc. Indexes: Each volume has a complete alphabetical name and keyword index.

★9955★ **Nurses and Nurses' Registries Directory**
infoUSA Inc.
5711 S 86th Cir.
Omaha, NE 68127-0347
Ph: (402)930-3500   Fax: (402)331-0176
Fr: 800-555-6124
URL: http://www.abii.com

Annual. Number of listings: 10,949. Entries include: Name, address, phone (including area code), size of advertisement, year first in "Yellow Pages," name of owner or manager, number of employees. Compiled from telephone company "Yellow Pages," nationwide. Arrangement: Geographical.

★9956★ **Nursing Career Directory**
Springhouse Office of Lippincott, Williams & Wilkins
PO Box 908
Spring House, PA 19477-0908
Ph: (215)646-8700   Fax: (215)646-4399
Fr: 800-346-7844
URL: http://www.springnet.com

Annual, January. $10.00. Covers nonprofit and investor-owned hospitals and departments of the United States government which hire nurses. Does not report specific positions available. Entries include: Unit name, location, areas of nursing specialization, educational requirements for nurses, licensing, facilities, benefits, etc. Arrangement: Geographical. Indexes: Geographical.

★9957★ **The Nursing Job Search Handbook**
University of Pennsylvania Press
4200 Pine St.
Philadelphia, PA 19104-4011
Ph: (215)898-6261   Fax: (215)898-0404
Fr: 800-445-9880

$17.95. Publication includes: Appendix listing state licensing boards and nursing organizations. Entries include: Name, address, phone. Principal content of publication is information on obtaining a job in the field of nursing. Indexes: Alphabetical.

★9958★ **Peterson's Guide to Nursing Programs**
Thomson Peterson's
Princeton Pke. Corporate Ctr., 2000 Lenox Dr.
PO Box 67005
Lawrenceville, NJ 08648
Ph: (609)896-1800   Fax: (609)896-4531
Fr: 800-338-3282

Annual, latest edition 2002. $26.95. Covers over 700 institutions offering approximately 2,000 accredited nursing programs in the U.S. and Canada. Entries include: Academic information, extracurricular issues, costs, financial aid.

★9959★ **Peterson's Job Opportunities for Health and Science Majors**
Thomson Peterson's
Princeton Pke. Corporate Ctr., 2000 Lenox Dr.
PO Box 67005
Lawrenceville, NJ 08648
Ph: (609)896-1800   Fax: (609)896-4531
Fr: 800-338-3282
URL: http://www.petersons.com

Irregular, latest edition 1999. $18.95. Covers approximately 1,300 research, consulting, government, and non-profit and profit service organizations that hire college and university graduates in science and health-related majors. Entries include: Organization name, address, phone, name and title of contact, type of organization, number of employees, Standard Industrial Classification (SIC) code; description of opportunities available including disciplines, level of education required, starting locations and salaries, level of experience accepted, benefits.

HANDBOOKS AND MANUALS

★9960★ **Anatomy of a Job Search: A Nurse's Guide to Finding and Landing the Job You Want**
Springhouse Corporation
P.O. Box 908
Springhouse, PA 19477-0908
Ph: (215)646-8700   Fax: (215)646-4508
Fr: 800-346-7844

Jeanna Bozell. 1999. $22.95 (paper).

★9961★ **Building and Managing a Career in Nursing: Strategies for Advancing Your Career**
Sigma Theta Tau International, Center for Nursing Press
550 W. North St.
Indianapolis, IN 46202
Ph: (317)634-8171   Fax: (317)634-8188
Fr: 888-634-7575

Terry W. Miller. May 2003. $24.95. Illustrated. 411 pages.

★9962★ Career Opportunities in Health Care (Career Opportunities)

Facts on File
132 W. 31st St., 17th Fl.
New York, NY 10001-2006
Ph: (212)967-8800   Fax: (212)967-8107
Fr: 800-322-8755

Shelly Field. Arthur E. Weintraub. 2002. Reprint. $18.95. 243 pages. Part of the Career Opportunities Series.

★9963★ Careers in Health Care

McGraw-Hill Trade
2 Penn Plaza
New York, NY 10121
Ph: (212)904-2000   Fr: 800-722-4726
E-mail: ntcpub@tribune.com

Barbara M. Swanson. Fourth edition, 2000. $17.95; $13.95 (paper). 320 pages. Describes job duties, work settings, salaries, licensing and certification requirements, educational preparation, and future outlook. Gives ideas on how to secure a job.

★9964★ Careers for Night Owls and Other Insomniacs

McGraw-Hill Trade
2 Penn Plaza
New York, NY 10121
Ph: (212)904-2000   Fr: 800-722-4726
E-mail: ntcpub@tribune.com

Louise Miller. 1995. $14.95; $9.95 (paper). 160 pages.

★9965★ Careers in Nursing

McGraw-Hill Trade
2 Penn Plaza
New York, NY 10121
Ph: (212)904-2000   Fr: 800-722-4726
E-mail: ntcpub@tribune.com

Terence J. Sacks. 1998. $17.95; 13.95 (paper). 278 pages.

★9966★ Developing Your Career in Nursing

Sage Publications Inc.
370 Lexington Ave.
New York, NY 10017-6503
Ph: (212)953-5858   Fax: (212)953-5944

Robert Newell, editor. 1996. $90.00.

★9967★ Expert Resumes for Health Care Careers

JIST Publishing
8902 Otis Ave.
Indianapolis, IN 46216-1033
Ph: (317)613-4200   Fax: 800-547-8329

December 2003. $16.95. 288 pages.

★9968★ Federal Jobs in Nursing and Health Sciences

Impact Publications
9104 Manassas Dr., Ste. N
Manassas Park, VA 20111-5211
Ph: (703)361-7300   Fax: (703)335-9486

Russ Smith. 1996. Part of Federal Jobs in...Series. $14.95. 130 pages.

★9969★ Health Care Career Starter: Finding and Getting a Great Job

LearningExpress, LLC
900 Broadway, Ste. 604
New York, NY 10003
Ph: (212)995-2566   Fax: (212)995-5512
Fr: 800-295-9556

Cheryl Jean Hancock. Brigit Dermott. Reprint. 2002. $15.95 (paper). 216 pages. Part of the Heath Care Career Starters Series.

★9970★ Health Careers Today

Elsevier-Health Sciences Division
The Curtis Center, Ste. 300E, 3rd Fl.
170 S. Independence Mall W.
Philadelphia, PA 19106
Ph: (215)238-7800   Fax: (215)238-7362
Fr: 800-523-4069

Gerdin. Revised edition. April 2004. $52.95.

★9971★ Healthcare Career Directory-Nurses and Physicians

Thomson Gale
27500 Drake Rd.
Farmington Hills, MI 48331-3535
Ph: (248)699-GALE   Fax: 800-414-5043
Fr: 800-877-GALE
E-mail: galeord@gale.com
URL: http://www.gale.com

Bradley Morgan. Second edition, 1993. $39.00. 300 pages. Out of print. Essays on specific careers provide an insider's perspective. Features extensive listings of contacts and entry-level job opportunities. Provides information on internships and sources of help-wanted ads.

★9972★ Mosby's Tour Guide to Nursing School: A Student's Road Survival Guide

Mosby Inc.
11830 Westline Industrial Dr.
St. Louis, MO 63146
Ph: (314)872-8370   Fax: 800-235-0256
Fr: 800-325-4177

Melodie Chenevert. Third edition. 1994. $21.95 (paper). 216 pages.

★9973★ The Nurses' Career Guide: Discovering New Horizons in Health Care

Sovereignty Press
1241 Johnson Ave., No. 353
San Luis Obispo, CA 93401
Ph: (805)543-6100   Fax: (805)543-1085
Fr: 888-201-2501

Zardoya E. Eagles and Marti Kock. 1999.

$17.95 (paper). Helps the reader identify work skills and achievements, clarify values and goals, explore career options, develop personal action plan, prepare cover letters and resumes, and conduct informational and job interviews. Also addresses the dramatic changes that nurses currently face in the workplace. Includes a 65-page resource section which lists references, samples of resumes and letters, professional magazines, organizations, and online resources.

★9974★ Nursing (Career Portraits)

McGraw-Hill Trade
2 Penn Plaza
New York, NY 10121
Ph: (212)904-2000   Fax: (212)755-564
Fr: 800-722-4726
E-mail: ntcpub@tribune.com

Blythe Camenson. 1995. $13.95. 335 pages

★9975★ The Nursing Experience: Trends, Challenges & Transitions

McGraw-Hill Professional
PO Box 545
Blacklick, OH 43004-0545
Fax: (614)755-5645   Fr: 800-722-472
Lucie Y. Kelly. Fourth edition, 2001. $34.95 (paper). 792 pages.

★9976★ Nursing Today: Transition and Trends

W.B. Saunders Co.
150 S. Independence Mall W
The Public Ledger Bldg., Ste. 1250
Philadelphia, PA 19106-3412
Ph: (215)238-5500   Fax: (215)238-8495
Fr: 800-654-2452

JoAnn Zerwekh and Jo C. Claborn, editors. Second edition, 1997.

★9977★ 101 Careers in Nursing

Springer Publishing Company, Inc.
536 Broadway, 11th Fl.
New York, NY 10012-3955
Ph: (212)431-4370   Fax: (212)941-7842

Jeanne M. Novotny, Doris T. Lippman, Nicole K. Sanders, Joyce J. Fitzpatrick. August 2003. $33.95 (paper). Illustrated. 240 pages.

★9978★ Opportunities in Environmental Careers

McGraw-Hill Trade
2 Penn Plaza
New York, NY 10121
Ph: (212)904-2000   Fr: 800-722-4726
E-mail: ntcpub@tribune.com

Odom Fanning. Revised, 2002. $12.95 (paper). 160 pages. Describes a broad range of opportunities in fields such as environmental health, recreation, physics, and hygiene, and provides job search advice. Part of Opportunities in...Series.

★9979★ **Opportunities in Health and Medical Careers**

McGraw-Hill Trade
2 Penn Plaza
New York, NY 10121
Ph: (212)904-2000   Fr: 800-722-4726

I. Donald Snook, Jr. and Leo D'Orazio. 1997. $14.95; $11.95 (paper). 202 pages. Covers the full range of medical and health occupations. Illustrated.

★9980★ **Opportunities in Mental Health Careers**

McGraw-Hill Trade
2 Penn Plaza
New York, NY 10121
Ph: (212)904-2000   Fr: 800-722-4726

Philip A. Perry and George Blake. 1996. $14.95; $11.95 (paper). 160 pages.

★9981★ **Opportunities in Nursing Careers**

McGraw-Hill Trade
2 Penn Plaza
New York, NY 10121
Ph: (212)904-2000   Fr: 800-722-4726

Keville Frederickson and Judith A. Ryan. 1995. $14.95; $11.95 (paper). 205 pages. Discusses the employment outlook and job-seeking techniques for LVN's, LPN's, RN's, nurse practitioners, nurse anesthetists, and other nurse members of the medical team. Includes a complete list of state nurses associations, state nursing boards, and specialty nursing organizations. Contains bibliography and illustrations.

★9982★ **Opportunities in Paramedical Careers**

McGraw-Hill/Contemporary Books
1221 Avenue of the Americas
New York, NY 10020
Ph: (212)904-2000   Fr: 800-323-4900
E-mail: ntcpub@tribune.com

Alex Kacen. Revised, 1999. $14.95; 11.95 (paper). 200 pages. Discusses a variety of opportunities in this field and how to pursue them. Illustrated.

★9983★ **Opportunities in Physician Assistant Careers**

McGraw-Hill Trade
2 Penn Plaza
New York, NY 10121
Ph: (212)904-2000   Fr: 800-722-4726

Terence J. Sacks. 2002. $14.95; $12.95 (paper). 160 pages.

★9984★ **Opportunities in State and Local Government Careers**

Vgm Career Horizons
1221 Avenue of the Americas
New York, NY 10020
Ph: (212)904-2000   Fr: 800-323-4900
E-mail: ntcpub@tribune.com

Neale J. Baxter. 1994. $14.95; $10.95 (paper). 160 pages. Points out the incentives and drawbacks of a government career. Describes hiring procedures and provides tips on filling out applications, taking physical and aptitude tests, handling interviews, and finding jobs. Describes the jobs in which 75% of all state and local government workers are employed. For each occupation, covers the nature of the work and the training required.

★9985★ **Real People Working in Health Care**

McGraw-Hill Contemporary Books
1221 Avenue of the Americas
New York, NY 10020
Ph: (212)904-2000   Fr: 800-323-4900
E-mail: ntcpub@tribune.com

Blythe Camenson, Jan Goldberg. 1996. $17.95; $12.95 (paper). Interviews and profiles of working professionals capture a range of opportunities in this field.

★9986★ **Real-Resumes for Nursing Jobs: Including Real Resumes Used to Change Careers and Resumes Used to Gain Federal Employment**

PREP Publishing
1110 1/2 Hay St., PMB 66
Fayetteville, NC 28305
Ph: (910)483-6611   Fax: (910)483-2439
Fr: 800-533-2814

April 2003. $16.95. 192 pages. Real-Resumes Series.

★9987★ **Reinventing Your Nursing Career: A Handbook for Success in the Age of Managed Care**

Jones and Bartlett Publishing
200 Orchard Ridge Dr., Ste. 200
Gaithersburg, MD 20878
Ph: (301)417-7500   Fax: (301)695-7931
Fr: 800-638-8437

Michael Newell and Mario Pinardo. 1997. $37.00 (paper). 272 pages. Helps nurses identify career goals and take practical steps to realize them using self-surveys, goal-setting methods, personal action plans, and networking techniques.

★9988★ **Resumes for the Health Care Professional**

John Wiley & Sons Inc.
111 River Rd.
Hoboken, NJ 07030-5774
Ph: (201)748-6000   Fax: (201)748-6088
Fr: 800-225-5945

Kim Marino. Second edition, 2000. $14.95 (paper). 224 pages.

★9989★ **Resumes for Health and Medical Careers**

McGraw-Hill Trade
2 Penn Plaza
New York, NY 10121
Ph: (212)904-2000   Fr: 800-722-4726

E-mail: ntcpub@tribune.com

1997. $9.95 (paper). 455 pages.

★9990★ **Resumes for Nursing Careers**

McGraw-Hill Professional
2 Penn Plaza
New York, NY 10121
Ph: (212)904-2000   Fr: 800-722-4726
E-mail: ntcpub@tribune.com

2001. $10.95 (paper). 160 pages.

★9991★ **Vocational & Personal Adjustments in Practical Nursing**

Mosby Inc.
11830 Westline Industrial Dr.
St. Louis, MO 63146
Ph: (314)872-8370   Fax: 800-235-0256
Fr: 800-325-4177

Betty G. Becker and Dolores T. Fendler. Seventh edition, 1994. $24.95 (paper). 194 pages.

★9992★ **Where the Jobs Are: The Hottest Careers for the 90s**

The Career Press, Inc.
3 Tice Rd.
PO Box 687
Franklin Lakes, NJ 07417-1322
Ph: (201)848-0310   Fax: (201)848-1727
Fr: 800-227-3371

Joyce Hadley. Third edition, 2000. $13.99 (paper). 400 pages. Out of print. Describes careers in fifteen general fields, from accounting to travel and hospitality.

★9993★ **Your Career in Nursing: Manage Your Future in the Changing World of Healthcare**

Kaplan Books
1230 Avenue of the Americas, 1st Fl.
New York, NY 10020
Ph: (212)698-7000   Fax: (212)698-7007
Fr: 800-223-2348

Annette Vallano. January 2003. $18.00 (paper). Illustrated. 368 Pages. Vocational guide.

★9994★ **Your First Year as a Nurse: Making the Transition from Total Novice to Successful Professional**

Prima Publishing
3000 Lava Ridge Ct.
Roseville, CA 95661
Ph: (916)787-7000   Fax: (916)787-7001

2001. $19.95 (paper).

EMPLOYMENT AGENCIES AND SEARCH FIRMS

★9995★ Educational Placement Service
1001 Craig Rd., Ste. 170
St. Louis, MO 63146
Ph: (314)991-5855   Fax: (314)991-5295
URL: http://www.educatorjobs.com

Employment agency. Focuses on teaching, administrative, and education-related openings.

★9996★ Harper Associates
29870 Middlebelt
Farmington Hills, MI 48334
Ph: (248)932-1170   Fax: (248)932-1214
E-mail: resumes@harperjobs.com
URL: http://www.harperjobs.com

Executive search firm and employment agency.

★9997★ Medical Personnel Services, Inc.
1707 L St. NW, Ste. 760
Washington, DC 20036
Ph: (202)466-2955

Employment agency specializing in permanent health/medical placements.

★9998★ Nursing Technomics
814 Sunset Hollow Rd.
West Chester, PA 19380-1848
Ph: (610)436-4551   Fax: (610)436-0255

Administrative nursing consultants offer expertise in the design and implementation of customized software applications for departments of nursing, organizational design and implementation, and executive nurse search. Also specializes in department staffing, scheduling and nurse recruitment. Serves private industries as well as government agencies.

★9999★ Professional Placement Associates, Inc.
287 Bowman Ave., Ste. 309
Purchase, NY 10577
Ph: (914)251-1000   Fax: (914)251-1055
E-mail: lschachter@ppasearch.com
URL: http://www.ppasearch.com

Executive search firm specializing in the health and medical field.

★10000★ Team Placement Service, Inc.
5113 Leesburg Pike, Ste. 510
Falls Church, VA 22041-3242
Ph: (703)820-8618   Fax: (703)820-3368
Fr: 800-495-6767
E-mail: 4jobs@teamplace.com
URL: http://www.teamplace.com

Temporary agency that also handles some permanent placements.

★10001★ Travcorps, Inc.
40 Eastern Ave.
Malden, MA 02148
Ph: (781)322-2600   Fax: 800-803-1186
Fr: 800-343-3270
URL: http://www.travcorps.com

Places staff in temporary assignments. Other locations nationwide.

ONLINE JOB SOURCES AND SERVICES

★10002★ GasWork.com: The Largest Internet Anesthesia Employment Resource
E-mail: support@atsgaswork.com
URL: http://www.gaswork.com

Description: The largest anesthesia employment resource. Lists positions for anesthesiologists, CRNA's, and more. Visitors may post or search jobs.

★10003★ Health Care Job Store
395 South End Ave., Ste. 15-D
New York, NY 10280
Ph: (212)912-0175
E-mail: jobs@atshealthcarejobstore.com
URL: http://www.healthcarejobstore.com/adag.html

Description: Job sites include every job title in the healthcare industry,every healthcare industry and every geographic location in the U.S.

★10004★ HealthCareerWeb
URL: http://www.healthcareerweb.com/

Description: Advertises jobs for healthcare professionals. **Main files include:** Jobs, Employers, Resumes, Jobwire. Relocation tools and career guidance resources available.

★10005★ MedExplorer
URL: http://www.medexplorer.com

Description: Employment postings make up one module of this general medical site. Other sections contain: Newsletter, Classifieds, and Discussion Forum.

★10006★ Medhunters.com
E-mail: info@medhunters.com
URL: http://www.medhunters.com

Description: Career search site for jobs in all health care specialties; educational resources; visa and licensing information for relocation; interesting articles; relocation tools; links to professional organizations and general resources.

★10007★ Medzilla
URL: http://www.medzilla.com

Description: General medical website which matches employers and job hunters to their ideal employees and jobs through search capabilities. **Main files include:** Post Jobs, Search Resumes, Post Resumes, Search Jobs, Head Hunters, Articles, Salary Survey.

★10008★ Monster Healthcare
E-mail: office@atsmedsearch.com
URL: http://myh.monster.com/

Description: H Monster delivers nationwide access to healthcare recruiting. Employers can post job listings or ads. Job seekers can post and code resumes, and search over 150,000 healthcare job listings, healthcare career advice columns, career resources information, and member employer profiles and services.

★10009★ NursesRX.com
E-mail: nursesrx@nursesrx.com
URL: http://www.nursesrx.com

Description: Job board site for travel nursing. In addition to traditional travel nursing, Nurses Rx provides staffing possibilities from temporary-to-permanent, traditional permanent placement, staffing/recruitment outsourcing, new graduate internship programs, and a full Canadian Placement Division.

TRADESHOWS

★10010★ American Association of Office Nurses Annual Meeting and Convention
American Association of Office Nurses
109 Kinderkamack Rd.
Montvale, NJ 07645
Ph: (201)391-2600   Fax: (201)573-8543
Fr: 800-457-7504
E-mail: aaonmail@aaon.org
URL: http://www.aaon.org

Annual. **Primary Exhibits:** Exhibits of interest to nurses.

★10011★ American Nephrology Nurses Association Symposium
Anthony J. Jannetti, Inc.
E. Holly Ave., Box 56
Pitman, NJ 08071
Ph: (856)256-2300   Fax: (856)589-7463

Annual. **Primary Exhibits:** Equipment, supplies, pharmaceuticals, and services related to the field of nephrology.

★10012★ American Organization of Nurse Executives Annual Meeting and Exposition
Dallas Hyatt Regency
300 Reunion Blvd.
Dallas, TX 75267
E-mail: ashhra@aha.org
URL: http://www.aha.org

Annual. **Primary Exhibits:** Patient-care equipment and supplies; computer hardware and software related to the administration of hospital nursing services; communications systems; intensive care units; medical supplies and equipment; recruiting and staffing services; and related equipment, supplies, and services. **Dates and Locations:** 2005 Apr 14-19; Chicago, IL • 2006 Apr 07-12; Orlando, FL.

★10013★ **AORN World Conference on Surgical Patient Care**

Association of Perioperative Registered Nurses (AORN)
2170 S. Parker Rd., Ste. 300
Denver, CO 80231-5711
Ph: (303)755-6300   Fax: (303)752-0299
Fr: 800-755-2676
URL: http://www.aorn.org

Biennial. **Primary Exhibits:** Equipment, supplies, and services used in operating room suites and pre-surgical areas.

★10014★ **Association of Perioperative Registered Nurses Annual Congress**

Association of Perioperative Registered Nurses (AORN)
2170 S. Parker Rd., Ste. 300
Denver, CO 80231-5711
Ph: (303)755-6300   Fax: (303)752-0299
Fr: 800-755-2676
URL: http://www.aorn.org

Annual. **Primary Exhibits:** Surgical equipment, supplies, and services; recruiting firms, computer software, endoscopes, on-line buying services. **Dates and Locations:** 2005 Apr 3-7; New Orleans, LA • 2006 Mar 19-23; Washington, DC.

★10015★ **Conference on Classification of Nursing Diagnosis**

North American Nursing Diagnosis Association
1211 Locust St.
Philadelphia, PA 19107
Ph: (215)545-8105   Fax: (215)545-8107
Fr: 800-647-9002
E-mail: nanda@nursecominc.com

Biennial. **Primary Exhibits:** Exhibits relating to the development of a taxonomy of diagnostic terminology for use by professional nurses. Booth publishers, electronic media publishers.

★10016★ **Conference of the National Association of Pediatric Nurse Associates and Practitioners**

National Association of Pediatric Nurse Associates and Practitioners
20 Brace Rd., Ste. 200
Cherry Hill, NJ 08034-1912
Ph: (856)857-9700   Fax: (856)857-1600
Fr: 877-662-7627
E-mail: info@napnap.org
URL: http://www.napnap.org

Annual. **Primary Exhibits:** Equipment, supplies, and services for pediatric, school, and family nurse practitioners.

★10017★ **Emergency Nurses Association Annual Meeting**

Emergency Nurses Association
915 Lee St.
Des Plaines, IL 60016-6569
Fax: (847)460-4001   Fr: 800-900-9659
E-mail: enainfo@iqnow.com
URL: http://www.ena.org

Annual. **Primary Exhibits:** Exhibits relating to emergency room care.

★10018★ **House of Delegates Meeting**

American Nurses Association
600 Maryland Ave. SW, Ste. 100 W
Washington, DC 20024-2571
Ph: (202)651-7203   Fax: (202)651-7003
E-mail: exhibits@ana.org
URL: http://www.nursingworld.org

Biennial. **Primary Exhibits:** Equipment, supplies, and services for nurses, including publications, uniforms and shoes, computers, laboratory services, medical equipment, and nutritional products.

★10019★ **International Society of Psychiatric-Mental Health Nurses Annual Conference**

International Society of Psychiatric - Mental Health Nurses
1211 Locust St.
Philadelphia, PA 19107
Ph: (215)545-2843   Fax: (215)545-8107
Fr: 800-826-2950
E-mail: ispn@nursecominc.com
URL: http://www.ispn-psych.org

Annual. **Primary Exhibits:** Psychiatric nursing equipment, supplies, and services.

★10020★ **NASN Annual Conference**

National Association of School Nurses
Lamplighter Ln.
PO Box 1300
Scarborough, ME 04070
Ph: (207)883-2117   Fax: (207)883-2683
E-mail: nasn@aol.com
URL: http://www.VRmedia.com/nurses

Annual. **Primary Exhibits:** School nursing equipment, supplies, and services.

★10021★ **National Association of Orthopedic Nurses Annual Congress**

Smith, Bucklin and Associates, Inc. (Chicago)
401 N. Michigan Ave.
Chicago, IL 60611-4267
Ph: (312)321-6610   Fax: (312)673-6670
Fr: 800-289-NAON
E-mail: info@smithbucklin.com
URL: http://www.sba.com

Annual. **Primary Exhibits:** Pharmaceuticals, medical equipment, medical instruments, and publications. **Dates and Locations:** 2005 May 14-18; Phoenix, AZ; Phoenix Hyatt Regency and Civic Plaza.

★10022★ **National League for Nursing Convention**

SLACK, Inc.
6900 Grove Rd.
Thorofare, NJ 08086
Ph: (609)848-1000   Fax: (609)848-3522

Biennial. **Primary Exhibits:** Equipment, supplies, and services for nurses and related healthcare professionals.

★10023★ **National Student Nurses' Association Convention**

National Student Nurses' Association
45 Main St., Ste. 606
Brooklyn, NY 11201
Ph: (718)210-0705   Fax: (718)210-0710
E-mail: nsna.net@internetmci.com
URL: http://www.nsna.org

Biennial. **Primary Exhibits:** Equipment, supplies, and services for the student nurse. **Dates and Locations:** 2004 Nov 11-14; Daytona Beach, FL • 2005 Apr 06-10; Salt Lake City, UT.

★10024★ **North Carolina Nurses Association Convention**

North Carolina Nurses Association
103 Enterprise St.
PO Box 12025
Raleigh, NC 27605
Ph: (919)821-4250   Fax: (919)829-5807
Fr: 800-626-2153
E-mail: ncnurses@ncnurses.org
URL: http://www.ncnurses.org

Annual. **Primary Exhibits:** Nursing equipment, supplies, and services, books.

★10025★ **Oncology Nursing Society Meeting**

Oncology Nursing Society
501 Holiday Dr.
Pittsburgh, PA 15220
Ph: (412)921-7373   Fax: (412)921-6565

Annual. **Primary Exhibits:** Oncology nursing equipment, supplies, and services.

★10026★ **Wisconsin Nurses Association Convention**

Wisconsin Nurses Association, Inc.
6117 Monona Dr.
Madison, WI 53716
Ph: (608)221-0383   Fax: (608)221-2788
E-mail: wna@execpc.com
URL: http://www.execpc.com/~wna

Annual. **Primary Exhibits:** Nursing equipment, supplies, and services.

OTHER SOURCES

★10027★ *American Almanac of Jobs and Salaries*

Morrow Avon
1350 Avenue of the Americas
New York, NY 10019
Ph: (212)261-6788   Fr: 800-242-7737

John W. Wright. Revised edition, 2000. $20.00 (paper). 672 pages. This is a comprehensive guide to the wages of hundreds of occupations in a wide variety of industries and organizations.

★10028★ American Assembly for Men in Nursing (AAMN)

11 Cornell Rd.
Latham, NY 12110-1499
Ph: (518)782-9400   Fax: (518)782-9530
E-mail: aamn@aamn.org
URL: http://aamn.org

Members: Registered nurses. **Purpose:** Works to help eliminate prejudice in nursing; interest men in the nursing profession; provide opportunities for the discussion of common problems; encourage education and promote further professional growth; advise and assist in areas of professional inequity; help develop sensitivities to various social needs; promote the principles and practices of positive health care. **Activities:** Acts as a clearinghouse for information on men in nursing. Conducts educational programs. Promotes education and research about men's health issues.

★10029★ American Association of Nurse Attorneys (TAANA)

7794 Grow Dr.
Pensacola, FL 32514
Ph: (850)474-3646   Fax: (850)484-8762
Fr: 877-532-2262
E-mail: taana@puetzamc.com
URL: http://www.taana.org

Members: Nurse attorneys, nurses in law school, and attorneys in nursing school. **Purpose:** Aims to better nurse attorneys and inform the public on matters of nursing, health care, and law. Goals are to facilitate communication and information sharing between professional groups; to establish an employment network; to assist new and potential nurse attorneys; to develop the profession; to promote the image of nurse attorneys as experts and consultants in nursing and law. **Activities:** Maintains educational foundation.

★10030★ American Health Care Association (AHCA)

1201 L St. NW
Washington, DC 20005
Ph: (202)842-4444   Fax: (202)842-3860
URL: http://www.ahca.org

Description: Federation of state associations of long-term health care facilities. Promotes standards for professionals in long-term health care delivery and quality care for patients and residents in a safe environment. Focuses on issues of availability, quality, affordability, and fair payment. Operates as liaison with governmental agencies, Congress, and professional associations. Compiles statistics.

★10031★ American Hospital Association (AHA)

1 N. Franklin
Chicago, IL 60606-3421
Ph: (312)422-3000   Fax: (312)422-4796
URL: http://www.aha.org

Description: Health care provider organizations. Seeks to advance the health of individuals and communities. Leads, represents, and serves health care provider organizations that are accountable to the community and committed to health improvement.

★10032★ American Nurses Association (ANA)

600 Maryland Ave. SW, Ste. 100 W.
Washington, DC 20024-2571
Ph: (202)651-7000   Fax: (202)651-7001
Fr: 800-274-4262
E-mail: memberinfo@ana.org
URL: http://www.nursingworld.org

Description: Membership association representing registered nurses.

★10033★ American School Health Association (ASHA)

PO Box 708
7263 State Route 43
Kent, OH 44240
Ph: (330)678-1601   Fax: (330)678-4526
Fr: 800-445-2742
E-mail: asha@ashaweb.org
URL: http://www.ashaweb.org

Description: School physicians, school nurses, dentist, nurses, nutritionists, health educators, dental hygienist, school-based professionals and public health workers. Promotes coordinated school health programs that include health education, health services, a healthful school environment, physical education, nutrition services, and psycho-social health services offered in schools collaboratively with families and other members of the community. Offers professional reference materials. Conducts pilot programs that inform materials development, provides technical assistance to school professionals, advocates for school health, and complies statistics.

★10034★ American Society of Extra-Corporeal Technology (AmSECT)

503 Carlisle Dr. No. 125
Herndon, VA 20170-4838
Ph: (703)435-8556   Fax: (703)435-0056
E-mail: gcate@amsect.org
URL: http://www.amsect.org

Description: Perfusionists, technologists, doctors, nurses, and others actively employed and using the applied skills relating to the practice of extracorporeal technology (involving heart-lung machines); student members. Disseminates information necessary to the proper practice of the technology. Conducts programs in continuing education and professional-public liaison and hands-on workshops. Maintains placement service.

★10035★ *EMTs, Nurses, Therapists, and Assistants*

Cambridge Educational
2572 Brunswick Ave.
Lawrenceville, NJ 08648-4128
Fax: 800-FAX-ON-US   Fr: 800-468-4227
URL: http://www.cambridgeeducational.com

$79.95. 1999. Part of the series "Exploring Health Occupations."

★10036★ *Exploring Health Occupations*

Cambridge Educational
2572 Brunswick Ave.
Lawrenceville, NJ 08648-4128
Fax: 800-FAX-ON-US   Fr: 800-468-4227
URL: http://www.cambridgeeducational.com

Two videos. $139.95. 1999.

★10037★ *Health Service Occupations*

Delphi Productions
3160 4th St.
Boulder, CO 80304
Fax: (303)443-4022   Fr: 888-443-2400
URL: http://www.delphivideo.com

$95.00. 50 minutes. Part of the Careers for the 21st Century Video Library.

★10038★ *Interviewing Skills for Nurses & Other Health Care Professionals: A Structured Approach*

Routledge
29 W. 35th St.
New York, NY 10001-2299
Ph: (212)216-7800   Fax: (212)564-7854
Fr: 800-634-7064

Robert Newell. 1994. $24.99 (paper). 208 pages. Out of print.

★10039★ *Medicine & Related Occupations*

Delphi Productions
3160 4th St.
Boulder, CO 80304
Fax: (303)443-4022   Fr: 888-443-2400
URL: http://www.delphivideo.com

$95.00. 45 minutes. Part of the Careers for the 21st Century Video Library.

★10040★ National Association of Pediatric Nurse Practitioners (NAPNAP)

20 Brace Rd., Ste. 200
Cherry Hill, NJ 08034-2633
Ph: (856)857-9700   Fax: (856)857-1600
E-mail: info@napnap.org
URL: http://www.napnap.org

Members: Pediatric, school, and family nurse practitioners and interested persons.

Purpose: Seeks to improve the quality of infant, child, and adolescent health care by making health care services accessible and providing a forum for continuing education of members. **Activities:** Facilitates and supports legislation designed to promote the role of pediatric nurse practitioners; promotes salary ranges commensurate with practitioners' responsibilities; facilitates exchange of information between prospective employers and job seekers in the field. Supports research programs; compiles statistics.

★10041★ **National League for Nursing (NLN)**

61 Broadway 33rd Fl.
New York, NY 10006-2701
Ph: (212)363-5555   Fax: (212)812-0393
Fr: 800-669-1656
E-mail: rcorcor@nln.org
URL: http://www.nln.org

Description: Champions the pursuit of quality nursing education. A professional association of nursing faculty, education agencies, healthcare agencies, allied/public agencies, and public members whose mission is to advance quality nursing education that prepares the nursing workforce to meet the needs of diverse populations in an ever-changing health care environment. Serves as the primary source of information about every type of nursing education, from the LVN and LPN to the EDD and PHD. There are 33 affiliated constituent leagues that provide a local forum for members. The National League for Nursing Accrediting Commission is an independent corporate affiliate of the NLN, responsible for providing accreditation services to all levels of nursing education. NLN's bimonthly update is available free of charge on the website and by email.

★10042★ **National Rural Health Association (NRHA)**

1 W Armour Blvd., Ste. 203
Kansas City, MO 64111-2087
Ph: (816)756-3140   Fax: (816)756-3144
E-mail: mail@nrharural.org
URL: http://www.nrharural.org

Description: Administrators, physicians, nurses, physician assistants, health planners, academicians, and others interested or involved in rural health care. Creates a better understanding of health care problems unique to rural areas; utilizes a collective approach in finding positive solutions; articulates and represents the health care needs of rural America; supplies current information to rural health care providers; serves as a liaison between rural health care programs throughout the country. Offers continuing education credits for medical, dental, nursing, and management courses.

★10043★ **National Student Nurses' Association (NSNA)**

45 Main St., Ste. 606
Brooklyn, NY 11201
Ph: (718)210-0705   Fax: (718)210-0710
E-mail: nsna@nsna.org
URL: http://www.nsna.org

Members: Students enrolled in state-approved schools for the preparation of registered nurses. **Purpose:** Seeks to aid in the development of the individual nursing student and to urge students of nursing, as future leaders and health professionals, to be aware of and to contribute to improving the health care of all people. Encourages programs and activities in state groups concerning nursing, health, and the community. Provides assistance for state board review, as well as materials for preparation for state RN licensing examination. Cooperates with nursing organizations in recruitment of nurses and in professional, community, and civic programs. Sponsors Foundation of the National Student Nurses' Association in

memory of Frances Tompkins to award scholarships to student nurses.

★10044★ **Nurses' House**

2113 Western Ave., Ste. 2
Guilderland, NY 12084-9559
Ph: (518)456-7858   Fax: (518)452-3760
E-mail: mail@nurseshouse.org
URL: http://www.nurseshouse.org

Members: Registered nurses and interested individuals united to assist registered nurses in financial and other crises. **Purpose:** Provides short-term financial aid for shelter, food, and utilities until nurses obtain entitlements or jobs. Offers counseling and referrals. Encourages homebound or retired nurses through a volunteer corps.

★10045★ *The Patient Care Nursing Team*

Cambridge Educational
2572 Brunswick Ave.
Lawrenceville, NJ 08648
Fax: 800-FAX-ON-US   Fr: 800-468-4227
URL: http://www.cambridgeeducational.com
$89.95. 2001. 18 minutes.

★10046★ **Visiting Nurse Associations of America (VNAA)**

99 Summer St., Ste. 1700
Boston, MA 02110
Ph: (617)737-3200   Fax: (617)737-1144
Fr: 800-426-2547
E-mail: vnaa@vnaa.org
URL: http://www.vnaa.org

Members: Voluntary, nonprofit home health care agencies. **Purpose:** Develops competitive strength among community-based nonprofit visiting nurse organizations; works to strengthen business resources and economic programs through contracting, marketing, governmental affairs and publications.

Reporters and Correspondents

SOURCES OF HELP-WANTED ADS

★10047★ Broadcasting & Cable
Reed Business Information
360 Park Ave. S
New York, NY 10010
Ph: (646)746-6400   Fax: (646)746-6734
URL: http://www.broadcastingcable.com

Weekly. $179.00/year for U.S.; $239.00/year for Canada. News magazine covering The Fifth Estate (radio, TV, cable, and satellite), and the regulatory commissions involved.

★10048★ Columbia Journalism Review
Columbia Journalism Review
2950 Broadway, Journalism Bldg.
Columbia University
New York, NY 10027
Ph: (212)854-1881   Fax: (212)854-8580
E-mail: cjr@columbia.edu
URL: http://www.cjr.org

Bimonthly. $18.00/year; $4.95 for single issue. Magazine focusing on journalism.

★10049★ Current
Heldref Publications
1319 18th St. NW
Washington, DC 20036-1802
Ph: (202)296-6267   Fax: (202)296-5149
Fr: 800-365-9753
URL: http://www.heldref.org/html/curr.html

Monthly. $38.00/year for individuals; $77.00/year for institutions, add $18 for postage outside the United States. Journal that reprints articles on education, politics, and other social issues.

★10050★ Editor & Publisher
Editor & Publisher Magazine
770 Broadway
New York, NY 10003-9595
Fax: (646)654-5360   Fr: 800-336-4380
URL: http://www.editorandpublisher.com

Weekly. $99.00/year for U.S. and Canada, includes exclusive web access; $130.00/year for other countries; $4.00 for single issue. Magazine focusing on newspaper journalism, advertising, printing equipment, and interactive services.

★10051★ Electronic Media
Crain Communications Inc.
1155 Gratiot Ave.
Detroit, MI 48207-2997
Ph: (313)446-6000
E-mail: info@crain.com
URL: http://www.crain.com/

Newspaper covering management, programming, cable and trends in the television and the media industry.

★10052★ The Hollywood Reporter
The Hollywood Reporter
5055 Wilshire Blvd.
Los Angeles, CA 90036-4396
Ph: (323)525-2000   Fax: (323)525-2377
E-mail: special-issues@hollywoodreporter.com
URL: http://www.hollywoodreporter.com

Daily. Film, TV, and entertainment trade newspaper.

★10053★ In These Times
Institute for Public Affairs Inc.
2040 N Milwaukee Ave., 2nd Fl.
Chicago, IL 60647-4002
Ph: (773)772-0100   Fax: (773)772-4180
Fr: 888-READ-ITT
E-mail: itt@inthesetimes.com
URL: http://www.inthesetimes.com

Biweekly. $36.95/year for individuals. National political newsmagazine.

★10054★ Metro Magazine
Bobit Publishing
21061 S Western Ave.
Torrance, CA 90501
Ph: (310)533-2400   Fax: (310)533-2500
E-mail: info@metro-magazine.com
URL: http://www.metro-magazine.com

$40.00/year; $6.00 for single issue; $60.00/year for Canada. Magazine on public transportation.

★10055★ The New Republic
The New Republic L.L.C.
1331 H St. NW, Ste. 700
Washington, DC 20005
Ph: (202)508-4444   Fax: (202)331-0275
E-mail: tnrcustserv@cdsfulfillment.com
URL: http://www.tnr.com

Monthly. $19.95/year for individuals. Journal featuring current events comments and reviews.

★10056★ Publishers Weekly
Publishers Weekly
360 Park Ave. S
New York, NY 10010
Ph: (646)746-6758   Fax: (646)746-6631
Fr: (866)436-0727
URL: http://http;//www.bookwire.com

Weekly. $215.80/year for individuals. Weekly trade news magazine.

★10057★ Writer's Digest
F & W Publications Inc.
4700 E Galbraith Rd.
Cincinnati, OH 45236-6708
Ph: (513)531-2690   Fax: (513)531-2902
Fr: 800-289-0963
E-mail: writersdig@fwpubs.com
URL: http://www.writersdigest.com

Monthly. $27.00/year for individuals; $3.49 for single issue. Professional magazine for writers.

PLACEMENT AND JOB REFERRAL SERVICES

★10058★ American Sportscasters Association (ASA)
225 Broadway, Ste. 2030
New York, NY 10009
Ph: (212)227-8080   Fax: (212)571-0556

E-mail: lschwa8918@aol.com
URL: http://
www.americansportscasters.com

Members: Radio and television sportscasters. **Purpose:** Sponsors seminars, clinics, and symposia for aspiring announcers and sportscasters. **Activities:** Compiles statistics. Operates speakers' bureau, placement service, hall of fame, and biographical archives. Maintains American Sportscaster Hall of Fame Trust. Is currently implementing Hall of Fame Museum, Community Programs.

★10059★ **Broadcast Foundation of College/University Students (BROADCAST)**

89 Longview Rd.
Port Washington, NY 11050
Ph: (516)883-2897   Fax: (516)883-0159
E-mail: rstarleton@aol.com

Members: College students interested in broadcasting and professional broadcasters interested in encouraging practical broadcasting experience in colleges and universities. **Activities:** Conducts annual survey of all professional broadcasting stations for part-time and summer employment for college students. Sponsors job advisory and placement service.

★10060★ **Education Writers Association (EWA)**

2122 P St. NW, No. 201
Washington, DC 20037
Ph: (202)452-9830   Fax: (202)452-9837
E-mail: ewa@ewa.org
URL: http://www.ewa.org/

Members: Education writers and reporters of daily and weekly newspapers, national magazines of general circulation, and radio and television stations; associate members are school and college public relations personnel and others with a serious interest in education writing. **Purpose:** Improves the quality of education reporting and interpretation; encourages the development of education coverage by the press; to help attract top-notch writers and reporters to the education field. **Activities:** Sponsors regional and special workshops. Provides job referral/bank services.

★10061★ **National Association of Broadcasters (NAB)**

1771 N St. NW
Washington, DC 20036
Ph: (202)429-5300   Fax: (202)429-4199
E-mail: nab@nab.org
URL: http://www.nab.org

Description: Representatives of radio and television stations and networks; associate members include producers of equipment and programs. Seeks to ensure the viability, strength, and success of free, over-the-air broadcasters; serves as an information resource to the industry. Monitors and reports on events regarding radio and television broadcasting. Maintains Broadcasting Hall of

Fame. Offers minority placement service and employment clearinghouse.

★10062★ **National Association of Hispanic Journalists (NAHJ)**

1000 National Press Bldg.
Washington, DC 20045-2100
Ph: (202)662-7145   Fax: (202)662-7144
Fr: 888-346-NAHJ
E-mail: nahj@nahj.org
URL: http://www.nahj.org

Description: Purpose is to organize and support Hispanics involved in news gathering and dissemination. Encourages journalism and communications study and practice by Hispanics. Seeks recognition for Hispanic members of the profession regarding their skills and achievements. Promotes fair and accurate media treatment of Hispanics; opposes job discrimination and demeaning stereotypes. Works to increase educational and career opportunities and development for Hispanics in the field. Seeks to foster greater awareness of members' cultural identity, interests, and concerns. Provides a united voice for Hispanic journalists with the aim of achieving national visibility. Offers placement services to Hispanic students. Activities include: a census of Hispanic media professionals nationwide; writing contest-for Hispanic students. Bestows National Hispanic Journalist Award; offers scholarships, seminars, and training workshops

★10063★ **Radio-Television News Directors Association (RTNDA)**

1600 K St. NW, Ste. 700
Washington, DC 20006-2838
Ph: (202)659-6510   Fax: (202)223-4007
Fr: 800-80-RTNDA
E-mail: rtnda@rtnda.org
URL: http://rtnda.org

Description: Professional society of heads of news departments for broadcast and cable stations and networks; associate members are journalists engaged in the preparation and presentation of broadcast news and teachers of electronic journalism; other members represent industry services, public relations departments of business firms, public relations firms, and networks. Works to improve standards of electronic journalism; defends rights of journalists to access news; promotes journalism training to meet specific needs of the industry. Operates placement service and speakers' bureau.

EMPLOYER DIRECTORIES AND NETWORKING LISTS

★10064★ *ANR National Directory of Community Newspapers*

American Newspaper Representatives Inc.
2075 W Big Beaver Rd., Ste. 310
Troy, MI 48084-3439
Ph: (248)643-7766   Fax: (248)643-0606
Fr: 800-550-7557

URL: http://www.anrinc.net/

Annual, May/June. $125.00. Number of listings: 7,000. Entries include: Name of weekly newspaper, address, county, type of area, circulation, day published, name of publisher, and information on advertising rates and production specifications. Arrangement: Geographical.

★10065★ *Broadcasting & Cable Yearbook*

R.R. Bowker L.L.C.
630 Central Ave.
New Providence, NJ 07974
Ph: (908)286-1090   Fax: (908)219-0098
Fr: 888-269-5372

Annual, March, latest edition 2003-2004. $179.95. Covers over 17,000 television and radio stations in the United States, its territories, and Canada; cable MSOs and their individual systems; television and radio networks, broadcast and cable group owners, station representatives, satellite networks and services, film companies, advertising agencies, government agencies, trade associations, schools, and suppliers of professional and technical services, including books, serials, and videos; communications lawyers. Entries include: Company name, address, phone, fax, names of executives. Station listings include broadcast power, other operating details. Arrangement: Stations and systems are geographical, others are alphabetical. Indexes: Alphabetical.

★10066★ *Burrelle's New York Media Directory*

Burrelle's Information Services
75 E. Northfield Rd.
Livingston, NJ 07039
Ph: (973)992-6600   Fax: (973)992-7675
Fr: 800-631-1160
URL: http://www.burrellesluce.com/media-data/regional.html

Annual. $200.00. Covers Print and electronic media in New York. Entries include: Name, address, phone, fax, names and titles of key personnel, geographical area served, subsidiary and branch names and locations, description. Arrangement: Geographical; magazines are arranged by subject. Indexes: Name, subject, geographical.

★10067★ *CPB Public Broadcasting Directory*

Corporation for Public Broadcasting
901 E St. NW
Washington, DC 20004-2037
Ph: (202)879-9600   Fax: (202)783-9700
URL: http://www.cpb.org/directory/home.html

Annual. $15.00. Covers public television and radio stations, national and regional public broadcasting organizations and networks, state government agencies and commissions, and other related organizations. Entries include: For radio and television stations-Station call letters, frequency or channel, address, phone, licensee name, licensee type, date on air, antenna height, area covered, names and titles of key personnel. For organizations-Name, address, phone, name and title of key personnel. Arrangement: National and regional listings are alphabetical; state groups and the public radio and television stations are each geographical; other organizations and agencies are alphabetical. Indexes: Geographical, personnel, call letter, licensee type (all in separate indexes for radio and television).

★10068★ **Directory of Leading Magazines and Newspapers**
Publisher Media
1145 N Second St.
El Cajon, CA 92021-5024
Ph: (619)588-2155   Fax: (619)588-9103
Annual, January. $14.95. Covers over 300 newspapers and 700 consumer and trade magazines; coverage also includes Canada. Entries include: Company name, address, description of services, circulation figures advertising information. Arrangement: Classified by subject.

★10069★ **Directory of Small Magazine-Press Editors and Publishers**
Dustbooks
PO Box 100
Paradise, CA 95967
Ph: (530)887-6110   Fax: (530)877-0222
Fr: 800-477-6110
URL: http://www.dustbooks.com/
Annual, September. $23.95. Covers about 7,500 publishers and editors. Entries include: Individual name, title of press or magazine, address and phone number. Arrangement: Alphabetical.

★10070★ **Editor & Publisher International Year Book**
Editor & Publisher Magazine
770 Broadway
New York, NY 10003-9595
Fax: (646)654-5370   Fr: 800-336-4380
URL: http://www.editorandpublisher.com
Annual, April. $230.00. Covers daily and Sunday newspapers in the United States and Canada; weekly newspapers; foreign daily newspapers; special service newspapers; newspaper syndicates; news services; journalism schools; foreign language and Black newspapers in the United States; news, picture, and press services; feature and news syndicates; comic and magazine services; advertising clubs; trade associations; clipping bureaus; house organs; journalism awards; also lists manufacturers of equipment and supplies. Entries include: For daily papers-Publication name, address, phone, fax, e-mail, web site URL, names of executives and departmental editors (business, financial, book, food, etc.), circulation and advertising data, production information including format of paper and equipment used. Similar but less detailed information for other publications. Arrangement: Publications and schools are geographical; most other lists are alphabetical.

★10071★ **Editorial Freelancers Association-Membership Directory**
Editorial Freelancers Association Inc.
71 W 23rd St., Ste. 1910
New York, NY 10010
Ph: (212)929-5400   Fax: (212)929-5439
URL: http://www.the-efa.org
Annual, spring. $25.00. Covers 1,100 member editorial freelancers. Entries include: Personal name, address, phone, services provided, specialties. Arrangement: Alphabetical. Indexes: Product/service, special interest, geographical, computer skills.

★10072★ **International Directory of Little Magazines and Small Presses**
Dustbooks
PO Box 100
Paradise, CA 95967
Ph: (530)887-6110   Fax: (530)877-0222
Fr: 800-477-6110
URL: http://www.dustbooks.com/lilmag.htm
Annual, September. $55.00 for cloth; $35.95 for paper. Covers over 5,000 small, independent magazines, presses, and papers. Entries include: Name, address, size, circulation, frequency, price, type of material used, number of issues or books published annually, and other pertinent data. Arrangement: Alphabetical. Indexes: Subject, regional.

★10073★ **International Television and Video Almanac**
Quigley Publishing Company Inc.
64 Wintergreen Ln.
Groton, MA 01450-4129
Fr: 800-231-8239
URL: http://hometown.aol.com/quigleypub/mp.html
Annual, January. $130.00. Covers "Who's Who in Motion Pictures and Television and Home Video," television networks, major program producers, major group station owners, cable television companies, distributors, firms serving the television and home video industry, equipment manufacturers, casting agencies, literary agencies, advertising and publicity representatives, television stations, associations, list of feature films produced for television; statistics, industry's year in review, award winners, satellite & wireless cable provider, primetime programming, video producers, distributors, wholesalers. Entries include: Generally, company name, address, phone; manufacturer and service listings may include description of products and services and name of contact; producing, distributing, and station listings include additional detail, and contacts for cable and broadcast networks. Arrangement: Classified by service or activity. Indexes: Full.

★10074★ **National Directory of Magazines**
Oxbridge Communications Inc.
186 5th Ave., 6th Fl.
New York, NY 10010
Ph: (212)741-0231   Fax: (212)633-2938
Fr: 800-955-0231
E-mail: custserv@oxbridge.com
URL: http://www.mediafinder.com
October. $895.00. Covers over 20,000 magazines; coverage includes Canada. Entries include: Title, publisher name, address, phone, fax number, names and titles of contact and key personnel, financial data, editorial and advertising information, circulation. Arrangement: Classified by subject. Indexes: Title, geographical, publisher.

★10075★ **The News Media**
Lucent Books Inc.
10911 Technology Pl.
San Diego, CA 92127-1811
Ph: (858)485-7424   Fax: (858)485-8019
Fr: 800-877-4253
$27.45. Publication includes: List of organizations to contact for further information about careers in the news media. Principal content of publication is an examination of a variety of careers in the news media. Indexes: Alphabetical.

★10076★ **RTNDA Communicator-Directory Issues**
Radio-Television News Directors Association
1600 K St. NW, No. 700
Washington, DC 20006
Ph: (202)659-6510   Fax: (202)223-4007
Fr: 800-807-8632
Semiannual, January and July. Number of listings: 3,000; membership includes Canada and some foreign countries. Entries include: Member name, address, phone; and name of radio or television station, network, or other news organization with which affiliated. Arrangement: Same information given in alphabetical and geographical arrangements.

★10077★ **Southern Newspaper Publishers Association Internship Directory**
Southern Newspaper Publishers Association
PO Box 28875
Atlanta, GA 30358
Latest edition 1995-96. $2.00. Covers a list of internship programs offered by the Association's member newspapers.

★10078★ **Sports Market Place**
Sportsguide L.L.C.
13901 N 73rd St., Ste. 219
Scottsdale, AZ 85260
Ph: (480)948-8885   Fax: (480)948-7701
Fr: 800-776-7877
E-mail: smp@sportsmarketplace.com
URL: http://www.sportsmarketplace.com
Annual, January. $249.00. Covers manufacturers, organizations, professional sports teams, broadcasting networks, sports arenas, syndicators, publications, trade shows, marketing services, corporate sports sponsors, and other groups concerned with the business and promotional aspects of sports

generally and with air sports, arm wrestling, auto sports, badminton, baseball, basketball, biathlon, bowling, boxing, curling, equestrian, exercise, fencing, field hockey, football, golf, gymnastics, ice hockey, lacrosse, martial arts, paddleball, paddle tennis, platform tennis, pentathlon, racquetball, rowing, rugby, running/jogging, skiing, soccer, softball, squash, swimming, table tennis, tennis, track and field, volleyball, water sports, weightlifting, and wrestling. Entries include: Name of company or organization, address, fax, e-mail, URL, name of key personnel with titles, and description of products or services. Arrangement: Classified by type of firm, sport, or activity. Indexes: Alphabetical, single sprt, media, sport sponsors, agencies, manufacturers, brand name, facilities, executive, and Geographical.

★10079★ **SRDS International Media Guide: Newspapers Worldwide**
SRDS
1700 .E Higgins Rd.
Des Plaines, IL 60018-5605
Ph: (847)375-5000   Fax: (847)375-5001
Fr: 800-851-7737
URL: http://www.srds.com

Annual. $350.00. Covers approximately 2,500 newspapers and color newspaper magazines/supplements from 200 countries, including the United States. Entries include: Publication name; publisher name, address, phone, fax, e-mail, URL, names of editor, advertising manager, and representatives in the United States and worldwide; advertising rates in U.S. dollars and/or local currency, circulation, mechanical data, ad closing, readership description, etc. Arrangement: Geographical.

★10080★ **Ulrich's Periodicals Directory**
R.R. Bowker L.L.C.
630 Central Ave.
New Providence, NJ 07974
Ph: (908)286-1090   Fax: (908)219-0098
Fr: 888-269-5372
E-mail: ulrichs@bowker.com
URL: http://www.ulrichsweb.com

Annual. $699.00. Covers nearly 165,000 current periodicals and newspapers published worldwide. Entries include: In main list-Publication title; Dewey Decimal Classification number, Library of Congress Classification Number (where applicable), CODEN designation (for sci-tech serials), British Library Document Supply Centre shelfmark number, country code, ISSN; subtitle, language(s) of text, year first published, frequency, subscription prices, sponsoring organization, publishing company name, address, phone, fax, e-mail and website addresses, editor and publisher names; regular features (reviews, advertising, abstracts, bibliographies, trade literature, etc.), indexes, circulation, format, brief description of content; availability of microforms and reprints; whether refereed; CD-ROM availability with vendor name; online availability with service name; services that index or abstract the periodical, with years covered; advertising rates and contact; right and permissions contact name and phone; availability through

document delivery services; Copyright Clearance Center participation; document type; former title and former ISSN history. For cessations-Title, name and address of publisher, publication status. For online and CD-ROM vendors-Company name, address, phone, fax, e-mail and URL addresses, titles of publications available. Arrangement: Main listing is classified by subject; U.S. general daily and weekly newspapers are listed in a separate volume; lists of cessations, online services, and CD-ROM vendors are alphabetical. Indexes: Cessations, subjects, title (including variant, former, and ceased titles), ISSN, periodicals available on CD-ROM, online periodical title, refereed serial, and international organization publication title.

HANDBOOKS AND MANUALS

★10081★ **Career Information Center**
Macmillan Publishing Co. Inc.
200 Old Tappan Rd.
Old Tappan, NJ 07675
Fr: 800-428-5331

Visual Education Center Staff. Seventh edition, 1999. $275.00. 2080 pages. This 13-volume set profiles over 600 occupations. Each occupational profile describes job duties, educational requirements, how to get the job, advancement possibilities, employment outlook, working conditions, earnings and benefits, and where to write for more information.

★10082★ **Career Opportunities for Writers**
Checkmark Books
132 W. 31st St., 17th Fl.
New York, NY 10001-2006
Ph: (212)967-8800   Fax: (212)967-9196
Fr: 800-322-8755
URL: http://www.factsonfile.com

Rosemary Ellen Guiley and Janet Frick. Fourth edition, 2000. $45.00. Part of the Career Opportunities Series. Describes more than 100 jobs in eight major fields, offering such details as duties, salaries, perquisites, employment and advancement opportunities, organizations to join, and opportunities for women and minorities.

★10083★ **Careers in Communications**
VGM Career Horizons
4255 W. Touhy Ave.
Lincolnwood, IL 60646-1975
Ph: (847)679-5500   Fax: (847)679-2494
Fr: 800-323-4900
E-mail: ntcpub@tribune.com

Shonan Noronha. Third edition, 1998. $17.95; $13.95 (paper). 418 pages. Examines the fields of journalism, photography, radio, television, film, public relations, and advertising. Gives concrete details on job locations and how to secure a job. Suggests many resources for job hunting.

★10084★ **Careers in Journalism**
Kogan Page
1221 Avenue of the Americas
New York, NY 10020
Ph: (212)904-2000   Fr: 800-323-4900
E-mail: ntcpub@tribune.com

Jan Goldberg. Second edition, 1999. $17.95; 13.95 (paper). 192 pages.

★10085★ **Careers for Mystery Buffs and Other Snoops and Sleuths**
McGraw-Hill Trade
2 Penn Plaza
New York, NY 10121
Ph: (212)904-2000   Fr: 800-722-4726
E-mail: ntcpub@tribune.com

Blythe Camenson. 1996. $14.95; $9.95 (paper). 210 pages.

★10086★ **Careers for Night Owls and Other Insomniacs**
McGraw-Hill Trade
2 Penn Plaza
New York, NY 10121
Ph: (212)904-2000   Fr: 800-722-4726
E-mail: ntcpub@tribune.com

Louise Miller. 1995. $14.95; $9.95 (paper). 160 pages.

★10087★ **Careers for Writers and Others Who Have a Way with Words**
McGraw-Hill Trade
2 Penn Plaza
New York, NY 10121
Ph: (212)904-2000   Fr: 800-722-4726
E-mail: ntcpub@tribune.com

Robert W. Bly. 1995. $14.95; $9.95 (paper). 295 pages.

★10088★ **Editorial Freelancing: A Practical Guide**
Aletheia Publications, Inc.
46 Bell Hollow Rd.
Putnam Valley, NY 10579
Ph: (914)526-2873   Fax: (914)526-2905

Trumbull Rogers. 1995. 200 pages. $19.95 (paper). Contains everything the freelancer needs to know about building a basic reference library, choosing a computer & appropriate software, marketing editorial services, determining & negotiating rates, billing, & setting up a retirement plan.

★10089★ **Great Jobs for Communications Majors**
McGraw-Hill Professional
2 Penn Plaza
New York, NY 10121
Ph: (212)904-2000   Fr: 800-722-4726
E-mail: ntcpub@tribune.com

Blythe Camenson. Second edition, 2001. $14.95 (paper). 256 pages.

★10090★ Great Jobs for English Majors

McGraw-Hill Trade
2 Penn Plaza
New York, NY 10121
Ph: (212)904-2000   Fr: 800-722-4726
E-mail: ntcpub@tribune.com

Julie DeGalan. Second edition, 2000. $12.95 (paper). 462 pages.

★10091★ Great Jobs for Liberal Arts Majors

McGraw-Hill Professional
2 Penn Plaza
New York, NY 10121
Ph: (212)904-2000   Fr: 800-722-4726
E-mail: ntcpub@tribune.com

Blythe Camenson. Second edition, 2001. $14.95 (paper). 256 pages.

★10092★ Guide to Careers in World Affairs

Impact Publications
9104-N Manassas Dr., Ste. N
Manassas Park, VA 20111-5211
Ph: (703)361-7300   Fax: (703)335-9486

Foreign Affairs Association Staff and Pamela Gerard. Third edition. 1993. $14.95. 331 pages. Out of print. Describes jobs in business, government, and nonprofit organizations. Explains the methods and credentials required to secure a job in many fields, including international law and journalism. Contains sections on internships and graduate programs.

★10093★ The Journalist's Road to Success

Pearson Allyn & Bacon
1230 Ave. of the Americas
New York, NY 10020
Ph: (212)782-3300   Fax: 800-445-6991
Fr: 800-666-9433

Annual, 1998. 148 pages. $4.00. Provides information on newspaper careers and salaries, and how to apply for a newspaper job. Explains how to choose a journalism school and lists colleges and universities offering journalism majors; describes undergraduate and graduate financial aid programs. Lists scholarships, fellowships, internships, and continuing education opportunities. Out of print.

★10094★ Magazines Career Directory

Thomson Gale
27500 Drake Rd.
Farmington Hills, MI 48331-3535
Ph: (248)699-GALE   Fax: (248)699-8069
Fr: 800-877-GALE
E-mail: galeord@gale.com
URL: http://www.galegroup.com

Bradley Morgan. Fifth edition, 1993. $39.00. Features extensive listings of contacts and entry-level job opportunities at many magazine publishing organizations. Includes articles by top professionals in the field on some of the industry's varied career paths: art,

editorial, sales, and business management. Part of Career Advisor series.

★10095★ Newspapers Career Directory

Thomson Gale
27500 Drake Rd.
Farmington Hills, MI 48331-3535
Ph: (248)699-GALE   Fax: 800-414-5043
Fr: 800-877-GALE
E-mail: galeord@gale.com
URL: http://www.gale.com

Bradley Morgan. Fourth edition, 1993. $39.00. 300 pages. Out of print. Features extensive listings of contacts and entry-level job opportunities at many newspaper organizations. Focuses on each area of the business, from reporting and editorial to sales and marketing to promotion and production.

★10096★ Opportunities in Journalism Careers

McGraw-Hill/Contemporary Books
1221 Avenue of the Americas
New York, NY 10020
Ph: (212)904-2000   Fr: 800-323-4900
E-mail: ntcpub@tribune.com

Jim Patten and Donald L. Ferguson. 1995. $14.95; $11.95 (paper). 160 pages. Outlines opportunities in every field of journalism, including newspaper reporting and editing, magazine and book publishing, corporate communications, advertising and public relations, freelance writing, and teaching. Covers how to prepare for and enter each field, outlining responsibilities, salaries, benefits, and job outlook for each specialty. Illustrated.

★10097★ Opportunities in Sports and Athletics Careers

McGraw-Hill Trade
2 Penn Plaza
New York, NY 10121
Ph: (212)904-2000   Fr: 800-722-4726
E-mail: ntcpub@tribune.com

William Ray Heitzmann. 1994. 160 pages. $14.95; $11.95 (paper). A guide to planning for and seeking opportunities in this growing field. Illustrated.

★10098★ Opportunities in Technical Writing and Communications Careers

McGraw-Hill Trade
2 Penn Plaza
New York, NY 10121
Ph: (212)904-2000   Fr: 800-722-4726
E-mail: ntcpub@tribune.com

Jay Gould and Wayne Losano. 1994. $14.95; $11.95 (paper). 160 pages. Provides advice on acquiring a position in medical, engineering, pharmaceutical, and other technical fields. Illustrated.

★10099★ Opportunities in Writing Careers

McGraw-Hill Contemporary Books
1221 Avenue of the Americas
New York, NY 10020
Ph: (212)904-2000   Fr: 800-323-4900
E-mail: ntcpub@tribune.com

Elizabeth Foote-Smith. 1999. $14.95; $11.95 (paper). 160 pages. Discusses opportunities in the print media, broadcasting, advertising or publishing. Business writing, public relations, and technical writing are among the careers covered. Contains bibliography and illustrations.

★10100★ Radio and Television Career Directory

Thomson Gale
27500 Drake Rd.
Farmington Hills, MI 48331-3535
Ph: (248)699-GALE   Fax: 800-414-5043
Fr: 800-877-GALE
E-mail: galeord@gale.com
URL: http://www.gale.com

Bradley Morgan. Second edition, 1993. $39.00. 300 pages. Features extensive listings of contacts and entry-level job opportunities. Provides information on internships and sources of help-wanted ads.

★10101★ Real People Working in Communications

McGraw-Hill Contemporary Books
1221 Avenue of the Americas
New York, NY 10020
Ph: (212)904-2000   Fr: 800-323-4900
E-mail: ntcpub@tribune.com

Jan Goldberg. 1996. $14.95; $12.95 (paper). Interviews and profiles of working professionals capture a range of opportunities in this field.

★10102★ Real-Resumes for Media, Newspaper, Broadcasting and Public Affairs Jobs

PREP Publishing
1110 1/2 Hay St., PMB 66
Fayetteville, NC 28305
Ph: (910)483-6611   Fax: (910)483-2439
Fr: 800-533-2814

Anne McKinney (Editor). October 2002. $16.95. Part of the Real-Resumes Series.

★10103★ Resumes for Communications Careers

McGraw-Hill Contemporary Books
1221 Avenue of the Americas
New York, NY 10020
Ph: (212)904-2000   Fr: 800-323-4900
E-mail: ntcpub@tribune.com

1998. $9.95 (paper). 464 pages.

EMPLOYMENT AGENCIES AND SEARCH FIRMS

★10104★ Joe Sullivan and Associates, Inc.

1202 Lexington Ave
PO Box 178
New York, NY 10028
Ph: (212)734-7890
E-mail: jsa612@aol.com
URL: http://www.joesullivanassociates.com

Executive search firm. Recruits for the broadcasting, media, and entertainment industries.

ONLINE JOB SOURCES AND SERVICES

★10105★ JournalismJobs.com

E-mail: contact@journalismjobs.com
URL: http://www.journalismjobs.com

Description: Career-related site for journalists and other media professionals. Seekers can search for jobs, post a resume online, and manage the search online with the Job Seeker Folder feature. They also can receive free job announcements by e-mail.

TRADESHOWS

★10106★ Radio-Television News Directors Association International Conference & Exhibition

Radio-Television News Directors Association
1600 K St. NW, No. 700
Washington, DC 20006-2838
Ph: (202)659-6510   Fax: (202)223-4007
Fr: 800-807-8632
E-mail: rtnda@rtnda.org
URL: http://www.rtnda.org/

Annual. **Primary Exhibits:** Equipment, supplies, and services for the radio and television news industries, including cameras, recorders, weather equipment, computers, and software. **Dates and Locations:** 2004 Sep 29 - Oct 2; Denver, CO; Denver Convention Center.

OTHER SOURCES

★10107★ Art Directors Club (ADC)

106 W 29th St.
New York, NY 10001
Ph: (212)643-1440   Fax: (212)643-4266
E-mail: info@adcny.org

URL: http://www.adcny.org

Members: Art directors of advertising magazines and agencies, visual information specialists, and graphic designers; associate members are artists, cinematographers, photographers, copywriters, educators, journalists, and critics. **Purpose:** Promotes and stimulates interest in the practice of art direction. **Activities:** Sponsors Annual Exhibition of Advertising, Editorial and Television Art and Design; International Traveling Exhibition; Hall of Fame. Provides educational, professional, and entertainment programs; on-premise art exhibitions; portfolio review program. Conducts panels for students and faculty.

★10108★ Asian American Journalists Association (AAJA)

1182 Market St., Ste. 320
San Francisco, CA 94102
Ph: (415)346-2051   Fax: (415)346-6343
E-mail: national@aaja.org
URL: http://www.aaja.org

Description: Educational and professional organization. Encourages Asian Pacific Americans to enter the ranks of journalism, to work for fair and accurate coverage of Asian Pacific Americans and to increase the number of Asian Pacific American Journalists and news managers in the industry.

★10109★ Association for Women in Communications

780 Ritchie Hwy., Ste. 28-S
Severna Park, MD 21146
Ph: (410)544-7442   Fax: (410)544-4640
E-mail: pat@womcom.org
URL: http://www.womcom.org

Description: Professional association of journalism and communications.

★10110★ Broadcast Education Association (BEA)

1771 N St. NW
Washington, DC 20036-2891
Ph: (202)429-3935   Fax: (202)775-2981
Fr: 888-380-7222
E-mail: beainfo@beaweb.org
URL: http://www.beaweb.org/

Description: Universities and colleges; faculty and students; promotes improvement of curriculum and teaching methods, broadcasting research, television and radio production, and programming teaching on the college level.

★10111★ Dow Jones Newspaper Fund (DJNF)

PO Box 300
Princeton, NJ 08543-0300
Ph: (609)452-2820   Fax: (609)520-5804
E-mail: newsfund@wsj.dowjones.com
URL: http://djnewspaperfund.dowjones.com

Description: Established by Dow Jones and Company, publisher of *The Wall Street Journal*, to encourage careers in journalism. Operates Newspapers Editing, and Sports

Copy Editing Internship Programs for all junior, senior, and graduate level college students interested in journalism. Also offers Business Reporting Intern Program for minority college sophomores and juniors to complete summer internships on daily newspapers as business reporters. Students receive monetary scholarships to return to school in the fall. Offers information on careers in journalism.

★10112★ Editorial Freelancers Association (EFA)

71 W 23rd St., Ste. 1910
New York, NY 10010
Ph: (212)929-5400   Fax: (212)929-5439
Fr: (866)929-5400
E-mail: info@the-efa.org
URL: http://www.the-efa.org

Description: Persons who work full- or part-time as freelance writers or editorial freelancers. Promotes professionalism and facilitates the exchange of information and support. Conducts professional training seminars; offers job listings.

★10113★ Education and Research Institute (ERI)

800 Maryland Ave. NE
Washington, DC 20002
Ph: (202)546-1710   Fax: (202)546-3489
E-mail: mal@nationaljournalismcenter.org
URL: http://www.nationaljournalismcenter.org/

Description: Organization dedicated to advancing awareness and understanding of America's traditional values and free enterprise system through the publication and distribution of studies on major issues of public policy. Conducts educational programs for youth. Founded and maintains the National Journalism Center to train college students in journalistic skills. Sponsors internship program that features research projects, writing assignments, and weekly seminars with professional journalists. Operates a job bank to match potential candidates with media-related jobs.

★10114★ International Security and Detective Alliance (ISDA)

PO Box 6303
Corpus Christi, TX 78466-6303
Fax: (361)888-8060

Members: Private investigators and security professionals, investigative reporters and writers, researchers, military personnel, and some interested laypersons. **Purpose:** Seeks to maintain an international registry of investigators for purpose of referral; support a more positive and accurate media image of P.I.s and security officers; provide a professional association for freelance operators; provide continuing education courses and materials. **Activities:** Provides professional certification in numerous specialty areas of investigation and security.

★10115★ *Interviewing Techniques for Newspapers*

State Mutual Book & Periodical Service, Ltd.
2183 Montauk Hwy.
Bridgehampton, NY 11932
Ph: (631)537-1104   Fax: (631)537-0412
Maurice Dunlevy. 1995. $20.00 (paper). 143 pages.

★10116★ *Media and the Arts Occupations*

Delphi Productions
3160 4th St.
Boulder, CO 80304
Fax: (303)443-4022   Fr: 888-443-2400
URL: http://www.delphivideo.com
$95.00. 50 minutes. Part of the Careers for the 21st Century Video Library.

★10117★ National Religious Broadcasters (NRB)

9510 Technology Dr.
Manassas, VA 20110
Ph: (703)330-7000   Fax: (703)330-7100
E-mail: adunlap@nrb.org
URL: http://www.nrb.org

Description: Christian communicators. Fosters electronic media access for the Gospel; promotes standards of excellence; integrity and accountability; and provides networking and fellowship opportunities for its members.

★10118★ Society of Professional Journalists (SPJ)

3909 N Meridian St.
Indianapolis, IN 46208-4011
Ph: (317)927-8000   Fax: (317)920-4789
E-mail: questions@spj.org
URL: http://www.spj.org

Members: Professional society - journalism. **Purpose:** Promotes a free and unfettered press; high professional standards and ethical behavior; journalism as a career. Conducts lobbying activities; maintains legal defense fund. Sponsors Pulliam/Kilgore Freedom of Information Internships in Washington, DC, and Indianapolis, IN. **Activities:** Holds forums on the free press.

★10119★ Women in Cable and Telecommunications (WIT)

14555 Avion Pkwy., Ste. 250
Chantilly, VA 20151
Ph: (703)234-9810   Fax: (703)817-1595
URL: http://www.wict.org

Description: Empowers and educate women to achieve their professional goals by providing opportunities for leadership, networking and advocacy.

Respiratory Therapists

★10120★ Health Careers Today

Elsevier-Health Sciences Division
The Curtis Center, Ste. 300E, 3rd Fl.
170 S. Independence Mall W.
Philadelphia, PA 19106
Ph: (215)238-7800   Fax: (215)238-7362
Fr: 800-523-4069

Gerdin. Revised edition. April 2004. $52.95.

SOURCES OF HELP-WANTED ADS

★10121★ AARC Times

Daedalus Enterprises Inc.
PO Box 29686
Dallas, TX 75229
Ph: (972)243-2272   Fax: (972)484-6010
URL: http://aarc.org

Monthly. $90.00/year; $10.00 for single issue. Professional magazine for respiratory therapists and other cardiopulmonary specialists.

★10122★ ADVANCE for Respiratory Care Practitioners

Merion Publications Inc.
2900 Horizon Dr.
PO Box 61556
King of Prussia, PA 19406-0956
Ph: (610)278-1400
URL: http://www.advanceforrcp.com

Biweekly. Free to qualified subscribers. Magazine for RRT's, CRTT's, and cardiopulmonary technologists across the country.

★10123★ Ambulatory Outreach

Society for Ambulatory Care Professionals
1 N Franklin, 31st Fl.
Chicago, IL 60606
Fax: (312)422-4577

Quarterly. Subscription included in membership; $95.00/year for nonmembers. Professional journal for ambulatory care personnel.

★10124★ American Review of Respiratory Disease

American Lung Association
61 Broadway
New York, NY 10019
Ph: (212)315-8700   Fax: (212)265-5642
E-mail: alahr@lungusa.org

Monthly. $130.00/year; $170.00/year. Medical journal focusing on lung diseases.

★10125★ ASRT Scanner

American Society of Radiologic Technologists
15000 Central Ave. SE
Albuquerque, NM 87123-3917
Ph: (505)298-4500   Fax: (505)298-5063
Fr: 800-444-2778

Monthly. Subscription included in membership. Professional magazine covering issues in radiology and medical technology. Includes calendar of events, member profiles, state affiliate news, educational opportunities, and research updates.

★10126★ Health Care Weekly Review

The Martin Group Inc.
24901 Northwestern Hwy., Ste. 316A
Southfield, MI 48075
Ph: (248)440-6080   Fax: (248)352-4801
E-mail: hcwr@compuserve.com

Weekly. $48.00/year for individuals. Professional newspaper covering the health care industry.

★10127★ Heart and Lung

Mosby Inc.
Curtis Ctr., 3rd Fl.
170 S. Independence Mall W
Philadelphia, PA 19106-3399
Ph: (215)238-7800
URL: http://www.mosby.com/hrtlng

Bimonthly. $66.00/year for individuals; $217.00/year for institutions. Journal offering articles prepared by nurse and physician members of the critical care team, recognizing the nurse's role in the care and management of major organ-system conditions in critically ill patients.

★10128★ Hospitals & Health Networks

Health Forum L.L.C.
One N Franklin
Chicago, IL 60606
Ph: (312)893-6800   Fax: (312)422-4600
Fr: 800-621-6902
E-mail: hhn@healthforum.com
URL: http://www.hhnmag.com

Monthly. Publication covering the health care industry.

★10129★ Journal of the American Society of Podiatric Medical Assistants

American Society of Podiatric Medical Assistants
2124 S Austin Blvd.
Cicero, IL 60804
Ph: (708)863-6303   Fax: (708)863-5375
Fr: 888-88A-SPMA

Quarterly. Subscription included in membership. Professional journal covering issues in podiatry.

★10130★ Journal of Cardiopulmonary Rehabilitation

Lippincott Williams & Wilkins
530 Walnut St.
Philadelphia, PA 19106
Ph: (215)521-8300   Fax: (215)521-8902
Fr: 800-638-3030
E-mail: gregg@breuningnagle.com
URL: http://www.jcrjournal.com/

Bimonthly. $99.95/year for individuals; $249.95/year for institutions; $99.95/year for other countries; $301.95/year for institutions, other countries. Medical journal.

★10131★ Journal of Health and Hospital Law

American Health Lawyers Association
1025 Connecticut NW, Ste. 600
Washington, DC 20036
Ph: (202)833-1100   Fax: (202)833-1105

Quarterly. $150.00/year. Professional journal covering healthcare issues and cases and their impact on the health care arena.

★10132★ Medicine and Health

Thomson Financial
195 Broadway
New York, NY 10007
Ph: (646)822-2000

Weekly. Professional publication covering the health care industry.

★10133★ Minority Health Today

Heritage Information Holdings Inc.
1101 Pennsylvania Ave. NW, Ste. 820
Washington, DC 20001

Bimonthly. Publication covering minority issues in health.

★10134★ Research in Healthcare Financial Management

International Society for Research in
  Healthcare Financial Management Ltd.
305 W Chesapeake Ave.
CSBA Ste. L-096
Towson, MD 21204

Annual. Publication covering issues in the healthcare industry.

★10135★ State Health Monitor

Atlantic Information Services Inc.
1100 17th St. NW, No. 300
Washington, DC 20036
Ph: (202)775-9008   Fax: (202)331-9542
Fr: 800-521-4323
E-mail: customerserv@aispub.com

Monthly. Publication covering health care.

★10136★ Trauma Reports

Thomson Medical Economics
5 Paragon Dr.
Montvale, NJ 07645-1742
Ph: (201)358-7200   Fax: (201)722-2680
URL: http://www.ahcpub.com/ahc_root_
html/products/newsletters/tr.

Bimonthly. $239.00/year for individuals. Professional publication covering health care.

PLACEMENT AND JOB REFERRAL SERVICES

★10137★ American Public Health Association (APHA)

800 I St. NW
Washington, DC 20001-3710
Ph: (202)777-2742   Fax: (202)777-2534
E-mail: comments@apha.org
URL: http://www.apha.org

Members: Professional organization of physicians, nurses, educators, academicians, environmentalists, epidemiologists, new professionals, social workers, health administrators, optometrists, podiatrists, pharmacists, dentists, nutritionists, health planners, other community and mental health specialists, and interested consumers. **Purpose:** Seeks

to protect and promote personal, mental, and environmental health. **Activities:** Services include promulgation of standards; establishment of uniform practices and procedures; development of the etiology of communicable diseases; research in public health; exploration of medical care programs and their relationships to public health. Sponsors job placement service.

EMPLOYER DIRECTORIES AND NETWORKING LISTS

★10138★ AHA Guide to the Health Care Field

American Hospital Association (AHA)
1 N. Franklin St., 27th Fl.
Chicago, IL 60606
Ph: (312)422-2050   Fax: (312)422-4700
Fr: 800-424-4301

Annual, August. $295.00. Covers hospitals, networks, multi-health care systems, freestanding ambulatory surgery centers, psychiatric facilities, long-term care facilities, substance abuse programs, and other health-related organizations. Entries include: For hospitals-Facility name, address, phone, administrator's name, number of beds, facilities and services, number of employees, expenses, other statistics. For other organizations-Name, address, phone, fax, name and title of contact. Arrangement: Geographical. Indexes: Hospital name.

★10139★ Directory of Hospital Personnel

Thomson Medical Economics
5 Paragon Dr.
Montvale, NJ 07645-1742
Ph: (201)358-7200   Fax: (201)722-2680

Annual, November. $325.00. Covers 200,000 executives at 7,000 U.S. hospitals. Entries include: Name of hospital, address, phone, number of beds, type and JCAHO status of hospital, names and titles of key department heads and staff, medical and nursing school affiliations; number of residents, interns, and nursing students. Arrangement: Geographical. Indexes: Hospital name, personnel, hospital size.

★10140★ Home Health Service Directory

infoUSA Inc.
5711 S 86th Cir.
Omaha, NE 68127-0347
Ph: (402)930-3500   Fax: (402)331-0176
Fr: 800-555-6124
URL: http://www.abii.com

Annual. Number of listings: 21,158. Entries include: Name, address, phone (including area code), size of advertisement, year first in "Yellow Pages," name of owl her or manager, number of employees. Compiled from telephone company "Yellow Pages," nationwide. Arrangement: Geographical.

★10141★ Hospital Blue Book

Billian/Transworld Publishing Inc.
2100 Powers Ferry Rd.
Ste. 300
Atlanta, GA 30339
Ph: (770)955-8484   Fax: (770)955-8485
Fr: 800-533-8484
E-mail: blu-book@billian.com

Annual, January. $285.00 for national edition; $160.00 for southern edition. Covers more than 6,687 hospitals; some listings also appear in a separate southern edition of this publication. Entries include: Name of hospital, accreditation, mailing address, phone, fax, number of beds, type of facility (nonprofit, general, state, etc.); list of administrative personnel and chiefs of medical services, with specific titles. Arrangement: Geographical.

★10142★ Medical and Health Information Directory

Thomson Gale
27500 Drake Rd.
Farmington Hills, MI 48331-3535
Ph: (248)699-4253   Fax: (248)699-8065
Fr: 800-877-GALE
E-mail: businessproducts@gale.com

Annual. $285.00 per volume; $675.00 per set. Covers in Volume 1, more than 26,500 medical and health oriented associations, organizations, institutions, and government agencies, including health maintenance organizations (HMOs), preferred provider organizations (PPOs), insurance companies, pharmaceutical companies, research centers, and medical and allied health schools. In Volume 2, over 12,000 medical book publishers; medical periodicals, directories, audiovisual producers and services, medical libraries and information centers, electronic resources, and health-related internet search engines. In Volume 3, more than 35,500 clinics, treatment centers, care programs, and counseling/diagnostic services for 34 subject areas. Entries include: Institution, service, or firm name, address, phone, fax, email and URL; many include names of key personnel and, when pertinent, descriptive annotation. Volume 3 was formerly listed separately as Health Services Directory. Arrangement: Classified by organization activity, service, etc. Indexes: Each volume has a complete alphabetical name and keyword index.

HANDBOOKS AND MANUALS

★10143★ Careers in Health Care

McGraw-Hill Trade
2 Penn Plaza
New York, NY 10121
Ph: (212)904-2000   Fr: 800-722-4726
E-mail: ntcpub@tribune.com

Barbara M. Swanson. Fourth edition, 2000. $17.95; $13.95 (paper). 320 pages. Describes job duties, work settings, salaries, licensing and certification requirements, educational preparation, and future outlook. Gives ideas on how to secure a job.

★10144★ **Expert Resumes for Health Care Careers**

JIST Publishing
8902 Otis Ave.
Indianapolis, IN 46216-1033
Ph: (317)613-4200   Fax: 800-547-8329
December 2003. $16.95. 288 pages.

★10145★ **Opportunities in Health and Medical Careers**

McGraw-Hill Trade
2 Penn Plaza
New York, NY 10121
Ph: (212)904-2000   Fr: 800-722-4726
I. Donald Snook, Jr. and Leo D'Orazio. 1997. $14.95; $11.95 (paper). 202 pages. Covers the full range of medical and health occupations. Illustrated.

★10146★ **Resumes for Health and Medical Careers**

McGraw-Hill Trade
2 Penn Plaza
New York, NY 10121
Ph: (212)904-2000   Fr: 800-722-4726
E-mail: ntcpub@tribune.com
1997. $9.95 (paper). 455 pages.

EMPLOYMENT AGENCIES AND SEARCH FIRMS

★10147★ **JPM International**

26060 Acero
Mission Viejo, CA 92691
Ph: (949)699-4300   Fax: (949)699-4333
Fr: 800-685-7856
E-mail: leslieo@jpmintl.com
URL: http://www.jpmintl.com
Executive search firm and employment agency.

★10148★ **Professional Placement Associates, Inc.**

287 Bowman Ave., Ste. 309
Purchase, NY 10577
Ph: (914)251-1000   Fax: (914)251-1055
E-mail: lschachter@ppasearch.com
URL: http://www.ppasearch.com
Executive search firm specializing in the health and medical field.

★10149★ **Travcorps, Inc.**

40 Eastern Ave.
Malden, MA 02148
Ph: (781)322-2600   Fax: 800-803-1186
Fr: 800-343-3270
URL: http://www.travcorps.com

Places staff in temporary assignments. Other locations nationwide.

ONLINE JOB SOURCES AND SERVICES

★10150★ **Medhunters.com**

E-mail: info@medhunters.com
URL: http://www.medhunters.com
Description: Career search site for jobs in all health care specialties; educational resources; visa and licensing information for relocation; interesting articles; relocation tools; links to professional organizations and general resources.

★10151★ **ProHealthJobs**

E-mail: sales@prohealthjobs.com
URL: http://www.prohealthjobs.com
Description: Career resources site for the medical and health care field. Lists professional opportunities, product information, continuing education and open positions.

★10152★ **RehabJobs Online**

PO Box 480536
Los Angeles, CA 90048
Ph: (213)938-7718   Fax: (213)938-9609
Fr: 800-43-REHAB
E-mail: support@atsrehabjobs.com
URL: http://www.rehabjobs.com
Description: @dq1On-line resource center for the professional therapist.@dq2 **Main files include:** Therapists Only, Therapy Forums, Nationwide Job Search (database), Therapy Job Outlook, Therapy Job Search Utilities, Therapy Links, Information for Employers and Recruiters.

OTHER SOURCES

★10153★ **American Association for Respiratory Care (AARC)**

9425 N MacArthur Blvd., Ste. 100
Irving, TX 75063-4706
Ph: (972)243-2272   Fax: (972)484-2720
E-mail: info@aarc.org
URL: http://www.aarc.org
Description: Allied health society of respiratory therapists and other respiratory caregivers employed by hospitals, skilled nursing facilities, home care companies, group practices, educational institutions, and municipal organizations. Encourages, develops, and provides educational programs for persons interested in the profession of respiratory care; and advances the science of respiratory care.

★10154★ **Committee on Accreditation for Respiratory Care (COARC)**

1248 Harwood Rd.
Bedford, TX 76021-4244
Ph: (817)283-2835   Fax: (817)354-8519
Fr: 800-874-5615
E-mail: info@coarc.com
URL: http://www.coarc.com
Description: Physicians (6); respiratory therapists (6); public representative (1). Purposes are to develop standards and requirements for accredited educational programs of respiratory therapy for recommendation to the American Medical Association; to conduct evaluations of educational programs that have applied for accreditation of the AMA and to make recommendations to the AMA's Committee on Allied Health Education and Accreditation; to maintain a working liaison with other organizations interested in respiratory therapy education and evaluation.

★10155★ **Exploring Health Occupations**

Cambridge Educational
2572 Brunswick Ave.
Lawrenceville, NJ 08648-4128
Fax: 800-FAX-ON-US   Fr: 800-468-4227
URL: http://www.cambridgeeducational.com
Two videos. $139.95. 1999.

★10156★ **Health Assessment & Treating Occupations**

Delphi Productions
3160 4th St.
Boulder, CO 80304
Fax: (303)443-4022   Fr: 888-443-2400
URL: http://www.delphivideo.com
$95.00. 50 minutes. Part of the Careers for the 21st Century Video Library.

★10157★ **Health Service Occupations**

Delphi Productions
3160 4th St.
Boulder, CO 80304
Fax: (303)443-4022   Fr: 888-443-2400
URL: http://www.delphivideo.com
$95.00. 50 minutes. Part of the Careers for the 21st Century Video Library.

★10158★ **Medicine & Related Occupations**

Delphi Productions
3160 4th St.
Boulder, CO 80304
Fax: (303)443-4022   Fr: 888-443-2400
URL: http://www.delphivideo.com
$95.00. 45 minutes. Part of the Careers for the 21st Century Video Library.

★10159★ **National Board for Respiratory Care (NBRC)**

8310 Nieman Rd.
Lenexa, KS 66214-1579
Ph: (913)599-4200   Fax: (913)541-0156

E-mail: mthomas@goAMP.com
URL: http://www.nbrc.org.

Description: Offers credentialing examinations for respiratory therapists, respiratory

therapy technicians, pulmonary technologists, and perinatal/pediatric respiratory care specialists.

Restaurant and Food Service Managers

SOURCES OF HELP-WANTED ADS

★10160★ **Airport Press**
P.A.T.I. Inc.
PO Box 879, JFK Sta.
Jamaica, NY 11430-0879
Ph: (718)244-6788   Fax: (718)995-3432
Fr: 800-982-5832
E-mail: airprtpres@aol.com

Monthly. $32.00/year for individuals. Newspaper for the airport industry.

★10161★ **Beverage World**
Beverage World
770 Broadway
New York, NY 10003-9595
Ph: (646)654-4500   Fax: (646)654-7727
E-mail: bevworld@aol.com
URL: http://www.beverageworld.com

Monthly. $70.00/year for individuals; $110.00 for two years; $125.00/year for other countries; $165.00 for two years, other countries; $8.00 for single issue. Trade magazine for corporate, marketing, distribution, production, and purchasing top and middle management in the multi-product beverage industry.

★10162★ **Chef**
Talcott Communications Corp.
2B W Kinzie, 12th Fl.
Chicago, IL 60610
Ph: (312)849-2220   Fax: (312)849-2174
Fr: 800-229-1967
E-mail: chef@talcott.com

$32.00/year for individuals; $2.95/year. Food information for chefs.

★10163★ **Food Management**
Penton Media Inc.
1300 E 9th St.
Cleveland, OH 44114-1503
Ph: (216)696-7000   Fax: (216)931-9799
URL: http://www.foodservicesearch.com/
Monthly. Free. Magazine for foodservice

professionals in the onsite "noncommercial" market.

★10164★ **FoodService Director**
VNU Business Publications
770 Broadway
New York, NY 10003
Ph: (646)654-5000   Fax: (646)654-4977
URL: http://www.fsd.com

Monthly. Tabloid newspaper of the noncommercial foodservice market.

★10165★ **Foodservice East**
The Newbury Street Group Inc.
165 New Boston St., No. 236
Woburn, MA 01801
Ph: (781)376-9080   Fax: (781)376-0010
Fr: 800-852-5212
E-mail: fdsvceast@.aol.com

$30.00/year for individuals. Compact Tabloid covering trends and analysis of the foodservice industry in the Northeast. A business-to-business publication featuring news, analysis and trends for the Northeast food service professional.

★10166★ **Hotel & Motel Management**
Advanstar Communications Inc.
7500 Old Oak Blvd.
Cleveland, OH 44130-3369
Ph: (440)243-8100   Fax: (440)891-2777
URL: http://https://www.advanstar.com/index_allpubs.html

Magazine (tabloid) covering the global lodging industry.

★10167★ **HOTELS**
Reed Business Information
360 Park Ave. S
New York, NY 10014
Ph: (646)746-7764
URL: http://www.hotelsmag.com/

Magazine covering management and operations as well as foodservice and design in the hospitality industry.

★10168★ **Institutional Distribution**
Institutional Distribution
770 Broadway
New York, NY 10003
Ph: (646)654-5000
E-mail: cleibman@bill.com
URL: http://www.billcom.com

Monthly. $66.00/year; $7.00 for single issue. Trade magazine for foodservice wholesalers and sales force.

★10169★ **Journal of the American Dietetic Association**
American Dietetic Association
120 S Riverside Plaza, Ste. 2000
Chicago, IL 60606-6995
Ph: (312)899-0040   Fax: (312)899-4817
Fr: 800-877-1600

Monthly. $115.00/year for individuals; $140.00/year for Canada; $190.00/year for other countries; $9.75 for single issue. Journal reporting original research on nutrition, diet therapy, education and administration.

★10170★ **Midwest Foodservice News**
Pinnacle Publishing Group
2736 Sawbury Blvd.
Columbus, OH 43235
Ph: (614)336-0710   Fax: (614)336-0713

Bimonthly. Free to qualified subscribers; $24.00/year for others. Food service trade magazine featuring new products and suppliers and other industry news including food news, restaurant association updates, news of chefs, restaurant concepts, earnings, and openings and closings.

★10171★ **Nightclub & Bar Magazine**
Oxford Publishing Inc.
307 W Jackson Ave.
Oxford, MS 38655
Ph: (601)236-5510   Fax: (601)236-5541
Fr: 800-247-3881
E-mail: ncb@nightclub.com
URL: http://www.nightclub.com

Monthly. Free to qualified subscribers; $25.00/year; $35.00/year for Canada; $85.00/year for other countries. Trade magazine covering management, lighting, sound, food, beverage, promotions, current trends, and other bar industry news.

★10172★ Restaurant Business

VNU Business Publications
770 Broadway
New York, NY 10003
Ph: (646)654-5000   Fax: (646)654-4977
E-mail: 200-4782@mcimail.com
URL: http://http://www.foodservicetoday.com

$105.00/year for individuals; $10.00 for single issue. Trade magazine for restaurants and commercial food service.

★10173★ Restaurant Hospitality

Penton Media Inc.
1300 E 9th St.
Cleveland, OH 44114-1503
Ph: (216)696-7000   Fax: (216)931-9799
E-mail: rheditors@aol.com

Monthly. Free to qualified subscribers; $60.00/year for individuals; $5.95 for single issue. Magazine for managers and other executives of restaurant chains, independent restaurants, and hotels - foodservice operations.

★10174★ Restaurants & Institutions

Reed Business Information
360 Park Ave. S
New York, NY 10014
Ph: (646)746-7764
E-mail: gdrummond@reedbusiness.com
URL: http://www.rimag.com

Magazine focusing on foodservice and lodging management.

★10175★ Southeast Food Service News

Southeast Publishing Company Inc.
PO Box 47719
Atlanta, GA 30362
Ph: (770)452-1807   Fax: (770)457-3829
E-mail: info@sfsn.com

$36.00/year for individuals. Magazine (tabloid) serving the food industry.

★10176★ Special Events

Miramar Communications Inc.
23805 Stuart Ranch Rd., Ste. 235
PO Box 8987
Malibu, CA 90265-8987
Ph: (310)317-4522   Fax: (310)317-0264
Fr: 800-543-4116
URL: http://www.specialevents.com

Monthly. Free to qualified subscribers. Magazine for special event professionals.

★10177★ Sunbelt Foodservice

Shelby Publishing Company Inc.
517 Green St.
Gainesville, GA 30501
Ph: (770)534-8380   Fax: (770)535-0110

Monthly. $25.00/year for individuals. Trade newspaper (tabloid) covering the food industry geared toward restaurant operators.

★10178★ Trends in the Hotel Industry

Pannell Kerr Forster
420 Lexington Ave.
New York, NY 10170
Ph: (212)867-8000

Quarterly. Trade publication covering the hotel industry.

★10179★ Western Itasca Review & Deerpath Shopper

Lebhar-Friedman Inc.
425 Park Ave.
New York, NY 10022-3556
Ph: (212)756-5088   Fax: (212)756-5120
Fr: 800-453-2427

Weekly. $34.50/year for individuals. Local newspaper and shopper.

PLACEMENT AND JOB REFERRAL SERVICES

★10180★ Les Amis d'Escoffier

1230 Main St., Rte. 9
Leicester, MA 01524
Ph: (508)892-9090   Fax: (508)892-3620
E-mail: info@castlerestaurant.com
URL: http://www.castlerestaurant.com/default.htm

Members: An educational organization of professionals in the food and wine industries. **Activities:** Maintains museum, speakers' bureau, hall of fame, and placement service. Sponsors charitable programs.

EMPLOYER DIRECTORIES AND NETWORKING LISTS

★10181★ College/University Foodservice Who's Who

Information Central Inc.
Box 3900
Prescott, AZ 86302
Ph: (520)778-1513   Fax: (520)778-1513

Triennial. $345.00. Covers over 2,700 food service programs in colleges and universities. Entries include: Institution name, address, phone, enrollment, total annual food purchases, number of meals served per day; name of management company, principal food service executive(s), services, fast food

chains on campus. Arrangement: Geographical. Indexes: Alphabetical.

★10182★ Directory of Chain Restaurant Operators

Chain Store Guide
3922 Coconut Palm Dr.
Tampa, FL 33619
Ph: (813)627-6800   Fax: (813)627-688
Fr: 800-927-9292
URL: http://www.csgis.com

Annual, April. $775.00 for CD-ROM; $975.0 for CD-ROM and directory. Covers chai restaurant operators, chain hotel operators nontraditional foodservice operators an food service management operators wh operate 2 or more food service locations Entries include: For chain restaurant opera tors-company name, address, phone and fa numbers; e-mail and web addresses; type c business; listing type; total annual sales food service sales; system wide sales; per cent of sales of alcohol; percent of sale from Internet; alcohol types served; tota units; company owned units; units franchise to and from; trade names; co-brande names and numbers; food service manage ment location types; trading areas; foreig trading areas; units by primary menu type and type of foodservice; self distributing an catering services indicators; franchise affilia tions names and locations; primary distribu tors names and locations; parent and sub sidiary company names and locations; re gional; divisional; and branch office loca tions; distribution centers locations; yea founded; public company indicator; key per sonnel with titles. For chain hotel operators includes number of restaurants in hotels. Fo food service management operators-in cludes number of food service managemen accounts and total number of locations served. Arrangement: Geographical. In dexes: Alphabetical, type of food service menu type, franchisee, food service man agement, state, exclusions.

★10183★ Directory of Hospital Personnel

Thomson Medical Economics
5 Paragon Dr.
Montvale, NJ 07645-1742
Ph: (201)358-7200   Fax: (201)722-268C

Annual, November. $325.00. Covers 200,000 executives at 7,000 U.S. hospitals. Entries include: Name of hospital, address, phone, number of beds, type and JCAHO status of hospital, names and titles of key department heads and staff, medical and nursing school affiliations; number of residents, interns, and nursing students. Arrangement: Geographical. Indexes: Hospital name, personnel, hospital size.

★10184★ Restaurants & Institutions- Annual 400 Issues

Reed Business Information
360 Park Ave. S
New York, NY 10014
Ph: (646)746-6400
E-mail: r&iedit@cahners.com

URL: http://www.rimag.com

Annual, July. $25.00. Publication includes: List of 400 largest away-from-home food service companies. Entries include: Company name, location, rank, food service volume and number of units for two preceding years, brief summary of activities and prospects. Arrangement: Ranked by sales volume. Indexes: Alphabetical, segment of industry.

★10185★ **School Foodservice Who's Who**

Information Central Inc.
Box 3900
Prescott, AZ 86302
Ph: (520)778-1513   Fax: (520)778-1513

Triennial, latest edition January 1999. $650.00. Covers about 5,800 food service programs in public and Catholic school systems with enrollments in excess of 1,500 students. Separate listings of the biggest buyers (school districts reporting over $1.5 million/year in foodservice purchases), state school foodservice officials, and co-op buying groups and food management companies involved in food service. Entries include: School district name, address, phone, fax; food service budget, key food service executive, number of meals served daily, types of food and services, food management company, fast food brands. Arrangement: Geographical. Indexes: School districts.

HANDBOOKS AND MANUALS

★10186★ **Best Impressions in Hospitality: Your Professional Image for Excellence**

Thomson Delmar Learning
PO Box 15015
Albany, NY 12212-5015
Ph: (518)348-2300   Fr: 800-998-7498

Angie Michael. 1999. $22.50 (paper). 240 pages.

★10187★ **Career Opportunities in the Food and Beverage Industry**

Facts on File, Inc.
132 W. 31st St., 17th Fl.
New York, NY 10001-2006
Ph: (212)967-8800   Fax: (212)967-8107
Fr: 800-322-8755
URL: http://www.factsonfile.com

Barbara Sims-Bell. Second edition, 2001. $18.95 (paper). Provides the job seeker with information about locating and landing 80 skilled and unskilled jobs in the industry. Includes detailed job descriptions for many specific positions and lists trade associations, recruiting organizations, and major agencies. Contains index and bibliography.

★10188★ **Career Opportunities in Travel and Tourism**

Checkmark Books, Inc.
132 W. 31st St., 17th Fl.
New York, NY 10001-2006
Ph: (212)967-8800   Fax: (212)967-9196
Fr: 800-322-8755
URL: http://www.factsonfile.com

John K. Hawks. 1996. $18.95 (paper). 224 pages. Includes detailed job descriptions, educational requirements, salary ranges, and advancement prospects for 70 different job opportunities in this fast-paced industry. Contains index and bibliography.

★10189★ **Careers for Gourmets and Others Who Relish Food**

McGraw-Hill Trade
2 Penn Plaza
New York, NY 10121
Ph: (212)904-2000   Fr: 800-722-4726
E-mail: ntcpub@tribune.com

Mary Donovan. Second edition, 2002. $15.95; $12.95 (paper). 192 pages. Discusses such job prospects as foods columnist, cookbook writer, test kitchen worker, pastry chef, recipe developer, food festival organizer, restaurant manager, and food stylist.

★10190★ **Careers for Health Nuts and Others Who Like to Stay Fit**

McGraw-Hill Trade
2 Penn Plaza
New York, NY 10121
Ph: (212)904-2000   Fr: 800-722-4726
E-mail: ntcpub@tribune.com

Blythe Camenson. 1996. $14.95; $9.95 (paper). 160 pages.

★10191★ **Careers for Night Owls and Other Insomniacs**

McGraw-Hill Trade
2 Penn Plaza
New York, NY 10121
Ph: (212)904-2000   Fr: 800-722-4726
E-mail: ntcpub@tribune.com

Louise Miller. 1995. $14.95; $9.95 (paper). 160 pages.

★10192★ **Careers in Travel, Tourism, and Hospitality**

McGraw-Hill Contemporary Books
1221 Avenue of the Americas
New York, NY 10020
Ph: (212)904-2000   Fr: 800-323-4900
E-mail: ntcpub@tribune.com

Marjorie Eberts, Linda Brothers, and Ann Gisler. 1997. $17.95; 13.95 (paper). 192 pages.

★10193★ **Choosing a Career in the Restaurant Industry**

Rosen Publishing Group, Inc.
29 E. 21st St.
New York, NY 10010
Ph: (212)777-3017   Fax: 888-436-4643
Fr: 800-237-9932

Eileen Beal. 1996. $17.95. 64 pages. Explores various jobs in the restaurant industry. Describes job duties, salaries, educational preparation, and job hunting. Contains information about fast food, catering, and small businesses.

★10194★ **Culinary Arts Career Starter**

LearningExpress, LLC
900 Broadway, Ste. 604
New York, NY 10003
Ph: (212)995-2566   Fax: (212)995-5512
Fr: 800-295-9556

Mary Masi. 1999. $14.95 (paper). 229 pages.

★10195★ **How to Get a Job with a Cruise Line**

Ticket to Adventure, Inc.
PO Box 41005
St. Petersburg, FL 33743-1005
Ph: (727)822-5029   Fax: (727)821-3409
Fr: 800-929-7447

Mary Fallon Miller. Fifth edition, 2001. $16.95 (paper). 336 pages. Explores jobs with cruise ships, describing duties, responsibilities, benefits, and training. Lists cruise ship lines and schools offering cruise line training. Offers job hunting advice.

★10196★ **Opportunities in Culinary Careers**

McGraw-Hill Contemporary Books
1221 Avenue of the Americas
New York, NY 10020
Ph: (212)904-2000   Fr: 800-323-4900
E-mail: ntcpub@tribune.com

Mary Deirdre Donovan. 1998. $14.95; $11.95 (paper). 160 pages. Describes the educational preparation and training of chefs and cooks and explores a variety of food service jobs in restaurants, institutions, and research and development. Lists major culinary professional associations and schools. Offers guidance on landing a first job in cooking and related fields.

★10197★ **Opportunities in Hospital Administration Careers**

McGraw-Hill/Contemporary Books
1221 Avenue of the Americas
New York, NY 10020
Ph: (212)904-2000   Fr: 800-323-4900
E-mail: ntcpub@tribune.com

I. Donald Snook. 1997. $14.95; $11.95 (paper). 160 pages. Discusses opportunities for administrators in a variety of management settings: hospital, department, clinic, group practice, HMO, mental health, and extended care facilities.

★10198★ Opportunities in Restaurant Careers
Vgm Career Horizons
1221 Avenue of the Americas
New York, NY 10020
Ph: (212)904-2000   Fr: 800-323-4900
E-mail: ntcpub@tribune.com
Carol Caprione Chmelynski. 1998. $14.95; $11.95 (paper). 160 pages. Covers opportunities in the food service industry and details salaries, benefits, training opportunities, and professional associations. Special emphasis is put on becoming a successful restaurant manager by working up through the ranks. Illustrated.

EMPLOYMENT AGENCIES AND SEARCH FIRMS

★10199★ The Alfus Group Inc.
353 Lexington Ave., Fl. 8
New York, NY 10016
Ph: (212)599-1000   Fax: (212)599-1523
Executive search firm. Specializes in the hospitality industry.

★10200★ Anderson & Associates
112 S. Tyron St.
Charlotte, NC 28284
Ph: (704)347-0090   Fax: (704)347-0064
Executive search firm. Branch in Cumming, Georgia.

★10201★ Bennett Search & Consulting Company Inc.
285-1 W. Naomi Dr.
Naples, FL 34104
Ph: (239)352-0219   Fax: (239)353-7719
Executive search firm.

★10202★ Bowman & Associates
1660 S Amphlett Blvd., Ste. 245
San Mateo, CA 94402
Ph: (650)573-0188   Fax: (650)573-8209
Executive search firm specializing in the hospitality industry.

★10203★ Carlson & Czeswik
740 Mississippi River Blvd., Ste. 18-G
St. Paul, MN 55116
Ph: (651)698-6400
Executive search firm.

★10204★ Cary & Associates
PO Box 2043
Winter Park, FL 32790
Ph: (407)647-1145
Executive search firm.

★10205★ The Cooper Executive Search Group Inc.
PO Box 375
Wales, WI 53183-0375
Ph: (262)968-9049   Fax: (262)968-9059
Executive search firm.

★10206★ CraigSearch
901 Waterfall Way, Ste. 107
Richardson, TX 75080
Ph: (972)644-3264
Executive search firm.

★10207★ Derba & Derba
7 Whispering Pines
Andover, MA 01810
Ph: (978)470-8270   Fax: (978)470-4592
Executive search firm focused on the hospitality industry.

★10208★ Drake Executive Search
9434 N. 134th Ave., Ste. 111
Owasso, OK 74055
Ph: (918)272-2608   Fax: (918)272-2612
Executive search firm for the hospitality industry.

★10209★ DSA-Dixie Search Associates
670 Village Trace, Bldg. 19, Ste. D
Marietta, GA 30067
Ph: (770)850-0250   Fax: (770)850-9295
Conducts employee recruitment and placement for U.S. and international firms within the food, beverage and hospitality industries.

★10210★ Employment Advisors
815 Nicollet Mall Ste 200
Minneapolis, MN 55402
Ph: (612)339-3944
E-mail: info@collegegraduateregistry.com
URL: http://www.collegegraduateregistry.com
Employment agency. Places candidates in variety of fields.

★10211★ Hospitality International
23 W 73rd St., Ste.100
New York, NY 10023
Ph: (212)769-8800   Fax: (212)769-2138
E-mail: jar@hospitalityinternational.com
URL: http://www.hospitalityinternational.com
Executive search firm. Branch office in New York, NY.

★10212★ J.D. Hersey and Associates
1695 Old Henderson Rd.
Columbus, OH 43220
Ph: (614)459-4555   Fax: (614)459-4544
E-mail: info@jdhersey.com
URL: http://www.jdhersey.com
Executive search firm for permanent and contingency placements.

★10213★ LW Foote Company
110-110th Ave. NE, Ste. 603
Bellevue, WA 98004-5840
Ph: (425)451-1660   Fax: (425)451-1535
Executive search firm.

★10214★ Personalized Management Associates
1950 Spectrum Cir., Ste. B310
Marietta, GA 30067
Ph: (770)916-1668   Fax: (770)916-1429
Fr: 800-466-7822
Mid-level to executive level management placement firm specializing in retail, restaurant and service management. Industries served: retail, restaurant, finance, sales, marketing, advertising.

★10215★ The Personnel Network, Inc.
1246 Lake Murray Blvd.
PO Box 1426
Irmo, SC 29063
Ph: (803)781-2087   Fax: (803)732-7986
E-mail: chuckirmo@aol.com
Executive search firm.

★10216★ Ritt-Ritt and Associates
5105 Tollview Dr., Ste. 100
Rolling Meadows, IL 60008
Ph: (847)483-9330   Fax: (847)483-9331
E-mail: info@rittsearch.com
URL: http://www.rittsearch.com
Food service and hospitality employment agency and executive search firm.

★10217★ Tempo Personnel Services
4 Moss Creek Ct.
PO Box 22448
Hilton Head Island, SC 29926
Ph: (843)681-9066   Fax: (843)689-6477
Full service employment agency that includes local temporary and permanent placements, medical home health provider and regional and national hospitality placement.

★10218★ Vip Temporaries
15600 N San Pedro, Ste. 203
San Antonio, TX 78232
Ph: (210)340-2000   Fax: (210)340-4089
Personnel consultants specializing in executive recruiting. Industries served: food, automotive aftermarket, financial services, and medical.

ONLINE JOB SOURCES AND SERVICES

★10219★ Bristol Associates, Inc.
URL: http://www.bristolassoc.com
Description: Executive search firm specializing in direct marketing, hospitality and food industries. Applicants can post their resumes online for recruiters' viewing and search current job databank. Also contains job tools and resources.

★10220★ Pioneer College Caterers Online
E-mail: careers@pcconline.com
URL: http://www.foodindustryjobs.com
Description: Job databank and resume submission service for food industry workers in Christian college cafeterias.

TRADESHOWS

★10221★ American School Food Service Association Annual National Conference
American School Food Service Association
700 S. Washington St., Ste. 300
Alexandria, VA 22314-4287
Ph: (703)739-3900   Fax: (703)739-3915
Fr: 800-877-8822
Annual. **Primary Exhibits:** Food service supplies and equipment, including educational services and computers.

★10222★ Annual Hotel, Motel, and Restaurant Supply Show of the Southeast
Leisure Time Unlimited, Inc.
708 Main St.
PO Box 332
Myrtle Beach, SC 29578
Ph: (843)448-9483   Fax: (843)626-1513
Fr: 800-261-5591
E-mail: ltushows@aol.com
URL: http://www.dickenschristmashow.com
Annual. **Primary Exhibits:** Carpeting, furniture, coffee makers, produce companies, wine and beer and food companies, and services to motels, hotels, and restaurants. **Dates and Locations:** 2005 Jan 25-27; Myrtle Beach, SC.

★10223★ Foodservice Expo
Kentucky Restaurant Association
133 N Evergreen Rd. Ste. 201
Louisville, KY 40243-1484
Ph: (502)896-0464   Fax: (502)896-0465
Fr: 800-896-0414
E-mail: info@kyra.org
URL: http://www.kyra.org

Annual. **Primary Exhibits:** Foodservice equipment, supplies, services, and products.

★10224★ Heart of America Hospitality Expo
Missouri Restaurant Association
1810 Craig Rd. Ste. 225
St. Louis, MO 65101
Annual. **Primary Exhibits:** Food service and hospitality industries equipment, supplies, and services.

★10225★ International Hotel & Restaurant Expo
Diversified Business Communications
121 Free St.
PO Box 7437
Portland, ME 04112-7437
Ph: (207)842-5504   Fax: (207)842-5505
URL: http://www.divbusiness.com
Primary Exhibits: Equipment, supplies, and services for the hotel and restaurant industries.

★10226★ Louisiana Foodservice Expo
Louisiana Restaurant Association
2700 N. Arnoult Rd.
Metairie, LA 70002-5916
Ph: (504)454-2277   Fax: (504)454-2663
Fr: 800-256-4572
E-mail: sandyr@lra.org
Annual. **Primary Exhibits:** Food service equipment, supplies, and services, food products.

★10227★ Midsouthwest Foodservice Convention and Exposition
Oklahoma Restaurant Association
3800 N. Portland
Oklahoma City, OK 73112
Ph: (405)942-8181   Fax: (405)942-0541
Fr: 800-375-8181
Annual. **Primary Exhibits:** Providers of foodservice and hospitality products, services and equipment.

★10228★ New York Restaurant & Food Service Show
Reed Exhibitions (North American Headquarters)
383 Main Ave.
PO Box 6059
Norwalk, CT 06851
Ph: (203)840-5402   Fax: (203)840-9402
E-mail: inquiry@reedexpo.com
URL: http://www.reedexpo.com
Annual. **Primary Exhibits:** Equipment, supplies, and services for the food products, foodservice, restaurant, and institutional food service industries.

★10229★ Northeast Food Service and Lodging Exposition and Conference
Reed Exhibitions (North American Headquarters)
383 Main Ave.
PO Box 6059
Norwalk, CT 06851
Ph: (203)840-5402   Fax: (203)840-9402
E-mail: inquiry@reedexpo.com
URL: http://www.reedexpo.com
Annual. **Primary Exhibits:** Food services, operating equipment, and services for the hospitality and institutional foodservice industry.

★10230★ South Carolina Foodservice Expo
South Carolina Foodservice Expo
111 Shannon Dr.
Spartanburg, SC 29301
Ph: (864)574-9323   Fax: (864)574-0784
E-mail: scsfsa@aol.com
Annual. **Primary Exhibits:** Food and food-service equipment, supplies, and services.

★10231★ Southeastern Restaurant, Hospitality & Foodservice Show
Reed Exhibitions (North American Headquarters)
383 Main Ave.
PO Box 6059
Norwalk, CT 06851
Ph: (203)840-5402   Fax: (203)840-9402
E-mail: inquiry@reedexpo.com
URL: http://www.reedexpo.com
Annual. **Primary Exhibits:** Equipment, supplies, and services for hotels, restaurants, and travel-related businesses.

★10232★ Upper Midwest Hospitality, Restaurant, and Lodging Show - UP Show
Hospitality Minnesota - Minnesota's Restaurant, Hotel, and Resort Associations
305 E. Roselawn Ave.
St. Paul, MN 55117
Ph: (651)778-2400   Fax: (651)778-2424
E-mail: info@hospitalitymn.com
URL: http://www.hospitalitymn.com
Annual. **Primary Exhibits:** Food, beverages, hospitality business services, lodging supplies, and foodservice equipment. **Dates and Locations:** 2004 Feb 22-24; Minneapolis, MN; Minneapolis Convention Center.

OTHER SOURCES

★10233★ Administration and Management Occupations
Delphi Productions
3160 4th St.
Boulder, CO 80304
Fax: (303)443-4022   Fr: 888-443-2400
URL: http://www.delphivideo.com

$95.00. 50 minutes. Part of the Careers for the 21st Century Video Library.

★10234★ **American Correctional Food Service Association (ACFSA)**
4248 Park Glen
Minneapolis, MN 55416
Ph: (952)928-4658   Fax: (952)929-1318
E-mail: info@acfsa.org
URL: http://www.acfsa.org
Description: Food service professionals from federal, state, and county correctional institutions and vendors that serve them. Works to advance skills and professionalism through education, information and networking.

★10235★ **Association for International Practical Training (AIPT)**
10400 Little Patuxent Pky., Ste. 250
Columbia, MD 21044-3519
Ph: (410)997-2200   Fax: (410)992-3924
E-mail: aipt@aipt.org
URL: http://www.aipt.org
Description: Providers worldwide on-the-job training programs for students and professionals seeking international career development and life-changing experiences. Arranges workplace exchanges in hundreds of professional fields, bringing employers and trainees together from around the world. Client list ranges from small farming communities to Fortune 500 companies.

★10236★ **Club Managers Association of America (CMAA)**
1733 King St.
Alexandria, VA 22314-2720
Ph: (703)739-9500   Fax: (703)739-0124
E-mail: cmaa@cmaa.org
URL: http://www.cmaa.org
Members: Professional managers and assistant managers of private golf, yacht, athletic, city, country, luncheon, university, and military clubs. **Purpose:** Encourages education and advancement of members and promotes efficient and successful club operations. **Activities:** Provides reprints of articles on club management. Supports courses in club management. Compiles statistics; maintains management referral service.

★10237★ *Food and Beverage Service Occupations*
Evon Publishing
832 N 7th Ave.
Iron River, MI 49935
Ph: (906)265-3190
Audiocassette. 1996. $16.95. 32 minutes. Part of the Careers and Vocational Guidance Series. Provides information about the nature of the work, educational requirements, employment outlook, earnings, and work

conditions as well as additional related information.

★10238★ **Food Distributors International**
201 Park Washington Ct.
Falls Church, VA 22046
Ph: (703)532-9400   Fax: (703)538-4673
Description: Comprised of food distribution companies that supply and service independent wholesale grocers and foodservice operations. Goal is to educate and inform members on industry events, government affairs, and technology.

★10239★ **International Council on Hotel, Restaurant, and Institutional Education (CHRIE)**
2613 N Parham Rd., 2nd Fl.
Richmond, VA 23294
Ph: (804)346-4800   Fax: (804)346-5009
E-mail: info@chrie.org
URL: http://www.chrie.org
Description: Schools and colleges offering specialized education and training in hospitals, recreation, tourism and hotel, restaurant, and institutional administration; individuals, executives, and students. Provides networking opportunities and professional development.

★10240★ **National Management Association (NMA)**
2210 Arbor Blvd.
Dayton, OH 45439
Ph: (937)294-0421   Fax: (937)294-2374
E-mail: nma@nma1.org
URL: http://www.nma1.org
Description: Business and industrial management personnel; membership comes from supervisory level, with the remainder from middle management and above. Seeks to develop and recognize management as a profession and to promote the free enterprise system. Prepares chapter programs on basic management, management policy and practice, communications, human behavior, industrial relations, economics, political education, and liberal education. Maintains speakers' bureau and hall of fame. Maintains educational, charitable, and research programs. Sponsors charitable programs.

★10241★ **National Restaurant Association (NRA)**
1200 17th St., NW
Washington, DC 20036
Ph: (202)331-5900   Fax: (202)331-2429
Fr: 800-424-5156
E-mail: info@dineout.org
URL: http://www.restaurant.org
Description: Restaurants, cafeterias, clubs, contract foodservice management, drive-ins,

caterers, institutional food services, and other members of the foodservice industry; also represents establishments belonging to nonaffiliated state and local restaurant associations in governmental affairs. Supports foodservice education and research in several educational institutions. Affiliated with the Educational Foundation of the National Restaurant Association to provide training and education for operators, food and equipment manufacturers, distributors, and educators. Has 300,000 member locations.

★10242★ **National Restaurant Association Educational Foundation (NRAEF)**
175 W Jackson Blvd., No. 1500
Chicago, IL 60604-2702
Ph: (312)715-1010   Fr: 800-765-2122
E-mail: info@foodtrain.org
URL: http://www.nraef.org
Description: Educational foundation supported by the National Restaurant Association and all segments of the foodservice industry including restaurateurs, foodservice companies, food and equipment manufacturers, distributors, and trade associations. Dedicated to the advancement of professional standards in the industry through education and research. Offers video training programs, management courses, and careers information. Conducts research. Maintains hall of fame.

★10243★ **Society for Foodservice Management (SFM)**
304 W. Liberty St., Ste. 201
Louisville, KY 40202
Ph: (502)583-3783   Fax: (502)589-3602
E-mail: ghobby@hqtrs.com
URL: http://www.sfm-online.org
Description: Member companies operate or maintain food service and vending facilities in businesses and industrial plants, or supply food products, equipment, or other essential industry services. Works to serve the needs and interests of onsite employee food service executives and management. Provides an opportunity for the exchange of experiences and opinions through study, discussion, and publications; develops greater efficiency and more economical methods of providing high-quality food and service at a reasonable cost; assists members in solving specific operating and management problems; keeps pace with the rapidly changing conditions of the employee food service segment of the industry. Develops and encourages the practice of high standards and professional conduct among management andexecutive personnel; provides job placement and management personnel recruiting service; sends representative to the U.S. Air Force Hennessey Award Team, which selects the Air Force base having the most superior food service

Retail Sales Representatives

SOURCES OF HELP-WANTED ADS

★10244★ Building Supply Home Centers

Reed Business Information
360 Park Ave. S
New York, NY 10014
Ph: (646)746-7764

Monthly. Free to qualified subscribers; $60.00/year for individuals. Magazine for owners, executives, and managers responsible for product selection and purchase, merchandising, marketing, and management within the building supply retail and home center market.

★10245★ Chain Store Age

Lebhar-Friedman Inc.
425 Park Ave.
New York, NY 10022-3556
Ph: (212)756-5088   Fax: (212)756-5120
Fr: 800-453-2427
URL: http://www.chainstoreage.com

Monthly. $79.00/year for individuals. Magazine for management of retail chain headquarters. Reports on marketing, merchandising, strategic planning, physical supports, and shopping center developments, retail technology credit and communications.

★10246★ The College Store

The College Store
500 E Lorain St.
Oberlin, OH 44074-1294
Ph: (216)775-7777   Fax: (216)775-4769
Fr: 800-622-7498
E-mail: thecollegestore@nacs.org
URL: http://www.nacs.org

Bimonthly. $64.00/year. Books and college supplies magazine.

★10247★ Counterman

Babcox
3550 Embassy Pkwy.
Akron, OH 44333-8318
Ph: (330)670-1234   Fax: (330)670-0874

E-mail: jowens@babcox.com
URL: http://www.counterman.com

Monthly. Free to qualified subscribers; $64.00/year for U.S.; $109.00 for two years, U.S.; $84.00/year for Canada and Mexico; $143.00 for two years, Canada and Mexico; $124.00/year for other countries; $211.00 for two years, other countries; $10.00 for single issue, U.S.; $15.00/year for single issue, other countries. Magazine devoted to improving the effectiveness of professional automotive parts counter-sales personnel.

★10248★ CRN

CMP Media L.L.C.
600 Community Dr.
Manhasset, NY 11030
Ph: (516)562-5000
URL: http://www.crn.com

Weekly. Free to qualified subscribers; $209.00/year. Newspaper for value added resellers, retailers, and distributors in the computer market.

★10249★ Daily News Record

Fairchild Publications Inc.
7 W 34th St.
New York, NY 10001
Ph: (212)630-4000
URL: http://www.dailynewsrecord.com

Dail. $62.00/year; $1.50 for single issue, Monday; $1.00 for single issue, Tuesday-Friday; $140.00/year for Canada and Mexico; $250.00/year for other countries. Daily newspaper reporting on men's and boys' clothing, retailing, and textiles.

★10250★ Discount Store News

Lebhar-Friedman Inc.
425 Park Ave.
New York, NY 10022-3556
Ph: (212)756-5088   Fax: (212)756-5120
Fr: 800-453-2427
E-mail: lliebeck@lf.com
URL: http://www.discountstorenews.com

Semimonthly. $99.00/year.

★10251★ Gifts & Decorative Accessories

Reed Business Information
360 Park Ave. S
New York, NY 10010
Ph: (646)746-7395   Fax: (646)746-7434
URL: http://www.giftsanddec.com

Monthly. $42.00/year for individuals. International magazine for retailers of gifts, greeting cards, decorative accessories, and stationery-related merchandise.

★10252★ Modern Grocer

GC Publishing Company Inc.
1 University Dr., Ste. 200
Hackensack, NJ 07601
Ph: (201)488-1800   Fax: (201)488-7357
URL: http://www.griffcomm.net

Monthly. $45.00/year for individuals. Magazine for food retailers, wholesalers, distributors, brokers, manufacturers, and packers in the metro New York and New Jersey marketing area.

★10253★ Money Making Opportunities

Success Publishing International
11071 Ventura Blvd.
Studio City, CA 91604-3548
Ph: (818)765-2344   Fax: (818)980-7829
URL: http://www.moneymakingopps.com

$8.00/year. Magazine Source for small business opportunity seekers.

★10254★ Music Inc.

Maher Publications Inc.
102 N Haven Rd.
Elmhurst, IL 60126
Ph: (630)941-2030   Fax: (630)941-3210
Fr: 800-535-7496
E-mail: musicincupbeat@worldnet.att.net

$16.50/year for individuals. Magazine serving retailers of music and sound products.

★10255★ *National Home Center News*
Lebhar-Friedman Inc.
425 Park Ave.
New York, NY 10022-3556
Ph: (212)756-5088   Fax: (212)756-5120
Fr: 800-453-2427
URL: http://www.homecenternews.com

$99.00/year for individuals; $119.00/year for Canada; $279.00/year for other countries. Business tabloid serving home center/building material retailers.

★10256★ *National Jeweler*
VNU Business Media
770 Broadway
New York, NY 10003-9595
Ph: (646)654-5000
E-mail: jwynn@mfi.com
URL: http://www.national-jeweler/com

Biweekly. $45.00/year for one year; $71.00 for two years. Jewelry industry magazine.

★10257★ *Photo Marketing*
Photo Marketing Association International
3000 Picture Pl.
Jackson, MI 49201
Ph: (517)788-8100   Fax: (517)788-8371
URL: http://www.pmai.org

Monthly. $30.00/year for individuals; $35.00/year for Canada; $50.00/year, international. Trade magazine for photo/video dealers and photo finishers.

★10258★ *Sales & Marketing Management*
Bill Communications Inc.
770 Broadway
New York, NY 10003-9595
Ph: (646)654-4500   Fax: (646)654-7212
E-mail: edit@salesandmarketing.com
URL: http://www.salesandmarketing.com

$48.00/year. Business magazine.

★10259★ *Sporting Goods Dealer*
Bill Communications Inc.
1115 Northmeadow Pkwy.
Roswell, GA 30076
Ph: (770)569-5105   Fax: (770)569-5105
Fr: 800-241-9034
URL: http://www.sgdealer.com

Monthly. Free to qualified subscribers; $100.00/year; $6.00/year for single issue. Magazine which offers expert reporting on trends affecting team dealers and ret ailers who service schools, colleges, pro and local teams.

★10260★ *Tire Business*
Crain Communications Inc.
1725 Merriman Rd.
Akron, OH 44313-5283
Ph: (330)836-9180   Fax: (330)836-2365

Semimonthly. $57.00/year for individuals; $104.00 for two years. Newspaper (tabloid) serving independent tire dealers, retreaders, tire wholesalers and others allied to the tire industry.

★10261★ *Tire Review*
Babcox
3550 Embassy Pkwy.
Akron, OH 44333-8318
Ph: (330)670-1234   Fax: (330)670-0874
E-mail: dmoniz@babcox.com
URL: http://www.tirereview.com

Monthly. Free to qualified subscribers; $64.00/year for U.S.; $109.00 for two years, U.S.; $84.00/year for Canada and Mexico; $143.00 for two years, Canada and Mexico; $124.00/year for other countries; $211.00 for two years, other countries; $10.00 for single issue, U.S.; $15.00/year for single issue, other countries. Magazine containing news and business information about the tire, custom wheel, automotive service, and retreading industries.

★10262★ *Visual Merchandising and Store Design*
ST Media Group International Inc.
407 Gilbert Ave.
Cincinnati, OH 45202
Ph: (513)421-2050   Fax: (513)421-5144
Fr: 800-925-1110
E-mail: vmsd@stmediagroup.com
URL: http://www.visualstore.com

Monthly. $42.00/year; $5.50/year, single copy. The leading magazine of the retail design industry covering the latest trends in retail design, store planning, and merchandise presentation.

★10263★ *Watch & Clock Review*
Golden Bell Press
2403 Champa St.
Denver, CO 80205
Ph: (303)296-1600   Fax: (303)295-2159

$19.50/year; $3.00 for single issue. Magazine on watches and clocks.

EMPLOYER DIRECTORIES AND NETWORKING LISTS

★10264★ *Directory of Department Stores*
Chain Store Guide
3922 Coconut Palm Dr.
Tampa, FL 33619
Ph: (813)627-6800   Fax: (813)627-6882
Fr: 800-927-9292
URL: http://www.csgis.com

Annual, October. $327.00. Covers 214 department store companies, 1,500 shoe store companies, 200 jewelry store companies, 95 optical store companies, and 70 leather and luggage store companies in the United States and Canada, with annual sales of at least $250,000. Entries include: Company name; physical and mailing addresses; phone and fax numbers, company e-mail and web addresses; listing type; total sales; industry sales; total selling square footage; store prototype sizes; total units; units by trade name; trading areas; projected openings and remodelings; self-distributing indicator; distribution center locations; resident buyers' name and location; leased departments area, name, and location; mail order catalog indicator; Internet order processing indicator; private label softlines, hardlines, and credit card indicators; furniture styles and price lines; average number of checkouts; year founded; public company indicator; parent company name and loction; subsidiaries' names and locations; regional and divisional office locations; key personnel with titles; store locations, with address, phone number, and manager name (department stores only). Arrangement: Geographical. Indexes: Alphabetical, product lines, exclusions.

★10265★ *Directory of Drug Store & HBC Chains*
Chain Store Guide
3922 Coconut Palm Dr.
Tampa, FL 33619
Ph: (813)627-6800   Fax: (813)627-6882
Fr: 800-927-9292
URL: http://www.csgis.com

Annual, May. $335.00. Covers 1,600 drug store chains operation two or more units, including mass merchants and grocers with pharmacies; 215 wholesale drug companies in the United States and Canada. Entries include: For retailers-company name; phone and fax numbers; physical and mailing addresses; company e-mail and web addresses; listing type; number of stores; product lines; percentage of sales by product line; total sales; prescription drug sales; percentage of prescriptions filled with generic drugs; number of prescriptions filled daily; percentage of prescriptions filled with private third party, cash, and Medicaid; number of stores by type; mail order pharmacy indicator; managed care division indicator; projected openings and remodelings; store prototype sizes; total selling square footage; trading area; franchise group headquarter's name and location; distribution center and primary wholesaler names and locations; number of specialty departments; packaged liquor indicators; private label indicators; computerized pharmacy indicator; average number of checkouts; year founded; public company indicator; parent company name and location; regional and divisional office locations; headquarters personnel with titles. For wholesalers-company name, address, phone, and fax; e-mail and web addresses; listing type; product lines; percentage of sales by product line; total sales; percentage of sales by customer type; total stores served; number of member and non-member stores served; trading area; group store trading names; wholesaler type; distribution center locations; private label indicator; year founded; public company indicator; headquarters personnel with titles. Arrangement: Separate geographical sections for retailers and wholesalers. Indexes: Alphabetical, exclusions.

★10266★ **Discount Store News-Top Chains Issue**
Chain Store Guides Inc.
425 Park Ave.
New York, NY 10022
Ph: (212)756-5000

Annual, July. $79.00. Entries include: Chain name, location, sales and earnings for the past two years, number of stores, net store square footage. Arrangement: Ranked by sales volume.

★10267★ **Florists-Retail Directory**
infoUSA Inc.
5711 S 86th Cir.
Omaha, NE 68127-0347
Ph: (402)930-3500   Fax: (402)331-0176
Fr: 800-555-6124
URL: http://www.abii.com

Annual. Number of listings: 50,501. Entries include: Name, address, phone (including area code), size of advertisement, year first in "Yellow Pages," name of owner or manager, number of employees. Regional editions available. Compiled from telephone company "Yellow Pages," nationwide. Arrangement: Geographical.

★10268★ **STORES-Top 100 Retailers Issue**
National Retail Federation
325 7th St. NW, Ste. 1100
Washington, DC 20004
Ph: (202)783-7971   Fax: (202)737-2849
Fr: 800-673-4692
URL: http://www.stores.org

Annual, July. $75.00. Publication includes: 100 U.S. retail companies having largest estimated sales during preceding year. Entries include: Name of store, city, number of stores included, and total sales. Arrangement: Ranked by sales.

★10269★ **Variety Stores Directory**
infoUSA Inc.
5711 S 86th Cir.
Omaha, NE 68127-0347
Ph: (402)930-3500   Fax: (402)331-0176
Fr: 800-555-6124
URL: http://www.abii.com

Annual. Number of listings: 12,400. Entries include: Name, address, phone (including area code), size of advertisement, year first in "Yellow Pages," name of owner or manager, number of employees. Compiled from telephone company "Yellow Pages," nationwide. Arrangement: Geographical.

HANDBOOKS AND MANUALS

★10270★ **Exploring Careers in the Computer Field**
Rosen Publishing Group, Inc.
29 E 21st St.
New York, NY 10010
Ph: (212)777-3017   Fax: 888-436-4643
Fr: 800-237-9932

Joseph Weintraub. Revised edition, 1993. $14.95; $9.95 (paper). Discusses entry into the field, salaries, future trends, and offers job search advice. Surveys the newest growth areas in the computer industry including artificial intelligence, desktop publishing, and personal computers. Out of stock.

★10271★ **Great Jobs for Business Majors**
McGraw-Hill Trade
2 Penn Plaza
New York, NY 10121
Ph: (212)904-2000   Fr: 800-722-4726
E-mail: ntcpub@tribune.com

Stephen Lambert. 1996. $11.95 (paper). 462 pages.

★10272★ **Opportunities in Retailing Careers**
McGraw-Hill Companies
1221 Avenue of the Americas
New York, NY 10020
Ph: (212)904-2000   Fr: 800-323-4900
E-mail: ntcpub@tribune.com

Roslyn Dolber. 1996. 160 pages. $14.95; $11.95 (paper). Discusses a number of opportunities in retailing, from entry-level to retail management.

★10273★ **Opportunities in Sales Careers**
McGraw-Hill Professional
2 Penn Plaza
New York, NY 10121
Ph: (212)904-2000   Fr: 800-722-4726
E-mail: ntcpub@tribune.com

James Brescoll and Ralph Dahm. 160 pages. 1995. $12.95; $11.95 (paper). Details sales in retail, wholesale and industrial sales, sales of services and intangibles, and sales management. Illustrated.

★10274★ **Real People Working in Sales and Marketing**
McGraw-Hill Contemporary Books
1221 Avenue of the Americas
New York, NY 10020
Ph: (212)904-2000   Fr: 800-323-4900
E-mail: ntcpub@tribune.com

Blythe Camenson, Jan Goldberg. 1997. $17.95; $12.95 (paper). 410 pages. Interviews and profiles of working sales and marketing professionals capture a range of opportunities in this field.

★10275★ **Where the Jobs Are: The Hottest Careers for the 90s**
The Career Press, Inc.
3 Tice Rd.
PO Box 687
Franklin Lakes, NJ 07417-1322
Ph: (201)848-0310   Fax: (201)848-1727
Fr: 800-227-3371

Joyce Hadley. Third edition, 2000. $13.99 (paper). 400 pages. Out of print. Describes careers in fifteen general fields, from accounting to travel and hospitality.

EMPLOYMENT AGENCIES AND SEARCH FIRMS

★10276★ **Allen Associates**
650 Westlake Ctr.
Cincinnati, OH 45242
Ph: (513)563-3040

Executive senior-level search firm.

★10277★ **Amherst Personnel Group Inc.**
PO Box 580
Hicksville, NY 11801-7848
Ph: (516)433-7610   Fax: (516)433-7848
E-mail: amherstgroup1@aol.com

Employment agency. Executive search firm. Other offices in Milltown, NJ, and Rochelle Park, NJ.

★10278★ **APA Search Inc.**
1 Byram Brook Pl., Ste. 201
Armonk, NY 10504
Ph: (914)273-6000   Fax: (914)273-8025

Employment agency specializing in the automotive, retail, and hardware industries.

★10279★ **Don Waldron and Associates, Inc.**
450 7th Ave., Ste. 507A
New York, NY 10123
Ph: (212)239-9110   Fax: (212)239-9114
E-mail: salepositions@comcast.net
URL: http://www.salespositions.com

Employment agency.

★10280★ **Ecruiters.net**
PO Box 1086
Chanhassen, MN 55317
Ph: (952)233-5750

Executive search firm.

★10281★ **Employment Advisors**
815 Nicollet Mall Ste 200
Minneapolis, MN 55402
Ph: (612)339-3944
E-mail: info@collegegraduateregistry.com
URL: http://

www.collegegraduateregistry.com

Employment agency. Places candidates in variety of fields.

★10282★   Fairfaxx Corp.

PO Box 320308
Fairfield, CT 06825-0308
Ph: (203)838-8300   Fax: (203)851-5844

Executive search consulting firm specializing in apparel and retail industry positions.

★10283★   J.D. Hersey and Associates

1695 Old Henderson Rd.
Columbus, OH 43220
Ph: (614)459-4555   Fax: (614)459-4544
E-mail: info@jdhersey.com
URL: http://www.jdhersey.com

Executive search firm for permanent and contingency placements.

★10284★   Joel H. Wilensky Associates, Inc.

PO Box 155
Sudbury, MA 01776
Ph: (978)443-5176   Fax: (978)443-3009
E-mail: jhwassoc@joelhwilensky.com
URL: http://www.joelhwilensky.com

Executive search firm.

★10285★   John J. Sudlow and Co.

1044 Water St., Ste. 223
Port Townsend, WA 98368
Ph: (360)385-0703

Offers counsel emphasizing executive development and recruiting, particularly for manufacturing and retail oriented businesses.

★10286★   National Register Columbus, Inc.

2700 E. Dublin Granville Rd., Ste. 555
Columbus, OH 43231-4097
Ph: (614)890-1200   Fax: (614)890-1259
E-mail: sales@nrcols.com
URL: http://www.nrcols.com

Employment agency. Offices in Akron and Toledo, OH.

★10287★   Personalized Management Associates

1950 Spectrum Cir., Ste. B310
Marietta, GA 30067
Ph: (770)916-1668   Fax: (770)916-1429
Fr: 800-466-7822

Mid-level to executive level management placement firm specializing in retail, restaurant and service management. Industries served: retail, restaurant, finance, sales, marketing, advertising.

★10288★   The Personnel Network, Inc.

1246 Lake Murray Blvd.
PO Box 1426
Irmo, SC 29063
Ph: (803)781-2087   Fax: (803)732-7986
E-mail: chuckirmo@aol.com

Executive search firm.

★10289★   Retail Connection, Inc.

271 Rte. 46 W., Ste. D105
Fairfield, NJ 07004
Ph: (973)882-6662   Fax: (973)575-5858
E-mail: retailconn@aol.com
URL: http://www.retailconnectioninc.com

Executive search firm serving retail executives.

★10290★   Retail Recruiters/Spectrum Consultants, Inc.

10 E Athens Ave., Ste.200
Ardmore, PA 19003
Ph: (610)645-9520
E-mail: rrspectrum@erols.com

Employment agency. Affiliate offices in many locations across the country.

ONLINE JOB SOURCES AND SERVICES

★10291★   Spherion Workforce Architects

URL: http://www.spherion.com

Description: Recruitment firm specializing in accounting and finance, sales and marketing, interim executives, technology, engineering, retail and human resources.

TRADESHOWS

★10292★   Florida Fashion Focus Show

Southern Apparel Exhibitors, Inc.
7220 N.W. 36 St., Ste. 309
Miami, FL 33166
Ph: (305)718-4320   Fax: (305)718-4323
Fr: 888-249-1377
E-mail: saefffshow@aol.com
URL: http://www.saemiami.com

5/yr. **Primary Exhibits:** Ladies ready-to-wear clothing; handbags, jewelry, and accessories. Order-writing for future delivery.

★10293★   Sales and Marketing Show and Conference

Flagg Management, Inc.
353 Lexington Ave.
New York, NY 10016
Ph: (212)286-0333   Fax: (212)286-0086
E-mail: flaggmgmt@msn.com
URL: http://www.flaggmgmt.com

Annual. **Primary Exhibits:** Sales and marketing products, customer support systems, sales administration services, Internet/Intranet systems, web site marketing services, client server solutions, sales automation, telecommunications, wireless, telemarketing, training, incentives, database management, and direct marketing.

OTHER SOURCES

★10294★   Automotive Aftermarket Industry Association (AAIA)

4600 East-West Hwy., Ste. 300
Bethesda, MD 20814-3415
Ph: (301)654-6664   Fax: (301)654-3299
E-mail: aaia@aftermarket.org
URL: http://www.aftermarket.org

Members: Automotive parts and accessories retailers, distributors, manufacturers, and manufacturers' representatives. **Activities:** Conducts research and compiles statistics. Conducts seminars and provides specialized education program.

★10295★   CBA

PO Box 62000
Colorado Springs, CO 80962-2000
Ph: (719)265-9895   Fax: (719)272-3510
Fr: 800-252-1950
E-mail: info@cbaonline.org
URL: http://www.cbaonline.org

Members: Trade association for retail stores selling Christian books, Bibles, gifts, and Sunday school and church supplies. **Activities:** Compiles statistics; conducts specialized education programs.

★10296★   Computing Technology Industry Association (CompTIA)

1815 S Meyers Rd., Ste. 300
Oakbrook Terrace, IL 60181
Ph: (630)678-8300   Fax: (630)627-2930
E-mail: info@comptia.org
URL: http://www.comptia.org

Description: Trade association of more than 19,000 companies and professional IT members in the rapidly converging computing and communications market. Has members in more than 89 countries and provides a unified voice for the industry in the areas of e-commerce standards, vendor-neutral certification, service metrics, public policy and workforce development. Serves as information clearinghouse and resource for the industry; sponsors educational programs.

★10297★   *Marketing & Sales Occupations*

Delphi Productions
3160 4th St.
Boulder, CO 80304
Fax: (303)443-4022   Fr: 888-443-2400
URL: http://www.delphivideo.com

$95.00. 50 minutes. Part of the Careers for the 21st Century Video Library.

★10298★ **National Association of College Stores (NACS)**
500 E Lorain St.
Oberlin, OH 44074
Ph: (440)775-7777   Fax: (440)775-4769
Fr: 800-622-7498
E-mail: membership@nacs.org
URL: http://www.nacs.org

Members: Institutional, private, leased, and cooperative college stores (2800) selling books, supplies, and other merchandise to college students, faculty, and staff; associate members include publishers and suppliers (1200). **Purpose:** Seeks to effectively serve higher education by providing educational research, advocacy and other to college stores and their suppliers. **Activities:** Maintains NACSCORP, Inc., a wholly owned subsidiary corporation, which distributes trade and mass market books and educa-

tional software. Sponsors seminars. Conducts manager certification, specialized education, and research programs. Maintains College Stores Research and Educational Foundation which provides grants for NACS educational programs and conducts research.

★10299★ **National Retail Federation (NRF)**
325 7th St. NW, Ste. 1100
Washington, DC 20004
Ph: (202)783-7971   Fax: (202)737-2849
Fr: 800-NRF-HOW2
E-mail: mullint@nrf.com
URL: http://www.nrf.com

Purpose: Represents 50 state retail association, several dozen national retail associations as well as large and small corporate members representing the breadth and diversity of the retail industry's establishment and employees. **Activities:** Conducts informational and educational conferences related to all phases of retailing including finan-

cial planning and cash management, taxation, economic forecasting, expense planning, shortage control, credit, electronic data processing, telecommunications, merchandise management, buying, traffic, security, supply, materials handling, store planning and construction, personnel administration, recruitment and training, and advertising and display.

★10300★ *Working with Children*
Cambridge Educational
2572 Brunswick Ave.
Lawrenceville, NJ 08648-4128
Fax: 800-FAX-ON-US   Fr: 800-468-4227
URL: http://www.cambridgeeducational.com

$89.95. 2000. 23 minutes. This program examines alternative positions offering the opportunity to work with children of different ages and the qualifications necessary for those jobs. A nanny, social worker, nonfaculty school worker, and retail salesperson describe their job responsibilities and explain why they find their work so enjoyable.

Roofers

SOURCES OF HELP-WANTED ADS

★10301★ Builder
Hanley-Wood L.L.C.
1 Thomas Cir., Ste. 600
Washington, DC 20005
Ph: (202)452-0800   Fax: (202)785-1974
URL: http://www.builderonline.com

Monthly. $29.95/year for individuals. Magazine covering housing and construction industry.

★10302★ Construction Digest
Construction Digest
5804 W 74th St.
Indianapolis, IN 46278
Ph: (317)293-6860   Fax: (317)293-7840
Fr: 888-893-6860

Semimonthly. $3.00 for single issue. Magazine for the public works and construction engineering industries.

★10303★ CONSTRUCTOR
Associated General Contractors
  Information
333 John Carlyle St., Ste. 200
Alexandria, VA 22314
Ph: (703)837-5355   Fax: (703)837-5402
URL: http://www.agc.org

Monthly. $15.00/year for members; $250.00/year for nonmembers; $4.00/year for single issue except July, November, and December; $25.00/year for single issue-November, December; $325.00 for single issue-July. Management magazine for the Construction Industry.

★10304★ Contractors Guide
G & M Communications
1050 Illinois Rte. 63, Ste. 200
Bensenville, IL 60106-1096
Ph: (847)588-3333   Fax: (847)647-7055
URL: http://www.constructiongroup.com

Monthly. Free to qualified subscribers; $25.00/year for individuals; $5.00 for single issue. Trade magazine on roofing and insulation.

★10305★ Professional Builder
Reed Business Information
360 Park Ave. S
New York, NY 10014
Ph: (646)746-7764
URL: http://www.probuilder.com

Monthly. $10.00 for single issue; $139.95/year for by mail.

★10306★ Professional Roofing
National Roofing Contractors Association
10255 W Higgins Rd., Ste. 600
Rosemont, IL 60018-5607
Ph: (847)299-9070   Fax: (847)299-1183
Fr: 800-323-9545
URL: http://www.nrca.net

Monthly. $30.00/year for individuals, U.S. and Canada; $70.00/year for other countries. Roofing industry magazine.

★10307★ Roofing Contractor
BNP Media, Inc.
2401 W Big Beaver Rd., Ste. 700
Troy, MI 48084
Ph: (248)362-3700   Fax: (248)362-0317
URL: http://www.roofingcontractor.com/

Monthly. Trade publication covering roofing and the construction industry.

★10308★ WIT
Northern New England Tradeswomen
189 N Main St., Ste. 9
Barre, VT 05641-4173
Ph: (802)476-4040   Fax: (802)476-3346

Description: Three issues/year. Provides a network of support, information, and skill sharing for women in skilled trades professions.

EMPLOYER DIRECTORIES AND NETWORKING LISTS

★10309★ ABC Today-Associated Builders and Contractors National Membership Directory Issue
Associated Builders & Contractors Inc.
4250 N Fairfax Dr., 9th Fl.
Arlington, VA 22203
Ph: (703)812-2000   Fax: (703)812-8203

Annual, December. $150.00. Publication includes: List of approximately 19,000 member construction contractors and suppliers. Entries include: Company name, address, phone, name of principal executive, code to volume of business, business specialty. Arrangement: Classified by chapter, then by work specialty.

★10310★ Constructor-AGC Directory of Membership and Services Issue
AGC Information Inc.
333 John Carlyle St., Ste. 200
Alexandria, VA 22314
Ph: (703)548-3118   Fax: (703)548-3119
URL: http://www.agc.org

Annual, July. $250.00 for nonmembers; $15.00 for members; $250.00 for other countries. Publication includes: List of over 8,500 member firms and 24,000 national associate member firms engaged in building, highway, heavy, industrial, municipal utilities, and railroad construction (SIC 1541, 1542, 1611, 1622, 1623, 1629); listing of state and local chapter officers. Entries include: For firms-Company name, address, phone, fax, names of principal executives, and code indicating type of construction undertaken. For officers-Name, title, address. Arrangement: Geographical, Alphabetical. Indexes: Company name.

★10311★ **ENR-Top 400 Construction Contractors Issue**

McGraw-Hill Companies
1221 Ave. of the Americas
New York, NY 10020
Ph: (212)512-2000   Fax: (212)512-3840

Annual, May issue of "Engineering News Record". $10.00. Publication includes: List of 400 United States contractors receiving largest dollar volumes of contracts in preceding calendar year. Separate lists of 50 largest design/construct management firms; 50 largest program and construction managers; 25 building contractors; 25 heavy contractors. Entries include: Company name, headquarters location, total value of contracts received in preceding year, value of foreign contracts, countries in which operated, construction specialities. Arrangement: By total value of contracts received.

★10312★ **National Roofing Contractors Association-Membership Directory**

National Roofing Contractors Association
10255 W Higgins Rd., Ste. 600
Rosemont, IL 60018-5607
Ph: (847)299-9070   Fax: (847)299-1183
Fr: 800-323-9545
URL: http://www.nrca.net

Annual, July. $55.00. Covers 5,000 contractors applying all types of commercial and residential roofing; 600 associate member manufacturers, suppliers, and distributors; 300 foreign members; and 100 institutions and related industries. Entries include: Company name, address, phone, and names of voting representatives. Arrangement: Alphabetical. Indexes: Geographical, voting representative, Alphabetical, member product guide.

★10313★ **Roofing Contractors Directory**

infoUSA Inc.
5711 S 86th Cir.
Omaha, NE 68127-0347
Ph: (402)930-3500   Fax: (402)331-0176
Fr: 800-555-6124
URL: http://www.abii.com

Annual. Number of listings: 38,704. Entries include: Name, address, phone (including area code), size of advertisement, year first in "Yellow Pages," name of owner or manager, number of employees. Compiled from telephone company "Yellow Pages," nationwide. Arrangement: Geographical.

HANDBOOKS AND MANUALS

★10314★ **Exploring Careers in the Construction Industry**

Rosen Publishing Group Inc.
29 E. 21st St.
New York, NY 10010
Ph: (212)777-3017   Fax: 888-436-4643
Fr: 800-237-9932

Elizabeth Stewart Lytle. Revised edition, 1994. $16.95; $9.95 (paper). Out of print.

★10315★ **Opportunities in Building Construction Trades**

McGraw-Hill Trade
2 Penn Plaza
New York, NY 10121
Ph: (212)904-2000   Fr: 800-722-4726

Michael Sumichrast. Second edition, 1998. $14.95; $11.95 (paper). 202 pages. From custom builder to rehabber, the many kinds of companies that employ craftspeople and contractors are explored. Includes job descriptions, requirements, and salaries for dozens of specialties within the construction industry. Contains a complete list of Bureau of Apprenticeship and Training state and area offices. Illustrated.

ONLINE JOB SOURCES AND SERVICES

★10316★ **National Roofing Contractors**
URL: http://nrca.net

Description: Members have the opportunity to have their resume and business listed free of charge and are accessed by the zip codes they serve. NRCA provides a complimentary hyperlink to a member's Web site if an address is provided. Also, (800) USA-ROOF: NRCA's contractor referral network is accessed by more than 8,000 consumers each year who are searching for professional roofing contractors. **Fee:** Membership fees depend on annual sales volume and begin at $330.

TRADESHOWS

★10317★ **Midwest Roofing Contractors Association Convention and Trade Show**

Midwest Roofing Contractors Association
4840 W. 15th St., Ste. 1000
Lawrence, KS 66049-3862
Ph: (785)843-4888   Fax: (785)843-7555
Fr: 800-497-6722
E-mail: mrca@mrca.org
URL: http://www.mrca.org

Annual. **Primary Exhibits:** Roofing products, materials, and related industries and services. **Dates and Locations:** 2004 Oct 06-08; Kansas City, MO; Center Exhibit Hall.

★10318★ **National Roofing Contractors Association Annual Convention and Exhibit**

National Roofing Contractors Association
O'Hare International Center
10255 W. Higgins Rd., Ste. 600
Rosemont, IL 60018-5607
Ph: (847)299-9070   Fax: (847)299-1183
Fr: 800-323-9545
E-mail: nrca@nrca.net
URL: http://www.nrca.net

Annual. **Primary Exhibits:** Roofing, urethane foam, waterproofing materials, and computer programs.

★10319★ **Southeast Roofing and Sheet Metal Spectacular Trade Exposition**

Florida Roofing, Sheet Metal, and Air Conditioning Contractors Association - FRSA
Box 4850
Winter Park, FL 32793
Ph: (407)671-3772   Fax: (407)679-0010
URL: http://www.floridaroof.com

Annual. **Primary Exhibits:** Roofing and sheet metal supplies, products and services. **Dates and Locations:** 2005 Jul 20-23; Orlando, FL; Orange County Convention Center and Peabody Hotel.

OTHER SOURCES

★10320★ **Associated Builders and Contractors (ABC)**

1300 N. 17th St., Ste. 800
Rosslyn, VA 22209
Ph: (703)812-2000   Fax: (703)812-8201
E-mail: info@abc.org
URL: http://www.abc.org

Description: Construction contractors, subcontractors, suppliers, and associates. Aim is to foster and perpetuate the principles of rewarding construction workers and management on the basis of merit. Sponsors management education programs and craft training; also sponsors apprenticeship and skill training programs. Disseminates technological and labor relations information.

★10321★ **Associated General Contractors of America (AGC)**

333 John Carlyle St., Ste. 200
Alexandria, VA 22314
Ph: (703)548-3118   Fax: (703)548-3119
E-mail: sandhers@agc.org
URL: http://www.agc.org

Description: General construction contractors; subcontractors; industry suppliers; service firms. Provides market services through its divisions. Conducts special conferences and seminars designed specifically for construction firms. Compiles statistics on job accidents reported by member firms. ors. Maintains 65 committees, including joint cooperative committees with other associations and liaison committees with federal agencies.

★10322★ **Associated Specialty Contractors (ASC)**
3 Bethesda Metro Ctr., Ste. 1100
Bethesda, MD 20814
Ph: (301)657-3110   Fax: (301)215-4500
E-mail: dgw@necanet.org
URL: http://www.assoc-spec-con.org

Description: Subcontractor associations with a total of 25,000 members representing electrical, heating, piping, mechanical, air conditioning, sheet metal, plumbing, ventilating, painting and decorating, and roofing and insulation contractors. Promotes liaison with general contractors, architects, and engineers on inter-industry matters, codes, bidding, and contracting procedures. Coordinates governmental affairs, research, and educational matters.

★10323★ *Building Trades*
Delphi Productions
3160 4th St.
Boulder, CO 80304
Fax: (303)443-4022   Fr: 888-443-2400
URL: http://www.delphivideo.com

$95.00. 46 minutes. Part of the Careers for the 21st Century Video Library.

★10324★ **COIN Career Guidance System**
COIN Educational Products
3361 Executive Pky., Ste. 302
Toledo, OH 43606
Ph: (419)536-5353   Fax: (419)536-7056
Fr: 800-274-8515
URL: http://www.coin3.com/highschool/guidance.asp

CD-ROM. Provides career information through seven cross-referenced files covering postsecondary schools, college majors, vocational programs, military service, apprenticeship programs, financial aid, and scholarships. Apprenticeship file describes national apprenticeship training programs, including information on how to apply, contact agencies, and program content. Military file describes more than 200 military occupations and training opportunities related to civilian employment.

★10325★ **National Association of Home Builders (NAHB)**
1201 15th St. NW
Washington, DC 20005
Ph: (202)266-8200   Fax: (202)822-0586
Fr: 800-368-5242
E-mail: info@nahb.com
URL: http://www.nahb.org

Description: Single and multifamily home builders, commercial builders, and others associated with the building industry. Lobbies on behalf of the housing industry and conducts public affairs activities to increase public understanding of housing and the economy. Collects and disseminates data on current developments in home building and home builders' plans through its Economics Department and nationwide Metropolitan Housing Forecast. Maintains NAHB Research Center, which functions as the research arm of the home building industry. Sponsors seminars and workshops on con-

struction, mortgage credit, labor relations, cost reduction, land use, remodeling, and business management. Compiles statistics; offers charitable program, spokesman training, and placement service; maintains speakers' bureau, and Hall of Fame. Subsidiaries include the National Council of the Housing Industry. Maintains over 50 committees in many areas of construction; operates National Commercial Builders Council, National Council of the Multifamily Housing Industry, National Remodelers Council, and National Sales and Marketing Council.

★10326★ **National Association of Women in Construction (NAWIC)**
327 S Adams St.
Fort Worth, TX 76104
Ph: (817)877-5551   Fax: (817)877-0324
Fr: 800-552-3506
E-mail: nawic@nawic.org
URL: http://www.nawic.org

Description: Seeks to enhance the success of women in the construction industry.

★10327★ **Roofing Industry Educational Institute (RIEI)**
10255 W. Higgins Rd., Ste. 600
Rosemont, IL 60018
Ph: (847)299-9070   Fax: (847)299-1183
E-mail: nrca@nrca.net
URL: http://www.nrca.net

Members: Participants are contractors, architects, specifiers, owners, consultants, and others involved in the roofing industry. **Activities:** Conducts seminars and educational programs covering all aspects of roofing, highlighting design, installation, and maintenance including topics such as thermal insulation, vapors and condensation, and fire and codes. Provides referral service; presents diplomas; awards credits in continuing education.

Sales Managers

SOURCES OF HELP-WANTED ADS

★10328★ The Customer Service Advantage

Progressive Business Publications
370 Technology Dr.
Malvern, PA 19355
Ph: (610)695-8600   Fax: (610)647-8089
Fr: 800-220-5000
URL: http://www.pbp.com

Description: Semimonthly. Presents practical methods for quantifying customer service benefits and motivating employees day in and day out. Recurring features include interviews, news of research, a calendar of events, news of educational opportunities, and a column titled Sharpen Your Judgment.

★10329★ Issues & Answers in Sales Management

Clement Communications Inc.
Concord Industrial Park
10 LaCrue Ave.
PO Box 500
Concordville, PA 19331
Ph: (610)459-1700   Fax: (610)459-0936
Fr: 800-345-8101
E-mail: editor@clement.com
URL: http://www.clement.com

Description: Biweekly. Provides sales managers and supervisors with techniques and strategies to improve customer service and profits. Includes topics such as the Internet, tradeshow tips, and cold-calling hints.

★10330★ Journal of Staff Development

National Staff Development Council
PO Box 240
Oxford, OH 45056
Ph: (513)523-6029   Fax: (513)523-0638
Fr: 800-727-7288

Quarterly. Professional journal covering administration issues.

★10331★ Master Salesmanship

Clement Communications Inc.
Concord Industrial Park
10 LaCrue Ave.
PO Box 500
Concordville, PA 19331
Ph: (610)459-1700   Fax: (610)459-0936
Fr: 800-345-8101
E-mail: editor@clement.com

Description: Biweekly. Designed to help sales managers motivate, train, and inform their salespeople. Offers pointers on improving old sales skills and developing new ones. Recurring features include a motivation column, Q&A (questions and answers), and Selling Slants.

★10332★ Sales and Marketing Executive Report

The Dartnell Corp.
PO Box 980
Horsham, PA 19044-0980
Fr: 800-621-5463

Description: Biweekly. Discusses topics of interest to managers, including motivating and training sales personnel, executive self-improvement, and advertising and public relations strategies. Recurring features include news of research, letters to the editor, book reviews, a calendar of events, and columns titled Sales/Marketing Briefs and Special Report.

★10333★ Sales & Marketing Report

Lawrence Ragan Communications Inc.
316 N Michigan Ave., Ste. 300
Chicago, IL 60601
Ph: (312)960-4100   Fax: (312)960-4105
Fr: 800-878-5331
URL: http://www.ragan.com

Description: Monthly. Provides information about strategic sales coaching, building a high performance sales team, boosting morale and productivity, and managing time more effectively.

★10334★ The Selling Advantage

Progressive Business Publications
370 Technology Dr.
Malvern, PA 19355
Ph: (610)695-8600   Fax: (610)647-8089
Fr: 800-220-5000

Description: Semimonthly. Explores new strategies and proven techniques to improve sales performance. Recurring features include book reviews and a column titled Tale of the Sale.

★10335★ Supply Chain Management Review

Reed Business Information
275 Washington St.
Newton, MA 02458-1630
Ph: (617)964-3030

Bimonthly. Publication covering business and management.

★10336★ What's Working in Sales Management

Progressive Business Publications
370 Technology Dr.
Malvern, PA 19355
Ph: (610)695-8600   Fax: (610)647-8089
Fr: 800-220-5000
URL: http://www.pbp.com

Description: Semimonthly. Acts as a time-saving resource for busy sales managers. Recurring features include interviews, news of research, a calendar of events, and news of educational opportunities.

EMPLOYER DIRECTORIES AND NETWORKING LISTS

★10337★ 4 Data Base

Hunt-Scanlon Publishing
20 Signal Rd.
Stamford, CT 06902-7907
Ph: (203)352-2920   Fax: (203)352-2930

Annual. $1,350.00 for individuals. Database covers more than 100,000 top and middle

management professionals in human resources, finance, sales and marketing, and
information technology at over 10,000 companies in the U.S. Entries include: Company
name, address, phone, number of employees, SIC codes, revenues, individual name,
title, phone number, industry specialization.

HANDBOOKS AND MANUALS

**★10338★ Career Opportunities in the
Retail and Wholesale Industry**
Facts on File
132 W. 31st St., 17th Fl.
New York, NY 10001-2006
Ph: (212)967-8800   Fax: (212)967-9196
Fr: 800-322-8755
Field, Shelly. 2001. $18.95 (Trade paper).
256 pages.

**★10339★ How to Make Hot Cold Calls:
Your Calling Card to Personal
Success**
General Distribution Services, Inc.
4500 Witmer Industrial, E.
Niagara Falls, NY 14305-1386
Fax: 800-481-6207   Fr: 800-805-1083
Steven J. Schwartz. Revised, 2001. 176
pages.

**★10340★ Opportunities in Retailing
Careers**
McGraw-Hill Contemporary Books
1221 Avenue of the Americas
New York, NY 10020
Ph: (212)904-2000   Fr: 800-323-4900
Dolber, Roslyn. 1996. $11.95 (Trade paper).
205 pages.

**★10341★ Opportunities in Sales
Careers**
McGraw-Hill Trade
2 Penn Plaza
New York, NY 10121
Ph: (212)904-2000   Fr: 800-722-4726
Dahm, Ralph M. and James Brescoll. 1994.
$10.95 (Trade paper). 160 pages.

★10342★ Retailing Career Starter
LearningExpress, LLC
900 Broadway, Suite 604
New York, NY 10003
Ph: (212)995-2566   Fax: (212)995-5512
Fr: 800-295-9556
Lipow, Valerie. 1998. $14.95 (Trade paper).
208 pages.

**★10343★ Sales Careers: The Ultimate
Guide to Getting a High-Paying Sales
Job**
JIST Publishing
8902 Otis Ave.
Indianapolis, IN 46216-1033
Ph: (317)613-4200   Fax: 800-547-8329
Edward R. Newill, Louise Kursmark. June
2003. $12.95. 208 pages.

**★10344★ Sales Management: A Career
Path Approach**
Thomson South-Western
5191 Natorp Blvd.
Mason, OH 45040
Ph: (513)229-1000   Fr: 800-354-9706
Hughes, G. David, Daryl McKee, and
Charles H. Singler. 1998. $98.95 (Cloth).
500 pages.

EMPLOYMENT AGENCIES AND
SEARCH FIRMS

★10345★ AG Fishkin & Associates
PO Box 34413
Bethesda, MD 20827
Ph: (301)983-0303   Fax: (301)983-0415
E-mail: afishkin@comcast.net
Executive search firm.

★10346★ Aries Search Group
9925 Haynes Bridge Rd., Ste. 200-146
Alpharetta, GA 30022
Ph: (770)569-4708   Fax: (770)569-4709
E-mail: cmcand6089@aol.com
Executive search firm.

★10347★ Austin Michaels Ltd. Inc.
7949 E Acoma Dr
Scottsdale, AZ 85260
Ph: (480)483-5000   Fax: (480)483-6068
E-mail: frank@austinmichaels.com
URL: http://www.austinmichaels.com
Executive search firm.

★10348★ The B & B Group
202 W Main St., Ste. B
Glen Carbon, IL 62034
Ph: (618)288-2927   Fax: (618)288-2950
E-mail: bandbgroup@aol.com
URL: http://www.bnbgrp.com
Executive search firm.

★10349★ Baldwin & Associates
3975 Erie Ave.
Cincinnati, OH 45208-1908
Ph: (513)272-2400
E-mail: office@baldwin-assoc.com
URL: http://www.baldwin-assoc.com
Executive search firm.

★10350★ BallResources
PO Box 480391
Kansas City, MO 64148
Ph: (816)322-2727
E-mail: ronball@swbell.net
Executive search firm.

★10351★ Barclay Consultants Inc.
16 Chestnut Ct., Ste. B
Brielle, NJ 08730
Ph: (732)223-1131
Executive search firm.

★10352★ Barcus Associates
PO Box 1059
Van Alstyne, TX 75495
Ph: (903)482-1362   Fax: (903)482-1365
E-mail: keithl@barcusassociates.com
URL: http://www.barcusassociates.com
Executive search firm.

★10353★ Barrett & Co. Inc.
59 Stiles Rd., Ste. 105
Salem, NH 03079
Ph: (603)890-1111   Fax: (603)890-1118
E-mail: info@barrettcompany.com
URL: http://www.barrettcompany.com
Executive search firm.

★10354★ BD Wallace & Associates
217 Georgetown Rd.
Annapolis, MD 21403
Ph: (410)268-2024   Fax: (410)267-8374
E-mail: info@bdwallace.com
URL: http://www.bdwallace.com
Executive search firm.

★10355★ The Bentley Group Inc.
2240 Woolbright Rd., Ste. 353
Boynton Beach, FL 33426
Ph: (561)734-3550   Fax: (561)734-3449
Fr: (866)734-3550
E-mail: Bennett@bentleygrp.com
URL: http://www.bentleygrp.com
Executive search firm.

★10356★ Bosch & Associates LLC
PO Box 1030
Greens Farms, CT 06436
Ph: (203)255-8700   Fax: (203)259-4959
E-mail: ebosch@sprintmail.com
URL: http://www.boschllc.com
Executive search firm.

**★10357★ Brownstone Sales &
Marketing Group Inc.**
312 S 22nd St., Ste. C
New York, NY 10010
Ph: (212)254-8700
E-mail: team@b-stone.com
URL: http://www.b-stone.com
Executive search firm.

★10358★ Bryant Bureau Sales Recruiters
2435 Kimberly Rd., Ste. 110 N
Bettendorf, IA 52722
Ph: (563)355-4411   Fax: (563)355-3635
E-mail: doug@bbureau.com
URL: http://www.bbureau.com
Executive search firm.

★10359★ CAA Search
5469 Sunbird Dr.
Loves Park, IL 61111
Ph: (815)654-8535   Fax: (815)654-0469
Executive search firm.

★10360★ Career Forum Inc.
165 S Union Blvd., Ste.1020
Lakewood, CO 80228
Ph: (303)279-9200   Fax: (303)279-9296
E-mail: inquiries@careerforum.com
URL: http://www.careerforum.com
Executive search firm.

★10361★ CareerConnections USA Inc.
12827 Westledge Lane
St. Louis, MO 63131
Ph: (314)909-8510   Fax: (314)909-8513
E-mail: deb@careerconnectionsusa.com
URL: http://www.careerconnectionsusa.com
Executive search firm.

★10362★ Carter/MacKay
777 Terrace Ave.
Hasbrouck Heights, NJ 07604
Ph: (201)288-5100   Fax: (201)288-2660
E-mail: info.nj@cartermackay.com
URL: http://www.cartermackay.com
Executive search firm.

★10363★ Century Associates Inc.
1420 Walnut St., Ste. 1402
Philadelphia, PA 19102
Ph: (215)732-4311   Fax: (215)735-1804
E-mail: century@centuryassociates.com
URL: http://www.centuryassociates.com
Executive search firm.

★10364★ Clanton & Co.
1 City Blvd. W, Ste. 820
Orange, CA 92868
Ph: (714)978-7100   Fax: (714)978-7103
E-mail: fssearch@aol.com
Executive search firm.

★10365★ Clinton, Charles, Wise & Co.
931 State Rd. 434, Ste. 1201-319
Altamonte Springs, FL 32714
Ph: (407)682-6790   Fax: (407)682-1697
E-mail: ccwc@cfl.rr.com
URL: http://www.recruitersofccwc.com
Executive search firm.

★10366★ Colton Bernard Inc.
870 Market St., Ste. 822
San Francisco, CA 94102
Ph: (415)399-8700   Fax: (415)399-0750
Executive search firm focused on textiles, apparel and retail industries.

★10367★ Corporate Dynamix
6619 N Scottsdale Rd.
Scottsdale, AZ 85250
Ph: (480)607-0040   Fax: (310)662-0054
E-mail: david@cdynamix.com
URL: http://www.cdynamix.com
Executive search firm.

★10368★ Corporate Resources, Stevens Inc.
110 N Potomac St.
Hagerstown, MD 21740
Ph: (301)797-3434   Fax: (301)797-3331
E-mail: jgocha1@aol.com
Executive search firm.

★10369★ Criterion Search Group Inc.
PO Box 466
Wayne, PA 19087
Ph: (610)581-0590   Fax: (610)581-0594
Executive search firm.

★10370★ Damon & Associates Inc.
5716 Portsmouth Ln
Dallas, TX 75252
Ph: (972)381-9055
E-mail: damonoffice@sbcglobal.net
Executive search firm.

★10371★ Dan Bolen & Associates LLC
9741 N 90th Pl., Ste. 200
Scottsdale, AZ 85258-5045
Ph: (480)767-9000   Fax: (480)767-0100
E-mail: danbolen@mindspring.com
URL: http://www.danbolenassoc.com
Executive search firm.

★10372★ David Aplin & Associates
10235 101st St.
2300 Oxford Tower
Edmonton, AB, Canada T5J 3G1
Ph: (780)428-6663   Fax: (780)421-4680
E-mail: edmonton@aplin.com
URL: http://www.aplin.com
Executive search firm.

★10373★ David Blevins & Associates Inc.
2261 Market St., Ste. 105
San Francisco, CA 94114
Ph: (707)495-3714
Executive search firm.

★10374★ David E. Clutter
5668 S Foresthill St.
Littleton, CO 80120
Ph: (303)730-6422
E-mail: dclutter@prodigy.net
Executive search firm.

★10375★ David Fockler & Associates Inc.
25944 Paseo Estribo, Ste. 100
Monterey, CA 93940
Ph: (831)649-6666   Fax: (831)649-0600
E-mail: dave@fockler.com
URL: http://www.fockler.com
Executive search firm.

★10376★ Despres & Associates Inc.
117 S Cook St., Ste. 304
Barrington, IL 60010
Ph: (847)382-0625   Fax: (847)382-1705
E-mail: rdespres@despres.net
URL: http://www.despres.net
Executive search firm.

★10377★ Don Allan Associates Inc.
PO Box 12988
La Jolla, CA 92039-2988
Ph: (858)587-4800   Fr: 800-291-6900
E-mail: resume@globalstaffing.com
URL: http://www.globalstaffing.com
Executive search firm.

★10378★ Don V. Poole and Associates, Inc
7700 S Glencoe Way
Centennial, CO 80122
Ph: (303)721-6644   Fax: (303)721-7724
E-mail: dvpoole@attglobal.net
Executive search firm.

★10379★ The Donnelly Group Sales Recruiters Inc.
12536 Glenlea Dr.
Hazelwood, MO 63043
Ph: (314)469-6400   Fax: (314)469-4880
E-mail: ddonnelly@primary.net
Executive search firm.

★10380★ Dorothy W. Farnath & Associates Inc.
104B Center Blvd.
Marlton, NJ 08053
Ph: (856)810-2200
E-mail: office@farnath.com
URL: http://www.farnath.com
Executive search firm.

★10381★ Ecruiters.net
PO Box 1086
Chanhassen, MN 55317
Ph: (952)233-5750
Executive search firm.

★10382★ Edwards & Associates
4015 Goshen Lake Dr. S
Augusta, GA 30906
Ph: (706)793-3679   Fax: (706)793-7262
E-mail: lisa.edwards@earthlink.net
URL: http://www.edwardsassociates.net

Executive search firm.

★10383★ The Excel Group Inc.
18573 Lime Cir
Fountain Valley, CA 92708
Ph: (714)593-5927
E-mail: frank@xlg.com
URL: http://www.xlg.com

Executive search firm.

★10384★ Execusearch
21 Mountainwood Dr.
Glenville, NY 12302
Ph: (518)384-2036   Fax: (518)384-1413
E-mail: esearch1@aol.com

Executive search firm.

★10385★ Executive Sales Search Inc.
1815 Habersham Terrace
Cumming, GA 30041
Ph: (770)889-9665   Fax: (770)889-9350
E-mail: lindamende@earthlink.net

Executive search firm.

★10386★ Fast Switch Ltd.
37 W Bridge St., Ste. 200
Dublin, OH 43017
Ph: (614)336-3690   Fax: (614)336-3695
E-mail: mark_pukita@fastswitch.com

Executive search firm.

★10387★ Fisher-Todd Associates
122 E 42nd St. 3rd Fl
New York, NY 10168
Ph: (212)986-9052   Fax: (212)661-7897
E-mail: fishertodd@winstonstaffing.com
URL: http://www.winstonresources.com

Executive search firm.

★10388★ Forsyte Associates Inc.
1749 Central St., Ste. 4
Stoughton, MA 02072
Ph: (781)344-8600   Fax: (781)344-1896
E-mail: resumes@forsyte.com
URL: http://www.forsyte.com

Executive search firm.

★10389★ Franklin Associates Inc.
2061 SE Pyramid Rd
Port St. Lucie, FL 34952
Ph: (772)219-0406   Fax: (772)219-0860
E-mail: employ011@bellsouth.net

Executive search firm.

★10390★ The Garrison Organization
14225 University Ave., Ste. 206
Greenview Corporate Bldg.
Waukee, IA 50263-8096
Ph: (515)309-4442   Fax: (509)479-1213
E-mail: info@garrisonorg.com
URL: http://www.garrisonorg.com

Executive search firm.

★10391★ Georgia Sales Development Inc.
2700 Mansell Rd., Ste. 220
Alpharetta, GA 30022
Ph: (770)625-5075   Fax: (770)992-1601
E-mail: sdijobs@mindspring.com
URL: http://www.sdijobs.com

Executive search firm.

★10392★ GlobalQuest Group
12 Greenway Plaza, Ste. 1100
Houston, TX 77046
Ph: (713)964-4007   Fax: (713)964-4006
E-mail: rjhsearch@aol.com
URL: http://www.globalquestgrp.com

Executive search firm.

★10393★ Gowdy Consultants
12059 Starcrest Dr.
San Antonio, TX 78247
Ph: (210)499-4444   Fax: (210)499-4676
E-mail: gowdycts@texas.net

Executive search firm.

★10394★ Greenwich Search Partners LLC
43 Hillcrest Park Rd
Old Greenwich, CT 06870-1020
Ph: (203)627-2260
E-mail: gsp01@attglobal.net

Executive search firm.

★10395★ Harbeck Associates Inc.
2003 Claremont Commons
Normal, IL 61761
Ph: (309)454-2456   Fax: (309)454-2332
E-mail: bill@harbeckassociates.com
URL: http://www.greatsalesjobs.com

Executive search firm.

★10396★ Heath/Norton Associates Inc.
545 8th Ave., 7th Fl.
New York, NY 10018-4307
Ph: (212)695-3600   Fax: (212)695-0025

Executive search firm.

★10397★ Holloway, Schulz & Partners
1188 W Georgia St., Ste. 1500
Vancouver, BC, Canada V6E 4A2
Ph: (604)688-9595   Fax: (604)688-3608
E-mail: info@recruiters.com
URL: http://www.recruiters.com

Executive search firm.

★10398★ The Howard-Sloan-Koller Group
300 E 42nd St., 15th Fl.
New York, NY 10017
Ph: (212)661-5250   Fax: (212)557-9178
E-mail: hsk@hsksearch.com
URL: http://www.hsksearch.com

Executive search firm.

★10399★ Hughes & Co.
1626 Belle View Blvd.
PO Box 7365
Alexandria, VA 22307-0365
Ph: (703)765-8853   Fax: (703)765-6828
E-mail: djh@webbox.com
URL: http://www.careerresources.com

Executive search firm.

★10400★ International Search Consultants
1956 E Vinedo Lane
Tempe, AZ 85284
Fax: 888-866-6625   Fr: 888-866-7276
E-mail: annr@iscjobs.com

Executive search firm.

★10401★ J H Dugan & Company
225 Crossroads Blvd., Ste. 416
Carmel, CA 93923
Ph: (831)655-5880   Fax: (831)655-5588

Executive search firm.

★10402★ Jivaro Group
5433 S Emporia Court
Greenwood Village, CO 80111
Ph: (303)740-0022   Fax: (303)843-9570
E-mail: sue@jivarogroup.com
URL: http://www.jivarogroup.com

Executive search firm.

★10403★ JS Robertson Retained Search
2242 Camden Ave., Ste. 203
San Jose, CA 95124
Ph: (408)879-8000   Fax: (408)879-8001
E-mail: info@jsrobertson.com
URL: http://www.jsrobertson.com

Executive search firm.

★10404★ KDK Associates LLC
575 Waterford Dr.
Lake Zurich, IL 60047
Ph: (847)726-2902   Fax: (847)726-2903
E-mail: kdkassociates@aol.com
URL: http://www.kdkassociates.com

Executive search firm.

★10405★ Kensington International Inc.
1415 W 22nd St., Ste. 500
Oak Brook, IL 60523
Ph: (630)571-0123   Fax: (630)571-3139
E-mail: info@kionline.com

URL: http://www.kionline.com
Executive search firm.

★10406★ **The Kirdonn Sales Pros**
4224 S Hocker, Ste.100
Independence, MO 64055
Ph: (816)474-0700   Fax: (816)474-0702
E-mail: salespros@kirdonn.net
URL: http://www.kirdonn.com
Executive search firm.

★10407★ **Kressenberg Associates**
1112 E Copeland, Ste. 340
Arlington, TX 76012
Ph: (817)226-8990   Fax: (817)226-8999
Fr: 800-551-5361
E-mail: sammye@kressenberg.attbbs.com
URL: http://
www.kressenbergassociates.com
Executive search firm.

★10408★ **A la Carte International Inc.**
3330 Pacific Ave., Ste. 500
Virginia Beach, VA 23451-2997
Ph: (757)425-6111   Fax: (757)425-8507
Fr: 800-446-3037
E-mail: alacarte@wedofood.com
URL: http://www.wedofood.com
Executive search firm.

★10409★ **Lawrence Glaser Associates Inc.**
505 S Lenola Rd., Ste. 202
Moorestown, NJ 08057
Ph: (856)778-9500   Fax: (856)778-4390
E-mail: larryg@lgasearch.com
URL: http://www.lgasearch.com
Executive search firm.

★10410★ **Management Decision Systems Inc.**
466 Kinderkamack Rd.
Oradell, NJ 07649
Ph: (201)986-1200   Fax: (201)986-1210
URL: http://www.mdsisearch.com
Executive search firm.

★10411★ **Marketing & Sales Resources Inc.**
14000 Military Trail
Delray Beach, FL 33484
Ph: (561)637-7711   Fax: (561)637-7555
E-mail: msresources@mindspring.com
Executive search firm.

★10412★ **Medical Recruiters Inc.**
1401 S Brentwood Blvd., Ste750
St. Louis, MO 63144
Ph: (314)222-4200   Fax: (314)222-4211
Executive search firm.

★10413★ **MH Executive Search Group**
35246 US Hwy. 19 N, Ste.108
Palm Harbor, FL 34684-1931
Ph: (727)442-2011
E-mail: pkgjobs@mhgroup.com
URL: http://www.mhgroup.com
Executive search firm.

★10414★ **Mid-American Placement Service Inc.**
1941 S 42nd St., Ste. 520
Omaha, NE 68105-2945
Ph: (402)341-3338   Fax: (402)341-6266
E-mail: jobs@nejobs.com
URL: http://www.nejobs.com
Executive search firm.

★10415★ **Morency Associates**
301 Newbury St., Ste. 237
Danvers, MA 01923
Ph: (978)750-4460
E-mail: mmorency@aol.com
Executive search firm.

★10416★ **MRI of Atlanta West**
4260 Veterans Memorial Hwy., Ste. A
Lithia Springs, GA 30122-1752
Ph: (770)948-5560   Fax: (770)948-5762
E-mail: stevekendall@bellsouth.net
Executive search firm.

★10417★ **MRI of the Baltimore Washington Corridor**
7240 Parkway Dr., Ste. 150
Hanover, MD 21076
Ph: (410)712-0770   Fax: (410)712-0510
E-mail: mribwi@recruitersgurus.com
URL: http://www.recruitergurus.com
Executive search firm.

★10418★ **MRI of Houston**
1360 Post Oak Blvd., Ste. 2015
Houston, TX 77056
Ph: (713)850-9850   Fax: (713)850-1429
E-mail: mrhouston@mrhouston.com
URL: http://www.mrhouston.com
Executive search firm.

★10419★ **MRI of Milwaukee North**
1333 W Towne Square Rd.
Mequon, WI 53092
Ph: (262)241-1600   Fax: (262)241-1640
E-mail: admin@lawlergroup.com
URL: http://www.recruiters-jobs.com
Executive search firm.

★10420★ **MRI of Morris County, NJ**
17 Hanover Rd., Ste. 450
Florham Park, NJ 07932
Ph: (973)593-0400   Fax: (973)593-0150
Executive search firm.

★10421★ **National Sales & Marketing Consultants Inc.**
5650 Greenwood Plz. Blvd., Ste. 206
Englewood, CO 80111-2307
Ph: (303)771-4201   Fax: (303)740-8640

Locates, hires, and trains sales representatives, and coordinates on-going activities of manufacturer's representatives for clients in healthcare, government, health and beauty aids, sporting goods, consumer products, hardware, and stationery/office supply industries. Assists clients in developing pricing, packaging, advertising, general sales, and promotional policies. Acts as national sales manager for multiple clients.

★10422★ **Navin Group**
80 Washington St., Ste. 27-28D
Norwell, MA 02061
Ph: (781)871-6770   Fax: (781)878-8703
Fr: 888-837-1300
E-mail: search@navingroup.com
URL: http://www.navingroup.com
Executive search firm.

★10423★ **Next Step Group, Inc**
PO Box 25038
San Mateo, CA 94402
Ph: (650)577-8000   Fax: (650)577-9000
E-mail: info@4nextstep.com
URL: http://www.4nextstep.com
Executive search firm.

★10424★ **Opus Marketing**
23151 Moulton Parkway
Laguna Hills, CA 92653
Ph: (949)581-0962   Fax: (949)581-1497
E-mail: resumes@opusmarketing.com
URL: http://www.opusmarketing.com
Executive search firm.

★10425★ **Page Staffing & Training**
289 Rte. 33 E, Ste. 6, Bldg. A
Manalapan, NJ 07726
Ph: (732)786-8210   Fax: (732)786-8110
Fr: (866)653-6844
E-mail: abrown@whodoyouknowfordough.com
URL: http://
www.whodoyouknowfordough.com
Executive search firm.

★10426★ **Pat Licata & Associates**
5001 Weston Pkwy., Ste.104
Cary, NC 27513
Ph: (919)653-1180   Fax: (919)653-1199
E-mail: pat@patlicata.com
URL: http://www.patlicata.com
Executive search firm.

★10427★ Paul J. Biestek Associates Inc.
800 E. NW Hwy., Ste. 700
PO Box 101
Palatine, IL 60074
Ph: (847)825-5131
Executive search firm.

★10428★ Price & Associates
1400 Midhurst Cir
Virginia Beach, VA 23464
Ph: (757)306-4777   Fax: (757)306-8943
E-mail: vprice@earthlink.net
Executive search firm.

★10429★ Pro Search National Recruiting Services
216 W Pacific Ave., Ste. 104
Spokane, WA 99201
Ph: (509)363-1986   Fax: (509)363-1987
E-mail: pat@prosearchnational.com
Executive search firm.

★10430★ Professional Recruiters Inc.
17641 Kettering Trail., Ste. 100
Lakeville, MN 55044
Ph: (952)892-3700   Fr: 800-594-8414
E-mail: bob@professionalrecruiters.com
URL: http://www.professionalrecruiters.com
Executive search firm.

★10431★ The Professional Sales Search Company Inc.
12915 50th Ave. Ct. NW
Gig Harbor, WA 98332
Ph: (253)851-3528   Fax: (253)851-7505
E-mail: execadmin@psscinc.com
URL: http://www.psscinc.com
Executive search firm.

★10432★ Roadrunner Personnel
4015 Carlisle Blvd. NE, Ste. C
Albuquerque, NM 87107
Ph: (505)881-1994
E-mail: mail@exec-recruiter.com
URL: http://www.exec-recruiter.com
Executive search firm.

★10433★ Sales Consultants of Ft. Lauderdale
3000 NE 30th Place, Ste.408
Ft. Lauderdale, FL 33306
Ph: (954)772-5100
E-mail: resumes@mri-sc-usa.com
URL: http://www.mri-sc-usa.com
Executive search firm.

★10434★ Sales Consultants of Indianapolis-Central
8200 Haverstick Rd., Ste. 240
Indianapolis, IN 46240-2472
Ph: (317)257-5411   Fax: (317)259-6886

E-mail: search@mriindy.com
URL: http://www.mriindy.com
Executive search firm.

★10435★ Sales Consultants of Laurel Park
17177 N Laurel Park Dr., Ste. 256
Livonia, MI 48152-2659
Ph: (734)542-9099
Executive search firm.

★10436★ Sales Consultants of Rhode Island
2348 Post Rd., Ste. 101
Airport Professional Park
Warwick, RI 02886-2271
Ph: (401)737-3200   Fax: (401)737-4322
E-mail: info@mrisales.net
URL: http://www.mrisales.net
Executive search firm.

★10437★ Sales Consultants of St. Petersburg
275 104th Ave., Unit A
Treasure Island, FL 33706
Ph: (727)367-8787   Fax: (727)367-8532
E-mail: scstpete@netscape.net
URL: http://www.brilliantpeople.com
Executive search firm.

★10438★ Sales Consultants of Scottsdale
17021 E Nicklaus Dr.
Fountain Hills, AZ 85268
Ph: (480)816-4526
E-mail: scscottsdale@extremezone.com
Executive search firm.

★10439★ Sales Consultants of Southampton
80 Second St., Ste. 10
Southampton, PA 18966
Ph: (215)364-7559   Fax: (215)364-7579
E-mail: infoscs@mriscs.com
URL: http://www.mriscs.com
Executive search firm.

★10440★ Sales Consultants of Syracuse
212 Highbridge St., Ste. B
Fayetteville, NY 13066
Ph: (315)637-0619   Fax: (315)637-0621
E-mail: dwelker@accucom.net
URL: http://www.scsyr.baweb.com/company.html
Executive search firm.

★10441★ Sanford Rose Associates-Norcross
9650 Ventana Way, Ste. 204
1 Medlock Crossing
Alpharetta, GA 30022
Ph: (770)232-9900   Fax: (770)232-1933

E-mail: sra@searchforsuccess.com
URL: http://www.searchforsuccess.com
Executive search firm.

★10442★ Satterfield & Associates Inc.
7875 Annesdale Dr.
Cincinnati, OH 45243
Ph: (513)561-3679
E-mail: info@satterfield3.com
URL: http://www.satterfield3.com
Executive search firm.

★10443★ Search Masters USA
4598 Hamlets Grove
Sarasota, FL 34235
Ph: (941)351-7307   Fax: (941)351-5416
E-mail: alexstevenson@sbcglobal.net
Executive search firm.

★10444★ Select Medical Solutions
16303 Autumn View Terrace
St. Louis, MO 63011
Ph: (636)405-0333   Fax: (636)458-4657
E-mail: steve@selectmedicalsolutions.com
Executive search firm.

★10445★ SilverSands International
201 Springview Ct.
Winter Springs, FL 32708
Ph: (407)327-2300
E-mail: jmulvey@minsoring.com
Executive search firm.

★10446★ Sondra Search
PO Box 101
Roswell, GA 30077-0101
Ph: (770)552-1910   Fax: (770)552-7340
E-mail: sondrasearch@earthlink.net
Executive search firm.

★10447★ SR & Associates
5001 Birch St.
Newport Beach, CA 92660
Ph: (949)756-3271
E-mail: sraross@srassociates.com
URL: http://www.srassociatesinc.com
Executive search firm.

★10448★ Strategic Associates Inc.
PO Box 203278
Austin, TX 78720-3278
Ph: (512)218-8222   Fax: (512)218-8102
E-mail: sai@strategicassociates.com
URL: http://www.strategicassociates.com
Executive search firm.

★10449★ Strategic Executive Search Solutions
14 Fernald Ave
PO Box 86
Corinna, ME 04928
Ph: (207)278-3800   Fax: 877-780-4777
Fr: 877-871-3800
E-mail: j.parker@strategicexecsearch.com
URL: http://www.strategicexecsearch.com
Executive search firm.

★10450★ Todd Arro Inc.
3024 Delaware Ave.
PO Box 172
Buffalo, NY 14217
Ph: (716)871-0993   Fax: (716)871-1376
Recruiting and search consultants specializing in sales and marketing management in the industrial, commercial, consumer product, pharmaceutical and medical areas.

★10451★ Weterrings & Agnew Inc.
132 Allens Creek Rd.
Rochester, NY 14618
Ph: (585)241-9040   Fax: (716)241-9044
E-mail: info@weterrings.com
URL: http://www.weterrings.com
Executive search firm.

★10452★ Whitney Group
850 3rd Ave., 11th Fl
New York, NY 10022
Ph: (212)508-3500   Fax: (212)508-3589
E-mail: recruiter@whitneygroup.com
URL: http://www.whitneygroup.com
Executive search firm.

★10453★ William Halderson Associates Inc.
PO Box 20056
St. Simons Island, GA 31522
Ph: (912)638-8430
E-mail: bill@haldersonsearch.com
URL: http://www.haldersonsearch.com
Executive search firm.

★10454★ The Wylie Group Ltd.
345 N Canal St., Ste. 1605
Chicago, IL 60606
Ph: (312)822-0333   Fax: (312)454-1375
E-mail: wrw@wyliegroup.net
Executive search firm.

ONLINE JOB SOURCES AND SERVICES

★10455★ Omni Search, Inc.
E-mail: omni@the-salesnet.com
URL: http://www.omnisearch.biz/opps.htm

Description: Job search engine for those in the sales and marketing positions in the pharmaceutical, medical and consumer industries.

★10456★ Spherion Workforce Architects
URL: http://www.spherion.com
Description: Recruitment firm specializing in accounting and finance, sales and marketing, interim executives, technology, engineering, retail and human resources.

TRADESHOWS

★10457★ ERA Conference and Exposition
Electronic Retailing Association
2101 Wilson Blvd., Ste. 1002
Arlington, VA 22201
Ph: (703)841-1751   Fax: (703)841-1860
Fr: 800-987-6462
URL: http://www.retailing.org
Annual. **Primary Exhibits:** Equipment, supplies, and services for the growth, development, and acceptance of electronic retailing worldwide. **Dates and Locations:** 2004 Sep 26-28; Las Vegas, NV; Paris Las Vegas.

★10458★ International Mass Retail Association Convention and Exhibits
International Mass Retail Association
1700 N. Moore St., Ste. 2250
Arlington, VA 22209
Ph: (703)841-2300   Fax: (703)841-1184
URL: http://www.imra.org
Annual. **Primary Exhibits:** Consumer products.

★10459★ Sales and Marketing Show and Conference
Flagg Management, Inc.
353 Lexington Ave.
New York, NY 10016
Ph: (212)286-0333   Fax: (212)286-0086
E-mail: flaggmgmt@msn.com
URL: http://www.flaggmgmt.com
Annual. **Primary Exhibits:** Sales and marketing products, customer support systems, sales administration services, Internet/Intranet systems, web site marketing services, client server solutions, sales automation, telecommunications, wireless, telemarketing, training, incentives, database management, and direct marketing.

OTHER SOURCES

★10460★ Administration and Management Occupations
Delphi Productions
3160 4th St.
Boulder, CO 80304
Fax: (303)443-4022   Fr: 888-443-2400
URL: http://www.delphivideo.com
$95.00. 50 minutes. Part of the Careers for the 21st Century Video Library.

★10461★ American Management Association (AMA)
1601 Broadway
New York, NY 10019-7420
Ph: (212)586-8100   Fax: (212)903-8168
Fr: 800-262-9699
E-mail: customerservice@amanet.org
URL: http://www.amanet.org
Members: American Management Association provides educational forums worldwide where members and their colleagues learn superior, practical business skills and explore best practices of world-class organizations through interaction with each other and expert faculty practitioners. **Purpose:** AMA's publishing program provides tools individuals use to extend learning beyond the classroom in a process of life-long professional growth and development through education.

★10462★ American Society of Association Executives (ASAE)
1575 I St. NW
Washington, DC 20005-1103
Ph: (202)626-2723   Fax: (202)371-8825
Fr: 888-950-2723
E-mail: pr@asaenet.org
URL: http://www.asaenet.org
Members: Professional society of paid executives of international, national, state, and local trade, professional, and philanthropic associations. **Purpose:** Seeks to educate association executives on effective management, including: the proper objectives, functions, and activities of associations; the basic principles of association management; the legal aspects of association activity; policies relating to association management; efficient methods, procedures, and techniques of association management; the responsibilities and professional standards of association executives. Maintains information resource center. **Activities:** Conducts resume, guidance, and consultation services; compiles statistics in the form of reports, surveys, and studies; carries out research and education. Maintains ASAE Services Corporation to provide special services and ASAE Foundation to do future-oriented research and make grant awards. Offers executive search services and insurance programs. Provides CEO center for chief staff executives. Conducts Certified Association Executive (CAE) program.

★10463★ *Marketing & Sales Occupations*

Delphi Productions
3160 4th St.
Boulder, CO 80304
Fax: (303)443-4022   Fr: 888-443-2400
URL: http://www.delphivideo.com

$95.00. 50 minutes. Part of the Careers for the 21st Century Video Library.

★10464★ **National Management Association (NMA)**

2210 Arbor Blvd.
Dayton, OH 45439
Ph: (937)294-0421   Fax: (937)294-2374
E-mail: nma@nma1.org
URL: http://www.nma1.org

Description: Business and industrial management personnel; membership comes from supervisory level, with the remainder from middle management and above. Seeks to develop and recognize management as a profession and to promote the free enterprise system. Prepares chapter programs on basic management, management policy and practice, communications, human behavior, industrial relations, economics, political education, and liberal education. Maintains speakers' bureau and hall of fame. Maintains educational, charitable, and research programs. Sponsors charitable programs.

Science Technicians

SOURCES OF HELP-WANTED ADS

★10465★ American Biotechnology Laboratory

International Scientific Communications Inc.
30 Controls Dr.
PO Box 870
Shelton, CT 06484-0870
Ph: (203)926-9300   Fax: (203)926-9310

$160.00/year for individuals. Biotechnology magazine.

★10466★ Annual Review of Genetics

Annual Reviews Inc.
PO Box 10139
Palo Alto, CA 94303-0139
Ph: (650)493-4400   Fax: (650)855-9815
Fr: 800-523-8635

Annual. Periodical covering issues in genetics and the biological sciences.

★10467★ Annual Review of Microbiology

Annual Reviews Inc.
PO Box 10139
Palo Alto, CA 94303-0139
Ph: (650)493-4400   Fax: (650)855-9815
Fr: 800-523-8635

Annual. Periodical covering microbiology and the biological sciences.

★10468★ Chemical Equipment

Reed Business Information
301 Gibraltar Dr.
Morris Plains, NJ 07950
Ph: (973)292-5100   Fax: (973)539-3476

Tabloid on the chemical process industry.

★10469★ Invertebrate Biology

Allen Press
810 E 10th
Lawrence, KS 66044
Ph: (785)843-1234   Fax: (785)843-1244
Fr: 800-627-0326
URL: http://www.invertebrate biology.org/ibgenl.htm

Quarterly. $38.00/year for individuals, includes membership; $19.00/year for students, includes membership; $48.00/year for Canada and Mexico; $52.00/year for elsewhere; $85.00/year for libraries in U.S., Canada and Mexico; $110.00/year for libraries elsewhere. Scientific journal covering the biology of invertebrate animals and research in the fields of cell and molecular biology, ecology, physiology, systematics, genetics, biogeography and behavior.

★10470★ Nature Biotechnology

Nature Publishing Group
345 Park Ave. S
New York, NY 10010-1707
Ph: (212)726-9200   Fax: (212)689-9711
Fr: 888-331-6288
E-mail: biotech@natureny.com
URL: http://www.biotechnology.nature.com

Monthly. $75.00/year for individuals; $545.00/year for institutions. Scientific research journal.

★10471★ Nature International Weekly Journal of Science

Nature Publishing Group
345 Park Ave. S
New York, NY 10010-1707
Ph: (212)726-9200   Fax: (212)689-9711
Fr: 888-331-6288
E-mail: nature@natureny.com
URL: http://www.nature.com

Weekly. $145.00/year for individuals; $495.00/year for institutions. Magazine covering science and technology, including the fields of biology, biochemistry, genetics, medicine, earth sciences, physics, pharmacology, and behavioral sciences.

★10472★ The Northeastern Naturalist

Humboldt Field Research Institute
PO Box 9
Steuben, ME 04680-0009
Ph: (207)546-2821   Fax: (207)546-3042
URL: http://www.eaglehill.us/jngeninf.html

Quarterly. $40.00/year for individuals; $60.00/year for institutions; $45.00/year for individuals, Canada; $65.00/year for institutions, Canada; $49.00/year for individuals, other countries; $69.00/year for institutions, other countries. Peer-reviewed interdisciplinary scientific journal covering field ecology, biology, behavior, biogeography, taxonomy, anatomy, physiology, geology and related fields in the northeastern United States.

★10473★ Popular Science

Time4 Media Inc.
2 Park Ave., 10th Fl.
New York, NY 10016
Ph: (212)779-5493   Fax: (212)779-5118

Monthly. $13.94/year; $2.00 for single issue. General interest science magazine.

★10474★ Science

American Association for the Advancement of Science
1200 New York Ave. NW
Washington, DC 20005
Ph: (202)326-6400   Fax: (202)371-9849
URL: http://htpp://www.sciencemag.org

Weekly. $105.00/year for individuals; $7.00 for single issue. Magazine devoted to science, scientific research, and public policy.

★10475★ The Scientist

The Scientist Inc.
3535 Market St., Ste. 200
Philadelphia, PA 19104-2645
Ph: (215)386-9601   Fax: (215)386-7542
Fr: 800-258-6008
E-mail: info@the-scientist.com
URL: http://www.the-scientist.com

Biweekly. $49.00/year for individuals; $149.00/year for institutions; $24.00/year for students; $82.00/year for other countries; $49.00/year for students, other countries; $174.00/year for institutions, other countries.

News journal (tabloid) for life scientists featuring news, opinions, research, and professional section.

★10476★ The Southeastern Naturalist
Humboldt Field Research Institute
PO Box 9
Steuben, ME 04680-0009
Ph: (207)546-2821   Fax: (207)546-3042
URL: http://www.eaglehill.us/jngeninf.html

Quarterly. $40.00/year for individuals; $60.00/year for institutions; $45.00/year for individuals, Canada; $65.00/year for institutions, Canada; $49.00/year for individuals, other countries; $69.00/year for institutions, other countries. Peer-reviewed interdisciplinary scientific journal covering field ecology, biology, behavior, biogeography, taxonomy, anatomy, physiology, geology and related fields in the southeastern United States.

★10477★ Wetlands
Society of Wetland Scientists
1313, Dolley Madison Blvd.Ste.402
McLean, VA 22101
Ph: (703)790-1745   Fax: (703)790-2672
Fr: 800-627-0629
URL: http://www.sws.org/wetlands/

Quarterly. $50.00/year for individuals, includes SWS membership; $25.00/year for students, includes SWS membership; $250.00/year for institutions, includes SWS membership; $125.00/year for libraries, includes SWS membership; $65.00/year for family, includes SWS membership; $35.00/year for emeritus, includes SWS membership. Scholarly journal covering all aspects of wetlands biology, ecology, hydrology, water chimstry, soil and sediment characteristics, management, and laws and regulations.

PLACEMENT AND JOB REFERRAL SERVICES

★10478★ American Society of Agronomy (ASA)
677 S. Segoe Rd.
Madison, WI 53711
Ph: (608)273-8080   Fax: (608)273-2021
E-mail: headquarters@agronomy.org
URL: http://www.agronomy.org

Description: Professional society of agronomists, plant breeders, physiologists, soil scientists, chemists, educators, technicians, and others concerned with crop production and soil management, and conditions affecting them. Sponsors fellowship program and student essay and speech contests. Provides placement service.

★10479★ American Society for Histocompatibility and Immunogenetics (ASHI)
17000 Commerce Pky., Ste. C
Mount Laurel, NJ 08054
Ph: (856)638-0428   Fax: (856)439-0525
E-mail: info@ashi-hla.org
URL: http://www.ashi-hla.org

Members: Scientists, physicians, and technologists involved in research and clinical activities related to histocompatibility testing (a state of mutual tolerance that allows some tissues to be grafted effectively to others). **Activities:** Conducts proficiency testing and educational programs. Maintains liaison with regulatory agencies; offers placement services and laboratory accreditation. Has co-sponsored development of histocompatability specialist and laboratory certification program.

★10480★ Korean Scientists and Engineers Association in America (KSEA)
1952 Gallows Rd., Ste. 300
Vienna, VA 22182
Ph: (703)748-1221   Fax: (703)748-1331
E-mail: sejong@ksea.org
URL: http://www.ksea.org

Description: Scientists and engineers holding single or advanced degrees. Goals are to: promote friendship and mutuality among Korean and American scientists and engineers; contribute to Korea's scientific, technological, industrial, and economic developments; strengthen the scientific, technological, and cultural bonds between Korea and the U.S. Sponsors symposium. Maintains speakers' bureau, placement service, and biographical archives. Compiles statistics. Maintains 100 volume library of scientific handbooks and yearbooks in Korean.

★10481★ Society for Range Management (SRM)
445 Union Blvd., Ste. 230
Lakewood, CO 80228
Ph: (303)986-3309   Fax: (303)986-3892
E-mail: srmweb@rangelands.org
URL: http://www.rangelands.org/

Members: Professional international society of scientists, technicians, ranchers, administrators, teachers, and students interested in the study, use, and management of rangeland resources for livestock, wildlife, watershed, and recreation. **Activities:** Sponsors placement service.

EMPLOYER DIRECTORIES AND NETWORKING LISTS

★10482★ Peterson's Job Opportunities in Engineering and Technology
Thomson Peterson's
PO Box 67005
Lawrenceville, NJ 08648-6105
Fr: 800-338-3282

Compiled by the Peterson's staff. Fourth edition, 1996. $21.95 (paper). 384 pages. Profiles 2,000 high-tech companies looking primarily for technical personnel in such fields as biotechnology, telecommunications, software, computers and peripherals, defense, and aerospace. Contains job-search strategies and career options to help match education and expertise to the job market. Indexed geographically, by industry, and by hiring needs.

HANDBOOKS AND MANUALS

★10483★ The Best Resumes for Scientists and Engineers
John Wiley & Sons Inc.
1 Wiley Dr.
Somerset, NJ 08873
Ph: (732)469-4400   Fr: 800-225-5945

Adele Lewis and David J. Moore. Second edition, 1993. $37.50; $19.95 (paper). 224 pages. Presents an extensive collection of scientific and engineering resumes, highlighting the important differences between these and resumes written for other occupations.

★10484★ Opportunities in Biological Science Careers
McGraw-Hill Trade
2 Penn Plaza
New York, NY 10121
Ph: (212)904-2000   Fr: 800-722-4726
E-mail: ntcpub@tribune.com

Charles A. Winter. 1998. $14.95; $11.95 (paper). 200 pages. Identifies employers and outlines opportunities in plant and animal biology, biological specialties, biomedical sciences, applied biology, and other areas. Illustrated.

★10485★ Opportunities in High Tech Careers
McGraw-Hill Trade
2 Penn Plaza
New York, NY 10121
Ph: (212)904-2000   Fr: 800-722-4726

Gary Colter and Deborah Yanuck. 1995. $14.95; $11.95 (paper). 160 pages. Explores high technology careers. Describes job opportunities, how to make a career decision, how to prepare for high technology jobs, job hunting techniques, and future trends.

★10486★ Opportunities in Research and Development Careers

McGraw-Hill/Contemporary Books
1221 Avenue of the Americas
New York, NY 10020
Ph: (212)904-2000   Fr: 800-323-4900
E-mail: ntcpub@tribune.com

Jan Goldberg. 1997. $14.95; $11.95 (paper). 204 pages.

★10487★ Opportunities in Science Technician Careers

Vgm Career Horizons
1221 Avenue of the Americas
New York, NY 10020
Ph: (212)904-2000   Fr: 800-323-4900
E-mail: ntcpub@tribune.com

JoAnn Chirico. 1996. 160 pages. $14.95; $11.95 (paper).

★10488★ Resumes for Science Careers

McGraw-Hill Professional
1221 Avenue of the Americas
New York, NY 10020
Ph: (212)904-2000   Fr: 800-323-4900
E-mail: ntcpub@tribune.com

1997. $9.95 (paper). 466 pages.

EMPLOYMENT AGENCIES AND SEARCH FIRMS

★10489★ Banner Personnel Service

125 S Wacker Dr., Ste.1250
Chicago, IL 60606
Ph: (312)580-2500   Fax: (312)580-2515

Employment agency. Executive search firm. Branch offices in Oak Brook and Schaumburg, IL.

★10490★ Bruce Edwards & Associates Inc.

PO Box 51206
Durham, NC 27717-1206
Ph: (919)489-5368

Executive search firm.

★10491★ Eastbourne Associates Inc.

104 Sandy Hollow Rd.
Northport, NY 11768
Ph: (631)757-1217   Fax: (631)757-1417

Executive search firm.

★10492★ Franklin Allen Consultants Ltd.

1205 Franklin Ave., Ste. 350
Garden City, NY 11530
Ph: (516)248-4511   Fax: (516)294-6646

Executive search firm.

★10493★ Intech Summit Group, Inc.

5075 Shoreham Pl., Ste. 280
San Diego, CA 92122
Ph: (858)452-2100   Fax: (858)452-8500
E-mail: isg@isgsearch.com
URL: http://www.isgsearch.com

Employment agency and executive recruiter with a branch in Carlsbad, CA.

TRADESHOWS

★10494★ American Association for the Advancement of Science Annual Meeting & Science Innovation Exposition

American Association for the Advancement of Science (AAAS)
1200 New York Ave. NW
Washington, DC 20005
Ph: (202)326-6400   Fax: (202)289-4021
URL: http://www.aaasmeetings.org

Annual. **Primary Exhibits:** Scientific supplies and services, including books and journals, educational and informational services, government agencies, and scientific associations.

★10495★ O-E/LASE - Optoelectronics and Laser Applications in Science and Engineering Exhibit

SPIE - International Society for Optical Engineering
PO Box 10
Bellingham, WA 98227-0010
Ph: (360)676-3290   Fax: (360)647-1445
E-mail: spie@spie.org
URL: http://www.spie.org/

Annual. **Primary Exhibits:** Laser applications, science, and engineering; optics and optomechanics; optical computing and holography; and mass data optical storage.

OTHER SOURCES

★10496★ American Chemical Society (ACS)

1155 16th St. NW
Washington, DC 20036
Ph: (202)872-4600   Fax: (202)776-8258
Fr: 800-227-5558
E-mail: webmaster@acs.org
URL: http://www.acs.org

Members: Scientific and educational society of chemists and chemical engineers. **Activities:** Conducts studies and surveys; special programs for disadvantaged persons; legislation monitoring, analysis, and reporting; courses for graduate chemists and chemical engineers; radio and television programming. Offers career guidance counseling; administers the Petroleum Research Fund and other grants and fellowship programs. Operates Employment Clearing Houses. Compiles statistics. Maintains speakers' bureau. Maintains 33 divisions.

★10497★ American Institute of Biological Sciences (AIBS)

1444 I St. NW, Ste. 200
Washington, DC 20005-2210
Ph: (202)628-1500   Fax: (202)628-1509
Fr: 800-992-2427
E-mail: rogrady@aibs.org
URL: http://www.aibs.org

Members: Professional member organization and federation of biological associations, laboratories, and museums whose members have an interest in the life sciences. **Purpose:** Promotes unity and effectiveness of effort among persons engaged in biological research, education, and application of biological sciences, including agriculture, environment, and medicine. Seeks to further the relationships of biological sciences to other sciences and industries. Conducts roundtable series; provides names of prominent biologists who are willing to serve as speakers and curriculum consultants; provides advisory committees and other services to the Department of Energy, Environmental Protection Agency, National Science Foundation, Department of Defense, and National Aeronautics and Space Administration. Maintains educational consultant panel.

★10498★ Association for International Practical Training (AIPT)

10400 Little Patuxent Pky., Ste. 250
Columbia, MD 21044-3519
Ph: (410)997-2200   Fax: (410)992-3924
E-mail: aipt@aipt.org
URL: http://www.aipt.org

Description: Providers worldwide on-the-job training programs for students and professionals seeking international career development and life-changing experiences. Arranges workplace exchanges in hundreds of professional fields, bringing employers and trainees together from around the world. Client list ranges from small farming communities to Fortune 500 companies.

★10499★ Minority Women In Science (MWIS)

Directorate for Education and Human Resources Programs
1200 New York Ave. NW
Washington, DC 20005
Ph: (202)326-7019   Fax: (202)371-9849
E-mail: sassefa@aaas.org

Description: A national network group of the American association for the Advancement of Science (AAAS), Education and Human Resources Directorate. The objectives of this group are: to identify and share information on resources and programs that could help in mentoring young women and minorities interested in science and engineering careers, and to strengthen communication among women and minorities in science and education.

Secondary School Teachers

SOURCES OF HELP-WANTED ADS

★10500★ AAEE Connections
American Association for Employment in Education
3040 Riverside Dr., Ste. 125
Columbus, OH 43221
Ph: (614)485-1111   Fax: (614)485-9609
Description: Quarterly. Publishes news of the Association, whose aim is "to enhance and promote the concept of career planning and placement as an integral part of the educational process and to undertake activities designed to help schools, colleges, and universities meet their educational staffing needs." Also concerned with teacher education and the supply of/demand for teachers. Recurring features include news of members, state and regional news, and announcements of upcoming conferences and meetings.

★10501★ Academic Exchange Quarterly
Rapid Intellect Group Inc.
PO Box 131
Stuyvesant Falls, NY 12174
Ph: (518)372-1347
E-mail: AEQ@rapidintellect.com
URL: http://rapidintellect.com/AEQweb/

Quarterly. $156.00/year for individuals; $116.00/year, professional rate; $39.00 for single issue. Periodical covering issues in education.

★10502★ The American Biology Teacher
National Association of Biology Teachers
12030 Sunrise Valley Dr., Ste. 110
Reston, VA 20191
Ph: (703)264-9696   Fax: (703)264-7778
Fr: 800-406-0775
E-mail: publication@nabt.org
URL: http://www.nabt.org

$125.00/year; $135.00/year for other countries; $10.00 for single issue. Journal featuring articles on biology, science, and educa-tion for elementary, high school and college level biology teachers. Includes audio-visual, book, computer, and research reviews.

★10503★ The Council Chronicle
National Council of Teachers of English
1111 W Kenyon Rd.
Urbana, IL 61801-1096
Ph: (217)328-3870   Fax: (217)328-0977
Fr: 800-369-6283
E-mail: chronicle@ncte.org
URL: http://www.ncte.org

$30.00/year for members. Newspaper for teachers of English or language arts at all levels who are members of the National Council of Teachers of English.

★10504★ Education Week
Editorial Projects in Education Inc.
6935 Arlington Rd., Ste. 100
Bethesda, MD 20814
Ph: (301)280-3100   Fax: (301)280-3250
E-mail: ew@epe.org
URL: http://www.edweek.org

Weekly. $79.94/year for individuals. Professional newspaper for elementary and secondary school educators.

★10505★ Educational Researcher
American Educational Research Association
1230 17th St. NW
Washington, DC 20036-3078
Ph: (202)223-9485   Fax: (202)775-1824
URL: http://www.aera.net

$41.00/year for individuals; $8.00 for single issue; $56.00/year for institutions; $50.00/year for out of country; free to members of AERA. Educational research journal.

★10506★ Electronic Learning
Scholastic Library Publishing Inc.
90 Old Sherman Tpke.
Danbury, CT 06816
Ph: (203)797-3500   Fax: (203)797-3657
Fr: 800-621-1115

$19.00/year. Magazine focusing on electronic education.

★10507★ Journal of Language, Identity, and Education
Lawrence Erlbaum Associates Inc.
10 Industrial Ave.
Mahwah, NJ 07430-2262
Ph: (201)236-9500   Fax: (201)236-0072
Fr: 800-9-BOOKS-9
E-mail: journals@erlbaum.com
URL: http://www.erlbaum.com/shop/tek9.asp?pg=products&specific=1

Quarterly. $40.00/year for individuals; $70.00/year for out of country; $225.00/year for institutions; $255.00/year for institutions, other countries. Scholarly, interdisciplinary journal covering issues in language, identity and education worldwide for academics, educators and policy specialists in a variety of disciplines, and others.

★10508★ Journal of Latinos and Education
Lawrence Erlbaum Associates Inc.
10 Industrial Ave.
Mahwah, NJ 07430-2262
Ph: (201)236-9500   Fax: (201)236-0072
Fr: 800-9-BOOKS-9
E-mail: journals@erlbaum.com
URL: http://www.erlbaum.com/shop/tek9.asp?pg=products&specific=1

Quarterly. $40.00/year for individuals; $70.00/year for out of country; $195.00/year for institutions; $225.00/year for institutions, other countries. Scholarly, multidisciplinary journal covering educational issues that impact Latinos for researchers, teaching professionals, academics, scholars, institutions, and others.

★10509★ Journal of Learning Disabilities
PRO-ED Inc.
8700 Shoal Creek Blvd.
Austin, TX 78757-6897
Ph: (512)451-3246   Fax: (512)451-8542
Fr: 800-897-3202

$49.00/year for individuals; $105.00/year for institutions; $115.00/year for other countries. Special education journal.

★10510★ Journal of Teacher Education
Boston College
McElroy Commons, No. 113
Chestnut Hill, MA 02467
Ph: (617)552-4820   Fax: (617)552-4823

Magazine of interest to educators.

★10511★ Matrix: The Magazine for Leaders in Higher Education
Professional Media Group L.L.C.
36 Clipper Ct., Ste. B
Mystic, CT 06355-2138

Bimonthly. Trade publication covering issues for higher education professionals.

★10512★ Music Educators Journal
MENC: The National Association for Music Education
1806 Robert Fulton Dr.
Reston, VA 20191
Ph: (703)860-4000   Fr: 800-336-3768

Bimonthly. Journal covering all levels of music education. Published on alternate months with Teaching Music.

★10513★ NJEA Review
New Jersey Education Association
180 W State St.
PO Box 1211
Trenton, NJ 08607
Ph: (609)599-4561   Fax: (609)392-6321
E-mail: lgalley@mgea.org

$25.00/year. Educational journal for public school employees.

★10514★ Perspective Atlas
Association of Teachers of Latin American Studies
PO Box 754
Flushing, NY 11362
Ph: (718)428-1237   Fax: (718)428-1237
URL: http://atlas0754.com

Description: Quarterly. Presents news of the Association, women's studies and teaching abroad programs, and conferences. Recurring features include notices of publications available, grant opportunities, and employment.

★10515★ The Physics Teacher
American Association of Physics Teachers
One Physics Ellipse
College Park, MD 20740-3845
Ph: (301)209-3350   Fax: (301)209-0845
E-mail: tpt@appstate.edu
URL: http:///www.aapt.org/tpt

$94.00/year for individuals; $47.00/year. Scientific education magazine.

★10516★ Scholastic Coach & Athletic Director
Scholastic Library Publishing Inc.
90 Old Sherman Tpke.
Danbury, CT 06816
Ph: (203)797-3500   Fax: (203)797-3657
Fr: 800-621-1115
E-mail: magazines@scholastic.ca
URL: http://secure.palmcoast.com/pcd/document?ikey=0473YIWEA

$14.98/year for individuals. Magazine on high school and college athletics.

★10517★ School and Community
Missouri State Teachers Association
PO Box 458
Columbia, MO 65205-0458
Ph: (573)442-3127   Fax: (573)443-5079
Fr: 800-392-0532
E-mail: publications@mail.msta.org
URL: http://www.msta.org

Quarterly. $15.00/year. Education magazine.

★10518★ The Science Teacher
National Science Teachers Association
1840 Wilson Blvd.
Arlington, VA 22201-3000
Ph: (703)243-7100   Fax: (703)243-7177
Fr: 800-722-6782
E-mail: thescienceteacher@nsta.org
URL: http://www.nsta.org

$65.00/year for individuals. Journal on science education.

★10519★ Strategies
American Alliance for Health, Physical Education, Recreation & Dance
1900 Association Dr.
Reston, VA 20191
Ph: (703)476-3400   Fax: (703)476-9527
Fr: 800-213-7193
E-mail: strategies@aahperd.org

$25.00/year for members; $40.00/year for individuals; $63.00/year for businesses, institutions, and libraries. Journal providing practical, hands-on information to physical educators and coaches.

★10520★ Teacher Magazine
Editorial Projects in Education Inc.
6935 Arlington Rd., Ste. 100
Bethesda, MD 20814
Ph: (301)280-3100   Fax: (301)280-3250
E-mail: tm@epe.org
URL: http://www.teachermagazine.org

$17.94/year; $3.00 for single issue. Professional magazine for elementary and secondary school teachers.

★10521★ Teaching Exceptional Children
Council for Exceptional Children
1110 N Glebe Rd., Ste. 300
Arlington, VA 22201
Ph: (703)620-3660   Fax: (703)264-9494
Fr: 888-232-7733

E-mail: tec@bc.edu

$58.00/year for individuals; $66.00/year for other countries by surface mail; $95.00/year for other countries by airmail; $10.50 for single issue. Journal exploring practical methods for teaching students who have exceptionalities and those who are gifted and talented.

★10522★ Tech Directions
Prakken Publications Inc.
PO Box 8623
Ann Arbor, MI 48107-8623
Ph: (734)975-2800   Fax: (734)975-2787
Fr: 800-530-WORD
E-mail: tdedit@techdirections.com
URL: http://www.techdirections.com

Free to qualified subscribers; $30.00/year for individuals. Magazine covering issues, programs, and projects in industrial education, technology education, trade and industry, and vocational-technical career education. Articles are geared for teacher and administrator use and reference from elementary school through postsecondary levels.

★10523★ The Technology Teacher
International Technology Education Association
1914 Association Dr., Ste. 201
Reston, VA 20191
Ph: (703)620-4146   Fax: (703)860-0353
E-mail: iteapubs@iris.com

$70.00/year. Magazine on technology education.

★10524★ Today's OEA
Oregon Education Association
6900 SW Atlanta St.
Portland, OR 97223-2513
Ph: (503)684-3300   Fax: (503)684-8063

Bimonthly. Free to qualified subscribers; $10.00/year for nonmembers. Membership magazine covering educational issues statewide and nationally.

PLACEMENT AND JOB REFERRAL SERVICES

★10525★ American Alliance for Health, Physical Education, Recreation and Dance (AAHPERD)
1900 Association Dr.
Reston, VA 20191-1598
Ph: (703)476-3400   Fax: (703)476-9527
Fr: 800-213-7193
URL: http://www.aahperd.org

Members: Students and educators in physical education, dance, health, athletics, safety education, recreation, and outdoor education. **Purpose:** Works to improve its fields of education at all levels through such services as consultation, periodicals and special publications, leadership development, determination of standards, and research. Sponsors placement service.

★10526★ American Association of Christian Schools (AACS)
PO Box 1097
Independence, MO 64051-0597
Ph: (816)252-9900   Fax: (816)252-6700
E-mail: national@aacs.org
URL: http://www.aacs.org
Description: Maintains teacher/administrator certification program and placement service. Participates in school accreditation program. Sponsors National Academic Tournament. Maintains American Christian Honor Society. Compiles statistics; maintains speakers' bureau and placement service.

★10527★ American Association of Teachers of French (A.A.T.F.)
Mail Code 4510
Southern Illinois University
Carbondale, IL 62901-4510
Ph: (618)453-5731   Fax: (618)453-5733
E-mail: abrate@siu.edu
URL: http://www.frenchteachers.org
Members: Teachers of French in public and private elementary and secondary schools, colleges, and universities. **Activities:** Sponsors National French Week each November to take French out of the classroom and into the schools and community. Conducts National French Contest in elementary and secondary schools and awards prizes at all levels. Maintains Materials Center with promotional and pedagogical materials; National French Honor Society (high school), Placement Bureau, Pen Pal Bureau, summer scholarships.

★10528★ American Association of Teachers of Spanish and Portuguese (AATSP)
423 Exton Commons
Exton, PA 19341-2951
Ph: (610)363-7005   Fax: (610)363-7116
E-mail: corporate@aatsp.org
URL: http://www.aatsp.org
Description: Teachers of Spanish and Portuguese languages and literatures and others interested in Hispanic culture. Operates placement bureau and maintains pen pal registry. Sponsors honor society, Sociedad Honoraria Hispanica and National Spanish Examinations for secondary school students.

★10529★ American Classical League (ACL)
Miami University
Oxford, OH 45056
Ph: (513)529-7741   Fax: (513)529-7742
E-mail: info@aclclassics.org
URL: http://www.aclclassics.org
Members: Teachers of classical languages in high schools and colleges. **Purpose:** To promote the teaching of Latin and other classical languages. Presents scholarship. **Activities:** Maintains placement service, teaching materials, and resource center at

Miami University in Oxford, OH to sell teaching aids to Latin and Greek teachers.

★10530★ Association for Direct Instruction (ADI)
PO Box 10252
Eugene, OR 97440
Ph: (541)485-1293   Fax: (541)683-7543
Fr: 800-995-2464
E-mail: info@adihome.org
URL: http://www.adihome.org
Members: Public school regular and special education teachers and university instructors. **Purpose:** Encourages, promotes, and engages in research aimed at improving educational methods. Promotes dissemination of developmental information and skills that facilitate the education of adults and children. **Activities:** Administers a preschool for developmentally delayed children. Offers educational training workshops for instructors. Maintains speakers' bureau, and placement service.

★10531★ Association of Southern Baptist Colleges and Schools (ASBCS)
PO Box 11655
Jackson, TN 38308-0127
Ph: (731)660-3497   Fax: (731)664-6459
E-mail: bob_agee@baptistschools.org
URL: http://www.baptistschools.org
Members: Southern Baptist senior colleges, universities, junior colleges, academies, and Bible schools. **Purpose:** Promotes Christian education through literature, faculty workshops, student recruitment, teacher placement, trustee orientation, statistical information, and other assistance to members.

★10532★ Christian Schools International (CSI)
3350 E Paris Ave. SE
Grand Rapids, MI 49512-3054
Ph: (616)957-1070   Fax: (616)957-5022
Fr: 800-635-8288
E-mail: info@csionline.org
URL: http://community.gospelcom.net/Brix?pageID=2831
Description: Christian elementary and secondary schools enrolling 100,000 pupils and employing 7800 teachers. Purposes are: to provide a medium for a united witness regarding the role of Christian schools in contemporary society; to promote the establishment of Christian schools; to help members function more effectively in areas of promotion, organization, administration, and curriculum; to help establish standards and criteria to guide the operation of its members; to foster high professional ideals and economic well-being among Christian school personnel; to establish and maintain communication with member schools, colleges, churches, government agencies, and the public. Encourages study, research, and writing that embodies Christian theories of education; conducts salary studies, research, andsurveys on operating costs; offers expert and confidential analysis of member school programs and operation. Spon-

sors meetings, workshops, and seminars; offers placement service. Administers the Christian School Pension and Trust Funds, Group Insurance Plans, and Life and Insurance Plans and Trust Funds.

★10533★ Independent Educational Services (IES)
221 S Alfred St.
Alexandria, VA 22314-3647
Ph: (703)548-9700   Fax: (703)548-7171
Description: Nonprofit consulting, head search, and teacher recruitment organization. Furnishes to independent (private) schools dossiers of qualified candidates for teaching and administrative positions. Offers to teachers and prospective teachers information concerning current requirements and qualifications for positions in the field of education and vacancies for which they qualify. Conducts searches for heads of schools. Offers specialized placement workshops, consulting, and in-service programs to independent schools.

★10534★ International Educator's Institute (TIE)
PO Box 513
Cummaquid, MA 02637
Ph: (508)362-1414   Fax: (508)362-1411
Fr: 877-375-6668
E-mail: tie@tieonline.com
URL: http://www.tieonline.com
Description: Facilitates the placement of teachers and administrators in American, British, and international schools. Seeks to create a network that provides for professional development opportunities and improved financial security of members. Offers advice and information on international school news, recent educational developments, job placement, and investment, consumer, and professional development opportunities. Makes available insurance and travel benefits. Operates International Schools Internship Program.

★10535★ Jewish Educators Assembly (JEA)
300 Forest Dr.
East Hills, NY 11548
Ph: (516)484-9585   Fax: (516)484-9586
E-mail: jewisheducators@aol.com
URL: http://www.jewisheducators.org/
Members: Educational and supervisory personnel serving Jewish educational institutions. **Purpose:** Seeks to advance the development of Jewish education in the congregation on all levels in consonance with the philosophy of the Conservative Movement; cooperate with the United Synagogue of America Commission on Jewish Education as the policy-making body of the educational enterprise; join in cooperative effort with other Jewish educational institutions and organizations; establish and maintain professional standards for Jewish educators; serve as a forum for the exchange of ideas; promote the values of Jewish education as a basis for the creative continuity of the Jewish

people. **Activities:** Maintains placement service and speakers' bureau.

★10536★ National Association for Sport and Physical Education (NASPE)
1900 Association Dr.
Reston, VA 20191
Ph: (703)476-3410   Fax: (703)476-8316
Fr: 800-213-7193
E-mail: naspe@aahperd.org
URL: http://www.aahperd.org

Description: Men and women professionally involved with physical activity and sports. Seeks to improve the total sport and physical activity experience in America. Conducts research and education programs in such areas as sport psychology, curriculum development, kinesiology, history, philosophy, sport sociology, and the biological and behavioral basis of human activity. Develops and distributes public information materials which explain the value of physical education programs. Supports councils involved in organizing and supporting elementary, secondary, and college physical education and sport programs; administers the National Council of Athletic Training in conjunction with the National Association for Girls and Women in Sport; serves the professional interests of coaches, trainers, and officials. Maintains hall of fame, placement service, and media resource center for public information and professional preparation. Member benefits include group insurance and discounts.

★10537★ National Association of Teachers' Agencies (NATA)
797 Kings Hwy.
Fairfield, CT 06432
Ph: (203)333-0611   Fax: (203)334-7224
E-mail: info@jobsforteachers.com
URL: http://www.jobsforteachers.com

Description: Private employment agencies engaged primarily in the placement of teaching and administration personnel. Works to standardize records and promote a strong ethical sense in the placement field. Maintains speakers' bureau.

★10538★ National Communication Association (NCA)
1765 N St. NW
Washington, DC 20036
Ph: (202)464-4622   Fax: (202)464-4600
E-mail: smorreale@natcom.org
URL: http://www.natcom.org

Members: Elementary, secondary, college, and university teachers, speech clinicians, media specialists, communication consultants, students, theater directors, and other interested persons; libraries and other institutions. **Purpose:** To promote study, criticism, research, teaching, and application of the artistic, humanistic, and scientific principles of communication, particularly speech communication. Sponsors the publication of scholarly volumes in speech. **Activities:** Conducts international debate tours in the

U.S. and abroad. Maintains placement service.

★10539★ U.S.-China Education Foundation (USCEF)
4140 Oceanside Blvd.
PMB 112, No. 159
Oceanside, CA 92056-6005
Ph: (760)644-0977
E-mail: SAGE.Kennedypres@cex.net
URL: http://www.sage-usa.net

Members: A project of the Society for the Advancement of Global Education. **Purpose:** Purposes are to promote the learning of the Chinese languages (including Mandarin, Cantonese, and minority languages such as Mongolian) by Americans, and the learning of English by Chinese. **Activities:** Conducts short-term travel-study program to prepare Americans and Chinese for stays of four, six, or eight months or one to four years in China or the U.S., respectively. Operates teacher placement service and speakers' bureau. A project of S.A.G.E. the Society for the Development of Global Education.

EMPLOYER DIRECTORIES AND NETWORKING LISTS

★10540★ Boarding Schools Directory
The Association of Boarding Schools
4455 Connecticut Ave., Ste. A200
Washington, DC 20008
Ph: (202)966-8705   Fax: (202)966-8708
Fr: 800-541-5908
URL: http://www.schools.com

Annual, August. Covers boarding schools that are members of the Association of Boarding Schools. Entries include: School name, address, phone, e-mail and url's, grades for which boarding students are accepted, enrollment, brief description. Arrangement: Classified by type of school. Indexes: Geographical; program; Alphabetical.

★10541★ Christian Schools International-Directory
Christian Schools International
3350 E Paris Ave. SE
Grand Rapids, MI 49512-3054
Ph: (616)957-1070   Fax: (616)957-5022
Fr: 800-635-8288
URL: http://www.gospelcom.net/csi

Annual, November. $52.00 for nonmembers. Covers nearly 450 Reformed Christian elementary and secondary schools; related associations; societies without schools. Entries include: For schools-School name, address, phone; name, title, and address of officers; names of faculty members. Arrangement: Geographical.

★10542★ Directory of Day Schools in the United States and Canada
Torah Umesorah National Society for Hebrew Day Schools
5723 18th Ave.
Brooklyn, NY 11204
Ph: (718)259-1223   Fax: (718)259-1795
E-mail: mail@tupublications.com

Annual, latest edition 2003. $15.00. Covers over 700 elementary and secondary Hebrew day schools in the U.S. and Canada. Entries include: School name, address, phone, names of administrative personnel, grades taught, language of instruction, year established (fax numbers and e-mail addresses when available). Arrangement: Geographical. Indexes: Schools & personnel.

★10543★ Directory of Public Elementary and Secondary Education Agencies
National Center for Education Statistics
1990 K St., NW
Washington, DC 20006
Ph: (202)502-7300   Fr: 800-424-1616

Annual. $22.00. Covers about 17,000 local education agencies in the United States, the District of Columbia, and five territories which operate their own schools or pay tuition to other local education agencies. Also lists intermediate education agencies. Entries include: Agency name, address, phone, county, description of district, grade span, membership, special education students, metropolitan status, number of high school graduates, teachers, and schools. Also available from Superintendent of Documents, U.S. Government Printing Office. Arrangement: Geographical, then by type of agency.

★10544★ Directory of Public School Systems in the U.S.
American Association for Employment in Education
3040 Riverside Dr., Ste. 125
Columbus, OH 43221
Ph: (614)485-1111   Fax: (614)485-9609

Annual, Winter. $80.00. Covers about 14,500 public school systems in the United States and their administrative personnel. Entries include: System name, address, phone, website address, name and title of personnel administrator, levels taught and approx. student population. Arrangement: Geographical by state.

★10545★ Educators Resource Directory
Grey House Publishing
PO Box 860
Millerton, NY 12546-0860
Ph: (518)789-8700   Fax: (518)789-0556
Fr: 800-562-2139
URL: http://www.greyhouse.com/education.htm

Biennial, latest edition 5th, 2003/04. $145.00 for softcover; $195.00 for online database; $280.00 for book and online database. Covers publishing opportunities, state by state information on enrollment, funding and grant resources, associations and conferences, teaching jobs abroad all geared toward elementary and secondary school professionals. Also covers online databases, textbook publishers, school suppliers, plus state and federal agencies. Entries include: Contact name, address, phone, fax, description, publications. A unique compilation of over 6,200 educational resources and over 130 tables and charts of education statistics and rankings Arrangement: By subject catagories. Indexes: Entry, subject, publisher.

★10546★ **Employment Opportunities, USA**

Washington Research Associates
1090 Vermont Ave., NW, Ste. 800
Washington, DC 20005
Ph: (202)408-7025

Annual, quarterly updates. $184.00. Publication includes: List of over 1,000 employment contacts in companies and agencies in the banking, arts, telecommunications, education, and 14 other industries and professions, including the federal government. Entries include: Company name, name of representative, address, description of products or services, hiring and recruiting practices, training programs, and year established. Principal content is industry overviews, career news, employment opportunity information on 14 different job markets, and comprehensive guidance to career resources on the Internet. Arrangement: Classified by industry. Indexes: Occupation.

★10547★ **Encyclopedia of Education**

Macmillan/McGraw-Hill
2 Penn Plz.
New York, NY 10121
Ph: (212)904-6749   Fax: (212)904-6637

$850.00. Publication includes: List of assessment and achievement tests with contact information; list of state departments of education; list of Internet resources. Principal content of publication is a variety of topics within the field of education including policy, curriculum, learning, assessment, legislation, history, and standards. Indexes: Alphabetical.

★10548★ **Fifty State Educational Directories**

Career Guidance Foundation
8090 Engineer Rd., Ste. B
San Diego, CA 92111
Ph: (858)560-8051   Fax: (858)278-8960
Fr: 800-854-2670
URL: http://www.cgf.org

Annual, latest edition June 1996. $89.00. Microfiche. Collection consists of reproductions of the state educational directories published by the departments of education of individual 50 states. Directory contents vary, but the majority contain listings of elementary and secondary schools, colleges and universities, and state education officials. Amount of detail in each also varies. Entries include: Usually, institution name, address, and name of one executive.

★10549★ **Ganley's Catholic Schools in America-Elementary/Secondary/College & University**

Fisher Publishing Co.
PO Box 15070
Scottsdale, AZ 85267
Ph: (480)657-9422   Fax: (480)657-9422
Fr: 800-759-7615
URL: http://www.ganleyscatholicschools.com

Annual, summer; latest edition 2003. $51.50. Covers over 8,400 Catholic K-12 Schools. Arrangement: Geographical by state, then alphabetical by Diocese name.

★10550★ **Handbook of Private Schools**

Porter Sargent Publishers Inc.
11 Beacon St., Ste. 1400
Boston, MA 02108-3099
Ph: (617)523-1670   Fax: (617)523-1021
Fr: 800-342-7470
E-mail: orders@portersargent.com

Annual, June. $99.00. Covers more than 1,600 elementary and secondary boarding and day schools in the United States. Entries include: School name, address, phone, fax, E-mail, URL, type of school (boarding or day), sex and age range, names and titles of administrators, grades offered, academic orientation, curriculum, new admissions yearly, tests required for admission, enrollment and faculty, graduate record, number of alumni, tuition and scholarship figures, summer session, plant evaluation and endowment, date of establishment, calendar, association membership, description of school's offerings and history, test score averages, uniform requirements, geographical, and demographic date. Arrangement: Geographical. Indexes: Alphabetical by school name, cross indexed by state, region, grade range, sexes accepted, school features and enrollment.

★10551★ **Independent School Guide for Washington DC and Surrounding Area**

Lift Hill Press Inc.
4930-A Eisenhower Ave.
Alexandria, VA 22304
Ph: (703)212-9113   Fax: (703)212-9114
Fr: 800-699-9113
URL: http://www.washingtonbk.com

Biennial. $15.95. Covers over 475 independent schools (including parochial schools) in the Washington, DC area, including Maryland and Virginia. Entries include: School name, address, phone, name and title of contact, number of faculty, geographical area served, tuition, courses, admission procedures, summer programs, LD/ED programs, scholarships available. Arrangement: Alphabetical. Indexes: Geographical.

★10552★ **Independent Schools Association of the Southwest-Membership List**

Independent Schools Association of the Southwest
4700 Bryant Irvin Ct., Ste. 204
Fort Worth, TX 76107
Ph: (817)569-9200   Fax: (817)569-9103
Fr: 800-688-5007
URL: http://www.isasw.org

Annual, August. Covers over 75 independent elementary and secondary schools accredited by the association. Entries include: School name, address, phone, chief administrative officer, structure, and enrollment. Arrangement: Geographical. Indexes: Alphabetical.

★10553★ **MDR's School Directories**

Market Data Retrieval
1 Forest Pkwy.
Shelton, CT 06484
Ph: (203)926-4800   Fax: (203)926-1826
Fr: 800-333-8802
URL: http://www.schooldata.com

Annual, October. $1,349.00 for set. Covers over 90,000 public, 8,000 Catholic, and 15,000 other private schools (grades K-12) in the United States; over 15,000 school district offices, and 76,000 school librarians; and 27,000 media specialists, 33,000 technology coordinators. Includes names of over 165,000 school district administrators and staff members in county and state education administration. Entries include: For districts: District name and address; telephone and fax number; number of schools; number of teachers in the district; district enrollment; special Ed students; limited-english proficient students; minority percentage by race, college bound students; expenditures per student for instructional materials; poverty level; title 1 dollars; site-based management; district open/close dates; construction indicator; technologies and quantities (instructional computer brands, multimedia computers; networks, VCRs, satellite dish, DVD Player/Drive High-Speed Internet Access URL); district-level adminstrators, *new superintendents shaded.* For schools: School name and address-new public shaded; telephone and fax number; principal new principal shaded; librarian, media specialist and technology coordinator; grade span; special programs and school type; student enrollment; technologies and quantities (instructional computer brand noting predominant brand); Multi-Media Computers; internet connection or access; Tech Sophistication Index. Arrangement: Geographical. Indexes: District County; District Personnel; Principal; New Public Schools and Key Personnel; District and School Telephone; District URLs.

★10554★ **National Association of Teachers' Agencies-Membership Directory**

National Association of Teachers' Agencies
797 Kings Hwy.
Fairfield, CT 06432
Ph: (203)333-0611   Fax: (203)334-7224

URL: http://www.jobsforteachers.com

Annual, January. Covers approximately 20 private employment agencies engaged primarily in the placement of teaching and administrative personnel in education. Entries include: Name, address, phone, names of key officials. Arrangement: Alphabetical.

★10555★ **National Directory of Alternative Schools**

National Coalition of Alternative Community Schools
1289 Jewett St.
Ann Arbor, MI 48104-6201
Ph: (734)668-9171   Fax: (734)769-9629
Fr: 888-771-9171

Biennial, odd years. $18.00. Covers over 500 alternative education programs, including home schools, and state and regional coalitions of alternative schools and colleges; also lists organizations and networks offering services and resources to those working with children; international coverage. Entries include: Name, address, phone, name of contact; many also include descriptions of programs. Arrangement: Schools are geographical. Indexes: Complete index of entries.

★10556★ **National Directory for Employment in Education**

American Association for Employment in Education
3040 Riverside Dr., Ste. 125
Columbus, OH 43221
Ph: (614)485-1111   Fax: (614)485-9609

Annual, Winter. $20.00 for institutions. Covers about 600 placement offices maintained by teacher-training institutions and 300 school district personnel officers and/or superintendents responsible for hiring professional staff. Entries include: Institution name, address, phone, contact name, email address, and website. Arrangement: Geographical. Indexes: Personal name, subject-field of teacher training, institutions which provide vacancy bulletins and placement services to non-enrolled students.

★10557★ **Opportunities Abroad for Educators**

Fulbright Teacher and Administrator Exchange Program
600 Maryland Ave. SW, Ste. 320
Washington, DC 20024-2520
Ph: (202)314-3527   Fax: (202)479-6806
Fr: 800-726-0479
URL: http://www.fulbrightexchanges.org

Annual. Covers opportunities available for elementary and secondary teachers, and two year college instructors, and school administrators to attend seminars or to teach abroad under the Mutual Educational and Cultural Exchange Act of 1961. Entries include: Countries of placement, dates, eligibility requirements, teaching assignments. Arrangement: Geographical.

★10558★ **Patterson's American Education**

Educational Directories Inc.
PO Box 68097
Schaumburg, IL 60168-0097
Ph: (847)891-1250   Fax: (847)891-0945
Fr: 800-357-6183
URL: http://www.ediusa.com

Annual, October; latest edition 2002. $87.00. Covers over 11,400 school districts in the United States; more than 34,000 public, private, and Catholic high schools, middle schools, and junior high schools; approximately 300 parochial superintendents; 400 state department of education personnel. Entries include: For school districts and schools-District and superintendent name, address, phone, fax, grade ranges, enrollment, school names, addresses, phone numbers, grade ranges, enrollment, names of principals. For postsecondary schools-School name, address, phone number, URL, e-mail, names of administrator or director of admissions. For private and Catholic high schools-Name, address, phone, fax, enrollment, grades offered, name of principal. Postsecondary institutions are covered in 'Patterson's Schools Classified'. Arrangement: Geographical by state, then alphabetical by city.

★10559★ **Private Independent Schools**

Bunting and Lyon Inc.
238 N Main St.
Wallingford, CT 06492
Ph: (203)269-3333   Fax: (203)269-5697
URL: http://www.buntingandlyon.com

Annual, February. $110.00. Covers 1,200 English-speaking elementary and secondary private schools and summer programs in North America and abroad. Entries include: School name, address, phone, fax, e-mail, website, enrollment, tuition and other fees, financial aid information, administrator's name and educational background, director of admission, regional accreditation, description of programs, curriculum, activities, learning differences grid. Arrangement: Geographical. Indexes: School name; geographical. Summer programs, general classification grid, learning differences reference grid.

★10560★ **QED's State-by-State School Guides**

Quality Education Data Inc.
1625 Broadway, Ste. 250
Denver, CO 80202
Ph: (303)209-9400   Fax: (303)209-9444
Fr: 800-525-5811
URL: http://www.qeddata.com/school-guide.htm

Annual, October. $1,345.00 for national set; $3,565.00 for electronic version; $4,175.00 for print and electronic. Covers over 100,000 public and private elementary and secondary schools in 16,000 school districts; in 52 volumes (national set). Entries include: School district name, address, phone, district enrollment, identification of site-based managed schools, number of teachers, number of schools, financial data, minority enrollment statistics, names and educational spe-

cializations of key personnel, list of member schools, including school name, address, phone, name of principal, name of librarian, grade levels taught, enrollment, services outsourced, number and brands of microcomputers used. Arrangement: Geographical - county within state. Indexes: School name, district name, geographical (county name), personal name.

★10561★ **Requirements for Certification of Teachers, Counselors, Librarians, Administrators for Elementary and Secondary Schools**

University of Chicago Press
Journals Division
PO Box 37005
Chicago, IL 60637
Ph: (773)753-3347   Fax: (773)753-0811
Fr: 877-705-1878

Annual, June. $44.00. Publication includes: List of state and local departments of education. Entries include: Office name, address, phone. Principal content of publication is summaries of each state's teaching and administrative certification requirements. Arrangement: Geographical.

HANDBOOKS AND MANUALS

★10562★ **Becoming a Secondary School Science Teacher**

Prentice Hall PTR
200 Old Tappan Rd.
Old Tappan, NJ 07675
Fax: 800-445-6991   Fr: 800-567-3800

Jazlin V. Ebenezer and Sharon M. Haggerty. 1999. $78.00 (paper).

★10563★ **Becoming a Teacher**

Pearson Allyn & Bacon
1230 Ave. of the Americas
New York, NY 10020
Ph: (212)782-3300   Fr: 800-634-7064

Gary Borich. 1995. $24.95 (paper). 140 pages. Part of The Falmer Press Teachers' Library Series No. 7.

★10564★ **Career Information Center**

Macmillan Publishing Co. Inc.
200 Old Tappan Rd.
Old Tappan, NJ 07675
Fr: 800-428-5331

Visual Education Center Staff. Seventh edition, 1999. $275.00. 2080 pages. This 13-volume set profiles over 600 occupations. Each occupational profile describes job duties, educational requirements, how to get the job, advancement possibilities, employment outlook, working conditions, earnings and benefits, and where to write for more information.

★10565★ Careers in Education
McGraw-Hill Professional
2 Penn Plaza
New York, NY 10121-2298
Ph: (212)904-2000   Fr: 800-722-4726
Roy A. Edelfelt, Alan Reiman. Fourth edition. $14.95. E-book, netLibrary.

★10566★ Careers in Horticulture and Botany
McGraw-Hill Trade
2 Penn Plaza
New York, NY 10121
Ph: (212)904-2000   Fr: 800-722-4726
E-mail: ntcpub@tribune.com
Jerry Garner. 1996. $17.95; 13.95 (paper). 255 pages. Includes bibliographical references

★10567★ Careers in Journalism
Kogan Page
1221 Avenue of the Americas
New York, NY 10020
Ph: (212)904-2000   Fr: 800-323-4900
E-mail: ntcpub@tribune.com
Jan Goldberg. Second edition, 1999. $17.95; 13.95 (paper). 192 pages.

★10568★ Customizing Your Resume for Teaching Positions
Rowman and Littlefield
4720 Boston Way
Lanham, MD 20706
Ph: (301)459-3366   Fax: (301)459-2118
Fr: 800-462-6420
Edward G. Pultorak. 1993. 52 pages.

★10569★ Educator's Job Search: The Ultimate Guide to Finding Positions in Education
National Education Association
PO Box 2035
Annapolis Junction, MD 20701
Fr: 800-229-4200
Martin Kimeldorf. 1993. $15.95 (paper). 88 pages.

★10570★ Great Jobs for English Majors
McGraw-Hill Trade
2 Penn Plaza
New York, NY 10121
Ph: (212)904-2000   Fr: 800-722-4726
E-mail: ntcpub@tribune.com
Julie DeGalan. Second edition, 2000. $12.95 (paper). 462 pages.

★10571★ Great Jobs for History Majors
McGraw-Hill Trade
2 Penn Plaza
New York, NY 10121
Ph: (212)904-2000   Fr: 800-722-4726
E-mail: ntcpub@tribune.com

Julie DeGalan and Stephen Lambert. 1994. $11.95 (paper). 442 pages.

★10572★ Great Jobs for Liberal Arts Majors
McGraw-Hill Professional
2 Penn Plaza
New York, NY 10121
Ph: (212)904-2000   Fr: 800-722-4726
E-mail: ntcpub@tribune.com
Blythe Camenson. Second edition, 2001. $14.95 (paper). 256 pages.

★10573★ Great Jobs for Music Majors
McGraw-Hill Companies
1221 Avenue of the Americas
New York, NY 10020
Ph: (212)904-2000   Fr: 800-323-4900
E-mail: ntcpub@tribune.com
Jan Goldberg, Stephen Lambert, Julie DeGalan. 1997. $11.95 (paper). 365 pages.

★10574★ Great Jobs for Theater Majors
McGraw-Hill Companies
1221 Avenue of the Americas
New York, NY 10020
Ph: (212)904-2000   Fr: 800-323-4900
E-mail: ntcpub@tribune.com
Jan Goldberg, Stephen Lambert, Julie DeGalan. 1998. $11.95 (paper). 388 pages.

★10575★ Handbook for Christian EFL Teachers: Christian Teacher-Preparation Programs, Overseas Teaching Opportunities, Instructional Materials and Resources
Institute for Cross-Cultural Training, Billy Graham Center, Wheaton College; Berry Pub. Services
PO Box 794
Wheaton, IL 60189
Ph: (630)752-7158   Fax: (630)752-7155
Lonna J. Dickerson and Dianne F. Dow. 1997. $9.00 (paper). 96 pages. Part of the Monograph Series.

★10576★ How to Get a Job in Education
Adams Media Corp.
57 Littlefield St.
Avon, MA 02322
Ph: (508)427-7100   Fax: (508)427-6790
Fr: 800-872-5627
URL: http://www.adamsmedia.com
Joel Levin. Second edition, 1995. $15.95. 320 pages. Out of print. Prepared for recent college graduates, seasoned educators, and career-changing professionals, this publication guides the job-seeker through the necessary steps to obtaining a job in education at the elementary, secondary, and university levels. Offers advice on how to prepare for state and local examinations, how to locate teaching opportunities nationwide, and how to obtain certification. Includes a nationwide

salary survey. Covers public, private, summer, and overseas opportunities.

★10577★ How to Get the Teaching Position You Want: Teacher Candidate Guide
Educational Enterprises
PO Box 1836
Spring Valley, CA 91979
Ph: (619)660-7720
Phyllis Murton. Second edition, revised, 1996. $9.95 (paper). 110 pages. This book provides a comprehensive guide for the teacher candidate's job search, as the format offers information that includes: interview questions most often asked in the teaching interview (grade-level & subject-matter specific); sample forms for applications, cover letters, & resumes that will impact principals & district personnel; strategies on preparing for the teaching interview; interview follow-up techniques; inside tips from a superintendent, a principal & a counselor.

★10578★ The Inside Secrets of Finding a Teaching Job
JIST Publishing
8902 Otis Ave.
Indianapolis, IN 46216
Ph: (317)613-4200   Fax: (317)613-4307
Fr: 800-648-5478
E-mail: jistworks@aol.com
URL: http://www.jist.com
Burt Beers, Jack Warner, Clyde Bryan and Diane Warner. 1997. $14.95. 186 pages. Tips from educators on finding an entry-level teaching position.

★10579★ Non-Profits and Education Job Finder
Planning Communications
7215 Oak Ave.
River Forest, IL 60305-1935
Ph: (708)366-5200   Fax: (708)366-5280
Fr: 888-366-5200
URL: http://jobfindersonline.com
Daniel Lauber. 1997. $32.95; $16.95 (paper). 336 pages. Covers 1600 sources. Discusses how to use sources of non-profit sector job vacancies in a number of specialties and state-by-state, including job-matching services, job hotlines, specialty periodicals with job ads, salary surveys, and directories. Covers a variety of fields from education to religion. Includes chapters on resume and cover letter preparation and interviewing.

★10580★ Opportunities in Overseas Careers
McGraw-Hill Trade
2 Penn Plaza
New York, NY 10121
Ph: (212)904-2000   Fr: 800-722-4726
Blythe Camenson. 1998. $14.95; $11.95 (paper). 106 pages.

★10581★ Opportunities in State and Local Government Careers

Vgm Career Horizons
1221 Avenue of the Americas
New York, NY 10020
Ph: (212)904-2000   Fr: 800-323-4900
E-mail: ntcpub@tribune.com

Neale J. Baxter. 1994. $14.95; $10.95 (paper). 160 pages. Points out the incentives and drawbacks of a government career. Describes hiring procedures and provides tips on filling out applications, taking physical and aptitude tests, handling interviews, and finding jobs. Describes the jobs in which 75% of all state and local government workers are employed. For each occupation, covers the nature of the work and the training required.

★10582★ Opportunities in Teaching Careers

McGraw-Hill/Contemporary Books
1221 Avenue of the Americas
New York, NY 10020
Ph: (212)904-2000   Fr: 800-323-4900
E-mail: ntcpub@tribune.com

Janet Fine. 2000. $14.95; $11.95 (paper). 200 pages. Discusses licensing and accreditation programs, sources of placement information, job-seeking correspondence, selection procedures, and paths to advancement. Also covers professional associations, non-traditional teaching opportunities, and jobs abroad.

★10583★ Opportunities in Technical Education Careers

McGraw-Hill/Contemporary Books
1221 Avenue of the Americas
New York, NY 10020
Ph: (212)904-2000   Fr: 800-323-4900
E-mail: ntcpub@tribune.com

Robert Connelly. 1998. 200 pages. $14.95; $11.95 (paper).

★10584★ Real People Working in Education

McGraw-Hill Contemporary Books
1221 Avenue of the Americas
New York, NY 10020
Ph: (212)904-2000   Fr: 800-323-4900
E-mail: ntcpub@tribune.com

Blythe Camenson, Jan Goldberg. 1997. $17.95; $12.95 (paper). Interviews and profiles of working professionals capture a range of opportunities in this field.

★10585★ Teaching (Career Portraits)

Vgm Career Horizons
1221 Avenue of the Americas
New York, NY 10020
Ph: (212)904-2000   Fr: 800-323-4900
E-mail: ntcpub@tribune.com

Marjorie Eberts and Margaret Gisler. 1994. $13.95. 320 pages.

★10586★ Teaching in the Middle and Secondary Schools

Prentice Hall PTR
200 Old Tappan Rd.
Old Tappan, NJ 07675
Fax: 800-445-6991   Fr: 800-223-1360

Joseph F. Callahan, Leonard H. Clark and Richard D. Kellough. Seventh edition, 2001. $60.00 (paper). 439 pages.

★10587★ Where the Jobs Are: The Hottest Careers for the 90s

The Career Press, Inc.
3 Tice Rd.
PO Box 687
Franklin Lakes, NJ 07417-1322
Ph: (201)848-0310   Fax: (201)848-1727
Fr: 800-227-3371

Joyce Hadley. Third edition, 2000. $13.99 (paper). 400 pages. Out of print. Describes careers in fifteen general fields, from accounting to travel and hospitality.

EMPLOYMENT AGENCIES AND SEARCH FIRMS

★10588★ Educational Placement Service

1001 Craig Rd., Ste. 170
St. Louis, MO 63146
Ph: (314)991-5855   Fax: (314)991-5295
URL: http://www.educatorjobs.com

Employment agency. Focuses on teaching, administrative, and education-related openings.

TRADESHOWS

★10589★ American Council on the Teaching of Foreign Languages Convention

American Council on the Teaching of Foreign Languages
6 Executive Plaza
Yonkers, NY 10701
Ph: (914)963-8830   Fax: (914)963-1275
URL: http://www.actfl.org

Annual. **Primary Exhibits:** Textbooks, tapes, and supplementary material in foreign languages.

★10590★ Association for Childhood Education International Annual International Conference & Exhibition

Association for Childhood Education International
17904 Georgia Ave., Ste. 215
Olney, MD 20832
Ph: (301)570-2111   Fax: (301)570-2212
Fr: 800-423-3563

E-mail: aceimc@aol.com
URL: http://www.acei.org

Annual. **Primary Exhibits:** Commercial and educational exhibits of interest to teachers, teacher educators, college students, day care personnel and other care givers.

★10591★ Family and Consumer Sciences Teachers Association of Texas Annual Educational Exhibits Show

Family and Consumer Sciences Teachers Association of Texas
4131 Spicewood Springs Rd., Ste. L-1
Austin, TX 78759-8652
Ph: (512)794-8370   Fax: (512)794-9080
Fr: 800-880-8438
E-mail: fcstat@fcstat.org
URL: http://www.fcstat.org

Annual. **Primary Exhibits:** Products related to family and consumer sciences program material.

★10592★ NARST Annual Meeting

National Association for Research in Science Teaching
c/o Arthur L. White
The Ohio State University
1929 Kenny Rd., Rm. 200E
Columbus, OH 43210
Ph: (614)292-3339   Fax: (614)292-1595
E-mail: white32@osu.edu

Annual. **Primary Exhibits:** Science education, publications, equipment, supplies, and services.

★10593★ National Art Education Association Convention

National Art Education Association
1916 Association Dr.
Reston, VA 20191
Ph: (703)860-8000   Fax: (703)860-2960
E-mail: naea@dgs.dgsys.com
URL: http://www.naea-reston.org

Annual. **Primary Exhibits:** Art materials; art-related books and magazines; art career education information; arts and crafts supplies. **Dates and Locations:** 2005 Mar 04-08; Boston, MA • 2006 Mar 22-26; Chicago, IL • 2004 Mar 14-18; New York, NY.

★10594★ National Association for the Education of Young Children Annual Conference

National Association for the Education of Young Children
1509 16th St., NW
Washington, DC 20036
Ph: (202)232-8777   Fax: (202)328-1846
Fr: 800-424-2460
E-mail: conference@naevc.org
URL: http://www.naevc.org

Annual. **Primary Exhibits:** Educational materials and equipment designed for children ages birth through eight years old. **Dates and Locations:** 2004 Nov 10-13; Anaheim, CA; Anaheim Convention Center.

★10595★ National Council for Geographic Education Conference

National Council for Geographic Education
206-A Martin Hall
Jacksonvill State University
Jacksonville, AL 36265-1602
Ph: (256)782-5293   Fax: (256)782-5336
E-mail: ncge@jsucc.jsu.edu
URL: http://www.ncge.org

Annual. **Primary Exhibits:** Geographic teaching aids and materials. **Dates and Locations:** 2004 Oct 20-23; Kansas City, MO; Marriott.

★10596★ National Council for the Social Studies Conference

National Council for the Social Studies
3501 Newark St., NW
Washington, DC 20016-3167
Ph: (202)966-7840   Fax: (202)966-2061
E-mail: ncss@ncss.org
URL: http://www.ncss.org

Annual. **Primary Exhibits:** Educational materials, software, publications, and textbooks.

★10597★ National Middle School Association Annual Conference & Exhibit

National Middle School Association
4151 Executive Pkwy., No. 300
Westerville, OH 43081-3867
Ph: (614)895-4730   Fax: (614)895-4750
Fr: 800-528-6672
URL: http://www.nmsa.org

Annual. **Primary Exhibits:** Educational materials and services relating to middle level school (ages 10-15). **Dates and Locations:** 2004 Nov 04-06; Minneapolis, MN.

OTHER SOURCES

★10598★ American Association for Health Education (AAHE)

1900 Association Dr.
Reston, VA 20191
Ph: (703)476-3437   Fax: (703)476-6638
Fr: 800-213-7193
E-mail: aahe@aahperd.org
URL: http://www.aahperd.org/aahe

Members: Professionals who have responsibility for health education in schools, colleges, communities, hospitals and clinics, and industries. **Purpose:** Works for the advancement of health education through program activities and federal legislation; encouragement of close working relationships between all health education and health service organizations; achievement of good health and well-being for all Americans automatically, without conscious thought and endeavor. Member of the American Alliance for Health, Physical Education, Recreation and Dance.

★10599★ American Association of Teachers of German (AATG)

112 Haddontowne Ct., No. 104
Cherry Hill, NJ 08034-3668
Ph: (856)795-5553   Fax: (856)795-9398
E-mail: headquarters@aatg.org
URL: http://www.aatg.org

Description: Teachers of German at all levels; individuals interested in German language and culture. Offers in-service teacher-training workshops, materials, student honor society, national German examination, and stipends/scholarships.

★10600★ American Federation of Teachers (AFT)

555 New Jersey Ave. NW
Washington, DC 20001
Ph: (202)879-4400   Fax: (202)879-4545
Fr: 800-238-1133
E-mail: online@aft.org
URL: http://www.aft.org

Description: Affiliated with the AFL-CIO. Works with teachers and other educational employees at the state and local level in organizing, collective bargaining, research, educational issues, and public relations. Conducts research in areas such as educational reform, teacher certification, and national assessments and standards. Represents members' concerns through legislative action; offers technical assistance. Also serves professionals with concerns similar to those of teachers, including state employees, healthcare workers, and paraprofessionals.

★10601★ American Mathematical Society (AMS)

201 Charles St.
Providence, RI 02904-2294
Ph: (401)455-4000   Fax: (401)331-3842
Fr: 800-321-4AMS
E-mail: ams@ams.org
URL: http://www.ams.org/

Description: Professional society of mathematicians and educators. Promotes the interests of mathematical scholarship and research. Holds institutes, seminars, short courses, and symposia to further mathematical research; awards prizes. Offers placement services; compiles statistics.

★10602★ American Orff-Schulwerk Association (AOSA)

PO Box 391089
Cleveland, OH 44139-8089
Ph: (440)543-5366   Fax: (440)543-2687
E-mail: info@aosa.org
URL: http://www.aosa.org

Description: Music and movement educators, music therapists, and church choir directors united to promote and encourage the philosophy of Carl Orff's (1895-1982, German composer) Schulwerk (Music for Children) in America. Distributes information on the activities and growth of Orff Schulwerk in America. Conducts research; offers information on teacher training. Operates clearinghouse.

★10603★ Association of Christian Schools International (ACSI)

731 Chapel Hills Dr.
Colorado Springs, CO 80920-1027
Ph: (719)528-6906   Fax: (719)531-063
Fr: 800-367-0798
E-mail: info@acsi.org
URL: http://www.acsi.org

Description: Seeks to enable Christian educators and schools worldwide to effectivel prepare students for life.

★10604★ Career Close-ups: School Teacher

AIMS Multimedia
9710 DeSoto Ave.
Chatsworth, CA 91311
Ph: (818)773-4300   Fax: (818)341-6700
Fr: 800-367-2467
URL: http://www.aimsmultimedia.com

Video. 1994. $69.95. 27 minutes. Profiles o outstanding teachers.

★10605★ Convention of American Instructors of the Deaf (CAID)

PO Box 377
Bedford, TX 76095-0377
Ph: (817)354-8414
E-mail: caid@swbell.net
URL: http://www.caid.org/

Members: Professional organization o teachers, administrators, and professionals in allied fields related to education of the deaf and hard-of-hearing. **Purpose:** Objec tives are to provide opportunities for a free interchange of views concerning methods and means of educating the deaf and hard of-hearing; to promote such education by the publication of reports, essays, and othe information; to develop more effective methods of teaching deaf and hard-of-hearing children.

★10606★ Education and Training

Cambridge Educational
2572 Brunswick Ave.
Lawrenceville, NJ 08648-4128
Fax: 800-FAX-ON-US   Fr: 800-468-4227
URL: http://www.cambridgeeducational.com

$89.95. 2002. 18 minutes.

★10607★ Friends Council on Education (FCE)

1507 Cherry St.
Philadelphia, PA 19102
Ph: (215)241-7245   Fax: (215)241-7299
E-mail: quakered@aol.com
URL: http://www.friendscouncil.org

Members: Representatives appointed by Friends Yearly Meetings; heads of Quaker secondary and elementary schools and colleges; members-at-large. **Purpose:** Acts as a clearinghouse for information on Quaker schools and colleges. **Activities:** Holds meetings and conferences on education and provides in-service training for teachers, administrators, and trustees in Friends schools.

★10608★ International Reading Association (IRA)

800 Barksdale Rd.
PO Box 8139
Newark, DE 19714-8139
Ph: (302)731-1600   Fax: (302)731-1057
E-mail: pubinfo@reading.org
URL: http://www.reading.org

Description: Teachers, reading specialists, consultants, administrators, supervisors, researchers, psychologists, librarians, and parents interested in promoting literacy. Seeks to improve the quality of reading instruction and promote literacy worldwide. Disseminates information pertaining to research on reading, including information on adult literacy, early childhood and literacy development, international education, literature for children and adolescents, and teacher education and professional development. Maintains over 40 special interest groups and over 70 committees.

★10609★ International Technology Education Association - Council for Supervisors (ITEA-CS)

Virginia Department of Education
PO Box 2120, 21st Fl.
Richmond, VA 23218-2120
Ph: (804)225-2839   Fax: (804)371-2456
URL: http://www.iteawww.org

Description: Technology education supervisors from the U.S. Office of Education; local school department chairpersons; state departments of education, local school districts, territories, provinces, and foreign countries. Works to improve instruction and supervision of programs in technology education. Conducts research; compiles statistics. Sponsors competitions. Maintains speakers' bureau.

★10610★ Jewish Education Service of North America (JESNA)

111 8th Ave., 11th Fl.
New York, NY 10011-5201
Ph: (212)284-6950   Fax: (212)284-6951
E-mail: jwoocher@jesna.org
URL: http://www.jesna.org

Description: Widely recognized leader in the areas of research and program evaluation, organizational change and innovative program design and dissemination. Operates the Mandell J. Berman Jewish Heritage Center for Research and Evaluation. Supports the Convenant Foundation, a joint venture with the Crown Family, which makes awards and grants for creativity in Jewish education.

★10611★ NAFSA/Association of International Educators (NAFSA)

1307 New York Ave. NW, 8th Fl.
Washington, DC 20005
Ph: (202)737-3699   Fax: (202)737-3657
E-mail: inbox@nafsa.org
URL: http://www.nafsa.org

Description: Individuals, organizations, and institutions dealing with international educational exchange, including foreign student advisers, overseas educational advisers, credentials and admissions officers, administrators and teachers of English as a second language, community support personnel, study-abroad administrators, and embassy cultural or educational personnel. Promotes self-regulation standards and responsibilities in international educational exchange; offers professional development opportunities primarily through publications, workshops, grants, and regional and national conferences. Advocates for increased awareness and support of international education and exchange on campuses, in government, and in communities. Offers services including: a job registry for employers and professionals involved with international education; a consultant referral service. Sponsors joint liaison activities with a variety of other educational and government organizations to conduct a census of foreign student enrollment in the U.S.; conducts workshops about specific subjects and countries.

★10612★ National Alliance of Black School Educators (NABSE)

310 Pennsylvania Ave. SE
Washington, DC 20003
Ph: (202)608-6310   Fax: (202)608-6319
Fr: 800-221-2654
E-mail: nabse@nabse.org
URL: http://www.nabse.org

Description: Black educators from all levels; others indirectly involved in the education of black youth. Purpose is to promote awareness, professional expertise, and commitment among black educators. Goals are to: eliminate and rectify the results of racism in education; work with state, local, and national leaders to raise the academic achievement level of all black students; increase members' involvement in legislative activities; facilitate the introduction of a curriculum that more completely embraces black America; improve the ability of black educators to promote problem resolution; create a meaningful and effective network of strength, talent, and professional support. Sponsors workshops, commission meetings, and special projects. Encourages research, especially as it relates to blacks, and the presentation of papers during national conferences. Plans to establish a National Black Educators Data Bank and offer placement service.

★10613★ National Art Education Association (NAEA)

1916 Association Dr.
Reston, VA 20191-1590
Ph: (703)860-8000   Fax: (703)860-2960
E-mail: naea@dgs.dgsys.com
URL: http://www.naea-reston.org

Members: Teachers of art at elementary, middle, secondary, and college levels; colleges, libraries, museums, and other educational institutions. **Purpose:** Studies problems of teaching art; encourages research and experimentation. **Activities:** Serves as clearinghouse for information on art education programs, materials, and methods of instruction. Sponsors special institutes. Cooperates with other national organizations for the furtherance of creative art experiences for youth.

★10614★ National Association of Blind Teachers (NABT)

1155 15th St. NW, Ste. 1004
Washington, DC 20005
Ph: (202)467-5081   Fax: (202)467-5085
Fr: 800-424-8666
E-mail: info@acb.org
URL: http://www.acb.org

Description: Public school teachers, college and university professors, and teachers in residential schools for the blind. Purpose is to promote employment and professional goals of blind persons entering the teaching profession or those established in their respective teaching fields. Serves as a vehicle for the dissemination of information and the exchange of ideas addressing special problems of members. Compiles statistics.

★10615★ National Association of Catholic School Teachers (NACST)

1700 Sansom St., Ste. 903
Philadelphia, PA 19103
Ph: (215)665-0993   Fax: (215)568-8270
Fr: 800-99-NACST
E-mail: nacst.nacst@verizon.net
URL: http://www.nacst.com

Description: Catholic school teachers. Purpose is to unify, advise, and assist Catholic school teachers in matters of collective bargaining. Promotes the welfare and rights of Catholic schools and teachers; determines needs of Catholic schools and teachers. Monitors legislation, trends, and statistics concerning Catholic education; promotes legislation favorable to nonpublic schools and Catholic school teachers; offers legal advice and addresses issues such as unemployment compensation; assists teachers in organizing and negotiating contracts. Maintains speakers' bureau.

★10616★ National Association of Episcopal Schools (NAES)

815 2nd Ave., Ste. 313
New York, NY 10017-4594
Ph: (212)716-6134   Fax: (212)286-9366
Fr: 800-334-7626
E-mail: info@episcopalschools.org
URL: http://www.naes.org

Description: Episcopal day and boarding schools and preschools. Promotes the educational ministry of the Episcopal Church. Provides publications, consultation services and conference focusing on Episcopal identity of schools, worship, religious education, spirituality, leadership development and governance for heads/directors, administrators, chaplains and teachers of religion, trustees, rectors and other church and school leaders.

★10617★ National Association of Independent Schools (NAIS)

1620 L St. NW, Ste. 1100
Washington, DC 20036-5695
Ph: (202)973-9700   Fax: (202)973-9790

E-mail: info@nais.org
URL: http://www.nais.org

Description: Independent elementary and secondary school members; regional associations of independent schools and related associations. Provides curricular and administrative research and services. Conducts educational programs; compiles statistics.

★10618★ National Association for Research in Science Teaching (NARST)

319A Erickson Hall
Michigan State University
East Lansing, MI 48824
Ph: (517)432-4648
E-mail: jwtillot@syr.edu
URL: http://www2.educ.sfu.ca/narstsite/

Description: Science teachers, supervisors, and science educators specializing in research and teacher education. Promotes and coordinates science education research and interprets and reports the results.

★10619★ National Association of State Directors of Special Education (NASDSE)

1800 Diagonal Rd., Ste. 320
Alexandria, VA 22314
Ph: (703)519-3800   Fax: (703)519-3808
E-mail: nasdse@nasdse.org
URL: http://www.nasdse.org

Members: Professional society of state directors; consultants, supervisors, and administrators who have statewide responsibilities for administering special education programs. **Purpose:** Provides services to state agencies to facilitate their efforts to maximize educational outcomes for individuals with disabilities.

★10620★ National Community Education Association (NCEA)

3929 Old Lee Hwy., Ste. 91-A
Fairfax, VA 22030
Ph: (703)359-8973   Fax: (703)359-0972
E-mail: ncea@ncea.com
URL: http://www.ncea.com

Description: Community school directors, principals, superintendents, professors, teachers, students, and laypeople. **Purpose:** Promotes and establishes community schools as an integral part of the educational plan of every community. Emphasizes community and parent involvement in the schools, lifelong learning, and enrichment of K-12 and adult education. Serves as a clearinghouse for the exchange of ideas and information, and the sharing of efforts. **Activities:** Offers leadership training.

★10621★ National Council for Accreditation of Teacher Education (NCATE)

2010 Massachusetts Ave. NW, Ste. 500
Washington, DC 20036-1023
Ph: (202)466-7496   Fax: (202)296-6620
E-mail: ncate@ncate.org
URL: http://www.ncate.org

Members: Representatives from constituent colleges and universities, state departments of education, school boards, teacher, and other professional groups. **Purpose:** Voluntary accrediting body devoted exclusively to evaluation and accreditation of institutions for preparation of elementary and secondary school teachers; preparation of school service personnel, including school principals, supervisors, superintendents, school psychologists, instructional technologists, and other specialists for school-oriented positions.

★10622★ National Council for Geographic Education (NCGE)

206A Martin Hall
Jacksonville State University
Jacksonville, AL 36265-1602
Ph: (256)782-5293   Fax: (256)782-5336
E-mail: ncge@jsucc.jsu.edu
URL: http://www.ncge.org

Description: Teachers of geography and social studies in elementary and secondary schools, colleges, and universities; geographers in governmental agencies and private businesses. Encourages the training of teachers in geographic concepts, practices, teaching methods, and techniques; works to develop effective geographic educational programs in schools and colleges and with adult groups; stimulates the production and use of accurate and understandable geographic teaching aids and materials.

★10623★ National Council of Teachers of Mathematics (NCTM)

1906 Association Dr.
Reston, VA 20191-1502
Ph: (703)620-9840   Fax: (703)476-2970
Fr: 800-235-7566

E-mail: orders@nctm.org
URL: http://www.nctm.org

Description: Dedicated to improving teaching and learning of mathematics. Toll-free number is for orders only.

★10624★ Organization of American Historians (OAH)

112 N. Bryan Ave.
Bloomington, IN 47408-4199
Ph: (812)855-7311   Fax: (812)855-0696
E-mail: oah@oah.org
URL: http://www.oah.org

Description: Professional historians, including college faculty members, secondary school teachers, graduate students, and other individuals in related fields; institutional subscribers are college, university, high school and public libraries, and historical agencies. Promotes historical research and study. Sponsors 12 prize programs for historical writing; maintains speakers' bureau. Conducts educational programs.

★10625★ Overseas Employment Opportunities for Educators: Department of Defense Dependents Schools

DIANE Publishing Co.
PO Box 1428
Collingdale, PA 19023-8428
Ph: (610)461-6200   Fax: (610)461-6130
Fr: 800-782-3833

Barry Leonard, editor. 1999. $20.00. 44 pages. An introduction to teachings positions in the Dept. of Defense Dependents Schools (DoDDS), a worldwide school system, operated by the DoD in 14 countries.

★10626★ Teaching & Related Occupations

Delphi Productions
3160 4th St.
Boulder, CO 80304
Fax: (303)443-4022   Fr: 888-443-2400
URL: http://www.delphivideo.com

$95.00. 50 minutes. Part of the Careers for the 21st Century Video Library.

Security Professionals and Investigators

SOURCES OF HELP-WANTED ADS

★10627★ ACJS Today
Academy of Criminal Justice Sciences
402 Nunn Hall
Northern Kentucky University
Newport, KY 41099
Ph: (606)572-5634   Fax: (606)572-6665
Fr: 800-757-ACJS

Description: Four issues/year. Contains criminal justice information.

★10628★ National Locksmith
National Publishing Company Inc.
1533 Burgundy Pkwy.
Streamwood, IL 60107
Ph: (630)837-2044   Fax: (630)837-1210
E-mail: natlock@aol.com
URL: http://www.thenationallocksmith.com

$41.00/year for individuals; $5.00 for single issue. Magazine focusing on physical security and locksmithing.

★10629★ Occupational Hazards
Penton Media Inc.
1300 E 9th St.
Cleveland, OH 44114-1503
Ph: (216)696-7000   Fax: (216)931-9799
URL: http://www.occupationalhazards.com

Monthly. $55.00/year; $5.00 for single issue. Monthly publication for safety professionals featuring information to meet OSHA and EPA compliance requirements, improve management of safety, industrial hygiene and environmental programs and find products and services to protect employees and property.

★10630★ Police & Security News
Days Communications
1208 Juniper St.
Quakertown, PA 18951-1520
Ph: (215)538-1240   Fax: (215)538-1208
E-mail: advertising@policeandsecuritynews.com

Bimonthly. $18.00/year; $54.00/year for other countries; $3.00 for single issue. Tabloid for the law enforcement and private security industries. Includes articles on training, new products, and new technology.

★10631★ SafetyHealth
National Safety Council
1121 Spring Lake Dr.
Itasca, IL 60143-3201
Ph: (630)285-1121   Fax: (630)285-1315
Fr: 800-621-7615

Monthly. $56.00/year; $5.00 for single issue. Publication focusing on workplace safety and health issues.

★10632★ SECURITY
Business News Publishing
1050 Rte. 83, No. 200
Bensenville, IL 60106
Ph: (630)616-0200   Fax: (630)227-0214
E-mail: security@cahners.com
URL: http://www.securitymagazine.com

Monthly. $89.00/year for individuals; $10.00 for single issue. Magazine presenting news and technology for loss prevention and asset protection.

★10633★ Security Sales
Bobit Publishing
21061 S Western Ave.
Torrance, CA 90501
Ph: (310)533-2400   Fax: (310)533-2500
E-mail: secsales@bobit.com
URL: http://www.securitysales.com

Monthly. $35.00/year for individuals; $42.00/year for Canada; $53.00/year for other countries. Magazine covering the security industry.

PLACEMENT AND JOB REFERRAL SERVICES

★10634★ Nine Lives Associates (NLA)
Executive Protection Institute
PO Box 802
Berryville, VA 22611-0802
Ph: (540)554-2540   Fax: (540)554-2558
E-mail: info@personalprotection.com
URL: http://www.personalprotection.com

Description: Law enforcement, correctional, military, and security professionals who have been granted Personal Protection Specialist certification through completion of the protective services program offered by the Executive Protection Institute; conducts research. EPI programs emphasize personal survival skills and techniques for the protection of others. Provides professional recognition for qualified individuals engaged in executive protection assignments. Maintains placement service. Operates speakers' bureau; compiles statistics

EMPLOYER DIRECTORIES AND NETWORKING LISTS

★10635★ Associated Locksmiths of America-Membership Directory
Associated Locksmiths of America
3003 Live Oak St.
Dallas, TX 75204
Ph: (214)827-1701   Fax: (214)827-1810

Annual, March. Publication includes: Roster of about 9,500 members of the association. Entries include: Name, address, phone. Arrangement: Alphabetical. Indexes: Geographical.

★10636★ Burglar Alarm Systems Wholesale Directory

infoUSA Inc.
5711 S 86th Cir.
Omaha, NE 68127-0347
Ph: (402)930-3500   Fax: (402)331-0176
Fr: 800-555-6124
URL: http://www.abii.com

Annual, January. Number of listings: 11,847. Entries include: Name, address, phone (including area code), size of advertisement, year first in "Yellow Pages," name of owner or manager, number of employees. Compiled from telephone company "Yellow Pages," nationwide. Arrangement: Geographical.

★10637★ Detective Agencies Directory

infoUSA Inc.
5711 S 86th Cir.
Omaha, NE 68127-0347
Ph: (402)930-3500   Fax: (402)331-0176
Fr: 800-555-6124
URL: http://www.abii.com

Annual. Number of listings: 2,025. Entries include: Name, address, phone (including area code), size of advertisement, year first in "Yellow Pages," name of owner or manager, number of employees. Compiled from telephone company "Yellow Pages," nationwide. Arrangement: Geographical.

★10638★ International Security Management Association-Membership Directory

International Security Management Association
PO Box 623
Buffalo, IA 52728
Ph: (563)381-4008   Fax: (563)381-4283

Covers member senior security officers of multinational firms and chief executive officers of security consultation services.

★10639★ Investigators Directory

infoUSA Inc.
5711 S 86th Cir.
Omaha, NE 68127-0347
Ph: (402)930-3500   Fax: (402)331-0176
Fr: 800-555-6124
URL: http://www.abii.com

Annual. Number of listings: 8,292. Entries include: Name, address, phone (including area code), size of advertisement, year first in "Yellow Pages," name of owner or manager, number of employees. Compiled from telephone company "Yellow Pages," nationwide. Arrangement: Geographical.

★10640★ Security Guard & Patrol Service Directory

infoUSA Inc.
5711 S 86th Cir.
Omaha, NE 68127-0347
Ph: (402)930-3500   Fax: (402)331-0176
Fr: 800-555-6124
URL: http://www.abii.com

Annual. Number of listings: 8,449. Entries

include: Name, address, phone (including area code), size of advertisement, year first in "Yellow Pages," name of owner or manager, number of employees. Compiled from telephone company "Yellow Pages," nationwide. Arrangement: Geographical.

★10641★ Security Letter Source Book

Security Letter
166 E 96th St.
New York, NY 10128
Ph: (212)348-1553   Fax: (212)534-2957

Biennial, June of odd years. $75.00. Covers over 3,000 companies and individuals that supply security services, equipment, and products, including armored car carriers and vehicle manufacturers, central alarm stations, consultants, guard companies, investigators, risk management and insurance services, polygraph and pre-employment screening services, and art theft specialists. Entries include: Company name, address, phone, fax, names of executives, number of employees, brand names, financial keys, services and products, major clients. Arrangement: Classified by type of service or product. Indexes: Subjects, corporate and organizational names.

★10642★ Security Systems Consultants Directory

infoUSA Inc.
5711 S 86th Cir.
Omaha, NE 68127-0347
Ph: (402)930-3500   Fax: (402)331-0176
Fr: 800-555-6124
URL: http://www.abii.com

Updated continuously; printed on request. Number of listings: 3,078. Entries include: Name, address, phone (including area code), size of advertisement, year first in "Yellow Pages," name of owner or manager, number of employees. Compiled from telephone company "Yellow Pages," nationwide. Arrangement: Geographical.

HANDBOOKS AND MANUALS

★10643★ America's Fastest Growing Jobs

JIST Works, Inc.
8902 Otis Ave.
Indianapolis, IN 46216-1033
Ph: (317)613-4200   Fax: (317)613-4307
Fr: 800-648-5478
E-mail: jistworks@aol.com
URL: http://www.jist.com

Seventh edition, 2002. $16.95 (paper). 438 pages. Each job profile explains the nature of the work, skills and abilities required, employment outlook, average earnings, related occupations, education and training requirements, and employment opportunities. Also contains career planning information and job search tips.

★10644★ Career Planning in Criminal Justice

Anderson Publishing Co.
2035 Reading Rd.
Cincinnati, OH 45202-1576
Ph: (513)421-4142   Fax: (513)562-8116
Fr: 800-582-7295

Robert C. DeLucia and Thomas J. Doyle. Third edition, 1998. 226 pages. $21.95. Surveys a wide range of career and employment opportunities in law enforcement, the courts, corrections, forensic science, and private security. Contains career planning and job hunting advice.

★10645★ Careers in Law Enforcement and Security

Rosen Publishing Group, Inc.
29 E. 21st St.
New York, NY 10010
Ph: (212)777-3017   Fax: 888-436-4643
Fr: 800-237-9932

Paul Cohen and Shari Cohen. Revised edition, 1994. $18.95. $9.95 (paper), out of print. Describes jobs such as police, sheriff, detective, FBI, CIA, and Secret Service agents, parole and probation officers, security guards, and private investigators. Covers job duties, qualifications, education, training, income, and advancement possibilities. Offers advice about where and how to apply for jobs.

★10646★ Careers for Legal Eagles and Other Law-and-Order Types

McGraw-Hill Trade
2 Penn Plaza
New York, NY 10121
Ph: (212)904-2000   Fr: 800-722-4726
E-mail: ntcpub@tribune.com

Blythe Camenson. 1998. $14.95; $9.95 (paper). 220 pages.

★10647★ 100 Best Careers in Crimefighting

Thomson Peterson's
P.O. Box 67005
Lawrenceville, NJ 08648-6105
Fr: 800-338-3282

Mary P. Lee. 1997. $15.95 (paper). 200 pages. Covers private security careers, government law enforcement positions, and more, with information on employment opportunities.

★10648★ Opportunities in Law Enforcement and Criminal Justice Careers

McGraw-Hill Contemporary Books
1221 Avenue of the Americas
New York, NY 10020
Ph: (212)904-2000   Fr: 800-323-4900
E-mail: ntcpub@tribune.com

James Stinchcomb. Revised edition, 1996. $14.95; $11.95 (paper). 160 pages. Offers information on opportunities at the city, county, state, military, and federal levels. Contains bibliography and illustrations.

★10649★ *Real People Working in Law*
McGraw-Hill Contemporary Books
1221 Avenue of the Americas
New York, NY 10020
Ph: (212)904-2000   Fr: 800-323-4900
E-mail: ntcpub@tribune.com

Blythe Camenson, Jan Goldberg. 1997. $14.95; $12.95 (paper). 405 pages. Interviews and profiles of working professionals capture a range of opportunities in this field.

EMPLOYMENT AGENCIES AND SEARCH FIRMS

★10650★ **Bill Young and Associates**
273 Oak Dale Ln.
Stuarts Draft, VA 24477
Ph: (540)337-5268
E-mail: byoung@billyoung.com
URL: http://www.billyoung.com

Employment agency. Executive recruiter.

★10651★ **Robert A. Borissoff, Security Consultant**
2016 Oakdale Ave.
San Francisco, CA 94124
Ph: (415)221-0600   Fax: (415)821-1164

Safety and security specialist in the development, design, and installation of personnel security programs, guard services, surveillance services, and personnel testing. Industries served: legal, security, and government agencies worldwide.

OTHER SOURCES

★10652★ **ASIS International**
1625 Prince St.
Alexandria, VA 22314-2818
Ph: (703)519-6200   Fax: (703)519-6299
E-mail: asis@asisonline.org
URL: http://www.asisonline.org

Purpose: Security professionals responsible for loss prevention, asset protection and security for businesses, government, or public organizations and institutions. Sponsors educational programs on security principles (basic through advanced levels) and current security issues. Administers professional certification programs (CPP, PCI, PSP). Offers networking opportunities to professionals; provides an online service for employment and resumes, publishes books, directories, and other resources.

★10653★ **Associated Locksmiths of America (ALOA)**
3003 Live Oak St.
Dallas, TX 75204
Ph: (214)827-1701   Fax: (214)827-1810
Fr: 800-532-2562

E-mail: charlie@aloa.org
URL: http://www.aloa.org

Members: Retail locksmiths; associate members are manufacturers and distributors of locks, keys, safes, and burglar alarms. **Purpose:** Works to educate and provide current information to individuals in the physical security industry. **Activities:** Maintains information and referral services for members; offers insurance and bonding programs. Holds annual five-day technical training classes and 3-day technical exhibit. Maintains museum.

★10654★ **Federal Criminal Investigators Association (FCIA)**
PO Box 23400
Washington, DC 20026
Fax: 800-528-3492   Fr: 800-961-7753
E-mail: info@fedcia.org
URL: http://www.fedcia.org

Description: Professional fraternal organization dedicated to the advancement of federal law enforcement officers and the citizens they serve. Their mission is to ensure law enforcement professionals have the tools and support network to meet the challenges of future criminal investigations while becoming more community oriented. Intends to pursue mission through promoting professionalism, enhancing the image of federal officers, fostering cooperation among all law enforcement professionals, providing a fraternal environment for the advancement of the membership and community. Deeply involved in charitable programs and organizations.

★10655★ *Human Services Occupations*
Delphi Productions
3160 4th St.
Boulder, CO 80304
Fax: (303)443-4022   Fr: 888-443-2400
URL: http://www.delphivideo.com

$95.00. 50 minutes. Part of the Careers for the 21st Century Video Library.

★10656★ **International Association of Campus Law Enforcement Administrators (IACLEA)**
342 W Main St.
West Hartford, CT 06117-2507
Ph: (860)586-7517   Fax: (860)586-7550
E-mail: info@iaclea.org
URL: http://www.iaclea.org

Description: Advances public safety for educational institutions by providing educational resources, advocacy, and professional development. Dedicated to promoting professional ideals and standards in the administration of campus security/public safety/law enforcement. Goal is to make campus security/public safety/law enforcement an integral part of the educational community.

★10657★ **International Association for Healthcare Security and Safety (IAHSS)**
PO Box 5038
Glendale Heights, IL 60139
Ph: (630)871-9936   Fax: (630)871-9938
Fr: 888-353-0990
E-mail: president@iahss.org
URL: http://www.iahss.org

Members: Administrative and supervisory personnel in the field of hospital security and safety. **Purpose:** To develop, promote, and coordinate better security/safety programs in medical care facilities. **Activities:** Offers placement services; conducts specialized education programs.

★10658★ **International Association of Professional Security Consultants (IAPSC)**
525 SW 5th St., Ste. A
Des Moines, IA 50309
Ph: (515)282-8192   Fax: (515)282-9117
E-mail: iapsc@iapsc.org
URL: http://www.iapsc.org

Description: Security management, technical, training, and forensic consultants. Promotes understanding and cooperation among members and industries or individuals requiring such services. Seeks to enhance members' knowledge through seminars, training programs, and educational materials. Works to foster public awareness of the security consulting industry; serves as a clearinghouse for consultants requirements. Maintains code of conduct, ethics, and professional standards. Offers consultant referral service; operates speakers' bureau.

★10659★ **International Security Management Association (ISMA)**
PO Box 623
Buffalo, IA 52728
Ph: (563)381-4008   Fax: 800-568-1894
Fr: 800-368-1894
E-mail: isma3@aol.com
URL: http://www.ismanet.com

Description: Senior security executives of multinational business firms and chief executive officers of full service security services companies. Purpose is to assist senior security executives in coordinating and exchanging information about security management and to establish high business and professional standards.

★10660★ *Math at Work: Women in Nontraditional Careers*
Her Own Words
PO Box 5264
Madison, WI 53705-0264
Ph: (608)271-7083   Fax: (608)271-0209
URL: http://www.herownwords.com/

Video. Jocelyn Riley. $95.00. 15 minutes. Resource guide also available for $45.00.

★10661★ National Association of Legal Investigators (NALI)
11643 Saginaw St.
PO Box 905
Grand Blanc, MI 48439
Fax: (810)694-7109   Fr: 800-266-6254
E-mail: laccardo@gfn.org
URL: http://www.nalionline.org/

Description: Legal investigators, both independent and law firm staff, who specialize in investigation of personal injury matters for the plaintiff and criminal defense. Goal is the professionalization of the legal investigator, accomplished by seminars and a professional certification program. Provides nationwide network of contact among members. Compiles statistics.

★10662★ *Professional Specialty Occupations*
Delphi Productions
3160 4th St.
Boulder, CO 80304
Fax: (303)443-4022   Fr: 888-443-2400
URL: http://www.delphivideo.com
$95.00. 53 minutes. Part of the Careers for the 21st Century Video Library.

★10663★ Society of Professional Investigators (SPI)
PO Box 1128
Bellmore, NY 11710
Ph: (516)781-1000   Fax: (516)783-0000
E-mail: info@spionline.org
URL: http://www.spionline.org

Description: Persons with at least 5 years' investigative experience for an official federal, state, or local government agency or for a quasi-official agency formed for law enforcement or related activities. Seeks to advance knowledge of the science and technology of professional investigation, law enforcement, and police science; maintains high standards and ethics; promotes efficiency of investigators in the services they perform.

Services Sales Representatives

SOURCES OF HELP-WANTED ADS

★10664★ Advertising Age
Crain Communications Inc.
711 Third Ave.
New York, NY 10017-4036
Ph: (212)210-0100   Fax: (212)210-0244
Fr: 800-446-1420

Weekly. $99.00/year; $3.00 for single issue. Advertising trade publication covering agency, media, and advertiser news and trends.

★10665★ BtoB Magazine
Crain Communications Inc.
711 Third Ave.
New York, NY 10017-4036
Ph: (212)210-0100   Fax: (212)210-0244
Fr: 800-446-1420
URL: http://www.btobonline.com

Monthly. $59.00/year for individuals. Trade magazine on business-to-business marketing news, strategy, and tactics.

★10666★ Money Making Opportunities
Success Publishing International
11071 Ventura Blvd.
Studio City, CA 91604-3548
Ph: (818)765-2344   Fax: (818)980-7829
URL: http://www.moneymakingopps.com

$8.00/year. Magazine Source for small business opportunity seekers.

★10667★ Sales & Marketing Management
Bill Communications Inc.
770 Broadway
New York, NY 10003-9595
Ph: (646)654-4500   Fax: (646)654-7212
E-mail: edit@salesandmarketing.com
URL: http://www.salesandmarketing.com

$48.00/year. Business magazine.

HANDBOOKS AND MANUALS

★10668★ America's Fastest Growing Jobs
JIST Works, Inc.
8902 Otis Ave.
Indianapolis, IN 46216-1033
Ph: (317)613-4200   Fax: (317)613-4307
Fr: 800-648-5478
E-mail: jistworks@aol.com
URL: http://www.jist.com

Seventh edition, 2002. $16.95 (paper). 438 pages. Each job profile explains the nature of the work, skills and abilities required, employment outlook, average earnings, related occupations, education and training requirements, and employment opportunities. Also contains career planning information and job search tips.

★10669★ Career Opportunities in Advertising and Public Relations (Career Opportunities Series)
Checkmark Books, Inc.
132 W. 31st St., 17th Fl.
New York, NY 10001-2006
Ph: (212)967-8800   Fax: (212)967-9196
Fr: 800-322-8755
URL: http://www.factsonfile.com

Shelly Field and Howard J. Rubenstein. Third edition, 2001. $14.95 (paper). 320 pages. Provides the job seeker with information about locating and landing the right position. Includes detailed job descriptions for many specific positions and lists trade associations, recruiting organizations, and major agencies. Contains index and bibliography.

★10670★ Career Opportunities in Travel and Tourism
Checkmark Books, Inc.
132 W. 31st St., 17th Fl.
New York, NY 10001-2006
Ph: (212)967-8800   Fax: (212)967-9196
Fr: 800-322-8755
URL: http://www.factsonfile.com

John K. Hawks. 1996. $18.95 (paper). 224 pages. Includes detailed job descriptions, educational requirements, salary ranges, and advancement prospects for 70 different job opportunities in this fast-paced industry. Contains index and bibliography.

★10671★ Careers for Talkative Types and Others with the Gift of Gab
McGraw-Hill Trade
2 Penn Plaza
New York, NY 10121
Ph: (212)904-2000   Fr: 800-722-4726
E-mail: ntcpub@tribune.com

Marjorie Eberts and Margaret Gisler. 1998. $14.95; $9.95 (paper). 160 pages.

★10672★ The I Hate Selling Book: Business-Building Advice for Consultants, Attorneys, Accountants, Engineers, Architects, and Other Professionals
Allan Boress & Associates
1500 University Dr., Suite 239
Coral Springs, FL 33071
Ph: (954)345-4666   Fax: (954)344-2453

Allan S. Boress. 2001. $29.95.

★10673★ Newspapers Career Directory
Thomson Gale
27500 Drake Rd.
Farmington Hills, MI 48331-3535
Ph: (248)699-GALE   Fax: 800-414-5043
Fr: 800-877-GALE
E-mail: galeord@gale.com
URL: http://www.gale.com

Bradley Morgan. Fourth edition, 1993. $39.00. 300 pages. Out of print. Features extensive listings of contacts and entry-level job opportunities at many newspaper organizations. Focuses on each area of the business, from reporting and editorial to sales and marketing to promotion and production.

★10674★ Opportunities in Medical Sales Careers

McGraw-Hill Trade
2 Penn Plaza
New York, NY 10121
Ph: (212)904-2000   Fr: 800-722-4726
Chad Ellis. 1997. $14.95; $11.95 (paper). 200 pages. Includes index.

★10675★ Opportunities in Sales Careers

McGraw-Hill Professional
2 Penn Plaza
New York, NY 10121
Ph: (212)904-2000   Fr: 800-722-4726
E-mail: ntcpub@tribune.com
James Brescoll and Ralph Dahm. 160 pages. 1995. $12.95; $11.95 (paper). Details sales in retail, wholesale and industrial sales, sales of services and intangibles, and sales management. Illustrated.

★10676★ Resumes for Sales and Marketing Careers

McGraw-Hill Professional
2 Penn Plaza
New York, NY 10121
Ph: (212)904-2000   Fr: 800-722-4726
E-mail: ntcpub@tribune.com
Chuck Cochran and Donna Peerce. Second edition, 1998. $10.95 (paper). 336 pages. Sample resumes and cover letters from all levels of the sales and marketing field.

★10677★ Where the Jobs Are: The Hottest Careers for the 90s

The Career Press, Inc.
3 Tice Rd.
PO Box 687
Franklin Lakes, NJ 07417-1322
Ph: (201)848-0310   Fax: (201)848-1727
Fr: 800-227-3371
Joyce Hadley. Third edition, 2000. $13.99 (paper). 400 pages. Out of print. Describes careers in fifteen general fields, from accounting to travel and hospitality.

EMPLOYMENT AGENCIES AND SEARCH FIRMS

★10678★ Amherst Personnel Group Inc.

PO Box 580
Hicksville, NY 11801-7848
Ph: (516)433-7610   Fax: (516)433-7848

E-mail: amherstgroup1@aol.com
Employment agency. Executive search firm. Other offices in Milltown, NJ, and Rochelle Park, NJ.

★10679★ The Culver Group

1810 Gateway Dr., Ste140
San Mateo, CA 94404
Ph: (650)356-1100   Fax: (650)356-1111
E-mail: gfagin@culvercareers.com
URL: http://www.culvercorp.com
Employment agency specializing in sales positions.

★10680★ Don Waldron and Associates, Inc.

450 7th Ave., Ste. 507A
New York, NY 10123
Ph: (212)239-9110   Fax: (212)239-9114
E-mail: salepositions@comcast.net
URL: http://www.salespositions.com
Employment agency.

★10681★ National Register Columbus, Inc.

2700 E. Dublin Granville Rd., Ste. 555
Columbus, OH 43231-4097
Ph: (614)890-1200   Fax: (614)890-1259
E-mail: sales@nrcols.com
URL: http://www.nrcols.com
Employment agency. Offices in Akron and Toledo, OH.

★10682★ Sales Executives Inc.

755 W. Big Beaver Rd., Ste. 2107
Troy, MI 48084
Ph: (248)362-1900
E-mail: dale@salesexecutives.com
URL: http://www.salesexecutives.com
Employment agency. Executive search firm.

★10683★ Selected Executives Inc.

36 Ash Ste., Ste102
Cambridge, MA 02138
Ph: (781)933-1500   Fax: (617)547-7333
E-mail: seilrs@aol.com
Executive search firm and employment agency.

TRADESHOWS

★10684★ National Agri-Marketing Association Conference

National Agri-Marketing Association
11020 King St., Ste. 205
Overland Park, KS 66210
Ph: (913)491-6500   Fax: (913)492-6502
E-mail: agrimktg@nama.org
URL: http://www.nama.org
Annual. **Primary Exhibits:** Marketing and communication suppliers, including trade publications, radio and television broadcast sales organizations, premium/incentive manufacturers, printers, marketing research firms, photographers, and related professionals.

★10685★ Support Services Conference & Expo - Washington DC

Keith Reed Media Events
303 Vintage Park Dr.
Foster City, CA 94404
Ph: (650)578-6897   Fax: (650)525-0193
Fr: 800-488-2883
E-mail: mtrask@zdcf.com
Primary Exhibits: Industry event for customer service and technical support professionals.

OTHER SOURCES

★10686★ Marketing & Sales Occupations

Delphi Productions
3160 4th St.
Boulder, CO 80304
Fax: (303)443-4022   Fr: 888-443-2400
URL: http://www.delphivideo.com
$95.00. 50 minutes. Part of the Careers for the 21st Century Video Library.

★10687★ Services Sales Representatives

Evon Publishing
832 N 7th Ave.
Iron River, MI 49935
Ph: (906)265-3190
Audiocassette. 1996. $16.95. 32 minutes. Part of the Careers and Vocational Guidance Series. Provides information about the nature of the work, educational requirements, employment outlook, earnings, and work conditions as well as additional related information.

Social Workers

SOURCES OF HELP-WANTED ADS

★10688★ American City and County
Primedia Business
6151 Powers Ferry Rd.
Atlanta, GA 30339
Ph: (770)955-2500   Fax: (770)618-0348
Monthly. $67.00/year for individuals. Municipal and county administration magazine.

★10689★ Children & Schools
National Association of Social Workers
750 1st St. NE, Ste. 700
Washington, DC 20002-4241
Ph: (202)408-8600   Fax: (202)336-8312
Quarterly. $45.00/year for members; $75.00/year for nonmembers; $105.00/year for institutions; $30.00/year for students. Journal.

★10690★ EAP Digest
Performance Resource Press Inc.
1270 Rankin Dr., Ste. F
Troy, MI 48083-2843
Ph: (248)588-7733   Fax: (248)588-6633
Fr: 800-453-7733
Quarterly. $10.00 for single issue; $36.00/year, U.S.; $45.00/year, Canada, Hawaii, and Alaska; $55.00/year for other countries; $65.00/year for air mail, other countries. Magazine covering planning, development, and administration of employee assistance programs.

★10691★ Family Therapy News
American Association for Marriage and
  Family Therapy
1133 15th St. NW, Ste. 300
Washington, DC 20005-2710
Ph: (202)452-0109
E-mail: ftn@aamft.org
Bimonthly. $20.00/year for individuals; $35.00/year for institutions, Canada; $10.00/year for out of country. Newspaper for professionals in family therapy and mental health-related issues.

★10692★ Journal of Family Social Work
The Haworth Press Inc.
10 Alice St.
Binghamton, NY 13904-1580
Ph: (607)722-5857   Fax: (607)722-1424
Fr: 800-429-6784
URL: http://www.haworthpress.com
Quarterly. $60.00/year for individuals, USA; $95.00/year for institutions, USA; $175.00/year for libraries, USA; $81.00/year for individuals, Canada; $128.25/year for institutions, Canada; $236.25/year for libraries, Canada; $87.00/year for individuals, other countries; $137.75/year for institutions, other countries; $123.75/year for libraries, other countries. Journal serves as a forum for family practitioners, scholars, and educators in the field of social work.

★10693★ Journal of Jewish Communal Service
Jewish Communal Service Association
3084 State Hwy. 27, Ste. 9
Kendall Park, NJ 08824-1657
Ph: (732)821-1871   Fax: (732)821-5335
Quarterly. $30.00/year for individuals. Journal covering Jewish communal service and social work.

★10694★ The Lutheran
Augsburg Fortress, Publishers
100 S Fifth St., Ste. 700
Minneapolis, MN 55402
Ph: (612)330-3300   Fax: (612)330-3521
Fr: 800-426-0115
E-mail: lutheran@elca.org
URL: http://www.thelutheran.org
Monthly. $15.95/year for individuals; $1.50 for single issue. Magazine of the Evangelical Lutheran Church in America.

★10695★ Mental Retardation
American Association on Mental
  Retardation
444 N Capitol St. NW, Ste. 846
Washington, DC 20001-1512
Ph: (202)387-1968   Fax: (202)387-2193
Fr: 800-424-3688

E-mail: staylo01@mailbox.syr.edu
Bimonthly. $115.00/year for nonmembers. Magazine featuring articles on mental retardation for professionals and parents.

★10696★ Modern Healthcare
Crain Communications Inc.
360 N Michigan Ave.
Chicago, IL 60601
Ph: (312)649-5200   Fax: (312)280-3174
Fr: 800-678-2724
E-mail: mhcedit@crain.com
URL: http://www.modernhealthcare.com
Weekly. $135.00/year. Weekly Business news magazine for Healthcare Management

★10697★ NASW News
National Association of Social Workers
750 1st St. NE, Ste. 700
Washington, DC 20002-4241
Ph: (202)408-8600   Fax: (202)336-8312
E-mail: naswnews@naswdc.org
URL: http://www.naswpress.org
Description: Ten issues/year. Recurring features include letters to the editor, job listings, notices of publications available, and columns titled From the President, From the Director, and Social Work in the Public Eye.

★10698★ The New Social Worker
White Hat Communications
PO Box 5390
Harrisburg, PA 17110-0390
Ph: (717)238-3787   Fax: (717)238-2090
URL: http://www.socialworker.com
$15.00/year for individuals. Publication offering career guidance for social work students.

★10699★ The Nonprofit Times
NPT Publishing Group Inc.
120 Littleton Rd., Ste. 120
Parsippany, NJ 07054-1803
Ph: (973)394-1800   Fax: (973)734-1771
E-mail: ednchief@nptimes.com
URL: http://www.nptimes.com
$8.95 for single issue; $59.00/year. Trade journal serving nonprofit organizations.

★10700★ The Pennsylvania Social Worker

National Association of Social Workers-Pennsylvania Chapter
1337 N Front St.
Harrisburg, PA 17102-2629
Ph: (717)232-4125   Fax: (717)232-4140
Fr: 800-272-6279

Description: Bimonthly. Provides information on state, local, and national Association activities. Tracks legislative actions. Recurring features include interviews, a calendar of events, news of educational opportunities, job listings, book reviews, and columns titled President's Report and Division Report.

★10701★ Psychiatric Services

Association of Partners for Public Lands
2401 Blueridge Ave., Ste. 303
Wheaton, MD 20902-4517
Ph: (301)946-9475   Fax: (301)946-9478
URL: http://www.appl.org/psjournal

Monthly. Interdisciplinary mental health journal covering clinical, legal, and public policy issues.

★10702★ Social Work

National Association of Social Workers
750 1st St. NE, Ste. 700
Washington, DC 20002-4241
Ph: (202)408-8600   Fax: (202)336-8312
E-mail: press@naswdc.org

Quarterly. Subscription included in membership; $80.00/year for nonmembers; $105.00/year for institutions. Journal for social workers.

★10703★ Teaching Exceptional Children

Council for Exceptional Children
1110 N Glebe Rd., Ste. 300
Arlington, VA 22201
Ph: (703)620-3660   Fax: (703)264-9494
Fr: 888-232-7733
E-mail: tec@bc.edu

$58.00/year for individuals; $66.00/year for other countries by surface mail; $95.00/year for other countries by airmail; $10.50 for single issue. Journal exploring practical methods for teaching students who have exceptionalities and those who are gifted and talented.

PLACEMENT AND JOB REFERRAL SERVICES

★10704★ Alliance for Children and Families (ACF)

11700 W Lake Park Dr.
Milwaukee, WI 53224-3099
Ph: (414)359-1040   Fax: (414)359-1074
Fr: 800-221-3726
E-mail: info@alliance1.org
URL: http://www.alliance1.org

Description: Membership organization of local agencies in more than 1000 communities providing family counseling, family life education and family advocacy services, and other programs to help families with parent-child, marital, mental health, and other problems of family living. Assists member agencies in developing and providing effective family services. Works with the media, government, and corporations to promote strong family life. Compiles statistics; conducts research. Maintains extensive files of unpublished materials from member agencies. Offers career placement services.

★10705★ American Association of Psychiatric Technicians (AAPT)

2000 "O" St., Ste. 250
Sacramento, CA 95814-5286
Ph: (916)443-1701   Fax: (916)329-9145
Fr: 800-391-7589
E-mail: hearn@psychtechs.org
URL: http://www.psychtechs.org

Description: Administers the Nationally Certified Psychiatric Technician examination to non-licensed direct-care workers in the fields of mental illness, developmental disabilities and substance abuse.

★10706★ American Public Health Association (APHA)

800 I St. NW
Washington, DC 20001-3710
Ph: (202)777-2742   Fax: (202)777-2534
E-mail: comments@apha.org
URL: http://www.apha.org

Members: Professional organization of physicians, nurses, educators, academicians, environmentalists, epidemiologists, new professionals, social workers, health administrators, optometrists, podiatrists, pharmacists, dentists, nutritionists, health planners, other community and mental health specialists, and interested consumers. **Purpose:** Seeks to protect and promote personal, mental, and environmental health. **Activities:** Services include promulgation of standards; establishment of uniform practices and procedures; development of the etiology of communicable diseases; research in public health; exploration of medical care programs and their relationships to public health. Sponsors job placement service.

★10707★ International Association of Counselors and Therapists (IACT)

10915 Bonita Beach Rd., Ste. 1101
Bonita Springs, FL 34135-9049
Ph: (239)498-9710   Fax: (239)498-1215
E-mail: iactnow@aol.com
URL: http://www.iact.org

Description: Mental health professionals, medical professionals, social workers, clergy, educators, hypnotherapists, counselors, and individuals interested in the helping professions. Promotes enhanced professional image and prestige for complementary therapy. Provides a forum for exchange of information and ideas among practitioners of traditional and nontraditional therapies and methodologies; fosters unity among "grassroots" practitioners and those with advanced academic credentials. Facilitates the development of new therapy programs. Conducts educational, research, and charitable programs. Awards credits for continuing education. Maintains speakers' bureau and library; operates referral and placement services; compiles statistics. Assists in the development of local chapters.

★10708★ National Staff Development and Training Association (NSDTA)

810 First St., NE, Ste. 500
Washington, DC 20002
Ph: (202)682-0100   Fax: (202)682-2328
E-mail: dpollard@aphsa.org
URL: http://nsdta.aphsa.org/

Description: Social welfare workers engaged in staff development and training. Attempts to: support people in the field; influence welfare policy-making on the national level; form a network of contacts for members. Provides technical assistance. Maintains speakers' bureau; offers placement services.

EMPLOYER DIRECTORIES AND NETWORKING LISTS

★10709★ American Group Psychotherapy Association-Membership Directory

American Group Psychotherapy Association Inc.
25 E 21st St., 6th Fl.
New York, NY 10023
Ph: (212)477-2677   Fax: (212)979-6627
Fr: 877-668-AGPA

Biennial, fall. $90.00. Covers 4,500 physicians, psychologists, clinical social workers, psychiatric nurses, and other mental health professionals interested in treatment of emotional problems by group methods. Entries include: Name, office or home address, highest degree held, office or home phone number. Arrangement: Alphabetical. Indexes: Geographical.

★10710★ Christian Association for Psychological Studies International-Membership Directory

Christian Association for Psychological Studies
PO Box 310400
New Braunfels, TX 78131-0400
Ph: (830)629-2277   Fax: (830)629-2342
URL: http://www.caps.net/dircoup.htm

Annual, June. $12.00 for other countries. Covers 2,300 Christians involved in psychology, psychiatry, counseling, sociology, social work, ministry, and nursing. Entries include: Name, office address and phone number, highest degree held, area of occupational specialization, and career data. Arrangement: Geographical. Indexes: Alphabetical.

★10711★ Directory of Catholic Charities USA Directories

Catholic Charities USA
1731 King St.
Alexandria, VA 22314
Ph: (703)549-1390   Fax: (703)549-1656
URL: http://www.catholiccharitiesusa.org

Annual. $25.00 for members; $40.00 for nonmembers. Covers nearly 1,200 Catholic community and social service agencies. Listings include diocesan agencies, state Catholic conferences. Entries include: Organization name, address, name and title of director, phone, fax. Arrangement: Geographical by state, then classified by diocese.

★10712★ Directory of Child Life Programs

Child Life Council Inc.
11820 Parklawn Dr., Ste. 202
Rockville, MD 20852-2529
Ph: (301)881-7090   Fax: (301)881-7092
URL: http://www.childlife.org/

Biennial. $15.00 for members; $20.00 for nonmembers. Covers over 400 child life programs. Entries include: Facility name, address, phone, name of child life department and director, reporting structure, staff statistics, educational requirements for employment, and internship or educational opportunities. Arrangement: Geographical. Indexes: Speciality areas, internship sessions, program size, fellowships.

★10713★ Mental Health Directory

Office of Consumer, Family & Public Information
Parklawn Bldg.
5600 Fishers Ln.
Rockville, MD 20857
Ph: (301)443-4795   Fax: (301)443-0284

Irregular, previous edition 1990; latest edition 1995. $23.00. Covers hospitals, treatment centers, outpatient clinics, day/night facilities, residential treatment centers for emotionally disturbed children, residential supportive programs such as halfway houses, and mental health centers offering mental health assistance; not included are substance abuse programs, Veteran's Administration programs, nursing homes, programs for the developmentally disabled, and organizations in which fees are retained by individual members. Entries include: Name, address, phone. Arrangement: Geographical.

★10714★ Mental Health Services Directory

infoUSA Inc.
5711 S 86th Cir.
Omaha, NE 68127-0347
Ph: (402)930-3500   Fax: (402)331-0176
Fr: 800-555-6124
URL: http://www.abii.com

Annual. Number of listings: 18,282. Entries include: Name, address, phone (including area code), size of advertisement, year first in "Yellow Pages," name of owner or manager, number of employees. Compiled from telephone company "Yellow Pages," nationwide. Arrangement: Geographical.

★10715★ Mental Help Net

CenterSite, LLC
570 Metro Place
Dublin, OH 43017
URL: http://www.mentalhelp.net

Covers resources for finding mental help including local therapists and self-help groups; Services including upcoming conferences, professional education, and universities offering degrees in mental health fields.

★10716★ National Directory of Children, Youth & Families Services

Penny K. Spencer, Publisher
14 Inverness Dr. E. Ste. D-144
Englewood, CO 80112
Ph: (303)662-8165   Fax: 800-845-6452
Fr: 800-343-6681
URL: http://www.childrenyouthfamilydir.com/

Annual, July. $159.00. Covers more than 45,000 key contacts in the areas of Social Services, Health & Mental Health Services, Juvenile Justice Agencies, Education Departments, Treatment Centers & Hospitals, Referral Networks, child, youth, and family-oriented social services, health and mental health services, and juvenile/family court and youth advocacy services, educational listings in state and private agencies, major cities, and 3,300 counties; also covers runaway youth centers, child abuse projects, congressional committees, clearinghouses, and national organizations concerned with family health and welfare; buyers' guide to specialized services and products. Entries include: Agency listings include agency name, address, phone, fax, after-hours phone, websites, names of principal executives and staff, description of services. Arrangement: Geographical.

★10717★ National Directory of Private Social Agencies

Croner Publications Inc.
10951 Sorrento Valley Rd., Ste. 1D
San Diego, CA 92121-1616
Ph: (619)546-1894   Fax: (858)546-1955
Fr: 800-441-4033
URL: http://www.sdic.net/croner

Base edition supplied upon order; monthly updates. $100.00. Number of listings: Over 10,000. Entries include: Agency name, address, phone, name and title of contact, description of services. Arrangement: Geographical. Indexes: Service, agency type.

★10718★ Public Human Services Directory

American Public Human Services Association
810 1st St. NE, Ste. 500
Washington, DC 20002
Ph: (202)682-0100   Fax: (202)289-6555
E-mail: pubs@aphsa.org
URL: http://www.aphsa.org

Annual, September. $120.00 for members; $155.00 for out of country. Covers federal, state, territorial, county, and major municipal public human service agencies. Entries include: Agency name, address, phone, fax, e-mail address, web site address, names of key personnel, program area. Arrangement: Geographical.

★10719★ Social Workers Directory

infoUSA Inc.
5711 S 86th Cir.
Omaha, NE 68127-0347
Ph: (402)930-3500   Fax: (402)331-0176
Fr: 800-555-6124
URL: http://www.abii.com

Annual. Number of listings: 4,859. Entries include: Name, address, phone (including area code), size of advertisement, year first in "Yellow Pages," name of owner or manager, number of employees. Compiled from telephone company "Yellow Pages," nationwide. Arrangement: Geographical.

HANDBOOKS AND MANUALS

★10720★ Career Information Center

Macmillan Publishing Co. Inc.
200 Old Tappan Rd.
Old Tappan, NJ 07675
Fr: 800-428-5331

Visual Education Center Staff. Seventh edition, 1999. $275.00. 2080 pages. This 13-volume set profiles over 600 occupations. Each occupational profile describes job duties, educational requirements, how to get the job, advancement possibilities, employment outlook, working conditions, earnings and benefits, and where to write for more information.

★10721★ Careers for Caring People and Other Sensitive Types

VGM Career Horizons
1221 Avenue of the Americas
New York, NY 10020
Ph: (212)904-2000   Fr: 800-323-4900
E-mail: ntcpub@tribune.com

Adrian Paradis. 1995. $14.95; $9.95 (paper). 205 pages.

★10722★ Careers for Good Samaritans and Other Humanitarian Types

McGraw-Hill Trade
2 Penn Plaza
New York, NY 10121
Ph: (212)904-2000   Fr: 800-722-4726
E-mail: ntcpub@tribune.com

Marjorie Eberts and Margaret Gisler. Second edition, 1998. $9.95 (paper). 274 pages. Contains hundreds of ideas for turning good work into paid work. Inventories opportunities in service organizations like the Red Cross, Goodwill, and the Salvation Army;

religious groups, VISTA, the Peace Corps, and UNICEF; and agencies at all levels of the government. Part of Careers for You series.

★10723★ *Careers in Health Care*
McGraw-Hill Trade
2 Penn Plaza
New York, NY 10121
Ph: (212)904-2000   Fr: 800-722-4726
E-mail: ntcpub@tribune.com

Barbara M. Swanson. Fourth edition, 2000. $17.95; $13.95 (paper). 320 pages. Describes job duties, work settings, salaries, licensing and certification requirements, educational preparation, and future outlook. Gives ideas on how to secure a job.

★10724★ *Careers in Social and Rehabilitation Services*
McGraw-Hill Trade
2 Penn Plaza
New York, NY 10121
Ph: (212)904-2000   Fr: 800-722-4726
E-mail: ntcpub@tribune.com

Geraldine O. Garner. Second edition, 2001. $19.95; 14.95 (paper). 128 pages.

★10725★ *Great Jobs for Liberal Arts Majors*
McGraw-Hill Professional
2 Penn Plaza
New York, NY 10121
Ph: (212)904-2000   Fr: 800-722-4726
E-mail: ntcpub@tribune.com

Blythe Camenson. Second edition, 2001. $14.95 (paper). 256 pages.

★10726★ *Great Jobs for Sociology Majors*
McGraw-Hill Trade
2 Penn Plaza
New York, NY 10121
Ph: (212)904-2000   Fr: 800-722-4726
E-mail: ntcpub@tribune.com

Stephen Lambert. 1996. $11.95 (paper). 514 pages.

★10727★ *A Guide to Careers in Community Development*
Island Press
1718 Connecticut Ave., NW, Suite 300
Washington, DC 20009-1148
Ph: (202)232-7933   Fax: (202)234-1328
Fr: 800-828-1302

Alice Shabecoff and Paul Brody. 2001. $35.00.

★10728★ *Non-Profits and Education Job Finder*
Planning Communications
7215 Oak Ave.
River Forest, IL 60305-1935
Ph: (708)366-5200   Fax: (708)366-5280
Fr: 888-366-5200

URL: http://jobfindersonline.com

Daniel Lauber. 1997. $32.95; $16.95 (paper). 336 pages. Covers 1600 sources. Discusses how to use sources of non-profit sector job vacancies in a number of specialties and state-by-state, including job-matching services, job hotlines, specialty periodicals with job ads, salary surveys, and directories. Covers a variety of fields from education to religion. Includes chapters on resume and cover letter preparation and interviewing.

★10729★ *100 Jobs in Social Change*
Hungry Minds Inc.
10475 Crosspoint Blvd.
Indianapolis, IN 46256
Ph: (317)572-2000   Fr: 800-428-5331

Harley Jebens. 1996. $14.95. 224 pages. Part of the One Hundred Jobs Series.

★10730★ *Opportunities in Child Care Careers*
McGraw-Hill Trade
2 Penn Plaza
New York, NY 10121
Ph: (212)904-2000   Fr: 800-722-4726

Renee Wittenberg. 1998. $14.95; $11.95 (paper). 210 pages. Discusses various job opportunities and how to secure a position. Illustrated.

★10731★ *Opportunities in Gerontology and Aging Services Careers*
McGraw-Hill Trade
2 Penn Plaza
New York, NY 10121
Ph: (212)904-2000   Fr: 800-722-4726

Ellen Williams. 1995. $14.95; $11.95 (paper). 200 pages. Covers jobs in community, health and medical programs, financial, legal, residential, travel and tourism, and counseling, and how to go after them. Includes bibliography and illustrations.

★10732★ *Opportunities in Health and Medical Careers*
McGraw-Hill Trade
2 Penn Plaza
New York, NY 10121
Ph: (212)904-2000   Fr: 800-722-4726

I. Donald Snook, Jr. and Leo D'Orazio. 1997. $14.95; $11.95 (paper). 202 pages. Covers the full range of medical and health occupations. Illustrated.

★10733★ *Opportunities in Social Work Careers*
McGraw-Hill/Contemporary Books
1221 Avenue of the Americas
New York, NY 10020
Ph: (212)904-2000   Fr: 800-323-4900
E-mail: ntcpub@tribune.com

Renee Wittenberg. 1997. 205 pages. $14.95; $11.95 (paper).

★10734★ *Opportunities in State and Local Government Careers*
Vgm Career Horizons
1221 Avenue of the Americas
New York, NY 10020
Ph: (212)904-2000   Fr: 800-323-4900
E-mail: ntcpub@tribune.com

Neale J. Baxter. 1994. $14.95; $10.95 (paper). 160 pages. Points out the incentives and drawbacks of a government career. Describes hiring procedures and provides tips on filling out applications, taking physical and aptitude tests, handling interviews, and finding jobs. Describes the jobs in which 75% of all state and local government workers are employed. For each occupation, covers the nature of the work and the training required.

★10735★ *Passion and Policy: A Social Workers Career*
Octavia Press
12127 Sperry Rd.
Chesterland, OH 44026-2230
Ph: (216)729-3252   Fax: (216)729-2003

Alvin L. Schorr. 1997. $29.95. 212 pages.

★10736★ *Resumes for Social Service Careers*
McGraw-Hill Trade
2 Penn Plaza
New York, NY 10121
Ph: (212)904-2000   Fr: 800-722-4726
E-mail: ntcpub@tribune.com

2000. $9.95 (paper). 460 pages.

★10737★ *Social Work Career Development: A Handbook for Job Hunting and Career Planning*
National Association of Social Workers
750 1st St., NE, Ste. 700
Washington, DC 20002-4241
Ph: (202)408-8600   Fax: (202)336-8312
Fr: 800-638-8799

Carol Nesslein Doelling, editor. 1997. $24.95 (paper). 730 pages.

ONLINE JOB SOURCES AND SERVICES

★10738★ **Delta T Group**
E-mail: staffing@sdelta-tgroup.com
URL: http://www.delta-tgroup.com

Description: Specialized contract temporary staffing source for healthcare professionals in the fields of social service, psychiatry, mental health, and substance abuse. Organizations may request services and staffing; job seekers may view services provided, submit a resume, or peruse jobs available.

★10739★ **RehabWorld**
URL: http://www.rehabworld.com

Description: Site for rehabilitation professionals to learn about the profession and locate jobs. Includes user groups, salary surveys, and chat capabilities. **Main files include:** Physical Therapy, Occupational Therapy, Speech Therapy, Mental Health, Employer World, Student World, International World, Forum.

★10740★ **Social Work and Social Services Jobs Online**
E-mail: cndoe@gwbweb.wustl.edu
URL: http://gwbweb.wustl.edu/jobs/

Description: Specialized database of social work and social services jobs gives a large list of openings sorted by location (both within and outside the United States). Employers may submit job openings. Site also contains career resources and links to related internet job sites.

TRADESHOWS

★10741★ **International Association of Pupil Personnel Workers Conference**
International Association of Pupil Personnel Workers
c/o Bill Chmela
2025 Juneway Dr.
Long Beach, IN 46360
Ph: (219)872-4975
E-mail: w.chmela@attbi.com

Annual. **Primary Exhibits:** Equipment, supplies, and services for school administrators, counselors, attendance officers, and school social workers.

★10742★ **National Association of Black Social Workers Convention**
National Black United Fund
40 Clinton St., 5th Fl.
Newark, NJ 07102

Annual. **Primary Exhibits:** Items of interest to social workers and others concerned with community welfare projects and programs.

OTHER SOURCES

★10743★ *American Almanac of Jobs and Salaries*
Morrow Avon
1350 Avenue of the Americas
New York, NY 10019
Ph: (212)261-6788   Fr: 800-242-7737

John W. Wright. Revised edition, 2000. $20.00 (paper). 672 pages. This is a comprehensive guide to the wages of hundreds of occupations in a wide variety of industries and organizations.

★10744★ **American Association of Mental Health Professionals in Corrections (AAMHPC)**
PO Box 160208
Sacramento, CA 95816-0208
Fax: (916)649-1080
E-mail: corrmentalhealth@aol.com

Description: Psychiatrists, psychologists, social workers, nurses, and other mental health professionals; individuals working in correctional settings. Fosters the progress of behavioral sciences related to corrections. Goals are: to improve the treatment, rehabilitation, and care of the mentally ill, mentally retarded, and emotionally disturbed; to promote research and professional education in psychiatry and allied fields in corrections; to advance standards of correctional services and facilities; to foster cooperation between individuals concerned with the medical, psychological, social, and legal aspects of corrections; to share knowledge with other medical practitioners, scientists, and the public. Conducts scientific meetings to contribute to the advancement of the therapeutic community in all its institutional settings, including correctional institutions, hospitals, churches, schools, industry, and the family.

★10745★ **American Society of Psychopathology of Expression (ASPE)**
74 Lawton St.
Brookline, MA 02446
Ph: (617)738-9821   Fax: (617)975-0411

Description: Psychiatrists, psychologists, art therapists, sociologists, art critics, artists, social workers, linguists, educators, criminologists, writers, and historians. At least two-thirds of the members must be physicians. Fosters collaboration among specialists in the United States who are interested in the problems of expression and in the artistic activities connected with psychiatric, sociological, and psychological research. Disseminates information about research and clinical applications in the field of psychopathology of expression. Sponsors consultations, seminars, and lectures on art therapy.

★10746★ **Association on Higher Education and Disability (AHEAD)**
PO Box 540666
Waltham, MA 02454
Ph: (781)788-0003   Fax: (781)788-0033
E-mail: ahead@ahead.org
URL: http://www.ahead.org.

Description: Individuals interested in promoting the equal rights and opportunities of disabled postsecondary students, staff, faculty, and graduates. Provides an exchange of communication for those professionally involved with disabled students; collects, evaluates, and disseminates information; encourages and supports legislation for the benefit of disabled students. Conducts surveys on issues pertinent to college students with disabilities; offers resource referral system and employment exchange for positions in disability student services. Conducts research programs; compiles statistics.

★10747★ **Child Welfare League of America (CWLA)**
440 1st St. NW, 3rd Fl.
Washington, DC 20001
Ph: (202)638-2952   Fax: (202)638-4004
E-mail: jjohnson@cwla.org
URL: http://www.cwla.org

Purpose: Works to improve care and services for abused, dependent, or neglected children, youth, and their families. **Activities:** Provides training and consultation; conducts research; maintains information service; develops standards for child welfare practice.

★10748★ **Counseling Association for Humanistic Education and Development (C-AHEAD)**
5999 Stevenson Ave.
Alexandria, VA 22304
Ph: (703)823-9800   Fax: 800-473-2329
Fr: 800-347-6647
E-mail: membership@counseling.org
URL: http://www.counseling.org

Description: A division of the American Counseling Association. Teachers, educational administrators, community agency workers, counselors, school social workers, and psychologists; others interested in the area of human development. Aims to assist individuals in improving their quality of life. Provides forum for the exchange of information about humanistically-oriented administrative and instructional practices. Supports humanistic practices and research on instructional and organizational methods for facilitating humanistic education; encourages cooperation among related professional groups.

★10749★ **Employee Assistance Society of North America (EASNA)**
230 E Ohio St., Ste. 400
Chicago, IL 60611-3265
Ph: (312)644-0828   Fax: (312)644-8557
E-mail: easna@bostrom.com
URL: http://www.easna.org

Description: Individuals in the field of employee assistance, including psychiatrists, psychologists, and managers. Facilitates communication among members; provides resource information; serves as a network for employee assistance programs nationwide. Conducts research.

★10750★ *Human Services Occupations*
Delphi Productions
3160 4th St.
Boulder, CO 80304
Fax: (303)443-4022   Fr: 888-443-2400
URL: http://www.delphivideo.com

$95.00. 50 minutes. Part of the Careers for the 21st Century Video Library.

★10751★ National Association of Social Workers (NASW)

750 First St. NE, Ste. 700
Washington, DC 20002-4241
Ph: (202)408-8600   Fax: (202)336-8312
Fr: 800-638-8799
E-mail: info@naswdc.org
URL: http://www.naswdc.org

Members: Regular members are persons who hold a minimum of a baccalaureate degree in social work. Associate members are persons engaged in social work who have a baccalaureate degree in another field. Student members are persons enrolled in accredited (by the Council on Social Work Education) graduate or undergraduate social work programs. **Purpose:** Works to create professional standards for social work practice; advocate sound public social policies through political and legislative action; provide a wide range of membership services, including continuing education opportunities and an extensive professional program. **Activities:** Operates National Center for Social Policy and Practice. Conducts research; compiles statistics.

★10752★ National Organization for Human Service Education (NOHSE)

Fort Greene SNAP
375 Myrtle Ave.
Brooklyn, NY 11205
Ph: (718)694-6957   Fax: (718)694-6958
E-mail: ftg_snap@hotmail.com
URL: http://www.nohse.com

Description: Human service professionals, faculty, and students. Works to foster excellence in teaching, research and curriculum planning in the human service area; to encourage and support the development of local, state, and national human services organizations; to aid faculty and professional members in their career development. Provides a medium for cooperation and communication among members; maintains registry of qualified consultants in human service education. Conducts professional development workshop; operates speakers' bureau.

★10753★ North American Association of Christians in Social Work (NACSW)

PO Box 121
Botsford, CT 06404-0121
Ph: (203)270-8780   Fax: (203)270-8780
Fr: 888-426-4712
E-mail: info@nacsw.org
URL: http://www.nacsw.org

Description: Professional social workers and related professionals, students, interested individuals. Supports the integration of Christian faith and professional social work practice in the lives of its members, the profession and the church, promoting love and justice in social service and social reform. Provides opportunities for Christian fellowship, education and service opportunities; articulates informed Christian voice on social welfare practice and policy to the social work profession; provides professional understanding and help for the social ministry of the church; and promotes social welfare services and policies in society which bring about greater justice and meet basic human needs.

★10754★ Social Workers

Evon Publishing
832 N 7th Ave.
Iron River, MI 49935
Ph: (906)265-3190

Audiocassette. 1996. $16.95. 32 minutes. Part of the Careers and Vocational Guidance Series. Provides information about the nature of the work, educational requirements, employment outlook, earnings, and work conditions as well as additional related information.

★10755★ Working with Children

Cambridge Educational
2572 Brunswick Ave.
Lawrenceville, NJ 08648-4128
Fax: 800-FAX-ON-US   Fr: 800-468-4227
URL: http://www.cambridgeeducational.com

$89.95. 2000. 23 minutes. This program examines alternative positions offering the opportunity to work with children of different ages and the qualifications necessary for those jobs. A nanny, social worker, non-faculty school worker, and retail salesperson describe their job responsibilities and explain why they find their work so enjoyable.

Sociologists

SOURCES OF HELP-WANTED ADS

★10756★ *American Studies Association Newsletter*
American Studies Association
1120 19th St. NW, Ste. 301
Washington, DC 20036
Ph: (202)467-4783   Fax: (202)467-4786
URL: http://www.georgetown.edu/cross-roads

Description: Four issues/year. Promotes the interdisciplinary study of American culture. Presents news of research, publications, and conferences. Also includes information on grants, employment opportunities, and Association activities.

★10757★ *The Gerontologist*
Gerontological Society of America
1030 15th St. NW, Ste. 250
Washington, DC 20005-1503
Ph: (202)842-1275   Fax: (202)842-1150
E-mail: tg@geri.duke.edu

Bimonthly. $77.00/year for individuals; $145.00/year for institutions; $87.00/year for individuals, foreign; $155.00/year for institutions, foreign. Multidisciplinary peer-reviewed journal presenting new concepts, clinical ideas, and applied research in gerontology. Includes book and audiovisual reviews.

★10758★ *Innovations*
National Council on the Aging
409 3rd St. SW, 2nd Fl.
Washington, DC 20024
Ph: (202)479-1200   Fax: (202)479-0735
E-mail: scott.parkin@ncoa.org

Quarterly. $95.00/year for individuals; $195.00/year for organizations; $47.50/year for students. Magazine exploring significant developments in the field of aging.

PLACEMENT AND JOB REFERRAL SERVICES

★10759★ *American Society of Criminology (ASC)*
1314 Kinnear Rd., Ste. 212
Columbus, OH 43212-1156
Ph: (614)292-9207   Fax: (614)292-6767
E-mail: ceskridge@unl.edu
URL: http://www.asc41.com

Description: Professional and academic criminologists; students of criminology in accredited universities; psychiatrists, psychologists, and sociologists. Works to develop criminology as a science and academic discipline; to aid in the construction of criminological curricula in accredited universities; to upgrade the practitioner in criminological fields (police, prisons, probation, parole, delinquency workers). Conducts research programs; sponsors three student paper competitions. Provides placement service at annual convention.

EMPLOYER DIRECTORIES AND NETWORKING LISTS

★10760★ *American Sociological Association-Directory of Members*
American Sociological Association
1307 New York Ave. NW, Ste. 700
Washington, DC 20005-4701
Ph: (202)383-9005   Fax: (202)638-0882
URL: http://www.asanet.org

Biennial, May of odd years. $30.00 for members; $20.00 for students; $50.00 for nonmembers; $50.00 for institutions. Covers 12,000 sociologists, worldwide. Entries include: Member name, preferred mailing address, educational background, and section memberships. Only the 1990 issue is biographical, others are cited as American Sociological Association-Directory of Members. Arrangement: Alphabetical. Indexes: Geographical.

★10761★ *Christian Association for Psychological Studies International-Membership Directory*
Christian Association for Psychological Studies
PO Box 310400
New Braunfels, TX 78131-0400
Ph: (830)629-2277   Fax: (830)629-2342
URL: http://www.caps.net/dircoup.htm

Annual, June. $12.00 for other countries. Covers 2,300 Christians involved in psychology, psychiatry, counseling, sociology, social work, ministry, and nursing. Entries include: Name, office address and phone number, highest degree held, area of occupational specialization, and career data. Arrangement: Geographical. Indexes: Alphabetical.

HANDBOOKS AND MANUALS

★10762★ *Career Information Center*
Macmillan Publishing Co. Inc.
200 Old Tappan Rd.
Old Tappan, NJ 07675
Fr: 800-428-5331

Visual Education Center Staff. Seventh edition, 1999. $275.00. 2080 pages. This 13-volume set profiles over 600 occupations. Each occupational profile describes job duties, educational requirements, how to get the job, advancement possibilities, employment outlook, working conditions, earnings and benefits, and where to write for more information.

★10763★ *Careers for Caring People and Other Sensitive Types*
VGM Career Horizons
1221 Avenue of the Americas
New York, NY 10020
Ph: (212)904-2000   Fr: 800-323-4900
E-mail: ntcpub@tribune.com

Adrian Paradis. 1995. $14.95; $9.95 (paper). 205 pages.

★10764★ Careers in Health Care

McGraw-Hill Trade
2 Penn Plaza
New York, NY 10121
Ph: (212)904-2000   Fr: 800-722-4726
E-mail: ntcpub@tribune.com

Barbara M. Swanson. Fourth edition, 2000. $17.95; $13.95 (paper). 320 pages. Describes job duties, work settings, salaries, licensing and certification requirements, educational preparation, and future outlook. Gives ideas on how to secure a job.

★10765★ Careers for Mystery Buffs and Other Snoops and Sleuths

McGraw-Hill Trade
2 Penn Plaza
New York, NY 10121
Ph: (212)904-2000   Fr: 800-722-4726
E-mail: ntcpub@tribune.com

Blythe Camenson. 1996. $14.95; $9.95 (paper). 210 pages.

★10766★ Careers in Sociology

Pearson Allyn & Bacon
1230 Ave. of the Americas
New York, NY 10020
Ph: (212)782-3300   Fr: 800-223-1360

W. Richard Stephens. Second edition, 1998. $6.00 (paper). 144 pages.

★10767★ Doing Fieldwork in Japan

University of Hawaii Press
2840 Kolowalu St.
Honolulu, HI 96822-1888
Ph: (808)956-8255   Fax: (808)988-6052

Victoria Lyon-Bestor. January 2003. $55.00. Illustrated. 424 pages. Exploring social sciences in Japan.

★10768★ Embarking upon a Career with an Undergraduate Sociology Major

American Sociological Association
1307 New York Ave. NW, Ste. 700
Washington, DC 20005-4701
Ph: (202)383-9005   Fax: (202)638-0882
E-mail: apap@asanet.org
URL: http://www.asanet.org

Janet Mancini Billson and Bettina J. Huber. 1999. $10.00, $6.00 (paper). 65 pages. Aimed at the new college graduate with a sociology major. Reviews job search strategies.

★10769★ Great Jobs for Sociology Majors

McGraw-Hill Trade
2 Penn Plaza
New York, NY 10121
Ph: (212)904-2000   Fr: 800-722-4726
E-mail: ntcpub@tribune.com

Stephen Lambert. 1996. $11.95 (paper). 514 pages.

★10770★ A Guide to Careers in Physical Anthropology

Greenwood Publishing Group Inc.
88 Post Rd. W
Westport, CT 06881
Fax: (203)222-1502   Fr: 800-225-5800

Alan S. Ryan. 2001. $67.95.

★10771★ 100 Jobs in Social Change

Hungry Minds Inc.
10475 Crosspoint Blvd.
Indianapolis, IN 46256
Ph: (317)572-2000   Fr: 800-428-5331

Harley Jebens. 1996. $14.95. 224 pages. Part of the One Hundred Jobs Series.

★10772★ Opportunities in Gerontology and Aging Services Careers

McGraw-Hill Trade
2 Penn Plaza
New York, NY 10121
Ph: (212)904-2000   Fr: 800-722-4726

Ellen Williams. 1995. $14.95; $11.95 (paper). 200 pages. Covers jobs in community, health and medical programs, financial, legal, residential, travel and tourism, and counseling, and how to go after them. Includes bibliography and illustrations.

★10773★ Opportunities in Research and Development Careers

McGraw-Hill/Contemporary Books
1221 Avenue of the Americas
New York, NY 10020
Ph: (212)904-2000   Fr: 800-323-4900
E-mail: ntcpub@tribune.com

Jan Goldberg. 1997. $14.95; $11.95 (paper). 204 pages.

★10774★ Opportunities in Social Science Careers

McGraw-Hill Companies
860 Taylor Station Rd.
Blacklick, OH 43004-0545
Fax: (614)755-5645   Fr: 800-722-4726

Rosanne J. Marek. March 2004. $22.95. 160 Pages. VGM Opportunities Series.

TRADESHOWS

★10775★ American Association for State and Local History Annual Meeting

American Association for State and Local History
1717 Church St.
Nashville, TN 37203-2991
Ph: (615)320-3203   Fax: (615)327-9013
E-mail: history@aaslh.org
URL: http://www.aaslh.org

Annual. **Primary Exhibits:** Products and services directed toward the museum and

history field, including publications, fund-raising devices, software, exhibit design, historic preservation, historic research and technical information. **Dates and Locations:** 2004 Sep 29-Oct 02.

★10776★ American Sociological Association Annual Meeting

American Sociological Association
1307 New York Ave. NW, Ste. 700
Washington, DC 20005-4701
Ph: (202)383-9005   Fax: (202)638-0882
E-mail: asanet@asanet.org
URL: http://www.asanet.org

Annual. **Primary Exhibits:** Scholarly book publishers, statistical software supplies, government agencies, and information/data centers. **Dates and Locations:** 2005 Aug 13-16; Philadelphia, PA; Philadelphia Marriott.

★10777★ Eastern Sociological Society Annual Meeting

Exhibit Promotions Plus
11620 Vixens Path
Ellicott City, MD 21043-1539
Ph: (410)997-0763   Fax: (410)997-0764
E-mail: exhibit@erols.com
URL: http://www.epponline.com

Annual. **Primary Exhibits:** Publishers with titles in fields of sociology, anthropology, and psychology.

OTHER SOURCES

★10778★ American Academy of Political and Social Science (AAPSS)

3814 Walnut St.
Philadelphia, PA 19104-6197
Ph: (215)746-6500   Fax: (215)898-1202
E-mail: rwpearso@sas.upenn.edu
URL: http://www.aapss.org

Members: Professionals and laymen concerned with the political and social sciences and related fields. **Purpose:** Promotes the progress of political and social science through publications and meetings. The academy does not take sides in controversial issues, but seeks to gather and present reliable information to assist the public in forming an intelligent and accurate judgment.

★10779★ American Society of Psychopathology of Expression (ASPE)

74 Lawton St.
Brookline, MA 02446
Ph: (617)738-9821   Fax: (617)975-0411

Description: Psychiatrists, psychologists, art therapists, sociologists, art critics, artists, social workers, linguists, educators, criminologists, writers, and historians. At least two-thirds of the members must be physicians. Fosters collaboration among specialists in the United States who are interested in the problems of expression and in the artistic activities connected with psychiatric, sociological, and psychological research. Disseminates information about research and clinical applications in the field of psychopathology of expression. Sponsors consultations, seminars, and lectures on art therapy.

★10780★ American Sociological Association (ASA)

1307 New York Ave. NW, Ste. 700
Washington, DC 20005
Ph: (202)383-9005   Fax: (202)638-0882
E-mail: executive.office@asanet.org
URL: http://www.asanet.org

Description: Sociologists, social scientists, and others interested in research, teaching, and application of sociology; graduate and undergraduate sociology students. Compiles statistics. Operates the ASA Teaching Resources Center, which develops a variety of materials useful in teaching sociology. Sponsors Minority Fellowship and Professional Development Programs and Teaching Project. Maintains 37 sections including: Aging; Criminology; Medical; Population.

★10781★ Institute for the Study of Man (ISM)

1133 13th St. NW, No. C-2
Washington, DC 20005
Ph: (202)371-2700   Fax: (202)371-1523
E-mail: iejournal@aol.com
URL: http://www.jies.org

Description: Purpose is to publish books and journals in areas related to anthropology, historical linguistics, and the human sciences.

★10782★ Population Association of America (PAA)

8630 Fenton St., Ste. 722
Silver Spring, MD 20910-3812
Ph: (301)565-6710   Fax: (301)565-7850
E-mail: info@popassoc.org
URL: http://www.popassoc.org

Description: Professional society of individuals interested in demography and its scientific aspects.

★10783★ Rural Sociological Society

104 Gentry Hall
University of Missouri
Columbia, MO 65211-7040
Ph: (573)882-9065   Fax: (573)882-1473
E-mail: ruralsoc@missouri.edu
URL: http://www.ruralsociology.org

Description: Educators and others employed in the field of rural sociology. Promotes the development of rural sociology through research, teaching, and extension work.

★10784★ Sociological Practice Association (SPA)

Southwest Missouri State University
Department of Anthropology and
    Sociology
901 S National Ave.
Springfield, MO 65804
Ph: (417)836-6954   Fax: (417)836-6416
E-mail: mgl300f@smsu.edu
URL: http://www.socpractice.org/

Purpose: Promotes the application of sociology to individual and social change and advances theory, research, and methods to this end; develops opportunities for the employment and use of clinically trained sociologists; provides a common ground for sociological practitioners, allied professionals, and interested scholars and students. Promotes training and educational opportunities to further sociological practice. **Activities:** Sponsors sessions and programs in clinical and applied sociology at national and regional meetings of other sociological associations. Has conducted a survey on skills, licenses, education, and experience of members. Conducts national certification program. certification program.

★10785★ Sociological Research Association (SRA)

1307 New York Ave. NW
Washington, DC 20005
Ph: (202)383-9005   Fax: (202)638-0882
URL: http://www.asanet.org

Description: Persons, elected from membership of the American Sociological Association, "who have made significant contributions to sociological research, other than a doctoral dissertation, and who maintain an active interest in the advancement of sociological knowledge."

★10786★ Sociologists

Evon Publishing
832 N 7th Ave.
Iron River, MI 49935
Ph: (906)265-3190

Audiocassette. 1996. $16.95. 32 minutes. Part of the Careers and Vocational Guidance Series. Provides information about the nature of the work, educational requirements, employment outlook, earnings, and work conditions as well as additional related information.

★10787★ Sociologists for Women in Society (SWS)

University of Akron
Dept. of Sociology
Akron, OH 44325-1905
Ph: (330)972-7918   Fax: (330)972-5377
E-mail: sws@uakron.edu
URL: http://www.socwomen.org

Description: Members are mainly national and international professional social scientists, sociologists and students of sociology, though membership is open to anyone interested in the purposes of the organization. Dedicated to: maximizing the effectiveness of and professional opportunities for women in sociology; exploring the contributions which sociology can, does, and should make to the investigation of and improvement in the status of women in society. Acts as watchdog of the American Sociological Association to ensure that it does not ignore the special needs of women in the profession. Has organized a job market service to bring potential jobs and applicants together; established a discrimination committee offering advice and organizational support for women who pursue cases charging sex discrimination; has aided women to establish social, professional, and intellectual contacts with each other. Supports minority scholarships, breast cancer research and academic mentoring activities.

Software Engineers

★10788★ Biotechnology Software

Mary Ann Liebert Inc. Publishers
2 Madison Ave.
Larchmont, NY 10538
Ph: (914)834-3100   Fax: (914)834-1388
Fr: 800-654-3237
URL: http://www.liebertpub.com

Description: Bimonthly. Reviews scientific software and hardware. Recurring features include letters to the editor, news of research, a calendar of events, job listings, and book reviews.

★10789★ Computerworld

101 Communications
9121 Oakdale Ave.
Chatsworth, CA 91311
Ph: (818)734-1520   Fax: (818)734-1522
URL: http://www.computerworld.com

Weekly. $48.00/year for individuals. Newspaper for information systems executives.

★10790★ Database Programming & Design

CMP Media L.L.C.
600 Community Dr.
Manhasset, NY 11030
Ph: (516)562-5000
E-mail: tgibb@cmp.com
URL: http://www.intelligententerprise.com/dbpdsearch.shtml

Monthly. Computer magazine.

★10791★ e-Business Advisor

e-Business Advisor
PO Box 429002
San Diego, CA 92142-9002
Ph: (858)278-5600   Fax: (858)278-0300
Fr: 800-336-6060
E-mail: CustomerService@Advisor.com
URL: http://www.advisor.com/

Magazine for developing strategies, prac-tices, and innovations for e-business appli-cations.

★10792★ Graduating Engineer & Computer Careers

Career Recruitment Media
211 W. Wacker Dr., No. 900
Chicago, IL 60606
Ph: (312)525-3100
URL: http://www.graduatingengineer.com

$16.00/year for individuals. Magazine focus-ing on employment, education, and career development for entry-level engineers and computer scientists.

★10793★ High Technology Careers Magazine

HTC
4701 Patrick Henry Dr., No. 1901
Santa Clara, CA 95054-1847
Ph: (408)970-8800   Fax: (408)567-0242
URL: http://www.hightechcareers.com

Bimonthly. $29.00/year; $35.00/year for Canada; $85.00/year for out of country. Magazine (tabloid) containing employment opportunity information for the engineering and technical community.

★10794★ IEEE Computer Graphics and Applications

IEEE Computer Society
PO Box 3014
Los Alamitos, CA 90720-1264
Ph: (714)821-8380   Fax: (714)821-4010
Fr: 800-272-6657
E-mail: rbaldwin@computer.org
URL: http://www.computer.org/cga/

Bimonthly. $32.00/year for members; $320.00/year for institutions. Magazine ad-dressing the interests and needs of profes-sional designers and users of computer graphics hardware, software, and systems.

★10795★ IEEE Software Magazine

IEEE Computer Society
PO Box 3014
Los Alamitos, CA 90720-1264
Ph: (714)821-8380   Fax: (714)821-4010
Fr: 800-272-6657
URL: http://computer.org

Bimonthly. Magazine covering the computer software industry for the community of lead-ing software practitioners.

★10796★ International Journal of Software Engineering and Knowledge Engineering

World Scientific Publishing Co. Inc.
1060 Main St., Ste. 202
River Edge, NJ 07661
Ph: (201)487-9655   Fax: (201)487-9656
Fr: 800-227-7562

Quarterly. $5.00/year for individuals. Journal focusing on the interplay between software engineering and knowledge engineering.

★10797★ Journal of Graphics Tools

A.K. Peters Ltd.
63 S Ave.
Natick, MA 01760
Ph: (508)655-9933   Fax: (508)655-5847
E-mail: jgt@akpeters.com
URL: http://www.acm.org/jgt

Quarterly. $50.00/year for individuals; $120.00/year for institutions, U.S. and Cana-da; $40.00 for single issue; $7.50/year for U.S., postage and handling; $25.00/year for elsewhere, postage and handling; $15.00/year for Canada, postage and handling. Journal containing research ideas for com-puter graphics professionals.

★10798★ Journal of Software Maintenance

John Wiley and Sons Inc.
111 River St.
Hoboken, NJ 07030
Ph: (201)748-8866   Fax: (201)748-8824

Bimonthly. $645.00/year for individuals. Journal devoted to maintaining the viability of software through swift software evolution cycles.

★10799★ PC WORLD

101 Communications
9121 Oakdale Ave.
Chatsworth, CA 91311
Ph: (818)734-1520   Fax: (818)734-1522
URL: http://www.pcworld.com

Monthly. $29.90/year for individuals; $5.95 for single issue.

★10800★ Scientific Programming

John Wiley and Sons Inc.
111 River St.
Hoboken, NJ 07030
Ph: (201)748-8866   Fax: (201)748-8824

Quarterly. $396.00/year for individuals. Journal containing information on the practical experience of software engineering and scientific computing.

★10801★ Software

John Wiley and Sons Inc.
111 River St.
Hoboken, NJ 07030
Ph: (201)748-8866   Fax: (201)748-8824
E-mail: altoft@wiley.compuserve.com

$1,935.00/year for individuals. Journal for those who design, implement, or maintain computer software.

★10802★ Software Process

John Wiley and Sons Inc.
111 River St.
Hoboken, NJ 07030
Ph: (201)748-8866   Fax: (201)748-8824

$175.00/year for individuals. Journal for those involved in the software development process. Features experience reports, research papers, and critical discussion.

★10803★ SWE

Society of Women Engineers
230 E Ohio St., No. 400
2135 Lamberton Rd.
Chicago, IL 60611-3265
Ph: (312)596-5223   Fax: (312)596-5252
E-mail: hq@swe.org
URL: http://www.swe.org

Bimonthly. $30.00/year for nonmembers. Magazine for engineering students and for women and men working in the engineering and technology fields. Covers career guidance, continuing development and topical issues.

PLACEMENT AND JOB REFERRAL SERVICES

★10804★ American Indian Science and Engineering Society (AISES)

PO Box 9828
Albuquerque, NM 87119-9828
Ph: (505)765-1052   Fax: (505)765-5608

E-mail: info@aises.org
URL: http://www.aises.org

Description: American Indian and non-Indian students and professionals in science, technology, and engineering fields; corporations representing energy, mining, aerospace, electronic, and computer fields. Seeks to motivate and encourage students to pursue undergraduate and graduate studies in science, engineering, and technology. Sponsors science fairs in grade schools, teacher training workshops, summer math/science sessions for 8th-12th graders, professional chapters, and student chapters in colleges. Offers scholarships. Adult members serve as role models, advisers, and mentors for students. Operates placement service.

★10805★ Engineering Society of Detroit (ESD)

26100 American Dr., Ste. 500
Southfield, MI 48034-6184
Ph: (248)355-2910   Fax: (248)355-1492
E-mail: esd@esd.org
URL: http://esd.org

Description: Engineers from all disciplines; scientists and technologists. Conducts technical programs and engineering refresher courses; sponsors conferences and expositions. Maintains speakers' bureau; offers placement services. Although based in Detroit, MI, society membership is international.

★10806★ Korean Scientists and Engineers Association in America (KSEA)

1952 Gallows Rd., Ste. 300
Vienna, VA 22182
Ph: (703)748-1221   Fax: (703)748-1331
E-mail: sejong@ksea.org
URL: http://www.ksea.org

Description: Scientists and engineers holding single or advanced degrees. Goals are to: promote friendship and mutuality among Korean and American scientists and engineers; contribute to Korea's scientific, technological, industrial, and economic developments; strengthen the scientific, technological, and cultural bonds between Korea and the U.S. Sponsors symposium. Maintains speakers' bureau, placement service, and biographical archives. Compiles statistics. Maintains 100 volume library of scientific handbooks and yearbooks in Korean.

★10807★ Society of Hispanic Professional Engineers (SHPE)

5400 E Olympic Blvd., Ste. 210
Los Angeles, CA 90022
Ph: (323)725-3970   Fax: (323)725-0316
E-mail: shpenational@shpe.org
URL: http://www.shpe.org

Description: Engineers, student engineers, and scientists seeking to increase the number of Hispanic engineers by providing motivation and support to students. Sponsors competitions and educational programs. Maintains placement service and speakers' bureau; compiles statistics.

EMPLOYER DIRECTORIES AND NETWORKING LISTS

★10808★ American Men and Women of Science

Thomson Gale
27500 Drake Rd.
Farmington Hills, MI 48331-3535
Ph: (248)699-4253   Fax: (248)699-8065
Fr: 800-877-GALE
E-mail: amws@galegroup.com

Biennial, latest edition December 2002. $975.00. Covers over 129,700 U.S. and Canadian scientists active in the physical, biological, mathematical, computer science, and engineering fields; includes references to previous edition for deceased scientists and nonrespondents. Entries include: Name, address, education, personal and career data, memberships, honors and awards, research interest. Arrangement: Alphabetical. Indexes: Discipline (in separate volume).

★10809★ Computer Directory

Computer Directories Inc.
23815 Nichols Sawmill Rd.
Hockley, TX 77447
Ph: (281)259-5959   Fax: (281)356-7980
Fr: 800-234-4353
URL: http://www.compdirinc.com

Annual, fall. Covers approximately 130,000 computer installations; 19 separate volumes for Alaska/Hawaii, Connecticut/New Jersey, Dallas/Ft. Worth, Eastern Seaboard, Far Midwest, Houston, Illinois, Midatlantic, Mid-central, Mideast, Minnesota/Wisconsin, North Central, New England, New York Metro, Northwest, Ohio, Pennsylvania/West Virginia, Southeast, and Southwest Texas. Entries include: Company name, address, phone, fax, email, name and title of contact, hardware used, software application, operating system, programming language, computer graphics, networking system. Arrangement: Geographical. Indexes: Alphabetical, industry, hardware.

★10810★ Computer Software Directory

infoUSA Inc.
5711 S 86th Cir.
Omaha, NE 68127-0347
Ph: (402)930-3500   Fax: (402)331-0176
Fr: 800-555-6124
URL: http://www.abii.com

Annual. Number of listings: 44,502. Entries include: Name, address, phone (including area code), size of advertisement, year first in "Yellow Pages," name of owner or manager, number of employees. Regional editions available. Compiled from telephone company "Yellow Pages," nationwide. Arrangement: Geographical.

★10811★ Directory of Contract Staffing Firms

C.E. Publications Inc.
PO Box 3006
Bothell, WA 98041-3006
Ph: (425)806-5200   Fax: (425)806-5585

URL: http://www.cjhunter.com/dcsf/overview.html

$15.00. Covers nearly 1,300 contract firms actively engaged in the employment of engineering, IT/IS, and technical personnel for 'temporary' contract assignments throughout the world. Entries include: Company name, address, phone, name of contact, email, web address. Arrangement: Alphabetical. Indexes: Geographical.

★10812★ Directory of Multi-Media Systems and Software

International Management Services Inc.
42 Harbour Passage Dr.
Hilton Head Island, SC 29926-1261
Ph: (843)342-9642   Fax: (843)342-9628

Annual, March. $135.00. Covers approximately 220 companies that manufacture or service products used in building and presenting multi-media programs; international coverage. Entries include: Company name, address, phone, descriptions of services, product/service. Arrangement: Classified by product/service. Indexes: Alphabetical.

★10813★ Directory of Software Data Sources

ERIC Document Reproduction Service
7420 Fullerton Rd., Ste. 110
Springfield, VA 22153-2852
Ph: (703)440-1400   Fax: (703)440-1408
Fr: 800-443-ERIC
URL: http://www.edrs.com/

$16.00; $20.10 for out of country. Covers companies that provide databases and on-line that describe software and other technological products designed for use in special education. Entries include: Name, address, phone of companies, description of product/service, name and title of contact. Arrangement: Alphabetical.

★10814★ GIS Markets and Opportunities

Daratech Inc.
255 Bent St.
Cambridge, MA 02141-2001
Ph: (617)354-2339   Fax: (617)354-7822
URL: http://www.daratech.com/research/gis/2003/index.php

Annual, September. $5,950.00; $7,500.00 for online version. Covers over 310 geographic information system software vendors and products. Entries include: Company name, address, phone, names and titles of key personnel, number of employees, geographical area served, financial data, subsidiary and branch names and locations, description of software. Arrangement: Alphabetical. Indexes: Name, product.

★10815★ Indiana Society of Professional Engineers-Directory

Indiana Society of Professional Engineers
PO Box 20806
Indianapolis, IN 46220
Ph: (317)255-2267   Fax: (317)255-2530

Annual, fall. $55.00. Covers member registered engineers, land surveyors, engineering students, and engineers in training. Entries include: Member name, address, phone, type of membership, business information, specialty. Arrangement: Alpha by chapter area.

★10816★ Information Sources: The IIA Annual Membership Directory

Software & Information Industry Association
1090 Vermont Ave. NW, 6th Fl.
Washington, DC 20005
Ph: (202)289-7442   Fax: (202)289-7097
URL: http://www.siia.net/

Annual, November. $75.00 for members; $300.00 for nonmember. Covers more than 800 companies involved in the creation, distribution, and use of information products, services, and technology. Entries are prepared by companies described. Entries include: Company name, address, phone, names of executives, international partners, regional offices, trade and brand names, and description of products and services. Arrangement: Alphabetical. Indexes: Product, personal name, trade name, geographical, corporate parents, international and niche markets.

★10817★ Northwest High Tech

Resolution Business Press Inc.
12307 NE 149th Ct.
Kirkland, WA 98034
Ph: (425)487-6248   Fax: (425)649-1897
E-mail: info@respress.com
URL: http://www.respress.com

Annual. $34.95. Covers over 2,000 computer-related companies in Washington, Oregon, and Idaho, and British Columbia and Alberta, Canada. Entries include: Company; name, address, phone, fax; toll-free number; names and titles of key personnel; product/service, programming languages, financial data, number of employees, operating systems, expansion plans (including hiring and site expansion plans), company market information, Standard Industrial Classification (SIC) code., internet addresses. Arrangement: Geographical. Indexes: Company name, SIC.

★10818★ Peterson's Hidden Job Market

Thomson Peterson's
Princeton Pike Corporate Center
2000 Lenox Dr.
PO Box 67005
Lawrenceville, NJ 08648
Ph: (609)896-1800   Fax: 800-277-2465
Fr: 800-338-3282
URL: http://www.petersons.com

Annual, June. $18.95. Covers approximately

2,000 technology firms with under 1,000 employees, which hire at four times the national rate. Entries include: Company name, address, phone, fax, name and title of contact, number of employees, year founded, number of employees added in last year, percentage of growth, line of business. Arrangement: Geographical by state, then by area code. Indexes: Alphabetical by industry.

★10819★ The Software Encyclopedia

R.R. Bowker L.L.C.
630 Central Ave.
New Providence, NJ 07974
Ph: (908)286-1090   Fax: (908)219-0098
Fr: 888-269-5372
URL: http://www.bowker.com

Annual, May, latest edition 2003. $335.00. Covers over 40,100 software programs from over 3,845 publishers of software programs. Entries include: For software-Title, version, release date, system requirements, price, ISBN, order number, description, publisher name. For publishers-Company name, address, phone, toll-free phone, fax, ISBN prefix, titles. Arrangement: Two alphabetical sections for software, one by title, the other by system/application; also, one alphabetical section for publishers. Indexes: Title, system/application.

★10820★ Software Engineering Bibliography

Data & Analysis Center for Software
775 Daedalian Dr.
Rome, NY 13442-4909
Ph: (315)334-4905   Fax: (315)334-4964
Fr: 800-214-7921
URL: http://www.dacs.dtic.mil/

Annual. $30.00. Database covers: Citations for over 100,000 technical reports, articles, theses, papers, an books concerned with software technology. Entries include: Title, author name, publisher name and address, number of pages, other bibliographic information, and abstract. Arrangement: By document accession number.

HANDBOOKS AND MANUALS

★10821★ The Best Home-Based Businesses for the 90s

Putnam Publishing Group
375 Hudson St.
New York, NY 10014
Ph: (212)366-2000   Fax: (212)366-2643
Fr: 800-331-4624

Paul Edwards and Sarah Edwards. Second edition, 1991. $11.95 (paper). 272 pages. Profiles 95 businesses and careers that can be conducted from one's home. Lists sources of additional information. Out of print.

★10822★ *Career Guide for the High-Tech Professional: Where the Jobs Are Now and How to Land Them*

Career Press, Inc.
3 Tice Rd.
PO Box 687
Franklin Lakes, NJ 07417
Ph: (201)848-0310   Fax: (201)848-1727
Fr: 800-227-3371

David Perry. May 2004. $15.99 (paper). Illustrated. 192 pages.

★10823★ *Career Insights: CEO's and CTO's from BEA, BMC, Peoplesoft and More on Achieving Personal and Professional Success*

Aspatore Books, Incorporated
264 Beacon St., 2nd Fl.
Boston, MA 02116
Ph: (617)249-1960   Fax: (617)249-1970

Aspatore Books. April 2004. $19.95 (paper).

★10824★ *Career Opportunities in Computers and Cyberspace*

Facts on File
132 W. 31st St., 17th Fl.
New York, NY 10001-2006
Ph: (212)967-8800   Fax: (212)967-8107
Fr: 800-322-8755

Harry Henderson. 1999. $26.95 (paper). Part of the Career Opportunities Series. 224 pages.

★10825★ *Careers for Computer Buffs and Other Technological Types*

VGM Career Horizons
1221 Avenue of the Americas
New York, NY 10020
Ph: (212)904-2000   Fr: 800-323-4900
E-mail: ntcpub@tribune.com

Marjorie Eberts, Margaret Gisler and Maria Olsen. Second edition, 1999. $14.95; $9.95 (paper).

★10826★ *Careers in Computers*

VGM Career Horizons
1221 Avenue of the Americas
New York, NY 10020
Ph: (212)904-2000   Fr: 800-323-4900
E-mail: ntcpub@tribune.com

Lila B. Stair and Leslie Stair. Third edition, 2002. $19.95; $14.95 (paper). Describes trends affecting computer careers and explores a wide range of job opportunities from programming to consulting. Provides job qualifications, salary data, job market information, personal and educational requirements, career paths, and the place of the job in the organizational structure. Offers advice on education, certification, and job search.

★10827★ *Careers in High Tech*

Vgm Career Horizons
McGraw-Hill Trade
1221 Avenue of the Americas
New York, NY 10020
Ph: (212)904-2000   Fr: 800-323-4900

E-mail: ntcpub@tribune.com

Nick Basta. Second edition, 1998. $17.95; $13.95 (paper). 104 pages. Examines new career opportunities in such fields as biotechnology, computers, aerospace, telecommunications, and others.

★10828★ *Careers Inside the World of Technology*

Rosen Publishing Group, Inc.
29 E. 21st St.
New York, NY 10010
Ph: (212)777-3017   Fax: 888-436-4643
Fr: 800-237-9932

Jean W. Spencer. Revised edition, 1998. $16.95. 64 pages. Describes computer-related careers for reluctant readers.

★10829★ *Careers for Number Crunchers and Other Quantitative Types*

McGraw-Hill Trade
2 Penn Plaza
New York, NY 10121
Ph: (212)904-2000   Fr: 800-722-4726
E-mail: ntcpub@tribune.com

Rebecca Burnett. Second edition, 2002. $15.95; $12.95 (paper). 192 pages. Provides information to math-oriented job hunters on how to become statisticians, field researchers, computer programmers, stock analysts, investment managers, bankers, engineers, accountants, underwriters, economists, market analysts, mathematicians, systems analysts, and more.

★10830★ *The Digital Frontier Job & Opportunity Finder*

Moon Lake Media
PO Box 251466
Los Angeles, CA 90025
Ph: (310)535-2453

Don B. Altman. 1996. $19.95 (paper). 256 pages.

★10831★ *Engineering Your Job Search: A Job-Finding Resource for Engineering Professionals*

Professional Publications, Inc.
1250 5th Ave.
Belmont, CA 94002
Ph: (650)593-9119   Fax: (650)592-4519
Fr: 800-426-1178

Compiled by Professional Publications, editors. 1995. $24.95 (paper). 154 pages. Out of print.

★10832★ *Expert Resumes for Computer and Web Jobs*

JIST Publishing
8902 Otis Ave.
Indianapolis, IN 46216-1033
Ph: (317)613-4200   Fax: (317)613-4307
Fr: 800-648-5478

Wendy Enelow and Louis Kursmark. 2001. $16.95 (paper).

★10833★ *Exploring Careers in the Computer Field*

Rosen Publishing Group, Inc.
29 E 21st St.
New York, NY 10010
Ph: (212)777-3017   Fax: 888-436-4643
Fr: 800-237-9932

Joseph Weintraub. Revised edition, 1993. $14.95; $9.95 (paper). Discusses entry into the field, salaries, future trends, and offers job search advice. Surveys the newest growth areas in the computer industry including artificial intelligence, desktop publishing, and personal computers. Out of stock.

★10834★ *Exploring High-Tech Careers*

Rosen Publishing Group, Inc.
29 E. 21st St.
New York, NY 10010
Ph: (212)777-3017   Fax: (212)777-0277
Fr: 800-237-9932

Scott Southworth. Revised edition, 1993. $14.95; $9.95 (paper). 118 pages. Out of print. Gives an orientation to the field of high technology and high-tech jobs. Describes educational preparation and job hunting. Includes a glossary and bibliography.

★10835★ *Game Developer's Marketplace: The Definitive Guide to Making it Big in the Interactive Game Industry*

Coriolis Group LLC
14455 N. Hayden Rd., Ste. 220
Scottsdale, AZ 85260-6949
Ph: (480)483-0192   Fax: (480)483-0193
Fr: 800-410-0192

Ben Sawyer. 1997. $49.99. 700 pages. Out of print. Covers the basics of game design, getting a job in the industry, and business plans along with other related topics.

★10836★ *Get Your IT Career in Gear!*

McGraw-Hill Professional
2 Penn Plaza
New York, NY 10121
Ph: (212)904-2000

Leslie Goff. 2001. $24.99 (paper).

★10837★ *Great Jobs for Computer Science Majors*

McGraw-Hill Companies
1221 Avenue of the Americas
New York, NY 10020
Ph: (212)904-2000   Fr: 800-323-4900
E-mail: ntcpub@tribune.com

Jan Goldberg, Stephen Lambert, Julie De-Galan. 1997. $11.95 (paper). 365 pages.

★10838★ *Hidden Job Market*

Thomson Peterson's
PO Box 67005
Lawrenceville, NJ 08648-6105
Fr: 800-338-3282

Ninth edition, 1999. $18.95 (paper). 319 pages. Guide to 2,000 fast-growing companies that are hiring now. Focuses on high technology companies in such fields as environmental consulting, genetic engineering, home health care, telecommunications, alternative energy systems, and others. Part of Peterson's Hidden Job Market series.

★10839★ **Job Seekers Guide to Silicon Valley Recruiters**
John Wily and Sons, Inc.
605 Third Ave., 4th Fl.
New York, NY 10158-0012
Ph: (212)850-6276   Fax: (212)850-8641
Christopher W. Hunt, Scott A. Scanlon. First edition, 1998. $19.95 (paper). 371 pages. Includes a list of 2,400 recruiters specializing in high technology positions and explains how to work with them.

★10840★ **The JobBank Guide to Computer and High-Tech Companies**
Adams Media Corp.
57 Littlefield St.
Avon, MA 02322
Ph: (508)427-7100   Fax: (508)427-6790
Fr: 800-872-5627
URL: http://www.adamsmedia.com
Second edition, 1999. $17.95 (paper). 704 pages. Contains profiles of more than 4,500 high-tech employers.

★10841★ **Majoring in Engineering: How to Get from Your Freshman Year to Your First Job**
Farrar, Straus & Giroux, Inc.
19 Union Sq., W
New York, NY 10003
Ph: (212)741-6900   Fax: (212)633-9385
Fr: 888-330-8477
John Garcia and Carol Carter, editors. 2000. $20.00; $10.00 (paper). 134 pages.

★10842★ **The National Business Employment Weekly Jobs Rated Almanac**
John Wiley & Sons Inc.
1 Wiley Dr.
Somerset, NJ 08873
Ph: (732)469-4400   Fr: 800-225-5945
Les Krantz. First edition, 1995. $16.95. 340 pages. Ranks 250 jobs by environment, salary, outlook, physical demands, stress, security, travel opportunities, and geographic location.

★10843★ **Opportunities in Engineering Careers**
McGraw-Hill Contemporary Books
1221 Avenue of the Americas
New York, NY 10020
Ph: (212)904-2000   Fr: 800-323-4900
E-mail: ntcpub@tribune.com
Nicholas Basta. Revised, 1995. $14.95; $11.95 (paper). 200 pages. Outlines typical job titles, salaries, career paths, and employment prospects.

★10844★ **Opportunities in High Tech Careers**
McGraw-Hill Trade
2 Penn Plaza
New York, NY 10121
Ph: (212)904-2000   Fr: 800-722-4726
Gary Colter and Deborah Yanuck. 1995. $14.95; $11.95 (paper). 160 pages. Explores high technology careers. Describes job opportunities, how to make a career decision, how to prepare for high technology jobs, job hunting techniques, and future trends.

★10845★ **Peterson's Job Opportunities in Engineering and Technology**
Thomson Peterson's
PO Box 67005
Lawrenceville, NJ 08648-6105
Fr: 800-338-3282
Compiled by the Peterson's staff. Fourth edition, 1996. $21.95 (paper). 384 pages. Profiles 2,000 high-tech companies looking primarily for technical personnel in such fields as biotechnology, telecommunications, software, computers and peripherals, defense, and aerospace. Contains job-search strategies and career options to help match education and expertise to the job market. Indexed geographically, by industry, and by hiring needs.

★10846★ **Preparing for an Outstanding Career in Computers: Questions and Answers for Professionals and Students**
Rafi Systems, Incorporated
750 N. Diamond Bar Blvd., Suite 224
Diamond Bar, CA 91765
Ph: (909)593-8124   Fax: (909)629-1034
Fr: 800-584-6706
Mohamed Rafiquzzaman. 2001. $19.95.

★10847★ **Professional Awareness in Software Engineering: Or Should a Software Engineer Wear a Suit?**
The McGraw-Hill Companies
2 Penn Plaza, 20th Fl.
New York, NY 10121-2298
Fr: 800-338-3987
Colin Myers, editor. 1995.

★10848★ **Resumes for Scientific and Technical Careers**
McGraw-Hill Contemporary Books
1221 Avenue of the Americas
New York, NY 10020
Ph: (212)904-2000   Fr: 800-323-4900
E-mail: ntcpub@tribune.com
1999. $9.95 (paper). 450 pages. Provides resume advice for individuals interested in working in scientific and technical careers. Includes sample resumes and cover letters.

★10849★ **Software Developer's Marketplace**
Coriolis Group LLC
14455 N. Hayden Rd., Ste. 220
Scottsdale, AZ 85260-6949
Ph: (480)483-0192   Fax: (480)483-0193
Fr: 800-410-0192
Ben Sawyer. First edition, 1998. $49.99 (paper). 700 pages. Out of print.

★10850★ **Software Engineer's Reference Book**
CRC Press LLC
2000 NW Corporate Blvd.
Boca Raton, FL 33431
Ph: (561)994-0555   Fax: (561)989-8732
Fr: 800-272-7737
John A. McDermid, editor. 1993. $89.95.

★10851★ **Ultimate Web Developers Sourcebook**
Coriolis Group LLC
14455 N. Hayden Rd., Ste. 220
Scottsdale, AZ 85260-6949
Ph: (480)483-0192   Fax: (480)483-0193
Fr: 800-410-0192
Ben Sawyer. 1996. $49.99 (paper). 600 pages. Out of print.

★10852★ **Unlocking the Clubhouse: Women in Computing**
MIT Press
5 Cambridge Ctr., Suite 4
Cambridge, MA 02142-1493
Ph: (617)253-5646   Fax: (617)253-6779
Fr: 800-356-0343
Jane Margolis and Allan Fisher. 2001. $24.95.

★10853★ **The Unofficial Guide to Getting a Job at Microsoft**
McGraw-Hill Education Group
800 Taylor Staion Rd.
Blacklick, OH 43004-0545
Fax: (614)755-5645   Fr: 800-722-4726
Rebecca Smith. 2000. $16.95 (paper).

★10854★ **Where the Jobs Are: The Hottest Careers for the 90s**
The Career Press, Inc.
3 Tice Rd.
PO Box 687
Franklin Lakes, NJ 07417-1322
Ph: (201)848-0310   Fax: (201)848-1727
Fr: 800-227-3371
Joyce Hadley. Third edition, 2000. $13.99 (paper). 400 pages. Out of print. Describes careers in fifteen general fields, from accounting to travel and hospitality.

★10855★ **Winning Resumes for Computer Personnel**

Barron's Educational Series, Inc.
250 Wireless Blvd.
Hauppauge, NY 11788-3917
Ph: (631)434-3311   Fax: (631)434-3723
Fr: 800-645-3476

Anne Hart. Second edition, 1998. $12.95 (paper). 320 pages.

★10856★ **Your Opportunities in Computers**

Energeia Publishing, Inc.
1307 Fairmount Ave., S
Salem, OR 97302-4313
Ph: (503)362-1480   Fax: (503)362-2123
Fr: 800-639-6048

John Tribbett. 1994. $2.50 (paper). 8 pages.

EMPLOYMENT AGENCIES AND SEARCH FIRMS

★10857★ **Amtec Engineering Corp.**

2749 Saturn St.
Brea, CA 92821
Ph: (714)993-1900   Fax: (714)993-2419
E-mail: staffing@amtec-eng.com
URL: http://www.amtec-eng.com

Employment agency.

★10858★ **The Arcus Group Inc.**

325 N. Saint Paul, Ste. 1340
Dallas, TX 75201
Ph: (214)871-3332   Fax: (214)871-1338

Executive search firm. Branch in Chicago.

★10859★ **Career Development Services**

706 East Ave.
Rochester, NY 14607-2105
Ph: (585)244-0750   Fax: (585)244-7115
Fr: 800-736-6710
E-mail: info@careerdev.org
URL: http://www.careerdev.org

Employment agency.

★10860★ **The Datafinders Group, Inc.**

25 E Spring Valley Ave.,Fl.3
Maywood, NJ 07607
Ph: (201)845-7700   Fax: (201)845-7365
E-mail: info@datafinders.net
URL: http://www.datafinders.net

Executive search firm.

★10861★ **Doleman Enterprises Ln.**

1151 Water Pointe
Reston, VA 20194-1035
Ph: (703)742-5454   Fax: (703)708-6992

Human resources firm specializes in recruiting for the high-tech, data and computer engineering, and pharmaceutical industries.

★10862★ **Erspamer Associates**

4010 W. 65th St., Ste. 100
Edina, MN 55435
Ph: (952)925-3747   Fax: (952)925-4022
E-mail: hdhuntrel@aol.com

Executive search firm specializing in technical management.

★10863★ **Huntington Personnel Consultants, Inc.**

PO Box 1077
Huntington, NY 11743-0640
Ph: (516)549-8888

Executive search firm and employment agency.

★10864★ **JES Search Firm Inc.**

950 E Paces Ferry Rd., Ste. 2245
Atlanta, GA 30326
Ph: (404)262-7222   Fax: (404)266-3533

Contract and permanent information technology search firm specializing in placing software developers as well as other information systems professionals.

★10865★ **JPM International**

26060 Acero
Mission Viejo, CA 92691
Ph: (949)699-4300   Fax: (949)699-4333
Fr: 800-685-7856
E-mail: leslieo@jpmintl.com
URL: http://www.jpmintl.com

Executive search firm and employment agency.

★10866★ **Main Line Personnel Service, Inc.**

Pagoda Blding.
100 Presidential Blvd. Ste. 200
Bala Cynwyd, PA 19004-0448
Ph: (610)667-1820   Fax: (610)668-5000
URL: http://www.mlpers.com

Employment agency.

★10867★ **Technical Talent Locators Ltd.**

5570 Sterrett Place, Ste.208
Columbia, MD 21044
Ph: (410)740-0091
URL: http://www.ttlgroup.com

Permanent employment agency working within the following fields: software and database engineering; computer, communication, and telecommunication system engineering; and other computer-related disciplines.

★10868★ **Techtronix Technical Search**

PO Box 17713
Milwaukee, WI 53217-0173
Ph: (414)466-3100   Fax: (414)466-3598

Firm specializes in recruiting executives for the engineering, information systems, manufacturing, marketing, finance, and human resources industries.

ONLINE JOB SOURCES AND SERVICES

★10869★ **Computerwork.com**
E-mail: candidate_support@computerwork.com
URL: http://computerwork.com/

Description: Job search and resume submission service for professionals in information technology.

★10870★ **Computerworld Careers**
URL: http://www.computerworld.com/cwi/careers/

Description: Offers career opportunities for IT (information technology) professionals. Job seekers may search the jobs database, register at the site, and read about job surveys and employment trends. Employers may post jobs.

★10871★ **Computing Research Association Job Announcements**
URL: http://www.cra.org/main/cra.jobs.html

Description: Contains dated links to national college and university computer technology positions.

★10872★ **Dice.com**
URL: http://www.dice.com

Description: Job search database for computer consultants and high-tech professionals, listing thousands of high tech permanent contract and consulting jobs for programmers, software engineers, systems administrators, web developers, and hardware engineers. Also free career advice e-mail newsletter and job posting e-alerts.

★10873★ **Guru**
URL: http://www.guru.com

Description: Job board specializing in contract jobs for creative and information technology professionals. Also provides online incorporation and educational opportunities for independent contractors along with articles and advice.

★10874★ **Ittalent.com**
E-mail: ewsmith@ITtalent.com
URL: http://www.ittalent.com

Description: Job search and resume submission service for professionals in information technology.

★10875★ **Jobs for Programmers**
E-mail: prgjobs@jfpresources.com
URL: http://www.prgjobs.com

Description: Job board site for computer programmers that allows them to browse through thousands of programming jobs, even search for special jobs with sign-on bonuses, relocation funding, and 4-day work weeks. Resume posting is free.

★10876★ **Softwarejobs.com**
E-mail: info@softwarejobs.com
URL: http://softwarejobs.techengine.com
Description: Job search website for software programmers. Registrants can post their resume and search available positions, review career resources, and activate e-mail job alerts. Registration is free.

★10877★ **ZDNet Tech Jobs**
URL: http://www.zdnet.com/special/filters/techjobs/
Description: Site houses a listing of national employment opportunities for professionals in high tech fields. Also contains resume building tips and relocation resources. Powered by Dice.com

OTHER SOURCES

★10878★ **American Association of Engineering Societies (AAES)**
1828 L St. NW, No. 906
Washington, DC 20036
Ph: (202)296-2237   Fax: (202)296-1151
Fr: 888-400-2237
E-mail: tprice@aaes.org
URL: http://www.aaes.org
Description: Coordinates the efforts of the member societies in the provision of reliable and objective information to the general public concerning issues which affect the engineering profession and the field of engineering as a whole; to collect, analyze, document, and disseminate data which will inform the general public of the relationship between engineering and the national welfare; to provide a forum for the engineering societies to exchange and discuss their views on matters of common interest; and to represent the U.S. engineering community aborad through representation in WFEO and UPADI.

★10879★ **Association of Computer Professionals (ACP)**
9 Forest Dr.
Plainview, NY 11803
Ph: (516)938-8223   Fax: (516)938-3073
E-mail: sybosworth@aol.com
Members: Authors, consultants, programmers, publishers, and teachers in the computer field who provide products or services to users or to other professionals. **Purpose:** Works to advance the art and science of computer professionals through educational means. Encourages education and instruction of the public regarding what the association views as the beneficial use of computers

and computer technology. **Activities:** Provides members with information on accounting, business management, creative marketing techniques, law, microcomputer advances, tax matters, technical developments, and special earning opportunities. Addresses issues of software protection, contract law, tax benefits, potential tax problems, and financial subjects such as sources of capital for new ventures and expanding businesses.

★10880★ **Association for Women in Computing (AWC)**
41 Sutter St., Ste. 1006
San Francisco, CA 94104
Ph: (415)905-4663
E-mail: info@awc-hq.org
URL: http://www.awc-hq.org
Members: Individuals interested in promoting the education, professional development, and advancement of women in computing.

★10881★ *Computer Occupations*
Delphi Productions
3160 4th St.
Boulder, CO 80304
Fax: (303)443-4022   Fr: 888-443-2400
URL: http://www.delphivideo.com
$95.00. 50 minutes. Part of the Careers for the 21st Century Video Library.

★10882★ *Information Technology Occupations*
Delphi Productions
3160 4th St.
Boulder, CO 80304
Fax: (303)443-4022   Fr: 888-443-2400
URL: http://www.delphivideo.com
$95.00. 52 minutes. Part of the Emerging Careers Video Library.

★10883★ *Information Technology Services*
Cambridge Educational
2572 Brunswick Ave.
Lawrenceville, NJ 08648-4128
Fax: 800-FAX-ON-US   Fr: 800-468-4227
URL: http://www.cambridgeeducational.com
$89.95. 2002. 18 minutes. Part of the Career Cluster Series.

★10884★ *Internet-Related Occupations*
Delphi Productions
3160 4th St.
Boulder, CO 80304
Fax: (303)443-4022   Fr: 888-443-2400
URL: http://www.delphi.video.com
$95.00. 47 minutes. Part of the Emerging Careers Video Library.

★10885★ **National Action Council for Minorities in Engineering (NACME)**
Empire State Bldg., Ste. 2212
350 Fifth Ave.
New York, NY 10118-2299
Ph: (212)279-2626   Fax: (212)629-5178
E-mail: webmaster@nacme.org
URL: http://www.nacme.org/
Description: Leads the national effort to increase access to careers in engineering and other science-based disciplines. Supported by the nation's leading technology-intensive companies, NACME conducts research and public policy analysis, develops and operates national demonstration programs at precollege and university levels, and disseminates information through publications, conferences, and electronic media. NACME is also the nation's largest privately funded source of scholarships for minority students in engineering.

★10886★ **National Society of Professional Engineers (NSPE)**
1420 King St.
Alexandria, VA 22314
Ph: (703)684-2800   Fax: (703)836-4875
Fr: 888-285-6773
E-mail: custserv@nspe.org
URL: http://www.nspe.org
Description: Professional engineers and engineers-in-training in all fields registered in accordance with the laws of states or territories of the U.S. or provinces of Canada; qualified graduate engineers, student members, and registered land surveyors. Is concerned with social, professional, ethical, and economic considerations of engineering as a profession; encompasses programs in public relations, employment practices, ethical considerations, education, and career guidance. Monitors legislative and regulatory actions of interest to the engineering profession.

★10887★ *Resumes for High Tech Careers*
Vgm Career Horizons
1221 Avenue of the Americas
New York, NY 10020
Ph: (212)904-2000   Fr: 800-323-4900
E-mail: ntcpub@tribune.com
Second edition, 1997. $9.95 (paper). 462 pages. Demonstrates how to tailor a resume that catches a high tech employer's attention. Part of Resumes for... series.

★10888★ **Society of Women Engineers (SWE)**
230 E Ohio St., No. 400
Chicago, IL 60611-3265
Ph: (312)596-5223   Fax: (312)596-5252
E-mail: hq@swe.org
URL: http://www.swe.org
Description: Educational and service organization representing both students and professional women in engineering and technical fields.

★10889★ **Special Interest Group for Computers and the Physically Handicapped (SIGCAPH)**
Church St. Sta.
PO Box 12115
New York, NY 10249
Ph: (212)626-0500   Fax: (212)944-1318
E-mail: chair_sigcaph@acm.org
URL: http://www.acm.org/sigcaph

Description: Promotes the professional interests of computing personnel with physical disabilities and the application of computing & information technology in solving relevant disability problems. Studies to educate the public to support careers for the disabled.

★10890★ *Women in Engineering*
Her Own Words
PO Box 5264
Madison, WI 53705-0264
Ph: (608)271-7083   Fax: (608)271-0209
URL: http://www.herownwords.com/

Video. Jocelyn Riley. $95.00. 15 minutes. Resource guide also available for $45.00.

Special Education Teachers

SOURCES OF HELP-WANTED ADS

★10891★ **Academic Exchange Quarterly**

Rapid Intellect Group Inc.
PO Box 131
Stuyvesant Falls, NY 12174
Ph: (518)372-1347
E-mail: AEQ@rapidintellect.com
URL: http://rapidintellect.com/AEQweb/

Quarterly. $156.00/year for individuals; $116.00/year, professional rate; $39.00 for single issue. Periodical covering issues in education.

★10892★ **Education and Training in Developmental Disabilities**

Council for Exceptional Children
1110 N Glebe Rd.
Arlington, VA 22201-5704
Ph: (703)620-3660   Fax: (703)264-9494
Fr: 888-232-7733
E-mail: etdd@asu.edu

Quarterly. $30.00/year for individuals; $34.00/year for other countries; $75.00/year for institutions; $79.50/year for institutions, other countries. Journal covering theory and research in eductation of individuals with mental retardation and/or developmental disabilities

★10893★ **Journal of Language, Identity, and Education**

Lawrence Erlbaum Associates Inc.
10 Industrial Ave.
Mahwah, NJ 07430-2262
Ph: (201)236-9500   Fax: (201)236-0072
Fr: 800-9-BOOKS-9
E-mail: journals@erlbaum.com
URL: http://www.erlbaum.com/shop/tek9.asp?pg=products&specific=1

Quarterly. $40.00/year for individuals; $70.00/year for out of country; $225.00/year for institutions; $255.00/year for institutions, other countries. Scholarly, interdisciplinary journal covering issues in language, identity and education worldwide for academics, educators and policy specialists in a variety of disciplines, and others.

★10894★ **Journal of Latinos and Education**

Lawrence Erlbaum Associates Inc.
10 Industrial Ave.
Mahwah, NJ 07430-2262
Ph: (201)236-9500   Fax: (201)236-0072
Fr: 800-9-BOOKS-9
E-mail: journals@erlbaum.com
URL: http://www.erlbaum.com/shop/tek9.asp?pg=products&specific=1

Quarterly. $40.00/year for individuals; $70.00/year for out of country; $195.00/year for institutions; $225.00/year for institutions, other countries. Scholarly, multidisciplinary journal covering educational issues that impact Latinos for researchers, teaching professionals, academics, scholars, institutions, and others.

★10895★ **The Journal of Special Education**

PRO-ED Inc.
8700 Shoal Creek Blvd.
Austin, TX 78757-6897
Ph: (512)451-3246   Fax: (512)451-8542
Fr: 800-897-3202

Quarterly. $39.00/year for individuals; $10.00 for single issue; $85.00/year for institutions; $95.00/year for other countries. Journal presents research findings in the field of special education.

★10896★ **Matrix: The Magazine for Leaders in Higher Education**

Professional Media Group L.L.C.
36 Clipper Ct., Ste. B
Mystic, CT 06355-2138

Bimonthly. Trade publication covering issues for higher education professionals.

★10897★ **Remedial and Special Education (RASE)**

PRO-ED Inc.
8700 Shoal Creek Blvd.
Austin, TX 78757-6897
Ph: (512)451-3246   Fax: (512)451-854?
Fr: 800-897-3202
E-mail: polloway@lynchburg.edu

Bimonthly. $39.00/year; $95.00/year for other countries; $10.00 for single issue. Journal interprets research and makes recommendations for practice in the fields of remedial and special education.

★10898★ **Rural Special Education Quarterly**

American Council on Rural Special Education
Bluemont Hall, No. 306
Kansas State University
Manhattan, KS 66506
Ph: (785)532-5717   Fax: (785)532-7732
E-mail: rseq@wvu.edu

Quarterly. $50.00/year for nonmembers; $75.00/year for libraries. Scholarly journal on rural special education.

★10899★ **Teacher Education and Special Education**

Boyd Printing Co.
49 Sheridan Ave.
Albany, NY 12210
Ph: (518)436-9686   Fax: (518)436-7433
Fr: 800-877-2693
E-mail: tese@uc.edu

Quarterly. $50.00/year for individuals; $55.00/year for individuals, other countries; $62.00/year, institutions; $67.00/year for institutions, other countries. Journal covering personnel preparation in special education.

★10900★ **Today's OEA**

Oregon Education Association
6900 SW Atlanta St.
Portland, OR 97223-2513
Ph: (503)684-3300   Fax: (503)684-8063

Bimonthly. Free to qualified subscribers; $10.00/year for nonmembers. Membership magazine covering educational issues state-wide and nationally.

EMPLOYER DIRECTORIES AND NETWORKING LISTS

★10901★ *Directory of Programs for Preparing Individuals for Careers in Special Education*

National Clearinghouse for Professions in Special Education
1110 N Glebe Rd., Ste. 300
Arlington, VA 22201-4795
Ph: (703)264-9476   Fax: (703)264-1637
Fr: 800-641-7824
URL: http://www.special-ed-careers.org

Irregular, previous edition 1991; latest edition 1999. $75.00. Covers approximately 850 institutions with programs in teacher preparation and administration in special education. Entries include: Institution name, program, contact name, address, coded description of program. Arrangement: Geographical.

★10902★ *Innovation & Development in Special Education Directory of Current Projects*

ERIC/OSEP Special Project
Council for Exceptional Children
110 N Glebe Rd.
Arlington, VA 22201-5704
Ph: (703)264-9495   Fax: (703)620-2521
URL: http://ericec.org

Annual, October. $9.00. Covers approximately 200 research projects funded by the Division of Innovation and Development, Office of Special Education Programs, U.S. Department of Education. Entries include: Project name, address, phone, description. Arrangement: Classified by primary focus of study. Indexes: Project name, subject, organization.

HANDBOOKS AND MANUALS

★10903★ *Becoming a Teacher*

Pearson Allyn & Bacon
1230 Ave. of the Americas
New York, NY 10020
Ph: (212)782-3300   Fr: 800-634-7064
Gary Borich. 1995. $24.95 (paper). 140 pages. Part of The Falmer Press Teachers' Library Series No. 7.

★10904★ *Building Blocks for Working with Exceptional Children & Youth: A Primer*

Houghton Mifflin Company
215 Park Ave., S.
New York, NY 10003
Ph: (212)420-5800   Fax: (212)420-5855
Nancy Hunt and Kathleen Marshall. 1999.

★10905★ *Educator's Job Search: The Ultimate Guide to Finding Positions in Education*

National Education Association
PO Box 2035
Annapolis Junction, MD 20701
Fr: 800-229-4200
Martin Kimeldorf. 1993. $15.95 (paper). 88 pages.

★10906★ *The Exceptional Teacher's Handbook: The First-Year Special Education Teacher's Guide for Success*

Corwin Press, Incorporated
2455 Teller Rd.
Thousand Oaks, CA 91320-2218
Ph: (805)499-9734   Fax: (805)499-0871
Carla F. Shelton and Alice B. Pollingue. 2000. $32.95 (paper).

★10907★ *Great Jobs for Liberal Arts Majors*

McGraw-Hill Professional
2 Penn Plaza
New York, NY 10121
Ph: (212)904-2000   Fr: 800-722-4726
E-mail: ntcpub@tribune.com
Blythe Camenson. Second edition, 2001. $14.95 (paper). 256 pages.

★10908★ *How to Get a Job in Education*

Adams Media Corp.
57 Littlefield St.
Avon, MA 02322
Ph: (508)427-7100   Fax: (508)427-6790
Fr: 800-872-5627
URL: http://www.adamsmedia.com
Joel Levin. Second edition, 1995. $15.95. 320 pages. Out of print. Prepared for recent college graduates, seasoned educators, and career-changing professionals, this publication guides the job-seeker through the necessary steps to obtaining a job in education at the elementary, secondary, and university levels. Offers advice on how to prepare for state and local examinations, how to locate teaching opportunities nationwide, and how to obtain certification. Includes a nationwide salary survey. Covers public, private, summer, and overseas opportunities.

★10909★ *How to Get the Teaching Position You Want: Teacher Candidate Guide*

Educational Enterprises
PO Box 1836
Spring Valley, CA 91979
Ph: (619)660-7720
Phyllis Murton. Second edition, revised, 1996. $9.95 (paper). 110 pages. This book provides a comprehensive guide for the teacher candidate's job search, as the format offers information that includes: interview questions most often asked in the teaching interview (grade-level & subject-matter specific); sample forms for applications, cover letters, & resumes that will impact principals & district personnel; strategies on preparing for the teaching interview; interview follow-up techniques; inside tips from a superintendent, a principal & a counselor.

★10910★ *The Inside Secrets of Finding a Teaching Job*

JIST Publishing
8902 Otis Ave.
Indianapolis, IN 46216
Ph: (317)613-4200   Fax: (317)613-4307
Fr: 800-648-5478
E-mail: jistworks@aol.com
URL: http://www.jist.com
Burt Beers, Jack Warner, Clyde Bryan and Diane Warner. 1997. $14.95. 186 pages. Tips from educators on finding an entry-level teaching position.

★10911★ *Opportunities in Special Education Careers*

McGraw-Hill Trade
2 Penn Plaza
New York, NY 10121
Ph: (212)904-2000   Fr: 800-722-4726
E-mail: ntcpub@tribune.com
Robert Connelly. 1995. 160 pages. $14.95; $11.95 (paper).

★10912★ *Opportunities in Teaching Careers*

McGraw-Hill/Contemporary Books
1221 Avenue of the Americas
New York, NY 10020
Ph: (212)904-2000   Fr: 800-323-4900
E-mail: ntcpub@tribune.com
Janet Fine. 2000. $14.95; $11.95 (paper). 200 pages. Discusses licensing and accreditation programs, sources of placement information, job-seeking correspondence, selection procedures, and paths to advancement. Also covers professional associations, non-traditional teaching opportunities, and jobs abroad.

★10913★ *Real People Working in Education*

McGraw-Hill Contemporary Books
1221 Avenue of the Americas
New York, NY 10020
Ph: (212)904-2000   Fr: 800-323-4900

E-mail: ntcpub@tribune.com

Blythe Camenson, Jan Goldberg. 1997. $17.95; $12.95 (paper). Interviews and profiles of working professionals capture a range of opportunities in this field.

★10914★ Special Education for All Teachers

McGraw-Hill Companies
Two Penn Plaza
New York, NY 10121-2298
Fr: 800-338-3987

Madava, Miller, and Osborne. 2001. $46.50.

★10915★ Survival Guide for the First-Year Special Education Teacher

Council for Exceptional Children
1920 Association Dr.
Reston, VA 20191-1589
Ph: (703)264-9455   Fax: (703)620-2521
Fr: 888-232-7733

Mary Kemper Cohen, Maureen Gale and Joyce M. Meyer. 1994. $13.20 (paper). 47 pages.

★10916★ Teaching Persons with Severe Disabilities

Prentice Hall PTR
200 Old Tappan Rd.
Old Tappan, NJ 07675
Ph: (201)236-7000   Fr: 800-223-1360

1999. $33.75. 688 pages.

EMPLOYMENT AGENCIES AND SEARCH FIRMS

★10917★ Educational Placement Service

1001 Craig Rd., Ste. 170
St. Louis, MO 63146
Ph: (314)991-5855   Fax: (314)991-5295
URL: http://www.educatorjobs.com

Employment agency. Focuses on teaching, administrative, and education-related openings.

TRADESHOWS

★10918★ Lifelong Learning for Adults with Special Learning Needs

National Association for Adults with Special Learning Needs
P.O. Box 716
Bryn Mawr, PA 19010
Ph: (610)446-6126   Fax: (610)466-6129

Annual. **Primary Exhibits:** Equipment, supplies, and services for educating adults with special learning needs.

OTHER SOURCES

★10919★ American Federation of Teachers (AFT)

555 New Jersey Ave. NW
Washington, DC 20001
Ph: (202)879-4400   Fax: (202)879-4545
Fr: 800-238-1133
E-mail: online@aft.org
URL: http://www.aft.org

Description: Affiliated with the AFL-CIO. Works with teachers and other educational employees at the state and local level in organizing, collective bargaining, research, educational issues, and public relations. Conducts research in areas such as educational reform, teacher certification, and national assessments and standards. Represents members' concerns through legislative action; offers technical assistance. Also serves professionals with concerns similar to those of teachers, including state employees, healthcare workers, and paraprofessionals.

★10920★ AVKO Dyslexia Research Foundation (AVKOEFR)

3084 W Willard Rd., Ste. W
Clio, MI 48420-7801
Ph: (810)686-9283   Fax: (810)686-1101
Fr: (866)AVKO-612
E-mail: donmccabe@aol.com
URL: http://www.spelling.org

Description: Teachers and individuals interested in helping others learn to read and spell and in developing reading training materials for individuals with dyslexia or other learning disabilities using a method involving audio, visual, kinesthetic, and oral (AVKO) techniques. Offers advice on the techniques of tutoring, classroom teaching, diagnosis, and remediation. Conducts research into the causes of reading, spelling, and writing disabilities. Publishes and disseminates information on research. Provides a reading and spelling center where children and adults with educational deficiencies can receive diagnostic attention and remediation. Sponsors adult community education courses to train adults in tutoring their spouses or children in reading and spelling skills. Maintains speakers' bureau; compiles statistics.

★10921★ Convention of American Instructors of the Deaf (CAID)

PO Box 377
Bedford, TX 76095-0377
Ph: (817)354-8414
E-mail: caid@swbell.net
URL: http://www.caid.org/

Members: Professional organization of teachers, administrators, and professionals in allied fields related to education of the deaf and hard-of-hearing. **Purpose:** Works to provide opportunities for a free interchange of views concerning methods and means of educating the deaf and hard-of-hearing; to promote such education by the publication of reports, essays, and other information; to develop more effective methods of teaching deaf and hard-of-hearing children.

★10922★ Council for Exceptional Children (CEC)

1110 N. Glebe Rd. Ste. 300
Arlington, VA 22201-4795
Ph: (703)620-3660   Fax: (703)264-949
Fr: 888-232-7733
E-mail: service@cec.sped.org
URL: http://www.cec.sped.org

Members: Administrators, teachers, parents, and others who work with and on behalf of children with disabilities and/or gifts. **Purpose:** Seeks to improve the educational success for individuals with exceptionalities - children, youth, and young adults with disabilities and/or gifts. **Activities:** Advocates for appropriate government policies provides information to the media. Operates the ERIC Clearinghouse on Disabilities and Gifted Education, and the National Clearinghouse for Professions in Special Education. Develops programs to help teachers, administrators, and related services professionals improve their practice.

★10923★ Council for Learning Disabilities (CLD)

PO Box 4014
Leesburg, VA 20177-8187
Ph: (571)258-1010   Fax: (571)258-101
E-mail: afalzarano@mcs-amc.com
URL: http://www.cldinternational.org

Description: Professionals interested in the study of learning disabilities. Works to promote the education and general welfare of individuals having specific learning disabilities by: improving teacher preparation programs and local special education programs; and resolving important research issues. Sponsors educational sessions.

★10924★ Education and Training

Cambridge Educational
2572 Brunswick Ave.
Lawrenceville, NJ 08648-4128
Fax: 800-FAX-ON-US   Fr: 800-468-4227
URL: http://www.cambridgeeducational.com

$89.95. 2002. 18 minutes.

★10925★ National Association of State Directors of Special Education (NASDSE)

1800 Diagonal Rd., Ste. 320
Alexandria, VA 22314
Ph: (703)519-3800   Fax: (703)519-3808
E-mail: nasdse@nasdse.org
URL: http://www.nasdse.org

Members: Professional society of state directors; consultants, supervisors, and administrators who have statewide responsibilities for administering special education programs. **Purpose:** Provides services to state agencies to facilitate their efforts to maximize educational outcomes for individuals with disabilities.

★10926★ **National Association of Vocational Education Special Needs Personnel (NAVESNP)**
3145 Longridge Way
Grove City, OH 43123-9506
Ph: (412)675-9065   Fax: (412)675-9067
E-mail: lvb6@psu.edu
Description: Employees in programs or services related to vocational special needs

education; interested individuals. To serve as a unifying association for development and operation of programs for special vocational education; to promote and maintain active leadership in vocational, career, and occupational education. Monitors submits committee reports.

★10927★ *Teaching & Related Occupations*
Delphi Productions
3160 4th St.
Boulder, CO 80304
Fax: (303)443-4022   Fr: 888-443-2400
URL: http://www.delphivideo.com
$95.00. 50 minutes. Part of the Careers for the 21st Century Video Library.

Speech-Language Pathologists and Audiologists

SOURCES OF HELP-WANTED ADS

★10928★ ADVANCE for Speech-Language Pathologists & Audiologists
Merion Publications Inc.
2900 Horizon Dr.
PO Box 61556
King of Prussia, PA 19406-0956
Ph: (610)278-1400
URL: http://www.advanceforspanda.com

Weekly. Free to qualified subscribers. Professional medical magazine for qualified speech-language pathologist and audiologists.

★10929★ American Annals of the Deaf
Conference of Educational Administrators
  Serving the Deaf
800 Florida Ave. NE
Washington, DC 20002
Ph: (202)651-5488   Fax: (202)651-5489
URL: http://sehs.gallaudet.edu/annals

$60.00/year for individuals; $66.00/year for Canada; $80.00/year for other countries. Journal focusing on education of the deaf.

★10930★ American Journal of Speech Language Pathology
American Speech-Language-Hearing
  Association
10801 Rockville Pke.
Rockville, MD 20852
Ph: (301)897-5700   Fax: (301)897-7358
Fr: 888-498-6699

Quarterly. $15.00/year for members; $25.00/year for nonmembers. Professional journal covering issues in speech, language, and hearing.

★10931★ Audiology Today
American Academy of Audiology
11730 Plaza America Dr., Ste. 300
Reston, VA 20190
Ph: (703)790-8466   Fax: (703)790-8631
Fr: 800-AAA-2336

Bimonthly. Professional magazine covering audiology.

★10932★ Topics in Language Disorders
Aspen Publishers Inc.
1185 Avenue of the Americas
New York, NY 10036
Ph: (212)597-0200   Fax: (212)597-0338
Fr: 800-234-1660
URL: http://www.lww.com

Quarterly. $81.95/year for individuals; $111.95/year for other countries; $201.95/year for institutions; $251.95/year for institutions, other countries. Journal intending to clarify the application of theory to practice in the treatment, rehabilitation, and education of individuals with language disorders.

★10933★ The Volta Review
Alexander Graham Bell Association for
  the Deaf
3417 Volta Pl. NW
Washington, DC 20007-2778
Ph: (202)337-5220   Fax: (202)337-8314

$62.00/year for institutions; $50.00/year for members; $30.00/year for students. Scholarly journal relating to the field of deafness.

PLACEMENT AND JOB REFERRAL SERVICES

★10934★ National Communication Association (NCA)
1765 N St. NW
Washington, DC 20036
Ph: (202)464-4622   Fax: (202)464-4600
E-mail: smorreale@natcom.org
URL: http://www.natcom.org

Members: Elementary, secondary, college, and university teachers, speech clinicians, media specialists, communication consultants, students, theater directors, and other interested persons; libraries and other institutions. **Purpose:** To promote study, criticism, research, teaching, and application of the artistic, humanistic, and scientific principles of communication, particularly speech communication. Sponsors the publication of scholarly volumes in speech. **Activities:** Conducts international debate tours in the U.S. and abroad. Maintains placement service.

EMPLOYER DIRECTORIES AND NETWORKING LISTS

★10935★ AHA Guide to the Health Care Field
American Hospital Association (AHA)
1 N. Franklin St., 27th Fl.
Chicago, IL 60606
Ph: (312)422-2050   Fax: (312)422-4700
Fr: 800-424-4301

Annual, August. $295.00. Covers hospitals, networks, multi-health care systems, freestanding ambulatory surgery centers, psychiatric facilities, long-term care facilities, substance abuse programs, and other health-related organizations. Entries include: For hospitals-Facility name, address, phone, administrator's name, number of beds, facilities and services, number of employees, expenses, other statistics. For other organizations-Name, address, phone, fax, name and title of contact. Arrangement: Geographical. Indexes: Hospital name.

★10936★ Directory of Hospital Personnel
Thomson Medical Economics
5 Paragon Dr.
Montvale, NJ 07645-1742
Ph: (201)358-7200   Fax: (201)722-2680

Annual, November. $325.00. Covers 200,000 executives at 7,000 U.S. hospitals.

ntries include: Name of hospital, address, hone, number of beds, type and JCAHO tatus of hospital, names and titles of key epartment heads and staff, medical and ursing school affiliations; number of resients, interns, and nursing students. Arangement: Geographical. Indexes: Hospital ame, personnel, hospital size.

10937★ Home Health Service Directory

foUSA Inc.
711 S 86th Cir.
maha, NE 68127-0347
h: (402)930-3500   Fax: (402)331-0176
r: 800-555-6124
RL: http://www.abii.com

nnual. Number of listings: 21,158. Entries clude: Name, address, phone (including rea code), size of advertisement, year first "Yellow Pages," name of owl her or anager, number of employees. Compiled om telephone company "Yellow Pages," ationwide. Arrangement: Geographical.

10938★ Hospital Blue Book

illian/Transworld Publishing Inc.
100 Powers Ferry Rd.
te. 300
tlanta, GA 30339
h: (770)955-8484   Fax: (770)955-8485
r: 800-533-8484
-mail: blu-book@billian.com

nnual, January. $285.00 for national edion; $160.00 for southern edition. Covers ore than 6,687 hospitals; some listings lso appear in a separate southern edition of his publication. Entries include: Name of ospital, accreditation, mailing address, hone, fax, number of beds, type of facility nonprofit, general, state, etc.); list of administrative personnel and chiefs of medical ervices, with specific titles. Arrangement: eographical.

10939★ Medical and Health Information Directory

homson Gale
7500 Drake Rd.
armington Hills, MI 48331-3535
h: (248)699-4253   Fax: (248)699-8065
r: 800-877-GALE
-mail: businessproducts@gale.com

nnual. $285.00 per volume; $675.00 per et. Covers in Volume 1, more than 26,500 nedical and health oriented associations, rganizations, institutions, and government gencies, including health maintenance oranizations (HMOs), preferred provider oranizations (PPOs), insurance companies, harmaceutical companies, research cenrs, and medical and allied health schools. n Volume 2, over 12,000 medical book ublishers; medical periodicals, directories, udiovisual producers and services, medical braries and information centers, electronic esources, and health-related internet earch engines. In Volume 3, more than 5,500 clinics, treatment centers, care prorams, and counseling/diagnostic services or 34 subject areas. Entries include: Institu-

tion, service, or firm name, address, phone, fax, email and URL; many include names of key personnel and, when pertinent, descriptive annotation. Volume 3 was formerly listed separately as Health Services Directory. Arrangement: Classified by organization activity, service, etc. Indexes: Each volume has a complete alphabetical name and keyword index.

HANDBOOKS AND MANUALS

★10940★ Careers in Health Care

McGraw-Hill Trade
2 Penn Plaza
New York, NY 10121
Ph: (212)904-2000   Fr: 800-722-4726
E-mail: ntcpub@tribune.com

Barbara M. Swanson. Fourth edition, 2000. $17.95; $13.95 (paper). 320 pages. Describes job duties, work settings, salaries, licensing and certification requirements, educational preparation, and future outlook. Gives ideas on how to secure a job.

★10941★ Careers in Social and Rehabilitation Services

McGraw-Hill Trade
2 Penn Plaza
New York, NY 10121
Ph: (212)904-2000   Fr: 800-722-4726
E-mail: ntcpub@tribune.com

Geraldine O. Garner. Second edition, 2001. $19.95; 14.95 (paper). 128 pages.

★10942★ Clinical Administration in Audiology and Speech-Language Pathology

Singular Publishing
7625 Empire Dr.
Florence, KY 41042
Ph: (859)525-6620   Fax: (859)525-0978
Fr: 800-347-7707

Stephen R. Rizzo, Jr. and Michael D. Trudeau, editors. 1993. $59.95 (paper). 306 pages.

★10943★ Funding Sources: A Guide for Future Audiologists, Speech-Language Pathologists, and Speech, Language, and Hearing Scientists

American Speech-Language Hearing Association
10801 Rockville Pke.
Rockville, MD 20852
Ph: (301)897-5700   Fax: (301)897-7355
Fr: 888-498-6699

1999. $20.00 (paper).

★10944★ Great Jobs for Communications Majors

McGraw-Hill Professional
2 Penn Plaza
New York, NY 10121
Ph: (212)904-2000   Fr: 800-722-4726
E-mail: ntcpub@tribune.com

Blythe Camenson. Second edition, 2001. $14.95 (paper). 256 pages.

★10945★ Guide to Successful Private Practice in Speech-Language Pathology

American Speech-Language Hearing Association
10801 Rockville Pke.
Rockville, MD 20852
Ph: (301)897-5700   Fax: (301)897-7355
Fr: 888-498-6699

Cole. 1996. $38.00 (ringbound).

★10946★ Making a Difference for America's Children: Speech Language Pathologists in Public Schools

Thinking Publications
P.O. Box 163
Eau Claire, WI 54702-0163
Ph: (715)832-2488   Fax: (715)832-9082
Fr: 800-225-4769

Barbara J. Moore-Brown and Judy K. Montgomery. 2001.

★10947★ On Your Own: A Resource Manual for Starting a Successful Private Practice as a Solo Practicioner in Speech-Language Pathology

PRO-ED, Incorporated
8700 Shoal Creek Blvd.
Austin, TX 78757-6897
Ph: (512)451-3246   Fax: (512)451-8542
Fr: 800-897-3202

Ann M. Coleman. 2000.

★10948★ Opportunities in Health and Medical Careers

McGraw-Hill Trade
2 Penn Plaza
New York, NY 10121
Ph: (212)904-2000   Fr: 800-722-4726

I. Donald Snook, Jr. and Leo D'Orazio. 1997. $14.95; $11.95 (paper). 202 pages. Covers the full range of medical and health occupations. Illustrated.

★10949★ Resumes for Health and Medical Careers

McGraw-Hill Trade
2 Penn Plaza
New York, NY 10121
Ph: (212)904-2000   Fr: 800-722-4726
E-mail: ntcpub@tribune.com

1997. $9.95 (paper). 455 pages.

★10950★ Survival Guide for School-Based Speech-Language Pathologists

Singular Publishing Group, Incorporated
401 W. A St., Suite 325
San Diego, CA 92101-7904
Ph: (619)238-6777   Fax: (619)238-6789
Fr: 800-521-8545

Ellen P. Dodge. 1999. $53.95 (paper).

EMPLOYMENT AGENCIES AND SEARCH FIRMS

★10951★ Educational Placement Service

1001 Craig Rd., Ste. 170
St. Louis, MO 63146
Ph: (314)991-5855   Fax: (314)991-5295
URL: http://www.educatorjobs.com

Employment agency. Focuses on teaching, administrative, and education-related openings.

ONLINE JOB SOURCES AND SERVICES

★10952★ Medhunters.com

E-mail: info@medhunters.com
URL: http://www.medhunters.com

Description: Career search site for jobs in all health care specialties; educational resources; visa and licensing information for relocation; interesting articles; relocation tools; links to professional organizations and general resources.

★10953★ ProHealthJobs

E-mail: sales@prohealthjobs.com
URL: http://www.prohealthjobs.com

Description: Career resources site for the medical and health care field. Lists professional opportunities, product information, continuing education and open positions.

★10954★ RehabJobs Online

PO Box 480536
Los Angeles, CA 90048
Ph: (213)938-7718   Fax: (213)938-9609
Fr: 800-43-REHAB
E-mail: support@atsrehabjobs.com
URL: http://www.rehabjobs.com

Description: @dq1On-line resource center for the professional therapist.@dq2 **Main files include:** Therapists Only, Therapy Forums, Nationwide Job Search (database), Therapy Job Outlook, Therapy Job Search Utilities, Therapy Links, Information for Employers and Recruiters.

★10955★ RehabWorld

URL: http://www.rehabworld.com

Description: Site for rehabilitation professionals to learn about the profession and locate jobs. Includes user groups, salary surveys, and chat capabilities. **Main files include:** Physical Therapy, Occupational Therapy, Speech Therapy, Mental Health, Employer World, Student World, International World, Forum.

TRADESHOWS

★10956★ American Speech-Language-Hearing Association Annual Convention

American Speech-Language-Hearing Association
10801 Rockville Pke.
Rockville, MD 20852
Ph: (301)897-5700   Fax: (301)571-0454
Fr: 800-498-2071
E-mail: convention@asha.org
URL: http://www.asha.org

Annual. **Primary Exhibits:** Scientific equipment, publications, and testing materials.

★10957★ National Student Speech Language Hearing Association Conference

National Student Speech Language Hearing Association
10801 Rockville Pike
Rockville, MD 20852
Ph: (301)897-5700   Fax: (301)571-0457

Annual. **Primary Exhibits:** Exhibits relating to speech-language pathology, speech and hearing sciences, and audiology.

★10958★ North Carolina Speech, Hearing, and Language Association Convention

North Carolina Speech, Hearing, and Language Association
PO Box 28359
Raleigh, NC 27611-8359
Ph: (919)833-3984   Fax: (919)832-0445
E-mail: ncshla@juno.com
URL: http://www.ncshla.org

Annual. **Primary Exhibits:** Equipment, supplies, and services for speech and language pathology and/or audiology. **Dates and Locations:** 2005 Apr 19-23; Winston-Salem, NC; Adam's Mark • 2006 Apr 05-08.

★10959★ Summer Institute of the Academy of Rehabilitative Audiology

Academy of Rehabilitative Audiology
PO Box 26532
Minneapolis, MN 55426
Ph: (952)920-0408   Fax: (952)920-6098
E-mail: ara@incnet.com
URL: http://www.audrehab.org

Primary Exhibits: Exhibits relating to audiology, language, speech pathology, and the education of the deaf.

OTHER SOURCES

★10960★ American Almanac of Jobs and Salaries

Morrow Avon
1350 Avenue of the Americas
New York, NY 10019
Ph: (212)261-6788   Fr: 800-242-773

John W. Wright. Revised edition, 2000. $20.00 (paper). 672 pages. This is a comprehensive guide to the wages of hundreds of occupations in a wide variety of industries and organizations.

★10961★ American Health Care Association (AHCA)

1201 L St. NW
Washington, DC 20005
Ph: (202)842-4444   Fax: (202)842-386
URL: http://www.ahca.org

Description: Federation of state associations of long-term health care facilities. Promotes standards for professionals in long term health care delivery and quality care for patients and residents in a safe environment. Focuses on issues of availability, quality, affordability, and fair payment. Operates as liaison with governmental agencies, Congress, and professional associations. Compiles statistics.

★10962★ Association on Higher Education and Disability (AHEAD)

PO Box 540666
Waltham, MA 02454
Ph: (781)788-0003   Fax: (781)788-003
E-mail: ahead@ahead.org
URL: http://www.ahead.org.

Description: Individuals interested in promoting the equal rights and opportunities of disabled postsecondary students, staff, faculty, and graduates. Provides an exchange of communication for those professionally involved with disabled students; collects, evaluates, and disseminates information; encourages and supports legislation for the benefit of disabled students. Conducts surveys on issues pertinent to college students with disabilities; offers resource referral system and employment exchange for positions in disability student services. Conducts research programs; compiles statistics.

★10963★ Association for Pediatric Therapists (APT)

2784 Lantz Ave.
San Jose, CA 95124
Ph: (408)377-3345

Members: Occupational, physical, and speech therapists, certified assistants, and students. **Purpose:** Promotes continuing professional development of members. Ac

tivities: Functions as a communication network linking members. Cooperates with other organizations representing professionals in related fields. Conducts continuing professional education programs.

★10964★ **Convention of American Instructors of the Deaf (CAID)**
PO Box 377
Bedford, TX 76095-0377
Ph: (817)354-8414
E-mail: caid@swbell.net
URL: http://www.caid.org/

Members: Professional organization of teachers, administrators, and professionals in allied fields related to education of the deaf and hard-of-hearing. **Purpose:** Objectives are to provide opportunities for a free interchange of views concerning methods and means of educating the deaf and hard-of-hearing; to promote such education by the publication of reports, essays, and other information; to develop more effective methods of teaching deaf and hard-of-hearing children.

★10965★ *Exploring Health Occupations*
Cambridge Educational
2572 Brunswick Ave.
Lawrenceville, NJ 08648-4128
Fax: 800-FAX-ON-US   Fr: 800-468-4227
URL: http://www.cambridgeeducational.com
Two videos. $139.95. 1999.

★10966★ *Health Assessment & Treating Occupations*
Delphi Productions
3160 4th St.
Boulder, CO 80304
Fax: (303)443-4022   Fr: 888-443-2400

URL: http://www.delphivideo.com
$95.00. 50 minutes. Part of the Careers for the 21st Century Video Library.

★10967★ *Health Service Occupations*
Delphi Productions
3160 4th St.
Boulder, CO 80304
Fax: (303)443-4022   Fr: 888-443-2400
URL: http://www.delphivideo.com
$95.00. 50 minutes. Part of the Careers for the 21st Century Video Library.

★10968★ *Medicine & Related Occupations*
Delphi Productions
3160 4th St.
Boulder, CO 80304
Fax: (303)443-4022   Fr: 888-443-2400
URL: http://www.delphivideo.com
$95.00. 45 minutes. Part of the Careers for the 21st Century Video Library.

★10969★ **Modern Language Association of America (MLA)**
26 Broadway, 3rd Fl.
New York, NY 10004-1789
Ph: (646)576-5000   Fax: (646)458-0300
E-mail: info@mla.org
URL: http://www.mla.org

Members: College and university teachers of English and of modern foreign languages. **Purpose:** Seeks to advance all aspects of literary and linguistic study. Under its Foreign Language Program, researches foreign language teaching primarily at the postsecondary level of U.S. education. Under its English Program, acts as a clearinghouse for information of interest to teachers of English

literature and composition. **Activities:** Conducts Job Information Service. Operates 84 divisions.

★10970★ **National Rehabilitation Association (NRA)**
633 S Washington St.
Alexandria, VA 22314
Ph: (703)836-0850   Fax: (703)836-0848
E-mail: info@nationalrehab.org
URL: http://www.nationalrehab.org/website/index.html

Description: Providing opportunities through knowledge and diversity for professionals in the fields of rehabilitation of people with disabilities.

★10971★ **Neuro-Developmental Treatment Association (NDTA)**
1540 S Coast Hwy., Ste. 203
Laguna Beach, CA 92651
Fax: (949)376-3456   Fr: 800-869-9295
E-mail: membership@ndta.org
URL: http://www.ndta.org

Members: Physical and occupational therapists, speech pathologists, special educators, physicians, parents, and others interested in neurodevelopmental treatment. (NDT is a form of therapy for individuals who suffer from central nervous system disorders resulting in abnormal movement. Treatment attempts to initiate or refine normal stages and processes in the development of movement.) **Purpose:** Informs members of new developments in the field and with ideas that will eventually improve fundamental independence. **Activities:** Locates articles related to NDT.

Sports Officials, Coaches, and Instructors

SOURCES OF HELP-WANTED ADS

★10972★ The American Journal of Sports Medicine

The American Orthopaedic Society for Sports Medicine
6300 N River Rd.
Rosemont, IL 60018
Ph: (847)292-4900   Fax: (847)292-4905
URL: http://www.ajsm.org

Bimonthly. $125.00/year for individuals; $145.00/year for out of country; $160.00/year for institutions; $25.00/year for single issue. Medical journal.

★10973★ NAIA News

National Association of Intercollegiate Athletics
23500 W 105th St.
PO Box 1325
Olathe, KS 66051-1325
Ph: (913)791-0044   Fax: (913)791-9555
E-mail: naianews@naia.org
URL: http://www.naia.org

Description: Daily. Provides news and information on the Association, which strives to "develop intercollegiate athletic programs as an integral part of the total educational program of the college rather than as a separate commercial or promotional adjunct." Aims toward uniformity and equity in policies and practices. Recurring features include news of members and events, notices of awards, and job listings. America Online, Inc.

★10974★ Sailing World

Miller Sports Group L.L.C.
79 Madison Ave.
New York, NY 10016-7802
Ph: (212)636-2700   Fr: 800-634-1953
E-mail: 70672.2725@compuserve.com
URL: http://www.sailingworld.com

$28.00/year for individuals. Magazine on performance sailing.

★10975★ Scholastic Coach & Athletic Director

Scholastic Library Publishing Inc.
90 Old Sherman Tpke.
Danbury, CT 06816
Ph: (203)797-3500   Fax: (203)797-3657
Fr: 800-621-1115
E-mail: magazines@scholastic.ca
URL: http://secure.palmcoast.com/pcd/document?ikey=0473YIWEA

$14.98/year for individuals. Magazine on high school and college athletics.

★10976★ Skiing Trade News

Time4 Media Inc.
2 Park Ave., 10th Fl.
New York, NY 10016
Ph: (212)779-5493   Fax: (212)779-5118
URL: http://www.skinet.com

$15.00/year for individuals. Trade newspaper for the ski industry. Includes trade show previews, company news, retail trends, personnel changes, and miscellaneous news.

PLACEMENT AND JOB REFERRAL SERVICES

★10977★ American Athletic Trainers Association and Certification Board (AATA)

146 E. Duarte Rd.
Arcadia, CA 91006
Ph: (626)445-1978   Fax: (626)574-1999
E-mail: americansportsmedicine@hotmail.com

Purpose: Works to qualify and certify active athletic trainers; to establish minimum competence standards for individuals participating in the prevention and care of athletic injuries; to inform communities nationwide of the importance of having competent leadership in the area of athletic training. **Activities:** Conducts continuing education and charitable programs; maintains placement service. Oldest athletic trainers association in the nation.

★10978★ American Sail Training Association (ASTA)

PO Box 1459
Newport, RI 02840
Ph: (401)846-1775   Fax: (401)849-5400
E-mail: asta@sailtraining.org
URL: http://tallships.sailtraining.org

Members: Organizations operating sail training programs; corporations and educational institutions supporting sail training; private citizens with an interest in sailing and sail training. **Purpose:** Promotes sail training as an educational and character-building experience for youth of all ages. Seeks to bring together the sail training ships of the world in a spirit of friendship and international goodwill. **Activities:** Sponsors Tall Ships events including sail training rallies. Maintains billet bank/placement service; compiles statistics.

★10979★ American Swimming Coaches Association (ASCA)

2101 N Andrews Ave., Ste. 107
Fort Lauderdale, FL 33311
Ph: (954)563-4930   Fax: (954)563-9813
Fr: 800-356-2722
E-mail: asca@swimmingcoach.org
URL: http://www.swimmingcoach.org

Members: Swimming coaches united for informational and educational purposes. **Activities:** Operates Swim America, a learn-to-swim program. Maintains placement service; conducts research programs; compiles statistics.

★10980★ Athletic Equipment Managers Association (AEMA)

460 Hunt Hill Rd.
Freeville, NY 13068
Ph: (607)539-6300   Fax: (607)539-6340
E-mail: dec13@cornell.edu
URL: http://www.aema1.com

Members: Athletic equipment managers and others who handle sports equipment for junior high and high schools, colleges, recreation centers, and professional sports; individuals involved in athletic management and coaching or the handling or purchasing of athletic, physical education, or recreational equipment. **Purpose:** Aims to improve the profession of equipment management and promote a better working relationship among those interested in problems of management. Works collectively to facilitate equipment improvement for greater safety among participants in all sports. **Activities:** Conducts workshops and clinics. Maintains job placement service.

★10981★ College Swimming Coaches Association of America (CSCAA)

PO Box 63285
Colorado Springs, CO 80962
Ph: (719)266-0064   Fax: (719)266-6844
E-mail: swimco@aol.com
URL: http://www.cscaa.org

Members: College and university swimming and diving coaches organized to promote college swimming. **Activities:** Disseminates information; maintains placement service and hall of fame.

★10982★ Exercise Safety Association (ESA)

PO Box 547916
Orlando, FL 32854-9716
Ph: (407)246-5090   Fax: (407)246-5090
E-mail: askesa@aol.com
URL: http://www.exercisesafety.com

Description: Fitness instructors, personal trainers, health spas, YMCAs, community recreation departments, and hospital wellness programs. Purposes are: to improve the qualifications of exercise instructors; to train instructors to develop safe exercise programs that will help people avoid injury while exercising; to prepare instructors for national certification. Offers training in aerobics and exercise and on the physiological aspects of exercise. Conducts exercise safety and research programs. Sponsors charitable program; maintains speakers' bureau. Offers instructor placement services.

★10983★ Jackie Robinson Foundation (JRF)

3 W 35th St., 11th Fl.
New York, NY 10001-2204
Ph: (212)290-8600   Fax: (212)290-8081
E-mail: general@jackierobinson.org
URL: http://www.jackierobinson.org

Description: Seeks to develop the leadership and achievement potential of minority and urban youth. Founded by the friends and family of Jackie Robinson (1919-72), the first black athlete to play major league baseball. Trains minority and poor youths for sports management careers. Provides counseling, support, and placement services. Awards full college scholarships to promising minority students. Maintains collection of Jackie Robinson memorabilia; has produced a national touring exhibit of archival materials pertaining to Robinson.

★10984★ National Association for Sport and Physical Education (NASPE)

1900 Association Dr.
Reston, VA 20191
Ph: (703)476-3410   Fax: (703)476-8316
Fr: 800-213-7193
E-mail: naspe@aahperd.org
URL: http://www.aahperd.org

Description: Men and women professionally involved with physical activity and sports. Seeks to improve the total sport and physical activity experience in America. Conducts research and education programs in such areas as sport psychology, curriculum development, kinesiology, history, philosophy, sport sociology, and the biological and behavioral basis of human activity. Develops and distributes public information materials which explain the value of physical education programs. Supports councils involved in organizing and supporting elementary, secondary, and college physical education and sport programs; administers the National Council of Athletic Training in conjunction with the National Association for Girls and Women in Sport; serves the professional interests of coaches, trainers, and officials. Maintains hall of fame, placement service, and media resource center for public information and professional preparation. Member benefits include group insurance and discounts.

★10985★ National Association of Underwater Instructors (NAUI)

1232 Tech Blvd.
Tampa, FL 33619-7832
Ph: (813)628-6284   Fax: (813)628-8253
Fr: 800-553-6284
E-mail: nauihq@nauiww.org
URL: http://www.naui.org/index-side.html

Members: Certified instructors of basic, advanced, and specialized courses in underwater diving. **Activities:** Offers instructor certification programs and training programs. Conducts seminars, workshops, and symposia. Sells diving education books. Sponsors competitions; maintains speakers' bureau and placement service; conducts charitable programs.

★10986★ National Athletic Trainers Association (NATA)

2952 Stemmons Fwy., Ste. 200
Dallas, TX 75247-6196
Ph: (214)637-6282   Fax: (214)637-2206
Fr: 800-879-6282
E-mail: ebd@nata.org
URL: http://www.nata.org

Members: Athletic trainers from universities, colleges, and junior colleges; professional football, baseball, basketball, and ice hockey; high schools, preparatory schools, military establishments, sports medicine clinics, and business/industrial health programs. **Activities:** Maintains hall of fame and placement service. Conducts research programs; compiles statistics.

★10987★ National Christian College Athletic Association (NCCAA)

302 W Washington St.
Greenville, SC 29601-1919
Ph: (864)250-1199   Fax: (864)250-1141
E-mail: info@thenccaa.org
URL: http://www.thenccaa.org

Members: Christian colleges. **Purpose:** Provides national competition for the Christian college movement in baseball, basketball (men's and women's) cross-country (men's and women's), football, golf, soccer (men's and women's), tennis (men's and women's), men's volleyball, women's volleyball, track and field (men's and women's), and softball. **Activities:** Maintains placement service; compiles statistics.

★10988★ Professional Association of Diving Instructors (PADI)

30151 Tomas
Rancho Santa Margarita, CA 92688-2125
Ph: (949)858-7234   Fax: (949)858-7264
Fr: 800-729-7234
E-mail: webmaster@padi.com
URL: http://www.padi.com

Purpose: Educates and certifies underwater scuba instructors. Sanctions instructor training courses nationwide and in 175 foreign countries. Provides training course criteria, training aids, and national requirements for all aspects of diving instruction. Instructor training courses are held at geographically central locations. **Activities:** Sponsors PADI Travel Network and a retail dive store program. Offers courses in diving specialties; conducts educational programs. Offers placement service; compiles statistics.

★10989★ Professional Skaters Association (PSA)

3006 Allegro Park SW
Rochester, MN 55902
Ph: (507)281-5122   Fax: (507)281-5491
E-mail: office@skatepsa.com
URL: http://skatepsa.com

Members: Professional ice skaters engaged in the teaching coaching and performing of ice skating. **Purpose:** Strives to form a cohesive body of all professional ice skaters for the benefit of the profession, to protect the interests of members' pupils, to advance all aspects of both ice figure skating and recreational skating, and to promote high ethical and professional standards in the field. **Activities:** Grades teachers on the basis of on-ice proficiency and oral examination, according to the official PSA Rating System. Operates placement service.

★10990★ United States Association of Independent Gymnastic Clubs (USAIGC)

22 River Terr., Ste. 200
New York, NY 10282
Ph: (212)227-9792   Fax: (212)227-9793
Fr: 800-480-0201
E-mail: usaigcpsny2@aol.com
URL: http://www.usaigc.com

Members: Gymnastic clubs and independent gymnastic club businesses (725) offering professional class instruction and coaching; manufacturers (25) of gymnastic equipment, apparel, and supplies. **Purpose:** Objectives are to provide services, programs, and business advice to help gymnastic businesses to grow and prosper; locate organizations and individuals that will provide needed services for members' clientele; further coaching knowledge; advance the U.S. in gymnastic competitions throughout the world. **Activities:** Offers certification for coaches and developmental-training programs for gymnasts to prepare for international competitions. Provides placement service; conducts research programs. Maintains Medical Advisory Board and hall of fame.

★10991★   United States Judo (USJ)

1 Olympic Plz., Ste. 202
Colorado Springs, CO 80909
Ph: (719)866-4730   Fax: (719)866-4733
Fr: (719)578-4733
E-mail: secusji@aol.com
URL: http://www.usjudo.org

Description: Judo groups and athletes, referees, judges, and interested individuals. Serves as national governing body for amateur judo in the United States. Promotes the sport of judo and trains athletes for competition. Develops eligibility and safety standards; conducts training courses for referees, coaches, and athletes. Sanctions and sponsors national amateur judo competitions. Maintains placement service; compiles statistics.

★10992★   United States Professional Diving Coaches Association (PDCA)

2210 Wrocklage Ave.
Louisville, KY 40205
Ph: (513)697-9509   Fax: (513)697-9609
Fr: 877-348-3246
E-mail: svoellmecke@cinci.rr.com
URL: http://www.uspdca.org

Description: Conducts educational programs; offers placement services. Maintains videotape library.

★10993★   United States Professional Tennis Association (USPTA)

3535 Briarpark Dr., Ste. 1
Houston, TX 77042
Ph: (713)978-7782   Fax: (713)978-7780
Fr: 800-USPTA-4U
E-mail: uspta@uspta.org
URL: http://www.uspta.com

Members: Professional tennis instructors, tennis-teaching professionals and college coaches. **Purpose:** Seeks to improve tennis instruction in the United States; maintains placement bureau and library. Offers specialized education; sponsors competitions; administrates an adult tennis league and a nationwide program to introduce children ages 3-10 to tennis. Sponsors annual "Tennis Across America" program each spring.

★10994★   U.S. Ski Coaches Association (USSCA)

1500 Kearns Blvd.
PO Box 100
Park City, UT 84060
Ph: (435)649-9090   Fax: (435)649-3613
E-mail: special2@ussa.org
URL: http://www.usskiteam.com

Description: Alpine, Nordic, and Freestyle ski and snowboard coaches and instructors; persons interested in sports medicine. Promotes the highest standards of Alpine, Nordic, and Freestyle ski coaching. Provides educational and technical materials, supplies, and equipment necessary to the function of the ski coach. Offers courses, clinics, films, and placement service. Provides high standards of certification, recertification, accreditation, and coaching ethics; handles problems of common concern to the ski coaching profession.

EMPLOYER DIRECTORIES AND NETWORKING LISTS

★10995★   *Blue Book of College Athletics for Senior, Junior & Community Colleges*

Athletic Publishing Company Inc.
P O Box 931
Montgomery, AL 36101
Ph: (334)263-4436   Fax: (334)263-4437
URL: http://www.athleticpubco.com

Annual, September. $44.95 for first copy; $38.00 for each additional copy. Covers over 2,400 colleges and universities that have athletic programs, conferences, and related associations; coverage includes the U.S.; Canada and Puerto Rico. Entries include: For colleges and universities-Name, address, phone, name and title of governing officials, athletic department phone number, enrollment, school colors, team nickname, band nickname and size, band director's name, stadium name and size, other athletic facilities, conference membership; names and phone numbers of athletic directors, coaches, assistants, and trainers; previous year's team records. For conferences and associations-Name, Headquarters address; names and titles of key personnel; name, address, phone commissioner; membership conference/associations championships for previous year. Arrangement: Classified by type of college, conference, or association, then alphabetical. Indexes: Senior colleges and universities in the U.S.; colleges of Canada, and Puerto Rico; senior conferences and associations, senior related associations and organizations; junior and community colleges; junior and community college conferences and associations.

★10996★   *Clell Wade Coaches Directory*

Clell Wade Coaches Directory Inc.
PO Box 177
Cassville, MO 65625
Ph: (417)847-2783   Fax: (417)847-5920

E-mail: info@coachesdirectory.com
URL: http://www.coachesdirectory.com

Annual, September. $11.95 for individual directory; $19.95 for national college directory; $69.95 for national high school directory. Published in 50 state and/or regional editions as well as 1 Canadian province editions, this series covers high school and college athletic programs and their personnel. Entries include: For each school-Name and titles of athletic director, superintendent, principal, cheerleader sponsor, band director, and trainer; school name, address, phone; enrollment; conference memberships; school colors, nickname; interscholastic sports, name of coach. College listings include name and seating capacity of the football stadium and basketball fieldhouse. Arrangement: Geographical.

★10997★   *Exercise and Physical Fitness Programs Directory*

infoUSA Inc.
5711 S 86th Cir.
Omaha, NE 68127-0347
Ph: (402)930-3500   Fax: (402)331-0176
Fr: 800-555-6124
URL: http://www.abii.com

Annual. Number of listings: 8,412. Entries include: Name, address, phone (including area code), size of advertisement, year first in "Yellow Pages," name of owner or manager, number of employees. Compiled from telephone company "Yellow Pages," nationwide. Arrangement: Geographical.

★10998★   *Health Clubs Studios & Gymnasiums Directory*

infoUSA Inc.
5711 S 86th Cir.
Omaha, NE 68127-0347
Ph: (402)930-3500   Fax: (402)331-0176
Fr: 800-555-6124
URL: http://www.abii.com

Updated continuously; printed on request. Number of listings: 17,012. Entries include: Name, address, phone (including area code). Compiled from telephone company "Yellow Pages," nationwide. Arrangement: Geographical.

★10999★   *Health & Fitness Program Consultants Directory*

infoUSA Inc.
5711 S 86th Cir.
Omaha, NE 68127-0347
Ph: (402)930-3500   Fax: (402)331-0176
Fr: 800-555-6124
URL: http://www.abii.com

Annual. Number of listings: 4,627. Entries include: Name, address, phone (including area code), size of advertisement, year first in "Yellow Pages," name of owner or manager, number of employees. Compiled from telephone company "Yellow Pages," nationwide. Arrangement: Geographical.

★11000★ **National Collegiate Athletic Association-Directory**

National Collegiate Athletic Association
700 W. Washington St.
PO Box 6222
Indianapolis, IN 46206-6222
Ph: (317)917-6222   Fax: (317)917-6888
URL: http://www.ncaa.org

Annual, October. $5.00 for members; $10.00 for nonmembers. Covers about 1,000 member institutions. Entries include: Name of institution, conference, address, phone, E-mail address, fax numbers, names and titles of key personnel. Arrangement: Alphabetical.

★11001★ **National Directory of College Athletics**

Collegiate Directories Inc.
PO Box 450640
Cleveland, OH 44145
Ph: (440)835-1172   Fax: (440)835-8835
Fr: 800-426-2232
URL: http://www.collegiatedirectories.com

Annual, August. $39.95. Covers men's athletic departments of 2,100 senior and junior colleges in the United States and Canada. Entries include: School name, address, enrollment, colors, team nicknames, stadium and/or gym capacity; names of president, men's athletic director, athletic administrative staff, physical education director and coaches for each sport; athletic department phones, faxes, etc.; association affiliations. Arrangement: Alphabetical. Indexes: Schools by program and division; Alphabetical by advertisers and products.

★11002★ **National Directory of High School Coaches**

Athletic Publishing Company Inc.
P O Box 931
Montgomery, AL 36101
Ph: (334)263-4436   Fax: (334)263-4437
URL: http://www.athleticpubco.comm

Annual, September. $64.95 for first copy; $48.00 for additional copies. Covers more than 240,000 high school coaches at over 19,500 high schools. Entries include: School name, address, phone, names of coaches, codes for sports coached, and ETS numbers. Arrangement: Geographical. Indexes: Advertiser, key to symbols, index of high schools by name, city & state.

★11003★ **National Sports and Fitness Association-Fitness Directory**

National Sports & Fitness Association
1945 Palo Verde, Ste. 202
Long Beach, CA 90815-3445
Ph: (562)682-3559   Fax: (562)799-3355

Annual, summer. Entries include: Name, address, phone, products or services, geographical area covered, sports and fitness interests. Arrangement: Alphabetical.

★11004★ **Recreational Sports Directory**

National Intramural-Recreational Sports Association
4185 SW Research Way
Corvallis, OR 97333-1067
Ph: (541)766-8211   Fax: (541)766-8284
URL: http://www.nirsa.org

Annual, December. $150.00 to corporate members; $40.00 to student members. Covers recreational sports programs in approximately 2,500 four-year colleges and universities, nearly 700 junior and community colleges, Canadian colleges and universities, and over 350 military installations. Entries include: Institution name and address; institution enrollment; name of president; names, phone numbers, fax numbers, Internet access, and job titles of recreational directors and staff; existing sports clubs; degrees offered in physical education and recreation; whether graduate assistantships or internships are available. A Buyer's Guide is included with supplier addresses and descriptions of products and services. Arrangement: Classified by institution type, then alphabetical. Indexes: Alphabetical, geographical, personal name, recreational sports program.

★11005★ **Skiing USA: Where to Ski, Where to Stay, Where to Eat in the 30 Best U.S. Ski Resorts**

Fodor's Travel Publications Inc.
1745 Broadway
New York, NY 10019
Ph: (212)782-9000   Fax: (212)782-9054
Fr: 800-733-3000

Biennial, even years. $17.00. Covers 30 top ski resorts in the U.S. Entries include: Resort name, address, phone; type of lifts, number of trails, snowmaking capabilities, length of season, hotels, restaurants, available transportation, other activities, and recommendations on the best trails for all levels. Arrangement: Geographical. Indexes: Resort name.

★11006★ **Sports Market Place**

Sportsguide L.L.C.
13901 N 73rd St., Ste. 219
Scottsdale, AZ 85260
Ph: (480)948-8885   Fax: (480)948-7701
Fr: 800-776-7877
E-mail: smp@sportsmarketplace.com
URL: http://www.sportsmarketplace.com

Annual, January. $249.00. Covers manufacturers, organizations, professional sports teams, broadcasting networks, sports arenas, syndicators, publications, trade shows, marketing services, corporate sports sponsors, and other groups concerned with the business and promotional aspects of sports generally and with air sports, arm wrestling, auto sports, badminton, baseball, basketball, biathlon, bowling, boxing, curling, equestrian, exercise, fencing, field hockey, football, golf, gymnastics, ice hockey, lacrosse, martial arts, paddleball, paddle tennis, platform tennis, pentathlon, racquetball, rowing, rugby, running/jogging, skiing, soccer, softball, squash, swimming, table tennis, tennis, track and field, volleyball, water sports, weightlifting, and wrestling. Entries include: Name of

company or organization, address, fax, e-mail, URL, name of key personnel with titles, and description of products or services. Arrangement: Classified by type of firm, sport, or activity. Indexes: Alphabetical, single sprt, media, sport sponsors, agencies, manufacturers, brand name, facilities, executive, and Geographical.

★11007★ **White Book of Ski Areas: U.S., Canada**

Inter-Ski Services Inc.
PO Box 3775
Washington, DC 20007
Ph: (202)342-0886   Fax: (202)338-1940
URL: http://www.inter-ski.com

Annual, latest edition 28th, 2004. $19.95. Covers about 500 lift-equipped ski areas and resorts. Entries include: Name of ski area, location, phone; snow condition phone numbers; ski statistics (elevation, lift capacity, etc.); season and rates; equipment and schooling available; lodging availability and phone, restaurants, apres-ski, and other recreational facilities in vicinity; shops; travel instructions. Special industry edition available with more comprehensive information; $395.00. Arrangement: Geographical within four regions-West, North Central, South, and Northeast. Indexes: Geographical.

★11008★ **Who's Who in Sports & Fitness**

National Sports & Fitness Association
1945 Palo Verde, Ste. 202
Long Beach, CA 90815-3445
Ph: (562)682-3559   Fax: (562)799-3355

Annual, January. Entries include: Name, address, phone, biographical data, products or services, geographical area covered. Arrangement: Alphabetical. Indexes: Geographical.

HANDBOOKS AND MANUALS

★11009★ **Athlete's Guide to Career Planning**

Human Kinetics Publishers
PO Box 5076
Champaign, IL 61825-5076
Ph: (217)351-5076   Fax: (217)351-2674
Fr: 800-747-4457

Al Petitpas, Delight Champagne, Judy Chartrand, Shane Murphy and Steven Danish. 1997. $17.95 (paper). 240 pages.

★11010★ **Career Game Plan for Student Athletes**

Prentice Hall PTR
One Lake St.
Upper Saddle River, NJ 07458
Ph: (201)236-7000

Jennifer Bohac. 1999. $34.00 (paper).

★11011★ Career Insights: Presidents/ GMs from the NFL, MLB, NHL and MLS on Achieving Personal and Professional Success

Aspatore Books, Incorporated
264 Beacon St., 2nd Fl.
Boston, MA 02116
Ph: (617)249-1960   Fax: (617)249-1970

Aspatore Books. April 2004. $19.95 (paper).

★11012★ Career Transitions in Sport: International Perspectives

Fitness Information Technology, Incorporated
P.O. Box 4425
Morgantown, WV 26504-4425
Ph: (304)599-3483   Fax: (304)599-3482
Fr: 800-477-4348

Editors: David Lavallee, Paul Wylleman. 2000. $39.00.

★11013★ Careers Inside the World of Sports and Entertainment

Rosen Publishing Group, Inc.
29 E. 21st St.
New York, NY 10010
Ph: (212)777-3017   Fax: 888-436-4643
Fr: 800-237-9932

Bruce McGothlin. 1995. $15.95. 64 pages. Out of print.

★11014★ Careers Without College: Fitness

Thomson Peterson's
PO Box 67005
Lawrenceville, NJ 08648-6105
Fr: 800-338-3282

Maura R. Curless. 1992. $7.95 (paper).

★11015★ Chronicle of Sports Careers

Chronicle Guidance Publications, Inc.
66 Aurora St.
Moravia, NY 13118-3576
Fax: (315)497-3359   Fr: 800-899-0454

Paul Downes, editor. 1994. $24.00.

★11016★ Developing a Career in the Sports Marketplace: The Sports Career Development Handbook

Global Sports Productions, Inc.
1223 Broadway, Ste. 102
Santa Monica, CA 90404
Ph: (310)454-9480   Fax: (310)454-6590

Ed Kobak, Jr. 1999. $24.95 (paper). 348 pages. Out of print.

★11017★ Developing a Lifelong Contract in the Sports Marketplace

Athletic Achievements
3036 Ontario Rd.
Little Canada, MN 55117
Ph: (612)484-8299   Fax: (612)484-8311
Fr: 800-680-8311

Greg J. Cylkowski. Second edition, revised,

1998. $20.95. 400 pages. A guide to seeking opportunities in a variety of sports positions.

★11018★ Exploring Coaching: A Step-by-Step Guide to a Fulfilling and Rewarding Career

LearnMore Publishing
2245 Eagles Nest Dr.
Lafayette, CO 80026-9334
Ph: (303)464-0110

Will Craig. April 2004. $9.95.

★11019★ Leading with the Heart: Coach K's Successful Strategies for Basketball, Business and Life

Warner Books, Incorporated
1271 Avenue of the Americas
New York, NY 10020
Ph: (212)522-7200

Mike Krzyzewski, Donald T. Phillips. 2000. $24.95 (paper).

★11020★ Opportunities in Sports and Athletics Careers

McGraw-Hill Trade
2 Penn Plaza
New York, NY 10121
Ph: (212)904-2000   Fr: 800-722-4726
E-mail: ntcpub@tribune.com

William Ray Heitzmann. 1994. 160 pages. $14.95; $11.95 (paper). A guide to planning for and seeking opportunities in this growing field. Illustrated.

★11021★ Opportunities in Sports Medicine Careers

McGraw-Hill Trade
2 Penn Plaza
New York, NY 10121
Ph: (212)904-2000   Fr: 800-722-4726
E-mail: ntcpub@tribune.com

William Ray Heitzmann. 1995. $14.95; $11.95 (paper). 160 pages. Discusses a variety of opportunities in this field and how to pursue them. Contains bibliography and illustrations.

★11022★ Real-Resumes for Sports Industry Jobs

PREP Publishing
1110 1/2 Hay St., PMB 66
Fayetteville, NC 28305
Ph: (910)483-6611   Fax: (910)483-2439
Fr: 800-533-2814

Anne McKinney (Editor). April 2004. $16.95 (paper). Illustrated. 192 pages. Real-Resumes Series.

ONLINE JOB SOURCES AND SERVICES

★11023★ Online Sports Career Center
E-mail: comments@atsonlinesports.com
URL: http://www.onlinesports.com/pages/careercenter.html

Description: Resource for sports-related career opportunities, as well as a resume bank for the perusal of potential employers within the sports and recreation industries. Job seekers may post resumes by sending files in ASCII text format to resumes@atsonlinesports.com. **Main files include:** Job Bank, Resume Bank, Newsletter, Work With Online Sports, Other Internet Resources.

OTHER SOURCES

★11024★ American Hockey Coaches Association (AHCA)

7 Concord St.
Gloucester, MA 01930
Ph: (781)245-4177   Fax: (978)281-2081
E-mail: jbertagna@hockeyeastonline.com
URL: http://www.ahcahockey.com

Description: University, college, and secondary school ice hockey coaches. Conducts coaches' clinics throughout the U.S.

★11025★ Black Coaches Association (BCA)

Pan American Plz.
201 S Capitol Ave., Ste. 495
Indianapolis, IN 46225
Ph: (317)829-5600   Fax: (317)829-5601
Fr: 877-789-1222
E-mail: fkeith@bcasports.org
URL: http://www.bcasports.org

Description: Blacks and other minorities in the coaching profession. Promotes the creation of a positive environment in which issues such as stereotyping, lack of significant media coverage, and discrimination can be exposed, discussed, and resolved. Provides member services. Petitions the NCAA legislative bodies to design, enact, and enforce diligent guidelines and policies to improve professional mobility for minorities.

★11026★ IDEA Health and Fitness Association

6190 Cornerstone Ct. E., Ste. 204
San Diego, CA 92121-3773
Ph: (858)535-8979   Fax: (858)535-8234
Fr: 800-999-IDEA
E-mail: member@ideafit.com
URL: http://www.ideafit.com

Purpose: Provides continuing education for fitness professionals including; fitness instructors, personal trainers, program directors, and club/studio owners. **Activities:**

Offers workshops for continuing education credits.

★11027★ **National Association for Girls and Women in Sport (NAGWS)**
1900 Association Dr.
Reston, VA 20191-1598
Ph: (703)476-3450   Fax: (703)476-9527
Fr: 800-213-7193
E-mail: nagws@aahperd.org
URL: http://www.aahperd.org/nagws/template.cfm?template=main.html
Members: An Association of the American Alliance for Health, Physical Education, Recreation, and Dance. Teachers, coaches, athletic trainers, officials, athletic administrators, and students. NAGWS has 8 main structures: Advocacy Coaching Enhancement; Minority Representation; Professional Development Publications, and Student Representation. **Purpose:** Supports and fosters the development of quality sports programs that will enrich the lives of all participants. **Activities:** Holds training sessions for leadership development. Maintains speakers' bureau. Conducts research programs; bestows awards.

★11028★ **National Association of Sports Officials (NASO)**
2017 Lathrop Ave.
Racine, WI 53405
Ph: (262)632-5448   Fax: (262)632-5460
E-mail: cservice@naso.org
URL: http://www.naso.org
Description: Active sports officials, umpires, companies, and individuals interested in sports. Develops programs to assist in the education of sports officials; engages in programs to instruct fans, coaches, players, and the media on the role of sports officials. Conducts clinics and camps; sponsors public service ads.

★11029★ **National High School Athletic Coaches Association (NHSACA)**
PO Box 4342
Hamden, CT 06514-2262
Ph: (203)288-7473   Fax: (203)288-8224
E-mail: office@hscoaches.org
URL: http://www.hscoaches.org
Description: High school coaches and athletic directors; athletic directors for school systems; executive secretaries of state high school coaches; state high school coaches associations. Public members are college coaches, former high school coaches, adult athletic trainers, principals, officials, and sporting goods salesmen. Formed to give greater national prestige and professional status to high school coaching and to promote cooperation among coaches, school administrators, the press, game officials, and the public. Promotes drug and alcohol abuse prevention through National Training Semi-

nars in Drug Prevention in conjunction with the Drug Enforcement Administration, Washington, DC. Conducts Sports medicine/Medical Aspects of Sports seminars in conjunction with national sports and medical groups, and National College Credit Program for coaches and athletic directors. Maintains National Awards Program to recognize outstanding high school athletic directors, coaches, and players. Presents numerous awards, including: National All-American awards in various sports; National High School Coach of the Year Award in football, boys' basketball, baseball, boys' and girls' track, wrestling, cross country, swimming, soccer, golf, tennis, softball, volleyball, and special sports; Distinguished Service Award. Maintains National High School Sports Committees in 17 sports areas.

★11030★ **National Strength and Conditioning Association (NSCA)**
PO Box 9908
Colorado Springs, CO 80932-0908
Ph: (719)632-6722   Fax: (719)632-6367
Fr: 800-815-6826
E-mail: nsca@nsca-lift.org
URL: http://www.nsca-lift.org
Description: Professionals in the sports science, athletic, and fitness industries. Promotes the total conditioning of athletes to a level of optimum performance, with the belief that a better conditioned athlete not only performs better but is less prone to injury. Gathers and disseminates information on strength and conditioning techniques and benefits. Conducts national, regional, state, and local clinics and workshops. Operates professional certification program.

★11031★ **NFHS Coaches Association**
PO Box 690
Indianapolis, IN 46206
Ph: (317)972-6900   Fax: (317)822-5700
E-mail: nfca@nfhs.org
URL: http://www.nfhs.org
Description: High school, middle school and youth athletic coaches. Promotes professional growth and image of interscholastic sports coaches; provides a forum for coaches to make suggestions on rules and procedures in high school sports in the United States. Cooperates with state high school athletic associations and uses extensive committee structure to ensure grass roots involvement and input from the local, state, and national levels. Maintains hall of fame.

★11032★ **Professional Golfers' Association of America (PGA)**
100 Ave. of Champions
Box 109601
Palm Beach Gardens, FL 33410-9601
Ph: (561)624-8400   Fax: (561)624-8430

E-mail: info@pga.com
URL: http://www.pga.com/
Members: Recruits and trains men and women to manage a variety of golf businesses, including golf clubs, courses, and tournaments. **Activities:** Sponsors PGA Championship, PGA Seniors' Championship, Ryder Cup Matches, PGA Grand Slam of Golf, Club Professional Championship, PGA Foundation, and Senior Club Professional Championship; PGA Junior Championship; PGA Assistants Championship. Conducts Professional Golf Management; certifies college programs in golf management at 14 universities. Sponsors winter tournament program for club professionals including tournaments held in south Florida. Offers complementary employment services for PGA members and employers, owns and operates PGA Golf Club and PGA Learning Center.

★11033★ **Professional Tennis Registry (USPTR)**
PO Box 4739
Hilton Head Island, SC 29938
Ph: (843)785-7244   Fax: (843)686-2033
Fr: 800-421-6289
E-mail: ptr@ptrtennis.org
URL: http://www.ptrtennis.org
Purpose: Tests, certifies, and registers international tennis teaching professionals. Certification requires successful completion of a written and on-court examinations. **Activities:** Sponsors workshops, tennis clinics, and charitable program. Holds competitions; compiles statistics; maintains placement service.

★11034★ **U.S. Lacrosse and The Lacrosse Museum and National Hall of Fame**
113 W. University Pkwy.
Baltimore, MD 21210
Ph: (410)235-6882   Fax: (410)366-6735
E-mail: info@uslacrosse.org
URL: http://www.uslacrosse.org
Description: The national governing body of men's and women's lacrosse. Also runs the Lacrosse Museum and National Hall of Fame.

★11035★ *Women in Nontraditional Careers: An Introduction*
Her Own Words
PO Box 5264
Madison, WI 53705
Ph: (608)271-7083   Fax: (608)271-0209
URL: http://www.herownwords.com/
Video. Jocelyn Riley. $95.00. 15 minutes. Resource guide also available for $45.00.

Statisticians

SOURCES OF HELP-WANTED ADS

★11036★ *Journal of Financial and Quantitative Analysis*
Journal of Financial & Quantitative Analysis
University of Washington
School of Business Administration
115 Lewis Hall
PO Box 353200
Seattle, WA 98195
Ph: (206)543-4598   Fax: (206)616-1894
E-mail: jfqa@u.washington.edu
URL: http://weber.u.washington.edu/~jfqa

Quarterly. $40.00/year; $25.00/year for students; $85.00/year. Journal on research in finance.

PLACEMENT AND JOB REFERRAL SERVICES

★11037★ International Society of Parametric Analysts (ISPA)
PO Box 6402
Town & Country Branch
Chesterfield, MO 63006-6402
Ph: (636)527-2955   Fax: (636)256-8358
E-mail: clydeperry@aol.com
URL: http://www.ispa-cost.org

Members: Engineers, designers, statisticians, estimators, and managers in industry, the military, and government who develop and use computerized, parametric cost-estimating models. **Activities:** Conducts educational activities aimed at promoting usage of parametric modeling techniques for purposes of cost estimating, risk analysis, and technology forecasting. Sponsors placement service.

EMPLOYER DIRECTORIES AND NETWORKING LISTS

★11038★ *American Men and Women of Science*
Thomson Gale
27500 Drake Rd.
Farmington Hills, MI 48331-3535
Ph: (248)699-4253   Fax: (248)699-8065
Fr: 800-877-GALE
E-mail: amws@galegroup.com

Biennial, latest edition December 2002. $975.00. Covers over 129,700 U.S. and Canadian scientists active in the physical, biological, mathematical, computer science, and engineering fields; includes references to previous edition for deceased scientists and nonrespondents. Entries include: Name, address, education, personal and career data, memberships, honors and awards, research interest. Arrangement: Alphabetical. Indexes: Discipline (in separate volume).

HANDBOOKS AND MANUALS

★11039★ *Careers for Number Crunchers and Other Quantitative Types*
McGraw-Hill Trade
2 Penn Plaza
New York, NY 10121
Ph: (212)904-2000   Fr: 800-722-4726
E-mail: ntcpub@tribune.com

Rebecca Burnett. Second edition, 2002. $15.95; $12.95 (paper). 192 pages. Provides information to math-oriented job hunters on how to become statisticians, field researchers, computer programmers, stock analysts, investment managers, bankers, engineers, accountants, underwriters, economists, market analysts, mathematicians, systems analysts, and more.

★11040★ *Opportunities in High Tech Careers*
McGraw-Hill Trade
2 Penn Plaza
New York, NY 10121
Ph: (212)904-2000   Fr: 800-722-4726

Gary Colter and Deborah Yanuck. 1995. $14.95; $11.95 (paper). 160 pages. Explores high technology careers. Describes job opportunities, how to make a career decision, how to prepare for high technology jobs, job hunting techniques, and future trends.

★11041★ *Opportunities in Research and Development Careers*
McGraw-Hill/Contemporary Books
1221 Avenue of the Americas
New York, NY 10020
Ph: (212)904-2000   Fr: 800-323-4900
E-mail: ntcpub@tribune.com

Jan Goldberg. 1997. $14.95; $11.95 (paper). 204 pages.

★11042★ *Opportunities in Social Science Careers*
McGraw-Hill Companies
860 Taylor Station Rd.
Blacklick, OH 43004-0545
Fax: (614)755-5645   Fr: 800-722-4726

Rosanne J. Marek. March 2004. $22.95. 160 Pages. VGM Opportunities Series.

★11043★ *Opportunities in Sports and Athletics Careers*
McGraw-Hill Trade
2 Penn Plaza
New York, NY 10121
Ph: (212)904-2000   Fr: 800-722-4726
E-mail: ntcpub@tribune.com

William Ray Heitzmann. 1994. 160 pages. $14.95; $11.95 (paper). A guide to planning for and seeking opportunities in this growing field. Illustrated.

EMPLOYMENT AGENCIES AND SEARCH FIRMS

★11044★ Analytic Recruiting, Inc.
12 E. 41st St., 9th Fl.
New York, NY 10017
Ph: (212)545-8511   Fax: (212)545-8520
E-mail: email@analyticrecruiting.com
URL: http://www.analyticrecruiting.com

Executive search firm.

★11045★ Biomedical Search Consultants
PO Box 721
Hawleyville, CT 06440-0721
Ph: (203)426-1445
E-mail: ta4nabio@cs.com

Employment agency.

★11046★ Placemart Personnel Service
766 Shrewsbury Ave E Office Fl. 5
Tinton Falls, NJ 07724
Ph: (732)212-0144   Fax: (732)212-0145
Fr: 800-394-7522
E-mail: info@placemart.com
URL: http://www.placemart.com

Executive search firm focusing on the field of clinical research.

TRADESHOWS

★11047★ Joint Statistical Meetings
American Statistical Association
1429 Duke St.
Alexandria, VA 22314
Ph: (703)684-1221   Fax: (703)684-2037

Annual. **Primary Exhibits:** Publications, software, federal agencies, recruiters, con-sulting firms. **Dates and Locations:** 2004 Aug 08-12; Toronto, ON, Canada.

OTHER SOURCES

★11048★ American Statistical Association (ASA)
1429 Duke St.
Alexandria, VA 22314-3415
Ph: (703)684-1221   Fax: (703)684-2037
Fr: 888-231-3473
E-mail: asainfo@amstat.org
URL: http://www.amstat.org

Members: Professional society of persons interested in the theory, methodology, and application of statistics to all fields of human endeavor.

★11049★ Caucus for Women in Statistics (CWS)
7732 Rydal Terr.
Rockville, MD 20855
E-mail: williams_janet@bls.gov
URL: http://www.geocities.com/ResearchT-riangle/System/2290

Description: Individuals, primarily statisti-cians, united to improve employment and professional opportunities for women in sta-tistics. Conducts technical sessions concern-ing statistical studies related to women. Maintains biographical archives.

★11050★ Institute of Mathematical Statistics (IMS)
PO Box 22718
Beachwood, OH 44122
Ph: (216)295-2340   Fax: (216)295-5661
E-mail: ims@imstat.org
URL: http://www.imstat.org/

Members: Professional society of mathema-ticians and others interested in mathematical statistics and probability theory. **Purpose:** Seeks to further research in mathematical statistics and probability.

★11051★ Mathematicians
Evon Publishing
832 N 7th Ave.
Iron River, MI 49935
Ph: (906)265-3190

Audiocassette. 1996. $16.95. 32 minutes. Part of the Careers and Vocational Guidance Series. Provides information about the na-ture of the work, educational requirements, employment outlook, earnings, and work conditions as well as additional related infor-mation.

★11052★ Professional Specialty Occupations
Delphi Productions
3160 4th St.
Boulder, CO 80304
Fax: (303)443-4022   Fr: 888-443-2400
URL: http://www.delphivideo.com

$95.00. 53 minutes. Part of the Careers for the 21st Century Video Library.

★11053★ Scientific, Engineering, and Technical Services
Cambridge Educational
2572 Brunswick Ave.
Lawrenceville, NJ 08648-4128
Fax: 800-FAX-ON-US   Fr: 800-468-4227
URL: http://www.cambridgeeducational.com

$89.95. 2002. 18 minutes. Part of the Career Cluster Series.

★11054★ Scientific Occupations
Delphi Productions
3160 4th St.
Boulder, CO 80304
Fax: (303)443-4022   Fr: 888-443-2400
URL: http://www.delphivideo.com

$95.00. 60 minutes. Part of the Careers for the 21st Century Video Library.

Stenographers and Court Reporters

Sources of Help-Wanted Ads

★11055★ Public Interest Employment Service Job Alert!

Public Interest Clearinghouse
47 Kearny St., Ste. 705
San Francisco, CA 94108
Ph: (415)834-0100   Fax: (415)834-0202
E-mail: pies@pic.org

Description: Semimonthly. Lists job openings in legal aid offices and public interest law organizations.

★11056★ Virginia Court Reporters Association Newsletter

Virginia Court Reporters Association
RR 74, Box 1034
Plain View, VA 23156
Ph: (804)556-4726   Fax: (804)556-2533

Description: Quarterly. Publishes anything educational, entertaining, or enlightening about court reporting. Recurring features include interviews, news of research, a calendar of events, reports of meetings, news of educational opportunities, job listings, and notices of publications available.

Employer Directories and Networking Lists

★11057★ Court & Convention Reporters Directory

infoUSA Inc.
5711 S 86th Cir.
Omaha, NE 68127-0347
Ph: (402)930-3500   Fax: (402)331-0176
Fr: 800-555-6124
URL: http://www.abii.com

Annual. Number of listings: 4,891. Entries include: Name, address, phone (including area code), size of advertisement, year first in "Yellow Pages," name of owner or manager, number of employees. Compiled from telephone company "Yellow Pages," nationwide. Arrangement: Geographical.

★11058★ Law and Legal Information Directory

Thomson Gale
27500 Drake Rd.
Farmington Hills, MI 48331-3535
Ph: (248)699-4253   Fax: (248)699-8065
Fr: 800-877-GALE
E-mail: businessproducts@gale.com

Biennial. $405.00. Covers more than 19,000 national and international organizations, bar associations, federal and highest state courts, federal regulatory agencies, law schools, firms and organizations offering continuing legal education, paralegal education, sources of scholarships and grants, awards and prizes, special libraries, information systems and services, research centers, publishers of legal periodicals, books, and audiovisual materials, lawyer referral services, legal aid offices, public defender offices, legislature manuals and registers, small claims courts, corporation departments of state, state law enforcement agencies, state agencies, including disciplinary agencies, and state bar requirements. Entries include: All entries include institution or firm name, address, phone; many include names and titles of key personnel and, when pertinent, descriptive annotations. Contents based in part on information selected from several other Gale directories. Arrangement: Classified by type of organization, activity, service, etc. Indexes: Individual sections have special indexes as required.

Handbooks and Manuals

★11059★ Career Planning in Criminal Justice

Anderson Publishing Co.
2035 Reading Rd.
Cincinnati, OH 45202-1576
Ph: (513)421-4142   Fax: (513)562-8116
Fr: 800-582-7295

Robert C. DeLucia and Thomas J. Doyle. Third edition, 1998. 226 pages. $21.95. Surveys a wide range of career and employment opportunities in law enforcement, the courts, corrections, forensic science, and private security. Contains career planning and job hunting advice.

★11060★ The Court Reporter's Guide to Cyberspace

Grras Publications
4022 E. Stanford Dr.
Phoenix, AZ 85018
Ph: (602)808-7771   Fax: (602)808-7773

Richard A. Sherman and Gary Robson. 1996. $24.95. 375 pages.

★11061★ Style and Sense For the Legal Profession: A Handbook for Court Reporters, Transcribers, Paralegals and Secretaries

ETC Publications
700 E. Vereda del Sur
Palm Springs, CA 92262
Ph: (760)325-5352   Fax: (760)325-8841
Fr: 800-382-7869

Audrey Fatooh and Barbara R. Mauk. Revised, 1996. $22.95.

Employment Agencies and Search Firms

★11062★ Attorney Resources, Inc.

750 North St. Paul, Ste. 540
Dallas, TX 75201
Ph: (512)922-8050   Fax: (512)871-3041
Fr: 800-324-4828
E-mail: dallas@attorneyresource.com
URL: http://www.attorneyresource.com

Employment agency. Offices in Fort Worth, TX, and Tulsa, OK. Provides staffing assistance on regular or temporary basis.

★11063★ **Beverly Hills Bar Association Personnel Service**
300 S. Beverly Dr., Ste. 214
Beverly Hills, CA 90212-4805
Ph: (310)553-4575   Fax: (310)553-6940
URL: http://www.bhba.org

Employment agency.

★11064★ **Hallmark Services**
1000 Second Ave., Ste. 1450
Seattle, WA 98104
Ph: (206)587-5360
URL: http://hallmarkservices.com/Default.htm

Employment agency. Fills openings for permanent employment.

★11065★ **Legal Placement Services, Inc.**
740 N Plankinton Ave., Ste.430
Milwaukee, WI 53203
Ph: (414)276-6689   Fax: (414)276-1418
E-mail: info@legalplacementservices.com
URL: http://
www.legalplacementservices.com

Employment agency. Periodically fills temporary placements as well.

★11066★ **Pathfinders, Inc.**
229 Peachtree St. NE
International Tower, Ste. 1500
Atlanta, GA 30303
Ph: (404)688-5940

Permanent employment agency focusing on the secretarial field.

ONLINE JOB SOURCES AND SERVICES

★11067★ **JournalismJobs.com**
E-mail: contact@journalismjobs.com
URL: http://www.journalismjobs.com

Description: Career-related site for journalists and other media professionals. Seekers can search for jobs, post a resume online, and manage the search online with the Job Seeker Folder feature. They also can receive free job announcements by e-mail.

OTHER SOURCES

★11068★ **National Court Reporters Association (NCRA)**
8224 Old Courthouse Rd.
Vienna, VA 22182
Ph: (703)556-6272   Fax: (703)556-6291
Fr: 800-272-6272
E-mail: msic@ncrahq.org
URL: http://www.ncraonline.org

Description: Independent state, regional, and local associations. Verbatim court reporters who work as official reporters for courts and government agencies, as freelance reporters for independent contractors, and as captioners for television programming; retired reporters, teachers of court reporting, and school officials; student court reporters. Conducts research; compiles statistics; offers several certification programs, publishes journal.

★11069★ *Stenographers*
Evon Publishing
832 N 7th Ave.
Iron River, MI 49935
Ph: (906)265-3190

Audiocassette. 1996. $16.95. 32 minutes. Part of the Careers and Vocational Guidance Series. Provides information about the nature of the work, educational requirements, employment outlook, earnings, and work conditions as well as additional related information.

Stockbrokers and Securities Analysts

SOURCES OF HELP-WANTED ADS

★11070★ Investment Dealers' Digest
Securities Data Publishing
195 Broadway, 10th Fl.
New York, NY 10007
Fr: 800-455-5844
E-mail: subscribe@iddis.com

Weekly. $625.00/year for individuals. Magazine focusing on securities and finance.

★11071★ Registered Rep.
Primedia Business
249 W 17th St., 3rd Fl.
New York, NY 10011-5300
Ph: (212)462-3586   Fax: (212)206-3622
URL: http://www.registeredrep.com

Monthly. $48.00/year for individuals; $60.00/year for out of country; $10.00 for single issue. Magazine providing comprehensive coverage of securities industry trends directly affecting the job performance and productivity of retail stockbrokers.

PLACEMENT AND JOB REFERRAL SERVICES

★11072★ Financial Women's Association of New York (FWA)
215 Park Ave. S, Ste. 1713
New York, NY 10003
Ph: (212)533-2141   Fax: (212)982-3008
E-mail: fwaoffice@fwa.org
URL: http://www.fwa.org

Members: Persons of professional status in the field of finance in the New York metropolitan area. **Purpose:** Works to promote and maintain high professional standards in the financial and business communities; provide an opportunity for members to enhance one another's professional contacts; achieve recognition of the contribution of women to the financial and business communities; encourage other women to seek professional positions within the financial and business communities. **Activities:** Activities include educational trips to foreign countries; college internship program including foreign student exchange; high school mentorship program; Washington and international briefings; placement service for members. Maintains speakers' bureau.

★11073★ New York Society of Security Analysts (NYSSA)
1601 Broadway, 11th Fl.
New York, NY 10019
Ph: (212)541-4530   Fax: (212)541-4677
Fr: 800-248-0108
E-mail: staff@nyssa.org
URL: http://www.nyssa.org

Members: Security analysts and portfolio managers employed primarily in New York by brokerage houses, banks, insurance companies, mutual funds, and other financial institutions. **Activities:** Conducts educational forums on topics relating to the securities markets. Maintains placement service.

EMPLOYER DIRECTORIES AND NETWORKING LISTS

★11074★ Bonds-Surety & Fidelity Directory
infoUSA Inc.
5711 S 86th Cir.
Omaha, NE 68127-0347
Ph: (402)930-3500   Fax: (402)331-0176
Fr: 800-555-6124
URL: http://www.abii.com

Annual. Number of listings: 4,927. Entries include: Name, address, phone (including area code), size of advertisement, year first in "Yellow Pages," name of owner or manager, number of employees. Compiled from telephone company "Yellow Pages," nationwide. Arrangement: Geographical.

★11075★ Career Opportunities in Banking, Finance, and Insurance
Facts on File Inc.
132 W 31st St., 17th Fl.
New York, NY 10001
Ph: (212)967-8800   Fax: 800-678-3633
Fr: 800-322-8755

$49.50. Publication includes: Lists of colleges with programs supporting banking, finance, and industry; professional associations; professional certifications; regulatory agencies; and Internet resources for career planning. Principal content of publication is job descriptions for professions in the banking, finance, and insurance industries. Indexes: Alphabetical.

★11076★ Institutional Investor-All America Research Team Issue
Aspen Publishers Inc.
1185 Avenue of the Americas
New York, NY 10036
Ph: (212)597-0200

Annual, October. $45.00. Publication includes: List of about 400 analysts at 35 firms judged to have been outstanding in their recommendations concerning stock transactions. Entries include: Analyst name, firm, ranking, comments by colleagues and clients. Arrangement: Classified by line of business.

★11077★ Institutional Investor-Ranking America's Biggest Brokers Issue
Aspen Publishers Inc.
1185 Avenue of the Americas
New York, NY 10036
Ph: (212)597-0200

Annual, April. $45.00. Publication includes: Top 100 brokerage firms selected on the basis of total capital. Entries include: Company name, total capital, excess net capital, number of employees, officers, and registered representatives. Arrangement: Ranked by total capital.

★11078★ Investment Securities Directory

infoUSA Inc.
5711 S 86th Cir.
Omaha, NE 68127-0347
Ph: (402)930-3500   Fax: (402)331-0176
Fr: 800-555-6124
URL: http://www.abii.com

Updated continuously; printed on request. Number of listings: 24,703. Entries include: Name, address, phone (including area code), size of advertisement, year first in "Yellow Pages," name of owner or manager, number of employees. Compiled from telephone company "Yellow Pages," nationwide. Arrangement: Geographical.

★11079★ National Association of Securities Dealers-Manual

CCH Inc.
2700 Lake Cook Rd.
Riverwoods, IL 60015
Ph: (847)267-7000   Fax: (847)267-2945
Fr: 888-224-7377

Loose-leaf format with eight updates per year. $452.00. Publication includes: List of about 2,900 members of the National Association of Securities Dealers. Entries include: Company name, address. Principal contents of the manual are association by-laws and industry rules, arbitration code and code of procedure, and association's rules of fair practice. Arrangement: Alphabetical.

★11080★ Securities Industry Yearbook

Securities Industry Association
120 Broadway, 35th Fl.
New York, NY 10271-0080
Ph: (212)608-1500   Fax: (212)968-0703
URL: http://www.sia.com.

Annual, August. $140.00 for nonmembers. Covers over 600 member securities firms, with about 480 of them covered in detail. Entries include: For firms covered in detail-Company name, name of parent company, address, phone, capital position and rank, number of offices and type, number of employees, area of specialization, names and titles of key personnel, number of registered representatives, departments with name of department head, dollar volume of underwriting and syndication by type, other financial data. For other firms-Company name, address, name of delegated liaison to the association. Arrangement: Alphabetical. Indexes: National firms ranked by capital with capital and rank for prior year, number of offices and rank, number of employees and rank, and number of registered representatives and rank. Same data given in separate ranked list for regional firms.

★11081★ Standard & Poor's Security Dealers of North America

Standard & Poor's
55 Water St.
New York, NY 10041
Ph: (212)438-1000
URL: http://www2.standardandpoors.com/s.com

Semiannual, March and September; supplements available every 6 weeks. $590.00 per set; $480.00 per issue without supplements; $210.00 for supplements. Covers over 12,000 security dealers; includes over 300 offices outside North America. Entries include: Company name, address, phone, main and branch offices, departments, names and titles of principal personnel, exchange memberships, teletype, wire systems, clearing facilities, employer identification number, and date established. Arrangement: Geographical.

HANDBOOKS AND MANUALS

★11082★ America's Fastest Growing Jobs

JIST Works, Inc.
8902 Otis Ave.
Indianapolis, IN 46216-1033
Ph: (317)613-4200   Fax: (317)613-4307
Fr: 800-648-5478
E-mail: jistworks@aol.com
URL: http://www.jist.com

Seventh edition, 2002. $16.95 (paper). 438 pages. Each job profile explains the nature of the work, skills and abilities required, employment outlook, average earnings, related occupations, education and training requirements, and employment opportunities. Also contains career planning information and job search tips.

★11083★ Careers in Banking and Finance

Rosen Publishing Group, Inc.
29 E. 21st St.
New York, NY 10010
Ph: (212)777-3017   Fax: 888-436-4643
Fr: 800-237-9932

Patricia Haddock. 2001. $16.95 139 pages. Offers advice on job hunting. Describes jobs at all levels in banking and finance. Contains information about the types of financial organizations where the jobs are found, educational requirements, job duties, and salaries.

★11084★ Careers for Financial Mavens and Other Money Movers

McGraw-Hill Trade
2 Penn Plaza
New York, NY 10121
Ph: (212)904-2000   Fr: 800-722-4726
E-mail: ntcpub@tribune.com

Marjorie Eberts and Margaret Gisler. 1998. $14.95; $9.95 (paper). 232 pages.

★11085★ Careers for Number Crunchers and Other Quantitative Types

McGraw-Hill Trade
2 Penn Plaza
New York, NY 10121
Ph: (212)904-2000   Fr: 800-722-4726

E-mail: ntcpub@tribune.com

Rebecca Burnett. Second edition, 2002. $15.95; $12.95 (paper). 192 pages. Provides information to math-oriented job hunters on how to become statisticians, field researchers, computer programmers, stock analysts, investment managers, bankers, engineers, accountants, underwriters, economists, market analysts, mathematicians, systems analysts, and more.

★11086★ Job Seekers Guide to Wall Street Recruiters

John Wiley & Sons Inc.
1 Wiley Dr.
Somerset, NJ 08873
Ph: (732)469-4400   Fr: 800-225-5945

Christopher W. Hunt and Scott A. Scanlon. 1998. $19.95 (paper). Lists recruiters covering investment banking, investment management, and the securities industry.

★11087★ Opportunities in Financial Careers

McGraw-Hill Trade
2 Penn Plaza
New York, NY 10121
Ph: (212)904-2000   Fr: 800-722-4726

Michael Sumichrast. 1997. $14.95; $11.95 (paper). 210 pages. A guide to planning for and seeking opportunities in this challenging field.

★11088★ Vault Career Guide to Sales and Trading

Vault.com
150 W. 22nd St., 5th Fl.
New York, NY 10011
Ph: (212)366-4212   Fax: (212)366-6117
Fr: 888-562-8285

April 2004. $29.95 (paper). 128 pages. Series of the Vault Career Library.

EMPLOYMENT AGENCIES AND SEARCH FIRMS

★11089★ Baker Scott and Co.

1259 U.S. Highway 46, Ste. 1
Parsippany, NJ 07054
Ph: (973)263-3355   Fax: (973)263-9255

Executive search firm.

★11090★ Erlanger Holdings Inc.

2 Soundview Dr.
Greenwich, CT 06830
Ph: (203)629-5410   Fax: (203)629-5444

Executive search firm with second location in North Palm Beach, FL.

★11091★ ESearch Group
30 Tower Ln.
Avon, CT 06001
Ph: (860)677-6770
Executive search firm.

★11092★ Essex Consulting Group Inc.
PO Box 550
Essex, MA 01929
Ph: (978)768-0030
Executive search firm.

★11093★ ExecuGroup Inc.
142 S. Main St.
PO Box 5040
Grenada, MS 38901
Ph: (662)226-9025   Fax: (662)226-9090
Executive search firm. Second location in Bethlehem, PA.

★11094★ Flagship Global Inc.
Flagship Wharf
197 8th St.
Boston, MA 02129
Ph: (617)241-9000
Executive search firm focused on the financial industry.

★11095★ Fogec Consultants Inc.
PO Box 28806
Milwaukee, WI 53228
Ph: (414)427-0690
Executive search firm focused on the financial industry.

★11096★ J.R. Scott and Associates
1 S Wacker Dr., Ste. 1616
Chicago, IL 60606-4616
Ph: (312)795-4300   Fax: (312)795-4329
E-mail: mark@esquirestaffing.com
URL: http://www.esquirestaffing.com
Executive search firm specializing in retail securities sales, investment banking, and equity and debt trading. A division of Esquire Personnel Services, Inc.

★11097★ Mark Elzweig Co. Ltd.
183 Madison Ave., Ste.1704
New York, NY 10016
Ph: (212)685-7070   Fax: (212)685-7761
E-mail: melzweig@elzweig.com
URL: http://www.elzweig.com
Executive search firm.

★11098★ Straight and Company
1002 Brown Thrasher Point
St. Mary's, GA 31558
Ph: (912)882-3480   Fax: (912)882-3487
E-mail: gary.straight@straightco.com
URL: http://www.straightco.com
Financial services executive search firm.

ONLINE JOB SOURCES AND SERVICES

★11099★ Glocapsearch.com
E-mail: comments@glocap.com
URL: http://www.glocapsearch.com
Description: Recruitment firm for the private equity, venture capital and hedge fund marketplaces. After registering with website, seekers will be notified weekly of positions available that may interest them. Through returned e-mail, the firm will forward resumes and schedule preliminary interviews with prospective employers.

OTHER SOURCES

★11100★ Association for Investment Management and Research (AIMR)
560 Ray C. Hunt Dr.
PO Box 3668
Charlottesville, VA 22903-0668
Ph: (434)951-5499   Fax: (434)951-5262
Fr: 800-247-8132
E-mail: info@aimr.org

URL: http://www.aimr.org
Description: Security and financial analyst association whose members are practicing investment analysts. Includes private, voluntary self-regulation program in which AIMR members are enrolled. Internationally renowned for its rigorous Chartered Financial Analyst (CFA) curriculum and examination program, which has more than 86,000 candidates from 143 countries enrolled for exams. In addition, AIMR is internationally recognized for its investment performance standards, which investment firms use to document and report investment results, as well as for its Code of Ethics and Standards of Professional Conduct.

★11101★ Financial Occupations
Delphi Productions
3160 4th St.
Boulder, CO 80304
Fax: (303)443-4022   Fr: 888-443-2400
URL: http://www.delphivideo.com
$95.00. 50 minutes. Part of the Careers for the 21st Century Video Library.

★11102★ Securities Industry Association (SIA)
120 Broadway, 35th Fl.
New York, NY 10271-0080
Ph: (212)608-1500   Fax: (212)968-0703
E-mail: info@sia.com
URL: http://www.sia.com
Description: Investment bankers, securities underwriters, and dealers in stocks and bonds. To represent and serve all segments of the securities industry and provide a unified voice in legislation, regulation, and public information. Conducts studies and compiles statistics on investment, securities markets, and related matters. Sponsors management development programs; conducts roundtables. Maintains offices in New York City, and Washington, DC.

Surgical Technicians

★11103★ Expert Resumes for Health Care Careers

JIST Publishing
8902 Otis Ave.
Indianapolis, IN 46216-1033
Ph: (317)613-4200   Fax: 800-547-8329

December 2003. $16.95. 288 pages.

★11104★ Health Careers Today

Elsevier-Health Sciences Division
The Curtis Center, Ste. 300E, 3rd Fl.
170 S. Independence Mall W.
Philadelphia, PA 19106
Ph: (215)238-7800   Fax: (215)238-7362
Fr: 800-523-4069

Gerdin. Revised edition. April 2004. $52.95.

SOURCES OF HELP-WANTED ADS

★11105★ Ambulatory Outreach

Society for Ambulatory Care Professionals
1 N Franklin, 31st Fl.
Chicago, IL 60606
Fax: (312)422-4577

Quarterly. Subscription included in membership; $95.00/year for nonmembers. Professional journal for ambulatory care personnel.

★11106★ American Journal of Surgery

Excerpta Medica Inc.
655 Avenue of the Americas
New York, NY 10010
Ph: (212)989-5800

Monthly. $69.00/year. Surgical journal.

★11107★ Anesthesiology

Lippincott Williams & Wilkins
530 Walnut St.
Philadelphia, PA 19106
Ph: (215)521-8300   Fax: (215)521-8902
Fr: 800-638-3030
E-mail: jderrico@lww.com

URL: http://www.anesthesiology.org

Monthly. $268.00/year for individuals; $491.00/year for institutions; $355.00/year for other countries; $551.00/year for institutions, other countries. Medical journal publishing original manuscripts and brief abstracts from current literature on anesthesiology.

★11108★ Annals of Surgery

Lippincott Williams & Wilkins
530 Walnut St.
Philadelphia, PA 19106
Ph: (215)521-8300   Fax: (215)521-8902
Fr: 800-638-3030
E-mail: bmorrill@lww.com
URL: http://www.annalsofsurgery.com/

Monthly. $190.00/year for individuals; $475.00/year for institutions; $290.00/year for other countries, including current and back issues; $602.00/year for institutions, other countries. Medical journal publishing original manuscripts promoting the advancement of surgical knowledge and practice.

★11109★ ASRT Scanner

American Society of Radiologic
   Technologists
15000 Central Ave. SE
Albuquerque, NM 87123-3917
Ph: (505)298-4500   Fax: (505)298-5063
Fr: 800-444-2778

Monthly. Subscription included in membership. Professional magazine covering issues in radiology and medical technology. Includes calendar of events, member profiles, state affiliate news, educational opportunities, and research updates.

★11110★ Clinical Nuclear Medicine

Lippincott Williams & Wilkins
530 Walnut St.
Philadelphia, PA 19106
Ph: (215)521-8300   Fax: (215)521-8902
Fr: 800-638-3030
E-mail: cnm@pond.com
URL: http://www.nuclearmed.com/

Monthly. $257.00/year for individuals; $447.00/year for institutions; $333.00/year

for other countries, current and back issues; $509.00/year for institutions, other countries. Journal publishing original manuscripts about scanning, imaging, and related subjects.

★11111★ Current Surgery

Lippincott Williams & Wilkins
530 Walnut St.
Philadelphia, PA 19106
Ph: (215)521-8300   Fax: (215)521-8902
Fr: 800-638-3030

Professional journal covering continuing education for surgical residents and general surgeons.

★11112★ Health Care Weekly Review

The Martin Group Inc.
24901 Northwestern Hwy., Ste. 316A
Southfield, MI 48075
Ph: (248)440-6080   Fax: (248)352-4801
E-mail: hcwr@compuserve.com

Weekly. $48.00/year for individuals. Professional newspaper covering the health care industry.

★11113★ Hospitals & Health Networks

Health Forum L.L.C.
One N Franklin
Chicago, IL 60606
Ph: (312)893-6800   Fax: (312)422-4600
Fr: 800-621-6902
E-mail: hhn@healthforum.com
URL: http://www.hhnmag.com

Monthly. Publication covering the health care industry.

★11114★ Journal of the American Society of Podiatric Medical Assistants

American Society of Podiatric Medical
   Assistants
2124 S Austin Blvd.
Cicero, IL 60804
Ph: (708)863-6303   Fax: (708)863-5375
Fr: 888-88A-SPMA

Quarterly. Subscription included in membership. Professional journal covering issues in podiatry.

★11115★ **Journal of Health and Hospital Law**

American Health Lawyers Association
1025 Connecticut NW, Ste. 600
Washington, DC 20036
Ph: (202)833-1100   Fax: (202)833-1105

Quarterly. $150.00/year. Professional journal covering healthcare issues and cases and their impact on the health care arena.

★11116★ **Medicine and Health**

Thomson Financial
195 Broadway
New York, NY 10007
Ph: (646)822-2000

Weekly. Professional publication covering the health care industry.

★11117★ **Minority Health Today**

Heritage Information Holdings Inc.
1101 Pennsylvania Ave. NW, Ste. 820
Washington, DC 20001

Bimonthly. Publication covering minority issues in health.

★11118★ **Research in Healthcare Financial Management**

International Society for Research in Healthcare Financial Management Ltd.
305 W Chesapeake Ave.
CSBA Ste. L-096
Towson, MD 21204

Annual. Publication covering issues in the healthcare industry.

★11119★ **State Health Monitor**

Atlantic Information Services Inc.
1100 17th St. NW, No. 300
Washington, DC 20036
Ph: (202)775-9008   Fax: (202)331-9542
Fr: 800-521-4323
E-mail: customerserv@aispub.com

Monthly. Publication covering health care.

★11120★ **Surgical Rounds**

Romaine Pierson Publishers Inc.
241 Forsgate Dr.
Jamesburg, NJ 08831
Ph: (732)656-0200   Fax: (732)656-1142

Monthly. Free to qualified subscribers; $76.00/year for individuals. Journal featuring clinical articles of interest to office-based and hospital-based surgeons, including residents, full-time staff, and surgical faculty.

★11121★ **Trauma Reports**

Thomson Medical Economics
5 Paragon Dr.
Montvale, NJ 07645-1742
Ph: (201)358-7200   Fax: (201)722-2680

URL: http://www.ahcpub.com/ahc_root_html/products/newsletters/tr.

Bimonthly. $239.00/year for individuals. Professional publication covering health care.

EMPLOYER DIRECTORIES AND NETWORKING LISTS

★11122★ **AHA Guide to the Health Care Field**

American Hospital Association (AHA)
1 N. Franklin St., 27th Fl.
Chicago, IL 60606
Ph: (312)422-2050   Fax: (312)422-4700
Fr: 800-424-4301

Annual, August. $295.00. Covers hospitals, networks, multi-health care systems, freestanding ambulatory surgery centers, psychiatric facilities, long-term care facilities, substance abuse programs, and other health-related organizations. Entries include: For hospitals-Facility name, address, phone, administrator's name, number of beds, facilities and services, number of employees, expenses, other statistics. For other organizations-Name, address, phone, fax, name and title of contact. Arrangement: Geographical. Indexes: Hospital name.

★11123★ **Directory of Hospital Personnel**

Thomson Medical Economics
5 Paragon Dr.
Montvale, NJ 07645-1742
Ph: (201)358-7200   Fax: (201)722-2680

Annual, November. $325.00. Covers 200,000 executives at 7,000 U.S. hospitals. Entries include: Name of hospital, address, phone, number of beds, type and JCAHO status of hospital, names and titles of key department heads and staff, medical and nursing school affiliations; number of residents, interns, and nursing students. Arrangement: Geographical. Indexes: Hospital name, personnel, hospital size.

★11124★ **Hospital Blue Book**

Billian/Transworld Publishing Inc.
2100 Powers Ferry Rd.
Ste. 300
Atlanta, GA 30339
Ph: (770)955-8484   Fax: (770)955-8485
Fr: 800-533-8484
E-mail: blu-book@billian.com

Annual, January. $285.00 for national edition; $160.00 for southern edition. Covers more than 6,687 hospitals; some listings also appear in a separate southern edition of this publication. Entries include: Name of hospital, accreditation, mailing address, phone, fax, number of beds, type of facility (nonprofit, general, state, etc.); list of administrative personnel and chiefs of medical services, with specific titles. Arrangement: Geographical.

★11125★ **Medical and Health Information Directory**

Thomson Gale
27500 Drake Rd.
Farmington Hills, MI 48331-3535
Ph: (248)699-4253   Fax: (248)699-8065
Fr: 800-877-GALE
E-mail: businessproducts@gale.com

Annual. $285.00 per volume; $675.00 per set. Covers in Volume 1, more than 26,500 medical and health oriented associations, organizations, institutions, and government agencies, including health maintenance organizations (HMOs), preferred provider organizations (PPOs), insurance companies, pharmaceutical companies, research centers, and medical and allied health schools. In Volume 2, over 12,000 medical book publishers; medical periodicals, directories, audiovisual producers and services, medical libraries and information centers, electronic resources, and health-related internet search engines. In Volume 3, more than 35,500 clinics, treatment centers, care programs, and counseling/diagnostic services for 34 subject areas. Entries include: Institution, service, or firm name, address, phone, fax, email and URL; many include names of key personnel and, when pertinent, descriptive annotation. Volume 3 was formerly listed separately as Health Services Directory. Arrangement: Classified by organization activity, service, etc. Indexes: Each volume has a complete alphabetical name and keyword index.

HANDBOOKS AND MANUALS

★11126★ **Careers in Health Care**

McGraw-Hill Trade
2 Penn Plaza
New York, NY 10121
Ph: (212)904-2000   Fr: 800-722-4726
E-mail: ntcpub@tribune.com

Barbara M. Swanson. Fourth edition, 2000. $17.95; $13.95 (paper). 320 pages. Describes job duties, work settings, salaries, licensing and certification requirements, educational preparation, and future outlook. Gives ideas on how to secure a job.

★11127★ **Careers for Night Owls and Other Insomniacs**

McGraw-Hill Trade
2 Penn Plaza
New York, NY 10121
Ph: (212)904-2000   Fr: 800-722-4726
E-mail: ntcpub@tribune.com

Louise Miller. 1995. $14.95; $9.95 (paper). 160 pages.

★11128★ **Opportunities in Health and Medical Careers**
McGraw-Hill Trade
2 Penn Plaza
New York, NY 10121
Ph: (212)904-2000   Fr: 800-722-4726
I. Donald Snook, Jr. and Leo D'Orazio. 1997. $14.95; $11.95 (paper). 202 pages. Covers the full range of medical and health occupations. Illustrated.

★11129★ **Opportunities in Paramedical Careers**
McGraw-Hill/Contemporary Books
1221 Avenue of the Americas
New York, NY 10020
Ph: (212)904-2000   Fr: 800-323-4900
E-mail: ntcpub@tribune.com
Alex Kacen. Revised, 1999. $14.95; 11.95 (paper). 200 pages. Discusses a variety of opportunities in this field and how to pursue them. Illustrated.

★11130★ **Resumes for Health and Medical Careers**
McGraw-Hill Trade
2 Penn Plaza
New York, NY 10121
Ph: (212)904-2000   Fr: 800-722-4726
E-mail: ntcpub@tribune.com
1997. $9.95 (paper). 455 pages.

★11131★ **Surgical Technologist**
R & E Publishers
2132 O'Toole Ave.
San Jose, CA 95131-1302
Ronald R. Smith. 1993. $2.50 (paper). 24 pages.

ONLINE JOB SOURCES AND SERVICES

★11132★ **Medhunters.com**
E-mail: info@medhunters.com
URL: http://www.medhunters.com
Description: Career search site for jobs in all health care specialties; educational re-sources; visa and licensing information for relocation; interesting articles; relocation tools; links to professional organizations and general resources.

★11133★ **ProHealthJobs**
E-mail: sales@prohealthjobs.com
URL: http://www.prohealthjobs.com
Description: Career resources site for the medical and health care field. Lists professional opportunities, product information, continuing education and open positions.

OTHER SOURCES

★11134★ **Association of Surgical Technologists (AST)**
7108-C S Alton Way
Englewood, CO 80112-2106
Ph: (303)694-9130   Fax: (303)694-9169
E-mail: bteutsch@ast.org
URL: http://www.ast.org
Description: Individuals who have received specific education and training to deliver surgical patient care in the operating room. Membership categories are available for both certified and student surgical technologists. Emphasis is placed on encouraging members to participate actively in a continuing education program. Aims are to study, discuss, and exchange knowledge, experience, and ideas in the field of surgical technology; to promote a high standard of surgical technology performance in the community for quality patient care; to stimulate interest in continuing education. Local groups sponsor workshops and institutes. Conducts research.

★11135★ **Exploring Health Occupations**
Cambridge Educational
2572 Brunswick Ave.
Lawrenceville, NJ 08648-4128
Fax: 800-FAX-ON-US   Fr: 800-468-4227
URL: http://www.cambridgeeducational.com
Two videos. $139.95. 1999.

★11136★ **Health Service Occupations**
Delphi Productions
3160 4th St.
Boulder, CO 80304
Fax: (303)443-4022   Fr: 888-443-2400
URL: http://www.delphivideo.com
$95.00. 50 minutes. Part of the Careers for the 21st Century Video Library.

★11137★ **Health Technologists & Technicians**
Delphi Productions
3160 4th St.
Boulder, CO 80304
Fax: (303)443-4022   Fr: 888-443-2400
URL: http://www.delphivideo.com
$95.00. 50 minutes. Part of the Careers for the 21st Century Video Library.

★11138★ **Medical Technicians and Technologists**
Cambridge Educational
2572 Brunswick Ave.
Lawrenceville, NJ 08648-4128
Fax: 800-FAX-ON-US   Fr: 800-468-4227
URL: http://www.cambridgeeducational.com
$79.95. 15 minutes. Part of the Exploring Health Occupations Series.

★11139★ **Medicine & Related Occupations**
Delphi Productions
3160 4th St.
Boulder, CO 80304
Fax: (303)443-4022   Fr: 888-443-2400
URL: http://www.delphivideo.com
$95.00. 45 minutes. Part of the Careers for the 21st Century Video Library.

★11140★ **Surgical Technicians**
Evon Publishing
832 N 7th Ave.
Iron River, MI 49935
Ph: (906)265-3190
Audiocassette. 1996. $16.95. 32 minutes. Part of the Careers and Vocational Guidance Series. Provides information about the nature of the work, educational requirements, employment outlook, earnings, and work conditions as well as additional related information.

Surveyors

SOURCES OF HELP-WANTED ADS

★11141★ **American City and County**
Primedia Business
6151 Powers Ferry Rd.
Atlanta, GA 30339
Ph: (770)955-2500   Fax: (770)618-0348

Monthly. $67.00/year for individuals. Municipal and county administration magazine.

★11142★ **Architectural Record**
McGraw-Hill Companies
1221 Avenue of the Americas
New York, NY 10020
Ph: (212)512-2000
URL: http://www.mcgraw-hill.com

$59.00/year for individuals; $7.00 for single issue. Magazine focusing on architecture.

★11143★ **Builder**
Hanley-Wood L.L.C.
1 Thomas Cir., Ste. 600
Washington, DC 20005
Ph: (202)452-0800   Fax: (202)785-1974
URL: http://www.builderonline.com

Monthly. $29.95/year for individuals. Magazine covering housing and construction industry.

★11144★ **The Municipality**
League of Wisconsin Municipalities
202 State St., Ste. 300
Madison, WI 53703-2215
Ph: (608)267-2380   Fax: (608)267-0645
Fr: 800-991-5502

Monthly. $12.00/year. Magazine for officials of Wisconsin's local municipal governments.

★11145★ **NAHRO Monitor**
National Association of Housing and
  Redevelopment Officials
630 I St. NW
Washington, DC 20001-3736
Ph: (202)289-3500   Fax: (202)289-8181
Fr: 877-866-2476
URL: http://www.nahro.org

Description: Semimonthly. Disseminates news on low-income housing and community development issues. Intended for member professionals and government officials.

★11146★ **PE & RS Photogrammetric Engineering & Remote Sensing**
The Imaging and Geospatial Information
  Society
5410 Grosvenor Ln., Ste. 210
Bethesda, MD 20814
Ph: (301)493-0290   Fax: (301)493-0208
E-mail: asprs@asprs.org

Monthly. $130.00/year. Journal covering photogrammetry, remote sensing, geographic information systems, cartography, and surveying, global positioning systems, digital photogrammetry.

★11147★ **Western City**
League of California Cities
1400 K St., 4th Fl.
Sacramento, CA 95814
Ph: (916)658-8223   Fax: (916)658-8289
Fr: 800-262-1801
URL: http://www.westerncity.com

Monthly. $39.00/year for individuals; $63.00 for two years. Municipal interest magazine.

PLACEMENT AND JOB REFERRAL SERVICES

★11148★ **Professional Women in Construction (PWC)**
315 E. 56th St.
New York, NY 10022-3730
Ph: (212)486-7745   Fax: (212)486-0228

E-mail: pwcusa1@aol.com
URL: http://www.pwcusa.org

Description: Management-level women and men in construction and allied industries; owners, suppliers, architects, engineers, field personnel, office personnel, and bonding/surety personnel. Provides a forum for exchange of ideas and promotion of political and legislative action, education, and job opportunities for women in construction and related fields; forms liaisons with other trade and professional groups; develops research programs. Strives to reform abuses and to assure justice and equity within the construction industry. Sponsors mini-workshops. Maintains Action Line which provides members with current information on pertinent legislation and on the association's activities and job referrals.

EMPLOYER DIRECTORIES AND NETWORKING LISTS

★11149★ **ABC Today-Associated Builders and Contractors National Membership Directory Issue**
Associated Builders & Contractors Inc.
4250 N Fairfax Dr., 9th Fl.
Arlington, VA 22203
Ph: (703)812-2000   Fax: (703)812-8203

Annual, December. $150.00. Publication includes: List of approximately 19,000 member construction contractors and suppliers. Entries include: Company name, address, phone, name of principal executive, code to volume of business, business specialty. Arrangement: Classified by chapter, then by work specialty.

★11150★ **Constructor-AGC Directory of Membership and Services Issue**
AGC Information Inc.
333 John Carlyle St., Ste. 200
Alexandria, VA 22314
Ph: (703)548-3118   Fax: (703)548-3119
URL: http://www.agc.org

Annual, July. $250.00 for nonmembers;

$15.00 for members; $250.00 for other countries. Publication includes: List of over 8,500 member firms and 24,000 national associate member firms engaged in building, highway, heavy, industrial, municipal utilities, and railroad construction (SIC 1541, 1542, 1611, 1622, 1623, 1629); listing of state and local chapter officers. Entries include: For firms-Company name, address, phone, fax, names of principal executives, and code indicating type of construction undertaken. For officers-Name, title, address. Arrangement: Geographical, Alphabetical. Indexes: Company name.

★11151★ **Indiana Society of Professional Engineers-Directory**

Indiana Society of Professional Engineers
PO Box 20806
Indianapolis, IN 46220
Ph: (317)255-2267   Fax: (317)255-2530

Annual, fall. $55.00. Covers member registered engineers, land surveyors, engineering students, and engineers in training. Entries include: Member name, address, phone, type of membership, business information, specialty. Arrangement: Alpha by chapter area.

★11152★ **Surveyors-Land Directory**

infoUSA Inc.
5711 S 86th Cir.
Omaha, NE 68127-0347
Ph: (402)930-3500   Fax: (402)331-0176
Fr: 800-555-6124
URL: http://www.abii.com

Annual. Number of listings: 15,492. Entries include: Name, address, phone (including area code), size of advertisement, year first in "Yellow Pages," name of owner or manager, number of employees. Compiled from telephone company "Yellow Pages," nationwide. Arrangement: Geographical.

HANDBOOKS AND MANUALS

★11153★ **Career Information Center**

Macmillan Publishing Co. Inc.
200 Old Tappan Rd.
Old Tappan, NJ 07675
Fr: 800-428-5331

Visual Education Center Staff. Seventh edition, 1999. $275.00. 2080 pages. This 13-volume set profiles over 600 occupations. Each occupational profile describes job duties, educational requirements, how to get the job, advancement possibilities, employment outlook, working conditions, earnings and benefits, and where to write for more information.

★11154★ **Opportunities in Real Estate Careers**

McGraw-Hill Professional
2 Penn Plaza
New York, NY 10121
Ph: (212)904-2000   Fr: 800-722-4726
E-mail: ntcpub@tribune.com

Mariwyn Evans. 2002. $15.95; $11.95 (paper). 160 pages.

TRADESHOWS

★11155★ **California Land Surveyors Association Conference**

California Land Surveyors Association
795 Farmers Ln., No. 11
PO Box 9098
Santa Rosa, CA 95405
Ph: (707)578-6016   Fax: (707)578-4406

Annual. **Primary Exhibits:** Land surveying equipment, computers, vehicles, software, and two-way communication systems.

OTHER SOURCES

★11156★ **American Congress on Surveying and Mapping (ACSM)**

6 Montgomery Village Ave., Ste .403
Gaithersburg, MD 20879
Ph: (240)632-9716   Fax: (240)632-1321
E-mail: info@acsm.net
URL: http://www.acsm.net/

Members: Professionals, technicians, and students in the field of surveying and mapping including surveying of all disciplines, land and geographic information systems, cartography, geodesy, photogrammetry, engineering, geophysics, geography, and computer graphics; American Association for Geodetic Surveying, American Cartographic Association, and National Society of Professional Surveyors. **Purpose:** Objectives are to advance the sciences of surveying and mapping; promote public understanding and use of surveying and mapping; speak on the national level as the collective voice of the profession; provide publications to serve the surveying and mapping community. Member organizations encourage improvement of university and college curricula for surveying and mapping.

★11157★ **ASPRS - The Imaging and Geospatial Information Society**

5410 Grosvenor Ln., Ste. 210
Bethesda, MD 20814-2160
Ph: (301)493-0290   Fax: (301)493-0208
E-mail: asprs@asprs.org
URL: http://www.asprs.org

Members: Firms, individuals, government employees, and academicians engaged in photogrammetry, photointerpretation, remote sensing, and geographic information systems and their application to such fields as archaeology, geographic information systems, military reconnaissance, urban planning, engineering, traffic surveys, meteorological observations, medicine, geology, forestry, agriculture, construction, and topographic mapping. Mission is to advance knowledge and improve understanding of these sciences and to promote responsible applications. **Activities:** Offers voluntary certification program open to persons associated with one or more functional area of photogrammetry, remote sensing, and GIS. Surveys the profession of private firms in photogrammetry and remote sensing in the areas of productsand services

★11158★ **Associated Builders and Contractors (ABC)**

1300 N. 17th St., Ste. 800
Rosslyn, VA 22209
Ph: (703)812-2000   Fax: (703)812-8201
E-mail: info@abc.org
URL: http://www.abc.org

Description: Construction contractors, subcontractors, suppliers, and associates. Aim is to foster and perpetuate the principles of rewarding construction workers and management on the basis of merit. Sponsors management education programs and craft training; also sponsors apprenticeship and skill training programs. Disseminates technological and labor relations information.

★11159★ **Associated General Contractors of America (AGC)**

333 John Carlyle St., Ste. 200
Alexandria, VA 22314
Ph: (703)548-3118   Fax: (703)548-3119
E-mail: sandhers@agc.org
URL: http://www.agc.org

Description: General construction contractors; subcontractors; industry suppliers; service firms. Provides market services through its divisions. Conducts special conferences and seminars designed specifically for construction firms. Compiles statistics on job accidents reported by member firms. ors. Maintains 65 committees, including joint cooperative committees with other associations and liaison committees with federal agencies.

★11160★ **National Association of Home Builders (NAHB)**

1201 15th St. NW
Washington, DC 20005
Ph: (202)266-8200   Fax: (202)822-0586
Fr: 800-368-5242
E-mail: info@nahb.com
URL: http://www.nahb.org

Description: Single and multifamily home builders, commercial builders, and others associated with the building industry. Lobbies on behalf of the housing industry and conducts public affairs activities to increase public understanding of housing and the economy. Collects and disseminates data on current developments in home building and home builders' plans through its Economics

Department and nationwide Metropolitan Housing Forecast. Maintains NAHB Research Center, which functions as the research arm of the home building industry. Sponsors seminars and workshops on construction, mortgage credit, labor relations, cost reduction, land use, remodeling, and business management. Compiles statistics; offers charitable program, spokesman training, and placement service; maintains speakers' bureau, and Hall of Fame. Subsidiaries include the National Council of the Housing Industry. Maintains over 50 committees in many areas of construction; operates National Commercial Builders Council, National Council of the Multifamily Housing Industry, National Remodelers Council, and National Sales and Marketing Council.

★11161★ National Association of Women in Construction (NAWIC)
327 S Adams St.
Fort Worth, TX 76104
Ph: (817)877-5551   Fax: (817)877-0324
Fr: 800-552-3506

E-mail: nawic@nawic.org
URL: http://www.nawic.org

Description: Seeks to enhance the success of women in the construction industry.

★11162★ National Center for Construction Education and Research
3600 NW 43rd St., Bldg. G
PO Box 141104
Gainesville, FL 32606-1104
Ph: (352)334-0911   Fax: (352)334-0932
Fr: 888-NCCER-20
E-mail: info@nccer.org
URL: http://www.nccer.org

Description: Education foundation committed to the development and publication of Contren(TM) Learning Series, the source of craft training, management education and safety resources for the construction industry.

★11163★ Surveyors
Evon Publishing
832 N 7th Ave.
Iron River, MI 49935
Ph: (906)265-3190

Audiocassette. 1996. $16.95. 32 minutes. Part of the Careers and Vocational Guidance Series. Provides information about the nature of the work, educational requirements, employment outlook, earnings, and work conditions as well as additional related information.

★11164★ Technical & Related Occupations
Delphi Productions
3160 4th St.
Boulder, CO 80304
Fax: (303)443-4022   Fr: 888-443-2400
URL: http://www.delphivideo.com

$95.00. 49 minutes. Part of the Careers for the 21st Century Video Library.

Talent Scouts and Agents

EMPLOYER DIRECTORIES AND NETWORKING LISTS

★11165★ Billboard's International Talent and Touring Directory

Billboard Books
770 Broadway
New York, NY 10003
Ph: (646)654-5000   Fax: (646)654-5487
Fr: 800-278-8477
URL: http://orderbillboard.com

Annual, October. $139.00. Covers over 12,900 artists, managers and agents from 76 countries worldwide, including the U.S.A. and Canada; tour facilities and services; venues; entertainers, booking agents, hotels, and others in the entertainment industry; international coverage. Entries include: Company name, address, phone, fax, names and titles of key personnel. Arrangement: Classified by line of business; venues are then geographical. Indexes: Product/service.

★11166★ Model & Talent Directory

Peter Glenn Publications
6040 NW 43rd Ter.
Boca Raton, FL 33496-4043
Ph: (561)999-8930   Fax: (561)999-8931
Fr: 888-332-6700
URL: http://www.pgdirect.com

Annual. $24.95. Covers over 2,200 listings of model and talent agencies worldwide. Arrangement: Geographical.

★11167★ Modeling Agencies Directory

infoUSA Inc.
5711 S 86th Cir.
Omaha, NE 68127-0347
Ph: (402)930-3500   Fax: (402)331-0176
Fr: 800-555-6124
URL: http://www.abii.com

Updated continuously; printed on request. Number of listings: 1,604. Entries include: Name, address, phone, size of advertisement, name of owner or manager, number of employees, year first in "Yellow Pages." Compiled from telephone company "Yellow

Pages," nationwide. Arrangement: Geographical.

★11168★ New York City Model Agency Directory

Peter Glenn Publications
6040 NW 43rd Ter.
Boca Raton, FL 33496-4043
Ph: (561)999-8930   Fax: (561)999-8931
Fr: 888-332-6700
URL: http://www.pgdirect.com

Annual. $13.95. Covers about 80 modeling agencies in New York City. Entries include: Company name, address, phone, fax, name and title of contact, type of modeling work handled, interview information, years of operation. Arrangement: Alphabetical. Indexes: Name.

★11169★ The Official Southwest Talent Directory

Cobb-Rendish Publishing
1920 Abrams Pkwy., Ste. 419
Dallas, TX 75214-6271
Fax: (214)855-0643

Annual, latest edition March, 1995. $25.00. Covers over 500 adult and juvenile actors, actresses, and models; motion picture and audio/videotape production facilities in the Southwest. Entries include: Name, acting or performing specialties, and agency contact; production services are presented in individual suppliers' ads. Arrangement: Talent classified by sex and age of performers; production sources classified by product or service. Indexes: Personal name, ethnic group, talent abilities.

★11170★ Theatrical Agencies Directory

infoUSA Inc.
5711 S 86th Cir.
Omaha, NE 68127-0347
Ph: (402)930-3500   Fax: (402)331-0176
Fr: 800-555-6124
URL: http://www.abii.com

Updated continuously; printed on request. Number of listings: 383. Entries include: Name, address, phone, size of advertisement, name of owner or manager, number of

employees, year first in "Yellow Pages." Compiled from telephone company "Yellow Pages," nationwide. Arrangement: Geographical.

HANDBOOKS AND MANUALS

★11171★ The Los Angeles Agent Book

Sweden Press
Box 1612
Studio City, CA 91604
Ph: (818)995-4250   Fax: (818)995-4399

K. Callan. Seventh edition, 2001. $17.95 (paper). 315 pages. Describes the actor-agent relationship, provides guidance for selecting the right agent, and gives a list of agents in Los Angeles with background information on each.

★11172★ The Media Jungle: A Survival Guide

Media Masters
872 Franklin Trace
Zionsville, IN 46077-1169
Ph: (317)733-9440   Fax: (317)873-4493

Carrie Van Dyke. 1996. $15.00. 92 pages.

★11173★ 100 Best Careers in Entertainment

Macmillan Publishing Co., Inc.
200 Old Tappan Rd.
Old Tappan, NJ 07675
Fr: 800-428-5331

Shelly Field. 1995. $14.95 (paper). 352 pages.

★11174★ Opportunities in Entertainment Careers

McGraw-Hill Trade
2 Penn Plaza
New York, NY 10121
Ph: (212)904-2000   Fr: 800-722-4726
E-mail: ntcpub@tribune.com

Jan Goldberg. 1999. $14.95; $11.95 (paper). 160 pages.

broadcasting, media, and entertainment industries.

EMPLOYMENT AGENCIES AND SEARCH FIRMS

★11175★ Executive Careers Ltd.
1801 Avenue of the Stars, Fl. 6
Los Angeles, CA 90067
Ph: (310)552-3455   Fax: (310)578-7524
Executive search firm.

★11176★ Joe Sullivan and Associates, Inc.
1202 Lexington Ave
PO Box 178
New York, NY 10028
Ph: (212)734-7890
E-mail: jsa612@aol.com
URL: http://www.joesullivanassociates.com
Executive search firm. Recruits for the

OTHER SOURCES

★11177★ Agents: Tell It Like It Is!
Joel Asher Studio
PO Box 4223
North Hollywood, CA 91617-4223
Ph: (818)785-1551
URL: http://www.joel-asher-studio.com
T. Michael. 1995. $29.95. This 50-minute videocassette introduces viewers to some veteran talent agents as well as to the nature of the job.

★11178★ Association of Talent Agents (ATA)
9255 Sunset Blvd., Ste. 930
Los Angeles, CA 90069
Ph: (310)274-0628   Fax: (310)274-5063
E-mail: shellie@agentassociation.com
URL: http://www.agentassociation.com/

Members: Talent agencies that have clients in the Screen Actors Guild, American Federation of Television and Radio Artists, Directors Guild of America, Writers Guild of America, East, and Writers Guild of America, West. **Purpose:** Negotiates terms of franchise agreements with these guilds and maintains liaison with their representatives. Assists members with contract problems, interpretations, rulings, residual matters, and arbitrations. Employs legal counsel to prepare opinions upon request and to file briefs in arbitrations and labor commission hearings. Initiates arbitration between ATA and the guilds on interpretations that have impact on the agency business. Maintains liaison with labor commission representatives in San Francisco and Los Angeles, CA, and intervenes on behalf of individual members having special problems. Has been successful in amending or defeating bills which the association claims would have had adverse effects on agents. **Activities:** Conducts seminars and symposia

Tax Examiners and Revenue Agents

SOURCES OF HELP-WANTED ADS

★11179★ **Assessment Journal**
International Association of Assessing Officers
130 E Randolph, Ste. 850
Chicago, IL 60601-6217
Ph: (312)819-6100   Fax: (312)819-6149
Bimonthly. Subscription included in membership; $200.00/year for nonmembers. Professional journal covering taxation.

★11180★ **Tax Advisor**
American Institute of Certified Public Accountants
1211 Avenue of the Americas
New York, NY 10036
Monthly. $98.00.

★11181★ **Taxes**
CCH Inc.
2700 Lake Cook Rd.
Riverwoods, IL 60015
Monthly. Publishes articles on legal, accounting, and economic aspects of federal and state taxes.

HANDBOOKS AND MANUALS

★11182★ **Getting Started in Tax Consulting**
Wiley Publishing
10475 Crosspoint Blvd.
Indianapolis, IN 46256
Gary Carter. April 2001. 304 pages.

★11183★ **Inside Careers Guide to the Tax Adviser's Profession**
Cambridge Market Intelligence Ltd.
Unit 3, The Quadrangle
49 Atlanta St.
London SW6 6TR, United Kingdom
Andrew Rogoff. 1999.

★11184★ **Revenue Agent**
National Learning Corporation
212 Michael Dr.
Syosset, NY 11791
Ph: (516)921-8888   Fax: (516)921-8743
Fr: 800-645-6337
Rudman, Jack. 1994. $29.95 (Trade paper).

★11185★ **Tax Examiner**
National Learning Corporation
212 Michael Dr.
Syosset, NY 11791
Ph: (516)921-8888   Fax: (516)921-8743
Fr: 800-645-6337
Rudman, Jack. 1994. $27.95 (Trade paper).

EMPLOYMENT AGENCIES AND SEARCH FIRMS

★11186★ **Boyce Cunnane Inc.**
PO Box 19064
Baltimore, MD 21284-9064
Ph: (410)583-5511
Executive search firm.

★11187★ **The Directorship Search Group Inc.**
8 Sound Shore Dr., Ste. 250
Greenwich, CT 06830
Ph: (203)618-7000   Fax: (203)618-7007
Executive search firm with a second office in New York.

★11188★ **ET Search Inc.**
1250 Prospect St., Ste. 101
La Jolla, CA 92037-3618
Ph: (858)459-3443   Fax: (858)459-4147
Executive search firm focused on the tax industry.

ONLINE JOB SOURCES AND SERVICES

★11189★ **Association of Certified Fraud Examiners**
URL: http://www.cfenet.com
Description: Website for membership organization contains Career Center with job databank, ability to post jobs and career resources and links. **Fee:** Must be a member of organization in order to access databank; annual dues depend on level of professional and begin at $95.

★11190★ **Society of Financial Examiners**
URL: http://www.sofe.org
Description: Website for membership organization contains classified advertisements for financial examiner positions as well as links to resources about the profession and an opportunity to enroll in an annual career development seminar. Visitors do not have to be members of the association to view job postings.

OTHER SOURCES

★11191★ **Accreditation Council for Accountancy and Taxation (ACAT)**
1010 N. Fairfax St.
Alexandria, VA 22314-1574
Ph: (703)549-2228   Fax: (703)549-2984
Fr: 888-289-7763
URL: http://www.acatcredentials.org

Members: Participants include accounting and tax practitioners, enrolled agents, certified public accountants, students, and others interested in attaining accreditation in accounting or taxation. **Purpose:** Strives to raise professional standards and improve the practices of accountancy and taxation; to identify persons with demonstrated knowledge of the principles and practices of accountancy and taxation, to ensure the continued professional growth of accredited individuals by setting stringent continuing education requirements, to foster increased recognition for the profession in the public, private, and educational sectors. **Activities:** Conducts semiannual accreditation examination in accountancy. Tax credentials obtained through coursework and examination. Designations are: Accredited in Accountancy/Accredited Business Accountant, Accredited Tax Advisor and Accredited Tax Preparer.

★11192★ American Society of Tax Professionals (ASTP)

PO Box 1213
Lynnwood, WA 98046-1213
Ph: (425)774-1996   Fax: (425)672-0461
Fr: 877-674-1996
E-mail: kraemerc@juno.com
URL: http://www.taxbeacon.com/astp

Members: Tax preparers, accountants, attorneys, bookkeepers, accounting services, and public accounting firms seeking to uphold high service standards in professional tax preparation. **Purpose:** Works to enhance the image of tax professionals and make tax practice more profitable; keep members abreast of tax law and service and delivery changes; promote networking among members for mutual assistance. **Activities:** Offers continuing education and training courses and public relations and marketing

planning and preparation services. Supports Certified Tax Preparer Program.

★11193★ Council on State Taxation

122 C St. NW, Ste. 330
Washington, DC 20001
Ph: (202)484-5222
URL: http://www.statetax.org

Description: Seeks to preserve equitable local taxation practices.

★11194★ *Financial Occupations*

Delphi Productions
3160 4th St.
Boulder, CO 80304
Fax: (303)443-4022   Fr: 888-443-2400
URL: http://www.delphivideo.com

$95.00. 50 minutes. Part of the Careers for the 21st Century Video Library.

★11195★ Institute for Professionals in Taxation

600 Northpark Town Center
1200 Abernathy Rd. NE, Ste. L-2
Atlanta, GA 30328
URL: http://www.ipt.org

Description: Offers networking and other job opportunities.

★11196★ Internal Revenue Service Agent

Vocational Biographies, Inc.
PO Box 31
Sauk Centre, MN 56378-0031
Fax: (612)352-5546   Fr: 800-255-0752

1995. $5.00. This pamphlet profiles a person working in the job. Includes information about job duties, working conditions, places

of employment, educational preparation, labor market outlook, and salaries.

★11197★ National Association of Enrolled Agents

1120 Connecticut Ave. NW, Ste. 460
Washington, DC 20036
Ph: (202)822-6232
URL: http://www.naea.org

Description: Professional society. Offers a career center.

★11198★ National Association of Tax Professionals (NATP)

720 Association Dr.
Appleton, WI 54914
Ph: (920)749-1040   Fax: 800-747-0001
Fr: 800-558-3402
E-mail: natp@natptax.com
URL: http://www.natptax.com

Description: Dedicated to excellence in the tax profession. Serves professionals who work in all areas of tax practice, including individual practitioners, enrolled agents, certified public accountants, accountants, attorneys, and certified financial planners.

★11199★ National Society of Tax Professionals

10818 NE Coxley Dr., Ste. A
Vancouver, WA 98662
Fr: 800-367-8130
URL: http://www.nstp.org

Description: Professional society.

Teacher Aides

$14.99/year for individuals. Magazine for elementary teachers.

★11211★ Tech Directions

Prakken Publications Inc.
PO Box 8623
Ann Arbor, MI 48107-8623
Ph: (734)975-2800   Fax: (734)975-2787
Fr: 800-530-WORD
E-mail: tdedit@techdirections.com
URL: http://www.techdirections.com

Free to qualified subscribers; $30.00/year for individuals. Magazine covering issues, programs, and projects in industrial education, technology education, trade and industry, and vocational-technical career education. Articles are geared for teacher and administrator use and reference from elementary school through postsecondary levels.

★11212★ Today's OEA

Oregon Education Association
6900 SW Atlanta St.
Portland, OR 97223-2513
Ph: (503)684-3300   Fax: (503)684-8063

Bimonthly. Free to qualified subscribers; $10.00/year for nonmembers. Membership magazine covering educational issues state-wide and nationally.

PLACEMENT AND JOB REFERRAL SERVICES

★11213★ American Montessori Society (AMS)

281 Park Ave. S, 6th Fl.
New York, NY 10010
Ph: (212)358-1250   Fax: (212)358-1256
E-mail: east@amshq.org
URL: http://www.amshq.org

Description: School affiliates and teacher training affiliates; heads of schools, teachers, parents, non-Montessori educators, and other interested individuals dedicated to stimulating the use of the Montessori teaching approach and promoting better education for all children. Formed to meet demands of growing interest in the Montessori approach to early learning. Developed in Italy in 1907 by Dr. Maria Montessori, the system "is based on the young child's instinctive love and need for purposeful work realized in an environment prepared with auto-educative, multi-sensory, manipulative learning devices for language, math, science, and practical life. Freedom within limits and individual growth fostered in classes with three year age mix and peer stimulation. Teacher's role is that of observer and catalyst." Assists in establishing schools; supplies information and limited services to member schools in other countries. Maintains school consultation and accreditation service; provides information service; assists research and gathers statistical data; offers placement service.

Maintains Montessori and related materials exhibit.

EMPLOYER DIRECTORIES AND NETWORKING LISTS

★11214★ Christian Schools International-Directory

Christian Schools International
3350 E Paris Ave. SE
Grand Rapids, MI 49512-3054
Ph: (616)957-1070   Fax: (616)957-5022
Fr: 800-635-8288
URL: http://www.gospelcom.net/csi

Annual, November. $52.00 for nonmembers. Covers nearly 450 Reformed Christian elementary and secondary schools; related associations; societies without schools. Entries include: For schools-School name, address, phone; name, title, and address of officers; names of faculty members. Arrangement: Geographical.

★11215★ Directory of Public School Systems in the U.S.

American Association for Employment in Education
3040 Riverside Dr., Ste. 125
Columbus, OH 43221
Ph: (614)485-1111   Fax: (614)485-9609

Annual, Winter. $80.00. Covers about 14,500 public school systems in the United States and their administrative personnel. Entries include: System name, address, phone, website address, name and title of personnel administrator, levels taught and approx. student population. Arrangement: Geographical by state.

★11216★ Employment Opportunities, USA

Washington Research Associates
1090 Vermont Ave., NW, Ste. 800
Washington, DC 20005
Ph: (202)408-7025

Annual, quarterly updates. $184.00. Publication includes: List of over 1,000 employment contacts in companies and agencies in the banking, arts, telecommunications, education, and 14 other industries and professions, including the federal government. Entries include: Company name, name of representative, address, description of products or services, hiring and recruiting practices, training programs, and year established. Principal content is industry overviews, career news, employment opportunity information on 14 different job markets, and comprehensive guidance to career resources on the Internet. Arrangement: Classified by industry. Indexes: Occupation.

★11217★ Fifty State Educational Directories

Career Guidance Foundation
8090 Engineer Rd., Ste. B
San Diego, CA 92111
Ph: (858)560-8051   Fax: (858)278-8960
Fr: 800-854-2670
URL: http://www.cgf.org

Annual, latest edition June 1996. $89.00. Microfiche. Collection consists of reproductions of the state educational directories published by the departments of education of individual 50 states. Directory contents vary, but the majority contain listings of elementary and secondary schools, colleges and universities, and state education officials. Amount of detail in each also varies. Entries include: Usually, institution name, address, and name of one executive.

★11218★ Ganley's Catholic Schools in America-Elementary/Secondary/College & University

Fisher Publishing Co.
PO Box 15070
Scottsdale, AZ 85267
Ph: (480)657-9422   Fax: (480)657-9422
Fr: 800-759-7615
URL: http://www.ganleyscatholicschools.com

Annual, summer; latest edition 2003. $51.50. Covers over 8,400 Catholic K-12 Schools. Arrangement: Geographical by state, then alphabetical by Diocese name.

★11219★ Handbook of Private Schools

Porter Sargent Publishers Inc.
11 Beacon St., Ste. 1400
Boston, MA 02108-3099
Ph: (617)523-1670   Fax: (617)523-1021
Fr: 800-342-7470
E-mail: orders@portersargent.com

Annual, June. $99.00. Covers more than 1,600 elementary and secondary boarding and day schools in the United States. Entries include: School name, address, phone, fax, E-mail, URL, type of school (boarding or day), sex and age range, names and titles of administrators, grades offered, academic orientation, curriculum, new admissions yearly, tests required for admission, enrollment and faculty, graduate record, number of alumni, tuition and scholarship figures, summer session, plant evaluation and endowment, date of establishment, calendar, association membership, description of school's offerings and history, test score averages, uniform requirements, geographical, and demographic date. Arrangement: Geographical. Indexes: Alphabetical by school name, cross indexed by state, region, grade range, sexes accepted, school features and enrollment.

★11220★ Independent Schools Association of the Southwest-Membership List

Independent Schools Association of the Southwest
4700 Bryant Irvin Ct., Ste. 204
Fort Worth, TX 76107
Ph: (817)569-9200   Fax: (817)569-9103
Fr: 800-688-5007
URL: http://www.isasw.org

Annual, August. Covers over 75 independent elementary and secondary schools accredited by the association. Entries include: School name, address, phone, chief administrative officer, structure, and enrollment. Arrangement: Geographical. Indexes: Alphabetical.

★11221★ MDR's School Directories

Market Data Retrieval
1 Forest Pkwy.
Shelton, CT 06484
Ph: (203)926-4800   Fax: (203)926-1826
Fr: 800-333-8802
URL: http://www.schooldata.com

Annual, October. $1,349.00 for set. Covers over 90,000 public, 8,000 Catholic, and 15,000 other private schools (grades K-12) in the United States; over 15,000 school district offices, and 76,000 school librarians; and 27,000 media specialists, 33,000 technology coordinators. Includes names of over 165,000 school district administrators and staff members in county and state education administration. Entries include: For districts: District name and address; telephone and fax number; number of schools; number of teachers in the district; district enrollment; special Ed students; limited-english proficient students; minority percentage by race, college bound students; expenditures per student for instructional materials; poverty level; title 1 dollars; site-based management; district open/close dates; construction indicator; technologies and quantities (instructional computer brands, multimedia computers; networks, VCRs, satellite dish, DVD Player/Drive High-Speed Internet Access URL); district-level adminstrators, *new superintendents shaded*. For schools: School name and address-new public shaded; telephone and fax number; principal new principal shaded; librarian, media specialist and technology coordinator; grade span; special programs and school type; student enrollment; technologies and quantities (instructional computer brand noting predominant brand); Multi-Media Computers; internet connection or access; Tech Sophistication Index. Arrangement: Geographical. Indexes: District County; District Personnel; Principal; New Public Schools and Key Personnel; District and School Telephone; District URLs.

★11222★ National Association of Teachers' Agencies-Membership Directory

National Association of Teachers' Agencies
797 Kings Hwy.
Fairfield, CT 06432
Ph: (203)333-0611   Fax: (203)334-7224

URL: http://www.jobsforteachers.com

Annual, January. Covers approximately 20 private employment agencies engaged primarily in the placement of teaching and administrative personnel in education. Entries include: Name, address, phone, names of key officials. Arrangement: Alphabetical.

★11223★ National Directory of Alternative Schools

National Coalition of Alternative Community Schools
1289 Jewett St.
Ann Arbor, MI 48104-6201
Ph: (734)668-9171   Fax: (734)769-9629
Fr: 888-771-9171

Biennial, odd years. $18.00. Covers over 500 alternative education programs, including home schools, and state and regional coalitions of alternative schools and colleges; also lists organizations and networks offering services and resources to those working with children; international coverage. Entries include: Name, address, phone, name of contact; many also include descriptions of programs. Arrangement: Schools are geographical. Indexes: Complete index of entries.

★11224★ National Directory for Employment in Education

American Association for Employment in Education
3040 Riverside Dr., Ste. 125
Columbus, OH 43221
Ph: (614)485-1111   Fax: (614)485-9609

Annual, Winter. $20.00 for institutions. Covers about 600 placement offices maintained by teacher-training institutions and 300 school district personnel officers and/or superintendents responsible for hiring profesional staff. Entries include: Institution name, address, phone, contact name, email address, and website. Arrangement: Geographical. Indexes: Personal name, subject-field of teacher training, institutions which provide vacancy bulletins and placement services to non-enrolled students.

★11225★ Private Independent Schools

Bunting and Lyon Inc.
238 N Main St.
Wallingford, CT 06492
Ph: (203)269-3333   Fax: (203)269-5697
URL: http://www.buntingandlyon.com

Annual, February. $110.00. Covers 1,200 English-speaking elementary and secondary private schools and summer programs in North America and abroad. Entries include: School name, address, phone, fax, e-mail, website, enrollment, tuition and other fees, financial aid information, administrator's name and educational background, director of admission, regional accreditation, description of programs, curriculum, activities, learning differences grid. Arrangement: Geographical. Indexes: School name; geographical. Summer programs, general classification grid, learning differences reference grid.

HANDBOOKS AND MANUALS

★11226★ Careers in Focus: Family and Consumer Sciences; Education and Communication, Science and Technology, Human Services, Business, Art

Goodheart-Wilcox Publisher
18604 W. Creek Dr.
Tinley Park, IL 60477-6243
Ph: (708)687-5000   Fax: 888-409-3900
Fr: 888-409-3900

Lee Jackson. September 2003. $45.00. Illustrated. 399 pages.

★11227★ How to Get a Job in Education

Adams Media Corp.
57 Littlefield St.
Avon, MA 02322
Ph: (508)427-7100   Fax: (508)427-6790
Fr: 800-872-5627
URL: http://www.adamsmedia.com

Joel Levin. Second edition, 1995. $15.95. 320 pages. Out of print. Prepared for recent college graduates, seasoned educators, and career-changing professionals, this publication guides the job-seeker through the necessary steps to obtaining a job in education at the elementary, secondary, and university levels. Offers advice on how to prepare for state and local examinations, how to locate teaching opportunities nationwide, and how to obtain certification. Includes a nationwide salary survey. Covers public, private, summer, and overseas opportunities.

★11228★ Opportunities in Child Care Careers

McGraw-Hill Trade
2 Penn Plaza
New York, NY 10121
Ph: (212)904-2000   Fr: 800-722-4726

Renee Wittenberg. 1998. $14.95; $11.95 (paper). 210 pages. Discusses various job opportunities and how to secure a position. Illustrated.

★11229★ Opportunities in Teaching Careers

McGraw-Hill/Contemporary Books
1221 Avenue of the Americas
New York, NY 10020
Ph: (212)904-2000   Fr: 800-323-4900
E-mail: ntcpub@tribune.com

Janet Fine. 2000. $14.95; $11.95 (paper). 200 pages. Discusses licensing and accreditation programs, sources of placement information, job-seeking correspondence, selection procedures, and paths to advancement. Also covers professional associations, non-traditional teaching opportunities, and jobs abroad.

EMPLOYMENT AGENCIES AND SEARCH FIRMS

★11230★ Educational Placement Service

1001 Craig Rd., Ste. 170
St. Louis, MO 63146
Ph: (314)991-5855   Fax: (314)991-5295
URL: http://www.educatorjobs.com

Employment agency. Focuses on teaching, administrative, and education-related openings.

OTHER SOURCES

★11231★ National Association of Independent Schools (NAIS)

1620 L St. NW, Ste. 1100
Washington, DC 20036-5695
Ph: (202)973-9700   Fax: (202)973-9790
E-mail: info@nais.org
URL: http://www.nais.org

Description: Independent elementary and secondary school members; regional associations of independent schools and related associations. Provides curricular and administrative research and services. Conducts educational programs; compiles statistics.

★11232★ National Community Education Association (NCEA)

3929 Old Lee Hwy., Ste. 91-A
Fairfax, VA 22030
Ph: (703)359-8973   Fax: (703)359-0972
E-mail: ncea@ncea.com
URL: http://www.ncea.com

Description: Community school directors, principals, superintendents, professors, teachers, students, and laypeople. **Purpose:** Promotes and establishes community schools as an integral part of the educational plan of every community. Emphasizes community and parent involvement in the schools, lifelong learning, and enrichment of K-12 and adult education. Serves as a clearinghouse for the exchange of ideas and information, and the sharing of efforts. **Activities:** Offers leadership training.

★11233★ Overseas Employment Opportunities for Educators: Department of Defense Dependents Schools

DIANE Publishing Co.
PO Box 1428
Collingdale, PA 19023-8428
Ph: (610)461-6200   Fax: (610)461-6130
Fr: 800-782-3833

Barry Leonard, editor. 1999. $20.00. 4 pages. An introduction to teachings positions in the Dept. of Defense Dependents Schools (DoDDS), a worldwide school system, operated by the DoD in 14 countries.

★11234★ Working with Children

Cambridge Educational
2572 Brunswick Ave.
Lawrenceville, NJ 08648-4128
Fax: 800-FAX-ON-US   Fr: 800-468-4227
URL: http://www.cambridgeeducational.com

$89.95. 2000. 23 minutes. This program examines alternative positions offering the opportunity to work with children of different ages and the qualifications necessary for those jobs. A nanny, social worker, non-faculty school worker, and retail salesperson describe their job responsibilities and explain why they find their work so enjoyable.

Telemarketing Representatives

SOURCES OF HELP-WANTED ADS

★11235★ **Customer Interaction Solutions**
Technology Marketing Corp.
1 Technology Plz.
Norwalk, CT 06854
Ph: (203)852-6800   Fax: (203)853-2845
Fr: 800-243-6002

Monthly. Publication covering issues in the telecommunications industry.

★11236★ **Journal of Municipal Telecommunications Policy**
National Association of Telecommunications Officers and Advisors
8405 Greensboro Dr., Ste. 800
McLean, VA 22102-5120
Ph: (703)506-3275   Fax: (703)506-3266

Quarterly. Professional journal covering issues for the telecommunications industry.

★11237★ **Online Learning**
VNU Business Media USA
770 Broadway
New York, NY 10003
Ph: (646)654-5000

Monthly. Publication covering the telecommunications industry.

★11238★ **R&B Airplay Monitor**
VNU Business Media USA
770 Broadway
New York, NY 10003
Ph: (646)654-5000
URL: http://www.vnubusinessmedia.com/box/bp/div_ent_music_airm.ht

Weekly. $295.00/year for individuals. Trade publication covering the radio and telecommunications industries.

PLACEMENT AND JOB REFERRAL SERVICES

★11239★ **International Customer Service Association (ICSA)**
401 N. Michigan Ave.
Chicago, IL 60611-4267
Ph: (312)321-6800   Fax: (312)245-1084
Fr: 800-360-ICSA
E-mail: icsa@sba.com
URL: http://www.icsa.com

Description: Customer service professionals in public and private sectors united to develop the theory and understanding of customer service and management. Goals are to: promote professional development; standardize terminology and phrases; provide career counseling and placement services; establish hiring guidelines, performance standards, and job descriptions. Provides a forum for shared problems and solutions. Compiles statistics.

EMPLOYER DIRECTORIES AND NETWORKING LISTS

★11240★ **American Teleservices Association-Membership Directory and Resource Guide**
American Teleservices Association
1620 I St. NW, Ste. 615
Washington, DC 20006
Ph: (202)293-2452   Fax: (202)463-8498
Fr: 877-779-3974
URL: http://www.ataconnect.org

Annual. $300.00 for nonmembers. Covers member companies in the teleservice industry; in-house call centers, service agencies, consultants and suppliers. Entries include: Company name, address, phone, name and title of contact, product or service provided, branch office location. Arrangement: Alphabetical, geographical, by business type. Indexes: Company, international/state member users of TM services, including agencies, consultants, and suppliers.

★11241★ **Quirk's Marketing Research Review-Telephone Interviewing Facilities Directory Issue**
Quirk Enterprises Inc.
8030 Cedar Ave. S.,Ste 229
Minneapolis, MN 55425
Ph: (952)854-5101   Fax: (952)854-8191
URL: http://www.quirks.com

Annual, May. $10.00. Publication includes: List of more than 550 telephone interviewing facilities that conduct marketing research projects. Entries include: Company name, address, phone, fax, description of interviewing stations. Arrangement: Geographical. Indexes: Geographical.

★11242★ **Telemarketing Services Directory**
infoUSA Inc.
5711 S 86th Cir.
Omaha, NE 68127-0347
Ph: (402)930-3500   Fax: (402)331-0176
Fr: 800-555-6124
URL: http://www.abii.com

Updated continuously; printed on request. Number of listings: 2,904. Entries include: Name, address, phone, size of advertisement, name of owner or manager, number of employees, year first in "Yellow Pages." Compiled from telephone company "Yellow Pages," nationwide. Arrangement: Geographical.

★11243★ **Who's Who Teleservices Agency Roundup**
Technology Marketing Corp.
1 Technology Plz.
Norwalk, CT 06854
Ph: (203)852-6800   Fax: (203)853-2845
Fr: 800-243-6002
URL: http://www.tcmnet.com

Annual, June. $7.00. Publication includes: List of more than 250 telemarketing and telecommunications companies that provide inbound, outbound, business-to-business, and business-to-consumer and/or interactive telemarketing services. Entries include: Company name, address, phone, services. Arrangement: Alphabetical. Indexes: Service.

HANDBOOKS AND MANUALS

★11244★ Careers Inside the World of Sales
Rosen Publishing Group, Inc.
29 E. 21st St.
New York, NY 10010
Ph: (212)777-3017   Fax: 888-436-4643
Fr: 800-237-9932

Carlienne Frisch. Revised edition, 1998. $17.95. 64 pages. Describes different sales careers for reluctant readers.

★11245★ Careers in Marketing
McGraw-Hill Trade
2 Penn Plaza
New York, NY 10121
Ph: (212)904-2000   Fr: 800-722-4726
E-mail: ntcpub@tribune.com

Lila B. Stair and Leslie Stair. Third edition, 2001. $19.95; $14.95 (paper). 192 pages. Surveys career opportunities in marketing and related areas such as marketing research, product development, and sales promotion. Includes a description of the work, places of employment, employment outlook, trends, and salaries. Offers job hunting advice.

★11246★ The Complete Job-Finding Guide for Secretaries and Administrative Support Staff
AMACOM
1601 Broadway, 12th Fl.
New York, NY 10019-7420
Ph: (518)891-1500   Fax: (518)903-8168
Fr: 800-250-5308

Paul Falcone. 1995. $16.95 (paper). 256 pages. Covers several secretarial and administrative staff support positions and includes tips on resume writing, interview preparation, and other aspects of the job search.

★11247★ How to Get Customers to Call, Buy and...Beg for More!
World Wide Publishing and Trading, LLC
5 Airport Rd.
Lakewood, NJ 08701
Ph: (732)364-1900   Fax: (732)364-3716
Fr: 800-545-4724

Kenneth J. Varga. 1997. $49.97.

★11248★ How to Make Hot Cold Calls: Your Calling Card to Personal Success
General Distribution Services, Inc.
4500 Witmer Industrial, E.
Niagara Falls, NY 14305-1386
Fax: 800-481-6207   Fr: 800-805-1083

Steven J. Schwartz. Revised, 2001. 176 pages.

★11249★ Opportunities in Direct Marketing
McGraw-Hill Contemporary Books
1221 Avenue of the Americas
New York, NY 10020
Ph: (212)904-2000   Fr: 800-323-4900
E-mail: ntcpub@tribune.com

Anne Basye. Revised, 2000. $14.95; $11.95 (paper). 160 pages. Examines opportunities with direct marketers, catalog companies, direct marketing agencies, telemarketing firms, mailing list brokers, and database marketing companies. Describes how to prepare for a career in direct marketing and how to break into the field. Includes sources of short-term professional training.

★11250★ Opportunities in Sales Careers
McGraw-Hill Professional
2 Penn Plaza
New York, NY 10121
Ph: (212)904-2000   Fr: 800-722-4726
E-mail: ntcpub@tribune.com

James Brescoll and Ralph Dahm. 160 pages. 1995. $12.95; $11.95 (paper). Details sales in retail, wholesale and industrial sales, sales of services and intangibles, and sales management. Illustrated.

★11251★ Opportunities in Telecommunications Careers
Vgm Career Horizons
1221 Avenue of the Americas
New York, NY 10020
Ph: (212)904-2000   Fr: 800-323-4900
E-mail: ntcpub@tribune.com

Jan Bone, Suzanne Nagle. 1995. $12.95; $11.95 (paper).

★11252★ Opportunities in Telemarketing Careers
Vgm Career Horizons
1221 Avenue of the Americas
New York, NY 10020
Ph: (212)904-2000   Fr: 800-323-4900
E-mail: ntcpub@tribune.com

Anne Basye. 1995. $14.95; $11.95 (paper). 160 pages. Discusses opportunities in inside sales, customer service, telesearch, multilingual marketing, and more.

★11253★ Real People Working in Sales and Marketing
McGraw-Hill Contemporary Books
1221 Avenue of the Americas
New York, NY 10020
Ph: (212)904-2000   Fr: 800-323-4900
E-mail: ntcpub@tribune.com

Blythe Camenson, Jan Goldberg. 1997. $17.95; $12.95 (paper). 410 pages. Interviews and profiles of working sales and marketing professionals capture a range of opportunities in this field.

★11254★ Resumes for Sales and Marketing Careers
McGraw-Hill Professional
2 Penn Plaza
New York, NY 10121
Ph: (212)904-2000   Fr: 800-722-4726
E-mail: ntcpub@tribune.com

Chuck Cochran and Donna Peerce. Second edition, 1998. $10.95 (paper). 336 pages. Sample resumes and cover letters from all levels of the sales and marketing field.

EMPLOYMENT AGENCIES AND SEARCH FIRMS

★11255★ Career Development Services
706 East Ave.
Rochester, NY 14607-2105
Ph: (585)244-0750   Fax: (585)244-7115
Fr: 800-736-6710
E-mail: info@careerdev.org
URL: http://www.careerdev.org

Employment agency.

★11256★ Churchill & Affiliates Inc.
180 E. Elizabeth Ln.
Richboro, PA 18954
Ph: (215)364-8070   Fax: (215)364-0519

Executive search firm focusing on the telecommunications industry.

★11257★ The Culver Group
1810 Gateway Dr., Ste140
San Mateo, CA 94404
Ph: (650)356-1100   Fax: (650)356-1111
E-mail: gfagin@culvercareers.com
URL: http://www.culvercorp.com

Employment agency specializing in sales positions.

★11258★ The Esquire Staffing Group Ltd.
1 S. Wacker Dr., Ste. 1616
Chicago, IL 60606-4616
Ph: (312)795-4300   Fax: (312)795-4329
E-mail: s.fischer@esquirestaffing.com
URL: http://www.esquirestaffing.com

Employment agency. Fills permanent as well as temporary openings.

★11259★ Winters and Ross
442 Main St.
Fort Lee, NJ 07024
Ph: (201)947-8400   Fax: (201)947-1035
E-mail: wintersandross@aol.com
URL: http://www.wintersandross.com

Permanent employment agency serving a variety of industries.

ONLINE JOB SOURCES AND SERVICES

★11260★ Spherion Workforce
  Architects
URL: http://www.spherion.com

Description: Recruitment firm specializing in accounting and finance, sales and marketing, interim executives, technology, engineering, retail and human resources.

OTHER SOURCES

★11261★ *Marketing & Sales
  Occupations*
Delphi Productions
3160 4th St.
Boulder, CO 80304
Fax: (303)443-4022   Fr: 888-443-2400
URL: http://www.delphivideo.com

$95.00. 50 minutes. Part of the Careers for the 21st Century Video Library.

Tissue Engineers

SOURCES OF HELP-WANTED ADS

★11262★ *Annual Review of Genetics*
Annual Reviews Inc.
PO Box 10139
Palo Alto, CA 94303-0139
Ph: (650)493-4400   Fax: (650)855-9815
Fr: 800-523-8635

Annual. Periodical covering issues in genetics and the biological sciences.

★11263★ *Engineering Times*
National Society of Professional
  Engineers
1420 King St.
Alexandria, VA 22314
Ph: (703)684-2875   Fax: (703)836-4875
E-mail: et@nspe.org
URL: http://http//:www.nspc.org/1et.asp

$30.00/year for individuals; $48.00/year for out of country. Magazine (tabloid) covering professional, legislative, and techology issues for an engineering audience.

★11264★ *ENR: Engineering News-Record*
McGraw-Hill Companies
1221 Avenue of the Americas
New York, NY 10020
Ph: (212)512-2000
URL: http://www.enr.com

Weekly. $74.00/year; $5.00 for single issue. Magazine focusing on engineering and construction.

★11265★ *High Technology Careers Magazine*
HTC
4701 Patrick Henry Dr., No. 1901
Santa Clara, CA 95054-1847
Ph: (408)970-8800   Fax: (408)567-0242
URL: http://www.hightechcareers.com

Bimonthly. $29.00/year; $35.00/year for Canada; $85.00/year for out of country. Magazine (tabloid) containing employment opportunity information for the engineering and technical community.

★11266★ *NSBE Magazine*
NSBE Publications
1454 Duke St.
Alexandria, VA 22314
Ph: (703)549-2207   Fax: (703)683-5312

$10.00/year for individuals; $2.00 for single issue. Journal providing information on engineering careers, self-development, and cultural issues for recent graduates with technical majors.

★11267★ *SWE*
Society of Women Engineers
230 E Ohio St., No. 400
2135 Lamberton Rd.
Chicago, IL 60611-3265
Ph: (312)596-5223   Fax: (312)596-5252
E-mail: hq@swe.org
URL: http://www.swe.org

Bimonthly. $30.00/year for nonmembers. Magazine for engineering students and for women and men working in the engineering and technology fields. Covers career guidance, continuing development and topical issues.

★11268★ *Tissue Engineering*
Mary Ann Liebert Inc. Pulishers
2 Madison Ave.
Larchmont, NY 10538
Fr: 800-654-3237

Monthly. Peer-reviewed journal that focuses on the engineering of new biologic tissues.

★11269★ *WEPANEWS*
Women in Engineering Programs &
  Advocates Network
Castle Point on the Hudson
Hoboken, NJ 07030
Ph: (201)216-5245   Fax: (201)216-5175
URL: http://www.wepan.org/newsletter.html

Description: Two issues/year. Seeks to provide greater access for women to careers in engineering. Includes news of graduate, undergraduate, freshmen, pre-college, and re-entry engineering programs for women. Recurring features include job listings, faculty, grant, and conference news, international engineering program news, action group news, notices of publications available, and a column titled Kudos.

EMPLOYER DIRECTORIES AND NETWORKING LISTS

★11270★ *Careers in Focus: Engineering*
Ferguson Publishing Co.
200 W Jackson Blvd.
Chicago, IL 60606
Ph: (312)692-0109

2nd edition, 2002. $22.95. Publication includes: List of resources to consult for more information. Principal content of publication is job descriptions, advancement opportunities, educational requirements, employment outlook, salary information, and working conditions for careers in the field of engineering. Indexes: Alphabetical.

★11271★ *Indiana Society of Professional Engineers-Directory*
Indiana Society of Professional Engineers
PO Box 20806
Indianapolis, IN 46220
Ph: (317)255-2267   Fax: (317)255-2530

Annual, fall. $55.00. Covers member registered engineers, land surveyors, engineering students, and engineers in training. Entries include: Member name, address, phone type of membership, business information, specialty. Arrangement: Alpha by chapter area.

HANDBOOKS AND MANUALS

★11272★ The Best Resumes for Scientists and Engineers

John Wiley & Sons Inc.
1 Wiley Dr.
Somerset, NJ 08873
Ph: (732)469-4400   Fr: 800-225-5945

Adele Lewis and David J. Moore. Second edition, 1993. $37.50; $19.95 (paper). 224 pages. Presents an extensive collection of scientific and engineering resumes, highlighting the important differences between these and resumes written for other occupations.

★11273★ Functional Tissue Engineering

Springer-Verlag New York, Inc.
175 Fifth Ave.
New York, NY 10010

Farshid Guilak, David Butler, Steven Goldstein, and David Mooney. July 2003. $149.00. 426 pages.

★11274★ Great Jobs for Engineering Majors

McGraw-Hill Professional
McGraw-Hill Higher Education
2 Penn Plaza
New York, NY 10121
Ph: (212)904-2000   Fr: 800-722-4726
E-mail: ntcpub@tribune.com

Geraldine O. Garner. Second edition, 2002. $14.95. 256 pages. Covers all the career options open to students majoring in engineering.

★11275★ Keys to Engineering Success

Prentice Hall PTR
One Lake St.
Upper Saddle River, NJ 07458
Ph: (201)236-7000

Jill S. Tietjen, Kristy A. Schloss, Carol Carter, Joyce Bishop, and Sarah Lyman. 2000. $32.00 (paper).

★11276★ Majoring in Engineering: How to Get from Your Freshman Year to Your First Job

Farrar, Straus & Giroux, Inc.
19 Union Sq., W
New York, NY 10003
Ph: (212)741-6900   Fax: (212)633-9385
Fr: 888-330-8477

John Garcia and Carol Carter, editors. 2000. $20.00; $10.00 (paper). 134 pages.

★11277★ The New Engineer's Guide to Career Growth & Professional Awareness

Institute of Electrical & Electronics Engineers Inc.
445 Hoes Ln.
PO Box 1331
Piscataway, NJ 08855-1331
Ph: (732)562-3967   Fax: (732)981-9334
Fr: 800-678-4333

Irving J. Gabelman, editor. 1996. $39.95 (paper). 275 pages.

★11278★ Orthopedic Tissue Engineering: Basic Science and Practices

Marcel Dekker Inc.
270 Madison Ave.
New York, NY 10016

Victor Goldbert and Arnold Caplan. January 2004. $185.00.

★11279★ Resumes for Engineering Careers

McGraw-Hill Trade
2 Penn Plaza
New York, NY 10121
Ph: (212)904-2000   Fr: 800-722-4726
E-mail: ntcpub@tribune.com

2000. $10.95 (paper). 456 pages. Contains sample resumes and cover letters applicable to any engineering field.

★11280★ Tissue Engineering

American Academy of Orthopaedic Surgeons
6300 N. River Rd.
Rosemont, IL 60018

L Sandell. 2004. $120.00.

★11281★ Tissue Engineering: Engineering Principles for the Design of Replacement Organs and Tissues

Oxford University Press Inc.
198 Madison Ave.
New York, NY 10016

W Mark Saltzman. $85.00. 544 pages.

★11282★ Tissue Engineering: Principles and Applications in Engineering

CRC Press LLC
2000 NW Corporate Blvd.
Boca Raton, FL 33431
Fr: 800-272-7737

Bernhard Pallson, Jeffrey A. Hubbell, Robert Pionsey and Joseph D. Bronzion. 2003. $99.95. 392 pages. Provides an overview of the major physiologic systems of current interest to biomedical engineers.

★11283★ Tissue Engineering, Stem Cells, and Gene Therapies

Kluwer Academic Publishers
101 Philip Dr.
Norwell, MA 02061

Y Murat Elcin. July 2003. $135.00. 340 pages.

EMPLOYMENT AGENCIES AND SEARCH FIRMS

★11284★ High Employee Services Ltd.

525 Greenfield Rd., 2nd Fl.
Lancaster, PA 17601
Ph: (717)396-7701   Fax: (717)396-7779

Personnel consultants serving all industries including business and finance, engineering, sales and marketing, and focusing on manufacturing, industrial, and transportation operations. Conducts full time, contract staffing, and temporary (clerical and skilled) placements. Serves private industries as well as government agencies.

★11285★ Techtronix Technical Search

PO Box 17713
Milwaukee, WI 53217-0173
Ph: (414)466-3100   Fax: (414)466-3598

Firm specializes in recruiting executives for the engineering, information systems, manufacturing, marketing, finance, and human resources industries.

★11286★ TRC Staffing Services Inc.

2110 15 Mile Rd., Ste. B
Sterling Heights, MI 48310
Ph: (586)939-3210   Fax: (586)978-0572

A full-service executive search company with permanent placements encompassing engineering, industrial sales, financial and computer science positions. Screen, interview, and verify past employment for all candidates prior to referral. Also assist personnel staffs in the attainment of their EEO/AAP goals with the placement of talented individuals in positions which are underutilized with minorities and/or women. In addition, firm has a clerical temporary service division, TRC Temporary Service; and an employment agency, TRC Staffing Services.

★11287★ Winters Technical Staffing Services

2025 Sheppard Ave. E, Ste. 4110
Willowdale, ON, Canada M2T 1V7
Ph: (416)495-7422   Fax: (416)495-8479

Technical staffing service for permanent and contract positions in all facets of engineering. Serves government agencies, consulting engineers, and all areas of manufacturing in Canada and northeast U.S.

TRADESHOWS

★11288★ American Society for Engineering Education Annual Conference and Exposition

American Society for Engineering Education
1818 N St., Ste. 600
Washington, DC 20036
Ph: (202)331-3500   Fax: (202)265-8504
URL: http://www.asee.org

Annual. **Primary Exhibits:** Publications, engineering supplies and equipment, computers, software, and research companies all products and services related to engineering education. **Dates and Locations:** 2005 Jun 12-15; Portland, OR • 2006 Jun 18-21; Chicago, IL • 2007 Jun 24-27; Honolulu, HI.

OTHER SOURCES

★11289★ American Association of Engineering Societies (AAES)

1828 L St. NW, No. 906
Washington, DC 20036
Ph: (202)296-2237   Fax: (202)296-1151
Fr: 888-400-2237
E-mail: tprice@aaes.org
URL: http://www.aaes.org

Description: Coordinates the efforts of the member societies in the provision of reliable and objective information to the general public concerning issues which affect the engineering profession and the field of engineering as a whole; to collect, analyze, document, and disseminate data which will inform the general public of the relationship between engineering and the national welfare; to provide a forum for the engineering societies to exchange and discuss their views on matters of common interest; and to represent the U.S. engineering community aborad through representation in WFEO and UPADI.

★11290★ American Engineering Association (AEA)

PO Box 820473
Fort Worth, TX 76182-0473
Ph: (972)264-6248
E-mail: info@aea.org
URL: http://www.aea.org

Description: Engineers and engineering professionals. Works to advance the engineering profession and U.S. engineering capabilities. Issues of concern include age discrimination, immigration laws, trade agreements, loss of U.S. manufacturing and engineering capability, and recruitment of foreign students. Testifies before Congress.

★11291★ American Institute of Engineers (AIE)

4630 Appian Way, Ste. 206
El Sobrante, CA 94803-1875
Ph: (510)758-6240   Fax: (510)758-6240
E-mail: aie@members-aie.org
URL: http://www.members-aie.org

Description: Professional Association for engineers, scientists, and mathematicians. Multi-disciplined, non-technical Association whose mission statement is to improve the stature and image of engineers, scientists, and mathematicians. Provides endorsements, awards and opportunities for small business start-ups within the AIE Councils. Sponsors "LA Engineer," a comedy-drama television series; produces annual "Academy Hall of Fame".

★11292★ American Society for Cell Biology (ASCB)

8120 Woodmont Ave., Ste. 750
Bethesda, MD 20814-2762
Ph: (301)347-9300   Fax: (301)347-9310
E-mail: ascbinfo@ascb.org
URL: http://www.ascb.org

Description: Scientists with educational or research experience in cell biology or an allied field. Offers placement service.

★11293★ Biomedical Engineering Society

8401 Corporate Dr., Ste. 225
Landover, MD 20785
Ph: (301)459-1999
URL: http://www.bmes.org

Description: Provides resources including relevant publications and career links.

★11294★ Engineering Society of Detroit (ESD)

26100 American Dr., Ste. 500
Southfield, MI 48034-6184
Ph: (248)355-2910   Fax: (248)355-1492
E-mail: esd@esd.org
URL: http://esd.org

Description: Engineers from all disciplines; scientists and technologists. Conducts technical programs and engineering refresher courses; sponsors conferences and expositions. Maintains speakers' bureau; offers placement services. Although based in Detroit, MI, society membership is international.

★11295★ Engineering Workforce Commission (EWC)

1828 L St. NW, Ste. 906
Washington, DC 20036-5110
Ph: (202)296-2237   Fax: (202)296-1151
Fr: 888-400-AAES
E-mail: mdoster@aaes.org
URL: http://www.ewc-online.org

Description: Commissioners appointed by member societies of the American Association of Engineering Societies to engage in studies and analyses of the supply, demand, use, and remuneration of engineering and technical personnel. Provides representation to government groups dealing with professional manpower policy; consults with industry. Gathers and disseminates information on the engineering profession. Conducts surveys of engineering school enrollments, degrees, and salaries; monitors federal labor statistics.

★11296★ International Federation of Professional and Technical Engineers (IFPTE)

8630 Fenton St., No. 400
Silver Spring, MD 20910-3803
Ph: (301)565-9016   Fax: (301)565-0018
URL: http://www.ifpte.org

Description: Labor union representing engineers, scientists, architects, technicians.

★11297★ Korean Scientists and Engineers Association in America (KSEA)

1952 Gallows Rd., Ste. 300
Vienna, VA 22182
Ph: (703)748-1221   Fax: (703)748-1331
E-mail: sejong@ksea.org
URL: http://www.ksea.org

Description: Scientists and engineers holding single or advanced degrees. Goals are to: promote friendship and mutuality among Korean and American scientists and engineers; contribute to Korea's scientific, technological, industrial, and economic developments; strengthen the scientific, technological, and cultural bonds between Korea and the U.S. Sponsors symposium. Maintains speakers' bureau, placement service, and biographical archives. Compiles statistics. Maintains 100 volume library of scientific handbooks and yearbooks in Korean.

★11298★ National Action Council for Minorities in Engineering (NACME)

Empire State Bldg., Ste. 2212
350 Fifth Ave.
New York, NY 10118-2299
Ph: (212)279-2626   Fax: (212)629-5178
E-mail: webmaster@nacme.org
URL: http://www.nacme.org/

Description: Leads the national effort to increase access to careers in engineering and other science-based disciplines. Supported by the nation's leading technology-intensive companies, NACME conducts research and public policy analysis, develops and operates national demonstration programs at precollege and university levels, and disseminates information through publications, conferences, and electronic media. NACME is also the nation's largest privately funded source of scholarships for minority students in engineering.

★11299★ National Society of Professional Engineers (NSPE)

1420 King St.
Alexandria, VA 22314
Ph: (703)684-2800   Fax: (703)836-4875
Fr: 888-285-6773
E-mail: custserv@nspe.org

URL: http://www.nspe.org

Description: Professional engineers and engineers-in-training in all fields registered in accordance with the laws of states or territories of the U.S. or provinces of Canada; qualified graduate engineers, student members, and registered land surveyors. Is concerned with social, professional, ethical, and economic considerations of engineering as a profession; encompasses programs in public relations, employment practices, ethical considerations, education, and career guidance. Monitors legislative and regulatory actions of interest to the engineering profession.

★11300★ **Society of Engineering Science (SES)**
College of Engineering
Virginia Tech
Blacksburg, VA 24061
Ph: (540)231-9171   Fax: (540)231-3031
E-mail: henneke@vt.edu
URL: http://www.sesinc.org

Members: Individuals with at least a baccalaureate degree who are engaged in any aspect of engineering science or in other pursuits that contribute to the advancement of engineering science. **Purpose:** Works to foster and promote the interchange of ideas and information among the various fields of engineering science and among engineering science and the fields of theoretical and applied physics, chemistry, and mathematics. Is dedicated to the advancement of interdisciplinary research and to the establishment of a bridge between science and engineering.

★11301★ **Society of Hispanic Professional Engineers (SHPE)**
5400 E Olympic Blvd., Ste. 210
Los Angeles, CA 90022
Ph: (323)725-3970   Fax: (323)725-0316
E-mail: shpenational@shpe.org
URL: http://www.shpe.org

Description: Engineers, student engineers, and scientists seeking to increase the number of Hispanic engineers by providing motivation and support to students. Sponsors competitions and educational programs. Maintains placement service and speakers' bureau; compiles statistics.

★11302★ **Society of Women Engineers (SWE)**
230 E Ohio St., No. 400
Chicago, IL 60611-3265
Ph: (312)596-5223   Fax: (312)596-5252
E-mail: hq@swe.org
URL: http://www.swe.org

Description: Educational and service organization representing both students and professional women in engineering and technical fields.

★11303★ **The Tissue Engineering Society International**
841B Southgate Drive, No. 15
State College, PA 16801
Ph: (814)237-7350   Fax: (814)237-7371

Description: Brings together the international community of persons engaged or interested in the field of tissue engineering and promotes education and research within the field of tissue engineering through regular meetings, publications and other forms of communication.

★11304★ **United Engineering Foundation (UEF)**
3 Park Ave., 27th Fl.
New York, NY 10016-5902
Ph: (212)591-7829   Fax: (212)591-7441
E-mail: engfnd@aol.com
URL: http://www.engfnd.org

Description: Federation of 5 major national engineering societies: American Institute of Chemical Engineers; American Institute of Mining, Metallurgical and Petroleum Engineers; American Society of Civil Engineers; American Society of Mechanical Engineers; Institute of Electrical and Electronics Engineers. Supports research in engineering and advances the engineering arts and sciences through its conference program.

Tool Programmers, Numerical Control

SOURCES OF HELP-WANTED ADS

★11305★ American Machinist

Penton Media Inc.
1300 E 9th St.
Cleveland, OH 44114-1503
Ph: (216)696-7000   Fax: (216)931-9799
URL: http://www.americanmachinist.com/

Monthly. Free for US residents; $81.00/year for Canada; $108.00/year for other countries. Magazine serving the metalworking marketplace, consisting of plants in industries primarily engaged in manufacturing durable goods and other metal products.

★11306★ Tooling & Production

Nelson Publishing Inc.
2500 Tamiami Trl. N
Nokomis, FL 34275-3482
Ph: (941)966-9521   Fax: (941)966-2590
Fr: 800-226-6113
URL: http://www.toolingandproduction.com

Monthly. $90.00/year for individuals. Magazine concerning metalworking.

PLACEMENT AND JOB REFERRAL SERVICES

★11307★ American Indian Science and Engineering Society (AISES)

PO Box 9828
Albuquerque, NM 87119-9828
Ph: (505)765-1052   Fax: (505)765-5608
E-mail: info@aises.org
URL: http://www.aises.org

Description: American Indian and non-Indian students and professionals in science, technology, and engineering fields; corporations representing energy, mining, aerospace, electronic, and computer fields. Seeks to motivate and encourage students to pursue undergraduate and graduate studies in science, engineering, and technology.

Sponsors science fairs in grade schools, teacher training workshops, summer math/science sessions for 8th-12th graders, professional chapters, and student chapters in colleges. Offers scholarships. Adult members serve as role models, advisers, and mentors for students. Operates placement service.

★11308★ Composites Manufacturing Association of the Society of Manufacturing Engineers (CMA/SME)

1 SME Dr.
Dearborn, MI 48121-0930
Ph: (313)271-2867   Fax: (313)271-2861
Fr: 800-733-4763
E-mail: service@sme.org
URL: http://www.sme.org/cma

Description: A division of the Society of Manufacturing Engineers. Composites manufacturing professionals and students in 21 countries. Addresses design, tooling, assembly, producibility, supportability, and future trends of composites materials and hardware; promotes advanced composites technology. Analyzes industry trends; evaluates composites usage. Conducts educational programs; facilitates exchange of information among members; operates placement service.

HANDBOOKS AND MANUALS

★11309★ Careers in Computers

VGM Career Horizons
1221 Avenue of the Americas
New York, NY 10020
Ph: (212)904-2000   Fr: 800-323-4900
E-mail: ntcpub@tribune.com

Lila B. Stair and Leslie Stair. Third edition, 2002. $19.95; $14.95 (paper). Describes trends affecting computer careers and explores a wide range of job opportunities from programming to consulting. Provides job qualifications, salary data, job market information, personal and educational requirements, career paths, and the place of the job in the organizational structure. Offers advice on education, certification, and job search.

★11310★ Careers for Number Crunchers and Other Quantitative Types

McGraw-Hill Trade
2 Penn Plaza
New York, NY 10121
Ph: (212)904-2000   Fr: 800-722-4726
E-mail: ntcpub@tribune.com

Rebecca Burnett. Second edition, 2002. $15.95; $12.95 (paper). 192 pages. Provides information to math-oriented job hunters on how to become statisticians, field researchers, computer programmers, stock analysts, investment managers, bankers, engineers, accountants, underwriters, economists, market analysts, mathematicians, systems analysts, and more.

★11311★ Opportunities in Computer-Aided Design and Computer-Aided Manufacturing

McGraw-Hill Trade
2 Penn Plaza
New York, NY 10121
Ph: (212)904-2000   Fr: 800-722-4726

Jan Bone. 1994. $14.95; $11.95 (paper). 160 pages. Defines CAD (computer-aided design), CAM (computer-aided manufacturing), and MAP (manufacturing automation protocol). Explains career opportunities in the CAD/CAM field, and education and training needed. Gives job-hunting tips.

EMPLOYMENT AGENCIES AND SEARCH FIRMS

★11312★ Mfg/Search, Inc.

431 E Colfax Ave., Ste.120
South Bend, IN 46617
Ph: (574)282-2547   Fr: 800-782-7976
E-mail: mfg@mfgsearch.com
URL: http://www.mfgsearch.com

Executive search firm. Offices in GA, IL, MI, NY.

★11313★ **Romac International, Inc.**
1001 E Palm Ave
Tampa, FL 33605
Ph: (813)552-5239   Fax: (813)552-2122
URL: http://www.romac.com

Executive search firm. More than 30 locations throughout the United States.

TRADESHOWS

★11314★ **Houston Tool and Manufacturing Exposition**
NTMA, Houston Chapter
PO Box 541583
Houston, TX 77254-1583
Ph: (713)928-6241   Fax: (713)928-6242

Biennial. **Primary Exhibits:** Industrial tools and machines.

★11315★ **METALFORM**
Precision Metalforming Association
6363 Oak Tree Blvd.
Independence, OH 44131
Ph: (216)901-8800   Fax: (216)901-9190
URL: http://www.metalforming.com

Annual. **Primary Exhibits:** Presses and stamping equipment, tooling and fabricating machines, management aids, and related materials.

★11316★ **Pacific Coast Industrial and Machine Tool Show**
Professional Trade Shows, Inc.
47817 Fremont Blvd.
Fremont, CA 94538
Ph: (510)354-3131   Fax: (510)354-3159
Fr: 800-548-1407
E-mail: showinfo@proshows.com
URL: http://www.proshows.com

Annual. **Primary Exhibits:** Industrial equipment, machine tools, business services, hand tools, and related equipment, supplies, and services.

★11317★ **Reno Industrial & Machine Tool Show**
Professional Trade Shows, Inc.
47817 Fremont Blvd.
Fremont, CA 94538
Ph: (510)354-3131   Fax: (510)354-3159
Fr: 800-548-1407

E-mail: showinfo@proshows.com
URL: http://www.proshows.com

Annual. **Primary Exhibits:** Industrial and machine tool products.

★11318★ **WESTEC - Advanced Productivity Exposition**
Society of Manufacturing Engineers (SME)
Expositions Division
1 SME Dr.
PO Box 930
Dearborn, MI 48121-0930
Ph: (313)271-1500   Fax: (313)240-8253
Fr: 800-733-3976
URL: http://www.sme.org

Annual. **Primary Exhibits:** Equipment, supplies, and services for the tool and manufacturing engineering industries.

OTHER SOURCES

★11319★ *Math at Work: Women in Nontraditional Careers*
Her Own Words
PO Box 5264
Madison, WI 53705-0264
Ph: (608)271-7083   Fax: (608)271-0209
URL: http://www.herownwords.com/

Video. Jocelyn Riley. $95.00. 15 minutes. Resource guide also available for $45.00.

★11320★ *Numerical Control Machine Tool Operators*
Evon Publishing
832 N 7th Ave.
Iron River, MI 49935
Ph: (906)265-3190

Audiocassette. 1996. $16.95. 32 minutes. Part of the Careers and Vocational Guidance Series. Provides information about the nature of the work, educational requirements, employment outlook, earnings, and work conditions as well as additional related information.

★11321★ **Precision Machined Products Association (PMPA)**
6700 W Snowville Rd.
Brecksville, OH 44141
Ph: (440)526-0300   Fax: (440)526-5803
E-mail: webmaster@pmpa.org
URL: http://www.pmpa.org

Description: Addresses the information, training, and technical needs of manufactur-

ers of component parts to customer's order, machined from rod, bar, or tube stock, of metal, fiber, plastic, or other material, using automatic or hand screw machines, automatic bar machines, and CNC machines.

★11322★ **Special Interest Group for Computers and the Physically Handicapped (SIGCAPH)**
Church St. Sta.
PO Box 12115
New York, NY 10249
Ph: (212)626-0500   Fax: (212)944-1318
E-mail: chair_sigcaph@acm.org
URL: http://www.acm.org/sigcaph

Description: Promotes the professional interests of computing personnel with physical disabilities and the application of computing & information technology in solving relevant disability problems. Studies to educate the public to support careers for the disabled.

★11323★ *Tool Programmers, Numerical Control*
Evon Publishing
832 N 7th Ave.
Iron River, MI 49935
Ph: (906)265-3190

Audiocassette. 1996. $16.95. 32 minutes. Part of the Careers and Vocational Guidance Series. Provides information about the nature of the work, educational requirements, employment outlook, earnings, and work conditions as well as additional related information.

★11324★ *Women in Machining*
Her Own Words
PO Box 5264
Madison, WI 53705-0264
Ph: (608)271-7083   Fax: (608)271-0209
URL: http://www.herownwords.com/

Video. Jocelyn Riley. $95.00. 15 minutes. Resource guide also available for $45.00.

★11325★ *Women in Nontraditional Careers: An Introduction*
Her Own Words
PO Box 5264
Madison, WI 53705
Ph: (608)271-7083   Fax: (608)271-0209
URL: http://www.herownwords.com/

Video. Jocelyn Riley. $95.00. 15 minutes. Resource guide also available for $45.00.

Tour Guides and Operators

SOURCES OF HELP-WANTED ADS

★11326★ Meeting News

Bill Communications Inc.
770 Broadway
New York, NY 10003-9595
Ph: (646)654-4500   Fax: (646)654-7212
URL: http://www.meetingnews.com

Free to qualified subscribers; $65.00/year. The newspaper for conventions, meetings, incentive travel and trade show professionals.

★11327★ Travel Agent

Universal Media Inc.
801 2nd Ave.
New York, NY 10017
Ph: (212)986-5100   Fax: (212)338-9445

Weekly. Free to qualified subscribers; $250.00/year. Travel industry magazine.

★11328★ Travel Trade

Travel Trade
15 W 44th St.
New York, NY 10036
Ph: (212)730-6600   Fax: (212)730-7137
E-mail: travelcat@aol.com

Weekly. $10.00/year. Travel industry magazine.

★11329★ Travel Weekly

Northstar Travel Media
500 Plaza Dr.
Secaucus, NJ 07094-3626
Ph: (201)902-2000   Fax: (201)902-2053
URL: http://www.traveler.net/two

Semiweekl. $9.00/year. Travel industry magazine.

★11330★ TravelAge West

Northstar Travel Media
500 Plaza Dr.
Secaucus, NJ 07094-3626
Ph: (201)902-2000   Fax: (201)902-2053

Weekly. Free to qualified subscribers; $25.00/year for individuals. Magazine for retail travel agents in western U.S. and western Canada.

PLACEMENT AND JOB REFERRAL SERVICES

★11331★ Connected International Meeting Professionals Association (CIMPA)

9200 Bayard Pl.
Fairfax, VA 22032
Ph: (703)286-2142   Fax: (703)291-2292
E-mail: info@meetingprofessionals.org
URL: http://www.cimpa.org

Members: Meeting planners, incentive organizers, travel agents, tour operators, and seminar organizers in 42 countries. **Purpose:** Works to improve the skills of professional conference and convention planners. Serves as a clearinghouse of information on new travel destinations and planning technologies, techniques, and strategies. **Activities:** Facilitates exchange of information among Internet professionals. Produces a television program on travel and meetings. Conducts educational courses and awards Certified Internet Meeting Professional designation. Conducts research programs and placement service. Sponsors training courses on the Internet.

★11332★ International Association of Tour Managers - North American Region (IATM-NAR)

9500 Rainier Ave. S, No. 603
Seattle, WA 98118
Ph: (206)725-7108   Fax: (206)725-4020
E-mail: iatmone@aol.com
URL: http://members.aol.com/iatmone/

Description: Travel agents, travel wholesalers, airlines, hotel associations, shipping lines, tourist organizations, restaurants, shops, and entertainment organizations. Works to maintain the highest possible standards of tour management; guarantee excellence of performance; educate the travel world on the role of the tour manager (also referred to as tour director, tour escort, or tour leader) in the successful completion of the tour itinerary and in bringing business to related industries. Represents members in influencing legislation and advising on travel policy. Trains tour managers to plan, research, and lead tours for domestic and foreign travelers; operates Advisory Board in Professional Tour Management; offers placement service; conducts Professional Tour Management, U.S.A. Certificate Program.

EMPLOYER DIRECTORIES AND NETWORKING LISTS

★11333★ Directory of Travel Agencies for the Disabled

Twin Peaks Press
PO Box 129
Vancouver, WA 98666-0129
Ph: (360)694-2462   Fax: (360)696-3210
URL: http://www.netm.com/mall/infoprod/twinpeak/helen.htm

Quarterly. $19.95. Number of listings: 370. Entries include: Company name, address, phone, fax, names and titles of key personnel, subsidiary and branch names and locations, description of services. Arrangement: Geographical.

★11334★ Specialty Travel Index: The Special Interest & Adventure Travel Directory

Alpine Hansen, Publishers
PO Box 458
San Anselmo, CA 94979
Ph: (415)455-1643   Fax: (415)455-1648
Fr: 888-624-4030

E-mail: info@specialitytravel.com
URL: http://www.specialtytravel.com

Semiannual, January and August. $6.00 per issue; $10.00 for annual subscription. Covers over 600 special interest tour operators, worldwide; all listings are paid. Entries include: Firm name, address, phone; description of tours offered, including nature of trip, destinations, sample cost and duration of trip. Arrangement: Alphabetical. Indexes: Special interest activity (with location of activity), Geographical (and the special interest activities possible).

★11335★ **Survey of State Tourism Offices**
Travel Industry Association of America
1100 New York Ave. NW, No. 450
Washington, DC 20005-3934
Ph: (202)408-8422   Fax: (202)408-1255
URL: http://www.tia.org

Annual, April. $495.00. Covers state and territorial government agencies responsible for travel and travel promotion in their states. Entries include: Agency name, address, phone, number of full- and part-time staff, number of professional staff directly involved in travel; name and title of state travel director, and length of service as director, length of service in agency, and whether employed under the Civil Service program; advertising director and agency and public relations director in separate sections. Extensive additional data is provided by a series of tables covering state activities in advertising, package tours, general promotion press and public relations, research, the establishment of welcome centers, and the department budget. Although addresses are not given, some listings do include name, title, and department of contact. Arrangement: By function (administration, advertising, etc.), then geographical.

★11336★ **Tours-Operators & Promoters Directory**
infoUSA Inc.
5711 S 86th Cir.
Omaha, NE 68127-0347
Ph: (402)930-3500   Fax: (402)331-0176
Fr: 800-555-6124
URL: http://www.abii.com

Annual. Number of listings: 6,743. Entries include: Name, address, phone (including area code), size of advertisement, year first in "Yellow Pages," name of owner or manager, number of employees. Compiled from telephone company "Yellow Pages," nationwide. Arrangement: Geographical.

★11337★ **Travel and Tourism Research Association-Membership Directory**
Travel and Tourism Research Association
PO Box 2133
Boise, ID 83701
Ph: (208)429-9511   Fax: (208)429-9512
URL: http://www.ttra.com

Annual, June. $125.00. Covers over 800 state and local tourism bureaus and other federal and provincial government agencies,

airlines, media, hotels, university bureaus of business research and other university departments, and research and consulting firms concerned with travel research, marketing, and promotion. Entries include: Firm or individual name, address, phone; company listings also include name and title of representative or alternate. Arrangement: Alphabetical. Indexes: Personal name, geographical, industry category.

HANDBOOKS AND MANUALS

★11338★ **Career Opportunities in Travel and Tourism**
Checkmark Books, Inc.
132 W. 31st St., 17th Fl.
New York, NY 10001-2006
Ph: (212)967-8800   Fax: (212)967-9196
Fr: 800-322-8755
URL: http://www.factsonfile.com

John K. Hawks. 1996. $18.95 (paper). 224 pages. Includes detailed job descriptions, educational requirements, salary ranges, and advancement prospects for 70 different job opportunities in this fast-paced industry. Contains index and bibliography.

★11339★ **Careers in Travel, Tourism, and Hospitality**
McGraw-Hill Contemporary Books
1221 Avenue of the Americas
New York, NY 10020
Ph: (212)904-2000   Fr: 800-323-4900
E-mail: ntcpub@tribune.com

Marjorie Eberts, Linda Brothers, and Ann Gisler. 1997. $17.95; 13.95 (paper). 192 pages.

★11340★ **A Coach Full of Fun: A Handbook of Creative Solutions and Ideas for Tour Escorts**
Shoreline Creations, Ltd.
2465 112th Ave.
Holland, MI 49424
Ph: (616)393-2077   Fax: (616)393-0085
Fr: 800-767-3489

Jeane S. Klender. 1995. $19.95 (paper). 214 pages. Provides advice on how to be successful in the group tour industry. Contains information on tour procedures, preparation, and finances.

★11341★ **Conducting Tours**
Thomson Delmar Learning
PO Box 15015
Albany, NY 12212-5015
Ph: (518)348-2300   Fax: (518)464-0393
Fr: 800-998-7498

Marc Mancini. Third edition, 2000. $30.75. 272 pages.

★11342★ **Cruise Ship Jobs: The Insider's Guide to Finding and Getting Jobs on Cruise Ships Around the World**
Portofino Publications
PO Box 97-0252
Coconut Creek, FL 33097
Ph: (972)380-2161   Fax: (972)380-9521
Fr: 800-522-4693

Richard B. Marin. 1998. $13.95 (paper). 144 pages.

★11343★ **Ecotourism Guidelines for Nature Tour Operator**
The International Ecotourism Society
PO Box 688
Burlington, VT 05402
Ph: (802)651-9818   Fax: (802)651-9819

1993. $8.00 (paper). 14 pages.

★11344★ **First Class: An Introduction to Travel and Tourism**
Glencoe/McGraw-Hill
8787 Orion Pl.
Columbus, OH 43240-4027
Ph: (614)890-1111   Fax: (614)899-4414
Fr: 800-848-1567

Dennis L. Foster. 1995.

★11345★ **Hospitality and Tourism Careers**
Prentice Hall PTR
200 Old Tappan Rd.
Old Tappan, NJ 07675
Ph: (201)236-7000   Fr: 800-223-1360

Melissa Dallas and Carl Riegel. First edition, 1997. $20.85 (paper). 252 pages.

★11346★ **How to Get a Job with a Cruise Line**
Ticket to Adventure, Inc.
PO Box 41005
St. Petersburg, FL 33743-1005
Ph: (727)822-5029   Fax: (727)821-3409
Fr: 800-929-7447

Mary Fallon Miller. Fifth edition, 2001. $16.95 (paper). 336 pages. Explores jobs with cruise ships, describing duties, responsibilities, benefits, and training. Lists cruise ship lines and schools offering cruise line training. Offers job hunting advice.

★11347★ **Opportunities in Travel Careers**
McGraw-Hill Contemporary Books
1221 Avenue of the Americas
New York, NY 10020
Ph: (212)904-2000   Fr: 800-323-4900
E-mail: ntcpub@tribune.com

Robert Scott Milne. 1996. $14.95; $11.95 (paper). 198 pages. Discusses what the jobs are and where to find them in airlines, shipping lines, and railroads. Discusses related opportunities in hotels, motels, resorts, travel agencies, public relation firms, and recreation departments. Illustrated.

★11348★ *Travel the World Free as an International Tour Director: How to Be an International Tour Director*

G.E. Mitchell & Associates, Inc.
PO Box 21199
Charleston, SC 29413
Ph: (803)723-7400   Fax: (803)723-0751
Fr: 800-894-8687

Gerald E. Mitchell. 1995. $59.95. 300 pages. Kit includes 250-page manual, 189-page site-inspection journal and resource start up kit with video.

EMPLOYMENT AGENCIES AND SEARCH FIRMS

★11349★ Travel Executive Search

5 Rose Ave.
Great Neck, NY 11021
Ph: (516)829-8829
E-mail: tsintl@aol.com

Executive search firm.

TRADESHOWS

★11350★ Tour Expo

Advanstar Communications Inc.
7500 Old Oak Blvd.
Cleveland, OH 44130
Ph: (440)891-2701   Fax: (440)891-2741
Fr: 800-225-4569
E-mail: info@advantstar.com
URL: http://www.advanstar.com

Primary Exhibits: Tours and tour packages sales agents.

★11351★ WTM - World Travel Market

Reed Exhibitions (North American
  Headquarters)
383 Main Ave.
PO Box 6059
Norwalk, CT 06851
Ph: (203)840-5402   Fax: (203)840-9402
E-mail: inquiry@reedexpo.com
URL: http://www.reedexpo.com

Annual. **Primary Exhibits:** Goods and services related to tourism and travel.

OTHER SOURCES

★11352★ United States Tour Operators Association (USTOA)

275 Madison Ave., Ste. 2014
New York, NY 10016-1101
Ph: (212)599-6599   Fax: (212)599-6744
E-mail: information@ustoa.com
URL: http://www.ustoa.com

Description: Wholesale tour operators, common carriers, associations, government agencies, suppliers, purveyors of travel services, trade press, communications media, and public relations and advertising representatives. Encourages and supports professional and financial integrity in tourism. Protects the legitimate interests of the consumer and the retail agent from financial loss from business conducted with members. Informs the travel trade, government agencies, and the public concerning the activities and objectives of tour operators, focusing attention on their contributions in furthering worldwide travel. Provides tour operators with an opportunity to formulate and express an independent industry voice on matters of common interest and self-regulation; works with other trade organizations and government agencies. Strives to facilitate and develop travel on a worldwide basis.

Traffic Technicians

SOURCES OF HELP-WANTED ADS

★11353★ Advanced Transportation Technology News
Business Communications Company Inc.
25 Van Zant St.
Norwalk, CT 06855-1781
Ph: (203)853-4266   Fax: (203)853-0348
Monthly. Publication covering technology and related news for the transportation industry.

★11354★ Highway Builder
TRIAD
6525 Busch Blvd.
Columbus, OH 43229
Ph: (614)846-8761   Fax: (614)846-8763
Fr: 800-288-7423
Quarterly. $15.00/year. Heavy highway construction and general transportation trade magazine.

★11355★ Maine Trails
Maine Better Transportation Association
146 State St.
Augusta, ME 04330
Ph: (207)623-2928   Fax: (207)623-2928
E-mail: mbta@mbtaonline.org
Bimonthly. $20.00/year. Magazine informing association members and the business community about Maine transportation issues.

★11356★ Traffic Safety
NSC Press
1121 Spring Lake Dr.
Itasca, IL 60143-3201
Ph: (630)285-1121   Fax: (630)285-1315
Fr: 800-621-7615
URL: http://nsc.org
Bimonthly. $24.00/year for members; $30.00/year for nonmembers; $4.25 for single issue. Vehicle collision prevention magazine includes information on driver training, traffic and road engineering, and law enforcement.

★11357★ Traffic World
Economist Group
33 Washington St., 13th Fl.
Newark, NJ 07102-3107
Fr: 800-245-8723
Weekly. $174.00/year. Transportation trade magazine.

★11358★ Transport Technology Today
Transportation Communications
2615 Three Oaks Rd.
Cary, IL 60013
Ph: (847)639-2200   Fax: (847)639-9542
Monthly. Trade publication covering the transportation industry.

★11359★ Transportation Journal
American Society of Transportation and Logistics Inc.
PO Box 55199
Atlanta, GA 30308-5199
Ph: (404)524-3555   Fax: (404)524-7776
Quarterly. $61.95/year for U.S. and Canada; $89.95/year for elsewhere; $115.90 for two years, U.S. and Canada; $245.90/year for two years, elsewhere; $17.00 for single issue. Trade journal covering transportation and logistics.

★11360★ Transportation Quarterly
Eno Transportation Foundation Inc.
1634 I St. NW, Ste. 500
Washington, DC 20006-4003
Ph: (202)879-4700   Fax: (202)879-4719
Quarterly. $55.00/year for individuals; $75.00/year for out of country. A journal of transportation policy, ideas, and commentary.

HANDBOOKS AND MANUALS

★11361★ Opportunities in Civil Engineering Careers
VGM Career Horizons
N T C Contemporary Publishing Company
1221 Avenue of the Americas
New York, NY 10020
Ph: (212)904-2000   Fr: 800-323-4900
E-mail: ntcpub@tribune.com
Joseph Hagerty, Louis F. Cohn, Philip Pessy, and Tom Cosgrove. 1996. $14.95; $11.95 (paper). 205 pages. Describes career opportunities in the different fields of civil engineering and tells how to prepare for and launch such a career.

★11362★ The Role of the Community College in Developing Traffic Specialists and Technicians
Books on Demand-UMI
300 N. Zeeb Rd.
Ann Arbor, MI 48106
Fr: 800-521-0600
Richard Bishop and Gordon Sheehe. 41 pages. Industry information.

EMPLOYMENT AGENCIES AND SEARCH FIRMS

★11363★ Copier Careers
PO Box 300140
Minneapolis, MN 55403
Ph: (612)332-4888   Fax: 800-464-3434
Fr: 888-733-4868
Executive search firm focused on technicians.

ONLINE JOB SOURCES AND SERVICES

★11364★ Civil Engineering Jobs
URL: http://www.civilengineeringjobs.com
Description: Job postings for all civil engineering disciplines including positions in traffic/transportation.

TRADESHOWS

★11365★ ATSSA Annual Convention and Traffic Expo
American Traffic Safety Services Association
15 Riverside Pkwy., Ste. 100
Fredericksburg, VA 22406
Ph: (540)368-1701   Fax: (540)368-1717
Fr: 800-272-8772
E-mail: general@atssa.com
URL: http://www.atssa.com

Annual. **Primary Exhibits:** Manufacturers or services oriented companies that provide traffic control, ITS, pavement marking, signing and various other roadway safety devices. **Dates and Locations:** 2005 Feb 20-22; Phoenix, AZ.

★11366★ International Municipal Signal Association
International Municipal Signal Association
165 E. Union St.
PO Box 539
Newark, NY 14513-0539
Ph: (315)331-2182   Fax: (315)331-8205
Fr: 800-723-4672
E-mail: info@imsasafety.org

Annual. **Primary Exhibits:** Public Safety equipment, supplies, and services, including traffic signals, street signs, alarms, roadway lighting, and communications equipment.

OTHER SOURCES

★11367★ American Association of State Highway and Transportation Officials
444 N. Capitol St. NW, Ste. 249
Washington, DC 20001
Ph: (202)624-5800   Fax: (202)624-5806
URL: http://transportation.org/aashto/organization.nsf

Description: Strives to advocate transportation policies, provide technical services, and demonstrate the contributions of transportation and facilitate change.

★11368★ American Highway Users Alliance
1776 Massachusetts Ave. NW, Ste. 500
Washington, DC 20036
Ph: (202)857-1200
URL: http://www.highways.org

Description: Serves as the voice of the transportation community promoting safe highways and the enhanced freedom of mobility.

★11369★ American Planning Association (APA)
122 S Michigan Ave., Ste. 1600
Chicago, IL 60603-6107
Ph: (312)431-9100   Fax: (312)431-9985
E-mail: research@planning.org
URL: http://www.planning.org

Description: Public and private planning agency officials, professional planners, planning educators, elected and appointed officials, and other persons involved in urban and rural development. Works to foster the best techniques and decisions for the planned development of communities and regions. Provides extensive professional services and publications to professionals and laypeople in planning and related fields; serves as a clearinghouse for information. Through Planning Advisory Service, a research and inquiry-answering service, provides, on an annual subscription basis, advice on specific inquiries and a series of research reports on planning, zoning, and environmental regulations. Supplies information on job openings and makes definitive studies on salaries and recruitment of professional planners. Conducts research; collaborates in joint projects with local, national, and international organizations.

★11370★ American Traffic Safety Services Association
15 Riverside Pkwy., Ste. 100
Fredericksburg, VA 22406
Fr: 800-272-8772
URL: http://www.atssa.com

Description: Represents individuals and companies in the traffic control and roadway safety industry.

★11371★ Association for Commuter Transportation
PO Box 15542
Washington, DC 20003
Ph: (202)393-3497   Fax: (202)347-8847
URL: http://tmi.cob.fsu.edu/act

Description: Professionals who specialize in commuter options and solutions.

★11372★ Association of Metropolitan Planning Organizations
1730 Rhode Island Ave., Ste. 608
Washington, DC 20036
Ph: (202)296-7051   Fax: (202)296-7054

Description: Offers a forum for transportation policy development, conferences and workshops, and research.

★11373★ Institute of Transportation Engineers
1099 14th St., Ste. 300 W
Washington, DC 20005
Ph: (202)289-0222   Fax: (202)289-7722
URL: http://www.ite.org

Description: Traffic engineers, transportation planners, and other related professionals.

★11374★ National Committee on Uniform Traffic Laws and Ordinances (NCUTLO)
107 S West St., No. 110
Alexandria, VA 22314
Ph: (540)465-4701   Fax: (540)465-5383
Fr: 800-807-5290
E-mail: ncutloceo@rica.net
URL: http://www.ncutlo.org

Members: Federal, state, and local highway, police, motor vehicle, and other officials; legislators; educational institutions; manufacturers of vehicles and equipment; insurance companies, motor clubs, and safety councils; other persons and organizations interested in uniform motor vehicle laws. **Activities:** Maintains small library on traffic law. Keeper of the Uniform Vehicle Code, Collection of model laws.

★11375★ National Highway Traffic Safety Administration
Office of Crash Avoidance Research
400 Seventh St. SW, NRD-51
Washington, DC 20590
Ph: (202)366-0388   Fax: (202)366-7237
URL: http://www.nhtsa.dot.gov

Description: Works to save lives, prevent injuries and reduce traffic-related health care.

★11376★ Roadway Safety Foundation
1776 Massachusetts Ave. NW, No. 500
Washington, DC 20036
Ph: (202)857-1239   Fax: (202)857-1220
URL: http://www.roadwaysafety.org

Description: Dedicated to reducing highway deaths and injuries by improving the physical characteristics of roadways.

★11377★ The Traffic Group, Inc.
9900 Franklin Square Dr.
Baltimore, MD 21236
Fr: 800-583-8411
URL: http://www.trafficgroup.com

Description: Consists of professionals in the Traffic Engineering and Transportation Planning fields.

★11378★ Transportation Research Board
2101 Constitution Ave. NW
Washington, DC 20418
Ph: (202)334-2963   Fax: (202)334-2003
URL: http://www4.trb.org

Description: Engineers, Scientists, and other transportation researchers and practitioners from the public and private sectors.

Facilitates the sharing of information, promotes innovation and progress, and stimulates research.

Translators and Interpreters

SOURCES OF HELP-WANTED ADS

★11379★ LSA Bulletin

Linguistic Society of America
1325 18th St. NW, Ste. 211
Washington, DC 20036-6501
Ph: (202)835-1714   Fax: (202)835-1717
URL: http://www.lsadc.org

Description: Quarterly. Covers activities of the linguistic community. Recurring features include a grants calendar, conference and job announcements, a calendar of events, reports of meetings, and job listings.

★11380★ Society of Federal Linguists Newsletter

Society of Federal Linguists
PO Box 7765
Washington, DC 20044
Ph: (202)588-0995

Description: Monthly, or bimonthly. Provides news of interest to translators, interpreters, and linguists working for the federal government. Contains information on technical advances in linguistics. Recurring features include announcements of new foreign language dictionaries and reference books, particularly those received by the Library of Congress, a listing of employment opportunities, news of members, and a column titled Professional Notes.

PLACEMENT AND JOB REFERRAL SERVICES

★11381★ African Studies Association (ASA)

Rutgers the State University of New Jersey
132 George St.- Douglass Campus
New Brunswick, NJ 08901-1400
Ph: (732)932-8173
E-mail: callasa@rci.rutgers.edu

Members: Persons specializing in teaching, writing, or research on Africa including political scientists, historians, geographers, anthropologists, economists, librarians, linguists, and government officials; persons who are studying African subjects; institutional members are universities, libraries, government agencies, and others interested in receiving information about Africa. **Purpose:** Seeks to foster communication and to stimulate research among scholars on Africa. **Activities:** Sponsors placement service; conducts panels and discussion groups; presents exhibits and films.

EMPLOYER DIRECTORIES AND NETWORKING LISTS

★11382★ American Translators Association-Membership Directory

American Translators Association
225 Reinekers Ln., Ste. 590
Alexandria, VA 22314
Ph: (703)683-6100   Fax: (703)683-6122

Annual, summer. $120.00. Includes more than 9,000 member translators, interpreters, and linguists in the United States and over 60 countries. Entries include: Name, address, phone, languages in which member has ATA certification. Arrangement: Alphabetical.

★11383★ ATA Directory of Translators and Interpreters

American Translators Association
225 Reinekers Ln., Ste. 590
Alexandria, VA 22314
Ph: (703)683-6100   Fax: (703)683-6122
URL: http://www.atanet.org

Covers over 5,000 member translators and interpreters. Entries include: Name, address, languages in which proficient, subject competencies, professional background. Arrangement: Alphabetical, area of specialization, language. Indexes: Language-subject competency (with state).

★11384★ Career Opportunities for Bilinguals and Multilinguals

Scarecrow Press Inc.
4501 Forbes Blvd., Ste. 200
Lanham, MD 20706
Ph: (301)459-3366   Fax: (301)429-5748
Fr: 800-462-6420

Latest edition 2nd 2002. $37.50. Covers 3,800 companies and organizations that hire people who are fluent in languages other than English; colleges and universities, libraries, books, and other educational resources for those wishing to learn other languages. Entries include: For employers-Name, address, phone, description of work, languages sought. For educational resources-Name, address, phone, languages. Arrangement: Separate sections for educational resources, U.S. opportunities, and overseas opportunities. Indexes: Language, educational background, geographical.

★11385★ International Literary Market Place

Information Today Inc.
143 Old Marlton Pke.
Medford, NJ 08055-8750
Ph: (609)654-6266   Fax: (609)654-4309
Fr: 800-300-9848
URL: http://www.literarymarketplace.com

Annual, September, latest edition 2004. $239.00. Covers over 10,799 publishers in over 180 countries outside the United States and Canada, and about 1,499 trade and professional organizations related to publishing abroad; includes major printers, binders, typesetters, book manufacturers, book dealers, libraries, literary agencies, translators, book clubs, reference books and journals, periodicals, prizes, and international reference section. Entries include: For publishers-Name, address, phone, fax, telex, names and titles of key personnel, branches, type of publications, subjects, ISBN prefix. Listings for others include similar information but less detail. Arrangement: Classified by business activities, then geographical. Indexes: Company name, subject, type of publication.

★11386★ *Literary Market Place*

Information Today Inc.
143 Old Marlton Pke.
Medford, NJ 08055-8750
Ph: (609)654-6266   Fax: (609)654-4309
Fr: 800-300-9848
URL: http://www.literarymarketplace.com

Annual, Octber, latest edition 2002. $299.00. Covers over 14,500 firms or organizations offering services related to the publishing industry, including book publishers in the United States and Canada who issued three or more books during the preceding year, plus a small press section of publishers who publish less than three titles per year or those who are self-published. Also included: book printers and binders; book clubs; book trade and literary associations; selected syndicates, newspapers, periodicals, and radio and TV programs that use book reviews or book publishing news; translators and literary agents. Entries include: For publishers-Company name, address, phone, address for orders, principal executives, editorial directors, and managers, date founded, number of titles in previous year, number of backlist titles in print, types of books published, ISBN prefixes, representatives, imprints, and affiliations. For suppliers, etc. - Listings usually show firm name, address, phone, executives, services, etc. Arrangement: Classified by line of business. Indexes: Principal index is 35,000-item combined index of publishers, publications, and personnel; several sections have geographical and/or subject indexes; translators are indexed by source and target language.

★11387★ *Translators & Interpretors Directory*

infoUSA Inc.
5711 S 86th Cir.
Omaha, NE 68127-0347
Ph: (402)930-3500   Fax: (402)331-0176
Fr: 800-555-6124
URL: http://www.abii.com

Updated continuously; printed on request.

Number of listings: 3,689. Entries include: Name, address, phone, size of advertisement, name of owner or manager, number of employees, year first in "Yellow Pages." Compiled from telephone company "Yellow Pages," nationwide. Arrangement: Geographical.

HANDBOOKS AND MANUALS

★11388★ *Careers in International Affairs*

Georgetown University Press
3600 O St. NW
Washington, DC 20007-0866
Ph: (202)687-5889   Fr: 800-246-9606

School of Foreign Service, Georgetown University Staff. Sixth edition, 1996. $17.95 (paper). 320 pages. Includes index and bibliography.

★11389★ *Foreign Languages and Your Career*

Jeffrey Norton Publishers, Inc. Audio-Forum
96 Broad St.
Guilford, CT 06437-2612
Ph: (203)453-9794   Fax: (203)453-9774
Fr: 800-243-1234

Edward Bourgoin. Fourth edition, 1993. 120 pages. $9.95. Includes index and bibliography.

★11390★ *Great Jobs for Foreign Language Majors*

McGraw-Hill Trade
2 Penn Plaza
New York, NY 10121
Ph: (212)904-2000   Fr: 800-722-4726
E-mail: ntcpub@tribune.com

Julie DeGalan and Stephen E. Lambert. 1994. $11.95 (paper). 412 pages. Part of Great Jobs for... Majors series.

★11391★ *Guide to Careers in World Affairs*

Impact Publications
9104-N Manassas Dr., Ste. N
Manassas Park, VA 20111-5211
Ph: (703)361-7300   Fax: (703)335-9486

Foreign Affairs Association Staff and Pamela Gerard. Third edition. 1993. $14.95. 331 pages. Out of print. Describes jobs in business, government, and nonprofit organizations. Explains the methods and credentials required to secure a job in many fields, including international law and journalism. Contains sections on internships and graduate programs.

★11392★ *Opportunities in Foreign Language Careers*

McGraw-Hill Contemporary Books
1221 Avenue of the Americas
New York, NY 10020
Ph: (212)904-2000   Fr: 800-323-4900
E-mail: ntcpub@tribune.com

Wilga Rivers. 1998. $14.95; $11.95 (paper). 198 pages. Explores a variety of foreign language careers and discusses how to pursue them. Contains bibliography and illustrations.

★11393★ *A Practical Guide for Translators*

Taylor and Francis, Inc.
325 Chestnut St.
Philadelphia, PA 19106
Ph: (215)625-8900   Fax: (215)625-2940
Fr: 800-634-7064

Geoffrey Samuelsson-Brown. Third edition, 1998. 290 pages. Part of Topics in Translation series. Provides information on becoming a translator.

Travel Agents and Managers

SOURCES OF HELP-WANTED ADS

★11394★ Business Travel News

VNU Business Media USA
770 Broadway
New York, NY 10003
Ph: (646)654-5000
URL: http://www.btnonline.com

Tabloid newspaper covering business travel.

★11395★ Meeting News

Bill Communications Inc.
770 Broadway
New York, NY 10003-9595
Ph: (646)654-4500   Fax: (646)654-7212
URL: http://www.meetingnews.com

Free to qualified subscribers; $65.00/year. The newspaper for conventions, meetings, incentive travel and trade show professionals.

★11396★ TIA Newsline

Travel Industry Association of America
1100 New York Ave. NW, No. 450
Washington, DC 20005-3934
Ph: (202)408-8422   Fax: (202)408-1255
URL: http://www.tia.org

Description: Monthly. Publishes news for the travel industry. Includes book reviews and notices of publications available, news of educational opportunities, and a calendar of events.

★11397★ Travel Agent

Universal Media Inc.
801 2nd Ave.
New York, NY 10017
Ph: (212)986-5100   Fax: (212)338-9445

Weekly. Free to qualified subscribers; $250.00/year. Travel industry magazine.

★11398★ Travel Trade

Travel Trade
15 W 44th St.
New York, NY 10036
Ph: (212)730-6600   Fax: (212)730-7137
E-mail: travelcat@aol.com

Weekly. $10.00/year. Travel industry magazine.

★11399★ Travel Weekly

Northstar Travel Media
500 Plaza Dr.
Secaucus, NJ 07094-3626
Ph: (201)902-2000   Fax: (201)902-2053
URL: http://www.traveler.net/two

Semiweekl. $9.00/year. Travel industry magazine.

★11400★ TravelAge West

Northstar Travel Media
500 Plaza Dr.
Secaucus, NJ 07094-3626
Ph: (201)902-2000   Fax: (201)902-2053

Weekly. Free to qualified subscribers; $25.00/year for individuals. Magazine for retail travel agents in western U.S. and western Canada.

PLACEMENT AND JOB REFERRAL SERVICES

★11401★ Connected International Meeting Professionals Association (CIMPA)

9200 Bayard Pl.
Fairfax, VA 22032
Ph: (703)286-2142   Fax: (703)291-2292
E-mail: info@meetingprofessionals.org
URL: http://www.cimpa.org

Members: Meeting planners, incentive organizers, travel agents, tour operators, and seminar organizers in 42 countries. **Purpose:** Works to improve the skills of professional conference and convention planners. Serves as a clearinghouse of information on new travel destinations and planning technologies, techniques, and strategies. **Activities:** Facilitates exchange of information among Internet professionals. Produces a television program on travel and meetings. Conducts educational courses and awards Certified Internet Meeting Professional designation. Conducts research programs and placement service. Sponsors training courses on the Internet.

★11402★ International Association of Tour Managers - North American Region (IATM-NAR)

9500 Rainier Ave. S, No. 603
Seattle, WA 98118
Ph: (206)725-7108   Fax: (206)725-4020
E-mail: iatmone@aol.com
URL: http://members.aol.com/iatmone/

Description: Travel agents, travel wholesalers, airlines, hotel associations, shipping lines, tourist organizations, restaurants, shops, and entertainment organizations. Works to maintain the highest possible standards of tour management; guarantee excellence of performance; educate the travel world on the role of the tour manager (also referred to as tour director, tour escort, or tour leader) in the successful completion of the tour itinerary and in bringing business to related industries. Represents members in influencing legislation and advising on travel policy. Trains tour managers to plan, research, and lead tours for domestic and foreign travelers; operates Advisory Board in Professional Tour Management; offers placement service; conducts Professional Tour Management, U.S.A. Certificate Program.

EMPLOYER DIRECTORIES AND NETWORKING LISTS

★11403★ American Society of Travel Agents-Membership Directory

American Society of Travel Agents
1101 King St., Ste. 200
Alexandria, VA 22314
Ph: (703)739-2782   Fax: (703)684-8319
URL: http://www.astanet.com

Annual, June. $195.00. Covers about 13,500 travel agents representing over 25,600 members in 130 countries. Entries include: Company name, address, phone, fax, telex, name of principal executive and other officials, services. Arrangement: Classified by membership category, then geographical. Indexes: Personal name, company name.

★11404★ Corporate Travel's Black Book

VNU Business Media
770 Broadway
New York, NY 10003-9595
Ph: (646)654-5000

Annual, October. $15.00. Covers approximately 2,000 airlines, hotels, car rentals, corporate charge cards, travel agencies, and other businesses offering travel packages to corporations. Entries include: Company name, address, phone, fax, name and title of contact. Arrangement: Classified by industry.

★11405★ Directory of Travel Agencies for the Disabled

Twin Peaks Press
PO Box 129
Vancouver, WA 98666-0129
Ph: (360)694-2462   Fax: (360)696-3210
URL: http://www.netm.com/mall/infoprod/twinpeak/helen.htm

Quarterly. $19.95. Number of listings: 370. Entries include: Company name, address, phone, fax, names and titles of key personnel, subsidiary and branch names and locations, description of services. Arrangement: Geographical.

★11406★ National Business Travel Association-Membership Directory

National Business Travel Association
110 N Royal St., 4th Fl.
Alexandria, VA 22314
Ph: (703)684-0836   Fax: (703)684-0263
URL: http://www.nbta.org

Annual. Covers over 1,900 corporate travel managers and supplier members in the United States. Entries include: Individual name, corporate name, type of membership, office address, phone, fax, e-mail, URL address. Arrangement: Alphabetical by individual/company name. Indexes: Geographical, member type, advertiser, company category listing.

★11407★ Specialty Travel Index: The Special Interest & Adventure Travel Directory

Alpine Hansen, Publishers
PO Box 458
San Anselmo, CA 94979
Ph: (415)455-1643   Fax: (415)455-1648
Fr: 888-624-4030
E-mail: info@specialitytravel.com
URL: http://www.specialtytravel.com

Semiannual, January and August. $6.00 per issue; $10.00 for annual subscription. Covers over 600 special interest tour operators, worldwide; all listings are paid. Entries include: Firm name, address, phone; description of tours offered, including nature of trip, destinations, sample cost and duration of trip. Arrangement: Alphabetical. Indexes: Special interest activity (with location of activity), Geographical (and the special interest activities possible).

★11408★ Survey of State Tourism Offices

Travel Industry Association of America
1100 New York Ave. NW, No. 450
Washington, DC 20005-3934
Ph: (202)408-8422   Fax: (202)408-1255
URL: http://www.tia.org

Annual, April. $495.00. Covers state and territorial government agencies responsible for travel and travel promotion in their states. Entries include: Agency name, address, phone, number of full- and part-time staff, number of professional staff directly involved in travel; name and title of state travel director, and length of service as director, length of service in agency, and whether employed under the Civil Service program; advertising director and agency and public relations director in separate sections. Extensive additional data is provided by a series of tables covering state activities in advertising, package tours, general promotion press and public relations, research, the establishment of welcome centers, and the department budget. Although addresses are not given, some listings do include name, title, and department of contact. Arrangement: By function (administration, advertising, etc.), then geographical.

★11409★ Travel Agencies & Bureaus Directory

infoUSA Inc.
5711 S 86th Cir.
Omaha, NE 68127-0347
Ph: (402)930-3500   Fax: (402)331-0176
Fr: 800-555-6124
URL: http://www.abii.com

Annual. Number of listings: 40,973. Entries include: Name, address, phone (including area code), size of advertisement, year first in "Yellow Pages," name of owner or manager, number of employees. Compiled from telephone company "Yellow Pages", nationwide. Arrangement: Geographical.

★11410★ Travel and Tourism Research Association-Membership Directory

Travel and Tourism Research Association
PO Box 2133
Boise, ID 83701
Ph: (208)429-9511   Fax: (208)429-9512
URL: http://www.ttra.com

Annual, June. $125.00. Covers over 800 state and local tourism bureaus and other federal and provincial government agencies, airlines, media, hotels, university bureaus of business research and other university departments, and research and consulting firms concerned with travel research, marketing, and promotion. Entries include: Firm or individual name, address, phone; company listings also include name and title of representative or alternate. Arrangement: Alphabetical. Indexes: Personal name, geographical, industry category.

HANDBOOKS AND MANUALS

★11411★ America's Fastest Growing Jobs

JIST Works, Inc.
8902 Otis Ave.
Indianapolis, IN 46216-1033
Ph: (317)613-4200   Fax: (317)613-4307
Fr: 800-648-5478
E-mail: jistworks@aol.com
URL: http://www.jist.com

Seventh edition, 2002. $16.95 (paper). 438 pages. Each job profile explains the nature of the work, skills and abilities required, employment outlook, average earnings, related occupations, education and training requirements, and employment opportunities. Also contains career planning information and job search tips.

★11412★ Career Opportunities in Travel and Tourism

Checkmark Books, Inc.
132 W. 31st St., 17th Fl.
New York, NY 10001-2006
Ph: (212)967-8800   Fax: (212)967-9196
Fr: 800-322-8755
URL: http://www.factsonfile.com

John K. Hawks. 1996. $18.95 (paper). 224 pages. Includes detailed job descriptions, educational requirements, salary ranges, and advancement prospects for 70 different job opportunities in this fast-paced industry. Contains index and bibliography.

★11413★ Careers in Travel, Tourism, and Hospitality

McGraw-Hill Contemporary Books
1221 Avenue of the Americas
New York, NY 10020
Ph: (212)904-2000   Fr: 800-323-4900
E-mail: ntcpub@tribune.com

Marjorie Eberts, Linda Brothers, and Ann Gisler. 1997. $17.95; 13.95 (paper). 192 pages.

★11414★ A Coach Full of Fun: A Handbook of Creative Solutions and Ideas for Tour Escorts

Shoreline Creations, Ltd.
2465 112th Ave.
Holland, MI 49424
Ph: (616)393-2077   Fax: (616)393-0085
Fr: 800-767-3489

Jeane S. Klender. 1995. $19.95 (paper). 214 pages. Provides advice on how to be successful in the group tour industry. Contains information on tour procedures, preparation, and finances.

★11415★ First Class: An Introduction to Travel and Tourism

Glencoe/McGraw-Hill
8787 Orion Pl.
Columbus, OH 43240-4027
Ph: (614)890-1111   Fax: (614)899-4414
Fr: 800-848-1567

Dennis L. Foster. 1995.

★11416★ Home-Based Travel Agent: How to Cash in on the Exciting New World of Travel Marketing

Intrepid Traveler
15200 NBN Way
Blue Ridge Summit, PA 17214

Kelly Monaghan. Third edition, 1999. $29.95 (paper). 400 pages. Includes an extensive resource section, mini sales program and subject index.

★11417★ Hospitality and Tourism Careers

Prentice Hall PTR
200 Old Tappan Rd.
Old Tappan, NJ 07675
Ph: (201)236-7000   Fr: 800-223-1360

Melissa Dallas and Carl Riegel. First edition, 1997. $20.85 (paper). 252 pages.

★11418★ How to Get a Job with a Cruise Line

Ticket to Adventure, Inc.
PO Box 41005
St. Petersburg, FL 33743-1005
Ph: (727)822-5029   Fax: (727)821-3409
Fr: 800-929-7447

Mary Fallon Miller. Fifth edition, 2001. $16.95 (paper). 336 pages. Explores jobs with cruise ships, describing duties, responsibilities, benefits, and training. Lists cruise ship lines and schools offering cruise line training. Offers job hunting advice.

★11419★ Opportunities in Travel Careers

McGraw-Hill Contemporary Books
1221 Avenue of the Americas
New York, NY 10020
Ph: (212)904-2000   Fr: 800-323-4900
E-mail: ntcpub@tribune.com

Robert Scott Milne. 1996. $14.95; $11.95 (paper). 198 pages. Discusses what the jobs are and where to find them in airlines, shipping lines, and railroads. Discusses related opportunities in hotels, motels, resorts, travel agencies, public relation firms, and recreation departments. Illustrated.

★11420★ Travel Career Development

Institute of Certified Travel Agents
148 Linden St.
PO Box 56
Wellesley, MA 02482
Ph: (781)237-0280   Fax: (781)237-3860

Patricia J. Gagnon and Bruno Ociepka. Sixth edition, 1997. $46.95 (paper).

★11421★ Travel the World Free as an International Tour Director: How to Be an International Tour Director

G.E. Mitchell & Associates, Inc.
PO Box 21199
Charleston, SC 29413
Ph: (803)723-7400   Fax: (803)723-0751
Fr: 800-894-8687

Gerald E. Mitchell. 1995. $59.95. 300 pages. Kit includes 250-page manual, 189-page site-inspection journal and resource start up kit with video.

★11422★ Where the Jobs Are: The Hottest Careers for the 90s

The Career Press, Inc.
3 Tice Rd.
PO Box 687
Franklin Lakes, NJ 07417-1322
Ph: (201)848-0310   Fax: (201)848-1727
Fr: 800-227-3371

Joyce Hadley. Third edition, 2000. $13.99 (paper). 400 pages. Out of print. Describes careers in fifteen general fields, from accounting to travel and hospitality.

EMPLOYMENT AGENCIES AND SEARCH FIRMS

★11423★ ChaseAmerica Inc.

7100-39 Fairway Dr., Ste. 223
Palm Beach Gardens, FL 33418
Ph: (561)622-1120

Executive search firm.

★11424★ The Elliot Group LLC

505 White Plains Rd., Ste. 228
Tarrytown, NY 10591
Ph: (914)631-4904   Fax: (914)631-6481

Executive search firm. Eight locations throughout the United States.

★11425★ Travel Executive Search

5 Rose Ave.
Great Neck, NY 11021
Ph: (516)829-8829

E-mail: tsintl@aol.com

Executive search firm.

TRADESHOWS

★11426★ WTM - World Travel Market

Reed Exhibitions (North American Headquarters)
383 Main Ave.
PO Box 6059
Norwalk, CT 06851
Ph: (203)840-5402   Fax: (203)840-9402
E-mail: inquiry@reedexpo.com
URL: http://www.reedexpo.com

Annual. **Primary Exhibits:** Goods and services related to tourism and travel.

OTHER SOURCES

★11427★ Administration and Management Occupations

Delphi Productions.
3160 4th St.
Boulder, CO 80304
Fax: (303)443-4022   Fr: 888-443-2400
URL: http://www.delphivideo.com

$95.00. 50 minutes. Part of the Careers for the 21st Century Video Library.

★11428★ American Society of Travel Agents (ASTA)

1101 King St., Ste. 200
Alexandria, VA 22314
Ph: (703)739-2782   Fax: (703)684-8319
Fr: 800-440-2782
E-mail: askasta@astahq.com
URL: http://www.astanet.com

Members: Travel agents; allied members are representatives of carriers, hotels, resorts, sightseeing and car rental companies, official tourist organizations, and other travel interests. **Purpose:** Purposes are to: promote and encourage travel among people of all nations; to promote the image and encourage the use of professional travel agents worldwide; serve as an information resource for the travel industry worldwide; promote and represent the views and interests of travel agents to all levels of government and industry; promote professional and ethical conduct in the travel agency industry worldwide; facilitate consumer protection and safety for the traveling public. **Activities:** Maintains biographical archives and travel hall of fame. Conducts research and education programs.

★11429★ Institute of Certified Travel Agents (ICTA)

148 Linden St., Ste. 305
PO Box 812059
Wellesley, MA 02482
Ph: (781)237-0280   Fax: (781)237-3860
Fr: 800-542-4282
E-mail: info@thetravelinstitute.com
URL: http://www.icta.com

Description: Individuals who have been accredited as Certified Travel Counselors (CTC) or Certified Travel Associates (CTA) must meet the institute's testing and experience requirements. Seeks to increase the level of competence in the travel industry. Provides continuing education, and examination and certification programs; conducts workshops and professional management seminars. Operates Travel Career Development Program to increase professional skills and Destination Specialist Programs to enhance the geographical knowledge of sales agents. Organizes study groups of instruction with enrolled student bodies in most major cities. student bodies in most major cities.

★11430★ Marketing & Sales Occupations

Delphi Productions
3160 4th St.
Boulder, CO 80304
Fax: (303)443-4022   Fr: 888-443-2400
URL: http://www.delphivideo.com

$95.00. 50 minutes. Part of the Careers for the 21st Century Video Library.

★11431★ Reservation and Transportation Ticket Agents, Travel Agents

Evon Publishing
832 N 7th Ave.
Iron River, MI 49935
Ph: (906)265-3190

Audiocassette. 1996. $16.95. 32 minutes. Part of the Careers and Vocational Guidance Series. Provides information about the nature of the work, educational requirements, employment outlook, earnings, and work conditions as well as additional related information.

★11432★ Society of Incentive and Travel Executives (SITE)

401 North Michigan Ave.
Chicago, IL 60611
Ph: (312)321-5148   Fax: (312)527-6783
E-mail: hq@site-intl.org
URL: http://www.site-intl.org

Description: Individuals responsible for the administration or sale of incentive programs including corporate users, incentive marketing companies, cruise lines, hotel chains, resort operators, airlines, and tourist boards. Unites individuals in the incentive industry and facilitates information exchange and problem solving on a personal and professional basis. Supports expansion of incentive programs through public relations, promotion, and speakers' bureau activities. Contributes to the continuing professional education of members through meetings, publications, and research services. Helps upgrade standards through educational services to nonmembers. Bestows Certified Incentive Travel Executive designation. Compiles statistics; provides placement service.

★11433★ Travel Agents

Evon Publishing
832 N 7th Ave.
Iron River, MI 49935
Ph: (906)265-3190

Audiocassette. 1996. $16.95. 32 minutes. Part of the Careers and Vocational Guidance Series. Provides information about the nature of the work, educational requirements, employment outlook, earnings, and work conditions as well as additional related information.

★11434★ U.S. Travel Data Center (USTDC)

1100 New York Ave. NW, Ste. 450
Washington, DC 20005-3934
Ph: (202)408-8422   Fax: (202)408-1255
URL: http://www.tia.org/Travel/default.asp

Description: Conducts statistical, economic, and market research concerning travel; encourages standardized travel research terminology and techniques. Program objectives include: monitoring trends in travel activity and the travel industry; measuring the economic impact of travel on geographic areas; evaluating the effect of government programs on travel and the travel industry; measuring the cost of travel in the U.S., forecasting travel activity and expenditures.

Typesetters and Compositors

on goals, printing philosophy, etc. Arrangement: Alphabetical. Indexes: Proprietor name, geographical.

★11442★ International Literary Market Place

Information Today Inc.
143 Old Marlton Pke.
Medford, NJ 08055-8750
Ph: (609)654-6266   Fax: (609)654-4309
Fr: 800-300-9848
URL: http://www.literarymarketplace.com

Annual, September, latest edition 2004. $239.00. Covers over 10,799 publishers in over 180 countries outside the United States and Canada, and about 1,499 trade and professional organizations related to publishing abroad; includes major printers, binders, typesetters, book manufacturers, book dealers, libraries, literary agencies, translators, book clubs, reference books and journals, periodicals, prizes, and international reference section. Entries include: For publishers-Name, address, phone, fax, telex, names and titles of key personnel, branches, type of publications, subjects, ISBN prefix. Listings for others include similar information but less detail. Arrangement: Classified by business activities, then geographical. Indexes: Company name, subject, type of publication.

★11443★ Literary Market Place

Information Today Inc.
143 Old Marlton Pke.
Medford, NJ 08055-8750
Ph: (609)654-6266   Fax: (609)654-4309
Fr: 800-300-9848
URL: http://www.literarymarketplace.com

Annual, Octber, latest edition 2002. $299.00. Covers over 14,500 firms or organizations offering services related to the publishing industry, including book publishers in the United States and Canada who issued three or more books during the preceding year, plus a small press section of publishers who publish less than three titles per year or those who are self-published. Also included: book printers and binders; book clubs; book trade and literary associations; selected syndicates, newspapers, periodicals, and radio and TV programs that use book reviews or book publishing news; translators and literary agents. Entries include: For publishers-Company name, address, phone, address for orders, principal executives, editorial directors, and managers, date founded, number of titles in previous year, number of backlist titles in print, types of books published, ISBN prefixes, representatives, imprints, and affiliations. For suppliers, etc. - Listings usually show firm name, address, phone, executives, services, etc. Arrangement: Classified by line of business. Indexes: Principal index is 35,000-item combined index of publishers, publications, and personnel; several sections have geographical and/or subject indexes; translators are indexed by source and target language.

★11444★ Publishers Directory

Thomson Gale
27500 Drake Rd.
Farmington Hills, MI 48331-3535
Ph: (248)699-4253   Fax: (248)699-8065
Fr: 800-877-GALE
E-mail: businessproducts@gale.com
URL: http://www.gale.com

Annual. $450.00. Covers over 20,000 new and established, commercial and nonprofit, private and alternative, corporate and association, government and institution publishing programs and their distributors; includes producers of books, classroom materials, prints, reports, and databases. Entries include: Firm name, address, phone, fax, company e-mail address, URL, year founded, ISBN prefix, Standard Address Number, whether firm participates in the Cataloging in Publication program of the Library of Congress, names of principal executives, personal e-mail addresses, number of titles in print, description of firm and its main subject interests, discount and returns policies, affiliated and parent companies, mergers and amalgamations, principal markets, imprints and divisions, alternate formats products are offered; distributors also list firms for which they distribute, special services, terms to publishers and regional offices. Arrangement: Alphabetical; distributors listed separately. Indexes: Subject, geographical, publisher, imprints, and distributor.

★11445★ Typesetting Directory

infoUSA Inc.
5711 S 86th Cir.
Omaha, NE 68127-0347
Ph: (402)930-3500   Fax: (402)331-0176
Fr: 800-555-6124
URL: http://www.abii.com

Annual. Number of listings: 10,120. Entries include: Name, address, phone (including area code), size of advertisement, year first in "Yellow Pages," name of owner or manager, number of employees. Compiled from telephone company "Yellow Pages," nationwide. Arrangement: Geographical.

★11446★ The Workbook

Scott & Daughters Publishing Inc.
940 N Highland Ave., Ste. A
Los Angeles, CA 90038
Ph: (323)856-0008   Fax: (323)856-0443
Fr: 800-547-2688
URL: http://www.workbook.com

Annual, February. $120.00. Covers 49,000 advertising agencies, art directors, photographers, freelance illustrators and designers, artists' representatives, interactive designers, pre-press services, and other graphic arts services in the U.S. Entries include: Company or individual name, address, phone, specialty. National in scope. Arrangement: Classified by product or service.

HANDBOOKS AND MANUALS

★11447★ Degree of Mastery: A Journey Through Book Arts Apprenticeship

Penguin Putnam, Incorporated
375 Hudson St.
New York, NY 10014
Ph: (212)366-2000   Fr: (212)366-2666

Annie Tremmel Wilcox. 2000. $12.95 (paper).

★11448★ Opportunities in Printing Careers

McGraw-Hill Trade
2 Penn Plaza
New York, NY 10121
Ph: (212)904-2000   Fr: 800-722-4726
E-mail: ntcpub@tribune.com

Irvin Borowsky. 1998. $14.95; $11.95 (paper). 160 pages. Offers detailed information on the variety of pre-press, press, and post-press jobs available. Covers apprenticeships, unions, salaries, and how to get ahead. Illustrated.

EMPLOYMENT AGENCIES AND SEARCH FIRMS

★11449★ Graphic Arts Employment Service, Inc.

409 N Pacific Coast Hwy., Ste.455
Redondo Beach, CA 90277
Ph: (310)316-1246   Fax: (310)937-3760
Fr: 800-499-9722
E-mail: info@gaes.com
URL: http://www.gaes.com

Employment agency specializing in the publishing and packaging industries.

★11450★ Graphic Search Associates Inc.

PO Box 373
Newtown Square, PA 19073
Ph: (610)359-1234   Fax: (610)353-8120
Fr: 800-342-1777
E-mail: info@graphsrch.com
URL: http://www.graphsrch.com

Executive search firm for the graphic arts industry.

★11451★ Stewart Associates

181 Windover Turn
Lancaster, PA 17601
Ph: (717)299-9242   Fax: (717)299-4879
E-mail: waltp@redrose.net

Executive search firm for the manufacturing industry.

OTHER SOURCES

★11452★ American Institute of Graphic Arts (AIGA)
164 5th Ave.
New York, NY 10010
Ph: (212)807-1990   Fax: (212)807-1799
Fr: 800-548-1634
E-mail: comments@aiga.org
URL: http://www.aiga.org

Description: Graphic designers, art directors, art directors, illustrators, packaging designers. Sponsors exhibits and projects in the public interest. Sponsors traveling exhibitions. Operates gallery. Maintains library of design books and periodicals; offers slide archives.

★11453★ *Compositors and Typesetters*
Evon Publishing
832 N 7th Ave.
Iron River, MI 49935
Ph: (906)265-3190

Audiocassette. 1996. $16.95. 32 minutes. Part of the Careers and Vocational Guidance Series. Provides information about the nature of the work, educational requirements, employment outlook, earnings, and work conditions as well as additional related information.

★11454★ Graphic Arts Technical Foundation (GATF)
200 Deer Run Rd.
Sewickley, PA 15143-2600
Ph: (412)741-6860   Fax: (412)741-2311
Fr: 800-910-GATF
E-mail: info@gatf.org
URL: http://www.gatf.org

Description: Scientific, research, technical, and educational organization serving the international graphic communications industries. Conducts research in all graphic processes and their commercial applications. Conducts seminars, workshops, and forums on graphic arts and environmental subjects. Conducts educational programs, including the publishing of graphic arts textbooks and learning modules, videotapes and CD-ROMs and broadcast video seminars. Conducts the GATF training and certification program in sheet-fed offset press operating, Web Offset press operating, Image Assembly, and desktop publishing. Produces test images and quality control devices for the industry. Performs technical services for the graphic arts industry, including problem-solving, material evaluation, and plant audits. A partner of the Printing Industries of America (PIA).

★11455★ National Association for Printing Leadership (NAPL)
75 W. Century Rd.
Paramus, NJ 07652-1408
Ph: (201)634-9600   Fax: (201)634-0325
Fr: 800-642-NAPL
E-mail: info@napl.org
URL: http://www.napl.org

Description: Commercial printers and suppliers to the commercial printing industry. Enables those in the industry to operate their businesses for maximum profitability. Offers following management products and services: sales and marketing, customer service, financial, human resources, operations, economic. **Activities:** Maintains Management Institute, which conducts Executive Certification Program. Compiles extensive economic statistics.

★11456★ Printing Brokerage/Buyers Association (PB/BAI)
PO Box 744
Palm Beach, FL 33480
Ph: (561)586-9391   Fax: (561)845-7130
Fr: (866)586-9391
E-mail: Info@pbbai.net
URL: http://www.pbbai.net

Description: Printing buyers/brokers/distributors, printers, typographers, binders, envelope and book manufacturers, packagers, color separation houses, pre-press service organizations, and related companies in the graphic arts industry. Promotes understanding, cooperation, and interaction among members while obtaining the highest standard of professionalism in the graphic arts industry. Gathers information on current technology in the graphic communications industry. Sponsors seminars for members to learn how to work with buyers, brokers and printers; also conducts technical and management seminars. Maintains referral service; compiles statistics. Conducts charitable programs.

★11457★ Printing Industries of America (PIA)
100 Daingerfield Rd.
Alexandria, VA 22314-2888
Ph: (703)519-8100   Fax: (703)548-3227
Fr: 800-742-2666
E-mail: gain@printing.org
URL: http://www.gain.net

Description: Commercial printing firms (lithography, letterpress, gravure, platemakers, typographic houses); allied firms in the graphic arts. Provides extensive management services for member companies, including government relations, industry research and statistical information, technology information and assistance, and management education and publications. Compiles statistical and economic data, including annual ratio study which provides a benchmark for printers to compare profits as a basis for improving individual member company and industry profits. Provides reporting system on provisions, rates, and other matters relating to union contracts in effect throughout the industry. Sponsors annual Premier Print Awards Competition.

★11458★ Type Directors Club (TDC)
127 W 25th St., Fl. 8
New York, NY 10001
Ph: (212)633-8943   Fax: (212)633-8944
E-mail: director@tdc.org
URL: http://www.tdc.org

Description: Professional society of typographic designers, type directors, and teachers of typography; sustaining members are individuals with interests in typographic education. Seeks to stimulate research and disseminate information. Provides speakers and offers presentations on new developments in typography.

★11459★ Typophiles
35 Schermerhorn St.
Brooklyn, NY 11201-4826

Description: Designers, printers, book collectors, artists, calligraphers, private press owners, wood engravers, and others interested in graphic arts.

Typists, Word Processors, and Data Entry Keyers

SOURCES OF HELP-WANTED ADS

★11460★ *OfficePRO*
Stratton Publishing and Marketing Inc.
5501 Backlick Rd., Ste. 240
Springfield, VA 22151
Ph: (703)914-9200   Fax: (703)914-6777
E-mail: officepromag@strattonpub.com

$25.00/year for individuals. Magazine for administrative assistants, office managers, and secretaries featuring information on trends in business, technology, career development, and management.

PLACEMENT AND JOB REFERRAL SERVICES

★11461★ Network and Systems Professionals Association (NASPA)
7044 S 13th St.
Oak Creek, WI 53154
Ph: (414)768-8000   Fax: (414)768-8001
E-mail: helpdesk@netstream.net
URL: http://www.naspa.net

Description: Technicians and technical management personnel in 90 countries who work in corporate data processing. Dedicated to enhancing the level of technical education among members through publications, public domain software, electronic information sharing, job and career assistance, and scholarships and grants. Conducts charitable and educational programs; maintains speakers' bureau and placement service; compiles statistics.

EMPLOYER DIRECTORIES AND NETWORKING LISTS

★11462★ *Northwest High Tech*
Resolution Business Press Inc.
12307 NE 149th Ct.
Kirkland, WA 98034
Ph: (425)487-6248   Fax: (425)649-1897
E-mail: info@respress.com
URL: http://www.respress.com

Annual. $34.95. Covers over 2,000 computer-related companies in Washington, Oregon, and Idaho, and British Columbia and Alberta, Canada. Entries include: Company; name, address, phone, fax; toll-free number; names and titles of key personnel; product/service, programming languages, financial data, number of employees, operating systems, expansion plans (including hiring and site expansion plans), company market information, Standard Industrial Classification (SIC) code., internet addresses. Arrangement: Geographical. Indexes: Company name, SIC.

HANDBOOKS AND MANUALS

★11463★ *Exploring Careers in Word Processing and Desktop Publishing*
Rosen Publishing Group Inc.
29 East 21st St.
New York, NY 10010

Jean Spencer. Offers an overview of desktop publishing.

★11464★ *Exploring High-Tech Careers*
Rosen Publishing Group, Inc.
29 E. 21st St.
New York, NY 10010
Ph: (212)777-3017   Fax: (212)777-0277
Fr: 800-237-9932

Scott Southworth. Revised edition, 1993. $14.95; $9.95 (paper). 118 pages. Out of print. Gives an orientation to the field of high technology and high-tech jobs. Describes educational preparation and job hunting. Includes a glossary and bibliography.

★11465★ *How to Prepare for the Civil Service Examinations for Stenographer, Typist, Clerk, and Office Manager*
Barron's Educational Series, Inc.
250 Wireless Blvd.
Hauppauge, NY 11788-3917
Ph: (631)434-3311   Fax: (631)434-3723
Fr: 800-645-3476

Jerry Bobrow. Fourth edition, 2000. $13.95 (paper). 384 pages.

★11466★ *Opportunities in Data and Word Processing Careers*
McGraw-Hill Contemporary Books
1221 Avenue of the Americas
New York, NY 10020
Ph: (212)904-2000   Fr: 800-323-4900
E-mail: ntcpub@tribune.com

Marianne Munday. Revised, 1996. $14.95; $11.95 (paper). 160 pages.

★11467★ *Opportunities in High Tech Careers*
McGraw-Hill Trade
2 Penn Plaza
New York, NY 10121
Ph: (212)904-2000   Fr: 800-722-4726

Gary Colter and Deborah Yanuck. 1995. $14.95; $11.95 (paper). 160 pages. Explores high technology careers. Describes job opportunities, how to make a career decision, how to prepare for high technology jobs, job hunting techniques, and future trends.

★11468★ *Opportunities in Office Occupations*
McGraw-Hill Trade
2 Penn Plaza
New York, NY 10121
Ph: (212)904-2000   Fr: 800-722-4726

Blanche Ettinger. 1994. $14.95; $11.95 (paper). 200 pages. Covers a variety of office positions and discusses trends for the next decade. Describes the job market, opportunities, job duties, educational preparation, the work environment, and earnings.

★11469★ Opportunities in Secretarial Careers

McGraw-Hill Trade
2 Penn Plaza
New York, NY 10121
Ph: (212)904-2000   Fr: 800-722-4726
E-mail: ntcpub@tribune.com

Blanche Ettinger. 1999. 160 pages. $14.95; $11.95 (paper). Includes a chapter on finding a secretarial job with sample resumes and interview questions.

★11470★ Opportunities in State and Local Government Careers

Vgm Career Horizons
1221 Avenue of the Americas
New York, NY 10020
Ph: (212)904-2000   Fr: 800-323-4900
E-mail: ntcpub@tribune.com

Neale J. Baxter. 1994. $14.95; $10.95 (paper). 160 pages. Points out the incentives and drawbacks of a government career. Describes hiring procedures and provides tips on filling out applications, taking physical and aptitude tests, handling interviews, and finding jobs. Describes the jobs in which 75% of all state and local government workers are employed. For each occupation, covers the nature of the work and the training required.

★11471★ Word Processing Profits at Home

Aames-Allen Publishing Company
18281 Gothard St., No. 105
Huntington Beach, CA 92648
Ph: (714)375-4889   Fax: (714)848-4566

Peggy Glenn. 1994. $18.95 (paper). Covers all aspects of running a home-based word processing business. Out of Print.

EMPLOYMENT AGENCIES AND SEARCH FIRMS

★11472★ Apple One Employment Services

990 Knox St.
Torrance, CA 90504
Ph: (310)516-1572
E-mail: cduque@appleonee.com
URL: http://www.appleone.com

Employment agency. Additional offices in Anaheim, Oakland, Cerritos, San Francisco, Manhattan Beach, and Glendale.

★11473★ The Aspire Group

52 Second Ave, 1st Fl
Waltham, MA 02451-1129
Fax: (718)890-1810   Fr: 800-546-5675
URL: http://www.bmanet.com

Employment agency.

★11474★ Beverly Hills Bar Association Personnel Service

300 S. Beverly Dr., Ste. 214
Beverly Hills, CA 90212-4805
Ph: (310)553-4575   Fax: (310)553-6940
URL: http://www.bhba.org

Employment agency.

★11475★ Davis-Smith, Inc.

27656 Franklin Rd.
Southfield, MI 48034
Ph: (248)354-4100   Fax: (248)354-6702
Fr: 800-541-4672
E-mail: info@davissmith.com
URL: http://www.davissmith.com

Employment agency. Executive search firm.

★11476★ The Esquire Staffing Group Ltd.

1 S. Wacker Dr., Ste. 1616
Chicago, IL 60606-4616
Ph: (312)795-4300   Fax: (312)795-4329
E-mail: s.fischer@esquirestaffing.com
URL: http://www.esquirestaffing.com

Employment agency. Fills permanent as well as temporary openings.

★11477★ Hallmark Services

1000 Second Ave., Ste. 1450
Seattle, WA 98104
Ph: (206)587-5360
URL: http://hallmarkservices.com/Default.htm

Employment agency. Fills openings for permanent employment.

★11478★ Pathfinders, Inc.

229 Peachtree St. NE
International Tower, Ste. 1500
Atlanta, GA 30303
Ph: (404)688-5940

Permanent employment agency focusing on the secretarial field.

OTHER SOURCES

★11479★ Association of Information Technology Professionals

401 N Michigan Ave., Ste. 2400
PO Box 809189
Chicago, IL 60611-4267
Ph: (312)245-1070   Fax: (312)527-6636
Fr: 800-224-9371
E-mail: aitp_hq@aitp.org

URL: http://www.aitp.org

Members: Managerial personnel, staff, educators, and individuals interested in the management of information resources. Founder of the Certificate in Data Processing examination program, now administered by an intersociety organization. **Purpose:** Maintains Legislative Communications Network. Professional education programs include EDP-oriented business and management principles self-study courses and a series of videotaped management development seminars. Sponsors student organizations around the country interested in information technology and encourages members to serve as counselors for the Scout computer merit badge. Conducts research projects, including a business information systems curriculum for two- and four-year colleges.

★11480★ Black Data Processing Associates (BDPA)

6301 Ivy Ln., Ste. 700
Greenbelt, MD 20770
Ph: (301)220-2180   Fax: (301)220-2185
Fr: 800-727-BDPA
E-mail: president@bdpa.org
URL: http://www.bdpa.org

Description: Persons employed in the information processing industry, including electronic data processing, electronic word processing, and data communications; others interested in information processing. Seeks to accumulate and share information processing knowledge and business expertise in order to increase the career and business potential of minorities in the information processing field. Conducts professional seminars, workshops, tutoring services, and community introductions to data processing. Makes annual donation to the United Negro College Fund.

★11481★ Data Entry Keyers

Evon Publishing
832 N 7th Ave.
Iron River, MI 49935
Ph: (906)265-3190

Audiocassette. 1996. $16.95. 32 minutes. Part of the Careers and Vocational Guidance Series. Provides information about the nature of the work, educational requirements, employment outlook, earnings, and work conditions as well as additional related information.

★11482★ Data Processing Industry

Evon Publishing
832 N 7th Ave.
Iron River, MI 49935
Ph: (906)265-3190

Audiocassette. 1996. $16.95. 32 minutes. Part of the Careers and Vocational Series. Provides information about the nature of the work, educational requirements, employment outlook, earnings, and work conditions as well as additional related information.

★11483★ *Typists and Word Processors*

Evon Publishing
832 N 7th Ave.
Iron River, MI 49935
Ph: (906)265-3190

Audiocassette. 1996. $16.95. 32 minutes. Part of the Careers and Vocational Guidance Series. Provides information about the nature of the work, educational requirements, employment outlook, earnings, and work conditions as well as additional related information.

★11484★ **Visually Impaired Data Processors International (VIDPI)**
1155 15th St. NW, Ste. 1004
Washington, DC 20005
Ph: (202)467-5081   Fr: 888-217-7373
E-mail: rrrogers@one.net
URL: http://www.acb.org/vidpi/

Description: Visually impaired electronic data processing employees; those seeking employment; employers, instructors, manufacturers, and students in the electronic data processing field. Advocates high standards in training visually impaired students. Seeks to increase employment opportunities; encourages the exchange of work technique ideas and the development of new equipment. Works with agencies to increase the availability of braille and recorded materials. Supports a speakers' bureau.

Underwriters

★11485★ Best's Review
A.M. Best Co.
Ambest Rd.
Oldwick, NJ 08858
Fax: (908)439-2200
E-mail: best'sreview@ambest.com
URL: http://www.bestreview.com

Monthly. $21.00/year for individuals; $7.50 for single issue. Magazine covering issues and trends for the management personnel of life/health insurers, the agents, and brokers who market their products.

★11486★ Business Insurance
Crain Communications Inc.
711 Third Ave.
New York, NY 10017-4036
Ph: (212)210-0100   Fax: (212)210-0244
Fr: 800-446-1420
URL: http://www.businessinsurance.com

Weekly. $97.00/year for individuals. International newsweekly reporting on corporate risk and employee benefit management news.

★11487★ National Underwriter Property and Casualty/Risk and Benefits Management
National Underwriter Co.
5081 Olympic Blvd.
Erlanger, KY 41018
Ph: (859)692-2100   Fax: 800-874-1916
Fr: 800-543-0874
E-mail: nup&c@nuco.com

Weekly. $89.00/year. Newsweekly for agents, brokers, executives, and managers in risk and benefit insurance.

★11488★ The Standard
Standard Publishing Corp.
155 Federal St., 13th Fl.
Boston, MA 02110
Ph: (617)457-0600   Fax: (617)482-7820
Fr: 800-682-5759

E-mail: stnd@earthlink.net

Weekly. $55.00/year for individuals. Trade newspaper covering insurance events, legislation, regulatory hearings, and court sessions for independent insurance agents in New England.

EMPLOYER DIRECTORIES AND NETWORKING LISTS

★11489★ Best's Insurance Reports
A.M. Best Co.
Ambest Rd.
Oldwick, NJ 08858
Ph: (908)439-2200   Fax: (908)439-2688
URL: http://www.ambest.com

Annual, summer. $1,495.00 for CD-ROM; $830.00 for print. Published in three editions: Life-health insurance, covering about 1,750 companies, property-casualty insurance, covering over 3,200 companies; and international, covering more than 1,200 insurers. Each edition lists state insurance commissioners and related companies and agencies (mutual funds, worker compensation funds, underwriting agencies, etc.). Entries include: For each company-Company name, address, phone; history; states in which licensed; names of officers and directors; financial data; financial analysis and Best's rating. Arrangement: Alphabetical.

★11490★ Business Insurance-Agent/ Broker Profiles Issue
Business Insurance
360 N Michigan Ave.
Chicago, IL 60601-3806
Ph: (312)649-5319   Fax: (312)280-3174
Fr: 800-678-2724
URL: http://www.businessinsurance.com/ cgi-bin/page.pl?pageId=121

Annual, July. $15.00. Publication includes: List of approximately 200 insurance agents and brokers specializing in commercial insurance. Entries include: Firm name, address, phone, fax, branch office locations, year established, names of subsidiaries,

gross revenues, premium volume, number of employees, principal officers, percent of revenue generated by commercial retail brokerage, acquisitions. Arrangement: Alphabetical, by company. Indexes: Geographical.

★11491★ Insurance Almanac
Underwriter Printing and Publishing Co.
50 E Palisade Ave.
Englewood, NJ 07631
Ph: (201)569-8808   Fax: (201)569-8817
Fr: 800-526-4700

Annual, July. $175.00. Covers over 3,000 insurance companies that write fire, casualty, accident and health, life, and Lloyd's policies; also lists mutual and reciprocal companies. Includes national, state, and local insurance associations; state insurance officials; and about 800 agents, brokers, actuaries, and adjusters. Entries include: For companies-Company name, address, phone, names of officers and directors, lines written, territory covered; for larger firms, some history and financial data. For associations-Name, address, names of staff and officers, place and date of meetings. For agents, brokers, etc.-Name, address. Arrangement: Classified by insurance lines, type of activity, etc. Indexes: Company name.

★11492★ Insurance Consultants & Advisors Directory
infoUSA Inc.
5711 S 86th Cir.
Omaha, NE 68127-0347
Ph: (402)930-3500   Fax: (402)331-0176
Fr: 800-555-6124
URL: http://www.abii.com

Annual. Number of listings: 11,032. Entries include: Name, address, phone (including area code), size of advertisement, year first in "Yellow Pages," name of owner or manager, number of employees. Compiled from telephone company "Yellow Pages," nationwide. Arrangement: Geographical.

★11493★ Insurance Phone Book and Directory

Douglas Publications Inc.
2807 N Parham Rd.,64 Bldg., Ste. 200
Richmond, VA 23294
Ph: (804)762-9600   Fax: (804)217-8999
Fr: 800-794-6086
URL: http://www.douglaspublications.com

Annual. $99.50. Covers about 4,000 life, accident and health, worker's compensation, auto, fire and casualty, marine, surety, and other insurance companies. Entries include: Company name, address, phone, fax, toll-free number, type of insurance provided. Arrangement: Alphabetical.

★11494★ Kirshner's Insurance Directories

National Underwriter Co.
5081 Olympic Blvd.
Erlanger, KY 41018
Ph: (859)692-2100   Fax: 800-874-1916
Fr: 800-543-0874
URL: http://www.nationalunderwriter.com/kirschners/

Annual, all editions except California and Pacific Northwest (semiannual). $19.95. Covers Insurance agents and agencies in all 50 states and the District of Columbia. Published in 24 separate editions for Southern California, Northern California, Pacific Northwest (AK, ID, HI, OR, WA, MT), Michigan, Illinois, New England states (CT, ME, MA, NH, RI, VT), Ohio, Rocky Mountain states (AZ, CO, NV, NM, UT, WY), South Central states (GA, AL, MS), Indiana, Texas, Kentucky/Tennessee, East Central states (VA, WV, NC, SC), South Central West states (AR, OK, LA), Wisconsin, Central states (KS, MO, NE), North Central states (IA, MN, ND, SD), Mid-Atlantic states (DE, MD, NJ, DC), Pennsylvania, Florida. Entries include: For companies-Name, address, key personnel (with addresses abd phone numbers). Arrangement: Separate alphabetical sections for insurance companies, wholesalers, field agents, and agencies. Indexes: Type of insurance.

★11495★ Mergent Bank and Finance Manual

Mergent Inc.
5250 77 Center Dr., Ste. 150
Charlotte, NC 28217
Ph: (704)559-7601   Fax: (704)559-6945
Fr: 800-342-5647
URL: http://www.mergent.com

Annual, July; supplements in 'Mergent Bank & Finance News Reports'. $2,095.00. Covers in four volumes, over 12,000 national, state, and private banks, savings and loans, mutual funds, unit investment trusts, and insurance and real estate companies in the United States. Entries include: Company name, headquarters and branch offices, phones, names and titles of principal executives, directors, history, Moody's rating, and extensive financial and statistical data. Arrangement: Classified by type of business. Indexes: Company name.

★11496★ New Jersey Telephone Tickler

Underwriter Printing and Publishing Co.
50 E Palisade Ave.
Englewood, NJ 07631
Ph: (201)569-8808   Fax: (201)569-8817
Fr: 800-526-4700

Annual, June. $12.50. Covers insurance companies, brokers, agents, and related suppliers in New Jersey. Entries include: Company name, address, phone. Arrangement: Alphabetical. Indexes: Product/service.

★11497★ Who's Who in Insurance

Underwriter Printing and Publishing Co.
50 E Palisade Ave.
Englewood, NJ 07631
Ph: (201)569-8808   Fax: (201)569-8817
Fr: 800-526-4700

Annual, February. $150.00. Covers over 5,000 insurance officials, brokers, agents, and buyers. Entries include: Name, title, company name, address, home address, educational background, professional club and association memberships, personal and career data. Arrangement: Alphabetical.

HANDBOOKS AND MANUALS

★11498★ Careers for Number Crunchers and Other Quantitative Types

McGraw-Hill Trade
2 Penn Plaza
New York, NY 10121
Ph: (212)904-2000   Fr: 800-722-4726
E-mail: ntcpub@tribune.com

Rebecca Burnett. Second edition, 2002. $15.95; $12.95 (paper). 192 pages. Provides information to math-oriented job hunters on how to become statisticians, field researchers, computer programmers, stock analysts, investment managers, bankers, engineers, accountants, underwriters, economists, market analysts, mathematicians, systems analysts, and more.

★11499★ Opportunities in Insurance Careers

McGraw-Hill/Contemporary Books
1221 Avenue of the Americas
New York, NY 10020
Ph: (212)904-2000   Fr: 800-323-4900
E-mail: ntcpub@tribune.com

Robert Schrayer. Revised, 1999. $14.95; $11.95 (paper). 148 pages. A guide to planning for and seeking opportunities in the field. Contains bibliography and illustrations.

★11500★ Successful Life Insurance Selling: How to Prosper in the Year 2000 and Beyond

Dearborn Trade Publishing
155 N. Wacker Dr.
Chicago, IL 60606-1719
Ph: (312)836-1021   Fax: (312)836-1021
Fr: 800-621-9621

Gary Schulte. 1994. $24.95. 256 pages. Out of print.

EMPLOYMENT AGENCIES AND SEARCH FIRMS

★11501★ Employment Advisors

815 Nicollet Mall Ste 200
Minneapolis, MN 55402
Ph: (612)339-3944
E-mail: info@collegegraduateregistry.com
URL: http://www.collegegraduateregistry.com

Employment agency. Places candidates in variety of fields.

★11502★ Godfrey Personnel Inc.

300 W. Adams, Ste. 612
Chicago, IL 60606-5194
Ph: (312)236-4455   Fax: (312)580-6292
E-mail: jim@godfreypersonnel.com
URL: http://ww.godfreypersonnel.com

Search firm specializing in insurance industry.

★11503★ International Insurance Personnel, Inc.

300 W. Wieuca Rd., Bldg. 2, Ste. 101
Atlanta, GA 30342
Ph: (404)255-9710
E-mail: info@intlinspersonnel.com
URL: http://www.intlinspersonnel.com/interimstafing.htm

Employment agency specializing in the area of insurance.

★11504★ Questor Consultants, Inc.

2515 N. Broad St.
Colmar, PA 18915
Ph: (215)997-9262   Fax: (215)997-9226
E-mail: jobs@questorconsultants.com
URL: http://www.questorconsultants.com

Executive search firm specializing in the insurance and legal fields.

ONLINE JOB SOURCES AND SERVICES

★11505★ UnderwritingJobs.com
E-mail: admin@uwjobs.com

URL: http://www.underwritingjobs.com
Description: Job search website for underwriters. Seekers may search databank by field of interest or geography, post their resume or visit career-related links.

TRADESHOWS

★11506★ CPCU Conferment Ceremony
American Institute for CPCU
720 Providence Rd.
PO Box 3016
Malvern, PA 19355-0716
Ph: (610)644-2100   Fax: (610)640-9576
Fr: 800-644-2101
E-mail: cserv@cpcuiia.org
URL: http://www.aicpcu.org

Annual. **Primary Exhibits:** Exhibits for insurance personnel and Chartered Property Casualty Underwriters (CPCUs). **Dates and Locations:** 2004 Oct 23-26; Los Angeles, CA.

★11507★ Financial Services Forum
Society of Financial Service Professionals
270 S. Bryn Mawr Ave.
Bryn Mawr, PA 19010
Ph: (610)526-2500   Fax: (610)527-1499

Annual. **Primary Exhibits:** Exhibitors who offer products and services for the leaders in the insurance and financial services industry.

★11508★ National Association of Insurance and Financial Advisors Annual Convention
National Association of Insurance and Financial Advisors
2901 Telestar Ct
Falls Church, VA 22042
Ph: (703)770-8100   Fax: (703)770-8229
Fr: 877-866-2432
E-mail: becker @naifa.org
URL: http://www.naifa.org

Annual. **Primary Exhibits:** Exhibits relating to life and health insurance, mutual funds, and financial services.

★11509★ National Association of Review Appraisers and Mortgage Underwriters Convention
National Association of Review Appraisers and Mortgage Underwriters
1224 North Nokomis NE
Alexandria, MN 56308-5072
Ph: (320)763-6870   Fax: (320)763-9290
E-mail: naramu@iami.org

Annual. **Primary Exhibits:** Real estate-related information and services.

★11510★ Physician Insurers Association of America Annual Meeting
Physician Insurers Association of America
2275 Research Blvd., Ste. 250
Rockville, MD 20850
Ph: (301)947-9000   Fax: (301)947-9090

Annual. **Primary Exhibits:** Exhibits related to physician liability insurance.

★11511★ Public Agency Risk Managers Association Convention
Public Agency Risk Managers Association
PO Box 6810
San Jose, CA 95150
Ph: (408)865-6930   Fax: 888-412-5913
Fr: 888-907-2762
E-mail: BFrancis@PARMA.com

Annual. **Primary Exhibits:** Risk management equipment, supplies, and services.

★11512★ Sales Congress of National Association of Insurance and Financial Adviors - New Hampshire
National Association of Insurance and Financial Advisors - New Hampshire
76 S. State St.
Concord, NH 03301-3520
Ph: (603)223-9973   Fax: (603)228-2118
Fr: 800-480-8719
E-mail: assnrhg@aol.com

Annual. **Primary Exhibits:** Equipment, supplies, and services for life and health insurance agents, brokers, and managers.

OTHER SOURCES

★11513★ American Almanac of Jobs and Salaries
Morrow Avon
1350 Avenue of the Americas
New York, NY 10019
Ph: (212)261-6788   Fr: 800-242-7737

John W. Wright. Revised edition, 2000. $20.00 (paper). 672 pages. This is a comprehensive guide to the wages of hundreds of occupations in a wide variety of industries and organizations.

★11514★ American Council of Life Insurers (ACLI)
101 Constitution Ave., NW, Ste. 700
Washington, DC 20001-2133
Ph: (202)624-2000   Fax: (202)624-2319
E-mail: acli@acli.com
URL: http://www.acli.com

Description: National trade association that represents the interests of legal reserve life insurance companies in legislative, regulatory and judicial matters at the federal, state and municipal levels of government and at the NAIC. Its member companies hold the overwhelming majority of the life insurance in force in the United States.

★11515★ American Institute for CPCU (CPCU)
720 Providence Rd.
PO Box 3016
Malvern, PA 19355-0716
Ph: (610)644-2100   Fax: (610)640-9576
Fr: 800-644-2101
E-mail: cserv@cpcuiia.org
URL: http://www.aicpcu.org

Purpose: Determines qualifications for professional certification of insurance personnel; conducts examinations and awards designation of Chartered Property Casualty Underwriter (CPCU).

★11516★ CPCU Society
Kahler Hall
720 Providence Rd.
PO Box 3009
Malvern, PA 19355-0709
Fax: (610)251-2780   Fr: 800-932-2728
E-mail: membercenter@cpcusociety.org
URL: http://www.cpcusociety.org

Description: Professional society of individuals who have passed national examinations of the American Institute for Chartered Property Casualty Underwriters, have 3 years of work experience, have agreed to be bound by a code of ethics, and have been awarded CPCU designation. Promotes education, research, social responsibility, and professionalism in the field. Holds seminars, symposia, and workshops.

★11517★ Insurance Information Institute (III)
110 William St.
New York, NY 10038
Ph: (212)346-5500   Fax: (212)791-1807
Fr: 800-331-9146
E-mail: info@iii.org
URL: http://www.iii.org

Description: Property and casualty insurance companies. Provides information and educational services to mass media, educational institutions, trade associations, businesses, government agencies, and the public.

★11518★ LOMA
2300 Windy Ridge Pkwy., Ste. 600
Atlanta, GA 30339-8443
Ph: (770)951-1770   Fax: (770)984-0441
E-mail: marketing@loma.org
URL: http://www.loma.org/

Description: Life and health insurance companies and financial services in the U.S. and Canada; and overseas in 45 countries; affiliate members are firms that provide professional support to member companies. Provides research, information, training, and educational activities in areas of operations and systems, human resources, financial planning and employee development. Administers FLMI Insurance Education Program, which awards FLMI (Fellow, Life Management Institute) designation to those who complete the ten-examination program.

★11519★ National Association of Health Underwriters (NAHU)
200 N 14th St., Ste. 450
Arlington, VA 22201
Ph: (703)276-0220   Fax: (703)841-7797
E-mail: nahu@atsnahu.org
URL: http://www.nahu.org

Description: Insurance agents and brokers engaged in the promotion, sale, and administration of disability income and health insurance. Sponsors advanced health insurance underwriting and research seminars. Testifies before federal and state committees on pending health insurance legislation. Sponsors Leading Producers Roundtable Awards for leading salesmen. Maintains a speakers' bureau and a political action committee.

★11520★ National Association of Insurance Women International (NAIW)
1847 E 15th St.
PO Box 4410
Tulsa, OK 74104
Fax: (918)743-1968   Fr: 800-766-6249
E-mail: joinnaiw@naiw.org

URL: http://www.naiw.org

Members: Insurance industry professionals. **Purpose:** Promotes continuing education and networking for the professional advancement of its members. **Activities:** Offers education programs, meetings, services, and leadership opportunities. Provides a forum to learn about other disciplines in the insurance industry.

★11521★ National Association of Review Appraisers and Mortgage Underwriters (NARA/MU)
1224 N Nokomis NE
Alexandria, MN 56308-5072
Ph: (320)763-6870   Fax: (320)763-9290
E-mail: nara@iami.org
URL: http://www.iami.org/nara

Description: Real estate professionals and mortgage underwriters who aid in determining value of property. Acts as umbrella group for real estate appraisers. Conducts educational seminars; maintains speakers' bureau; operates placement service.

★11522★ Society of Financial Service Professionals (SFSP)
270 S Bryn Mawr Ave.
Bryn Mawr, PA 19010-2195
Ph: (610)526-2500   Fax: (610)527-1499
Fr: 800-927-2427
E-mail: custserv@financialpro.org
URL: http://www.financialpro.org

Description: Professional society of insurance and financial advisers. Foster dedication to continuing professional development and adherence to a strict code of ethical business practices.

★11523★ Underwriters
Evon Publishing
832 N 7th Ave.
Iron River, MI 49935
Ph: (906)265-3190

Audiocassette. 1996. $16.95. 32 minutes. Part of the Careers and Vocational Guidance Series. Provides information about the nature of the work, educational requirements, employment outlook, earnings, and work conditions as well as additional related information.

Urban and Regional Planners

EMPLOYER DIRECTORIES AND NETWORKING LISTS

★11536★ City, Regional & Town Planners Directory

infoUSA Inc.
5711 S 86th Cir.
Omaha, NE 68127-0347
Ph: (402)930-3500   Fax: (402)331-0176
Fr: 800-555-6124
URL: http://www.abii.com

Updated continuously; printed on request. Number of listings: 1,335. Entries include: Name, address, phone (including area code), size of advertisement, year first in "Yellow Pages," name of owner or manager, number of employees. Compiled from telephone company "Yellow Pages," nationwide. Arrangement: Geographical.

★11537★ ENR-Top 500 Design Firms Issue

McGraw-Hill Companies
1221 Ave. of the Americas
New York, NY 10020
Ph: (212)512-2000   Fax: (212)512-3840

Annual, April. $10.00. Publication includes: List of 500 leading architectural, engineering, and specialty design firms selected on basis of annual billings. Entries include: Company name, headquarters location, type of firm, current and prior year rank in billings, types of services, countries in which operated in preceding year. Arrangement: Ranked by billings.

★11538★ ENR-Top International Design Firms Issue

McGraw-Hill Companies
1221 Ave. of the Americas
New York, NY 10020
Ph: (212)512-2000   Fax: (212)512-3840

Annual, July issue of "Engineering News Record". $10.00. Publication includes: List of 200 design firms (including United States firms) competing outside their own national borders who received largest dollar volume of foreign contracts in preceding calendar year. Entries include: Company name, headquarters location, type of firm, current and previous year rankings in total billings, types of services, countries in which operated in preceding year. Arrangement: By amount billed to international clients in previous year.

HANDBOOKS AND MANUALS

★11539★ Career Information Center

Macmillan Publishing Co. Inc.
200 Old Tappan Rd.
Old Tappan, NJ 07675
Fr: 800-428-5331

Visual Education Center Staff. Seventh edition, 1999. $275.00. 2080 pages. This 13- volume set profiles over 600 occupations. Each occupational profile describes job duties, educational requirements, how to get the job, advancement possibilities, employment outlook, working conditions, earnings and benefits, and where to write for more information.

★11540★ Opportunities in Environmental Careers

McGraw-Hill Trade
2 Penn Plaza
New York, NY 10121
Ph: (212)904-2000   Fr: 800-722-4726
E-mail: ntcpub@tribune.com

Odom Fanning. Revised, 2002. $12.95 (paper). 160 pages. Describes a broad range of opportunities in fields such as environmental health, recreation, physics, and hygiene, and provides job search advice. Part of Opportunities in...Series.

★11541★ Opportunities in Social Science Careers

McGraw-Hill Companies
860 Taylor Station Rd.
Blacklick, OH 43004-0545
Fax: (614)755-5645   Fr: 800-722-4726

Rosanne J. Marek. March 2004. $22.95. 160 Pages. VGM Opportunities Series.

★11542★ Planners on Planning: Leading Planners Offer Real-Life Lessons on What Works, What Doesn't and Why

Jossey-Bass, Inc. Publishers
350 Sansome St.
San Francisco, CA 94104-1342
Ph: (415)433-1740   Fax: (415)433-0499
Fr: 888-378-2537

Bruce W. McClendon and Anthony J.Catanese. 1996. $35.00. 320 pages. Provides career advice from professionals in the planning industry.

★11543★ Resumes for Architecture and Related Careers

McGraw-Hill Trade
2 Penn Plaza
New York, NY 10121
Ph: (212)904-2000   Fr: 800-722-4726

VGM Career Horizons Editors. 1996. $9.95 (paper). 160 pages.

OTHER SOURCES

★11544★ American Institute of Certified Planners (AICP)

1776 Massachusetts Ave. NW, Ste. 400
Washington, DC 20036-1904
Ph: (202)872-0611   Fax: (202)872-0643
Fr: 800-954-1669
E-mail: aicp@planning.org

URL: http://www.planning.org/aicp

Description: The Professional Institute of the American Planning Association. **Members:** Members of the APA who have met the requirements of education, practice, and examination established for the professional practice of public planning. **Activities:** Provides continuing education and a written professional examination. Maintains code of ethics; conducts research.

★11545★ American Planning Association (APA)

122 S Michigan Ave., Ste. 1600
Chicago, IL 60603-6107
Ph: (312)431-9100   Fax: (312)431-9985
E-mail: research@planning.org
URL: http://www.planning.org

Description: Public and private planning agency officials, professional planners, planning educators, elected and appointed officials, and other persons involved in urban and rural development. Works to foster the best techniques and decisions for the planned development of communities and regions. Provides extensive professional services and publications to professionals and laypeople in planning and related fields; serves as a clearinghouse for information. Through Planning Advisory Service, a research and inquiry-answering service, provides, on an annual subscription basis, advice on specific inquiries and a series of research reports on planning, zoning, and environmental regulations. Supplies information on job openings and makes definitive studies on salaries and recruitment of professional planners. Conducts research; collaborates in joint projects with local, national, and international organizations.

★11546★ ASPRS - The Imaging and Geospatial Information Society

5410 Grosvenor Ln., Ste. 210
Bethesda, MD 20814-2160
Ph: (301)493-0290   Fax: (301)493-0208
E-mail: asprs@asprs.org
URL: http://www.asprs.org

Members: Firms, individuals, government employees, and academicians engaged in photogrammetry, photointerpretation, remote sensing, and geographic information systems and their application to such fields as archaeology, geographic information systems, military reconnaissance, urban planning, engineering, traffic surveys, meteorological observations, medicine, geology, forestry, agriculture, construction, and topographic mapping. Mission is to advance knowledge and improve understanding of these sciences and to promote responsible applications. **Activities:** Offers voluntary certification program open to persons associated with one or more functional area of photogrammetry, remote sensing, and GIS. Surveys the profession of private firms in photogrammetry and remote sensing in the areas of productsand services

★11547★ Environmental Occupations: Professional

Delphi Productions
3160 4th St.
Boulder, CO 80304
Fax: (303)443-4022   Fr: 888-443-2400
URL: http://www.delphivideo.com

$95.00. 49 minutes. Part of the Emerging Careers Video Library.

★11548★ National Urban Fellows (NUF)

59 John St., Rm. 310
New York, NY 10038-3709
Ph: (212)349-6200   Fax: (212)349-7478
E-mail: lbenitez@nuf.org
URL: http://www.nuf.org

Description: Program designed to make top leadership opportunities in government and rural development available to minority group members. Recipients of the 14-month fellowships are selected competitively and must be U.S. citizens who have a bachelor's degree; have experience in solving urban or rural problems; have three-five years of employment experience in an administrative or managerial capacity; have demonstrated ability, leadership qualities, and a commitment to the solution of urban or rural problems. Program is aimed at meeting the need for competent urban and rural administrators, particularly minority group members and women, by combining a nine month, on-the-job assignment as special assistant to an experienced practitioner with several kinds of academic work. A master's degree in public administration is awarded to qualified fellows at the end of the fellowship.

★11549★ Professional Specialty Occupations

Delphi Productions
3160 4th St.
Boulder, CO 80304
Fax: (303)443-4022   Fr: 888-443-2400
URL: http://www.delphivideo.com

$95.00. 53 minutes. Part of the Careers for the 21st Century Video Library.

★11550★ Urban and Regional Planners

Evon Publishing
832 N 7th Ave.
Iron River, MI 49935
Ph: (906)265-3190

Audiocassette. 1996. $16.95. 32 minutes. Part of the Careers and Vocational Guidance Series. Provides information about the nature of the work, educational requirements, employment outlook, earnings, and work conditions as well as additional related information.

Veterinarians

★11551★ Expert Resumes for Health Care Careers

JIST Publishing
8902 Otis Ave.
Indianapolis, IN 46216-1033
Ph: (317)613-4200   Fax: 800-547-8329

December 2003. $16.95. 288 pages.

★11552★ Health Careers Today

Elsevier-Health Sciences Division
The Curtis Center, Ste. 300E, 3rd Fl.
170 S. Independence Mall W.
Philadelphia, PA 19106
Ph: (215)238-7800   Fax: (215)238-7362
Fr: 800-523-4069

Gerdin. Revised edition. April 2004. $52.95.

SOURCES OF HELP-WANTED ADS

★11553★ American Journal of Veterinary Research

American Veterinary Medical Association
1931 N Meacham Rd., Ste. 100
Schaumburg, IL 60173-4360
Ph: (847)925-8070   Fax: (847)925-1329

Monthly. $150.00/year for individuals. Veterinary research journal reporting on nutrition and diseases of domestic, wild, and furbearing animals.

★11554★ Animal Keepers' Forum

American Association of Zoo Keepers Inc.
3601 SW 29th St., Ste. 133
Topeka, KS 66614-2054
Ph: (785)273-9149   Fax: (785)273-1980
Fr: 800-242-4519
E-mail: akfeditor@kscoxmail.com
URL: http://aazk.org

Monthly. $40.00/year for individuals; $125.00/year for institutions; $4.00 for single issue. Professional journal of the American Association of Zoo Keepers, Inc.

★11555★ The Chronicle of the Horse

The Chronicle of the Horse Inc.
PO Box 46
Middleburg, VA 20118
Ph: (540)687-6341   Fax: (540)687-3937
E-mail: staff@chronofhorse.com

Weekly. $49.00/year; $2.95 for single issue. Magazine covering English riding and horse sports.

★11556★ Dog World

Fancy Publications
PO Box 57900
Los Angeles, CA 90057
Ph: (213)385-2222   Fax: (213)385-8565
E-mail: dogworld3@aol.com
URL: http://www.dogworldmag.com

Monthly. $28.00/year for individuals; $3.99 for single issue. Magazine serving breeders, exhibitors, hobbyists and professionals in kennel operations, groomers, veterinarians, animal hospitals/clinics and pet suppliers.

★11557★ DVM Newsmagazine

Advanstar Communications Inc.
7500 Old Oak Blvd.
Cleveland, OH 44130-3369
Ph: (440)243-8100   Fax: (440)891-2777
E-mail: dvmnewsmagazine@advanstar.com
URL: http://www.dvmnewsmagazine.com

Monthly. $39.00/year; $4.00 for single issue. Magazine for veterinarians in private practices in the United States.

★11558★ Equus

Primedia Equine Group
656 Quince Orchard Rd., Ste. 600
Gaithersburg, MD 20878
Ph: (301)977-3900   Fax: (301)990-9015
E-mail: equuslts@aol.com

Monthly. $24.00/year for individuals; $3.99 for single issue. Magazine featuring health, care, and understanding of horses.

★11559★ Journal of the American Veterinary Medical Association

American Veterinary Medical Association
1931 N Meacham Rd., Ste. 100
Schaumburg, IL 60173-4360
Ph: (847)925-8070   Fax: (847)925-1329

Semimonthly. Trade journal for veterinary medical professionals.

★11560★ Journal of Animal Science

American Society of Animal Science
1111 N Dunlap Ave.
Savoy, IL 61874
Ph: (217)356-3182   Fax: (217)398-4119

Monthly. Professional journal covering animal science.

★11561★ Journal of Avian Medicine and Surgery

Allen Press
810 E 10th
Lawrence, KS 66044
Ph: (785)843-1234   Fax: (785)843-1244
Fr: 800-627-0326
E-mail: aavpubs@aol.com
URL: http://www.aav.org/publications.html

Quarterly. Subscription included in membership. Medical journal for veterinarians treating birds, students and technicians with an interest in the field.

★11562★ Lab Animal

Nature Publishing Group
345 Park Ave. S
New York, NY 10010-1707
Ph: (212)726-9200   Fax: (212)689-9711
Fr: 888-331-6288
E-mail: labanimal@natureny.com
URL: http://www.labanimal.com

Free. Life science magazine.

★11563★ The Morgan Horse

American Morgan Horse Association
PO Box 960
Shelburne, VT 05482-0960
Ph: (802)985-4944   Fax: (802)985-8897

Monthly. $27.50/year for individuals; $4.00 for single issue. Magazine for Morgan horse enthusiasts.

★11564★ New Methods

Ronald S. Lippert, A.H.T.
PO Box 22605
San Francisco, CA 94122-0605
Ph: (707)459-4535

Description: Monthly. Examines common problems and concerns in the field of animal health technology. "Provides professionals with the best in network sources" as well as items on animal care and protection and medical breakthroughs. Recurring features include letters to the editor, interviews, notices of publications available, job listings, news of educational opportunities, and news of research.

★11565★ Newsletter-Animal Behavior Society

Animal Behavior Society
Animal Behavior Office
Indiana University
2611 E 10th St., Office 170
Bloomington, IN 47408-2603
Ph: (812)856-5541   Fax: (812)856-5542
URL: http://www.animalbehavior.org

Description: Quarterly. Informs members of the Society of activities, events, meetings, announcements and opportunities in the field of animal behavior. Recurring features include a news of educational opportunities, job listings, and notices of publications available.

★11566★ TRENDS Magazine

American Animal Hospital Association
PO Box 150899
Denver, CO 80215-0899
Ph: (303)986-2800   Fax: (303)986-1700
Fr: 800-252-2242
E-mail: trendsmagazine@aahanet.org

Bimonthly. $60.00/year for U.S. and Canada; $70.00/year for other countries. Professional magazine covering the management of small animal veterinary practices.

★11567★ Veterinary and Human Toxicology

Comparative Toxicology Laboratories
Kansas State University
1800 Denison Ave. M213 Morier Hall
Manhattan, KS 66506-5705
Ph: (785)532-4334   Fax: (785)532-4481
E-mail: vhtox@vet.ksu.edu

Bimonthly. $80.00/year for individuals; $90.00/year for Canada; $100.00/year for other countries, surface; $130.00/year for other countries, air mail. Professional journal containing refereed scientific articles, news, and reports from the field of toxicology.

Includes reports of past meetings, announcements of forthcoming meetings, book reviews, job opportunities, membership, and other news from the several organizations in toxicology that sponsor this publication.

★11568★ Western Horseman

Western Horseman
PO Box 7980
Colorado Springs, CO 80933
Ph: (719)633-5524   Fax: (719)633-1392
Fr: 800-874-6774

Monthly. $20.00/year for individuals; $27.00/year for other countries; $2.95 for single issue. Magazine covering forms of horsemanship and all breeds of horses; emphasizing western stock horses and western lifestyle.

PLACEMENT AND JOB REFERRAL SERVICES

★11569★ American Veterinary Medical Association (AVMA)

1931 N Meacham Rd., Ste. 100
Schaumburg, IL 60173-4360
Ph: (847)925-8070   Fax: (847)925-1329
Fr: 800-248-2862
E-mail: awhitsett@avma.org
URL: http://www.avma.org

Description: Professional society of veterinarians. Conducts educational and research programs. Provides placement service. Sponsors American Veterinary Medical Association Foundation (also known as AVMF Foundation) and Educational Commission for Foreign Veterinary Graduates. Compiles statistics. Accredits veterinary medical education programs and veterinary technician education programs.

EMPLOYER DIRECTORIES AND NETWORKING LISTS

★11570★ American Association of Bovine Practitioners-Directory

American Association of Bovine Practitioners
Box 1755
Rome, GA 30162-1755
Ph: (706)232-2220   Fax: (706)232-2232

Triennial, latest edition June 1996; annual supplements. Covers 5,000 member veterinarians who have a special interest in treatment of dairy and beef cattle. Entries include: Name, office address and phone. Arrangement: Alphabetical. Indexes: Alphabetical.

★11571★ American College of Veterinary Pathologists-Membership Directory

American College of Veterinary Pathologists
7600 Terrace Ave., Ste. 203
Middleton, WI 53562

Annual, March. $350.00. Covers 1,200 veterinary anatomic pathologists and veterinary clinical pathologists. Entries include: Name, office address, phone, e-mail. Arrangement: Alphabetical.

★11572★ American Society of Veterinary Ophthalmology-Directory

American Society of Veterinary Ophthalmology
1416 W Liberty
Stillwater, OK 74075
Ph: (405)377-4388   Fax: (405)744-6265

Annual, December. Covers 250 member veterinarians interested in animal ophthalmology. Entries include: Name, address, office and home phone numbers, and year of graduation. Arrangement: Geographical. Indexes: Alphabetical, chronological.

★11573★ American Veterinary Medical Association-Directory

American Veterinary Medical Association
1931 N Meacham Rd., Ste. 100
Schaumburg, IL 60173-4360
Ph: (847)925-8070   Fax: (847)925-1329
URL: http://www.avma.org

Annual, January. $125.00 for U.S.; $150.00 for other countries. Covers 68,000 veterinarians; not limited to AVMA members. Entries include: Name, spouse's name, address, email, phones and codes for practice activity, type of employer, institution granting degree, and year received. Arrangement: Geographical & alphabetical. Indexes: Alphabetical.

★11574★ Animal Hospitals Directory

infoUSA Inc.
5711 S 86th Cir.
Omaha, NE 68127-0347
Ph: (402)930-3500   Fax: (402)331-0176
Fr: 800-555-6124
URL: http://www.abii.com

Annual. Number of listings: 15,285. Entries include: Name, address, phone (including area code), size of advertisement, year first in "Yellow Pages," name of owner or manager, number of employees. Compiled from telephone company "Yellow Pages" nationwide. Arrangement: Geographical.

★11575★ Directory of Animal Care and Control Agencies

American Humane Association
63 Inverness Dr. E
Englewood, CO 80112-5117
Ph: (303)792-9900   Fax: (303)792-5333
Fr: 800-227-4645

Updated continuously; printed on request. $125.00 base edition to nonprofits; $800.00

base edition to others; $3.00 state edition to nonprofits; $15.00 state edition to others. Covers over 6,000 animal protection agencies; Canadian and some other foreign agencies are available; national and individual state editions are available. Entries include: Agency name, address, phone, contact. Arrangement: Geographical.

★11576★ Programs in Veterinary Technology

American Veterinary Medical Association
1931 N Meacham Rd., Ste. 100
Schaumburg, IL 60173-4360
Ph: (847)925-8070   Fax: (847)925-1329
URL: http://www.avma.org

Semiannual, June and December. Covers colleges and universities that offer accredited veterinary technology programs. Entries include: Institution name, address; department name, address, phone, name of departmental contact, degree offered, length of program, type of accreditation. Arrangement: Geographical.

★11577★ Veterinarian Hospitals Directory

infoUSA Inc.
5711 S 86th Cir.
Omaha, NE 68127-0347
Ph: (402)930-3500   Fax: (402)331-0176
Fr: 800-555-6124
URL: http://www.abii.com

Annual. Number of listings: 15,285. Entries include: Name, address, phone, size of advertisement, name of owner or manager, number of employees, year first in "Yellow Pages." Compiled from telephone company "Yellow Pages," nationwide. Arrangement: Geographical.

★11578★ Veterinarians Directory

infoUSA Inc.
5711 S 86th Cir.
Omaha, NE 68127-0347
Ph: (402)930-3500   Fax: (402)331-0176
Fr: 800-555-6124
URL: http://www.abii.com

Annual. Number of listings: 46,503. Entries include: Name, address, phone (including area code), size of advertisement, year first in "Yellow Pages," name of owner or manager, number of employees. Regional editions available; Eastern, $780.00; Western, $645.00. Compiled from telephone company "Yellow Pages" nationwide. Arrangement: Geographical.

HANDBOOKS AND MANUALS

★11579★ Career Choices for Veterinarians: Beyond Private Practice

Smith Veterinary Services
PO Box 254
Leavenworth, WA 98826
Ph: (509)763-2052   Fax: (509)763-2112

Carin A. Smith. 1998. $27.95 (paper). 256 pages.

★11580★ Career Information Center

Macmillan Publishing Co. Inc.
200 Old Tappan Rd.
Old Tappan, NJ 07675
Fr: 800-428-5331

Visual Education Center Staff. Seventh edition, 1999. $275.00. 2080 pages. This 13-volume set profiles over 600 occupations. Each occupational profile describes job duties, educational requirements, how to get the job, advancement possibilities, employment outlook, working conditions, earnings and benefits, and where to write for more information.

★11581★ Careers with Dogs

Barron's Educational Series, Inc.
250 Wireless Blvd.
Hauppauge, NY 11788-3917
Ph: (631)434-3311   Fax: (631)434-3723
Fr: 800-645-3476

Audrey Pavia. 1998. $8.95 (paper). 112 pages. Covers various types of work available for animal lovers. Includes information on salaries, qualifications, and job-hunting.

★11582★ Careers in Veterinary Medicine

Rosen Publishing Group, Inc.
29 E. 21st St.
New York, NY 10010
Ph: (212)777-3017   Fax: 888-436-4643
Fr: 800-237-9932

Jane Caryl Duncan. Revised edition, 1994. $16.95; $9.95 (paper). Contains advice from a real veterinarian and a description of her work.

★11583★ Marketing Your Veterinary Practice

American Veterinary Publications
11830 Westline Industrial Dr.
St. Louis, MO 63146
Ph: (314)872-8370   Fax: 800-235-0256
Fr: 800-325-4177

Shawn Messonnier. Volume 2. 1997. $28.95 (paper). 176 pages.

★11584★ 101 Secrets of a High-Performance Veterinary Practice

Veterinary Healthcare Communications
8033 Flint St.
Lenexa, KS 66214
Ph: (913)492-4300   Fax: (913)492-4157
Fr: 800-255-6864

Bob Levoy. 1996. $19.95 (paper). 101 pages.

★11585★ Opportunities in Animal and Pet Care Careers

McGraw-Hill Trade
2 Penn Plaza
New York, NY 10121
Ph: (212)904-2000   Fax: (212)755-5645
Fr: 800-722-4726

Mary Price Lee and Richard S. Lee. 2001. $12.95. 160 pages. Covers the field from small animal medicine to large animal medicine, and provides job-hunting advice. Illustrated.

★11586★ Opportunities in Environmental Careers

McGraw-Hill Trade
2 Penn Plaza
New York, NY 10121
Ph: (212)904-2000   Fr: 800-722-4726
E-mail: ntcpub@tribune.com

Odom Fanning. Revised, 2002. $12.95 (paper). 160 pages. Describes a broad range of opportunities in fields such as environmental health, recreation, physics, and hygiene, and provides job search advice. Part of Opportunities in...Series.

★11587★ Opportunities in Health and Medical Careers

McGraw-Hill Trade
2 Penn Plaza
New York, NY 10121
Ph: (212)904-2000   Fr: 800-722-4726

I. Donald Snook, Jr. and Leo D'Orazio. 1997. $14.95; $11.95 (paper). 202 pages. Covers the full range of medical and health occupations. Illustrated.

★11588★ Opportunities in Zoo Careers

McGraw-Hill Trade
2 Penn Plaza
New York, NY 10121
Ph: (212)904-2000   Fr: 800-722-4726
E-mail: ntcpub@tribune.com

Blythe Camenson. 1997. $14.95; $11.95 (paper).

★11589★ Wild Careers!: Working with Animals

SeaWorld, Incorporated
500 SeaWorld Dr.
San Diego, CA 92109
Ph: (619)225-4275   Fax: (619)226-3634
Fr: 800-237-4268

Loran Wlodarski. 2002. $7.99. Illustrated. 88

pages. Exploring a career in the animal industry.

★11590★ *Working with Animals: The UK, Europe and Worldwide*

Vacation Work Publications
9 Park End St.
Oxford OX1 1HJ, United Kingdom

Victoria Pybus. Second edition. 2003. $19.95. Illustrated. 288 pages. Educating on a career as a vetinarian.

EMPLOYMENT AGENCIES AND SEARCH FIRMS

★11591★ **Management Search, Inc.**

3013 NW 59th St.,Ste.A-1
Oklahoma City, OK 73112
Ph: (405)842-3173   Fax: (405)842-8360
E-mail: dorwig@mgmtsearch.com
URL: http://www.mgmtsearch.com

Executive search firm specializing in the field of agri-business.

ONLINE JOB SOURCES AND SERVICES

★11592★ **Medhunters.com**
E-mail: info@medhunters.com
URL: http://www.medhunters.com

Description: Career search site for jobs in all health care specialties; educational resources; visa and licensing information for relocation; interesting articles; relocation tools; links to professional organizations and general resources.

★11593★ **ProHealthJobs**
E-mail: sales@prohealthjobs.com
URL: http://www.prohealthjobs.com

Description: Career resources site for the medical and health care field. Lists professional opportunities, product information, continuing education and open positions.

★11594★ **VeterinaryLife.com**
URL: http://www.veterinarylife.com

Description: Posts classified ads for veterinarian and clinic jobs available worldwide.

TRADESHOWS

★11595★ **ACVS Veterinary Symposium**

American College of Veterinary Surgeons
4401 East West Hwy., No. 205
Bethesda, MD 20814-4523
Ph: (301)913-9550   Fax: (301)913-2034
E-mail: acvs@aol.com
URL: http://www.acvs.org

Annual. **Primary Exhibits:** Veterinary surgery equipment, supplies, and services. **Dates and Locations:** 2004 Oct 07-10; Denver, CO; Adams Mark.

★11596★ **American Animal Hospital Association Annual Meeting**

American Animal Hospital Association
PO Box 150899
Denver, CO 80215-0899
Ph: (303)986-2800   Fax: (303)986-1700
Fr: 800-252-2242

Annual. **Primary Exhibits:** Scientific displays related to small-animal veterinary care, computer software, marketing consulting services, pet care products, and pet foods.

★11597★ **American Association of Bovine Practitioners Annual Conference**

American Association of Bovine Practitioners
Box 1755
Rome, GA 30162-1755
Ph: (706)232-2220   Fax: (706)232-2232
E-mail: exhibits@aabp.org

Annual. **Primary Exhibits:** Pharmaceutical & biological manufacturers, equipment companies, agricultural related companies, and computer programs and supplies. **Dates and Locations:** 2004 Sep 23-25; Fort Worth, TX • 2005 Sep 24-26; Salt Lake City, UT; Salt Palace • 2006 Sep 21-23; St. Paul, MN.

★11598★ **American College of Veterinary Ophthalmologists Conference**

Grana Enterprises
24832 N. 91st Ave.
Peoria, AZ 85383-1243
Ph: (602)841-8793   Fax: (602)864-3734

Annual. **Primary Exhibits:** Veterinary ophthalmology equipment, supplies, and services.

★11599★ **American College of Veterinary Pathologists Annual Meeting**

American College of Veterinary Pathologists
6700 Terrace Ave., Ste. 203
Middleton, WI 53562-3174
E-mail: info@acvp.org
URL: http://www.acvp.org

Annual. **Primary Exhibits:** Veterinary pathology (origin, nature, and course of diseases in animals) equipment, supplies, and services.

★11600★ **American Humane Association Annual Meeting and Training Conference/Animal Protection**

American Humane Association
63 Inverness Dr., E.
Englewood, CO 80112-5117
Ph: (303)792-9900   Fax: (303)792-5333

Annual. **Primary Exhibits:** Animal welfare equipment including pet food, cages, trucks, ID programs, and health and veterinary products.

★11601★ **American Society of Veterinary Ophthalmology Meeting**

American Society of Veterinary Ophthalmology
1416 W. Liberty Ave.
Stillwater, OK 74075
Ph: (405)377-4388

Annual. **Primary Exhibits:** Veterinary ophthalmology equipment, supplies, and services.

★11602★ **American Veterinary Medical Association Annual Convention - 137th Salt Lake City**

American Veterinary Medical Association
1931 N. Meacham Rd., Ste. 100
Schaumburg, IL 60173-4360
Ph: (847)925-8070   Fax: (847)925-1329
E-mail: 103176.3374@compuserve.com

Annual. **Primary Exhibits:** Products, materials, equipment, data, and services for veterinary medicine.

★11603★ **International Congress on Veterinary Acupuncture**

International Veterinary Acupuncture Society
PO Box 271395
Fort Collins, CO 80527-1395
Ph: (303)682-1167   Fax: (303)682-1168
E-mail: ivasoffice@aol.com

Annual. **Primary Exhibits:** Veterinary acupuncture equipment, supplies, and services.

★11604★ **International Wildlife Rehabilitation Council Conference**

International Wildlife Rehabilitation Council
4437 Central Pl., Ste. B-4
Suisun City, CA 94585-1633
Ph: (707)864-1761   Fax: (707)864-3106
E-mail: iwrc@inreach.com
URL: http://iwrc-online.org

Annual. **Primary Exhibits:** Equipment, supplies, and services for the rehabilitation of wildlife, including the handling and care of sick and injured wild animals. T-shirts books, jewelry, artwork, etc.

★11605★ Joint Annual Meeting of the American Dairy Science Association and the American Society of Animal Science

Federation of Animal Science Societies
1111 North Dunlap Ave.
Savoy, IL 61874
Ph: (217)356-3182   Fax: (217)398-4119
E-mail: fass@assochq.org
URL: http://www.fass.org

Annual. **Primary Exhibits:** Exhibits related to the investigation, instruction, or extension in animal science and in the production, processing, and dissemination of livestock and livestock products. **Dates and Locations:** 2005 Jul 24-28; Cincinnati, OH; Convention Center.

★11606★ MASAAV Annual Conference on Avian Medicine and Surgery

Mid-Atlantic States Association of Avian Veterinarians
Memorial Bldg., Ste. 291
610 N. Main St.
Blacksburg, VA 24060-3311
Ph: (540)951-2559   Fax: (540)953-0230
E-mail: office@masaav.org
URL: http://masaav.org

Annual. **Primary Exhibits:** Equipment, supplies, and services for the avian veterinary medicine. **Dates and Locations:** 2005 Apr 24-26.

★11607★ Southwest International Veterinary Symposium Expo

Texas Veterinary Medical Association
6633 Hwy. 290 E., Ste. 201
Austin, TX 78723
Ph: (512)452-4224   Fax: (512)452-6633
E-mail: tvma.org@aol.com

Annual. **Primary Exhibits:** Pharmaceuticals, publications, computer equipment, surgical and X-ray equipment, veterinary supplies, pet nutritional products, biologicals, and testing laboratories, pesticides, livestock equipment.

★11608★ Washington State Veterinary Medical Association Convention

Washington State Veterinary Medical Association
PO Box 962
Bellevue, WA 98009
Ph: (206)454-8381   Fax: (206)454-8381
E-mail: wsvma1@aol.com
URL: http://www.wsvma.org

Annual. **Primary Exhibits:** Veterinary drugs, medical supplies, and equipment.

★11609★ Western Veterinary Conference

Western Veterinary Conference
2425 E. Oquendo Rd.
Las Vegas, NV 89120
Ph: (702)739-6698   Fax: (702)739-6420
E-mail: info@westernveterinary.org
URL: http://www.wvc.org

Annual. **Primary Exhibits:** Veterinary equip-

ment, supplies, and services, including drugs.

★11610★ Wisconsin Veterinary Medical Association Annual Convention

Wisconsin Veterinary Medical Association
301 N. Broom St.
Madison, WI 53703
Ph: (608)257-3665   Fax: (608)257-8989
E-mail: wvma@wvma.org

Annual. **Primary Exhibits:** Veterinary supplies, pharmaceuticals, pet food, business systems, and record-keeping equipment.

OTHER SOURCES

★11611★ American Academy of Clinical Toxicology (AACT)

777 E Park Dr.
PO Box 8820
Harrisburg, PA 17105-8820
Ph: (717)558-7847   Fax: (717)558-7845
Fr: 888-633-5784
E-mail: jreisinger@pamedsoc.org
URL: http://www.clintox.org

Members: Physicians, veterinarians, pharmacists, nurses research scientists, and analytical chemists. **Purpose:** Works to unite medical scientists and facilitate the exchange of information; encourage the development of therapeutic methods and technology. **Activities:** Conducts professional training in poison information and emergency service personnel.

★11612★ American Association of Zoo Veterinarians (AAZV)

6 N Pennell Rd.
Media, PA 19063
Ph: (610)892-4812   Fax: (610)892-4813
E-mail: aazv@aol.com
URL: http://www.aazv.org/aazv_001.htm

Description: Veterinarians actively engaged in the practice of zoo and wildlife medicine for at least four years; veterinarians who do not qualify for active membership; persons interested in diseases of wildlife; students of veterinary medicine in any accredited veterinary school. Purposes are to: advance programs for preventive medicine, husbandry, and scientific research dealing with captive and free-ranging wild animals; provide a forum for the presentation and discussion of problems related to the field; enhance and uphold the professional ethics of veterinary medicine.

★11613★ Association for Women Veterinarians (AWV)

310 North Indian Hill Blvd., Box 337
Claremont, CA 91711-4611
E-mail: lapancho@ra.msstate.edu
URL: http://www.awv-women-veterinarians.org

Description: Works to support veterinary medicine by providing leadership in women's issues.

★11614★ Exploring Health Occupations

Cambridge Educational
2572 Brunswick Ave.
Lawrenceville, NJ 08648-4128
Fax: 800-FAX-ON-US   Fr: 800-468-4227
URL: http://www.cambridgeeducational.com

Two videos. $139.95. 1999.

★11615★ Health Service Occupations

Delphi Productions
3160 4th St.
Boulder, CO 80304
Fax: (303)443-4022   Fr: 888-443-2400
URL: http://www.delphivideo.com

$95.00. 50 minutes. Part of the Careers for the 21st Century Video Library.

★11616★ International Veterinary Acupuncture Society (IVAS)

PO Box 271395
Fort Collins, CO 80527-1395
Ph: (970)266-0660   Fax: (970)266-0777
E-mail: office@ivas.org
URL: http://www.ivas.org

Description: Veterinarians and veterinary students. Encourages knowledge and research of the philosophy, technique, and practice of veterinary acupuncture. Fosters high standards in the field; promotes scientific investigation. Accumulates resources for scientific research and education; collects data concerning clinical and research cases where animals have been treated with acupuncture; disseminates information to veterinary students, practitioners, other scientific groups, and the public. Offers 120 contact hour basic veterinary acupuncture course; administers certification examination; also offers advanced traditional Chinese herbal veterinary medicine.

★11617★ Medicine & Related Occupations

Delphi Productions
3160 4th St.
Boulder, CO 80304
Fax: (303)443-4022   Fr: 888-443-2400
URL: http://www.delphivideo.com

$95.00. 45 minutes. Part of the Careers for the 21st Century Video Library.

★11618★ National Association of Federal Veterinarians (NAFV)

1101 Vermont Ave. NW, Ste. 710
Washington, DC 20005-6308
Ph: (202)289-6334   Fax: (202)842-4360
E-mail: dboyle@nafv.org
URL: http://users.erols.com/nafv/

Description: Professional society of veterinarians employed by the U.S. Government. Maintains speakers' bureau.

★11619★ *Veterinarians*
Evon Publishing
832 N 7th Ave.
Iron River, MI 49935

Ph: (906)265-3190

Audiocassette. 1996. $16.95. 32 minutes. Part of the Careers and Vocational Guidance Series. Provides information about the nature of the work, educational requirements, employment outlook, earnings, and work conditions as well as additional related information.

Visual Artists

SOURCES OF HELP-WANTED ADS

★11620★ Adweek
VNU Business Media USA
770 Broadway
New York, NY 10003
Ph: (646)654-5000
E-mail: info@adweek.com
URL: http://www.adweek.com

Weekly. $149.00/year for individuals; $3.95 for single issue. Advertising news magazine.

★11621★ AFTERIMAGE
Visual Studies Workshop Press
31 Prince St.
Rochester, NY 14607
Ph: (585)442-8676
E-mail: afterimage@vsw.org
URL: http://www.vsw.org

$30.00/year for individuals; $5.00 for single issue; $60.00/year for institutions; $45.00/ year for out of country. Publication providing independent critical commentary on issues in media arts, including scholarly research, in-depth reviews, investigative journalism, interviews, and the largest list of exhibitions, festivals, position announcements and calls for work of its kind.

★11622★ American Artist
VNU Business Media USA
770 Broadway
New York, NY 10003
Ph: (646)654-5000
URL: http://www.vnubusinessmedia.com/E-Mail

Monthly. $28.95/year for individuals; $3.95 for single issue. Art and educational journal.

★11623★ Art in America
Brant Publications Inc.
575 Broadway
New York, NY 10012-3230
Ph: (212)941-2884   Fax: (212)941-2844

$39.95/year for individuals; $5.00 for single issue. Art magazine.

★11624★ Art Calendar
Art Calendar
PO Box 2675
Salisbury, MD 21802
Ph: (410)749-9625   Fax: (410)749-9626
Fr: (866)4AR-TCAL
URL: http://www.artcalendar.com

Description: Monthly, (except August). Lists art grants, shows, and commissions. Features articles on the psychology of creativity. Recurring features include interviews, a calendar of events, news of educational opportunities, job listings, book reviews, notices of publications available, and columns titled Marketing Strategies, Art Law, Perspective, and Federal Updates.

★11625★ The Artist's Magazine
F & W Publications Inc.
4700 E Galbraith Rd.
Cincinnati, OH 45236-6708
Ph: (513)531-2690   Fax: (513)531-2902
Fr: 800-289-0963
E-mail: tamedit@fwpubs.com

Monthly. $27.00/year for individuals; $24.00/ year for libraries; $19.96/year, group introductory rate; $3.49 for single issue. Magazine by artists for artists. Covers artwork, working methods, tools, and materials.

★11626★ ARTnews Magazine
Art News L.L.C.
48 W 38th St.
New York, NY 10018-6238
Ph: (212)398-1690   Fax: (212)819-0394
E-mail: service@artnewsonline.com

Monthly. $39.95/year; $6.00 for single issue. News magazine reporting on art, personalities, issues, trends, and events that shape the international art world.

★11627★ C Magazine
C The Visual Arts Foundation
PO Box 5, Sta. B
Toronto, ON, Canada M5T 2T2
Ph: (416)539-9495   Fax: (416)539-9903
Fr: 800-745-6312

Quarterly. Periodical covering the visual and performing arts.

★11628★ DM News
DM News
100 6th Ave.of the Americas
New York, NY 10013
Ph: (212)925-7300   Fax: (212)925-8752
E-mail: inquiry@dmnews.com
URL: http://www.dmnews.com

Weekly. $75.00/year. Tabloid newspaper for publishers, fund raisers, financial marketers, catalogers, package goods advertisers and their agencies, and other marketers who use direct mail, mail order advertising, catalogs, or other direct response media to sell their products or services.

★11629★ Editor & Publisher
Editor & Publisher Magazine
770 Broadway
New York, NY 10003-9595
Fax: (646)654-5360   Fr: 800-336-4380
URL: http://www.editorandpublisher.com

Weekly. $99.00/year for U.S. and Canada, includes exclusive web access; $130.00/ year for other countries; $4.00 for single issue. Magazine focusing on newspaper journalism, advertising, printing equipment, and interactive services.

★11630★ FIBERARTS
Altamont Press
67 Broadway St.
Asheville, NC 28801-2919
Ph: (828)253-0467   Fax: (828)253-7952
URL: http://www.larkbooks.com/fiberarts

$24.00/year. Art magazine.

★11631★ GNSI Newsletter

Guild of Natural Science Illustrators Inc.
PO Box 652, Ben Franklin Sta.
Washington, DC 20044
Ph: (301)309-1514   Fax: (301)309-1514

Description: Ten issues/year. Serves as a forum for member professional scientific illustrators and technical artists. Provides information on supplies, techniques, methods, and materials for production of highly-rendered and accurate illustrations of natural science subjects. Also discusses business practices of interest to professional as well as aspiring illustrators. Recurring features include announcements of Guild activities, examples of members' work, book reviews and notices of publications available, and job listings.

★11632★ Graphic Arts Monthly

Reed Business Information
360 Park Ave. S
New York, NY 10010
Ph: (646)746-7395   Fax: (646)746-7434
URL: http://www.gammag.com

Monthly. $99.90/year for U.S. and territories; $176.90/year for Canada; $154.90/year for Mexico; $212.90/year for foreign, surface mail; $260.90/year for foreign, air mail. Magazine featuring commercial printing and graphic arts, including digital technologies.

★11633★ HOW

F & W Publications Inc.
4700 E Galbraith Rd.
Cincinnati, OH 45236-6708
Ph: (513)531-2690   Fax: (513)531-2902
Fr: 800-289-0963
E-mail: editorial@howdesign.com

Bimonthly. $49.00/year for individuals; $7.95 for single issue, Jan/Feb or May/June; $9.95 for single issue, Mar/April or July/Aug; $11.95/year for single issue, Sept/Oct or Nov/Dec. Instructional trade magazine.

★11634★ Jobline News

Graphic Artists Guild
90 John St., Ste. 403
New York, NY 10038
Ph: (212)791-3400   Fax: (212)791-0333
E-mail: jobline@gag.org

Description: Weekly. Lists jobs for freelance and staff artists in areas such as graphic design, illustration, and art education. Lists jobs from across the country; quantity and locales vary weekly.

★11635★ Modernism Magazine

David Rago
333 N Main St.
Lambertville, NJ 08530
Ph: (609)397-4104   Fax: (609)397-9377
Fr: 888-847-6464
E-mail: info@modernismmagazine.com

Quarterly. $19.95/year for individuals; $6.95 for single issue. Publication covering the visual arts and design.

★11636★ NSS News Bulletin

National Sculpture Society
237 Park Ave.
New York, NY 10017
Fax: (212)764-5651

Description: Bimonthly. Covers sculpture competitions, awards, grants, exhibitions, and commissions. Reports members' works and activities. Recurring features include news of research, a calendar of events, reports of meetings, news of educational opportunities, job listings, notices of publications available, and Seeking and Offering.

★11637★ Paperboard Packaging Worldwide

Advanstar Communications Inc.
7500 Old Oak Blvd.
Cleveland, OH 44130-3369
Ph: (440)243-8100   Fax: (440)891-2777
URL: http://www.packaging-online.com

Monthly. $30.00/year for individuals. Trade magazine for the corrugated container, folding carton, and rigid box converting industry.

★11638★ PIX

VNU Business Media USA
770 Broadway
New York, NY 10003
Ph: (646)654-5000

Monthly. Trade publication covering the arts and entertainment industries.

★11639★ Producers Masterguide

Producers Masterguide
60 E 8th St., 34th Fl.
New York, NY 10003-6514
Ph: (212)777-4002   Fax: (212)777-4101
URL: http://www.producers.masterguide.com

Annual. $145.00/year for U.S.; $155.00/year for Canada; $175.00/year for other countries. An international film and TV production directory and guide for the professional motion picture, broadcast television, feature film, TV commercial, cable/satellite, digital and videotape industries in the U.S., Canada, the UK, the Caribbean Islands, Mexico, Australia, New Zealand, Europe, Israel, Morocco, the Far East, and South America.

★11640★ Publishers Weekly

Publishers Weekly
360 Park Ave. S
New York, NY 10010
Ph: (646)746-6758   Fax: (646)746-6631
Fr: (866)436-0727
URL: http://http;//www.bookwire.com

Weekly. $215.80/year for individuals. Weekly trade news magazine.

★11641★ SignCraft

Signcraft Publishing Company Inc.
PO Box 60031
Fort Myers, FL 33906
Ph: (239)939-4644   Fax: (239)939-0607
Fr: 800-204-0204

E-mail: signcraft@signcraft.com

Bimonthly. $30.00/year for individuals; $5.95 for single issue. Trade magazine.

★11642★ Stained Glass Magazine

Stained Glass Association of America
10009 E 62nd St.
Raytown, MO 64133
Ph: (816)737-2090   Fax: (816)737-2801
Fr: 800-438-9581
E-mail: sgmagaz@kcnet.com
URL: http://www.stainedglass.org

Quarterly. $30.00/year for U.S.; $8.50 for single issue; $46.00/year for other countries. Magazine on architectural stained and decorative art glass.

★11643★ State of the Arts

Montana Arts Council
316 N Park Ave., Ste. 252
PO Box 202201
Helena, MT 59620
Ph: (406)444-6430   Fax: (406)444-6548

Description: Five issues/year. Contains artists profiles; news of educational opportunities; updates of legislation and government support programs, especially the National Endowment for the Arts; news of conferences and Council activities; grant announcements; calls for exhibit entries; notices of publications available; a calendar of events; and job listings.

★11644★ Stone in America

American Monument Association
70 N Market St.
Mount Sterling, OH 43143
Ph: (740)869-9990   Fax: (740)869-9991

Monthly. $30.00/year for individuals; $54.00 for two years; $36.00/year for Canada; $60.00/year for Canada; $37.00/year for other countries; $61.00/year for other countries. Magazine for the North American memorial stone industry.

PLACEMENT AND JOB REFERRAL SERVICES

★11645★ Association of Medical Illustrators (AMI)

5475 Mark Dabling Rd., Ste. 108
Colorado Springs, CO 80918-3847
Ph: (719)598-8622   Fax: (719)599-3075
E-mail: hq@ami.org
URL: http://www.ami.org

Description: Medical illustrators and individuals engaged in related pursuits. Promotes the study and encourages the advancement of medical illustration and allied fields of visual education. Works to advance medical education and to promote understanding and cooperation with medical and related professions; accredits six postgraduate medical illustration programs. Offers continuing education program; provides professional certification; compiles statistics.

★11646★ **BDA**
2029 Century Park East, Ste. 555
Los Angeles, CA 90067-2906
Ph: (310)789-1509   Fax: (310)712-0039
E-mail: bonnie@promax.tv
URL: http://www.bda.tv

Members: Designers, artists, art directors, illustrators, photographers, animators, and other motion graphic professionals in the electronic media industry; educators and students; commercial and industrial companies that manufacture products related to design. **Purpose:** Objectives are to promote understanding between designers, clients, and management; to stimulate innovative ideas and techniques; to encourage and provide a resource for young talent; and to provide a forum for discussion on industry issues and concerns. **Activities:** Maintains placement service; conducts surveys and compiles statistics.

★11647★ **Health Sciences Communications Association (HESCA)**
39 Wedgewood Dr., Ste. A
Jewett City, CT 06351
Ph: (860)376-5915   Fax: (860)376-6621
E-mail: hesca@hesca.org
URL: http://www.hesca.org/

Description: Media managers, graphic artists, biomedical librarians, producers, faculty members of health science and veterinary medicine schools, health professional organizations, and industry representatives. Acts as a clearinghouse for information used by professionals engaged in health science communications. Coordinates Media Festivals Program which recognizes outstanding media productions in the health sciences. Offers placement service.

★11648★ **Institute of American Indian Arts (IAIA)**
83 Avan Nu Po Rd.
Santa Fe, NM 87505
Ph: (505)424-2300   Fax: (505)424-4500
Fr: 800-804-6423
E-mail: webmaster@iaiancad.org
URL: http://www.iaiancad.org

Description: Federally chartered private institution. Offers learning opportunities in the arts and crafts to Native American youth (Indian, Eskimo, or Aleut). Emphasis is placed upon Indian traditions as the basis for creative expression in fine arts including painting, sculpture, museum studies, creative writing, printmaking, photography, communications, design, and dance, as well as training in metal crafts, jewelry, ceramics, textiles, and various traditional crafts. Students are encouraged to identify with their heritage and to be aware of themselves as members of a race rich in architecture, the fine arts, music, pageantry, and the humanities. All programs are based on elements of the Native American cultural heritage that emphasize differences between Native American and non-Native Americancultures.

Sponsors Indian arts-oriented junior college offering Associate of Fine Arts degrees in various fields as well as seminars, an exhibition program, and traveling exhibits. Maintains extensive library, museum, and biographical archives. Provides placement service

EMPLOYER DIRECTORIES AND NETWORKING LISTS

★11649★ *American Art Directory*
LexisNexis Group
121 Chanlon Rd.
New Providence, NJ 07974
Ph: (908)464-6800   Fax: (908)771-7704
Fr: 800-526-4902
URL: http://nationalregisterpub.com

Biennial. $299.00. Covers over 7,000 museums, art libraries, and art organizations, and 1,700 art schools; also includes lists of state directors and supervisors of art education in schools, traveling exhibition booking agencies, corporations having art holdings for public viewing, newspapers that carry art notes, art scholarships and fellowships; and 190 national, regional, and state open art exhibitions. Entries include: For museums-Name, address, phone, fax, electronic mail address, name of curator; days and hours of operation, collection, budget, publications. For exhibits-Name, address, phone, fax, electronic mail address, name of contact; date, deadline. For schools-Name, address, phone, name of director, names of faculty members, majors or degrees offered, tuition fees; summer school or adult hobby class information. For newspapers-Name, address, phone, name of art editor. Arrangement: Geographical. Indexes: Geographical, collection/subject/name, personal name, institution name.

★11650★ *American Showcase Illustration*
American Showcase Inc.
915 Broadway, 14th Fl.
New York, NY 10010
Ph: (212)673-6600   Fax: (212)673-9795
Fr: 800-894-7469

Annual. $95.00. Covers illustrators and graphic designers. Entries include: Name, address, phone, sample of work. Arrangement: Geographical.

★11651★ *Artists-Commercial Directory*
infoUSA Inc.
5711 S 86th Cir.
Omaha, NE 68127-0347
Ph: (402)930-3500   Fax: (402)331-0176
Fr: 800-555-6124
URL: http://www.abii.com

Annual. Number of listings: 5,786 (U.S. edition); 637 (Canadian edition). Entries include: Name, address, phone (including area code), size of advertisement, year first in

"Yellow Pages," name of owner or manager, number of employees. Compiled from telephone company "Yellow Pages," nationwide. Arrangement: Geographical.

★11652★ *Artists-Fine Arts Directory*
infoUSA Inc.
5711 S 86th Cir.
Omaha, NE 68127-0347
Ph: (402)930-3500   Fax: (402)331-0176
Fr: 800-555-6124
URL: http://www.abii.com

Annual. Number of listings: 5,597. Entries include: Name, address, phone (including area code), size of advertisement, year first in "Yellow Pages," name of owner or manager, number of employees. Compiled from telephone company "Yellow Pages," nationwide. Arrangement: Geographical.

★11653★ *Artist's & Graphic Designer's Market*
Writer's Digest Books
4700 E Galbraith Rd.
Cincinnati, OH 45236
Ph: (513)531-2690   Fr: 800-289-0963
E-mail: artdesign@fwpubs.com

Annual, September. $24.99. Covers 2,500 buyers of free-lance art work, including ad agencies, art studios, galleries, clip art firms, audiovisual firms, television film producers, periodicals, record companies, book publishers; coverage includes Canada. Entries include: Name of buyer, address, phone, payment rates, special submission requirements, reporting time, how to break in. Arrangement: Classified by type of market.

★11654★ *Below-the-Line Guide*
IFILM Publishing
1024 N Orange Dr.
Hollywood, CA 90038
Ph: (323)308-3490   Fax: (323)308-3493
E-mail: lrossini@ifilm.com
URL: http://www.loneeagle.com

Annual, latest edition 9th. $49.95. Covers approximately 2,500 motion picture and television cinematographers, editors, production designers, and costume designers, now includes set decorators. Entries include: Personal name; name, address, phone of agent or contact; chronological list of films or shows. Arrangement: Classified by line of business. Indexes: Film/show title, contact name, agents and managers.

★11655★ *Black Book Photography*
Black Book Marketing Group
10 Astor Pl., 6th Fl.
New York, NY 10003
Ph: (212)539-9800   Fax: (212)539-9801
Fr: 800-841-1246
URL: http://www.BlackBook.com

Annual, January. $110.00. Publication includes over 19,000 art directors, creative directors, photographers and photographic services, design firms, advertising agencies, and other firms whose products or services are used in advertising. Entries include:

Company name, address, phone. Principal content of publication is 4-color samples from the leading commercial photographers. Arrangement: Classified by product/service.

★11656★ Chicago Sourcebook
Black Book Marketing Group
10 Astor Pl., 6th Fl.
New York, NY 10003-6935
Ph: (212)539-9800   Fax: (212)539-9801

Annual, November. Covers commercial artists and photographers and graphic designers in Chicago, Illinois area. Entries include: Firm name, address, phone; other details as provided by firm. Arrangement: Alphabetical.

★11657★ Contemporary Designers
St. James Press
27500 Drake Rd.
Farmington Hills, MI 48331-3535
Ph: (248)699-4253   Fax: (248)699-8062
Fr: 800-877-4253

Irregular, 3rd edition 1996. $190.00. Covers 685 living designers and outstanding deceased designers from the recent past in the fields of art, architecture, industry, environment, textile, fashion, furniture, theater, film, graphic arts, and interior design; international coverage. Entries include: Name, date and place of birth, address, spouse's and children's names, educational background, area of specialization, projects completed, exhibitions, memberships; bibliography of materials by or about the entrant; signed critical essay. Arrangement: Alphabetical. Indexes: Nationality, designer type.

★11658★ Directory of American Professional Artists & Craftspeople
American Society of Artists
PO Box 1326
Palatine, IL 60078-1326
Ph: (312)751-2500

Annual, March. Covers about 20,000 plus artists and craftspeople. Entries include: Name, address, art medium; members' listings may also include works available, slides or photos on file, shows in which participated. Arrangement: Geographical by name, state, then by ZIP code or by address, by zip.

★11659★ Employment Opportunities, USA
Washington Research Associates
1090 Vermont Ave., NW, Ste. 800
Washington, DC 20005
Ph: (202)408-7025

Annual, quarterly updates. $184.00. Publication includes: List of over 1,000 employment contacts in companies and agencies in the banking, arts, telecommunications, education, and 14 other industries and professions, including the federal government. Entries include: Company name, name of representative, address, description of products or services, hiring and recruiting practices, training programs, and year established. Principal content is industry over-

views, career news, employment opportunity information on 14 different job markets, and comprehensive guidance to career resources on the Internet. Arrangement: Classified by industry. Indexes: Occupation.

★11660★ International Directory of Corporate Art Collections
ARTnews
PO Box 1608
Largo, FL 33779
Ph: (813)581-7328   Fax: (813)585-6398

Biennial, March of even years. $109.95. Covers about 1,300 art collections maintained or sponsored by businesses and corporations in the United States, Canada, Europe, and Japan. Entries include: Collection name; company name, name of contact, address, phone; line of business, description of collection, size and location of collection; publications, exhibitions, loan and viewing policies, other corporate arts activities. Arrangement: Alphabetical. Indexes: Geographical, personal name, media and type of art, type of business, collection status.

★11661★ National Directory of Arts Internships
National Network for Artist Placement
935 W. Ave. 37
Los Angeles, CA 90065
Ph: (323)222-4035   Fax: (323)225-5711
URL: http://www.artistplacement.com/intern.htm

Biennial, odd years. $85.00. Covers over 5,000 internship opportunities in dance, music, theater, art, design, film, and video & over 1,250 host organizations Entries include: Name of sponsoring organization, address, name of contact; description of positions available, eligibility requirements, stipend or salary (if any), application procedures. Arrangement: Classified by discipline, then geographical.

★11662★ National Directory of Magazines
Oxbridge Communications Inc.
186 5th Ave., 6th Fl.
New York, NY 10010
Ph: (212)741-0231   Fax: (212)633-2938
Fr: 800-955-0231
E-mail: custserv@oxbridge.com
URL: http://www.mediafinder.com

October. $895.00. Covers over 20,000 magazines; coverage includes Canada. Entries include: Title, publisher name, address, phone, fax number, names and titles of contact and key personnel, financial data, editorial and advertising information, circulation. Arrangement: Classified by subject. Indexes: Title, geographical, publisher.

★11663★ The Official Southwest Talent Directory
Cobb-Rendish Publishing
1920 Abrams Pkwy., Ste. 419
Dallas, TX 75214-6271
Fax: (214)855-0643

Annual, latest edition March, 1995. $25.00. Covers over 500 adult and juvenile actors, actresses, and models; motion picture and audio/videotape production facilities in the Southwest. Entries include: Name, acting or performing specialties, and agency contact; production services are presented in individual suppliers' ads. Arrangement: Talent classified by sex and age of performers; production sources classified by product or service. Indexes: Personal name, ethnic group, talent abilities.

★11664★ Printworld Directory of Contemporary Prints and Prices
Printworld International Inc.
PO Box 1957
West Chester, PA 19380
Ph: (610)431-6654   Fax: (610)431-6653
Fr: 800-788-9101
URL: http://www.printworlddirectory.com

Irregular, previous edition 1991; latest edition 2003, 10th edition. $285.00. Publication includes: Biographical data on 5,000 international artists in contemporary printmaking; thousands of galleries who handle prints and hundreds of print publishers, and 600,000 print/price listings. Entries include: For artists-Name, address, personal and educational data, major exhibits, collections, publishers, printers, galleries, awards, teaching positions and documentation of prints. For galleries and publishers-Name, address. Arrangement: Alphabetical. Indexes: Artist name, printer/print workshop, publisher, gallery, art appraiser.

★11665★ RSVP: The Directory of Illustration and Design
RSVP: The Directory of Illustration and Design
253 Washington Ave., No. D4
Brooklyn, NY 11205
Ph: (718)857-9267   Fax: (718)783-2376
URL: http://www.rsvpdirectory.com

Annual, January/February latest edition 2003. $20.00. Covers about 250 illustrators and designers in the graphic arts industry. All listings are paid. Entries include: Name, address, phone, sample of work. Arrangement: Separate sections for illustrators and designers; each subdivided into color and black and white. Indexes: Specialty (with phone), geographical, alphabetical.

★11666★ Society of Illustrators-Annual of American Illustration
Society of Illustrators
128 E 63rd St.
New York, NY 10021-1303
Ph: (212)838-2560   Fax: (212)838-2561

Annual, January. $49.95. Covers 800 illustrators and art directors. Entries include:

Personal or firm name, address, clients. Arrangement: Alphabetical.

★11667★ *Who's Who in American Art*
Marquis Who's Who
121 Chanlon Rd.
New Providence, NJ 07974
Ph: (908)673-1101   Fax: (908)673-1189
Fr: 800-473-7020
E-mail: art@renp.com
URL: http://www.marquiswhoswho.com

Biennial, Spring of odd years. $265.00. Covers about 11,800 people active in visual arts, including sculptors, painters, illustrators, printmakers, collectors, curators, writers, educators, dealers, critics, patrons, and museum executives. Also includes cumulative necrology from 1953. Entries include: Name, professional classification, address; artists' listings include dealer's name and address, preferred media, works in public collections, awards, publications, teaching positions, etc.; other listings may include same information plus statement of research interests, etc. Arrangement: Alphabetical. Indexes: Geographical, professional classification.

★11668★ *The Workbook*
Scott & Daughters Publishing Inc.
940 N Highland Ave., Ste. A
Los Angeles, CA 90038
Ph: (323)856-0008   Fax: (323)856-0443
Fr: 800-547-2688
URL: http://www.workbook.com

Annual, February. $120.00. Covers 49,000 advertising agencies, art directors, photographers, freelance illustrators and designers, artists' representatives, interactive designers, pre-press services, and other graphic arts services in the U.S. Entries include: Company or individual name, address, phone, specialty. National in scope. Arrangement: Classified by product or service.

HANDBOOKS AND MANUALS

★11669★ *The Art Business Encyclopedia*
Allworth Press
10 E. 23rd St., Ste. 510
New York, NY 10010
Ph: (212)777-8395   Fax: (212)777-8261
Fr: 800-491-2808

Leonard DuBoff. 1994. $29.95; $18.95 (paper). 320 pages.

★11670★ *Art and Reality: the Standard Reference Guide and Business Plan for Actively Developing Your Career As an Artist*
Seven Locks Press
3100 W. Warner Ave., Ste. 8
Santa Ana, CA 92704
Ph: (714)545-2526   Fax: (714)545-1572
Fr: 800-354-5348

Robert J. Abbott. Second edition, 1997. $29.95 (paper). 248 pages.

★11671★ *An Artist's Guide: Making It in New York City*
Allworth Press
10 E. 23rd St., Suite 510
New York, NY 10010
Ph: (212)777-8395   Fax: (212)777-8261
Fr: 800-491-2808

Daniel Grant. 2001. $19.95 (paper).

★11672★ *Becoming a Computer Graphics Designer Artist*
John Wiley & Sons Inc.
111 River St.
Hoboken, NJ 07030-5774
Ph: (201)748-6000   Fax: (201)748-6088

Gardner. 2000. $29.95 (paper).

★11673★ *Becoming a Successful Artist*
F & W Publications, Inc.
4700 E Galbraith Rd.
Cincinnati, OH 45236
Ph: (513)531-2690   Fax: (513)531-4082
Fr: 800-289-0963

Lewis B. Lehrman. 1996. $24.99 (paper). 144 pages.

★11674★ *Career Information Center*
Macmillan Publishing Co. Inc.
200 Old Tappan Rd.
Old Tappan, NJ 07675
Fr: 800-428-5331

Visual Education Center Staff. Seventh edition, 1999. $275.00. 2080 pages. This 13-volume set profiles over 600 occupations. Each occupational profile describes job duties, educational requirements, how to get the job, advancement possibilities, employment outlook, working conditions, earnings and benefits, and where to write for more information.

★11675★ *Career Opportunities in Theater and the Performing Arts*
Facts on File, Inc.
132 W. 31st St., 17th Fl.
New York, NY 10001-2006
Ph: (212)967-8800   Fax: (212)967-9196
Fr: 800-322-8755
URL: http://www.factsonfile.com

Shelly Field. Second edition, 1999. $29.95; $18.95 (paper). 256 pages. Offers a complete range of information about job opportu-

nities in the performing arts. Part of Career Opportunities Series.

★11676★ *Career Solutions for Creative People: How to Balance Artistic Goals with Career Security*
Allworth Press
10 E. 23rd St., Suite 510
New York, NY 10010
Ph: (212)777-8395   Fax: (212)777-8261
Fr: 800-491-2808

Ronda Ormont. 2001. $19.95 (paper).

★11677★ *Careers for Color Connoisseurs and Other Visual Types*
VGM Career Horizons
1221 Avenue of the Americas
New York, NY 10020
Ph: (212)904-2000   Fr: 800-323-4900
E-mail: ntcpub@tribune.com

Jan Goldberg. 1999. $14.95; $9.95 (paper). 212 pages.

★11678★ *Careers for Crafty People and Other Dexterous Types*
VGM Career Horizons
1221 Avenue of the Americas
New York, NY 10020
Ph: (212)904-2000   Fr: 800-323-4900
E-mail: ntcpub@tribune.com

Mark Rowh. Second Edition, 2002. $14.95; $9.95 (paper). 192 pages.

★11679★ *Careers for Culture Lovers and Other Artsy Types*
VGM Career Horizons
1221 Avenue of the Americas
New York, NY 10020
Ph: (212)904-2000   Fr: 800-323-4900
E-mail: ntcpub@tribune.com

Marjorie Eberts and Margaret Gisler. Second edition, 1999. $14.95; $9.95 (paper). 234 pages. Describes how to get work in a variety of fields related to art and culture. Opportunities include picture framer, curator, art restorer, symphony manager, disk jockey, music reviewer, dance teacher, choreographer, costume designer, theater manager, light designer, drama teacher, bookstore owner, interior decorator, antique store owner, and others.

★11680★ *Careers by Design: A Headhunter's Secrets for Success and Survival in Graphic Design*
Allworth Press
10 E. 23rd St., Ste. 510
New York, NY 10010
Ph: (212)777-8395   Fax: (212)777-8261
Fr: 800-491-2808

Roz Goldfarb. Third edition, 2002. 256 pages.

★11681★ Careers for Film Buffs and Other Hollywood Types

VGM Career Horizons
1221 Avenue of the Americas
New York, NY 10020
Ph: (212)904-2000   Fr: 800-323-4900
E-mail: ntcpub@tribune.com

Jaq Greenspon. 1994. $14.95; $9.95 (paper). 250 pages. Describes job descriptions in production, camera, sound, special effects, grips, electrical, makeup, costumes, etc.

★11682★ Careers in the Graphic Arts

Rosen Publishing Group, Inc.
29 E. 21st St.
New York, NY 10010
Ph: (212)777-3017   Fax: 888-436-4643
Fr: 800-237-9932

Erin McGuire-Lytle. Revised edition, 1997. $16.95; $9.95 (paper). 152 pages. Discusses a career in graphic arts; outlines educational requirements, training, and skills needed to become an illustrator, layout artist, designer, and paste-up artist. Gives job hunting advice, describes how to write a resume, prepare a portfolio, and interview preparation. Gives a state-by-state listing of schools offering graphic arts.

★11683★ Careers in Health Care

McGraw-Hill Trade
2 Penn Plaza
New York, NY 10121
Ph: (212)904-2000   Fr: 800-722-4726
E-mail: ntcpub@tribune.com

Barbara M. Swanson. Fourth edition, 2000. $17.95; $13.95 (paper). 320 pages. Describes job duties, work settings, salaries, licensing and certification requirements, educational preparation, and future outlook. Gives ideas on how to secure a job.

★11684★ Careers in the Visual Arts: A Guide to Jobs, Money, Opportunities, and an Artistic Life

Watson-Guptill Publications, Inc.
BPI Communications, Inc.
770 Broadway
New York, NY 10003
Ph: (646)654-5400   Fax: (646)654-5486
Fr: 800-323-9432

Dee Ito. 1993. $14.95 (paper). 320 pages. Out of print. Gives a broad overview of each field included, with educational requirements and employment opportunities. Includes ideas on how to get started.

★11685★ Chronicle Artistic Occupations Guidebook

Chronicle Guidance Publications, Inc.
66 Aurora St.
Moravia, NY 13118-3576
Fax: (315)497-3359   Fr: 800-899-0454

Paul Downes, editor. Revised, 1994. $81.80.

★11686★ Exploring High-Tech Careers

Rosen Publishing Group, Inc.
29 E. 21st St.
New York, NY 10010
Ph: (212)777-3017   Fax: (212)777-0277
Fr: 800-237-9932

Scott Southworth. Revised edition, 1993. $14.95; $9.95 (paper). 118 pages. Out of print. Gives an orientation to the field of high technology and high-tech jobs. Describes educational preparation and job hunting. Includes a glossary and bibliography.

★11687★ The Fine Artist's Career Guide

Allworth Press
10 E. 23rd St.
New York, NY 10010
Ph: (212)777-8395   Fax: (646)654-5486
Fr: 800-323-9432

Daniel Grant. 1998. $18.95 (paper). 304 pages. Covers the fine and applied arts.

★11688★ The Fine Artist's Guide to Marketing and Self-Promotion: Innovative Techniques to Build Your Career As an Artist

Allworth Press
10 E. 23rd St., Ste. 510
New York, NY 10010
Ph: (212)777-8395   Fax: (212)777-8261
Fr: 800-491-2808

Julius Vitali. 1996. $18.95 (paper). 224 pages. Covers a variety of self-promotion techniques for artists, including preparing a resume.

★11689★ Get Noticed!: Self Promotion for Creative Professionals

F & W Publications Inc.
4700 E Galbraith Rd.
Cincinnati, OH 45236
Ph: (513)531-2690   Fax: (513)531-4082
Fr: 800-289-0963

Sheree Clark, Kristen Lennert. 2000. $29.99 (paper).

★11690★ Graphic Design: A Career Guide and Educational Directory

American Institute of Graphic Arts
164 Fifth Ave.
New York, NY 10010-5900
Ph: (212)807-1990

Sharon H. Poggenpohl, editor. 1993. $25.00 (paper). 160 pages.

★11691★ Graphic Designer's Ultimate Resource Directory

F & W Publications, Inc.
4700 E Galbraith Rd.
Cincinnati, OH 45236
Ph: (513)531-2690   Fax: (513)531-4082
Fr: 800-289-0963

Poppy Evans. 1999. $28.99 (paper). 192 pages.

★11692★ Great Jobs for Art Majors

McGraw-Hill Contemporary Books
1221 Avenue of the Americas
New York, NY 10020
Ph: (212)904-2000   Fr: 800-323-4900
E-mail: ntcpub@tribune.com

Blythe Camenson, Stephen Lambert, Julie DeGalan. 1997. $11.95 (paper). 345 pages. Includes bibliographical references and index.

★11693★ How to Start and Succeed as an Artist

Allworth Press
10 E. 23rd St., Ste. 510
New York, NY 10010
Ph: (212)777-8395   Fax: (212)777-8261
Fr: 800-491-2808

Daniel Grant. Second edition, 1997. $18.95. 224 pages.

★11694★ How to Survive and Prosper as an Artist: Selling Yourself Without Selling Your Soul

Henry Holt and Co., LLC
115 W. 18th St., 5th Fl.
New York, NY 10011
Ph: (212)886-9200   Fax: (212)633-0748
Fr: 800-672-2054

Caroll Michels. Fourth edition, 1997. $16.00. 336 pages. Includes index and bibliographical references.

★11695★ The Lost Soul Companion: Comfort & Constructive Advice for Struggling Actors, Musicians, Artists, Writers & Other Free Spirits

Puckitt Press, Incorporated
P.O. Box 3248
Bloomington, IN 47402-3248
Ph: (812)331-4337

Susan M. Brackney. 2000. $10.00

★11696★ The Madness of Art: A Guide to Living and Working in Chicago

Chicago Review Press
814 N. Franklin St.
Chicago, IL 60610
Ph: (312)337-0747   Fax: (312)337-5985
Fr: 800-888-4741

Adam Langer. 1996. $12.95 (paper). 268 pages.

★11697★ Magazines Career Directory

Thomson Gale
27500 Drake Rd.
Farmington Hills, MI 48331-3535
Ph: (248)699-GALE   Fax: (248)699-8069
Fr: 800-877-GALE
E-mail: galeord@gale.com
URL: http://www.galegroup.com

Bradley Morgan. Fifth edition, 1993. $39.00. Features extensive listings of contacts and entry-level job opportunities at many magazine publishing organizations. Includes articles by top professionals in the field on some of the industry's varied career paths: art, editorial, sales, and business management. Part of Career Advisor series.

★11698★ **New Media Careers for Artists and Designers**
AuthorHouse
1663 Liberty Dr., Ste. 200
Bloomington, IN 47403
Fax: (812)339-8654   Fr: 800-839-8640

Brenda S. Faison. February 2003. $13.95. 136 pages.

★11699★ **Newspapers Career Directory**
Thomson Gale
27500 Drake Rd.
Farmington Hills, MI 48331-3535
Ph: (248)699-GALE   Fax: 800-414-5043
Fr: 800-877-GALE
E-mail: galeord@gale.com
URL: http://www.gale.com

Bradley Morgan. Fourth edition, 1993. $39.00. 300 pages. Out of print. Features extensive listings of contacts and entry-level job opportunities at many newspaper organizations. Focuses on each area of the business, from reporting and editorial to sales and marketing to promotion and production.

★11700★ **100 Best Careers for Writers and Artists**
Thomson Peterson's
PO Box 67005
Lawrenceville, NJ 08648-6105
Fr: 800-338-3282

Shelly Field. 1997. $15.95 (paper). 288 pages. Identifies job opportunities in communications and the arts.

★11701★ **Opportunities in Arts and Crafts Careers**
McGraw-Hill Contemporary Books
1221 Avenue of the Americas
New York, NY 10020
Ph: (212)904-2000   Fr: 800-323-4900
E-mail: ntcpub@tribune.com

Betty Gardner. 1998. $14.95; $11.95 (paper). 202 pages.

★11702★ **Opportunities in Commercial Art and Graphic Design Careers**
McGraw-Hill Trade
2 Penn Plaza
New York, NY 10121
Ph: (212)904-2000   Fr: 800-722-4726

Barbara Gordon. Second edition, 1997. $12.95; $11.95 (paper). 160 pages. Provides a survey of job opportunities in advertising and public relations, publishing, fashion, architecture, and newspapers, as well as in a variety of specialty markets. Illustrated.

★11703★ **Opportunities in Crafts Careers**
McGraw-Hill Trade
2 Penn Plaza
New York, NY 10121
Ph: (212)904-2000   Fr: 800-722-4726

Marianne Munday. 1994. $14.95; $11.95 (paper). 160 pages. Provides information about careers and job opportunities in such areas as fine and applied arts, antiques and collectibles, ceramics, woodworking, sewing and needlecraft, and more. Illustrated. Out of stock.

★11704★ **Opportunities in Drafting Careers**
McGraw-Hill Trade
2 Penn Plaza
New York, NY 10121
Ph: (212)904-2000   Fr: 800-722-4726

Mark Rowh. 1994. $14.95; $11.95 (paper). 298 pages. Provides information on opportunities in mechanical, landscape, marine, and topographical drafting in civil service, architecture, electronics, and other fields. Contains index and illustrations.

★11705★ **Opportunities in Magazine Publishing Careers**
McGraw-Hill Trade
2 Penn Plaza
New York, NY 10121
Ph: (212)904-2000   Fr: 800-722-4726
E-mail: ntcpub@tribune.com

S. William Pattis. 1994. $13.95; $12.95 (paper). 160 pages. Covers the scope of magazine publishing and addresses how to identify and pursue available positions. Illustrated.

★11706★ **Opportunities in Printing Careers**
McGraw-Hill Trade
2 Penn Plaza
New York, NY 10121
Ph: (212)904-2000   Fr: 800-722-4726
E-mail: ntcpub@tribune.com

Irvin Borowsky. 1998. $14.95; $11.95 (paper). 160 pages. Offers detailed information on the variety of pre-press, press, and post-press jobs available. Covers apprenticeships, unions, salaries, and how to get ahead. Illustrated.

★11707★ **Opportunities in Publishing Careers**
McGraw-Hill Professional
2 Penn Plaza
New York, NY 10121
Ph: (212)904-2000   Fr: 800-722-4726
E-mail: ntcpub@tribune.com

Robert A. Carter and S. William Pattis. 1995. $14.95; $11.95 (paper). 160 pages. Covers all positions in book and magazine publishing, including new opportunities in multimedia publishing.

★11708★ **Opportunities in Visual Arts Careers**
McGraw-Hill Trade
2 Penn Plaza
New York, NY 10121
Ph: (212)904-2000   Fr: 800-722-4726
E-mail: ntcpub@tribune.com

Mark Salmon. 1994. $14.95; $11.95 (paper). 160 pages. Points the way to a career in the visual arts, examining opportunities for designers, painters, sculptors, illustrators, animators, photographers, art therapists, educators, and others. Offers a view of the pros and cons of working for an art or design company or on your own.

★11709★ **Taking the Leap: Building a Career as a Visual Artist**
Chronicle Books LLC
85 Second St.
San Francisco, CA 94105
Ph: (415)537-4200   Fax: (415)537-4460
Fr: 800-722-6657

Cay Lang. 1998. $16.95. 224 pages.

★11710★ **2002 Artist's & Graphic Designer's Market**
Writer's Digest Books
F & W Publications, Inc.
1507 Dana Ave.
Cincinnati, OH 45207
Ph: (513)531-2690   Fax: (513)531-4082
Fr: 800-289-0963

Mary Cox, editor. 2001. $24.99 (paper). 720 pages.

EMPLOYMENT AGENCIES AND SEARCH FIRMS

★11711★ **Claremont-Branan, Inc.**
1298 Rockbridge Rd., Ste. B
Stone Mountain, GA 30087
Ph: (770)925-2915   Fax: (770)925-2601

Employment agency. Executive search firm.

★11712★ **Graphic Arts Employment Service, Inc.**
409 N Pacific Coast Hwy., Ste.455
Redondo Beach, CA 90277
Ph: (310)316-1246   Fax: (310)937-3760
Fr: 800-499-9722
E-mail: info@gaes.com
URL: http://www.gaes.com

Employment agency specializing in the publishing and packaging industries.

★11713★ **Graphic Search Associates Inc.**
PO Box 373
Newtown Square, PA 19073
Ph: (610)359-1234   Fax: (610)353-8120
Fr: 800-342-1777

E-mail: info@graphsrch.com
URL: http://www.graphsrch.com
Executive search firm for the graphic arts industry.

★11714★ **Randolph Associates, Inc.**
950 Massachusetts Ave., Ste. 105
Cambridge, MA 02139-3174
Ph: (617)441-8777   Fax: (617)441-8778
E-mail: jobs@greatjobs.com
URL: http://www.greatjobs.com
Employment agency. Provides regular or temporary placement of staff.

ONLINE JOB SOURCES AND SERVICES

★11715★ **ArtJob Online**
1743 Wazee St., Ste. 300
Denver, CO 80202
Ph: (303)629-1166   Fax: (303)629-9717
Fr: 888-JOBS-232
E-mail: artjob@westaf.org
URL: http://www.artjob.org
Description: Contains up-to-date national and international listings of arts employment and related opportunities in the arts: full- & part-time employment, internships, grants, public art projects, residencies – can search by region, art discipline, type of organization. **Fee:** Subscribers pay $25 for 3 months, $40 for six months and $75 for one year.

★11716★ **Graphic Artists Guild**
URL: http://www.gag.org
Description: JOBLine News section of Guild Resources page contains weekly e-mail newsletter of job listings. **Fee:** Must subscribe to e-mail newsletter non-member six-month rates start at $80. Visitors may download a free sample.

TRADESHOWS

★11717★ **International Black Writers and Artists Convention**
International Black Writers and Artists
PO Box 43576
Los Angeles, CA 90043
Ph: (213)964-3721   Fax: (213)938-0556
E-mail: lahughes@aol.com
Annual. **Primary Exhibits:** Books and artwork.

OTHER SOURCES

★11718★ **Aid to Artisans (ATA)**
331 Wethersfield Ave.
Hartford, CT 06114
Ph: (860)947-3344   Fax: (860)947-3350
E-mail: clare_smith@aidtoartisans.org
URL: http://www.aidtoartisans.org/
Description: Dedicated to creating employment opportunities for disadvantaged artisans worldwide. Functions as a consultative agency, helping other organizations establish craft programs and market Third World crafts. Provides technical assistance to needy craft producers in impoverished areas of the U.S. and other countries.

★11719★ **American Institute of Graphic Arts (AIGA)**
164 5th Ave.
New York, NY 10010
Ph: (212)807-1990   Fax: (212)807-1799
Fr: 800-548-1634
E-mail: comments@aiga.org
URL: http://www.aiga.org
Description: Graphic designers, art directors, art directors, illustrators, packaging designers. Sponsors exhibits and projects in the public interest. Sponsors traveling exhibitions. Operates gallery. Maintains library of design books and periodicals; offers slide archives.

★11720★ **American Society of Artists (ASA)**
PO Box 1326
Palatine, IL 60078
Ph: (312)751-2500
E-mail: asoa@webtv.net
URL: http://www.americansocietyofartists.com
Description: Professional artists and craftspeople. Maintains art referral service and information exchange service. Sponsors art and craft festivals and a Lecture and Demonstration Service. The Special Arts Services Division aids disabled individuals to either practice or enjoy the visual arts. Presents demonstrations in visual arts to better acquaint the public with various processes in different media.

★11721★ **American Society of Psychopathology of Expression (ASPE)**
74 Lawton St.
Brookline, MA 02446
Ph: (617)738-9821   Fax: (617)975-0411
Description: Psychiatrists, psychologists, art therapists, sociologists, art critics, artists, social workers, linguists, educators, criminologists, writers, and historians. At least two-thirds of the members must be physicians. Fosters collaboration among specialists in the United States who are interested in the problems of expression and in the artistic activities connected with psychiatric, sociological, and psychological research. Disse-

minates information about research and clinical applications in the field of psychopathology of expression. Sponsors consultations, seminars, and lectures on art therapy.

★11722★ **Art Directors Club (ADC)**
106 W 29th St.
New York, NY 10001
Ph: (212)643-1440   Fax: (212)643-4266
E-mail: info@adcny.org
URL: http://www.adcny.org
Members: Art directors of advertising magazines and agencies, visual information specialists, and graphic designers; associate members are artists, cinematographers, photographers, copywriters, educators, journalists, and critics. **Purpose:** Promotes and stimulates interest in the practice of art direction. **Activities:** Sponsors Annual Exhibition of Advertising, Editorial and Television Art and Design; International Traveling Exhibition; Hall of Fame. Provides educational, professional, and entertainment programs; on-premise art exhibitions; portfolio review program. Conducts panels for students and faculty.

★11723★ **Cartoonists Northwest (CNW)**
PO Box 31122
Seattle, WA 98103
Ph: (425)226-7623   Fax: (425)227-0511
E-mail: cartoonistsnw@aol.com
URL: http://www.cartoonists.net
Description: Cartoonists, writers, publishers, illustrators, agents, and others interested in cartooning. Members are accepted nationwide and internationally. Provides information on all aspects of the cartooning profession to amateur, aspiring, and practicing cartoonists. Promotes cartooning as an art form. Provides networking opportunities and referral services. Conducts educational programs.

★11724★ **College Art Association (CAA)**
275 7th Ave.
New York, NY 10001
Ph: (212)691-1051   Fax: (212)627-2381
E-mail: nyoffice@collegeart.org
URL: http://www.collegeart.org
Description: Professional organization of artists, art historians and fine art educators, museum directors, and curators. Seeks to raise the standards of scholarship and of the teaching of art and art history throughout the country.

★11725★ **Graphic Arts Technical Foundation (GATF)**
200 Deer Run Rd.
Sewickley, PA 15143-2600
Ph: (412)741-6860   Fax: (412)741-2311
Fr: 800-910-GATF
E-mail: info@gatf.org
URL: http://www.gatf.org
Description: Scientific, research, technical, and educational organization serving the international graphic communications indus-

tries. Conducts research in all graphic processes and their commercial applications. Conducts seminars, workshops, and forums on graphic arts and environmental subjects. Conducts educational programs, including the publishing of graphic arts textbooks and learning modules, videotapes and CD-ROMs and broadcast video seminars. Conducts the GATF training and certification program in sheet-fed offset press operating, Web Offset press operating, Image Assembly, and desktop publishing. Produces test images and quality control devices for the industry. Performs technical services for the graphic arts industry, including problem-solving, material evaluation, and plant audits. A partner of the Printing Industries of America (PIA).

★11726★ **Media and the Arts Occupations**
Delphi Productions
3160 4th St.
Boulder, CO 80304
Fax: (303)443-4022   Fr: 888-443-2400
URL: http://www.delphivideo.com
$95.00. 50 minutes. Part of the Careers for the 21st Century Video Library.

★11727★ **Society of Illustrators (SI)**
128 E 63rd St.
New York, NY 10021-7303
Ph: (212)838-2560   Fax: (212)838-2561
E-mail: sil901@aol.com
URL: http://www.societyillustrators.org
Description: Professional society of illustrators and art directors. Maintains Museum of American Illustration which sponsors continuous exhibits; holds annual exhibit (February-April) of best illustrations of the year; conducts benefit and sale in gallery in December. Awards annual scholarships to students of accredited college-level art schools. Participates in annual U.S. Air Force exhibits. Maintains hall of fame. Traveling exhibition.

★11728★ **Southeastern Theatre Conference (SETC)**
PO Box 9868
Greensboro, NC 27429-0868
Ph: (336)272-3645   Fax: (336)272-8810
E-mail: setc@mindspring.com
URL: http://www.setc.org/
Members: Individuals and theatre organizations involved in university, college, community, professional, children's, and secondary school theatres. **Purpose:** Purpose is to bring together people interested in theatre and theatre artists and craftsmen from 10 southeastern states of the U.S. in order to promote high standards and to stimulate creativity in all phases of theatrical endeavor. **Activities:** Services include: central office for business and communication; job contact service; new play project; annual auditions for summer indoor and outdoor theatres; fall auditions for professional theatres. Compiles statistics.

★11729★ **Women's Caucus for Art (WCA)**
Canal Street Sta.
PO Box 1498
New York, NY 10013
Ph: (212)634-0007
E-mail: info@nationalwca.com
URL: http://www.nationalwca.com
Members: Professional women in visual art fields including artists, critics, art historians, museum and gallery professionals, arts administrators, educators and students, and collectors of art. **Purpose:** Objectives are to increase recognition for contemporary and historical achievements of women in art; ensure equal opportunity for employment, art commissions, and research grants; encourage professionalism and shared information among women in art; stimulate and publicize research and publications on women in the visual arts. **Activities:** Conducts workshops, periodic affirmative action research, and statistical surveys. Presents annual honor awards to senior women in the visual arts.

Website Designers

SOURCES OF HELP-WANTED ADS

★11730★ *Computer Graphics World*
PennWell Corp.
98 Spit Brook Rd.
Nashua, NH 03062-5737
Ph: (603)891-0123   Fax: (603)891-0574
URL: http://cgw.pennnet.com/home.cfm

Monthly. $55.00/year for individuals; $75.00/year for Canada and Mexico; $115.00/year for other countries; $90.00 for two years; $104.00 for two years, Canada and Mexico; $160.00/year for two years, other countries. Publication reporting on the use of modeling, animation, and multimedia in the areas of science and engineering, art and entertainment, and presentation and training.

★11731★ *e-Business Advisor*
e-Business Advisor
PO Box 429002
San Diego, CA 92142-9002
Ph: (858)278-5600   Fax: (858)278-0300
Fr: 800-336-6060
E-mail: CustomerService@Advisor.com
URL: http://www.advisor.com/

Magazine for developing strategies, practices, and innovations for e-business applications.

★11732★ *IEEE Computer Graphics and Applications*
IEEE Computer Society
PO Box 3014
Los Alamitos, CA 90720-1264
Ph: (714)821-8380   Fax: (714)821-4010
Fr: 800-272-6657
E-mail: rbaldwin@computer.org
URL: http://www.computer.org/cga/

Bimonthly. $32.00/year for members; $320.00/year for institutions. Magazine addressing the interests and needs of professional designers and users of computer graphics hardware, software, and systems.

★11733★ *Journal of Graphics Tools*
A.K. Peters Ltd.
63 S Ave.
Natick, MA 01760
Ph: (508)655-9933   Fax: (508)655-5847
E-mail: jgt@akpeters.com
URL: http://www.acm.org/jgt

Quarterly. $50.00/year for individuals; $120.00/year for institutions, U.S. and Canada; $40.00 for single issue; $7.50/year for U.S., postage and handling; $25.00/year for elsewhere, postage and handling; $15.00/year for Canada, postage and handling. Journal containing research ideas for computer graphics professionals.

★11734★ *PC WORLD*
101 Communications
9121 Oakdale Ave.
Chatsworth, CA 91311
Ph: (818)734-1520   Fax: (818)734-1522
URL: http://www.pcworld.com

Monthly. $29.90/year for individuals; $5.95 for single issue.

EMPLOYER DIRECTORIES AND NETWORKING LISTS

★11735★ *Computer Directory*
Computer Directories Inc.
23815 Nichols Sawmill Rd.
Hockley, TX 77447
Ph: (281)259-5959   Fax: (281)356-7980
Fr: 800-234-4353
URL: http://www.compdirinc.com

Annual, fall. Covers approximately 130,000 computer installations; 19 separate volumes for Alaska/Hawaii, Connecticut/New Jersey, Dallas/Ft. Worth, Eastern Seaboard, Far Midwest, Houston, Illinois, Midatlantic, Midcentral, Mideast, Minnesota/Wisconsin, North Central, New England, New York Metro, Northwest, Ohio, Pennsylvania/West Virginia, Southeast, and Southwest Texas. Entries include: Company name, address, phone, fax, email, name and title of contact, hardware used, software application, operating system, programming language, computer graphics, networking system. Arrangement: Geographical. Indexes: Alphabetical, industry, hardware.

★11736★ *Computers-System Designers and Consultants Directory*
infoUSA Inc.
5711 S 86th Cir.
Omaha, NE 68127-0347
Ph: (402)930-3500   Fax: (402)331-0176
Fr: 800-555-6124
URL: http://www.abii.com

Annual. Number of listings: 35,936. Entries include: Name, address, phone (including area code), size of advertisement, year first in "Yellow Pages," name of owner or manager, number of employees. Compiled from telephone company "Yellow Pages," nationwide. Arrangement: Geographical.

HANDBOOKS AND MANUALS

★11737★ *Career Opportunities in Computers and Cyberspace*
Facts on File
132 W. 31st St., 17th Fl.
New York, NY 10001-2006
Ph: (212)967-8800   Fax: (212)967-8107
Fr: 800-322-8755

Harry Henderson. 1999. $26.95 (paper). Part of the Career Opportunities Series. 224 pages.

★11738★ *Careers for Color Connoisseurs and Other Visual Types*
VGM Career Horizons
1221 Avenue of the Americas
New York, NY 10020
Ph: (212)904-2000   Fr: 800-323-4900
E-mail: ntcpub@tribune.com

Jan Goldberg. 1999. $14.95; $9.95 (paper). 212 pages.

★11739★ *Creating Online Media: A Guide to Research, Writing and Design on the Internet*
McGraw-Hill Companies
860 Taylor Station Rd.
Blacklick, OH 43004-0545
Fax: (614)755-5645   Fr: 800-722-4726

Carole Rich. 1998. $34.50.

★11740★ *The Digital Frontier Job & Opportunity Finder*
Moon Lake Media
PO Box 251466
Los Angeles, CA 90025
Ph: (310)535-2453

Don B. Altman. 1996. $19.95 (paper). 256 pages.

★11741★ *Expert Resumes for Computer and Web Jobs*
JIST Publishing
8902 Otis Ave.
Indianapolis, IN 46216-1033
Ph: (317)613-4200   Fax: (317)613-4307
Fr: 800-648-5478

Wendy Enelow and Louis Kursmark. 2001. $16.95 (paper).

★11742★ *Exploring Careers in Cyberspace*
Rosen Publishing Group, Inc.
29 E. 21st St.
New York, NY 10010
Ph: (212)777-3017   Fax: 888-436-4643
Fr: 800-237-9932

Michael Fulton. 1997. $18.95. Over 100 pages. Provides information on preparation for cyberspace careers and available jobs.

★11743★ *Game Developer's Marketplace: The Definitive Guide to Making it Big in the Interactive Game Industry*
Coriolis Group LLC
14455 N. Hayden Rd., Ste. 220
Scottsdale, AZ 85260-6949
Ph: (480)483-0192   Fax: (480)483-0193
Fr: 800-410-0192

Ben Sawyer. 1997. $49.99. 700 pages. Out of print. Covers the basics of game design, getting a job in the industry, and business plans along with other related topics.

★11744★ *Get Your IT Career in Gear!*
McGraw-Hill Professional
2 Penn Plaza
New York, NY 10121
Ph: (212)904-2000

Leslie Goff. 2001. $24.99 (paper).

★11745★ *Job Seekers Guide to Silicon Valley Recruiters*
John Wily and Sons, Inc.
605 Third Ave., 4th Fl.
New York, NY 10158-0012
Ph: (212)850-6276   Fax: (212)850-8641

Christopher W. Hunt, Scott A. Scanlon. First edition, 1998. $19.95 (paper). 371 pages. Includes a list of 2,400 recruiters specializing in high technology positions and explains how to work with them.

★11746★ *The JobBank Guide to Computer and High-Tech Companies*
Adams Media Corp.
57 Littlefield St.
Avon, MA 02322
Ph: (508)427-7100   Fax: (508)427-6790
Fr: 800-872-5627
URL: http://www.adamsmedia.com

Second edition, 1999. $17.95 (paper). 704 pages. Contains profiles of more than 4,500 high-tech employers.

★11747★ *Opportunities in High Tech Careers*
McGraw-Hill Trade
2 Penn Plaza
New York, NY 10121
Ph: (212)904-2000   Fr: 800-722-4726

Gary Colter and Deborah Yanuck. 1995. $14.95; $11.95 (paper). 160 pages. Explores high technology careers. Describes job opportunities, how to make a career decision, how to prepare for high technology jobs, job hunting techniques, and future trends.

★11748★ *Preparing for an Outstanding Career in Computers: Questions and Answers for Professionals and Students*
Rafi Systems, Incorporated
750 N. Diamond Bar Blvd., Suite 224
Diamond Bar, CA 91765
Ph: (909)593-8124   Fax: (909)629-1034
Fr: 800-584-6706

Mohamed Rafiquzzaman. 2001. $19.95.

★11749★ *Software Developer's Marketplace*
Coriolis Group LLC
14455 N. Hayden Rd., Ste. 220
Scottsdale, AZ 85260-6949
Ph: (480)483-0192   Fax: (480)483-0193
Fr: 800-410-0192

Ben Sawyer. First edition, 1998. $49.99 (paper). 700 pages. Out of print.

★11750★ *Ultimate Web Developers Sourcebook*
Coriolis Group LLC
14455 N. Hayden Rd., Ste. 220
Scottsdale, AZ 85260-6949
Ph: (480)483-0192   Fax: (480)483-0193
Fr: 800-410-0192

Ben Sawyer. 1996. $49.99 (paper). 600 pages. Out of print.

★11751★ *Unlocking the Clubhouse: Women in Computing*
MIT Press
5 Cambridge Ctr., Suite 4
Cambridge, MA 02142-1493
Ph: (617)253-5646   Fax: (617)253-6779
Fr: 800-356-0343

Jane Margolis and Allan Fisher. 2001. $24.95.

★11752★ *The Unofficial Guide to Getting a Job at Microsoft*
McGraw-Hill Education Group
800 Taylor Staion Rd.
Blacklick, OH 43004-0545
Fax: (614)755-5645   Fr: 800-722-4726

Rebecca Smith. 2000. $16.95 (paper).

★11753★ *Winning Resumes for Computer Personnel*
Barron's Educational Series, Inc.
250 Wireless Blvd.
Hauppauge, NY 11788-3917
Ph: (631)434-3311   Fax: (631)434-3723
Fr: 800-645-3476

Anne Hart. Second edition, 1998. $12.95 (paper). 320 pages.

★11754★ *Your Opportunities in Computers*
Energeia Publishing, Inc.
1307 Fairmount Ave., S
Salem, OR 97302-4313
Ph: (503)362-1480   Fax: (503)362-2123
Fr: 800-639-6048

John Tribbett. 1994. $2.50 (paper). 8 pages.

EMPLOYMENT AGENCIES AND SEARCH FIRMS

★11755★ **Capitol Search**
215 E. Ridgewood Ave., Ste. 205
Ridgewood, NJ 07450
Ph: (201)444-6666

Employment agency.

★11756★ **Graphic Arts Employment Service, Inc.**
409 N Pacific Coast Hwy., Ste.455
Redondo Beach, CA 90277
Ph: (310)316-1246   Fax: (310)937-3760
Fr: 800-499-9722
E-mail: info@gaes.com
URL: http://www.gaes.com

Employment agency specializing in the publishing and packaging industries.

ONLINE JOB SOURCES AND SERVICES

★11757★ Aquent.com
URL: http://www.aquent.com/work/index.html
Description: Aquent finds contract, project-based, and permanent work for a broad range of creative and information technology professionals. Applicants submit their applications, which are reviewed by an Aquent agent and, if qualifications match job opportunities, they will be called in for an interview and skills assessment. If skills and experience are appropriate, then will then be assigned an Aquent agent who will get to work finding contract or permanent jobs. Also offers free career resources.

★11758★ ComputerJobs.com
URL: http://www.computerjobs.com
Description: The site is an employment tool for technology professionals. Information on positions is updated hourly for seekers. Jobs may be searched by skill, or by location nationally or in a specific state or city job market. Contains thousands of job postings. National jobs may be posted for free. Also career resources for IT professionals.

★11759★ Computerwork.com
E-mail: candidate_support@computerwork.com
URL: http://computerwork.com/
Description: Job search and resume submission service for professionals in information technology.

★11760★ Computerworld Careers
URL: http://www.computerworld.com/cwi/careers/
Description: Offers career opportunities for IT (information technology) professionals.

Job seekers may search the jobs database, register at the site, and read about job surveys and employment trends. Employers may post jobs.

★11761★ Computing Research Association Job Announcements
URL: http://www.cra.org/main/cra.jobs.html
Description: Contains dated links to national college and university computer technology positions.

★11762★ Dice.com
URL: http://www.dice.com
Description: Job search database for computer consultants and high-tech professionals, listing thousands of high tech permanent contract and consulting jobs for programmers, software engineers, systems administrators, web developers, and hardware engineers. Also free career advice e-mail newsletter and job posting e-alerts.

★11763★ Guru
URL: http://www.guru.com
Description: Job board specializing in contract jobs for creative and information technology professionals. Also provides online incorporation and educational opportunities for independent contractors along with articles and advice.

★11764★ Ittalent.com
E-mail: ewsmith@ITtalent.com
URL: http://www.ittalent.com
Description: Job search and resume submission service for professionals in information technology.

★11765★ ZDNet Tech Jobs
URL: http://www.zdnet.com/special/filters/techjobs/

Description: Site houses a listing of national employment opportunities for professionals in high tech fields. Also contains resume building tips and relocation resources. Powered by Dice.com

---

OTHER SOURCES

★11766★ Computer Occupations
Delphi Productions
3160 4th St.
Boulder, CO 80304
Fax: (303)443-4022   Fr: 888-443-2400
URL: http://www.delphivideo.com

$95.00. 50 minutes. Part of the Careers for the 21st Century Video Library.

★11767★ Internet Careers: College Not Required
Cambridge Educational
2572 Brunswick Ave.
Lawrenceville, NJ 08648-4128
Fax: 800-FAX-ON-US   Fr: 800-468-4227
URL: http://www.cambridgeeducational.com

Video. 1998. $79.95. 28 minutes. Covers careers and job opportunities related to developing, programming, and managing Internet sites.

★11768★ Internet-Related Occupations
Delphi Productions
3160 4th St.
Boulder, CO 80304
Fax: (303)443-4022   Fr: 888-443-2400
URL: http://www.delphi.video.com

$95.00. 47 minutes. Part of the Emerging Careers Video Library.

Wedding Consultants

SOURCES OF HELP-WANTED ADS

★11769★ Special Events

Miramar Communications Inc.
23805 Stuart Ranch Rd., Ste. 235
PO Box 8987
Malibu, CA 90265-8987
Ph: (310)317-4522   Fax: (310)317-0264
Fr: 800-543-4116
URL: http://www.specialevents.com

Monthly. Free to qualified subscribers. Magazine for special event professionals.

EMPLOYER DIRECTORIES AND NETWORKING LISTS

★11770★ National Bridal & Gift Registry Directory

National Tabletop & Giftware Association
355 Lexington Ave., 17th Fl.
New York, NY 10017
Ph: (212)661-4261   Fax: (212)370-9047

Annual, January. $50.00. Covers approximately 120 retail and specialty stores with bridal gift registry services in the U.S. Entries include: Store name, address, phone, names and titles of key personnel. Arrangement: Alphabetical. Indexes: Geographical.

★11771★ Wedding Announcements & Invitations Directory

infoUSA Inc.
5711 S 86th Cir.
Omaha, NE 68127-0347
Ph: (402)930-3500   Fax: (402)331-0176
Fr: 800-555-6124
URL: http://www.abii.com

Updated continuously; printed on request. Number of listings: 1,585. Entries include: Name, address, phone (including area code), size of advertisement, year first in "Yellow Pages," name of owner or manager, number of employees. Compiled from tele-

phone company "Yellow Pages," nationwide. Arrangement: Geographical.

★11772★ Wedding Consultants/ Planning/Arranging Directory

infoUSA Inc.
5711 S 86th Cir.
Omaha, NE 68127-0347
Ph: (402)930-3500   Fax: (402)331-0176
Fr: 800-555-6124
URL: http://www.abii.com

Annual. Number of listings: 6,167. Entries include: Name, address, phone (including area code), size of advertisement, year first in "Yellow Pages," name of owner or manager, number of employees. Compiled from telephone company "Yellow Pages," nationwide. Arrangement: Geographical.

HANDBOOKS AND MANUALS

★11773★ The Best Home-Based Businesses for the 90s

Putnam Publishing Group
375 Hudson St.
New York, NY 10014
Ph: (212)366-2000   Fax: (212)366-2643
Fr: 800-331-4624

Paul Edwards and Sarah Edwards. Second edition, 1991. $11.95 (paper). 272 pages. Profiles 95 businesses and careers that can be conducted from one's home. Lists sources of additional information. Out of print.

★11774★ Business of Wedding Photography

Watson-Guptill Publications, Inc.
770 Broadway
New York, NY 10003
Ph: (646)654-5400   Fax: (646)654-5486
Fr: 800-323-9432

Ann Monteith. 1996. $35.00 (paper). 192 pages. Subtitled, "A Professional's Guide to Marketing and Managing a Successful Stu-

dio With Profiles of 30 Top Portrait Photographers."

★11775★ FabJob Guide to Become a Wedding Planner

Fabjob
4603 NE University Village, No. 224
Seattle, WA 98105
Ph: (403)949-4980

2003. $39.95. 224 pages. Provides a step-by-step guide on how to plan a wedding. Includes advice for planning the wedding ceremony and reception, and how to chose reputable vendors (e.g. bridal shop, caterer, florist, limousine company, photographer, stationer, etc.)

★11776★ How to Start a Home-Based Event Planning Business

Globe Pequot Press
246 Goose Lane
Guilford, CT 06437
Ph: 888-249-7586   Fr: 800-820-2329
URL: http://www.globepequot.com

Jill Moran. 2004. $12.57. 197 pages. This insider's handbook reveals how to start a successful business planning a wide variety of events from home.

★11777★ The National Business Employment Weekly Jobs Rated Almanac

John Wiley & Sons Inc.
1 Wiley Dr.
Somerset, NJ 08873
Ph: (732)469-4400   Fr: 800-225-5945

Les Krantz. First edition, 1995. $16.95. 340 pages. Ranks 250 jobs by environment, salary, outlook, physical demands, stress, security, travel opportunities, and geographic location.

★11778★ Planning a Wedding to Remember

Wilshire Publications
12021 Wilshire Blvd., Ste. 208
Los Angeles, CA 90025
Beverly Clark. Fifth edition, 1999. $18.95 (paper). 248 pages.

★11779★ Small Business Profiles

Thomson Gale
27500 Drake Rd.
Farmington Hills, MI 48331-3535
Ph: (248)699-GALE   Fax: (248)699-8069
Fr: 800-877-GALE
E-mail: galeord@gale.com
URL: http://www.galegroup.com

Third edition, 1998. $95.00. Publication cancelled.

★11780★ Start Your Own Wedding Consulting Business: Your Step-By-Step Guide to Success

McGraw-Hill Trade
2 Penn Plaza
New York, NY 10121
Ph: (212)904-2000   Fr: 800-722-4726

Eileen Figure Sandlin. 2003. $10.47. 180 pages. Provides information for someone who is starting their wedding consulting business.

ONLINE JOB SOURCES AND SERVICES

★11781★ Coordinators' Corner
URL: http://www.coordinatorscorner.com

Description: Offers access to articles on managing a wedding consultant business. Provides information from the industry's top experts.

OTHER SOURCES

★11782★ American Society of Wedding Professionals (ASWP)

268 Griggs Ave.
Teaneck, NJ 07666
Ph: (973)472-1800   Fax: (201)836-8895
Fr: 800-526-0497
E-mail: lawrence@carroll.com
URL: http://www.sellthebride.com

Members: Professionals in the wedding industry. **Purpose:** Promotes the wedding professional and educates brides on the experience of working with a consultant. **Activities:** Provides trends, etiquette, marketing, consulting information, directory listing, referrals, networking, and co-op advertising. Offers local forums for information exchange among members. Compiles statistics and conducts educational programs and seminars.

★11783★ Association of Bridal Consultants (ABC)

200 Chestnutland Rd.
New Milford, CT 06776-2521
Ph: (860)355-0464   Fax: (860)354-1404
E-mail: office@bridalassn.com
URL: http://www.bridalassn.com

Members: Independent bridal and wedding consultants; persons employed by companies in wedding-related businesses and novices looking to get into the business. **Purpose:** Strives to improve professionalism and recognition of bridal and wedding consultants. **Activities:** Offers professional development program, start-up manual and seminars. Provides advertising, publicity, referrals, and information services. Operates speakers' bureau; compiles statistics.

★11784★ Association of Certified Professional Wedding Consultants

7791 Prestwick Cir.
San Jose, CA 95135
URL: http://www.acpwc.com

Description: Professional society. Offers personalized training courses.

★11785★ Association of Wedding Professionals

PO Box 600468
Dallas, TX 75360
URL: http://www.awpdallas.com

Description: Dedicated to helping its members grow through networking opportunities, education programs, and special event showcases.

★11786★ Association for Wedding Professionals International

6700 Freeport Blvd., Ste. 282
Sacramento, CA 95822
URL: http://www.afwpi.com

Description: Acts as a central source of information and referrals.

★11787★ Bridal Association of America

531 H St.
Bakersfield, CA 93304
Ph: (661)633-1949
URL: http://www.bridalassociationofamerica.com

Description: Acts as a forum for wedding professionals.

★11788★ Wedding and Portrait Photographers International (WPPI)

1312 Lincoln Blvd.
PO Box 2003
Santa Monica, CA 90406-2003
Ph: (310)451-0090   Fax: (310)395-9058
URL: http://www.wppinow.com/index2.tml

Description: Wedding portrait and digital photographers and photographers employed at general photography studios. Promotes high artistic and technical standards in wedding photography. Serves as a forum for the exchange of technical knowledge and experience; makes available the expertise of top professionals in the field of photographic arts and technology, advertising, sales promotion, marketing, public relations, accounting, business management, tax, and profit planning. Members are offered the opportunity to purchase special products and services.

Wholesale and Retail Buyers

★11789★ Aftermarket Business

Advanstar Communications Inc.
7500 Old Oak Blvd.
Cleveland, OH 44130-3369
Ph: (440)243-8100   Fax: (440)891-2777
URL: http://https://www.advanstar.com/index_allpubs.html

Magazine (tabloid) for purchasing professionals in the retail automotive aftermarket.

★11790★ AudioVideo International

AudioVideo International
275 Madison Ave.
New York, NY 10016
Ph: (212)682-3755   Fax: (212)682-2730
E-mail: avi@dempa-us.com

Monthly. $40.00/year; $4.00 for single issue. Magazine for domestic retailers of consumer electronics products. Feature stories include trends and developments in audio, hi-fi, TV, video, car stereo, and home and personal electronics products.

★11791★ Benchmarking Purchasing

American Purchasing Society
8 E Galena Blvd., Ste. 203
Aurora, IL 60506-5035
Ph: (630)859-0250   Fax: (630)859-0270

Annual. Professional journal covering issues in purchasing.

★11792★ Chain Store Age

Lebhar-Friedman Inc.
425 Park Ave.
New York, NY 10022-3556
Ph: (212)756-5088   Fax: (212)756-5120
Fr: 800-453-2427
URL: http://www.chainstoreage.com

Monthly. $79.00/year for individuals. Magazine for management of retail chain headquarters. Reports on marketing, merchandising, strategic planning, physical supports, and shopping center developments, retail technology credit and communications.

★11793★ Children's Business

Fairchild Publications Inc.
7 W 34th St.
New York, NY 10001
Ph: (212)630-4000

Monthly. Magazine serving retailers, wholesalers, and manufacturers in the children's apparel, furniture and footwear markets.

★11794★ Daily News Record

Fairchild Publications Inc.
7 W 34th St.
New York, NY 10001
Ph: (212)630-4000
URL: http://www.dailynewsrecord.com

Dail. $62.00/year; $1.50 for single issue, Monday; $1.00 for single issue, Tuesday-Friday; $140.00/year for Canada and Mexico; $250.00/year for other countries. Daily newspaper reporting on men's and boys' clothing, retailing, and textiles.

★11795★ Discount Store News

Lebhar-Friedman Inc.
425 Park Ave.
New York, NY 10022-3556
Ph: (212)756-5088   Fax: (212)756-5120
Fr: 800-453-2427
E-mail: lliebeck@lf.com
URL: http://www.discountstorenews.com

Semimonthly. $99.00/year.

★11796★ Earnshaw's Review

Earnshaw Publications Inc.
112 W 34th St. Ste. 1515
New York, NY 10120
Ph: (212)563-2742   Fax: (212)629-3249

Monthly. $24.00/year. Fashion and business magazine for retailers, manufacturers, licensees, and fiber companies in the children's apparel industry.

★11797★ EBN

CMP Media L.L.C.
600 Community Dr.
Manhasset, NY 11030
Ph: (516)562-5000
E-mail: brayner@cmp.com
URL: http://www.mfi.com

Weekly. $89.00/year; free to qualified subscribers. Reports business and technology trends of the electronics industry.

★11798★ Electronic Business

Reed Business Information
275 Washington St.
Newton, MA 02458
Ph: (617)558-4900   Fax: (617)630-3830
Fr: 800-357-4745
URL: http://www.eb-mag.com

Monthly. Free to qualified readers; $83.90/year, nonqualified; $115.90/year for Canada; $104.90/year for Mexico. Magazine for purchasing managers and buyers of electronic components and materials used in end product manufacture.

★11799★ Gifts & Decorative Accessories

Reed Business Information
360 Park Ave. S
New York, NY 10010
Ph: (646)746-7395   Fax: (646)746-7434
URL: http://www.giftsanddec.com

Monthly. $42.00/year for individuals. International magazine for retailers of gifts, greeting cards, decorative accessories, and stationery-related merchandise.

★11800★ LDB Interior Textiles

E.W. Williams Publications
2125 Center Ave., Ste. 305
Fort Lee, NJ 07024
Ph: (201)592-7007   Fax: (201)592-7171

Monthly. $72.00/year for individuals; $115.00/year for other countries; $7.00 for single issue; $125.00/year for Canada; $150.00/year for elsewhere. Magazine for buyers of home fashions, including bed, bath and table linens, hard and soft window treatments, home fragrances, decorative pillows and home accessories, accent rugs, and decorative fabrics.

★11801★ **Music Inc.**
Maher Publications Inc.
102 N Haven Rd.
Elmhurst, IL 60126
Ph: (630)941-2030   Fax: (630)941-3210
Fr: 800-535-7496
E-mail: musicincupbeat@worldnet.att.net

$16.50/year for individuals. Magazine serving retailers of music and sound products.

★11802★ **Music Trades**
Music Trades Corp.
80 W St.
Englewood, NJ 07631
Ph: (201)871-1965   Fax: (201)871-0455
Fr: 800-423-6530

Monthly. $12.00/year; $3.00 for single issue. Music trade magazine.

★11803★ **National Home Center News**
Lebhar-Friedman Inc.
425 Park Ave.
New York, NY 10022-3556
Ph: (212)756-5088   Fax: (212)756-5120
Fr: 800-453-2427
URL: http://www.homecenternews.com

$99.00/year for individuals; $119.00/year for Canada; $279.00/year for other countries. Business tabloid serving home center/building material retailers.

★11804★ **National Jeweler**
VNU Business Media
770 Broadway
New York, NY 10003-9595
Ph: (646)654-5000
E-mail: jwynn@mfi.com
URL: http://www.national-jeweler/com

Biweekly. $45.00/year for one year; $71.00 for two years. Jewelry industry magazine.

★11805★ **Purchasing Magazine**
Reed Business Information
275 Washington St.
Newton, MA 02458-1630
Ph: (617)964-3030
URL: http://www.purchasing.com

Semimonthly. $99.00/year. Magazine for buying professionals.

★11806★ **Small World**
Earnshaw Publications Inc.
112 W 34th St. Ste. 1515
New York, NY 10120
Ph: (212)563-2742   Fax: (212)629-3249

Monthly. $18.00/year. Product and business magazine for retailers and manufacturers of juvenile products.

★11807★ **Southern PHC Magazine**
Southern Trade Publications Inc.
Box 7344
Greensboro, NC 27417
Ph: (336)454-3516   Fax: (336)454-3649

Bimonthly. Free to qualified subscribers; $10.00/year for others. Trade magazine covering plumbing, heating, and air conditioning, targeted to contractors and wholesalers in 14 southern states.

★11808★ **Sporting Goods Dealer**
Bill Communications Inc.
1115 Northmeadow Pkwy.
Roswell, GA 30076
Ph: (770)569-5105   Fax: (770)569-5105
Fr: 800-241-9034
URL: http://www.sgdealer.com

Monthly. Free to qualified subscribers; $100.00/year; $6.00/year for single issue. Magazine which offers expert reporting on trends affecting team dealers and ret ailers who service schools, colleges, pro and local teams.

★11809★ **Tire Business**
Crain Communications Inc.
1725 Merriman Rd.
Akron, OH 44313-5283
Ph: (330)836-9180   Fax: (330)836-2365

Semimonthly. $57.00/year for individuals; $104.00 for two years. Newspaper (tabloid) serving independent tire dealers, retreaders, tire wholesalers and others allied to the tire industry.

★11810★ **Tire Review**
Babcox
3550 Embassy Pkwy.
Akron, OH 44333-8318
Ph: (330)670-1234   Fax: (330)670-0874
E-mail: dmoniz@babcox.com
URL: http://www.tirereview.com

Monthly. Free to qualified subscribers; $64.00/year for U.S.; $109.00 for two years, U.S.; $84.00/year for Canada and Mexico; $143.00 for two years, Canada and Mexico; $124.00/year for other countries; $211.00 for two years, other countries; $10.00 for single issue, U.S.; $15.00/year for single issue, other countries. Magazine containing news and business information about the tire, custom wheel, automotive service, and retreading industries.

★11811★ **TWICE**
Reed Business Information
360 Park Ave. S
New York, NY 10010
Ph: (646)746-6400   Fax: (646)746-6734
E-mail: ssmith@cahners.com
URL: http://www.twice.com

Semiweekly. $35.00/year; $150.00/year for Canada; $200.00/year for other countries. Trade tabloid covering consumer electronics, appliance, and camera industries for retailers, manufacturers, and distributors.

EMPLOYER DIRECTORIES AND NETWORKING LISTS

★11812★ **Directory of Department Stores**
Chain Store Guide
3922 Coconut Palm Dr.
Tampa, FL 33619
Ph: (813)627-6800   Fax: (813)627-6882
Fr: 800-927-9292
URL: http://www.csgis.com

Annual, October. $327.00. Covers 214 department store companies, 1,500 shoe store companies, 200 jewelry store companies, 95 optical store companies, and 70 leather and luggage store companies in the United States and Canada, with annual sales of at least $250,000. Entries include: Company name; physical and mailing addresses; phone and fax numbers, company e-mail and web addresses; listing type; total sales; industry sales; total selling square footage; store prototype sizes; total units; units by trade name; trading areas; projected openings and remodelings; self-distributing indicator; distribution center locations; resident buyers' name and location; leased departments area, name, and location; mail order catalog indicator; Internet order processing indicator; private label softlines, hardlines, and credit card indicators; furniture styles and price lines; average number of checkouts; year founded; public company indicator; parent company name and loction; subsidiaries' names and locations; regional and divisional office locations; key personnel with titles; store locations, with address, phone number, and manager name (department stores only). Arrangement: Geographical. Indexes: Alphabetical, product lines, exclusions.

★11813★ **Directory of Drug Store & HBC Chains**
Chain Store Guide
3922 Coconut Palm Dr.
Tampa, FL 33619
Ph: (813)627-6800   Fax: (813)627-6882
Fr: 800-927-9292
URL: http://www.csgis.com

Annual, May. $335.00. Covers 1,600 drug store chains operation two or more units, including mass merchants and grocers with pharmacies; 215 wholesale drug companies in the United States and Canada. Entries include: For retailers-company name; phone and fax numbers; physical and mailing addresses; company e-mail and web addresses; listing type; number of stores; product lines; percentage of sales by product line; total sales; prescription drug sales; percentage of prescriptions filled with generic drugs; number of prescriptions filled daily; percentage of prescriptions filled with private third party, cash, and Medicaid; number of stores by type; mail order pharmacy indicator; managed care division indicator; projected openings and remodelings; store prototype sizes; total selling square footage; trading area; franchise group headquarter's name and location; distribution center and primary wholesaler names and locations; number of specialty departments; packaged liquor indicators; private label indicators; computerized pharmacy indicator; average number of checkouts; year founded; public company indicator; parent company name and location; regional and divisional office locations; headquarters personnel with titles. For wholesalers-company name, address, phone, and fax; e-mail and web addresses; listing type; product lines; percentage of sales by product line; total sales; percentage of sales by customer type; total stores served; number of member and non-member stores served; trading area; group store trading names; wholesaler type; distribution center locations; private label indicator; year founded; public company indicator; headquarters personnel with titles. Arrangement: Separate geographical sections for retailers and wholesalers. Indexes: Alphabetical, exclusions.

★11814★ **Discount Store News-Top Chains Issue**
Chain Store Guides Inc.
425 Park Ave.
New York, NY 10022
Ph: (212)756-5000

Annual, July. $79.00. Entries include: Chain name, location, sales and earnings for the past two years, number of stores, net store square footage. Arrangement: Ranked by sales volume.

★11815★ **STORES-Top 100 Retailers Issue**
National Retail Federation
325 7th St. NW, Ste. 1100
Washington, DC 20004
Ph: (202)783-7971   Fax: (202)737-2849
Fr: 800-673-4692
URL: http://www.stores.org

Annual, July. $75.00. Publication includes: 100 U.S. retail companies having largest estimated sales during preceding year. Entries include: Name of store, city, number of stores included, and total sales. Arrangement: Ranked by sales.

★11816★ **Variety Stores Directory**
infoUSA Inc.
5711 S 86th Cir.
Omaha, NE 68127-0347
Ph: (402)930-3500   Fax: (402)331-0176
Fr: 800-555-6124
URL: http://www.abii.com

Annual. Number of listings: 12,400. Entries include: Name, address, phone (including area code), size of advertisement, year first in "Yellow Pages," name of owner or manager, number of employees. Compiled from telephone company "Yellow Pages," nationwide. Arrangement: Geographical.

★11817★ **The Wholesaler-'The Wholesaling 100' Issue**
TMB Publishing Inc.
1838 Techny Ct.
Northbrook, IL 60062
Ph: (847)564-1127   Fax: (847)564-1264
URL: http://www.technotribe.net/clients/tmb/production/tw_res.htm

Annual, July. $50.00. Publication includes: Ranks 100 leading wholesalers of plumbing, heating, air conditioning, refrigeration equipment, and industrial pipe, valves and fittings. Entries include: Company name, address, phone, fax, names and titles of key personnel, number of employees, business breakdown (percentage). Arrangement: Ranked by sales.

HANDBOOKS AND MANUALS

★11818★ **Opportunities in Fashion Careers**
McGraw-Hill Trade
2 Penn Plaza
New York, NY 10121
Ph: (212)904-2000   Fr: 800-722-4726

Roslyn Dolber. 1994. $14.95; $11.95 (paper). 160 pages. Covers job opportunities in the textile industry, design and manufacturing, apparel production, and fashion merchandising, and how to pursue them. Illustrated.

★11819★ **Opportunities in Retailing Careers**
McGraw-Hill Companies
1221 Avenue of the Americas
New York, NY 10020
Ph: (212)904-2000   Fr: 800-323-4900
E-mail: ntcpub@tribune.com

Roslyn Dolber. 1996. 160 pages. $14.95; $11.95 (paper). Discusses a number of opportunities in retailing, from entry-level to retail management.

★11820★ **Resumes for Sales and Marketing Careers**
McGraw-Hill Professional
2 Penn Plaza
New York, NY 10121
Ph: (212)904-2000   Fr: 800-722-4726
E-mail: ntcpub@tribune.com

Chuck Cochran and Donna Peerce. Second edition, 1998. $10.95 (paper). 336 pages. Sample resumes and cover letters from all levels of the sales and marketing field.

EMPLOYMENT AGENCIES AND SEARCH FIRMS

★11821★ **The Aspire Group**
52 Second Ave, 1st Fl
Waltham, MA 02451-1129
Fax: (718)890-1810   Fr: 800-546-5675
URL: http://www.bmanet.com

Employment agency.

★11822★ **Britt Associates Inc.**
3533 Lake Shore Dr.
Joliet, IL 60431-8820
Ph: (815)436-8300   Fax: (815)436-9617
E-mail: brittassoc@aol.com

Employment agency.

★11823★ **Colli Associates**
404 Caboose Ln.
Valrico, FL 33594
Ph: (813)681-2145   Fax: (813)661-5217
E-mail: colli@gte.net

Employment agency. Executive search firm.

TRADESHOWS

★11824★ **Great Lakes Industrial Show**
North American Exposition Co.
33 Rutherford Ave.
Charlestown, MA 02129
Ph: (617)242-6092   Fax: (617)242-1817
Fr: 800-225-1577
E-mail: naexpo@hotmail.com

Annual. **Primary Exhibits:** Industrial products, machine tools, hand tools, pneumatics, hydraulics, plant engineering, and maintenance, paper and packaging, plastics, rubber products, material handling equipment, and dies and stampings.

★11825★ **The NAMSB Show**
NSI
309 5th Ave., Ste. 303
New York, NY 10016-6509
Ph: (212)685-4550   Fax: (212)685-4688
Fr: 800-936-2672
E-mail: info@nsi-shows.com
URL: http://www.nsi-shows.com

Semiannual. **Primary Exhibits:** Product lines include mens' and boy's clothing, sportswear, footwear, streetwear, unisex, and accessories.

★11826★ **Supermarket Industry Convention and Educational Exposition**
Food Marketing Institute
655 15th St., NW
Washington, DC 20005
Ph: (202)452-8444   Fax: (202)429-4519

E-mail: fmi@fmi.org
URL: http://www.fmi.org

Annual. **Primary Exhibits:** Products, equipment, supplies, and services available to and through the supermarket industry, including grocery products, perishables, general merchandise, health and beauty aids, food service equipment, store design services, data processing equipment, advertising, and warehouse services. **Dates and Locations:** 2005 May 01-03; Chicago, IL.

OTHER SOURCES

★11827★ **National Association of College Stores (NACS)**
500 E Lorain St.
Oberlin, OH 44074
Ph: (440)775-7777   Fax: (440)775-4769
Fr: 800-622-7498

E-mail: membership@nacs.org
URL: http://www.nacs.org

Members: Institutional, private, leased, and cooperative college stores (2800) selling books, supplies, and other merchandise to college students, faculty, and staff; associate members include publishers and suppliers (1200). **Purpose:** Seeks to effectively serve higher education by providing educational research, advocacy and other to college stores and their suppliers. **Activities:** Maintains NACSCORP, Inc., a wholly owned subsidiary corporation, which distributes trade and mass market books and educational software. Sponsors seminars. Conducts manager certification, specialized education, and research programs. Maintains College Stores Research and Educational Foundation which provides grants for NACS educational programs and conducts research.

★11828★ **National Retail Federation (NRF)**
325 7th St. NW, Ste. 1100
Washington, DC 20004
Ph: (202)783-7971   Fax: (202)737-2849
Fr: 800-NRF-HOW2
E-mail: mullint@nrf.com
URL: http://www.nrf.com

Purpose: Represents 50 state retail association, several dozen national retail associations as well as large and small corporate members representing the breadth and diversity of the retail industry's establishment and employees. **Activities:** Conducts informational and educational conferences related to all phases of retailing including financial planning and cash management, taxation, economic forecasting, expense planning, shortage control, credit, electronic data processing, telecommunications, merchandise management, buying, traffic, security, supply, materials handling, store planning and construction, personnel administration, recruitment and training, and advertising and display.

Writers and Editors

SOURCES OF HELP-WANTED ADS

★11829★ Adweek
VNU Business Media USA
770 Broadway
New York, NY 10003
Ph: (646)654-5000
E-mail: info@adweek.com
URL: http://www.adweek.com

Weekly. $149.00/year for individuals; $3.95 for single issue. Advertising news magazine.

★11830★ Columbia Journalism Review
Columbia Journalism Review
2950 Broadway, Journalism Bldg.
Columbia University
New York, NY 10027
Ph: (212)854-1881   Fax: (212)854-8580
E-mail: cjr@columbia.edu
URL: http://www.cjr.org

Bimonthly. $18.00/year; $4.95 for single issue. Magazine focusing on journalism.

★11831★ Daily Variety
Reed Business Information
5700 Wilshire Blvd., Ste. 120
Los Angeles, CA 90036
Ph: (323)857-6600   Fax: (323)965-2475

Daily. Global entertainment newspaper (tabloid).

★11832★ Directory Marketplace
Todd Publications
PO Box 635
Nyack, NY 10960
Ph: (845)358-6213   Fax: (845)358-6213
Fr: (866)896-0916
URL: http://www.toddpublications.com

Description: Quarterly. Serves as a means for directory and reference book publishers to advertise their publications. Listings for more than 300 directories & reference books for sale.

★11833★ Editor & Publisher
Editor & Publisher Magazine
770 Broadway
New York, NY 10003-9595
Fax: (646)654-5360   Fr: 800-336-4380
URL: http://www.editorandpublisher.com

Weekly. $99.00/year for U.S. and Canada, includes exclusive web access; $130.00/year for other countries; $4.00 for single issue. Magazine focusing on newspaper journalism, advertising, printing equipment, and interactive services.

★11834★ Food Writer
Page One
21 W Spring Ave.
Ardmore, PA 19003
Ph: (610)896-2879
E-mail: foodwriter@aol.com
URL: http://www.booklocker.com

Description: Monthly. Provides ideas, media contracts, and marketing listings to individuals who write about food. Recurring features include letters to the editor, interviews, news of educational opportunities, book reviews, job listings, notices of publications available, and columns titled Food Trends, and Self-Publishing. Available online only.

★11835★ History News
American Association for State & Local History
1717 Church St.
Nashville, TN 37203-2991
Ph: (615)320-3203   Fax: (615)327-9013
URL: http://www.aaslh.org

Quarterly. $50.00/year, includes membership; $75.00/year for institutions, includes membership. Magazine for employees of historic sites, museums, and public history agencies. Coverage includes museum education programs and techniques for working with volunteers.

★11836★ HOW
F & W Publications Inc.
4700 E Galbraith Rd.
Cincinnati, OH 45236-6708
Ph: (513)531-2690   Fax: (513)531-2902
Fr: 800-289-0963
E-mail: editorial@howdesign.com

Bimonthly. $49.00/year for individuals; $7.95 for single issue, Jan/Feb or May/June; $9.95 for single issue, Mar/April or July/Aug; $11.95/year for single issue, Sept/Oct or Nov/Dec. Instructional trade magazine.

★11837★ Independent Publisher Online
Jenkins Group Inc.
400 W Front St., No. 4A
Traverse City, MI 49684-2206
Ph: (231)933-0445   Fax: (231)933-0448

Monthly. Free. Online magazine containing book reviews and articles about independent publishing.

★11838★ Metro Magazine
Bobit Publishing
21061 S Western Ave.
Torrance, CA 90501
Ph: (310)533-2400   Fax: (310)533-2500
E-mail: info@metro-magazine.com
URL: http://www.metro-magazine.com

$40.00/year; $6.00 for single issue; $60.00/year for Canada. Magazine on public transportation.

★11839★ The New Republic
The New Republic L.L.C.
1331 H St. NW, Ste. 700
Washington, DC 20005
Ph: (202)508-4444   Fax: (202)331-0275
E-mail: tnrcustserv@cdsfulfillment.com
URL: http://www.tnr.com

Monthly. $19.95/year for individuals. Journal featuring current events comments and reviews.

★11840★ **PR Marcom Jobs East**
Rachel P.R. Services
208 E 51st St., No. 1600
New York, NY 10022
Description: Biweekly. Provides news of job openings in public relations, marketing, journalism, communications, public relations agencies and corporations, and freelance and temporary writing positions. Focuses on the New York City, Washington, D.C., Boston, and surrounding states. Recurring features include a calendar of events, job listings, book reviews, and notices of publications available.

★11841★ **Producers Masterguide**
Producers Masterguide
60 E 8th St., 34th Fl.
New York, NY 10003-6514
Ph: (212)777-4002   Fax: (212)777-4101
URL: http://
www.producers.masterguide.com

Annual. $145.00/year for U.S.; $155.00/year for Canada; $175.00/year for other countries. An international film and TV production directory and guide for the professional motion picture, broadcast television, feature film, TV commercial, cable/satellite, digital and videotape industries in the U.S., Canada, the UK, the Caribbean Islands, Mexico, Australia, New Zealand, Europe, Israel, Morocco, the Far East, and South America.

★11842★ **Publishers Weekly**
Publishers Weekly
360 Park Ave. S
New York, NY 10010
Ph: (646)746-6758   Fax: (646)746-6631
Fr: (866)436-0727
URL: http://http://www.bookwire.com

Weekly. $215.80/year for individuals. Weekly trade news magazine.

★11843★ **Sojourners**
Sojourners
2401 15th St. NW
Washington, DC 20009
Ph: (202)328-8842   Fax: (202)328-8757
Fr: 800-714-7474
URL: http://www.sojo.net

Bimonthly. $4.95 for single issue; $30.00/year. Independent, ecumenical Christian magazine which analyzes faith, politics, and culture from a progressive, justice-oriented perspective.

★11844★ **Tech Comments**
Society for Technical Communication, Southeastern Michigan Chapter
PO Box 1289
Ann Arbor, MI 48106
URL: http://www.stc.org/region4/smc
Description: Monthly. Keeps chapter members informed of events and shares information about the work of technical communicators. Recurring features include letters to the editor, a calendar of events, reports of meetings, news of educational opportunities,

job listings, book reviews, notices of publications available, and messages from chapter president and regional director.

★11845★ **The Writer Magazine**
Kalmbach Publishing Co.
PO Box 1612
Waukesha, WI 53187-1612
Ph: (262)796-8776   Fax: (262)796-1615
Fr: 800-533-6644
URL: http://www.writermag.com

Monthly. $29.00/year for individuals; $39.00/year for other countries; $4.95 for single issue. Magazine for freelance writers. Publishing practical information and advice on how to write publishable material and where to sell it.

★11846★ **Writer's Digest**
F & W Publications Inc.
4700 E Galbraith Rd.
Cincinnati, OH 45236-6708
Ph: (513)531-2690   Fax: (513)531-2902
Fr: 800-289-0963
E-mail: writersdig@fwpubs.com
URL: http://www.writersdigest.com

Monthly. $27.00/year for individuals; $3.49 for single issue. Professional magazine for writers.

★11847★ **Writing World**
Fern Reiss
44 Tarleton Rd.
Newton Center, MA 02459
Description: Bimonthly. Gives "the juiciest tidbits of interest to writers," such as free publications and products, and offers basic information on finding an agent, book proposals, and query letters. Profiles other writing organizations and each issues spotlights a special genre. Recurring features include letters to the editor, interviews, news of educational opportunities, job listings, book reviews, and notices of publications available.

PLACEMENT AND JOB REFERRAL SERVICES

★11848★ **Associated Writing Programs (AWP)**
George Mason University
Carty House, Mail Stop 1E3
Fairfax, VA 22030
Ph: (703)993-4301
E-mail: awp@gmu.edu
URL: http://www.awpwriter.org

Description: Writers; students and teachers in creative writing programs in university departments of English; editors, publishers, and freelance creative and professional writers. Fosters literary talent and achievement; advocates the craft of writing as primary to a liberal and humane education; provides pub-

lications and services to the makers and readers of contemporary literature. Operates career services and job listings; sponsors literary competitions.

★11849★ **Catholic Press Association (CPA)**
3555 Veterans Memorial Hwy., Unit 0
Ronkonkoma, NY 11779
Ph: (631)471-4730   Fax: (631)471-4804
E-mail: rosep@catholicpress.org
URL: http://www.catholicpress.org

Description: Publishers of Catholic newspapers, magazines, pamphlets, and books; Catholic writers, illustrators, and teachers. Sponsors research and specialized education programs. Maintains placement service. Maintains 25 committees, including Freedom of Information, News Service Liaison, and Research.

★11850★ **Education Writers Association (EWA)**
2122 P St. NW, No. 201
Washington, DC 20037
Ph: (202)452-9830   Fax: (202)452-9837
E-mail: ewa@ewa.org
URL: http://www.ewa.org/

Members: Education writers and reporters of daily and weekly newspapers, national magazines of general circulation, and radio and television stations; associate members are school and college public relations personnel and others with a serious interest in education writing. **Purpose:** Improves the quality of education reporting and interpretation; encourages the development of education coverage by the press; to help attract top-notch writers and reporters to the education field. **Activities:** Sponsors regional and special workshops. Provides job referral/bank services.

★11851★ **Health Sciences Communications Association (HESCA)**
39 Wedgewood Dr., Ste. A
Jewett City, CT 06351
Ph: (860)376-5915   Fax: (860)376-6621
E-mail: hesca@hesca.org
URL: http://www.hesca.org/

Description: Media managers, graphic artists, biomedical librarians, producers, faculty members of health science and veterinary medicine schools, health professional organizations, and industry representatives. Acts as a clearinghouse for information used by professionals engaged in health science communications. Coordinates Media Festivals Program which recognizes outstanding media productions in the health sciences. Offers placement service.

★11852★ **National Association of Hispanic Journalists (NAHJ)**
1000 National Press Bldg.
Washington, DC 20045-2100
Ph: (202)662-7145   Fax: (202)662-7144
Fr: 888-346-NAHJ
E-mail: nahj@nahj.org

URL: http://www.nahj.org

Description: Purpose is to organize and support Hispanics involved in news gathering and dissemination. Encourages journalism and communications study and practice by Hispanics. Seeks recognition for Hispanic members of the profession regarding their skills and achievements. Promotes fair and accurate media treatment of Hispanics; opposes job discrimination and demeaning stereotypes. Works to increase educational and career opportunities and development for Hispanics in the field. Seeks to foster greater awareness of members' cultural identity, interests, and concerns. Provides a united voice for Hispanic journalists with the aim of achieving national visibility. Offers placement services to Hispanic students. Activities include: a census of Hispanic media professionals nationwide; writing contest for Hispanic students. Bestows National Hispanic Journalist Award; offers scholarships, seminars, and training workshops

EMPLOYER DIRECTORIES AND NETWORKING LISTS

★11853★ American Society of Journalists and Authors-Directory

American Society of Journalists & Authors
1501 Broadway, Ste. 302
New York, NY 10036
Ph: (212)997-0947   Fax: (212)768-7414
URL: http://www.asja.org

Annual, January. $98.00. Covers 1,050 member freelance nonfiction writers. Entries include: Writer's name, home and office addresses and phone numbers, specialties, areas of expertise; name, address and phone of agent; memberships; books; periodicals to which contributed; awards. Arrangement: Alphabetical. Indexes: Subject specialty, type of material written, geographical.

★11854★ ANR National Directory of Community Newspapers

American Newspaper Representatives Inc.
2075 W Big Beaver Rd., Ste. 310
Troy, MI 48084-3439
Ph: (248)643-7766   Fax: (248)643-0606
Fr: 800-550-7557
URL: http://www.anrinc.net/

Annual, May/June. $125.00. Number of listings: 7,000. Entries include: Name of weekly newspaper, address, county, type of area, circulation, day published, name of publisher, and information on advertising rates and production specifications. Arrangement: Geographical.

★11855★ Association of American University Presses-Directory

Association of American University Presses
71 W 23rd St., Ste. 901
New York, NY 10010-4102
Ph: (212)989-1010   Fax: (212)989-0275

Annual, November. $18.00; $23.00 postpaid. Covers 124 presses and affiliates worldwide. Entries include: Press name, address, phone, e-mail, URL; titles and names of complete editorial and managerial staffs; editorial program; mailing, warehouse, printing, and/or customer service addresses; other details. Arrangement: Classified by press affiliation, alphabetical by press name. Indexes: Personal name.

★11856★ Association of Professional Communication Consultants-Membership Directory

Association of Professional Communication Consultants
c/o Reva Daniel
Dynamic Business Writing
104 Trace Ridge
Clinton, MS 39056-6153
Ph: (601)924-2173   Fax: (601)925-4414
E-mail: revadaniel@aol.com

Annual. $100.00. Covers 200 members. Entries include: Company or individual name, address, phone, areas of consulting expertise, services. Arrangement: Geographical and alphabetical.

★11857★ Burrelle's New York Media Directory

Burrelle's Information Services
75 E. Northfield Rd.
Livingston, NJ 07039
Ph: (973)992-6600   Fax: (973)992-7675
Fr: 800-631-1160
URL: http://www.burrellesluce.com/media-data/regional.html

Annual. $200.00. Covers Print and electronic media in New York. Entries include: Name, address, phone, fax, names and titles of key personnel, geographical area served, subsidiary and branch names and locations, description. Arrangement: Geographical; magazines are arranged by subject. Indexes: Name, subject, geographical.

★11858★ Children's Writer's & Illustrator's Market

Writer's Digest Books
4700 E Galbraith Rd.
Cincinnati, OH 45236
Ph: (513)531-2690   Fr: 800-289-0963
URL: http://www.writersdigest.com

Annual, January. $24.99. Covers about 800 book and magazine publishers that publish works by authors and illustrators for young audiences; sponsors of writing and illustrating contests and awards; writers' organizations; and workshops. Entries include: For Publishers-Name, address, phone, name and title of contact, type of business, type and number of books published annually, average length of material bought, list of

recently published material, reporting times, terms of payment to authors. Arrangement: Separate sections for book and magazine publishers. Indexes: Age level for books, general, magazine.

★11859★ Contemporary Theatre, Film, and Television

Thomson Gale
27500 Drake Rd.
Farmington Hills, MI 48331-3535
Ph: (248)699-4253   Fax: (248)699-8065
Fr: 800-877-GALE
URL: http://www.gale.com

Bimonthly. $175.00. Covers in 47 volumes, more than 15,000 leading and up-and-coming performers, directors, writers, producers, designers, managers, choreographers, technicians, composers, executives, and dancers in the United States, Canada, Great Britain and the world. Each volume includes updated biographies for people listed in previous volumes and in "Who's Who in the Theatre," which this series has superseded. Entries include: Name, agent and/or office addresses, personal and career data; stage, film, and television credits; writings, awards, other information. Arrangement: Alphabetical. Indexes: Cumulative name index also covers entries in "Who's Who in the Theatre" editions 1-17 and in "Who Was Who in the Theatre".

★11860★ Directory of Leading Magazines and Newspapers

Publisher Media
1145 N Second St.
El Cajon, CA 92021-5024
Ph: (619)588-2155   Fax: (619)588-9103

Annual, January. $14.95. Covers over 300 newspapers and 700 consumer and trade magazines; coverage also includes Canada. Entries include: Company name, address, description of services, circulation figures advertising information. Arrangement: Classified by subject.

★11861★ Directory of Poetry Publishers

Dustbooks
PO Box 100
Paradise, CA 95967
Ph: (530)887-6110   Fax: (530)877-0222
Fr: 800-477-6110
URL: http://www.dustbooks.com/poet-pub.htm

Annual, September. $23.95; $76.00 for four year subscription. Covers about 2,000 magazines, small presses, commercial presses, and university presses that accept poetry for publication. Entries include: Publisher name and address, number of submissions accepted, percentage of submissions published, deadlines, reporting time, list of recent contributors, rights purchased, and method of payment. Arrangement: Alphabetical. Indexes: Subject, geographical.

★11862★ Directory of Small Magazine-Press Editors and Publishers

Dustbooks
PO Box 100
Paradise, CA 95967
Ph: (530)887-6110   Fax: (530)877-0222
Fr: 800-477-6110
URL: http://www.dustbooks.com/

Annual, September. $23.95. Covers about 7,500 publishers and editors. Entries include: Individual name, title of press or magazine, address and phone number. Arrangement: Alphabetical.

★11863★ Do the Write Thing

Myriad Press
12535 Chandler Blvd., No. 3
North Hollywood, CA 91607
Ph: (818)508-6296   Fax: (818)508-6296
E-mail: cywrite@juno.com
URL: http://www.geocities.com/Athens/1980/writers.html

Published 1994. $18.95. Publication includes: Lists of publishers, trade associations, and government agencies of interest to aspiring professional writers. Entries include: Company, organization, or personal name, address, and service provided. Indexes: Organization name, subject.

★11864★ The Dramatists Guild Resource Directory

The Dramatists Guild of America Inc.
1501 Broadway, Ste. 701
New York, NY 10036-3988
Ph: (212)398-9366   Fax: (212)944-0420

Annual, September. Publication includes: Lists of Broadway and off-Broadway producers; theater & producing organizations; agents; regional theaters; sources of grants, fellowships, residencies; conferences and festivals; playwriting ontests; and sources of financial assistance. Entries include: For producers-Name, address, credits, types of plays accepted for consideration. For groups-Name, address, contact name, type of material accepted for consideration, future commitment, hiring criteria, response time. For agents-Name, address. For theaters-Theater name, address, contact name, submission procedure, types of plays accepted for consideration, maximum cast, limitations, equity contract, opportunities, response time. For grants, fellowships, residencies, financial assistance, conferences, and festivals-Name, address, contact name, description, eligibility and application requirements, deadline. For play contests-Name, address, prize, deadline, description. Arrangement: Contests are by deadline; others are classified.

★11865★ Editor & Publisher International Year Book

Editor & Publisher Magazine
770 Broadway
New York, NY 10003-9595
Fax: (646)654-5370   Fr: 800-336-4380
URL: http://www.editorandpublisher.com

Annual, April. $230.00. Covers daily and Sunday newspapers in the United States and Canada; weekly newspapers; foreign daily newspapers; special service newspapers; newspaper syndicates; news services; journalism schools; foreign language and Black newspapers in the United States; news, picture, and press services; feature and news syndicates; comic and magazine services; advertising clubs; trade associations; clipping bureaus; house organs; journalism awards; also lists manufacturers of equipment and supplies. Entries include: For daily papers-Publication name, address, phone, fax, e-mail, web site URL, names of executives and departmental editors (business, financial, book, food, etc.), circulation and advertising data, production information including format of paper and equipment used. Similar but less detailed information for other publications. Arrangement: Publications and schools are geographical; most other lists are alphabetical.

★11866★ Editorial Freelancers Association-Membership Directory

Editorial Freelancers Association Inc.
71 W 23rd St., Ste. 1910
New York, NY 10010
Ph: (212)929-5400   Fax: (212)929-5439
URL: http://www.the-efa.org

Annual, spring. $25.00. Covers 1,100 member editorial freelancers. Entries include: Personal name, address, phone, services provided, specialties. Arrangement: Alphabetical. Indexes: Product/service, special interest, geographical, computer skills.

★11867★ Freelance Editorial Association Yellow Pages & Code of Fair Practice

Freelance Editorial Association
71 W 23rd St., Ste. 1910
New York, NY 10010
Ph: (212)929-5400   Fax: (212)929-5439
URL: http://www.tiac.net/users/freelanc

Annual. $47.50. Covers services offered by hundreds of freelance editors, indexers, proofreaders, translators, desktop publishers, researchers, illustrators, and writers; member are located throughout the United States. Entries include: Name, address, phone, and brief descriptions. Arrangement: Classified by editorial skill. Indexes: Name, geographical, specialty.

★11868★ Hudson's Washington News Media Contacts Directory

Howard Penn Hudson Associates Inc.
PO Box 311
Rhinebeck, NY 12572
Ph: (845)876-2081   Fax: (845)876-2561
Fr: 800-572-3451
URL: http://www.hudsonsdirectory.com

Annual, Dec.; updates in Feb., May, and Aug.; online updates 24 hrs./day. $269.00. Covers nearly 5,000 editors, free-lance writers, and news correspondents, plus 4,624 United States, Canadian, and foreign newspapers, radio-TV networks and stations, magazines, and periodicals based or represented in Washington, D.C. Entries include: For publications and companies-Name, address, phone, and name of editor or key personnel. For individuals-Name, assignment. Arrangement: Classified by activity (e.g., correspondents), media type, etc; newspapers and radio-TV stations sections are arranged geographically; specialized periodicals section is arranged by subject. Indexes: Subject.

★11869★ International Directory of Children's Literature

George Kurian Reference Books
Box 519
Baldwin Place, NY 10505
Ph: (914)962-3287   Fax: (914)962-5287

Irregular, previous edition 1990; latest edition 2001. $48.95. Covers about 5,000 children's book and magazine publishers, organizations, children's libraries and special collections, fairs, seminars, and conferences concerned with children's literature; worldwide coverage. Entries include: For book publishers, children's literature organizations, and major children's libraries and special collections-Name, address, purpose of activity. For periodicals, prizes, and events-Name, responsible organization, address, frequency or time period, subject. Arrangement: Geographical.

★11870★ International Directory of Little Magazines and Small Presses

Dustbooks
PO Box 100
Paradise, CA 95967
Ph: (530)887-6110   Fax: (530)877-0222
Fr: 800-477-6110
URL: http://www.dustbooks.com/lilmag.htm

Annual, September. $55.00 for cloth; $35.95 for paper. Covers over 5,000 small, independent magazines, presses, and papers. Entries include: Name, address, size, circulation, frequency, price, type of material used, number of issues or books published annually, and other pertinent data. Arrangement: Alphabetical. Indexes: Subject, regional.

★11871★ International Literary Market Place

Information Today Inc.
143 Old Marlton Pke.
Medford, NJ 08055-8750
Ph: (609)654-6266   Fax: (609)654-4309
Fr: 800-300-9848
URL: http://www.literarymarketplace.com

Annual, September, latest edition 2004. $239.00. Covers over 10,799 publishers in over 180 countries outside the United States and Canada, and about 1,499 trade and professional organizations related to publishing abroad; includes major printers, binders, typesetters, book manufacturers, book dealers, libraries, literary agencies, translators, book clubs, reference books and journals, periodicals, prizes, and international reference section. Entries include: For publishers-Name, address, phone, fax, telex, names and titles of key personnel, branches, type of publications, subjects, ISBN prefix. Listings for others include similar information but less detail. Arrangement: Classified by business activities, then geographical. Indexes: Company name, subject, type of publication.

★11872★ Literary Market Place

Information Today Inc.
143 Old Marlton Pke.
Medford, NJ 08055-8750
Ph: (609)654-6266   Fax: (609)654-4309
Fr: 800-300-9848
URL: http://www.literarymarketplace.com

Annual, Octber, latest edition 2002. $299.00. Covers over 14,500 firms or organizations offering services related to the publishing industry, including book publishers in the United States and Canada who issued three or more books during the preceding year, plus a small press section of publishers who publish less than three titles per year or those who are self-published. Also included: book printers and binders; book clubs; book trade and literary associations; selected syndicates, newspapers, periodicals, and radio and TV programs that use book reviews or book publishing news; translators and literary agents. Entries include: For publishers-Company name, address, phone, address for orders, principal executives, editorial directors, and managers, date founded, number of titles in previous year, number of backlist titles in print, types of books published, ISBN prefixes, representatives, imprints, and affiliations. For suppliers, etc. - Listings usually show firm name, address, phone, executives, services, etc. Arrangement: Classified by line of business. Indexes: Principal index is 35,000-item combined index of publishers, publications, and personnel; several sections have geographical and/or subject indexes; translators are indexed by source and target language.

★11873★ Magazine & Bookseller-Who's Who of the Publishing & Distribution Industry Issue

North American Publishing Co.
401 N. Broad St., Fifth Fl.
837 Villa Ridge Rd.
Philadelphia, PA 19108
Ph: (215)238-5482   Fax: (215)238-5412
Fr: 800-777-8074

Annual, December; new edition expected 1999. $49.00. Publication includes: Lists of magazine publishers, paperback publishers, national distributors, industry services associations and magazine paperback wholesalers. Entries include: Most listings include company name, address, phone, and key personnel; other details such as magazine frequency, name of distributor, cover price or distributor's number of titles carried may also be given. Arrangement: Classified by type of magazine or line of business.

★11874★ Midwest Travel Writers Association-Membership Directory

Midwest Travel Writers Association
PO Box 83542
Lincoln, NE 68501-3542
Ph: (402)438-2253   Fax: (402)438-2253

URL: http://www.mtwa.org

Annual, February. $50.00; $65.00 for book and CD. Covers over 100 travel writers, editors, and representatives of the travel and tourism industry, located in 13 midwestern states. Entries include: Name, spouse's name, address, phone; title, year membership began, publications, professional affiliations, writing specialties. Arrangement: Alphabetical. Indexes: Geographical.

★11875★ National Directory of Arts Internships

National Network for Artist Placement
935 W. Ave. 37
Los Angeles, CA 90065
Ph: (323)222-4035   Fax: (323)225-5711
URL: http://www.artistplacement.com/intern.htm

Biennial, odd years. $85.00. Covers over 5,000 internship opportunities in dance, music, theater, art, design, film, and video & over 1,250 host organizations Entries include: Name of sponsoring organization, address, name of contact; description of positions available, eligibility requirements, stipend or salary (if any), application procedures. Arrangement: Classified by discipline, then geographical.

★11876★ National Directory of Magazines

Oxbridge Communications Inc.
186 5th Ave., 6th Fl.
New York, NY 10010
Ph: (212)741-0231   Fax: (212)633-2938
Fr: 800-955-0231
E-mail: custserv@oxbridge.com
URL: http://www.mediafinder.com

October. $895.00. Covers over 20,000 magazines; coverage includes Canada. Entries include: Title, publisher name, address, phone, fax number, names and titles of contact and key personnel, financial data, editorial and advertising information, circulation. Arrangement: Classified by subject. Indexes: Title, geographical, publisher.

★11877★ Novel & Short Story Writer's Market

Writer's Digest Books
4700 E Galbraith Rd.
Cincinnati, OH 45236
Ph: (513)531-2690   Fr: 800-289-0963

Annual, January, latest edition 2004. $24.99. Publication includes: List of 2,000 literary magazines, general periodicals, small presses, book publishers, and authors' agents; contests awards; and writers' organizations. Entries include: For markets-Publication name (if a periodical), publisher name and address, phone, name of editor or other contact; description of periodical or type of work published; frequency and circulation for periodicals, number of titles published for others; needs, method of contact, terms, payment, advice, comments, or tips given by firm. For contests and awards-Name, sponsoring organization name and address, name and title of contact, frequency; pur-

pose, requirements, other information. Arrangement: Contests and awards are alphabetical; markets are classified by type of publisher or type of periodical. Indexes: Market category.

★11878★ Poet's Market

Writer's Digest Books
4700 E Galbraith Rd.
Cincinnati, OH 45236
Ph: (513)531-2690   Fr: 800-289-0963
E-mail: poetsmarket@fwpubs.com

Annual, August. $24.99. Covers 1,800 publishers, periodicals, and other markets accepting poetry for publication. Entries include: Name, address, phone, name and title of contact, types of poetry accepted, submission requirements. Arrangement: Alphabetical. Indexes: Subject, geographical, chapbook publishers.

★11879★ Professional Freelance Writers Directory

The National Writers Association
3140 S. Peoria St., No. 295PMB
Aurora, CO 80014-3155
Ph: (303)841-0246   Fax: (303)841-2607
URL: http://www.nationalwriters.com

Annual. Free. Database covers: 200 professional members selected from the club's membership on the basis of significant articles or books, or production of plays or movies. Entries include: Name, address, phone (home and business numbers), special fields of writing competence, titles of books published by royalty firms, mention of contributions to specific magazines, journals, newspapers or anthologies, recent awards received, relevant activities and skills (photography, etc.). Arrangement: Alphabetical. Indexes: By author alphabetical, by state, by subject.

★11880★ Publishers Directory

Thomson Gale
27500 Drake Rd.
Farmington Hills, MI 48331-3535
Ph: (248)699-4253   Fax: (248)699-8065
Fr: 800-877-GALE
E-mail: businessproducts@gale.com
URL: http://www.gale.com

Annual. $450.00. Covers over 20,000 new and established, commercial and nonprofit, private and alternative, corporate and association, government and institution publishing programs and their distributors; includes producers of books, classroom materials, prints, reports, and databases. Entries include: Firm name, address, phone, fax, company e-mail address, URL, year founded, ISBN prefix, Standard Address Number, whether firm participates in the Cataloging in Publication program of the Library of Congress, names of principal executives, personal e-mail addresses, number of titles in print, description of firm and its main subject interests, discount and returns policies, affiliated and parent companies, mergers and amalgamations, principal markets, imprints and divisions, alternate formats products are offered; distributors also list firms for which they distribute, special services, terms to publishers and regional offices. Arrangement: Alphabetical; distributors listed separately. Indexes: Subject, geographical, publisher, imprints, and distributor.

★11881★ **Publishers, Distributors, and Wholesalers of the United States**
R.R. Bowker L.L.C.
630 Central Ave.
New Providence, NJ 07974
Ph: (908)286-1090   Fax: (908)219-0098
Fr: 888-269-5372
URL: http://www.booksinprint.com

Annual, October, latest edition 2003-2004. $349.00. Covers over 140,670 publishers, distributors, and wholesalers; includes associations, museums, software producers and manufacturers, and others not included in 'Books in Print'. Entries include: Publisher name, editorial and ordering addresses, e-mail, websites, phone, Standard Address Numbers (SANs), International Standard Book Number prefix. Arrangement: Alphabetical; distributors and wholesalers are listed separately. Indexes: ISBN prefix, abbreviation, type of business, imprint name, geographical, inactive and out of business company name, toll-free phone and fax, wholesaler and distributor.

★11882★ **Self-Employed Writers and Artists Network-Directory**
Self-Employed Writers and Artists
Network Inc.
PO Box 440
Paramus, NJ 07653
Ph: (201)967-1313
URL: http://www.swan-net.com

Annual, spring. Covers over 135 freelance writers, graphic designers, illustrators, photographers, and other graphic arts professionals in northern New Jersey and New York city providing services in advertising, marketing, sales promotion, public relations, and telecommunications. Entries include: Name, address, phone, biographical data, description of services provided. Arrangement: Alphabetical. Indexes: Line of business.

★11883★ **Self-Publishing Manual**
Para Publishing
PO Box 8206-240
Santa Barbara, CA 93118-8206
Ph: (805)968-7277   Fax: (805)968-1379
Fr: 800-PAR-APUB
URL: http://www.parapublishing.com

Biennial, odd years. $19.95; $23.95 for California residents. Publication includes: Lists of wholesalers, reviewers, exporters, suppliers, direct mailing list sources, publishing organizations, and others of assistance in publishing. Entries include: Organization or company name, address, email addresses and web address. Arrangement: Classified by ZIP code. Indexes: General subject.

★11884★ **Society of American Travel Writers-Membership Directory**
Society of American Travel Writers
1500 Sunday Dr., Ste. 102
Raleigh, NC 27607
Ph: (919)861-5586   Fax: (919)787-4916
URL: http://www.satw.org/satw/index.asp?SId=27

Annual, February. $195.00; $75.00 for members. Covers about 550 newspaper and magazine travel editors, writers, columnists, photo journalists, and broadcasters in the United States and Canada. Also covers separately 300 executives in public relations who handle tourist attractions and travel industry accounts. Entries include: For regular members-Name, business address, phone, year joined; awards, publications, specialties, publications contributed to; spouse's name. For public relations executives-Name, address, phone, year joined, clients. Arrangement: Classified by type of membership. Indexes: Geographical, travel editor affiliation, free lance travel writers, public relations executive affiliation.

★11885★ **Southern Newspaper Publishers Association Internship Directory**
Southern Newspaper Publishers
Association
PO Box 28875
Atlanta, GA 30358

Latest edition 1995-96. $2.00. Covers a list of internship programs offered by the Association's member newspapers.

★11886★ **Space Coast Writers Guild-Membership Information/Directory**
Space Coast Writers Guild Inc.
PO Box 804
Melbourne, FL 32902-0804
Ph: (321)723-7345

Annual. Covers about 350 professional and aspiring writers in Florida. Entries include: Name, address, phone, area and form of specialty. Arrangement: Alphabetical. Indexes: By genre.

★11887★ **SRDS International Media Guide: Newspapers Worldwide**
SRDS
1700 .E Higgins Rd.
Des Plaines, IL 60018-5605
Ph: (847)375-5000   Fax: (847)375-5001
Fr: 800-851-7737
URL: http://www.srds.com

Annual. $350.00. Covers approximately 2,500 newspapers and color newspaper magazines/supplements from 200 countries, including the United States. Entries include: Publication name; publisher name, address, phone, fax, e-mail, URL, names of editor, advertising manager, and representatives in the United States and worldwide; advertising rates in U.S. dollars and/or local currency, circulation, mechanical data, ad closing, readership description, etc. Arrangement: Geographical.

★11888★ **Ulrich's Periodicals Directory**
R.R. Bowker L.L.C.
630 Central Ave.
New Providence, NJ 07974
Ph: (908)286-1090   Fax: (908)219-0098
Fr: 888-269-5372
E-mail: ulrichs@bowker.com
URL: http://www.ulrichsweb.com

Annual. $699.00. Covers nearly 165,000 current periodicals and newspapers published worldwide. Entries include: In main list-Publication title; Dewey Decimal Classification number, Library of Congress Classification Number (where applicable), CODEN designation (for sci-tech serials), British Library Document Supply Centre shelfmark number, country code, ISSN; subtitle, language(s) of text, year first published, frequency, subscription prices, sponsoring organization, publishing company name, address, phone, fax, e-mail and website addresses, editor and publisher names; regular features (reviews, advertising, abstracts, bibliographies, trade literature, etc.), indexes, circulation, format, brief description of content; availability of microforms and reprints; whether refereed; CD-ROM availability with vendor name; online availability with service name; services that index or abstract the periodical, with years covered; advertising rates and contact; right and permissions contact name and phone; availability through document delivery services; Copyright Clearance Center participation; document type; former title and former ISSN history. For cessations-Title, name and address of publisher, publication status. For online and CD-ROM vendors-Company name, address, phone, fax, e-mail and URL addresses, titles of publications available. Arrangement: Main listing is classified by subject; U.S. general daily and weekly newspapers are listed in a separate volume; lists of cessations, online services, and CD-ROM vendors are alphabetical. Indexes: Cessations, subjects, title (including variant, former, and ceased titles), ISSN, periodicals available on CD-ROM, online periodical title, refereed serial, and international organization publication title.

★11889★ **Washington Independent Writers-Directory**
Washington Independent Writers
Woodward Bldg., 733 15th St. NW, Ste. 220
733 Fifteenth St. NW
Washington, DC 20005
Ph: (202)737-9500   Fax: (202)638-7800

Biennial. $20.00. Covers about 2,500 member freelance writers in the Washington, D.C. area. Entries include: Name, address, home and office phone, area of specialization; personal and career data usually included. Arrangement: Alphabetical. Indexes: Specialty.

★11890★ **Who's Who in American Art**
Marquis Who's Who
121 Chanlon Rd.
New Providence, NJ 07974
Ph: (908)673-1101   Fax: (908)673-1189
Fr: 800-473-7020

E-mail: art@renp.com
URL: http://www.marquiswhoswho.com

Biennial, Spring of odd years. $265.00. Covers about 11,800 people active in visual arts, including sculptors, painters, illustrators, printmakers, collectors, curators, writers, educators, dealers, critics, patrons, and museum executives. Also includes cumulative necrology from 1953. Entries include: Name, professional classification, address; artists' listings include dealer's name and address, preferred media, works in public collections, awards, publications, teaching positions, etc.; other listings may include same information plus statement of research interests, etc. Arrangement: Alphabetical. Indexes: Geographical, professional classification.

★11891★ *Who's Who in the Motion Picture Industry*
Packard Publishing Co.
PO Box 2187
Beverly Hills, CA 90213
Ph: (626)791-5367

Annual, February; supplement. $24.95. Covers about 1,200 cinematographers, directors, producers, writers, and studio executives in the theatrical and television motion picture industries. Entries include: For production companies and studios-Name, address, phone, names and titles of key personnel. For others-Name, company or agent name, address, phone, credits. Arrangement: Classified by professional status (director, studio executive, etc.) in separate sections for theatrical and television films. Indexes: Alphabetical.

★11892★ *Working Press of the Nation*
R.R. Bowker L.L.C.
630 Central Ave.
New Providence, NJ 07974
Ph: (908)286-1090   Fax: (908)219-0098
Fr: 888-269-5372
E-mail: wpn@bowker.com

Annual, September. $530.00 for set; $295.00 each volume. Covers in three separate volumes, syndicates and over 8,500 daily and weekly newspapers; 1,750 newsletters; over 16,800 radio and television stations; 5,500 magazines; 1,000 internal publications. Entries include: Name of publication or station, address, phone, fax, e-mail and URL, names of executives, editors, writers, etc., as appropriate. Broadcasting and magazine volumes include data on kinds of material accepted. Technical and mechanical requirements for publications are given. Arrangement: Magazines are classified by subject; newspapers and broadcasting stations are geographical. Indexes: Newspaper department/editor by interest, metro area, feature syndicate subject; magazine subject, publication title; television director/personnel by subject, radio personnel and director by subject.

★11893★ *Writers Directory*
infoUSA Inc.
5711 S 86th Cir.
Omaha, NE 68127-0347
Ph: (402)930-3500   Fax: (402)331-0176
Fr: 800-555-6124
URL: http://www.abii.com

Updated continuously; printed on request. Number of listings: 2,400. Entries include: Name, address, phone, size of advertisement, name of owner or manager, number of employees, year first in "Yellow Pages." Compiled from telephone company "Yellow Pages," nationwide. Arrangement: Geographical.

★11894★ *Writer's Guide to Book Editors, Publishers, and Literary Agents*
Prima Publishing
3000 Lava Ridge Ct.
Roseville, CA 95661
Ph: (916)787-7000   Fax: (916)787-7003
Fr: 800-632-8676

Annual, latest edition 2002-2003. $29.95. Covers more than 300 publishing houses and their editors. Entries include: Name of press, description, editors and their specialties. Appendixes list agents, model book proposal, and author-agency agreement. Indexes: Extensive.

★11895★ *The Writer's Handbook*
Kalmbach Publishing Co.
PO Box 1612
Waukesha, WI 53187-1612
Ph: (262)796-8776   Fax: (262)796-1615
Fr: 800-533-6644

Annual, October. $29.95. Publication includes: Compilation of 50-plus articles for publication, many by recognized authors and editors. Features list of 3,000-plus markets for the sale of manuscripts (fiction, nonfiction, poetry, drama, greeting card), plus lists of American literary agents, writers' organizations, literary contests, and writing conferences. Entries include: Markets- name of firm or publication, contact information, editorial preferences, payment rate. Agents-agency name, contact information, submission guidelines, commission rates. Organizations-name, contact information, description of purpose and activities. Contests-name, contact information, prize or award, deadline. Conferences-name, contact information, date/place, description of workshops/activities. Arrangement: Markets are classified by type: magazine (nonfiction and fiction/poetry) and book (general, juvenile, religious); other resources are alphabetical. Indexes: Alphabetical.

★11896★ *Writer's Market*
Writer's Digest Books
4700 E Galbraith Rd.
Cincinnati, OH 45236
Ph: (513)531-2690   Fr: 800-289-0963
E-mail: writersmarker@fwpubs.com
URL: http://www.writersmarket.com/wmns/about.asp

Annual, September. $29.99. Covers over 8,000 buyers of books, articles, short stories, plays, gags, verse, fillers, and other original written material. Includes book and periodical publishers, greeting card publishers, play producers and publishers, audiovisual material producers, syndicates, and contests and awards. Entries include: Name and address of buyer, phone, payment rates, editorial requirements, reporting time, how to break in. Arrangement: Classified by type of publication. Indexes: Subject, alphabetical.

★11897★ *WritersNet*
Internet Concepts L.L.C.
6200 Gisholt Dr., Ste. 105
Madison, WI 53713
URL: http://www.writersnet.com

Database covers: Internet resources, books, and other materials for writers.

HANDBOOKS AND MANUALS

★11898★ *Achieving Financial Independence As a Freelance Writer*
Blue Heron Publishing
4205 SW Washington St., Suite 303
Portland, OR 97204
Ph: (503)221-6841   Fax: (503)221-6843
Raymond Dreyfack. 2000. $16.95 (paper).

★11899★ *Be a Successful Writer: New Expanded Common Sense Program for Anyone Who Wants to Write*
Diamond Editions
3808 Georgia St., Apt. 212
San Diego, CA 92103-4673
Ph: (619)224-8907
Carolan Gladden. 1995. 112 pages.

★11900★ *Career Information Center*
Macmillan Publishing Co. Inc.
200 Old Tappan Rd.
Old Tappan, NJ 07675
Fr: 800-428-5331

Visual Education Center Staff. Seventh edition, 1999. $275.00. 2080 pages. This 13-volume set profiles over 600 occupations. Each occupational profile describes job duties, educational requirements, how to get the job, advancement possibilities, employment outlook, working conditions, earnings and benefits, and where to write for more information.

★11901★ *Career Opportunities for Writers*
Checkmark Books
132 W. 31st St., 17th Fl.
New York, NY 10001-2006
Ph: (212)967-8800   Fax: (212)967-9196
Fr: 800-322-8755
URL: http://www.factsonfile.com

Rosemary Ellen Guiley and Janet Frick. Fourth edition, 2000. $45.00. Part of the Career Opportunities Series. Describes more than 100 jobs in eight major fields, offering such details as duties, salaries, perquisites, employment and advancement opportunities, organizations to join, and opportunities for women and minorities.

★11902★ **Careers in Communications**
VGM Career Horizons
4255 W. Touhy Ave.
Lincolnwood, IL 60646-1975
Ph: (847)679-5500   Fax: (847)679-2494
Fr: 800-323-4900
E-mail: ntcpub@tribune.com

Shonan Noronha. Third edition, 1998. $17.95; $13.95 (paper). 418 pages. Examines the fields of journalism, photography, radio, television, film, public relations, and advertising. Gives concrete details on job locations and how to secure a job. Suggests many resources for job hunting.

★11903★ **Careers for Culture Lovers and Other Artsy Types**
VGM Career Horizons
1221 Avenue of the Americas
New York, NY 10020
Ph: (212)904-2000   Fr: 800-323-4900
E-mail: ntcpub@tribune.com

Marjorie Eberts and Margaret Gisler. Second edition, 1999. $14.95; $9.95 (paper). 234 pages. Describes how to get work in a variety of fields related to art and culture. Opportunities include picture framer, curator, art restorer, symphony manager, disk jockey, music reviewer, dance teacher, choreographer, costume designer, theater manager, light designer, drama teacher, bookstore owner, interior decorator, antique store owner, and others.

★11904★ **Careers in Health Care**
McGraw-Hill Trade
2 Penn Plaza
New York, NY 10121
Ph: (212)904-2000   Fr: 800-722-4726
E-mail: ntcpub@tribune.com

Barbara M. Swanson. Fourth edition, 2000. $17.95; $13.95 (paper). 320 pages. Describes job duties, work settings, salaries, licensing and certification requirements, educational preparation, and future outlook. Gives ideas on how to secure a job.

★11905★ **Careers for Health Nuts and Others Who Like to Stay Fit**
McGraw-Hill Trade
2 Penn Plaza
New York, NY 10121
Ph: (212)904-2000   Fr: 800-722-4726
E-mail: ntcpub@tribune.com

Blythe Camenson. 1996. $14.95; $9.95 (paper). 160 pages.

★11906★ **Careers in Journalism**
Kogan Page
1221 Avenue of the Americas
New York, NY 10020
Ph: (212)904-2000   Fr: 800-323-4900
E-mail: ntcpub@tribune.com

Jan Goldberg. Second edition, 1999. $17.95; 13.95 (paper). 192 pages.

★11907★ **Careers for Mystery Buffs and Other Snoops and Sleuths**
McGraw-Hill Trade
2 Penn Plaza
New York, NY 10121
Ph: (212)904-2000   Fr: 800-722-4726
E-mail: ntcpub@tribune.com

Blythe Camenson. 1996. $14.95; $9.95 (paper). 210 pages.

★11908★ **Careers for Writers and Others Who Have a Way with Words**
McGraw-Hill Trade
2 Penn Plaza
New York, NY 10121
Ph: (212)904-2000   Fr: 800-722-4726
E-mail: ntcpub@tribune.com

Robert W. Bly. 1995. $14.95; $9.95 (paper). 295 pages.

★11909★ **Editorial Freelancing: A Practical Guide**
Aletheia Publications, Inc.
46 Bell Hollow Rd.
Putnam Valley, NY 10579
Ph: (914)526-2873   Fax: (914)526-2905

Trumbull Rogers. 1995. 200 pages. $19.95 (paper). Contains everything the freelancer needs to know about building a basic reference library, choosing a computer & appropriate software, marketing editorial services, determining & negotiating rates, billing, & setting up a retirement plan.

★11910★ **Exploring High-Tech Careers**
Rosen Publishing Group, Inc.
29 E. 21st St.
New York, NY 10010
Ph: (212)777-3017   Fax: (212)777-0277
Fr: 800-237-9932

Scott Southworth. Revised edition, 1993. $14.95; $9.95 (paper). 118 pages. Out of print. Gives an orientation to the field of high technology and high-tech jobs. Describes educational preparation and job hunting. Includes a glossary and bibliography.

★11911★ **Great Jobs for Communications Majors**
McGraw-Hill Professional
2 Penn Plaza
New York, NY 10121
Ph: (212)904-2000   Fr: 800-722-4726
E-mail: ntcpub@tribune.com

Blythe Camenson. Second edition, 2001. $14.95 (paper). 256 pages.

★11912★ **Great Jobs for English Majors**
McGraw-Hill Trade
2 Penn Plaza
New York, NY 10121
Ph: (212)904-2000   Fr: 800-722-4726
E-mail: ntcpub@tribune.com

Julie DeGalan. Second edition, 2000. $12.95 (paper). 462 pages.

★11913★ **Great Jobs for Liberal Arts Majors**
McGraw-Hill Professional
2 Penn Plaza
New York, NY 10121
Ph: (212)904-2000   Fr: 800-722-4726
E-mail: ntcpub@tribune.com

Blythe Camenson. Second edition, 2001. $14.95 (paper). 256 pages.

★11914★ **Guide to Careers in World Affairs**
Impact Publications
9104-N Manassas Dr., Ste. N
Manassas Park, VA 20111-5211
Ph: (703)361-7300   Fax: (703)335-9486

Foreign Affairs Association Staff and Pamela Gerard. Third edition. 1993. $14.95. 331 pages. Out of print. Describes jobs in business, government, and nonprofit organizations. Explains the methods and credentials required to secure a job in many fields, including international law and journalism. Contains sections on internships and graduate programs.

★11915★ **How to Make a Living as a Travel Writer**
Marlowe & Co.
841 Broadway, 4th Fl.
New York, NY 10003
Ph: (212)614-7880   Fax: (212)614-7887
Fr: 800-788-3123

Susan Farewell. Second edition, 1997. $10.95 (paper). 192 pages.

★11916★ **How to Write and Sell Your Articles**
Writer, Inc.
21027 Crossroads Cir.
Waukesha, WI 53187
Ph: (262)796-8776   Fax: (262)798-6592
Fr: 800-553-6644

Sylvia K. Burack, editor. 1997. $8.95 (paper). 112 pages.

★11917★ **How to Write What You Love and Make a Living at It**
WaterBrook Press
2375 Telstar Dr., Suite 160
Colorado Springs, CO 80920
Ph: (719)590-4999   Fax: (719)590-8977
Fr: 800-603-7051

Dennis E. Hensley. 2000. $12.99 (paper).

★11918★ The Journalist's Road to Success

Pearson Allyn & Bacon
230 Ave. of the Americas
New York, NY 10020
Ph: (212)782-3300   Fax: 800-445-6991
Fr: 800-666-9433

Annual, 1998. 148 pages. $4.00. Provides information on newspaper careers and salaries, and how to apply for a newspaper job. Explains how to choose a journalism school and lists colleges and universities offering journalism majors; describes undergraduate and graduate financial aid programs. Lists scholarships, fellowships, internships, and continuing education opportunities. Out of print.

★11919★ The Lost Soul Companion: Comfort & Constructive Advice for Struggling Actors, Musicians, Artists, Writers & Other Free Spirits

Puckitt Press, Incorporated
P.O. Box 3248
Bloomington, IN 47402-3248
Ph: (812)331-4337

Susan M. Brackney. 2000. $10.00

★11920★ Magazines Career Directory

Thomson Gale
7500 Drake Rd.
Farmington Hills, MI 48331-3535
Ph: (248)699-GALE   Fax: (248)699-8069
Fr: 800-877-GALE
E-mail: galeord@gale.com
URL: http://www.galegroup.com

Bradley Morgan. Fifth edition, 1993. $39.00. Features extensive listings of contacts and entry-level job opportunities at many magazine publishing organizations. Includes articles by top professionals in the field on some of the industry's varied career paths: art, editorial, sales, and business management. Part of Career Advisor series.

★11921★ Making Money Writing Newsletters

EFG, Inc.
3460 Hampton Ave.
Ste. 103
St. Louis, MO 63139
Ph: (314)353-6100   Fax: (314)353-1272
Fr: 800-264-6305

Elaine Floyd. 1994. $29.95 (paper). 132 pages. How to start a newsletter writing and design service.

★11922★ Newspapers Career Directory

Thomson Gale
27500 Drake Rd.
Farmington Hills, MI 48331-3535
Ph: (248)699-GALE   Fax: 800-414-5043
Fr: 800-877-GALE
E-mail: galeord@gale.com
URL: http://www.gale.com

Bradley Morgan. Fourth edition, 1993. $39.00. 300 pages. Out of print. Features extensive listings of contacts and entry-level job opportunities at many newspaper organizations. Focuses on each area of the business, from reporting and editorial to sales and marketing to promotion and production.

★11923★ 100 Best Careers for Writers and Artists

Thomson Peterson's
PO Box 67005
Lawrenceville, NJ 08648-6105
Fr: 800-338-3282

Shelly Field. 1997. $15.95 (paper). 288 pages. Identifies job opportunities in communications and the arts.

★11924★ Opportunities in Desktop Publishing Careers

McGraw-Hill Trade
2 Penn Plaza
New York, NY 10121
Ph: (212)904-2000   Fr: 800-722-4726

Kenny Schiff. 1994. $14.95; $11.95 (paper). 160 pages. Out of stock.

★11925★ Opportunities in High Tech Careers

McGraw-Hill Trade
2 Penn Plaza
New York, NY 10121
Ph: (212)904-2000   Fr: 800-722-4726

Gary Colter and Deborah Yanuck. 1995. $14.95; $11.95 (paper). 160 pages. Explores high technology careers. Describes job opportunities, how to make a career decision, how to prepare for high technology jobs, job hunting techniques, and future trends.

★11926★ Opportunities in Journalism Careers

McGraw-Hill/Contemporary Books
1221 Avenue of the Americas
New York, NY 10020
Ph: (212)904-2000   Fr: 800-323-4900
E-mail: ntcpub@tribune.com

Jim Patten and Donald L. Ferguson. 1995. $14.95; $11.95 (paper). 160 pages. Outlines opportunities in every field of journalism, including newspaper reporting and editing, magazine and book publishing, corporate communications, advertising and public relations, freelance writing, and teaching. Covers how to prepare for and enter each field, outlining responsibilities, salaries, benefits, and job outlook for each specialty. Illustrated.

★11927★ Opportunities in Magazine Publishing Careers

McGraw-Hill Trade
2 Penn Plaza
New York, NY 10121
Ph: (212)904-2000   Fr: 800-722-4726
E-mail: ntcpub@tribune.com

S. William Pattis. 1994. $13.95; $12.95 (paper). 160 pages. Covers the scope of magazine publishing and addresses how to identify and pursue available positions. Illustrated.

★11928★ Opportunities in Publishing Careers

McGraw-Hill Professional
2 Penn Plaza
New York, NY 10121
Ph: (212)904-2000   Fr: 800-722-4726
E-mail: ntcpub@tribune.com

Robert A. Carter and S. William Pattis. 1995. $14.95; $11.95 (paper). 160 pages. Covers all positions in book and magazine publishing, including new opportunities in multimedia publishing.

★11929★ Opportunities in Technical Writing and Communications Careers

McGraw-Hill Trade
2 Penn Plaza
New York, NY 10121
Ph: (212)904-2000   Fr: 800-722-4726
E-mail: ntcpub@tribune.com

Jay Gould and Wayne Losano. 1994. $14.95; $11.95 (paper). 160 pages. Provides advice on acquiring a position in medical, engineering, pharmaceutical, and other technical fields. Illustrated.

★11930★ Opportunities in Writing Careers

McGraw-Hill Contemporary Books
1221 Avenue of the Americas
New York, NY 10020
Ph: (212)904-2000   Fr: 800-323-4900
E-mail: ntcpub@tribune.com

Elizabeth Foote-Smith. 1999. $14.95; $11.95 (paper). 160 pages. Discusses opportunities in the print media, broadcasting, advertising or publishing. Business writing, public relations, and technical writing are among the careers covered. Contains bibliography and illustrations.

★11931★ The Playwright's Companion, 1999: A Practical Guide to Script Opportunities in the U.S.A.

Feedback Theatrebooks and Prospero Press
PO Box 220
Brooklin, ME 04616
Ph: (207)359-2781   Fax: (207)359-5532
Fr: 800-800-8671

Mollie A. Meserve, editor. First edition, revised, 1998. $20.95 (paper). 400 pages. Out of print.

★11932★ Power Freelancing: Home-Based Careers for Writers, Designers, & Consultants

Mid-List Press
4324 12th Ave., S
Minneapolis, MN 55407-3218
Ph: (612)822-3733   Fax: (612)823-8387
Fr: 888-543-1138

George Sorenson. 1995. $14.95 (paper). 192 pages.

★11933★ Quit Your Day Job: Develop a Successful Career As a Freelance Writer

Quill Driver Books
8386 N. Madsen Ave.
Clovis, CA 93611-8636
Ph: (209)322-5917   Fax: (209)322-5967
Fr: 800-497-4909

Robert Spiegel. 1998. $14.95 (paper).

★11934★ Radio and Television Career Directory

Thomson Gale
27500 Drake Rd.
Farmington Hills, MI 48331-3535
Ph: (248)699-GALE   Fax: 800-414-5043
Fr: 800-877-GALE
E-mail: galeord@gale.com
URL: http://www.gale.com

Bradley Morgan. Second edition, 1993. $39.00. 300 pages. Features extensive listings of contacts and entry-level job opportunities. Provides information on internships and sources of help-wanted ads.

★11935★ Real People Working in Communications

McGraw-Hill Contemporary Books
1221 Avenue of the Americas
New York, NY 10020
Ph: (212)904-2000   Fr: 800-323-4900
E-mail: ntcpub@tribune.com

Jan Goldberg. 1996. $14.95; $12.95 (paper). Interviews and profiles of working professionals capture a range of opportunities in this field.

★11936★ Resumes for Advertising Careers

McGraw-Hill Contemporary Books
1221 Avenue of the Americas
New York, NY 10020
Ph: (212)904-2000   Fr: 800-323-4900
E-mail: ntcpub@tribune.com

1998. $9.95 (paper). 392 pages. Aimed at job seekers trying to enter or advance in advertising. Provides sample resumes for copywriters, art directors, account managers, ad managers, and media people at all levels of experience. Furnishes sample cover letters.

★11937★ Resumes for Communications Careers

McGraw-Hill Contemporary Books
1221 Avenue of the Americas
New York, NY 10020
Ph: (212)904-2000   Fr: 800-323-4900
E-mail: ntcpub@tribune.com

1998. $9.95 (paper). 464 pages.

★11938★ Stage Writers Handbook: A Complete Business Guide for Playwrights, Composers, Lyricists, and Librettists

Theatre Communications Group
520 Eighth Ave., 24th Fl.
New York, NY 10018-4156
Ph: (212)609-5900   Fax: (212)609-5901

Dana Singer. 1996. $18.95 (paper). 192 pages.

★11939★ Stein on Writing: A Master Editor of Some of the Most Successful Writers of Our Century Shares His Craft Techniques & Strategies

St. Martin's Press, LLC
175 5th Ave.
New York, NY 10010
Ph: (212)726-0200   Fax: (212)686-9491
Fr: 800-470-4767

Sol Stein. 2000. $14.95 (paper). 320 pages.

★11940★ Technical Writing for Technicians: How to Build a Career As a Hardware Technical Writer

Contemax Publishers
17815 24th Ave., N.
Plymouth, MN 55447
Ph: (612)473-6436

Warren R. Freeman. 1995. $19.95 (paper). 160 pages. This publication explains each step in writing a typical hardware technical manual.

★11941★ 30-Minute Writer: How to Write & Sell Short Pieces

iUniverse, Inc.
2021 Pine Lake Rd, Ste. 100
Lincoln, NE 68512
Ph: (402)323-7800   Fax: (402)323-7824
Fr: 877-288-4737

Connie Emerson. 2000. $17.95 (paper). 260 pages.

★11942★ 30 Steps to Becoming a Writer & Getting Published

Writer's Digest Books
F & W Publications, Inc.
1507 Dana Ave.
Cincinnati, OH 45207
Ph: (513)531-2690   Fax: (513)531-4082
Fr: 800-289-0963

Scott Edelstein. 1993. $16.99. 176 pages.

★11943★ Twenty Questions: Answers for the Inquiring Writer

Browder Springs Books
6238 Glennox Ln.
Dallas, TX 75214
Ph: (214)368-4360   Fax: (214)739-9149

Clay Reynolds. 1997. $12.95 (paper). Novelist Clay Reynolds provides "how to" advice on becoming a best-selling author.

★11944★ Where the Jobs Are: The Hottest Careers for the 90s

The Career Press, Inc.
3 Tice Rd.
PO Box 687
Franklin Lakes, NJ 07417-1322
Ph: (201)848-0310   Fax: (201)848-1727
Fr: 800-227-3371

Joyce Hadley. Third edition, 2000. $13.99 (paper). 400 pages. Out of print. Describes careers in fifteen general fields, from accounting to travel and hospitality.

★11945★ Write Your Way to Riches: How to Make a Fortune As a Technical Writer

J. G. Communications
200 Berkeley St.
Methuen, MA 01844
Ph: (978)682-4106

Joseph Gregg. 1998. $19.95. 114 pages.

★11946★ A Writer's Guide to Getting Published in Magazines

Aletheia Publications Inc.
46 Bell Hollow Rd.
Putnam Valley, NY 10579
Ph: (914)526-2873   Fax: (914)526-2905

JJ Despain. 2000. $19.95 (paper).

★11947★ The Writer's Handbook

Writer, Inc.
21027 Crossroads Cir.
Waukesha, WI 53187
Ph: (262)796-8776   Fax: (262)798-6592
Fr: 800-553-6644

Elfrieda Abbe, editor. 2001. 1024 pages.

★11948★ Writing for Results: Keys to Success for the Public Relations Writer

Alta Villa Publishing, Incorporated
P.O. Box 17684
Indianapolis, IN 46217-0684
Ph: (317)885-1918

Ray Begovich. 2001. $12.00 (paper).

EMPLOYMENT AGENCIES AND SEARCH FIRMS

★11949★ Amtec Engineering Corp.

2749 Saturn St.
Brea, CA 92821
Ph: (714)993-1900   Fax: (714)993-2419
E-mail: staffing@amtec-eng.com
URL: http://www.amtec-eng.com

Employment agency.

★11950★ Ariel Associates
141 E. 89 St., Ste. 9-H
New York, NY 10128-2330
Ph: (212)348-9600
Executive search firm specializing in media, advertising and publishing.

**★11951★ Bert Davis Publishing
Placement Consultants**
425 Madison Ave., Fl. 14
New York, NY 10017
Ph: (212)838-4000   Fax: (212)935-3291
E-mail: info@bertdavis.com
URL: http://www.bertdavis.com
Executive search firm.

★11952★ Career Development Services
706 East Ave.
Rochester, NY 14607-2105
Ph: (585)244-0750   Fax: (585)244-7115
Fr: 800-736-6710
E-mail: info@careerdev.org
URL: http://www.careerdev.org
Employment agency.

★11953★ Chaloner Associates
36 Milford St.
Boston, MA 02118
Ph: (617)451-5170   Fax: (617)451-8160
E-mail: info@chaloner.com
URL: http://www.chaloner.com
Executive search firm.

**★11954★ The Esquire Staffing Group
Ltd.**
1 S. Wacker Dr., Ste. 1616
Chicago, IL 60606-4616
Ph: (312)795-4300   Fax: (312)795-4329
E-mail: s.fischer@esquirestaffing.com
URL: http://www.esquirestaffing.com
Employment agency. Fills permanent as well as temporary openings.

**★11955★ Howard-Sloan Professional
Search Inc.**
1140 Ave. of the Americas
New York, NY 10036
Ph: (212)704-0444   Fax: (212)869-7999
Fr: 800-221-1326
E-mail: info@howardsloan.com
URL: http://www.howardsloan.com
Executive search firm.

★11956★ Max Brown
3208 Q St. NW
Washington, DC 20007
Ph: (202)338-2727   Fax: (202)338-3131
Executive recruiter to the magazine and book publishing industries. Employment placements in all publishing disciplines, including operation and financial management, new product development, marketing, advertising sales, editorial, graphic design, production, manufacturing, circulation, distri-

bution, corporate communications, promotion, and administration. Secondary concentrations include management advising for publishers, providing the following services: marketing and product positioning for new and existing publications, market research and development, business planning and financial projections, publishing models, launch strategies and start-up operations, and acquisitions and mergers counsel.

**★11957★ Technical Talent Locators
Ltd.**
5570 Sterrett Place, Ste.208
Columbia, MD 21044
Ph: (410)740-0091
URL: http://www.ttlgroup.com
Permanent employment agency working within the following fields: software and database engineering; computer, communication, and telecommunication system engineering; and other computer-related disciplines.

ONLINE JOB SOURCES AND SERVICES

★11958★ Guru
URL: http://www.guru.com
Description: Job board specializing in contract jobs for creative and information technology professionals. Also provides online incorporation and educational opportunities for independent contractors along with articles and advice.

★11959★ JournalismJobs.com
E-mail: contact@journalismjobs.com
URL: http://www.journalismjobs.com
Description: Career-related site for journalists and other media professionals. Seekers can search for jobs, post a resume online, and manage the search online with the Job Seeker Folder feature. They also can receive free job announcements by e-mail.

TRADESHOWS

**★11960★ International Black Writers
and Artists Convention**
International Black Writers and Artists
PO Box 43576
Los Angeles, CA 90043
Ph: (213)964-3721   Fax: (213)938-0556
E-mail: lahughes@aol.com
Annual. **Primary Exhibits:** Books and artwork.

OTHER SOURCES

**★11961★ American Almanac of Jobs
and Salaries**
Morrow Avon
1350 Avenue of the Americas
New York, NY 10019
Ph: (212)261-6788   Fr: 800-242-7737
John W. Wright. Revised edition, 2000. $20.00 (paper). 672 pages. This is a comprehensive guide to the wages of hundreds of occupations in a wide variety of industries and organizations.

**★11962★ American Society of
Business Publication Editors (ASBPE)**
710 E Ogden Ave., Ste. 600
Naperville, IL 60563-8603
Ph: (630)579-3288   Fax: (630)369-2488
E-mail: info@asbpe.org
URL: http://www.asbpe.org
Description: Professional association for editors and writers working for business, trade, association, professional, technical magazines and their associated print and Internet publications. Serves to enhance editorial standards and quality and raise the level of publication management skills of its members.

**★11963★ American Society of
Journalists and Authors (ASJA)**
1501 Broadway, Ste. 302
New York, NY 10036
Ph: (212)997-0947   Fax: (212)768-7414
E-mail: staff@asja.org
URL: http://www.asja.org
Description: Freelance writers of nonfiction magazine articles and books. Seeks to elevate the professional and economic position of nonfiction writers, provide a forum for discussion of common problems among writers and editors, and promote a code of ethics for writers and editors. Operates writer referral Service for individuals, institutions, or companies seeking writers for special projects; sponsors Llewellyn Miller Fund to aid professional writers no longer able to work due to age, disability, or extraordinary professional crisis.

**★11964★ American Society of
Magazine Editors (ASME)**
810 7th Ave., 24th Fl.
New York, NY 10019
Ph: (212)872-3737   Fax: (212)906-0128
E-mail: president@magazine.org
URL: http://asme.magazine.org
Purpose: Professional organization for magazine editors. **Activities:** Sponsors annual editorial internship program for college juniors and the National Magazine Awards.

★11965★ American Society of Psychopathology of Expression (ASPE)

74 Lawton St.
Brookline, MA 02446
Ph: (617)738-9821   Fax: (617)975-0411

Description: Psychiatrists, psychologists, art therapists, sociologists, art critics, artists, social workers, linguists, educators, criminologists, writers, and historians. At least two-thirds of the members must be physicians. Fosters collaboration among specialists in the United States who are interested in the problems of expression and in the artistic activities connected with psychiatric, sociological, and psychological research. Disseminates information about research and clinical applications in the field of psychopathology of expression. Sponsors consultations, seminars, and lectures on art therapy.

★11966★ Art Directors Club (ADC)

106 W 29th St.
New York, NY 10001
Ph: (212)643-1440   Fax: (212)643-4266
E-mail: info@adcny.org
URL: http://www.adcny.org

Members: Art directors of advertising magazines and agencies, visual information specialists, and graphic designers; associate members are artists, cinematographers, photographers, copywriters, educators, journalists, and critics. **Purpose:** Promotes and stimulates interest in the practice of art direction. **Activities:** Sponsors Annual Exhibition of Advertising, Editorial and Television Art and Design; International Traveling Exhibition; Hall of Fame. Provides educational, professional, and entertainment programs; on-premise art exhibitions; portfolio review program. Conducts panels for students and faculty.

★11967★ Asian American Journalists Association (AAJA)

1182 Market St., Ste. 320
San Francisco, CA 94102
Ph: (415)346-2051   Fax: (415)346-6343
E-mail: national@aaja.org
URL: http://www.aaja.org

Description: Educational and professional organization. Encourages Asian Pacific Americans to enter the ranks of journalism, to work for fair and accurate coverage of Asian Pacific Americans and to increase the number of Asian Pacific American Journalists and news managers in the industry.

★11968★ Association for Business Communication (ABC)

Baruch College
Communication Studies
One Bernard Baruch Way
Box B8-240
New York, NY 10010
Ph: (646)312-3726   Fax: (646)349-5297
E-mail: abcrjm@cs.com
URL: http://
www.businesscommunication.org

Description: College teachers of business communication; management consultants in business communications; training directors and correspondence supervisors of business firms, direct mail copywriters, public relations writers, and others interested in communication for business.

★11969★ Association for Women in Communications

780 Ritchie Hwy., Ste. 28-S
Severna Park, MD 21146
Ph: (410)544-7442   Fax: (410)544-4640
E-mail: pat@womcom.org
URL: http://www.womcom.org

Description: Professional association of journalism and communications.

★11970★ Copywriter's Council of America (CCA)

CCA Bldg.
7 Putter Ln.
PO Box 102
Middle Island, NY 11953-0102
Ph: (631)924-8555   Fax: (631)924-5890
E-mail: cca4dmcopy@att.net
URL: http://www.lgroup.addr.com/CCA.htm

Description: Advertising copywriters, marketing and public relations consultants, copyeditors, proofreaders, and other individuals involved in print, radio, broadcast, video, and telecommunications. Provides freelance work; acts as agent for members; negotiates on members' behalf. Serves as a forum for professional and social contact between freelance communications professionals. Offers courses on copywriting, direct marketing, mail order, publishing screenplays, and how to get published. Conducts charitable programs. Maintains speakers' bureau, hall of fame, and word processing consultation service.

★11971★ Council of Writers Organizations (CWO)

12724 Sagamore Rd.
Leawood, KS 66209
Ph: (913)451-9023   Fax: (913)451-4866
E-mail: hurleypr@sound.net

Description: Serves as an umbrella agency for organizations representing writers Provides a means of sharing information among the organizations and their members as well as a voice for professional writers. Promotes and monitors pertinent legislation. Offers group insurance and other benefits.

★11972★ Dow Jones Newspaper Fund (DJNF)

PO Box 300
Princeton, NJ 08543-0300
Ph: (609)452-2820   Fax: (609)520-5804
E-mail: newsfund@wsj.dowjones.com
URL: http://djnewspaperfund.dowjones.com

Description: Established by Dow Jones and Company, publisher of *The Wall Street Journal*, to encourage careers in journalism. Operates Newspapers Editing, and Sports Copy Editing Internship Programs for all junior, senior, and graduate level college students interested in journalism. Also offers Business Reporting Intern Program for minority college sophomores and juniors to complete summer internships on daily newspapers as business reporters. Students receive monetary scholarships to return to school in the fall. Offers information on careers in journalism.

★11973★ Editorial Freelancers Association (EFA)

71 W 23rd St., Ste. 1910
New York, NY 10010
Ph: (212)929-5400   Fax: (212)929-5439
Fr: (866)929-5400
E-mail: info@the-efa.org
URL: http://www.the-efa.org

Description: Persons who work full- or part-time as freelance writers or editorial freelancers. Promotes professionalism and facilitates the exchange of information and support. Conducts professional training seminars; offers job listings.

★11974★ Evangelical Press Association (EPA)

PO Box 28129
Crystal, MN 55428
Ph: (763)535-4793   Fax: (763)535-4794
E-mail: director@epassoc.org
URL: http://www.gospelcom.net/epa

Members: Editors and publishers of Christian periodicals. **Activities:** Maintains placement service.

★11975★ International Black Writers (IBW)

PO Box 43576
Los Angeles, CA 90043
E-mail: ibwa_la@yahoo.com
URL: http://members.tripod.com/~ibwa/home.htm

Description: Seeks to discover and support new black writers. Conducts research and monthly seminars in poetry, fiction, nonfiction, music, and jazz. Operates a lending library of 500 volumes on black history for members only. Provides writing services and children's services. Maintains library and speakers' bureau. Offers referral service. Plans to establish hall of fame, biographical archives, and museum.

★11976★ International Security and Detective Alliance (ISDA)

PO Box 6303
Corpus Christi, TX 78466-6303
Fax: (361)888-8060

Members: Private investigators and security professionals, investigative reporters and writers, researchers, military personnel, and some interested laypersons. **Purpose:** Seeks to maintain an international registry of investigators for purpose of referral; support a more positive and accurate media image of P.I.s and security officers; provide a professional association for freelance operators; provide continuing education courses and materials. **Activities:** Provides professiona certification in numerous specialty areas of investigation and security.

★11977★ International Women's Writing Guild (IWWG)
Box 810, Gracie Sta.
New York, NY 10028-0082
Ph: (212)737-7536   Fax: (212)737-9469
E-mail: dirhahn@aol.com
URL: http://www.iwwg.com

Members: Women writers in 24 countries interested in expressing themselves through the written word professionally and for personal growth regardless of portfolio. **Purpose:** Seeks to empower women personally and professionally through writing. **Activities:** Facilitates manuscript submissions to literary agents and independent presses. Participates in international network. Maintains health insurance program at group rates.

★11978★ Media Alliance (MA)
814 Mission St., Ste. 205
San Francisco, CA 94103
Ph: (415)546-6334   Fax: (415)546-6218
E-mail: info@media-alliance.org
URL: http://www.media-alliance.org

Description: Writers, photographers, editors, broadcast workers, public relations practioners, videographers, filmmakers, commercial artists and other media workers and aspiring media workers. Supports free press and independent, alternative journalism that services progressive politics and social justice.

★11979★ National Association of African-American Sportswriters and Broadcasters
308 Deer Park Ave.
Dix Hills, NY 11746
Ph: (631)462-3933
E-mail: clydesports@aol.com

Members: African-American men and women involved in the sports industry. **Purpose:** Provides job information in the areas of sports medicine, sports law, and sports management. **Activities:** Offers children's services; sponsors research and educational programs.

★11980★ National Writers Association (ABWA)
3140 S Peoria St., Ste. 295
Aurora, CO 80014-3155
Ph: (303)841-0246   Fax: (303)841-2607
E-mail: ExecDirSandyWhelchel@nationalwriters.com
URL: http://www.nationalwriters.com

Members: Professional full- or part-time freelance writers who specialize in business writing. **Purpose:** Objective is to serve as a marketplace whereby business editors can easily locate competent writing talent. **Activities:** Establishes communication among editors and writers.

★11981★ Society of American Business Editors and Writers (SABEW)
134 Neff Annex
Columbia, MO 65211
Ph: (573)882-7862   Fax: (573)884-1372
E-mail: padenc@missouri.edu
URL: http://www.sabew.org

Members: Active business, economic, and financial news writers and editors for newspapers, magazines, and other publications; broadcasters of business news; teachers of business or journalism at colleges and universities. **Activities:** Plans periodic seminars on problems and techniques in business news coverage and occasional special meetings with business, financial, government and labor leaders, and other experts. Maintains the Resume Bank, a service which keeps resumes of SABEW members on file. Editors looking for job candidates can re-

quest the resumes of candidates that meet their requirements.

★11982★ Society of Professional Journalists (SPJ)
3909 N Meridian St.
Indianapolis, IN 46208-4011
Ph: (317)927-8000   Fax: (317)920-4789
E-mail: questions@spj.org
URL: http://www.spj.org

Members: Professional society - journalism. **Purpose:** Promotes a free and unfettered press; high professional standards and ethical behavior; journalism as a career. Conducts lobbying activities; maintains legal defense fund. Sponsors Pulliam/Kilgore Freedom of Information Internships in Washington, DC, and Indianapolis, IN. **Activities:** Holds forums on the free press.

★11983★ Women in Scholarly Publishing (WISP)
1070 Beacon St., Apt. 6D
Brookline, MA 02446-3951
E-mail: sworst@comcast.net
URL: http://www.womeninscholarlypublishing.org

Description: Women involved in scholarly publishing and men who support the organization's goals. Promotes professional development and advancement, management skills, and opportunities for women in scholarly publishing. Concerns include career development, job-sharing information, and surveys of salaries and job opportunities for women, and practical workshops or other training opportunities. Provides a forum and network for communication among women in presses throughout the U.S. Sponsors educational workshops, programs, and seminars, in conjunction with the Association of American University Presses. Compiles statistics.

Broad Sources of Job-Hunting Information

REFERENCE WORKS

★11984★ Adams Electronic Job Search Almanac

Adams Media Corp.
57 Littlefield St.
Avon, MA 02322
Ph: (508)427-7100   Fax: (508)427-6790
Fr: 800-872-5627

Annual. $10.95. Covers job listings on the Internet; bulletin boards, Web networking, and online services for finding a job. Entries include: Firm or organization name, address, phone, name and title of contact; description of organization, headquarters location, typical titles for entry- and middle-level positions, educational backgrounds desired, fringe benefits offered, stock exchange listing, training programs, internships, parent company, number of employees, revenues, e-mail and web address, projected number of hires. Arrangement: Alphabetical.

★11985★ Adams Jobs Almanac

Adams Media Corp.
57 Littlefield St.
Avon, MA 02322
Ph: (508)427-7100   Fax: (508)427-6790
Fr: 800-872-5627

Annual. $16.95. Covers job listings nationwide. Entries include: Firm or organization name, address, phone, name and title of contact; description of organization, headquarters location, typical titles for entry- and middle-level positions, educational backgrounds desired, fringe benefits offered, stock exchange listing, training programs, internships, parent company, number of employees, revenues, e-mail and web address, projected number of hires. Indexes: Alphabetical.

★11986★ American Directory of Job and Labor Market Information

Career Communications
PO Box 169
Harleysville, PA 19438

$29.95. Covers resources providing information on jobs and labor markets, including state and federal government personnel departments, job information centers, employment service centers, databases, libraries, and publications. Arrangement: Classified by type of resource.

★11987★ America's Career InfoNet

U.S. Department of Labor
Administrative Services Ctr.
200 Constitution Ave. NW
Washington, DC 20210
URL: http://www.acinet.org/acinet

Covers links to and information about job banks, employment service providers, career education, and nationwide employer contacts.

★11988★ Atlanta JobBank

Adams Media Corp.
57 Littlefield St.
Avon, MA 02322
Ph: (508)427-7100   Fax: (508)427-6790
Fr: 800-872-5627
URL: http://www.adamsmedia.com/reference

$16.95. Covers 3,900 employers in the state of Georgia, including Albany, Columbus, Macon, and Savannah. Entries include: Firm or organization name, address, local phone, toll-free phone, fax, description of organization, subsidiaries, other locations, recorded jobline, name and title of contact, typical titles for common positions, educational backgrounds desired, number of employees, benefits offered, training programs, internships, parent company, revenues, e-mail and URL address, projected number of hires. Arrangement: Classified by industry. Indexes: Alphabetical.

★11989★ The Austin/San Antonio JobBank

Adams Media Corp.
57 Littlefield St.
Avon, MA 02322
Ph: (508)427-7100   Fax: (508)427-6790
Fr: 800-872-5627

Biennial. $16.95. Covers more than 5,100 companies in metro Austin, metro San Anto-

nio, and the surrounding area, including El Paso. Entries include: Firm or organization name, address, phone, name and title of contact; description of organization, headquarters location, typical titles for entry- and middle-level positions, educational backgrounds desired, fringe benefits offered, stock exchange listing, training programs, internships, parent company, number of employees, revenues, e-mail and web address, projected number of hires. Indexes: Alphabetical.

★11990★ Authoritative Guide to the Top 100 Careers to Year 2005

Research and Education Association
61 Ethel Rd., W
Piscataway, NJ 08854
Ph: (732)819-8880   Fax: (732)819-8808
Fr: 800-822-0830

1997. $19.95 (paper). 368 pages.

★11991★ The Baby Boomer's Guide to a Successful Job Search

AuthorHouse
1663 Liberty Dr., Ste. 200
Bloomington, IN 47403
Ph: (812)961-1023   Fax: (812)339-8654
Fr: 800-839-8640

Don Theeuwes. April 2004. $13.95 (paper). 108 pages.

★11992★ The Best Home-Based Businesses for the 90s

Putnam Publishing Group
375 Hudson St.
New York, NY 10014
Ph: (212)366-2000   Fax: (212)366-2643
Fr: 800-331-4624

Paul Edwards and Sarah Edwards. Second edition, 1991. $11.95 (paper). 272 pages. Profiles 95 businesses and careers that can be conducted from one's home. Lists sources of additional information. Out of print.

★11993★ Boston JobBank

Adams Media Corp.
57 Littlefield St.
Avon, MA 02322
Ph: (508)427-7100   Fax: (508)427-6790
Fr: 800-872-5627
URL: http://www.adamsmedia.com/reference

Annual. $16.95. Covers over 7,000 employers in Massachusetts. Entries include: Firm or organization name, address, local phone, toll-free phone, fax, e-mail, URL, recorded jobline, hours, names of management, name and title of contact, titles of common positions, entry-level positions, fringe benefits offered, stock exchange listing, description of organization, subsidiaries, location of headquarters, educational background desired, projected number of hires, training programs, internships, parent company, number of employees, revenues, other U.S. locations, international locations. Arrangement: Classified by industry. Indexes: Alphabetical.

★11994★ The Career Fitness Program: Exercising Your Options

Prentice Hall PTR
200 Old Tappan Rd.
Old Tappan, NJ 07675
Ph: (201)236-7000   Fr: 800-567-3800

Diane Sukiennik. Sixth edition, 2000. Out of print. Textbook, with second half devoted to the job search process.

★11995★ Career Information Center

Macmillan Publishing Co. Inc.
200 Old Tappan Rd.
Old Tappan, NJ 07675
Fr: 800-428-5331

Visual Education Center Staff. Seventh edition, 1999. $275.00. 2080 pages. This 13-volume set profiles over 600 occupations. Each occupational profile describes job duties, educational requirements, how to get the job, advancement possibilities, employment outlook, working conditions, earnings and benefits, and where to write for more information.

★11996★ CareerXRoads: The Directory to Job, Resume and Career Management Sites on the Web

MMC GROUP
4545 Fuller Drive, Suite 222
Irving, TX 75038
Ph: (972)893-0100   Fax: (972)893-0099

Latest edition 2002. $26.95. Covers nearly 3,000 job and resume web sites with reviews and descriptions of the top 500. Indexes: Colleges; Corporations; Diversity; Specialty/Industry; Location; Listing services.

★11997★ Change Your Job, Change Your Life: High Impact Strategies for Finding Great Jobs in the 21st Century

Impact Publications
9104 Manassas Dr., Ste. N
Manassas Park, VA 20111-5211
Ph: (703)361-7300   Fax: (703)335-9486

Ronald Krannich. Seventh edition, 1999. $17.95 (paper). 317 pages. Details trends in the marketplace, how to identify opportunities, how to retrain for them, and how to land jobs. Includes a chapter on starting a business. Contains index, bibliography, and illustrations.

★11998★ Chicago JobBank

Adams Media Corp.
57 Littlefield St.
Avon, MA 02322
Ph: (508)427-7100   Fax: (508)427-6790
Fr: 800-872-5627
URL: http://www.adamsmedia.com/reference

Annual. $16.95. Covers about 5,500 major employers in northern and central Illinois including Aurora, Peoria, Rockford, and Springfield. Entries include: Firm or organization name, address, local phone, toll-free phone, fax, e-mail, URL, description of organization, hours, recorded jobline, subsidiaries, names of management, name and title of contact, names of management, headquarters locations, typical titles for entry-level and middle-level positions, educational backgrounds desired, company benefits, stock exchange listing, training programs, internships, parent company, number of employees, revenues, other U.S. locations, international locations. Arrangement: Classified by industry. Indexes: Alphabetical.

★11999★ Coming Alive from Nine to Five: The Career Search Handbook

Mayfield Publishing Co.
1280 Villa St.
Mountain View, CA 94041-1176
Ph: (650)960-3222   Fax: (650)960-0328
Fr: 800-433-1279

Betty Neville Michelozzi. Sixth edition, 1999. In addition to general job-hunting advice, provides special information for women, young adults, minorities, older workers, and persons with handicaps.

★12000★ The Connecticut JobBank

Adams Media Corp.
57 Littlefield St.
Avon, MA 02322
Ph: (508)427-7100   Fax: (508)427-6790
Fr: 800-872-5627
URL: http://www.careercity.com

Biennial. $16.95. Covers approximately 2,000 employers, career resources, industry associations, and employment services in Connecticut. Entries include: Company name, address, phone, fax, e-mail, and web address; names and titles of key personnel; number of employees; geographical area served; financial data; subsidiary names and

addresses; description of services; Standard Industrial Classification (SIC) code. Indexes: Alphabetical.

★12001★ Damn, I Need a Job. Again!

Kanianthra Press
PO Box 23311
Seattle, WA 98102

March 2004. $14.99.

★12002★ Directory of New Jersey & Delaware Valley Human Resources Top Executives

Corfacts Publishing
39 E. Hanover Ave.
Morris Plains, NJ 07950-2456
Ph: (973)394-2990   Fax: (973)326-9188
Fr: 800-678-2565
URL: http://www.corfacts.com

Covers more than 5,000 human resources New Jersey and Delaware Valley in companies with more than 100 employees. Entries include: Company name, address, phone, fax, year founded, revenues, employee size, business codes, description, parent company, human resource contacts and title. Arrangement: Alphabetical, geographical, industry.

★12003★ Directory: Who's Who in Career Services & HR/Staffing

National Association of Colleges and Employers
62 Highland Ave.
Bethlehem, PA 18017
Ph: (610)868-1421   Fax: (610)868-0208
Fr: 800-544-5272
URL: http://www.jobweb.org/

Annual, latest edition January 1999. $47.95. Covers about 1,760 college and university offices concerned with securing employment for graduates and about 1,430 companies with staff assigned to recruiting and hiring college graduates. Entries include: For colleges-College name and address; names, titles, phone, fax, and URL and e-mail addresses of career planning and placement personnel; interview dates for undergraduates and graduates; months of graduation; whether alumni placement is also handled, student enrollment (including minority data), and dates of career/job fairs. For employers-Company name; names, addresses, phone, fax and e-mail addresses of recruitment staff; names of secondary contacts; nature of business; number of employees. Arrangement: Colleges are geographical; employers are alphabetical. Indexes: Institutional name, personal name (college personnel); geographical, personal name (in company recruitment).

★12004★ Dr. Job's Complete Career Guide: Advice for Getting Ahead in Your Career

McGraw-Hill Trade
2 Penn Plaza
New York, NY 10121
Ph: (212)904-2000   Fr: 800-722-4726

E-mail: ntcpub@tribune.com

Sandra Pesmen. 1995. $14.95 (paper). 192 pages. Out of print.

★12005★ **The Don't Sweat Guide to Your Job Search: Finding a Career Your Really Love**
Hyperion Press
77 W. 66th St., 11th Fl.
New York, NY 10023-6298
Ph: (212)456-0100   Fax: (212)456-0108
Fr: 800-759-0190

$10.70 (paper). 208 pages.

★12006★ **The Edge: Job Search Advice from the Hiring Side of the Desk**
Transition Strategy, Inc.
5813 Summers Grove Rd.
Alexandria, VA 22304

Donna Bernard, Carl Henrickson. February 2004. $19.95.

★12007★ **Effective Strategies for Career Success**
JIST Publishing
8902 Otis Ave.
Indianapolis, IN 46216-1033
Ph: (317)613-4200   Fax: (317)613-4307
Fr: 800-648-5478
E-mail: customerservice@chronicleguidance.com

$9.95 (paper). 380 pages.

★12008★ **Employment Opportunities, USA**
Washington Research Associates
1660 S. Albion, Ste. 390
Denver, CO 80222
Ph: (303)398-7025   Fax: (303)415-2500

Annual, quarterly updates. $184.00. Publication includes: List of over 1,000 employment contacts in companies and agencies in the banking, arts, telecommunications, education, and 14 other industries and professions, including the federal government. Entries include: Company name, name of representative, address, description of products or services, hiring and recruiting practices, training programs, and year established. Principal content is industry overviews, career news, employment opportunity information on 14 different job markets, and comprehensive guidance to career resources on the Internet. Arrangement: Classified by industry. Indexes: Occupation.

★12009★ **Employment Opportunity Career Locator**
Prentice Hall PTR
One Lake St.
Upper Saddle River, NJ 07458
Ph: (201)236-7000

Alan L. Moss and Donald G. Yale. 1999. $20.00.

★12010★ **The Enhanced Guide for Occupational Exploration**
JIST Publishing
8902 Otis Ave.
Indianapolis, IN 46216-1033
Ph: (317)613-4200   Fax: (317)613-4307
Fr: 800-648-5478

Marilyn Maze, Donald Mayall and J. Michael Farr. Second edition, 1995. $44.95; $29.95 (paper). 704 pages. Provides descriptions for 2800 jobs. Each description includes skills, abilities, academic and physical requirements, work environment, salary, and outlook. Contains indices to career alternatives based on interests, skills, industry, and education.

★12011★ **Find and Get Your Dream Job**
Socrates Media LLC
227 W. Monroe, Ste. 500
Chicago, IL 60606
Fax: (312)762-5601   Fr: 800-822-4566

$5.95. Laminated. Career tool.

★12012★ **The First Job Hunt Survival Guide**
DBM Publishing
275 Broad Hollow Rd., Ste. 300
Melville, NY 11747
Ph: (516)752-3789   Fax: (516)756-2571
Fr: 800-345-5627
URL: http://www.dbm.com

Pat Morton and Marcia R. Fox, editors. 1995. $11.95 (paper). 176 pages. Helps new graduates navigate the entry-level job market.

★12013★ **First Stop for Jobs and Industries**
Thomson Gale
27500 Drake Rd.
Farmington Hills, MI 48331-3535
Ph: (248)699-4253   Fax: (248)699-8065
Fr: 800-877-GALE
URL: http://www.gale.com

Annual. $125.00. Covers 1,000 industries, 500 occupations, and reviews of top companies. Entries include: For companies—Contact information.

★12014★ **4 Data Base**
Hunt-Scanlon Publishing
20 Signal Rd.
Stamford, CT 06902-7907
Ph: (203)352-2920   Fax: (203)352-2930

Annual. $1,350.00 for individuals. Database covers more than 100,000 top and middle management professionals in human resources, finance, sales and marketing, and information technology at over 10,000 companies in the U.S. Entries include: Company name, address, phone, number of employees, SIC codes, revenues, individual name, title, phone number, industry specialization.

★12015★ **Games Companies Play: The Job Hunter's Guide to Playing Smart and Winning Big in the High Stakes Hiring Game**
Ten Speed Press
555 Richmond St. W.
Ste. 405, Box 702
Toronto, ON, Canada M5V 3B1
Ph: (416)703-7775   Fax: (416)703-9992
Fr: 800-841-2665

Pierre Mornell. March 2004. $17.95 (paper). Illustrated. 216 pages.

★12016★ **Get A Job! Put Your Degree to Work**
Donna Kozik
2828 University Ave., Ste. 227
San Diego, CA 92104
Ph: (619)297-1749

Donna Kozik. 2004. $19.95

★12017★ **Get That Job!: Job Openings**
McGraw-Hill Contemporary Books
1221 Avenue of the Americas
New York, NY 10020
Ph: (212)904-2000   Fr: 800-323-4900

1997. $4.66 (paper).

★12018★ **Get That Job!: Work Experience**
McGraw-Hill Contemporary Books
1221 Avenue of the Americas
New York, NY 10020
Ph: (212)904-2000   Fr: 800-323-4900

1997. $4.66 (paper).

★12019★ **Getting the Job You Really Want**
JIST Publishing
8902 Otis Ave.
Indianapolis, IN 46216-1033
Ph: (317)613-4200   Fax: (317)613-4307
Fr: 800-648-5478
E-mail: jistworks@aol.com
URL: http://www.jist.com

J. Michael Farr. Fourth edition, 2001. $12.95 (paper). 208 pages. A step-by-step guide to career planning, job seeking, and job survival.

★12020★ **Getting, Keeping, and Growing in Your Job**
Beckett-Highland Publishing
1429 Chase Ct.
Carmel, IN 46032-7502
Ph: (317)844-8622   Fax: (317)573-0239
Fr: 800-222-0590
E-mail: energ123@aol.com

William G. Corbin and Kim Corbin. 1994. $9.95. 245 pages. Covers job hunting topics such as writing resumes and cover letters, interviews, and starting a new job.

★12021★ Getting Your Foot in the Door When You Don't Have a Leg to Stand On

McGraw-Hill Trade
2 Penn Plaza
New York, NY 10121
Ph: (212)904-2000

Rob Sullivan. 2001. $12.95 (paper).

★12022★ Great Jobs

Scholastic Library Publisher Inc.
90 Old Sherman Tpke.
Danbury, CT 06816
Ph: (203)797-3500   Fax: (203)797-3657
Fr: 800-621-1115

2004. $20.00. Career search.

★12023★ Guide for the Pissed-off-Job-Seeker: Angry? Good! Use That Anger to Get Work!

iUniverse, Inc.
2021 Pine Lake Rd., Ste. 100
Lincoln, NE 68512
Ph: (402)323-7824   Fax: (402)323-7824
Fr: 877-288-4737

Irv Zuckerman, David Abel. May 2004. $14.95 (paper). 132 pages.

★12024★ Guide for the Unemployed Workbook

Prosperity and Profits Unlimited
PO Box 416
Denver, CO 80201-0416
Ph: (303)575-5676   Fax: (970)292-2136

Frieda Carrol. 1997. $24.95 (ringbound). 60 pages.

★12025★ The Harvard Business School Guide to Finding Your Next Job

Harvard Business School Press
60 Harvard Way
Boston, MA 02163
Ph: (617)783-7400   Fax: (617)783-7492
Fr: 888-500-1016

Robert S. Gardella. 2000. $16.95 (paper).

★12026★ Have No Career Fear: A College Grad's Guide to Snagging a Job, Trekking the Career Path, and Reaching Job Nirvana

Natavi Guides
276 First Ave., No. 6G
New York, NY 10009
Fr: (866)425-4218

Ben Cohen-Leadholm, Rachel Skerritt, Ari Gerzon-Kessler. April 2004. $13.95 (paper). 206 pages.

★12027★ Help Wanted: An Inexperienced Job Seekers Complete Guide to Career Success

Waveland Press, Inc.
PO Box 400
Prospect Heights, IL 60070
Ph: (847)634-0081   Fax: (847)634-9501

Ann M. Gill and Stephen M. Lewis. 1996. $18.95 (paper). 212 pages.

★12028★ Houston JobBank

Adams Media Corp.
57 Littlefield St.
Avon, MA 02322
Ph: (508)427-7100   Fax: (508)427-6790
Fr: 800-872-5627
URL: http://www.adamsmedia.com/reference

Annual. $16.95. Covers over 3,500 employers in Houston, Texas and the surrounding areas including Bayton, Beaumont, Galveston, Pasadena. Entries include: Firm or organization name, address, local phone, toll-free phone, fax, recorded jobline, e-mail, URL, hours, name and title of contact; description of organization; headquarters location, subsidiaries, operations at the facility, names of management, typical titles for common positions, educational backgrounds desired, number of projected hires, fringe benefits offered, stock exchange listing, training programs, internships, parent company, number of employees, revenues, other U.S. locations, international locations. Arrangement: Classified by industry. Indexes: Alphabetical.

★12029★ How to Choose Your Next Employer

Oakhill Press
461 Layside Dr., Suite 102
Winchester, VA 22602-2123
Ph: (540)877-1689   Fax: (540)877-1360
Fr: 800-322-6657

Roger E. Herman. 2000.

★12030★ How to Find the Work You Love

Penguin Putnam, Inc.
375 Hudson St.
New York, NY 10014
Ph: (212)366-2000   Fax: (212)366-2666
Fr: 800-788-6262

Laurence G. Boldt. 1996. $10.95 (paper). 192 pages.

★12031★ How to Get Any Job with Any Major: A New Look at Career Launch

Ten Speed Press
555 Richmond St. W.
Ste. 405, Box 702
Toronto, ON, Canada M5V 3B1
Ph: (416)703-7775   Fax: (416)703-9992
Fr: 800-841-2665

Donald Asher. June 2004. $14.95 (paper). 336 pages.

★12032★ How to Get a Better Job in This Crazy World

NAL
375 Hudson St.
New York, NY 10014-3657
Ph: (212)366-2000   Fax: (212)366-2666
Fr: 800-331-4624

Robert Half. 1994. $5.50. 256 pages.

★12033★ How to Get Hired Today!

McGraw-Hill Trade
2 Penn Plaza
New York, NY 10121
Ph: (212)904-2000   Fr: 800-722-4726
E-mail: ntcpub@tribune.com

George E. Kent. 1994. $7.95 (paper). 120 pages. Directed at individuals who know the type of job they are looking for. Focuses the reader on activities that are likely to lead to a job and eliminates those that won't. Shows how to establish productive contacts and discover, evaluate, and pursue strong job leads.

★12034★ How to Get a Job & Keep It

Ferguson Publishing Company
200 W. Jackson Blvd., 7th Flr.
Chicago, IL 60606-3412
Ph: (312)692-1000   Fax: (312)692-1020
Fr: 800-306-9941

Susan Morem. 2001.

★12035★ How to Get the Job You Desire

Dorrance Publishing Company, Inc.
701 Smithfield St.
Pittsburgh, PA 15222
Ph: (412)288-4543   Fax: (412)434-8430
Fr: 800-788-7654

Peggy Redman. March 2004. $14.95 (paper). 40 pages.

★12036★ How to Get That Job

Pilot Books
127 Sterling Ave.
PO Box 2102
Greenport, NY 11944-0893
Ph: (516)477-1094   Fax: (516)477-0978
Fr: 800-797-4568
URL: http://www.pilotbooks.com

Ruby N. Gorter. 1997. $8.95. 94 pages. Provides information for first-time job seekers as well as those who want to change careers.

★12037★ How to Get Your Dream Job in 60 Days: For College Graduates

Althemus
PO Box 8634
Northridge, CA 91327
Fax: (818)831-1316

Kerry Gardette. February 2004. $12.95 (paper). Illustrated. 163 pages.

★12038★ How to Land a Better Job

McGraw-Hill Trade
2 Penn Plaza
New York, NY 10121
Ph: (212)904-2000　　Fr: 800-722-4726
E-mail: ntcpub@tribune.com

Catherine S. Lott and Oscar C. Lott. Third edition, 1994. $8.95 (paper). 144 pages. Tells the job seeker how to enhance his or her credentials, overcome past weaknesses, uncover job leads, get appointments, organize an appealing resume, and score points in interviews. A special section devoted to getting a better job without changing companies covers the process of transferring departments and gives pointers on moving up to the boss's job. Out of print.

★12039★ How to Locate Jobs and Land Interviews

The Career Press, Inc.
3 Tice Rd.
PO Box 687
Franklin Lakes, NJ 07417-1322
Ph: (201)848-0310　　Fax: (201)848-1727
Fr: 800-227-3371

Albert L. French. Second edition, 1993. $10.95 (paper). 192 pages. Shows readers how to tap into the unadvertised, hidden job market and guides them through the resume, cover letter, and interview preparation process. Out of print.

★12040★ How to Market Your College Degree

McGraw-Hill Trade
2 Penn Plaza
New York, NY 10121
Ph: (212)904-2000　　Fr: 800-722-4726
E-mail: ntcpub@tribune.com

Dorothy Rogers. 1993. $12.95 (paper). 168 pages. Provides a guide to self-marketing as a key component of an effective job search. Helps job seekers to develop a strategic marketing plan that targets niches with needs that match their skills, differentiate themselves from the competition by positioning themselves against other candidates, evaluate their potential worth from the employer's perspective, and manage their careers as they move up the career ladder or into another field.

★12041★ How to Move from College into a Secure Job

McGraw-Hill Trade
2 Penn Plaza
New York, NY 10121
Ph: (212)904-2000　　Fr: 800-722-4726
E-mail: ntcpub@tribune.com

Mary Dehner. 1993. $12.95 (paper). 192 pages.

★12042★ Hunt-Scanlon's Executive Recruiters of North America - Contingency Firms

Hunt-Scanlon Publishing
20 Signal Rd.
Stamford, CT 06902-7907
Ph: (203)352-2920　　Fax: (203)352-2930

Annual. $225.00 for individuals. Covers more than 3,000 executive recruiters in a cross-section of contingency search firms in North America. Entries include: Individual and company name, phone number, and revenue statistics. Arrangement: Alphabetical. Indexes: Geographical, business sector.

★12043★ Hunt-Scanlon's Executive Recruiters of North America - Retained Firms

Hunt-Scanlon Publishing
20 Signal Rd.
Stamford, CT 06902-7907
Ph: (203)352-2920　　Fax: (203)352-2930

Annual. $225.00 for individuals. Covers more than 3,600 retained executive recruiters in the U.S., Canada, and Mexico. Entries include: Individual name, phone number, specialization, revenue, professional memberships, salary levels.

★12044★ Hunt-Scanlon's Select Guide to Human Resource Executives

Hunt-Scanlon Publishing
20 Signal Rd.
Stamford, CT 06902-7907
Ph: (203)352-2920　　Fax: (203)352-2930

Annual. $265.00 for individuals. Covers more than 23,000 human resource executives, personnel managers, and compensation, benefits, and training professionals in 9,500 companies in the U.S. Entries include: Company and individual name, title.

★12045★ The Indiana JobBank

Adams Media Corp.
57 Littlefield St.
Avon, MA 02322
Ph: (508)427-7100　　Fax: (508)427-6790
Fr: 800-872-5627

Biennial. $16.95. Covers 3,200 employers in Indiana, including Evansville, Fort Wayne, Gary, New Albany, and South Bend. Entries include: Firm or organization name, address, phone, name and title of contact; description of organization, headquarters location, typical titles for entry- and middle-level positions, educational backgrounds desired, fringe benefits offered, stock exchange listing, training programs, internships, parent company, number of employees, revenues, e-mail and web address, projected number of hires. Indexes: Alphabetical.

★12046★ Job Hotlines USA: A National Telephone Directory of Employer Joblines

Career Communications
PO Box 169
Harleysville, PA 19438

Published 1994. $24.95. Covers over 1,000 government agencies, hospitals, colleges, companies, and federal job information centers that have employment hotlines. Entries include: company name, address, voice telephone number, job hotline number, and industry classification.

★12047★ The Job Hunter's Catalog

John Wiley & Sons Inc.
1 Wiley Dr.
Somerset, NJ 08873
Ph: (732)469-4400　　Fr: 800-225-5945

Peggy Schmidt. First edition, 1996. $10.95 (paper). 192 pages.

★12048★ Job Hunting for Dummies

Running Press Book Publishers
125 S. 22nd St.
Philadelphia, PA 19103-4399
Ph: (215)567-5080　　Fax: (215)568-2919
Fr: 800-345-5359

Robert Half, Max Massmer, Jr. 2002. $4.95. 128 pages. A one-stop reference.

★12049★ Job Hunting Made Easy

LearningExpress LLC
900 Broadway, Ste. 604
New York, NY 10003
Ph: (212)995-2566　　Fax: (212)995-5512
Fr: 800-295-9556
E-mail: ntcpub@tribune.com

Carol Sonnenblick. 1997. $12.95 (paper). 160 pages.

★12050★ Job Search: Career Planning Guide

Brooks/Cole Publishing Company
511 Forest Lodge Rd.
Pacific Grove, CA 93950
Ph: (831)373-0728　　Fax: (831)375-6414

Robert D. Lock. Third edition, 1995. $20.75 (paper). Assists the reader in a productive job search. Part of Career Planning Guide series.

★12051★ Job Search 101

Marketing Directions
8902 Otis Ave.
Indianapolis, IN 46216-1033
Ph: (317)613-4200　　Fax: (317)613-4307
Fr: 800-648-5478
E-mail: jistworks@aol.com
URL: http://www.jist.com

Marcia Fox and Pat Morton. 1997. $12.95. 325 pages. An introductory guide to entry-level jobs.

★12052★ Job Seeker's Guide
Thomson Gale
27500 Drake Rd
Farmington Hills, MI 48331
Ph: (248)699-4253   Fax: (214)746-6799
$10.00 for members; $15.00 for nonmembers. Covers top 100 employers in the Dallas area, information on employment agencies, and labor market projections.

★12053★ Job Wise: 150 Tips to Help You Survive & Thrive in Your Career
John Wiley & Sons, Incorporated
605 Third Ave., 4th Fl.
New York, NY 10158-0012
Ph: (212)850-6276   Fax: (212)850-8641
Steve Klein. 1999. $19.95.

★12054★ JobSmarts 50 Top Careers
HarperTrade
10 E. 53rd St.
New York, NY 10022
Ph: (212)207-7000   Fax: (212)207-7633
Fr: 800-242-7737
Bradley G. Richardson. 1997. $16.00 (paper). 400 pages.

★12055★ Joyce Lain Kennedy's Career Book
McGraw-Hill Contemporary Books
1221 Avenue of the Americas
New York, NY 10020
Ph: (212)904-2000   Fr: 800-323-4900
E-mail: ntcpub@tribune.com
Joyce Lain Kennedy and Dr. Darryl Laramore. Third edition, 1996. $29.95; $17.95 (paper). 448 pages. Guides the reader through the entire career-planning and job-hunting process. Addresses how to find the kinds of jobs available and what to do once the job is secured. Provides a number of case histories to give examples.

★12056★ Knock 'Em Dead: The Ultimate Job Seeker's Handbook
Adams Media Corp.
57 Littlefield St.
Avon, MA 02322
Ph: (508)427-7100   Fax: (508)427-6790
Fr: 800-872-5627
URL: http://www.adamsmedia.com
Martin Yate. Revised edition, 2002. $12.95 (paper). Prepares the job seeker for the interview with advice on dress, manner, how to answer the toughest questions, and how to spot illegal questions. Discusses how to respond to questions of salary to maximize income. Features sections on executive search firms and drug testing. 352 pages.

★12057★ Last Minute Job Search Tips
Career Press, Inc.
PO Box 687
3 Tice Rd.
Franklin Lakes, NJ 07417
Ph: (201)848-0310   Fax: (201)848-1727
Fr: 800-227-3371

URL: http://www.CareerPress.com
Brandon Toropov. 1996. $7.99 (paper). 168 pages.

★12058★ Los Angeles JobBank
Adams Media Corp.
57 Littlefield St.
Avon, MA 02322
Ph: (508)427-7100   Fax: (508)427-6790
Fr: 800-872-5627
URL: http://www.adamsmedia.com/reference
Annual. $16.95. Covers over 7,900 southern California employers including Orange, Riverside, San Bernadino, San Diego, Santa Barbara and Ventura counties. Entries include: Firm or organization name, address, local phone, toll-free phone, fax, e-mail, URL, recorded jobline, hours, subsidiaries, other locations, names of management, name and title of contact, description of organization, number of employees, headquarters location, typical titles for common positions, educational backgrounds desired, fringe benefits offered, stock exchange listing, training programs, internships, parent company, number of employees, revenues, corporate headquarters, and number of projected hires. Arrangement: Classified by industry. Indexes: Alphabetical.

★12059★ Major Employers Directory
Greater Philadelphia Chamber of Commerce
200 S. Broad St., Ste. 700
Philadelphia, PA 19102
Ph: (215)545-1234   Fax: (215)790-3700
$20.00 for members; $28.00 for nonmembers. Covers Top employers and pertinent information for all 11 greater Philadelphia counties.

★12060★ Making a Life, Making a Living: Reclaiming Your Purpose and Passion in Business and in Life
Warner Books, Incorporated
1271 Avenue of the Americas
New York, NY 10020
Ph: (212)522-7200
Mark Albion. 2000.

★12061★ Metro New York JobBank
Adams Media Corp.
57 Littlefield St.
Avon, MA 02322
Ph: (508)427-7100   Fax: (508)427-6790
Fr: 800-872-5627
URL: http://www.adamsmedia.com/reference
$16.95. Covers over 7,900 New York City Northern New Jersey, Southwestern Connecticut, Long Island, and Westchester employers. Entries include: Firm or organization name, address, local phone, toll-free phone, fax, e-mail, URL, recorded jobline, hours, name and title of contact; description of organization, subsidiaries, other locations, names of management, headquarters loca-

tion, typical titles for common positions, educational backgrounds desired, fringe benefits offered, stock exchange listing, training programs, internships, parent company, number of employees, revenues, projected number of hires. Arrangement: Classified by industry. Indexes: Alphabetical.

★12062★ Metro Washington DC JobBank
Adams Media Corp.
57 Littlefield St.
Avon, MA 02322
Ph: (508)427-7100   Fax: (508)427-6790
Fr: 800-872-5627
URL: http://www.adamsmedia.com/reference
$16.95. Covers 6,900 employers in Washington, D.C., greater Baltimore, and northern Virginia. Entries include: Firm or organization name, address, local phone, toll-free phone, fax, recorded jobline, name and title of contact, description of organization, subsidiaries, other locations, names of management, hours, titles for common positions, educational backgrounds desired, company benefits, stock exchange listing, location of headquarters, training programs, internships, parent company, number of employees, revenues, email and URL address, projected number of hires. Arrangement: Classified by industry. Indexes: Alphabetical.

★12063★ Moving on in Your Career
Routledge
29 W. 35th St.
New York, NY 10001-2299
Ph: (212)216-7800   Fax: (212)564-7854
Lynda Ali and Barbara Graham. 2000. $75.00.

★12064★ Nail It! Get a Job in 24 Hours Using 10 Insider Secrets
Entrepreneur Media Inc.
2445 McCabe Way, Ste. 400
Irvine, CA 92614-6244
Ph: (949)261-2325   Fax: (949)261-7729
Fr: 800-864-6864
Todd Bermont. February 2004. $17.95 (paper). 208 pages.

★12065★ National JobBank
Adams Media Corp.
57 Littlefield St.
Avon, MA 02322
Ph: (508)427-7100   Fax: (508)427-6790
Fr: 800-872-5627
URL: http://www.adamsmedia.com/reference
Annual. $395.00. Covers over 21,000 employers nationwide. Entries include: Firm or organization name, address, local phone, toll-free phone, fax, contact name and title, description of organization, headquarters location, names of management, number of employees, other locations, subsidiaries, parent company, projected number of hires, training offered, internships, hours, recorded jobline, typical titles for common positions,

educational backgrounds desired, stock exchange (if listed), fringe benefits offered. Several state and regional volumes are available and described separately. Arrangement: Geographical. Indexes: Geographical and classified by industry.

★12066★ **Network Your Way to Job and Career Success**

Impact Publications
9104 Manassas Dr., Ste. N
Manassas Park, VA 20111-5211
Ph: (703)361-7300   Fax: (703)335-9486

Ronald L. Krannich and Caryl R. Krannich. Third edition, 1995. $15.95 (paper). 181 pages. Out of print. Based on a comprehensive career planning framework, each chapter outlines the best strategies for identifying, finding, and transforming networks to gather information and obtain advice and referrals that lead to job interviews and offers. Includes exercises, sample interviewing dialogues, and a directory of organizations for initiating and sustaining networking activities.

★12067★ **The New Jersey JobBank**

Adams Media Corp.
57 Littlefield St.
Avon, MA 02322
Ph: (508)427-7100   Fax: (508)427-6790
Fr: 800-872-5627
URL: http://www.careercity.com

Biennial. $16.95. Covers approximately 4,000 employers, career resources, industry associations, and employment services in the Garden State. Entries include: Company name, address, phone, fax, email, and web address; names and titles of key personnel; number of employees; geographical area served; financial data; subsidiary names and addresses; description of services; standard industrial classification (sic) code. Indexes: Alphabetical.

★12068★ **Occupational Outlook Handbook**

U.S. Bureau of Labor Statistics
2 Massachusetts Ave. NE, Rm. 2135
Washington, DC 20212
Ph: (202)606-7828   Fax: (202)691-7890
E-mail: OOHinfo@bls.gov
URL: http://www.bls.gov/ocol

Biennial, January of even years. $57.00 for hardcover; $53.00 for softcover. Publication includes: Various occupational organizations that provide career information on hundreds of occupations. Entries include: For organizations-Organization name, address. Principal content of publication is profiles of various occupations, which include description of occupation, educational requirements, job outlook, and expected earnings. Arrangement: Organizations are classified by occupation.

★12069★ **The Ohio JobBank**

Adams Media Corp.
57 Littlefield St.
Avon, MA 02322
Ph: (508)427-7100   Fax: (508)427-6790
Fr: 800-872-5627

Biennial. $16.95. Covers 4,800 employers and employment services in Ohio. Entries include: Firm or organization name, address, phone, name and title of contact; description of organization, headquarters location, typical titles for entry- and middle-level positions, educational backgrounds desired, fringe benefits offered, stock exchange listing, training programs, internships, parent company, number of employees, revenues, e-mail and web address, projected number of hires. Arrangement: Alphabetical.

★12070★ **The Only Job Hunting Guide You'll Ever Need**

Simon & Schuster Inc.
1230 Ave. of the Americas
New York, NY 10020
Ph: (212)698-7000   Fax: (212)698-7007
Fr: 800-897-7650

Kathryn and Ross Petras. 1995. $15.00 (paper). 400 pages. Covers the full range of the job search process for job hunters and career switchers.

★12071★ **Outwitting the Job Market: Everything You Need to Locate and Land a Great Position**

Globe Pequot Press
246 Goose Ln.
Guilford, CT 06437
Ph: (203)458-4500   Fax: (203)458-4604
Fr: 800-243-0495

Chandra Prasad. May 2004. $13.95 (paper). 256 pages. Part of the Outwitting Series.

★12072★ **The Overnight Job Change Strategy**

Ten Speed Press
PO Box 7123
Berkeley, CA 94707
Ph: (510)559-1600   Fax: (510)559-1629
Fr: 800-841-2665

Donald Asher. 1993. $7.95 (paper). 265 pages. Subtitled "How to Plan a Comprehensive, Systematic Job Search in One Evening". Incorporates sales and marketing techniques into a six-stage job search process. Out of print.

★12073★ **The Perfect Job Reference**

John Wiley & Sons Inc.
1 Wiley Dr.
Somerset, NJ 08873
Ph: (732)469-4400   Fr: 800-225-5945

Jeffrey G. Allen. 1990. $9.95 (paper). 192 pages. Step-by-step methods for securing a written or verbal recommendation.

★12074★ **Peterson's Hidden Job Market**

Thomson Peterson's
Princeton Pike Corporate Center
2000 Lenox Dr.
PO Box 67005
Lawrenceville, NJ 08648
Ph: (609)896-1800   Fax: 800-277-2465
Fr: 800-338-3282
URL: http://www.petersons.com

Annual, June. $18.95. Covers approximately 2,000 technology firms with under 1,000 employees, which hire at four times the national rate. Entries include: Company name, address, phone, fax, name and title of contact, number of employees, year founded, number of employees added in last year, percentage of growth, line of business. Arrangement: Geographical by state, then by area code. Indexes: Alphabetical by industry.

★12075★ **The Practical Job-Search Guide**

Ten Speed Press
PO Box 7123
Berkeley, CA 94707
Fax: (510)559-1629   Fr: 800-841-2665

Donna Ferris. 1996. $14.95 (paper). 565 pages. Out of print. Includes action plan and workbook for job hunters.

★12076★ **The Procrastinator's Guide to the Job Hunt**

NAL
375 Hudson St.
New York, NY 10014-3657
Ph: (212)366-2000   Fax: (212)366-2666
Fr: 800-331-4624

Lorelei Lanum. June 2004. $14.00 (paper). 240 pages.

★12077★ **San Francisco Bay Area JobBank**

Adams Media Corp.
57 Littlefield St.
Avon, MA 02322
Ph: (508)427-7100   Fax: (508)427-6790
Fr: 800-872-5627
URL: http://www.adamsmedia.com/reference

$16.95. Covers about 5,600 employers in the San Francisco Bay area and the Northern half of California including Oakland, Sacramento, San Jose, and Silicon Valley. Entries include: Firm or organization name, address, local phone, toll-free phone, fax, e-mail, URL, recorded jobline, hours, description of organization, subsidiaries, other locations, number of employees, name and title of contact, headquarters location, typical titles for common positions, educational backgrounds desired, company benefits, stock exchange listing, training programs, internships, parent company, number of employees, revenues, corporate headquarters, and number of projected hires. Arrangement: Classified by industry. Indexes: Alphabetical.

★12078★ *Stay in Control: How to Cope and Still Get the Job You Really Want*

DBM Publishing
Drake Beam Morin, Inc.
275 Broad Hollow Rd., Suite 300
Melville, NY 11747
Ph: (516)752-3789   Fax: (516)756-2571
Fr: 800-345-5627
URL: http://www.dbm.com

Carla-Krystin Andrade. $14.95. 1994. 212 pages. Focuses on stress management during the job search process.

★12079★ *The Student's Guide to Finding a Superior Job*

Jossey-Bass Inc. Publishers
350 Sansome St.
San Francisco, CA 94104-1342
Ph: (415)433-1740   Fax: (415)433-0499
Fr: 800-956-7739

William A. Cohen. Second edition, 1993. $9.95 (paper). 108 pages. Aimed at the new college graduate. Out of print.

★12080★ *The Successful Job Search: A Step-by-Step Guide for a Successful Job Search in the 1990s*

Rogers Resource, Inc.
713 Ashworth Rd.
West Des Moines, IA 50265-3617
Ph: (515)225-1650   Fax: (515)225-6835

Roxanne S. Rogers. 1993. $29.95 (paper). 320 pages. The book covers the trauma & recovery processes for job loss, the special problems of first time job seekers, & guidance for total career changes.

★12081★ *Super Job Search: The Complete Manual for Job-Seekers and Career-Changers*

Jamenair Ltd.
PO Box 241957
Los Angeles, CA 90024-9757
Ph: (310)470-6688   Fax: (310)470-8106
Fr: 800-581-5953

Peter Studner. Third edition, 1998. $22.95 (paper). 352 pages. A step-by-step guidebook for getting a job, with sections on getting started, how to present accomplishments, networking strategies, telemarketing tips, and negotiating tactics.

★12082★ *Taking Charge of Your Career Direction*

Brooks/Cole Publishing Company
511 Forest Lodge Rd.
Pacific Grove, CA 93950
Ph: (831)373-0728   Fax: (831)375-6414

Robert D. Lock. Third edition, 1996. Three volumes. Provides guidance for the job search process.

★12083★ *303 Off-the-Wall Ways to Get a Job*

Career Press Inc.
3 Tice Rd.
Franklin Lakes, NJ 07417-1322
Ph: (201)848-0310   Fax: (201)848-1727
Fr: 800-227-3371

Brandon Toropov. 1995. $12.99 (paper). 312 pages. Provides a creative perspective on job hunting.

★12084★ *Tips for Finding the Right Job*

U.S. Government Printing Office
Superintendent of Documents
PO Box 371954
Pittsburgh, PA 15250-7954
Fr: (866)512-1800
URL: http://www.access.gpo.gov/su_docs/

Booklet 029-014-002445. 1996. $2.50. 27 pages. General advice for job seekers. See website for current list of available publications.

★12085★ *The Top 10 Fears of Job Seekers*

Berkley Publishing Group
375 Hudson St.
New York, NY 10014
Ph: (212)366-2000   Fax: (212)366-2385

Gary J. Grappo. 1996. 128 pages. $12.00 (paper). Shows effective ways to overcome common fears associated with job hunting.

★12086★ *Turn Your Degree into a Career: The Step-by-Step Guide to Choosing and Getting Your First Job*

How to Books
3 Newtec Pl., Magdalen Rd.
Oxford OX4 1RE, United Kingdom

Michael Collins, Benjamin Scott. January 2004. $15.75 (paper). 144 pages.

★12087★ *The Two Best Ways to Find a Job*

JIST Publishing
8902 Otis Ave.
Indianapolis, IN 46216-1033
Ph: (317)613-4200   Fax: (317)613-4307
Fr: 800-648-5478
URL: http://www.cambridgeol.com

Michael J. Farr and Susan Christophersen. $7.95. 248 pages. Presents techniques that emphasize nontraditional job search methods.

★12088★ *The Very Quick Job Search: Get a Better Job in Half the Time*

JIST Publishing
8902 Otis Ave.
Indianapolis, IN 46216-1033
Ph: (317)613-4200   Fax: (317)613-4307
Fr: 800-648-5478

J. Michael Farr. Second edition, 1996. $29.95. 460 pages.

★12089★ *The Virginia JobBank*

Adams Media Corp.
57 Littlefield St.
Avon, MA 02322
Ph: (508)427-7100   Fax: (508)427-6790
Fr: 800-872-5627

Biennial. $16.95. Covers 3,700 employers in Virginia and West Virginia. Entries include: Firm or organization name, address, phone, name and title of contact; description of organization, headquarters location, typical titles for entry- and middle-level positions, educational backgrounds desired, fringe benefits offered, stock exchange listing, training programs, internships, parent company, number of employees, revenues, e-mail and web address, projected number of hires. Indexes: Alphabetical.

★12090★ *What Color Is Your Parachute*

Ten Speed Press
PO Box 7123
Berkeley, CA 94707
Ph: (510)559-1600   Fax: (510)559-1629
Fr: 800-841-2665

Richard N. Bolles. 2001. $24.95. Publication cancelled. 368 pages. Subtitled: "A Practical Manual for Job-Hunters and Career-Changers". One of the best-known works on job hunting, this book provides detailed and strategic advice on all aspects of the job search.

★12091★ *What Employers Really Want: The Insider's Guide to Getting a Job*

McGraw-Hill Trade
2 Penn Plaza
New York, NY 10121
Ph: (212)904-2000   Fr: 800-722-4726

Barbara S. Hawk. 1998. $14.95 (paper). 224 pages.

★12092★ *Where the Jobs Are: The Hottest Careers for the 90s*

The Career Press, Inc.
3 Tice Rd.
PO Box 687
Franklin Lakes, NJ 07417-1322
Ph: (201)848-0310   Fax: (201)848-1727
Fr: 800-227-3371

Joyce Hadley. Third edition, 2000. $13.99 (paper). 400 pages. Out of print. Describes careers in fifteen general fields, from accounting to travel and hospitality.

★12093★ *You Have the Whole World in Your Hands: A Handbook and Workout Book on Choosing the Right Career Job*

Dorrance Publishing Company, Inc.
701 Smithfield St.
Pittsburgh, PA 15222
Ph: (412)288-4543   Fax: (412)434-8430
Fr: 800-788-7654

Hazel Elmore. May 2004. $9.00 (paper).

★12094★ You're Certifiable: The Alternative Career Guide to More than 700 Certificate Programs, Trade Schools and Job Opportunities
Simon & Schuster Inc.
1230 Avenue of the Americas
New York, NY 10020
Ph: (212)698-7000   Fax: (212)698-7007
Lee Naftali and Joel Naftali. 1999. $15.00 (paper).

NEWSPAPERS, MAGAZINES, AND JOURNALS

★12095★ Kennedy's Career Strategist
Career Strategies
1150 Willmette Ave.
Wilmette, IL 60091
Ph: (847)251-1661   Fax: (847)251-5191
Fr: 800-728-1709
Description: Ten issues/year. Offers advice on job hunting and discusses such topics as "how to win at office politics." Follows employment trends in various industries. Recurring features include interviewing techniques, salary strategies, and advice column.

★12096★ Occupational Outlook Quarterly
U.S. Government Printing Office
PO Box 371954
Pittsburgh, PA 15250-7954
Ph: (202)512-1800   Fax: (202)512-2250
E-mail: ooginfo@bls.gov
URL: http://www.bls.gov/opub/ooq/o-oqhome.htm
Quarterly. $14.00/year. Magazine providing occupational and employment information.

AUDIO/VISUAL RESOURCES

★12097★ Accommodating
Cambridge Educational
PO Box 931
Monmouth Junction, NJ 08852-0931
Fax: 800-FAX-ON-US   Fr: 800-468-4227
URL: http://www.cambridgeeducational.com
$69.95. 25 minutes. Part of the Video GOE series.

★12098★ Artistic
Cambridge Educational
PO Box 931
Monmouth Junction, NJ 08852-0931
Fax: 800-FAX-ON-US   Fr: 800-468-4227
URL: http://www.cambridgeeducational.com
$69.95. 45 minutes. Part of the Video GOE series.

★12099★ Behind the Scenes: Industrial Field Trips
Cambridge Educational
PO Box 931
Monmouth Junction, NJ 08852-0931
Fax: 800-FAX-ON-US   Fr: 800-468-4227
URL: http://www.cambridgeeducational.com
$239.95. Three videos.

★12100★ Business Detail
Cambridge Educational
PO Box 931
Monmouth Junction, NJ 08852-0931
Fax: 800-FAX-ON-US   Fr: 800-468-4227
URL: http://www.cambridgeeducational.com
$69.95. 25 minutes. Part of the Video GOE series.

★12101★ Career Cluster Series
Cambridge Educational
PO Box 931
Monmouth Junction, NJ 08852-0931
Fax: 800-FAX-ON-US   Fr: 800-468-4227
URL: http://www.cambridgeeducational.com
4 videos. $319.95. 18 minutes each. Includes education and training, health services, information technology services, and scientific, engineering, and technical services.

★12102★ Career Evaluation
Cambridge Educational
PO Box 931
Monmouth Junction, NJ 08852-0931
Fax: 800-FAX-ON-US   Fr: 800-468-4227
URL: http://www.cambridgeeducational.com
$69.95. 15 minutes.

★12103★ Career Exploration: You're in the Driver's Seat
Cambridge Educational
PO Box 931
Monmouth Junction, NJ 08852-0931
Fax: 800-FAX-ON-US   Fr: 800-468-4227
URL: http://www.cambridgeeducational.com
2 videos. $149.95. Covers mapping your career plan and tracking your interests and abilities.

★12104★ Careers in Science: From Archaeologist to Zoologist
Cambridge Educational
PO Box 931
Monmouth Junction, NJ 08852-0931
Fax: 800-FAX-ON-US   Fr: 800-468-4227
URL: http://www.cambridgeeducational.com
$79.95. 20 minutes.

★12105★ Careers Without College: Jobnet
Cambridge Educational
PO Box 931
Monmouth Junction, NJ 08852-0931
Fax: 800-FAX-ON-US   Fr: 800-468-4227
URL: http://www.cambridgeeducational.com
Video. 1996. $79.95. 30 minutes. Covers career opportunities and other options for high school graduates.

★12106★ Choices Today for Career Satisfaction Tomorrow
Cambridge Educational
PO Box 931
Monmouth Junction, NJ 08852-0931
Fax: 800-FAX-ON-US   Fr: 800-468-4227
URL: http://www.cambridgeeducational.com
Three videos. $189.95. 30 minutes each; includes student/teacher manual. Topics covered are preparing for an occupation, investigating the world of work, and self-awareness.

★12107★ The Complete Job Search System
Cambridge Educational
PO Box 931
Monmouth Junction, NJ 08852-0931
Fax: 800-FAX-ON-US   Fr: 800-468-4227
URL: http://www.cambridgeeducational.com
Five videos. 1997. $295.95/set. 15-20 minutes each. Individual titles cover career planning, career evaluation, finding a job, interviewing for a job, and succeeding on the job.

★12108★ Directing Your Successful Job Search
Cambridge Educational
PO Box 931
Monmouth Junction, NJ 08852-0931
Fax: 800-FAX-ON-US   Fr: 800-468-4227
URL: http://www.cambridgeeducational.com
Video. $69.95. 45 minutes. Describes the tools needed for a successful job search, networking, traditional sources of leads, and interviewing. Comes with an adapted version of the Cambridge Job Search Guide.

★12109★ Exceptional Employee: A Guide To Success On The Job
Cambridge Educational
PO Box 931
Monmouth Junction, NJ 08852-0931
Fax: 800-FAX-ON-US   Fr: 800-468-4227
URL: http://www.cambridgeeducational.com
$79.95. 1998. 25 minutes.

★12110★ Feedback on the Job: Accepting Criticism
Cambridge Educational
PO Box 931
Monmouth Junction, NJ 08852-0931
Fax: 800-FAX-ON-US   Fr: 800-468-4227
URL: http://www.cambridgeeducational.com
$99.95. 1999. 22 minutes.

★12111★ Finding a Job
Cambridge Educational
PO Box 931
Monmouth Junction, NJ 08852-0931
Fax: 800-FAX-ON-US   Fr: 800-468-4227
URL: http://www.cambridgeeducational.com

Video. 1997. $69.95. 16 minutes. Covers conventional and unconventional job search methods.

★12112★ Humanitarian
Cambridge Educational
PO Box 931
Monmouth Junction, NJ 08852-0931
Fax: 800-FAX-ON-US   Fr: 800-468-4227
URL: http://www.cambridgeeducational.com

$69.95. 25 minutes. Part of the Video GOE series.

★12113★ Industrial
Cambridge Educational
PO Box 931
Monmouth Junction, NJ 08852-0931
Fax: 800-FAX-ON-US   Fr: 800-468-4227
URL: http://www.cambridgeeducational.com

$69.95. 21 minutes. Part of the Video GOE series.

★12114★ Investigating the World of Work
Cambridge Educational
PO Box 931
Monmouth Junction, NJ 08852-0931
Fax: 800-FAX-ON-US   Fr: 800-468-4227
URL: http://www.cambridgeeducational.com

Video. $69.95. 30 minutes. Demonstrates techniques for relating knowledge of oneself to the world of work. Includes student/teacher manual.

★12115★ Job Survival Kit
Cambridge Educational
PO Box 931
Monmouth Junction, NJ 08852-0931
Fax: 800-FAX-ON-US   Fr: 800-468-4227
URL: http://www.cambridgeeducational.com

$79.95. 30 minutes. Includes book.

★12116★ Mechanical I
Cambridge Educational
PO Box 931
Monmouth Junction, NJ 08852-0931
Fax: 800-FAX-ON-US   Fr: 800-468-4227
URL: http://www.cambridgeeducational.com

$69.95. 45 minutes. Part of the Video GOE series.

★12117★ Mechanical II
Cambridge Educational
PO Box 931
Monmouth Junction, NJ 08852-0931
Fax: 800-FAX-ON-US   Fr: 800-468-4227
URL: http://www.cambridgeeducational.com

$69.95. 45 minutes. Part of the Video GOE series.

★12118★ The Networking Process
DBM Publishing
100 Park Ave.
New York, NY 10017
Ph: (212)692-7700   Fax: (212)297-0426
Fr: 800-345-5627
E-mail: generalinfo@dbm.com
URL: http://www.dbm.com

Video. $49.95. Presents networking techniques to find the job of your choice.

★12119★ Occupational Preparation
Cambridge Educational
PO Box 931
Monmouth Junction, NJ 08852-0931
Fax: 800-FAX-ON-US   Fr: 800-468-4227
URL: http://www.cambridgeeducational.com

Video. $69.95. 30 minutes. Shows how to develop and implement an effective educational and training program. Includes student/teacher manual.

★12120★ Physical Performing
Cambridge Educational
PO Box 931
Monmouth Junction, NJ 08852-0931
Fax: 800-FAX-ON-US   Fr: 800-468-4227
URL: http://www.cambridgeeducational.com

$69.95. 30 minutes. Part of the Video GOE series.

★12121★ Planning Your Career
Cambridge Educational
PO Box 931
Monmouth Junction, NJ 08852-0931
Fax: 800-FAX-ON-US   Fr: 800-468-4227
URL: http://www.cambridgeeducational.com

$69.95. 1997. 13 minutes. Part of the "Complete Job Search System" series.

★12122★ Plants and Animals
Cambridge Educational
PO Box 931
Monmouth Junction, NJ 08852-0931
Fax: 800-FAX-ON-US   Fr: 800-468-4227
URL: http://www.cambridgeeducational.com

$69.95. 30 minutes. Part of the Video GOE series.

★12123★ Protective
Cambridge Educational
PO Box 931
Monmouth Junction, NJ 08852-0931
Fax: 800-FAX-ON-US   Fr: 800-468-4227
URL: http://www.cambridgeeducational.com

$69.95. 25 minutes. Part of the Video GOE series.

★12124★ Researching the Job Market
DBM Publishing
100 Park Ave.
New York, NY 10017
Ph: (212)692-7700   Fax: (212)297-0426
Fr: 800-345-5627
E-mail: generalinfo@dbm.com
URL: http://www.dbm.com

Video. $49.95. Follows three successful job seekers who use careful, planned research.

★12125★ Scientific
Cambridge Educational
PO Box 931
Monmouth Junction, NJ 08852-0931
Fax: 800-FAX-ON-US   Fr: 800-468-4227
URL: http://www.cambridgeeducational.com

$69.95. 45 minutes. Part of the Video GOE series.

★12126★ Selling
Cambridge Educational
PO Box 931
Monmouth Junction, NJ 08852-0931
Fax: 800-FAX-ON-US   Fr: 800-468-4227
URL: http://www.cambridgeeducational.com

$69.95. 45 minutes. Part of the Video GOE series.

★12127★ Shhh! I'm Finding a Job: The Library and Your Self-Directed Job Search
Cambridge Educational
PO Box 931
Monmouth Junction, NJ 08852-0931
Fax: 800-FAX-ON-US   Fr: 800-468-4227
URL: http://www.cambridgeeducational.com

$79.95. 1993. 30 minutes. Includes workbook.

★12128★ Taking Charge of Your Job Search
DBM Publishing
100 Park Ave.
New York, NY 10017
Ph: (212)692-7700   Fax: (212)297-0426
Fr: 800-345-5627
E-mail: generalinfo@dbm.com
URL: http://www.dbm.com

Video. $25.00. Workbook. $25.00. Designed to supplement an inhouse outplacement program for departing employees.

★12129★ 10 Basics of Business Etiquette
Cambridge Educational
PO Box 931
Monmouth Junction, NJ 08852-0931
Fax: 800-FAX-ON-US   Fr: 800-468-4227
URL: http://www.cambridgeeducational.com

$99.95. 22 minutes.

★12130★ Ten Ways to Get a Great Job: Back to the Basics
Cambridge Educational
PO Box 931
Monmouth Junction, NJ 08852-0931
Fax: 800-FAX-ON-US   Fr: 800-468-4227
URL: http://www.cambridgeeducational.com
Video. 1994. $79.95. 30 minutes. Reminds viewers of job search basics.

★12131★ Tough Times: Finding the Jobs
Cambridge Educational
PO Box 931
Monmouth Junction, NJ 08852-0931
Fax: 800-FAX-ON-US   Fr: 800-468-4227
URL: http://www.cambridgeeducational.com
$69.95. 1993. 30 minutes. Part of the Series "Tough Times Job Strategies."

★12132★ Tough Times Job Strategies
Cambridge Educational
PO Box 931
Monmouth Junction, NJ 08852-0931
Fax: 800-FAX-ON-US   Fr: 800-468-4227
URL: http://www.cambridgeeducational.com
Series of two videos. 1993. $129.95/set. 30 minutes each. Includes "Tough Times: Finding the Jobs" and "Tough Times: Making the Most of Your Job." Examines factors influencing today's job market.

★12133★ The Video Guide to Occupational Exploration
Cambridge Educational
PO Box 931
Monmouth Junction, NJ 08852-0931
Fax: 800-FAX-ON-US   Fr: 800-468-4227
URL: http://www.cambridgeeducational.com
14 videos. $749.95.

★12134★ Vocational Visions Career Series
Cambridge Educational
PO Box 931
Monmouth Junction, NJ 08852-0931
Fax: 800-FAX-ON-US   Fr: 800-468-4227
URL: http://www.cambridgeeducational.com
10 videos. $299.95. 15 minutes each. Topics include auto mechanic, band director, florist, park ranger, potter, chef, insurance agent, physical therapist, letter carrier, and paralegal.

★12135★ The Winning Look
Cambridge Educational
PO Box 931
Monmouth Junction, NJ 08852-0931
Fax: 800-FAX-ON-US   Fr: 800-468-4227
URL: http://www.cambridgeeducational.com
$49.95. 12 minutes. Explains the importance of dressing appropriately in the business world–for job interviewing as well as for continued success on the job.

ONLINE AND DATABASE SERVICES

★12136★ CareerMagazine
URL: http://www.careermag.com
Description: Online magazine containing many columns, features and articles about job hunting. Also holds job listings for browsers. **Main files include:** Job Openings, Employers, Articles, Resume Bank, Career Forum, On Campus, Diversity, Be Your Own Boss, Job Fairs, Recruiter Directory, Consultant Directory, Products & Services, Relocation Resources, Career Links, Post Your Jobs. Has information section for self-employed and freelance workers.

★12137★ CareerPerfect.com
URL: http://www.careerperfect.com
Description: Provides links to career software and books; lists FAQ's on career planning, resumes, job searching, and interviewing; identifies online job databases; accepts resumes for posting.

★12138★ CollegeGrad.com
URL: http://www.collegegrad.com
Description: "Your link to life after college." Site contains the online version of the College Grad Job Hunter - an entry level job search book. **Main files include:** Preparation, Resumes and Cover Letters, Job Postings, Interviews and Negotiations, New Job. Employers may also search for candidates fitting positions.

★12139★ 4Work.com
E-mail: info@ats4work.com
URL: http://www.4work.com
Description: Job hunting site with the option of searching by job, internship, part-time, or volunteer position. Also searchable by keyword and state. Employers may also post positions available. **Fee:** $100 first month, $100 each additional month

★12140★ 4Anything Network: 4Careers.com
URL: http://www.4careers.com
Description: Job hunters may search job ads placed by employers. Jobs are arranged in sub-categories. Also sections on personality assessments, salary research, and career counseling.

★12141★ JobStar
E-mail: electrajobstar@earthlink.net
URL: http://jobstar.org/
Description: Job search guide based in California. Includes career guides and information on local, national and international career counseling centers, resumes, salaries, and hidden jobs.

★12142★ MonsterTRAK
URL: http://www.jobtrak.com/
Description: College-targeted job hunting and recruiting site. Students and alumni may enter a user profile or resume to be reviewed by potential employers, or search job listings without doing so. Employers may enter full-time, part-time, temporary, and internship opportunities into the database to be reviewed by students and recent graduates, and may review resumes.

★12143★ NYU Stern School of Business
E-mail: ocd@stern.nyu.edu
URL: http://www.stern.nyu.edu
Description: Office of Career Development section of website provides career resources for business graduates, along with resume databases arranged by classes. Many resources restricted to Stern students and alumni.

★12144★ Quintessential Careers
E-mail: randall@quintcareers.com
URL: http://www.quintcareers.com
Description: Job search mega-site that links to several job board, provides information on every step of the job search process, and additional information on earning advanced degrees and certificates to increase one's value as a professional.

★12145★ Recruiters Online Network
URL: http://www.recruitersonline.com/
Description: Site is used by over 8,000 recruiters, search firms, employment agencies, and employment professionals. Job seekers may read the Careers Online Magazine, post resumes, and search jobs. **Fee:** Free to job seekers; fee for recruiters.

★12146★ The Riley Guide
E-mail: webmaster@rileyguide.com
URL: http://www.rileyguide.com
Description: Job search portal site. Also contains resources on writing and distributing resumes, targeting employers, interviewing, salary negotiations and more.

★12147★ What Color Is Your Parachute? Job Hunters Bible
URL: http://www.jobhuntersbible.com/
Description: Companion internet guide to the best selling job-hunting book, What Color is Your Parachute? Includes lists of helpful links to other resources on the internet. **Main files include:** Jobs, Resumes, Counseling, Contacts, Research, Dealing With Depression.

★12148★ The World Wide Web Employment Office
URL: http://www.employmentoffice.net/
Description: Portal to job and resume banks and board for employers and job hunters.

★12149★ Yahoo! Careers
URL: http://careers.yahoo.com/

Description: Contains over 360,000 jobs for job seekers to search and post resumes for, as well as weekly features, relocation resources, a daily column, and links to resume banks and services and temp agencies. Special sections are devoted to industry research, company research, advice, high tech jobs, and first jobs and internships. Powered by Career Builder.

SOFTWARE

★12150★ Mike Farr's Get a Job Workshop on CD-ROM
JIST Publishing
8902 Otis Ave.
Indianapolis, IN 46216
Fr: 800-648-5478

E-mail: jistworks@aol.com
URL: http://www.jist.com

CD-ROM. Professional edition, $295.00. Network edition, $995.00. Nearly three hours of instruction.

★12151★ Multimedia Job Search
Cambridge Educational
PO Box 931
Monmouth Junction, NJ 08852-0931
Fax: 800-FAX-ON-US   Fr: 800-468-4227
URL: http://www.cambridgeeducational.com

CD-ROM. $99.95. Includes videos, narration, and on-screen text. Users learn about getting a competitive edge in today's job market, traditional and nontraditional job search tools, resumes and cover letters, and interviewing skills.

OTHER SOURCES

★12152★ National Self-Help Clearinghouse (NSHC)
365 5th Ave., Ste. 3300
New York, NY 10016
Ph: (212)817-1822   Fax: (212)817-1561
E-mail: info@selfhelpweb.org
URL: http://www.selfhelpweb.org

Description: Clearinghouse on self-help groups; provides referral services. Conducts research and training activities. Maintains speakers' bureau.

Career Transitions and Alternatives

REFERENCE WORKS

★12153★ America's Career InfoNet
U.S. Department of Labor
Administrative Services Ctr.
200 Constitution Ave. NW
Washington, DC 20210
URL: http://www.acinet.org/acinet
Covers links to and information about job banks, employment service providers, career education, and nationwide employer contacts.

★12154★ Authoritative Guide to the Top 100 Careers to Year 2005
Research and Education Association
61 Ethel Rd., W
Piscataway, NJ 08854
Ph: (732)819-8880   Fax: (732)819-8808
Fr: 800-822-0830

1997. $19.95 (paper). 368 pages.

★12155★ Career Bounce-Back!: The Professionals in Transition Guide to Recovery and Reemployment
AMACOM
1601 Broadway, 12th Fl.
New York, NY 10019-7420
Ph: (518)891-1500   Fax: (518)903-8168
Fr: 800-250-5308

J. Damian Birkel and Stacey J. Miller. 1997. $14.95 (paper). 224 pages.

★12156★ Career Directions
McGraw-Hill Higher Education
PO Box 545
Blacklick, OH 43004-0545

Donna J. Yena. Third edition, 1996. $17.50. 288 pages.

★12157★ Career Transition: A Guide for Federal Employees in a Time of Turmoil
FPMI Communications, Inc.
4901 Univ. St., Ste. 3
Huntsville, AL 35816
Ph: (256)539-1850   Fax: (256)539-0911

Robert Carey. 1996. $14.95 (paper). 105 pages.

★12158★ Career Transitions in Sport: International Perspectives
Fitness Information Technology, Incorporated
P.O. Box 4425
Morgantown, WV 26504-4425
Ph: (304)599-3483   Fax: (304)599-3482
Fr: 800-477-4348

David Lavalle and Paul Wylleman. 2000. $39.00.

★12159★ Career Transitions in Turbulent Times: Exploring Work, Learning and Careers
Counseling and Psychological Services, Inc.
201 Ferguson Bldg., UNCG
Greensboro, NC 27402-6171
Ph: (336)334-4114   Fax: (336)334-4116
Fr: 800-414-9769

Rich Feller and Garry Walz, editors. 1996. $29.95 (paper). 780 pages.

★12160★ Career & Vocational Counseling Directory
infoUSA Inc.
5711 S 86th Cir.
Omaha, NE 68127-0347
Ph: (402)930-3500   Fax: (402)331-0176
Fr: 800-555-6124
URL: http://www.abii.com

Annual. Number of listings: 2,971. Entries include: Name, address, phone (including area code), size of advertisement, year first in "Yellow Pages," name of owner or manager, number of employees. Compiled from telephone company "Yellow Pages," nationwide. Arrangement: Geographical.

★12161★ CareerXRoads: The Directory to Job, Resume and Career Management Sites on the Web
MMC GROUP
4545 Fuller Drive, Suite 222
Irving, TX 75038
Ph: (972)893-0100   Fax: (972)893-0099

Latest edition 2002. $26.95. Covers nearly 3,000 job and resume web sites with reviews and descriptions of the top 500. Indexes: Colleges; Corporations; Diversity; Specialty/Industry; Location; Listing services.

★12162★ Change Your Job, Change Your Life: High Impact Strategies for Finding Great Jobs in the 21st Century
Impact Publications
9104 Manassas Dr., Ste. N
Manassas Park, VA 20111-5211
Ph: (703)361-7300   Fax: (703)335-9486

Ronald Krannich. Seventh edition, 1999. $17.95 (paper). 317 pages. Details trends in the marketplace, how to identify opportunities, how to retrain for them, and how to land jobs. Includes a chapter on starting a business. Contains index, bibliography, and illustrations.

★12163★ College Majors and Careers: A Resource Guide for Effective Life Planning
Facts on File Inc.
132 W 31st St., 17th Fl.
New York, NY 10001
Ph: (212)967-8800   Fax: 800-678-3633
Fr: 800-322-8755
E-mail: holli@inil.com
URL: http://www.fergpubco.com

Irregular, latest edition 1997; previous edition 1987. $14.95. Publication includes: Lists of organizations and other sources of information on choosing a college field of concentration and a subsequent career path. Entries include: Organization name, address, phone. Principal content of publication is descriptions of 60 of the most popular major fields and discussions of their attributes.

★12164★ *Complete Idiot's Guide to Changing Careers*
Macmillan Publishing Co. Inc.
200 Old Tappan Rd.
Old Tappan, NJ 07675
Fr: 800-428-5331
1998. $17.95 (paper).

★12165★ *Dare to Change Your Job and Your Life*
Master Media
8902 Otis Ave.
Indianapolis, IN 46216-1033
Ph: (317)613-4200   Fax: (317)613-4307
Fr: 800-648-5478
E-mail: jistworks@aol.com
URL: http://www.jist.com
Carole Kanchier. Second edition, 1999. $14.95. 460 pages. Based on a survey of more than 5,000 adults.

★12166★ *Directory of Outplacement and Career Management Firms*
Kennedy Information Inc.
One Phoenix Mill Ln., 5th Fl.
Peterborough, NH 03458
Ph: (603)924-1006   Fax: (603)924-4460
Fr: 800-531-0007
Annual, latest edition 2003. $149.95. Covers over 380 consulting firms with special interest in career management and "outplacement" or "de-hiring" counseling executive employees being terminated because of poor performance, plant closings, etc., and assisting them in finding new jobs; firms that are compensated only by employers and those that also accept compensation from individuals are listed. Entries include: Firm name, address, phone, fax, E-mail, description of philosophy and services, names and titles of principals, branches, area served, year established, revenue (within wide ranges), professional associations, minimum salary of positions handled, number of staff, percentage of business devoted to outplacement. Arrangement: Separate sections on basis of compensation arrangements, then alphabetical. Indexes: Industries, key principals, firm.

★12167★ *Do What You Love for the Rest of Your Life: A Practical Guide to Career Change and Personal Renewal*
Ballantine Books
1540 Broadway, 11th Fl.
New York, NY 10036
Ph: (212)782-9000   Fax: (212)940-7539
Fr: 800-733-3000
Bob Griffiths. December 2003. $13.95 (paper). 336 pages.

★12168★ *Effective Strategies for Career Success*
JIST Publishing
8902 Otis Ave.
Indianapolis, IN 46216-1033
Ph: (317)613-4200   Fax: (317)613-4307
Fr: 800-648-5478

E-mail: customerservice@chronicleguidance.com
$9.95 (paper). 380 pages.

★12169★ *The Enhanced Guide for Occupational Exploration*
JIST Publishing
8902 Otis Ave.
Indianapolis, IN 46216-1033
Ph: (317)613-4200   Fax: (317)613-4307
Fr: 800-648-5478
Marilyn Maze, Donald Mayall and J. Michael Farr. Second edition, 1995. $44.95; $29.95 (paper). 704 pages. Provides descriptions for 2800 jobs. Each description includes skills, abilities, academic and physical requirements, work environment, salary, and outlook. Contains indices to career alternatives based on interests, skills, industry, and education.

★12170★ *Get a Job You Love!*
Dearborn Trade, A Kaplan Professional Co.
155 N. Wacker Dr.
Chicago, IL 60606-1719
Ph: (312)836-4400   Fax: (312)836-1021
Fr: 800-621-9621
Roxanne S. Rogers. 1995. $19.95 (paper). 270 pages. Out of print.

★12171★ *Good News! You're Fired! A Comprehensive Guide for People in Career Transition*
Nebbadoon Press
PO Box 333
Etna, NH 03750
Ph: (603)643-0400   Fax: (603)643-0404
Fr: 800-500-9086
Elizabeth Tansey. 1998. $17.00. 137 pages.

★12172★ *How to Change Your Career*
McGraw-Hill Trade
2 Penn Plaza
New York, NY 10121
Ph: (212)904-2000   Fr: 800-722-4726
E-mail: ntcpub@tribune.com
Kent Banning and Ardelle Friday. 1993. $9.95 (paper). 192 pages. Provides checklists, worksheets, and exercises to help career-changers identify and successfully enter new careers. Guides the reader in the production of a career-change resume.

★12173★ *How to Find the Work You Love*
Penguin Putnam, Inc.
375 Hudson St.
New York, NY 10014
Ph: (212)366-2000   Fax: (212)366-2666
Fr: 800-788-6262
Laurence G. Boldt. 1996. $10.95 (paper). 192 pages.

★12174★ *How to Get That Job*
Pilot Books
127 Sterling Ave.
PO Box 2102
Greenport, NY 11944-0893
Ph: (516)477-1094   Fax: (516)477-0978
Fr: 800-797-4568
URL: http://www.pilotbooks.com
Ruby N. Gorter. 1997. $8.95. 94 pages. Provides information for first-time job seekers as well as those who want to change careers.

★12175★ *JobSmarts 50 Top Careers*
HarperTrade
10 E. 53rd St.
New York, NY 10022
Ph: (212)207-7000   Fax: (212)207-7633
Fr: 800-242-7737
Bradley G. Richardson. 1997. $16.00 (paper). 400 pages.

★12176★ *Mid-Career Changes: Strategies for Success*
Career Publishing, Inc.
910 Main St.
PO Box 5486
Orange, CA 92863-5486
Ph: (714)771-5155   Fax: (714)532-0180
Fr: 800-854-4014
John D. Shingleton and James Anderson. 1993. $16.95 (paper). 270 pages. Out of print. Provides information about today's changing workplace. Offers advice on identifying goals and adjusting to change.

★12177★ *Occupational Outlook Handbook*
U.S. Bureau of Labor Statistics
2 Massachusetts Ave. NE, Rm. 2135
Washington, DC 20212
Ph: (202)606-7828   Fax: (202)691-7890
E-mail: OOHinfo@bls.gov
URL: http://www.bls.gov/ocol
Biennial, January of even years. $57.00 for hardcover; $53.00 for softcover. Publication includes: Various occupational organizations that provide career information on hundreds of occupations. Entries include: For organizations-Organization name, address. Principal content of publication is profiles of various occupations, which include description of occupation, educational requirements, job outlook, and expected earnings. Arrangement: Organizations are classified by occupation.

★12178★ *Outside the Ivory Tower: A Guide for Academics Considering Alternative Careers*
Harvard University, Office of Career Services
54 Dunster St.
Cambridge, MA 02138
Ph: (617)495-2595   Fax: (617)495-3584
Margaret Newhouse. 1993. $13.00 (paper). 164 pages.

★12179★ The Overnight Job Change Strategy

Ten Speed Press
PO Box 7123
Berkeley, CA 94707
Ph: (510)559-1600   Fax: (510)559-1629
Fr: 800-841-2665

Donald Asher. 1993. $7.95 (paper). 265 pages. Subtitled "How to Plan a Comprehensive, Systematic Job Search in One Evening". Incorporates sales and marketing techniques into a six-stage job search process. Out of print.

★12180★ Parting Company: How to Survive the Loss of a Job and Find Another Successfully

Harcourt Trade Publishers
6277 Sea Harbor Dr.
Orlando, FL 32887
Fax: 800-235-0256   Fr: 800-543-1918
URL: http://www.dbm.com

William J. Morin and James C. Cabrera. 1991 $13.00 (paper). 416 pages. Covers the entire spectrum of termination issues.

★12181★ Preparing to Tack: When Physicians Change Careers

Vantage Press, Inc.
516 W. 34th St.
New York, NY 10001
Ph: (212)736-1767   Fax: (212)736-2273
Fr: 800-882-3273

Jack Kushner. 1996. $13.95. Out of print.

★12182★ Professional Careers Sourcebook

Thomson Gale
27500 Drake Rd.
Farmington Hills, MI 48331-3535
Ph: (248)699-GALE   Fax: (248)699-8069
Fr: 800-877-GALE
E-mail: galeord@gale.com
URL: http://www.galegroup.com

Sixth edition, 1999. Next edition expected 1999. $105.00. 1000 pages. Directs users to career information sources related to specific professions, such as civil engineering, psychology, law, public relations, dance and choreography, and more. Provides a listing of state professional and occupational licensing agencies and occupational rankings and statistics. Includes over 110 professional career profiles containing information on general career guides, career information and services provided by professional associations, standards and certification agencies, directories of educational programs and institutions, basic reference guides and handbooks related to the profession, professional and trade periodicals, and more. Indexes: Alphabetical.

★12183★ Quick Prep Careers: Good Jobs in One Year or Less

Ferguson Publishing Co.
200 W Jackson Blvd.
Chicago, IL 60606
Ph: (312)692-0109

$18.95. Publication includes: Lists of associations for further consultation for each of 75 jobs featured. Principal content of publication is detailed information on each job. Arrangement: By job. Indexes: Alphabetical.

★12184★ Resumes for Midcareer Job Changes

Vgm Career Horizons
1221 Avenue of the Americas
New York, NY 10020
Ph: (212)904-2000   Fr: 800-323-4900
E-mail: ntcpub@tribune.com

1994. $9.95 (paper). 160 pages. Out of print.

★12185★ Starting Over: How to Change Careers or Start Your Own Business

Warner Books, Inc.
1271 Ave. of the Americas
New York, NY 10020
Ph: (212)522-7200   Fax: 800-286-9471
Fr: 800-759-0190

Stephen M. Pollan and Mark Levine. 1997. $15.99 (paper). 241 pages.

★12186★ Survive and Profit from a Mid-Career Change

NewStar Media, Incorporated
8955 Beverly Blvd.
Los Angeles, CA 90048
Ph: (310)786-1600   Fax: (310)247-2924
Fr: 800-368-3007

Moreau. 1996. $17.95 (paper). Shows how to handle layoffs, burnout, job hunting, and more. Out of Print.

★12187★ Take This Job and Love It: A Personal Guide to Career Empowerment

Sourcebooks, Inc.
1935 Brookdale Rd., Ste. 139
Naperville, IL 60563
Ph: (630)961-3900   Fax: (630)961-2168
Fr: 800-432-7444

Diane Tracy. 2001. $14.95 (paper). 208 pages. Out of print.

★12188★ Taking Charge of Your Career Direction

Brooks/Cole Publishing Company
511 Forest Lodge Rd.
Pacific Grove, CA 93950
Ph: (831)373-0728   Fax: (831)375-6414

Robert D. Lock. Third edition, 1996. Three volumes. Provides guidance for the job search process.

★12189★ Ten Insider Secrets Career Transition Workshop: Your Complete Guide to Discovering the Ideal Job!

10 Step Publications
1151 N. State Pkwy., No. 253
Chicago, IL 60610
Ph: (312)493-0582   Fax: (312)873-3777

Todd Bermont. January 2004. $14.95.

★12190★ Vocational Careers Sourcebook

Thomson Gale
27500 Drake Rd.
Farmington Hills, MI 48331-3535
Ph: (248)699-GALE   Fax: (248)699-8069
Fr: 800-877-GALE
E-mail: galeord@gale.com
URL: http://www.galegroup.com

Fourth edition, 1999. $110.00. 700 pages. Directs users to career information sources related to specific occupations, such as insurance and real estate sales, corrections and police work, mechanics, armed forces options, agriculture and forestry, production work, and the trades. Contains information on general career guides, career information and services provided by trade associations, standards and certification agencies, directories of educational programs and institutions, basic reference guides and handbooks related to the occupation, trade periodicals, and more. Indexes: Alphabetical.

AUDIO/VISUAL RESOURCES

★12191★ Getting Fired, Getting Hired: Job Hunting from A to Z

CareerLab Books
304 Inverness Way S, Ste. 465
Englewood, CO 80112
Ph: (303)790-0505   Fax: (303)790-0606
Fr: 800-723-9675
URL: http://www.careerlab.com

Series of 6 videos. $14.95/set. 30 minutes each. Individual titles cover aspects of the job search following job loss.

★12192★ Rebounding from Job Loss

Cambridge Educational
PO Box 931
Monmouth Junction, NJ 08852-0931
Fax: 800-FAX-ON-US   Fr: 800-468-4227
URL: http://www.cambridgeeducational.com
$89.95. 2000. 17 minutes.

★12193★ Unemployment: Understanding The Grieving Process

Cambridge Educational
PO Box 931
Monmouth Junction, NJ 08852-0931
Fax: 800-FAX-ON-US   Fr: 800-468-4227
URL: http://www.cambridgeeducational.com
$89.95. 1999. 30 minutes. Includes section on taking action to find a new job.

ONLINE AND DATABASE SERVICES

★12194★ Career Leader
E-mail: wba@world.std.com
URL: http://www.careerdiscovery.com

Description: Online career assessment tool for job seekers, emphasis on business careers. **Fee:** Several levels of assessment available; starts at $95.

★12195★ CareerAdvantage.com
E-mail: advfdbk@bridges.com
URL: http://careeradvantage.com

Description: Career planning website with skills and interest aptitude assessments, daily feed of new career articles, exclusive library of career profiles and interviews with people in the field to help guide and direct professional development. **Fee:** Subscription to services $19.95.

★12196★ Keirsey Temperament Sorter and Temperament Web Site
E-mail: keirsey@orci.com
URL: http://www.keirsey.com

Description: Online personality questionnaire that identifies temperament and interest traits that may be applied towards career searches.

SOFTWARE

★12197★ CareerMax Vocational Transition Program
Career Impact Ministries International
18 Edenfield Cove
Little Rock, AR 72212
Ph: (501)217-0385
URL: http://www.careerimpact.org

$99.00-$500.00, depending on services. Combination of vocational assessment, audio/manual based training, personal coaching and job search tools to allow people to discover their unique design and secure the right career.

OTHER SOURCES

★12198★ Career Planning and Adult Development Network (CPADN)
PO Box 1484
Pacifica, CA 94044
Ph: (650)359-6911   Fax: (650)359-3089
E-mail: admin@careernetwork.org
URL: http://www.careernetwork.org

Description: Counselors, trainers, consultants, therapists, educators, personnel specialists, and graduate students who work in business, educational, religious, and governmental organizations, and focus on career planning and adult development issues. Seeks to: establish a link between professionals working with adults in a variety of settings; identify and exchange effective adult development methods and techniques; develop a clearer understanding of the directions and objectives of the career planning and the adult development movement. Keeps members informed of developments in career decision-making, career values clarification, preretirement counseling, dual-career families, job search techniques, and mid-life transitions. Cosponsors professional seminars; maintains biographical archives.

★12199★ New Ways to Work (NWW)
425 Market St., Ste 2200
San Francisco, CA 94105
Ph: (415)995-9860   Fax: (415)995-9867
E-mail: info@nww.org
URL: http://www.nww.org

Purpose: Goal is to provide a work world that responds to the needs of both workers and institutions. Provides information, training, and support to individuals and organizations interested in new work options. Promotes the concepts of flextime, compressed work weeks, job sharing, work sharing, and voluntary reduced work time to satisfy the requirements of people who want and need flexible schedules. **Activities:** Offers technical assistance, including problem analysis and assistance in program facilitation for interested employees, employers, or unions.

Electronic Job Search Information

REFERENCE WORKS

★12200★ Adams Electronic Job Search Almanac

Adams Media Corp.
57 Littlefield St.
Avon, MA 02322
Ph: (508)427-7100   Fax: (508)427-6790
Fr: 800-872-5627

Annual. $10.95. Covers job listings on the Internet; bulletin boards, Web networking, and online services for finding a job. Entries include: Firm or organization name, address, phone, name and title of contact; description of organization, headquarters location, typical titles for entry- and middle-level positions, educational backgrounds desired, fringe benefits offered, stock exchange listing, training programs, internships, parent company, number of employees, revenues, e-mail and web address, projected number of hires. Arrangement: Alphabetical.

★12201★ Be Your Own Headhunter

Random House, Inc.
1540 Broadway
New York, NY 10036
Ph: (212)782-9000   Fax: (212)302-7985
Fr: 800-726-0600

P. Dickson and S. Tiersten. 1995. $16.00 (paper). 256 pages.

★12202★ Cyberspace Resume Kit

JIST Publishing
8902 Otis Ave.
Indianapolis, IN 46216-1033
Ph: (317)613-4200   Fax: (317)613-4307
Fr: 800-648-5478
E-mail: jistworks@aol.com
URL: http://www.jist.com

Fred E. Jandt and Mary B. Nemnich. Second edition, 2000. $18.95. 586 pages. Teaches how to develop and post electronic resumes.

★12203★ Electronic Job Search Almanac

Adams Media Corp.
57 Littlefield St.
Avon, MA 02322
Ph: (508)427-7100   Fax: (508)427-6790
Fr: 800-872-5627

Edited by Adams Media Corp. staff. 2000. $10.95 (paper). 320 pages.

★12204★ Electronic Job Search Revolution

John Wiley & Sons Inc.
1 Wiley Dr.
Somerset, NJ 08873
Ph: (732)469-4400   Fr: 800-225-5945

Joyce Lain Kennedy and Thomas J. Morrow. Second edition, 1995. $12.95 (paper). 183 pages. Discusses new technologies being used in job searching.

★12205★ Electronic Resume Revolution

John Wiley & Sons Inc.
1 Wiley Dr.
Somerset, NJ 08873
Ph: (732)469-4400   Fr: 800-225-5945

Joyce Lain Kennedy and Thomas J. Morrow. Second edition, 1995. $12.95 (paper). 228 pages. Explains how to write a resume that a computer can read. Includes 30 model resumes.

★12206★ Electronic Resumes for the New Job Market

Impact Publications
9104 Manassas Dr., Ste. N
Manassas Park, VA 20111-5211
Ph: (703)361-7300   Fax: (703)335-9486

Peter D. Weddle. 1994. $11.95 (paper). 161 pages. Explains how to use electronic job banks and design resumes that best meet electronic job bank specifications.

★12207★ Electronic Resumes and Online Networking: How to Use the Internet to Do a Better Job Search, Including a Complete, Up-to-Date Resource Guide

Career Press, Inc.
3 Tice Rd.
PO Box 687
Franklin Lakes, NJ 07417-1322
Ph: (201)848-0310   Fax: (201)848-1727
Fr: 800-227-3371

Rebecca Smith. Second edition, 2000. $13.99 (paper). Provides information on using the Internet as a resume networking tool. Covers locating employers, evaluating electronic resume options, and web pages. 400 pages.

★12208★ Electronic Resumes: The Complete Guide to Putting Your Resume On-Line

The McGraw-Hill Companies
2 Penn Plaza, 20th Fl.
New York, NY 10121-2298
Ph: (212)904-4509   Fr: 800-338-3987

Wayne M. Gonyea and James C. Gonyea. 1996. $19.95. 277 pages. Explains the basics of online, multimedia, video, and audio resumes in nontechnical language. Disk includes software that enables users to create their own electronic resume to upload via modem onto online resume databases.

★12209★ Finding a Job on the Internet

The McGraw-Hill Companies
2 Penn Plaza, 20th Fl.
New York, NY 10121-2298
Ph: (212)904-4509   Fr: 800-338-3987

Alfred Glossbrenner. 1995. $17.95 (paper). 272 pages. Out of print. Describes how to use the Internet to find job openings. Covers online database searches, posting your resume online, researching employers and unannounced job openings, and tapping newsgroups, mailing lists, and World Wide Web sites.

★12210★ The Guide to Internet Job Searching

McGraw-Hill Trade
2 Penn Plaza
New York, NY 10121
Ph: (212)904-2000　　Fr: 800-722-4726
URL: http://www.cambridgeol.com

Margaret Riley, Frances E. Roehm, Steve Oserman. $14.95. 1998-99. 224 pages. Helps readers develop an effective Internet job application, quickly locate major job listing sites in each career area, and use the computer to search for job opportunities.

★12211★ Head Hunters Revealed

Hunter Arts Publishing
PO Box 66578K
Los Angeles, CA 90066
Ph: (310)821-6303　　Fax: (310)821-6308
Fr: 877-4-HEADHUNT

Quarterly. $14.95. Covers online career sites, career associations, and organizations.

★12212★ Hook Up, Get Hired! The Internet Job Search Revolution

John Wiley & Sons Inc.
1 Wiley Dr.
Somerset, NJ 08873
Ph: (732)469-4400　　Fr: 800-225-5945

Joyce Lain Kennedy. 1995. $95.00. 250 pages. Provides an Internet roadmap for networking, researching companies, searching job ads, and creating an Internet-friendly resume. Includes e-mail addresses and access numbers to online career centers, newsgroups, bulletin boards, and resume marquees.

★12213★ How to Get Your Dream Job Using the Internet

Coriolis Group LLC
14455 N. Hayden Rd., Ste. 220
Scottsdale, AZ 85260-6949
Ph: (480)483-0192　　Fax: (480)483-0193
Fr: 800-410-0192

Shannon Bounds and Arthur Karl. 1997. $34.99 (paper). 448 pages. Out of print. Includes CD-ROM containing web page creation software, interview simulator, resume tools, and direct links to online recruiters, job and resume banks, etc.

★12214★ Internet Resumes

Impact Publications
9104 Manassas Dr., Ste. N
Manassas Park, VA 20111-5211
Ph: (703)361-7300　　Fax: (703)335-9486
URL: http://www.cambridgeol.com

Peter D. Weddle. 1998. $14.95 (paper). 536 pages. Shows how to communicate qualifications to potential employers over the Internet.

★12215★ Job Searching Online for Dummies

John Wiley & Sons Inc.
1 Wiley Dr.
Somerset, NJ 08873
Ph: (732)469-4400

Pam Dixon. Second edition, 2000. $24.99 (paper). 295 pages. Includes CD-ROM. Techniques for finding a job online through the Internet.

★12216★ Job-Seeker's Guide to On-Line Resources

Kennedy Information Inc.
1 Kennedy Pl.
Rte. 12 S.
Fitzwilliam, NH 03447
Ph: (603)585-3101　　Fax: (603)585-6401
Fr: 800-531-0007

Alice Snell. Second edition, 1995. $14.95 (paper). 98 pages. Out of print. Describes available services and how to use them. Identifies 140 candidate databases, job-posting services, and related resources accessible with a computer and modem.

★12217★ 110 Best Job Search Sites on the Internet

Linx Educational Publishing, Inc.
PO Box 331547
Atlantic Beach, FL 32233
Ph: (904)220-5469　　Fax: (904)221-2696
Fr: 800-717-5469
URL: http://www.cambridgeol.com

Katherine K. Yonge. $10.95. 1998. 80 pages. Also includes tips on electronic resumes and other information.

★12218★ Plunkett's Employers' Internet Sites with Careers Information: The Only Complete Guide to Careers Websites Operated by Major Employers

Plunkett Research, Ltd.
PO Box 541737
Houston, TX 77254-1737
Ph: (713)932-0000　　Fax: (713)932-7080

Jack W. Plunkett. Revised, 2002. $179.99 (includes CD-ROM). Provides profiles of Internet sites for major employers. Job hunters can use the profiles or indexes to locate the Internet job sites that best fit their needs. 697 pages.

★12219★ Professional's Job Finder

Planning Communications
7215 Oak Ave.
River Forest, IL 60305-1935
Ph: (708)366-5200　　Fax: (708)366-5280
Fr: 888-366-5200
E-mail: projf@planningcommunications.com
URL: http://jobfindersonline.com

New edition expected 2003. $18.95. Covers over 3,000 sources of jobs in the private sector of the United States, including job matching services, job hotlines, periodicals and directories, internet job sites, salary surveys, databases, and electronic online

job services. Includes coupons for over $200 in discounts and free job resources. Entries include: For job services-Name, sponsor or operator name, address, phone, length of registration period, cost, description (including number of job vacancies listed). For publications-Title, publisher name, address, phone, frequency of publication, price, description (including number of job vacancies listed). Arrangement: Classified by occupational specialty; geographical by state. Indexes: Subject.

★12220★ The Quick Internet Guide to Career and Education Information

JIST Publishing
8902 Otis Ave.
Indianapolis, IN 46216-1033
Ph: (317)613-4200　　Fax: (317)613-4309
Fr: 800-648-5478

$16.95. Covers utilizing the Internet to research colleges, financial aid, distance learning, careers, job openings, military careers, contract work, and other college and career-related information. Entries include: Web site address, summary of source.

★12221★ Using the Internet and the World Wide Web in Your Job Search

JIST Publishing
8902 Otis Ave.
Indianapolis, IN 46216-1033
Ph: (317)264-3720　　Fax: (317)613-4307
Fr: 800-648-5478

Fred Jandt and Mary Nemnich. Second edition, 1996. $16.95 (paper). 300 pages. Explains how to connect to the Internet, find job listings, research potential employers, use news groups to get leads, and adapt standard resumes to electronic formats.

AUDIO/VISUAL RESOURCES

★12222★ Connect on the Net: Finding a Job on the Internet

Cambridge Educational
PO Box 931
Monmouth Junction, NJ 08852-0931
Fax: 800-FAX-ON-US　　Fr: 800-468-4227
URL: http://www.cambridgeeducational.com

Video. $79.95. 30 minutes. Viewers learn how to use traditional and non-traditional job search strategies as they navigate job search directories and bulletin boards on the Internet.

★12223★ Networking on the WWW and Beyond

Cambridge Educational
PO Box 931
Monmouth Junction, NJ 08852-0931
Fax: 800-FAX-ON-US　　Fr: 800-468-4227
URL: http://www.cambridgeeducational.com

Video. 1997. $79.95. 30 minutes. This three-part video includes an introduction to search engines, how to network and find jobs using Internet resources, and interviewing via the Internet.

★12224★ Web Resumes
Cambridge Educational
PO Box 931
Monmouth Junction, NJ 08852-0931
Fax: 800-FAX-ON-US   Fr: 800-468-4227
URL: http://www.cambridgeeducational.com

Video. 1998. $89.95. 30 minutes. Topics covered include Web and electronic resumes, creative resumes, target resumes, and mid-life and reentry resumes.

ONLINE AND DATABASE SERVICES

★12225★ Academic Position Network
E-mail: info@apnjobs.com
URL: http://www.apnjobs.com/

Description: Online position announcement service. Announcements include faculty, administration, and staff positions as well as announcements for graduate assistant and fellowship positions. **Fee:** Free searching and browsing features.

★12226★ Academic360.com
E-mail: webmaster@atsacademic360.com
URL: http://www.academic360.com/

Description: Site is a collection of internet resources gathered for the academic job hunter. Contains links to over 1,400 colleges and universities that advertise job openings online. Positions listed are not limited to teaching positions.

★12227★ Accountingjobs.com
E-mail: jobs@atsaccountingjobs.com
URL: http://www.accountingjobs.com

Description: Site holds national employment opportunities for accounting and finance professionals. Job seekers may search over 1,000 available positions posted by employers. Employers may browse through resumes posted by the job seekers. Employer profiles are also housed on the site, as well as links to other financial/accounting resources on the web.

★12228★ American Academy of Ophthalmology Professional Choices Career Center
American Academy of Ophthalmology
655 Beach St.
PO Box 7424
San Francisco, CA 94120-7424
Ph: (415)561-8500   Fax: (415)561-8595
E-mail: pchoices@atsaao.org
URL: http://secure3.aao.org/professional-choices/index.cfm

Description: A site providing regularly updated ophthalmology positions. Applicants

for jobs contact the AAO with resume, cover letter, and listing reference number. Job hunters may also join the Applicant Database which allows access to a greater number of employers. **Fee:** $70 for nonmembers, $60 for members to subscribe to the Applicant Database.

★12229★ American Academy of Physician Assistants Career Opportunities
URL: http://www.medical-admart.com/aapa

Description: Online newsletter of the AAPA. Job opportunities may be searched by state or type. Members may also post position wanted on AAPA website.

★12230★ American Accounting Association Placement Advertising
URL: http://aaahq.org/placements/default.cfm

Description: Visitors may apply for membership to the Association at this site. **Main files include:** Placement Postings, Placement Submission Information, Faculty Development, Marketplace, more.

★12231★ American Association of Anatomists Career Center
URL: http://www.anatomy.org/public/pages/index.cfm?pageid=117

Description: Job advertisers include academic sites in the U.S. and Canada. Job seekers may review these posted jobs through "Positions Offered" or post their own needs under "Positions Wanted." Offerings for Postdoctoral Positions also available. Contains Career Resources sections and links to online career resources.

★12232★ American Chemical Society: JobSpectrum.org
E-mail: jobmaster@jobspectrum.org
URL: http://www.jobspectrum.org

Description: JobSpectrum is a joint venture of the ACS Publications Division and the ACS Membership Division. Offers online interviewing between employers and potential employees, postings for positions available and situations wanted, and regularly updated career advice and information for American Chemical Society members only.

★12233★ American Institute of Aeronautics and Astronautics Career Planning and Placement Services
URL: http://www.aiaa.org/members/index.hfm?memo=0

Description: Site for AIAA members to place recruitment advertisements, browse career opportunities listings, post resumes, and seek additional employment assistance. Non-members may become members though this site.

★12234★ American Institute of Biological Sciences Classifieds
URL: http://spars.aibs.org/aibsclassifieds/txtintro.html

Description: Section of the American Institute of Biological Sciences website used for posting available positions, research awards and fellowships, and other classified ads.

★12235★ American Library Association Education and Employment
URL: http://www.ala.org/education

Description: Contains links to monthly job and career leads lists posted in *American Libraries* and *College & Research Libraries NewsNet* and other sources, as well as a Conference Placement Service and accreditation information.

★12236★ American Oil Chemists Society Career Opportunities
E-mail: kathya@aocs.org
URL: http://www.aocs.org/member/jobcent/

Description: Section of the AOCS homepage intended to aid members in finding jobs in the oil chemistry field. Job areas include analytical, health and nutrition, processing, surfactants and detergents, general fats and oils/chemistry, and others. Jobs may be posted and searched.

★12237★ American Society of Landscape Architects JobLink
American Society of Landscape Architects
636 Eye St. NW
Washington, DC 20001-3736
Ph: (202)898-2444   Fax: (202)898-1185
URL: http://www.asla.org/nonmembers/joblink.cfm

Description: A job-search site of the American Society of Landscape Architects. **Fee:** Resume postings cost $100 (nonmembers) or $10 (members) for a two-month listing. Job postings cost $450 (nonmembers) or $200 (members) for a two-month listing.

★12238★ American Society of Plant Biologists Job Bank
E-mail: dgordon@aspb.org
URL: http://www.aspb.org/jobbank/

Description: A service of the American Society of Plant Biologists, intended to aid its members in locating jobs and job resources. Site lists new jobs weekly in its job bank. **Fee:** A fee of $150 is charged for all academic/government/industry permanent positions and for all positions, regardless of rank, posted by private companies. Postdoctoral Positions; Research/Technical Positions (non-Ph.D.); and Assistantships, Fellowships, and Internships at universities and not-for-profit agencies are published at no charge.

★12239★ America's Job Bank
URL: http://www.ajb.dni.us/index.html

Description: Provides detailed job listings in all areas. Use the site's self-directed search feature to find a job opening in a particular field, browse by company name, or connect to one of the local job banks in each state. **Main files include:** Employers, Job Seekers, Job Market Info, Search Tips, Instructions, America's Talent Bank, and America's Career Infonet.

★12240★ **AppleOne.com**
URL: http://www.appleone.com
Description: Search site with job databank, resume posting and online e-newsletter subscriptions. Applicants can also interview with prospective employers online. Registration is free.

★12241★ **ArtJob Online**
1743 Wazee St., Ste. 300
Denver, CO 80202
Ph: (303)629-1166   Fax: (303)629-9717
Fr: 888-JOBS-232
E-mail: artjob@westaf.org
URL: http://www.artjob.org
Description: Contains up-to-date national and international listings of arts employment and related opportunities in the arts: full- & part-time employment, internships, grants, public art projects, residencies – can search by region, art discipline, type of organization. **Fee:** Subscribers pay $25 for 3 months, $40 for six months and $75 for one year.

★12242★ **Best Jobs USA**
E-mail: rci@atsbestjobsusa.com
URL: http://www.bestjobsusa.com
Description: Employment search engine and database offering employment ads from @IT1Employment Review Magazine@IT2. **Main files include:** Career Guide (job opportunities, resume posting, career fairs, company profiles); HR Solutions (trends, statistics, resume searching); News to Peruse (industry information and news).

★12243★ **Bio.com Career Center**
URL: http://career.bio.com/pages/index.cfm
Description: Contains a job index searchable by employer name, discipline, or location. Suitable for job hunters tracking down specific medical, biological, biochemical, or pharmaceutical companies and positions. Also references at Career Guide and Career Forum sections.

★12244★ **BioView.com**
URL: http://www.bioview.com
Description: Provides information on bio-pharmaceutical jobs, news, and resources. Job hunters may search jobs by keyword, state, and job title or discipline. **Main files include:** Submit Company Summary, CareerView, CompanyView, NewsView, InvestorView, MarketView. **Fee:** Single Job Posting - $225/60 days Unlimited Job Postings $2,000/month. Posting packages also available.

★12245★ **Bioview.com Career Opportunities**
URL: http://www.biolinks.com/career
Description: An internet search engine designed by scientists for scientists. Offers searchable career and candidate listings and options to post jobs or resumes. **Main files include:** BioBoard, Medline, Databases and Research Tools, Journals, Medical Sites, Scientific Companies, and more.

★12246★ **Brass Ring**
URL: http://www.brassring.com
Description: Site offers a database of over 15,000 job listings searchable by job title, technology, and location/company. Also provides a resume posting service, career article search, salary calculator, and Human Resource Center, as well as schedules for career fairs and expos.

★12247★ **California Society of Certified Public Accountants Classifieds**
E-mail: tiffany.gilroy@calcpa.org
URL: http://www.calcpa.org/community/classifieds/index.html
Description: An accounting job search tool for CPAs in California. Details steps to become a CPA, provides job search posting opportunities for seekers and candidates' pages for employers looking to fill positions.

★12248★ **Career Engine Network**
E-mail: info@careerengine.com
URL: http://www.careerengine.com
Description: Job board where seekers may search for jobs, recruit a job search agent to assist them, and take advantage of relocation tools. Provides links to specific field information and diversity-concentrated sites.

★12249★ **Career Mag**
URL: http://www.careermag.com
Description: Searchable database with resume bank. **Main files include:** Post Your Jobs; Post Internships; Relocation Assistance Center, Resume Writing Advice; Featured Employers.

★12250★ **Careerbuilder**
URL: http://www.careerpath.com
Description: Employment database featuring job listings from national and international newspapers. Employers may also post jobs. Listings are updated on a daily basis. Also contains sections on resumes, interviews, relocation services, and more. Also links to Resumezapper.com for rapid resume distribution. E-mail system for job lead alert.

★12251★ **CareerBuilder.com**
URL: http://www.careerbuilder.com
Description: Job-seekers may search job board through several different career headers, such as field of interest, location or keyword search, also may post resume to Career Builder database. Employers and recruiters may log on to post jobs and review resumes. Also contains resume and career resources, e-mail alerts.

★12252★ **Career.com**
E-mail: info@atscareer.com
URL: http://www.career.com
Description: Users can perform job searches by company, location, discipline, and for new graduates. Other features include "Hot Jobs," CyberFair, and a resume save option.

★12253★ **CareerFairs.com**
URL: http://www.careerfairs.com
Description: An online guide to upcoming career fairs and the employers who will attend them. Includes a free resume database.

★12254★ **CareerMagazine**
URL: http://www.careermag.com
Description: Online magazine containing many columns, features and articles about job hunting. Also holds job listings for browsers. **Main files include:** Job Openings, Employers, Articles, Resume Bank, Career Forum, On Campus, Diversity, Be Your Own Boss, Job Fairs, Recruiter Directory, Consultant Directory, Products & Services, Relocation Resources, Career Links, Post Your Jobs. Has information section for self-employed and freelance workers.

★12255★ **CareerMart**
E-mail: info@atscareermart.com
URL: http://www.careermart.com
Description: Site where users can scan job postings and learn about specific employers. Users can conduct job searches customized by state/region, job category, and company. **Main files include:** Job Search; Companies; Post Job; Post Resume; College Index; Alliances.

★12256★ **CareerPerfect.com**
URL: http://www.careerperfect.com
Description: Provides links to career software and books; lists FAQ's on career planning, resumes, job searching, and interviewing; identifies online job databases; accepts resumes for posting.

★12257★ **Careers In Business**
URL: http://www.careers-in-business.com/
Description: Site contains information on jobs in the business sector, primarily in accounting, finance, and consulting. Provides detailed information on job search aids and employer profiles, with job areas broken down into subject. Data on salaries, skill requirements, trends and other important factors are expanded from each subject-specific occupation listing. There are also many links to other job-seeking related sites and dozens of company sites on the Internet. **Main files include:** Careers in Finance;

Careers in Accounting; Careers in Management; Other Career Sites; Recommended Books.

★12258★ CareerShop.com
URL: http://www.careershop.com
Description: Database of resume profiles and employment opportunites. Job hunters can post resumes and perform job searches. Employers can search resumes and post job openings. Also AutoHire system offers the ability to enhance the recruiting section of an organization's current web site. It can also be used as a stand-alone site for organizations that have no current site.

★12259★ CareerSite
URL: http://www.careersite.com
Description: Job seekers can scan job opportunities either by employer or by type of work, and reply electronically to job listings. They can submit a resume and confidential profile to be placed in the database. The job seeker's identity is released to employers only with the listee's permission.

★12260★ Chronicle of Higher Education Career Network
E-mail: careers@atschronicle.com
URL: http://www.chronicle.com/jobs/
Description: Provided by the Chronicle of Higher Education, a fully searchable online listing of jobs currently available at univeristies and colleges in the U.S. and abroad. Position listings include faculty, research, administrative and executive openings. Also provides an e-mail notification service for specific jobs, job market news, and links.

★12261★ CollegeGrad.com
URL: http://www.collegegrad.com
Description: "Your link to life after college." Site contains the online version of the @it1College Grad Job Hunter@it2 - an entry level job search book. **Main files include:** Preparation, Resumes and Cover Letters, Job Postings, Interviews and Negotiations, New Job. Employers may also search for candidates fitting positions.

★12262★ ComputerJobs.com
URL: http://www.computerjobs.com
Description: The site is an employment tool for technology professionals. Information on positions is updated hourly for seekers. Jobs may be searched by skill, or by location nationally or in a specific state or city job market. Contains thousands of job postings. National jobs may be posted for free. Also career resources for IT professionals.

★12263★ Computerworld Careers
URL: http://www.computerworld.com/cwi/careers/
Description: Offers career opportunities for IT (information technology) professionals. Job seekers may search the jobs database,

register at the site, and read about job surveys and employment trends. Employers may post jobs.

★12264★ Computing Research Association Job Announcements
URL: http://www.cra.org/main/cra.jobs.html
Description: Contains dated links to national college and university computer technology positions.

★12265★ Contract Job Hunter
E-mail: staff@cjhunter.com
URL: http://www.cjhunter.com/#
Description: Contains information on immediate and anticipated contract job openings throughout the United States, Canada, and overseas. All jobs listed are temporary technical jobs that are usually higher paying than similar direct jobs. Jobs database is updated every hour. Hosts Subscribers' Lounge, advertisers section, a guest area, and links. Also directory of contract staffing firms.

★12266★ Delta T Group
E-mail: staffing@sdelta-tgroup.com
URL: http://www.delta-tgroup.com
Description: Specialized contract temporary staffing source for healthcare professionals in the fields of social service, psychiatry, mental health, and substance abuse. Organizations may request services and staffing; job seekers may view services provided, submit a resume, or peruse jobs available.

★12267★ Dice.com
URL: http://www.dice.com
Description: Job search database for computer consultants and high-tech professionals, listing thousands of high tech permanent contract and consulting jobs for programmers, software engineers, systems administrators, web developers, and hardware engineers. Also free career advice e-mail newsletter and job posting e-alerts.

★12268★ The Digital Financier
URL: http://www.dfin.com
Description: Job postings from financial companies. Offers links to major job search websites. Has leads for further training and allows companies to post their own job links.

★12269★ EmployMED: Healthcare Job Listings
E-mail: ashrafn@aol.com
URL: http://www.employmed.com/
Description: Lists practice opportunities throughout North America for all medical specialties. Contains job listings directory. Posting option is available for those who wish to advertise jobs. **Fee:** $25 per month per posting for minimum of 2 months.

★12270★ Employment Guide.com
URL: http://www.employmentguide.com/

Description: Users may search job listings, file their resume online, hunt for international jobs, search employers, and visit the specialized healthcare job database. Employers may list jobs and search resumes. Site also lists affiliated and associated job sites. Contains JobWire Instant interview process.

★12271★ Employment Resourcers for People with Disabilities
E-mail: careers@atsdisserv.stu.umn.edu
URL: http://www.disserv.stu.umn.edu/TC/Grants/COL/listing/disemp/
Description: Site offering employment and career-related links to job seekers with disabilities.

★12272★ Employment911.com
E-mail: contact@employment911.com
URL: http://www.employment911.com
Description: Seekers can access free email, resume posting, job search organizer & personal web calendar. Also contains job meta-search engine, career resources, and links to online education. Registration is free.

★12273★ eResourcing North America
URL: http://na.eresourcing.tmp.com/
Description: Corporate recruiting firm's website presence; job seekers can search job databank and submit their resume to the firm for posting to employers.

★12274★ FASEB Career Resources
9650 Rockville Pike
Bethesda, MD 20814
Ph: (301)530-7020   Fax: (301)571-0699
E-mail: jroberts@atsfaseb.org
URL: http://ns2.faseb.org/careerweb
Description: A career opportunity site combined with a development service that attempts to pair applicants at all career levels with employers who hire biomedical scientists and technicians. Biomedical career development is highlighted through career resource tools. **Main files include:** Careers OnLine DataNet, Career OnLine Classified.

★12275★ FCS - The 1st Choice in Psychiatric Recruitment
1711 Ashley Cir., Ste. 6
Bowling Green, KY 42104-5801
Fax: (502)782-1055   Fr: 800-783-9152
E-mail: fcsinfo@atsfcspsy.com
URL: http://www.fcspsy.com
Description: Physician search firm specializing in the recruitment of psychiatrists. After the applicant fills out an interest survey, a tailored search is run on the jobs database. Confidential and free.

★12276★ FedWorld Federal Job Search
E-mail: helpdesk@atsfedworld.gov
URL: http://www.fedworld.gov/jobs/job-search.html

Description: Database containing employment information in the public sector. Listings include address, job title and information, contact information, geographic location, and data of availability, among others. **Main files include:** NTIS Federal Job Opportunities; Atlanta Regional Federal Jobs; Chicago Regional Federal Jobs; Dallas Regional Federal Jobs; Philadelphia Regional Federal Jobs; San Francisco Regional Federal Jobs; Washington DC Regional Federal Jobs; National Federal Jobs; S&S Federal Positions Available; Public Health Service Positions; Federal Jobs Listed by State; Atlantic Overseas; Pacific Overseas; Puerto Rico; Virgin Islands; Information on Downloading Files; Federal Jobs EMail Forum; Exit to Main Menu; and Enter Jobs File Library. **Fee:** Free.

★12277★ **Financial Job Network**
E-mail: info@atsfjn.com
URL: http://www.fjn.com

Description: Contains information on international and national employment opportunities for those in the financial job market. Job listings may be submitted, as well as resumes. **Main files include:** Testimonials, Calendar, Corporate Listings, FJN Clients, more. **Fee:** Free to candidates.

★12278★ **First Steps in the Hunt: Daily News for Online Job Hunters**
E-mail: suggestions@atsinterbiznet.com
URL: http://www.interbiznet.com/hunt/index.html

Description: Database provides a wide variety of information on job hunting on the Internet, as well as links to other sources of information. Included are examples of online web page resumes and links to information about publishing them. Also includes current and archived articles, company job sites, and a listing of job hunting tools and products that may help in the job search. **Main files include:** Sponsors; Tools; Archives; Products; and Info.

★12279★ **FlipDog.com**
URL: http://www.flipdog.com

Description: Job search site with job board, resume posting, automated job finders with e-mail alert, resume coaching and broadcasting, career resource center and semimonthly newsletter. Registration is free.

★12280★ **4Work.com**
E-mail: info@ats4work.com
URL: http://www.4work.com

Description: Job hunting site with the option of searching by job, internship, part-time, or volunteer position. Also searchable by keyword and state. Employers may also post positions available. **Fee:** $100 first month, $100 each additional month

★12281★ **4Anything Network: 4Careers.com**
URL: http://www.4careers.com

Description: Job hunters may search job ads placed by employers. Jobs are arranged in sub-categories. Also sections on personality assessments, salary research, and career counseling.

★12282★ **Freeality Online Career and Job Search**
E-mail: webmaster@freeality.com
URL: http://www.freeality.com/jobst.htm

Description: Listing of career-related search engines, along with links to other career resources.

★12283★ **FreeJobSearchEngines.com**
E-mail: cs@free-job-search-engines.com
URL: http://free-job-search-engines.com/

Description: Job board meta-search engine grouping jobs by geography. Seekers can search in the United States, the United Kingdom, Australia, Canada and Hong Kong.

★12284★ **GasWork.com: The Largest Internet Anesthesia Employment Resource**
E-mail: support@atsgaswork.com
URL: http://www.gaswork.com

Description: The largest anesthesia employment resource. Lists positions for anesthesiologists, CRNA's, and more. Visitors may post or search jobs.

★12285★ **Genetics Society of America:Positions Open**
E-mail: dprice@atsgenetics.faseb.org
URL: http://www.faseb.org/genetics/g-gsa/open_positions.shtml

Description: Listing of position announcements formerly published in @it1Genetics@it2. Members may e-mail job listings to the site to be posted.

★12286★ **Graduate School of Library and Information Science Resources**
URL: http://www.lis.uiuc.edu/gslis/resources/jobs.html

Description: Database contains links to site posting library science related jobs available.

★12287★ **GrantsNet**
E-mail: grantsnet@atsaaas.org
URL: http://www.grantsnet.org

Description: Grant-locating site intended for scientists in training who may become vulnerable in an era of competitive funding. Includes a directory of over 600 programs with contact information within a searchable database.

★12288★ **Great Insurance Jobs**
URL: http://www.greatinsurancejobs.com

Description: Contains varied insurance positions. Job seekers may browse employee profiles, post resumes, and read descriptions of hundreds of recently-posted insurance jobs.

★12289★ **Guru**
URL: http://www.guru.com

Description: Job board specializing in contract jobs for creative and information technology professionals. Also provides online incorporation and educational opportunities for independent contractors along with articles and advice.

★12290★ **Health Care Job Store**
395 South End Ave., Ste. 15-D
New York, NY 10280
Ph: (212)912-0175
E-mail: jobs@atshealthcarejobstore.com
URL: http://www.healthcarejobstore.com/adag.html

Description: Job sites include every job title in the healthcare industry,every healthcare industry and every geographic location in the U.S.

★12291★ **Health Care Recruitment Online**
E-mail: rich@atshealthcarerecruitment.com
URL: http://www.healthcareers-online.com/

Description: Helps seekers find healthcare positions through on-line postings with national staffing companies and hospital partners. **Main files include:** Featured Employers, Job Search, Immediate Openings, Relocating, Career Management, State boards, and more.

★12292★ **Health Search USA**
E-mail: info@atshealthsearchusa.com
URL: http://www.healthsearchusa.com

Description: A site for national physician recruitment. Offers job postings classified by region and salary comparison.

★12293★ **HealthCareerWeb**
URL: http://www.healthcareerweb.com/

Description: Advertises jobs for healthcare professionals. **Main files include:** Jobs, Employers, Resumes, Jobwire. Relocation tools and career guidance resources available.

★12294★ **HelpWanted.com**
E-mail: editor@atshelpwanted.com
URL: http://www.helpwanted.com

Description: Site providing job postings, resume service, and listing of employment agencies and recruiters. Caters to job seekers, employers, and agencies.

★12295★ **Illinois Certified Public Accountant Society Career Services**
URL: http://www.icpas.org/icpas/career-services/career-services.asp

Description: Offers job hunting aid to members of the Illinois CPA Society only. Opportunity for non-members to join online. **Main files include:** Overview of Services, Resume Match, Career Seminars, Career Resources, Free Job Listings, Per Diem Pool, and Career Bibliographies.

★12296★ Institute of Food Technologists - IFT Web Express
E-mail: info@atsift.org
URL: http://www.ift.org/employment/index.shtml

Description: Offers job information and resources for those considering the Food Science and Technology field. Employers may post for full- or part-time positions and have the option of receiving a resume file of current job seekers. IFT members may register for a six-month confidential service to have their credentials reviewed by food industry employers. Job seekers who list credentials will receive the monthly Jobs Available bulletin. **Main files include:** Employment and Salary Information, How to Find Your First Job in the Food Sciences, Resources for Non-US Job Seekers, and more.

★12297★ Insurance National Search, Inc.
E-mail: stacy@atsinsurancerecruiters.com
URL: http://www.insurancerecruiters.com

Description: Contains lists of recruiters (listed by department and line of business) and available insurance positions. **Main files include:** Recruiter Resources, Recruiters Roundtable Discussion Forum, Job Listing Submission Form, Candidate Listing Submission Form. Visitors can also search by job position.

★12298★ Internet Career Connection
URL: http://www.iccweb.com/

Description: Online career and employment guidance agency. Site's services include: Help Wanted USA – job seekers can access one million help wanted ads; U.S. Government Employment Opportunities; Worldwide Resume/Talent Bank – job seekers can post resumes. Employers may view over 50,000 Resumes and career advice articles.

★12299★ The Internet Job Locator
URL: http://www.joblocator.com

Description: Visitors may post their resume and search job board. Registration is free.

★12300★ Job.com
E-mail: jobseekersupport@job.com
URL: http://www.job.com

Description: Seekers can post resume free, search through job databank and use website "powertools" such as resume coaching and distribution, career direction report, personal salary report, online education and self-employment links, and more.

★12301★ JobFind.com
E-mail: jobfind@jobfind.com
URL: http://www.jobfind.com

Description: Job site that includes job search board, resume posting with HTML capabilities, "inbox" for e-mail job alerts, corporate profiles, job fair search and career resources.

★12302★ JobHunt: On-Line Job Meta-list
URL: http://www.job-hunt.org/

Description: Database containing list of career search websites from various sources in the United States. **Main files include:** Categories: Academia; Classified Ads; Companies; General; Newsgroup Searches; Recruiting Agencies; Science, Engineering, and Medicine. Other Job Resources: Commercial Services; Other Meta-lists; Reference Material; Resume Banks; University Career Resource Centers. Also contains links to other job sites and free PDF file on choosing a career search site.

★12303★ JobListings.net
URL: http://www.joblistings.net

Description: Job search and resume posting site. Registration and posting is free.

★12304★ Jobs.com
E-mail: info@atswantedtech.com
URL: http://hoovers.wantedjobs.com/wjo/search.jsp?cb=hoovers

Description: Search engine for job postings.

★12305★ JobStar
E-mail: electrajobstar@earthlink.net
URL: http://jobstar.org/

Description: Job search guide based in California. Includes career guides and information on local, national and international career counseling centers, resumes, salaries, and hidden jobs.

★12306★ JobWeb
URL: http://www.jobweb.org/

Description: Site is maintained by the National Association of Colleges and Employers (NACE). Provides career-related information and job listings to college students and graduates.

★12307★ Law.com: Law Jobs
URL: http://www.lawjobs.com

Description: Visitors can post job openings for attorneys, legal support staff and temporary workers. Also resources for legal recruiters and temporary staffing agencies.

★12308★ Library and Information Technology Association Job Listing
URL: http://www.lita.org/jobs/index.html

Description: Contains weekly postings of available library jobs. Searchable by region.

★12309★ Library Job Postings on the Internet
E-mail: sarah@libraryjobpostings.org
URL: http://www.libraryjobpostings.org

Description: Employers may post library position announcements. Also contains links to around 250 library employment sites and links to library-related e-mail lists. Positions are searchable by region and type of library.

★12310★ Mandy's International Film and TV Production Directory
E-mail: Directory@atsmandy.com
URL: http://www.mandy.com/1/filmtvjobs.cfm

Description: Employment site intended for film and tv professionals. Employers may post free Jobs Offered listings. Job seekers may post free Jobs Wanted ads.

★12311★ MBA Careers
E-mail: support@mbacareers.com
URL: http://www.mbacareers.com

Description: Job site that provides resume posting, databank search and e-mail alert services to MBA and other advanced graduate degree holders.

★12312★ Med Source Consultants
20 Summer Ct.
Stamford, CT 06901
Ph: (203)324-0388   Fax: (203)324-0551
Fr: 800-575-2880
URL: http://www.psychiatricresources.com

Description: Site houses a physician search and consulting company for psychiatrists. Consultants attempt to match job seekers to positions according to the individual's personal and professional needs. This page also aids institutions looking to recruit psychiatrists.

★12313★ Medbulletin Medical Career Resource Center
E-mail: medbulletin@atsmedbulletin.com
URL: http://www.medbulletin.com

Description: Offers free specialized update service, resume posting, recruiter directory, varied job listings, and relocation services.

★12314★ MedExplorer
URL: http://www.medexplorer.com

Description: Employment postings make up one module of this general medical site. Other sections contain: Newsletter, Classifieds, and Discussion Forum.

★12315★ MEDMarket
URL: http://www.medmarket.com/

Description: Site provides links to employers who wish to make current employment listings available to interested persons in the healthcare manufacturing industry.

★12316★ Medzilla
URL: http://www.medzilla.com

Description: General medical website which matches employers and job hunters to their ideal employees and jobs through search capabilities. **Main files include:** Post Jobs, Search Resumes, Post Resumes, Search Jobs, Head Hunters, Articles, Salary Survey.

★12317★ Military Career Guide Online
URL: http://www.militarycareers.com

Description: Site provides details on many enlisted and officer occupations and describes training, advancement, and educational services within each of the major services. Includes browsing capabilities to match positions with interests.

★12318★ The Monster Board
E-mail: webmaster@atsmonster.com
URL: http://www.monster.com

Description: An interactive, continually expanding database of current job openings, including an online career fair, career search help, employer profiles, and a resume posting service. Searching is available by industry, location, company, discipline and keyword. Users can search over 50,000 of position openings, advertise openings, or submit resumes. Employers pay a fee for posting position openings and company profiles. An online form allows for contact with the producers of the database. **Main files include:** Press Box, Career Center, Job Search Agent, Recruiters' Center. **Fee:** Free to job seekers; fees for job advertisers.

★12319★ Monster Healthcare
E-mail: office@atsmedsearch.com
URL: http://myh.monster.com/

Description: H Monster delivers nationwide access to healthcare recruiting. Employers can post job listings or ads. Job seekers can post and code resumes, and search over 150,000 healthcare job listings, healthcare career advice columns, career resources information, and member employer profiles and services.

★12320★ MonsterTRAK
URL: http://www.jobtrak.com/

Description: College-targeted job hunting and recruiting site. Students and alumni may enter a user profile or resume to be reviewed by potential employers, or search job listings without doing so. Employers may enter full-time, part-time, temporary, and internship opportunities into the database to be reviewed by students and recent graduates, and may review resumes.

★12321★ NationJob Network
URL: http://www.nationjob.com/

Description: Online job database containing job listings and company profiles. **Main files include:** Specialty Pages; Custom Jobs Pages; Community Pages; Customer Success Stories.

★12322★ Net Temps
URL: http://www.net-temps.com/

Description: Site specializing in the Staffing industry serving direct placement and temporary (contract) professionals. Net-Temps provides a convenient and free method to post resumes, inquire about available positions and apply for jobs online. Recruiters utilize Net-Temps to publicize available employment opportunities and search the Resume Bank to identify qualified job candidates

★12323★ NetJobs
E-mail: info@atsnetjobs.com
URL: http://www.netjobs.com

Description: Source for Canadian job hunters and employers. Job seekers may post resumes online and search through job openings. Searches can be performed by job category, company name, or location, or on listings posted within the last ten days.

★12324★ Online Sports Career Center
E-mail: comments@atsonlinesports.com
URL: http://www.onlinesports.com/pages/careercenter.html

Description: Resource for sports-related career opportunities, as well as a resume bank for the perusal of potential employers within the sports and recreation industries. Job seekers may post resumes by sending files in ASCII text format to resumes@atsonlinesports.com. **Main files include:** Job Bank, Resume Bank, Newsletter, Work With Online Sports, Other Internet Resources.

★12325★ Premier Careers, Inc.
1345 S. Missouri Ave., Ste. 120
Clearwater, FL 33756
Ph: (727)467-0220   Fax: (727)467-0222
E-mail: info@atspremiercareers.com
URL: http://www.premiercareers.com

Description: Contains a database with information on candidates searching for jobs in the property and casualty insurance industry and with national sales organizations. Houses resumes and letters of reference. Candidate searches may be run by industry, geography, job title, years of experience, compensation, education, and/or accreditation. Also offers resume writing and interviewing tips to job hunters.

★12326★ PrintJobs.com
PO Box 135
Bowmansville, NY 14026
Ph: (716)686-9251   Fax: (716)686-9258
E-mail: newhouse@atsprintjobs.com
URL: http://www.printjobs.com

Description: Aims to find suitable graphic arts jobs for qualified candidates. Over a hundred jobs are maintained and updated on the site. **Fee:** Must be paid by employers using the site; no registration charge for job hunters.

★12327★ RadWorking.com
E-mail: info@atsradworking.com
URL: http://www.RadWorking.com

Description: Employment resource dedicated to the profession of radiology. Site is divided into various job-search sections based on job type or nature of support position.

★12328★ Recruiters Online Network
URL: http://www.recruitersonline.com/

Description: Site is used by over 8,000 recruiters, search firms, employment agencies, and employment professionals. Job seekers may read the Careers Online Magazine, post resumes, and search jobs. **Fee:** Free to job seekers; fee for recruiters.

★12329★ RehabJobs Online
PO Box 480536
Los Angeles, CA 90048
Ph: (213)938-7718   Fax: (213)938-9609
Fr: 800-43-REHAB
E-mail: support@atsrehabjobs.com
URL: http://www.rehabjobs.com

Description: @dq1On-line resource center for the professional therapist.@dq2 **Main files include:** Therapists Only, Therapy Forums, Nationwide Job Search (database), Therapy Job Outlook, Therapy Job Search Utilities, Therapy Links, Information for Employers and Recruiters.

★12330★ RehabWorld
URL: http://www.rehabworld.com

Description: Site for rehabilitation professionals to learn about the profession and locate jobs. Includes user groups, salary surveys, and chat capabilities. **Main files include:** Physical Therapy, Occupational Therapy, Speech Therapy, Mental Health, Employer World, Student World, International World, Forum.

★12331★ Resume-Net
E-mail: info@atsresume-net.com
URL: http://www.resumenet.com

Description: Online resume publishing service. Assists job seekers in creating online resumes. Resumes are searchable by location and profession.

★12332★ Resume Safari
URL: http://resumesafari.com/affilfag.cfm

Description: Site serves as a resume distribution service. Once submitted, a job hunter's resume will be distributed to over 1,500 locations on the web **Fee:** $60 or $80 depending on tier.

★12333★ Saludos.com
E-mail: info@atssaludos.com

URL: http://www.saludos.com

Description: Supported by @IT1Saludos Hispanos@IT2 magazine, this site is devoted to promoting Hispanic careers and education. It is a prime resource for employers to gain access to the resumes of bilingual college graduates. Online job listings and a resume pool are offered, as well as a career center, links to Hispanic resources, career links, and access to @IT1Saludos@IT2 Magazine.

★12334★ The SciWeb Biotechnology Career Home Page
URL: http://www.biocareer.com

Description: Career resource center resulting from the collaboration of the Biotechnology Industry Organization (BIO) and *SciWeb*. Aims to connect job seekers with recruiters in the biotechnology industry. **Main files include:** Post Resume, Search Resume, Post Job, Search Job, Career Resources. **Fee:** Normal Listing Fees: $150.00 for the first two months, $75.00 per additional monthly renewal. Academic PostDoctoral Listings are posted for free.

★12335★ Social Work and Social Services Jobs Online
E-mail: cndoe@gwbweb.wustl.edu
URL: http://gwbweb.wustl.edu/jobs/

Description: Specialized database of social work and social services jobs gives a large list of openings sorted by location (both within and outside the United States). Employers may submit job openings. Site also contains career resources and links to related internet job sites.

★12336★ Society of Broadcast Engineers Job Line
URL: http://www.sbe.org/jobline.html

Description: Job Line is one benefit of membership in the Society of Broadcast Engineers. Includes a resume service to distribute resumes to employers, job contact information, and descriptions of job openings. Also accessible via telephone.

★12337★ Summer Jobs
URL: http://www.summerjobs.com

Description: Database listing seasonal and part-time job opportunities. Job listings are organized by country, state, region, and city. Primary focus is on summer jobs for students and education professionals.

★12338★ Telecommuting Jobs
E-mail: contact@atstjobs.com
URL: http://www.tjobs.com

Description: Job hunters may enter a resume or post a job-wanted listing. Employers may search talent available and post job availabilities. Site also includes tools to connect telecommuters with employers and job news about telecommuting.

★12339★ TopEchelon.com
E-mail: info@topechelon.com
URL: http://www.topechelon.com

Description: Online placement recruiter network. Job seekers may search job board compiled by network member recruiters. They can also create an online profile for recruiters' reviews. They can also contact specific member recruiters in their field of business.

★12340★ United Search Associates: Health Network USA
E-mail: info@atsunitedsearch.com
URL: http://www.hnusa.com/usaindex.html

Description: Visitors may explore healthcare positions, submit an electronic resume, or advertise with the site.

★12341★ USAJOBS - United States Office of Personnel Management
URL: http://www.usajobs.opm.gov

Description: Provides information about jobs that are available in the Federal government. The online search program allows users to search job announcements on the bulletin board by either series number or job title. Also has resume builder and e-mail alert services. **Fee:** Free.

★12342★ Vault.com
E-mail: feedback@staff.vault.com
URL: http://www.vault.com

Description: Job board website with searches emphasizing jobs in legal, business, consulting and finance fields of practice. Contains online profile posting, resume review, company research, salary calculators and relocation tools.

★12343★ Wall Street Journal Executive Career Site
URL: http://www.careerjournal.com

Description: Wall Street Journal CareerJournal.com contains numerous job-related resources, search engines and resume databases for job-seekers, employers and executive recruiters. Contains career columnists, salary negotiating instruments, discussion forums and e-mail alerting system. **Fee:** Must be subscribers to WSJ.com in order to fully utilize resources; year's subscription is $175.

★12344★ WetFeet.com
E-mail: services@wetfeet.com
URL: http://www.wetfeet.com

Description: Job board website with free membership for job seekers. Contains job board, resume listing, self assessment guides, company and city research, discussion forums, e-guides and online bookstore, salary calculators and listings of internship opportunities.

★12345★ What Color Is Your Parachute? Job Hunters Bible
URL: http://www.jobhuntersbible.com/

Description: Companion internet guide to the best selling job-hunting book, @it1What Color is Your Parachute?@it2 Includes lists of helpful links to other resources on the internet. **Main files include:** Jobs, Resumes, Counseling, Contacts, Research, Dealing With Depression.

★12346★ Women at Work
E-mail: womenatwork@atsearthlink.net
URL: http://www.womenatwork1.org/

Description: Site of nonprofit job and career resource center, serving the greater Los Angeles area.

★12347★ W.O.O. Zone
E-mail: Lbooker@atsbrassring.com
URL: http://www.nsbe.org/service/jobs.html

Description: W.O.O. stands for Window of Opportunity - a section of the website of the National Society of Black Engineers. **Main files include:** Job Search (includes full-time, co-ops, internships, and student jobs), Post a Job, Post a Resume, Company Site Search. **Fee:** $100 per month for posting a job.

★12348★ Work from Home
URL: http://www.jobs-telecommuting.com

Description: Contains a listing of over 700 companies currently looking for telecommuters. Employers may add or remove job listings. Also information on starting a home business available.

★12349★ WorkTree.com
E-mail: support@worktree.com
URL: http://www.worktree.com

Description: Job search engine portal, listing career-related search engines and websites by geography, field of practice, experience level, company and more. Also lists links to career resources such as resume coaching and interviewing tips. Resume broadcast service available. **Fee:** Membership available in several levels, depending on length of membership desired; three months' unlimited access is $47.

★12350★ The World Wide Web Employment Office
URL: http://www.employmentoffice.net/

Description: Portal to job and resume banks and board for employers and job hunters.

★12351★ WSA Executive Job Search Center
E-mail: info@atswsacorp.com
URL: http://www.wsacorp.com/index.asp

Description: A site intended for $50K-$700K range executives. Offers resume preparation, critiques and distribution, and interview preparation.

★12352★ Yahoo! Careers
URL: http://careers.yahoo.com/
Description: Contains over 360,000 jobs for job seekers to search and post resumes for, as well as weekly features, relocation resources, a daily column, and links to resume banks and services and temp agencies. Special sections are devoted to industry research, company research, advice, high tech jobs, and first jobs and internships. Powered by Career Builder.

★12353★ Yahoo! Hotjobs
E-mail: support@hotjobs.com
URL: http://www.hotjobs.yahoo.com/

Description: Job board searchable by fields, company or geographic location. Seekers may also post resumes and receive e-mail alerts. Also resources for relocation, resumes and interview tips, salary negotiation and self-assessment.

★12354★ ZDNet Tech Jobs
URL: http://www.zdnet.com/special/filters/techjobs/

Description: Site houses a listing of national employment opportunities for professionals in high tech fields. Also contains resume building tips and relocation resources. Powered by Dice.com

SOFTWARE

★12355★ Multimedia Job Search
Cambridge Educational
PO Box 931
Monmouth Junction, NJ 08852-0931
Fax: 800-FAX-ON-US   Fr: 800-468-4227
URL: http://www.cambridgeeducational.com

CD-ROM. $99.95. Includes videos, narration, and on-screen text. Users learn about getting a competitive edge in today's job market, traditional and nontraditional job search tools, resumes and cover letters, and interviewing skills.

Environmental Opportunities

REFERENCE WORKS

★12356★ Agricultural Research Institute-Membership Directory

Agricultural Research Institute
505 Capito Ct.
Washington, DC 20002
Ph: (202)675-8333   Fax: (202)675-8334

Annual. $50.00. Covers 125 member institutions; also lists study panels and committees interested in environmental issues, pest control, agricultural meteorology, biotechnology, food irradiation, agricultural policy, research and development, food safety, technology transfer, and remote sensing. Entries include: Name, title of primary contact, address, phone, fax. Arrangement: Alphabetical.

★12357★ Association of Consulting Foresters-Membership Specialization Directory

Association of Consulting Foresters
732 N Washington St., Ste. 4A
Alexandria, VA 22314-1921
Ph: (703)548-0990   Fax: (703)548-6395

Annual, August. Free. Covers nearly 500 member forestry consulting firms and professional foresters who earn the largest part of their income from consulting. Entries include: Name, address, phone, specialties, background, career data, staff (if a consulting firm), geographic area served, capabilities, including equipment available and foreign language proficiency. Arrangement: Alphabetical. Indexes: Name, office location, language, international capability.

★12358★ Canadian Environmental Directory

Thomson Gale
27500 Drake Rd.
Farmington Hills, MI 48331-3535
Ph: (248)699-GALE   Fax: (248)699-8069
Fr: 800-877-GALE
E-mail: galeord@gale.com
URL: http://www.galegroup.com

Ninth edition, 1994. 1400 pages. Out of print.

Directory of individuals, agencies, firms, and associations active in environment-related activities in Canada. Main alphabetical listings are organized by government, organization, and education/research establishments. Provides listing of legal, ecological, and management consultants.

★12359★ Careers in the Environment

VGM Career Horizons
N T C Publishing Group
1221 Avenue of the Americas
New York, NY 10020
Ph: (212)904-2000   Fr: 800-323-4900
E-mail: ntcpub@tribune.com

Michael Fasulo and Paul Walker. Second edition, 2000. $17.95; $13.95 (paper). 275 pages. Comprehensive information on the diverse career opportunities available in environmental services.

★12360★ Careers for Environmental Types and Others Who Respect the Earth

VGM Career Horizons
N T C Publishing Group
1221 Avenue of the Americas
New York, NY 10020
Ph: (212)904-2000   Fr: 800-323-4900
E-mail: ntcpub@tribune.com

Jane Kinney and Mike Fasulo. Second edition, 2001. $15.95; $12.95 (paper). 192 pages. Describes environmentally friendly positions with corporations, government, and environmental organizations.

★12361★ Careers for Health Nuts and Others Who Like to Stay Fit

McGraw-Hill Trade
2 Penn Plaza
New York, NY 10121
Ph: (212)904-2000   Fr: 800-722-4726
E-mail: ntcpub@tribune.com

Blythe Camenson. 1996. $14.95; $9.95 (paper). 160 pages.

★12362★ The Complete Guide to Environmental Careers in the 21st Century

Island Press
1718 Connecticut Ave. NW, Ste. 300
Washington, DC 20009-1148
Ph: (202)232-7933   Fax: (202)234-1328
Fr: 800-828-1302

Environmental Careers Organization Staff. Third edition, 1998. $17.95 (paper). 280 pages.

★12363★ Conservation Directory

National Wildlife Federation
11100 Wildlife Center Dr.
Reston, VA 20190
Ph: (703)638-6000   Fax: (703)438-6061
E-mail: cdadmin@nwf.org
URL: http://www.nwf.org/conservationdirectory

Annual, January. $70.00. Covers over 3,000 organizations, agencies, colleges and universities with conservation programs and more than 18,000 officials concerned with environmental conservation, education, and natural resource use and management. Entries include: Agency name, address, branch or subsidiary office name and address, names and titles of key personnel, descriptions of program areas, size of membership (where appropriate), telephone, fax, e-mail and URL addresses. Arrangement: Classified by type of organization. Indexes: Personal name, keyword, geographic, organization.

★12364★ Directory of Internships, Work Experience Programs, and On-the-Job Training Opportunities

Ready Reference Press
PO Box 5249
Santa Monica, CA 90405
Ph: (310)475-4895   Fr: 800-424-5627

$89.50. Lists internship opportunities in many fields of interest, including, but not limited to arts, journalism, public relations, education, law, environmental affairs, business, engineering, and computer science. In addition, cites summer internship opportunities, work/study programs, and specialized opportunities for high school and undergraduate students. Indexed by subject, geography, and program.

★12365★ **Education for the Earth**

Thomson Peterson's
Princeton Pike Corporate Center
2000 Lenox Dr.
PO Box 67005
Lawrenceville, NJ 08648
Ph: (609)896-1800   Fax: 800-277-2465
Fr: 800-338-3282
URL: http://www.petersons.com

Published 1994. $14.95. Covers over 300 colleges and universities offering programs in environmental studies. Entries include: College or university name, address, phone, description of program, major area of concentration, employment results, names of employers who recently recruited on campus. Arrangement: Classified by area of study. Indexes: Geographical; alphabetical.

★12366★ **EI Environmental Services Directory**

Environmental Information Ltd.
5775 Wazata Blvd., Ste. 820
St. Louis Park, MN 55416-1234
Ph: (952)831-2473   Fax: (952)831-6550
URL: http://www.envirobiz.com

Annual. $995.00. Covers over 620 waste-handling facilities, 600 transportation firms, 500 spill response firms, 2,100 consultants, 470 laboratories, 450 soil boring/well drilling firms; also includes incineration services, polychlorinated biphenyl (PCB) detoxification and mobile solvent-recovery services, asbestos services and underground tank services, summaries of states' regulatory programs. Entries include: Company name, address, phone, description of services, regulatory status, on and off site processes used, type of waste handled. Arrangement: Geographical. Indexes: Service.

★12367★ **Exploring Careers in the National Parks**

Rosen Publishing Group, Inc.
29 E. 21st St.
New York, NY 10010
Ph: (212)777-3017   Fax: 888-436-4643
Fr: 800-237-9932

Bob Gartner. Revised edition, 1999. $18.95. 192 pages. Describes working for the park service and how to get a job there.

★12368★ **Green at Work**

Island Press
1718 Connecticut Ave., NW
Ste. 300
Washington, DC 20009-1148
Ph: (202)232-7933   Fax: (202)234-1328
Fr: 800-828-1302

Susan Cohn, Horst Rechelbacher. 1995. $19.95 (paper). 400 pages. Identifies career options with an environmental focus and profiles more than 250 companies with environmental initiatives.

★12369★ **Hazardous Waste Consultant-Directory of Commercial Hazardous Waste Management Facilities Issue**

Elsevier Science Inc.
360 Park Ave. S, No. 11
New York, NY 10010-1710
Ph: (212)989-5800

Semiannual. $115.00. Publication includes: List of 170 licensed commercial facilities that treat and/or dispose of hazardous waste in North America. Entries include: Facility name, address, phone, contact name, type of waste handled, methods of on-site treatment and/or disposal, Environmental Protection Agency permit status and identification number, restrictions, description of other services. Arrangement: Geographical. Indexes: Organization name.

★12370★ **Hidden Job Market**

Thomson Peterson's
PO Box 67005
Lawrenceville, NJ 08648-6105
Fr: 800-338-3282

Ninth edition, 1999. $18.95 (paper). 319 pages. Guide to 2,000 fast-growing companies that are hiring now. Focuses on high technology companies in such fields as environmental consulting, genetic engineering, home health care, telecommunications, alternative energy systems, and others. Part of Peterson's Hidden Job Market series.

★12371★ **Job Opportunities in the Environment 1995**

Thomson Peterson's
PO Box 67005
Lawrenceville, NJ 08648-6105
Fr: 800-338-3282

Second edition, 1994. $18.95 (paper). 265 pages. Out of print.

★12372★ **National Parks: Index**

U.S. National Park Service
Harpers Ferry Center
PO Box 50
Harpers Ferry, WV 25425-0050
Ph: (202)208-4747   Fax: (304)535-6144
URL: http://www.nps.gov/

Biennial, odd years. $6.50. Covers over 379 areas administered by the National Park Service, including parks, shores, historic sites, 80 national trails, and wild and scenic rivers. Entries include: Name, location, address, acreage (federal, non-federal, and gross), federal facilities, brief description. Arrangement: Most areas are alphabetical by state; geographical and historical by state; wild and scenic rivers and national trails are alphabetical by state. Indexes: Alphabetical by state.

★12373★ **Nature (Career Portraits)**

McGraw-Hill Trade
2 Penn Plaza
New York, NY 10121
Ph: (212)904-2000   Fax: (212)755-5645
Fr: 800-722-4726

Marjorie Eberts. 1996. $13.95. 310 pages.

Highlights a range of careers that focus on the environment, with descriptions of a typical day on the job and interactive exercises for readers.

★12374★ **The New Complete Guide to Environmental Careers**

Island Press
1718 Connecticut Ave., NW
Ste. 300
Washington, DC 20009-1148
Ph: (202)232-7933   Fax: (202)234-1328
Fr: 800-828-1302

Bill Sharp. Second edition, 1993. $17.95 (paper). 364 pages. Covers job outlook, entry requirements, examples of actual jobs, and in-depth interviews with more than 100 professionals.

★12375★ **100 Jobs in the Environment**

Hungry Minds Inc.
10475 Crosspoint Blvd.
Indianapolis, IN 46256
Ph: (317)572-2000   Fr: 800-428-5331

Debra Quintana. 1996. $14.95 (paper). 224 pages. Each job profile includes prospects for finding work and describes a typical day.

★12376★ **Opportunities in Energy Careers**

McGraw-Hill Trade
2 Penn Plaza
New York, NY 10121
Ph: (212)904-2000   Fr: 800-722-4726
E-mail: ntcpub@tribune.com

Nicholas Basta. 1995. $13.95; $10.95 (paper). 160 pages. Discusses opportunities in a variety of fields, including petroleum, nuclear, and thermal energy, and how to pursue employment. Illustrated. Out of print.

★12377★ **Opportunities in Environmental Careers**

McGraw-Hill Trade
2 Penn Plaza
New York, NY 10121
Ph: (212)904-2000   Fr: 800-722-4726
E-mail: ntcpub@tribune.com

Odom Fanning. Revised, 2002. $12.95 (paper). 160 pages. Describes a broad range of opportunities in fields such as environmental health, recreation, physics, and hygiene, and provides job search advice. Part of Opportunities in...Series.

★12378★ **Opportunities in Forestry Careers**

McGraw-Hill Trade
2 Penn Plaza
New York, NY 10121
Ph: (212)904-2000   Fr: 800-722-4726
E-mail: ntcpub@tribune.com

Christopher M. Wille. 1998. $11.95 (paper). 204 pages. Describes the forestry opportunities available in governmental agencies, commercial enterprises, education, and private conservation association, and how to pursue openings. Illustrated. Part of Opportunities in...Series.

★12379★ **Opportunities in Waste Management Careers**
McGraw-Hill Trade
2 Penn Plaza
New York, NY 10121
Ph: (212)904-2000   Fr: 800-722-4726
E-mail: ntcpub@tribune.com

Mark Rowh. 1994. $14.95; $11.95 (paper). 160 pages. Outlines the diverse opportunities in waste management and examines the duties, working conditions, salaries, and future of a variety of positions. Profiles jobs and opportunities in solid waste and waste water management, environmental engineering, soil and wildlife conservation, and related career areas.

★12380★ **Peterson's Hidden Job Market**
Thomson Peterson's
Princeton Pike Corporate Center
2000 Lenox Dr.
PO Box 67005
Lawrenceville, NJ 08648
Ph: (609)896-1800   Fax: 800-277-2465
Fr: 800-338-3282
URL: http://www.petersons.com

Annual, June. $18.95. Covers approximately 2,000 technology firms with under 1,000 employees, which hire at four times the national rate. Entries include: Company name, address, phone, fax, name and title of contact, number of employees, year founded, number of employees added in last year, percentage of growth, line of business. Arrangement: Geographical by state, then by area code. Indexes: Alphabetical by industry.

★12381★ **Resumes for Environmental Careers**
McGraw-Hill Trade
2 Penn Plaza
New York, NY 10121
Ph: (212)904-2000   Fr: 800-722-4726
E-mail: ntcpub@tribune.com

2002. $9.95 (paper). 160 pages. Provides resume advice tailored to people pursuing careers focusing on the environment. Includes sample resumes and cover letters.

★12382★ **Seasonal Employment**
U.S. National Park Service
Harpers Ferry Center
PO Box 50
Harpers Ferry, WV 25425-0050
Ph: (202)208-4747   Fax: (304)535-6144
URL: http://www.nps.gov

Updated as needed; go to "InfoZone" to access. Publication includes: List of 10 regional offices and branches of the National Park Service that accept applications for seasonal jobs. Entries include: Name, address, phone, geographical area served. Principal content of publication is information on seasonal jobs offered by the National Park Services, with description of duties,

qualifications, and application procedures for each type of job offered. Arrangement: Geographical.

NEWSPAPERS, MAGAZINES, AND JOURNALS

★12383★ **Appalachian Trailway News**
Appalachian Trail Conference
PO Box 807
Harpers Ferry, WV 25425
Ph: (304)535-6331   Fax: (304)535-2667
Fr: 888-287-8673

$15.00/year for individuals. Magazine on hiking, Appalachian Trail protection, and general conservation issues.

★12384★ **Applied Occupational & Environmental Hygiene**
Applied Industrial Hygiene Inc.
1330 Kemper Meadow Dr., Ste. 600
Cincinnati, OH 45240
Ph: (513)742-2020   Fax: (513)742-3355
E-mail: comm@acgih.org

Monthly. $159.00/year for individuals; $269.00/year for institutions. Peer-reviewed journal presenting applied solutions for the prevention of occupational and environmental disease and injury.

★12385★ **CJE Newsletter**
Coalition for Jobs and the Environment
PO Box 645
Abingdon, VA 24210-0645

Description: Bimonthly. Covers issues relating to employment, jobs, and environmental safety. Recurring features include letters to the editor, news, interviews, a calendar of events, news of members, and columns titled Action Needed and Resources.

★12386★ **Earth Work**
Student Conservation Association
PO Box 550
Charlestown, NH 03603
Ph: (603)543-1700   Fax: (603)543-1828
E-mail: earthwork@sca-inc.org
URL: http://www.sca-inc.org

Description: Eleven issues/year. Contains listings of environmental positions, ranging from internships and administrative assistants for environmental groups to camp directors, state natural resource managers, and biologists.

★12387★ **Job Line...and News from CPRS**
California Park & Recreation Society Inc.
7971 Freeport Blvd.
Sacramento, CA 95832-9701
Ph: (916)665-2777   Fax: (916)665-9149

Description: Monthly. Discusses parks and recreation news of interest.

★12388★ **The Job Seeker**
The Job Seeker
24313 Destiny Ave.
Tomah, WI 54660-4367
Ph: (608)378-4450   Fax: (608)378-4450

Description: Semimonthly. Specializes "in environmental and natural resource vacancies nationwide." Lists current vacancies from federal, state, local, private, and nonprofit employers. Also available via e-mail.

★12389★ **Journal of Forestry**
Society of American Foresters
5400 Grosvenor Ln.
Bethesda, MD 20814-2198
Ph: (301)897-8720   Fax: (301)897-3690
URL: http://www.safnet.org

Monthly. $55.00/year; $100.00/year for institutions. Journal of forestry serves to advance the profession by keeping professionals informed about significant developments and ideas in forest science, natural resource management, and forest policy.

★12390★ **Nature International Weekly Journal of Science**
Nature Publishing Group
345 Park Ave. S
New York, NY 10010-1707
Ph: (212)726-9200   Fax: (212)689-9711
Fr: 888-331-6288
E-mail: nature@natureny.com
URL: http://www.nature.com

Weekly. $145.00/year for individuals; $495.00/year for institutions. Magazine covering science and technology, including the fields of biology, biochemistry, genetics, medicine, earth sciences, physics, pharmacology, and behavioral sciences.

★12391★ **NRPA Job Bulletin**
National Recreation and Park Association, Professional Services Div.
22377 Belmont Ridge Rd.
Ashburn, VA 20148
Ph: (703)858-0784   Fax: (703)858-0707
Fr: 800-626-6772
URL: http://www.nrpa.org

Description: Semimonthly. Provides listings of employment opportunities in the park, recreation, and leisure services field.

★12392★ **Recycling Today**
G.I.E. Media, MC
4012 Bridge Ave.
Cleveland, OH 44113
Ph: (216)961-4130   Fax: (216)961-0364
Fr: 800-456-0707
E-mail: dsandoval@recyclingtoday.com
URL: http://www.recyclingtoday.com

Monthly. $30.00/year for individuals; $47.00/year for Canada; $105.00/year for other countries; $212.00/year for other countries by air mail; $51.00/year for two years. Magazine covering recycling of secondary raw materials and solid-waste management.

★12393★ *Resource Recycling*

Resource Recycling
PO Box 42270
Portland, OR 97242-0270
Ph: (503)233-1305   Fax: (503)233-1356
E-mail: info@resource-recycling.com

$52.00/year for individuals; $5.00 for single issue. Journal reporting on all aspects of recycling and composting of solid waste, from collection and materials processing to markets and governmental policies.

★12394★ *Water Environment Research*

Water Environment Federation
601 Wythe St.
Alexandria, VA 22314-1994
Ph: (703)684-2400   Fax: (703)684-2492
Fr: 800-666-0206
E-mail: msc@wef.org

Bimonthly. $40.00/year for members; $158.00/year for nonmembers. Technical journal covering municipal and industrial water pollution control, water quality, and hazardous wastes.

OTHER SOURCES

★12395★ **Air and Waste Management Association (A&WMA)**

1 Gateway Ctr., 3rd Fl.
420 Duquesne Blvd.
Pittsburgh, PA 15222
Ph: (412)232-3444   Fax: (412)232-3450
Fr: 800-270-3444
E-mail: info@awma.org
URL: http://www.awma.org

Description: Environmental, educational, and technical organization. **Purpose:** Seeks to provide a neutral forum for the exchange of technical information on a wide variety of environmental topics.

★12396★ **American Academy of Environmental Engineers (AAEE)**

130 Holiday Ct., No. 100
Annapolis, MD 21401
Ph: (410)266-3311   Fax: (410)266-7653
E-mail: academy@aaee.net
URL: http://www.aaee.net

Members: Environmentally oriented registered professional engineers certified by examination as Diplomates of the Academy. **Purpose:** Works to improve the standards of environmental engineering; to certify those with special knowledge of environmental engineering; to furnish lists of those certified to the public. **Activities:** Maintains speakers' bureau. Recognizes areas of specialization: Air Pollution Control; General Environmental; Hazardous Waste Management; Industrial Hygiene; Radiation Protection; Solid Waste Management; Water Supply and Wastewater. Requires written and oral examinations for certification. Works with other professional organizations on environmentally oriented activities. Identifies potential employment candidates through Talent Search Service.

★12397★ **American Public Health Association (APHA)**

800 I St. NW
Washington, DC 20001-3710
Ph: (202)777-2742   Fax: (202)777-2534
E-mail: comments@apha.org
URL: http://www.apha.org

Members: Professional organization of physicians, nurses, educators, academicians, environmentalists, epidemiologists, new professionals, social workers, health administrators, optometrists, podiatrists, pharmacists, dentists, nutritionists, health planners, other community and mental health specialists, and interested consumers. **Purpose:** Seeks to protect and promote personal, mental, and environmental health. **Activities:** Services include promulgation of standards; establishment of uniform practices and procedures; development of the etiology of communicable diseases; research in public health; exploration of medical care programs and their relationships to public health. Sponsors job placement service.

★12398★ **Environmental Careers Organization (ECO)**

179 South St.
Boston, MA 02111
Ph: (617)426-4375   Fax: (617)423-0998
E-mail: info@eco.org
URL: http://www.eco.org

Description: Seeks to protect and enhance the environment through the development of professionals, the promotion of careers, and the inspiration of individual action. Offers paid internships, career development educational programs and related publications. Participants in programs are mostly upper-level undergraduate, graduate, and doctoral students, or recent graduates seeking professional experience relevant to careers in the environmental fields. Individual subject areas of placement service include biology, chemistry, community development, hazardous waste, natural resources, pollution, public/occupational health, transportation, and wildlife.

★12399★ **Environmental Technology Council (ETC)**

734 15th St. NW, Ste. 720
Washington, DC 20005-1013
Ph: (202)783-0870   Fax: (202)737-2038
E-mail: comments@etc.org
URL: http://www.etc.org

Description: Firms dedicated to the use of high technology treatment in the management of hazardous wastes and to the restricted use of land disposal facilities in the interests of protecting human health and the environment. Advocates minimization of hazardous wastes and the use of alternative technologies in their treatment, including chemical and biological treatments, fixation, neutralization, reclamation, recycling, and thermal treatments such as incineration. Encourages land disposal prohibitions. Promotes reductions in the volume of hazardous waste generated annually and expansion of EPA hazardous waste list. Advocates use of treatment technology as a more cost-effective approach to Superfund site cleanups. Works with state, national, and international officials and firms to assist in development of programs that utilize treatment and minimize land disposal. Provides technical and placement assistance to members; sponsors special studies, technical seminars, and workshops; participates in federal legislation, litigation, and regulatory development. Maintains library of materials on new technologies; operates speakers' bureau; compiles statistics and mailing list.

★12400★ **National Association of Conservation Districts (NACD)**

509 Capitol Ct. NE
Washington, DC 20002-4946
Ph: (202)547-6223   Fax: (202)547-6450
E-mail: washington@nacdnet.org
URL: http://www.nacdnet.org

Description: Soil and water conservation districts organized by the citizens of watersheds, counties, or communities under provisions of state laws. Directs and coordinates, through local self-government efforts, the conservation and development of soil, water, and related natural resources. Districts include over 90% of the nation's privately owned land. Conducts educational programs and children's services.

★12401★ **National Environmental Health Association (NEHA)**

720 S Colorado Blvd., Ste. 970, S Tower
Denver, CO 80246-1925
Ph: (303)756-9090   Fax: (303)691-9490
E-mail: staff@neha.org
URL: http://www.neha.org

Description: Represents all professionals in environmental health and protection, including Registered Sanitarians, Registered Environmental Health Specialists, Registered Environmental Technicians, Certified Environmental Health Technicians, Registered Hazardous Substances Professionals and Registered Hazardous Substances Specialists. NEHA's mission is to advance the environmental health and protection profession for the purpose of providing a healthful environment for all. Educational materials, publications, credentials and meetings are available to NEHA members and non-member professionals who strive to improve the environment.

★12402★ **Student Conservation Association (SCA)**

PO Box 550
Charlestown, NH 03603
Ph: (603)543-1700   Fax: (603)543-1828
E-mail: ask-us@theSCA.org
URL: http://www.theSCA.org

Description: Works to build the next generation of conservation leaders and inspire lifelong stewardship of the environment and communities by engaging young people in hands-on service to the land. Provides conservation service opportunities, outdoor education and leadership development for young people. Offers college and graduate students, as well as older adults expense-paid conservation internships. These positions include wildlife research, wilderness patrols and interpretive opportunities and provide participants with valuable hands-on career experience. Also places 15-19 year old high school students in four-week volunteer conservation crews in national parks forests and refuges across the country each summer to accomplish a range of trail building and habitat conservation projects. Offers year-round diversity conservation programs for young women and young persons of color in leading metropolitan areas of U.S.

★12403★ United States Committee for the United Nations Environment Program (US UNEP)
47914 252nd St.
Sioux Falls, SD 57198-0001
Ph: (605)594-6117   Fax: (605)594-6119
E-mail: webmaster@www.na.unep.net
URL: http://grid2.cr.usgs.gov
Description: Individuals interested in raising public awareness of the importance of a global environmental effort. Encourages activism in support of the United Nations Environment Program. Acts as a liason

between the UNEP and the public. Sponsors educational programs and children's services. Offers placement services to job seekers in international environmental work. Maintains speakers' bureau.

★12404★ U.S. Public Interest Research Group (U.S.PIRG)
218 D. St. SE
Washington, DC 20003
Ph: (202)546-9707   Fax: (202)546-2461
E-mail: uspirg@pirg.org
URL: http://www.pirg.org
Description: Individuals who contribute time, effort, or funds toward public interest research and advocacy. Conducts research, monitors corporate and government actions, and lobbies for reforms on consumer, environmental, energy, and governmental issues. Current efforts include support for: laws to protect consumers from unsafe products and unfair banking practices; laws to reduce the use of toxic chemicals; strengthening clean air laws; efforts to reduce global warming and ozone depletion; energy conservation and use of safe, renewable energy sources. Sponsors internships for college students; provides opportunities for students to receive academic credit for activities such as legislative research, lobbying, and public

education and organizing. Offers summer jobs.

★12405★ Water Environment Federation (WEF)
601 Wythe St.
Alexandria, VA 22314-1994
Ph: (703)684-2452   Fax: (703)684-2492
Fr: 800-666-0206
E-mail: csc@wef.org
URL: http://www.wef.org
Description: Technical societies representing chemists, biologists, ecologists, geologists, operators, educational and research personnel, industrial wastewater engineers consultant engineers, municipal officials equipment manufacturers, and university professors and students dedicated to the enhancement and preservation of water quality and resources. Seeks to advance fundamental and practical knowledge concerning the nature, collection, treatment, and disposal of domestic and industrial wastewaters, and the design, construction, operation and management of facilities for these purposes. Disseminates technical information promotes good public relations and regulations that improve water quality and the status of individuals working in this field Conducts educational and research programs.

Government Agencies

★12406★ Equal Employment Opportunity Commission

1801 L Street NW
Washington, DC 20507
Ph: (202)663-4900   Fr: 800-669-4000
URL: http://www.eeoc.gov

The Equal Employment Opportunity Commission enforces laws which prohibit discrimination based on race, color, religion, sex, national origin, disability, or age in hiring, promoting, firing, setting wages, testing, training, apprenticeship, and all other terms and conditions of employment. The Commission conducts investigations of alleged discrimination; makes determinations based on gathered evidence; attempts conciliation when discrimination has taken place; files lawsuits; and conducts voluntary assistance programs for employers, unions, and community organizations. The Commission also has adjudicatory and oversight responsibility for all compliance and enforcement activities relating to equal employment opportunity among Federal employees and applicants, including discrimination against individuals with disabilities.

★12407★ Federal Labor Relations Authority

607 Fourteenth Street NW
Washington, DC 20424-0001
Ph: (202)482-6560
URL: http://www.flra.gov

The Federal Labor Relations Authority oversees the Federal service labor-management relations program. It administers the law that protects the right of employees of the Federal Government to organize, bargain collectively, and participate through labor organizations of their own choosing in decisions affecting them. The Authority also ensures compliance with the statutory rights and obligations of Federal employees and the labor organizations that represent them in their dealings with Federal agencies.

★12408★ Federal Mediation and Conciliation Service

2100 K Street NW
Washington, DC 20427
Ph: (202)606-8100

URL: http://www.fmcs.gov

The Federal Mediation and Conciliation Service assists labor and management in resolving disputes in collective bargaining contract negotiation through voluntary mediation and arbitration services; provides training to unions and management in cooperative processes to improve long-term relationships under the Labor Management Cooperation Act of 1978, including Federal sector partnership training authorized by Executive Order 12871; provides alternative dispute resolution services and training to Government agencies, including the facilitation of regulatory negotiations under the Administrative Dispute Resolution Act and the Negotiated Rule-making Act of 1996; and awards competitive grants to joint labor-management committees to encourage innovative approaches to cooperative efforts.

★12409★ Merit Systems Protection Board

1615 M Street NW, Fifth Floor
Washington, DC 20419
Ph: (202)653-7200   Fax: (202)653-7130
Fr: 800-209-8960
URL: http://www.mspb.gov

The Merit Systems Protection Board protects the integrity of Federal merit systems and the rights of Federal employees working in the systems. In overseeing the personnel practices of the Federal Government, the Board conducts special studies of the merit systems, hears and decides charges of wrongdoing and employee appeals of adverse agency actions, and orders corrective and disciplinary actions when appropriate.

★12410★ National Labor Relations Board

1099 Fourteenth Street NW
Washington, DC 20570
Ph: (202)273-1000
URL: http://www.nlrb.gov

The National Labor Relations Board is vested with the power to prevent and remedy unfair labor practices committed by private sector employers and unions and to safeguard employees' rights to organize and

determine whether to have unions as their bargaining representative.

★12411★ Occupational Safety and Health Review Commission

1120 Twentieth Street NW
Washington, DC 20036-3419
Ph: (202)606-5398   Fax: (202)606-5050
URL: http://www.oshrc.gov

The Occupational Safety and Health Review Commission works to ensure the timely and fair resolution of cases involving the alleged exposure of American workers to unsafe or unhealthy working conditions.

★12412★ Office of Personnel Management

1900 E Street NW
Washington, DC 20415
Ph: (202)606-1800
URL: http://www.opm.gov

The Office of Personnel Management (OPM) administers a merit system to ensure compliance with personnel laws and regulations and assists agencies in recruiting, examining, and promoting people on the basis of their knowledge and skills, regardless of their race, religion, sex, political influence, or other nonmerit factors. OPM's role is to provide guidance to agencies in operating human resources programs which effectively support their missions and to provide an array of personnel services to applicants and employees. OPM supports Government program managers in their human resources management responsibilities and provide benefits to employees, retired employees, and their survivors.

★12413★ U.S. Commission on Civil Rights

624 Ninth Street NW, Suite 500
Washington, DC 20425
Ph: (202)376-7533
URL: http://www.usccr.gov

The Commission on Civil Rights collects and studies information on discrimination or denials of equal protection of the laws because of race, color, religion, sex, age, disability, national origin, or in the administration of justice in such areas as voting rights, enforcement of Federal civil rights laws, and equal opportunity in education, employment, and housing.

★12414★ U.S. Department of Justice Civil Rights Division

950 Pennsylvania Ave., NW
Washington, DC 20530
Ph: (202)514-4609   Fax: (202)514-0293
URL: http://www.usdoj.gov/crt

The Division is the primary institution within the Federal Government responsible for enforcing Federal statutes prohibiting discrimination on the basis of race, sex, disability, religion, and national origin.

★12415★ U.S. Department of Labor

200 Constitution Avenue NW
Washington, DC 20210
Fr: (866)487-2365
URL: http://www.dol.gov

The purpose of the Department of Labor is to foster, promote, and develop the welfare of the wage earners of the United States, to improve their working conditions, and to advance their opportunities for profitable employment. In carrying out this mission, the Department administers a variety of Federal labor laws guaranteeing workers' rights to safe and healthful working conditions, a minimum hourly wage and overtime pay, freedom from employment discrimination, unemployment insurance, and workers' compensation. The Department also protects workers' pension rights; provides for job training programs; helps workers find jobs; works to strengthen free collective bargaining; and keeps track of changes in employment, prices, and other national economic measurements. As the Department seeks to assist all Americans who need and want to work, special efforts are made to meet the unique job market problems of older workers, youths, minority group members, women, the handicapped, and other groups.

★12416★ U.S. Department of Labor Adult Services

200 Constitution Avenue NW
Washington, DC 20210
Fr: 877-872-5625
URL: http://www.doleta.gov

The Adult Services Administration is responsible for planning and developing policies, legislative proposals, goals, strategies, budgets, and resource allocation for the operation of comprehensive services to adults in the work force investment system; designing, developing, and administering employment and training services for welfare recipients, Native Americans, migrant and seasonal farm workers, older workers, individuals with disabilities, and individuals dislocated due to mass layoffs and emergencies; and providing direction for the investigation of worker petitions and the preparation of industry impact studies relating to trade adjustment assistance.

★12417★ U.S. Department of Labor Bureau of International Labor Affairs

200 Constitution Avenue NW
Washington, DC 20210
Ph: (202)693-4770   Fax: (202)693-4780
URL: http://www.dol.gov/ilab

The Bureau of International Labor Affairs assists in formulating international economic, social, trade, and immigration policies affecting American workers, with a view to maximizing higher wage and higher value U.S. jobs derived from global economic integration; gathers and disseminates information on child labor practices worldwide; promotes respect for international labor standards to protect the economic and physical well-being of workers in the United States and around the world; gathers and disseminates information on foreign labor markets and programs so that U.S. employment policy formulation might benefit from international experiences; carries out overseas technical assistance projects; assists in the administration of U.S. labor attaché programs at embassies abroad; and conducts research on the labor market consequences of immigration proposals and legislation.

★12418★ U.S. Department of Labor Bureau of Labor Statistics

2 Massachusetts Avenue NW, Room 4110
Washington, DC 20212
Ph: (202)691-5200
URL: http://www.bls.gov

The Bureau of Labor Statistics (BLS) is the principal fact-finding agency of the Federal Government in the broad field of labor economics and statistics. The Bureau is an independent national statistical agency that collects, processes, analyzes, and disseminates essential statistical data to the American public, Congress, other Federal agencies, State and local governments, businesses, and labor.

★12419★ U.S. Department of Labor Employment Standards Administration

200 Constitution Avenue NW
Washington, DC 20210
Fr: (866)487-2365
URL: http://www.dol.gov/esa

The Employment Standards Administration is responsible for managing and directing employment standards programs dealing with minimum wage and overtime standards; registration of farm labor contractors; determining prevailing wage rates to be paid on Government contracts and subcontracts; nondiscrimination and affirmative action for minorities, women, veterans, and handicapped Government contract and subcontract workers; workers' compensation programs for Federal and certain private employers and employees; safeguarding the financial integrity and internal democracy of labor unions; and administering statutory programs to certify employee protection provisions for various federally sponsored transportation programs.

★12420★ U.S. Department of Labor Employment and Training Administration

200 Constitution Avenue NW
Washington, DC 20210
Fr: 877-872-5625
URL: http://www.doleta.gov

The Employment and Training Administration fulfills responsibilities assigned to the Secretary of Labor that relate to employment services, job training, and unemployment insurance. Component offices and services administer a Federal/State employment security system; fund and oversee programs to provide work experience and training for groups having difficulty entering or returning to the work force; formulate and promote apprenticeship standards and programs; and conduct continuing programs of research, development, and evaluation.

★12421★ U.S. Department of Labor Mine Safety and Health Administration

1100 Wilson Boulevard, 21st Floor
Arlington, VA 22209-3939
Ph: (202)693-9400   Fax: (202)693-9401
URL: http://www.msha.gov

The Mine Safety and Health Administration is responsible for safety and health in the Nation's mines. The Administration develops and promulgates mandatory safety and health standards, ensures compliance with such standards, assesses civil penalties for violations, and investigates accidents. It cooperates with and provides assistance to the States in the development of effective State mine safety and health programs; improves and expands training programs in cooperation with the States and the mining industry; and contributes to the improvement and expansion of mine safety and health research and development. All of these activities are aimed at preventing and reducing mine accidents and occupational diseases in the mining industry.

★12422★ U.S. Department of Labor Occupational Safety and Health Administration

200 Constitution Avenue NW
Washington, DC 20210
Fr: 800-321-6742
URL: http://www.osha.gov

The Administration sets and enforces workplace safety and health standards and assists employers in complying with those standards.

★12423★ U.S. Department of Labor Office of Apprenticeship

200 Constitution Avenue NW
Washington, DC 20210
Fr: 877-872-5625
URL: http://www.doleta.gov

The Administration is responsible for developing materials and conducting a program of public awareness to secure the adoption of training in skilled occupations and related training policies and practices used by employers, unions, and other organizations;

developing policies and plans to enhance opportunities for minority and female participation in skilled training; and coordinating the effective use of Federal, labor, and employer resources to create a clear training-to-employment corridor for customers of the work force development system.

★12424★ **U.S. Department of Labor Office of Federal Contract Compliance Programs**

200 Constitution Avenue NW
Washington, DC 20210
Fr: (866)487-2365
URL: http://www.dol.gov/esa

The Office of Federal Contract Compliance Programs (OFCCP) ensures that companies that do business with the Government promote affirmative action and equal employment opportunity on behalf of minorities, women, the disabled, and Vietnam veterans.

★12425★ **U.S. Department of Labor Office of Labor-Management Standards**

200 Constitution Avenue NW
Washington, DC 20210
Fr: (866)487-2365
URL: http://www.dol.gov/esa

The Office of Labor-Management Standards conducts criminal and civil investigations to safeguard the financial integrity of unions and to ensure union democracy, and conducts investigative audits of labor unions to uncover and remedy criminal and civil violations of the Labor-Management Reporting and Disclosure Act and related statutes.

★12426★ **U.S. Department of Labor Office of Small Business Programs**

200 Constitution Avenue NW
Washington, DC 20210
Fr: (866)487-2365
URL: http://www.dol.gov/osbp

The Office of Small Business Programs administers the Department's efforts to ensure procurement opportunities for small, small disadvantaged, women-owned small businesses, HUBZone businesses, and businesses owned by service-disabled veterans.

★12427★ **U.S. Department of Labor Office of Workers' Compensation Programs**

200 Constitution Avenue NW, Room S-3524
Washington, DC 20210
Fr: (866)487-2365
URL: http://www.dol.gov/esa

The Office of Workers' Compensation Programs is responsible for programs providing workers' compensation for Federal employees; benefits to employees in private enterprise while engaged in maritime employment on navigable waters in the United States; benefits to coal miners who are totally disabled due to pneumoconiosis, a respiratory disease contracted after prolonged inhalation of coal mine dust, and to their survivors when the miner's death is due to pneumoconiosis; and to energy employees who contract occupational illnesses.

★12428★ **U.S. Department of Labor Pension and Welfare Benefits Administration**

200 Constitution Avenue NW
Washington, DC 20210
Fr: (866)444-3272
URL: http://www.dol.gov/ebsa

The Pension and Welfare Benefits Administration (PWBA) is responsible for promoting and protecting the pension, health, and other benefits of the over 150 million participants and beneficiaries in over 6 million private sector employee benefit plans. In administering its responsibilities, PWBA assists workers in understanding their rights and protecting their benefits; facilitates compliance by plan sponsors, plan officials, service providers, and other members of the regulated community; encourages the growth of employment-based benefits; and deters and corrects violations of the relevant statutes. ERISA is enforced through 15 PWBA field offices nationwide and the national office in Washington, DC.

★12429★ **U.S. Department of Labor Veterans' Employment and Training Service**

200 Constitution Avenue NW
Washington, DC 20210
Fr: (866)487-2365
URL: http://www.dol.gov/vets

The Veterans' Employment and Training Service (VETS) is responsible for administering veterans' employment and training programs and activities to ensure that legislative and regulatory mandates are accomplished.

★12430★ **U.S. Department of Labor Wage and Hour Division**

200 Constitution Avenue NW, Room S-3502
Washington, DC 20210
Fr: (866)487-2365
URL: http://www.dol.gov/esa

The Wage and Hour Division is responsible for planning, directing, and administering programs dealing with a variety of Federal labor legislation. These programs are designed to protect low-wage incomes; safeguard the health and welfare of workers by discouraging excessively long hours of work; safeguard the health and well-being of minors; prevent curtailment of employment and earnings for students, trainees, and handicapped workers; minimize losses of income and job rights caused by indebtedness; and direct a program of farm labor contractor registration designed to protect the health, safety, and welfare of migrant and seasonal agricultural workers.

★12431★ **U.S. Department of Labor Women's Bureau**

200 Constitution Avenue NW
Washington, DC 20210
Fr: 800-827-5335
URL: http://www.dol.gov/wb

The Women's Bureau is responsible for formulating standards and policies that promote the welfare of wage earning women, improve their working conditions, increase their efficiency, and advance their opportunities for profitable employment.

★12432★ **U.S. Department of Labor Workforce Security**

200 Constitution Avenue NW
Washington, DC 20210
Fr: 877-872-5625
URL: http://www.doleta.gov

The Administration is responsible for interpreting Federal legislative requirements for State unemployment compensation and employment service programs and one-stop systems; guiding and assisting States in adopting laws, regulations, and policies that conform with and support Federal law; developing, negotiating, and monitoring reimbursable agreements with States to administer the Targeted Jobs Tax Credit Program; providing policy guidance for the Immigration and Nationality Act concerning aliens seeking admission into the United States in order to work; and overseeing the development and implementation of the Nation's labor market information system.

★12433★ **U.S. Department of Labor Youth Services**

200 Constitution Avenue NW
Washington, DC 20210
Ph: (202)693-3030   Fr: 877-872-5625
URL: http://www.doleta.gov

The Administration is responsible for planning, developing, and recommending objectives, policies, and strategies for operations of a comprehensive youth employment and training system; and providing policy guidance and program performance oversight for Job Corps youth employment and training services and youth services grant programs authorized under the Workforce Investment Act and the school-to-work system.

Government Employment Opportunities

★12434★ **The Access Guide to International Affairs Internships in The Washington, DC Area**
Access: A Security Information Service
1701 K St. NW, Ste. 11
Washington, DC 20006-1503
Ph: (202)223-7949   Fax: (202)223-7946
Fr: 800-888-6033

Bruce Seymore II and Susan D. Krutt, editors. 1994. $17.95 (paper). 133 pages. Publication cancelled.

★12435★ **The Book of U.S. Government Jobs: Where They Are, What's Available, and How to Get One**
KSB Promotions
55 Honey Creek Ave. NE
Ada, MI 49301-9768
Ph: (616)676-0758   Fax: (616)676-0759

$21.95. Publication includes: Lists of Washington, D.C. departments and agencies, web sites, and job centers nationwide. Indexes: Alphabetical.

★12436★ **Career Transition: A Guide for Federal Employees in a Time of Turmoil**
FPMI Communications, Inc.
4901 Univ. St., Ste. 3
Huntsville, AL 35816
Ph: (256)539-1850   Fax: (256)539-0911

Robert Carey. 1996. $14.95 (paper). 105 pages.

★12437★ **Careers in Horticulture and Botany**
McGraw-Hill Trade
2 Penn Plaza
New York, NY 10121
Ph: (212)904-2000   Fr: 800-722-4726
E-mail: ntcpub@tribune.com

Jerry Garner. 1996. $17.95; 13.95 (paper).

255 pages. Includes bibliographical references

★12438★ **Careers Inside the World of the Government**
Rosen Publishing Group, Inc.
29 E. 21st St.
New York, NY 10010
Ph: (212)777-3017   Fax: 888-436-4643
Fr: 800-237-9932

Sue Hurwitz. Revised edition, 1995 $15.95. 64 pages.

★12439★ **Careers in Law**
McGraw-Hill Contemporary Books
1221 Avenue of the Americas
New York, NY 10020
Ph: (212)904-2000   Fr: 800-323-4900
E-mail: ntcpub@tribune.com

Gary Munneke. Second edition, 1997. $17.95; $13.95 (paper). 406 pages. Overview of opportunities available to lawyers in private practice, corporate law, in federal, state, and local governments, and in teaching. Provides information on the typical law school curriculum plus opportunities in internships and clerkships.

★12440★ **Carroll's Federal Directory**
Carroll Publishing
145 Taylor St., NE
Washington, DC 20017
Ph: (202)281-2410   Fax: (202)281-2408
Fr: 800-336-4240
URL: http://www.carrollpub.com

Bimonthly. $395.00. Covers about 40,000 executive managers in federal government offices in Washington, DC, including executive, congressional and judicial branches; members of Congress and Congressional committees and staff. Entries include: Agency names, titles, office address (including room numbers), e-mail addresses, and telephone and fax numbers. Also available as part of a "library edition" titled "Federal Directory Annual". Arrangement: By cabinet department or administrative agency. Indexes: Keyword, personal name (with phone) and e-mail addresses.

★12441★ **Carroll's State Directory**
Carroll Publishing
145 Taylor St., NE
Washington, DC 20017
Ph: (202)281-2410   Fax: (202)281-2408
Fr: 800-336-4240
URL: http://www.carrollpub.com

Three times per year. $350.00. Covers about 43,000 state government officials in all branches of government; officers, committees and members of state legislatures; managers of boards and authorities. Entries include: Name, address, phone, fax, title. Arrangement: Geographical; separate sections for state offices and legislatures. Indexes: Personal name (with phone and e-mail address), organizational, keyword.

★12442★ **Complete Guide to Public Employment**
Impact Publications
9104 Manassas Dr., Ste. N
Manassas Park, VA 20111-5211
Ph: (703)361-7300   Fax: (703)335-9486

Triennial, latest edition 1994. $34.95 for cloth copy; $19.95 for paper copy. Publication includes: List of federal, state, and local government agencies and departments, trade and professional associations, contracting and consulting firms, nonprofit organizations, foundations, research organizations, political support groups, and other organizations offering public service career opportunities. Entries include: Organization name, address, phone, name and title of contact. Complete title is "Complete Guide to Public Employment: Opportunities and Strategies with Federal, State, and Local Government; Trade and Professional Associations; Contracting and and Consulting Firms; Foundations; Research Organizations; and Political Support Groups." Arrangement: Classified by type of service. Indexes: Subject.

★12443★ **Congressional Directory**
Capitol Advantage
PO Box 2018
Order Department
Merrifield, VA 22116
Ph: (703)550-9500   Fax: (703)550-0406
Fr: 877-827-3321

URL: http://congress.nw.dc.us

Annual. $14.95. Covers 100 current senators and 440 House of Representative members. Entries include: Name, district office address, phone, fax; names and titles of key staff; committee and subcommittee assignments; biographical data, percentage of votes won, photo. Arrangement: Available in separate alphabetical, geographical, or condensed editions. Indexes: Name.

★12444★ **Contractor's Directory**

Government Data Publications Inc.
2300 M St., N.W.
Washington, DC 20037
Fr: 800-275-4688
URL: http://www.govdata.com

Annual, February. $49.50 for diskette; $49.95 for CD-ROM. Covers contractors who have received government contract under Public Law 95-507, which requires preferential treatment of small business for subcontracts. Entries include: Contractor name and address. Supplementary to 'Small Business Preferential Subcontracts Opportunities Monthly,' which lists companies with government contracts over $500,000 ($1,000,000 for construction). Arrangement: Same information given alphabetically and by ZIP code.

★12445★ **Employment Guide for the Military, Intelligence and Special Operations Communities**

The Graduate Group
PO Box 370351
West Hartford, CT 06137-0351
Ph: (860)233-2330   Fr: 800-484-7280

Mark W. Merritt. 1997. $30.00.

★12446★ **Employment Opportunities, USA**

Washington Research Associates
1090 Vermont Ave., NW, Ste. 800
Washington, DC 20005
Ph: (202)408-7025

Annual, quarterly updates. $184.00. Publication includes: List of over 1,000 employment contacts in companies and agencies in the banking, arts, telecommunications, education, and 14 other industries and professions, including the federal government. Entries include: Company name, name of representative, address, description of products or services, hiring and recruiting practices, training programs, and year established. Principal content is industry overviews, career news, employment opportunity information on 14 different job markets, and comprehensive guidance to career resources on the Internet. Arrangement: Classified by industry. Indexes: Occupation.

★12447★ **Employment Service-Government Company Fraternal Directory**

infoUSA Inc.
5711 S 86th Cir.
Omaha, NE 68127-0347
Ph: (402)930-3500   Fax: (402)331-0176
Fr: 800-555-6124
URL: http://www.abii.com

Updated continuously; printed on request. Number of listings: 884. Entries include: Name, address, phone, size of advertisement, name of owner or manager, number of employees, year first in "Yellow Pages." Compiled from telephone company "Yellow Pages," nationwide. Arrangement: Geographical.

★12448★ **Encyclopedia of Governmental Advisory Organizations**

Thomson Gale
27500 Drake Rd.
Farmington Hills, MI 48331-3535
Ph: (248)699-4253   Fax: (248)699-8065
Fr: 800-877-GALE
E-mail: businessproducts@gale.com

Annual. $685.00. Covers more than 7,300 boards, panels, commissions, committees, presidential conferences, and other groups that advise the President, Congress, and departments and agencies of federal government; includes interagency committees and federally sponsored conferences. Also includes historically significant organizations. Entries include: Unit name, address, phone, URL and email (if active), name of principal executive, legal basis for the unit, purpose, reports and publications, findings and recommendations, description of activities, members. Arrangement: Classified by general subject. Indexes: Alphabetical/keyword, personnel, publication, federal department/agency, presidential administration.

★12449★ **Federal Career Opportunities**

Federal Research Service Inc.
7360 McWhorter Pl., Ste. 201
PO Box 1708
Annandale, VA 22003
Ph: (703)281-0200   Fax: (703)281-7639
Fr: 800-822-5627
URL: http://www.fedjobs.com/index.html

Biweekly. $7.95 per copy. Covers more than 3,000 current federal job vacancies in the United States and overseas; includes permanent, part-time, and temporary positions. Entries include: Position title, location, series and grade, job requirements, special forms, announcement number, closing date, application address. Arrangement: Classified by occupation.

★12450★ **Federal Jobs for College Graduates**

Prentice Hall PTR
One Lake St.
Upper Saddle River, NJ 07458
Ph: (201)236-7000

Robert Goldenkoff. 1991. $15.95 (paper). 400 pages. Identifies job opportunities in numerous government agencies.

★12451★ **Federal Jobs Digest**

Federal Jobs Digest
325 Pennsylvania Ave. SE
Washington, DC 20003
Ph: (914)366-0333   Fax: (914)366-0059
Fr: 800-824-5000
URL: http://www.jobsfed.com

Biweekly. $5.50 per issue; $34.00 for three months; $125.00 for year. Covers over 10,000 specific job openings in the federal government in each issue. Vacancies from over 300 Federal Agencies are covered. Entries include: Position name, title, General Schedule (GS) grade, and Wage Grade (WG), closing date for applications, announcement number, application address, phone, and name of contact. Arrangement: By federal department or agency, then geographical.

★12452★ **Federal Law-Related Careers Directory**

Federal Reports Inc.
1010 Vermont Ave. NW, Ste. 408
Washington, DC 20005
Ph: (202)393-3311   Fax: (202)393-1553
Fr: 800-296-9611
URL: http://www.attorneyjobs.com

Irregular, previous edition 1991; latest edition October 1994. $27.45 for individuals; $52.50 for institutions. Publication includes: Listings of over 1,000 federal government recruiting offices. Entries include: Agency name, address, how to apply, and hiring procedure. Principal content of publication is the description of over 150 law-related careers in the U.S. government for which a law degree is an asset, but not a requirement, including contract specialist, criminal investigator, legal research analyst, and labor relations specialist. Arrangement: Classified by subject. Indexes: Subject.

★12453★ **Federal Staff Directory**

CQ Press
1255 22nd St. NW, Ste. 400
Washington, DC 20037
Ph: (202)729-1800   Fax: 800-380-3810
Fr: (866)427-7737
URL: http://www.cqdirectories.com

3x/year. $379.00. Covers approximately 45,000 persons in federal government offices and independent agencies, with biographies of 2,600 key executives; includes officials at policy level in agencies of the Office of the President, Cabinet-level departments, independent and regulatory agencies, military commands, federal information centers, and libraries, and United States attorneys, marshals, and ambassadors. Entries include: Name, title, location (indicating building, address, and/or room), phone, fax, e-mail address, website, symbols indicating whether position is a presidential appointment and whether senate approval is required. Arrangement: Classified by department/agency. Indexes: Personal name, subject.

★12454★ Federal Yellow Book

Leadership Directories Inc.
104 5th Ave.
New York, NY 10011
Ph: (212)627-4140   Fax: (212)645-0931
E-mail: federal@leadershipdirectories.com
URL: http://www.leadershipdirectories.com/fyb.htm

Quarterly. $375.00 for first annual subscription; $262.00 for each additional subscription. Covers federal departments, including the Executive Office of the President, the Office of the Vice President, the Office of Management and Budget, the Cabinet, and the National Security Council, and over 40,000 key personnel; over 70 independent federal agencies. Entries include: For personnel-Name, address, phone, fax, e-mails, titles. For departments and agencies-Office, or branch name and address; names and titles of principal personnel, with their room numbers, direct-dial phone numbers, and E-mails. Arrangement: Classified by department or agency. Indexes: Subject, organization, individuals' names.

★12455★ Find a Federal Job Fast! How to Cut the Red Tape and Get Hired

Impact Publications
9104 Manassas Dr., Ste. N
Manassas Park, VA 20111-5211
Ph: (703)361-7300   Fax: (703)335-9486

Ronald Krannich and Caryl Krannich. Fourth edition, revised, 1998. $15.95 (paper). 256 pages. Out of print. Presents advice on cutting through the red tape, locating job vacancies, completing the SF-171 form, marketing oneself to the federal job market, and obtaining information quickly on a wide variety of jobs.

★12456★ Government Job Finder

Planning Communications
7215 Oak Ave.
River Forest, IL 60305-1935
Ph: (708)366-5200   Fax: (708)366-5280
Fr: 888-366-5200
URL: http://jobfindersonline.com

Daniel Lauber. Third edition, 1997. 336 pages. Covers 1800 sources. Discusses how to use sources of local, state, and federal government job vacancies in a number of specialties and state-by-state, including job-matching services, job hotlines, specialty periodicals with job ads, salary surveys, and directories. Explains how local, state, and federal hiring systems work. Includes chapters on resume and cover letter preparation and interviewing.

★12457★ Insider's Guide to Finding a Job in Washington

Congressional Quarterly
1414 22nd St. NW
Washington, DC 20037
Ph: (202)729-1817   Fax: 800-380-3810
Fr: 800-432-2250

$29.50. Publication includes: Contact details for organizations; Web sites for government job hunting. Principal content of publication is jobs and careers available in public policy in Washington, including internship positions, congressional jobs, jobs within federal agencies or departments, interest group positions, trade association or labor union jobs, or media jobs. Indexes: Bibliography, subject, contact.

★12458★ Internships in Federal Government

The Graduate Group
PO Box 370351
West Hartford, CT 06137-0351
Ph: (860)233-2330   Fr: 800-484-7280

Seventh edition, 1995. $27.50.

★12459★ Internships in State Government

The Graduate Group
PO Box 370351
West Hartford, CT 06137-0351
Ph: (860)233-2330   Fr: 800-484-7280

Sixth edition, 1995. $27.50.

★12460★ Job Hotlines USA: A National Telephone Directory of Employer Joblines

Career Communications
PO Box 169
Harleysville, PA 19438

Published 1994. $24.95. Covers over 1,000 government agencies, hospitals, colleges, companies, and federal job information centers that have employment hotlines. Entries include: company name, address, voice telephone number, job hotline number, and industry classification.

★12461★ 9 Steps to a Great Federal Job

LearningExpress, LLC
900 Broadway, Ste. 604
New York, NY 10003
Ph: (212)995-2566   Fax: (212)995-5512
Fr: 800-295-9556

Lee Wherry Brainerd, C. Roebuck Reed. February 2004. $19.95. Illustrated. 180 pages.

★12462★ Opportunities in Federal Government Careers

McGraw-Hill Trade
2 Penn Plaza
New York, NY 10121
Ph: (212)904-2000   Fr: 800-722-4726
E-mail: ntcpub@tribune.com

Neale Baxter. Second edition, 1994. $14.95; $10.95 (paper). 160 pages. Describes the spectrum of government employment, including professional, administrative, scientific, blue-collar, clerical, and technical opportunities, and how to land a job. Illustrated. Part of Opportunities in...Series.

★12463★ Opportunities in Government Careers

McGraw-Hill Trade
2 Penn Plaza
New York, NY 10121
Ph: (212)904-2000   Fax: (614)755-5645
Fr: 800-722-4726

Neale J. Baxter. 2003. $15.95. 160 pages. VGM Opportunities Series.

★12464★ Opportunities in Overseas Careers

McGraw-Hill Trade
2 Penn Plaza
New York, NY 10121
Ph: (212)904-2000   Fr: 800-722-4726

Blythe Camenson. 1998. $14.95; $11.95 (paper). 106 pages.

★12465★ Opportunities in State and Local Government Careers

Vgm Career Horizons
1221 Avenue of the Americas
New York, NY 10020
Ph: (212)904-2000   Fr: 800-323-4900
E-mail: ntcpub@tribune.com

Neale J. Baxter. 1994. $14.95; $10.95 (paper). 160 pages. Points out the incentives and drawbacks of a government career. Describes hiring procedures and provides tips on filling out applications, taking physical and aptitude tests, handling interviews, and finding jobs. Describes the jobs in which 75% of all state and local government workers are employed. For each occupation, covers the nature of the work and the training required.

★12466★ The Paralegal's Guide to U.S. Government Jobs: How to Land a Job in 140 Law-Related Career Fields

Federal Reports, Inc.
1010 Vermont Ave. NW, Ste. 408
Washington, DC 20005
Ph: (202)393-3311

Richard L. Hermann, Jeanette J. Sobajian and Linda P. Sutherland. Seventh edition, 1996. $19.95. 140 pages. Explains U.S. Government procedures and describes 140 law-related federal careers for which paralegals may qualify. Includes a directory of several hundred Federal Agency personnel offices that hire the most paralegal and law-related talents.

★12467★ Real Resumes and Other Resumes for Federal Government Jobs: Including Samples of Real Resumes Used to Apply for Federal Government Jobs

PREP Publishing
1110 1/2 Hay St., PMB 66
Fayetteville, NC 28305
Ph: (910)483-6611   Fax: (910)483-2439
Fr: 800-533-2814

Anne McKinney (Editor). March 2003.

$24.95. Illustrated. 224 pages. Government Job Series.

★12468★ **State Yellow Book**
Leadership Directories Inc.
104 5th Ave.
New York, NY 10011
Ph: (212)627-4140   Fax: (212)645-0931
E-mail: state@leadershipdirectories.com
URL: http://www.leadershipdirectories.com

Quarterly. $356.00. Covers over 37,000 elected and appointed officials in the executive branch, and state legislators and their committees. Entries include: Name, address, phone, fax, organization name, government information, email and internet addresses. Arrangement: Alphabetical. Indexes: Subject, personnel.

★12469★ **Storming Washington: An Intern's Guide to National Government**
American Political Science Association
1527 New Hampshire Ave., NW
Washington, DC 20036-1206
Ph: (202)483-2512   Fax: (202)483-2657

Stephen E. Frantzich. Fourth edition, 1994. $6.00 (paper). 63 pages.

★12470★ **United States Government Manual**
Office of the Federal Register
National Archives and Records Administration
Washington, DC 20408
Ph: (202)741-6040   Fax: (202)741-6012
URL: http://www.access.gpo.gov/su_docs/

Annual, September; latest edition 2002-2003. $40.00. The "Manual" is the official handbook of the United States government, and includes descriptions and lists of principal personnel of agencies and other bodies in the legislative, judicial, and executive branches; the executive branch is covered in greatest depth. (The "Manual" devotes roughly 40 of 700 pages to the legislative branch and 20 to the judicial; the "Congressional Directory," described in a separate listing, devotes roughly 260 of 1,200 pages to the executive branch and 60 to the judicial.) Text of the listings is primarily concerned with programs and activities rather than administrative structure, but general organization charts are given. The "Congressional Directory" and the "Manual" comprise the "database" for principal federal government organizations and personnel. Entries include: For each cabinet department and independent agency or other unit, titles of major administrative posts and the names of incumbents are given, along with a description of the unit's responsibilities. Additional listings of subordinate offices and bureaus give similar information. Addresses and phone numbers are provided for units at most levels, as well as for obtaining detailed information on consumer activities, contracts and grants, employment, publications, and other areas of public interest. Arrangement: Classified by department and agency. Indexes: Personal name, agency/subject.

★12471★ **Vault Guide to Capitol Hill Careers: An Inside Look Inside the Beltway**
Vault.com
150 W. 22nd St., 5th Fl.
New York, NY 10011
Ph: (212)366-4212   Fax: (212)366-6117
Fr: 888-562-8285

William McCarthy. November 2003. $29.95 (paper). 128 pages. Part of the Vault Career Library.

★12472★ **Vault Guide to the Top Government and Non-Profit Legal Employers**
Vault.com
150 W. 22nd St., 5th Fl.
New York, NY 10011
Ph: (212)366-4212   Fax: (212)366-6117
Fr: 888-562-8285

Marcy Lerner. October 2003. $29.95 (paper). 176 pages. Part of the Vault Career Library Series.

★12473★ **Washington Information Directory**
CQ Press
1255 22nd St. NW, Ste. 400
Washington, DC 20037
Ph: (202)729-1800   Fax: 800-380-3810
Fr: (866)427-7737
URL: http://www.cqpress.com

Annual, latest edition 2003. $120.00. Covers 5,000 governmental agencies, congressional committees, and non-governmental associations considered competent sources of specialized information. Entries include: Name of agency, committee, or association; address, phone, fax, and internet; annotation concerning function or activities of the office; and name of contact. Arrangement: Classified by activity or competence (economics and business, housing and urban affairs, etc.). Indexes: Subject, agency/organization name, contact name.

★12474★ **Washington Job Source**
Benjamin Scott Publishing
20 E. Colorado Blvd., No. 202
Pasadena, CA 91105
Ph: (626)449-1339   Fax: (626)449-1389
Fr: 800-448-4959

Fifth edition, 2002.

★12475★ **Who's Who in Local Government Management**
International City/County Management Association
777 N Capitol St. NE, Ste. 500
Washington, DC 20002-4201
Ph: (202)289-4262   Fax: (202)962-3500
Fr: 800-746-8780
URL: http://www.icma.org

Annual, September. Covers 8,000 appointed administrators of cities, counties, and councils of governments. Entries include: Name, position, office address, educational history, career data, offices held in ICMA. Arrangement: Alphabetical by individual name.

NEWSPAPERS, MAGAZINES, AND JOURNALS

★12476★ **Federal Acquisition Report**
Management Concepts Inc.
8230 Leesburg Pke.
Vienna, VA 22182
Ph: (703)790-9595   Fax: (703)790-1371
Fr: 800-506-4450
E-mail: publications@managementconcepts.com
URL: http://www.managementconcepts.com

Description: Monthly. Focuses on developments in federal contracting, legislation, changes in rules and regulations, and recent decisions by the board of contract appeals and by the courts. Features job listings and guest essays.

★12477★ **Federal Times**
Army Times Publishing Co.
6883 Commercial Dr.
Springfield, VA 22159-0001
Ph: (703)750-9000   Fax: (703)750-8767
E-mail: mcofed@aol.com
URL: http://www.armytimes.com

Weekly. $52.00/year for individuals; $2.00 for single issue. Federal bureaucracy; technology in government.

★12478★ **FEW's News and Views**
Federally Employed Women Inc.
PO Box 28129
Washington, DC 20038-8129
Ph: (202)898-0994
E-mail: editor@few.org

Description: Three issues/year. Concerned with women's issues, particularly those involving women in the federal government. Reports on administration actions affecting the status of women and analyzes significant legislation. Recurring features include letters to the editor, news of members, a calendar of events, book reviews, and notices of career development and training opportunities.

★12479★ **Government Finance Officers Association Newsletter**
Government Finance Officers Association
203 N LaSalle St.
Chicago, IL 60601-7401
Ph: (312)977-9700   Fax: (312)977-4806

Description: Semimonthly. Provides updates on current events, innovations, and federal legislation affecting public finance management for state and local government finance officers. Covers cash management, budgeting, accounting, auditing, and financial reporting, public employee retirement administration, and related issues. Recurring features include news of research, news of members, a calendar of events, and columns titled Career Notes and Employment Opportunities. Subscription includes the bimonthly magazine Government Finance Review.

★12480★ _The Municipality_

League of Wisconsin Municipalities
202 State St., Ste. 300
Madison, WI 53703-2215
Ph: (608)267-2380   Fax: (608)267-0645
Fr: 800-991-5502

Monthly. $12.00/year. Magazine for officials of Wisconsin's local municipal governments.

★12481★ _New Technology Week_

King Communications Group Inc.
627 National Press Bldg.
Washington, DC 20045
Ph: (202)662-9745   Fax: (202)662-9744
URL: http://www.kingpublishing.com

Description: Weekly. Carries news on evolving technologies, especially those in defense-related fields. Follows legislation and government agency action affecting defense and high-tech industries. Lists recipients of foundation and research grants in the U.S. Recurring features include a calendar of events and news of employment opportunities.

★12482★ _Postal Record_

National Association of Letter Carriers
100 Indiana Ave. NW
Washington, DC 20001-2144
Ph: (202)393-4695

Monthly. Subscription included in membership. Magazine for active and retired letter carriers.

ONLINE AND DATABASE SERVICES

★12483★ ExecSearches.com

E-mail: question@execsearches.com
URL: http://execsearches.com

Description: Job site specializing in matching seekers with non-profit, public sector, academic and "socially conscious" positions. Contains job board, resume databank, e-mail alert system and reference articles. Employers may also post jobs and check resume references.

SOFTWARE

★12484★ Quick and Easy Federal Jobs Kit

Datatech Software, Inc.
4800 Linglestown Rd., No. 201
Harrisburg, PA 17112
Ph: (717)652-4334   Fax: (717)652-3222
Fr: 800-556-7526
URL: http://www.quickandeasy.com

$49.95 (personal version), $129.95 (office pack), $499.95 (professional version). Requires Windows 95. Designed to ensure that federal job applicants include all of the required information on the necessary forms.

OTHER SOURCES

★12485★ African Studies Association (ASA)

Rutgers the State University of New Jersey
132 George St.- Douglass Campus
New Brunswick, NJ 08901-1400
Ph: (732)932-8173
E-mail: callasa@rci.rutgers.edu

Members: Persons specializing in teaching, writing, or research on Africa including political scientists, historians, geographers, anthropologists, economists, librarians, linguists, and government officials; persons who are studying African subjects; institutional members are universities, libraries, government agencies, and others interested in receiving information about Africa. **Purpose:** Seeks to foster communication and to stimulate research among scholars on Africa. **Activities:** Sponsors placement service; conducts panels and discussion groups; presents exhibits and films.

★12486★ Civil Service Employees Association (CSEA)

143 Washington Ave.
PO Box 125
Albany, NY 12210
Ph: (518)257-1000   Fax: (518)462-3639
Fr: 800-342-4146
URL: http://www.csealocal1000.org

Description: AFL-CIO. Members are state and local government employees from all public employee classifications. Negotiates work contracts; represents members in grievances; provides legal assistance for on-the-job problems; provides advice and assistance on federal, state, and local laws affecting public employees. Conducts training and education programs. Compiles statistics; conducts research.

★12487★ Federally Employed Women (FEW)

1666 K St. NW, Ste. 440
Washington, DC 20006
Ph: (202)898-0994   Fax: (202)898-1535

E-mail: few@few.org
URL: http://www.few.org

Members: Men and women employed by the federal government. **Purpose:** Seeks to end sex discrimination in government service; to increase job opportunities for women in government service and to further the potential of all women in the government; to improve the merit system in government employment; to assist present and potential government employees who are discriminated against because of sex; to work with other organizations and individuals concerned with equal employment opportunity in the government. **Activities:** Provides speakers and sponsors seminars to publicize the Federal Women's Program; furnishes members with information on pending legislation designed to end discrimination against working women; informs and provides members opportunities for training to improve their job potential; issues fact sheets interpreting civil service rules and regulations and other legislative issues; provides annual training conference for over 3,000 women and men.

★12488★ National Alliance of Postal and Federal Employees (NAPFE)

1628 11th St. NW
Washington, DC 20001
Ph: (202)939-6325   Fax: (202)939-6389
E-mail: headquarters@napfe.org
URL: http://www.napfe.com

Description: Independent. Works to eliminate employment discrimination.

★12489★ National Association of Civil Service Employees (NACSE)

6829 Park Ridge Blvd.
San Diego, CA 92120
Ph: (619)466-3150

Description: Federal, state, county, and city civil service employees; association employees and counselors. Assists nonprofit charitable, educational, and scientific organizations in promoting social welfare. Conducts service and product consumer research and educational programs and symposia; sponsors competitions; maintains placement service.

★12490★ National Association of Government Communicators (NAGC)

10366 Democracy Ln., Ste. B
Fairfax, VA 22030
Ph: (703)691-0037   Fax: (703)706-9583
E-mail: info@nagc.com
URL: http://www.nagc.com/

Members: Government employees, retired persons, non-government affiliates, and students. **Purpose:** Seeks to advance communications as an essential professional resource at every level of national, state, and local government by disseminating information; encouraging professional development, public awareness, and exchange of ideas and experience; improving internal communications. **Activities:** Maintains placement service.

★12491★ **National Association of Government Employees (NAGE)**
159 Burgin Pkwy.
Quincy, MA 02169
Ph: (617)376-0220   Fax: (617)376-0285
URL: http://www.nage.org
Members: Union of civilian federal government employees with locals and members in military agencies, Internal Revenue Service, Post Office, Veterans Administration, General Services Administration, Federal Aviation Administration, and other federal agencies, as well as state and local agencies. **Activi-** ties: Activities include direct legal assistance, information service, legislative lobbying and representation, trained leadership in contract negotiations, employment protection, and insurance. Offers seminars; sponsors competitions.

★12492★ **National Association of Hispanic Federal Executives (NAHFE)**
PO Box 469
Herndon, VA 20172-0469
Ph: (703)787-0291   Fax: (703)787-4675
E-mail: nahfe@cs.com
URL: http://www.nahfe.org
Members: Hispanic and other federal employees ranked GS-12 and above; individuals in the private sector whose positions are equivalent to rank GS-12. **Purpose:** Promotes the federal government as a model employer by encouraging qualified individuals to apply for federal government positions. **Activities:** Offers increased productivity training to federal employees. Maintains speakers' bureau and placement service. Offers educational programs; compiles statistics; conducts research.

Help-Wanted Ads

URL: http://www.rbitem.com

$80.00/year for individuals; $80.00 for single issue. Design magazine about measurement and control of electromagnetic interference.

★12502★ National Ad Search
National Ad Search Inc.
PO Box 2083
Milwaukee, WI 53201
Ph: (414)351-1398   Fax: (414)351-0836
Fr: 800-992-2832
URL: http://www.nationaladsearch.com

Weekly. $250.00/year; $155.00 for six months; $80.00 for three months; $29.00 for four weeks. Magazine (tabloid) on occupations, careers, and professional employment.

★12503★ The Nonprofit Times
NPT Publishing Group Inc.
120 Littleton Rd., Ste. 120
Parsippany, NJ 07054-1803
Ph: (973)394-1800   Fax: (973)734-1771
E-mail: ednchief@nptimes.com
URL: http://www.nptimes.com

$8.95 for single issue; $59.00/year. Trade journal serving nonprofit organizations.

ONLINE AND DATABASE SERVICES

★12504★ HelpWanted.com
URL: http://www.helpwanted.com
Description: Job postings.

Identifying Prospective Employers

★12505★ American Manufacturers Directory

infoUSA Inc.
5711 S 86th Cir.
Omaha, NE 68127-0347
Ph: (402)930-3500   Fax: (402)331-0176
Fr: 800-555-6124
URL: http://www.abii.com

Annual, January. $295.00; $595.00 for print and CD-ROM. Covers more than 150,000 manufacturing companies with 20 or more employees. CD-ROM version lists all 531,000 U.S. manufacturers, in all employee size ranges. Entries include: Company name, address, phone, contact name, Standard Industrial Classification (SIC) codes, number of employees, sales volume code, credit rating scores. Arrangement: Entries listed alphabetically, geographically, and by Standard Industrial Classification (SIC) code. Indexes: Geographical.

★12506★ America's Corporate Families

Dun & Bradstreet Information Services
899 Eaton Ave.
Bethlehem, PA 18025
Ph: (610)882-7000   Fax: (610)882-7269
Fr: 800-526-0651

1996. Volume I lists all American divisions and subsidiaries; Volume II lists all international divisions and subsidiaries. $495.00.

★12507★ Career Employment Opportunities Directory

Ready Reference Press
1652 N Pepper Dr.
Pasadena, CA 91104
Ph: (310)474-4895   Fr: 800-424-5627

Biennial, October of odd years. $47.50 per volume; $190.00 per set. Covers about 1,250 companies that employ college graduates; separate editions available for "Liberal Arts and Social Sciences," "Business Administration," "Engineering and Computer Sciences," and "Sciences" Entries include: Company name, general description of com-pany and career opportunities, job locations, special programs, and contact address. Arrangement: Alphabetical. Indexes: Discipline, geographical.

★12508★ The Career Guide-Dun's Employment Opportunities Directory

Dun & Bradstreet
3 Sylvan Way
Parsippany, NJ 07054-3896
Fax: (973)605-6911   Fr: 800-526-0651

Annual. $425.00 to public libraries; $495.00 commercially. Covers more than 5,000 companies on leading employers throughout the U.S. that provide career opportunities in sales, marketing, management, engineering, life and physical sciences, computer science, mathematics, statistics planning, accounting and finance, liberal arts fields, and other technical and professional areas; based on data supplied on questionnaires and through personal interviews. Also covers personnel consultants; includes some public sector employers (governments, schools, etc.) usually not found in similar lists. Entries include: Company name, location of headquarters and other offices or plants; entries may also include name, title, address, and phone of employment contact; disciplines or occupational groups hired; brief overview of company, discussion of types of positions that may be available, training and career development programs, benefits offered, internship and work-study programs. Arrangement: Employers are alphabetical; geographically by industry, employer branch offices geographically, discilines hired geographically, employees offering work-study or internship programs and personnel consultants. Indexes: Geographical, SIC code.

★12509★ Corporate Affiliations Library

LexisNexis Group
121 Chanlon Rd.
New Providence, NJ 07974
Ph: (908)464-6800   Fax: (908)771-7704
Fr: 800-526-4902

Annual, June. $1,399.00. An 8-volume set listing public and private companies worldwide. Entries include: Parent company name, address, phone, fax, telex, e-mail addresses, names and titles of key personnel, financial data, fiscal period, type and line of business, SIC codes; names and locations of subsidiaries, divisions, and affiliates, outside service firms (accountants, legal counsel, etc.) Arrangement: Alphabetical within each volume. Indexes: Each volume includes company name index; separate Master Index volumes list all company names in the set in one alphabetic sequence in five indexes including private, public, international, alphabetical, geographical, brand name, SIC, and corporate responsibilities.

★12510★ The Corporate Directory of U.S. Public Companies

Thomson Gale
27500 Drake Rd.
Farmington Hills, MI 48331-3535
Ph: (248)699-GALE   Fax: (248)699-8069
Fr: 800-877-GALE
E-mail: galeord@gale.com
URL: http://www.galegroup.com

Annual. $360.00. 2600 pages. Provides information on more than 9,500 publicly-traded firms having at least $5,000,000 in assets. Entries include: General background, including name, address and phone, number of employees; stock data; description of areas of business; major subsidiaries; officers; directors; owners; and financial data. Indexes: Officers and directors, owners, subsidiary/parent, geographic, SIC, stock exchange, company rankings, and newly registered corporations.

★12511★ D & B Million Dollar Directory

Dun & Bradstreet
3 Sylvan Way
Parsippany, NJ 07054-3896
Fax: (973)605-6911   Fr: 800-526-0651
URL: http://www.dnbmdd.com

Annual. $1,395.00. Covers 1,600,000 public and private businesses with either a net worth of $500,000 or more, 250 or more employees at that location, or $25,000,000 or more in sales volume; includes industrial corporations, utilities, transportation companies, bank and trust companies, stock brokers, mutual and stock insurance companies, wholesalers, retailers, and domestic subsidiaries of foreign corporations. Entries include: Company name, address, phone, state of incorporation; annual sales; number of employees, company ticker symbol on stock exchange, Standard Industrial Classification (SIC) number, line of business; principal bank, accounting firm; parent company name, current ownership date, division names and functions, directors or trustees; names, titles, functions of principal executives, number of employees, import/export designation. Arrangement: Alphabetical, cross referenced geographically and by industry classification. Indexes: Geographical (with address and SIC), product by SIC (with address).

★12512★ **Directory of Career Training and Development Programs**

Ready Reference Press
PO Box 5249
Santa Monica, CA 90405
Ph: (310)475-4895   Fr: 800-424-5627

$47.50. Provides details on hundreds of professional career training programs offered by some of America's top corporations. Each company profile contains type of training, length of training, and qualifications.

★12513★ **Directory: Who's Who in Career Services & HR/Staffing**

National Association of Colleges and Employers
62 Highland Ave.
Bethlehem, PA 18017
Ph: (610)868-1421   Fax: (610)868-0208
Fr: 800-544-5272
URL: http://www.jobweb.org/

Annual, latest edition January 1999. $47.95. Covers about 1,760 college and university offices concerned with securing employment for graduates and about 1,430 companies with staff assigned to recruiting and hiring college graduates. Entries include: For colleges-College name and address; names, titles, phone, fax, and URL and e-mail addresses of career planning and placement personnel; interview dates for undergraduates and graduates; months of graduation; whether alumni placement is also handled, student enrollment (including minority data), and dates of career/job fairs. For employers-Company name; names, addresses, phone, fax and e-mail addresses of recruitment staff; names of secondary contacts; nature of business; number of employees. Arrangement: Colleges are geographical; employers are alphabetical. Indexes: Institutional name, personal name (college personnel); geographical, personal name (in company recruitment).

★12514★ **Employment Opportunities, USA**

Washington Research Associates
1090 Vermont Ave., NW, Ste. 800
Washington, DC 20005
Ph: (202)408-7025

Annual, quarterly updates. $184.00. Publication includes: List of over 1,000 employment contacts in companies and agencies in the banking, arts, telecommunications, education, and 14 other industries and professions, including the federal government. Entries include: Company name, name of representative, address, description of products or services, hiring and recruiting practices, training programs, and year established. Principal content is industry overviews, career news, employment opportunity information on 14 different job markets, and comprehensive guidance to career resources on the Internet. Arrangement: Classified by industry. Indexes: Occupation.

★12515★ **Finding a Job Just Got a Lot Easier!**

Village WordSmith
931 S. Mission Rd., Suite B
Fallbrook, CA 92028
Ph: (760)728-1884   Fax: (760)728-1025
Fr: 800-200-1884

2001. $24.95. Made for individuals who have been recently fired or quit and now need a job; individuals scheduled for an interview but don't have a current resume; individuals entering or returning to the workforce but don't know how; individuals over 40, 50, 60 and considering a career change. Also provides assistance with focusing on appropriate jobs, composing your resume, targeting prospective employees, or preparing for the job interview.

★12516★ **Forbes-Up-and-Comers 200: Best Small Companies in America Issue**

Forbes Magazine
60 5th Ave.
New York, NY 10011
Ph: (212)620-2200   Fax: (212)206-5174
URL: http://www.forbes.com

Weekly. $6.99. Publication includes: List of 200 small companies judged to be high quality and fast-growing on the basis of 5-year return on equity and other qualitative measurements. Also includes a list of the 100 best small companies outside the U.S. Note: Issue does not carry address or CEO information for the foreign companies. Entries include: Company name, shareholdings data on chief executive officer; financial data. Arrangement: Alphabetical. Indexes: Ranking.

★12517★ **Headquarters USA**

Omnigraphics Inc.
615 Griswold St., Ste. 1400
Detroit, MI 48226
Ph: (313)961-1340   Fax: (313)961-1383
Fr: 800-234-1340
URL: http://www.omnigraphics.com/prod-

uct_view.php?ID=711

Annual, latest edition 2002. $185.00. Covers approximately 123,000 U.S. businesses, federal, state, and local government offices, banks, colleges and universities, associations, labor unions, political organizations, newspapers, magazines, TV and radio stations, foundations, postal and shipping services, hospitals, office equipment suppliers, airlines, hotels and motels, profiles of top cities, accountants, law firms, computer firms, foreign corporations, overseas trade contacts, and other professional services. Also covers internet access providers; internet mailing lists, publications, and sources; freenets. Personal names now included. Entries include: Company, organization, agency, or firm name, address, phone, fax, website addresses as available, toll-free phone. Arrangement: Arranged alphabetically by name (white pages) and in a classified subject arrangement (yellow pages). Indexes: Classified headings.

★12518★ **Hidden Job Market**

Thomson Peterson's
PO Box 67005
Lawrenceville, NJ 08648-6105
Fr: 800-338-3282

Ninth edition, 1999. $18.95 (paper). 319 pages. Guide to 2,000 fast-growing companies that are hiring now. Focuses on high technology companies in such fields as environmental consulting, genetic engineering, home health care, telecommunications, alternative energy systems, and others. Part of Peterson's Hidden Job Market series.

★12519★ **How to Locate Jobs and Land Interviews**

The Career Press, Inc.
3 Tice Rd.
PO Box 687
Franklin Lakes, NJ 07417-1322
Ph: (201)848-0310   Fax: (201)848-1727
Fr: 800-227-3371

Albert L. French. Second edition, 1993. $10.95 (paper). 192 pages. Shows readers how to tap into the unadvertised, hidden job market and guides them through the resume, cover letter, and interview preparation process. Out of print.

★12520★ **Inc.-The Inc. 500 Issue**

Gruner & Jahr USA Publishing
375 Lexington Ave., 10th Fl.
New York, NY 10017-4024
Ph: (212)499-2119   Fax: (212)499-2097
URL: http://www.inc.com

Annual, October. $3.50. Publication includes: List of 500 fastest-growing privately held companies based on percentage increase in sales over the five year period prior to compilation of current year's list. Entries include: Company name, headquarters city, description of business, year founded, number of employees, sales five years earlier and currently, profitability range, and growth statistics. Arrangement: Ranked by sales growth.

★12521★ International Directory of Company Histories

St. James Press
27500 Drake Rd.
Farmington Hills, MI 48331-3535
Ph: (248)699-4253   Fax: (248)699-8062
Fr: 800-877-4253

Most recent volume (55) August 2003. $197.00. Covers 55 volumes, over 5,700 leading companies world-wide. Entries include: Company name, address, phone, names of subsidiaries, dates of founding, sales data, SICs or NAICS, products or services, company history, key dates, principal subsidiaries, principal competitors, sources for further reading. Arrangement: Alphabetical. Indexes: Company, industry, geographical.

★12522★ Manufacturing and Distribution USA

Thomson Gale
27500 Drake Rd.
Farmington Hills, MI 48331-3535
Ph: (248)699-4253   Fax: (248)699-8065
Fr: 800-877-GALE
E-mail: ecdi@statrom.com
URL: http://www.gale.com

Biennial. $395.00. Publication includes: Lists of up to 75 leading companies for each manufacturing industry (Standard Industrial Classification (SIC) code range 2011 to 3999), selected on the basis of annual sales. Entries include: Company name, address, phone, name of chief executive, type of company, annual sales, number of employees. Principal content of publication is statistical profiles of 458 manufacturing industries and over 21,000 public and private companies. Each industry division includes tables, graphs, and maps that provide general statistics on number of firms and employees, compensation, and production; change in these statistics since 1982 (through 1998 where available); materials consumed statistics; outputs; product share breakdowns by subsector; occupations of employees in the industry, and industry data by state. Arrangement: Classified by industry, then ranked by annual sales. Indexes: Company name, product, occupation, SIC.

★12523★ National Directory of Minority-Owned Business Firms

Business Research Services Inc.
4201 Connecticut Ave. NW, Ste. 610
Washington, DC 20008
Ph: (202)364-6473   Fax: (202)686-3228
Fr: 800-845-8420
URL: http://www.clickdata.com

Annual. $295.00. Covers over 30,000 minority-owned businesses. Entries include: Company name, address, phone, name and title of contact, minority group, certification status, date founded, number of employees, description of products or services, sales volume, government contracting experience, references. Arrangement: Standard Industrial Classification (SIC) code, geographical. Indexes: Alphabetical by company name, SIC by name.

★12524★ National Directory of Nonprofit Organizations

The Taft Group
27500 Drake Rd.
Farmington Hills, MI 48331-3535
Ph: (248)699-4253   Fax: (248)699-8052
Fr: 800-877-GALE
E-mail: businessproducts@gale.com
URL: http://www.gale.com

Annual. $650.00. Covers over 265,000 nonprofit organizations; volume 1 covers organizations with annual incomes of over $100,000; volume 2 covers organizations with incomes between $25,000 and $99,999. Entries include: Organization name, address, phone, annual income, IRS filing status, employer identification number, tax deductible status, activity description. Arrangement: Alphabetical. Indexes: Area of activity, geographical.

★12525★ National Directory of Woman-Owned Business Firms

Business Research Services Inc.
4201 Connecticut Ave. NW, Ste. 610
Washington, DC 20008
Ph: (202)364-6473   Fax: (202)686-3228
Fr: 800-845-8420

Annual. $295.00. Covers 28,000 woman-owned businesses. Entries include: Company name, address, phone, name and title of contact, minority group, certification status, date founded, number of employees, description of products or services, sales volume, government contracting experience, references. Arrangement: Standard Industrial Classification (SIC) code, geographical. Indexes: Alphabetical by company.

★12526★ Network of Small Businesses-Membership Directory

Network of Small Businesses
5420 Mayfield Rd., Ste. 205
Lyndhurst, OH 44124
Ph: (440)442-5600

Approximately annual; previous edition April 1992; latest edition November 1999. $495.00. Covers owners and others involved in small businesses (defined as 250 employees or less), including investors, venture funders, business owners, business buyers, business sellers, and investing partners. Entries include: Company name, address, phone, names and titles of key personnel. Arrangement: Alphabetical. Indexes: Company owner.

★12527★ The 100 Best Companies to Work for in America

Pearson Addison Wesley
1185 Ave Of The Americas
New York, NY 10001
Ph: (212)782-3300   Fax: (212)492-9700
Fr: 800-223-6834

Robert Levering and Milton Moskowitz. 1993. $27.50. 528 pages. Describes the best companies to work for in America, based on such factors as salary, benefits, job security, and ambience. The authors base their 'top

100' rating on surveys and personal visits to hundreds of firms.

★12528★ Peterson's Hidden Job Market

Thomson Peterson's
Princeton Pike Corporate Center
2000 Lenox Dr.
PO Box 67005
Lawrenceville, NJ 08648
Ph: (609)896-1800   Fax: 800-277-2465
Fr: 800-338-3282
URL: http://www.petersons.com

Annual, June. $18.95. Covers approximately 2,000 technology firms with under 1,000 employees, which hire at four times the national rate. Entries include: Company name, address, phone, fax, name and title of contact, number of employees, year founded, number of employees added in last year, percentage of growth, line of business. Arrangement: Geographical by state, then by area code. Indexes: Alphabetical by industry.

★12529★ Peterson's Job Opportunities for Business Majors

Thomson Peterson's
Princeton Pke. Corporate Ctr., 2000 Lenox Dr.
PO Box 67005
Lawrenceville, NJ 08648
Ph: (609)896-1800   Fax: (609)896-4531
Fr: 800-338-3282
URL: http://www.petersons.com

Irregular, latest edition 2000 - 16th ed. $18.95. Covers the 2,000 largest U.S. employers hiring in several fields, including financial services, management consulting, consumer products, and media/ entertainment. Entries include: Organization name, address, phone, name and title of contact, number of employees, type of organization. Arrangement: Alphabetical. Indexes: Type of organization.

★12530★ Peterson's Job Opportunities in Engineering and Technology

Thomson Peterson's
PO Box 67005
Lawrenceville, NJ 08648-6105
Fr: 800-338-3282

Compiled by the Peterson's staff. Fourth edition, 1996. $21.95 (paper). 384 pages. Profiles 2,000 high-tech companies looking primarily for technical personnel in such fields as biotechnology, telecommunications, software, computers and peripherals, defense, and aerospace. Contains job-search strategies and career options to help match education and expertise to the job market. Indexed geographically, by industry, and by hiring needs.

★12531★ *Plunkett's Employers' Internet Sites with Careers Information: The Only Complete Guide to Careers Websites Operated by Major Employers*
Plunkett Research, Ltd.
PO Box 541737
Houston, TX 77254-1737
Ph: (713)932-0000   Fax: (713)932-7080
Jack W. Plunkett. Revised, 2002. $179.99 (includes CD-ROM). Provides profiles of Internet sites for major employers. Job hunters can use the profiles or indexes to locate the Internet job sites that best fit their needs. 697 pages.

★12532★ *Standard & Poor's Register of Corporations, Directors and Executives*
Standard & Poor's
55 Water St.
New York, NY 10041
Ph: (212)438-1000
URL: http://www2.standardandpoors.com/
Annual, January; supplements in April, July, and October. $675.00. Covers over 55,000 public and privately held corporations in the United States, including names and titles of over 400,000 officials (Volume 1); 70,000 biographies of directors and executives (Volume 2). Entries include: For companies-Name, address, phone, names of principal executives and accountants; primary bank, primary law firm, number of employees, estimated annual sales, outside directors, Standard Industrial Classification (SIC) code, product or service provided. For directors and executives-Name, home and principal business addresses, date and place of birth, fraternal organization memberships, business affiliations. Arrangement: Alphabetical. Indexes: Volume 3 indexes companies geographically, by Standard Industrial Classification (SIC) code, and by corporate family groups.

★12533★ *Thomas Register of American Manufacturers*
Thomas Publishing Co.
5 Penn Plz.
New York, NY 10001
Ph: (212)695-0500   Fax: (212)290-7362
URL: http://www.thomasregister.com
Annual, January. More than 168,000 manufacturing firms are listed in this 34 volume set. Volumes 1-23 list the firms under 68,000 product headings. Thomas Register is enhanced with over 8,000 manufacturers' catalogs and is available in print, CD-ROM, DVD or online. Logistics Guide, a reference manual for freight and shipping sourcing. Arrangement: Volumes 1-23, classified by product or service; Volumes 24-26 alphabetical by company; Volumes 27-34 company catalogs alphabetical by company. Indexes: Product/service, brand/trade name (Volume 22).

★12534★ *Walker's Manual of Western Corporations*
Walker's Western Research
1650 Borel Pl., No. 130
San Mateo, CA 94402-3506
Ph: (415)341-1110   Fr: 800-258-5737
1995. $595.00. 2400 pages. Publicly-held corporations in 13 western states. Indexed geographically and by industry.

★12535★ *Ward's Business Directory of U.S. Private and Public Companies 2001*
Thomson Gale
27500 Drake Rd.
Farmington Hills, MI 48331-3535
Ph: (248)699-GALE   Fax: (248)699-8069
Fr: 800-877-GALE
E-mail: galeord@gale.com
URL: http://www.galegroup.com
Annual. Eight volumes. $2670.00/set. Comprehensive directory of companies. Part of Ward's Business Directory of U.S. Private and Public Companies series.

NEWSPAPERS, MAGAZINES, AND JOURNALS

★12536★ *The Network Connection*
Resources for Women Inc.
8421 E Shiloh St.
Tucson, AZ 85710-2939
Ph: (520)881-4506   Fax: (520)881-1955
Description: Monthly. Focuses on professional and personal networking while providing information about member businesses. Recurring features include interviews, a calendar of events, reports of meetings, job listings, and book reviews.

AUDIO/VISUAL RESOURCES

★12537★ *Effective Use of the Telephone in Your Job Search*
Cambridge Educational
PO Box 931
Monmouth Junction, NJ 08852-0931
Fax: 800-FAX-ON-US   Fr: 800-468-4227
URL: http://www.cambridgeeducational.com
Video. 1998. $98.95. 23 minutes. Covers using the telephone to identify potential employers and set up interviews.

ONLINE AND DATABASE SERVICES

★12538★ *CareerFairs.com*
URL: http://www.careerfairs.com
Description: An online guide to upcoming career fairs and the employers who will attend them. Includes a free resume database.

International Job Opportunities

★12539★ Alternative Travel Directory

Transitions Abroad Publishing
PO Box 745
Bennington, VT 05201
Ph: (802)442-4827   Fax: (802)442-4827
URL: http://www.transitionsabroad.com/publications/atd/index.shtm

Annual, January. $19.95. Covers over 3,000 sources of information on international employment, education, and specialty travel opportunities. Entries include: Source name, address, phone, decription, cost dates. Arrangement: Classified by subject and country. Indexes: Geographical.

★12540★ Career Opportunities for Bilinguals and Multilinguals

Scarecrow Press Inc.
4501 Forbes Blvd., Ste. 200
Lanham, MD 20706
Ph: (301)459-3366   Fax: (301)429-5748
Fr: 800-462-6420

Latest edition 2nd 2002. $37.50. Covers 3,800 companies and organizations that hire people who are fluent in languages other than English; colleges and universities, libraries, books, and other educational resources for those wishing to learn other languages. Entries include: For employers-Name, address, phone, description of work, languages sought. For educational resources-Name, address, phone, languages. Arrangement: Separate sections for educational resources, U.S. opportunities, and overseas opportunities. Indexes: Language, educational background, geographical.

★12541★ Careers in International Affairs

Georgetown University Press
3600 O St. NW
Washington, DC 20007-0866
Ph: (202)687-5889   Fr: 800-246-9606

School of Foreign Service, Georgetown University Staff. Sixth edition, 1996. $17.95

(paper). 320 pages. Includes index and bibliography.

★12542★ Careers in International Business

McGraw-Hill Trade
2 Penn Plaza
New York, NY 10121
Ph: (212)904-2000   Fr: 800-722-4726
E-mail: ntcpub@tribune.com

Ed Halloran. 1996. $17.95; 13.95 (paper). 160 pages.

★12543★ Craighead's International Business, Travel, and Relocation Guide to 81 Countries

Thomson Gale
27500 Drake Rd.
Farmington Hills, MI 48331-3535
Ph: (248)699-GALE   Fax: (248)699-8069
Fr: 800-877-GALE
E-mail: galeord@gale.com
URL: http://www.galegroup.com

First edition, 2002. $750.00. 5,180 pages. Arranged geographically into regions of Asia, Africa, Europe, the Mideast, and the Americas. Profiles include information on maps, statistics, travel restrictions, currency, transportation, and health. A separate section covers details of international travel such as instructions for passports and visas and information on transportation and shopping. An international relocation chapter covers financial planning, legal matters, insurance, education, housing, and other family concerns.

★12544★ Directory of American Firms Operating in Foreign Countries

Uniworld Business Publications Inc.
257 Central Park W., Ste. 10A
New York, NY 10024
Ph: (212)496-2448   Fax: (212)316-4098
URL: http://www.uniworldbp.com

Biennial, odd years; latest edition January 2003. $355.00. Covers about 3,000 American corporations with 36,300 subsidiaries or affiliates outside the United States. Entries include: Company name, address, phone;

names and titles of key personnel; number of employees, annual sales, NAICS code, web address, locations and types of facilities in foreign countries, number of employees, product/service. Separate country editions also available. Arrangement: Alphabetical. Indexes: Foreign operation by country.

★12545★ Directory of International Internships

Dean's Office of International Studies and Programs
International Ctr., Rm. 209
East Lansing, MI 48824
Ph: (517)353-5589   Fax: (517)353-7254

Irregular, first edition 1987; latest edition 2003. $42.95; $30.00 for students. Covers international internships sponsored by academic institutions, private sector, and the federal government. Entries include: Institution name, address, phone, names and titles of key personnel, subject areas in which internships are available, number available, location, duration, financial data, academic credit available, evaluation procedures, application deadline, requirements of participation. Arrangement: Classified by type of sponsor, then alphabetical. Indexes: Sponsor, subject, geographical.

★12546★ Directory of Summer Jobs Abroad

Vacation Work Publications
9 Park End St.
Oxford OX1 1HJ, United Kingdom
Ph: 865 241978   Fax: 865 790885

Annual, November; supplement in May. $7.99; $6.00. Covers more than 30,000 jobs worldwide. Entries include: Name of employer, address, length of employment, number of positions available, pay rates, how and when to apply, name of contact. Arrangement: Geographical, then classified by type of job.

★12547★ Federal Career Opportunities

Federal Research Service Inc.
7360 McWhorter Pl., Ste. 201
PO Box 1708
Annandale, VA 22003
Ph: (703)281-0200   Fax: (703)281-7639
Fr: 800-822-5627
URL: http://www.fedjobs.com/index.html

Biweekly. $7.95 per copy. Covers more than 3,000 current federal job vacancies in the United States and overseas; includes permanent, part-time, and temporary positions. Entries include: Position title, location, series and grade, job requirements, special forms, announcement number, closing date, application address. Arrangement: Classified by occupation.

★12548★ Finding Work Overseas: How and Where to Contact International Recruitment Agencies, Consultants and Employers

Trans-Atlantic Publications, Inc.
311 Bainbridge St.
Philadelphia, PA 19147
Ph: (215)925-5083   Fax: (215)925-1912

Matthew Cunningham. 1996. 205 pages. Part of the Living and Working Abroad Series.

★12549★ Great Jobs for Foreign Language Majors

McGraw-Hill Trade
2 Penn Plaza
New York, NY 10121
Ph: (212)904-2000   Fr: 800-722-4726
E-mail: ntcpub@tribune.com

Julie DeGalan and Stephen E. Lambert. 1994. $11.95 (paper). 412 pages. Part of Great Jobs for... Majors series.

★12550★ Guide to Careers in World Affairs

Impact Publications
9104-N Manassas Dr., Ste. N
Manassas Park, VA 20111-5211
Ph: (703)361-7300   Fax: (703)335-9486

Foreign Affairs Association Staff and Pamela Gerard. Third edition. 1993. $14.95. 331 pages. Out of print. Describes jobs in business, government, and nonprofit organizations. Explains the methods and credentials required to secure a job in many fields, including international law and journalism. Contains sections on internships and graduate programs.

★12551★ How to Get a Job in Europe

Surrey Books, Inc.
230 E. Ohio St., Ste. 120
Chicago, IL 60611
Ph: (312)751-7330   Fax: (312)751-7334
Fr: 800-326-4430

Robert Sanborn and Cheryl Matherly. Fifth edition, 2001. Directory of employers, associations, job referral services, and other sources of employment information. Part of Insider's Guide series.

★12552★ International Employment Hotline

International Employment Hotline
1088 Middle River Rd.
Stanardsville, VA 22973
Ph: (804)985-6444   Fax: (804)985-6828
Fr: 800-291-4618
E-mail: lisa@internationaljobs.org

Monthly. $69.00. Covers temporary and career job openings overseas and advice for international job hunters. Entries include: Company name, address, job title, description of job, requirements, geographic location of job. Arrangement: Geographical.

★12553★ International Jobs Directory

Impact Publications
9104 Manassas Dr., Ste. N
Manassas Park, VA 20111-5211
Ph: (703)361-7300   Fax: (703)335-9486

Ronald L. Krannich and Caryl R. Krannich. 1999. $19.95 (paper).

★12554★ International Jobs: Where They Are & How to Get Them

Perseus Books Group
10 E. 53rd St.
New York, NY 10022
Ph: (212)207-7817   Fr: 800-386-5656

Eric Kocher. Fourth edition, 2000. $16.00 (paper). 448 pages. Discusses over 500 different job opportunities in a variety of sectors. Out of print.

★12555★ Jobs in Japan

Global Press
697 College Pkwy.
Rockville, MD 20850

Irregular, previous edition 1991; latest edition 1993. $14.95. Publication includes: Lists of private schools in Japan and other organizations useful to native English-speaking job-seekers; directory of Japanese companies that hire non-Japanese workers. Entries include: Organization or company name, address, phone, name and title of contact. Principal content of publication is advice on jobs available for foreigners in Japan including teaching journalism, acting, office work, etc. It also explains how to negotiate with employers and obtain the right visas, and gives tips on living and working in Japan.

★12556★ Korea Calling: The Essential Handbook for Teaching English and Living in South Korea

Woodpecker Press
41 N. Palmer Dr.
Port Townsend, WA 98368-9427
Ph: (360)379-0297

Jay Freeborne and Allegra Specht. 1996. $14.95 (paper). 174 pages.

★12557★ Major Companies of Europe

Graham and Whiteside, Limited
Tuition House, 5-6 Francis Grove
Wimbledon SW19 4DT, United Kingdom
Ph: 020 8947 1011   Fax: 020 8947 1163

2001. Four volumes. $360.00/vol. Listings are organized by country.

★12558★ Major Companies of the Far East and Australasia

Thomson Gale
27500 Drake Rd.
Farmington Hills, MI 48331-3535
Ph: (248)699-GALE   Fax: (248)699-8069
Fr: 800-877-GALE
E-mail: galeord@gale.com
URL: http://www.galegroup.com

Seventeenth edition, 2000. Three volumes. $1,395.00/set. Listings are organized by country.

★12559★ The New Relocating Spouse's Guide to Employment

Impact Publications
9104 Manassas Dr., Ste. N
Manassas Park, VA 20111-5211
Ph: (703)361-7300   Fax: (703)335-9486
URL: http://www.impactpublications.com/

Irregular, previous edition 1989, latest edition 1993. $14.95. Publication includes: List of 133 professional associations and 54 federal job centers. Entries include: Organization name, address, phone. Principal content of publication is discussion of the job market, employment trends, and other useful information for those facing a move to a city where they have no job waiting. Arrangement: Alphabetical.

★12560★ Opportunities Abroad for Educators

Fulbright Teacher and Administrator Exchange Program
600 Maryland Ave. SW, Ste. 320
Washington, DC 20024-2520
Ph: (202)314-3527   Fax: (202)479-6806
Fr: 800-726-0479
URL: http://www.fulbrightexchanges.org

Annual. Covers opportunities available for elementary and secondary teachers, and two year college instructors, and school administrators to attend seminars or to teach abroad under the Mutual Educational and Cultural Exchange Act of 1961. Entries include: Countries of placement, dates, eligibility requirements, teaching assignments. Arrangement: Geographical.

★12561★ Opportunities in International Business Careers

McGraw-Hill Trade
2 Penn Plaza
New York, NY 10121
Ph: (212)904-2000   Fr: 800-722-4726

Jeffrey Arpan. 1994. $11.95 (paper). 200 pages. Describes what types of jobs exist in international business, where they are located, what challenges and rewards they bring, and how to prepare for and obtain jobs in international business.

★12562★ Opportunities in Overseas Careers

McGraw-Hill Trade
2 Penn Plaza
New York, NY 10121
Ph: (212)904-2000   Fr: 800-722-4726

Blythe Camenson. 1998. $14.95; $11.95 (paper). 106 pages.

★12563★ Overseas Employment Opportunities for Educators: Department of Defense Dependents Schools

DIANE Publishing Co.
PO Box 1428
Collingdale, PA 19023-8428
Ph: (610)461-6200   Fax: (610)461-6130
Fr: 800-782-3833

Barry Leonard, editor. 1999. $20.00. 44 pages. An introduction to teachings positions in the Dept. of Defense Dependents Schools (DoDDS), a worldwide school system, operated by the DoD in 14 countries.

★12564★ Overseas Exotic Jobs-$100 to $1000 Daily: For Unskilled, Skilled, Professionals

Zinks International Career Guidance
PO Box 587
Marshall, MI 49068-0587

Richard M. Zink. Eighth edition, 1995. $14.95 (paper). 80 pages.

★12565★ Overseas Jobs: The New Offshore & Oilfield Manual

Zinks International Career Guidance
PO Box 587
Marshall, MI 49068-0587

Richard M. Zink. Fifth edition, 1995. $14.95 (paper). 64 pages.

★12566★ Part Time Prospects: International Comparison of Part Time Work in Europe, North America and the Pacific Rim

Routledge
29 W. 35th St.
New York, NY 10001-2299
Ph: (212)216-7800   Fax: (212)564-7854
Fr: 800-634-7064

Jacqueline O'Reilly and Colette Fagan. 1998. $29.99 (paper). 272 pages.

★12567★ Peterson's Job Opportunities for Business Majors

Thomson Peterson's
Princeton Pke. Corporate Ctr., 2000 Lenox Dr.
PO Box 67005
Lawrenceville, NJ 08648
Ph: (609)896-1800   Fax: (609)896-4531
Fr: 800-338-3282

URL: http://www.petersons.com

Irregular, latest edition 2000 - 16th ed. $18.95. Covers the 2,000 largest U.S. employers hiring in several fields, including financial services, management consulting, consumer products, and media/ entertainment. Entries include: Organization name, address, phone, name and title of contact, number of employees, type of organization. Arrangement: Alphabetical. Indexes: Type of organization.

★12568★ Peterson's Job Opportunities in Engineering and Technology

Thomson Peterson's
PO Box 67005
Lawrenceville, NJ 08648-6105
Fr: 800-338-3282

Compiled by the Peterson's staff. Fourth edition, 1996. $21.95 (paper). 384 pages. Profiles 2,000 high-tech companies looking primarily for technical personnel in such fields as biotechnology, telecommunications, software, computers and peripherals, defense, and aerospace. Contains job-search strategies and career options to help match education and expertise to the job market. Indexed geographically, by industry, and by hiring needs.

★12569★ Resumes for Overseas & Stateside Jobs

Zinks International Career Guidance
PO Box 587
Marshall, MI 49068-0587

Richard M. Zink. 1994. $14.95 (paper). 80 pages.

★12570★ Summer Jobs Britain

Thomson Peterson's
PO Box 67005
Lawrenceville, NJ 08648-6105
Fr: 800-338-3282

Compiled by Peterson's Staff. Third edition, 2001. $16.95 (paper). 528 pages. Part of Summer Jobs Britain series.

★12571★ Vacation Work's Overseas Summer Jobs

Thomson Peterson's
Princeton Pke. Corporate Ctr., 2000 Lenox Dr.
PO Box 67005
Lawrenceville, NJ 08648
Ph: (609)896-1800   Fax: (609)896-4531
Fr: 800-338-3282

Annual. $17.95. Covers over 30,000 summer jobs worldwide. Entries include: Complete job data, length of employment, number of openings, pay, job description, qualifications needed, application/contact information.

NEWSPAPERS, MAGAZINES, AND JOURNALS

★12572★ Center for European Studies Newsletter

Center for European Studies
309 Social Science Bldg.
Minneapolis, MN 55455
Ph: (612)625-1557   Fax: (612)626-2242
URL: http://cla.umn.edu/europe

Description: Bimonthly. Announces events, visiting scholars, fellowships, scholarships, and grants at the Center. Recurring features include a calendar of events, news of educational opportunities, notes from the director, and job listings.

★12573★ International Living

Agora Inc.
1217 St. Paul St.
Baltimore, MD 21202-4702
Ph: (410)234-0515   Fax: (410)837-1999

Description: Monthly. Features articles about international travel, lifestyles, investments, retirement, employment, and real estate. Includes monthly currency reports. Recurring features include news briefs, letters to the editor, book reviews, and a calendar of events.

★12574★ International Studies Newsletter

International Studies Association
Social Sciences, No. 314
University of Arizona
Tucson, AZ 85721
Ph: (520)621-7715   Fax: (520)621-5780
URL: http://www.csf.colorado.edu/is/newsletter/

Description: Eight issues/year. Promotes the Association's interest in a multidisciplinary approach to international affairs and cross-cultural studies. Acts as a forum for discussion among scholars, students, and the general public. Recurring features include Association news; information on publications by members; notices of employment opportunities; calls for papers; and announcements of meetings, conferences, lectures, awards, grants, and fellowships.

★12575★ NewsNet, the Newsletter of the AAASS

American Association for the Advancement of Slavic Studies (AAASS)
8 Story St.
Cambridge, MA 02138
Ph: (617)495-0677   Fax: (617)495-0680
E-mail: newsnet@fas.harvard.edu

Description: Bimonthly, during the academic year. Reports on Association activities and on Slavic study research in institutions throughout the world. Alerts readers to research grants, internships, and fellowship opportunities as well as to employment opportunities in universities across the country. Announces awards, upcoming conferences, courses, new scholarly publications, and annual research.

★12576★ **United Nations Jobs Newsletter**
Thomas F. Burola & Associates
6477 Telephone Rd., Ste. 7R
Ventura, CA 93003
Fax: (805)654-1708

Description: Monthly. Focuses on employment conditions within the United Nations System and lists vacancy notices. Covers the World Bank, Canadian International Development Agency (CIDA), Overseas Development Agency (ODA), United States Agency for International Development (USAID), Asian Development Bank, European Bank for Reconstruction and Development, International Red Cross, and related private sector consulting companies.

ONLINE AND DATABASE SERVICES

★12577★ **FreeJobSearchEngines.com**
E-mail: cs@free-job-search-engines.com
URL: http://free-job-search-engines.com/

Description: Job board meta-search engine grouping jobs by geography. Seekers can search in the United States, the United Kingdom, Australia, Canada and Hong Kong.

OTHER SOURCES

★12578★ **Association for International Practical Training (AIPT)**
10400 Little Patuxent Pky., Ste. 250
Columbia, MD 21044-3519
Ph: (410)997-2200   Fax: (410)992-3924
E-mail: aipt@aipt.org
URL: http://www.aipt.org

Description: Providers worldwide on-the-job training programs for students and professionals seeking international career development and life-changing experiences. Arranges workplace exchanges in hundreds of professional fields, bringing employers and trainees together from around the world. Client list ranges from small farming communities to Fortune 500 companies.

★12579★ **Chinese Christian Mission (CCM)**
PO Box 750759
Petaluma, CA 94975
Ph: (707)762-1314   Fax: (707)762-1713

E-mail: ccm@ccmusa.org
URL: http://www.ccmusa.org

Purpose: Serves as an evangelical faith mission dedicated to reaching Chinese people around the world with the gospel of Jesus Christ. Broadcasts radio programs to foster Christianity in China. **Activities:** Operates placement service providing ministers with churches. Sponsors short-term mission trips to Latin America and East Asia.

★12580★ **International Educator's Institute (TIE)**
PO Box 513
Cummaquid, MA 02637
Ph: (508)362-1414   Fax: (508)362-1411
Fr: 877-375-6668
E-mail: tie@tieonline.com
URL: http://www.tieonline.com

Description: Facilitates the placement of teachers and administrators in American, British, and international schools. Seeks to create a network that provides for professional development opportunities and improved financial security of members. Offers advice and information on international school news, recent educational developments, job placement, and investment, consumer, and professional development opportunities. Makes available insurance and travel benefits. Operates International Schools Internship Program.

★12581★ **NAFSA/Association of International Educators (NAFSA)**
1307 New York Ave. NW, 8th Fl.
Washington, DC 20005
Ph: (202)737-3699   Fax: (202)737-3657
E-mail: inbox@nafsa.org
URL: http://www.nafsa.org

Description: Individuals, organizations, and institutions dealing with international educational exchange, including foreign student advisers, overseas educational advisers, credentials and admissions officers, administrators and teachers of English as a second language, community support personnel, study-abroad administrators, and embassy cultural or educational personnel. Promotes self-regulation standards and responsibilities in international educational exchange; offers professional development opportunities primarily through publications, workshops, grants, and regional and national conferences. Advocates for increased awareness and support of international education and exchange on campuses, in government, and in communities. Offers services including: a job registry for employers and professionals involved with international education; a consultant referral service. Sponsors joint liaison activities with a variety of other educational and government organizations to conduct a census of foreign student enrollment in the U.S.; conducts workshops about specific subjects and countries.

★12582★ **U.S.-China Education Foundation (USCEF)**
4140 Oceanside Blvd.
PMB 112, No. 159
Oceanside, CA 92056-6005
Ph: (760)644-0977
E-mail: SAGE.Kennedypres@cex.net
URL: http://www.sage-usa.net

Members: A project of the Society for the Advancement of Global Education. **Purpose:** Purposes are to promote the learning of the Chinese languages (including Mandarin, Cantonese, and minority languages such as Mongolian) by Americans, and the learning of English by Chinese. **Activities:** Conducts short-term travel-study program to prepare Americans and Chinese for stays of four, six, or eight months or one to four years in China or the U.S., respectively. Operates teacher placement service and speakers' bureau. A project of S.A.G.E. the Society for the Development of Global Education.

★12583★ **United States Committee for the United Nations Environment Program (US UNEP)**
47914 252nd St.
Sioux Falls, SD 57198-0001
Ph: (605)594-6117   Fax: (605)594-6119
E-mail: webmaster@www.na.unep.net
URL: http://grid2.cr.usgs.gov

Description: Individuals interested in raising public awareness of the importance of a global environmental effort. Encourages activism in support of the United Nations Environment Program. Acts as a liaison between the UNEP and the public. Sponsors educational programs and children's services. Offers placement services to job seekers in international environmental work. Maintains speakers' bureau.

★12584★ **YMCA International Camp Counselor Program (ICCP)**
5 W 63rd St., 2nd Fl.
New York, NY 10010
Ph: (212)727-8800   Fax: (212)727-8814
Fr: 888-477-9622
E-mail: ips@ymcanyc.org
URL: http://www.ymcaiccp.org

Description: A work-travel program designed to introduce international university students and teachers and social workers aged 19-30 to life in America. The students spend 8 to 9 weeks counseling in children's camps across the country, followed by a period of independent or group travel. Also sponsors ICCP-Abroad placement service for American university students aged 18-25 wishing to serve as camp counselors in Africa, Asia, Australia, Hungary, New Zealand, and South America.

Interviewing Skills

REFERENCE WORKS

★12585★ A Better Job Interview: Questions and Techniques

PushButtonPress.com, Inc.
PO Box 1364
Greenwich, CT 06836-1364
Ph: (203)550-7383

Damen Choy. May 2004. $17.95 (paper).

★12586★ Dynamite Networking for Dynamite Jobs: 101 Interpersonal Telephone and Electronic Techniques for Getting Job Leads, Interviews, and Offers

Impact Publications
9104 Manassas Dr., Ste. N
Manassas Park, VA 20111-5211
Ph: (703)361-7300   Fax: (703)335-9486

Caryl R. Krannich and Ronald L. Kannich. 1996. $15.95 (paper). 320 pages.

★12587★ Effective Interviewing for Paralegals

Anderson Publishing Co.
2035 Reading Rd.
Cincinnati, OH 45202-1576
Ph: (513)421-4142   Fax: (513)562-8116
Fr: 800-582-7295

Fred E. Jandt. Second edition, 1995. $28.95. 300 pages.

★12588★ Essential Interviewing: A Programmed Approach to Effective Communication

Thomson Wadsworth
10 Davis Dr.
Belmont, CA 94002
Ph: (650)598-9757   Fax: (831)375-6414

Allen Ivey, Margaret T. Hearn, Max R. Uhlemann and David R. Evans. Fifth edition, 1998. 273 pages.

★12589★ 50 Winning Answers to Interview Questions

DBM Publishing
275 Broad Hollow Rd., Ste. 300
Melville, NY 11747
Ph: (516)752-3789   Fax: (516)756-2571
Fr: 800-345-5627
URL: http://www.dbm.com

Charles F. Albrecht, Jr., editor. 1995. $10.95 (paper). 160 pages. Provides question-by-question guidance.

★12590★ A Funny Thing Happened at the Interview: Wit, Wisdom, and War Stories from the Job Hunt

Edin Books, Inc.
102 Sunrise Dr.
Gillette, NJ 07933
Ph: (908)647-3346   Fax: (908)580-1008
Fr: 800-334-6477

Gregory F. Farrell. 1996. $12.95 (paper). 272 pages. Humorous, true job interview stories.

★12591★ Get That Interview: The Indispensable Guide for College Grads

Barron's Educational Series, Inc.
250 Wireless Blvd.
Hauppauge, NY 11788-3917
Ph: (631)434-3311   Fax: (631)434-3723
Fr: 800-645-3476

R. Theodore Moock, Jr. 1996. $8.95 (paper). 160 pages. Offers strategies, tactics, and advice for the recent college graduate.

★12592★ Get That Job!: Interviews

McGraw-Hill Contemporary Books
1221 Avenue of the Americas
New York, NY 10020
Ph: (212)904-2000   Fr: 800-323-4900

Susan Echaore-McDavid. 1997. $4.66 (paper). 32 pages.

★12593★ Government Job Finder

Planning Communications
7215 Oak Ave.
River Forest, IL 60305-1935
Ph: (708)366-5200   Fax: (708)366-5280
Fr: 888-366-5200
URL: http://jobfindersonline.com

Daniel Lauber. Third edition, 1997. 336 pages. Covers 1800 sources. Discusses how to use sources of local, state, and federal government job vacancies in a number of specialties and state-by-state, including job-matching services, job hotlines, specialty periodicals with job ads, salary surveys, and directories. Explains how local, state, and federal hiring systems work. Includes chapters on resume and cover letter preparation and interviewing.

★12594★ How to Have a Winning Job Interview

McGraw-Hill Trade
2 Penn Plaza
New York, NY 10121
Ph: (212)904-2000   Fr: 800-722-4726
E-mail: ntcpub@tribune.com

Deborah Perlmutter Bloch. Third edition, 1998. $14.95 (paper). 480 pages. Guides the reader through the steps of making the best impression on a future employer, including getting the appointment for the interview and planning an approach, what to emphasize, and what to minimize.

★12595★ How to Locate Jobs and Land Interviews

The Career Press, Inc.
3 Tice Rd.
PO Box 687
Franklin Lakes, NJ 07417-1322
Ph: (201)848-0310   Fax: (201)848-1727
Fr: 800-227-3371

Albert L. French. Second edition, 1993. $10.95 (paper). 192 pages. Shows readers how to tap into the unadvertised, hidden job market and guides them through the resume, cover letter, and interview preparation process. Out of print.

★12596★ *How to Turn an Interview into a Job*
Simon & Schuster Inc.
1230 Avenue of the Americas
New York, NY 10020
Ph: (212)698-7000   Fax: (212)698-7007
Fr: 800-897-7650

Jeffrey Allen. April 2004. $11.00 (paper). 128 pages.

★12597★ *Information Interviewing: How to Tap Your Hidden Job Market*
Ferguson Publishing Co.
200 W. Jackson Blvd., 7th Fl.
Chicago, IL 60606-3412
Ph: (312)692-1000   Fax: (312)692-1020
Fr: 800-306-9941

Martha Stoodley. Second edition, 1996. 510 pages. Details the why, how, and where of information interviewing and provides suggestions for incorporating this technique into an effective job search.

★12598★ *Interview Handbook*
Kendall Hunt Publishing Co.
4050 Westmark Dr.
PO Box 1840
Dubuque, IA 52002
Ph: (319)589-1000   Fax: 800-772-9165
Fr: 800-228-0810

Second edition, 1995. $9.95. 48 pages. Out of print.

★12599★ *Interview Strategies That Will Get You the Job You Want*
F & W Publications, Inc.
4700 E Galbraith Rd.
Cincinnati, OH 45236
Ph: (513)531-2690   Fax: (513)531-4082
Fr: 800-289-0963

Andrea Kay. 1996. $12.99 (paper). 144 pages.

★12600★ *Interview for Success: A Practical Guide to Increasing Job Interviews, Offers, and Salaries*
Impact Publications
9104 Manassas Dr., Ste. N
Manassas Park, VA 20111-5211
Ph: (703)361-7300   Fax: (703)335-9486

Ronald Krannich and Caryl Krannich. Seventh edition, 1998. $15.95 (paper). 334 pages. Subtitled: "A Practical Guide to Increasing Job Interviews, Offers and Salaries". Offers hundreds of tips for more successful job interviews.

★12601★ *Interviewing & Helping Skills for Health Professionals*
Jones & Bartlett Publishers, Inc.
40 Tall Pine Dr.
Sudbury, MA 01776
Ph: (978)443-5000   Fax: (978)443-8000
Fr: 800-832-0034

Cormier. Second edition, 1999. $37.50 (paper). 352 pages.

★12602★ *Interviewing Principles and Practices*
Brown and Benchmark
25 Kessel Ct.
Madison, WI 53711
Ph: (608)273-0040   Fr: 800-338-5578

Charles J. Stewart and William B. Cash. Eighth edition, 1997. $25.50 (paper). 320 pages.

★12603★ *Interviewing: Skills & Applications*
Gorsuch Scarisbrick Publishers
6207 N. Cattle Track Rd., No. 1
Scottsdale, AZ 85250-4607

James E. Sayer and Lilburn P. Hoehn. 1993. $31.50 (paper). Out of print.

★12604★ *Interviewing Skills for Nurses & Other Health Care Professionals: A Structured Approach*
Routledge
29 W. 35th St.
New York, NY 10001-2299
Ph: (212)216-7800   Fax: (212)564-7854
Fr: 800-634-7064

Robert Newell. 1994. $24.99 (paper). 208 pages. Out of print.

★12605★ *Interviewing Techniques for Newspapers*
State Mutual Book & Periodical Service, Ltd.
2183 Montauk Hwy.
Bridgehampton, NY 11932
Ph: (631)537-1104   Fax: (631)537-0412

Maurice Dunlevy. 1995. $20.00 (paper). 143 pages.

★12606★ *Job Interview Tips for People with Not-So-Hot Backgrounds: How to Put Red Flags Behind You*
Impact Publications
9104 Manassas Dr., Ste. N
Manassas Park, VA 20111-9486
Ph: (703)361-7900   Fax: (703)335-9486

Ron Krannich. March 2004. $14.95 (paper). 160 pages.

★12607★ *Job Interviewing for College Students*
McGraw-Hill Contemporary Books
1221 Avenue of the Americas
New York, NY 10020
Ph: (212)904-2000   Fr: 800-323-4900
E-mail: ntcpub@tribune.com

John D. Singleton. 1995. $11.95 (paper). 112 pages.

★12608★ *Job Interviews for Dummies*
Hungry Minds, Inc.
10475 Crosspoint Blvd.
Indianapolis, IN 46256
Fax: (317)572-4000   Fr: 800-667-1115

Joyce L. Kennedy. Second edition, 2000. $14.99 (paper). Covers basic steps of interviewing from preparation to salary negotiation. Part of For Dummies series. 264 pages.

★12609★ *Job Interviews Made Easy*
McGraw-Hill Trade
2 Penn Plaza
New York, NY 10121
Ph: (212)904-2000   Fr: 800-722-4726
E-mail: ntcpub@tribune.com

1995. $6.95 (paper). 288 pages.

★12610★ *Job Interviews That Mean Business*
Random House Reference & Information Publishing
400 Hahn Rd.
Westminster, MD 21157
Ph: (410)848-1900   Fr: 800-726-0600

David R. Eyler. 1999. $12.95 (paper). 240 pages.

★12611★ *Key Words to Nail Your Job Interview: What to Say to Win Your Dream Job*
Impact Publications
9104 Manassas Dr., Ste. N
Manassas Park, VA 20111-5211
Ph: (703)361-7300   Fax: (703)335-9486

Wendy S. Enelow. March 2004. $17.95 (paper). 222 pages.

★12612★ *Knock 'Em Dead: The Ultimate Job Seeker's Handbook*
Adams Media Corp.
57 Littlefield St.
Avon, MA 02322
Ph: (508)427-7100   Fax: (508)427-6790
Fr: 800-872-5627
URL: http://www.adamsmedia.com

Martin Yate. Revised edition, 2002. $12.95 (paper). Prepares the job seeker for the interview with advice on dress, manner, how to answer the toughest questions, and how to spot illegal questions. Discusses how to respond to questions of salary to maximize income. Features sections on executive search firms and drug testing. 352 pages.

★12613★ *Last Minute Interview Tips*
Career Press Inc.
PO Box 687
3 Tice Rd.
Franklin Lakes, NJ 07417-1322
Ph: (201)848-0310   Fax: (201)848-1727
Fr: 800-227-3371
URL: http://www.CareerPress.com

Brandon Toropov. 1996. $9.99 (paper). 172 pages.

★12614★ Make Your Job Interview a Success

Hungry Minds, Inc.
10475 Crosspoint Blvd.
Indianapolis, IN 46256
Fax: (317)572-4000   Fr: 800-667-1115

Jacob I. Biegeleisen. Fourth edition, 1994. $12.95 (paper). 240 pages. Out of stock.

★12615★ The Medical Job Interview

Blackwell Science, Incorporated
Commerce Pl.
350 Main St.
Malden, MA 02148-5018
Ph: (617)388-8250   Fax: (781)388-8255
Fr: 800-759-6102

Colin Mumford. 2000. $23.95 (paper).

★12616★ More Successful Less Stressful Interviewing for Women: A Guide to Improving Your Interviewing Skills While Reducing Stress

StellWest Publishing Co., Inc.
PO Box 190
River Edge, NJ 07661
Ph: (201)692-8306   Fax: (201)692-0302

Jessica Woods. 1995. $9.95 (paper). 105 pages. Specialty publication geared toward women which teaches interviewing and personal skills to gain the edge over competitors.

★12617★ The New Job Interview

P P I Publishing
PO Box 292239
Kettering, OH 45429
Ph: (937)294-5057   Fax: (937)294-9442
Fr: 800-773-6825

Dinah Tallent. 1995. $6.95 (paper). 149 pages.

★12618★ The 90 Minute Interview Prep Book

Thomson Peterson's
PO Box 67005
Lawrenceville, NJ 08648-6105
Fr: 800-338-3282

Peggy Schmidt. 1996. $15.95 (paper). 160 pages. Includes diskette. Provides step-by-step instructions for conducting practice interviews. Software allows users to evaluate the practice interviews.

★12619★ 101 Great Answers to the Toughest Interview Questions

The Career Press, Inc.
3 Tice Rd.
PO Box 687
Franklin Lakes, NJ 07417-1322
Ph: (201)848-0310   Fax: (201)848-1727
Fr: 800-237-3371

Ronald Fry. Fourth edition, 2000. $11.99 (paper). 246 pages. Identifies some of the toughest interview questions and provides proven responses.

★12620★ The 101 Toughest Interview Questions: And Answers That Win the Job!

Ten Speed Press
555 Richmond St. W.
Ste. 405, Box 702
Toronto, ON, Canada M5V 3B1
Ph: (416)703-7775   Fax: (416)703-9992
Fr: 800-841-2665

Frances Bolles Haynes, Daniel Porot. March 2004. $12.95 (paper). Illustrated. 240 pages.

★12621★ The Perfect Interview: How to Get the Job You Really Want

AMACOM
1601 Broadway, 12th Fl.
New York, NY 10019-7420
Ph: (518)891-1500   Fax: (518)903-8168
Fr: 800-250-5308

John D. Drake. Second edition, 1996. $17.95 (paper). 208 pages. Contains skill-building exercises and tips on preparing for the interview, framing good questions, and following through.

★12622★ Power Interviews: Job-Winning Tactics from Fortune 500 Recruiters

John Wiley & Sons Inc.
1 Wiley Dr.
Somerset, NJ 08873
Ph: (732)469-4400   Fr: 800-225-5945

Neil Yeager and Lee Hough. 1998. $15.95 (paper). 256 pages.

★12623★ Preparing for the Interview

Marketing Directions Inc.
615 Queen St.
Southington, CT 06489
Fax: (860)276-2453   Fr: 800-562-4357
URL: http://www.marketingdirections.com

$1.45. 20 pages. Strategies for preparing for job interviews.

★12624★ The Quick Interview & Salary Negotiation Book: Dramatically Improve Your Interviewing Skills & Pay in a Matter of Hours

JIST Publishing
8902 Otis Ave.
Indianapolis, IN 46216-1033
Ph: (317)613-4200   Fax: (317)613-4307
Fr: 800-648-5478

Michael J. Farr. 1995. $14.95 (paper). 690 pages.

★12625★ Resumes, Application Forms, Cover Letters, and Interviews

Consumer Information Center
U.S. General Services Administration
PO Box 100
Pueblo, CO 81002
Ph: (719)948-4000   Fax: (719)948-9724
URL: http://www.pueblo.gsa.gov

$1.25. 7 pages. Provides tips for better resumes, cover letters, and interviews. Out of Print.

★12626★ Resumes, Cover-Letters & Interviewing: Setting the Stage for Success

Thomson South-Western
5101 Madison Rd.
Cincinnati, OH 45227
Ph: (513)527-1989   Fax: (513)527-6137
Fr: 800-543-0487

Clifford W. Eischen and Lynn A. Eischen. 1999. $18.95 (paper). Professional resume using today's business technologies including the Internet & E-mail. Specifically targeted to help individuals with a two-year degree showcase their skills & experiences to get the job they want. Scanable resumes, Internet-based resumes, & etiquette for sending resumes via fax or E-mail are addressed to prepare readers to apply for jobs using today's business technologies. Dedicated chapter on the interview process coaches readers on proper interview attire, preparing for interview questions, introductions, & how to follow up after an interview. Exercises on listing qualifications, producing a first draft, gathering references, & drafting a follow-up letter, all help readers build a finished resume step by step.

★12627★ Successful Interviewing & Beyond

Thomson Delmar Learning
P.O. Box 15015
Albany, NY 12212-5015
Ph: (518)348-2300   Fax: (518)464-0393
Fr: 800-998-7498

Lois Pigford. 2000. $18.75 (paper).

★12628★ Successful Interviewing for College Seniors

McGraw-Hill Trade
2 Penn Plaza
New York, NY 10121
Ph: (212)904-2000   Fr: 800-722-4726
E-mail: ntcpub@tribune.com

John Shingleton. 1993. $11.95 (paper). Specifically tailored to the needs of college seniors and recent graduates. Includes what to expect in an interview, how to prepare for it, and how to excel in a sometimes tense situation. 112 pages. Out of print.

★12629★ Tips for Finding the Right Job

U.S. Government Printing Office
Superintendent of Documents
PO Box 371954
Pittsburgh, PA 15250-7954
Fr: (866)512-1800
URL: http://www.access.gpo.gov/su_docs/

Booklet 029-014-002445. 1996. $2.50. 27 pages. General advice for job seekers. See website for current list of available publications.

★12630★ **Top Answers to Job Interview Questions: Which Questions the Applicant Should Ask**
Rampant TechPress
PO Box 511
Kittrell, NC 27544
Ph: (252)431-0050   Fax: (252)433-9311
Fr: (866)729-8145

Donald Burleson, Robert Strickland. April 2004. $16.95 (paper).

★12631★ **Your First Interview**
The Career Press, Inc.
3 Tice Rd.
PO Box 687
Franklin Lakes, NJ 07417-1322
Ph: (201)848-0310   Fax: (201)848-1727
Fr: 800-227-3371

Ronald Fry. Fourth edition, 2001. $11.99 (paper). 192 pages. Takes the reader from making the initial contact with a prospective employer to negotiating salary.

AUDIO/VISUAL RESOURCES

★12632★ **Access Unlimited: The Job Search Series for People with Disabilities**
Cambridge Educational
PO Box 931
Monmouth Junction, NJ 08852-0931
Fax: 800-FAX-ON-US   Fr: 800-468-4227
URL: http://www.cambridgeeducational.com

Three videos. 1998. $199.00/set. Three 30-minute videos cover job search tactics, resumes and applications, and job interviewing.

★12633★ **Common Mistakes People Make in Interviews**
Cambridge Educational
PO Box 931
Monmouth Junction, NJ 08852-0931
Fax: 800-FAX-ON-US   Fr: 800-468-4227
URL: http://www.cambridgeeducational.com

Video. 1995. $79.95. 40 minutes. Helps job seekers anticipate what interviewers are looking for.

★12634★ **The Complete Job Search System**
Cambridge Educational
PO Box 931
Monmouth Junction, NJ 08852-0931
Fax: 800-FAX-ON-US   Fr: 800-468-4227
URL: http://www.cambridgeeducational.com

Five videos. 1997. $295.95/set. 15-20 minutes each. Individual titles cover career planning, career evaluation, finding a job, interviewing for a job, and succeeding on the job.

★12635★ **Effective Use of the Telephone in Your Job Search**
Cambridge Educational
PO Box 931
Monmouth Junction, NJ 08852-0931
Fax: 800-FAX-ON-US   Fr: 800-468-4227
URL: http://www.cambridgeeducational.com

Video. 1998. $98.95. 23 minutes. Covers using the telephone to identify potential employers and set up interviews.

★12636★ **Exceptional Interviewing Tips: A View from the Inside**
Cambridge Educational
PO Box 931
Monmouth Junction, NJ 08852-0931
Fax: 800-FAX-ON-US   Fr: 800-468-4227
URL: http://www.cambridgeeducational.com

Video. 1996. $79.95. 30 minutes. Includes workbook. Representative from successful businesses cover what to do before, during, and after a job interview.

★12637★ **Extraordinary Answers to Common Interview Questions**
Cambridge Educational
PO Box 931
Monmouth Junction, NJ 08852-0931
Fax: 800-FAX-ON-US   Fr: 800-468-4227
URL: http://www.cambridgeeducational.com

Video. 1995. $79.95. 30 minutes. Follows a quiz format, with advice from career experts.

★12638★ **First Impressions: The Key to Turning Job Interviews into Job Offers**
JIST Works, Inc.
8902 Otis Ave.
Indianapolis, IN 46216
Fax: 800-547-8329   Fr: 800-648-5478
E-mail: info@jist.com
URL: http://www.jist.com

Video. 2001. $199.00. 22 minutes. A humorous, informative look at making a good first impression on a potential employer. Also available in Spanish.

★12639★ **From Parole to Payroll**
Cambridge Educational
PO Box 931
Monmouth Junction, NJ 08852-0931
Fax: 800-FAX-ON-US   Fr: 800-468-4227
URL: http://www.cambridgeeducational.com

Three videos. 1997. $275.95/set. Three videos cover finding a job (15 minutes), resumes and job applications (15 minutes), and the job interview (15 minutes).

★12640★ **Interviewing for a Job**
Cambridge Educational
PO Box 931
Monmouth Junction, NJ 08852-0931
Fax: 800-FAX-ON-US   Fr: 800-468-4227
URL: http://www.cambridgeeducational.com

Video. 1997. $69.95. 20 minutes.

★12641★ **Interviewing Skills for Non-Exempt Staff**
DBM Publishing
100 Park Ave.
New York, NY 10017
Ph: (212)692-7700   Fax: (212)297-0426
Fr: 800-345-5627
E-mail: generalinfo@dbm.com
URL: http://www.dbm.com

Video. $49.95. This video will help job seekers to develop and refine their interviewing skills and learn what to expect during common interview situations.

★12642★ **Interviewing Skills Video**
DBM Publishing
100 Park Ave.
New York, NY 10017
Ph: (212)692-7700   Fax: (212)297-0426
Fr: 800-345-5627
E-mail: generalinfo@dbm.com
URL: http://www.dbm.com

Video. $49.95. Available in two versions, one for professionals and one for executives.

★12643★ **The Job Interview**
Cambridge Educational
PO Box 931
Monmouth Junction, NJ 08852-0931
Fax: 800-FAX-ON-US   Fr: 800-468-4227
URL: http://www.cambridgeeducational.com

$98.95. 1997. 15 minutes. Part of the From Parole to Payroll Series.

★12644★ **Job Interviewing for People with Disabilities**
Cambridge Educational
PO Box 931
Monmouth Junction, NJ 08852-0931
Fax: 800-FAX-ON-US   Fr: 800-468-4227
URL: http://www.cambridgeeducational.com

$89.95. 30 minutes. Part of the series "Access Unlimited: The Job Search Series for People with Disabilities."

★12645★ **Networking on the WWW and Beyond**
Cambridge Educational
PO Box 931
Monmouth Junction, NJ 08852-0931
Fax: 800-FAX-ON-US   Fr: 800-468-4227
URL: http://www.cambridgeeducational.com

Video. 1997. $79.95. 30 minutes. This three-part video includes an introduction to search engines, how to network and find jobs using Internet resources, and interviewing via the Internet.

★12646★ **Power Interviewing Skills: Both Sides of the Desk**
Cambridge Educational
PO Box 931
Monmouth Junction, NJ 08852-0931
Fax: 800-FAX-ON-US   Fr: 800-468-4227
URL: http://www.cambridgeeducational.com

Two videos. 1998. $149.95/set. Two videos:

Strategies for the Interviewer and *Strategies for the Interviewee* look at the interview process from both sides.

★12647★ **Strategies For The Interviewee**
Cambridge Educational
PO Box 931
Monmouth Junction, NJ 08852-0931
Fax: 800-FAX-ON-US   Fr: 800-468-4227
URL: http://www.cambridgeeducational.com

$79.95. 1999. 28 minutes. Part of the Series "Power Interviewing Skills Both Sides of the Desk."

★12648★ **Your First Resume and Interview**
Cambridge Educational
PO Box 931
Monmouth Junction, NJ 08852-0931
Fax: 800-FAX-ON-US   Fr: 800-468-4227
URL: http://www.cambridgeeducational.com

Video. 1998. $89.95. 15 minutes.

SOFTWARE

★12649★ **Adams Job Interview Almanac**
Adams Media Corp.
57 Littlefield St.
Avon, MA 02322
Ph: (508)427-7100
URL: http://www.adamsmedia.com

1996. $12.95 (book only); $19.95 (book and Windows software).

★12650★ **Interview Skills of the Future: Interview Challenges for Minorities, Women, and People with Disabilities**
Program Development Associates
PO Box 2038
Syracuse, NY 13220-2038
Ph: (315)452-0643   Fax: (315)452-0710
Fr: 800-543-2119
E-mail: info@pdassoc.com

URL: http://www.pdassoc.com

$199.00. Teaches a tactful and positive response to challenging interview questions for those having a hard time breaking through the traditional hiring barriers.

★12651★ **Multimedia Job Search**
Cambridge Educational
PO Box 931
Monmouth Junction, NJ 08852-0931
Fax: 800-FAX-ON-US   Fr: 800-468-4227
URL: http://www.cambridgeeducational.com

CD-ROM. $99.95. Includes videos, narration, and on-screen text. Users learn about getting a competitive edge in today's job market, traditional and nontraditional job search tools, resumes and cover letters, and interviewing skills.

Legal Information

REFERENCE WORKS

★12652★ Age Discrimination in the American Workplace: Old at a Young Age
Rutgers University Press
100 Joyce Kilmer Ave.
Piscataway, NJ 08854-8099
Ph: (732)445-7762   Fax: 888-471-9014
Fr: 800-446-9323

Gregory, Raymond F. 2001. $28.00 (Trade cloth). 283 pages.

★12653★ Disability, Discrimination, and Equal Opportunities: A Comparative Study of the Employment Rights of Disabled Persons
Continuum International Publishing Group, Inc.
15 E 26th St., Ste. 1703
New York, NY 10010
Ph: (212)953-5858   Fax: (212)953-5944

Doyle, Brian. 1995. $110.00 (Trade cloth). 320 pages.

★12654★ Eastman on Defending Your Employee Rights: Preventing and Stopping Discriminatory and Wrongful Terminations
Northern Star Publishing
181 Springbrook Tr.
Sparta, NJ 07871
Ph: (973)729-9508   Fax: (973)729-9508

Eastman, J. D. $49.95 (Trade paper). 140 pages.

★12655★ The Employee Rights Handbook: The Essential Guide for People on the Job
Warner Books, Inc.
1271 Avenue of the Americas
New York, NY 10020
Ph: (212)522-7200   Fr: 800-759-0190

Sack, Steven Mitchell. 2000. $13.95 (Trade paper). 480 pages.

★12656★ Employee Rights in the Workplace
Oceana Publications, Inc.
75 Main St.
Dobbs Ferry, NY 10522-1601
Ph: (914)693-8100   Fax: (914)693-0402
Fr: 800-831-0758

Jasper, Margaret C. 1997. $25.50 (Cloth). 120 pages.

★12657★ Employment Discrimination Based on Sexual Orientation
William S. Hein & Company, Inc.
1285 Main St.
Buffalo, NY 14209-1987
Ph: (716)882-2600   Fax: (716)883-8100
Fr: 800-828-7571

Nugent, Gabriel M. 1998. $46.00 (Trade cloth). 68 pages.

★12658★ Federal Employees Legal Survival Guide: How to Protect and Enforce Your Job Rights
National Employee Rights Institute
911 Mercantile Library Bldg.
414 Walnut St.
Cincinnati, OH 45202
Ph: (513)241-8137   Fax: (513)241-7863
Fr: 800-469-6374

1999. 516 pages.

★12659★ Fired, Downsized, or Laid Off: Negotiating Secrets from the No. 1 Severance Attorney
Henry Holt & Company, LLC
115 W. 18th St., 5th Fl.
New York, NY 10011
Ph: (212)886-9200   Fax: (212)633-0748

Sklover, Alan L. 2000. $15.00 (Trade paper). 352 pages.

★12660★ Getting Fired: What to Do If You're Fired, Downsized, Laid off, Restructured, Discharged, Terminated or Forced to Resign
DIANE Publishing Co.
P.O. Box 1428
Collingdale, PA 19023-8428
Ph: (610)461-6200   Fax: (610)461-6130
Fr: 800-782-3833

Sack, Steven Mitchell. 2001. $24.00 (Trade cloth). 370 pages.

★12661★ Job Discrimination II: How to Fight, How to Win
R & R Writers Agents, Inc.
364 Mauro Rd.
Englewood Cliffs, NJ 07632
Ph: (201)567-8986   Fax: (201)567-8987
Fr: 888-567-6785

Bernbach, Jeffrey M. 1998. $15.00 (Trade paper). 192 pages.

★12662★ Job Rights and Survival Strategies: A Handbook for Terminated Employees
National Employee Rights Institute
911 Mercantile Library Bldg.
414 Walnut St.
Cincinnati, OH 45202
Ph: (513)241-8137   Fax: (513)241-7863
Fr: 800-469-6374

Tobias, Paul H. and Susan Sauter. 1997. $19.95 (Trade paper). 160 pages.

★12663★ The Law of the Workplace: Rights of Employers & Employees
BNA Books
P.O. Box 7814
Edison, NJ 08818-7814
Fax: (732)346-1624   Fr: 800-960-1220

Hunt, James W. and Patricia K. Strongin. 1997. $45.00 (Trade paper). 318 pages.

★12664★ Legal Rights of Persons with Disabilities: An Analysis of Federal Law

LRP Publications
P.O. Box 980
Horsham, PA 19044-0980
Ph: (215)784-0941   Fax: (215)784-9014
Fr: 800-341-7874

Tucker, Bonnie Poitras and Bruce A. Goldstein. 1991. $115.00.

★12665★ Meeting the Needs of Employees with Disabilities

Resources for Rehabilitation
33 Bedford St., No. 19A
Lexington, MA 02420-4460
Ph: (781)862-6455   Fax: (781)861-7517

Biennial, odd years. $44.95. Publication includes: Descriptions of organizations and products that assist those involved in the employment of people with disabilities. Entries include: Organization name, address, phone, requirements for membership, admission, or eligibility, description, prices of product. Principal content of publication is information and advice for employers and counselors who recruit and retain employees with disabilities, including coverage of government programs and laws, supported employment, environmental adaptations, mobility impairments, vision impairments, and communication impairments (hearing and speech). Chapters on assistive technology, environmental modification, transition from school to work, and older workers. Arrangement: Alphabetical. Indexes: Organizations.

★12666★ Mothers on the Job: Maternity Policy in the U. S. Workplace

Rutgers University Press
100 Joyce Kilmer Ave.
Piscataway, NJ 08854
Fr: 800-446-9323

Vogel, Lise. 1993. $34.00 (Cloth). 200 pages.

★12667★ Personnel Law

Prentice Hall PTR
One Lake St.
Upper Saddle River, NJ 07458
Ph: (201)236-7000   Fr: 800-567-3800

Sovereign, Kenneth L. 1998. $46.00 (Trade paper). 362 pages.

★12668★ Psychiatric Disabilities, Employment and the Americans with Disabilities Act (ADA)

DIANE Publishing Company
P.O. Box 1428
Collingdale, PA 19023-8428
Ph: (610)461-6200   Fax: (610)461-6130
Fr: 800-782-3833

1994. $20.00 (Paper). 136 pages.

★12669★ Regulation, Litigation and Dispute Resolution under the Americans with Disabilities Act: A Practitioner's Guide to Implementation

American Bar Association
750 N. Lake Shore Dr.
Chicago, IL 60611
Ph: (312)988-5561   Fax: (312)988-6030

1996. $35.00 (Trade paper).

★12670★ Sexual Identity on the Job: Issues and Services

Haworth Press, Inc.
10 Alice St.
Binghamton, NY 13904-1580
Ph: (607)722-5857   Fax: (607)722-6362
Fr: 800-429-6784

Ellis, Alan L.; and Ellen D. Riggle (Editors). 1996. $39.95 (Trade cloth). 108 pages.

★12671★ State Individual Employment Rights Laws: Labor Relations, Employee Leave, Employee Rights & Protections

CCH, Inc.
2700 Lake Cook Rd.
Riverwoods, IL 60015
Ph: (847)267-7000   Fr: 800-248-3248

2000. $125.00 (Trade paper). 1500 pages.

★12672★ A Working Woman's Guide to Her Job Rights

Gordon Press Publishers
P.O. Box 459, Bowling Green Sta.
New York, NY 10004
Ph: (212)969-8419   Fax: (718)624-8419

1992. $250 (Library binding).

★12673★ Workplace Accommodations under the ADA

Thompson Publishing Group, Inc.
1725 K St., NW, Suite 700
Washington, DC 20006
Ph: (202)739-9642   Fax: (202)739-9578

Magill, Barbara Gamble. 1999. $79.00 (Trade paper).

★12674★ Workplace Law Advisor: From Harassment and Discrimination Policies to Hiring & Firing Guidelines - What Every Manager and Employee Needs to Know

Perseus Books Group
10 E. 53rd St.
New York, NY 10022
Ph: (212)207-7817   Fr: 800-386-5656

Covey, Anne. 2000. $17.00 (Paper). 272 pages.

★12675★ Your Rights in the Workplace

Nolo.com
950 Parker St.
Berkeley, CA 94710
Ph: (510)549-1976   Fax: (510)548-5902
Fr: 800-992-6656

Repa, Barbara K. 2000. $29.95 (Trade paper). 560 pages.

NEWSPAPERS, MAGAZINES, AND JOURNALS

★12676★ Alabama Employment Law Letter

M. Lee Smith Publishers L.L.C.
5201 Virginia Way
PO Box 5094
Brentwood, TN 37024-5094
Ph: (615)373-7517   Fax: 800-785-9212
Fr: 800-274-6774
URL: http://www.mleesmith.com

Description: Monthly. Covers laws regulating employment activities in Alabama.

★12677★ American Academy of Psychiatry and the Law Newsletter

American Academy of Psychiatry and the Law
One Regency Dr.
PO Box 30
Bloomfield, CT 06002-0030
Ph: (860)242-5450   Fax: (860)286-0787
Fr: 800-331-1389

Description: Three issues/year. Discusses psychiatry as it relates to the law. Recurring features include recent legal cases, legislative updates, letters to the editor, notices of publications available, news of educational opportunities, job listings, a calendar of events, and columns.

★12678★ Bank Employment Law Report

A.S. Pratt & Sons
1911 Fort Myer Dr., Ste. 308
Arlington, VA 22209
Ph: (703)528-0145   Fax: (703)528-1736
Fr: 800-572-2797

Description: Monthly. Presents legal matters for financial institutions' human resources officers.

★12679★ BNA's Corporate Counsel Weekly

Bureau of National Affairs Inc.
1231 25th St. NW
Washington, DC 20037
Ph: (202)452-4200   Fax: (202)452-4644
Fr: 800-372-1033
URL: http://www.bna.com/hub/bna/legal/ccwhigh.htm1

Description: Weekly. Covers law that affects business, including corporate law, securities law, antitrust law, and employment law. Carries brief reports of court cases, looks at government regulation of trade and the environment, and focuses each week on a topic of current importance. Includes texts of regulatory material and practitioner analysis.

★12680★ **California Employer Advisor**

Employer Resource Institute Inc.
9 Main St., Ste. 700
Tiburon, CA 94920
Fax: (415)435-9679   Fr: 800-695-7178
URL: http://www.employeradvice.com

Description: Monthly. The award-winning guide to California employment law and employee relations.

★12681★ **California Employment Law Monitor**

M. Lee Smith Publishers L.L.C.
5201 Virginia Way
PO Box 5094
Brentwood, TN 37024-5094
Ph: (615)373-7517   Fax: 800-785-9212
Fr: 800-274-6774
URL: http://www.mleesmith.com

Description: Monthly. Provides coverage of court cases and other situations involving employment laws in California.

★12682★ **California Labor and Employment ALERT Newsletter**

Castle Publications Ltd.
PO Box 580
Van Nuys, CA 91408
Ph: (818)708-3208   Fax: (818)708-9287
URL: http://www.castlepublications.com

Description: Bimonthly. Reports on current developments in California and federal laws concerning personnel and employment issues. Recurring features include notices of publications available.

★12683★ **California Labor and Employment Law Quarterly**

State Bar of California
180 Howard St.
San Francisco, CA 94105
Ph: (415)538-2590   Fax: (415)538-2368

Description: Quarterly. Contains information and news on California's labor and employment laws and regulations.

★12684★ **Colorado Employment Law Letter**

M. Lee Smith Publishers L.L.C.
5201 Virginia Way
PO Box 5094
Brentwood, TN 37024-5094
Ph: (615)373-7517   Fax: 800-785-9212
Fr: 800-274-6774

Description: Monthly. Addresses litigation and court decisions affecting employment issues.

★12685★ **Commercial Laws of the World**

Foreign Tax Law Inc.
PO Box 2189
Ormond Beach, FL 32175-2189
Ph: (386)253-5785   Fax: (386)257-3003
URL: http://www.foreignlaw.com

Description: Biweekly. Provides loose-leaf supplements covering commercial laws for countries across the world. Includes amendments to laws of over 100 countries translated into English. Covers commercial registers, employment of foreigners, branches of foreign companies, registration of foreigners, cost of registration, cost of business, commercial acts, brokers, limited partnerships, joint ventures, distribution of profits, legal reserves, treatment of foreigners, foreign judgments, balance sheets, nature and kinds of companies, forms of company contracts, foreign corporations, partnerships, dissolution, mergers, prescription period, capital stock, insurance companies, and formation expenses.

★12686★ **Compensation**

Bureau of National Affairs Inc.
1231 25th St. NW
Washington, DC 20037
Ph: (202)452-4200   Fax: (202)452-4644
Fr: 800-372-1033

Description: Weekly. Offers legal clarification and practical advice on employers' pay and benefit policies. Discusses such topics as health care cost containment, payroll laws and taxes, workers compensation laws, pension law (ERISA), job evaluation, benefit plans, compensation administration, incentive systems, and independent contractors. Compensation is part of the BNA Policy and Practice Series, and can be purchased separately or in any combination with other binder sets entitled Fair Employment Practices, Labor Relations, Personnel Management, or Wages and Hours.

★12687★ **Connecticut Employment Law Letter**

M. Lee Smith Publishers L.L.C.
5201 Virginia Way
PO Box 5094
Brentwood, TN 37024-5094
Ph: (615)373-7517   Fax: 800-785-9212
Fr: 800-274-6774

Description: Monthly. Addresses legislation and court decisions affecting employment issues.

★12688★ **Disability Issues**

Information Center for Individuals With Disabilities
PO Box 750119
Arlington Heights, MA 02475-0119
E-mail: contact@disability.net
URL: http://disability.net

Description: Quarterly. Addresses persons with disabilities, their relatives and friends, and service providers through articles on education, employment, transportation, housing, legislation, equipment, and entertainment. Recurring features include a calendar of events and columns titled Resources, Sports Scoop, Book Shelf, Support Column, On Screen, To Your Health, and Disability and the law.

★12689★ **Employee Advocate**

National Employment Lawyers Association
44 Montgomery St., Ste. 2080
San Francisco, CA 94104
Ph: (415)296-7629   Fax: (415)677-9445

Description: Quarterly. Contains NELA activities, latest developments in employment law, best practice tips, briefs, and articles of interest to NELA members.

★12690★ **Employment Discrimination Law Update**

Oakstone Legal & Business Publishing
11975 Portland Ave., Ste. 110
Burnsville, MN 55337-1530
Ph: (612)808-0550   Fax: (612)808-0700
Fr: 800-365-4900

Description: Monthly. Contains judicial decisions, legislation, administrative regulations, and Law Review articles impacting employment issues, specifically on discrimination.

★12691★ **Employment Law Counselor No. 078**

Business Laws Inc.
11630 Chillicothe Rd.
Chesterland, OH 44026
Ph: (440)729-7996   Fax: (440)729-0645
Fr: 800-759-0929

Description: Monthly. Describes developments in all areas of employee relations law. Discusses such topics as Title VII, age discrimination, the Americans with Disabilities Act, reasonable accommodation, OSHA, wrongful discharge, employment contracts, drug testing, smoking in the workplace, employee benefit laws, arbitration, privacy in the workplace, and immigration laws. Recurring features include forms, checklists, policy statements, a calendar of events, case summaries, summaries of pending legislation, and the Executive Legal Summaries.

★12692★ **Employment Law Report**

Oakstone Legal & Business Publishing
11975 Portland Ave., Ste. 110
Burnsville, MN 55337-1530
Ph: (612)808-0550   Fax: (612)808-0700
Fr: 800-365-4900

Description: Monthly. Covers court cases and late-breaking legislation along with the most recent law review articles affecting employment. Summarizes federal and state appellate court decisions, with the full legal citation supplied for each case.

★12693★ **Employment Law Update**
Rutkowski & Associates Inc.
Box 15250
Evansville, IN 47716-0250
Ph: (812)476-4520

Description: Monthly. Covers legislation, court cases, and current trends in employment law. Contains sample policies.

★12694★ **Employment Law Week**
Bureau of National Affairs Inc.
1231 25th St. NW
Washington, DC 20037
Ph: (202)452-4200   Fax: (202)452-4644
Fr: 800-372-1033

Description: Weekly. Covers developments in employment law.

★12695★ **Employment Litigation Reporter**
Andrews Publications
175 Strafford Ave., Bldg. 4, Ste. 140
Wayne, PA 19087
Ph: (610)225-0510   Fax: (610)225-0501
Fr: 800-328-4880

Description: Biweekly. Reports on job termination lawsuits alleging tort and contract claims against employers. Follows pretrial, trial, and appellate proceedings and reprints complete texts of important case documents.

★12696★ **Fair Employment Practices**
Bureau of National Affairs Inc.
1231 25th St. NW
Washington, DC 20037
Ph: (202)452-4200   Fax: (202)452-4644
Fr: 800-372-1033

Description: Weekly. Provides a notification and reference service covering developments affecting fair employment practices. Includes federal laws, orders, and regulations; policy guides and discussions of federal court decisions; and state and local fair employment practice laws.

★12697★ **Fair Employment Practices Summary of Latest Developments**
Bureau of National Affairs Inc.
1231 25th St. NW
Washington, DC 20037
Ph: (202)452-4200   Fax: (202)452-4644
Fr: 800-372-1033

Description: Biweekly. Highlights developments in employment opportunity and affirmative actions, and affirmative action programs. Reports on federal and state court decisions, Equal Employment Opportunity Commission (EEOC) rulings and Office of Federal Contract Compliance Programs (OFCCP) decisions, new laws, regulations, and agency directives. Also provides information on special programs for minorities, the handicapped, women, and older workers.

★12698★ **Fair Employment Report**
Clarity Publishing
1894 Brown School Rd.
PO Box 665
St. Joseph, MI 49085
Ph: (616)429-8590   Fax: (616)429-8595

Description: Biweekly. Focuses on developments on the state and national levels regarding employment practices and discrimination. Emphasizes important legal decisions and governmental activities, particularly those of the Equal Employment Opportunity Commission, the Office of Federal Contract Compliance Programs, the Supreme Court, federal courts, Congress, state legislatures, state courts, and state agencies. Covers the efforts of businesses to comply with EEO, affirmative action, and diversity standards.

★12699★ **Florida Employment Law Letter**
M. Lee Smith Publishers L.L.C.
5201 Virginia Way
PO Box 5094
Brentwood, TN 37024-5094
Ph: (615)373-7517   Fax: 800-785-9212
Fr: 800-274-6774
URL: http://www.mleesmith.com

Description: Monthly. Addresses legal issues in employment and labor relations.

★12700★ **Georgia Employment Law Letter**
M. Lee Smith Publishers L.L.C.
5201 Virginia Way
PO Box 5094
Brentwood, TN 37024-5094
Ph: (615)373-7517   Fax: 800-785-9212
Fr: 800-274-6774
URL: http://www.mleesmith.com

Description: Monthly. Covers court cases involving employment issues. Outlines employers' legal rights and responsibilities.

★12701★ **Health Employment Law Update**
Rutkowski & Associates Inc.
Box 15250
Evansville, IN 47716-0250
Ph: (812)476-4520

Description: Monthly. Provides information on employment and labor law topics such as discrimination, drug testing, alcoholism, accommodation of the disabled, smoking rules, and employment policies. Covers current legislation and legal decisions, issues, and trends; policy concerns; and legal analysis. Recurring features include sample policies and clauses, and checklists.

★12702★ **HR Fact Finder**
Jamestown Area Labor-Management
  Committee Inc.
PO Box 819
1093 E 2 St. No. 309
Jamestown, NY 14702-0819
Ph: (716)665-3654   Fax: (716)665-8060
Fr: 800-542-7869

URL: http://www.jalmc.org

Description: Monthly. Summarizes articles from various publications on such topics as company benefits, health, the Family Leave Act, Americans with Disabilities Act, hiring practices, employment law, workers compensation, budgets, and sexual harassment.

★12703★ **HR Manager's Legal Reporter**
Ransom & Benjamin Publishers L.L.C.
PO Box 160
Mystic, CT 06355
Ph: (860)536-2000   Fax: (860)536-1545
Fr: 800-334-3352
URL: http://www.newsletters.com

Description: Monthly. Provides information, news, and how-to articles on employment law. Recurring features include columns titled Washington Watch, You Be the Judge, From the States, and In Brief.

★12704★ **Human Resources Practice Ideas**
Warren, Gorham & Lamont Inc.
117 E Stevens Ave.
Valhalla, NY 10595-1254
Fr: 800-950-1216

Description: Monthly. Provides information about employment laws and regulations.

★12705★ **Illinois Employment Law Letter**
M. Lee Smith Publishers L.L.C.
5201 Virginia Way
PO Box 5094
Brentwood, TN 37024-5094
Ph: (615)373-7517   Fax: 800-785-9212
Fr: 800-274-6774
URL: http://www.mleesmith.com

Description: Monthly. Addresses Illinois legislation and court decisions affecting employment issues.

★12706★ **Indiana Employment Law Letter**
M. Lee Smith Publishers L.L.C.
5201 Virginia Way
PO Box 5094
Brentwood, TN 37024-5094
Ph: (615)373-7517   Fax: 800-785-9212
Fr: 800-274-6774
URL: http://www.mleesmith.com

Description: Monthly. Contains legal information pertinent to employers in Indiana.

★12707★ **Kentucky Employment Law Letter**
M. Lee Smith Publishers L.L.C.
5201 Virginia Way
PO Box 5094
Brentwood, TN 37024-5094
Ph: (615)373-7517   Fax: 800-785-9212
Fr: 800-274-6774
URL: http://www.mleesmith.com

Description: Monthly. Addresses the legal rights of employees and obligations of employers as dictated by Kentucky law. Contains case summaries.

★12708★ **Labor and Employment Law**

Section of Labor and Employment Law
750 N Lake Shore Dr.
Chicago, IL 60611-3319
Ph: (312)988-6076   Fax: (312)988-6081

Description: Quarterly. Discusses labor and employment law. Recurring features include a calendar of events, reports of meetings, news of educational opportunities, and notices of publications available.

★12709★ **Labor & Employment Law Section Newsletter**

New York State Bar Association
1 Elk St.
Albany, NY 12207
Ph: (518)463-3200   Fax: (518)463-8844
Fr: 800-582-2452

Description: Four issues/year. Provides topical information about labor and employment law. Recurring features include chair's comments, article from the editor, cartoon, biographical updates, and columns titled Ethics Matters and Legislative Update.

★12710★ **Labor Relations Bulletin**

Bureau of Business Practice
125 Eugene O'Neill Dr., Ste. 103
New London, CT 06320
Ph: (860)442-4365   Fax: (860)437-3150
Fr: 800-876-9105
URL: http://www.bbpnews.com

Description: Quarterly. Provides information and insight to management and labor officials to help them avoid or resolve conflicts. Recurring features include reports on current developments in labor law and relations, discipline and grievance cases based on actual arbitration, a question and answer column on labor and employment relations, and a column titled Reflections of an Arbitrator, offering the insight and experience of prominent national arbitrators.

★12711★ **Louisiana Employment Law Letter**

M. Lee Smith Publishers L.L.C.
5201 Virginia Way
PO Box 5094
Brentwood, TN 37024-5094
Ph: (615)373-7517   Fax: 800-785-9212
Fr: 800-274-6774
URL: http://www.mleesmith.com

Description: Monthly. Addresses legislation and court decisions affecting employment issues.

★12712★ **Managing Today's Federal Employees**

LRP Publications
747 Dresher Rd., Ste. 500
PO Box 980
Horsham, PA 19044
Ph: (215)784-0910   Fax: (215)784-0870
Fr: 800-341-7874

Description: Monthly. Provides information about federal employment law concerning government employees.

★12713★ **Maryland Employment Law Letter**

M. Lee Smith Publishers L.L.C.
5201 Virginia Way
PO Box 5094
Brentwood, TN 37024-5094
Ph: (615)373-7517   Fax: 800-785-9212
Fr: 800-274-6774
URL: http://www.mleesmith.com

Description: Monthly. Covers Maryland laws and court cases involving employment-related issues.

★12714★ **Massachusetts Employment Law Letter**

M. Lee Smith Publishers L.L.C.
5201 Virginia Way
PO Box 5094
Brentwood, TN 37024-5094
Ph: (615)373-7517   Fax: 800-785-9212
Fr: 800-274-6774
URL: http://www.mleesmith.com

Description: Monthly. Addresses legal issues of interest to employers and employees in Massachusetts.

★12715★ **Michigan Employment Law Letter**

M. Lee Smith Publishers L.L.C.
5201 Virginia Way
PO Box 5094
Brentwood, TN 37024-5094
Ph: (615)373-7517   Fax: 800-785-9212
Fr: 800-274-6774
URL: http://www.mleesmith.com

Description: Monthly. Addresses employers' legal responsibilities and employee rights as dictated by Michigan law.

★12716★ **Minnesota Employment Law Letter**

M. Lee Smith Publishers L.L.C.
5201 Virginia Way
PO Box 5094
Brentwood, TN 37024-5094
Ph: (615)373-7517   Fax: 800-785-9212
Fr: 800-274-6774
URL: http://www.mleesmith.com

Description: Monthly. Contains analysis of issues regarding employment law in Minnesota.

★12717★ **Missouri Employment Law Letter**

M. Lee Smith Publishers L.L.C.
5201 Virginia Way
PO Box 5094
Brentwood, TN 37024-5094
Ph: (615)373-7517   Fax: 800-785-9212
Fr: 800-274-6774
URL: http://www.mleesmith.com

Description: Monthly. Presents issues in Missouri employment law.

★12718★ **National Partnership News**

National Partnership for Women & Families
1875 Connecticut Ave. NW, Ste. 650
Washington, DC 20009
Ph: (202)986-2600   Fax: (202)986-2539
URL: http://www.nationalpartnership.org

Description: Four issues/year. Monitors developments in employment discrimination, reproductive health, family leave policies, quality health care issues, and areas of sex discrimination law that affect women's status. Contains updates on the organization's services and activities and discussions of women's rights issues.

★12719★ **New Jersey Employment Law Letter**

M. Lee Smith Publishers L.L.C.
5201 Virginia Way
PO Box 5094
Brentwood, TN 37024-5094
Ph: (615)373-7517   Fax: 800-785-9212
Fr: 800-274-6774
URL: http://www.mleesmith.com

Description: Monthly. Addresses legislation and court decisions affecting employment issues.

★12720★ **New Jersey Labor and Employment Law Quarterly**

New Jersey State Bar Association
New Jersey Law Ctr.
1 Constitution Sq.
New Brunswick, NJ 08901-1500
Ph: (732)249-5000   Fax: (732)828-0034

Description: Quarterly. Deals with labor and employment legal matters and legislation in New Jersey, including grievances, mediation, and arbitration. Recurring features include Section news and columns titled Editor's Corner and Director's Corner.

★12721★ **North Carolina Employment Law Letter**

M. Lee Smith Publishers L.L.C.
5201 Virginia Way
PO Box 5094
Brentwood, TN 37024-5094
Ph: (615)373-7517   Fax: 800-785-9212
Fr: 800-274-6774
URL: http://www.mleesmith.com

Description: Monthly. Contains information on court cases and legislation affecting employment law in North Carolina.

★12722★ Ohio Employment Law Letter
M. Lee Smith Publishers L.L.C.
5201 Virginia Way
PO Box 5094
Brentwood, TN 37024-5094
Ph: (615)373-7517   Fax: 800-785-9212
Fr: 800-274-6774
URL: http://www.mleesmith.com
Description: Monthly. Addresses legal issues of interest to Ohio employers.

★12723★ Oklahoma Employment Law Letter
M. Lee Smith Publishers L.L.C.
5201 Virginia Way
PO Box 5094
Brentwood, TN 37024-5094
Ph: (615)373-7517   Fax: 800-785-9212
Fr: 800-274-6774
Description: Monthly. Addresses legislation and court decisions affecting employment issues.

★12724★ Payroll Administration Guide
Bureau of National Affairs Inc.
1231 25th St. NW
Washington, DC 20037
Ph: (202)452-4200   Fax: (202)452-4644
Fr: 800-372-1033
Description: Biweekly. Concerned with federal and state employment tax, and wage-hour and wage-payment laws.

★12725★ Payroll Legal Alert
Alexander Hamilton Institute
70 Hilltop Rd.
Ramsey, NJ 07446-1119
Ph: (201)825-3377   Fax: (201)825-8696
Fr: 800-879-2441
E-mail: payla@ahipubs.com
Description: Monthly. Covers aspects of payroll operations, including key tax and benefits laws, regulations, rulings, and cases. Includes new trends in tax law, ideas on benefits, wage and hour traps, and unemployment issues.

★12726★ Pennsylvania Employment Law Letter
M. Lee Smith Publishers L.L.C.
5201 Virginia Way
PO Box 5094
Brentwood, TN 37024-5094
Ph: (615)373-7517   Fax: 800-785-9212
Fr: 800-274-6774
URL: http://www.mleesmith.com
Description: Monthly. Details court cases and laws affecting employer/employee rights and responsibilities in Pennsylvania.

★12727★ Personnel Legal Alert
Alexander Hamilton Institute
70 Hilltop Rd.
Ramsey, NJ 07446-1119
Ph: (201)825-3377   Fax: (201)825-8696
Fr: 800-879-2441

E-mail: pla@ahipubs.com
URL: http://www.ahipubs.com
Description: Semimonthly. Provides information about employment law. Topics include court opinions and government regulations.

★12728★ Personnel Management
Bureau of National Affairs Inc.
1231 25th St. NW
Washington, DC 20037
Ph: (202)452-4200   Fax: (202)452-4644
Fr: 800-372-1033
Description: Weekly. Provides legal clarification and practical advice on employers' pay and benefit policies, including detailed discussions of pertinent federal and state laws. Discusses such topics as health care compensation laws, pension law (ERISA), job evaluation, benefit plans, compensation administration, incentive systems, and independent contractors. Part of the BNA Policy and Practice Series; can be purchased alone or in any combination with other binder sets titled Compensation, Fair Employment Practices, Wages and Hours, and Labor Relations.

★12729★ Planning Newsletter
Sachnoff & Weaver Ltd.
30 S Wacker Dr., No. 2900
Chicago, IL 60606
Ph: (312)207-1000   Fax: (312)207-6400
Description: Quarterly. Reviews developments in a variety of areas of law affecting closely-held businesses, including labor and employment issues, tax issues, intellectual property, and employee benefits. Discusses recent court decisions and new laws passed.

★12730★ Public Employment Law Report
Oakstone Legal & Business Publishing
11975 Portland Ave., Ste. 110
Burnsville, MN 55337-1530
Ph: (612)808-0550   Fax: (612)808-0700
Fr: 800-365-4900
Description: Monthly. Reports court cases and late-breaking legislation along with the most recent law review articles affecting public employment. Summarizes federal and state appellate court decisions, with the full legal citation supplied for each case.

★12731★ South Carolina Employment Law Letter
M. Lee Smith Publishers L.L.C.
5201 Virginia Way
PO Box 5094
Brentwood, TN 37024-5094
Ph: (615)373-7517   Fax: 800-785-9212
Fr: 800-274-6774
URL: http://www.mleesmith.com
Description: Monthly. Addresses legislation and court decisions affecting employment issues.

★12732★ State Labor Laws
Bureau of National Affairs Inc.
1231 25th St. NW
Washington, DC 20037
Ph: (202)452-4200   Fax: (202)452-4644
Fr: 800-372-1033
URL: http://www.bna.com
Description: Biweekly. Provides full texts, digests, and charts of state labor laws, covering their scope, jurisdiction, administration, and enforcement. Also discusses how state labor law relates to federal laws affecting labor relations and employment regulation and provides directories of state agencies that administer and enforce these laws. Self-contained reference service that is also available as part of Labor Relations Reporter or in any combination with other LRRM sets titled "Summary and Analysis" and "Labor Relations Expediter."

★12733★ Supervisors Legal Update
Progressive Business Publications
370 Technology Dr.
Malvern, PA 19355
Ph: (610)695-8600   Fax: (610)647-8089
Fr: 800-220-5000
URL: http://www.pbp.com
Description: Semimonthly. Supplies brief updates on employment law for supervisors. Review a column titled Sharpen Your Judgment.

★12734★ Tennessee Employment Law Update
M. Lee Smith Publishers L.L.C.
5201 Virginia Way
PO Box 5094
Brentwood, TN 37024-5094
Ph: (615)373-7517   Fax: 800-785-9212
Fr: 800-274-6774
Description: Monthly. Profiles legal issues of interest to employers in Tennessee.

★12735★ Texas Employment Law Letter
M. Lee Smith Publishers L.L.C.
5201 Virginia Way
PO Box 5094
Brentwood, TN 37024-5094
Ph: (615)373-7517   Fax: 800-785-9212
Fr: 800-274-6774
URL: http://www.mleesmith.com
Description: Monthly. Covers laws and legislation affecting Texas employers.

★12736★ Unemployment Insurance Reports with Social Security
CCH Inc.
2700 Lake Cook Rd.
Riverwoods, IL 60015
Ph: (847)267-7000   Fax: (847)267-2945
Fr: 888-224-7377
URL: http://www.cch.com
Description: Weekly. Issues of CCH's Unemployment Insurance Reports with Social Security provide timely information on social security and federal/state unemployment

insurance taxes, coverage, and benefits. Pertinent federal and state laws are reported promptly and reflected in place in the explanatory guides, as are regulations, judicial and administrative decisions, rulings, releases, and forms. Explanatory guides include examples showing how rules apply and offer practical information regarding the tax management, coverage, and benefit aspects of the social security and unemployment insurance systems.

★12737★ **Virginia Employment Law Letter**

M. Lee Smith Publishers L.L.C.
5201 Virginia Way
PO Box 5094
Brentwood, TN 37024-5094
Ph: (615)373-7517   Fax: 800-785-9212
Fr: 800-274-6774

URL: http://www.mleesmith.com

Description: Monthly. Examines legal issues pertinent to employers in Virginia.

★12738★ **What's Working in Human Resources**

Progressive Business Publications
370 Technology Dr.
Malvern, PA 19355
Ph: (610)695-8600   Fax: (610)647-8089
Fr: 800-220-5000

Description: Semimonthly. Reports on the latest trends in Human Resources, including the latest employment law rulings. Recurring features include interviews, news of research, a calendar of events, news of educational opportunities, and a column titlted Sharpen Your Judgment.

★12739★ **You & the Law**

National Institute of Business Management
1750 Old Meadow Rd., Ste. 302
McLean, VA 22102
Ph: (703)905-8000   Fax: (703)905-8042
Fr: 800-543-2049
E-mail: customer@nibm.net

Description: Monthly. Covers the employment law area. Provides information for managers and business owners interested in the relationship between the law and their business.

Looking to Relocate

REFERENCE WORKS

★12740★ Atlanta JobBank

Adams Media Corp.
57 Littlefield St.
Avon, MA 02322
Ph: (508)427-7100   Fax: (508)427-6790
Fr: 800-872-5627
URL: http://www.adamsmedia.com/reference

$17.95. Covers 3,900 employers in the state of Georgia, including Albany, Columbus, Macon, and Savannah. Entries include: Firm or organization name, address, local phone, toll-free phone, fax, description of organization, subsidiaries, other locations, recorded jobline, name and title of contact, typical titles for common positions, educational backgrounds desired, number of employees, benefits offered, training programs, internships, parent company, revenues, e-mail and URL address, projected number of hires. Arrangement: Classified by industry. Indexes: Alphabetical.

★12741★ Baltimore Job Source: Everything You Need to Know to Land the Internship, Entry-Level, or Middle Management Job of Your Choice

Benjamin Scott Publishing
20 E. Colorado Blvd., No. 202
Pasadena, CA 91105
Ph: (626)449-1339   Fax: (626)449-1389
Fr: 800-448-4959

Mary McMahon, Parker Webb, Ruth E. Thaler-Carter and Betty Glascoe. 1996. $15.95. 308 pages.

★12742★ Boston JobBank

Adams Media Corp.
57 Littlefield St.
Avon, MA 02322
Ph: (508)427-7100   Fax: (508)427-6790
Fr: 800-872-5627
URL: http://www.adamsmedia.com/reference

Annual. $16.95. Covers over 7,000 employ-

ers in Massachusetts. Entries include: Firm or organization name, address, local phone, toll-free phone, fax, e-mail, URL, recorded jobline, hours, names of management, name and title of contact, titles of common positions, entry-level positions, fringe benefits offered, stock exchange listing, description of organization, subsidiaries, location of headquarters, educational background desired, projected number of hires, training programs, internships, parent company, number of employees, revenues, other U.S. locations, international locations. Arrangement: Classified by industry. Indexes: Alphabetical.

★12743★ California Job Journal

California Job Journal
2033 Howe Ave., Ste. 100
Sacramento, CA 95825
Ph: (916)925-0800   Fax: (916)925-0101
Fr: 800-655-5627
E-mail: cjj@jobjournal.com
URL: http://www.jobjournal.com

Weekly. $135.00. Covers employment issues and job openings in California from entry-level to executive positions. Entries include: Company name, address, phone, type of business, name and title of contact; comprehensive description of position and required skills/background, salary and/or benefits offered. Arrangement: Classified by field of employment.

★12744★ Carolina JobBank

Adams Media Corp.
57 Littlefield St.
Avon, MA 02322
Ph: (508)427-7100   Fax: (508)427-6790
Fr: 800-872-5627
URL: http://www.adamsmedia.com/reference

$16.95. Covers 4,600 employers in North Carolina and South Carolina. Entries include: Firm or organization name, address, local phone, toll-free phone, fax, e-mail, URL, recorded jobline, description of organization, subsidiaries, other locations, hours, names of management, name and title of contact, location of headquarters, typical titles for common positions, educational

backgrounds desired, projected number of hires, company benefits, stock exchange listing, training programs and internships, parent company, number of employees, revenues. Arrangement: Classified by industry. Indexes: Alphabetical.

★12745★ Central Florida Career Guide

Edge Publishing
2175 N Forsyth Rd.
Orlando, FL 32807-5262
Fax: (407)673-9981

Semiannual, January and November. $19.95. Covers employment needs of over 400 firms in the Orlando metropolitan area. Entries include: Company name, address, phone, name and title of contact, number of employees, products or services provided, staffing needs. Arrangement: Classified by line of business.

★12746★ Chicago JobBank

Adams Media Corp.
57 Littlefield St.
Avon, MA 02322
Ph: (508)427-7100   Fax: (508)427-6790
Fr: 800-872-5627
URL: http://www.adamsmedia.com/reference

Annual. $16.95. Covers about 5,500 major employers in northern and central Illinois including Aurora, Peoria, Rockford, and Springfield. Entries include: Firm or organization name, address, local phone, toll-free phone, fax, e-mail, URL, description of organization, hours, recorded jobline, subsidiaries, names of management, name and title of contact, names of management, headquarters locations, typical titles for entry-level and middle-level positions, educational backgrounds desired, company benefits, stock exchange listing, training programs, internships, parent company, number of employees, revenues, other U.S. locations, international locations. Arrangement: Classified by industry. Indexes: Alphabetical.

★12747★ Craighead's International Business, Travel, and Relocation Guide to 81 Countries

Thomson Gale
27500 Drake Rd.
Farmington Hills, MI 48331-3535
Ph: (248)699-GALE   Fax: (248)699-8069
Fr: 800-877-GALE
E-mail: galeord@gale.com
URL: http://www.galegroup.com

First edition, 2002. $750.00. 5,180 pages. Arranged geographically into regions of Asia, Africa, Europe, the Mideast, and the Americas. Profiles include information on maps, statistics, travel restrictions, currency, transportation, and health. A separate section covers details of international travel such as instructions for passports and visas and information on transportation and shopping. An international relocation chapter covers financial planning, legal matters, insurance, education, housing, and other family concerns.

★12748★ Dallas/Ft. Worth JobBank

Adams Media Corp.
57 Littlefield St.
Avon, MA 02322
Ph: (508)427-7100   Fax: (508)427-6790
Fr: 800-872-5627
URL: http://www.adamsmedia.com/reference

Annual. $17.95. Covers 4,000 employers in the Dallas/Ft. Worth, Texas, area including Abilene, Amarillo, Arlington, Garland, Irving, Lubbock, Plano. Entries include: Firm or organization name, address, local phone, toll-free phone, fax, e-mail, URL, recorded jobline, hours, description of organization, subsidiaries, names of management, name and title of contact, location of headquarters, typical titles for common positions, educational backgrounds desired, company benefits, stock exchange listing, training programs, internships, parent company, number of employees, revenues, projected number of hires. Arrangement: Classified by industry. Indexes: Alphabetical.

★12749★ Denver JobBank

Adams Media Corp.
57 Littlefield St.
Avon, MA 02322
Ph: (508)427-7100   Fax: (508)427-6790
Fr: 800-872-5627
URL: http://www.adamsmedia.com/reference

$16.95. Covers 3,500 employers in Denver and the rest of Colorado including Aurora, Boulder, Colorado Springs, Lakewood. Entries include: Firm or organization name, address, local phone, toll-free phone, fax, e-mail, URL, description of organization, subsidiaries, other locations, hours, recorded jobline, names of management, name and title of contact, headquarters location, projected number of hires; listings may also include typical titles for common positions, educational backgrounds desired, company benefits, stock exchange listing, training programs, internships, parent company, number of employees, revenues. Arrange-

ment: Classified by industry. Indexes: Alphabetical.

★12750★ Detroit JobBank

Adams Media Corp.
57 Littlefield St.
Avon, MA 02322
Ph: (508)427-7100   Fax: (508)427-6790
Fr: 800-872-5627
URL: http://www.adamsmedia.com/reference

Annual. $16.95. Covers 4,200 employers throughout Michigan including Dearborn, Flint, Grand Rapids, Lansing. Entries include: Firm or organization name, address, local phone, toll-free phone, fax, e-mail, URL, recorded jobline, description of organization, other locations, subsidiaries, names of management, name and title of contact, location of headquarters, typical titles for common positions, educational backgrounds desired, projected number of hires, company benefits, stock exchange listing, training programs, internships, parent company, number of employees, revenues. Arrangement: Classified by industry. Indexes: Alphabetical.

★12751★ Florida JobBank

Adams Media Corp.
57 Littlefield St.
Avon, MA 02322
Ph: (508)427-7100   Fax: (508)427-6790
Fr: 800-872-5627
URL: http://www.adamsmedia.com/reference

$16.95. Covers 5,500 employers in Florida including Fort Lauderdale, Jacksonville, Miami, Orlando, Tampa. Entries include: Firm or organization name, address, local phone, toll-free phone, fax, e-mail addresses, web addresses, description of organization, subsidiaries, hours, recorded jobline, name and title of contact, headquarters location, typical titles for common positions, educational backgrounds desired, number of projected hires, company benefits, stock exchange listing, training programs, internships, parent company, number of employees, revenues, other U.S. locations, international locations. Arrangement: Classified by industry. Indexes: Alphabetical.

★12752★ Greater Orlando Major Employers Guide

Greater Orlando Chamber of Commerce
75 S. Ivanhoe Blvd.
PO Box 1234
Orlando, FL 32804
Ph: (407)425-1234   Fax: (407)839-5020
URL: http://www.orlando.org

Latest edition 2001, previous edition 1992. $25.99. Covers over 500 firms in metropolitan Orlando that have 100 or more employees. Entries include: Company name, address, phone, Standard Industrial Classification (SIC) code, name and title of contacts, number of employees. Arrangement: Alphabetical. Indexes: Line of business.

★12753★ Greater Philadelphia JobBank

Adams Media Corp.
57 Littlefield St.
Avon, MA 02322
Ph: (508)427-7100   Fax: (508)427-6790
Fr: 800-872-5627
URL: http://www.adamsmedia.com/reference

Annual. $16.95. Covers 5,200 employers in the metropolitan Philadelphia, the eastern half of Pennsylvania, and southern New Jersey, and Delaware. Entries include: Firm or organization name, address, phone, description of organization, name and title of contact, typical titles for entry-level and middle-level positions, educational backgrounds desired, company benefits, stock exchange listing, training programs, internships, parent company, number of employees, revenues, world wide web address, e-mail address, corporate headquarters, and projected number of hires for this location in the next year. Arrangement: Classified by industry. Indexes: Alphabetical.

★12754★ Houston JobBank

Adams Media Corp.
57 Littlefield St.
Avon, MA 02322
Ph: (508)427-7100   Fax: (508)427-6790
Fr: 800-872-5627
URL: http://www.adamsmedia.com/reference

Annual. $16.95. Covers over 3,500 employers in Houston, Texas and the surrounding areas including Bayton, Beaumont, Galveston, Pasadena. Entries include: Firm or organization name, address, local phone, toll-free phone, fax, recorded jobline, e-mail, URL, hours, name and title of contact; description of organization; headquarters location, subsidiaries, operations at the facility, names of management, typical titles for common positions, educational backgrounds desired, number of projected hires, fringe benefits offered, stock exchange listing, training programs, internships, parent company, number of employees, revenues, other U.S. locations, international locations. Arrangement: Classified by industry. Indexes: Alphabetical.

★12755★ How to Get a Job in Atlanta

Surrey Books, Inc.
230 E. Ohio St., Ste. 120
Chicago, IL 60611
Ph: (312)751-7330   Fax: (312)751-7334
Fr: 800-326-4430

Robert Sanborn, A. Tariq Shakoor and Rosita Jackson. Fourth edition, 1997. $16.95 (paper). 450 pages. Directory of employers, associations, job referral services, and other sources of employment information. Part of How to get a Job series.

★12756★ How to Get a Job in Boston, or Anywhere Else
The Globe Pequot Press
PO Box 480
Guilford, CT 06437-0480
Fax: 800-820-2329   Fr: 800-243-0495
Renee Levine. Fourth edition, revised, 1983. $7.95. 146 pages. Out of print. (paper). 456 pages. Directory of employers, associations, job referral services, and other sources of employment information.

★12757★ How to Get a Job in Chicago
Surrey Books, Inc.
230 E. Ohio St., Ste. 120
Chicago, IL 60611
Ph: (312)751-7330   Fax: (312)751-7334
Fr: 800-326-4430
Robert Sanborn and Susan Schwartz. Eighth edition, 2000. $18.95 (paper). 459 pages. Directory of employers, associations, job referral services, and other sources of employment information. Out of print. Part of How to get a Job series.

★12758★ How to Get a Job in Dallas and Fort Worth
Surrey Books, Inc.
230 E. Ohio St., Ste. 120
Chicago, IL 60611
Ph: (312)751-7330   Fax: (312)751-7334
Fr: 800-326-4430
Robert Sanborn and Richard Citrin. Sixth edition, 1998. $17.95 (paper). 456 pages. Directory of employers, associations, job referral services, and other sources of employment information.

★12759★ How to Get a Job in Denver and Central Colorado
Surrey Books, Inc.
230 E. Ohio St., Ste. 120
Chicago, IL 60611
Ph: (312)751-7330   Fax: (312)751-7334
Fr: 800-326-4430
Robert Sanborn and Christopher Ott. 1999. $18.95 (paper). 363 pages. Directory of employers, associations, job referral services, and other sources of employment information. Part of How to get a Job series.

★12760★ How to Get a Job in Europe
Surrey Books, Inc.
230 E. Ohio St., Ste. 120
Chicago, IL 60611
Ph: (312)751-7330   Fax: (312)751-7334
Fr: 800-326-4430
Robert Sanborn and Cheryl Matherly. Fifth edition, 2001. Directory of employers, associations, job referral services, and other sources of employment information. Part of Insider's Guide series.

★12761★ How to Get a Job in Houston
Surrey Books, Inc.
230 E. Ohio St., Ste. 120
Chicago, IL 60611
Ph: (312)751-7330   Fax: (312)751-7334
Fr: 800-326-4430
Robert Sanborn and Thomas M. Camden. Second edition, 1993. $15.95. 400 pages. Out of print. Directory of employers, associations, job referral services, and other sources of employment information. Part of How to get a Job series.

★12762★ How to Get a Job in New York City and the Metropolitan Area
Surrey Books, Inc.
230 E. Ohio St.. Ste. 120
Chicago, IL 60611
Ph: (312)751-7330   Fax: (312)751-7334
Fr: 800-326-4430
Robert Sanborn and Eva Lederman. Sixth edition, 1998. $17.95 (paper). 360 pages. Directory of employers, associations, job referral services, and other sources of employment information. Part of Insider's Guide series.

★12763★ How to Get a Job in the San Francisco Bay Area
Surrey Books, Inc.
230 E. Ohio St., Ste. 120
Chicago, IL 60611
Ph: (312)751-7330   Fax: (312)751-7334
Fr: 800-326-4430
Robert Sanborn and Will Flowers. Fifth edition, 1998. $17.95 (paper). 460 pages. Directory of employers, associations, job referral services, and other sources of employment information. Part of Insider's Guide series.

★12764★ How to Get a Job in Seattle/Portland
Surrey Books, Inc.
230 E. Ohio St., Ste. 120
Chicago, IL 60611
Ph: (312)751-7330   Fax: (312)751-7334
Fr: 800-326-4430
Robert Sanborn and Marc Snyder. Third edition, 1996. $16.95 (paper). 492 pages. Directory of employers, associations, job referral services, and other sources of employment information. Part of Insider's Guide series. Out of print.

★12765★ How to Get a Job in Southern California
Surrey Books, Inc.
230 E. Ohio St., Ste. 120
Chicago, IL 60611
Ph: (312)751-7330   Fax: (312)751-7334
Fr: 800-326-4430
Robert Sanborn and Naomi Sandweiss. Seventh edition, 1999. $18.95 (paper). 330 pages. Directory of employers, associations, job referral services, and other sources of employment information. Part of How to get a Job series.

★12766★ How to Get a Job in Washington, D.C.
Surrey Books, Inc.
230 E. Ohio St., Ste. 120
Chicago, IL 60611
Ph: (312)751-7330   Fax: (312)751-7334
Fr: 800-326-4430
Thomas M. Camden and Kathy Strawser. Second edition, 1993. $15.95 (paper). 380 pages. Out of print. Directory of employers, associations, job referral services, and other sources of employment information. Part of How to get a Job series.

★12767★ Job Relocation: Managing People on the Move
John Wiley & Sons Inc.
1 Wiley Dr.
Somerset, NJ 08873
Ph: (732)469-4400   Fr: 800-225-5945
Anthony G. Munton. 1993. $60.00 (paper). 184 pages. Out of print.

★12768★ Los Angeles JobBank
Adams Media Corp.
57 Littlefield St.
Avon, MA 02322
Ph: (508)427-7100   Fax: (508)427-6790
Fr: 800-872-5627
URL: http://www.adamsmedia.com/reference
Annual. $16.95. Covers over 7,900 southern California employers including Orange, Riverside, San Bernadino, San Diego, Santa Barbara and Ventura counties. Entries include: Firm or organization name, address, local phone, toll-free phone, fax, e-mail, URL, recorded jobline, hours, subsidiaries, other locations, names of management, name and title of contact, description of organization, number of employees, headquarters location, typical titles for common positions, educational backgrounds desired, fringe benefits offered, stock exchange listing, training programs, internships, parent company, number of employees, revenues, corporate headquarters, and number of projected hires. Arrangement: Classified by industry. Indexes: Alphabetical.

★12769★ Metro New York JobBank
Adams Media Corp.
57 Littlefield St.
Avon, MA 02322
Ph: (508)427-7100   Fax: (508)427-6790
Fr: 800-872-5627
URL: http://www.adamsmedia.com/reference
$16.95. Covers over 7,900 New York City Northern New Jersey, Southwestern Connecticut, Long Island, and Westchester employers. Entries include: Firm or organization name, address, local phone, toll-free phone, fax, e-mail, URL, recorded jobline, hours, name and title of contact; description of organization, subsidiaries, other locations,

names of management, headquarters location, typical titles for common positions, educational backgrounds desired, fringe benefits offered, stock exchange listing, training programs, internships, parent company, number of employees, revenues, projected number of hires. Arrangement: Classified by industry. Indexes: Alphabetical.

★12770★ **Metro Washington DC JobBank**
Adams Media Corp.
57 Littlefield St.
Avon, MA 02322
Ph: (508)427-7100   Fax: (508)427-6790
Fr: 800-872-5627
URL: http://www.adamsmedia.com/reference

$17.95. Covers 6,900 employers in Washington, D.C., greater Baltimore, and northern Virginia. Entries include: Firm or organization name, address, local phone, toll-free phone, fax, recorded jobline, name and title of contact, description of organization, subsidiaries, other locations, names of management, hours, titles for common positions, educational backgrounds desired, company benefits, stock exchange listing, location of headquarters, training programs, internships, parent company, number of employees, revenues, email and URL address, projected number of hires. Arrangement: Classified by industry. Indexes: Alphabetical.

★12771★ **Minneapolis/St. Paul JobBank**
Adams Media Corp.
57 Littlefield St.
Avon, MA 02322
Ph: (508)427-7100   Fax: (508)427-6790
Fr: 800-872-5627
URL: http://www.adamsmedia.com/reference

$16.95. Covers approximately 2,800 employers in Minneapolis-St. Paul, Minnesota including the Twin Cities, Duluth, and Rochester. Entries include: Firm or organization name, address, local phone, toll-free phone, fax, e-mail, URL, description of organization, subsidiaries, other locations, recorded jobline, hours, names of management, name and title of contact, location of headquarters, typical titles for common positions, educational backgrounds desired, projected number of hires, company benefits, stock exchange listing, training programs, internships, parent company, number of employees, revenues. Arrangement: Classified by industry. Indexes: Alphabetical.

★12772★ **Missouri JobBank**
Adams Media Corp.
57 Littlefield St.
Avon, MA 02322
Ph: (508)427-7100   Fax: (508)427-6790
Fr: 800-872-5627
URL: http://www.adamsmedia.com/reference

$16.95. Covers 3,700 employers in Missouri, Southern Illinois, and the Kansas City area. Entries include: Firm or organization name, address, local phone, toll-free phone, fax, e-

mail, URL, recorded jobline, hours, description of organization, name and title of contact, location of headquarters, typical titles for entry-level and middle-level positions, educational backgrounds desired, projected number of hires, company benefits, stock exchange listing, training programs, internships, parent company, projected hiring, number of employees, revenues. Arrangement: Classified by industry. Indexes: Alphabetical.

★12773★ **Multinational Firms & International Relocation**
Edward Elgar Publishing, Inc.
136 West ST., Ste. 202
Northampton, MA 01060
Ph: (413)584-5551   Fax: (413)584-9933
Peter J. Buckley and Jean Louis Mucchielli, editors. 1997. 272 pages. $90.00.

★12774★ **National JobBank**
Adams Media Corp.
57 Littlefield St.
Avon, MA 02322
Ph: (508)427-7100   Fax: (508)427-6790
Fr: 800-872-5627
URL: http://www.adamsmedia.com/reference

Annual. $450.00. Covers over 20,000 employers nationwide. Entries include: Firm or organization name, address, local phone, toll-free phone, fax, contact name and title, description of organization, headquarters location, names of management, number of employees, other locations, subsidiaries, parent company, projected number of hires, training offered, internships, hours, recorded jobline, typical titles for common positions, educational backgrounds desired, stock exchange (if listed), fringe benefits offered. Several state and regional volumes are available and described separately. Arrangement: Geographical. Indexes: Geographical and classified by industry.

★12775★ **Nevada in Your Future: The Complete Relocation Guide for Job-Seekers, Retirees and Snowbirds**
DiscoverGuides
P.O. Box 231954
Las Vegas, NV 89123
Ph: (702)558-8242   Fax: (702)558-4355
Don W. Martin and Betty W. Martin. 2000.

★12776★ **The New Relocating Spouse's Guide to Employment**
Impact Publications
9104 Manassas Dr., Ste. N
Manassas Park, VA 20111-5211
Ph: (703)361-7300   Fax: (703)335-9486
URL: http://www.impactpublications.com/

Irregular, previous edition 1989, latest edition 1993. $14.95. Publication includes: List of 133 professional associations and 54 federal job centers. Entries include: Organization name, address, phone. Principal content of publication is discussion of the job market, employment trends, and other useful

information for those facing a move to a city where they have no job waiting. Arrangement: Alphabetical.

★12777★ **Phoenix JobBank**
Adams Media Corp.
57 Littlefield St.
Avon, MA 02322
Ph: (508)427-7100   Fax: (508)427-6790
Fr: 800-872-5627
URL: http://www.adamsmedia.com/reference

$16.95. Covers 2,100 employers in the Arizona, area including Tucson, Phoenix, Flagstaff, and Yuma. Entries include: Firm or organization name, address, local phone, toll-free phone, fax, e-mail, URL, recorded jobline, description of organization, hours, names of management, name and title of contact, location of headquarters, typical titles for common positions, educational backgrounds desired, projected number of hires, company benefits, stock exchange listing, training programs, internships, parent company, number of employees, revenues. Arrangement: Classified by industry. Indexes: Alphabetical.

★12778★ **San Francisco Bay Area JobBank**
Adams Media Corp.
57 Littlefield St.
Avon, MA 02322
Ph: (508)427-7100   Fax: (508)427-6790
Fr: 800-872-5627
URL: http://www.adamsmedia.com/reference

$16.95. Covers about 5,600 employers in the San Francisco Bay area and the Northern half of California including Oakland, Sacramento, San Jose, and Silicon Valley. Entries include: Firm or organization name, address, local phone, toll-free phone, fax, e-mail, URL, recorded jobline, hours, description of organization, subsidiaries, other locations, number of employees, name and title of contact, headquarters location, typical titles for common positions, educational backgrounds desired, company benefits, stock exchange listing, training programs, internships, parent company, number of employees, revenues, corporate headquarters, and number of projected hires. Arrangement: Classified by industry. Indexes: Alphabetical.

★12779★ **Seattle JobBank**
Adams Media Corp.
57 Littlefield St.
Avon, MA 02322
Ph: (508)427-7100   Fax: (508)427-6790
Fr: 800-872-5627
URL: http://www.adamsmedia.com/reference

$17.95. Covers about 4,800 employers in Washington state, including Spokane, Tacoma, and Bellevue. Entries include: Firm or organization name, address, local phone, toll-free phone, fax, e-mail, URL, description of organization, subsidiaries, name and title of contact, headquarters location, recorded jobline, typical titles for common positions, educational backgrounds desired, projected number of hires, company benefits, stock exchange listing, training programs, internships, parent company, number of employees, revenues. Arrangement: Classified by industry. Indexes: Alphabetical.

★12780★ Tennessee JobBank
Adams Media Corp.
57 Littlefield St.
Avon, MA 02322
Ph: (508)427-7100   Fax: (508)427-6790
Fr: 800-872-5627
URL: http://www.adamsmedia.com/conference

Biennial. $16.95. Covers 2,700 employers in Tennessee, including Chattanooga, Knoxville, Memphis, and Nashville. Entries include: Firm or organization name, address, local phone, toll-free phone, fax, e-mail, URL, recorded jobline, description of organization, subsidiaries, hours, names of management, name and title of contact, location of headquarters, typical titles for common positions, educational backgrounds desired, projected number of hires, company benefits, stock exchange listing, training programs, internships, parent company, number of employees, revenues. Arrangement: Classified by industry. Indexes: Alphabetical.

NEWSPAPERS, MAGAZINES, AND JOURNALS

★12781★ Arizona Business Gazette
Phoenix Newspapers Inc.
200 E Van Buren St.
Phoenix, AZ 85004-2238
Ph: (602)444-8000   Fax: (602)444-7363
URL: http://www.abgnews.com

Weekly. $35.00/year for individuals. Business and legal newspaper.

★12782★ Arkansas Business
Arkansas Business Publishing Group
122 E Second St.
PO Box 3686
Little Rock, AR 72203
Ph: (501)372-1443   Fax: (501)375-7933
E-mail: abnews@abnews.com
URL: http://www.abnews.com

Weekly. $48.95/year for individuals. Business magazine on the Arkansas business community, covering people and recent news events statewide.

★12783★ Atlanta Business Chronicle
American City Business Journals Inc.
120 W Morehead St., Ste. 200
Charlotte, NC 28202
Ph: (704)973-1000   Fax: (704)973-1001
E-mail: bizchron@mindspring.com
URL: http://atlanta.bizjournals.com/atlanta/

Weekly. $84.00/year for individuals; $153.00 for two years. Local business newspaper.

★12784★ Austin Business Journal
Austin Business Journal Inc.
111 Congress Ave., Ste. 750
Austin, TX 78701
Ph: (512)494-2500   Fax: (512)494-2525

Weekly. $75.00/year; $110.00 for two years; $150.00 for three years. Newspaper (tabloid) serving business and industry in Central Texas.

★12785★ Baltimore Business Journal
American City Business Journals Inc.
120 W Morehead St., Ste. 200
Charlotte, NC 28202
Ph: (704)973-1000   Fax: (704)973-1001
E-mail: baltimore@bizjournals.com
URL: http://baltimore.bizjournals.com/baltimore/

Weekly. $85.00/year for individuals; $140.00 for two years. Newspaper reporting Baltimore business news.

★12786★ Boston Business Journal
MCP Inc.
200 High St.
Boston, MA 02110
Ph: (617)330-1000   Fax: (617)330-1016

Weekly. $64.00/year for individuals. Business newspaper specializing in local and regional business for upper management and CEO's of large and mid-sized businesses.

★12787★ Business First of Buffalo
American City Business Journals Inc.
120 W Morehead St., Ste. 200
Charlotte, NC 28202
Ph: (704)973-1000   Fax: (704)973-1001
E-mail: buffalo@bizjournals.com
URL: http://www.bizjournals.com/buffalo

$84.00/year for individuals; $145.00 for two years. Business Newspaper.

★12788★ The Business Journal of Charlotte
American City Business Journals Inc.
120 W Morehead St., Ste. 200
Charlotte, NC 28202
Ph: (704)973-1000   Fax: (704)973-1001
E-mail: charlotte@bizjournals.com
URL: http://www.bizjournals.com/charlotte

Weekly. $78.00/year for individuals; $130.00 for two years. Newspaper for the business community of Charlotte and the surrounding thirteen-county area.

★12789★ Business Times
Choice Media L.L.C.
PO Box 580
New Haven, CT 06513-0580
Ph: (203)782-1420   Fax: (203)782-3793
E-mail: cbtimes@ctbusinesstimes.com

URL: http://www.ctbusinesstimes.com

Monthly. $36.00/year for individuals. Business journal (tabloid).

★12790★ Capital District Business Review
American City Business Journals Inc.
120 W Morehead St., Ste. 200
Charlotte, NC 28202
Ph: (704)973-1000   Fax: (704)973-1001
E-mail: albany@bizjournals.com
URL: http://www.bizjournals.com

$81.00/year for individuals; $142.00 for two years. Business tabloid providing local business news for Capital Region area.

★12791★ Crain's Chicago Business
Crain Communications Inc.
360 N Michigan Ave.
Chicago, IL 60601
Ph: (312)649-5200   Fax: (312)280-3174
Fr: 800-678-2724
URL: http://www.chicagobusiness.com/mag

Weekly. $89.00/year in the Midwest; $109.00/year outside the Midwest; $151.00/year for other countries. Newspaper covering news stories about various aspects of business and labor activity in the Chicago market.

★12792★ Crain's Cleveland Business
Crain Communications Inc.
700 W St. Clair, Ste. 310
Cleveland, OH 44113
Ph: (216)522-1383   Fax: (216)694-4264
E-mail: cthompso@crain.com
URL: http://www.crainscleveland.com

Weekly. $49.00/year for individuals. Metropolitan business newspaper serving seven counties.

★12793★ Crain's Detroit Business
Crain Communications Inc.
1155 Gratiot Ave.
Detroit, MI 48207-2997
Ph: (313)446-6000   Fax: (313)446-0347
Fr: 800-678-9595
URL: http://www.crainsdetroit.com

Weekly. $59.00/year for individuals. Local business tabloid covering Wayne, Macomb, Oakland, Livingston, and Washtenaw counties.

★12794★ Crain's New York Business
Crain Communications Inc.
711 Third Ave.
New York, NY 10017-4036
Ph: (212)210-0100   Fax: (212)210-0244
Fr: 800-446-1420
URL: http://www.crainsny.com

Weekly. $62.00/year. Regional business tabloid.

★12795★ Daily Journal of Commerce

New Orleans Publishing Group
PO Box 52031
New Orleans, LA 70152
Ph: (504)368-8900   Fax: (504)368-8999

$270.00/year for individuals. Trade newspaper covering construction news in Louisiana and Mississippi.

★12796★ Des Moines Business Record

Business Publications Corp.
The Depot at Fourth
100 4th St.
Des Moines, IA 50309
Ph: (515)288-3336   Fax: (515)288-0309
URL: http://www.businessrecord.com

Weekly. $59.95/year for individuals. Newspaper covering local business news.

★12797★ Florida Trend

Trend Magazines Inc.
490 First Ave. S
St. Petersburg, FL 33731
Ph: (727)822-5000
E-mail: custrelations@floridatrend.com
URL: http://www.floridatrend.com

Monthly. Business.

★12798★ Houston Business Journal

American City Business Journals Inc.
120 W Morehead St., Ste. 200
Charlotte, NC 28202
Ph: (704)973-1000   Fax: (704)973-1001
E-mail: houston@bizjournals.com
URL: http://www.bizjournals.com/houston

$85.00/year for individuals; $122.00 for two years. Magazine (tabloid) for metropolitan Houston business community.

★12799★ Long Island

Long Island Association Inc.
80 Hauppauge Rd.
Commack, NY 11725-4495
Ph: (631)499-4400   Fax: (631)499-2194
Fr: 800-JOIN-LIA
E-mail: info@longislandassociation.org

$30.00/year for individuals; $2.95 for single issue. Long Island Association magazine.

★12800★ Long Island Business News

Long Island Business News
2150 Smithtown Ave.
Ronkonkoma, NY 11779-7358
Ph: (631)737-1700   Fax: (631)737-1890
Fr: 800-LIB-NEWS
E-mail: editor@libn.com
URL: http://www.libn.com

Weekly. $1.50 for single issue; $75.00/year. Business tabloid serving Long Island.

★12801★ The Los Angeles Business Journal

The Los Angeles Business Journal
5700 Wilshire, No. 170
Los Angeles, CA 90036
Ph: (213)549-5225   Fax: (213)549-5255
E-mail: labjtalk@aol.com

Weekly. $79.95/year for individuals. Newspaper (tabloid) covering local business news, business trends, executive profiles, and information for the Los Angeles area executive.

★12802★ Miami Today

Today Enterprises Inc.
PO Box 1368
Miami, FL 33101
Ph: (305)358-2663
E-mail: miamitodaynews.com
URL: http://www.miamitodaynews.com

Weekly. $79.00/year for individuals; $1.00 for single issue. Newspaper (tabloid) covering business and community information targeted to the upper management levels.

★12803★ Nashville Business Journal

Nashville Business Journal
344 Fourth Ave. N, Ste. 610
Nashville, TN 37219
Ph: (615)248-2222   Fax: (615)248-6246
E-mail: nashville@bizjournals.com
URL: http://www.bizjournals.com

Weekly. $64.00/year. Regional business newspaper.

★12804★ Northeast Pennsylvania Business Journal

The Scranton Times
149 Penn Ave.
PO Box 3311
Scranton, PA 18505-3311
Ph: (570)348-9154   Fax: (570)348-9135

Monthly. $28.00/year for individuals. Business publication serving 19 counties.

★12805★ Orlando Business Journal

American City Business Journals Inc.
120 W Morehead St., Ste. 200
Charlotte, NC 28202
Ph: (704)973-1000   Fax: (704)973-1001
E-mail: orlando@bizjournals.com
URL: http://www.bizjournals.com/orlando/

$75.00/year for individuals. Newspaper (tabloid) covering local business news, trends, and ideas of interest to industry, trade, agribusiness, finance, and commerce.

★12806★ Pacific Business News

American City Business Journals Inc.
120 W Morehead St., Ste. 200
Charlotte, NC 28202
Ph: (704)973-1000   Fax: (704)973-1001
E-mail: pacific@bizjournals.com
URL: http://www.amcity.com/pacific/

$79.95/year for individuals. Business tabloid.

★12807★ Philadelphia Business Journal

Philadelphia Business Journal
400 Market St., Ste. 300
Philadelphia, PA 19106
Ph: (215)238-1450   Fax: (215)238-9489
E-mail: pbjnews@pbj.com
URL: http://www.philadelphia.bcentral.com

Weekly. $85.00/year for individuals. Regional and general business newspaper.

★12808★ Pittsburgh Business Times

American City Business Journals Inc.
120 W Morehead St., Ste. 200
Charlotte, NC 28202
Ph: (704)973-1000   Fax: (704)973-1001
E-mail: pittsburgh@bizjournals.com
URL: http://pittsburgh.bizjournals.com/pittsburgh

$94.00/year for individuals; $156.00 for two years. Metropolitan business newspaper (tabloid).

★12809★ Providence Business News

Providence Business News
300 Richmond St. Ste. 202
Providence, RI 02903
Ph: (401)273-2201   Fax: (401)274-0270
E-mail: circulation@pbn.com
URL: http://www.pbn.com

Weekly. $84.00/year for individuals; $126.00 for two years; $168.00 for three years. Newspaper (tabloid) covering business news in Southeastern New England. Regular editorial focus sections include banking/finance, computers, boating, industry, real estate and health care.

★12810★ Puget Sound Business Journal

American City Business Journals Inc.
120 W Morehead St., Ste. 200
Charlotte, NC 28202
Ph: (704)973-1000   Fax: (704)973-1001
E-mail: seattle@amcity.com
URL: http://bizjournals.com

Weekly. $75.95/year. Regional business newspaper (tabloid).

★12811★ St. Louis Business Journal

American City Business Journals Inc.
120 W Morehead St., Ste. 200
Charlotte, NC 28202
Ph: (704)973-1000   Fax: (704)973-1001
E-mail: stlouis@bizjournals.com
URL: http://stlouis.bizjournals.com/stlouis/

Weekly. $81.00/year for individuals. Business newspaper.

★12812★ St. Louis Countian

Legal Communications Corp.
612 N 2nd St., 4th Fl.
PO Box 88910
St. Louis, MO 63102
Ph: (314)421-1880   Fax: (314)421-0436

$175.00/year. Business and legal newspaper.

★12813★ The San Antonio Business Journal
American City Business Journals Inc.
120 W Morehead St., Ste. 200
Charlotte, NC 28202
Ph: (704)973-1000   Fax: (704)973-1001
E-mail: sanantonio@bizjournals.com
URL: http://www.bizjournals.com/sanantonio

Daily. $82.00/year for individuals. Newspaper featuring news and information about the San Antonio and south Texas business community.

★12814★ San Diego Business Journal
San Diego Business Journal
4909 Murphy Canyon Rd., No. 200
San Diego, CA 92123
Ph: (858)277-6359   Fax: (858)571-3628

Weekly (Mon.). $58.00/year for individuals. Metropolitan business newspaper specializing in investigative and enterprise reporting on San Diego County businesses and related issues.

★12815★ San Diego Daily Transcript
San Diego Daily Transcript
2131 3rd Ave.
Box 85469
San Diego, CA 92101
Ph: (619)232-4381   Fax: (619)231-4866
Fr: 800-697-6397
E-mail: webmaster@sddt.com
URL: http://www.sddt.com

Daily. $200.00/year for individuals; $337.50 for two years. Local business newspaper.

★12816★ San Francisco Business Times
American City Business Journals Inc.
120 W Morehead St., Ste. 200
Charlotte, NC 28202
Ph: (704)973-1000   Fax: (704)973-1001
E-mail: sanfrancisco@bizjournals.com
URL: http://www.sanfrancisco.bcentral.com

$88.00/year for individuals; $140.00 for two years. Local business newspaper (tabloid) serving the San Francisco Bay Area.

★12817★ Vermont Business Magazine
Elk Publishing Inc.
181 S Union St.
Burlington, VT 05401-5275
Ph: (802)860-0003   Fax: (802)860-0005
Fr: 800-499-0447
E-mail: vtbizmag@together.net

Monthly. $28.00/year for individuals; $2.95 for single issue. Regional business magazine.

★12818★ Washington Business Journal
American City Business Journals Inc.
120 W Morehead St., Ste. 200
Charlotte, NC 28202
Ph: (704)973-1000   Fax: (704)973-1001

E-mail: washington@bizjournals.com
URL: http://www.amcity.com/washington

$86.00/year for individuals; $146.00 for two years. Metropolitan business newspaper (tabloid).

ONLINE AND DATABASE SERVICES

★12819★ BostonSearch.com
E-mail: webmaster@bostonsearch.com
URL: http://www.bostonsearch.com/
Description: Job search site for those interested in relocating to or remaining in the Boston, MA area. Visitors may post resume, search job databank and activate e-mail alert service.

★12820★ Corporate Search Consultants
E-mail: resumes@rothberg.com
URL: http://www.rothberg.com
Description: Job search consultants located in Atlanta. Job board and resume posting for jobs nationwide, but mainly located in the US Southeast.

★12821★ JobBus.com
E-mail: contact@jobbus.com
URL: http://www.jobbus.com
Description: Job search engine portal for those looking to remain in or relocate to Canada. Contains career resources and articles.

★12822★ PensacolaJobs.com
E-mail: contact@pensacolajobs.com
URL: http://www.pensacolajobs.com/
Description: Job search and resume posting database for those interested in remaining in or relocating to the Pensacola, Florida area.

OTHER SOURCES

★12823★ Aberdeen Area Chamber of Commerce
516 S. Main
PO Box 1179
Aberdeen, SD 57402-1179
Ph: (605)225-2860   Fax: (605)225-2437
Fr: 800-874-9038
E-mail: info@aberdeen-chamber.com
URL: http://www.aberdeen-chamber.com

Promotes business and community development in the Aberdeen and Brown County, SD area.

★12824★ Abilene Chamber of Commerce
174 Cypress St., Ste. 200
PO Box 2281
Abilene, TX 79604-2281
Ph: (325)677-7241
E-mail: chamber@abilene.com
URL: http://www.abilene.com/chamber

Promotes business and community development in Abilene, TX.

★12825★ Affiliated Chambers of Greater Springfield
1441 Main St., 1st Fl.
Springfield, MA 01103-1449
Ph: (413)787-1555
E-mail: denver@myonlinechamber.com
URL: http://www.myonlinechamber.com

Promotes business and community development in the Springfield, MA area.

★12826★ Aiken Chamber of Commerce
121 Richland Ave. E
PO Box 892
Aiken, SC 29802
Ph: (803)641-1111
E-mail: chamber@aikenchamber.net
URL: http://www.aikenchamber.net

Promotes business and community development in Aiken, SC.

★12827★ Alaska State Chamber of Commerce
217 2nd St., Ste. 201
Juneau, AK 99801-1267
Ph: (907)586-2323
E-mail: asccjuno@ptialaska.net
URL: http://www.alaskachamber.com

Promotes business and community development in Alaska.

★12828★ Alexandria Chamber of Commerce
801 N. Fairfax St., Ste. 402
PO Box 359
Alexandria, VA 22314
Ph: (703)549-1000
E-mail: kmoore@alexchamber.com
URL: http://www.alexchamber.com

Promotes business and community development in Alexandria, VA.

★12829★ Amarillo Chamber of Commerce
1000 S. Polk St.
PO Box 9480
Amarillo, TX 79105-9480
Ph: (806)373-7800
E-mail: chamber@amarillo-chamber.org
URL: http://www.amarillo-chamber.org

Promotes business and community development in Amarillo, TX.

★12830★ Anaheim Chamber of Commerce

201 E. Center St.
Anaheim, CA 92805
Ph: (714)758-0222
E-mail: info@anaheimchamber.org
URL: http://www.anaheimchamber.org

Promotes business and community development in Anaheim, CA.

★12831★ Anchorage Chamber of Commerce

441 W. 5th Ave., Ste. 300
Anchorage, AK 99501-2309
Ph: (907)272-2401
E-mail: info@anchoragechamber.org
URL: http://www.anchoragechamber.org

Promotes business and community development in Anchorage, AK.

★12832★ Ann Arbor Chamber of Commerce

425 S. Main St., Ste. 103
Ann Arbor, MI 48104
Ph: (734)665-4433   Fax: (734)665-4191
URL: http://www.annarborchamber.org

Promotes business and community development in Ann Arbor, MI.

★12833★ Arizona Chamber of Commerce

1221 E. Osborn Rd., Ste. 100
Phoenix, AZ 85014-5539
Ph: (602)248-9172   Fax: (602)265-1262
Fr: 800-498-6973
E-mail: info@azchamber.com
URL: http://www.azchamber.com

Promotes business and community development in Arizona.

★12834★ Arkansas State Chamber of Commerce

410 S. Cross
PO Box 3645
Little Rock, AR 72203-3645
Ph: (501)374-9225
E-mail: rrussell@ascc-aia.org
URL: http://statechamber-aia.dina.org

Promotes business and community development in Arkansas.

★12835★ Arlington Chamber of Commerce

505 E. Border St.
Arlington, TX 76010
Ph: (817)275-2613
E-mail: info@arlingtontx.com
URL: http://www.arlingtontx.com

Promotes business and community development in the Arlington, TX area. Seeks to create job opportunities and diversify the city's economic base. Represents business leadership on policy issues affecting city's economic growth.

★12836★ Arvada Chamber of Commerce

7305 Grandview Ave.
Arvada, CO 80002-9960
Ph: (303)424-0313
E-mail: director@arvadachamber.org
URL: http://www.arvadachamber.org

Promotes business and community development in the Arvada and Westminster, CO area. Facilitates communication and cooperation among area business people.

★12837★ Association of Commerce And Industry of New Mexico

PO Box 9706
Albuquerque, NM 87119
Ph: (505)842-0644   Fax: (505)842-0734
URL: http://www.technet.nm.org/aci

Promotes business and community development in the state of New Mexico.

★12838★ Association of Washington Business

1414 S. Cherry
PO Box 658
Olympia, WA 98507
Ph: (360)943-1600   Fax: (360)943-5811
URL: http://www.awb.org

Promotes business and community development in the state of Washington.

★12839★ Athens Area Chamber of Commerce

220 College Ave., Ste. 7
Athens, GA 30601-4505
Ph: (706)549-6800
E-mail: info@athenschamber.net
URL: http://www.athenschamber.net

Promotes business and community development in the Athens, GA area.

★12840★ Atlanta Chamber of Commerce, Metro

235 Andrew Young International Blvd. NW
Atlanta, GA 30301-1740
Ph: (404)880-9000
E-mail: info@macoc.com
URL: http://www.metroatlantachamber.com

Promotes business and community development in Atlanta, GA.

★12841★ Aurora Chamber of Commerce

562 Sable Blvd., No. 200
Aurora, CO 80011-0809
Ph: (303)344-1500
E-mail: info@aurorachamber.org
URL: http://www.aurorachamber.org

Promotes business and community development in the Aurora, IL area.

★12842★ Baltimore - Washington Corridor Chamber of Commerce

312 Marshall Ave., Ste. 104
Laurel, MD 20707-4824
Ph: (410)792-9714
E-mail: bwcc@baltwashchamber.org
URL: http://www.baltwashchamber.org

Promotes business and community development along the Baltimore, MD-Washington, DC corridor.

★12843★ Beaumont Chamber of Commerce

1110 Park St.
PO Box 3150
Beaumont, TX 77704-3150
Ph: (409)838-6581
E-mail: jimrich@bmtcoc.org
URL: http://www.bmtcoc.org

Promotes business and community development in Beaumont and southeast Texas.

★12844★ Bellevue Chamber of Commerce

10500 NE 8th St., Ste. 212
Bellevue, WA 98004
Ph: (425)454-2464
E-mail: staffteam@bellevuechamber.org
URL: http://www.bellevuechamber.org

Promotes business and community development in Bellevue, WA.

★12845★ Birmingham Regional Chamber of Commerce

Financial Center
505 20th St. N., Ste. 200
Birmingham, AL 35203
Ph: (205)324-2100
E-mail: president@birminghamchamber.com
URL: http://www.birminghamchamber.com

Promotes business and community development in the Birmingham, AL region.

★12846★ Bismarck - Mandan Chamber of Commerce

2000 Shafer St.
PO Box 1675
Bismarck, ND 58502-1675
Ph: (701)223-5660
E-mail: info@bismarckmandan.com
URL: http://www.bismarckmandan.com

Promotes business and community development in the Bismarck, ND Area.

★12847★ Boise Area Chamber of Commerce

250 S. 5th St., Ste. 800
PO Box 2368
Boise, ID 83701
Ph: (208)472-5200
URL: http://www.boisechamber.org

Promotes business and community development in the Boise, ID area.

★12848★ Bridgeport Regional Business Council
10 Middle St.
PO Box 999
Bridgeport, CT 06601-0999
Ph: (203)335-3800
E-mail: info@brbc.org
URL: http://www.brbc.org

Promotes business and community development in the Bridgeport, CT area.

★12849★ Brownsville Chamber of Commerce
1600 E. Elizabeth St.
Brownsville, TX 78520
Ph: (956)542-4341
E-mail: brnsvlle@hiline.net
URL: http://www.brownsvillechamber.com

Promotes business and community development in Brownsville, TX.

★12850★ Buffalo Niagara Partnership
665 Main St., Ste. 200
Buffalo, NY 14203-1487
Ph: (716)852-7100
URL: http://www.thepartnership.org

Promotes business and community development in the Buffalo, NY area.

★12851★ Burbank Chamber of Commerce
200 W. Magnolia Blvd.
Burbank, CA 91502-1724
Ph: (818)846-3111
E-mail: info@burbankchamber.org
URL: http://www.burbankchamber.org

Promotes business and community development in Burbank, CA.

★12852★ Business Council of Alabama
PO Box 76
Montgomery, AL 36101
Ph: (334)834-6000   Fax: (334)262-7371
URL: http://www.bcatoday.org

Promotes business and community development in the state of Alabama.

★12853★ Business Council of New York State, Inc.
The Schuler Building
152 Washington Avenue
Albany, NE 12210
Ph: (518)465-7511   Fax: (518)465-4389
Fr: 800-358-1202
URL: http://www.bcnys.org/

Promotes business and community development in the state of New York.

★12854★ California Chamber of Commerce
1215 K St., Ste. 1400
Sacramento, CA 95812-1736
Ph: (916)444-6670

E-mail: information@calchamber.com
URL: http://www.calchamber.com

Acts as legislative advocate for all California business interests. Offers educational seminars.

★12855★ Cambridge Chamber of Commerce
859 Massachusetts Ave.
Cambridge, MA 02139
Ph: (617)876-4100
E-mail: ccinfo@cambridgechamber.org
URL: http://www.cambridgechamber.org

Promotes business and community development in Cambridge, MA.

★12856★ Cedar Rapids Area Chamber of Commerce
424 1st Ave. NE
Cedar Rapids, IA 52401-1196
Ph: (319)398-5317
E-mail: chamber@cedarrapids.org
URL: http://www.cedarrapids.org

Promotes business and community development in the Cedar Rapids, IA area.

★12857★ Chamber of Commerce of Cape Coral
2051 Cape Coral Pkwy. East
PO Box 100747
Cape Coral, FL 33910-0747
Ph: (239)549-6900   Fax: (239)549-9609
Fr: 800-226-9609
E-mail: info@capecoralchamber.com
URL: http://www.capecoralchamber.com

Promotes business and community development in Cape Coral, FL.

★12858★ Chamber of Commerce of Huntsville/Madison County
225 Church St.
PO Box 408
Huntsville, AL 35804-0408
Ph: (256)535-2000
E-mail: hcc@hsvchamber.org
URL: http://www.hsvchamber.org

Promotes business and community development in Huntsville and Madison County, AL.

★12859★ ChamberWest
3540 S. 4000 W, Ste. 400
West Valley City, UT 84120-3691
Ph: (801)969-8755
E-mail: chamber@chamberwest.com
URL: http://www.chamberwest.com

The Chamber of Commerce for West Valley City, Taylorsville and Kearns, UT.

★12860★ Chandler Chamber of Commerce
25 S. Arizona Place, No. 201
Chandler, AZ 85225-5538
Ph: (480)963-4571
E-mail: becky@chandlerchamber.com
URL: http://www.chandlerchamber.com

Promotes business and community development in Chandler, AZ.

★12861★ Charlotte Chamber of Commerce
330 S. Tryon St.
PO Box 32785
Charlotte, NC 28232
Ph: (704)378-1300
URL: http://www.charlottechamber.org

Promotes business and community development in Charlotte, NC.

★12862★ Chattanooga Area Chamber of Commerce
811 Broad St.
Chattanooga, TN 37402
Ph: (423)756-2121
E-mail: info@chattanooga-chamber.com
URL: http://www.chattanoogachamber.com/

Promotes regional business growth that creates prosperity and enhances quality of life.

★12863★ Chicagoland Chamber of Commerce
One IBM Plz., No. 2800
Chicago, IL 60611
Ph: (312)494-6700
E-mail: staff@chicagolandchamber.org
URL: http://www.chicagolandchamber.org

Promotes business and community development in Chicago, IL.

★12864★ Chula Vista Chamber of Commerce
233 4th Ave.
Chula Vista, CA 91910-2611
Ph: (619)420-6602
E-mail: lisa@chulavistachamber.org
URL: http://www.chulavistachamber.org

Promotes business and community development in Chula Vista, CA.

★12865★ Clarksville Area Chamber of Commerce
312 Madison St.
PO Box 883
Clarksville, TN 37041-0883
Ph: (931)647-2331
E-mail: caccdir@clarksville.tn.us
URL: http://www.clarksville.tn.us

Promotes business and community development in the Clarksville, TN area.

★12866★ Clearwater Regional Chamber of Commerce
1130 Cleveland St.
PO Box 2457
Clearwater, FL 33757-2457
Ph: (727)461-0011
E-mail: info@clearwaterflorida.org
URL: http://www.clearwaterflorida.org

Promotes business and community development in the Clearwater, FL area. Provides networking opportunities and small business assistance.

★12867★ Colorado Association of Commerce and Industry

1600 Broadway, No. 1000
Denver, CO 80202
Ph: (303)831-7411   Fax: (303)860-1439
URL: http://www.cochamber.com/

Promotes business and community development in the state of Colorado.

★12868★ Connecticut Business and Industry Association

350 Church St.
Hartford, CT 06103
Ph: (860)244-1900
URL: http://www.cbia.com

Promotes business and community development in the state of Connecticut.

★12869★ Corona Chamber of Commerce

904 E. 6th St.
Corona, CA 92879
Ph: (909)737-3350
E-mail: info@coronachamber.org
URL: http://www.coronachamber.org

Promotes business and community development in Corona, CA.

★12870★ Corpus Christi Chamber of Commerce

1201 N. Shoreline Blvd.
Corpus Christi, TX 78401
Ph: (361)881-1800   Fax: (361)888-5627
E-mail: members@thecccchamber.org
URL: http://www.corpuschristichamber.org

Promotes business and community development in Corpus Christi, TX.

★12871★ Costa Mesa Chamber of Commerce

1700 Adams Ave., Ste. 101
Costa Mesa, CA 92626
Ph: (714)885-9090
E-mail: efawcett@costamesachamber.com
URL: http://www.costamesachamber.com

Promotes business and community development in Costa Mesa, CA.

★12872★ Daly City - Colma Chamber of Commerce

355 Gellert Blvd., No. 138
Daly City, CA 94015-2665
Ph: (650)755-3900
E-mail: staff@dalycity-colmachamber.org
URL: http://www.dalycity-colmachamber.org

Promotes business and community development in the Daly City/Colma, CA area.

★12873★ Dayton Area Chamber of Commerce

1 Chamber Plaza
Dayton, OH 45402-2400
Ph: (937)226-1444
E-mail: info@dacc.org
URL: http://www.daytonchamber.org

Promotes business and community development in Dayton, OH.

★12874★ Delaware State Chamber of Commerce

1201 N. Orange St., Ste. 200
PO Box 671
Wilmington, DE 19899-0671
Ph: (302)655-7221
E-mail: dscc@dscc.com
URL: http://www.dscc.com

Promotes business and community development in Delaware.

★12875★ Denver Metro Chamber of Commerce

1445 Market St.
Denver, CO 80202-1729
Ph: (303)534-8500
E-mail: membership@den-chamber.org
URL: http://www.denverchamber.org

Promotes business and community development in the Denver, CO area.

★12876★ Detroit Regional Chamber

1 Woodward Ave.
PO Box 33840
Detroit, MI 48232-0840
Ph: (313)964-4000
URL: http://www.detroitchamber.com

Promotes business and community development in the southeastern Michigan counties of Lapeer, Livingston, Macomb, Monroe, Oakland, St. Clair, Washtenaw, and Wayne.

★12877★ District of Columbia Chamber of Commerce

1213 K. St. NW
Washington, DC 20005
Ph: (202)347-7201
URL: http://www.dcchamber.org

Promotes business and community development in Washington, DC.

★12878★ El Monte-South El Monte Chamber of Commerce

10505 Valley Blvd., Ste. 312
PO Box 5866
El Monte, CA 91734-1866
Ph: (626)443-0180
E-mail: chamber@ksb8.com
URL: http://www.emsem.com

Promotes business and community development in the El Monte, CA area.

★12879★ Erie Area Chamber of Commerce

208 E. Bayfront Pky.
Erie, PA 16507
Ph: (814)454-7191
E-mail: erie-chamber@erie.net
URL: http://www.eriechamber.com

Promotes business and community development in Erie County, PA.

★12880★ Escondido Chamber of Commerce

720 N. Broadway
Escondido, CA 92025-1893
Ph: (760)745-2125
E-mail: info@escondidochamber.org
URL: http://www.escondidochamber.org

Promotes business and community development in Escondido, CA.

★12881★ Eugene Area Chamber of Commerce

1401 Willamette St.
PO Box 1107
Eugene, OR 97440-1107
Ph: (541)484-1314
E-mail: info@eugenechamber.com
URL: http://www.eugenechamber.com

Promotes business and community development in the Eugene, OR area.

★12882★ Fayetteville Chamber of Commerce

201 Hay St.
PO Box 9
Fayetteville, NC 28302-0009
Ph: (910)483-8133
E-mail: bmartin@fayettevillechamber.org
URL: http://www.fayettevillencchamber.org

Promotes business and community development in the Fayetteville, NC area.

★12883★ Flint Area Chamber of Commerce

519 S Saginaw St., Ste. 200
Flint, MI 48502-1802
Ph: (810)232-7101
URL: http://flintchamber.org

Business and professional organizations that promote business and community development in the Flint, MI area.

★12884★ Florida Chamber of Commerce

136 S. Bronough St.
PO Box 11309
Tallahassee, FL 32302-3309
Ph: (850)521-1200
E-mail: sliner@chamber.com
URL: http://www.flchamber.com

Promotes business and community development in the state of Florida.

★12885★ Fontana Chamber of Commerce

8435 Sierra Ave.
Fontana, CA 92335-3805
Ph: (909)822-4433
E-mail: fontana@sbcglobal.net
URL: http://www.fontanaacc.org

Promotes business and community development in the Fontana, CA area.

★12886★ Fort Collins Area Chamber of Commerce

225 S. Meldrum St.
PO Drawer D
Fort Collins, CO 80522
Ph: (970)482-3746
E-mail: general@fcchamber.org
URL: http://www.fortcollinschamber.com

Promotes business and community development in the Ft. Collins, CO area.

★12887★ Fort Worth Chamber of Commerce

777 Taylor, No. 900
Fort Worth, TX 76102-4997
Ph: (817)336-2491
URL: http://www.fortworthchamber.com

Promotes business and community development in Ft. Worth, TX.

★12888★ Fremont Chamber of Commerce

39488 Stevenson Pl., Ste. 100
Fremont, CA 94539-3085
Ph: (510)795-2244
E-mail: fmtcc@fremontbusiness.com
URL: http://www.fremontbusiness.com

Promotes business and community development in Fremont, CA. Conducts business education and assistance programs.

★12889★ Fresno Chamber of Commerce

2331 Fresno St.
PO Box 1469
Fresno, CA 93716-1469
Ph: (559)495-4800
E-mail: sdean@fresnochamber.com
URL: http://www.fresnochamber.com

Promotes business and community development in the Fresno County, CA area.

★12890★ Fullerton Chamber of Commerce

219 E. Commonwealth Ave.
PO Box 529
Fullerton, CA 92832-0529
Ph: (714)871-3100
E-mail: info@fullertonchamber.com
URL: http://www.fullertonchamber.com

Promotes business and community development in Fullerton, CA.

★12891★ Garden Grove Chamber of Commerce

12866 Main St., Ste. 102
Garden Grove, CA 92840-5298
Ph: (714)638-7950   Fax: (714)636-6672
Fr: 800-959-5560
E-mail: connie.margolin@gardengrovechamber.org
URL: http://gardengrovechamber.org

Promotes business and community development in Garden Grove, CA.

★12892★ Garland Chamber of Commerce

914 S. Garland Ave.
Garland, TX 75040
Ph: (972)272-7551
E-mail: paul@garlandchamber.com
URL: http://www.garlandchamber.com

Promotes business and community development in Garland, TX.

★12893★ Gary Chamber of Commerce

504 Broadway, No. 328
Gary, IN 46402
Ph: (219)885-7407
URL: http://www.garychamber.com

Promotes business and community development in the Gary, IN area.

★12894★ Georgia Chamber of Commerce

235 Peachtree St. NE, Ste. 900
Atlanta, GA 30303-1504
Ph: (404)233-2264
URL: http://www.gachamber.com

Promotes business and community development in the state of Georgia.

★12895★ Gilbert Chamber of Commerce

202 N. Gilbert Rd.
PO Box 527
Gilbert, AZ 85299-0527
Ph: (480)892-0056
E-mail: info@gilbertchamber.com
URL: http://www.gilbertaz.com

Promotes business and community development in Gilbert, AZ.

★12896★ Glendale Chamber of Commerce

7501 N. 59th Ave.
PO Box 249
Glendale, AZ 85311
Ph: (623)937-4754   Fax: (623)937-3333
Fr: 800-IDS-UNNY
E-mail: info@glendaleazchamber.org
URL: http://www.glendaleazchamber.org

Promotes business and community development in Glendale, AZ.

★12897★ Glendale Chamber of Commerce

200 S. Louise St.
Glendale, CA 91205
Ph: (818)240-7870
URL: http://www.glendalechamber.com

Promotes business and community development in Glendale, CA.

★12898★ Grand Prairie Chamber of Commerce

900 Conover Dr.
PO Box 531227
Grand Prairie, TX 75051
Ph: (972)264-1558
E-mail: info@grandprairiechamber.org
URL: http://www.grandprairiechamber.org

Promotes business and community development in Grand Prairie, TX.

★12899★ Grand Rapids Area Chamber of Commerce

111 Pearl St. NW
Grand Rapids, MI 49503-2831
Ph: (616)771-0300
URL: http://www.grandrapids.org/

Promotes business and community development in the Grand Rapids, MI area.

★12900★ Greater Akron Chamber of Commerce

1 Cascade Plaza, 17th Fl.
Akron, OH 44308-1192
Ph: (330)376-5550
E-mail: info@greaterakronchamber.org
URL: http://www.greaterakronchamber.org

Promotes business and community development in Akron, OH.

★12901★ Greater Albuquerque Chamber of Commerce

115 Gold Ave. SW, 2nd Fl.
PO Box 25100
Albuquerque, NM 87125-5100
Ph: (505)764-3700
E-mail: gaccinfo@gacc.org
URL: http://www.gacc.org

Promotes business and community development in Albuquerque, NM.

★12902★ Greater Aurora Chamber of Commerce

40 W. Downer Pl.
Aurora, IL 60506
Ph: (630)897-9214
URL: http://www.aurorachamber.com

Promotes business and community development in the Aurora, IL area.

★12903★ Greater Austin Chamber of Commerce

210 Barton Springs Rd., Ste. 400
PO Box 1967
Austin, TX 78767-1967
Ph: (512)478-9383

E-mail: info@austinchamber.org
URL: http://www.austinchamber.org

Promotes business and community development in Austin, TX.

★12904★ Greater Bakersfield Chamber of Commerce

1725 Eye St.
PO Box 1947
Bakersfield, CA 93303-1947
Ph: (661)327-4421
E-mail: info@bakersfieldchamber.org
URL: http://www.bakersfieldchamber.org

Promotes business and community development in the Bakersfield, CA area.

★12905★ Greater Baton Rouge Chamber of Commerce

564 Laurel St.
PO Box 3217
Baton Rouge, LA 70821-3217
Ph: (225)381-7125
E-mail: info@brchamber.org
URL: http://www.brchamber.org

Promotes business and community development in the Baton Rouge, LA area.

★12906★ Greater Bethesda-Chevy Chase Chamber of Commerce

7910 Woodmont Ave., Ste. 1204
Bethesda, MD 20814-3015
Ph: (301)652-4900
E-mail: info@bcchamber.org
URL: http://www.bcchamber.org

Promotes business and community development in the Bethesda and Chevy Chase communities within Maryland.

★12907★ Greater Bloomington Chamber of Commerce

400 W. 7th St., Ste. 102
PO Box 1302
Bloomington, IN 47402-1302
Ph: (812)336-6381
E-mail: showard@chamber.bloomington.in.us
URL: http://www.chamber.bloomington.in.us

Promotes business and community development in the Bloomington, IN area.

★12908★ Greater Boston Chamber of Commerce

75 State St., 2nd Fl.
Boston, MA 02109
Ph: (617)227-4500
E-mail: info@bostonchamber.com
URL: http://www.bostonchamber.com

Promotes business and community development in the Boston, MA area.

★12909★ Greater Cincinnati Chamber of Commerce

300 Carew Tower
441 Vine St.
Cincinnati, OH 45202-2812
Ph: (513)579-3100
URL: http://www.cincinnatichamber.com

Promotes business and community development in the Cincinnati, OH area.

★12910★ Greater Cleveland Growth Association

200 Tower City Center
50 Public Sq.
Cleveland, OH 44113
Ph: (216)621-3300   Fax: (216)621-6013
Fr: 888-304-GROW
URL: http://www.clevelandgrowth.com

Promotes business and community development in the Cleveland, OH area.

★12911★ Greater Colorado Springs Chamber of Commerce

Vanion Bldg.
2 N. Cascade Ave., Ste. 110
PO Drawer B
Colorado Springs, CO 80901-3002
Ph: (719)635-1551
E-mail: info@cscc.org
URL: http://www.coloradospringschamber.org

Promotes business and community development in Colorado Springs, CO.

★12912★ Greater Columbia Chamber of Commerce

930 Richland St.
PO Box 1360
Columbia, SC 29202-1360
Ph: (803)733-1110
E-mail: lmcleese@columbiachamber.com
URL: http://www.columbiachamber.com

Promotes business in Columbia, SC.

★12913★ Greater Columbus Area Chamber of Commerce

37 N. High St.
Columbus, OH 43215
Ph: (614)221-1321
E-mail: membership@columbus.org
URL: http://www.columbus-chamber.org

Promotes business and community development in the Columbus, OH area.

★12914★ Greater Columbus Chamber of Commerce

PO Box 1200
Columbus, GA 31902-1200
Ph: (706)327-1566
E-mail: mgaymon@columbusgachamber.com
URL: http://www.columbusgachamber.com

Promotes business and community development in Columbus, GA.

★12915★ Greater Concord Chamber of Commerce

2280 Diamond Blvd., Ste. 200
Concord, CA 94520-5750
Ph: (925)685-1181
E-mail: info@concordchamber.com
URL: http://www.concordchamber.com

Promotes business and community development in Concord, CA.

★12916★ Greater Dallas Chamber of Commerce

700 N. Pearl, Ste. 1200
Dallas, TX 75201
Ph: (214)746-6600
URL: http://www.dallaschamber.org

Promotes business and community development in the Dallas, TX area.

★12917★ Greater Des Moines Chamber of Commerce

22030 7th Ave. S., Ste. 104
Des Moines, WA 98198
Ph: (206)878-7000
E-mail: desmoineschamber@aol.com
URL: http://www.desmoineswa.org

Promotes business and community development in the Des Moines, IA area.

★12918★ Greater Des Moines Partnership

700 Locust St., Ste. 100
Des Moines, IA 50309
Ph: (515)286-4950   Fax: (515)286-4974
Fr: 800-451-2625
E-mail: info@desmoinesmetro.com
URL: http://www.desmoinesmetro.com

Promotes business and community development in the greater Des Moines, IA area.

★12919★ Greater Durham Chamber of Commerce

300 W. Morgan St., No. 1400
PO Box 3829
Durham, NC 27702-3829
Ph: (919)682-2133
E-mail: info@durhamchamber.org
URL: http://www.durhamchamber.org

Promotes business and community development in the Durham, NC area.

★12920★ Greater El Paso Chamber of Commerce

10 Civic Center Plaza
El Paso, TX 79901
Ph: (915)534-0500   Fax: (915)534-0513
Fr: 800-651-8065
E-mail: info@elpaso.org
URL: http://www.elpaso.org

Promotes business and community development in El Paso, TX.

★12921★ Greater Elizabeth Chamber of Commerce
456 N. Broad St., 2nd Fl.
Elizabeth, NJ 07208-3365
Ph: (908)355-7600
E-mail: gecc@juno.com
URL: http://www.elizabethchamber.com

Promotes business and community development in Elizabeth, NJ.

★12922★ Greater Fairbanks Chamber of Commerce
250 Cushman St., Ste. 2D
Fairbanks, AK 99701-4665
Ph: (907)452-1105
E-mail: staff@fairbankschamber.org
URL: http://www.fairbankschamber.org

Promotes business and community development in the Greater Fairbanks, AK area.

★12923★ Greater Fort Lauderdale Chamber of Commerce
512 NE 3rd Ave.
Fort Lauderdale, FL 33301-3236
Ph: (954)462-6000
E-mail: info@ftlchamber.com
URL: http://www.ftlchamber.com

Promotes business, tourism, and community development in the Greater Ft. Lauderdale, FL area.

★12924★ Greater Fort Wayne Chamber of Commerce
826 Ewing St.
Fort Wayne, IN 46802
Ph: (260)424-1435
E-mail: administration@fwchamber.org
URL: http://www.fwchamber.org

Promotes business and community development in the Ft. Wayne, IN area.

★12925★ Greater Hollywood Chamber of Commerce
330 N. Federal Hwy.
Hollywood, FL 33020
Ph: (954)923-4000   Fax: (954)923-8737
Fr: 800-231-5562
E-mail: tourism@hollywoodchamber.org
URL: http://www.hollywoodchamber.org

Promotes business and community development in the Hollywood, FL area.

★12926★ Greater Hot Springs Chamber of Commerce
659 Ouachita
PO Box 6090
Hot Springs, AR 71902-6090
Ph: (501)321-1700
E-mail: jay@hotspringschamber.com
URL: http://www.hotspringschamber.com

Promotes business and community development in the Hot Springs, AR area.

★12927★ Greater Houston Partnership
1200 Smith St.
2 Allen Blvd., Ste. 700
Houston, TX 77002-4400
Ph: (713)844-3600
E-mail: ghp@houston.org
URL: http://www.houston.org

Promotes business and community development in the Houston, TX area.

★12928★ Greater Irving - Las Colinas Chamber of Commerce
3333 N. MacArthur Blvd., No. 100
Irving, TX 75062
Ph: (972)252-8484
E-mail: chamber@irvingchamber.com
URL: http://www.irvingchamber.com

Promotes business and community development in Irving, TX.

★12929★ Greater Kansas City Chamber of Commerce
911 Main St., Ste. 2600
Kansas City, MO 64105
Ph: (816)221-2424
URL: http://www.kcchamber.com

Promotes business and community development in the Greater Kansas City, MO area.

★12930★ Greater Lafayette (IN) Chamber of Commerce
337 Columbia St.
PO Box 348
Lafayette, IN 47902-0348
Ph: (765)742-4041
E-mail: dana@lafayettechamber.com
URL: http://www.lafayettechamber.com

Promotes business and community development in the Lafayette, IN area.

★12931★ Greater Lafayette (LA) Chamber of Commerce
804 E. Saint Mary Blvd.
PO Box 51307
Lafayette, LA 70503-1307
Ph: (337)233-2705
E-mail: rob@lafchamber.org
URL: http://www.lafchamber.org

Promotes business and community development in the Lafayette, LA area.

★12932★ Greater Las Cruces Chamber of Commerce
760 W. Picacho
PO Drawer 519
Las Cruces, NM 88004-0519
Ph: (505)524-1968
E-mail: chamber@huntleigh.net
URL: http://www.lascruces.org

Promotes business and community development in Las Cruces, NM.

★12933★ Greater Lehigh County Chamber of Commerce
462 Walnut St.
Allentown, PA 18102-5497
Ph: (610)437-9661
E-mail: info@lehighvalleychamber.org
URL: http://www.lehighvalleychamber.org

Seeks to improve the economy and quality of life in Allentown and the Lehigh Valley, PA area.

★12934★ Greater Lexington Chamber of Commerce
330 E Main St., Ste. 100
PO Box 1968
Lexington, KY 40588-1968
Ph: (859)254-4447
E-mail: info@lexchamber.com
URL: http://www.lexchamber.com

Promotes business and community development in the Lexington, KY area.

★12935★ Greater Louisville - The Metro Chamber
614 W. Main St.
Louisville, KY 40202-2949
Ph: (502)625-0000
E-mail: info@greaterlouisville.com
URL: http://www.greaterlouisville.com

Promotes business and community development in Louisville, KY.

★12936★ Greater Lowell Chamber of Commerce
144 Merrimack St., Ste. 403
Lowell, MA 01852
Ph: (978)459-8154
E-mail: info@greaterlowellchamber.org
URL: http://www.glcc.biz

Promotes business and community development in the Lowell, MA area.

★12937★ Greater Madison Chamber of Commerce
615 E. Washington Ave., 2nd Fl.
PO Box 71
Madison, WI 53701-0071
Ph: (608)256-8348
E-mail: info@greatermadisonchamber.com
URL: http://www.greatermadisonchamber.com/

Promotes business and community development in Madison and Dane County, WI.

★12938★ Greater Manchester Chamber of Commerce
889 Elm St.
Manchester, NH 03101-2000
Ph: (603)666-6600
E-mail: info@manchester-chamber.org
URL: http://www.manchester-chamber.org

Promotes business and community development in Manchester and northern Hillsborough County, NH.

★12939★ Greater Miami Chamber of Commerce

1601 Biscayne Blvd.
Ballroom Level
Miami, FL 33132-1260
Ph: (305)350-7700
E-mail: chamber1@greatermiami.com
URL: http://www.greatermiami.com

Promotes business and community development in the Miami, FL area.

★12940★ Greater New Haven Chamber of Commerce

900 Chapel St., 10th Fl.
PO Box 1445
New Haven, CT 06510-2865
Ph: (203)787-6735
E-mail: info@gnhcc.com
URL: http://www.newhavenchamber.com

Promotes business and community development in the New Haven, CT area.

★12941★ Greater New Orleans, Inc.

601 Poydras St., Ste. 1700
New Orleans, LA 70130
Ph: (504)527-6900   Fax: (504)527-6950
E-mail: fdesk@gnoinc.org
URL: http://www.norcc.org

Promotes business and community development in the New Orleans, LA area.

★12942★ Greater North Dakota Association/State Chamber of Commerce

2000 Schafer St.
PO Box 2639
Bismarck, ND 58502-2639
Ph: (701)222-0929   Fax: (701)222-1611
Fr: 800-382-1405
E-mail: gnda@gnda.com
URL: http://www.gnda.com

Promotes business and community development in the state of North Dakota.

★12943★ Greater Oklahoma City Chamber of Commerce

123 Park Ave.
Oklahoma City, OK 73102-9031
Ph: (405)297-8900
E-mail: dburpee@okcchamber.com
URL: http://www.okcchamber.com

Promotes business and community development in Oklahoma City, OK.

★12944★ Greater Omaha Chamber of Commerce

1301 Harney St.
Omaha, NE 68102-1804
Ph: (402)346-5000
E-mail: gocc@accessomaha.com
URL: http://accessomaha.com

Promotes business and community development in the Omaha, NE area.

★12945★ Greater Paterson Chamber of Commerce

100 Hamilton Plaza, Ste. 1201
Paterson, NJ 07505
Ph: (973)881-7300
E-mail: gpcc@greaterpatersoncc.org
URL: http://www.greaterpatersoncc.org

Promotes business and community development in the Paterson, NJ area.

★12946★ Greater Philadelphia Chamber of Commerce

200 S. Broad St., Ste. 700
Philadelphia, PA 19102
Ph: (215)545-1234
URL: http://www.philachamber.com

Promotes business and community development in the greater Philadelphia area (includes Delaware, New Jersey, and Pennsylvania).

★12947★ Greater Phoenix Chamber of Commerce

201 N. Central, Ste. 2700
Phoenix, AZ 85073
Ph: (602)254-5521
E-mail: info@phoenixchamber.com
URL: http://www.phoenixchamber.com

Supports the growth and development of business and the quality of life in the Phoenix, AZ area.

★12948★ Greater Pittsburgh Chamber of Commerce

425 6th Ave., 6th Fl.
Pittsburgh, PA 15219-1811
Ph: (412)392-4500
URL: http://www.pittsburghchamber.com

Promotes business and community development in the Pittsburgh, PA area.

★12949★ Greater Portland Chamber of Commerce

60 Pearl St.
Portland, ME 04101
Ph: (207)772-2811
E-mail: chamber@portlandregion.com
URL: http://www.portlandregion.com

Promotes business and community development in the Portland, ME area.

★12950★ Greater Portsmouth Chamber of Commerce

500 Market St.
PO Box 239
Portsmouth, NH 03802-0239
Ph: (603)436-3988
E-mail: info@portsmouthchamber.org
URL: http://www.portsmouthchamber.org

Promotes business and community development in the Portsmouth, New Hampshire area and southwestern Maine.

★12951★ Greater Providence Chamber of Commerce

30 Exchange Terrace
Providence, RI 02903-1793
Ph: (401)521-5000
E-mail: chamber@provchamber.com
URL: http://www.providencechamber.com

Promotes business and community development in the Providence, RI area.

★12952★ Greater Pueblo Chamber of Commerce

302 N. Santa Fe Ave.
PO Box 697
Pueblo, CO 81002
Ph: (719)542-1704
E-mail: info@pueblochamber.org
URL: http://www.pueblochamber.org

Promotes business and community development in Pueblo County, CO.

★12953★ Greater Raleigh Chamber of Commerce

800 S. Salisbury St.
PO Box 2978
Raleigh, NC 27602-2978
Ph: (919)664-7000
E-mail: info@the-chamber.org
URL: http://www.raleighchamber.org

Promotes business and community development in Raleigh and Wake County, NC.

★12954★ Greater Richmond Chamber of Commerce

201 E. Franklin St.
PO Box 12280
Richmond, VA 23241-2280
Ph: (804)648-1234
E-mail: chamber@grcc.com
URL: http://www.grcc.com

Promotes business and community development in the Richmond, VA area.

★12955★ Greater Riverside Chamber of Commerce

3985 University Ave.
Riverside, CA 92501-3256
Ph: (909)683-7100
E-mail: rchamber@riverside-chamber.com
URL: http://www.riverside-chamber.com

Promotes business and community development in the Riverside, CA area.

★12956★ Greater San Antonio Chamber of Commerce

602 E. Commerce
PO Box 1628
San Antonio, TX 78296
Ph: (210)229-2100
E-mail: info@sachamber.org
URL: http://www.sachamber.org

Promotes business and community development in the San Antonio, TX area.

★12957★ Greater Sarasota Chamber of Commerce
1945 Fruitville Rd.
Sarasota, FL 34236-4203
Ph: (941)955-8187
E-mail: info@sarasotachamber.org
URL: http://www.sarasotachamber.org

Promotes business and community development in Sarasota County, FL.

★12958★ Greater Scranton Chamber of Commerce
222 Mulberry St.
PO Box 431
Scranton, PA 18501-0431
Ph: (570)342-7711
E-mail: sweiland@scrantonchamber.com
URL: http://www.scrantonchamber.com

Promotes business and community development in the greater Scranton, PA area.

★12959★ Greater Seattle Chamber of Commerce
1301 5th Ave., Ste. 2400
Seattle, WA 98101-2611
Ph: (206)389-7200
URL: http://www.seattlechamber.com

Promotes business and community development in the Seattle, WA area.

★12960★ Greater Shreveport Chamber of Commerce
400 Edwards St.
PO Box 20074
Shreveport, LA 71120-0074
Ph: (318)677-2500   Fax: (318)677-2541
Fr: 800-448-5432
E-mail: info@shreveportchamber.org
URL: http://www.shreveportchamber.org

Promotes business and community development in Shreveport/Bossier City, LA area.

★12961★ Greater Southwest Houston Chamber of Commerce
6900 S. Rice Ave.
PO Box 788
Bellaire, TX 77402-0788
Ph: (713)666-1521
E-mail: swcinfo@gswhcc.org
URL: http://
www.southwesthoustonchamber.com

Promotes business and community development in Bellaire and Greater Southwest Houston, TX.

★12962★ Greater Springfield Chamber of Commerce
3 S. Old State Capitol Plaza
Springfield, IL 62701-1593
Ph: (217)525-1173
E-mail: boer@gscc.org
URL: http://www.gscc.org

Promotes business and community development in the Springfield, IL area.

★12963★ Greater Stockton Chamber of Commerce
445 W. Weber Ave., No. 220
Stockton, CA 95203
Ph: (209)547-2770
E-mail: schamber@stocktonchamber.org
URL: http://www.stocktonchamber.org

Promotes business and community development in the Stockton, CA area.

★12964★ Greater Syracuse Chamber of Commerce
572 S. Salina St.
Syracuse, NY 13202-3320
Ph: (315)470-1800
E-mail: info@syracusechamber.com
URL: http://www.syracusechamber.com

Promotes business and community development in the Syracuse, NY area.

★12965★ Greater Tampa Chamber of Commerce
615 Channelside Dr., Ste. 108
Tampa, FL 33602
Ph: (813)228-7777   Fax: (813)223-7899
Fr: 800-298-2672
E-mail: info@tampachamber.com
URL: http://www.tampachamber.com

Promotes business and community development in Tampa, FL area.

★12966★ Greater Topeka Chamber of Commerce
120 SE 6th St., Ste. 110
Topeka, KS 66603-3515
Ph: (785)234-2644
E-mail: topekainfo@topekachamber.org
URL: http://www.topekachamber.org

Promotes business and community development in the Topeka, KS area.

★12967★ Greater Vancouver Chamber of Commerce
1101 Broadway, Ste. 120
Vancouver, WA 98660
Ph: (360)694-2588
E-mail: info@vancouverusa.com
URL: http://www.vancouverusa.com

Promotes business and community development in the Vancouver and Clark County, WA areas.

★12968★ Greater Waco Chamber of Commerce
101 S. University Parks Dr.
PO Box 1220
Waco, TX 76703-1220
Ph: (254)752-6551
E-mail: info@wacochamber.com
URL: http://www.wacochamber.com

Promotes business and community development in the Waco, TX area.

★12969★ Greater Waterbury Chamber of Commerce
83 Bank St.
PO Box 1469
Waterbury, CT 06721-1469
Ph: (203)757-0701
E-mail: info@waterburychamber.org
URL: http://www.waterburychamber.org

Promotes business and community development in the greater Waterbury, CT area.

★12970★ Greater Winston-Salem Chamber of Commerce
601 W. 4th St.
PO Box 1408
Winston-Salem, NC 27102-1408
Ph: (336)725-2361
URL: http://www.winstonsalem.com

Promotes business and community development in the Winston-Salem, NC area.

★12971★ Green Bay Area Chamber of Commerce
400 S. Washington St.
PO Box 1660
Green Bay, WI 54305-1660
Ph: (920)437-8704
E-mail: pres@titletown.org
URL: http://www.titletown.org

Promotes business and community development in the Green Bay, WI area.

★12972★ Greensboro Area Chamber of Commerce
342 N. Elm St.
PO Box 3246
Greensboro, NC 27402-3246
Ph: (336)275-8675
E-mail: info@greensboro.org
URL: http://www.greensborochamber.com

Promotes business and community development in Greensboro, NC.

★12973★ Hampton Roads Chamber of Commerce - Headquarters
420 Bank St.
PO Box 327
Norfolk, VA 23501-0327
Ph: (757)622-2312
E-mail: info@hrccva.com
URL: http://
www.hamptonroadschamber.com

Promotes business and community development in Norfolk and the Chesapeake, VA area.

★12974★ Hawaii Island Chamber of Commerce
106 Kamehameha Ave.
Hilo, HI 96720
Ph: (808)935-7178
E-mail: hicc@interpac.net
URL: http://www.hawaiiislandchamber.org

Promotes business and community development in the Hawaiian Islands.

★12975★ Hayward Chamber of Commerce
22561 Main St.
Hayward, CA 94541
Ph: (510)537-2424
E-mail: info@hayward.org
URL: http://www.hayward.org

Promotes business and community development in Hayward, CA.

★12976★ Henderson Chamber of Commerce
590 S. Boulder Hwy.
Henderson, NV 89015-7512
Ph: (702)565-8951
E-mail: info@hendersonchamber.com
URL: http://www.hendersonchamber.com

Promotes business and community development in Henderson, NV.

★12977★ Hialeah Chamber of Commerce and Industry
1840 W. 49th St., Ste. 700
Hialeah, FL 33012
Ph: (305)828-9898
E-mail: info@hialeahchamber.com
URL: http://www.hialeahchamber.com

Seeks to promote and develop the economy through trade missions and government relations.

★12978★ Hudson County Chamber of Commerce
253 Washington St.
Jersey City, NJ 07302
Ph: (201)435-7400
E-mail: info@hudsonchamber.org
URL: http://www.hudsonchamber.org

Promotes business and community development in Jersey City and Hudson County, NJ.

★12979★ Huntington Beach Chamber of Commerce
2100 Main St., Ste. 200
Huntington Beach, CA 92648-2461
Ph: (714)536-8888
E-mail: hbchamber@hbcoc.com
URL: http://www.hbchamber.org

Strives to promote a favorable business climate to support and develop the city.

★12980★ Idaho Association of Commerce and Industry
PO Box 389
Boise, ID 83701
Ph: (208)343-1849   Fax: (208)338-5623
URL: http://www.iaci.org/

Promotes business and community development in the state of Idaho.

★12981★ Illinois State Chamber of Commerce
311 S. Wacker Dr., Ste. 1500
Chicago, IL 60606-6619
Ph: (312)983-7100

E-mail: info@ilchamber.org
URL: http://www.ilchamber.org

Promotes business and community development in Illinois.

★12982★ Independence Chamber of Commerce
210 W. Truman Rd.
PO Box 1077
Independence, MO 64051
Ph: (816)252-4745
E-mail: rhemmingsen@independencechamber.org
URL: http://www.independencechamber.com

Promotes business and community development in Independence, MO.

★12983★ Indiana Chamber of Commerce
115 W. Washington St., Ste. 850S
Indianapolis, IN 46204-3407
Ph: (317)264-3110
E-mail: kbrinegar@indianachamber.com
URL: http://www.indianachamber.com

Businesses and other organizations. Promotes free enterprise and the preservation and advancement of the business climate. Monitors legislative activity. Holds seminars and workshops.

★12984★ Indianapolis Chamber of Commerce
320 N. Meridian St., Ste. 200
Indianapolis, IN 46204-1777
Ph: (317)464-2200
URL: http://www.indychamber.com

Promotes business and community development in Indianapolis, IN.

★12985★ Inglewood - Airport Area Chamber of Commerce
330 E. Queen St.
Inglewood, CA 90301-1817
Ph: (310)677-1121
URL: http://www.inglewoodchamber.com

Promotes business and community development in Inglewood, CA.

★12986★ Irvine Chamber of Commerce
17755 Sky Park E, Ste. 101
Irvine, CA 92614-6400
Ph: (949)660-9112
E-mail: icc@irvinechamber.com
URL: http://www.irvinechamber.com

Promotes business and community development in Irvine, CA.

★12987★ Jacksonville Regional Chamber of Commerce
3 Independent Dr.
Jacksonville, FL 32202-5004
Ph: (904)366-6600
URL: http://www.myjaxchamber.com

Promotes business and community development in Jacksonville, FL.

★12988★ Joliet Region Chamber of Commerce and Industry
63 N. Chicago St.
PO Box 752
Joliet, IL 60434-0752
Ph: (815)727-5371
E-mail: info@jolietchamber.com
URL: http://www.jolietchamber.com

Promotes business and community development in the Joliet, IL area.

★12989★ Kansas Chamber of Commerce and Industry
835 SW Topeka Blvd.
Topeka, KS 66612-1671
Ph: (785)357-6321
E-mail: kcci@kansaschamber.org
URL: http://www.kansaschamber.org

Promotes business and community development in Kansas.

★12990★ Kansas City, Kansas Area Chamber of Commerce
727 Minnesota Ave.
PO Box 171337
Kansas City, KS 66117-0337
Ph: (913)371-3070
E-mail: chamber@kckchamber.com
URL: http://www.kckchamber.com

Promotes business and community development in the Kansas City, KS area.

★12991★ Kentucky Chamber of Commerce
464 Chenault Rd.
Frankfort, KY 40601
Ph: (502)695-4700
E-mail: kcc@kychamber.com
URL: http://www.kychamber.com

Promotes business and community development in Kentucky.

★12992★ Knoxville Area Chamber Partnership
601 W. Summit Hill Dr., Ste. 300
Knoxville, TN 37902-2021
Ph: (865)637-4550
E-mail: partnership@kacp.com
URL: http://www.knoxvillechamber.com

Promotes business and community development in the Knoxville, TN, area.

★12993★ Lake Champlain Region Chamber of Commerce
60 Main St., Ste. 100
Burlington, VT 05401-8418
Ph: (802)863-3489   Fax: (802)863-1538
Fr: 877-686-5253
E-mail: vermont@vermont.org
URL: http://www.vermont.org

Promotes business and community development in Burlington and Chittenden County, VT.

★12994★ Lancaster Chamber of Commerce and Industry

100 S. Queen St.
PO Box 1558
Lancaster, PA 17608-1558
Ph: (717)397-3531
E-mail: info@lcci.com
URL: http://www.lancaster-chamber.com

Promotes business and community development in Lancaster, PA.

★12995★ Lansing Regional Chamber of Commerce

300 E. Michigan Ave., No. 300
PO Box 14030
Lansing, MI 48901
Ph: (517)487-6340
E-mail: wsepic@lansingchamber.org
URL: http://www.lansingchamber.org

Promotes business and community development in the Lansing, MI area.

★12996★ Laredo - Webb County Chamber of Commerce

2310 San Bernardo Ave.
PO Box 790
Laredo, TX 78042-0790
Ph: (956)722-9895
E-mail: chamber@laredochamber.com
URL: http://www.laredochamber.com

Promotes business and community development in Laredo, TX.

★12997★ Las Vegas Chamber of Commerce

3720 Howard Hughes Pkwy.
Las Vegas, NV 89109-0937
Ph: (702)641-5822
E-mail: info@lvchamber.com
URL: http://www.lvchamber.com

Promotes business and community development in Las Vegas, NV.

★12998★ Lincoln Chamber of Commerce

1135 M St., Ste. 200
PO Box 83006
Lincoln, NE 68501-3006
Ph: (402)436-2350
E-mail: glpwell@lcoc.com
URL: http://www.lcoc.com

Promotes business and community development in Lincoln, NE.

★12999★ Little Rock Regional Chamber of Commerce

One Chamber Plz.
Little Rock, AR 72201-2486
Ph: (501)374-2001
E-mail: chamber@littlerockchamber.com
URL: http://www.littlerockchamber.com

Promotes business and community development in the Little Rock, AR area.

★13000★ Livonia Chamber of Commerce

15401 Farmington Rd.
Livonia, MI 48154-2892
Ph: (734)427-2122
E-mail: chamber@livonia.org
URL: http://www.livonia.org

Business association that promotes economic and community development in the city of Livonia, MI.

★13001★ Long Beach Area Chamber of Commerce

1 World Trade Center, Ste. 206
Long Beach, CA 90831-0206
Ph: (562)436-1251
E-mail: jdonley@lbchamber.com
URL: http://www.lbchamber.com

Promotes business and community development in the Long Beach, CA area.

★13002★ Los Angeles Area Chamber of Commerce

350 S. Bixel St., No. 201
Los Angeles, CA 90017
Ph: (213)580-7500
E-mail: info@lachamber.org
URL: http://www.lachamber.org

Promotes business and community development in the Los Angeles, CA area.

★13003★ Louisiana Association of Business and Industry

3113 Valley Creek Dr.
PO Box 80258
Baton Rouge, LA 70898
Ph: (225)928-5388   Fax: (225)929-6054
URL: http://www.labi.org

Promotes business and community development in the state of Louisiana.

★13004★ Lubbock Chamber of Commerce

1301 Broadway, Ste. 101
Lubbock, TX 79401
Ph: (806)761-7000   Fax: (806)761-7010
Fr: 800-321-5822
URL: http://www.lubbockchamber.com

Promotes business and community development in the Lubbock, TX area.

★13005★ Maine State Chamber of Commerce

7 University Dr.
Augusta, ME 04330-9412
Ph: (207)623-4568   Fr: 800-821-2230
E-mail: info@mainechamber.org
URL: http://www.mainechamber.org

Promotes business and community development in Maine.

★13006★ Maryland Chamber of Commerce

60 West St., Ste. 100
Annapolis, MD 21401
Ph: (410)269-0642
E-mail: mcc@mdchamber.org
URL: http://www.mdchamber.org

Promotes business and community development in the state of Maryland.

★13007★ Massachusetts Chamber of Commerce

34 Market Street
Everett, MA 02149
Ph: (617)389-4900   Fax: (617)387-0051
URL: http://www.masschamber.com

Promotes business and community development in the state of Massachusetts.

★13008★ McAllen Chamber of Commerce

1200 Ash Ave.
PO Box 790
McAllen, TX 78505-0790
Ph: (956)682-2871   Fax: (956)687-2917
Fr: 877-622-5536
E-mail: steve@mcallenchamber.com
URL: http://www.mcallenchamber.com

Promotes business and community development in McAllen, TX.

★13009★ Memphis Regional Chamber of Commerce

22 N. Front St., Ste. 200
PO Box 224
Memphis, TN 38101-0224
Ph: (901)543-5333
E-mail: info@memphischamber.com
URL: http://www.memphischamber.com

Promotes business and community development in the Memphis, TN area.

★13010★ Mesa Chamber of Commerce

120 N. Center St.
Mesa, AZ 85201
Ph: (480)969-1307
E-mail: info@mesachamber.org
URL: http://www.mesachamber.org

Promotes business, tourism, and community development in Mesa, AZ. Conducts annual Business Showcase.

★13011★ Mesquite Chamber of Commerce and CVB

617 N. Ebrite
Mesquite, TX 75149-3453
Ph: (972)285-0211   Fax: (972)285-3535
Fr: 800-541-2355
E-mail: info@mesquitechamber.com
URL: http://www.mesquitechamber.com

Promotes business and community development in the Mesquite, TX area.

★13012★ Metro Augusta Chamber of Commerce

600 Broad St. Plaza
PO Box 1837
Augusta, GA 30903-1837
Ph: (706)821-1300
E-mail: info@augustagausa.com
URL: http://www.augustagausa.com

Promotes business and community development in the Augusta, GA area.

★13013★ Metro Evansville Chamber of Commerce

100 NW 2nd St., Ste. 100
Evansville, IN 47708-2101
Ph: (812)425-8147
E-mail: info@evansvillechamber.com
URL: http://www.evansvillechamber.com

Promotes business and community development in the Evansville, IN area.

★13014★ Metro Hartford Chamber of Commerce

31 Pratt St., 5th Fl.
Hartford, CT 06103-1602
Ph: (860)525-4451
E-mail: info@metrohartford.com
URL: http://www.metrohartford.com

Promotes business and community development in Hartford, CT. Promotes business and community development in Hawaii, including Honolulu.

★13015★ Metro Jackson Chamber of Commerce

Historic Central Fire Sta.
201 S President St.
Jackson, MS 39201
Ph: (601)948-7575
E-mail: doneill@metrochamber.com
URL: http://www.metrochamber.com

Promotes business and community development in Jackson, MS.

★13016★ Metro Milwaukee Association of Commerce

756 N. Milwaukee St.
Milwaukee, WI 53202
Ph: (414)287-4100
URL: http://www.mmac.org

Promotes business and community development in the Milwaukee, WI area.

★13017★ Metro Tulsa Chamber of Commerce

Williams Ctr. Tower II
2 W. 2nd St., Ste. 150
Tulsa, OK 74103
Ph: (918)585-1201
E-mail: webmaster@tulsachamber.com
URL: http://www.tulsachamber.com

Promotes business and community development in the Tulsa and northeastern Oklahoma area.

★13018★ Metrocrest Chamber of Commerce

1204 Metrocrest Dr.
Carrollton, TX 75006-5735
Ph: (972)416-6600
E-mail: ed@metrocrestchamber.com
URL: http://metrocrestchamber.com

Promotes business and community development in Carrollton, TX.

★13019★ Michigan Chamber of Commerce

600 S. Walnut St.
Lansing, MI 48933-2200
Ph: (517)371-2100   Fax: (517)371-7224
Fr: 800-748-0266
E-mail: info@michamber.com
URL: http://www.michamber.com

Promotes business and community development in the state of Michigan.

★13020★ Minneapolis Regional Chamber of Commerce

81 S 9th St., Ste. 200
Minneapolis, MN 55402-3223
Ph: (612)370-9100
E-mail: info@minneapolischamber.org
URL: http://www.minneapolischamber.org

Promotes business and community development in the Minneapolis, MN area.

★13021★ Miramar-Pembroke Pines Regional Chamber of Commerce

10100 Pines Blvd., 4th Fl.
Pembroke Pines, FL 33026-3900
Ph: (954)432-9808
URL: http://
www.miramarpembrokepines.org/

Promotes business and community development in Miramar and Pembroke Pines, FL.

★13022★ Mississippi Economic Council

PO Box 23276
Jackson, MS 39225
Ph: (601)969-0022   Fax: (601)353-0247
URL: http://www.msmec.com

Promotes business and community development in the state of Mississippi.

★13023★ Missoula Area Chamber of Commerce and Convention and Visitors' Bureau

825 E. Front
PO Box 7577
Missoula, MT 59802-7577
Ph: (406)543-6623
E-mail: info@missoulachamber.com
URL: http://www.missoulachamber.com

Promotes business and community development in the Missoula, MT area.

★13024★ Missouri Chamber of Commerce

428 E. Capitol Ave., PO Box 149
Jefferson City, MO 65102
Ph: (573)634-3511   Fax: (573)634-8855
URL: http://www.Mochamber.org

Promotes business and community development in the state of Missouri.

★13025★ Mobile Area Chamber of Commerce

451 Government St.
PO Box 2187
Mobile, AL 36652-2187
Ph: (334)433-6951
E-mail: info@mobilechamber.com
URL: http://www.mobilechamber.com

Promotes business and community development in the Mobile, AL area.

★13026★ Modesto Chamber of Commerce

1114 J St.
PO Box 844
Modesto, CA 95353-0844
Ph: (209)577-5757
E-mail: info@modchamber.org
URL: http://www.modchamber.org

Promotes business and community development in Modesto, CA.

★13027★ Montana Chamber of Commerce

2030 11th Ave., Ste. 21
PO Box 1730
Helena, MT 59624-1730
Ph: (406)442-2405
URL: http://www.montanachamber.com

Promotes business and community development in the state of Montana.

★13028★ Montgomery Area Chamber of Commerce

41 Commerce St.
PO Box 79
Montgomery, AL 36101-0079
Ph: (334)834-5200
URL: http://www.montgomerychamber.com

Promotes business and community development in the Montgomery, AL area.

★13029★ Morgantown Area Chamber of Commerce

1009 University Ave.
PO Box 658
Morgantown, WV 26507-0658
Ph: (304)292-3311
E-mail: frontdesk@morgantownchamber.org
URL: http://www.mgnchamber.org

Promotes business and community development in the Morgantown, WV area.

★13030★ Naperville Area Chamber of Commerce
131 W. Jefferson Ave.
Naperville, IL 60540-5310
Ph: (630)355-4141
E-mail: chamber@naperville.net
URL: http://www.naperville.net

Promotes business and community development in the Naperville, IL area.

★13031★ Nashville Area Chamber of Commerce
211 Commerce St., Ste. 100
Nashville, TN 37201-1806
Ph: (615)743-3000
E-mail: info@nashvillechamber.com
URL: http://www.nashvillechamber.com

Promotes business and community development in the Nashville, TN area.

★13032★ Nebraska Chamber of Commerce and Industry
PO Box 95128
1320 Lincoln Mall
Lincoln, NE 68509-5128
Ph: (402)474-4422
E-mail: nechamber@nechamber.com
URL: http://www.nechamber.com

Promotes business and community development in Nebraska.

★13033★ New Hampshire State Chamber of Commerce
1001 Islingon St., No. 37
Portsmouth, NH 03801
Ph: (603)422-8824   Fr: 800-709-2810

Promotes business and community development in the state of New Hampshire.

★13034★ New Jersey Chamber of Commerce
216 W. State St.
Trenton, NJ 08608
Ph: (609)989-7888   Fax: (609)989-9696
URL: http://www.njchamber.com

Promotes business and community development in the state of New Jersey.

★13035★ New York City Partnership and Chamber of Commerce
1 Battery Park Plaza, 5th Fl.
New York, NY 10004-1479
Ph: (212)493-7400
E-mail: info@nycp.org
URL: http://www.nycp.org

Promotes business and community development in New York City, NY.

★13036★ Newport County Chamber of Commerce
45 Valley Rd.
Middletown, RI 02842-6377
Ph: (401)847-1600
URL: http://www.newportchamber.com

Promotes business and community development in Newport County, RI.

★13037★ North Carolina Citizens for Business and Industry
225 Hillsborough St., No. 460
PO Box 2508
Raleigh, NC 27602
Ph: (919)836-1400   Fax: (919)836-1425
URL: http://www.nccbi.org

Promotes business and community development in the state of North Carolina.

★13038★ North Las Vegas Chamber of Commerce
2290 McDaniel St.
North Las Vegas, NV 89030
Ph: (702)642-9595
E-mail: spowers@nlvchamber.com
URL: http://www.nlvchamber.com

Promotes business and community development in North Las Vegas, NV and neighboring communities.

★13039★ Norwalk Chamber of Commerce
12040 Foster Rd.
Norwalk, CA 90650
Ph: (562)864-7785
URL: http://www.norwalkchamber.com

Promotes business and community development in Norwalk, CA.

★13040★ Oakland Metro Chamber of Commerce
475 14th St.
Oakland, CA 94612
Ph: (510)874-4800
E-mail: hmaster@oaklandchamber.com
URL: http://www.oaklandchamber.com

Promotes business and community development in Oakland, CA.

★13041★ Oceanside Chamber of Commerce
928 N. Coast Hwy.
Oceanside, CA 92054
Ph: (760)722-1534   Fax: (760)722-8336
Fr: 800-350-7873
E-mail: info@oceansidechamber.com
URL: http://www.oceansidechamber.com

Promotes business and community development in Oceanside, CA.

★13042★ Ohio Chamber of Commerce
230 E. Town
PO Box 15159
Columbus, OH 43215-0159
Ph: (614)228-4201   Fax: (614)228-6403
Fr: 800-622-1893
E-mail: occ@ohiochamber.com
URL: http://www.ohiochamber.com

Businesses organized to foster economic and industrial growth in Ohio. Serves as liaison between government and business. Keeps members informed of employment conditions, economic developments, and pertinent regulations. Conducts lobbying activities.

★13043★ Orlando Regional Chamber of Commerce
75 S. Ivanhoe Blvd.
PO Box 1234
Orlando, FL 32802-1234
Ph: (407)425-1234
URL: http://www.orlando.org

Promotes business and community development in Orange, Osceola, and Seminole, FL.

★13044★ Overland Park Chamber of Commerce
9001 W. 110th, Ste. 150
Overland Park, KS 66210
Ph: (913)491-3600
E-mail: opcc@opks.org
URL: http://www.opks.org

Promotes business and community development in Overland Park and Johnson County, KS.

★13045★ Oxnard Chamber of Commerce
400 S. A St.
PO Box 867
Oxnard, CA 93032
Ph: (805)385-8860
E-mail: ross@oxnardchamber.org
URL: http://www.oxnardchamber.org

Promotes business and community development in Oxnard, CA area.

★13046★ Palmdale Chamber of Commerce
817 E. Ave. Q9
Palmdale, CA 93550
Ph: (661)273-3232
E-mail: bbarnard@palmdalechamber.org
URL: http://www.palmdalechamber.org

Promotes business and community development in Palmdale, CA.

★13047★ Pasadena Chamber of Commerce
4334 Fairmont Pkwy.
Pasadena, TX 77504-3306
Ph: (281)487-7871
URL: http://www.pasadenachamber.org

Promotes business and community development in Pasadena, TX.

★13048★ Pasadena Chamber of Commerce and Civic Association
865 E. Del Mar Blvd.
Pasadena, CA 91101
Ph: (626)795-3355
E-mail: pasadenacoc@earthlink.net
URL: http://www.pasadena-chamber.org

Promotes business and community development in Pasadena, CA.

★13049★ **Pennsylvania Chamber of Business and Industry**

417 Walnut St.
Harrisburg, PA 17101-1918
Ph: (717)255-3252   Fax: (717)255-3298
Fr: 800-225-7224
E-mail: info@pachamber.org
URL: http://www.pachamber.org

Promotes business and community development in Pennsylvania.

★13050★ **Peoria Area Chamber of Commerce**

124 SW Adams St., Ste. 300
Peoria, IL 61602-1388
Ph: (309)676-0755
E-mail: chamber@chamber.h-p.org
URL: http://www.peoriachamber.org

Promotes business and community development in the Peoria, IL area.

★13051★ **Peoria Chamber of Commerce**

8355 W. Peoria Ave.
PO Box 70
Peoria, AZ 85380
Ph: (623)979-3601
E-mail: info@peoriachamber.com
URL: http://www.peoriachamber.com

Promotes business and community development in the Peoria, AZ area.

★13052★ **Plano Chamber of Commerce**

1200 E. 15th St.
PO Drawer 940287
Plano, TX 75094-0287
Ph: (972)424-7547
E-mail: info@planocc.org
URL: http://www.planocc.org

Promotes business and community development in Plano, TX.

★13053★ **Portland Business Alliance**

221 NW Second Ave.
Portland, OR 97209-3999
Ph: (503)228-9411
URL: http://www.portlandalliance.com

Promotes business and community development in Portland, OR.

★13054★ **Provo-Orem Chamber of Commerce**

51 S. University Ave., Ste. 215
Provo, UT 84601
Ph: (801)379-2555
E-mail: info@thechamber.org
URL: http://www.thechamber.org

Promotes business and community development in Provo and Orem, UT.

★13055★ **Rancho Cucamonga Chamber of Commerce**

7945 Vineyard Ave., Ste. D-5
Rancho Cucamonga, CA 91730-2314
Ph: (909)987-1012
E-mail: info@ranchochamber.org
URL: http://www.ranchochamber.org

Promotes business and community development in Rancho Cucamonga, CA.

★13056★ **Regional Business Partnership**

National Newark Bldg.
744 Broad St., 26th Fl.
Newark, NJ 07102-3802
Ph: (973)522-0099   Fax: (973)824-6587
E-mail: rbp@rbp.org
URL: http://www.rbp.org

Promotes business and community development in the Newark, NJ area.

★13057★ **Reno-Sparks Chamber of Commerce**

1 E. 1st. St., 16th Fl.
PO Box 3499
Reno, NV 89505
Ph: (775)337-3030
E-mail: info@reno-sparkschamber.org
URL: http://www.reno-sparkschamber.org

Promotes business and community development in the northern NV area.

★13058★ **Rochester Area Chamber of Commerce**

220 S. Broadway, Ste. 100
Rochester, MN 55904-6517
Ph: (507)288-1122
E-mail: chamber@rochestermnchamber.com
URL: http://www.rochestermnchamber.com

Promotes business and community development in the Rochester, MN area.

★13059★ **Rochester Business Alliance**

930 East Ave.
Rochester, NY 14604-2296
Ph: (585)244-1800
E-mail: angelam@RBAlliance.com
URL: http://www.RBAlliance.com

Promotes business and community development in the Rochester, NY area.

★13060★ **Rockford Area Chamber of Commerce**

515 N. Court St.
PO Box 1747
Rockford, IL 61110-0247
Ph: (815)987-8100
E-mail: cservice@rockfordchamber.com
URL: http://www.rockfordchamber.com

Promotes business and community development in the Rockford, IL area.

★13061★ **Sacramento Metro Chamber of Commerce**

917 7th St.
Sacramento, CA 95814
Ph: (916)552-6800
E-mail: chamber@metrochamber.org
URL: http://www.metrochamber.org

Promotes business and community development in the Sacramento, CA area.

★13062★ **St. Louis Regional Chamber and Growth Association**

1 Metropolitan Sq., Ste. 1300
St. Louis, MO 63102
Ph: (314)231-5555   Fax: (314)206-3277
E-mail: RCGAInfo@stlrcga.org
URL: http://www.stlrcga.org

Promotes business and community development in the St. Louis, MO area.

★13063★ **St. Paul Area Chamber of Commerce**

401 N. Robert St., Ste. 150
St. Paul, MN 55101
Ph: (651)223-5000
E-mail: info@saintpaulchamber.com
URL: http://www.saintpaulchamber.com

Promotes business and community development in the St. Paul and east metro areas.

★13064★ **St. Petersburg Area Chamber of Commerce**

100 2nd Ave. N, Ste. 150
PO Box 1371
St. Petersburg, FL 33731-1371
Ph: (727)821-4069
E-mail: mcornish@mindspring.com
URL: http://www.stpete.com

Promotes business and community development in the St. Petersburg, FL area.

★13065★ **Salem Area Chamber of Commerce**

1110 Commercial St. NE
Salem, OR 97301-1020
Ph: (503)581-1466
E-mail: info@salemchamber.org
URL: http://www.salemchamber.org

Promotes business and community development in Salem, Marion and Polk counties, OR.

★13066★ **Salinas Valley Chamber of Commerce**

119 E. Alisal St.
PO Box 1170
Salinas, CA 93902-1170
Ph: (831)424-7611
E-mail: salinas@salinaschamber.com
URL: http://www.salinaschamber.com

Promotes business and community development in the Salinas, CA area.

★13067★ Salt Lake Chamber
175 E. 400 S., Ste. 600
Salt Lake City, UT 84111-2329
Ph: (801)364-3631
E-mail: info@saltlakechamber.org
URL: http://www.saltlakechamber.org
Promotes business and community development in the Salt Lake City, UT area.

★13068★ San Diego Regional Chamber of Commerce
402 W. Broadway, Ste. 1000
San Diego, CA 92101
Ph: (619)544-1300
E-mail: webinfo@sdchamber.org
URL: http://www.sdchamber.org
Promotes business and community development in the San Diego, CA area.

★13069★ San Francisco Chamber of Commerce
235 Montgomery St., 12th fl.
San Francisco, CA 94104
Ph: (415)392-4520
E-mail: info@sfchamber.com
URL: http://www.sfchamber.com
Promotes business and community development in San Francisco, CA.

★13070★ San Jose - Silicon Valley Chamber of Commerce
310 S. 1st St.
San Jose, CA 95113
Ph: (408)291-5250
E-mail: info@sjchamber.com
URL: http://www.sjchamber.com
Promotes business and community development in San Jose and the Silicon Valley area of CA.

★13071★ Santa Ana Chamber of Commerce
PO Box 205
202 N. Broadway, 2nd Fl.
Santa Ana, CA 92702-0205
Ph: (714)541-5353
URL: http://www.santaanachamber.com
Promotes business and community development in the Santa Ana, CA area.

★13072★ Santa Clara Chamber of Commerce and Convention and Visitors Bureau
1850 Warburton Ave., Ste. 101
PO Box 387
Santa Clara, CA 95052-0387
Ph: (408)244-8244   Fax: (408)244-7830
Fr: 800-272-6822
URL: http://www.santaclara.org
Promotes business, community development, tourism and the convention trade in Santa Clara, CA.

★13073★ Santa Clarita Valley Chamber of Commerce
23920 Valencia Blvd., Ste. 100
Santa Clarita, CA 91355-2175
Ph: (661)259-4787
E-mail: info@scvchamber.com
URL: http://www.scvchamber.com
Promotes business and community development in the Santa Clarita Valley, CA area. Sponsors business expo.

★13074★ Santa Rosa Chamber of Commerce
637 1st St.
Santa Rosa, CA 95404
Ph: (707)545-1414
URL: http://www.santarosachamber.com
Promotes business and community development in Santa Rosa, CA.

★13075★ Savannah Area Chamber of Commerce
101 E. Bay St.
PO Box 1628
Savannah, GA 31402-1628
Ph: (912)644-6400
URL: http://www.savannahchamber.com
Promotes business and community development in the Savannah, GA area.

★13076★ Scottsdale Area Chamber
7343 Scottsdale Mall
Scottsdale, AZ 85251-4498
Ph: (480)945-8481   Fax: (480)947-4523
Fr: 800-877-1117
URL: http://www.scottsdalechamber.com
Promotes business and community development in the Scottsdale, AZ area.

★13077★ Simi Valley Chamber of Commerce
40 W. Cochran St., No. 100
Simi Valley, CA 93065
Ph: (805)526-3900
E-mail: info@sjchamber.org
URL: http://simivalleychamber.org
Promotes business and community development in Simi Valley, CA.

★13078★ Sioux Falls Area Chamber of Commerce
200 N. Phillips Ave., Ste. 102
PO Box 1425
Sioux Falls, SD 57101-1425
Ph: (605)336-1620
E-mail: sfacc@siouxfalls.com
URL: http://www.siouxfalls.com
Promotes business and community development in the Sioux Falls, SD area.

★13079★ South Carolina Chamber of Commerce
1201 Main St., Ste. 1810
Columbia, SC 29201-3254
Ph: (803)799-4601   Fax: (803)779-6043
Fr: 800-799-4601
E-mail: chamber@sccc.net
URL: http://www.scchamber.org
Promotes business and community development in South Carolina.

★13080★ South Dakota Chamber of Commerce and Industry
PO Box 190
Pierre, SD 57501
Ph: (605)224-6161   Fax: (605)224-7198
Fr: 800-742-8112
E-mail: sdchamber@dtgnet.com
URL: http://www.sdchamber.biz/
Promotes business and community development in the state of South Dakota.

★13081★ Spokane Regional Chamber of Commerce
801 W. Riverside Ave.
PO Box 2147
Spokane, WA 99201
Ph: (509)624-1393
E-mail: info@chamber.spokane.net
URL: http://www.spokanechamber.org
Promotes business and community development in the Spokane, WA area.

★13082★ Springfield Area Chamber of Commerce
202 S. John Q. Hammons Pkwy.
PO Box 1687
Springfield, MO 65801-1687
Ph: (417)862-5567
E-mail: info@springfieldchamber.com
URL: http://www.springfieldchamber.com
Promotes business and community development in the Springfield, MO area.

★13083★ Stamford Chamber of Commerce
733 Summer St., Ste. 104
Stamford, CT 06901-1019
Ph: (203)359-4761
URL: http://www.stamfordchamber.com
Promotes business and community development in Stamford, CT.

★13084★ State Chamber - Oklahoma's Association of Business and Industry
330 NE 10th St.
Oklahoma City, OK 73104-3220
Ph: (405)235-3669
E-mail: info@okstatechamber.com
URL: http://www.okstatechamber.com
Promotes business and community development in Oklahoma.

★13085★ Sterling Heights Area Chamber of Commerce

12900 Hall Rd., Ste. 110
Sterling Heights, MI 48313
Ph: (586)731-5400
E-mail: ladams@suscc.com
URL: http://www.suscc.com

Promotes business and community development in the Sterling Heights, Utica, Shelby Township, MI area.

★13086★ Sunnyvale Chamber of Commerce

101 W. Olive Ave.
Sunnyvale, CA 94086-6193
Ph: (408)736-4971
E-mail: sblackman@svcoc.org
URL: http://www.svcoc.org

Promotes business and community development in Sunnyvale, CA.

★13087★ Tacoma-Pierce County Chamber of Commerce

950 Pacific Ave., Ste. 300
PO Box 1933
Tacoma, WA 98401-1933
Ph: (253)627-2175
E-mail: info@tacomachamber.org
URL: http://www.tacomachamber.org

Promotes business and community development in Pierce County, WA.

★13088★ Tallahassee Chamber of Commerce

100 N. Duval St.
PO Box 1639
Tallahassee, FL 32302
Ph: (850)224-8116
E-mail: info@talchamber.com
URL: http://www.talchamber.com

Promotes business and community development in Tallahassee, FL.

★13089★ Tempe Chamber of Commerce

909 E. Apache Blvd.
PO Box 28500
Tempe, AZ 85285-8500
Ph: (480)967-7891
E-mail: info@tempechamber.org
URL: http://www.tempechamber.org

Promotes business and community development in Tempe, AZ.

★13090★ Tennessee Chamber of Commerce and Industry

611 Commerce St., Ste. 3030
Nashville, TN 37203-3742
Ph: (615)256-5141   Fax: (615)256-6726
E-mail: info@tnchamber.org
URL: http://www.tennbiz.org

Promotes business and community development in the state of Tennessee.

★13091★ Texas Association of Business and Chamber of Commerce

1209 Nueces St.
Austin, TX 78701
Ph: (512)477-6721
E-mail: info@txbiz.org
URL: http://www.txbiz.org

Promotes business and community development in the state of Texas.

★13092★ Thousand Oaks - Westlake Village Chamber of Commerce

600 Hampshire Rd., Ste. 200
Westlake Village, CA 91361-2571
Ph: (805)370-0035
E-mail: jlevett@towlvchamber.org
URL: http://www.towlvchamber.org

Promotes business and community development in Thousand Oaks and Westlake Village, CA. Offers networking opportunities.

★13093★ Toledo Area Chamber of Commerce

Enterprise Ste. 200
300 Madison Ave.
Toledo, OH 43604-1575
Ph: (419)243-8191
E-mail: joinus@toledochamber.com
URL: http://www.toledochamber.com

Promotes business and community development in the Toledo, OH area.

★13094★ Torrance Area Chamber of Commerce Foundation

3400 Torrance Blvd, Ste. 100
Torrance, CA 90503
Ph: (310)540-5858
E-mail: barbara@torrancechamber.com
URL: http://www.torrancechamber.com

Promotes business and community development in the Torrance, CA area.

★13095★ Tucson Metropolitan Chamber of Commerce

465 W. St. Mary's Rd.
PO Box 991
Tucson, AZ 85702-0991
Ph: (520)792-2250
URL: http://www.tucsonchamber.org

Promotes business and community development in the Tucson, AZ area.

★13096★ Utah State Chamber of Commerce

2274 S. 1300 E., No. G8-147
Salt Lake City, UT 84106
Ph: (801)621-8300   Fax: (801)932-7609
URL: http://www.commerce.state.ut.us/

Promotes business and community development in the state of Utah.

★13097★ Vallejo Chamber of Commerce

2 Florida St.
Vallejo, CA 94590
Ph: (707)644-5551
URL: http://www.vallejochamber.com

Promotes business and community development in Vallejo, CA.

★13098★ Ventura Chamber of Commerce

801 S. Victoria Ave., Ste. 200
Ventura, CA 93003
Ph: (805)676-7500
E-mail: info@ventura-chamber.org
URL: http://www.ventura-chamber.org

Promotes business and community development in the Ventura, CA area.

★13099★ Vermont Chamber of Commerce

PO Box 37
Montpelier, VT 05601-0037
Ph: (802)223-3443
E-mail: info@vtchamber.com
URL: http://www.vtchamber.com

Promotes business and community development in the state of Vermont. Conducts educational programs. Lobbies state government.

★13100★ Virginia Chamber of Commerce

9 S. 5th St.
Richmond, VA 23219
Ph: (804)644-1607
URL: http://www.vachamber.com

Promotes business and community development in Virginia.

★13101★ Virginia Peninsula Chamber of Commerce

1919 Commerce Dr., Ste. 320
PO Box 7269
Hampton, VA 23666-0269
Ph: (757)262-2000   Fax: (757)262-2009
Fr: 800-556-1822
E-mail: vpcc@vpcc.org
URL: http://www.vpcc.org

Promotes the economic and business interests of the Virginia Peninsula.

★13102★ Warren - Center Line - Sterling Heights Chamber of Commerce

30500 Van Dyke Ave., Ste. 118
Warren, MI 48093-2178
Ph: (586)751-3939
E-mail: info@wcschamber.com
URL: http://www.wcschamber.com

Promotes business and community development in Warren, Centerline, and Sterling Heights, MI.

★13103★ West Chamber of Commerce Serving Jefferson County

PO Box 280748
Lakewood, CO 80228-0748
Ph: (303)233-5555
E-mail: info@westchamber.org
URL: http://www.westchamber.org

Promotes business and community development in Lakewood and Jefferson County, CO.

★13104★ West Covina Chamber of Commerce

811 S. Sunset Ave.
West Covina, CA 91790-5512
Ph: (626)338-8496   Fax: (626)960-0511
Fr: 888-763-3232
E-mail: sdunn@westcovinachamber.com
URL: http://www.westcovinachamber.com

Promotes business and community development in West Covina, CA.

★13105★ West Virginia Chamber of Commerce

PO Box 2789
Charleston, WV 25330-2789
Ph: (304)342-1115
E-mail: forjobs@wvchamber.com
URL: http://www.wvchamber.com

Promotes business and community development in West Virginia. Sponsors seminars.

★13106★ Wichita Area Chamber of Commerce

350 W. Douglas
Wichita, KS 67202-2970
Ph: (316)265-7771
E-mail: info@wacc.org
URL: http://www.wichitakansas.org

Promotes business and community development in the Wichita, KS area.

★13107★ Wichita Falls Board of Commerce and Industry

900 8th St., No. 218
PO Box 1860
Wichita Falls, TX 76307
Ph: (940)723-2741
E-mail: wfbci@wf.net
URL: http://www.wichitafallscommerce.com

Promotes business and community development in Wichita Falls, TX.

★13108★ Wisconsin Manufacturers and Commerce

501 E. Washington Ave.
PO Box 352
Madison, WI 53701
Ph: (608)258-3400   Fax: (608)258-3413
URL: http://www.wmc.org

Promotes business and community development in the state of Wisconsin.

★13109★ Worcester Area Chamber of Commerce

339 Main St.
Worcester, MA 01608-1581
Ph: (508)753-2924
URL: http://www.worcesterchamber.org

Promotes business and community development in the Worcester, MA area.

★13110★ Yonkers Chamber of Commerce

20 S. Broadway, Ste. 1207
Yonkers, NY 10701
Ph: (914)963-0332
E-mail: info@yonkerschamber.com
URL: http://www.yonkerschamber.com

Promotes business and community development in Yonkers, NY.

Negotiating Compensation Packages

REFERENCE WORKS

★13111★ American Almanac of Jobs and Salaries

Morrow Avon
1350 Avenue of the Americas
New York, NY 10019
Ph: (212)261-6788   Fr: 800-242-7737

John W. Wright. Revised edition, 2000. $20.00 (paper). 672 pages. This is a comprehensive guide to the wages of hundreds of occupations in a wide variety of industries and organizations.

★13112★ American Salaries and Wages Survey

Thomson Gale
27500 Drake Rd.
Farmington Hills, MI 48331-3535
Ph: (248)699-GALE   Fax: (248)699-8069
Fr: 800-877-GALE
E-mail: galeord@gale.com
URL: http://www.galegroup.com

Sixth edition, 2001. $135.00. About 770 pages. Provides salary information for thousands of occupations at different experience levels, as well as for specific areas of the country. Entries include occupation, specialization, and industry; location; frequency of salary cited; the low, mid, and/or high salary ranges; source, and survey or publication date. Part of American Salaries and Wages Survey series.

★13113★ Dynamite Salary Negotiations: Know What You're Worth and Get It

Impact Publications
9104 Manassas Dr., Ste. N
Manassas Park, VA 20111-5211
Ph: (703)361-7300   Fax: (703)335-9486

Ronald L. Krannich and Caryl Krannich. Fourth edition, 2000. 219 pages.

★13114★ Getting a Raise Made Easy

McGraw-Hill Trade
2 Penn Plaza
New York, NY 10121
Ph: (212)904-2000   Fr: 800-722-4726
E-mail: ntcpub@tribune.com

Patty Marler and Jan B. Mattia. 1996. $6.95 (paper). 96 pages.

★13115★ How to Negotiate the Raise You Deserve

McGraw-Hill Trade
2 Penn Plaza
New York, NY 10121
Ph: (212)904-2000
E-mail: ntcpub@tribune.com

Mark Satterfield. 1994. $9.95 (paper). 160 pages.

★13116★ Interview for Success: A Practical Guide to Increasing Job Interviews, Offers, and Salaries

Impact Publications
9104 Manassas Dr., Ste. N
Manassas Park, VA 20111-5211
Ph: (703)361-7300   Fax: (703)335-9486

Ronald Krannich and Caryl Krannich. Seventh edition, 1998. $15.95 (paper). 334 pages. Subtitled: "A Practical Guide to Increasing Job Interviews, Offers and Salaries". Offers hundreds of tips for more successful job interviews.

★13117★ Knock 'Em Dead: The Ultimate Job Seeker's Handbook

Adams Media Corp.
57 Littlefield St.
Avon, MA 02322
Ph: (508)427-7100   Fax: (508)427-6790
Fr: 800-872-5627
URL: http://www.adamsmedia.com

Martin Yate. Revised edition, 2002. $12.95 (paper). Prepares the job seeker for the interview with advice on dress, manner, how to answer the toughest questions, and how to spot illegal questions. Discusses how to respond to questions of salary to maximize income. Features sections on executive search firms and drug testing. 352 pages.

★13118★ Negotiate Your Job Offer: A Step by Step Guide to a Win-Win Situation

John Wiley & Sons Inc.
1 Wiley Dr.
Somerset, NJ 08873
Ph: (732)469-4400   Fr: 800-225-5945

Mary Simon. 1997. $17.95 (paper). Covers important strategies in the negotiation process. 253 pages.

★13119★ The Quick Interview & Salary Negotiation Book: Dramatically Improve Your Interviewing Skills & Pay in a Matter of Hours

JIST Publishing
8902 Otis Ave.
Indianapolis, IN 46216-1033
Ph: (317)613-4200   Fax: (317)613-4307
Fr: 800-648-5478

Michael J. Farr. 1995. $14.95 (paper). 690 pages.

AUDIO/VISUAL RESOURCES

★13120★ Negotiating Your Job Offer

DBM Publishing
100 Park Ave.
New York, NY 10017
Ph: (212)692-7700   Fax: (212)297-0426
Fr: 800-345-5627
E-mail: generalinfo@dbm.com
URL: http://www.dbm.com

Video. $49.95. Shows an actual job offer negotiation session.

ONLINE AND DATABASE SERVICES

★13121★ JobStar Central
URL: http://www.jobstar.org

Description: Offers salary negotiation strategies and links to other resources.

★13122★ **Salary.com**
URL: http://www.salary.com

Description: Offers salary reports based upon occupation. Also provides self-tests, learning and career links.

★13123★ **SalaryExpert.com**
URL: http://salaryexpert.com

Description: Salary reports.

★13124★ **WageWeb.com**
URL: http://wageweb.com

Description: Provides salaries according to industry. Also offers consulting services.

Networking

REFERENCE WORKS

★13125★ Dynamite Networking for Dynamite Jobs: 101 Interpersonal Telephone and Electronic Techniques for Getting Job Leads, Interviews, and Offers

Impact Publications
9104 Manassas Dr., Ste. N
Manassas Park, VA 20111-5211
Ph: (703)361-7300   Fax: (703)335-9486

Caryl R. Krannich and Ronald L. Kannich. 1996. $15.95 (paper). 320 pages.

★13126★ Electronic Resumes and Online Networking: How to Use the Internet to Do a Better Job Search

Career Press, Inc.
3 Tice Rd.
Franklin Lakes, NJ 07417
Fr: 800-227-3371

Rebecca Smith. 224 pages. Explains how to use the Internet as a marketing tool for getting noticed in an increasingly online job market.

★13127★ A Foot in the Door: Networking Your Way into the Hidden Job Market

Ten Speed Press
555 Richmond St. West, Ste. 405, Box 702
Toronto, ON, Canada M5V 3B1

Katherine Hansen. March 2004. $14.95. 192 pages. Fundamentals of effective networking.

★13128★ Networking for Job Search and Career Success

JIST Publishing
8902 Otis Ave.
Indianapolis, IN 46216
Fr: 800-648-5478
E-mail: info@jist.com

Michelle Tullier. $16.95. 400 pages. Debunks the myths and misconceptions about networking while demonstrating how to cultivate and maintain rewarding professional relationships.

★13129★ The Networking Survival Guide: Get the Success You Want by Tapping into People You Know

McGraw-Hill Trade
2 Penn Plaza
New York, NY 10121
Ph: (212)904-2000

Diane Darling. 2003. Walks readers through the process of networking, including setting goals, identifying and developing potential contacts, and following up on leads and turning them into opportunities.

★13130★ Networking Works!: The WetFeet Insider Guide to Networking

WetFeet, Inc.
609 Mission St., Ste. 400
San Francisco, CA 94105
Ph: (415)284-7900   Fax: (415)284-7910

2004. $16.95. 122 pages. Shows how to network effectively by tapping into an existing network, reading about alternative means of networking, and using alternative means of networking.

★13131★ Power Networking: Using the Contacts You Don't Even Know You Have to Succeed in the Job You Want

McGraw-Hill Trade
2 Penn Plaza
New York, NY 10121
Ph: (212)904-2000

Marc Kramer. 1998. $17.95.

★13132★ Practical Networking: How to Give and Get Help with Jobs

AuthorHouse
1663 Liberty Dr., Ste. 200
Bloomington, IN 47403
Fax: (812)339-8654

Edward L. Flippen. October 2003. $22.95. 108 pages. Provides creative networking ideas for establishing contacts.

★13133★ SOS Guide to Effective Networking: The Best Way to Get the Job You Want

SOS Associates-Zack Press
2004 Westchester Dr.
Wheaton, MD 20902
Ph: (301)649-0842

Susan Saidman. 1993. 28 pages.

★13134★ Success Runs in Our Race: The Complete Guide to Effective Networking in the Black Community

HarperTrade
10 E. 53rd St.
New York, NY 10022
Ph: (212)207-7000

Demonstrates how to network for information, for influence, and for resources.

★13135★ Table Talk: The Savvy Girl's Alternative to Networking

AuthorHouse
1663 Liberty Dr., Ste. 200
Bloomington, IN 47403
Fax: (812)339-8654
E-mail: 1stbooks@1stbooks.com

Diane K. Danielson. April 2003. $17.50. 196 pages.

AUDIO/VISUAL RESOURCES

★13136★ Job Search Methods that Get Results

RMI Media
1365 N. Winchester St.
Olathe, KS 66061
Fr: 800-745-5480

Video. $99.00. 20 minutes. Discusses methods of networking and receiving job referrals from people you already know.

★13137★ Job Search Strategies
Cambridge Educational
2572 Brunswick Ave.
Lawrenceville, NJ 08648
Ph: 800-468-4227

Video. $99.00. 23 minutes. Covers sources of job leads, including the use of personal contacts.

★13138★ Learning Seed's Job Search Strategies
The Learning Seed
330 Telser Rd.
Lake Zurich, IL 60047

Video. $89.00. 23 minutes. Learn how to network with companies without going through the personnel department.

★13139★ Networking Your Way to Success
Cambridge Educational
2572 Brunswick Ave.
Lawrenceville, NJ 08648
Fr: 800-468-4227

Video. $79.95. 26 minutes. Shows how to succeed with the right contacts.

ONLINE AND DATABASE SERVICES

★13140★ Monster Networking
URL: http://network.monster.com

An online community of professionals that provide jobseekers with the opportunity to learn about various companies, industries, and fields through personal contact.

★13141★ Naked Meetings
URL: http://www.nakedmeetings.com

Arranges speed networking opportunities for jobseekers featuring fifteen or more five minute meetings with business executives on one night.

OTHER SOURCES

★13142★ Business Network International
545 College Commerce Way
Upland, CA 91786
Fr: 800-825-8286

Description: Offers a structured system of giving and receiving business by providing an environment in which individuals can develop personal relationships with other business professionals.

★13143★ Networks Unlimited, Inc.
337 44th St., No. 6
Brooklyn, NY 11220

Description: Individuals in business who are interested in furthering the process of networking.

★13144★ Professional International Network Society
280 Blocks Mill Valley
Dawsonville, GA 30534
Ph: (706)216-2611   Fax: (706)216-2720

Description: Individuals interested in networking professionally for business advancement and personal enrichment. Works to create strong professional relationships locally and internationally; to assist members and enhance their professional skills to meet the challenges of the business world; and to bring professionals together in receptive, stimulating environments.

★13145★ Small Business Network
PO Box 30149
Baltimore, MD 21270
Ph: (410)581-1373

Description: Maintains Business and Consumer Market-Sharing Network.

Non-Profit Opportunities

REFERENCE WORKS

★13146★ Alternatives to the Peace Corps: A Directory of Third World and U.S. Volunteer Opportunities

Food First Books
398 60th St.
Oakland, CA 94618
Ph: (510)654-4400   Fax: (510)654-4551
URL: http://www.cdsbooks.com;
www.foodfirst.org

Annual, latest edition spring 2001. $9.95. Covers more than 75 foreign service organizations (excluding the Peace Corps) that offer long- or short-term volunteer service or travel opportunities in developing countries and U.S.-based volunteer opportunities. Entries include: Program name, address, phone, e-mail, website, description of program, including geographical areas served and admission requirements. Arrangement: Classified by type of program. Indexes: Organization.

★13147★ Careers for Good Samaritans and Other Humanitarian Types

McGraw-Hill Trade
2 Penn Plaza
New York, NY 10121
Ph: (212)904-2000   Fr: 800-722-4726
E-mail: ntcpub@tribune.com

Marjorie Eberts and Margaret Gisler. Second edition, 1998. $9.95 (paper). 274 pages. Contains hundreds of ideas for turning good work into paid work. Inventories opportunities in service organizations like the Red Cross, Goodwill, and the Salvation Army; religious groups, VISTA, the Peace Corps, and UNICEF; and agencies at all levels of the government. Part of Careers for You series.

★13148★ Complete Guide to Public Employment

Impact Publications
9104 Manassas Dr., Ste. N
Manassas Park, VA 20111-5211
Ph: (703)361-7300   Fax: (703)335-9486

Triennial, latest edition 1994. $34.95 for cloth copy; $19.95 for paper copy. Publication includes: List of federal, state, and local government agencies and departments, trade and professional associations, contracting and consulting firms, nonprofit organizations, foundations, research organizations, political support groups, and other organizations offering public service career opportunities. Entries include: Organization name, address, phone, name and title of contact. Complete title is "Complete Guide to Public Employment: Opportunities and Strategies with Federal, State, and Local Government; Trade and Professional Associations; Contracting and and Consulting Firms; Foundations; Research Organizations; and Political Support Groups." Arrangement: Classified by type of service. Indexes: Subject.

★13149★ Directory of Catholic Charities USA Directories

Catholic Charities USA
1731 King St.
Alexandria, VA 22314
Ph: (703)549-1390   Fax: (703)549-1656
URL: http://www.catholiccharitiesusa.org

Annual. $25.00 for members; $40.00 for nonmembers. Covers nearly 1,200 Catholic community and social service agencies. Listings include diocesan agencies, state Catholic conferences. Entries include: Organization name, address, name and title of director, phone, fax. Arrangement: Geographical by state, then classified by diocese.

★13150★ Federal Support for Nonprofits

Thomson Gale
27500 Drake Rd.
Farmington Hills, MI 48331-3535
Ph: (248)699-GALE   Fax: (248)699-8069
Fr: 800-877-GALE
E-mail: galeord@gale.com

URL: http://www.galegroup.com
Cynthia R. Spomer. 1995. $150.00. 986 pages.

★13151★ Great Jobs for Business Majors

McGraw-Hill Trade
2 Penn Plaza
New York, NY 10121
Ph: (212)904-2000   Fr: 800-722-4726
E-mail: ntcpub@tribune.com

Stephen Lambert. 1996. $11.95 (paper). 462 pages.

★13152★ Guide to Careers in World Affairs

Impact Publications
9104-N Manassas Dr., Ste. N
Manassas Park, VA 20111-5211
Ph: (703)361-7300   Fax: (703)335-9486

Foreign Affairs Association Staff and Pamela Gerard. Third edition. 1993. $14.95. 331 pages. Out of print. Describes jobs in business, government, and nonprofit organizations. Explains the methods and credentials required to secure a job in many fields, including international law and journalism. Contains sections on internships and graduate programs.

★13153★ How to Form Your Own Profit or Non-Profit Corporation Without a Lawyer

Do-It-Yourself Legal Publishers
60 Park Pl., Suite 1013
Newark, NJ 07102
Ph: (973)639-0400   Fax: (973)639-1801

Benji O. Anosike. 1999. $25.95.

★13154★ How to Successfully Start a Grassroots Non-Profit Organization

Achievement U.S.A. Corporation
P.O. Box 9328
Washington, DC 20005
Ph: (202)319-9057   Fr: 800-891-3296

Darryl Webster. 2001. $20.00 The author provides a unique grassroots perspective on the pros & cons in getting started in the non-profit world. This book was written to save its reader's money, time & energy looking for information to help them start a non-profit organization. Some of the subjects covered in the book are: incorporating, obtaining tax exemption, garnering community support, marketing, proposal writing for grants, fundraising, getting publicity, giving interviews, & also comments on the significance & impact that grass-roots' citizens are having in the non-profit sector. Students, teachers, professors, community organizers, & citizens of all persuasions will greatly benefit from this book. Webster graduated from George Washington University (1987) & Catholic University of America (MSW/PA). A grass-roots community organizer who started a non-profit organization that won him numerous awards & honors, including: 1991 National Achievement Against the Odds Award; 1989 USA Today News: Hero Award; 1989 Washingtonian of the Year; Ebony Magazine: Future Leader of America. Highly recommended for both academic & public libraries. Volume discounts available from the publisher.

★13155★ **Jobs & Careers with Nonprofit Organizations**
Impact Publications
9104 Manassas Dr., Ste. N
Manassas Park, VA 20111-5211
Ph: (703)361-7300   Fax: (703)335-9486

Ronald L. Krannich and Caryl R. Krannich. Second edition, 1998. $17.95 (paper). 450 pages. Out of print.

★13156★ **A Legal Guide to Starting and Managing a Nonprofit Organization**
John Wiley & Sons Inc.
1 Wiley Dr.
Somerset, NJ 08873
Ph: (732)469-4400   Fr: 800-225-5945

Bruce R. Hopkins. Second edition, 1993. $26.95 (paper). 320 pages.

★13157★ **National Directory of Nonprofit Organizations**
The Taft Group
27500 Drake Rd.
Farmington Hills, MI 48331-3535
Ph: (248)699-4253   Fax: (248)699-8052
Fr: 800-877-GALE
E-mail: businessproducts@gale.com
URL: http://www.gale.com

Annual. $650.00. Covers over 265,000 non-profit organizations; volume 1 covers organizations with annual incomes of over $100,000; volume 2 covers organizations with incomes between $25,000 and $99,999. Entries include: Organization name, address, phone, annual income, IRS filing status, employer identification number, tax deductible status, activity description. Arrangement: Alphabetical. Indexes: Area of activity, geographical.

★13158★ **National Directory of Private Social Agencies**
Croner Publications Inc.
10951 Sorrento Valley Rd., Ste. 1D
San Diego, CA 92121-1616
Ph: (619)546-1894   Fax: (858)546-1955
Fr: 800-441-4033
URL: http://www.sdic.net/croner

Base edition supplied upon order; monthly updates. $100.00. Number of listings: Over 10,000. Entries include: Agency name, address, phone, name and title of contact, description of services. Arrangement: Geographical. Indexes: Service, agency type.

★13159★ **Non-Profits and Education Job Finder**
Planning Communications
7215 Oak Ave.
River Forest, IL 60305-1935
Ph: (708)366-5200   Fax: (708)366-5280
Fr: 888-366-5200
URL: http://jobfindersonline.com

Daniel Lauber. 1997. $32.95; $16.95 (paper). 336 pages. Covers 1600 sources. Discusses how to use sources of non-profit sector job vacancies in a number of specialties and state-by-state, including job-matching services, job hotlines, specialty periodicals with job ads, salary surveys, and directories. Covers a variety of fields from education to religion. Includes chapters on resume and cover letter preparation and interviewing.

★13160★ **Opportunities in Nonprofit Organizations**
McGraw-Hill Trade
2 Penn Plaza
New York, NY 10121
Ph: (212)904-2000   Fr: 800-722-4726

Adrian Paradis. 1994. $14.95; $11.95 (paper). 160 pages. Covers a range of career opportunities with nonprofit organizations.

★13161★ **Public Human Services Directory**
American Public Human Services Association
810 1st St. NE, Ste. 500
Washington, DC 20002
Ph: (202)682-0100   Fax: (202)289-6555
E-mail: pubs@aphsa.org
URL: http://www.aphsa.org

Annual, September. $120.00 for members; $155.00 for out of country. Covers federal, state, territorial, county, and major municipal public human service agencies. Entries include: Agency name, address, phone, fax, e-mail address, web site address, names of key personnel, program area. Arrangement: Geographical.

★13162★ **Real Resumes for Jobs in Non-Profit Organizations**
PREP Publishing
1110 1/2 Hay St., PMB 66
Fayetteville, NC 28305
Ph: (910)483-6611   Fax: (910)483-2439
Fr: 800-533-2814

Anne McKinney (Editor). April 2004. $16.95 (paper). Illustrated. 192 pages. Real-Resumes Series.

★13163★ **Search: Winning Strategies to Get Your Next Job in the Nonprofit World**
Piemonte Press
PO Box 639
Glen Echo, MD 20812
Ph: (301)320-0680   Fax: (301)320-9471

Larry Slesinger. March 2004. $16.95. Illustrated. 104 pages.

★13164★ **Vault Guide to the Top Government and Non-Profit Legal Employers**
Vault.com
150 W. 22nd St., 5th Fl.
New York, NY 10011
Ph: (212)366-4212   Fax: (212)366-6117
Fr: 888-562-8285

Marcy Lerner. October 2003. $29.95 (paper). 176 pages. Part of the Vault Career Library Series.

NEWSPAPERS, MAGAZINES, AND JOURNALS

★13165★ **The Chronicle of Philanthropy**
The Chronicle of Philanthropy
1255 23rd St. NW, Ste. 700
Washington, DC 20037
Ph: (202)466-1200   Fax: (202)466-2078
E-mail: editor@philanthropy.com
URL: http://philanthropy.com

Biweekly. $69.50/year for individuals. Magazine covering fundraising, philanthropy, and non-profit organizations. Includes information on tax rulings, new grants, and statistics, reports on grant makers, and profiles of foundations.

★13166★ **The Nonprofit Times**
NPT Publishing Group Inc.
120 Littleton Rd., Ste. 120
Parsippany, NJ 07054-1803
Ph: (973)394-1800   Fax: (973)734-1771
E-mail: ednchief@nptimes.com
URL: http://www.nptimes.com

$8.95 for single issue; $59.00/year. Trade journal serving nonprofit organizations.

★13167★ Public Interest Employment Service Job Alert!

Public Interest Clearinghouse
47 Kearny St., Ste. 705
San Francisco, CA 94108
Ph: (415)834-0100   Fax: (415)834-0202
E-mail: pies@pic.org

Description: Semimonthly. Lists job openings in legal aid offices and public interest law organizations.

★13168★ United Nations Jobs Newsletter

Thomas F. Burola & Associates
6477 Telephone Rd., Ste. 7R
Ventura, CA 93003
Fax: (805)654-1708

Description: Monthly. Focuses on employment conditions within the United Nations System and lists vacancy notices. Covers the World Bank, Canadian International Development Agency (CIDA), Overseas Development Agency (ODA), United States Agency for International Development (USAID), Asian Development Bank, European Bank for Reconstruction and Development, International Red Cross, and related private sector consulting companies.

AUDIO/VISUAL RESOURCES

★13169★ Humanitarian

Cambridge Educational
PO Box 931
Monmouth Junction, NJ 08852-0931
Fax: 800-FAX-ON-US   Fr: 800-468-4227
URL: http://www.cambridgeeducational.com

$69.95. 25 minutes. Part of the Video GOE series.

ONLINE AND DATABASE SERVICES

★13170★ American Society of Association Executives
E-mail: career@asaenet.org

URL: http://www.asaenet.org

Description: Membership site for executives of non-profit associations. "Career Headquarters" section contains resources both for searching for employees and new positions. Executives can also search resumes and review a list of executive recruiters, plus read information on a number of employment-related issues. You do not have to be a member to view job boards.

★13171★ ExecSearches.com
E-mail: question@execsearches.com
URL: http://execsearches.com

Description: Job site specializing in matching seekers with non-profit, public sector, academic and "socially conscious" positions. Contains job board, resume databank, e-mail alert system and reference articles. Employers may also post jobs and check resume references.

★13172★ OpportunityNOCs.org
E-mail: nocs@tmcenter.org
URL: http://www.opportunitynocs.org

Description: Job board website for those interested in careers in non-profit organizations. Visitors may search job bank, receive listserv, and subscribe to free updates e-newsletter. Also contains career resources.

OTHER SOURCES

★13173★ ACCESS: Networking in the Public Interest

1001 Connecticut Ave. NW, Ste. 838
Washington, DC 20036
Ph: (202)785-4233   Fax: (202)785-4212
E-mail: accesscntr@aol.com

Description: Serves as a clearinghouse of information related to employment opportunities in the non-profit sector. Provides career counseling and other job seeking related services.

★13174★ Intercristo

19303 Fremont Ave. N
Seattle, WA 98133
Ph: (206)546-7330   Fax: (206)546-7375
Fr: 800-251-7740
E-mail: careerhelp@intercristo.com
URL: http://www.jobsinaflash.org

Members: Division of CRISTA Ministries.
Purpose: Provides job exploration and job information service with computerized referrals on current openings with Christian organizations. Career counseling also available using The Birkman Method Assessment Tool.

★13175★ Third Sector Search Associates

1155 University St., Ste. 1414
Montreal, QC, Canada H3B 3A7
Ph: (514)906-1333   Fax: (514)878-2473
Fr: (866)273-8796

An executive search firm dedicated to not-for-profit organizations.

★13176★ U.S. Public Interest Research Group (U.S.PIRG)

218 D. St. SE
Washington, DC 20003
Ph: (202)546-9707   Fax: (202)546-2461
E-mail: uspirg@pirg.org
URL: http://www.pirg.org

Description: Individuals who contribute time, effort, or funds toward public interest research and advocacy. Conducts research, monitors corporate and government actions, and lobbies for reforms on consumer, environmental, energy, and governmental issues. Current efforts include support for: laws to protect consumers from unsafe products and unfair banking practices; laws to reduce the use of toxic chemicals; strengthening clean air laws; efforts to reduce global warming and ozone depletion; energy conservation and use of safe, renewable energy sources. Sponsors internships for college students; provides opportunities for students to receive academic credit for activities such as legislative research, lobbying, and public education and organizing. Offers summer jobs.

Opportunities for Disabled Workers

REFERENCE WORKS

★13177★ Adult Agencies: Linkages for Adolescents in Transition

PRO-ED, Incorporated
8700 Shoal Creek Blvd.
Austin, TX 78757-6897
Ph: (512)451-3246   Fax: (512)451-8542
Fr: 800-897-3202

Gary Cozzens. 1999.

★13178★ Affirmative Action Register

Affirmative Action Inc.
8356 Olive Blvd.
St. Louis, MO 63132
Ph: (314)991-1335   Fax: (314)997-1788
Fr: 800-537-0655
URL: http://www.aar-eeo.com

Monthly. $1.50 for single issue. Covers in each issue, about 300 positions at a professional level (most requiring advanced study) available to women, minorities, veterans, and the handicapped; listings are advertisements placed by employers with affirmative action programs. Entries include: Company or organization name, address, contact name; description of position including title, requirements, duties, application procedure, salary, etc. Arrangement: Classified by profession.

★13179★ Career Planning and Employment Strategies for Postsecondary Students with Disabilities

National Clearinghouse on Postsecondary
   Education for Individuals with Disabilities
1 Dupont Cir. NW, Ste. 800
Washington, DC 20036
Ph: (202)939-9320   Fax: (202)833-4760
Fr: 800-544-3284
URL: http://www.accnet.edu/Programs/
HEATH

Annual. Free. Covers about 30 educational institutions and organizations offering career placement programs for handicapped postsecondary students. Entries include: Institution name, address, phone, name and title of contact, program name, description of program. Arrangement: Classified by type of program.

★13180★ Coming Alive from Nine to Five: The Career Search Handbook

Mayfield Publishing Co.
1280 Villa St.
Mountain View, CA 94041-1176
Ph: (650)960-3222   Fax: (650)960-0328
Fr: 800-433-1279

Betty Neville Michelozzi. Sixth edition, 1999. In addition to general job-hunting advice, provides special information for women, young adults, minorities, older workers, and persons with handicaps.

★13181★ Demystifying Job Development: Field-Based Approaches to Job Development for People with Disabilities

Training Resource Network, Incorporated
P.O. Box 439
St. Augustine, FL 32085-0439
Ph: (904)823-9800   Fax: (904)823-3554
Fr: (866)823-9800

David Hoff, Cecilia Gandolfo, Marty Gold, and Melanie Jordan. 2000. $29.95 (paper).

★13182★ Directory of Information Resources for the Handicapped

Ready Reference Press
PO Box 5249
Santa Monica, CA 90405
Ph: (310)475-4895   Fr: 800-424-5627

$47.50. Three separate volumes provide a guide to information resources and services for the handicapped, covering the fields of employment, vocational rehabilitation, and education and training, among others. Discusses how to locate specialized career placement services.

★13183★ No More Job Interviews!: Self-Employment Strategies for People with Disabilities

Training Resource Network, Incorporated
P.O. Box 439
St. Augustine, FL 32085-0439
Ph: (904)823-9800   Fax: (904)823-3554
Fr: (866)823-9800

Alice Weiss. 2000. $29.95 (paper).

★13184★ Shoot for the Moon

Saunderstown Press
PO Box 307
Saunderstown, RI 02874-0307
Ph: (401)295-8810

Allen A. Johnson. Second edition, 1996. $12.95 (paper). 37 pages. Designed for people starting or reentering employment, with special emphasis on handicapped and minorities.

★13185★ So You're On Disability...& You Think You Might Want to Get Back into Action

Daniel Thomas McAneny
1417 Bexley Dr.
Wilmington, NC 28412-2001

Daniel T. McAneny. 1995. $7.95 (paper). 124 pages. This book includes over 40 stories of people who have successfully gotten jobs or started businesses after long term disability.

★13186★ Thriving and Surviving at Work: Disabled People's Employment Strategies

Policy Press
University of Bristol, 4th Fl.
Beacon House, Queens Rd., Clifton
Bristol BS8 1QU, United Kingdom

Alan Roulstone, Lorraine Gradwell, Jeni Price, Lesley Child. July 2003. $23.95 (paper). 45 pages.

NEWSPAPERS, MAGAZINES, AND JOURNALS

★13187★ Fair Employment Practices Summary of Latest Developments

Bureau of National Affairs Inc.
1231 25th St. NW
Washington, DC 20037
Ph: (202)452-4200   Fax: (202)452-4644
Fr: 800-372-1033

Description: Biweekly. Highlights developments in employment opportunity and affirmative actions, and affirmative action programs. Reports on federal and state court decisions, Equal Employment Opportunity Commission (EEOC) rulings and Office of Federal Contract Compliance Programs (OFCCP) decisions, new laws, regulations, and agency directives. Also provides information on special programs for minorities, the handicapped, women, and older workers.

★13188★ JADARA Update

JADARA
PO Box 727
Lusby, MD 20657-0727
Ph: (410)495-8440   Fax: (410)495-8442

Description: Quarterly. Surveys news events, resources, legislation, and developments in services related to the deaf. Recurring features include notices of employment opportunities, news of the national Association and its local chapters, information on new publications, announcements of awards granted, and a calendar of events.

★13189★ NAPH National Newsletter

National Association of the Physically
   Handicapped Inc.
4230 Emerick
Saginaw, MI 48603-6614
Ph: (517)799-3060   Fax: (517)792-7549

Description: Quarterly. Carries "news items about or of concern to the physically handicapped." Covers such subjects as legislation, employment, travel, and barrier-free architecture. Recurring features include items on local chapter events.

★13190★ Opportunity

Public Relations Department
1901 N Beauregard St., Ste. 200
Alexandria, VA 22311-1727
Ph: (703)998-0770   Fax: (703)671-9053
Fr: 800-433-2304
URL: http://www.nib.org

Description: Quarterly. Publishes news and feature articles on agencies for individuals who are blind and describes industries, agencies, and projects that employ blind workers. Recurring features include legislative updates, conference news, and news of programs and events of various associations employing blind individuals.

★13191★ Paraplegia News

Paraplegia News
2111 E Highland Ave., Ste. 180
Phoenix, AZ 85016-4702
Ph: (602)224-0500   Fax: (602)224-0507
Fr: 888-888-2201
URL: http://www.pn-magazine.com

Description: Monthly. Presents articles and briefs on wheelchair living, education, employment, housing, transportation, travel, spinal cord injury, research, legislation, new products, and sports and recreation for the wheelchair user.

★13192★ SIGCAPH Newsletter

Special Interest Group on Programming
   Languages
1515 Broadway
New York, NY 10036
Ph: (212)869-7440   Fax: (212)302-5826
Fr: 800-342-6626

Description: Quarterly. Supports the Group's concern to promote professional interests of computing personnel with the physically handicapped; promotes the "application of computing and information technology toward solutions of disability problems and to perform a public education function in support of computing careers for suitably trained blind, deaf, or motor impaired persons."

★13193★ Tapping New Talent for Business Success

Rehabilitation Research and Training
   Center on Workplace Supports
PO Box 842011
Richmond, VA 23284-2011
Ph: (804)828-1851   Fax: (804)828-2193
E-mail: tcblanke@saturn.vcu.edu
URL: http://www.worksupport.com

Description: Irregular. Reports on diversity and disabilities in the workplace. Publishes original research, new resources, and human interest features.

★13194★ Vendorscope

Randolph-Sheppard Vendors of America
1527 Royal Rd.
Aberdeen, SD 57401

Description: Quarterly. Reports on issues pertinent to the Business Enterprise Program for Blind Vendors. Recurring features include letters to the editor, interviews, news of research, a calendar of events, reports of meetings, news of educational opportunities, job listings, book reviews, notices of publications available, news of conventions and legislative action, and a column titled Mini-Mumbles from "Mean Dean." Also available on audiocassette.

AUDIO/VISUAL RESOURCES

★13195★ Access Unlimited: The Job Search Series for People with Disabilities

Cambridge Educational
PO Box 931
Monmouth Junction, NJ 08852-0931
Fax: 800-FAX-ON-US   Fr: 800-468-4227
URL: http://www.cambridgeeducational.com

Three videos. 1998. $199.00/set. Three 30-minute videos cover job search tactics, resumes and applications, and job interviewing.

★13196★ Everybody's Working Video

Attainment Co., Inc.
PO Box 930160
Verona, WI 53593
Ph: (608)845-7880   Fax: (608)845-8040
Fr: 800-327-4269
URL: http://www.attainmentcompany.com/

1997. $59.00 This 22-minute videocassette features success stories of five employees with disabilities.

★13197★ Everyone Can Work Video

Attainment Co., Inc.
PO Box 930160
Verona, WI 53593
Ph: (608)845-7880   Fax: (608)845-8040
Fr: 800-327-4269
URL: http://www.attainmentcompany.com/

Paul Wehman and Pamela Sherron. 1996. $79.00. This 55-minute videocassette provides information on employment for persons with disabilities. Covers advantages of supported employment, including job coaches. Includes interviews with employers.

★13198★ Job Interviewing for People with Disabilities

Cambridge Educational
PO Box 931
Monmouth Junction, NJ 08852-0931
Fax: 800-FAX-ON-US   Fr: 800-468-4227
URL: http://www.cambridgeeducational.com

$89.95. 30 minutes. Part of the series "Access Unlimited: The Job Search Series for People with Disabilities."

★13199★ Job Search Tactics for People with Disabilities

Cambridge Educational
PO Box 931
Monmouth Junction, NJ 08852-0931
Fax: 800-FAX-ON-US   Fr: 800-468-4227
URL: http://www.cambridgeeducational.com

$89.95. 30 minutes. Part of the series "Access Unlimited: The Job Search Series for People with Disabilities."

★13200★ *Resumes and Applications for People with Disabilities*

Cambridge Educational
PO Box 931
Monmouth Junction, NJ 08852-0931
Fax: 800-FAX-ON-US   Fr: 800-468-4227
URL: http://www.cambridgeeducational.com

$89.95. 1998. 30 minutes. Part of the series "Access Unlimited: The Job Search Series for People with Disabilities."

SOFTWARE

★13201★ **Interview Skills of the Future: Interview Challenges for Minorities, Women, and People with Disabilities**

Program Development Associates
PO Box 2038
Syracuse, NY 13220-2038
Ph: (315)452-0643   Fax: (315)452-0710
Fr: 800-543-2119
E-mail: info@pdassoc.com
URL: http://www.pdassoc.com

$199.00. Teaches a tactful and positive response to challenging interview questions for those having a hard time breaking through the traditional hiring barriers.

OTHER SOURCES

★13202★ **AFL-CIO Working for America Institute**

815 16th St. NW
Washington, DC 20006
Ph: (202)974-8102   Fax: (202)974-8101
E-mail: info@workingforamerica.org
URL: http://www.workingforamerica.org

Purpose: Serves as the employment and training arm of the AFL-CIO. Works to assure full labor participation in employment and training programs funded under the Job Training Partnership Act. Assists in developing JTPA programs for dislocated and economically disadvantaged workers; provides technical services in support of labor-operated programs. **Activities:** Offers job search and placement services for disabled persons and early intervention and return-to-work services for recently disabled union members. Sponsors demonstration program to develop effective ways of improving workers' skills through structured workplace training; also offers workplace literacy study. Works with affected labor groups to help workers displaced by plant closings. Provides education and training to labor members of JTPA planning councils, labor leaders, and employment and training professionals.

★13203★ **Goodwill Industries International (GII)**

9200 Rockville Pike
Bethesda, MD 20814
Ph: (301)530-6500   Fax: (301)530-1516
Fr: 800-741-0186
E-mail: contactus@goodwill.org
URL: http://www.goodwill.org

Description: Federation of Goodwill Industries organizations across North America and the world are concerned primarily with providing employment, training, evaluation, counseling, placement, job training, and other vocational rehabilitation services and opportunities for individual growth for people with disabilities and other special needs. Member Goodwill Industries organizations collect donated goods and sell them in Goodwill retail stores as a means of providing employment and generating income. Conducts seminars and training programs; compiles statistics.

★13204★ **Helen Keller National Center for Deaf-Blind Youths and Adults (HKNC)**

111 Middle Neck Rd.
Sands Point, NY 11050
Ph: (516)944-8900   Fax: (516)944-7302
E-mail: hkncinfo@rcn.com
URL: http://helenkeller.org/national/

Description: Provides diagnostic evaluations, comprehensive vocational and personal adjustment training, job preparation and placement for people who are deaf-blind from every state and territory. Field services include information and referral and advocacy and technical assistance to professionals, consumers, and families. Sponsors annual National Helen Keller Deaf-Blind Awareness Week.

★13205★ **Inspiration Ministries (CLH)**

PO Box 948
Corner State Rd. 67 and County F
Walworth, WI 53184-0948
Ph: (262)275-6131   Fax: (262)275-3355
E-mail: tschnake@elknet.net
URL: http://www.inspirationministries.org

Members: Seeks to provide fully accessible, permanent residence with attendant care in room and board facility for physically disabled adults. Conducts summer camping program for disabled persons and retreat opportunities for groups.

★13206★ **Job Accommodation Network (JAN)**

WVU PO Box 6080
Morgantown, WV 26506-6080
Ph: (304)293-7186   Fax: (304)293-5407
Fr: 800-526-7234
E-mail: jan@jan.icdi.wvu.edu
URL: http://janweb.icdi.wvu.edu

Description: A service of U.S. Department of Labor's Office of Disability Employment Policy. **Purpose:** An international toll-free consulting service that provides information about job accommodation and the employability of people with disabilities. Calls are answered by consultants who understand the limitations associated with disabilities and who have instant access to the most comprehensive and up-to-date information about accommodation methods, devices, and strategies.

★13207★ **Just One Break (JOB)**

120 Wall St., 20th Fl.
New York, NY 10005-3904
Ph: (212)785-7300   Fax: (212)785-4513
E-mail: jobs@justonebreak.com
URL: http://www.justonebreak.com/

Description: Employment service for people with disabilities, to help them find jobs and lead productive lives. JOB finds competitive employment for people with disabilities by bringing together leading employers and qualified JOB applicants. JOB concentrates efforts in New York, and is working to include New Jersey and Connecticut, but advises companies nationwide. Offers placement services, employment counseling, skills evaluation, college recruitment, resume writing assistance service referrals, and computer access. JOB's Student Internship Program (SIP) provides hands-on work experience for college students with disabilities and works in collaboration with college disability and career service offices. JOB provides on-site disability awareness training to support initiatives related to interviewing, hiring, and retaining employees with disabilities.

★13208★ **National Association of the Deaf (NAD)**

814 Thayer Ave., Ste. 250
Silver Spring, MD 20910-4500
Ph: (301)587-1788   Fax: (301)587-1791
E-mail: nadinfo@nad.org
URL: http://www.nad.org

Description: Safeguards accessibility and civil rights of America's deaf population in areas of education, employment, healthcare, and telecommunications.

★13209★ **National Business and Disability Council**

201 I.I. Willets Rd.
Albertson, NY 11507
Ph: (516)465-1515   Fax: (516)465-3730
E-mail: info@business-disability.com
URL: http://www.business-disability.com/

Description: Acts as a resource for employers seeking to integrate people with disabilities into the workplace and companies seeking to reach them in the consumer market.

★13210★ **National Center for Disability Services (NCDS)**

201 I.U. Willets Rd.
Albertson, NY 11507
Ph: (516)465-1470   Fax: (516)746-3298
E-mail: ecortez@ncds.org
URL: http://www.ncds.org

Description: Serves as a center providing educational, vocational, rehabilitation, and research opportunities for persons with disabilities. Work is conducted through the following: Abilities Health and Rehabilitation Services, a New York state licensed diagnostic and treatment center which offers comprehensive outpatient programs in physical therapy, occupational therapy, speech therapy, and psychological services; Career and Employment Institute, which evaluates, trains, and counsels more than 600 adults with disabilities each year, with the goal of productive competitive employment; Henry Viscardi School, which conducts early childhood, elementary, and secondary programs, as well as adult and continuing education programs; Research and Training Institute, which conducts research on the education, employment, and career development of persons with disabilities, and holds seminars and workshops for rehabilitation services professionals. Maintains library and speakers' bureau; compiles statistics; offers placement service; conducts research and educational programs.

★13211★ NTID's Center on Employment (NCE)
Rochester Institute of Technology
52 Lomb Memorial Dr.
Rochester, NY 14623-5604
Ph: (585)479-6219   Fax: (585)475-7570
E-mail: ntidcoe@rit.edu
URL: http://www.ntid.rit.edu/nce

Members: Operated by the National Technical Institute for the Deaf. **Purpose:** Promotes successful employment of Rochester Institute of Technology's deaf students and graduates. Also offers resources and training for employers.

★13212★ Special Interest Group for Computers and the Physically Handicapped (SIGCAPH)
Church St. Sta.
PO Box 12115
New York, NY 10249
Ph: (212)626-0500   Fax: (212)944-1318
E-mail: chair_sigcaph@acm.org
URL: http://www.acm.org/sigcaph

Description: Promotes the professional interests of computing personnel with physical disabilities and the application of computing & information technology in solving relevant disability problems. Studies to educate the public to support careers for the disabled.

Opportunities for Ex-Offenders

REFERENCE WORKS

★13213★ *The Ex-Offender's Job Search Companion*
Cambridge Career Products
PO Box 2153
Charleston, WV 25328-2153
Ph: (304)744-9323   Fax: (304)744-9351
Fr: 800-468-4227
URL: http://www.cambridgeol.com

1997. $9.95. 68 pages. This workbook covers all of the situations, problems, and obstacles the job hunter will encounter.

★13214★ *I Need a Job!: The Ex-Offender's Job Search Manual*
ConquestHouse, Inc.
Po Box 73873
Washington, DC 20056-3873
Ph: (202)723-2014   Fax: (202)291-1759

Louis Jones. September 2003. $15.00. 50 pages.

★13215★ *Prisoners' Assistance Directory*
National Prison Project
733 15th St. NW, Ste. 620
Washington, DC 20005
Ph: (202)393-4930   Fax: (202)393-4931

Biennial. $30.00. Covers organizations in the U.S. offering assistance to prisoners and their families, including legal, ex-offender, and family support services. Entries include: Organization name, address, phone, fax, URL, name and title of contact, geographical area served, subsidiary and branch names and locations, description of services. Arrangement: Geographical by state. Indexes: Geographical.

AUDIO/VISUAL RESOURCES

★13216★ *Finding a Job*
Cambridge Educational
PO Box 931
Monmouth Junction, NJ 08852-0931
Fax: 800-FAX-ON-US   Fr: 800-468-4227
URL: http://www.cambridgeeducational.com

Video. $98.95. 15 minutes. Covers conventional and unconventional job search methods, and which are more likely to work for ex-offenders.

★13217★ *From Parole to Payroll*
Cambridge Educational
PO Box 931
Monmouth Junction, NJ 08852-0931
Fax: 800-FAX-ON-US   Fr: 800-468-4227
URL: http://www.cambridgeeducational.com

Three videos. 1997. $275.95/set. Three videos cover finding a job (15 minutes), resumes and job applications (15 minutes), and the job interview (15 minutes).

★13218★ *The Job Interview*
Cambridge Educational
PO Box 931
Monmouth Junction, NJ 08852-0931
Fax: 800-FAX-ON-US   Fr: 800-468-4227
URL: http://www.cambridgeeducational.com

$98.95. 1997. 15 minutes. Part of the From Parole to Payroll Series.

★13219★ *Life after Prison: Success on the Outside*
Cambridge Educational
PO Box 931
Monmouth Junction, NJ 08852-0931
Fax: 800-FAX-ON-US   Fr: 800-468-4227
URL: http://www.cambridgeeducational.com

Video. 1999. $98.95. 40 minutes. Contains interviews and covers where to look for employment.

★13220★ *Resumes and Job Applications*
Cambridge Educational
PO Box 931
Monmouth Junction, NJ 08852-0931
Fax: 800-FAX-ON-US   Fr: 800-468-4227
URL: http://www.cambridgeeducational.com

$98.95. 1997. 20 minutes. Part of the From Parole to Payroll Series.

OTHER SOURCES

★13221★ **Court Services and Offender Supervision Agency**
633 Indiana Ave., NW
Washington, DC 20004

Description: Provides services for individuals on parole and probation.

★13222★ **Delancey Street Foundation**
600 Embarcadero
San Francisco, CA 94107

Description: Provides a structured educational and living environment for ex-felons. Teaches life skills.

★13223★ **Fortune Society (FS)**
53 W 23rd St., 8th Fl.
New York, NY 10010
Ph: (212)691-7554   Fax: (212)255-4948
E-mail: dhirsh@fortunesociety.org
URL: http://www.fortunesociety.org

Description: Ex-offenders and others interested in penal reform. Addresses the needs of ex-offenders and high-risk youth. Promotes greater public awareness of the prison system and of the problems confronting inmates before, after, and during incarceration. Works on a personal basis with men and women recently released from prison; helps ex-offenders find jobs. Offers educational services including literacy training and G.E.D. preparation. Sends teams of ex-offenders to talk to school, church, and civic groups and on radio and television to relate first-hand experiences of prison life and to create a greater understanding of the causes of crime in the United States. Conducts Alternatives to Incarceration programs; offers AIDS and general counseling services. Acts as referral agency for half-way houses and drug and alcohol addiction programs.

★13224★ **Osborne Association**
36-31 38th St.
Long Island City, NY 11101
URL: http://www.osborneny.org
Description: Provides assessment, testing, career and educational counseling for ex-offenders.

★13225★ **Sentencing Project**
514 Tenth St. NW, Ste. 1000
Washington, DC 20004
URL: http://www.sentencingproject.org

Description: Training and technical assistance.

★13226★ **Wildcat Service Corporation (WSC)**
17 Battery Place
New York, NY 10004-3875
Ph: (212)209-6000   Fax: (212)635-3875
E-mail: info@wildcat-at-work.org
URL: http://www.wildcatatwork.org

Description: Provides transitional employment and training for chronically unemployed persons (former substance abusers, ex-offenders, welfare mothers, out-of-school youth, and illiterate and delinquent youth). Systematically prepares and grooms employees to accept the full responsibility of full-time work within a 12-month time period. Placement rate of terminees is about 70% in a variety of industries. Operates clerical school in basic and advanced office practices; conducts specialized "life skills" edu-

cational program. Compiles statistics; maintains placement service. Operates three high schools.

★13227★ **Women's Prison Association (WPA)**
110 2nd Ave.
New York, NY 10003
Ph: (212)674-1163   Fax: (212)677-1981
E-mail: ajacobs@wpaonline.org
URL: http://www.wpaonline.org

Purpose: Service agency that aids women involved in the criminal justice system and their families. Promotes alternatives to incarceration; sponsors transitional programs for women being released from prison; assists homeless ex-offenders seeking to reunite with their children who are in kinship or foster-care.

Opportunities for Gay and Lesbian Workers

REFERENCE WORKS

★13228★ **Career and Life Planning With Gay, Lesbian, and Bisexual Persons**
American Counseling Association
5999 Stevenson Ave.
Alexandria, VA 22304-3300
Ph: (703)823-9800   Fax: (703)823-0252
Fr: 800-422-2648
Susan Owre Gelberg and Joseph T. Cho-jnacki. 1996. $35.95. Addresses the issues of overt and covert discrimination in the workplace. Designed by combining career theory and application within a counseling framework specific to the needs of gay, lesbian, and bisexual persons. 200 pages.

★13229★ **Community Yellow Pages**
G & L Community Yellow Pages
8235 Santa Monica Blvd., Ste. 400
West Hollywood, CA 90046
Ph: (323)848-3033   Fax: (323)848-7633
Fr: 800-745-5669
URL: http://www.gaycommunitydirectory.com
Annual, January. Covers approximately 2,500 gay and lesbian-owned businesses; professionals and organizations serving the gay and lesbian community in the Los Angeles, Ventura, Inland Empire, and Long Beach/Orange County, areas. Entries include: Company, organization, or individual name, address, phone and display advertising. Arrangement: Classified by type of service or profession.

★13230★ **Corporate Closet: The Professional Lives of Gay Men in America**
The Free Press
1230 Ave. of the Americas
New York, NY 10020
Ph: (212)698-7000   Fr: 800-223-2348
James D. Woods and Jay H. Lucas. 1994. $14.95. Addresses the risks and benefits of coming out on the job in the United States. 331 pages.

★13231★ **Gay Issues in the Workplace**
St. Martin's Press LLC
16365 James Madison Hwy.
Gordonsville, VA 22942
Ph: (540)672-7600   Fax: 800-672-2054
Fr: 888-330-8477
Brian McNaught. 1994. $11.95. Deals with homophobia in the workplace, the importance of dealing with gay issues within corporations, and techniques for encouraging understanding between all employees. The book includes a sample workshop outline and a list of resources for companies and individuals. Part of Stonewall Inn Edition series.

★13232★ **Gayellow Pages: A Classified Directory of Gay Services and Businesses in USA and Canada**
Gayellow Pages
PO Box 533, Village Sta.
New York, NY 10014-0544
Ph: (212)674-0120   Fax: (212)420-1126
URL: http://gayellowpages.com/
Annual, latest edition March 2000. $16.00; $12.00 for regional editions. Covers gay- or lesbian-oriented business enterprises, organizations, resources, churches, bars, restaurants, and publications; many AIDS/HIV resources. Includes a separate listing of national organizations. Entries include: Name, address, phone, business hours, and an annotation describing programs, products, or services. Also available in regional editions. Arrangement: Geographical; national listings are classified by subject category.

★13233★ **The 100 Best Companies for Gay Men and Lesbians**
Pocket Books
1230 Ave. of the Americas
New York, NY 10020
Ph: (212)698-7000   Fr: 800-223-2348
Ed Mickens. 1994. $12.00 (paper). 288 pages. Provides profiles of 100 "gay-friendly" companies and their policies and benefits. Also includes a discussion of gay and lesbian workplace issues and opportunities.

★13234★ **Out in the Workplace: The Pleasures and Perils of Coming Out on the Job**
Alyson Publications
6922 Hollywood Blvd., Ste. 1000
Los Angeles, CA 90028
Ph: (323)860-6065   Fax: (323)467-0152
Fr: 800-464-4574
Richard A. Rasi and Lourdes Rodriguez-Nogues. 1995. $12.95 (paper). 256 pages. Out of print.

★13235★ **Outing Yourself: How to Come Out to Your Family, Your Friends, & Your Coworkers**
Random House Value Publishing, Inc.
201 E. 50th St.
New York, NY 10022
Ph: (212)572-2400   Fr: 800-733-3000
Michelangelo Signorile. 1997. $4.99.

★13236★ **Personal Financial Planning for Gays and Lesbians**
McGraw-Hill Education Group
PO Box 545
Blacklick, OH 43004-0545
Fax: (614)755-5645   Fr: 800-722-4726
Peter M. Berkery, Jr. 1996. $24.95. Addresses challenges of financial planning and achieving financial goals. 336 pages.

★13237★ **Sexual Orientation in the Workplace: Gay Men, Lesbians, Bisexuals, & Heterosexuals Working Together**
Sage Publications, Inc.
2455 Teller Rd.
Thousand Oaks, CA 91320-2218
Ph: (805)499-0721   Fax: (805)499-0871
Amy J. Zuckerman and George F. Simons. 1995. $31.95 (paper). 96 pages.

★13238★ *Straight Jobs, Gay Lives*
Simon and Schuster Trade
1230 Ave. of the Americas
New York, NY 10020
Ph: (212)698-7000   Fax: (212)698-7007
Fr: 800-897-7650

Annette Friskopp and Sharon Silverstein. 1996. $16.00. Provides an in-depth look at the careers and lives of a wide array of gay professionals. Also provides over 200 contact listings. 528 pages.

NEWSPAPERS, MAGAZINES, AND JOURNALS

★13239★ *The Advocate*
Liberation Publications Inc.
6922 Hollywood Blvd., 10th Fl.
Los Angeles, CA 90028
Ph: (323)871-1225   Fax: (323)467-0173
E-mail: newsroom@advocate.com
URL: http://www.advocate.com

Biweekly. $44.00/year for individuals; $74.00/year for out of country; $3.95 for single issue. National gay and lesbian news and lifestyle magazine.

★13240★ *Fair Employment Practices Summary of Latest Developments*
Bureau of National Affairs Inc.
1231 25th St. NW
Washington, DC 20037
Ph: (202)452-4200   Fax: (202)452-4644
Fr: 800-372-1033

Description: Biweekly. Highlights developments in employment opportunity and affirmative actions, and affirmative action programs. Reports on federal and state court decisions, Equal Employment Opportunity Commission (EEOC) rulings and Office of Federal Contract Compliance Programs (OFCCP) decisions, new laws, regulations, and agency directives. Also provides information on special programs for minorities, the handicapped, women, and older workers.

★13241★ *Out & About*
PlanetOut Corp.
995 Market St.
San Francisco, CA 94103
Ph: (415)486-2501   Fax: (415)229-1793
Fr: 800-929-2268
E-mail: publisher@outandabout.com
URL: http://www.outandabout.com

Description: Ten issues/year. Provides "travel information free from bias for experienced lesbian and gay travelers and their travel agents." Explores U.S. and international destinations and experiences that are gay or gay-friendly. Recurring features include letters to the editor, calendar of events, book reviews, notices of publications available, and columns titled Out at the Inn, Three Ways to Save, Ask the Experts, Editor's Letter, and Traveler's Diary.

ONLINE AND DATABASE SERVICES

★13242★ **Chicago Area Gay and Lesbian Chamber of Commerce**
URL: http://www.glchamber.org/
Description: Site offering business, consumer and travel information to gays and lesbians in the Chicago area. Also includes classified ads for job huntering members.

★13243★ **Queer Net Online Policy Group**
E-mail: majordomo@atsqueernet.org
URL: http://groups.queernet.org/
General e-mail news and discussion list dealing with gay, lesbian, bisexual, and transgender issues within the workplace. To subscribe, send e-mail to majordomo@atsqueernet.org, with the words "subscribe glbt-workplace" or "subscribe glbt-workplace-digest" in the body of the message.

OTHER SOURCES

★13244★ **Association for Gay, Lesbian, and Bisexual Issues in Counseling (AGLBIC)**
Texas State University - San Marcos
Department of Educational Administration and Psychological S
Pecos Bldg., 2nd Fl., No. 201
601 University Dr.
San Marcos, TX 78666
Ph: (512)245-8677   Fax: (512)245-9627
E-mail: cc32@txstate.edu
URL: http://www.aglbic.org

Members: Counselors and personnel and guidance workers concerned with lesbian and gay issues. **Purpose:** Seeks to eliminate discrimination against and stereotyping of gay and lesbian individuals, particularly gay counselors. Works to educate heterosexual counselors on how to overcome homophobia and to best help homosexual clients. **Activities:** Provides a referral network and support for gay counselors and administrators; encourages objective research on gay issues. Organizational affiliate of the American Counseling Association.

★13245★ **Gay and Lesbian Medical Association (GLMA)**
459 Fulton St., Ste. 107
San Francisco, CA 94102
Ph: (415)255-4547   Fax: (415)255-4784
E-mail: info@glma.org
URL: http://www.glma.org

Members: Healthcare professionals. **Purpose:** Seeks elimination of discrimination on the basis of gender identity and sexual orientation in the health profession; promotes unprejudiced medical care for LGBT patients through advocacy and education. Maintains a referral and support program for HIV infected health care workers. Sponsors annual continuing medical education (CME, CEU) symposium on LGBT issues. Offers support to lesbian, gay, bisexual, and transgendered health care workers; encourages research into the health needs of gays and lesbians. Maintains liaison with medical schools and other organizations concerning needs of gay patients and professionals; fosters communication and cooperation among members and other groups and individuals supportive of gay and lesbian physicians. Sponsors Lesbian Health Fund for researching lesbian health needs.

★13246★ **Lesbian, Bisexual, Gay and Transgendered United Employees at AT&T (LEAGUE)**
AT&T, Ste. 1H
12508 E. Briarwood Ave.
Englewood, CO 80112
Ph: (703)713-7820
E-mail: ATTLEAGUE@aol.com
URL: http://www.league-att.org

Members: Individuals employed at or retired from AT&T or any of its subsidiaries. **Purpose:** Fosters the value of mutual respect and appreciation of cultural differences among employees. **Activities:** Offers educational programs and support groups to address issues that affect lesbian, gay, and bisexual employees, and their friends and families. Acts as an information clearinghouse on homosexuality, bisexuality, and lesbian and gay issues. Provides referral services to support groups and community and service organizations.

★13247★ **Lesbian, Gay, Bisexual, and Transgender People in Medicine (LGBPM)**
1902 Association Dr.
Reston, VA 20191
Ph: (703)620-6600   Fax: (703)620-5873
Fr: 800-767-2266
E-mail: amsa@amsa.org
URL: http://www.amsa.org

Description: Advocacy Group of the American Medical Student Association. Physicians and physicians in training; others interested in gay/lesbian issues. Purposes are to improve the quality of health care for gay patients; to improve working conditions and professional status of gay health professionals and students. Administers educational workshops for health professionals; designs training materials; conducts research on the health problems of gay people and surveys on admissions, hiring, and promotion policies of medical schools and hospitals; provides referrals; sponsors support groups for gay professionals to meet, socialize, and organize; presses for legislative and political action to end discrimination against gay people. Maintains speakers' bureau.

★13248★ Lesbian Resource Center (LRC)

227 S Orcas St.
Seattle, WA 98108
Ph: (206)322-3953   Fax: (206)322-0586
E-mail: lrc@lrc.net
URL: http://www.lrc.net

Description: Provides classes, groups, workshops, and information on housing, employment, and lesbian community groups and events. Represents the lesbian community in areas of political and social concern.

★13249★ National Association of Social Workers National Committee on Lesbian, Gay and Bisexual Issues (NASW)

750 First St. NE, Ste. 700
Washington, DC 20002-4241
Ph: (202)408-8600   Fax: (202)336-8327
Fr: 800-638-8799
E-mail: gwaller@naswdc.org
URL: http://www.socialworkers.org/governance/cmtes/nclgbi.asp

Description: A committee of the National Association of Social Workers. Seeks to ensure equal employment opportunities for lesbian, gay and bisexual individuals. Informs the NASW about: domestic, racial, and antigay violence; civil rights; family and primary associations. Encourages the NASW to support legislation, regulations, policies, judicial review, political action, and other activities that seek to establish and protect equal rights for all persons without regard to their affectional and/or sexual orientation. Advises government bodies and political candidates regarding the needs and concerns of social workers and lesbian and gay people; reviews proposed legislation.

★13250★ National Center for Lesbian Rights (NCLR)

870 Market St., Ste. 570
San Francisco, CA 94102
Ph: (415)392-6257   Fax: (415)392-8442
Fr: 800-528-6257
E-mail: info@nclrights.org
URL: http://www.nclrights.org

Description: A legal resource center specializing in sexual orientation discrimination cases, particularly those involving lesbians. Activities include: legal counseling and representation, community education, and technical assistance. Provides legal services to lesbian, gay and transgender youths, adults and elders on issues of custody and foster parenting, visitation rights second parent adoption.

★13251★ National Gay and Lesbian Task Force (NGLTF)

1325 Massachusetts Ave. NW, Ste. 600
Washington, DC 20005
Ph: (202)393-5177   Fax: (202)393-2241
E-mail: ngltf@ngltf.org
URL: http://www.ngltf.org

Description: Works to end violence and discrimination against gay, lesbian, bisexual, and transgendered people at the state, local, and federal level. Does grassroots organizing, training, and legislative advocacy. Monitors and tracks legislation in 50 states. Houses GLBT think tank producing research and analysis on GLBT issues. Maintains speakers' bureau.

★13252★ National Organization of Gay and Lesbian Scientists and Technical Professionals (NOGLSTP)

PO Box 91803
Pasadena, CA 91109
Ph: (626)791-7689   Fax: (626)791-7689
E-mail: office@noglstp.org
URL: http://www.noglstp.org/

Members: Gay and lesbian individuals employed or interested in high-technology or scientific fields; interested organizations. **Purpose:** Works to educate the public, especially the gay and scientific communities; improve members' employment and professional environment; oppose anti-gay discrimination and stereotypes; interact with professional organizations; foster intercity contacts among members. **Activities:** Addresses issues of discrimination in the provision of security clearances, employment, and immigration. Disseminates information. Organizes symposiums and workshops.

Opportunities for Independent Contractors and Freelance Workers

REFERENCE WORKS

★13253★ *Achieving Financial Independence As a Freelance Writer*
Blue Heron Publishing
4205 SW Washington St., Suite 303
Portland, OR 97204
Ph: (503)221-6841   Fax: (503)221-6843
Raymond Dreyfack. 2000. $16.95 (paper).

★13254★ *Editorial Freelancing: A Practical Guide*
Aletheia Publications, Inc.
46 Bell Hollow Rd.
Putnam Valley, NY 10579
Ph: (914)526-2873   Fax: (914)526-2905
Trumbull Rogers. 1995. $19.95 (paper). Presents what a freelancer needs to know about building a basic reference library, choosing a computer and appropriate software, marketing editorial services, determining and negotiating rates, billing, and setting up a retirement plan. Offers guidelines for establishing and equipping the home office, finding and keeping clients, and maintaining business records. 200 pages.

★13255★ *Freelance Editorial Association Yellow Pages & Code of Fair Practice*
Freelance Editorial Association
71 W 23rd St., Ste. 1910
New York, NY 10010
Ph: (212)929-5400   Fax: (212)929-5439
URL: http://www.tiac.net/users/freelanc
Annual. $47.50. Covers services offered by hundreds of freelance editors, indexers, proofreaders, translators, desktop publishers, researchers, illustrators, and writers; member are located throughout the United States. Entries include: Name, address, phone, and brief descriptions. Arrangement: Classified by editorial skill. Indexes: Name, geographical, specialty.

★13256★ *Freelance Teaching and Tutoring: How to Earn Good Money by Teaching Others What You Know*
Trans-Atlantic Publications, Inc.
311 Bainbridge St.
Philadelphia, PA 19147
Ph: (215)925-5083   Fax: (215)925-1912
John T. Wilson. 1997. 118 pages. Part of the Jobs and Careers Series.

★13257★ *Guidelines for Freelancers*
MasAir Publications
4918 Newman Rd.
Abilene, TX 79601
Ph: (915)672-3087   Fax: (915)673-0430
Fr: 800-277-5984
Nancy R. Masters. Second edition, 1996. $13.95 (paper). 120 pages. Out of print.

★13258★ *In Concert: The Freelance Musician's Keys to Financial Success*
Preludes Nouveaux, Ltd.
1506 E. Fox. Ln.
Milwaukee, WI 53217-2853
Ph: (414)241-9711
Gail Nelson and Pamela Fourd. 1994. $16.95 (paper). 96 pages.

★13259★ *The Joy of Working from Home: Making a Life While Making a Living*
Berrett-Koehler Publishers
235 Montgomery St., Suite 650
San Francisco, CA 94104
Ph: (415)288-0260   Fax: (415)362-2512
Fr: 800-929-2929
Jeff Berner. 1994. $12.95 (paper). 240 pages.

★13260★ *Make Money Freelance News Writing*
Seven Hills Book Distributors
1531 Tremont St.
Cincinnati, OH 45214-1458
Ph: (513)471-4300   Fax: (513)471-4311
Fr: 800-545-2005
Ian McCrone. 1997. $15.95 (paper). Out of print.

★13261★ *Making It Big in the $100 Billion Outsource Contracting Industry: Turn Your Knowledge Experience and Commitment into Lifetime Strategic Partnerships*
Westfield Press
3711 W. 101st Ave.
Westminster, CO 80030-2435
Ph: (303)466-7558   Fax: (303)438-5512
Robert W. Jennings. 1997. $49.95. Outlines how to use career experiences and strengths to tap into the market. 227 pages.

★13262★ *Marketing for the Home-based Business*
Adams Media Corp.
57 Littlefield St.
Avon, MA 02322
Ph: (508)427-7100   Fax: (508)427-6790
Fr: 800-872-5627
URL: http://www.adamsmedia.com
Jeffrey P. Davidson. Second edition, 1999. $10.95 (paper). 242 pages. Addresses how to market the home-based business after you've started it.

★13263★ *On Your Own: A Guide to Working Happily, Productively & Successfully at Home*
Prentice Hall PTR
200 Old Tappan Rd.
Old Tappan, NJ 07675
Ph: (201)236-7000   Fr: 800-223-1360
Lionel L. Fisher. 1994. $10.95 (paper). 228 pages.

★13264★ *100 Best Freelance Careers*

Macmillan Publishing Co., Inc.
200 Old Tappan Rd.
Old Tappan, NJ 07675
Fr: 800-428-5331

Kelly Reno. 1997. $14.95. 256 pages.

★13265★ *The Perfect Business: How to Make a Million from Home with No Payroll, No Employee Headaches, No Debt, and No Sleepless Nights*

Simon & Schuster Inc.
1230 Ave. of the Americas
New York, NY 10020
Ph: (212)698-7000   Fax: (212)698-7007
Fr: 800-223-2336

Michael LeBoeuf. 1997. $12.00 (paper).

★13266★ *Photos That Sell: The Art of Successful Freelance Photography*

Watson-Guptill Publications, Incorporated
770 Broadway
New York, NY 10003
Ph: (646)654-5400   Fax: (646)654-5486
Fr: 800-323-9432

Lee Frost. 2001. $24.95 (paper).

★13267★ *The Quick Internet Guide to Career and Education Information*

JIST Publishing
8902 Otis Ave.
Indianapolis, IN 46216-1033
Ph: (317)613-4200   Fax: (317)613-4309
Fr: 800-648-5478

$16.95. Covers utilizing the Internet to research colleges, financial aid, distance learning, careers, job openings, military careers, contract work, and other college and career-related information. Entries include: Web site address, summary of source.

★13268★ *Rocky Mountain Publishing Professionals Guild-Directory*

Rocky Mountain Publishing Professionals
 Guild
PO Box 17721
Boulder, CO 80308-7721
URL: http://www.rmppg.org

Annual. Covers approximately 60 freelancers serving the publishing industry nationwide. Entries include: Name, address, phone, fax, description of services offered, list of representative clients, year founded. Arrangement: Alphabetical. Indexes: Service.

★13269★ *Self-Employed Writers and Artists Network-Directory*

Self-Employed Writers and Artists
 Network Inc.
PO Box 440
Paramus, NJ 07653
Ph: (201)967-1313
URL: http://www.swan-net.com

Annual, spring. Covers over 135 freelance writers, graphic designers, illustrators, pho-

tographers, and other graphic arts professionals in northern New Jersey and New York city providing services in advertising, marketing, sales promotion, public relations, and telecommunications. Entries include: Name, address, phone, biographical data, description of services provided. Arrangement: Alphabetical. Indexes: Line of business.

★13270★ *Self-Publishing Manual*

Para Publishing
PO Box 8206-240
Santa Barbara, CA 93118-8206
Ph: (805)968-7277   Fax: (805)968-1379
Fr: 800-PAR-APUB
URL: http://www.parapublishing.com

Biennial, odd years. $19.95; $23.95 for California residents. Publication includes: Lists of wholesalers, reviewers, exporters, suppliers, direct mailing list sources, publishing organizations, and others of assistance in publishing. Entries include: Organization or company name, address, email addresses and web address. Arrangement: Classified by ZIP code. Indexes: General subject.

★13271★ *Streetwise Guide to Freelance Design and Illustration*

F & W Publications, Inc.
4700 E Galbraith Rd.
Cincinnati, OH 45236
Ph: (513)531-2690   Fax: (513)531-4082
Fr: 800-289-0963

Theo S. Williams. 1998. $24.99 (paper). 144 pages.

★13272★ *Successfully Self-Employed*

Upstart Pub. Co.
155 N. Wacker Dr.
Chicago, IL 60606-1719
Ph: (312)836-4400   Fax: (312)836-1021
Fr: 800-621-9621

Gregory Brennan. 1996. $16.95 (paper). 175 pages. Out of print.

★13273★ *Working Solo Sourcebook: Essential Resources for Independent Entrepreneurs*

John Wiley & Sons Inc.
1 Wiley Dr.
Somerset, NJ 08873
Ph: (732)469-4400   Fr: 800-225-5945

Terri Lonier. First edition, 1998. $14.95 (paper).

★13274★ *WritersNet*

Internet Concepts L.L.C.
6200 Gisholt Dr., Ste. 105
Madison, WI 53713
URL: http://www.writersnet.com

Database covers: Internet resources, books, and other materials for writers.

ONLINE AND DATABASE SERVICES

★13275★ FreeAgent
URL: http://www.freeagent.com
Description: Information site provides free job board for freelance and independent contractors. Site also contains resources for hosted e-presence, tax services, and business opportunities.

★13276★ FreelanceWorkExchange.com
E-mail: support@freelanceworkexchange.com
URL: http://www.freelanceworkexchange.com
Description: Project and contract search board for the freelance worker. E-mail newsletters and freelancing e-books available.
Fee: Must register as a member; pricing based on length of membership; one month is $19.95. Trial seven-day membership available.

★13277★ Guru
URL: http://www.guru.com
Description: Job board specializing in contract jobs for creative and information technology professionals. Also provides online incorporation and educational opportunities for independent contractors along with articles and advice.

★13278★ Work from Home
URL: http://www.jobs-telecommuting.com
Description: Contains a listing of over 700 companies currently looking for telecommuters. Employers may add or remove job listings. Also information on starting a home business available.

OTHER SOURCES

★13279★ American Society of Journalists and Authors (ASJA)
1501 Broadway, Ste. 302
New York, NY 10036
Ph: (212)997-0947   Fax: (212)768-7414
E-mail: staff@asja.org
URL: http://www.asja.org

Description: Freelance writers of nonfiction magazine articles and books. Seeks to elevate the professional and economic position of nonfiction writers, provide a forum for discussion of common problems among writers and editors, and promote a code of ethics for writers and editors. Operates writer referral Service for individuals, institutions, or companies seeking writers for special projects; sponsors Llewellyn Miller Fund to aid professional writers no longer able to work due to age, disability, or extraordinary professional crisis.

★13280★ **American Society of Media Photographers (ASMP)**

150 N 2nd St.
Philadelphia, PA 19106
Ph: (215)451-2767   Fax: (215)451-0880
E-mail: mopsik@asmp.org
URL: http://www.asmp.org

Members: Professional society of freelance photographers. **Purpose:** Works to evolve trade practices for photographers in communications fields. Provides business information to photographers and their potential clients; promotes ethics and rights of members. **Activities:** Holds educational programs and seminars. Compiles statistics.

★13281★ **Associated Writing Programs (AWP)**

George Mason University
Carty House, Mail Stop 1E3
Fairfax, VA 22030
Ph: (703)993-4301
E-mail: awp@gmu.edu
URL: http://www.awpwriter.org

Description: Writers; students and teachers in creative writing programs in university departments of English; editors, publishers, and freelance creative and professional writers. Fosters literary talent and achievement; advocates the craft of writing as primary to a liberal and humane education; provides publications and services to the makers and readers of contemporary literature. Operates career services and job listings; sponsors literary competitions.

★13282★ **Association of Food Journalists (AFJ)**

38309 Genesee Lake Rd.
Oconomowoc, WI 53066
Ph: (262)965-3251
E-mail: carolafj@execpc.com
URL: http://www.afjonline.com

Description: Individuals employed as food journalists by newspapers, magazines, internet services, and broadcasters; freelance food journalists. Goals are to encourage communication and professional development among food journalists and to increase members' knowledge of food and food-related issues. Promotes professional ethical standards.

★13283★ **Copywriter's Council of America (CCA)**

CCA Bldg.
7 Putter Ln.
PO Box 102
Middle Island, NY 11953-0102
Ph: (631)924-8555   Fax: (631)924-5890
E-mail: cca4dmcopy@att.net
URL: http://www.lgroup.addr.com/CCA.htm

Description: Advertising copywriters, marketing and public relations consultants, copyeditors, proofreaders, and other individuals involved in print, radio, broadcast, video, and telecommunications. Provides freelance work; acts as agent for members; negotiates on members' behalf. Serves as a forum for professional and social contact between freelance communications professionals. Offers courses on copywriting, direct marketing, mail order, publishing screenplays, and how to get published. Conducts charitable programs. Maintains speakers' bureau, hall of fame, and word processing consultation service.

★13284★ **Dance Critics Association (DCA)**

10592 Perry Hwy.
Wexford, PA 15090-9244
Ph: (412)363-4321   Fax: (412)363-4320
E-mail: dancecritics@hotmail.com

Description: Critics who review dance as a major professional responsibility either on a regular basis or as a freelance reviewer, in print and/or broadcast media; teachers, historians, publicists, and other individuals interested in dance writing. Encourages excellence in dance criticism through education, research, and the exchange of ideas. Conducts clinics on practical topics of interest to critics.

★13285★ **National Court Reporters Association (NCRA)**

8224 Old Courthouse Rd.
Vienna, VA 22182
Ph: (703)556-6272   Fax: (703)556-6291
Fr: 800-272-6272
E-mail: msic@ncrahq.org
URL: http://www.ncraonline.org

Description: Independent state, regional, and local associations. Verbatim court reporters who work as official reporters for courts and government agencies, as freelance reporters for independent contractors, and as captioners for television programming; retired reporters, teachers of court reporting, and school officials; student court reporters. Conducts research; compiles statistics; offers several certification programs, publishes journal.

★13286★ **National Writers Association (ABWA)**

3140 S Peoria St., Ste. 295
Aurora, CO 80014-3155
Ph: (303)841-0246   Fax: (303)841-2607
E-mail: ExecDirSandyWhelchel@nationalwriters.com
URL: http://www.nationalwriters.com

Members: Professional full- or part-time freelance writers who specialize in business writing. **Purpose:** Is to serve as a marketplace whereby business editors can easily locate competent writing talent. **Activities:** Establishes communication among editors and writers.

★13287★ **National Writers Union (NWU)**

113 University Place, 6th Fl.
New York, NY 10003-4527
Ph: (212)254-0279   Fax: (212)254-0673
E-mail: nwu@nwu.org
URL: http://www.nwu.org

Members: Freelance writers; journalists, authors, poets, and technical and public relations writers who are not represented by any existing union. **Purpose:** Engages in collective bargaining and provides other services for members such as grievance handling and health insurance. Works to raise rates and improve treatment of freelance writers by magazine and book publishers. Holds conferences on legal, economic, trade, and craft issues affecting writers.

Opportunities for Liberal Arts Graduates

REFERENCE WORKS

★13288★ Career Employment Opportunities Directory
Ready Reference Press
1652 N Pepper Dr.
Pasadena, CA 91104
Ph: (310)474-4895   Fr: 800-424-5627
Biennial, October of odd years. $47.50 per volume; $190.00 per set. Covers about 1,250 companies that employ college graduates; separate editions available for "Liberal Arts and Social Sciences," "Business Administration," "Engineering and Computer Sciences," and "Sciences" Entries include: Company name, general description of company and career opportunities, job locations, special programs, and contact address. Arrangement: Alphabetical. Indexes: Discipline, geographical.

★13289★ The Career Guide-Dun's Employment Opportunities Directory
Dun & Bradstreet
3 Sylvan Way
Parsippany, NJ 07054-3896
Fax: (973)605-6911   Fr: 800-526-0651
Annual. $425.00 to public libraries; $495.00 commercially. Covers more than 5,000 companies on leading employers throughout the U.S. that provide career opportunities in sales, marketing, management, engineering, life and physical sciences, computer science, mathematics, statistics planning, accounting and finance, liberal arts fields, and other technical and professional areas; based on data supplied by questionnaires and through personal interviews. Also covers personnel consultants; includes some public sector employers (governments, schools, etc.) usually not found in similar lists. Entries include: Company name, location of headquarters and other offices or plants; entries may also include name, title, address, and phone of employment contact; disciplines or occupational groups hired; brief overview of company, discussion of types of positions that may be available, training and career development programs, benefits offered, internship and work-study programs. Arrange-ment: Employers are alphabetical; geographically by industry, employer branch offices geographically, disciplines hired geographically, employees offering work-study or internship programs and personnel consultants. Indexes: Geographical, SIC code.

★13290★ Career Planning & Development for College Students & Recent Graduates
McGraw-Hill Trade
2 Penn Plaza
New York, NY 10121
Ph: (212)904-2000   Fr: 800-722-4726
E-mail: ntcpub@tribune.com
John E. Steele and Marilyn S. Morgan. 1995. $29.95; $17.95 (paper). 448 pages.

★13291★ Careers for Culture Lovers and Other Artsy Types
VGM Career Horizons
1221 Avenue of the Americas
New York, NY 10020
Ph: (212)904-2000   Fr: 800-323-4900
E-mail: ntcpub@tribune.com
Marjorie Eberts and Margaret Gisler. Second edition, 1999. $14.95; $9.95 (paper). 234 pages. Describes how to get work in a variety of fields related to art and culture. Opportunities include picture framer, curator, art restorer, symphony manager, disk jockey, music reviewer, dance teacher, choreographer, costume designer, theater manager, light designer, drama teacher, bookstore owner, interior decorator, antique store owner, and others.

★13292★ Choices and Challenges: Job Search Strategies for Liberal Arts Students
IU Custom Publishing
2715 E. Tenth St.
Bloomington, IN 47405
Ph: (812)855-9337   Fax: (812)855-1463
1998. $16.95 (paper). 197 pages.

★13293★ College Grad Job Hunter: Insider Techniques and Tactics for Finding a Top-Paying Entry Level Job
Adams Media Corp.
57 Littlefield St.
Avon, MA 02322
Ph: (508)427-7100   Fax: (508)427-6790
Fr: 800-872-5627
URL: http://www.adamsmedia.com
Brian D. Krueger. Fourth edition, 1998. $14.95 (paper). 352 pages.

★13294★ Great Jobs for English Majors
McGraw-Hill Trade
2 Penn Plaza
New York, NY 10121
Ph: (212)904-2000   Fr: 800-722-4726
E-mail: ntcpub@tribune.com
Julie DeGalan. Second edition, 2000. $12.95 (paper). 462 pages.

★13295★ Great Jobs for Foreign Language Majors
McGraw-Hill Trade
2 Penn Plaza
New York, NY 10121
Ph: (212)904-2000   Fr: 800-722-4726
E-mail: ntcpub@tribune.com
Julie DeGalan and Stephen E. Lambert. 1994. $11.95 (paper). 412 pages. Part of Great Jobs for... Majors series.

★13296★ Great Jobs for History Majors
McGraw-Hill Trade
2 Penn Plaza
New York, NY 10121
Ph: (212)904-2000   Fr: 800-722-4726
E-mail: ntcpub@tribune.com
Julie DeGalan and Stephen Lambert. 1994. $11.95 (paper). 442 pages.

★13297★ Great Jobs for Liberal Arts Majors
McGraw-Hill Professional
2 Penn Plaza
New York, NY 10121
Ph: (212)904-2000   Fr: 800-722-4726
E-mail: ntcpub@tribune.com

Blythe Camenson. Second edition, 2001. $14.95 (paper). 256 pages.

★13298★ The Liberal Arts Advantage: How to Turn Your Degree into a Great Job
Avon Books
1350 Ave. of the Americas
New York, NY 10019
Ph: (212)261-6788   Fr: 800-242-7737

Gregory Giangrande. 1998. $12.00 (paper). 208 pages.

★13299★ Opening Doors: A Job Search Guide for Graduates
The Graduate Group
PO Box 370351
West Hartford, CT 06137-0351
Ph: (860)233-2330   Fr: 800-484-7280

Janet G. Revelt. 1996. $27.50 (paper).

★13300★ Path: A Career Workbook for Liberal Arts Students
Sulzburger & Graham Publishing, Ltd.
793 Arbuckle Ave.
Woodmere, NY 11598-2723
Ph: (212)947-0100   Fax: (212)947-0360
Fr: 800-366-7086

Howard E. Figler. 1993. $13.50. 128 pages.

★13301★ Peterson's Job Opportunities for Business Majors
Thomson Peterson's
Princeton Pke. Corporate Ctr., 2000 Lenox Dr.
PO Box 67005
Lawrenceville, NJ 08648
Ph: (609)896-1800   Fax: (609)896-4531
Fr: 800-338-3282
URL: http://www.petersons.com

Irregular, latest edition 2000 - 16th ed. $18.95. Covers the 2,000 largest U.S. employers hiring in several fields, including financial services, management consulting, consumer products, and media/ entertainment. Entries include: Organization name, address, phone, name and title of contact, number of employees, type of organization. Arrangement: Alphabetical. Indexes: Type of organization.

★13302★ Real Life Guide to Starting Your Career: How to Get the Right Job Right Now!
TIPS Technical Publishing, Inc.
108 E. Main St., Ste. 4
Carrboro, NC 27510-2374
Ph: (919)933-2629   Fax: (919)832-9717

Margot C. Lester. 1998. $16.95 (paper). Part of the "Real Life Guides Series."

★13303★ The Student's Guide to Finding a Superior Job
Jossey-Bass Inc. Publishers
350 Sansome St.
San Francisco, CA 94104-1342
Ph: (415)433-1740   Fax: (415)433-0499
Fr: 800-956-7739

William A. Cohen. Second edition, 1993. $9.95 (paper). 108 pages. Aimed at the new college graduate. Out of print.

ONLINE AND DATABASE SERVICES

★13304★ College Job Board.com
E-mail: contac-tus@collegejobboard.zzn.com
URL: http://www.collegejobboard.com

Description: Job search site specializing in the career search of recent college, vocational and grad school graduates. Free resume posting, job board search, job tracking, scholarship and loan search and career resources.

★13305★ True Careers: College Edition
URL: http://www.jobdirect.com

Description: Recent college graduates can post their resume and search for jobs. Also contains interviewing tips and career resources, and career expert advice posting.

Opportunities for Military Personnel and Veterans

REFERENCE WORKS

★13306★ **Affirmative Action Register**
Affirmative Action Inc.
8356 Olive Blvd.
St. Louis, MO 63132
Ph: (314)991-1335   Fax: (314)997-1788
Fr: 800-537-0655
URL: http://www.aar-eeo.com

Monthly. $1.50 for single issue. Covers in each issue, about 300 positions at a professional level (most requiring advanced study) available to women, minorities, veterans, and the handicapped; listings are advertisements placed by employers with affirmative action programs. Entries include: Company or organization name, address, contact name; description of position including title, requirements, duties, application procedure, salary, etc. Arrangement: Classified by profession.

★13307★ **America's Top Military Careers: The Official Guide to Occupations in the Armed Forces**
JIST Publishing
8902 Otis Ave.
Indianapolis, IN 46216-1033
Ph: (317)613-4200   Fax: (317)613-4307
Fr: 800-648-5478

JIST Publishing staff. Third edition, 2000. $19.95 (paper). 427 pages.

★13308★ **Career Progression Guide for Soldiers**
Stackpole Books
5067 Ritter Rd.
Mechanicsburg, PA 17055
Ph: (717)796-0411   Fax: (717)796-0412
Fr: 800-732-3669

Audie G. Lewis. 1998. $12.95 (paper).

★13309★ **The Civilian Career Guide**
Grant's Guide, Inc.
PO Box 613
Lake Placid, NY 12946
Ph: (518)523-3498   Fax: (518)523-2974
Fr: 800-922-1923

James Grant, editor. 1993. $9.95 (paper). 220 pages.

★13310★ **Employment Guide for the Military, Intelligence and Special Operations Communities**
The Graduate Group
PO Box 370351
West Hartford, CT 06137-0351
Ph: (860)233-2330   Fr: 800-484-7280

Mark W. Merritt. 1997. $30.00.

★13311★ **Financial Aid for Veterans, Military Personnel, and Their Dependents**
Reference Service Press
5000 Windplay Dr., Ste. 4
El Dorado Hills, CA 95762
Ph: (916)939-9620   Fax: (916)939-9626

Biennial, January of even years, latest edition 2004-2006 edition. $40.00. Covers organizations that offer approximately 1,100 scholarships, fellowships, loans, grants, awards, and internships to veterans, military personnel, and their families. Entries include: Organization name, address, phone, financial data, requirements for eligibility, duration, special features and limitations, deadline, number of awards. Arrangement: Classified by type of program and target audience. Indexes: Organization name, program, residency, tenability, subject, and deadline date.

★13312★ **From Air Force Blue to Corporate Gray: A Career Transition Guide for Air Force Personnel**
Impact Publications
9104 Manassas Dr., Ste. N
Manassas Park, VA 20111-5211
Ph: (703)361-7300   Fax: (703)335-9486

Carl S. Savino and Ronald L. Krannich. Second edition, 1997. Out of print.

★13313★ **From Army Green to Corporate Gray: A Career Transition Guide for Army Personnel**
Impact Publications
9104 Manassas Dr., Ste. N
Manassas Park, VA 20111-5211
Ph: (703)361-7300   Fax: (703)335-9486

Carl S. Savino and Ronald L. Krannich. Second edition, 1997. $13.95 (paper). 367 pages. Out of print.

★13314★ **From Navy Blue to Corporate Gray: A Career Transition Guide for Navy & Marine Corps Personnel**
Impact Publications
9104 Manassas Dr., Ste. N
Manassas Park, VA 20111-5211
Ph: (703)361-7300   Fax: (703)335-9486

Carl S. Savino and Ronald L. Krannich. Second edition, 1997. $17.95 (paper). Out of print.

★13315★ **Future Career Management Systems for U.S. Military Officers**
Rand Corp.
PO Box 2138
Santa Monica, CA 90407-2138
Ph: (310)393-0411   Fax: (310)451-6996

Harry Thie and Roger Brown. 1994. $15.00 (paper).

★13316★ **A Guide to Civilian Jobs for Enlisted Naval Personnel**
Barron's Educational Series, Inc.
250 Wireless Blvd.
Hauppauge, NY 11788-3917
Ph: (631)434-3311   Fax: (631)434-3723
Fr: 800-645-3476

Rodney Voelker. 1996. $14.95 (paper). 432 pages.

★13317★ *IMCEA-Membership Directory*

International Military Community
   Executives Association (IMCEA)
23514 Beachwood Blvd.
Beachwood, OH 44122-1411

Annual, May. $345.00. Covers about 1,000 Navy, Army, Air Force, Marine Corps, and Coast Guard personnel who manage military clubs and golf and bowling centers; supplier members are also listed. Entries include: For military club and Morale, Welfare and Recreation (MWR) personnel-Name, office address and phone. For suppliers-Company name, address, product or service. Arrangement: Personnel are alphabetical; suppliers are classified by product, then alphabetical. Indexes: Geographical, product.

★13318★ *In or Out of the Military: How to Make Your Own Best Decision*

Pepper Press
1254 W. Pioneer Way, Ste. A266
Oak Harbor, WA 98277-3288

D.F. Reardon. 1993. $14.95 (paper). 144 pages.

★13319★ *Job Search: Marketing Your Military Experience*

Stackpole Books
5067 Ritter Rd.
Mechanicsburg, PA 17055
Ph: (717)796-0411   Fax: (717)796-0412
Fr: 800-732-3669

David G. Henderson. 1995. $14.95 (paper). 192 pages.

★13320★ *Opportunities in Aerospace Careers*

McGraw-Hill Contemporary Books
1221 Avenue of the Americas
New York, NY 10020
Ph: (212)904-2000   Fr: 800-323-4900
E-mail: ntcpub@tribune.com

Wallace R. Maples. 1995. $14.95; $11.95 (paper). Surveys jobs with the airlines, airports, the government, the military, in manufacturing, and in research and development. Includes information on job opportunities with NASA in the U.S. space program.

★13321★ *Opportunities in Law Enforcement and Criminal Justice Careers*

McGraw-Hill Contemporary Books
1221 Avenue of the Americas
New York, NY 10020
Ph: (212)904-2000   Fr: 800-323-4900
E-mail: ntcpub@tribune.com

James Stinchcomb. Revised edition, 1996. $14.95; $11.95 (paper). 160 pages. Offers information on opportunities at the city, county, state, military, and federal levels. Contains bibliography and illustrations.

★13322★ *Opportunities in Military Careers*

McGraw-Hill Contemporary Books
1221 Avenue of the Americas
New York, NY 10020
Ph: (212)904-2000   Fr: 800-323-4900
E-mail: ntcpub@tribune.com

Adrian A. Paradis. 1999. $14.95; $11.95 (paper). 160 pages. Illustrates what it's like to work in a variety of job situations unique to the armed forces. Opportunities for civilian employment are also included. Illustrated.

★13323★ *Out of Uniform: A Career Transition Guide for Ex-Military Personnel*

McGraw-Hill Trade
2 Penn Plaza
New York, NY 10121
Ph: (212)904-2000   Fr: 800-722-4726
E-mail: ntcpub@tribune.com

Harry N. Drier. 1994. $12.95 (paper). 192 pages. Part of Professional Careers series. Out of stock indefinitely.

★13324★ *Punching Out: Launching a Post-Military Career*

Palgrave Macmillan
175 Fifth Ave.
New York, NY 10010
Ph: (212)982-9300   Fax: (212)777-6359
Fr: 800-221-7945

Fred Mastin. 1994.

★13325★ *The Quick Internet Guide to Career and Education Information*

JIST Publishing
8902 Otis Ave.
Indianapolis, IN 46216-1033
Ph: (317)613-4200   Fax: (317)613-4309
Fr: 800-648-5478

$16.95. Covers utilizing the Internet to research colleges, financial aid, distance learning, careers, job openings, military careers, contract work, and other college and career-related information. Entries include: Web site address, summary of source.

★13326★ *Resume and Job Search: Letters for Transitioning Military Personnel*

Impact Publications
9104 Manassas Dr., Suite N
Manassas Park, VA 20111-5211
Ph: (703)361-7300   Fax: (703)335-9486
URL: http://www.CareerBookstore.com

Carl S. Savino and Ronald L. Krannich. 1998. 272 pages. $17.95. Helps members of the military service communicate their skills for civilian positions. Out of print.

★13327★ *Resumes for Ex-Military Personnel*

McGraw-Hill Trade
2 Penn Plaza
New York, NY 10121
Ph: (212)904-2000   Fr: 800-722-4726

E-mail: ntcpub@tribune.com

1995. $9.95 (paper). 462 pages. Part of VGM Professional Resume series. Out of print.

★13328★ *Yes, There Is Life after Aerospace: Career Transition from Military Defense Aerospace to Commercial Civilian Life*

A B P Associates
116 W. Santa Fe Ave.
Placentia, CA 92870-5632
Ph: (909)982-7595

Marie H. Reichelt. 1994. $14.95 (paper). 132 pages.

NEWSPAPERS, MAGAZINES, AND JOURNALS

★13329★ *Air Force Times*

Army Times Publishing Co.
6883 Commercial Dr.
Springfield, VA 22159-0001
Ph: (703)750-9000   Fax: (703)750-8767
E-mail: mcoair@aol.com

Weekly. $48.00/year. Independent newspaper serving Air Force personnel worldwide.

★13330★ *Armed Forces Journal International*

Defense News Media Group
6883 Commercial Dr.
Springfield, VA 22159
Ph: (703)750-9000   Fax: (703)848-0480
URL: http://www.afji.com

Free. Magazine concerning the armed services, national security, and defense.

★13331★ *Army Aviation Magazine*

Army Aviation Publications Inc.
755 Main St. Ste. 4D
Monroe, CT 06468-2830
E-mail: magazine@quad-a.org

$30.00/year for individuals; $3.00 for single issue. Army aviation magazine.

★13332★ *Checkpoint*

Veterans of Foreign Wars of the United
   States
VFW Bldg.
34th and Broadway
Kansas City, MO 64111
Ph: (816)756-3390   Fax: (816)968-1169
URL: http://www.vfw.org

Description: Six issues/year. Concerned with the organization's work of promoting patriotism. Covers national news of the VFW's community service activities, holiday observances, patriotic promotion campaigns, youth activities, safety, etc. Recurring features include editorials, legislation updates, veterans services, employment opportunities, and national security/foreign affairs.

★13333★ Military Medicine
Association of Military Surgeons of the U.S. (AMSUS)
9320 Old Georgetown Rd.
Bethesda, MD 20814
Ph: (301)897-8800   Fax: (301)530-5446
Fr: 800-761-9320
E-mail: milmed@amsus.org

Monthly. $65.00/year for individuals; $70.00/year for other countries; $6.00 for single issue. Journal for professional personnel affiliated with the Federal medical services.

★13334★ National Military Family Association Public Relations & Marketing
National Military Family Association Inc.
2500 N Van Dorn St., Ste. 102
Alexandria, VA 22302
Ph: (703)931-6632   Fax: (703)931-4600
URL: http://www.nmfa.org

Description: Monthly. Reports on current and proposed legislation affecting military families, quality of military life, and problems facing military families. Covers topics such as health care, relocation and housing, spouse employment, education, and retirement and survivor benefits. Recurring features include Association news and legislative updates.

★13335★ Navy Times
Army Times Publishing Co.
6883 Commercial Dr.
Springfield, VA 22159-0001
Ph: (703)750-9000   Fax: (703)750-8767
E-mail: navydesk@aol.com

Weekly. $52.00/year for individuals; $2.25 for single issue. Independent newspaper serving Navy, Marine, and Coast Guard personnel.

★13336★ The Officer
The Reserve Officers Association
1 Constitution Ave. NE
Washington, DC 20002
Ph: (202)479-2200   Fax: (202)479-0416

$12.00/year for individuals; $1.15 for single issue. Magazine for active and reserve officers of all uniformed services.

ONLINE AND DATABASE SERVICES

★13337★ Military Career Guide Online
URL: http://www.militarycareers.com
Description: Site provides details on many enlisted and officer occupations and describes training, advancement, and educational services within each of the major

services. Includes browsing capabilities to match positions with interests.

SOFTWARE

★13338★ COIN Career Guidance System
COIN Educational Products
3361 Executive Pky., Ste. 302
Toledo, OH 43606
Ph: (419)536-5353   Fax: (419)536-7056
Fr: 800-274-8515
URL: http://www.coin3.com/highschool/guidance.asp

CD-ROM. Provides career information through seven cross-referenced files covering postsecondary schools, college majors, vocational programs, military service, apprenticeship programs, financial aid, and scholarships. Apprenticeship file describes national apprenticeship training programs, including information on how to apply, contact agencies, and program content. Military file describes more than 200 military occupations and training opportunities related to civilian employment.

OTHER SOURCES

★13339★ Air Force Association (AFA)
1501 Lee Hwy.
Arlington, VA 22209
Ph: (703)247-5800   Fax: (703)247-5853
Fr: 800-727-3337
E-mail: polcom@afa.org
URL: http://www.afa.org

Description: Promoter public understanding of aerospace power and the pivotal role it plays in the security of the nation.

★13340★ American Military Retirees Association (AMRA)
22 US Oval, Suite 1200
Plattsburgh, NY 12903
Ph: (518)563-9479   Fax: (518)324-5204
Fr: 800-424-2969
E-mail: info@amra1973.org
URL: http://www.amra1973.org

Description: Persons honorably retired for length of service or disability from all branches and grades of the armed forces and their widows or widowers; persons still on active duty. Goals: to maintain "COLA" Program; authorization for all military retirees regardless of age; to maintain adequate care at military/VA medical facilities. Works to support or oppose Legislation in the best interests of members and to protect the earned privileges and benefits of military retirees. Testifies before Congress on Legislation affecting members. Sponsors Letter-writing campaigns. Offers supplemental

health insurance program. Member of National Military & Veterans Alliance.

★13341★ Army Aviation Association of America (AAAA)
755 Main St., Ste. 4D
Monroe, CT 06468-2830
Ph: (203)268-2450   Fax: (203)268-5870
E-mail: aaaa@quad-a.org
URL: http://www.quad-a.org

Description: Commissioned officers, warrant officers, and enlisted personnel serving in U.S. Army aviation assignments in the active U.S. Army, Army National Guard, and Army Reserve; Department of Army civilian personnel and industry representatives affiliated with army aviation. Fosters fellowship among military and civilian persons connected with army aviation, past or present; seeks to advance status, overall esprit, and general knowledge of professionals engaged in army aviation. Activities include locator and placement services, technical assistance, and biographical archives. Sponsors speakers' bureau; maintains hall of fame.

★13342★ Army and Navy Union, U.S.A. (ANU)
213 Prospect
Dover, OH 44622
Ph: (330)784-0388
E-mail: anu@armynavy.net
URL: http://www.armynavy.net/

Description: Servicemen and veterans of the armed forces during peace or war. Participates in veterans service work of all types. Provides children's services. Maintains nine county councils and 11 departments.

★13343★ Association of Graduates of the United States Air Force Academy (AOG)
3116 Academy Dr.
USAF Academy, CO 80840-4475
Ph: (719)472-0300   Fax: (719)333-4194
URL: http://www.aog-usafa.org

Description: Graduates and friends of the U.S. Air Force Academy. Promotes interest in and dedication to the mission, ideals, objectives, activities, and history of the Academy; encourages young people to attend the Academy; encourages and supports fundraising for the Academy; fosters camaraderie among Academy graduates and U.S. armed forces officer corps; professional development of the armed forces officer corps. Sponsors annual class reunions/homecomings. Offers scholarships to graduates of the academy and their dependents; provides placement service. Operates charitable program, including humanitarian support for next-of-kin of academy graduates. Compiles statistics.

★13344★ Association of the United States Army (AUSA)

2425 Wilson Blvd.
Arlington, VA 22201-3385
Ph: (703)841-4300   Fax: (703)525-9039
Fr: 800-336-4570
E-mail: ausa-info@ausa.org
URL: http://www.ausa.org

Members: Professional society of active, retired, and reserve military personnel; West Point and Army ROTC cadets; civilians interested in national defense. **Purpose:** Seeks to advance the security of the United States and consolidate the efforts of all who support the United States Army as an indispensable instrument of national security. **Activities:** Conducts industrial symposia for manufacturers of Army weapons and equipment, and those in the Department of the Army who plan, develop, test, and use weapons and equipment. Symposia subjects have included guided missiles, army aviation, electronics and communication, telemedicine, vehicles, and armor. Sponsors monthly PBS TV series America's Army.

★13345★ Blinded Veterans Association (BVA)

477 H St. NW
Washington, DC 20001
Ph: (202)371-8880   Fax: (202)371-8258
Fr: 800-669-7079
E-mail: bva@bva.org
URL: http://www.bva.org

Description: Veterans who lost their sight as a result of military service in the armed forces of the U.S.; associate members are veterans whose loss of sight was not connected with military service. Assists blinded veterans in attaining benefits and employment and with reestablishing themselves as adjusted, active, and productive citizens in their communities. Offers placement service; supports research programs; compiles statistics. Constructs initiatives designed to improve blind rehabilitation programs for veterans.

★13346★ Federal Employees Veterans Association (FEVA)

PO Box 183
Merion Station, PA 19066
Members: Federal government employees who have veterans' preference in federal employment under the G. I. Bill. **Purpose:** Works to maintain and increase veterans' preference in federal employment and prevent "the discrimination against the veteran that was rampant in federal agencies in the post-World War II era."

★13347★ Marine Corps Association (MCA)

715 Broadway Ave.
Quantico, VA 22134-0775
Ph: (703)640-6161   Fax: (703)640-0823
Fr: 800-336-0291
E-mail: mca@mca-marines.org
URL: http://www.mca-marines.org
Description: Comprised of active duty, re-

serve, retired, Fleet Reserve, honorably discharged Marines, and members of other services who have served with Marine Corps units. Disseminates information about the military arts and sciences to members; assists members' professional advancement; fosters the spirit and works to preserve the traditions of the United States Marine Corps. Maintains discount book service and group insurance plan for members. Association founded by members of the Second Provisional Marine Brigade at Guantanamo Bay, Cuba.

★13348★ Marine Corps Reserve Officers' Association (MCROA)

337 Potomac Ave.
Quantico, VA 22134
Ph: (703)630-3772   Fax: (703)630-1904
Fr: 800-927-6270
E-mail: gygreen@aol.com

Description: Marine Corps Reserve officers who have served on active duty in peace or war. Seeks to: advance the professional skills of reserve officers; promote the interest of reserve officers in the U.S. Marine Corps and the interest of the Marine Corps in its reserve officers; represent and assist individual members; promote the interests of the U.S. Marine Corps in order to advance the welfare and preserve the security of the United States. Maintains speakers' bureau and placement service.

★13349★ Military Officers Association of America (MOAA)

201 N Washington St.
Alexandria, VA 22314-2539
Ph: (703)549-2311   Fax: (703)838-8173
Fr: 800-234-6622
E-mail: pr@moaa.org
URL: http://www.moaa.org

Members: Active duty, retired, National Guard, Reserve, former commissioned officers, warrant officers of the following uniformed services: Army, Marine Corps, Navy, Air Force, Coast Guard, Public Health Service, NOAA. **Purpose:** Supports strong national defense and represents and assists members, their dependents and survivors with active duty and retirement issues and benefits. **Activities:** Sponsors educational assistance program, survivor assistance, and travel, insurance, and career transition services.

★13350★ National Association for Uniformed Services (NAUS)

5535 Hempstead Way
Springfield, VA 22151
Ph: (703)750-1342   Fax: (703)354-4380
Fr: 800-842-3451
E-mail: gwillis@naus.org
URL: http://www.naus.org

Members: Members of the uniformed military services, active, retired or reserve, veteran, enlisted and officers, and their spouses or widows. **Purpose:** To develop and support legislation that upholds the security of the U.S., sustains the morale of the uniformed services, and provides fair

and equitable consideration for all service people. Primary function is protection and improvement of compensation, entitlements, and benefits. **Activities:** Provides discount rates on travel, insurance, auto rentals, charge cards, prescription medicine, and legal services.

★13351★ National Naval Officers Association (NNOA)

PO Box 10871
Alexandria, VA 22310-0871
Ph: (703)997-1068   Fax: (703)997-1068
E-mail: board@nnoa.org
URL: http://www.nnoa.org

Members: Active, reserve, and retired Navy, Marine, and Coast Guard officers and students in college and military sea service programs. **Purpose:** Promotes and assists recruitment, retention, and career development of minority officers in the naval service. **Activities:** Conducts specialized education; maintains counseling, referral, and mentorship. Makes available non-ROTC grants-in-aid. Sponsors competitions; operates charitable program.

★13352★ National Veterans Outreach Program (NVOP)

5038 W. 127th St.
Alsip, IL 60803
Ph: (708)371-9800   Fax: (708)371-1150

Description: A program sponsored by the American G.I. Forum of United States, funded by local, state, and national government contracts. **Purpose:** Provides services to the economically disadvantaged, recently separated veterans (within the last 48 months), and Vietnam era veterans. **Activities:** Counsels veterans in making a smooth transition to the civilian community and mobilizes and coordinates all available resources serving veterans. Provides family counseling to Vietnam veterans who served in or near Vietnam between 1961-1972. Works with the private sector and local, state, and national employment services in order to place the economically disadvantaged and veterans in meaningful jobs. Offers V.A. benefit counseling and outreach follow-up and referral, including field counseling, home contacts, public service announcements, and street leaflet distribution.

★13353★ Non Commissioned Officers Association of the United States of America (NCOA)

PO Box 33610
San Antonio, TX 78265
Ph: (210)653-6161   Fax: (210)637-3337
Fr: 800-662-2620
E-mail: tkish@ncoausa.org
URL: http://www.ncoausa.org

Description: Noncommissioned and petty officers of the United States military serving in grades E1 through E9 from all five branches of the U.S. Armed Forces; includes active duty and retired personnel, members of the Reserve and National Guard components, and personnel who held the rank of NCO/PO at the time of separation from active duty under honorable conditions. Formed for patriotic, fraternal, social, and benevolent purposes. Offers veterans job assistance, legislative representation, and grants. Conducts charitable program.

★13354★ Organization of African-American Veterans (AAV)
2316 Elmwood Ln.
Sierra Vista, AZ 85635-5050
Ph: (602)458-7245   Fax: (602)458-7245
E-mail: allengeorgem@cs.com

Description: Veterans and active personnel of all branches of the U.S. military. Promotes the physical, mental, social, and economic rehabilitation of veterans; works to obtain compensation, medical care, employment, and business assistance for veterans. Assists and represents veterans and their

families in filing benefit claims. Sponsors and supports beneficial legislation.

★13355★ Vietnam Veterans Against the War (VVAW)
PO Box 408594
Chicago, IL 60640
Ph: (773)276-4189
E-mail: vvaw@vvaw.org
URL: http://www.vvaw.org

Description: Works for improved VA conditions and job opportunities; eliminating the possibility of future military conflicts such as Vietnam; no draft or registration; testing and treatment of Agent Orange poisoning. Offers traumatic stress disorder counseling and discharge upgrading; provides Agent Orange selfhelp information.

★13356★ Vietnam Veterans of America (VVA)
8605 Camerson St., Ste. 400
Silver Spring, MD 20910-3710
Ph: (301)585-4000   Fax: (301)585-0519
Fr: 800-882-1316
E-mail: communications@vva.org
URL: http://www.vva.org

Members: Congressionally chartered, nationwide veterans service organization formed specifically for Vietnam veterans. **Purpose:** Objectives are to work for the employment, education benefits, improved psychological assistance, and health care of Vietnam veterans. **Activities:** Provides referral services and research and public information programs to help veterans in developing a positive identification with their Vietnam service and with fellow veterans. Offers annual training for veterans service representatives.

Opportunities for Minorities

★13357★ *Affirmative Action Register*
Affirmative Action Inc.
8356 Olive Blvd.
St. Louis, MO 63132
Ph: (314)991-1335   Fax: (314)997-1788
Fr: 800-537-0655
URL: http://www.aar-eeo.com

Monthly. $1.50 for single issue. Covers in each issue, about 300 positions at a professional level (most requiring advanced study) available to women, minorities, veterans, and the handicapped; listings are advertisements placed by employers with affirmative action programs. Entries include: Company or organization name, address, contact name; description of position including title, requirements, duties, application procedure, salary, etc. Arrangement: Classified by profession.

★13358★ *Best Careers for Bilingual Latinos*
McGraw-Hill Contemporary Books
1221 Avenue of the Americas
New York, NY 10020
Ph: (212)904-2000   Fr: 800-323-4900
E-mail: ntcpub@tribune.com

Graciela Kenig. 1998. $14.95 (paper). 256 pages.

★13359★ *Big Book of Minority Opportunities*
Ferguson Publishing Co.
200 W. Jackson Blvd., Ste. 700
Chicago, IL 60606
Ph: (312)692-1000   Fax: (312)692-0120
E-mail: holli@imil.com
URL: http://www.fergpubco.com

Irregular, previous edition 1995, latest edition 1997. $39.95. Covers About 2,000 private and governmental agencies offering 4,000 financial aid, employment assistance, and career guidance programs for minorities. Entries include: Organization or agency name, address, phone, contact name, type of organization, purpose, description of ser-

vices and activities in the equal opportunity employment area. Arrangement: Alphabetical. Indexes: Alphabetical, type of program.

★13360★ *The Big Book of Minority Opportunities: The Directory of Special Programs for Minority Group Members*
Ferguson Publishing Co.
200 W. Jackson Blvd., 7th Fl.
Chicago, IL 60606-3412
Ph: (312)692-1000   Fax: (312)692-1020
Fr: 800-306-9941

Elizabeth Oakes. Seventh edition, 1997. $39.95 (paper). 630 pages. Out of print.

★13361★ *Black Enterprise-Top Black Businesses Issue*
Earl Graves Publishing Co.
130 5th Ave.,10th Fl.
New York, NY 10011-4399
Ph: (212)242-8000   Fax: (212)886-9600
Fr: 800-727-7777
E-mail: besubscribe@blackenterprise.com
URL: http://www.blackenterprise.com

Annual, June. $3.95; $5.00 for back issues. Publication includes: Lists of 100 Black-owned industrial/service companies with sales of $18 million or above; 25 banks with total assets of $3.6 billion or more; 10 insurance companies with total assets of about $689 million or more; and 100 auto dealers with sales of $17 million or above; 20 advertising agencies with total billings of $795 million or more; 15 investment banks with issues totalling $123 billion. Entries include: Company name, city and state, name of chief executive, year founded, number of employees, financial data. Arrangement: In categories, with rankings by financial size.

★13362★ *Career Counseling for African Americans*
Lawrence Erlbaum Associates, Incorporated
10 Industrial Ave.
Mahwah, NJ 07430-2262
Ph: (201)236-9500   Fax: (201)236-0072
Fr: 800-926-6579

Bruce W. Walsh, Michael T. Brown, and Connie M. Ward, Editors. 2000. $45.00.

★13363★ *Career Guide and Directory for Immigrant Professionals: Washington Metropolitan Area*
Scarecrow Press Inc.
4501 Forbes Blvd., Ste. 200
Lanham, MD 20706
Ph: (301)459-3366   Fax: (301)429-5748
Fr: 800-462-6420

$22.95. Covers Federal, state, local, and private career resources in the District of Columbia, Maryland, and northern Virginia. Also included is information on all aspects of advancing in the American workplace.

★13364★ *Career Opportunities for Minority College Graduates*
Paoli Publishing Inc.
1708 E Lancaster Ave., Ste. 287
Paoli, PA 19301
Ph: (610)640-9889   Fax: (610)296-9266
E-mail: collegeindex@aol.com

Annual, March. Free. Covers over 900 companies, organizations and schools representing 24 occupational fields and five continuing educational alternatives. Entries include: Name, address, personnel contact name or department; phone and fax number listed in many entries. Arrangement: Classified by occupation then geographical.

★13365★ *Coming Alive from Nine to Five: The Career Search Handbook*
Mayfield Publishing Co.
1280 Villa St.
Mountain View, CA 94041-1176
Ph: (650)960-3222   Fax: (650)960-0328
Fr: 800-433-1279

Betty Neville Michelozzi. Sixth edition, 1999.

In addition to general job-hunting advice, provides special information for women, young adults, minorities, older workers, and persons with handicaps.

★13366★ Council of Asian American Business Associations of California-Directory

Council of Asian American Business Associations of California
1670 Pine St.
San Francisco, CA 94109
Ph: (415)921-5910   Fax: (415)921-0182

Annual, April. $50.00. Covers over 2,000 Asian-American professional, commercial, and industrial firms; 10 plus trade associations. Entries include: Company name, address, phone, name of contact, product or service provided, number of employees, whether minority certified, market area, licenses; some listings include clients. Arrangement: Classified by Standard Industrial Classification (SIC) code, alphabetical. Indexes: Company name, association name, SIC number.

★13367★ Directorio Profesional Hispano

Blanca Balbi
PO Box 408
Flushing, NY 11352
Ph: (718)762-1432   Fax: (718)762-1432

Annual, January. Covers over 5,000 Hispanic doctors, optometrists, dentists, lawyers, architects, and accountants, with offices in the eastern United States. Entries include: Name, address, phone. Arrangement: Classified by profession. Indexes: Medical specialists.

★13368★ Directory of Career Resources for Minorities

Ready Reference Press
PO Box 5249
Santa Monica, CA 90405
Ph: (310)475-4895   Fr: 800-424-5627

$89.50. Offers details on hundreds of programs and services, including job referral services, talent banks, re-entry programs, special training programs, career counseling, resume preparation, workshops, and others. Entries include organization name, general information, resources offered, special features, hours, fees (if any), and address. Subject and geographic indexes.

★13369★ Directory of Indian Owned Businesses

All Indian Pueblo Council Inc.
2301 Yale SE, Ste. C-B
Albuquerque, NM 87106
Ph: (505)766-9200   Fax: (505)766-8840

Annual. $5.00. Covers about 200 firms offering professional, commercial, and industrial products and services in New Mexico. Entries include: Firm name, address, phone, name and title of owner or chief executive, product or service. Arrangement: Classified

by Standard Industrial Classification (SIC) code. Indexes: Product/service.

★13370★ Finding Diversity: A Directory of Recruiting Resources

Independent Publishers Group
814 N Franklin St.
Chicago, IL 60610
Ph: (312)337-0747   Fax: (312)337-5985
Fr: 800-888-4741

$49.95. Covers 300 advertising outlets that will reach diverse and qualified candidates for jobs. Entries include: Outlet Name, address, phone, fax, type and frequency of publication, description, circulation, geographic coverage, rates, audience characteristics, and name of contact person. Indexes: Alphabetical; Geographical; Type; Language; Name of organization.

★13371★ Finding a Job in the United States

McGraw-Hill Trade
2 Penn Plaza
New York, NY 10121
Ph: (212)904-2000   Fr: 800-722-4726
E-mail: ntcpub@tribune.com

John E. Friedenberg and Curtis H. Bradley. Third edition, 1994. $7.95 (paper). 128 pages. Written for those whose native language is not English. Contains job information based on the successful experience of job seekers, plus advice from the U.S. Department of Labor. Includes information about American job customs and laws related to immigration, as well as a systematic plan for job hunting.

★13372★ Inside Corporate America: A Guide for African-Americans

Berkley Publishing Group
375 Hudson St.
New York, NY 10014
Ph: (212)366-2000   Fax: (212)366-2385
Fr: 800-847-5515

Wilson Simmons. 1996. $12.00 (paper). 224 pages. Out of stock.

★13373★ Migrant Education: A Reference Handbook

ABC-CLIO
130 Cremona Dr.
Santa Barbara, CA 93117
Ph: (805)968-1911   Fax: (805)685-9685
Fr: 800-368-6868

$45.00. Publication includes: List of additional resources for further information about migrant education. Principal content of publication is discussion of issues facing educators who work with migrant families. Indexes: Alphabetical.

★13374★ Minority Business Information Center

National Minority Supplier Development Council
1040 Avenue of the Americas, 2nd Fl.
New York, NY 10018
Ph: (212)944-2430   Fax: (212)719-9611
URL: http://www.nmsdcus.org/infocenter/facts.html

Current. Updated as needed. Database covers: Approximately 15,000 companies that are certified by the NMSDC as minority owned. Database includes: Company name, address, phone, parent company name, Standard Industrial Classification (SIC) code/North American Industry Classification System (NAICS), description of products and services, year founded, ownership structure, number of employees; name, title, ethnicity, and sex of owners; major customers, annual sales, geographical area served, most recent certification date and accrediting council.

★13375★ The Minority Executive's Handbook

HarperTrade
10 E. 53rd St.
New York, NY 10022
Ph: (212)207-7000   Fax: (212)207-7633
Fr: 800-242-7737

Randolph W. Cameron. Revised edition, 1997. $11.95 (paper). 282 pages.

★13376★ Multicultural and Diversity Education: A Reference Handbook

ABC-CLIO
130 Cremona Dr.
Santa Barbara, CA 93117
Ph: (805)968-1911   Fax: (805)685-9685
Fr: 800-368-6868

$45.00. Publication includes: List of associations and organizations for further information about multicultural and diversity education. Principal content of publication is discussion of the trends, challenges, approaches, and future of diversity education. Indexes: Alphabetical.

★13377★ National American Indian Business Directory

National Center for American Indian Enterprise Development
953 E Juanita Ave.
Mesa, AZ 85204
Ph: (480)545-1298   Fax: (480)545-4208
Fr: 800-462-2433
URL: http://www.ncaied.org

Annual, May. $25.00. Covers firms offering professional, commercial, and industrial products and services. Entries include: Firm name, address, phone, name and title of owner or chief executive, product or service, year established, work locations, license type/specialty, bonding capacity/sales. Arrangement: Classified by line of business.

★13378★ **National Directory of Minority-Owned Business Firms**

Business Research Services Inc.
4201 Connecticut Ave. NW, Ste. 610
Washington, DC 20008
Ph: (202)364-6473   Fax: (202)686-3228
Fr: 800-845-8420
URL: http://www.clickdata.com

Annual. $295.00. Covers over 30,000 minority-owned businesses. Entries include: Company name, address, phone, name and title of contact, minority group, certification status, date founded, number of employees, description of products or services, sales volume, government contracting experience, references. Arrangement: Standard Industrial Classification (SIC) code, geographical. Indexes: Alphabetical by company name, SIC by name.

★13379★ **Native American Education: A Reference Handbook**

ABC-CLIO
130 Cremona Dr.
Santa Barbara, CA 93117
Ph: (805)968-1911   Fax: (805)685-9685
Fr: 800-368-6868

$45.00. Publication includes: List of American Indian organizations. Principal content of publication is a discussion of issues facing educators of American Indians. Indexes: Alphabetical.

★13380★ **SER Network Directory**

SER-Jobs for Progress National Inc.
1925 W John Carpenter Fwy., Ste. 575
Irving, TX 75063
Ph: (972)506-7815   Fax: (972)506-7832

Annual, April. Covers approximately 130 affiliated agencies in 90 U.S. cities of SER ("Service, Employment, Redevelopment")-Jobs for Progress National, Inc., an organization of Hispanics that provides employment and training, services to disadvantaged youth and adults, especially Hispanics. Entries include: Organization name, address, phone, name of president, services provided, satellite offices, if any. Arrangement: Geographical.

★13381★ **Shoot for the Moon**

Saunderstown Press
PO Box 307
Saunderstown, RI 02874-0307
Ph: (401)295-8810

Allen A. Johnson. Second edition, 1996. $12.95 (paper). 37 pages. Designed for people starting or reentering employment, with special emphasis on handicapped and minorities.

★13382★ **TRY US National Minority Business Directory**

Diversity Information Resources
2105 Central Ave. NE
Minneapolis, MN 55418
Ph: (612)781-6819   Fax: (612)781-0109
URL: http://www.diversityinforesources.com

Annual, January. $75.00 for print; $120.00 for CD-ROM; $175.00 for print and CD-ROM. Covers over 7,000 minority-owned companies capable of supplying their goods and services on national or regional levels. Entries include: Company name, address, phone, fax, name of principal executive, number of employees, date established, trade and brand names, financial keys, products or services, names of three customers, certification status, minority identification, gross sales. Arrangement: Classified by product or service, then geographical and alphabetical. Indexes: Company, product/service, keyword.

NEWSPAPERS, MAGAZINES, AND JOURNALS

★13383★ **CAA Voice**

Chinese for Affirmative Action
17 Walter U. Lum Pl.
San Francisco, CA 94108
Ph: (415)274-6750   Fax: (415)397-8770
URL: http://www.caasf.org

Description: Quarterly. Reports on legislation and court rulings which affect the civil rights of Chinese Americans. Publicizes recent acts of discrimination against Chinese Americans and examines media stereotypes of Asians. Supports affirmative action programs and informs readers of career counseling services, and employment and apprenticeship opportunities. Promotes bilingual education and services; announces events of the organization.

★13384★ **Chinese American Medical Society Newsletter**

Chinese American Medical Society
281 Edgewood Ave.
Teaneck, NJ 07666
Ph: (201)833-1506   Fax: (201)833-8252
URL: http://www.camsociety.org

Description: Three to Four issues/year. Publishes Society news for Chinese-American physicians, Recurring features include editorials, news of research letters to the editor, news of members, job listings, and a calendar of events.

★13385★ **Fair Employment Practices Summary of Latest Developments**

Bureau of National Affairs Inc.
1231 25th St. NW
Washington, DC 20037
Ph: (202)452-4200   Fax: (202)452-4644
Fr: 800-372-1033

Description: Biweekly. Highlights developments in employment opportunity and affirmative actions, and affirmative action programs. Reports on federal and state court decisions, Equal Employment Opportunity Commission (EEOC) rulings and Office of Federal Contract Compliance Programs (OFCCP) decisions, new laws, regulations,

and agency directives. Also provides information on special programs for minorities, the handicapped, women, and older workers.

★13386★ **Hispanic Link Weekly Report**

Hispanic Link News Service
1420 N St. NW
Washington, DC 20005
Ph: (202)234-0280   Fax: (202)234-4090
E-mail: zapoteco@aol.com

Description: Weekly. Covers Hispanic issues nationwide, including politics, employment, education, arts and entertainment, and relevant events. Recurring features include interviews, news of research, a calendar of events, reports of meetings, news of educational opportunities, and job listings.

★13387★ **Hispanic Times Magazine**

Hispanic Times Magazine
PO Box 579
Winchester, CA 92596
Ph: (909)926-2119

$30.00/year for individuals; $3.50 for single issue. Magazine focusing on business and careers (English and Spanish).

★13388★ **Indian Heritage Council Quarterly**

Indian Heritage Council Publishing
PO Box 2302
Morristown, TN 37816
Ph: (423)277-1103

Description: Quarterly. Covers issues of interest to Native Americans. Recurring features include letters to the editor, interviews, news of research, a calendar of events, reports of meetings, news of educational opportunities, job listings, book reviews, and notices of publications available.

★13389★ **Item-Interference Technology Engineers Master**

Robar Industries Inc.
3 Union Hill Rd.
West Conshohocken, PA 19428-2788
Ph: (610)834-0400   Fax: (610)834-7337
E-mail: item@rbitem.com
URL: http://www.rbitem.com

$80.00/year for individuals; $80.00 for single issue. Design magazine about measurement and control of electromagnetic interference.

★13390★ **National Association of Black Accountants-News Plus**

National Association of Black Accountants Inc.
7249-A Hanover Pkwy.
Greenbelt, MD 20770
Ph: (301)474-6222   Fax: (301)474-3114

Description: Quarterly. Addresses concerns of black business professionals, especially in the accounting profession. Reports on accounting education issues, developments affecting the profession, and the Association's activities on the behalf of minorities in the accounting profession. Recurring features include member profiles, job listings, reports of meetings, news of research, and a calendar of events.

★13391★ *Saludos Hispanos*

Saludos Hispanos
73121 Fred Waring Dr., No. 100
Palm Desert, CA 92260
Ph: (619)776-1206   Fax: (619)776-1214
Fr: 800-371-4456
URL: http://www.saludos.com

Magazine showcasing successful Hispanic Americans and promoting higher education (English and Spanish).

ONLINE AND DATABASE SERVICES

★13392★ BlackVoices.com Career Center

URL: http://new.blackvoices.com/classified/jobs/
Description: Visitors can post resume, search for jobs, contribute to discussion forums and read career resource guides.

★13393★ Latpro

E-mail: support@latpro.com
URL: http://www.latpro.com
Description: Job site dedicated to finding jobs for Spanish, Portuguese and bilingual workers. Seekers may post resumes, search the job databank and receive job alerts via e-mail. Contains e-mail newsletters, recruiter lists, relocation tools and salary calculators and ESL education opportunities, among other resources. Also available in Spanish and Portuguese.

★13394★ MBA Careers

E-mail: support@mbacareers.com
URL: http://www.mbacareers.com
Description: Job site that provides resume posting, databank search and e-mail alert services to MBA and other advanced graduate degree holders.

★13395★ W.O.O. Zone

E-mail: Lbooker@atsbrassring.com
URL: http://www.nsbe.org/service/jobs.html
Description: W.O.O. stands for Window of Opportunity - a section of the website of the National Society of Black Engineers. **Main files include:** Job Search (includes full-time, co-ops, internships, and student jobs), Post a Job, Post a Resume, Company Site Search. **Fee:** $100 per month for posting a job.

SOFTWARE

★13396★ Interview Skills of the Future: Interview Challenges for Minorities, Women, and People with Disabilities

Program Development Associates
PO Box 2038
Syracuse, NY 13220-2038
Ph: (315)452-0643   Fax: (315)452-0710
Fr: 800-543-2119
E-mail: info@pdassoc.com
URL: http://www.pdassoc.com
$199.00. Teaches a tactful and positive response to challenging interview questions for those having a hard time breaking through the traditional hiring barriers.

OTHER SOURCES

★13397★ American Indian Science and Engineering Society (AISES)

PO Box 9828
Albuquerque, NM 87119-9828
Ph: (505)765-1052   Fax: (505)765-5608
E-mail: info@aises.org
URL: http://www.aises.org
Description: American Indian and non-Indian students and professionals in science, technology, and engineering fields; corporations representing energy, mining, aerospace, electronic, and computer fields. Seeks to motivate and encourage students to pursue undergraduate and graduate studies in science, engineering, and technology. Sponsors science fairs in grade schools, teacher training workshops, summer math/science sessions for 8th-12th graders, professional chapters, and student chapters in colleges. Offers scholarships. Adult members serve as role models, advisers, and mentors for students. Operates placement service.

★13398★ Asian American Architects and Engineers

1670 Pine St.
San Francisco, CA 94109
Ph: (415)928-5910   Fax: (415)921-0182
E-mail: info@asianinc.org
URL: http://www.asianinc.org
Members: Minorities. **Purpose:** Provides contracts and job opportunities for minorities in the architectural and eningeering fields. **Activities:** Serves as a network for the promotion in professional fields.

★13399★ Chinese for Affirmative Action (CAA)

17 Walter U. Lum Pl.
San Francisco, CA 94108
Ph: (415)274-6750   Fax: (415)397-8770
E-mail: caa@caasf.org
URL: http://www.caasf.org

Description: Works towards equal rights and justice for Asian Americans, women and other people of color. Conducts policy advocacy in the areas of education, employment, hate crimes and affirmative action. Provides direct services for people interested in non-traditional blue collar work where women and people of color have been historically underrepresented.

★13400★ Ludot Personnel Services Inc.

6056 N Sheldon Rd.
Canton, MI 48187
Ph: (248)353-9720   Fax: (248)459-2012
Professional placement and executive search in regard to professionals from entry level through senior managers. Also maintains a specialized division for recruitment of females and minorities. Conducts human resources management studies and recommendations in regard to personnel and organization planning, wage and salary, and recruitment within small to medium-size businesses. Industries served: automotive and allied suppliers, chemical and petrochemical, defense/electronics, consumer products, heavy manufacturing, research and development, and legal, as well as government agencies.

★13401★ National Association for the Advancement of Colored People (NAACP)

4805 Mt. Hope Dr.
Baltimore, MD 21215
Ph: (410)521-4939   Fax: (410)358-3818
Fr: 877-NAA-CP98
URL: http://www.naacp.org/
Description: Persons "of all races and religions" who believe in the objectives and methods of the NAACP. To achieve equal rights through the democratic process and eliminate racial prejudice by removing racial discrimination in housing, employment, voting, schools, the courts, transportation, recreation, prisons, and business enterprises. Offers referral services, tutorials, job referrals, and day care. Sponsors seminars; maintains law library. Sponsors the NAACP National Housing Corporation to assist in the development of low and moderate income housing for families. Compiles statistics.

★13402★ National Association of Cuban-American Women of the U.S.A. (NACAW-USA)

PO Box 614
Union City, NJ 07087
Ph: (201)271-9384   Fax: (201)223-0036
Description: Addresses current issues, concerns, and problems affecting Hispanic and minority women, and to achieve goals such as equal education and training, fair immigration policy, and meaningful work with adequate compensation. Coordinates activities with national Hispanic and other minority organizations; responds to female concerns from minority and majority populations; encourages participation in related task forces,

legislative activities, and professional endeavors; acts as clearinghouse and referral center. Supports bilingual and bicultural education at the local, state, and national levels. Disseminates information on postsecondary educational opportunities and sources of financial aid in particular cities. Produces biweekly bilingual radio program. Conducts placement service; compiles statistics.

★13403★ **National Association of Hispanic Journalists (NAHJ)**
1000 National Press Bldg.
Washington, DC 20045-2100
Ph: (202)662-7145   Fax: (202)662-7144
Fr: 888-346-NAHJ
E-mail: nahj@nahj.org
URL: http://www.nahj.org

Description: Purpose is to organize and support Hispanics involved in news gathering and dissemination. Encourages journalism and communications study and practice by Hispanics. Seeks recognition for Hispanic members of the profession regarding their skills and achievements. Promotes fair and accurate media treatment of Hispanics; opposes job discrimination and demeaning stereotypes. Works to increase educational and career opportunities and development for Hispanics in the field. Seeks to foster greater awareness of members' cultural identity, interests, and concerns. Provides a united voice for Hispanic journalists with the aim of achieving national visibility. Offers placement services to Hispanic students. Activities include: a census of Hispanic media professionals nationwide; writing contest for Hispanic students. Bestows National Hispanic Journalist Award; offers scholarships, seminars, and training workshops

★13404★ **National Black MBA Association (NBMBAA)**
180 N Michigan Ave., Ste. 1400
Chicago, IL 60601
Ph: (312)236-2622   Fax: (312)236-0390
E-mail: mail@nbmbaa.org
URL: http://www.nbmbaa.org

Description: Business professionals, lawyers, accountants, and engineers concerned with the role of blacks who hold advanced management degrees. Works to create economic and intellectual wealth for the black community. Encourages blacks to pursue continuing business education; assists students preparing to enter the business world. Provides programs for minority youths, students, and professionals, and entrepreneurs including workshops, panel discussions, and Destination MBA seminar. Sponsors job fairs. Works with graduate schools. Operates job placement service.

★13405★ **National Coalition of 100 Black Women (NCBW)**
38 W. 32nd St., Ste. 1610
New York, NY 10001-3816
Ph: (212)947-2196   Fax: (212)947-2477
E-mail: ncloobw@aol.com
URL: http://www.ncbw.org

Description: African-American women actively involved with issues such as economic development, health, employment, education, voting, housing, criminal justice, the status of black families, and the arts. Seeks to provide networking and career opportunities for African-American women in the process of establishing links between the organization and the corporate and political arenas. Encourages leadership development; sponsors role-model and mentor programs to provide guidance to teenage mothers and young women in high school or who have graduated from college and are striving for career advancement.

★13406★ **National Puerto Rican Forum (NPRF)**
1946 Webster Ave., 3rd Fl.
Bronx, NY 10457-4249
Ph: (646)792-1010   Fax: (646)792-1020
E-mail: kofib@nprf.org
URL: http://www.nprf.org

Description: Concerned with the overall improvement of Puerto Rican and Hispanic communities throughout the U.S. Seeks to identify the obstacles preventing the advancement of the Puerto Rican and Hispanic communities and to develop strategies to remove them. Designs and implements programs in areas of job counseling, training and placement, and English language skills, to deal effectively with the problems of Puerto Ricans and other Hispanics. Sponsors Career Services and Job Placement Program at the national level. Also provides specialized programs in New York, such as: Employment Placement Initiative, Access and Family Services in the schools, and job counseling.

★13407★ **National Society of Hispanic MBAs (NSHMBA)**
1303 W Walnut Hill Ln., Ste. 300
Irving, TX 75038
Fax: (214)596-9325   Fr: 877-467-4622
E-mail: agonzalez@nshmba.org
URL: http://www.nshmba.org

Description: Hispanic MBA professional business network dedicated to economic and philanthropic advancement.

★13408★ **Organization of Chinese American Women (OCAW)**
4641 Montgomery Ln, Ste. 208
Bethesda, MD 20814
Ph: (301)907-3898   Fax: (301)907-3899
E-mail: ocawwomen@aol.com
URL: http://www.ocawwomen.org

Description: Advances the cause of Chinese American women in the U.S. and fosters public awareness of their special needs and concerns. Seeks to integrate Chinese American women into the mainstream of women's activities and programs. Addresses issues such as equal employment opportunities at both the professional and nonprofessional levels; overcoming stereotypes; racial and sexual discrimination and restrictive traditional beliefs; assistance to poverty-stricken recent immigrants; access to leadership and policymaking positions. Networking for Chinese American women. Sponsors annual opera and Mother's Day and Award Banquet. Conducts Biennual National Training Conferences; establishes scholarships for middle school girls in rural China.

★13409★ **SER - Jobs for Progress National**
1925 W John Carpenter Fwy., Ste. 5D
Irving, TX 75063-3224
Ph: (972)541-0616   Fax: (972)650-1860
Fr: 800-427-2306
URL: http://www.ser-national.org

Description: Aims to provide employment training and opportunities for Spanish-speaking and disadvantaged Americans. Seeks to increase business and economic opportunities for minority communities and ensure optimum participation by the Hispanic community in public policy forums. Most SER performance contracts are funded by the federal government. Each local office organizes its own training and management program and is responsible for recruitment and selection of job trainees, counseling, pre-job orientation and vocational preparation, basic education, employer relations, and follow-up services to trainees after training and job placement.

★13410★ **Xavier Associates Inc.**
266 Main St., 2nd Fl.
North Easton, MA 02356
Ph: (508)359-8294   Fax: (508)359-5902

Executive search firm with special focus on the recruitment and placement of minority professionals. Industries served: financial, insurance, hi-tech, and manufacturing.

Opportunities for Older Workers

REFERENCE WORKS

★13411★ Affirmative Action Register

Affirmative Action Inc.
8356 Olive Blvd.
St. Louis, MO 63132
Ph: (314)991-1335   Fax: (314)997-1788
Fr: 800-537-0655
URL: http://www.aar-eeo.com

Monthly. $1.50 for single issue. Covers in each issue, about 300 positions at a professional level (most requiring advanced study) available to women, minorities, veterans, and the handicapped; listings are advertisements placed by employers with affirmative action programs. Entries include: Company or organization name, address, contact name; description of position including title, requirements, duties, application procedure, salary, etc. Arrangement: Classified by profession.

★13412★ Coming Alive from Nine to Five: The Career Search Handbook

Mayfield Publishing Co.
1280 Villa St.
Mountain View, CA 94041-1176
Ph: (650)960-3222   Fax: (650)960-0328
Fr: 800-433-1279

Betty Neville Michelozzi. Sixth edition, 1999. In addition to general job-hunting advice, provides special information for women, young adults, minorities, older workers, and persons with handicaps.

★13413★ How to Find a New Career upon Retirement

McGraw-Hill Trade
2 Penn Plaza
New York, NY 10121
Ph: (212)904-2000   Fr: 800-722-4726
E-mail: ntcpub@tribune.com

Duane Brown. 1994. $9.95 (paper).160 pages.

★13414★ Jobs for People Over 50: 101 Companies That Hire Senior Workers

Brattle Communications
24 Computer Dr., W.
Albany, NY 12205

Arthur Kuman, Jr. and Richard D. Salmon. 1994. 128 pages.

★13415★ New Work Opportunities for Older Americans

iUniverse, Inc.
2021 Pine Lake Rd. Ste. 100
Lincoln, NE 68512
Ph: (402)323-7800   Fax: (402)323-7824
Fr: 877-288-4737

Robert S. Menchin. 2000. $18.95 (paper). 356 pages.

★13416★ Part-Time Employment for the Low-Income Elderly: Experiences from the Field

Garland Publishing, Inc.
29 W. 35th St., Fl. 10
New York, NY 10001-2299
Ph: (212)216-7800   Fax: (212)564-7854
Fr: 800-627-6273

Leslie B. Alexander and Lenard W. Kaye. 1997. $44.00. Part of Issues in Aging series. 204 pages.

★13417★ Resumes for the 50 Plus Job Hunter

McGraw-Hill Trade
2 Penn Plaza
New York, NY 10121
Ph: (212)904-2000

2002.

★13418★ Resumes for Re-Entering the Job Market

McGraw-Hill Trade
2 Penn Plaza
New York, NY 10121
Ph: (212)904-2000   Fr: 800-722-4726
E-mail: ntcpub@tribune.com

1995. $9.95 (paper). 464 pages. Part of VGM Professional Resumes series.

★13419★ Unretirement: A Career Guide for the Retired...the Soon-to-Be Retired...the Never Want-to-Be-Retired

AMACOM
1601 Broadway, 12th Fl.
New York, NY 10019-7420
Ph: (518)891-1500   Fax: (518)903-8168
Fr: 800-250-5308

Catherine D. Fyock and Anne M. Dorton. 1994. $17.95 (paper).

NEWSPAPERS, MAGAZINES, AND JOURNALS

★13420★ Fair Employment Practices Summary of Latest Developments

Bureau of National Affairs Inc.
1231 25th St. NW
Washington, DC 20037
Ph: (202)452-4200   Fax: (202)452-4644
Fr: 800-372-1033

Description: Biweekly. Highlights developments in employment opportunity and affirmative actions, and affirmative action programs. Reports on federal and state court decisions, Equal Employment Opportunity Commission (EEOC) rulings and Office of Federal Contract Compliance Programs (OFCCP) decisions, new laws, regulations, and agency directives. Also provides information on special programs for minorities, the handicapped, women, and older workers.

ONLINE AND DATABASE SERVICES

★13421★ Senior Job Bank
URL: http://www.seniorjobbank.com
Description: JOb postings for seniors.

★13422★ Seniors 4 Hire
URL: http://www.seniors4hire.org
Description: Online career center for people 50 and over.

★13423★ SeniorsJobs.com
URL: http://www.seniorsjobs.com
Description: Job postings for seniors.

OTHER SOURCES

★13424★ Experience Works
2200 Clarendon Blvd., Ste. 1000
Arlington, VA 22201
Ph: (703)522-7272   Fax: (703)522-0141
Fr: (866)EXP-WRKS
E-mail: allison_hadley@experienceworks.org
URL: http://www.experienceworks.org
Description: Provides training and employment services for mature workers. Reaches more than 125,000 mature individuals.

★13425★ National Council on the Aging
300 D St. SW, Ste. 801
Washington, DC 20024
Description: Offers MaturityWorks-a partnership that places mature workers with jobs.

★13426★ Senior Employment Resources
4201 John Marr Dr., Ste. 236
Annandale, VA 22003
Ph: (703)750-1936
URL: http://www.seniorjobs.org
Description: Job placement service that matches companies and job seekers age 50 and above.

Opportunities for Teenagers

REFERENCE WORKS

★13427★ Cents-Able Summer Self-Employment: An Entrepreneurial Guide for High School & College Students
Tamarax Press
PO Box 450
2A Taylor Way
Washington Crossing, PA 18977
Ph: (215)493-2136   Fax: (215)493-2057

E.K. Shepard. 1994. $12.95 (paper). 220 pages.

★13428★ Coming Alive from Nine to Five: The Career Search Handbook
Mayfield Publishing Co.
1280 Villa St.
Mountain View, CA 94041-1176
Ph: (650)960-3222   Fax: (650)960-0328
Fr: 800-433-1279

Betty Neville Michelozzi. Sixth edition, 1999. In addition to general job-hunting advice, provides special information for women, young adults, minorities, older workers, and persons with handicaps.

★13429★ Directory of Internships, Work Experience Programs, and On-the-Job Training Opportunities
Ready Reference Press
PO Box 5249
Santa Monica, CA 90405
Ph: (310)475-4895   Fr: 800-424-5627

$89.50. Lists internship opportunities in many fields of interest, including, but not limited to arts, journalism, public relations, education, law, environmental affairs, business, engineering, and computer science. In addition, cites summer internship opportunities, work/study programs, and specialized opportunities for high school and undergraduate students. Indexed by subject, geography, and program.

★13430★ How to Get a Job If You're a Teenager
Highsmith Incorporated
PO Box 800
Fort Atkinson, WI 53538-0800
Ph: (920)563-9571   Fax: 800-835-2329
Fr: 800-558-2110
E-mail: service@highsmith.com
URL: http://www.highsmith.com

Cindy Pervola and Debby Hobgood. Second edition, revised 2000. $13.95 (paper). 68 pages. Covers the different steps in getting a job.

★13431★ Opportunities in Summer Camp Careers
McGraw-Hill Trade
2 Penn Plaza
New York, NY 10121
Ph: (212)904-2000   Fr: 800-722-4726

Blythe Camenson. 1998. $11.95 (paper). 210 pages. Part of Opportunities in...Series.

★13432★ Peterson's Guide to College for Careers in Allied Health
Thomson Peterson's
Princeton Pike Corporate Center
2000 Lenox Dr.
PO Box 67005
Lawrenceville, NJ 08648
Ph: (609)896-1800   Fax: 800-277-2465
Fr: 800-338-3282

$14.95. Publication includes: College-level programs in allied health. Principal content of publication is career information on what it's like to work in the field, skills required, job outlook, career paths, education needed, and where to get more information.

★13433★ Peterson's Guide to College for Careers in Business
Thomson Peterson's
Princeton Pike Corporate Center
2000 Lenox Dr.
PO Box 67005
Lawrenceville, NJ 08648
Ph: (609)896-1800   Fax: 800-277-2465
Fr: 800-338-3282

$14.95. Publication includes: College-level programs in business. Principal content of publication is career information on what it's like to work in the field, skills required, job outlook, career paths, education needed and where to get more information.

★13434★ Peterson's Guide to College for Careers in Computing
Thomson Peterson's
Princeton Pke. Corporate Ctr., 2000 Lenox Dr.
PO Box 67005
Lawrenceville, NJ 08648
Ph: (609)896-1800   Fax: (609)896-4531
Fr: 800-338-3282

$14.95. Publication includes: College-level programs in computing. Principal content of publication is career information on what it's like to work in the field, skills required, job outlook, career paths, education needed and where to get more information.

★13435★ Peterson's Guide to College for Careers in Teaching
Thomson Peterson's
Princeton Pike Corporate Center
2000 Lenox Dr.
PO Box 67005
Lawrenceville, NJ 08648
Ph: (609)896-1800   Fax: 800-277-2465
Fr: 800-338-3282

$14.95. Publication includes: College-level programs in the field of teaching. Principal content of publication is career information on what it's like to work in the field, skills required, job outlook, career paths, education needed, and where to get more information.

★13436★ Peterson's International Directory of Summer Opportunities for Kids & Teenagers
Thomson Peterson's
PO Box 67005
Lawrenceville, NJ 08648-6105
Fr: 800-338-3282

1995. $29.95 (paper). 110 pages.

★13437★ Peterson's Summer Jobs for Students

Thomson Peterson's
Princeton Pke. Corporate Ctr., 2000
  Lenox Dr.
PO Box 67005
Lawrenceville, NJ 08648
Ph: (609)896-1800   Fax: (609)896-4531
Fr: 800-338-3282

Annual, latest edition 2002. $18.95. Covers over 650 camps, resorts, amusement parks, hotels, businesses, national parks, conference and training centers, ranches, and restaurants offering about 45,000 temporary summer jobs; listings are paid. Entries include: Name and address, length of employment, pay rate, fringe benefits, duties, qualifications, application deadline and procedure. Arrangement: Geographical, then type of job. Indexes: Job title.

★13438★ Peterson's Summer Opportunities for Kids and Teenagers

Thomson Peterson's
PO Box 67005
Lawrenceville, NJ 08648-6105
Fr: 800-338-3282

First edition, 2000 (annual). $29.95 (paper). 1,426 pages. In addition to information about 1,400 summer activities and programs, covers job opportunities for high school and college students. Part of Summer Opportunities for Kids and Teenagers series.

★13439★ Resumes for High School Graduates

McGraw-Hill Trade
2 Penn Plaza
New York, NY 10121
Ph: (212)904-2000
E-mail: ntcpub@tribune.com

Second edition, 1999. $9.95. Designed for the person with little or no full-time work experience. Shows how to emphasize part-work experience and highlight educational, extra-curricular and volunteer experience. Provides sample resumes and cover letters.

★13440★ Teen Guide to Getting Started in the Arts

Greenwood Publishing Group Inc.
80 Post Rd. W
Westport, CT 06881
Fax: (203)222-1502   Fr: 800-225-5800

Carol L. Ritzenthaler. 2001. $39.95.

★13441★ A Teen's Guide to Finding a Job

New Bee-ginnings
2722 Village Pkwy.
San Antonio, TX 78251
Ph: (210)258-4510

Naomi Vernon. 2000. $19.95 (paper).

★13442★ Your First Interview

The Career Press, Inc.
3 Tice Rd.
PO Box 687
Franklin Lakes, NJ 07417-1322
Ph: (201)848-0310   Fax: (201)848-1727
Fr: 800-227-3371

Ronald Fry. Fourth edition, 2001. $11.99 (paper). 192 pages. Takes the reader from making the initial contact with a prospective employer to negotiating salary.

AUDIO/VISUAL RESOURCES

★13443★ Teens for Hire

Cambridge Educational
PO Box 931
Monmouth Junction, NJ 08852-0931
Fax: 800-FAX-ON-US   Fr: 800-468-4227
URL: http://www.cambridgeeducational.com
$89.95. 1999. 15 minutes.

OTHER SOURCES

★13444★ National Youth Employment Coalition (NYEC)

1836 Jefferson Pl., NW
Washington, DC 20036
Ph: (202)659-1064   Fax: (202)659-0339
E-mail: nyec@nyec.org
URL: http://www.nyec.org

Members: A network of over 180 community-based organizations, research organizations, public interest groups, policy analysis organizations, and others dedicated to promoting improved policies and practices related to youth employment/development, to help youth succeed in becoming lifelong learners, productive workers and self-sufficient citizens.

★13445★ Operation Enterprise (OE)

AMSIO-ACG-ARMS-OSC
Bldg. 350, 5th Fl.
Rock Island, IL 61299
Fr: 800-797-7483
E-mail: govops@openterprise.com
URL: http://www.openterprise.com/

Description: Gives high school and college students an opportunity to learn about management by working with executives and managers. Learning techniques used include small group discussions, panel forums, a business simulation, and role playing. Sponsors two programs: Operation Enterprise, in which top managers and executives help students explore the concepts and skills of professional management, and Career Skills, to encourage development of job skills. Candidates are sponsored in a variety of ways by companies, civic organizations, or individuals.

★13446★ Vocationals Foundation, Inc. (VFI)

1 Hanson Pl., 14th Fl.
Brooklyn, NY 11243-2907
Ph: (718)230-3100   Fax: (718)230-8784
E-mail: hthompson@vfinyc.org
URL: http://www.vfinyc.org

Description: A free voluntary vocational training, guidance, and job placement service for economically and educationally disadvantaged young people (ages 16-21) who are referred by other accredited public and voluntary agencies in New York City. **Purpose:** Seeks to aid high school dropouts and young people with correctional and drug abuse histories. GED prop and testing.

★13447★ WAVE

525 School St. SW, Ste. 500
Washington, DC 20024
Ph: (202)484-0103   Fax: (202)484-7595
Fr: 800-274-2005
E-mail: mail@waveinc.org
URL: http://www.waveinc.org

Description: Organization, funded in part by the U.S. Department of Labor and grants from corporations and foundations, that helps disadvantaged 16-21 year old high school dropouts and students at risk of dropping out to find unsubsidized jobs and careers. Dropouts attend classes to prepare for their high school equivalency diplomas and to learn basic living skills, such as how to find an apartment, how to dress for a job interview, and how to balance a checkbook. In schools WAVE's youth organization, holds seminars and competitions that foster motivation and leadership and conducts national employment and training seminars for enrollees, and annual staff training institutes. Sponsors National Youth Professionals' Institute.

Opportunities for Temporary Workers

REFERENCE WORKS

★13448★ America's Career InfoNet

U.S. Department of Labor
Administrative Services Ctr.
200 Constitution Ave. NW
Washington, DC 20210
URL: http://www.acinet.org/acinet
Covers links to and information about job banks, employment service providers, career education, and nationwide employer contacts.

★13449★ CareerXRoads: The Directory to Job, Resume and Career Management Sites on the Web

MMC GROUP
4545 Fuller Drive, Suite 222
Irving, TX 75038
Ph: (972)893-0100   Fax: (972)893-0099
Latest edition 2002. $26.95. Covers nearly 3,000 job and resume web sites with reviews and descriptions of the top 500. Indexes: Colleges; Corporations; Diversity; Specialty/ Industry; Location; Listing services.

★13450★ Directory of Outplacement and Career Management Firms

Kennedy Information Inc.
One Phoenix Mill Ln., 5th Fl.
Peterborough, NH 03458
Ph: (603)924-1006   Fax: (603)924-4460
Fr: 800-531-0007
Annual, latest edition 2003. $149.95. Covers over 380 consulting firms with special interest in career management and "outplacement" or "de-hiring" counseling executive employees being terminated because of poor performance, plant closings, etc., and assisting them in finding new jobs; firms that are compensated only by employers and those that also accept compensation from individuals are listed. Entries include: Firm name, address, phone, fax, E-mail, description of philosophy and services, names and titles of principals, branches, area served, year established, revenue (within wide ranges), professional associations, minimum salary of positions handled, number of staff, percentage of business devoted to outplacement. Arrangement: Separate sections on basis of compensation arrangements, then alphabetical. Indexes: Industries, key principals, firm.

★13451★ Directory of Summer Jobs Abroad

Vacation Work Publications
9 Park End St.
Oxford OX1 1HJ, United Kingdom
Ph: 865 241978   Fax: 865 790885
Annual, November; supplement in May. $7.99; $6.00. Covers more than 30,000 jobs worldwide. Entries include: Name of employer, address, length of employment, number of positions available, pay rates, how and when to apply, name of contact. Arrangement: Geographical, then classified by type of job.

★13452★ Employment Contractors-Temporary Help Directory

infoUSA Inc.
5711 S 86th Cir.
Omaha, NE 68127-0347
Ph: (402)930-3500   Fax: (402)331-0176
Fr: 800-555-6124
URL: http://www.abii.com
Annual. Number of listings: 22,959. Entries include: Name, address, phone (including area code), size of advertisement, year first in "Yellow Pages," name of owner or manager, number of employees. Compiled from telephone company "Yellow Pages," nationwide. Arrangement: Geographical.

★13453★ Half a Job: Bad and Good Part-Time Jobs in Changing Labor Market

Temple University Press
University Services Bldg., Rm. 305
1601 N. Broad St.
Philadelphia, PA 19122-6099
Ph: (215)204-8787   Fax: (215)204-4719
Fr: 800-447-1656
Chris Tilly. 1996. $22.95 (paper). 256 pages.

★13454★ Peterson's Summer Jobs for Students

Thomson Peterson's
Princeton Pke. Corporate Ctr., 2000
Lenox Dr.
PO Box 67005
Lawrenceville, NJ 08648
Ph: (609)896-1800   Fax: (609)896-4531
Fr: 800-338-3282
Annual, latest edition 2002. $18.95. Covers over 650 camps, resorts, amusement parks, hotels, businesses, national parks, conference and training centers, ranches, and restaurants offering about 45,000 temporary summer jobs; listings are paid. Entries include: Name and address, length of employment, pay rate, fringe benefits, duties, qualifications, application deadline and procedure. Arrangement: Geographical, then type of job. Indexes: Job title.

★13455★ Quick Prep Careers: Good Jobs in One Year or Less

Ferguson Publishing Co.
200 W Jackson Blvd.
Chicago, IL 60606
Ph: (312)692-0109
$18.95. Publication includes: Lists of associations for further consultation for each of 75 jobs featured. Principal content of publication is detailed information on each job. Arrangement: By job. Indexes: Alphabetical.

★13456★ Temp by Choice

Career Press, Inc.
3 Tice Rd.
PO Box 687
Franklin Lakes, NJ 07417-1322
Ph: (201)848-0310   Fax: (201)848-1727
Fr: 800-227-3371
Diane Thrailkill. 1994. $10.95 (paper). 224 pages. Out of print.

★13457★ **Temp: How to Survive and Thrive in the World of Temporary Employment**
Shambhala Publications, Incorporated
Horticultural Hall, 300 Massachusetts Ave.
Boston, MA 02115
Ph: (617)424-0030   Fax: (617)236-1563
Smith. 1994. $15.95 (paper). 144 pages. Explains working with agencies, self-marketing, short- and long-term assignments, and more.

★13458★ **The Temp Track: Make One of the Hottest Job Trends of the 90s Work for You**
Thomson Peterson's
PO Box 67005
Lawrenceville, NJ 08648-6105
Fr: 800-338-3282
Peggy O. Justice. 1993. $12.95 (paper). 208 pages.

★13459★ **The Temp Worker's Guide to Self-Fulfillment: How to Slack Off, Achieve Your Dreams, and Get Paid for It!**
Breakout Productions, Inc.
PO Box 1643
Port Townsend, WA 98368
Ph: (360)379-1965   Fax: (360)379-3794
Fr: 800-380-2230
Dennis Fiery. 1997. $12.95 (paper). 156 pages.

★13460★ **VGM's Guide to Temporary Employment**
McGraw-Hill Trade
2 Penn Plaza
New York, NY 10121
Ph: (212)904-2000   Fr: 800-722-4726
Lewis Baratz. 1995. $11.95 (paper). 176 pages.

★13461★ **Workstyles to Fit Your Lifestyle: Everyone's Guide to Temporary Employment**
Prentice Hall PTR
200 Old Tappan Rd.
Old Tappan, NJ 07675
Ph: (201)236-7000   Fr: 800-223-1360
John Fanning. 1993. $11.95 (paper). Out of print.

OTHER SOURCES

★13462★ **American Staffing Association (ASA)**
277 S. Washington St., Ste. 200
Alexandria, VA 22314-3646
Ph: (703)253-2020   Fax: (703)253-2053
E-mail: asa@staffingtoday.net
URL: http://www.staffingtoday.net
Description: Promotes and represents the staffing industry through legal and legislative advocacy, public relations, education, and the establishment of high standards of ethical conduct.

★13463★ **National Association of Part-Time and Temporary Employees (NAPTE)**
5800 Barton, Ste. 201
PO Box 3805
Shawnee, KS 66203
Ph: (913)962-7740
URL: http://www.members.tripod.com/~napte
Purpose: Promotes the economic and social interests of persons working on a part-time, contingent, or temporary basis through research, advocacy, and member services. Offers short-term portable health insurance.

Opportunities for Women

REFERENCE WORKS

★13464★ Affirmative Action Register

Affirmative Action Inc.
8356 Olive Blvd.
St. Louis, MO 63132
Ph: (314)991-1335   Fax: (314)997-1788
Fr: 800-537-0655
URL: http://www.aar-eeo.com

Monthly. $1.50 for single issue. Covers in each issue, about 300 positions at a professional level (most requiring advanced study) available to women, minorities, veterans, and the handicapped; listings are advertisements placed by employers with affirmative action programs. Entries include: Company or organization name, address, contact name; description of position including title, requirements, duties, application procedure, salary, etc. Arrangement: Classified by profession.

★13465★ Big Opportunities for Women: The Directory of Women's Organizations

Ferguson Publishing Co.
200 W. Jackson, 7th Fl.
Chicago, IL 60606-3412
Ph: (312)692-1000   Fax: (312)692-1020
Fr: 800-306-9941

Elizabeth A. Olson, editor. 1996. $39.95 (paper). 450 pages. Out of print.

★13466★ Coming Alive from Nine to Five: The Career Search Handbook

Mayfield Publishing Co.
1280 Villa St.
Mountain View, CA 94041-1176
Ph: (650)960-3222   Fax: (650)960-0328
Fr: 800-433-1279

Betty Neville Michelozzi. Sixth edition, 1999. In addition to general job-hunting advice, provides special information for women, young adults, minorities, older workers, and persons with handicaps.

★13467★ Directory of Career Resources for Women

Ready Reference Press
PO Box 5249
Santa Monica, CA 90405
Ph: (310)475-4895   Fr: 800-424-5627

$89.50. Offers details on hundreds of programs and services, including job referral services, talent banks, re-entry programs, special training programs, career counseling, resume preparation, workshops, and others. Entries include organization name, general information, resources offered, special features, hours, fees (if any), and address. Subject and geographic indexes.

★13468★ Directory of Non-Traditional Training and Employment Programs Serving Women

DIANE Publishing Co.
PO Box 1428
Collingdale, PA 19023-8428
Ph: (610)461-6200   Fax: (610)461-6130
Fr: 800-782-3833

1993. $35.00 (paper). 157 pages. Directory of programs that assist women in obtaining training and employment in skilled nontraditional jobs, including apprenticeship.

★13469★ Directory of Women Entrepreneurs

Wind River Publications Inc.
2359 Henderson Mill Ct.
Atlanta, GA 30345
Fax: (404)496-5986

Annual, February. $79.95. Covers approximately 3,200 women-owned businesses; companies with minority and women professional development programs, women's groups and organizations, and minority business assistance offices. Entries include: For women-owned businesses-Company name, address, phone, names and titles of key personnel, year founded, financial data, Standard Industrial Classification (SIC) code, description of products or services. For others-Name, address, phone. Arrangement: Alphabetical. Indexes: Geographical, Standard Industrial Classification (SIC) code.

★13470★ Every Woman's Essential Job Hunting & Resume Book

Adams Media Corp.
57 Littlefield St.
Avon, MA 02322
Ph: (508)427-7100   Fax: (508)427-6790
Fr: 800-872-5627
URL: http://www.adamsmedia.com

Laura Morin. 1994. $11.95 (paper).

★13471★ Finding the Work You Love: A Woman's Career Guide

Resource Publications, Inc.
160 E. Virginia St., No. 290
San Jose, CA 95112-5876
Ph: (408)286-8505   Fax: (408)287-8748
Fr: 888-273-7782

Astrid Berg. 1994. $15.95 (paper). 154 pages.

★13472★ Going Part-Time: The Insider's Guide for Professional Women Who Want a Career and a Life

Morrow Avon
1350 Ave. of the Americas
New York, NY 10019
Ph: (212)261-6788   Fr: 800-242-7737

Cindy Tolliver and Nancy Chambers. 1997. $12.00 (paper). 256 pages. Out of print.

★13473★ If You Can Raise Kids, You Can Get a Good Job

HarperCollins Publishers Inc.
10 E. 53rd St.
New York, NY 10022-5299
Ph: (212)207-7000

Katherine Goldman. 1995. $16.50. Uses real-life examples to illustrate how mothers can successfully return to the work force. Out of print.

★13474★ International Association for Personnel Women-Membership Roster

National Human Resources Association (NHRA)
PO Box 803
Pewaukee, WI 53072-0803
Fax: (414)475-5959   Fr: (866)523-4417

Latest edition November, 1994. $150.00. Covers 1,200 members-at-large and members of affiliated chapters. Entries include: Individual name, title, company name, mailing address, office phone. Arrangement: Classified by type of membership.

★13475★ Looking for More than a Few Good Women in Traditionally Male Fields

Center for Women Policy Studies
1211 Connecticut Ave., NW, Ste. 312
Washington, DC 20036-2701
Ph: (202)872-1770   Fax: (202)296-8962
Fr: 888-SAT-BIAS

Julie K. Ehrhart, Bernice R. Sandler. $5.00 (paper). Out of print.

★13476★ National Directory of Woman-Owned Business Firms

Business Research Services Inc.
4201 Connecticut Ave. NW, Ste. 610
Washington, DC 20008
Ph: (202)364-6473   Fax: (202)686-3228
Fr: 800-845-8420

Annual. $295.00. Covers 28,000 woman-owned businesses. Entries include: Company name, address, phone, name and title of contact, minority group, certification status, date founded, number of employees, description of products or services, sales volume, government contracting experience, references. Arrangement: Standard Industrial Classification (SIC) code, geographical. Indexes: Alphabetical by company.

★13477★ The New Relocating Spouse's Guide to Employment

Impact Publications
9104 Manassas Dr., Ste. N
Manassas Park, VA 20111-5211
Ph: (703)361-7300   Fax: (703)335-9486
URL: http://www.impactpublications.com/

Irregular, previous edition 1989, latest edition 1993. $14.95. Publication includes: List of 133 professional associations and 54 federal job centers. Entries include: Organization name, address, phone. Principal content of publication is discussion of the job market, employment trends, and other useful information for those facing a move to a city where they have no job waiting. Arrangement: Alphabetical.

★13478★ 101 Best Extra-Income Opportunities for Women

Prima Lifestyles
401 Franklin Ave.
Garden City, NY 11530
Ph: (516)873-4561   Fax: (516)873-4714

Jennifer Basye Sandom. 1997. 192 pages.

★13479★ Professional by Choice: Milady's Career Development Guide

Milady Publishing Co.
3 Columbia Cir., Box 15015
Albany, NY 12212-5015
Ph: (518)464-3500   Fax: (518)464-0357
Fr: 800-347-7707

Victoria Harper. 1994. $20.95 (paper). 143 pages. Part of Salon Ovations series.

★13480★ Resumes for Women

Macmillan Publishing Co., Inc.
200 Old Tappan Rd.
Old Tappan, NJ 07675
Fr: 800-428-5331

Eva Shaw. 1995. $10.00 (paper).

★13481★ The Self-Employed Woman's Guide to Launching a Home-Based Business

Prima Publishing
3000 Lava Ridge Ct.
Roseville, CA 95661
Ph: (916)787-7000   Fax: (916)787-7001

Priscilla Huff. 2002. $14.95 (paper).

★13482★ The Smart Woman's Guide to Career Success

Chelsea House Publishers
1974 Sproul Rd., Ste. 400
Broomall, PA 19008-0914
Ph: (610)353-5166   Fax: (610)359-1439
Fr: 800-848-2665

Janet Hauter. 1996. $19.95. Part of the "Smart Woman's Guides Series."

★13483★ The Smart Woman's Guide to Interviewing and Salary Negotiations

Chelsea House Publishers
1974 Sproul Rd., Ste. 400
Broomall, PA 19008-0914
Ph: (610)353-5166   Fax: (610)359-1439
Fr: 800-848-2665

Julie A. King. 1997. $19.95 (paper). Part of the "Smart Woman's Guide Series."

★13484★ The Smart Woman's Guide to Resumes and Job Hunting

Chelsea House Publishers
1974 Sproul Rd., Ste. 400
Broomall, PA 19008-0914
Ph: (610)353-5166   Fax: (610)359-1439
Fr: 800-848-2665

Julie Adair King and Betsy Sheldon. 1996. $19.95. 271 pages. Addresses job-search challenges unique to women in the '90s. Discusses breaking through the glass ceiling and other gender barriers, commanding a fair salary, networking to hidden job opportunities, using "power language", translating volunteer experiences into powerful accomplishments, and offers other guidance. Takes the reader through a resume-creating process.

★13485★ The Smart Woman's Guide to Starting a Business

Career Press, Inc.
3 Tice Rd.
PO Box 687
Franklin Lakes, NJ 07417-1322
Ph: (201)848-0310   Fax: (201)848-1727
Fr: 800-227-3371

Vickie Montgomery. Second edition, 1998. $15.99. Part of Smart Woman's Guide series. Out of print.

★13486★ Unlocking the Clubhouse: Women in Computing

MIT Press
5 Cambridge Ctr., Suite 4
Cambridge, MA 02142-1493
Ph: (617)253-5646   Fax: (617)253-6779
Fr: 800-356-0343

Jane Margolis and Allan Fisher. 2001. $24.95.

★13487★ What Works!: The Working Women Count Honor Roll Report

DIANE Publishing Co.
PO Box 1428
Collingdale, PA 19023-8428
Ph: (610)461-6200   Fax: (610)461-6130
Fr: 800-782-3833

Ida L. Castro. 1998. $30.00 (paper). Provides information on the programs and policies of the Working Women Count Honor Roll.

★13488★ Wisconsin Women's Resources

Wisconsin Women's Council
14 W Mifflin St., Ste. 212
Madison, WI 53702
Ph: (608)266-2219   Fax: (608)261-2432
URL: http://www.cstate.wi.us

Latest edition 2001. Covers agencies, organizations, services, and other programs of interest to and concerned with women, including career planning, displaced homemaker services, legal aid, women's studies programs, child care services, etc. Entries include: Organization name, address, phone, e-mail, URL, purpose. Arrangement: Classified by area of concern.

★13489★ Women's Business Resource Guide

McGraw-Hill Contemporary Books
130 E Randolph St., Ste. 400
Chicago, IL 60601-6213
Ph: (847)679-5500   Fax: (847)679-2494
Fr: 800-323-4900

Biennial, June of even years. $18.95. Covers over 600 training, technical assistance, and counseling programs, information sources, government agencies, membership organizations, and other associations of interest to women in business. Entries include: Resource name, address, phone, geographical area served, description. Arrangement: Classified by topic. Indexes: Product/service, organization name, subject.

★13490★ Women's Yellow Pages

Nancy Sardella
13547 Ventura Blvd., No. 374
Sherman Oaks, CA 91423
Ph: (818)995-6646
URL: http://www.referral-guide.com/

Annual, Spring. $10.95. Covers over 1,400 women's businesses, services, and organizations in Los Angeles and Orange counties and nearby areas of southern California; and community resources. Entries include: Company or organization name, address, phone; product or service provided, field of interest. Arrangement: Classified by type of business or organization.

★13491★ Work of Her Own: A Woman's Guide to Success off the Career Track

Putnam Publishing Group
375 Hudson St.
New York, NY 10014
Ph: (212)366-2000   Fax: (212)366-2643
Fr: 800-788-6262

Susan W. Albert. 1994. $12.95 (paper). 272 pages. Out of print.

NEWSPAPERS, MAGAZINES, AND JOURNALS

★13492★ BusinessWoman Magazine

Business and Professional Women/USA
1900 M St. NW, Ste. 310
Washington, DC 20036
Ph: (202)293-1100   Fax: (202)861-0298
E-mail: businesswoman@bpwusa.org
URL: http://www.bpwusa.org/businesswoman

$12.00/year. Magazine for working women that promotes workplace equity issues.

★13493★ Center for Research on Women-Standpoint

Center for Research on Women
The University of Memphis
339 Clement Hall
Memphis, TN 38152-3530
Ph: (901)678-2770   Fax: (901)678-3652
URL: http://cas.memphis.edu/isc/crow

Description: Two issues/year. Features news on issues of concern to women, including careers, education, ethnic minority affairs, sexual harrassment, violence, and economics. Includes information on Center activities and conferences, and Race, Class, and Gender Scholarship.

★13494★ Fair Employment Practices Summary of Latest Developments

Bureau of National Affairs Inc.
1231 25th St. NW
Washington, DC 20037
Ph: (202)452-4200   Fax: (202)452-4644
Fr: 800-372-1033

Description: Biweekly. Highlights developments in employment opportunity and affirmative actions, and affirmative action programs. Reports on federal and state court decisions, Equal Employment Opportunity Commission (EEOC) rulings and Office of Federal Contract Compliance Programs (OFCCP) decisions, new laws, regulations, and agency directives. Also provides information on special programs for minorities, the handicapped, women, and older workers.

★13495★ FEW's News and Views

Federally Employed Women Inc.
PO Box 28129
Washington, DC 20038-8129
Ph: (202)898-0994
E-mail: editor@few.org

Description: Three issues/year. Concerned with women's issues, particularly those involving women in the federal government. Reports on administration actions affecting the status of women and analyzes significant legislation. Recurring features include letters to the editor, news of members, a calendar of events, book reviews, and notices of career development and training opportunities.

★13496★ Gaea

Association for Women Geoscientists
PO Box 280
Broomfield, CO 80038-0280
E-mail: gaea@awg.org

Description: Bimonthly. Serves as an exchange of technical and professional information for the purpose of enhancing the professional growth and advancement of women in the geosciences. Explores opportunities and careers available in the geosciences and announces workshops and seminars on job hunting techniques, management skills, and career and life planning. Recurring features include news of members, Association updates, and notices of awards granted.

★13497★ Math/Science Network-Broadcast

Math/Science Network
Mills College
5000 Macarthur Blvd.
Oakland, CA 94613
Ph: (510)430-2222   Fax: (510)430-2090

Description: Quarterly. Carries news of the Network, which is interested in promoting the continuing development in mathematics and science of all people, with special emphasis on the needs of women. Recurring features include information on career education conferences, teacher education programs which encourage girls and women to pursue scien-

tific careers, and news of resources available.

★13498★ The NAWIC Image

National Association of Women in Construction (NAWIC)
327 S Adams St.
Fort Worth, TX 76104-1002
Ph: (817)877-5551   Fax: (817)877-0324
Fr: 800-552-3506

Description: Bimonthly. Fosters career advancement for women in construction. Features women business owners, training for construction trades and educational programs. Recurring features include columns titled "Issues and Trends," "Road to Success," "Chapter Highlights," "Members on the Move," and "Q&A."

★13499★ Southern Association for Women Historians Newsletter

Southern Association for Women Historians
c/o Dr. Melissa Walker
Dept. of History and Politics
Converse College
Spartanburg, SC 29302
E-mail: h-sawh@h-net.msu.edu

Description: Three issues/year. Informs members of the Association's activities aimed at advancing the professional development of women historians and historians of women. Carries minutes of the annual meeting, announcements of awards and prizes available for work published in a variety of areas, and calls for papers at various conferences. Recurring features include notices of publications available, job listings, and member updates.

★13500★ WEPANEWS

Women in Engineering Programs & Advocates Network
Castle Point on the Hudson
Hoboken, NJ 07030
Ph: (201)216-5245   Fax: (201)216-5175
URL: http://www.wepan.org/newsletter.html

Description: Two issues/year. Seeks to provide greater access for women to careers in engineering. Includes news of graduate, undergraduate, freshmen, pre-college, and re-entry engineering programs for women. Recurring features include job listings, faculty, grant, and conference news, international engineering program news, action group news, notices of publications available, and a column titled Kudos.

★13501★ WIN News

Women's International Network
187 Grant St.
Lexington, MA 02420-2126
Ph: (781)862-9431   Fax: (781)862-1734
E-mail: winnews@igc.org
URL: http://feminist.com/win.htm

Description: Quarterly. Acts as "a worldwide open communication system by, for, and about women of all backgrounds, beliefs, nationalities, and age-groups." Provides news and commentary on women and health, female genital mutilation, violence, the environment, human rights, science, media, and the United Nations. Contains reports from North America, Latin America, Europe, Africa, the Middle East, Asia, and the Pacific. Recurring features include names/addresses of all report and contact persons, statistics, book reviews, news of conferences, a calendar of events, and a section on career opportunities in the international field.

★13502★ *WIT*
Northern New England Tradeswomen
189 N Main St., Ste. 9
Barre, VT 05641-4173
Ph: (802)476-4040   Fax: (802)476-3346

Description: Three issues/year. Provides a network of support, information, and skill sharing for women in skilled trades professions.

★13503★ *Women in Business*
The ABWA Company Inc.
9100 Ward Pkwy.
PO Box 8728
Kansas City, MO 64114-0728
Ph: (816)361-6621   Fax: (816)361-4991
Fr: 800-228-0007
E-mail: abwa@abwa.org

Bimonthly. $20.00/year for individuals; $24.00/year for other countries. Women's business magazine.

★13504★ *Women as Managers*
The Economic Press Inc.
12 Daniel Rd.
Fairfield, NJ 07004-2565
Ph: (973)227-1224   Fax: (973)227-8360
Fr: 800-526-2554

Description: Biweekly. Offers suggestions to women in management who seek higher career levels. Discusses career-influencing women's issues. Presents management skills and techniques, and details problems and strengthens women face on the job.

★13505★ *Women Work!*
Women Work!-The National Network for
  Women's Employment
1625 K. St. NW, Ste. 300
Washington, DC 20006
Ph: (202)467-6346   Fax: (202)467-5366
Fr: 800-235-2732

Description: Quarterly. Provides information on some of the issues women in transition face in their lives. Recurring features include legislative information and columns titled Career Ladder, which provides career tips; Occupation Profile, which highlights a high-wage growth occupation; Money Issues, which provides financial tips; Health Watch, which focuses on women's health issues; and President's Message.

AUDIO/VISUAL RESOURCES

★13506★ *Math at Work: Women in Nontraditional Careers*
Her Own Words
PO Box 5264
Madison, WI 53705-0264
Ph: (608)271-7083   Fax: (608)271-0209
URL: http://www.herownwords.com/

Video. Jocelyn Riley. $95.00. 15 minutes. Resource guide also available for $45.00.

★13507★ *Women in Building Construction*
Her Own Words
PO Box 5264
Madison, WI 53705-0264
Ph: (608)271-7083   Fax: (608)271-0209
URL: http://www.herownwords.com/

Video. Jocelyn Riley. $95.00. 15 minutes. Resource guide also available for $45.00.

★13508★ *Women in Dentistry*
Her Own Words
PO Box 5264
Madison, WI 53705-0264
Ph: (608)271-7083   Fax: (608)271-0209
URL: http://www.herownwords.com/

Video. Jocelyn Riley. $95.00. 15 minutes. Resource guide also available for $45.00.

★13509★ *Women in Engineering*
Her Own Words
PO Box 5264
Madison, WI 53705-0264
Ph: (608)271-7083   Fax: (608)271-0209
URL: http://www.herownwords.com/

Video. Jocelyn Riley. $95.00. 15 minutes. Resource guide also available for $45.00.

★13510★ *Women in Firefighting*
Her Own Words
PO Box 5264
Madison, WI 53705-0264
Ph: (608)271-7083   Fax: (608)271-0209
URL: http://www.herownwords.com/

Video. Jocelyn Riley. $95.00. 15 minutes. Resource guide also available for $45.00.

★13511★ *Women in Highway Construction*
Her Own Words
PO Box 5264
Madison, WI 53705-0264
Ph: (608)271-7083   Fax: (608)271-0209
URL: http://www.herownwords.com/

Video. Jocelyn Riley. $95.00. 15 minutes. Resource guide also available for $45.00.

★13512★ *Women in Machining*
Her Own Words
PO Box 5264
Madison, WI 53705-0264
Ph: (608)271-7083   Fax: (608)271-0209
URL: http://www.herownwords.com/

Video. Jocelyn Riley. $95.00. 15 minutes. Resource guide also available for $45.00.

★13513★ *Women in Nontraditional Careers: An Introduction*
Her Own Words
PO Box 5264
Madison, WI 53705
Ph: (608)271-7083   Fax: (608)271-0209
URL: http://www.herownwords.com/

Video. Jocelyn Riley. $95.00. 15 minutes. Resource guide also available for $45.00.

★13514★ *Women in Policing*
Her Own Words
PO Box 5264
Madison, WI 53705
Ph: (608)271-7083   Fax: (608)271-0209
URL: http://www.herownwords.com/

Video. Jocelyn Riley. $95.00. 15 minutes. Resource guide also available for $45.00.

★13515★ *Work Talk: Women in Nontraditional Careers in Their Own Words*
Her Own Words
PO Box 5264
Madison, WI 53705
Ph: (608)271-7083   Fax: (608)271-0209
URL: http://www.herownwords.com/

Video. Jocelyn Riley. $95.00. 15 minutes. Resource guide also available for $45.00.

ONLINE AND DATABASE SERVICES

★13516★ MBA Careers
E-mail: support@mbacareers.com
URL: http://www.mbacareers.com

Description: Job site that provides resume posting, databank search and e-mail alert services to MBA and other advanced graduate degree holders.

★13517★ Women at Work
E-mail: womenatwork@atsearthlink.net
URL: http://www.womenatwork1.org/

Description: Site of nonprofit job and career resource center, serving the greater Los Angeles area.

SOFTWARE

★13518★ Interview Skills of the Future: Interview Challenges for Minorities, Women, and People with Disabilities

Program Development Associates
PO Box 2038
Syracuse, NY 13220-2038
Ph: (315)452-0643   Fax: (315)452-0710
Fr: 800-543-2119
E-mail: info@pdassoc.com
URL: http://www.pdassoc.com

$199.00. Teaches a tactful and positive response to challenging interview questions for those having a hard time breaking through the traditional hiring barriers.

OTHER SOURCES

★13519★ Association for Women Geoscientists (AWG)

PO Box 30645
Lincoln, NE 68503-0645
Fax: (402)489-8122
E-mail: office@awg.org
URL: http://www.awg.org

Members: Men and women geologists, geophysicists, petroleum engineers, geological engineers, hydrogeologists, paleontologists, geochemists, and other geoscientists. **Purpose:** Aims to: encourage the participation of women in the geosciences; exchange educational, technical, and professional information; enhance the professional growth and advancement of women in the geosciences. Provides information through web site on opportunities and careers available to women in the geosciences. **Activities:** Sponsors educational booths and programs at geological society conventions. Operates charitable program. Maintains speakers' bureau, and Association for Women Geoscientists Foundation (educational arm).

★13520★ Business and Professional Women's Foundation (BPWF)

1900 M St. NW, Ste. 310
Washington, DC 20036
Ph: (202)293-1100   Fax: (202)861-0298
E-mail: nharrison@bpwusa.org
URL: http://www.bpwusa.org

Purpose: Dedicated to improving the economic status of workingwomen through their integration into all occupations. **Activities:** Conducts and supports research on women and work, with special emphasis on economic issues. Maintains Marguerite Rawalt Resource Center of 20,000 items on economic issues involving women and work and provides public reference and referral service.

★13521★ Catalyst

120 Wall St., 5th Fl.
New York, NY 10005-3904
Ph: (212)514-7600   Fax: (212)514-8470
E-mail: info@catalystwomen.org
URL: http://www.catalystwomen.org

Description: Nonprofit research and advisory organization working to advance women in business. Considered to be the leading source of information on women in business for past four decades. Helps companies and women maximize their potential. Holds current statistics, print media, and research materials on issues related to women in business.

★13522★ Center for Economic Options

214 Capitol St., Ste. 200
Charleston, WV 25301
Ph: (304)345-1298   Fax: (304)342-0641
E-mail: info@economicoptions.org
URL: http://www.centerforeconoptions.org

Description: Seeks to improve the economic position and quality of life for women, especially low-income and minority women. Works to provide access to job training and employment options to women. Supports self-employed women and small business owners by offering training and technical assistance and information. Advocates women's legal right to employment, training, education, and credit. Seeks to inform the public on economic issues related to women. While activities are conducted on local and state levels, group cooperates with national and international organizations on issues relating to employment and economic justice for women. Maintains speakers' bureau and library. Compiles statistics; conducts research.

★13523★ Federally Employed Women (FEW)

1666 K St. NW, Ste. 440
Washington, DC 20006
Ph: (202)898-0994   Fax: (202)898-1535
E-mail: few@few.org
URL: http://www.few.org

Members: Men and women employed by the federal government. **Purpose:** Seeks to end sex discrimination in government service; to increase job opportunities for women in government service and to further the potential of all women in the government; to improve the merit system in government employment; to assist present and potential government employees who are discriminated against because of sex; to work with other organizations and individuals concerned with equal employment opportunity in the government. **Activities:** Provides speakers and sponsors seminars to publicize the Federal Women's Program; furnishes members with information on pending legislation designed to end discrimination against working women; informs and provides members opportunities for training to improve their job potential; issues fact sheets interpreting civil service rules and regulations and other legislative issues; provides annual training conference for over 3,000 women and men.

★13524★ Ludot Personnel Services Inc.

6056 N Sheldon Rd.
Canton, MI 48187
Ph: (248)353-9720   Fax: (248)459-2012

Professional placement and executive search in regard to professionals from entry level through senior managers. Also maintains a specialized division for recruitment of females and minorities. Conducts human resources management studies and recommendations in regard to personnel and organization planning, wage and salary, and recruitment within small to medium-size businesses. Industries served: automotive and allied suppliers, chemical and petrochemical, defense/electronics, consumer products, heavy manufacturing, research and development, and legal, as well as government agencies.

★13525★ National Association of Cuban-American Women of the U.S.A. (NACAW-USA)

PO Box 614
Union City, NJ 07087
Ph: (201)271-9384   Fax: (201)223-0036

Description: Addresses current issues, concerns, and problems affecting Hispanic and minority women, and to achieve goals such as equal education and training, fair immigration policy, and meaningful work with adequate compensation. Coordinates activities with national Hispanic and other minority organizations; responds to female concerns from minority and majority populations; encourages participation in related task forces, legislative activities, and professional endeavors; acts as clearinghouse and referral center. Supports bilingual and bicultural education at the local, state, and national levels. Disseminates information on postsecondary educational opportunities and sources of financial aid in particular cities. Produces biweekly bilingual radio program. Conducts placement service; compiles statistics.

★13526★ National Coalition of 100 Black Women (NCBW)

38 W. 32nd St., Ste. 1610
New York, NY 10001-3816
Ph: (212)947-2196   Fax: (212)947-2477
E-mail: ncloobw@aol.com
URL: http://www.ncbw.org

Description: African-American women actively involved with issues such as economic development, health, employment, education, voting, housing, criminal justice, the status of black families, and the arts. Seeks to provide networking and career opportunities for African-American women in the process of establishing links between the organization and the corporate and political arenas. Encourages leadership development; sponsors role-model and mentor programs to provide guidance to teenage mothers and young women in high school or who have graduated from college and are striving for career advancement.

★13527★ 9 to 5, National Association of Working Women

152 W Wisconsin Ave., Ste. 408
Milwaukee, WI 53203
Ph: (414)274-0925   Fax: (414)272-2870
Fr: 800-522-0925
E-mail: 9to5@9to5.org
URL: http://www.9to5.org

Description: Women office workers. Seeks to build a national network of local office worker chapters that strives to gain better pay, proper use of office automation, opportunities for advancement, elimination of sex and race discrimination, and improved working conditions for women office workers. Works to introduce legislation or regulations at state level to protect video display terminal operators. Produces studies and research in areas such as reproductive hazards of Video Display Terminals (VDTs), automation's effect on clerical employment, family and medical leaves, and stress. Conducts annual summer school for working women. Maintains speakers' bureau.

★13528★ 9 to 5 Working Women Education Fund (WWEF)

152 W Wisconsin Ave., Ste. 408
Milwaukee, WI 53203
Ph: (414)274-0925   Fax: (414)272-2870
Fr: 800-522-0925
E-mail: 9to5@9to5.org
URL: http://www.9to5.org/

Purpose: Conducts research on the concerns of women workers. Topics include: work/family, anti-discrimination, welfare/workfare, contingent work. **Activities:** Conducts public presentations and seminars upon request; provides speakers and trainers on sexual harassment. Compiles statistics of women in the workforce.

★13529★ Organization of Chinese American Women (OCAW)

4641 Montgomery Ln, Ste. 208
Bethesda, MD 20814
Ph: (301)907-3898   Fax: (301)907-3899
E-mail: ocawwomen@aol.com

URL: http://www.ocawwomen.org

Description: Advances the cause of Chinese American women in the U.S. and fosters public awareness of their special needs and concerns. Seeks to integrate Chinese American women into the mainstream of women's activities and programs. Addresses issues such as equal employment opportunities at both the professional and nonprofessional levels; overcoming stereotypes; racial and sexual discrimination and restrictive traditional beliefs; assistance to poverty-stricken recent immigrants; access to leadership and policymaking positions. Networking for Chinese American women. Sponsors annual opera and Mother's Day and Award Banquet. Conducts Biennual National Training Conferences; establishes scholarships for middle school girls in rural China.

★13530★ Wider Opportunities for Women (WOW)

1001 Connecticut Ave. NW, No. 930
Washington, DC 20036
Ph: (202)464-1596   Fax: (202)464-1660
E-mail: info@wowonline.org
URL: http://www.wowonline.org

Description: To expand employment opportunities for women through information, employment training, technical assistance, and advocacy. Works to overcome barriers to women's employment and economic equity, including occupational segregation, sex stereotypic education and training, discrimination in employment practices and wages. Sponsors Women's Work Force Network, a national network of 500 women's employment programs and advocates. The network monitors current policies to increase the priority given to employment needs of women; provides information to congressional staffs to clarify the impact of various legislative proposals on women; issues public policy alerts and informational materials when relevant federal policy is being proposed or undergoing revision; conducts investigative projects toassess how legislative programs are implemented and their impact on women. Offers technical assistance to

education institutions, government agencies, and private industry on programs to increase women's participation in non-traditional employment and training. Maintains National Commission on Working Women and Industry Advisory Councils

★13531★ Women Employed Institute (WEI)

111 N. Wabash, 13th Fl.
Chicago, IL 60602
Ph: (312)782-3902   Fax: (312)782-5249
E-mail: info@womenemployed.org
URL: http://www.womenemployed.org

Description: Research and education division of Women Employed devoted to promoting economic equity for women. Analyzes government programs and employer policies; develops recommendations for public and corporate policy to promote equal opportunity. Sponsors advocacy programs to increase women's accessibility to vocational education and training for higher paying, nontraditional jobs. Develops model employment awareness/readiness programs for disadvantaged women. Conducts research projects; compiles statistics on women's economic status.

★13532★ Women Work! The National Network for Women's Employment

1625 K St. NW, Ste. 300
Washington, DC 20006
Ph: (202)467-6346   Fax: (202)467-5366
Fr: 800-235-2732
E-mail: womenwork@womenwork.org
URL: http://www.womenwork.org

Displaced homemakers and single parents, women's training services, persons from related organizations, and supporters. Fosters development of programs and services for women preparing for the workforce. Acts as clearinghouse to provide communications, technical assistance, public information, data collection, legislative monitoring, funding information, and other services. Compiles statistics. Provides referrals, information on research in progress, and publication distribution.

Outplacement

REFERENCE WORKS

★13533★ The Changing Outplacement Process: New Methods and Opportunities for Transition Management
Greenwood Publishing Group Inc.
88 Post Rd. W
Westport, CT 06881
Johm Meyer and Carolyn Shadle. $78.95. 312 pages.

★13534★ Complete Guide to Outplacement Services
LEA
10 Industrial Ave.
Mahwah, NJ 07430
Alan Pickman. 176 pages.

★13535★ Directory of Outplacement and Career Management Firms
Kennedy Information Inc.
One Phoenix Mill Ln., 5th Fl.
Peterborough, NH 03458
Ph: (603)924-1006   Fax: (603)924-4460
Fr: 800-531-0007

Annual, latest edition 2003. $149.95. Covers over 380 consulting firms with special interest in career management and "outplacement" or "de-hiring" counseling executive employees being terminated because of poor performance, plant closings, etc., and assisting them in finding new jobs; firms that are compensated only by employers and those that also accept compensation from individuals are listed. Entries include: Firm name, address, phone, fax, E-mail, description of philosophy and services, names and titles of principals, branches, area served, year established, revenue (within wide ranges), professional associations, minimum salary of positions handled, number of staff, percentage of business devoted to outplacement. Arrangement: Separate sections on basis of compensation arrangements, then alphabetical. Indexes: Industries, key principals, firm.

★13536★ Your Outplacement Handbook: Redesigning Your Career
St. Lucie Press
2000 Corporate Blvd. NW
Boca Raton, FL 33431-7372
Ph: (561)274-9906   Fax: (561)274-9927
Fr: 800-272-7737

Fern Lebo. 1996. $25.95.

NEWSPAPERS, MAGAZINES, AND JOURNALS

★13537★ Self-Employed America
National Association for the Self-Employed
2121 Precinct Line Rd.
Hurst, TX 76054
Ph: (817)428-4243   Fax: (817)428-4210
URL: http://www.nase.org

Bimonthly. Subscription included in membership; $12.00/year for nonmembers. Magazine deseminating information on topics of interest to small-business owners, such as marketing, management, and pertinent legislative developments. Also presents success stories concerning Association members and describes Association activities.

AUDIO/VISUAL RESOURCES

★13538★ Getting Fired, Getting Hired: Job Hunting from A to Z
CareerLab Books
304 Inverness Way S, Ste. 465
Englewood, CO 80112
Ph: (303)790-0505   Fax: (303)790-0606
Fr: 800-723-9675
URL: http://www.careerlab.com

Series of 6 videos. $14.95/set. 30 minutes each. Individual titles cover aspects of the job search following job loss.

OTHER SOURCES

★13539★ Association of Career Management Consulting Firms International (AOCFI)
204 E St. NE
Washington, DC 20002
Ph: (202)547-6344   Fax: (202)547-6348
E-mail: aocfi@aocfi.org
URL: http://www.aocfi.org

Members: Firms providing displaced employees, who are sponsored by their organization, with counsel and assistance in job searching and the techniques and practices of choosing a career. **Purpose:** To develop, improve, and encourage the art and science of outplacement consulting and the professional standards of competence, objectivity, and integrity in the service of clients. Cooperates with other industrial, technical, educational, professional, and governmental bodies in areas of mutual interest and concern.

★13540★ CareerSoar
KANDR Bldg.
22 IBM Rd., Ste. 103
Poughkeepsie, NY 12601
Ph: (845)462-2291
URL: http://www.careersoar.com

Description: Provides consulting services solutions.

★13541★ Five O'Clock Club
300 E. 40th St., Ste. 6L
New York, NY 10016
URL: http://www.fiveoclockclub.com
Description: Career Counseling network.

★13542★ National Career Development Association (NCDA)
10820 E 45th St., Ste. 210
Tulsa, OK 74146
Ph: (918)663-7060   Fax: (918)663-7058
Fr: (866)367-6232
E-mail: dpennington@ncda.org
URL: http://www.ncda.org

Description: A division of the American

Counseling Association. **Members:** Professionals and others interested in career development or counseling in various work environments. **Purpose:** Supports counselors, education and training personnel, and allied professionals working in schools, colleges, business/industry, community and government agencies, and in private practice. **Activities:** Provides publications, support for state and local activities, human equity programs, and continuing education and training for these professionals. Pro-

vides networking opportunities for career professionals in business, education, and government.

★13543★ **National Self-Help Clearinghouse (NSHC)**
365 5th Ave., Ste. 3300
New York, NY 10016
Ph: (212)817-1822   Fax: (212)817-1561
E-mail: info@selfhelpweb.org

URL: http://www.selfhelpweb.org

Description: Clearinghouse on self-help groups; provides referral services. Conducts research and training activities. Maintains speakers' bureau.

Self Employment

REFERENCE WORKS

★13544★ Becoming Self-Employed

Live Oak Publications
1515 23rd St.
PO Box 2193
Boulder, CO 80306
Ph: (303)448-1169   Fax: (303)447-8684

Susan Elliot. Second edition, 1994. $9.95 (paper). 160 pages. Illustrated.

★13545★ Being Self-Employed

Allyear Tax Guides
20484 Glen Brae Dr.
Saratoga, CA 95070
Ph: (408)867-2626   Fax: (408)867-6466

Holmes F. Crouch. Second edition, 1998. Part of the Series 100 Tax Guides: Individuals and Families. $19.95. 224 pages.

★13546★ The Bootstrapper's Bible: How to Start and Build a Business with a Great Idea And (Almost) No Money

Dearborn Trade, A Kaplan Professional Co.
155 N. Wacker Dr.
Chicago, IL 60606-1719
Ph: (312)836-4400   Fax: (312)836-1021
Fr: 800-621-9621

Seth Godin. 1998. $22.95 (paper). 288 pages.

★13547★ Business Incubators of North America

National Business Incubation Association (NBIA)
20 Circle Dr., Ste. 190
Athens, OH 45701-3211
Ph: (740)593-4331   Fax: (740)593-1996
URL: http://www.nbia.org

Biennial. $10.00 for members; $395.00 for nonmembers. Covers approximately 800 facilities that house small businesses in the beginning stage of development; coverage includes Canada and Mexico. Entries include: Facility name, address, phone, fax, e-mail; name and title of contact; type of incubator; year opened; sponsorship; square footage; number of clients; incubator sponsor information. Arrangement: Geographical.

★13548★ Careers for Self-Starters and Other Entrepreneurial Types

McGraw-Hill Contemporary Books
1221 Avenue of the Americas
New York, NY 10020
Ph: (212)904-2000   Fr: 800-323-4900

Blythe Camenson. 1997. $9.95 (paper). 190 pages.

★13549★ Change Your Job, Change Your Life: High Impact Strategies for Finding Great Jobs in the 21st Century

Impact Publications
9104 Manassas Dr., Ste. N
Manassas Park, VA 20111-5211
Ph: (703)361-7300   Fax: (703)335-9486

Ronald Krannich. Seventh edition, 1999. $17.95 (paper). 317 pages. Details trends in the marketplace, how to identify opportunities, how to retrain for them, and how to land jobs. Includes a chapter on starting a business. Contains index, bibliography, and illustrations.

★13550★ A Consumer Guide to Buying a Franchise

Franchise Rule Information Hotline
Federal Trade Commission
6th and Pennsylvania Ave. NW
Washington, DC 20580
Ph: (202)326-2222
URL: http://www.ftc.gov

21 pages. Describes owning and selecting a franchise.

★13551★ The Directory of Home-Based Business Resources

Pilot Books
127 Sterling Ave.
PO Box 2102
Greenport, NY 11944-0893
Ph: (516)477-1094   Fax: (516)477-1094
Fr: 800-797-4568
URL: http://www.pilotbooks.com

$7.95. Provides information on starting and running a homebased business and lists sources of additional information.

★13552★ Entrepreneur's Be Your Own Boss

Entrepreneur Media Inc.
2445 McCabe Way, Ste. 400
Irvine, CA 92614
Ph: (949)261-2325   Fax: (949)261-0234
URL: http://www.entrepreneur.com

Three times per year. $3.95; $5.99 for Canada. Covers over 1,100 franchise and business opportunities; coverage includes Canada; Feb issue: low-investment franchises; May issue: directory of homebased franchises and business opportunites; Sept issue: completed directory of franchise and business opportunities. Entries include: Company name, address, phone, description of opportunity, geographical areas available, costs. Arrangement: Classified by line of business.

★13553★ Fired Up: The Proven Principles of Successful Entrepreneurs

Viking Penguin
375 Hudson St.
New York, NY 10014-3657
Ph: (212)366-2000   Fax: (212)366-2952
Fr: 800-331-4624

Michael Gill. 1999. $8.95 (paper).

★13554★ Free Help from Uncle Sam to Start Your Own Business or Expand the One You Have
Puma Publishing Co.
1670 Coral Dr.
Santa Maria, CA 93454
Ph: (805)925-3216 Fax: (805)925-2656
Fr: 800-255-5730

William M. Alarid. Fifth edition, 2000. $17.95 (paper). 304 pages.

★13555★ Generation E: The Entrepreneurial Guide for Twentysomethings and Other Corporate Rejects
Ten Speed Press
PO Box 7123
Berkeley, CA 94707
Ph: (510)559-1600 Fax: (510)559-1629
Fr: 800-841-2665

Joel Ross and Lee Naftali. 1997. $11.95. "How-to" guide offers advice to those interested in starting their own small business.

★13556★ Government Giveaways for Entrepreneurs III
Information USA Inc.
U.S. Dept. of State
2201 C St. NW
Washington, DC 20520
Ph: (202)647-4000
URL: http://www.lesko.com

Biennial, even years. $37.95. Covers about 300 government programs and 9,000 sources of free help for persons wanting to start or expand a business. Arrangement: Geographical.

★13557★ Guide to Self-Employment
John Wiley & Sons Inc.
1 Wiley Dr.
Somerset, NJ 08873
Ph: (732)469-4400 Fr: 800-225-5945

National Business Employment Weekly staff. 1996. $12.95 (paper). 256 pages.

★13558★ Home Business Made Easy
Todd Publications
PO Box 635
Nyack, NY 10960
Ph: (845)358-6213 Fax: (845)358-6213
Fr: (866)896-0916
URL: http://www.toddpublications.com/todd-pubs/index.htm

Latest edition 1999. $25.00. Covers 175 different business that can be run from home full or part time based on interest, lifestyle, and finances.

★13559★ The Home Office and Small Business Success Book
Henry Holt and Co. LLC
115 W. 18th St., 5th Fl.
New York, NY 10011
Ph: (212)886-9200 Fax: (212)633-0748
Fr: 800-672-2054

Janet Attard. 1996. $45.00; $19.95 (paper).

560 pages. Guide covering telecommunications and telecommuting trends. Publication cancelled.

★13560★ How to Become Successfully Self-Employed
Adams Media Corp.
57 Littlefield St.
Avon, MA 02322
Ph: (508)427-7100 Fax: (508)427-6790
Fr: 800-872-5627
URL: http://www.adamsmedia.com

Brian R. Smith. Second edition, 1997. $9.95 (paper). 304 pages. Out of print. Offers practical advice and removes the myths surrounding self-employment.

★13561★ How to Have a Brilliant Career Without Ever Having a Proper Job: The Active Guide to Self-Employment
Trans-Atlantic Publications, Inc.
311 Bainbridge St.
Philadelphia, PA 19147
Ph: (215)925-5083 Fax: (215)925-1912

Stuart Crainer. 1995. 250 pages. Out of print.

★13562★ How to Run Your Own Home Business
McGraw-Hill Trade
2 Penn Plaza
New York, NY 10121
Ph: (212)904-2000 Fr: 800-722-4726
E-mail: ntcpub@tribune.com

Coralee Smith Kern and Tammara Hoffman Wolfgram. Third edition, 1994. $10.95 (paper). 224 pages. Helps the reader determine if he/she is suited to working at home, choose a product or service, set up a comfortable, efficient working environment, and keep abreast of zoning and tax laws.

★13563★ How to Write What You Love and Make a Living at It
WaterBrook Press
2375 Telstar Dr., Suite 160
Colorado Springs, CO 80920
Ph: (719)590-4999 Fax: (719)590-8977
Fr: 800-603-7051

Dennis E. Hensley. 2000. $12.99 (paper).

★13564★ The Ideal Entrepreneurial Business for You
John Wiley & Sons Inc.
1 Wiley Dr.
Somerset, NJ 08873
Ph: (732)469-4400 Fr: 800-225-5945

Glenn Desmond and Monica Faulkner. $40.00.

★13565★ Independent Practice for the Mental Health Professional: Growing a Private Practice for the 21st Century
Brunner-Routledge
325 Chestnut St., 8th Fl.
Philadelphia, PA 19106
Ph: (215)625-8900 Fax: (215)625-2940

Ralph Earle. 1999. $24.95.

★13566★ Kiss off Corporate America: A Young Professional's Guide to Independence
Andrews McMeel Publishing
4520 Main St.
Kansas City, MO 64111
Ph: (816)932-6700 Fax: (816)932-6749
Fr: 800-826-4216

Lisa Kivirist. 1998. $12.95 (paper). 216 pages.

★13567★ Lifescripts For the Self Employed
Hungry Minds, Inc.
10475 Crosspoint Blvd.
Indianapolis, IN 46256
Fax: (317)572-4000 Fr: 800-667-1115

Mark Levine. 1999. $14.95. Part of Lifescripts series.

★13568★ Making Money Writing Newsletters
EFG, Inc.
3460 Hampton Ave.
Ste. 103
St. Louis, MO 63139
Ph: (314)353-6100 Fax: (314)353-1272
Fr: 800-264-6305

Elaine Floyd. 1994. $29.95 (paper). 132 pages. How to start a newsletter writing and design service.

★13569★ Marketing for the Home-based Business
Adams Media Corp.
57 Littlefield St.
Avon, MA 02322
Ph: (508)427-7100 Fax: (508)427-6790
Fr: 800-872-5627
URL: http://www.adamsmedia.com

Jeffrey P. Davidson. Second edition, 1999. $10.95 (paper). 242 pages. Addresses how to market the home-based business after you've started it.

★13570★ Mind Your Own Business!
Tower Publishing
561 Chula Brookfield Rd.
Chula, GA 31733
Ph: (229)387-0057 Fax: (317)613-4307
Fr: 800-648-5478
E-mail: jistworks@aol.com
URL: http://www.jist.com

LaVerne L. Ludden and Bonnie R. Maitlen. 1993. $9.95. 305 pages. Explains how to get started as an entrepreneur.

★13571★ Minority Business Information Resource Directory

Diversity Information Resources
2105 Central Ave. NE
Minneapolis, MN 55418
Ph: (612)781-6819   Fax: (612)781-0109
URL: http://www.diversityinforesources.com

Annual, January. $52.00. Covers business opportunity fairs, seminars, and workshops; National Supplier Development Council regional offices; Small Business Administration and Minority Business Development Administration offices; minority and women-owned business directories; and other resources for minority and women-owned businesses.

★13572★ Modern Moonlighting: How to Earn Thousands Extra without Leaving Your Day Job

McGraw-Hill Trade
2 Penn Plaza
New York, NY 10121
Ph: (212)904-2000   Fax: (212)755-5645
Fr: 800-722-4726

Roger Woodson. 1997. $14.95 (paper). 288 pages. Explores part-time selfemployment business opportunities.

★13573★ Money Smart Secrets for the Self-Employed

Random House, Inc.
1540 Broadway
New York, NY 10036
Ph: (212)782-9000   Fax: (212)302-7985
Fr: 800-726-0600

Linda Stern. 1997. $20.00 (paper).

★13574★ Network of Small Businesses-Membership Directory

Network of Small Businesses
5420 Mayfield Rd., Ste. 205
Lyndhurst, OH 44124
Ph: (440)442-5600

Approximately annual; previous edition April 1992; latest edition November 1999. $495.00. Covers owners and others involved in small businesses (defined as 250 employees or less), including investors, venture funders, business owners, business buyers, business sellers, and investing partners. Entries include: Company name, address, phone, names and titles of key personnel. Arrangement: Alphabetical. Indexes: Company owner.

★13575★ No More Job Interviews!: Self-Employment Strategies for People with Disabilities

Training Resource Network, Incorporated
P.O. Box 439
St. Augustine, FL 32085-0439
Ph: (904)823-9800   Fax: (904)823-3554
Fr: (866)823-9800

Alice Weiss. 2000. $29.95 (paper).

★13576★ On Your Own: A Guide to Working Happily, Productively & Successfully at Home

Prentice Hall PTR
200 Old Tappan Rd.
Old Tappan, NJ 07675
Ph: (201)236-7000   Fr: 800-223-1360

Lionel L. Fisher. 1994. $10.95 (paper). 228 pages.

★13577★ Opportunities in Franchising Careers

McGraw-Hill Trade
2 Penn Plaza
New York, NY 10121
Ph: (212)904-2000   Fr: 800-722-4726

Kent B. Banning and Brook Carey. Revised, 1995. $14.95; $11.95 (paper). 160 pages.

★13578★ The Perfect Business: How to Make a Million from Home with No Payroll, No Employee Headaches, No Debt, and No Sleepless Nights

Simon & Schuster Inc.
1230 Ave. of the Americas
New York, NY 10020
Ph: (212)698-7000   Fax: (212)698-7007
Fr: 800-223-2336

Michael LeBoeuf. 1997. $12.00 (paper).

★13579★ Secrets of Self-Employment: Surviving and Thriving on the Ups and Downs at Being Your Own Boss

Putnam Publishing Group
375 Hudson St.
New York, NY 10014
Ph: (212)366-2000   Fax: (212)366-2643
Fr: 800-847-5515

Paul Edwards and Sarah Edwards. 1996. $15.95 (paper). Part of the Working from Home Series.

★13580★ The Self-Employed Woman's Guide to Launching a Home-Based Business

Prima Publishing
3000 Lava Ridge Ct.
Roseville, CA 95661
Ph: (916)787-7000   Fax: (916)787-7001

Priscilla Huff. 2002. $14.95 (paper).

★13581★ Self-Employment: From Dream to Reality!

JIST Publishing
8902 Otis Ave.
Indianapolis, IN 46216-1033
Ph: (317)613-4200   Fax: (317)613-4307
Fr: 800-648-5478
E-mail: jistworks@aol.com
URL: http://www.jist.com

Linda Gilkeson and Theresia Paauwe. 1997. $16.95. 345 pages. An interactive workbook for starting a small business.

★13582★ The Self-Employment Survival Manual: How to Start and Operate a One-Person Business Successfully

A. William Benitez Ltd.
PO Box 150266
Austin, TX 78715-0266
Ph: (512)447-4744   Fax: (512)292-1778
Fr: 800-887-4017

A. William Benitez. 1993. $18.95 (paper). 120 pages. The book helps individuals to discover the work they are best suited for & then teaches them how to get started & organized, get & keep customers, how to price work, handle complaints & all other aspects of small business operation.

★13583★ Small Business Network-National Directory

Small Business Network
3 Woodthorne Ct.
Owings Mills, MD 21117
Ph: (410)581-1373
URL: http://www.ameribiz.com

Annual, summer. Covers businesses involved in assisting the development and support of small business.

★13584★ Small Business Sourcebook

Thomson Gale
27500 Drake Rd.
Farmington Hills, MI 48331-3535
Ph: (248)699-4253   Fax: (248)699-8065
Fr: 800-877-GALE
E-mail: businessproducts@gale.com
URL: http://www.gale.com

Annual. $380.00. Contains profiles for 341 specific types of small business. Each profile contains sources of start-up information, associations, educational programs, reference works, sources of supplies, statistical sources, trade periodicals, videos, trade shows and conventions, consultants, franchises, databases, business systems and software, libraries, research centers, and Internet databases. Publications also lists 99 general small business topics of interest to entrepreneurs, and sources of small business information and assistance, including federal and state government agencies; professional associations; small business development centers; educational programs; consultants; venture capital firms; SCORE (Service Corps of Retired Executives) offices; incubators; and related publications. Contact information, including fax, and toll free, email & URL addresses are provided whenever possible. Entries include: Organization, individual, event, or publication name, address, contact numbers; description of contents, activities, services, publications, or programs; and other details relevant to the type of source, such as show dates and location, investment preferences and limitations, etc. Arrangement: Volume 1 contains small business profiles A-Z; Volume 2 contains general small business topics, state listings, federal government assistance. Indexes: Alphabetical.

★13585★ *Small Time Operator: How to Start Your Own Small Business, Keep Your Books, Pay Your Taxes, and Stay out of Trouble!*

Bell Springs Publishing
PO Box 1240
106 State St.
Willits, CA 95490
Ph: (707)459-6372   Fax: (707)459-8614
Fr: 800-515-8050

Bernard Kamoroff. Sixth edition, 2001. $16.95 (paper). 224 pages.

★13586★ *Solo Success*

Random House Value Publishing, Inc.
201 E. 50th St.
New York, NY 10022
Ph: (212)572-2400   Fr: 800-733-3000

David Perlstein. 1999. $1.99 (paper).

★13587★ *Start Small, Finish Big: 15 Key Lessons to Start - and Run - Your Own Successful Business*

Warner Books, Incorporated
1271 Avenue of the Americas
New York, NY 10020
Ph: (212)522-7200

Fred DeLuca and John P. Hayes. 2000. $25.95.

★13588★ *Start Up Financing: An Entrepreneur's Guide to Financing a New or Growing Business*

The Career Press, Inc.
3 Tice Rd.
PO Box 687
Franklin Lakes, NJ 07417-1322
Ph: (201)848-0310   Fax: (201)848-1727
Fr: 800-227-3371

William J. Stolze. 1997 $16.99. Written for the reader about to embark on a new venture or who has started a business within the past few years. Addresses key problems crucial to the small business owner, such as adequacy of funding and how to write a business plan.

★13589★ *Starting Over: How to Change Careers or Start Your Own Business*

Warner Books, Inc.
1271 Ave. of the Americas
New York, NY 10020
Ph: (212)522-7200   Fax: 800-286-9471
Fr: 800-759-0190

Stephen M. Pollan and Mark Levine. 1997. $15.99 (paper). 241 pages.

★13590★ *The States and Small Business: A Directory of Programs and Activities*

Office of Advocacy
409 3rd St. SW
Washington, DC 20416
Ph: (202)205-6531   Fax: (202)205-6928

Irregular, previous edition March 1989; latest edition March 1993. $21.00. Covers over 750 state government small business offices, legislative committees, small business conferences. Entries include: Agency name, address, phone; name and title of contact; description of activities; summary of small business legislation, etc. Arrangement: Geographical.

★13591★ *Successfully Self-Employed*

Upstart Pub. Co.
155 N. Wacker Dr.
Chicago, IL 60606-1719
Ph: (312)836-4400   Fax: (312)836-1021
Fr: 800-621-9621

Gregory Brennan. 1996. $16.95 (paper). 175 pages. Out of print.

★13592★ *Supplier Diversity Information Resource Guide*

Diversity Information Resources
2105 Central Ave. NE
Minneapolis, MN 55418
Ph: (612)781-6819   Fax: (612)781-0109
URL: http://www.diversityinforesources.com

Annual, January. $65.00. Covers business opportunity fairs, seminars, and workshops; National Supplier Development Council regional offices; Small Business Administration and Minority Business Development Administration offices; minority and women-owned business directories; and other resources for minority and women-owned businesses.

★13593★ *The Twentysomething Guide to Creative Self-Employment: Making Money While Keeping Your Freedom*

Prima Publishing
3000 Lava Ridge Ct.
Roseville, CA 95661
Ph: (916)787-7000   Fax: (916)787-7001

Jeff Porten. 1996. $14.95 (paper). 288 pages. Out of print.

★13594★ *Venture Capital Directory*

Forum Publishing Co.
383 E. Main St.
Centerport, NY 11721
Ph: (631)754-5000   Fax: (631)754-0630
Fr: 800-635-7654
URL: http://www.hometownparkmall.com

Annual, February. $12.95. Covers over 400 members of the Small Business Administration and the Small Business Investment Company that provide funding for small and minority businesses. Entries include: Company name, address, phone, names and titles of key personnel, geographical area served, financial data, branch office or subsidiary names, description of services and projects. Arrangement: Alphabetical.

★13595★ *Working Solo Sourcebook: Essential Resources for Independent Entrepreneurs*

John Wiley & Sons Inc.
1 Wiley Dr.
Somerset, NJ 08873
Ph: (732)469-4400   Fr: 800-225-5945

Terri Lonier. First edition, 1998. $14.95 (paper).

NEWSPAPERS, MAGAZINES, AND JOURNALS

★13596★ *Entrepreneur Magazine*

Entrepreneur Media Inc.
2445 McCabe Way, Ste. 400
Irvine, CA 92614
Ph: (949)261-2325   Fax: (949)261-0234
E-mail: entmag@entrepreneur.com
URL: http://www.entrepreneur.com

Monthly. $19.97/year for individuals; $4.99 for single issue. Magazine covering small business management and operation.

★13597★ *Franchising World*

International Franchise Association
1350 New York Ave. NW, Ste. 900
Washington, DC 20005-4709
Ph: (202)628-8000   Fax: (202)628-0812
Fr: 800-543-1038

$18.00/year for individuals; $3.50 for single issue. Trade magazine covering topics of interest to franchise company executives and the business world.

★13598★ *Income Opportunities*

IO Publications Inc.
1500 Broadway
New York, NY 10036-4015
Ph: (212)642-0600   Fax: (212)768-3769
Fr: 800-289-7852
E-mail: incomeed@aol.com

$19.95/year. Magazine focusing on money making opportunities.

★13599★ *innkeeping*

Professional Association of Innkeepers International
PO Box 90710
Santa Barbara, CA 93190
Ph: (805)569-1853   Fax: (805)682-1016

Description: Monthly. Addresses topics of interest to innkeepers who own and operate bed and breakfast operations. Recurring features include letters to the editor, news of research, news of educational opportunities, and notices of publications available.

★13600★ *Self-Employed America*
National Association for the Self-
 Employed
2121 Precinct Line Rd.
Hurst, TX 76054
Ph: (817)428-4243   Fax: (817)428-4210
URL: http://www.nase.org

Bimonthly. Subscription included in membership; $12.00/year for nonmembers. Magazine deseminating information on topics of interest to small-business owners, such as marketing, management, and pertinent legislative developments. Also presents success stories concerning Association members and describes Association activities.

★13601★ *Spare Time*
Kipen Publishing Corp.
5810 W Oklahoma Ave.
Milwaukee, WI 53219-4300
Ph: (414)543-8110   Fax: (414)543-9767
URL: http://www.sparetimemagazine.com
$16.95/year for individuals; $42.00/year for other countries; $2.50/year for single issue. Magazine featuring articles on business start-up and money-making opportunities.

ONLINE AND DATABASE SERVICES

★13602★ Home Workers Jobs Digest
E-mail: hr@intlhomeworkers.com
URL: http://Homeworkers.com
Description: Job databank and resource site for the self-employed. Contains links, online courses, resume submission and more. **Fee:** Lifetime membership is $77.

OTHER SOURCES

★13603★ National Association for the Self-Employed (NASE)
PO Box 612067
DFW Airport
Dallas, TX 75261-2067
Fax: 800-551-4446   Fr: 800-232-6273
URL: http://www.nase.org
Members: Self-employed and small independent businesspersons. **Purpose:** Acts as an advocate at the state and federal levels for self-employed people. Provides discounts on products and services important to self-employed and small business owners.

Using Recruiters and Employment Agencies

REFERENCE WORKS

★13604★ Adams Executive Recruiters Almanac

Adams Media Corp.
57 Littlefield St.
Avon, MA 02322
Ph: (508)427-7100   Fax: (508)427-6790
Fr: 800-872-5627

$17.95. Covers executive recruiters in the United States. Entries include: Firm or organization name, address, phone, name and title of contact; description of organization, headquarters location, typical titles for entry- and middle-level positions, educational backgrounds desired, fringe benefits offered, stock exchange listing, training programs, internships, parent company, number of employees, revenues, e-mail and web address, projected number of hires. Indexes: Alphabetical and by specialization.

★13605★ American Directory of Job and Labor Market Information

Career Communications
PO Box 169
Harleysville, PA 19438

$29.95. Covers resources providing information on jobs and labor markets, including state and federal government personnel departments, job information centers, employment service centers, databases, libraries, and publications. Arrangement: Classified by type of resource.

★13606★ The Career Makers: America's Top 150 Executive Recruiters

Random House Value Publishing, Inc.
201 E. 50th St.
New York, NY 10022
Ph: (212)572-2400   Fr: 800-733-3000

John Sibbald. 1995. $4.99. 384 pages. Out of print. Profiles of top recruiters and guidance for working with search firms. Includes industry/functional cross-indexing.

★13607★ The Directory of Executive Recruiters

Kennedy Information Inc.
1 Kennedy Pl.
Rte. 12 S.
Fitzwilliam, NH 03447
Ph: (603)585-3101   Fax: (603)585-6401
Fr: 800-531-0007

First edition, 2001. $179.95. 2100 pages. Lists and describes more than 3,200 firms in North America and indexes these by function, industry, and geographic area. Names key principals of recruiting firms. Includes narrative section on executive search and how it affects job candidates. Also available: Corporate Edition, expanded for use by corporate staffs, $99.00 (hardcover).

★13608★ Employment Agencies & Opportunities Directory

infoUSA Inc.
5711 S 86th Cir.
Omaha, NE 68127-0347
Ph: (402)930-3500   Fax: (402)331-0176
Fr: 800-555-6124
URL: http://www.abii.com

Annual. Number of listings: 30,462. Entries include: Name, address, phone (including area code), size of advertisement, year first in "Yellow Pages," name of owner or manager, number of employees. Compiled from telephone company "Yellow Pages," nationwide. Arrangement: Geographical.

★13609★ Employment Contractors-Temporary Help Directory

infoUSA Inc.
5711 S 86th Cir.
Omaha, NE 68127-0347
Ph: (402)930-3500   Fax: (402)331-0176
Fr: 800-555-6124
URL: http://www.abii.com

Annual. Number of listings: 22,959. Entries include: Name, address, phone (including area code), size of advertisement, year first in "Yellow Pages," name of owner or manager, number of employees. Compiled from telephone company "Yellow Pages," nationwide. Arrangement: Geographical.

★13610★ Executive Recruitment Firms

JNN International Inc.
6821 Sutherland Ct.
Mentor, OH 44060

Annual, September. $7.00. Covers firms providing services such as executive search, job counseling, and marketing (resume preparation, mailing, etc.); personnel agencies and job registers. Published in 18 industry-specific volumes under title "Executive Recruitment Firms Specializing in (industry name)" and a general volume titled "Executive Recruitment Firms Specializing in Most Industries." Entries include: Company name, contact name, address. Arrangement: Separate geographical sections for firms that do not charge fees and those that do charge.

★13611★ Executive Search Consultants Directory

infoUSA Inc.
5711 S 86th Cir.
Omaha, NE 68127-0347
Ph: (402)930-3500   Fax: (402)331-0176
Fr: 800-555-6124
URL: http://www.abii.com

Annual. Number of listings: 8,320. Entries include: Name, address, phone (including area code), size of advertisement, year first in "Yellow Pages," name of owner or manager, number of employees. Compiled from telephone company "Yellow Pages," nationwide. Arrangement: Geographical.

★13612★ Executive Search Firms and Employment Agencies in Seattle: Job-Search Resources for the Executive, Manager and Professional

Barrett Street Productions
PO Box 99642
Seattle, WA 98199
Ph: (206)284-8202   Fax: (206)352-0944

Linda Carlson. 1998. $21.95 (paper). 200 pages.

★13613★ Executive Search Research Directory
Recruiting & Search Report
PO Box 9433
Panama City, FL 32417
Ph: (850)235-3733   Fax: (850)233-9695
Fr: 800-634-4548
E-mail: esrd11@aol.com
URL: http://www.rsronline.com

Biennial, with yearly updates; May 2004, 11th Edition. $100.00. Covers over 400 freelance executive search researchers that specialize in candidate locating, screening, and development for executive recruiters and corporate (in-house) recruiters; publishers of directories, books, periodicals, and other resources related to recruitment research. Entries include: For researchers-Name, address, phone, rates, year established, first year listed, a description of services and specialties, hourly rates. Arrangement: Researchers are geographical by zip code. Indexes: Geographical; means of industry or functional concentration; unusual expertise; specialty.

★13614★ Finding Work Overseas: How and Where to Contact International Recruitment Agencies, Consultants and Employers
Trans-Atlantic Publications, Inc.
311 Bainbridge St.
Philadelphia, PA 19147
Ph: (215)925-5083   Fax: (215)925-1912

Matthew Cunningham. 1996. 205 pages. Part of the Living and Working Abroad Series.

★13615★ Head Hunters Revealed
Hunter Arts Publishing
PO Box 66578K
Los Angeles, CA 90066
Ph: (310)821-6303   Fax: (310)821-6308
Fr: 877-4-HEADHUNT

Quarterly. $14.95. Covers online career sites, career associations, and organizations.

★13616★ Hunt-Scanlon's Executive Recruiters of North America - Contingency Firms
Hunt-Scanlon Publishing
20 Signal Rd.
Stamford, CT 06902-7907
Ph: (203)352-2920   Fax: (203)352-2930

Annual. $225.00 for individuals. Covers more than 3,000 executive recruiters in a cross-section of contingency search firms in North America. Entries include: Individual and company name, phone number, and revenue statistics. Arrangement: Alphabetical. Indexes: Geographical, business sector.

★13617★ Hunt-Scanlon's Executive Recruiters of North America - Retained Firms
Hunt-Scanlon Publishing
20 Signal Rd.
Stamford, CT 06902-7907
Ph: (203)352-2920   Fax: (203)352-2930

Annual. $225.00 for individuals. Covers more than 3,600 retained executive recruiters in the U.S., Canada, and Mexico. Entries include: Individual name, phone number, specialization, revenue, professional memberships, salary levels.

★13618★ Job Seeker's Guide
Thomson Gale
27500 Drake Rd
Farmington Hills, MI 48331
Ph: (248)699-4253   Fax: (214)746-6799

$10.00 for members; $15.00 for nonmembers. Covers top 100 employers in the Dallas area, information on employment agencies, and labor market projections.

★13619★ Job Seekers Guide to Executive Recruiters
John Wiley & Sons Inc.
1 Wiley Dr.
Somerset, NJ 08873
Ph: (732)469-4400   Fr: 800-225-5945

Christopher W. Hunt and Scott A. Scanlon. 1997. $34.95 (paper). Provides listings for executive search consultants, as well as advice on interviewing and resume preparation.

★13620★ Job Seekers Guide to Silicon Valley Recruiters
John Wily and Sons, Inc.
605 Third Ave., 4th Fl.
New York, NY 10158-0012
Ph: (212)850-6276   Fax: (212)850-8641

Christopher W. Hunt, Scott A. Scanlon. First edition, 1998. $19.95 (paper). 371 pages. Includes a list of 2,400 recruiters specializing in high technology positions and explains how to work with them.

★13621★ Job Seekers Guide to Wall Street Recruiters
John Wiley & Sons Inc.
1 Wiley Dr.
Somerset, NJ 08873
Ph: (732)469-4400   Fr: 800-225-5945

Christopher W. Hunt and Scott A. Scanlon. 1998. $19.95 (paper). Lists recruiters covering investment banking, investment management, and the securities industry.

★13622★ Knock 'Em Dead: The Ultimate Job Seeker's Handbook
Adams Media Corp.
57 Littlefield St.
Avon, MA 02322
Ph: (508)427-7100   Fax: (508)427-6790
Fr: 800-872-5627

URL: http://www.adamsmedia.com

Martin Yate. Revised edition, 2002. $12.95 (paper). Prepares the job seeker for the interview with advice on dress, manner, how to answer the toughest questions, and how to spot illegal questions. Discusses how to respond to questions of salary to maximize income. Features sections on executive search firms and drug testing. 352 pages.

★13623★ National Directory of Personnel Service Firms
National Association of Personnel Services
10905 Fort Washington Rd., Ste. 400
Fort Washington, MD 20744-5807
Ph: (301)203-6700   Fax: (301)203-4346

Annual, spring. $15.95. Covers Over 1,100 member private (for-profit) personnel service firms and temporary service firms. Entries include: Firm name, address, phone, fax, contact, area of specialization. Arrangement: Same information given geographically by employment specialty.

★13624★ Navigating Your Career: 21 of America's Leading Headhunters Tell You How It's Done
John Wiley & Sons Inc.
1 Wiley Dr.
Somerset, NJ 08873
Ph: (732)469-4400   Fr: 800-225-5945

Christopher W. Hunt and Scott A. Scanlon. 1998. $16.95 (paper). Provides job-hunting advice from executive recruiters.

★13625★ O'Dwyer's New York Public Relations Directory
J.R. O'Dwyer Company Inc.
271 Madison Ave.
New York, NY 10016
Ph: (212)679-2471   Fax: (212)683-2750

Annual. $50.00. Covers approximately 600 public relations firms, 750 corporations, 225 trade associations, and 500 public relations service firms; over 50 executive recruiters and employment agencies. Entries include: Contact information.

★13626★ The Recruiter's Research Blue Book
Kennedy Information Inc.
One Kennedy Pl., Rte. 12 S.
Fitzwilliam, NH 03447
Ph: (603)585-3101   Fax: (603)585-9555
Fr: 800-531-0007

$179.00. Publication includes an annotated bibliography of print and Internet resources in 220 categories. Principal content of publication is a guide book to the executive search process for professional recruiters and human resources departments.

ONLINE AND DATABASE SERVICES

★13627★ Association of Executive Search Consultants
E-mail: aesc@aesc.org
URL: http://www.aesc.org
Description: Partnership with BlueSteps.com allows member search consultants to add their names to a directory of firms, which may then be referred to senior executives who contact the organization to help fill executive vacancies within their own organizations. **Fee:** For referral service, $10 administration fee, for directory access, $35 month. Search consultants who wish to post themselves must be registered members of association.

★13628★ BrillantPeople.com
E-mail: help@brilliantpeople.com
URL: http://www.brilliantpeople.com
Description: Management-level job seekers can review job board and/or contact an executive recruiter seeking for prospective candidates. Site also contains resume building and career transitioning resources.

★13629★ Corporate Search Consultants
E-mail: resumes@rothberg.com
URL: http://www.rothberg.com
Description: Job search consultants located in Atlanta. Job board and resume posting for jobs nationwide, but mainly located in the US Southeast.

★13630★ FutureStep
E-mail: info@futurestep.com
URL: http://www.futurestep.com
Description: An executive search service for management professionals brought to you by Korn/Ferry International, the world's largest executive search firm. Seekers can register for free, and search for jobs posted. Also contains assessment information, career resources, and useful links.

★13631★ Glocapsearch.com
E-mail: comments@glocap.com
URL: http://www.glocapsearch.com
Description: Recruitment firm for the private equity, venture capital and hedge fund marketplaces. After registering with website, seekers will be notified weekly of positions available that may interest them. Through returned e-mail, the firm will forward resumes and schedule preliminary interviews with prospective employers.

★13632★ Spherion Workforce Architects
URL: http://www.spherion.com
Description: Recruitment firm specializing in accounting and finance, sales and marketing, interim executives, technology, engineering, retail and human resources.

SOFTWARE

★13633★ Executive Search System
Custom Databanks, Inc.
60 Sutton Pl. S, Ste. 14BN
New York, NY 10022-4168
Fr: 800-445-3557
E-mail: info@CustomDatabanks.com
URL: http://www.customdatabanks.com
$200.00 (latest update); $500.00 (annual subscription). Diskette. Contains 8,900+ search firms. Can download and merge data directly into your cover letters.

Working at Home

REFERENCE WORKS

★13634★ **Complete Work-at-Home Companion: Everything You Need to Know to Prosper as a Home-Based Entrepreneur or Employee**
Prima Publishing
3000 Lava Ridge Ct.
Roseville, CA 95661
Ph: (916)787-7000   Fax: (916)787-7001

Herman Holtz. Second edition, 1994. $14.95 (paper). 368 pages.

★13635★ **The Directory of Home-Based Business Resources**
Pilot Books
127 Sterling Ave.
PO Box 2102
Greenport, NY 11944-0893
Ph: (516)477-1094   Fax: (516)477-1094
Fr: 800-797-4568
URL: http://www.pilotbooks.com

$7.95. Provides information on starting and running a homebased business and lists sources of additional information.

★13636★ **The Home-Based Entrepreneur: The Complete Guide to Working at Home**
Upstart Pub. Co.
155 N. Wacker Dr.
Chicago, IL 60606-1719
Ph: (312)836-4400   Fax: (312)836-1021
Fr: 800-621-9621

Linda Pinson and Jerry A. Jinnett. Second edition, 1993. $19.95 (paper). 178 pages. Out of print.

★13637★ **Home Business Made Easy**
Todd Publications
PO Box 635
Nyack, NY 10960
Ph: (845)358-6213   Fax: (845)358-6213
Fr: (866)896-0916
URL: http://www.toddpublications.com/todd-pubs/index.htm

Latest edition 1999. $25.00. Covers 175 different business that can be run from home full or part time based on interest, lifestyle, and finances.

★13638★ **The Home Office and Small Business Success Book**
Henry Holt and Co. LLC
115 W. 18th St., 5th Fl.
New York, NY 10011
Ph: (212)886-9200   Fax: (212)633-0748
Fr: 800-672-2054

Janet Attard. 1996. $45.00; $19.95 (paper). 560 pages. Guide covering telecommunications and telecommuting trends. Publication cancelled.

★13639★ **The Home Team: How Couples Can Make a Life and a Living by Working at Home**
Bookhome Publishing
PO Box 5900
Navarre, FL 32566
Ph: (850)936-4050   Fax: (850)939-4953

Scott Gregory. 1999. $14.95 (paper).

★13640★ **Homemade Money**
Betterway Books
4700 E Galbraith Rd.
Cincinnati, OH 45236
Ph: (513)531-2690   Fax: (513)891-7185
Fr: 800-666-0963

Irregular, latest edition August 1997. $31.99. Publication includes: A special 76 page, updated "A-Z Crash Course" on business basics and a directory of 300 listings. Entries include: Supplier name, address, description of information, price, order information. Principal content of the book is editorial matter on beginning and developing a home-based business. Arrangement: Classified by subject. Indexes: Alphabetical.

★13641★ **How to Run Your Own Home Business**
McGraw-Hill Trade
2 Penn Plaza
New York, NY 10121
Ph: (212)904-2000   Fr: 800-722-4726
E-mail: ntcpub@tribune.com

Coralee Smith Kern and Tammara Hoffman Wolfgram. Third edition, 1994. $10.95 (paper). 224 pages. Helps the reader determine if he/she is suited to working at home, choose a product or service, set up a comfortable, efficient working environment, and keep abreast of zoning and tax laws.

★13642★ **The Ideal Entrepreneurial Business for You**
John Wiley & Sons Inc.
1 Wiley Dr.
Somerset, NJ 08873
Ph: (732)469-4400   Fr: 800-225-5945

Glenn Desmond and Monica Faulkner. $40.00.

★13643★ **The Joy of Working from Home: Making a Life While Making a Living**
Berrett-Koehler Publishers
235 Montgomery St., Suite 650
San Francisco, CA 94104
Ph: (415)288-0260   Fax: (415)362-2512
Fr: 800-929-2929

Jeff Berner. 1994. $12.95 (paper). 240 pages.

★13644★ **Making Money with Your Computer at Home**
The Putnam Publishing Group
375 Hudson St.
New York, NY 10014
Ph: (212)366-2000   Fax: (212)366-2643

Paul Edwards and Sarah Edwards. Second edition, revised, 1997. $15.95 (paper). 320 pages. Profiles 75 different home-based computer businesses.

★13645★ Marketing for the Home-based Business

Adams Media Corp.
57 Littlefield St.
Avon, MA 02322
Ph: (508)427-7100   Fax: (508)427-6790
Fr: 800-872-5627
URL: http://www.adamsmedia.com

Jeffrey P. Davidson. Second edition, 1999. $10.95 (paper). 242 pages. Addresses how to market the home-based business after you've started it.

★13646★ Mompreneurs: A Mother's Step-by-Step Guide to Work-at-Home Success

Berkley Publishing Group
375 Hudson St.
New York, NY 10014
Ph: (212)366-2000   Fax: (212)366-2385
Fr: 800-631-8571

Ellen H. Parlapiano and Patricia Cobe. Revised, 2002. $14.95 (paper). 320 pages.

★13647★ Moneymaking Moms: How Work at Home Can Work for You

Carol Publishing Group
120 Enterprise Ave.
Secaucus, NJ 07094
Ph: (201)866-0490   Fax: (201)866-8159
Fr: 800-447-2665

Caroline Hull. 1998. $12.00 (paper).

★13648★ On Your Own: A Guide to Working Happily, Productively & Successfully at Home

Prentice Hall PTR
200 Old Tappan Rd.
Old Tappan, NJ 07675
Ph: (201)236-7000   Fr: 800-223-1360

Lionel L. Fisher. 1994. $10.95 (paper). 228 pages.

★13649★ The Perfect Business: How to Make a Million from Home with No Payroll, No Employee Headaches, No Debt, and No Sleepless Nights

Simon & Schuster Inc.
1230 Ave. of the Americas
New York, NY 10020
Ph: (212)698-7000   Fax: (212)698-7007
Fr: 800-223-2336

Michael LeBoeuf. 1997. $12.00 (paper).

★13650★ The Road to Self-Employment: A Practical Guide to Microbusiness Development

Women's Business Training Center
PO Box 126305
San Diego, CA 92101
Ph: (619)239-9282   Fax: (619)238-5205

Gerri P. Norington. 1997. $24.95. Part of The Rose Program Series. Deals with personal growth as a tool for business success and lets the reader know what to expect from and how to prepare for microbusiness development.

★13651★ The Selling-From-Home Sourcebook

F & W Publications, Inc.
4700 E Galbraith Rd.
Cincinnati, OH 45236
Ph: (513)531-2690   Fax: (513)531-4082
Fr: 800-289-0963

Kathryn Caputo. 1996. $17.99 (paper). 272 pages.

★13652★ Starting a Home Based Business (Full or Part-Time)

Carol Publishing Group
120 Enterprise Ave.
Secaucus, NJ 07094
Ph: (201)866-0490   Fax: (201)866-8159
Fr: 800-447-2665

Irene Korn and Bill Zanker. 1993. $8.95 (paper).

★13653★ Thy Neighbor's Talent-Directory of Cottage Industry Show Dates

Zoe McClintock
HCR 1, Box 75
Baldwin, ND 58521
Ph: (701)255-0352

Monthly. $18.95. Covers over 1,000 arts and crafts fairs, flea markets, and specialty show dates in Idaho, Minnesota, Montana, North Dakota, South Dakota, Washington, Wisconsin, and Wyoming. Entries include: Event name, date of occurrence, location, phone, and contact name and address. Arrangement: Chronological.

★13654★ Word Processing Profits at Home

Aames-Allen Publishing Company
18281 Gothard St., No. 105
Huntington Beach, CA 92648
Ph: (714)375-4889   Fax: (714)848-4566

Peggy Glenn. 1994. $18.95 (paper). Covers all aspects of running a home-based word processing business. Out of Print.

★13655★ Work-at-Home Sourcebook

Live Oak Publications
1515 23rd St.
PO Box 2193
Boulder, CO 80306
Ph: (303)448-1169   Fax: (303)447-8684

Biennial, January of even years. $19.95. Covers over 1,000 companies and home business franchises that employ home workers. Entries include: Company name, address, contact person, description of job position, pay scale, requirements, equipment, and training provided. Arrangement: Classified by occupational category. Indexes: Alphabetical, geographical.

★13656★ Work at Home Wisdom

Dearborn Trade, A Kaplan Professional Co.
155 N. Wacker Dr.
Chicago, IL 60606-1719
Ph: (312)836-4400   Fax: (312)836-1021
Fr: 800-621-9621

Andi Axman. 1998. $9.95 (paper). Offers advice on how to work smarter from home, including balancing the demands of home, work, and family.

★13657★ Working from Home: Everything You Need to Know About Living and Working Under the Same Roof

Putnam Publishing Group
375 Hudson St.
New York, NY 10014
Ph: (212)366-2000   Fax: (212)366-2643
Fr: 800-331-4624

Paul Edwards. Fifth edition, 1999. $18.95. 664 pages.

★13658★ Working at Home While the Kids Are There Too

Career Press, Inc.
3 Tice Rd.
PO Box 687
Franklin Lakes, NJ 07417-1322
Ph: (201)848-0310   Fax: (201)848-1727
Fr: 800-227-3371

Loriann H. Oberlin. 1997. $12.99 (paper).

★13659★ Working and Living Spaces: Working at Home

Watson-Guptill Publications, Incorporated
770 Broadway
New York, NY 10003
Ph: (646)654-5400   Fax: (646)654-5486
Fr: 800-323-9432

Aurora Cuito. 2000. $35.00 (paper).

★13660★ Working Smarter from Home: Your Day, Your Way

Crisp Publications, Inc.
1200 Hamilton Ct.
Menlo Park, CA 94025
Ph: (650)323-6100   Fax: (650)323-5800
Fr: 800-442-7477

Nancy Struck. 1995. $12.95 (paper). 111 pages. Part of Fifty-Minute series.

NEWSPAPERS, MAGAZINES, AND JOURNALS

★13661★ The Home Business Report

The Kerner Group Inc.
1319 Howard Ln.
Palmer, PA 18045-2153

Description: Monthly. Provides information on how to operate a home-based business or work from home. Features real life success stories, "how-to" articles on marketing, and strategies to keep focused on goals. Recurring features include letters to the editor, interviews, news of research, job listings, book reviews, and notices of publications available.

★13662★ *Our Place*
Home-Based Working Moms
PO Box 500164
Austin, TX 78750-0164
Ph: (512)266-0900
URL: http://www.hbwm.com

Description: Ten issues/year. Advocates home employment and home businesses to allow parents more time with their children. Offers ideas, marketing tips, member profiles to promote successful employment at home. Recurring features include interviews, job listings, and book reviews.

★13663★ *Spare Time*
Kipen Publishing Corp.
5810 W Oklahoma Ave.
Milwaukee, WI 53219-4300
Ph: (414)543-8110   Fax: (414)543-9767

URL: http://www.sparetimemagazine.com
$16.95/year for individuals; $42.00/year for other countries; $2.50/year for single issue. Magazine featuring articles on business start-up and money-making opportunities.

ONLINE AND DATABASE SERVICES

★13664★ **FreelanceWorkExchange.com**
E-mail: support@freelanceworkexchange.com
URL: http://www.freelanceworkexchange.com

Description: Project and contract search board for the freelance worker. E-mail newsletters and freelancing e-books available.
Fee: Must register as a member; pricing based on length of membership; one month is $19.95. Trial seven-day membership available.

★13665★ **Home Workers Jobs Digest**
E-mail: hr@intlhomeworkers.com
URL: http://Homeworkers.com

Description: Job databank and resource site for the self-employed. Contains links, online courses, resume submission and more. **Fee:** Lifetime membership is $77.

★13666★ **Telecommuting Jobs**
E-mail: contact@atstjobs.com
URL: http://www.tjobs.com

Description: Job hunters may enter a resume or post a job-wanted listing. Employers may search talent available and post job availabilities. Site also includes tools to connect telecommuters with employers and job news about telecommuting.

★13667★ **Work from Home**
URL: http://www.jobs-telecommuting.com

Description: Contains a listing of over 700 companies currently looking for telecommuters. Employers may add or remove job listings. Also information on starting a home business available.

Working Part-Time, Summer Employment, and Internships

REFERENCE WORKS

★13668★ *The Access Guide to International Affairs Internships in The Washington, DC Area*
Access: A Security Information Service
1701 K St. NW, Ste. 11
Washington, DC 20006-1503
Ph: (202)223-7949   Fax: (202)223-7946
Fr: 800-888-6033

Bruce Seymore II and Susan D. Krutt, editors. 1994. $17.95 (paper). 133 pages. Publication cancelled.

★13669★ *Administration of Justice: An Internship Guide to the Quest for Justice*
Kendall Hunt Publishing Co.
4050 Westmark Dr.
PO Box 1840
Dubuque, IA 52002
Ph: (319)589-1000   Fax: (319)589-1046
Fr: 800-228-0810

Carol Fine. 2000. $55.95 (paper). 340 pages.

★13670★ *Baltimore Job Source: Everything You Need to Know to Land the Internship, Entry-Level, or Middle Management Job of Your Choice*
Benjamin Scott Publishing
20 E. Colorado Blvd., No. 202
Pasadena, CA 91105
Ph: (626)449-1339   Fax: (626)449-1389
Fr: 800-448-4959

Mary McMahon, Parker Webb, Ruth E. Thaler-Carter and Betty Glascoe. 1996. $15.95. 308 pages.

★13671★ *The Best 106 Internships*
The Princeton Review
2315 Broadway
New York, NY 10024-4332
Ph: (212)362-6900

$21.00. Covers more than 20,000 internship opportunities. Entries include: Summary of the internship program and contact information.

★13672★ *Cents-Able Summer Self-Employment: An Entrepreneurial Guide for High School & College Students*
Tamarax Press
PO Box 450
2A Taylor Way
Washington Crossing, PA 18977
Ph: (215)493-2136   Fax: (215)493-2057

E.K. Shepard. 1994. $12.95 (paper). 220 pages.

★13673★ *Creating a Flexible Workplace: How to Select & Manage Alternative Work Options*
AMACOM
1601 Broadway, 12th Fl.
New York, NY 10019
Ph: (518)891-1500   Fax: (518)903-8168
Fr: 800-250-5308

Barney Olmsted and Suzanne Smith. Second edition, 1994. $59.95. 402 pages.

★13674★ *Directory of Child Life Programs*
Child Life Council Inc.
11820 Parklawn Dr., Ste. 202
Rockville, MD 20852-2529
Ph: (301)881-7090   Fax: (301)881-7092
URL: http://www.childlife.org/

Biennial. $15.00 for members; $20.00 for nonmembers. Covers over 400 child life programs. Entries include: Facility name, address, phone, name of child life department and director, reporting structure, staff statistics, educational requirements for employment, and internship or educational opportunities. Arrangement: Geographical. Indexes: Speciality areas, internship sessions, program size, fellowships.

★13675★ *Directory of International Internships*
Dean's Office of International Studies and Programs
International Ctr., Rm. 209
East Lansing, MI 48824
Ph: (517)353-5589   Fax: (517)353-7254

Irregular, first edition 1987; latest edition 2003. $42.95; $30.00 for students. Covers international internships sponsored by academic institutions, private sector, and the federal government. Entries include: Institution name, address, phone, names and titles of key personnel, subject areas in which internships are available, number available, location, duration, financial data, academic credit available, evaluation procedures, application deadline, requirements of participation. Arrangement: Classified by type of sponsor, then alphabetical. Indexes: Sponsor, subject, geographical.

★13676★ *Directory of Internships, Work Experience Programs, and On-the-Job Training Opportunities*
Ready Reference Press
PO Box 5249
Santa Monica, CA 90405
Ph: (310)475-4895   Fr: 800-424-5627

$89.50. Lists internship opportunities in many fields of interest, including, but not limited to arts, journalism, public relations, education, law, environmental affairs, business, engineering, and computer science. In addition, cites summer internship opportunities, work/study programs, and specialized opportunities for high school and undergraduate students. Indexed by subject, geography, and program.

★13677★ *Directory of Public Garden Internships*
American Association of Botanical Gardens and Arboreta (AABGA)
100 W 10th St., Ste. 614
Wilmington, DE 19801-6604
Ph: (302)655-7100   Fax: (302)655-8100
E-mail: bvincent@aabga.org

Annual, November. $10.00 for members; $15.00 for nonmembers. Covers 700 student internships and summer jobs at public gardens throughout North America. Entries include: Name of institution, address, name of contact, deadline for application, number of students hired, whether internships are available, employment period, hours, rate of pay, whether housing is available, other comments. Arrangement: Alphabetical. Indexes: By position, by state/province.

★13678★ Directory of Summer Jobs Abroad
Vacation Work Publications
9 Park End St.
Oxford OX1 1HJ, United Kingdom
Ph: 865 241978   Fax: 865 790885

Annual, November; supplement in May. $7.99; $6.00. Covers more than 30,000 jobs worldwide. Entries include: Name of employer, address, length of employment, number of positions available, pay rates, how and when to apply, name of contact. Arrangement: Geographical, then classified by type of job.

★13679★ Everything You Need to Get a Psychology Internship
Windmill Lane Press
1009 S. Bedford St.
Los Angeles, CA 90035-2101
Fax: (310)815-9865   Fr: 800-566-3659

Carl Levinger and Itzchack Schefres. 1996. $24.95 (paper). 153 pages.

★13680★ Going Part-Time: The Insider's Guide for Professional Women Who Want a Career and a Life
Morrow Avon
1350 Ave. of the Americas
New York, NY 10019
Ph: (212)261-6788   Fr: 800-242-7737

Cindy Tolliver and Nancy Chambers. 1997. $12.00 (paper). 256 pages. Out of print.

★13681★ Grants, Fellowships, and Prizes of Interest to Historians
American Historical Association
400 A St., S.E.
Washington, DC 20003-3889
Ph: (202)544-2422   Fax: (202)544-8307
E-mail: grantguide@theaha.org
URL: http://www.theaha.org/members/grants/index.cfm

Annual, September. Covers over 450 sources of funding (scholarships, fellowships, internships, awards, and book and essay prizes) in the United States and abroad for graduate students, postdoctoral researchers, and institutions in the humanities. Entries include: Name of source, institution name or contact, address, phone, eligibility and proposal requirements, award or stipend amount, location requirements for research, application deadlines. Arrangement: Alphabetical in three categories: support for individual research and teaching; grants for groups and organizations for research and education; and book, article, essay, and manuscript prizes.

★13682★ A Guide to a Successful Legal Internship
Anderson Publishing Co.
2035 Reading Rd.
Cincinnati, OH 45202-1576
Ph: (513)421-4142   Fax: (513)562-8116
Fr: 800-582-7295

Hedi Nasheri and Peter C. Kratcoski. 1996. $22.95 (paper). 176 pages.

★13683★ Half a Job: Bad and Good Part-Time Jobs in Changing Labor Market
Temple University Press
University Services Bldg., Rm 305
1601 N. Broad St.
Philadelphia, PA 19122-6099
Ph: (215)204-8787   Fax: (215)204-4719
Fr: 800-447-1656

Chris Tilly. 1996. $49.95. 256 pages.

★13684★ The Imaginative Soul's Guide to Foreign Internships: A Roadmap to Envision, Create and Arrange Your Own Experience
Ivy House
PO Box 391262
Cambridge, MA 02139
Ph: (617)489-0599

Laura Hitchcock. 1993. $16.95 (paper). 128 pages.

★13685★ International Directory for Youth Internships
Council on International & Public Affairs
777 United Nations Plz., No.3C
New York, NY 10017
Ph: (212)972-9877   Fax: 800-316-2739
Fr: 800-316-2739

Latest edition 1993. $7.50. Covers United Nations agencies and nongovernmental organizations offering intern and volunteer opportunities. Entries include: Agency, organization, or office name, address, description of internship. Arrangement: Classified by type of organization.

★13686★ Internship Bible
Princeton Review Publishing Corp.
2315 Broadway
New York, NY 10024
Ph: (212)874-8282   Fax: (212)874-0775
Fr: 800-273-8439

Mark Oldman and Samer Hamadeh. 2002. 656 pages.

★13687★ The Internship, Practicum and Field Placement Handbook: A Guide for the Helping Professions
Prentice Hall PTR
200 Old Tappan Rd.
Old Tappan, NJ 07675
Ph: (201)236-7000   Fr: 800-223-1360

Brian N. Baird. Third edition, 2001. $45.00. 224 pages.

★13688★ Internship Selection in Professional Psychology: A Comprehensive Guide for Students, Faculty, and Training Directors
Charles C. Thomas Publisher, Ltd.
2600 S. 1st St.
PO Box 19265
Springfield, IL 62794-9265
Ph: (217)789-8980   Fax: (217)789-9130
Fr: 800-258-8980

Mary E. Oehlert, Scott Sumerall and Shane J. Lopez. 1998. $44.95. 172 pages.

★13689★ Internships
Macmillan/Arco
15 Columbus Circle
New York, NY 10023
Ph: (212)373-8200   Fax: (212)373-8642
Fr: 800-257-5755

Irregular, Published in 1995. $18.95. Covers 25,000 internship positions worldwide in a variety of fields, including architecture, computers, journalism, pharmaceuticals, sports and others. Entries include: Company name, address, phone, telex, names and titles of key personnel, branch office or subsidiary names and addresses, description of company, internship openings and requirements. Arrangement: Geographical, alphabetical with geographic areas. Indexes: Product, subject, geographic.

★13690★ Internships in Communications
Iowa State University Press
2121 S. State Ave.
Ames, IA 50014-8300
Ph: (515)292-0140   Fax: (515)292-3348
Fr: 800-862-6657

James P. Alexander. 1995. $16.95 (paper). 216 pages.

★13691★ Internships in Federal Government
The Graduate Group
PO Box 370351
West Hartford, CT 06137-0351
Ph: (860)233-2330   Fr: 800-484-7280

Seventh edition, 1995. $27.50.

★13692★ Internships Leading to Careers
The Graduate Group
PO Box 370351
West Hartford, CT 06137-0351
Ph: (860)233-2330   Fr: 800-484-7280

Sixth edition, 2001. $27.50.

★13693★ Internships in Recreation and Leisure Services: A Practical Guide for Students

Venture Publishing, Inc.
1999 Cato Ave.
State College, PA 16801
Ph: (814)234-4561   Fax: (814)234-1651

Edward E. Seagle, Ralph W. Smith and Lola M. Dalton. Second edition, 1997. $19.95 (paper).

★13694★ Internships in State Government

The Graduate Group
PO Box 370351
West Hartford, CT 06137-0351
Ph: (860)233-2330   Fr: 800-484-7280

Sixth edition, 1995. $27.50.

★13695★ Internships: The Hotlist for Job Hunters

Hungry Minds, Inc.
10475 Crosspoint Blvd.
Indianapolis, IN 46256
Fax: (317)572-4000   Fr: 800-667-1115

Sara D. Gilbert. Second edition, 1996. $19.95 (paper). 432 pages. Part of Arco Internships series.

★13696★ Internships: The Largest Source of Internships Available

Thomson Peterson's
PO Box 67005
Lawrenceville, NJ 08648-6105
Fr: 800-338-3282

1998. $24.95 (paper). Lists 35,000 paid and unpaid internships. 648 pages. Part of Peterson's Guides series.

★13697★ The JobBank Guide to Health Care Companies

Adams Media Corp.
57 Littlefield St.
Avon, MA 02322
Ph: (508)427-7100   Fax: (508)427-6790
Fr: 800-872-5627

$17.95. Covers Jobs nationwide in health care companies. Entries include: Firm or organization name, address, phone, name and title of contact; description of organization, headquarters location, typical titles for entry- and middle-level positions, educational backgrounds desired, fringe benefits offered, stock exchange listing, training programs, internships, parent company, number of employees, revenues, e-mail and web address, projected number of hires. Indexes: Alphabetical.

★13698★ Jobs in Paradise

HarperCollins Publishers, Inc.
10 E. 53rd. St.
New York, NY 10022-5299
Ph: (212)207-7000   Fax: (212)207-7145
Fr: 800-242-7737

Jeffrey Maltzman. Revised, 1993. $16.00 (paper). 448 pages.

★13699★ Magazines Career Directory

Thomson Gale
27500 Drake Rd.
Farmington Hills, MI 48331-3535
Ph: (248)699-GALE   Fax: (248)699-8069
Fr: 800-877-GALE
E-mail: galeord@gale.com
URL: http://www.galegroup.com

Bradley Morgan. Fifth edition, 1993. $39.00. Features extensive listings of contacts and entry-level job opportunities at many magazine publishing organizations. Includes articles by top professionals in the field on some of the industry's varied career paths: art, editorial, sales, and business management. Part of Career Advisor series.

★13700★ Megargee's Guide to Obtaining a Psychological Internship

Hemisphere Publishing Corp.
325 Chestnut St., 8th Fl.
Philadelphia, PA 19106
Fax: (215)269-0363   Fr: 800-821-8312

Edwin I. Megaree. Third edition, 1997. $21.95 (paper). 255 pages.

★13701★ Modern Moonlighting: How to Earn Thousands Extra without Leaving Your Day Job

McGraw-Hill Trade
2 Penn Plaza
New York, NY 10121
Ph: (212)904-2000   Fax: (212)755-5645
Fr: 800-722-4726

Roger Woodson. 1997. $14.95 (paper). 288 pages. Explores part-time selfemployment business opportunities.

★13702★ National Directory of Arts Internships

National Network for Artist Placement
935 W. Ave. 37
Los Angeles, CA 90065
Ph: (323)222-4035   Fax: (323)225-5711
URL: http://www.artistplacement.com/intern.htm

Biennial, odd years. $85.00. Covers over 5,000 internship opportunities in dance, music, theater, art, design, film, and video & over 1,250 host organizations Entries include: Name of sponsoring organization, address, name of contact; description of positions available, eligibility requirements, stipend or salary (if any), application procedures. Arrangement: Classified by discipline, then geographical.

★13703★ National Directory of Internships

National Society for Experiential Education
9001 Braddock Rd., Ste. 380
Springfield, VA 22151-1002
Ph: (703)933-0017   Fax: (703)933-1053

Biennial, fall of odd years. $33.35. Covers thousands of internship opportunities in 85 fields (in government, nonprofit, and corporate settings) in the U.S. for youth and adults. Entries include: Organization name, address, phone, contact name, description of internship opportunities, including application procedures and deadlines, remuneration, and eligibility requirements. Arrangement: Classified by type of organization. Indexes: Geographical, organization name, career field.

★13704★ New Internships

The Graduate Group
PO Box 370351
West Hartford, CT 06137-0351
Ph: (860)233-2330   Fr: 800-484-7280

1997. $27.50.

★13705★ New Jersey Internship Guide

Resource Communications Group, Inc.
3274 Jefferson St., Ste. 318
Austin, TX 78731
Ph: (512)458-2021   Fax: (512)458-2059
Fr: 800-331-5076

Tyiana Steptoe, Lauren Dixon and Jeanne Graves. 1999. $24.95 (paper). 91 pages.

★13706★ Opportunities in Part-Time and Summer Jobs

McGraw-Hill Trade
2 Penn Plaza
New York, NY 10121
Ph: (212)904-2000   Fr: 800-722-4726

Adrian A. Paradis. 1997. $14.95; $11.95 (paper). 215 pages.

★13707★ Opportunities in Summer Camp Careers

McGraw-Hill Trade
2 Penn Plaza
New York, NY 10121
Ph: (212)904-2000   Fr: 800-722-4726

Blythe Camenson. 1998. $11.95 (paper). 210 pages. Part of Opportunities in...Series.

★13708★ Paralegal Internships: Finding, Managing & Transitioning Your Career

Thomson Delmar Learning
PO Box 15015
Albany, NY 12212-5015
Ph: (518)348-2300   Fax: (518)464-0393
Fr: 800-998-7498

Post. 1998. $27.95 (paper). 267 pages. Part of the Paralegal Series. Text covers all stages of the internship experience, including identifying learning objectives, finding the "right office," managing "office politics," self-monitoring & documentation & finally how to use the internship to land a permanent job.

★13709★ Part-Time Employment: A Bridge or a Trap?
Ashgate Publishing Co.
2252 Ridge Rd.
Brookfield, VT 05036-9704
Ph: (802)276-3162   Fax: (802)276-3837
Fr: 800-535-9544

May Tam. 1997. 288 pages.

★13710★ Part-Time Employment for the Low-Income Elderly: Experiences from the Field
Garland Publishing, Inc.
29 W. 35th St., Fl. 10
New York, NY 10001-2299
Ph: (212)216-7800   Fax: (212)564-7854
Fr: 800-627-6273

Leslie B. Alexander and Lenard W. Kaye. 1997. $44.00. Part of Issues in Aging series. 204 pages.

★13711★ Part Time Prospects: International Comparison of Part Time Work in Europe, North America and the Pacific Rim
Routledge
29 W. 35th St.
New York, NY 10001-2299
Ph: (212)216-7800   Fax: (212)564-7854
Fr: 800-634-7064

Jacqueline O'Reilly and Colette Fagan. 1998. $29.99 (paper). 272 pages.

★13712★ Peterson's Internships
Thomson Peterson's
Princeton Pke. Corporate Ctr., 2000 Lenox Dr.
PO Box 67005
Lawrenceville, NJ 08648
Ph: (609)896-1800   Fax: (609)896-4531
Fr: 800-338-3282
URL: http://www.petersons.com

Annual, latest edition 2003. $40.95. Covers 50,000 career-oriented internship positions with over 2,000 organizations in the U.S. ranging from business to theater, communications to science. Entries include: Company name, address, phone, name and title of contact, types of internships available, number of internships offered, salary where applicable, qualifications, how to apply. Arrangement: Classified by career field. Indexes: Geographical.

★13713★ Peterson's Job Opportunities for Business Majors
Thomson Peterson's
Princeton Pke. Corporate Ctr., 2000 Lenox Dr.
PO Box 67005
Lawrenceville, NJ 08648
Ph: (609)896-1800   Fax: (609)896-4531
Fr: 800-338-3282
URL: http://www.petersons.com

Irregular, latest edition 2000 - 16th ed. $18.95. Covers the 2,000 largest U.S. employers hiring in several fields, including financial services, management consulting, consumer products, and media/ entertainment. Entries include: Organization name, address, phone, name and title of contact, number of employees, type of organization. Arrangement: Alphabetical. Indexes: Type of organization.

★13714★ Peterson's Job Opportunities in Engineering and Technology
Thomson Peterson's
PO Box 67005
Lawrenceville, NJ 08648-6105
Fr: 800-338-3282

Compiled by the Peterson's staff. Fourth edition, 1996. $21.95 (paper). 384 pages. Profiles 2,000 high-tech companies looking primarily for technical personnel in such fields as biotechnology, telecommunications, software, computers and peripherals, defense, and aerospace. Contains job-search strategies and career options to help match education and expertise to the job market. Indexed geographically, by industry, and by hiring needs.

★13715★ Peterson's Summer Jobs for Students
Thomson Peterson's
Princeton Pke. Corporate Ctr., 2000 Lenox Dr.
PO Box 67005
Lawrenceville, NJ 08648
Ph: (609)896-1800   Fax: (609)896-4531
Fr: 800-338-3282

Annual, latest edition 2002. $18.95. Covers over 650 camps, resorts, amusement parks, hotels, businesses, national parks, conference and training centers, ranches, and restaurants offering about 45,000 temporary summer jobs; listings are paid. Entries include: Name and address, length of employment, pay rate, fringe benefits, duties, qualifications, application deadline and procedure. Arrangement: Geographical, then type of job. Indexes: Job title.

★13716★ Peterson's Summer Opportunities for Kids and Teenagers
Thomson Peterson's
PO Box 67005
Lawrenceville, NJ 08648-6105
Fr: 800-338-3282

First edition, 2000 (annual). $29.95 (paper). 1,426 pages. In addition to information about 1,400 summer activities and programs, covers job opportunities for high school and college students. Part of Summer Opportunities for Kids and Teenagers series.

★13717★ Seasonal Employment
U.S. National Park Service
Harpers Ferry Center
PO Box 50
Harpers Ferry, WV 25425-0050
Ph: (202)208-4747   Fax: (304)535-6144
URL: http://www.nps.gov

Updated as needed; go to "InfoZone" to access. Publication includes: List of 10 regional offices and branches of the National Park Service that accept applications for seasonal jobs. Entries include: Name, address, phone, geographical area served. Principal content of publication is information on seasonal jobs offered by the National Park Services, with description of duties, qualifications, and application procedures for each type of job offered. Arrangement: Geographical.

★13718★ Sixth Annual Internships Leading to Careers
The Graduate Group
PO Box 370351
West Hartford, CT 06137-0351
Ph: (860)233-2330   Fr: 800-484-7280

2001. $27.50.

★13719★ Southern Newspaper Publishers Association Internship Directory
Southern Newspaper Publishers Association
PO Box 28875
Atlanta, GA 30358

Latest edition 1995-96. $2.00. Covers a list of internship programs offered by the Association's member newspapers.

★13720★ Storming Washington: An Intern's Guide to National Government
American Political Science Association
1527 New Hampshire Ave., NW
Washington, DC 20036-1206
Ph: (202)483-2512   Fax: (202)483-2657

Stephen E. Frantzich. Fourth edition, 1994. $6.00 (paper). 63 pages.

★13721★ Student Advantage Guide to America's Top Internships, 1998
Random House, Inc.
1540 Broadway
New York, NY 10036
Ph: (212)782-9000   Fax: (212)302-7985
Fr: 800-726-0600

Lishing. 1999. $21.00 (paper).

★13722★ Summer Jobs Britain
Thomson Peterson's
PO Box 67005
Lawrenceville, NJ 08648-6105
Fr: 800-338-3282

Compiled by Peterson's Staff. Third edition, 2001. $16.95 (paper). 528 pages. Part of Summer Jobs Britain series.

★13723★ Summer Theater Directory
American Theatre Works Inc.
PO Box 510
Dorset, VT 05251
Ph: (802)867-2223   Fax: (802)867-0144
URL: http://www.theatredirectories.com

Annual, December. $20.95. Covers summer theater companies, theme parks and cruise lines that offer employment opportunities in acting, design, production, and management; summer theater training programs. Entries include: Company name, address, phone, name and title of contact; type of company, activities and size of house; whether union affiliated, whether nonprofit or commercial; year established; hiring procedure and number of positions hired annually, season; description of stage; internships; description of company's artistic goals and audience. Arrangement: Geographical. Indexes: Company name.

★13724★ **Survival Jobs: 118 Ways to Make Money While Pursuing Your Dreams**
Windtree Pub
1540 Broadway
New York, NY 10036
Ph: (212)354-6500   Fax: (212)782-8338
Fr: 800-223-6834

Deborah Jacobson. 1998. $14.00 (paper). 256 pages.

★13725★ **Vacation Work's Overseas Summer Jobs**
Thomson Peterson's
Princeton Pke. Corporate Ctr., 2000 Lenox Dr.
PO Box 67005
Lawrenceville, NJ 08648
Ph: (609)896-1800   Fax: (609)896-4531
Fr: 800-338-3282

Annual. $17.95. Covers over 30,000 summer jobs worldwide. Entries include: Complete job data, length of employment, number of openings, pay, job description, qualifications needed, application/contact information.

★13726★ **Washington Job Source**
Benjamin Scott Publishing
20 E. Colorado Blvd., No. 202
Pasadena, CA 91105
Ph: (626)449-1339   Fax: (626)449-1389
Fr: 800-448-4959

Fifth edition, 2002.

★13727★ **Yale Daily News Guide to Internships**
Kaplan Books
1230 Ave. of the Americas, 1st Fl.
New York, NY 10020
Ph: (212)698-7000   Fax: (212)698-7007
Fr: 800-223-2348

2001. $25.00 (paper). Publication cancelled.

NEWSPAPERS, MAGAZINES, AND JOURNALS

★13728★ **Earth Work**
Student Conservation Association
PO Box 550
Charlestown, NH 03603
Ph: (603)543-1700   Fax: (603)543-1828
E-mail: earthwork@sca-inc.org
URL: http://www.sca-inc.org

Description: Eleven issues/year. Contains listings of environmental positions, ranging from internships and administrative assistants for environmental groups to camp directors, state natural resource managers, and biologists.

★13729★ **Job Line...and News from CPRS**
California Park & Recreation Society Inc.
7971 Freeport Blvd.
Sacramento, CA 95832-9701
Ph: (916)665-2777   Fax: (916)665-9149

Description: Monthly. Discusses parks and recreation news of interest.

★13730★ **NRPA Job Bulletin**
National Recreation and Park Association, Professional Services Div.
22377 Belmont Ridge Rd.
Ashburn, VA 20148
Ph: (703)858-0784   Fax: (703)858-0707
Fr: 800-626-6772
URL: http://www.nrpa.org

Description: Semimonthly. Provides listings of employment opportunities in the park, recreation, and leisure services field.

★13731★ **Spare Time**
Kipen Publishing Corp.
5810 W Oklahoma Ave.
Milwaukee, WI 53219-4300
Ph: (414)543-8110   Fax: (414)543-9767
URL: http://www.sparetimemagazine.com

$16.95/year for individuals; $42.00/year for other countries; $2.50/year for single issue. Magazine featuring articles on business start-up and money-making opportunities.

ONLINE AND DATABASE SERVICES

★13732★ **College Job Board.com**
E-mail: contactus@collegejobboard.zzn.com
URL: http://www.collegejobboard.com

Description: Job search site specializing in the career search of recent college, vocational and grad school graduates. Free resume posting, job board search, job tracking,

scholarship and loan search and career resources.

★13733★ **WetFeet.com**
E-mail: services@wetfeet.com
URL: http://www.wetfeet.com

Description: Job board website with free membership for job seekers. Contains job board, resume listing, self assessment guides, company and city research, discussion forums, e-guides and online bookstore, salary calculators and listings of internship opportunities.

OTHER SOURCES

★13734★ **Association of Psychology Postdoctoral and Internship Centers (APPIC)**
10 G St., NW Ste. 750
Washington, DC 20002
Ph: (202)589-0600   Fax: (202)589-0603
E-mail: appic@aol.com
URL: http://www.appic.org

Description: Veterans Administration hospitals, medical centers, state hospitals, university counseling centers, and other facilities that provide internship and postdoctoral programs in professional psychology. Promotes activities that assist in the development of professional psychology training programs. Serves as a clearinghouse to provide Ph.D. candidates with internship placement assistance at member facilities. Conducts workshops and seminars on training procedures in clinical psychology at the Ph.D. level.

★13735★ **INROADS**
10 S Broadway, Ste. 700
St. Louis, MO 63102
Ph: (314)241-7488   Fax: (314)241-9325
E-mail: info@INROADS.org
URL: http://www.INROADS.org

Description: Participants are U.S. corporations that sponsor internships for minority students and pledge to develop career opportunities for the interns. Prepares black, Hispanic, and Native American high school and college students for leadership positions within major American business corporations and in their own communities. Screens and places over 6000 individuals for paid internships with close to 1000 American business corporations per year. Offers professional training seminars on time management, business presentation skills, team building, and decision making. Provides personal and professional guidance to pre-college and college interns. Operates in the U.S., Mexico City, Toronto, Canada and Johannesburg, South Africa.

★13736★ National Association of Part-Time and Temporary Employees (NAPTE)
5800 Barton, Ste. 201
PO Box 3805
Shawnee, KS 66203
Ph: (913)962-7740
URL: http://www.members.tripod.com/ ~napte

Purpose: Promotes the economic and social interests of persons working on a part-time, contingent, or temporary basis through research, advocacy, and member services. Offers short-term portable health insurance.

★13737★ New Ways to Work (NWW)
425 Market St., Ste 2200
San Francisco, CA 94105
Ph: (415)995-9860   Fax: (415)995-9867
E-mail: info@nww.org
URL: http://www.nww.org

Purpose: Goal is to provide a work world that responds to the needs of both workers and institutions. Provides information, training, and support to individuals and organizations interested in new work options. Promotes the concepts of flextime, compressed work weeks, job sharing, work sharing, and voluntary reduced work time to satisfy the requirements of people who want and need flexible schedules. **Activities:** Offers technical assistance, including problem analysis and assistance in program facilitation for interested employees, employers, or unions.

★13738★ U.S. Public Interest Research Group (U.S.PIRG)
218 D. St. SE
Washington, DC 20003
Ph: (202)546-9707   Fax: (202)546-2461
E-mail: uspirg@pirg.org
URL: http://www.pirg.org

Description: Individuals who contribute time, effort, or funds toward public interest research and advocacy. Conducts research, monitors corporate and government actions, and lobbies for reforms on consumer, environmental, energy, and governmental issues. Current efforts include support for: laws to protect consumers from unsafe products and unfair banking practices; laws to reduce the use of toxic chemicals; strengthening clean air laws; efforts to reduce global warming and ozone depletion; energy conservation and use of safe, renewable energy sources. Sponsors internships for college students; provides opportunities for students to receive academic credit for activities such as legislative research, lobbying, and public education and organizing. Offers summer jobs.

Writing Resumes and Other Job-Search Correspondence

REFERENCE WORKS

★13739★ Adams Cover Letter Almanac
Adams Media Corp.
57 Littlefield St.
Avon, MA 02322
Ph: (508)427-7100
URL: http://www.adamsmedia.com

1996. $12.95 (book only); $19.95 (book and FastLetter Windows software). 735 pages. Contains more than 600 sample cover letters. Software includes word processing, tutorial, and suggested opening sentences, following paragraphs, and closings for cover letters.

★13740★ Adams Resume Almanac
Adams Media Corp.
57 Littlefield St.
Avon, MA 02322
Ph: (508)427-7100
URL: http://www.adamsmedia.com

1996. $12.95 (book only); $19.95 (book and FastResume Windows software). 770 pages. Contains more than 600 sample resumes. Software includes word processing and tutorial.

★13741★ The Best Resumes for Scientists and Engineers
John Wiley & Sons Inc.
1 Wiley Dr.
Somerset, NJ 08873
Ph: (732)469-4400   Fr: 800-225-5945

Adele Lewis and David J. Moore. Second edition, 1993. $37.50; $19.95 (paper). 224 pages. Presents an extensive collection of scientific and engineering resumes, highlighting the important differences between these and resumes written for other occupations.

★13742★ Best Resumes for $75,000 Plus Executive Jobs
John Wiley & Sons Inc.
1 Wiley Dr.
Somerset, NJ 08873
Ph: (732)469-4400   Fr: 800-225-5945

William E. Montag. Second edition, 1998. The revised edition covers launching a job search campaign, interviewing, job selection criteria, and a guide to the Internet aimed at executives. $15.95. 304 pages.

★13743★ Better Resumes for Executives and Professionals
Barron's Educational Series, Inc.
250 Wireless Blvd.
PO Box 8040
Hauppauge, NY 11788-3917
Ph: (631)434-3311   Fax: (631)434-3723
Fr: 800-645-3476

Robert F. Wilson and Adele Lewis. Fourth edition, 2000. $13.95 (paper). Explains how to write resumes and cover letters for executives and professionals in most fields.

★13744★ Better Resumes in 3 Easy Steps
Thomson Delmar Learning
PO Box 15015
Albany, NY 12212-5015
Ph: (518)348-2300   Fax: (518)464-0393
Fr: 800-998-7498

Wright Field. 1999. Covers how to write an effective resume and cover letter. $11.25; $18.95. 77 pages.

★13745★ Blue Collar Resumes
Career Press Inc.
PO Box 687
3 Tice Rd.
Franklin Lakes, NJ 07417
Ph: (201)848-0310   Fax: (201)848-1727
Fr: 800-227-3371
URL: http://www.CareerPress.com

Steve Provanzano. 1999. $11.99 (paper). 404 pages. Includes hundreds of examples.

★13746★ The Business Writer's Companion
St. Martin's Press LLC
16365 James Madison Hwy.
Gordonsville, VA 22942
Ph: (540)672-7600   Fax: 800-672-2054
Fr: 888-330-8477

Gerald J. Alred. Third edition, 2001. $19.50 (paper).

★13747★ The Complete Resume Guide
Hungry Minds Inc.
10475 Crosspoint Blvd.
Indianapolis, IN 46256
Ph: (317)572-2000   Fr: 800-428-5331

Marian Faux. Fifth edition, 1995. $8.95 (paper). 192 pages.

★13748★ Cover Letters for Dummies
John Wiley & Sons Inc.
1 Wiley Dr.
Somerset, NJ 08873
Ph: (732)469-4400   Fr: 800-225-5945
URL: http://www.cambridgeol.com

Joyce Lane Kennedy. Second edition, 2000. $16.99, $14.99 (paper). 284 pages. Includes dozens of examples.

★13749★ Cover Letters Made Easy
McGraw-Hill Trade
2 Penn Plaza
New York, NY 10121
Ph: (212)904-2000   Fr: 800-722-4726
E-mail: ntcpub@tribune.com

Jan B. Mattia and Patty Marley. 1995. $6.95 (paper). 96 pages. Part of Made Easy series. 284 pages.

★13750★ Cover Letters That Knock 'em Dead
Adams Media Corp.
57 Littlefield St.
Avon, MA 02322
Ph: (508)427-7100   Fax: (508)427-6790
Fr: 800-872-5627
URL: http://www.adamsmedia.com

Martin Yate. Fourth edition, 2000. $10.95

(paper). Discusses the fundamentals of writing a superior cover letter; how to match the letter style with the resume it accompanies; which format is right for which applicant; what always goes in, what always stays out, and why. Includes a number of samples. Part of Cover Letters That Knock 'em Dead series. 580 pages.

★13751★ Creating Your High School Portfolio

JIST Publishing
8902 Otis Ave.
Indianapolis, IN 46216-1033
Ph: (317)613-4200   Fax: (317)613-4307
Fr: 800-648-5478
URL: http://www.cambridgeol.com

1998. $6.95. 378 pages. This workbook shows students how to collect and store essential documents needed to apply for first jobs or college.

★13752★ Creating Your High School Resume

JIST Publishing
8902 Otis Ave.
Indianapolis, IN 46216-1033
Ph: (317)613-4200   Fax: (317)613-4307
Fr: 800-648-5478
URL: http://www.cambridgeol.com

1998. $6.95. 342 pages. This workbook provides a step-by-step guide to preparing an effective resume for a career or college.

★13753★ Customizing Your Resume for Teaching Positions

Rowman and Littlefield
4720 Boston Way
Lanham, MD 20706
Ph: (301)459-3366   Fax: (301)459-2118
Fr: 800-462-6420

Edward G. Pultorak. 1993. 52 pages.

★13754★ CV's and Job Applications

Oxford University Press, Inc.
198 Madison Ave.
New York, NY 10016-4314
Ph: (212)726-6000   Fax: (212)726-6440
Fr: 800-445-9714

Judith Leigh. John Seely. 2004. Paper. Illustrated. 144 pages.

★13755★ Cyberspace Resume Kit

JIST Publishing
8902 Otis Ave.
Indianapolis, IN 46216-1033
Ph: (317)613-4200   Fax: (317)613-4307
Fr: 800-648-5478
E-mail: jistworks@aol.com
URL: http://www.jist.com

Fred E. Jandt and Mary B. Nemnich. Second edition, 2000. $18.95. 586 pages. Teaches how to develop and post electronic resumes.

★13756★ The Damn Good Resume Guide

Ten Speed Press
PO Box 7123
Berkeley, CA 94707
Ph: (510)559-1600   Fax: (510)559-1629
Fr: 800-841-2665

Yana Parker. Third edition, 1996. $7.95 (paper). 205 pages. Concentrates on producing an effective resume, with examples of functional and chronological resumes.

★13757★ Designing the Perfect Resume

Barron's Educational Series, Inc.
250 Wireless Blvd.
Hauppauge, NY 11788-3917
Ph: (631)434-3311   Fax: (631)434-3723
Fr: 800-645-3476

Pat Criscito. Second edition, 2000. $14.95 (paper). 314 pages. Focuses on resume appearance. Includes hundreds of sample resumes created using WordPerfect software.

★13758★ Dynamic Cover Letters

Ten Speed Press
PO Box 7123
Berkeley, CA 94707
Ph: (510)559-1600   Fax: (510)559-1629
Fr: 800-841-2665

Katherine Hansen and Randall S. Hansen. Revised edition, 2001. $12.95 (paper). 368 pages. Helps sell the employer with a cover letter that will get a resume read, get an interview, and get the job.

★13759★ The Edge Resume and Job Search Strategy

JIST Publishing
8902 Otis Ave.
Indianapolis, IN 46216-1033
Ph: (317)613-4200   Fax: (317)613-4207
Fr: 800-648-5478
E-mail: jistworks@aol.com
URL: http://www.jist.com

Third edition, 1999. $24.95. 490 pages. A unique collection of fancy resumes in full color and unusual shapes.

★13760★ Effective Resume Writing: A Guide to Successful Employment

Neal Publications, Inc.
127 W. Indiana
PO Box 451
Perrysburg, OH 43551
Ph: (419)874-4787

James E. Neal Jr. Second edition, 1996. $7.95 (paper). 132 pages.

★13761★ Electronic Resume Revolution

John Wiley & Sons Inc.
1 Wiley Dr.
Somerset, NJ 08873
Ph: (732)469-4400   Fr: 800-225-5945

Joyce Lain Kennedy and Thomas J. Morrow. Second edition, 1995. $12.95 (paper). 228 pages. Explains how to write a resume that a computer can read. Includes 30 model resumes.

★13762★ Electronic Resumes for the New Job Market

Impact Publications
9104 Manassas Dr., Ste. N
Manassas Park, VA 20111-5211
Ph: (703)361-7300   Fax: (703)335-9486

Peter D. Weddle. 1994. $11.95 (paper). 161 pages. Explains how to use electronic job banks and design resumes that best meet electronic job bank specifications.

★13763★ Electronic Resumes and Online Networking: How to Use the Internet to Do a Better Job Search, Including a Complete, Up-to-Date Resource Guide

Career Press, Inc.
3 Tice Rd.
PO Box 687
Franklin Lakes, NJ 07417-1322
Ph: (201)848-0310   Fax: (201)848-1727
Fr: 800-227-3371

Rebecca Smith. Second edition, 2000. $13.99 (paper). Provides information on using the Internet as a resume networking tool. Covers locating employers, evaluating electronic resume options, and web pages. 400 pages.

★13764★ Electronic Resumes: The Complete Guide to Putting Your Resume On-Line

The McGraw-Hill Companies
2 Penn Plaza, 20th Fl.
New York, NY 10121-2298
Ph: (212)904-4509   Fr: 800-338-3987

Wayne M. Gonyea and James C. Gonyea. 1996. $19.95. 277 pages. Explains the basics of online, multimedia, video, and audio resumes in nontechnical language. Disk includes software that enables users to create their own electronic resume to upload via modem onto online resume databases.

★13765★ Every Woman's Essential Job Hunting & Resume Book

Adams Media Corp.
57 Littlefield St.
Avon, MA 02322
Ph: (508)427-7100   Fax: (508)427-6790
Fr: 800-872-5627
URL: http://www.adamsmedia.com

Laura Morin. 1994. $11.95 (paper).

★13766★ Expert Resumes for Computer and Web Jobs

JIST Publishing
8902 Otis Ave.
Indianapolis, IN 46216-1033
Ph: (317)613-4200   Fax: (317)613-4307
Fr: 800-648-5478

Wendy Enelow and Louis Kursmark. 2001. $16.95 (paper).

★13767★ The Federal Resume Guidebook

JIST Publishing
8902 Otis Ave.
Indianapolis, IN 46216-1033
Ph: (317)613-4200   Fax: (317)613-4307
Fr: 800-648-5478
E-mail: jistworks@aol.com
URL: http://www.jist.com

Kathryn K. Troutman. Second edition, 1997. $34.95. 240 pages. Covers finding and analyzing federal job announcements as well as writing federal resumes. Out of print.

★13768★ The Five-Minute Interview

John Wiley & Sons Inc.
1 Wiley Dr.
Somerset, NJ 08873
Ph: (732)469-4400   Fr: 800-225-5945

Richard H. Beatty. Second edition, 1997. $14.95 (paper). 206 pages.

★13769★ Gallery of Best Resumes

JIST Publishing
8902 Otis Ave.
Indianapolis, IN 46216-1033
Ph: (317)613-4200   Fax: (317)613-4307
Fr: 800-648-5478
E-mail: jistworks@aol.com
URL: http://www.jist.com

David F. Noble. 2000. $18.95. 978 pages. Includes a wide range of styles, formats, designs, occupations, and situations.

★13770★ Get That Job!: Job Applications

McGraw-Hill Contemporary Books
1221 Avenue of the Americas
New York, NY 10020
Ph: (212)904-2000   Fr: 800-323-4900

Susan Echaore-McDavid and Winifred H. Roderman. 1998.

★13771★ Government Job Finder

Planning Communications
7215 Oak Ave.
River Forest, IL 60305-1935
Ph: (708)366-5200   Fax: (708)366-5280
Fr: 888-366-5200
URL: http://jobfindersonline.com

Daniel Lauber. Third edition, 1997. 336 pages. Covers 1800 sources. Discusses how to use sources of local, state, and federal government job vacancies in a number of specialties and state-by-state, including job-matching services, job hotlines, spe-

cialty periodicals with job ads, salary surveys, and directories. Explains how local, state, and federal hiring systems work. Includes chapters on resume and cover letter preparation and interviewing.

★13772★ Guide to Basic Resume Writing

McGraw-Hill Trade
2 Penn Plaza
New York, NY 10121
Ph: (212)904-2000   Fr: 800-722-4726
E-mail: ntcpub@tribune.com

Public Library Association Job and Career Information Staff. 1995. $7.95 (paper). 96 pages. Important resource for semiskilled and unskilled workers who need to compile a simple resume and write a cover letter. Out of print.

★13773★ High Impact Resumes and Letters: How to Communicate Your Qualifications to Employers

Impact Publications
9104 Manassas Dr., Ste. N
Manassas Park, VA 20111-5211
Ph: (703)361-7300   Fax: (703)335-9486

Ronald L. Krannich and William J. Banis. Seventh edition, 1997. $19.95 (paper). 812 pages.

★13774★ How to Prepare Your Curriculum Vitae

McGraw-Hill Trade
2 Penn Plaza
New York, NY 10121
Ph: (212)904-2000   Fr: 800-722-4726
E-mail: ntcpub@tribune.com

Acy L. Jackson. Second edition, 1996. $14.95 (paper). 550 pages. Dozens of examples from academics in all disciplines and at all career levels illustrate the principles of writing an effective C.V. Worksheets guide the reader through a step-by-step process that begins with describing, in draft form, all pertinent experiences, and then helps shape, organize, and edit experiences and credentials into a professional curriculum vitae. Includes sample cover letters tailored to academic institutions.

★13775★ How to Write Better Resumes

Barron's Educational Series, Inc.
250 Wireless Blvd.
Hauppauge, NY 11788-3917
Ph: (631)434-3311   Fax: (631)434-3723
Fr: 800-645-3476

Gary J. Grappo and Adele Lewis. Fifth edition, 1998. $11.95 (paper). 282 pages.

★13776★ How to Write an Effective Resume

The Saunderstown Press
P.O. Box 307
Saunderstown, RI 02874-0307
Ph: (401)295-8810

URL: http://www.amanet.org

Allen A. Johnson. Twenty-first edition, 1996. $7.95 17 pages.

★13777★ How to Write a Winning Resume

McGraw-Hill Trade
2 Penn Plaza
New York, NY 10121
Ph: (212)904-2000   Fr: 800-722-4726
E-mail: ntcpub@tribune.com

Deborah Perlmutter Bloch. Fourth edition, 1998. $14.95 (paper). 564 pages. Explains what a resume does, the various kinds that exist, and occasions where it should be used. Contains advice on what and what not to include in a resume, how to respond to the want ads, and an appendix of job descriptions.

★13778★ Internet Resumes

Impact Publications
9104 Manassas Dr., Ste. N
Manassas Park, VA 20111-5211
Ph: (703)361-7300   Fax: (703)335-9486
URL: http://www.cambridgeol.com

Peter D. Weddle. 1998. $14.95 (paper). 536 pages. Shows how to communicate qualifications to potential employers over the Internet.

★13779★ Last Minute Cover Letters

Career Press Inc.
PO Box 687
3 Tice Rd.
Franklin Lakes, NJ 07417-1322
Ph: (201)848-0310   Fax: (201)848-1727
Fr: 800-227-3371
URL: http://www.CareerPress.com

Brandon Toropov. 1998. $9.99 (paper). 288 pages. Provides templates for cover letters.

★13780★ Non-Profits and Education Job Finder

Planning Communications
7215 Oak Ave.
River Forest, IL 60305-1935
Ph: (708)366-5200   Fax: (708)366-5280
Fr: 888-366-5200
URL: http://jobfindersonline.com

Daniel Lauber. 1997. $32.95; $16.95 (paper). 336 pages. Covers 1600 sources. Discusses how to use sources of non-profit sector job vacancies in a number of specialties and state-by-state, including job-matching services, job hotlines, specialty periodicals with job ads, salary surveys, and directories. Covers a variety of fields from education to religion. Includes chapters on resume and cover letter preparation and interviewing.

★13781★ 101 Best Resumes: Endorsed by the Professional Association of Resume Writers

McGraw-Hill Professional
2 Penn Plaza
New York, NY 10121
Ph: (212)904-2000   Fr: 800-722-4726

Jay A. Block and Michael Betrus. 1997. $12.95 (paper). 197 pages.

★13782★ 101 Great Resumes

Career Press, Inc.
PO Box 687
3 Tice Rd.
Franklin Lakes, NJ 07417-1322
Ph: (201)848-0310   Fax: (201)848-1727
Fr: 800-227-3371
URL: http://www.CareerPress.com

Ron Fry. Revised, 2002. $11.99 (paper). 216 pages. Sample resumes cover 39 common situations and 62 career fields.

★13783★ 175 High-Impact Resumes

John Wiley & Sons Inc.
1 Wiley Dr.
Somerset, NJ 08873
Ph: (732)469-4400   Fr: 800-225-5945

Richard Beatty. Third edition, 2002. $14.95 (paper). Includes information on preparing electronic resumes for posting on the Internet. 336 pages.

★13784★ The Perfect Cover Letter

John Wiley & Sons Inc.
1 Wiley Dr.
Somerset, NJ 08873
Ph: (732)469-4400   Fr: 800-225-5945

Richard H. Beatty. Second edition, 1996. $12.95 (paper). 192 pages. Provides examples and analysis of a range of letters, including executive search, advertising response, networking, personal introduction, and general broadcast targeted pieces. Also contains tips on what information to include or omit, as well as proper letter design.

★13785★ The Perfect Resume: Today's Ultimate Job Search Tool

Broadway Books
1540 Broadway
New York, NY 10036
Ph: (212)354-6500   Fax: (212)782-8338
Fr: 800-223-6834

Tom Jackson. June 2004. $12.95 (paper). 240 pages.

★13786★ Power Resumes

John Wiley & Sons Inc.
1 Wiley Dr.
Somerset, NJ 08873
Ph: (732)469-4400   Fr: 800-225-5945

Ron Tepper. Third edition, 1998. $14.95 (paper). Covers the key parts and techniques that make for a successful resume. 272 pages.

★13787★ Professional Resumes for Executives, Managers and Other Administrators: A New Gallery of Best Resumes

JIST Publishing
8902 Otis Ave.
Indianapolis, IN 46216-1033
Ph: (317)613-4200   Fax: (317)613-4307
Fr: 800-648-5478

David F. Noble. 1998. $19.95. 1406 pages.

★13788★ The Quick Resume and Cover Letter Book

JIST Works, Inc.
8902 Otis Ave.
Indianapolis, IN 46216-1033
Ph: (317)613-4200   Fax: 800-547-8329
Fr: 800-648-5478
E-mail: jistworks@aol.com
URL: http://www.jist.com

1999. $14.95. 670 pages. Explains how to write and use a resume in one day.

★13789★ Real Life Resumes That Work!

DBM Publishing
Drake Beam Morin, Inc.
275 Broad Hollow Rd., Suite 300
Melville, NY 11747
Ph: (516)752-3789   Fax: (516)756-2571
Fr: 800-345-5627
URL: http://www.dbm.com

1995. 176 pages. Bob Stirling and Pat Morton, editors. $11.00 (paper). Includes a wide range of sample resumes as well as networking, ad response, and follow-up letters.

★13790★ The Resume Catalog: 200 Damn Good Examples

Ten Speed Press
PO Box 7123
Berkeley, CA 94707
Ph: (510)559-1600   Fax: (510)559-1629
Fr: 800-841-2665

Yana Parker. Revised edition, 1996. $15.95 (paper). 670 pages. Contains a range and variety of 200 sample resumes. Indexed and cross-referenced for ease of use.

★13791★ Resume and Cover Letter Writing Guide

Voc-Offers
PO Box 700252
San Jose, CA 95170-0252
Ph: (408)255-6579

Carey E. Harbin. Second edition, 1996. $8.95 (paper). 36 pages.

★13792★ The Resume Handbook

Adams Media Corp.
57 Littlefield St.
Avon, MA 02322
Ph: (508)427-7100   Fax: (508)427-6790
Fr: 800-872-5627
URL: http://www.adamsmedia.com

Arthur D. Rosenberg and David V. Hizer. Third edition, 1996. $7.95 (paper). 216 pages. Includes specific examples of excellent resumes and cover letters and examples of how weaker resumes and cover letters can be improved. Presents resumes for many types of job hunters, including recent college graduates, seasoned professionals, and women re-entering the job market. Chapters on cover letters and 'personal sales' letters and design and layout of resumes are also included.

★13793★ Resume and Job Search: Letters for Transitioning Military Personnel

Impact Publications
9104 Manassas Dr., Suite N
Manassas Park, VA 20111-5211
Ph: (703)361-7300   Fax: (703)335-9486
URL: http://www.CareerBookstore.com

Carl S. Savino and Ronald L. Krannich. 1998. 272 pages. $17.95. Helps members of the military service communicate their skills for civilian positions. Out of print.

★13794★ The Resume Kit

John Wiley & Sons Inc.
1 Wiley Dr.
Somerset, NJ 08873
Ph: (732)469-4400   Fr: 800-225-5945

Richard H. Beatty. Fourth edition, 2000. $12.95 (paper). 350 pages. Details effective resume preparation. Discusses both chronological and functional resumes. Includes sample resumes and cover letters.

★13795★ Resume Magic: Trade Secrets of a Professional Resume Writer

JIST Works, Inc.
8902 Otis Ave.
Indianapolis, IN 46216-1033
Ph: (317)613-4200   Fax: (317)613-4307
Fr: 800-648-5478
E-mail: jistworks@aol.com
URL: http://www.jist.com

Susan Britton Whitcomb. 1999. $18.95. 350 pages. Covers every element of resume writing, with nearly 100 "before and after" examples.

★13796★ The Resume Makeover: The Resume Writing Guide That Includes Personalized Feedback

John Wiley & Sons Inc.
1 Wiley Dr.
Somerset, NJ 08873
Ph: (732)469-4400   Fr: 800-225-5945

Jeffrey G. Allen. 2001. $14.95 (paper). 312 pages.

★13797★ **Resume Power: Selling Yourself on Paper**

Mount Vernon Press
1750 112th St. NE, C-224
Bellevue, WA 98004
Ph: (425)454-6982   Fax: (425)455-4729

Tom Washington. Sixth edition, 2000. $14.95 (paper). 265 pages.

★13798★ **Resume Service Directory**

infoUSA Inc.
5711 S 86th Cir.
Omaha, NE 68127-0347
Ph: (402)930-3500   Fax: (402)331-0176
Fr: 800-555-6124
URL: http://www.abii.com

Annual. Number of listings: 4,239. Entries include: Name, address, phone (including area code), size of advertisement, year first in "Yellow Pages," name of owner or manager, number of employees. Compiled from telephone company "Yellow Pages," nationwide. Arrangement: Geographical.

★13799★ **The Resume Solution**

JIST Works, Inc.
8902 Otis Ave.
Indianapolis, IN 46216-1033
Ph: (317)613-4200   Fax: (317)613-4307
Fr: 800-648-5478
E-mail: jistworks@aol.com
URL: http://www.jist.com

David Swanson. 1994 Second edition. $12.95. 560 pages. Covers how to use and write resumes, with more than 90 pages of sample resumes and worksheets. Out of print.

★13800★ **Resume Winners from the Pros: 177 of the Best from the Professional Association of Resume Writer**

Impact Publications
9104 Manassas Dr., Ste. N
Manassas Park, VA 20111-5211
Ph: (703)361-7300   Fax: (703)335-9486

Wendy S. Enelow. 1998. $17.95 (paper). 970 pages.

★13801★ **The Resume Writer's Handbook**

HarperCollins Publishers, Inc.
10 E. 53rd St.
New York, NY 10022-5299
Ph: (212)207-7000   Fax: (212)207-7145
Fr: 800-242-7737

Michael Holley Smith. 1994. $4.99 (paper). A writing guide aimed at people at all job levels. Provides examples and advice on common problems. 240 pages.

★13802★ **Resume Writing Made Easy**

Prentice Hall PTR
200 Old Tappan Rd.
Old Tappan, NJ 07675
Ph: (201)236-7000   Fr: 800-223-1360

Lola Brown. Seventh edition, 2001. $16.00. 160 pages.

★13803★ **Resumes for Advertising Careers**

McGraw-Hill Contemporary Books
1221 Avenue of the Americas
New York, NY 10020
Ph: (212)904-2000   Fr: 800-323-4900
E-mail: ntcpub@tribune.com

1998. $9.95 (paper). 392 pages. Aimed at job seekers trying to enter or advance in advertising. Provides sample resumes for copywriters, art directors, account managers, ad managers, and media people at all levels of experience. Furnishes sample cover letters.

★13804★ **Resumes, Application Forms, Cover Letters, and Interviews**

Consumer Information Center
U.S. General Services Administration
PO Box 100
Pueblo, CO 81002
Ph: (719)948-4000   Fax: (719)948-9724
URL: http://www.pueblo.gsa.gov

$1.25. 7 pages. Provides tips for better resumes, cover letters, and interviews. Out of Print.

★13805★ **Resumes for Banking and Financial Careers**

McGraw-Hill Contemporary Books
1221 Avenue of the Americas
New York, NY 10020
Ph: (212)904-2000   Fr: 800-323-4900
E-mail: ntcpub@tribune.com

2001. $10.95 (paper). 468 pages.

★13806★ **Resumes for Better Jobs**

Prentice Hall PTR
200 Old Tappan Rd.
Old Tappan, NJ 07675
Ph: (201)236-7000   Fr: 800-223-1360

Lawrence Brennan. Seventh edition, 1996. $10.95 (paper). Sample resumes that correspond to over 200 jobs. Publication cancelled.

★13807★ **Resumes for Business Management Careers**

McGraw-Hill Contemporary Books
1221 Avenue of the Americas
New York, NY 10020
Ph: (212)904-2000   Fr: 800-323-4900
E-mail: ntcpub@tribune.com

Jeffrey S. Johnson. Second edition, 2000. $10.95 (paper). 156 pages. Resume guide for supervisors and line and staff managers. Provides advice on compiling a business management resume; includes a number of

sample resumes and cover letters. Part of VGM Professional Resumes series.

★13808★ **Resumes for College Students and Recent Graduates**

McGraw-Hill Contemporary Books
1221 Avenue of the Americas
New York, NY 10020
Ph: (212)904-2000   Fr: 800-323-4900
E-mail: ntcpub@tribune.com

Revised edition, 1998. $9.95 (paper). 462 pages. Shows how to write a resume that capitalizes on pertinent work experience, academic background, and volunteer and extracurricular activities. Includes sample resumes and cover letters.

★13809★ **Resumes for Communications Careers**

McGraw-Hill Contemporary Books
1221 Avenue of the Americas
New York, NY 10020
Ph: (212)904-2000   Fr: 800-323-4900
E-mail: ntcpub@tribune.com

1998. $9.95 (paper). 464 pages.

★13810★ **Resumes, Cover-Letters & Interviewing: Setting the Stage for Success**

Thomson South-Western
5101 Madison Rd.
Cincinnati, OH 45227
Ph: (513)527-1989   Fax: (513)527-6137
Fr: 800-543-0487

Clifford W. Eischen and Lynn A. Eischen. 1999. $18.95 (paper). Professional resume using today's business technologies including the Internet & E-mail. Specifically targeted to help individuals with a two-year degree showcase their skills & experiences to get the job they want. Scanable resumes, Internet-based resumes, & etiquette for sending resumes via fax or E-mail are addressed to prepare readers to apply for jobs using today's business technologies. Dedicated chapter on the interview process coaches readers on proper interview attire, preparing for interview questions, introductions, & how to follow up after an interview. Exercises on listing qualifications, producing a first draft, gathering references, & drafting a follow-up letter, all help readers build a finished resume step by step.

★13811★ **Resumes for Engineering Careers**

McGraw-Hill Trade
2 Penn Plaza
New York, NY 10121
Ph: (212)904-2000   Fr: 800-722-4726
E-mail: ntcpub@tribune.com

2000. $10.95 (paper). 456 pages. Contains sample resumes and cover letters applicable to any engineering field.

★13812★ Resumes for Environmental Careers

McGraw-Hill Trade
2 Penn Plaza
New York, NY 10121
Ph: (212)904-2000   Fr: 800-722-4726
E-mail: ntcpub@tribune.com

2002. $9.95 (paper). 160 pages. Provides resume advice tailored to people pursuing careers focusing on the environment. Includes sample resumes and cover letters.

★13813★ Resumes Etc.

Prototype Career Press
1086 Seventh St., W.
St. Paul, MN 55102-3829
Fax: (612)224-5526   Fr: 800-368-3197
URL: http://www.getajob

Amy Lindgren. $2.95. 112 pages. Covers resumes, cover letters, follow-up letters, and applications.

★13814★ Resumes for Ex-Military Personnel

McGraw-Hill Trade
2 Penn Plaza
New York, NY 10121
Ph: (212)904-2000   Fr: 800-722-4726
E-mail: ntcpub@tribune.com

1995. $9.95 (paper). 462 pages. Part of VGM Professional Resume series. Out of print.

★13815★ Resumes for the 50 Plus Job Hunter

McGraw-Hill Trade
2 Penn Plaza
New York, NY 10121
Ph: (212)904-2000

2002.

★13816★ Resumes for the First-Time Job Hunter

McGraw-Hill Trade
2 Penn Plaza
New York, NY 10121
Ph: (212)904-2000   Fr: 800-722-4726
E-mail: ntcpub@tribune.com

1995. $9.95 (paper). 460 pages.

★13817★ Resumes that Get Jobs

Marketing Directions Inc.
615 Queen St.
Southington, CT 06489
Ph: (860)276-2452   Fax: (860)276-2453
Fr: 800-562-4357
URL: http://www.marketingdirections.com

Brian Jud. $1.45. 20 pages. Provides tips on resume writing.

★13818★ Resumes for Government Careers

Vgm Career Horizons
1221 Avenue of the Americas
New York, NY 10020
Ph: (212)904-2000   Fr: 800-323-4900
E-mail: ntcpub@tribune.com

1996. $9.95 (paper). 464 pages.

★13819★ Resumes for Health and Medical Careers

McGraw-Hill Trade
2 Penn Plaza
New York, NY 10121
Ph: (212)904-2000   Fr: 800-722-4726
E-mail: ntcpub@tribune.com

1997. $9.95 (paper). 455 pages.

★13820★ Resumes for High School Graduates

McGraw-Hill Trade
2 Penn Plaza
New York, NY 10121
Ph: (212)904-2000
E-mail: ntcpub@tribune.com

Second edition, 1999. $9.95. Designed for the person with little or no full-time work experience. Shows how to emphasize part-work experience and highlight educational, extra-curricular and volunteer experience. Provides sample resumes and cover letters.

★13821★ Resumes for High Tech Careers

Vgm Career Horizons
1221 Avenue of the Americas
New York, NY 10020
Ph: (212)904-2000   Fr: 800-323-4900
E-mail: ntcpub@tribune.com

Second edition, 1997. $9.95 (paper). 462 pages. Demonstrates how to tailor a resume that catches a high tech employer's attention. Part of Resumes for... series.

★13822★ Resumes for Higher Paying Positions: A Complete Guide to Resume Writing for a More Rewarding Career

Best Seller Publications, Inc.
12146 Island View Cir.
Germantown, MD 20874
Ph: (301)869-0072   Fax: (301)972-4456

Cory Schulman. 1997. $17.95 (paper). 187 pages.

★13823★ Resumes for Law Careers

McGraw-Hill Professional
2 Penn Plaza
New York, NY 10121
Ph: (212)904-2000   Fr: 800-722-4726
E-mail: ntcpub@tribune.com

2001. $10.95 (paper). 160 pages.

★13824★ Resumes for Midcareer Job Changes

Vgm Career Horizons
1221 Avenue of the Americas
New York, NY 10020
Ph: (212)904-2000   Fr: 800-323-4900
E-mail: ntcpub@tribune.com

1994. $9.95 (paper). 160 pages. Out of print.

★13825★ Resumes for Nursing Careers

McGraw-Hill Professional
2 Penn Plaza
New York, NY 10121
Ph: (212)904-2000   Fr: 800-722-4726
E-mail: ntcpub@tribune.com

2001. $10.95 (paper). 160 pages.

★13826★ Resumes for Overseas & Stateside Jobs

Zinks International Career Guidance
PO Box 587
Marshall, MI 49068-0587

Richard M. Zink. 1994. $14.95 (paper). 80 pages.

★13827★ Resumes for Performing Arts Careers

Vgm Career Horizons
1221 Avenue of the Americas
New York, NY 10020
Ph: (212)904-2000   Fr: 800-323-4900
E-mail: ntcpub@tribune.com

1997. $9.95 (paper). 462 pages.

★13828★ Resumes & Personal Statements for Health Professionals

Galen Press, Ltd.
PO Box 64400
Tucson, AZ 85728-4400
Ph: (520)577-8363   Fax: (520)529-6459
Fr: 800-442-5369

James W. Tysinger. Second edition, 1998. $18.95 (paper).

★13829★ Resumes for Re-Entering the Job Market

McGraw-Hill Trade
2 Penn Plaza
New York, NY 10121
Ph: (212)904-2000   Fr: 800-722-4726
E-mail: ntcpub@tribune.com

1995. $9.95 (paper). 464 pages. Part of VGM Professional Resumes series.

★13830★ Resumes for Sales and Marketing Careers

McGraw-Hill Professional
2 Penn Plaza
New York, NY 10121
Ph: (212)904-2000   Fr: 800-722-4726
E-mail: ntcpub@tribune.com

Chuck Cochran and Donna Peerce. Second edition, 1998. $10.95 (paper). 336 pages.

Sample resumes and cover letters from all levels of the sales and marketing field.

★13831★ **Resumes for Science Careers**

McGraw-Hill Professional
1221 Avenue of the Americas
New York, NY 10020
Ph: (212)904-2000   Fr: 800-323-4900
E-mail: ntcpub@tribune.com

1997. $9.95 (paper). 466 pages.

★13832★ **Resumes for Scientific and Technical Careers**

McGraw-Hill Contemporary Books
1221 Avenue of the Americas
New York, NY 10020
Ph: (212)904-2000   Fr: 800-323-4900
E-mail: ntcpub@tribune.com

1999. $9.95 (paper). 450 pages. Provides resume advice for individuals interested in working in scientific and technical careers. Includes sample resumes and cover letters.

★13833★ **Resumes for Social Service Careers**

McGraw-Hill Trade
2 Penn Plaza
New York, NY 10121
Ph: (212)904-2000   Fr: 800-722-4726
E-mail: ntcpub@tribune.com

2000. $9.95 (paper). 460 pages.

★13834★ **Resumes That Knock 'Em Dead**

Adams Media Corp.
57 Littlefield St.
Avon, MA 02322
Ph: (508)427-7100   Fax: (508)427-6790
Fr: 800-872-5627
URL: http://www.adamsmedia.com

Martin Yate. Fourth edition, 2000. $10.95 (paper). 572 pages. Presents resumes that were successfully used by individuals to obtain jobs. Resumes target the most commonly-sought positions on all levels.

★13835★ **Resumes for Women**

Macmillan Publishing Co., Inc.
200 Old Tappan Rd.
Old Tappan, NJ 07675
Fr: 800-428-5331

Eva Shaw. 1995. $10.00 (paper).

★13836★ **The Smart Woman's Guide to Resumes and Job Hunting**

Chelsea House Publishers
1974 Sproul Rd., Ste. 400
Broomall, PA 19008-0914
Ph: (610)353-5166   Fax: (610)359-1439
Fr: 800-848-2665

Julie Adair King and Betsy Sheldon. 1996. $19.95. 271 pages. Addresses job-search challenges unique to women in the '90s. Discusses breaking through the glass ceiling

and other gender barriers, commanding a fair salary, networking to hidden job opportunities, using "power language", translating volunteer experiences into powerful accomplishments, and offers other guidance. Takes the reader through a resume-creating process.

★13837★ **Sure-Hire Resumes**

Impact Publications
9104 Manassas Dr., Ste. N
Manassas Park, VA 20111-5211
Ph: (703)361-7300   Fax: (703)335-9486

Robbie M. Kaplan. Second edition, 1998. $14.95 (paper). Includes 'ideal' cover letters written by personnel directors. Presents 25 actual resumes (indexed by occupation) and includes discussions of useful resume-writing software and word processing. 545 pages.

★13838★ **200 Letters for Job Hunters**

Ten Speed Press
PO Box 7123
Berkeley, CA 94707
Ph: (510)559-1600   Fax: (510)559-1629
Fr: 800-841-2665

William S. Frank. Revised edition, 1993. $21.95 (paper). 750 pages. Provides over 250 letters to cover a variety of situations.

★13839★ **201 Dynamite Job Search Letters**

Impact Publications
9104 Manassas Dr., Suite N
Manassas Park, VA 20111-5211
Ph: (703)361-7300   Fax: (703)335-9486
URL: http://www.cambridgeol.com

2001. $19.95. 800 pages. Shows how to write nine different types of letters.

★13840★ **Winning Cover Letters**

John Wiley & Sons Inc.
1 Wiley Dr.
Somerset, NJ 08873
Ph: (732)469-4400   Fr: 800-225-5945

Robin Ryan. 1997. $12.95 (paper). Covers the techniques needed to draft an effective cover letter. 192 pages. Part of Career Coach series.

★13841★ **Winning Resumes**

John Wiley & Sons Inc.
1 Wiley Dr.
Somerset, NJ 08873
Ph: (732)469-4400   Fr: 800-225-5945

Robin Ryan. 1997. $14.95 (paper). 224 pages.

★13842★ **Write a Winning Resume**

McGraw-Hill Contemporary Books
1221 Avenue of the Americas
New York, NY 10020
Ph: (212)904-2000   Fr: 800-323-4900

Deborah P. Bloch. 1997. $12.95 (paper). 128 pages. Part of Here's How series.

★13843★ **Writing Resumes That Work: A How-to-Do-It Manual for Librarians**

Neal-Schuman Publishers, Inc.
100 Varick St.
New York, NY 10013
Ph: (212)925-8650   Fax: (212)219-8916

Robert R. Newlen. 1998. $39.95 (paper). 151 pages. Provides ideas for alternate library careers in this new edition of a 1980 publication. Most of the 62 contributors have information science, academic, and other adult-focused backgrounds; four come from the fields of children's and elementary school media services and one from the YA ranks.

★13844★ **Your First Resume**

The Career Press Inc.
3 Tice Rd.
PO Box 687
Franklin Lakes, NJ 07417-1322
Ph: (201)848-0310   Fax: (201)848-1727
Fr: 800-227-3371

Ronald W. Fry. Fifth edition, 2001. $11.99 (paper). 332 pages. Subtitled: "The Comprehensive Guide for College Students or Anyone Preparing to Enter or Reenter the Job Market."

★13845★ **Your Resume: Key to a Better Job**

Hungry Minds, Inc.
10475 Crosspoint Blvd.
Indianapolis, IN 46256
Fax: (317)572-4000   Fr: 800-667-1115

Leonard Corwen. Sixth edition, 1996. $24.95 (paper). 200 pages. Provides guidelines for resume writing; explains what employers look for in a resume, including contents and style. Includes model resumes for high-demand careers such as computer programmers, health administrators, and high-tech professionals. Notes basic job-getting information and strategies.

AUDIO/VISUAL RESOURCES

★13846★ **Access Unlimited: The Job Search Series for People with Disabilities**

Cambridge Educational
PO Box 931
Monmouth Junction, NJ 08852-0931
Fax: 800-FAX-ON-US   Fr: 800-468-4227
URL: http://www.cambridgeeducational.com

Three videos. 1998. $199.00/set. Three 30-

minute videos cover job search tactics, resumes and applications, and job interviewing.

★13847★ **Defining and Developing Your Portfolio**
Cambridge Educational
PO Box 931
Monmouth Junction, NJ 08852-0931
Fax: 800-FAX-ON-US   Fr: 800-468-4227
URL: http://www.cambridgeeducational.com
$79.95. 2000. 17 minutes.

★13848★ **Effective Resumes: Reading Between The Lines**
Cambridge Educational
PO Box 931
Monmouth Junction, NJ 08852-0931
Fax: 800-FAX-ON-US   Fr: 800-468-4227
URL: http://www.cambridgeeducational.com
$79.95. 60 minutes.

★13849★ **From Parole to Payroll**
Cambridge Educational
PO Box 931
Monmouth Junction, NJ 08852-0931
Fax: 800-FAX-ON-US   Fr: 800-468-4227
URL: http://www.cambridgeeducational.com
Three videos. 1997. $275.95/set. Three videos cover finding a job (15 minutes), resumes and job applications (15 minutes), and the job interview (15 minutes).

★13850★ **The Ideal Resume**
Cambridge Educational
PO Box 931
Monmouth Junction, NJ 08852-0931
Fax: 800-FAX-ON-US   Fr: 800-468-4227
URL: http://www.cambridgeeducational.com
Video. 1997. $79.95. 21 minutes. Appropriate for both adults and youth.

★13851★ **The Portfolio Resume Series**
Cambridge Educational
PO Box 931
Monmouth Junction, NJ 08852-0931
Fax: 800-FAX-ON-US   Fr: 800-468-4227
URL: http://www.cambridgeeducational.com
Two videos. $150.95. 2000. Topics include defining and developing your portfolio and using and maintaining your portfolio.

★13852★ **Resumes and Applications for People with Disabilities**
Cambridge Educational
PO Box 931
Monmouth Junction, NJ 08852-0931
Fax: 800-FAX-ON-US   Fr: 800-468-4227
URL: http://www.cambridgeeducational.com
$89.95. 1998. 30 minutes. Part of the series "Access Unlimited: The Job Search Series for People with Disabilities."

★13853★ **Resumes and Job Applications**
Cambridge Educational
PO Box 931
Monmouth Junction, NJ 08852-0931
Fax: 800-FAX-ON-US   Fr: 800-468-4227
URL: http://www.cambridgeeducational.com
$98.95. 1997. 20 minutes. Part of the From Parole to Payroll Series.

★13854★ **Ten Commandments of Resumes**
Cambridge Educational
PO Box 931
Monmouth Junction, NJ 08852-0931
Fax: 800-FAX-ON-US   Fr: 800-468-4227
URL: http://www.cambridgeeducational.com
1997. $79.95. 35 minutes. This videocassette contains ten important tips for writing an excellent resume, providing the knowledge needed to stand out in a crowd of job seekers.

★13855★ **Using and Maintaining Your Portfolio**
Cambridge Educational
PO Box 931
Monmouth Junction, NJ 08852-0931
Fax: 800-FAX-ON-US   Fr: 800-468-4227
URL: http://www.cambridgeeducational.com
$79.95. 2000. 21 minutes. Part of the Portfolio Resume Series.

★13856★ **Web Resumes**
Cambridge Educational
PO Box 931
Monmouth Junction, NJ 08852-0931
Fax: 800-FAX-ON-US   Fr: 800-468-4227
URL: http://www.cambridgeeducational.com
Video. 1998. $89.95. 30 minutes. Topics covered include Web and electronic resumes, creative resumes, target resumes, and mid-life and reentry resumes.

★13857★ **Your First Resume and Interview**
Cambridge Educational
PO Box 931
Monmouth Junction, NJ 08852-0931
Fax: 800-FAX-ON-US   Fr: 800-468-4227
URL: http://www.cambridgeeducational.com
Video. 1998. $89.95. 15 minutes.

ONLINE AND DATABASE SERVICES

★13858★ **CareerXpress.com**
E-mail: service@careerxpress.com
URL: http://www.careerxpress.com
Description: Resume writing and distribution service. **Fee:** Pricing depending on desired range of search; begins at $79.

★13859★ **Resume Safari**
URL: http://resumesafari.com/affilfag.cfm
Description: Site serves as a resume distribution service. Once submitted, a job hunter's resume will be distributed to over 1,500 locations on the web **Fee:** $60 or $80 depending on tier.

★13860★ **SeeMeResumes.com**
URL: http://www.seemeresumes.com
Description: Resume coaching and distribution service. Confidential e-mail inboxes available. **Fee:** Pricing based on desired intensity and range of search; starts at $39.

SOFTWARE

★13861★ **Adams Cover Letter Almanac**
Adams Media Corp.
57 Littlefield St.
Avon, MA 02322
Ph: (508)427-7100
URL: http://www.adamsmedia.com
1996. $12.95 (book only); $19.95 (book and FastLetter Windows software). 735 pages. Contains more than 600 sample cover letters. Software includes word processing, tutorial, and suggested opening sentences, following paragraphs, and closings for cover letters.

★13862★ **Adams Resume Almanac**
Adams Media Corp.
57 Littlefield St.
Avon, MA 02322
Ph: (508)427-7100
URL: http://www.adamsmedia.com
1996. $12.95 (book only); $19.95 (book and FastResume Windows software). 770 pages. Contains more than 600 sample resumes. Software includes word processing and tutorial.

★13863★ **Multimedia Job Search**
Cambridge Educational
PO Box 931
Monmouth Junction, NJ 08852-0931
Fax: 800-FAX-ON-US   Fr: 800-468-4227
URL: http://www.cambridgeeducational.com
CD-ROM. $99.95. Includes videos, narration, and on-screen text. Users learn about getting a competitive edge in today's job market, traditional and nontraditional job search tools, resumes and cover letters, and interviewing skills.

★13864★ **Professional Everyday Guide to Business Writing**
Queue Inc.
1450 Barnum Ave., Ste. 207
Bridgeport, CT 06610
Ph: (203)335-0906   Fax: (203)336-2481
Fr: 800-232-2224

URL: http://www.queueinc.com

CD-ROM. Windows. $39.95. Self-help tutorials on routine memos, persuasive letters, short reports, resumes, letters of employment and more.

★13865★ **Resume Pro**
Cambridge Educational
PO Box 931
Monmouth Junction, NJ 08852-0931
Fax: 800-FAX-ON-US   Fr: 800-468-4227
URL: http://www.cambridgeol.com

CD-ROM. 1998. $69.95. Requires Widows

95 or higher. Teaches resume formats and includes a word processor.

★13866★ **Resumes Quick & Easy**
Individual Software, Inc.
4255 Hopyard Rd., Ste. 2
Pleasanton, CA 94588
Ph: (925)734-6767   Fax: (925)734-8337
Fr: 800-822-3522
E-mail: customerservice@individual software.com
URL: http://www.individualsoftware.com

CD-ROM. $19.95. Helps create resumes, write cover letters, find your salary range,

manage contacts, and fax or email your resume.

★13867★ **WinWay Resume on CD-ROM Deluxe**
JIST Publishing
8902 Otis Ave.
Indianapolis, IN 46216
Fr: 800-648-5478
E-mail: jistworks@aol.com
URL: http://www.jist.com

CD-ROM. Version 9.0. Windows. $49.95. Includes hundreds of examples and more than 12,000 job descriptions.

Index to Information Sources

This Index is an alphabetical listing of all entries contained in both Parts One and Two. Index references are to **entry numbers** rather than to page numbers. Publication and film titles are rendered in italics.

American Catholic Philosophical
Association **2057**
American Ceramic Society **7332**
American Ceramic Society Annual Meeting
and Exposition **7374**
American Chamber of Commerce
Executives **4934**
American Chemical Society **1601, 1688,
10496**
American Chemical Society:
JobSpectrum.org **1593, 1683, 12232**
American Chiropractic Association **1746**
American Chiropractic Association Annual
Convention and Exhibition **1745**
American City and County **1753, 2513,
2630, 4310, 5674, 5986, 6028, 9780,
10688, 11141, 11524**
American Classical League **1960, 10529**
American Clinical Laboratory **1864**
American Clinical Neurophysiology Society
Annual Meeting and Short Courses **3600,
3630**
American College of Cardiology Annual
Scientific Session **3631**
American College of Chest
Physicians **8834**
American College of Clinical
Pharmacy **8313**
American College of Foot and Ankle
Surgeons Annual Meeting and Scientific
Seminar **9117**
American College of Forensic
Examiners **4419**
American College Health Association **5156,
8835**
American College of Health Care
Administrators **5157**
American College of Healthcare
Executives **5254**
American College of Managed Care
Administrators **5158**
American College of Medical
Administrators **5255**
American College of Medical Quality **5159,
8836**
American College of Nurse-Midwives **9939**
American College of Occupational and
Environmental Medicine **8837**
American College of Osteopathic
Internists **8838**
American College of Osteopathic
Obstetricians and Gynecologists Annual
Convention **8954**
American College of Osteopathic
Surgeons **8839**
American College Personnel
Association **2734, 3484**
American College of Physician
Executives **8840**
American College of Radiology **8973**
American College of Sports Medicine **4350,
8974**
American College of Sports Medicine Annual
Meeting **8955**
American College of Surgeons Annual
Clinical Congress **8956**
American College of Veterinary
Ophthalmologists Conference **11598**
American College of Veterinary Pathologists
Annual Meeting **11599**
*American College of Veterinary Pathologists-
Membership Directory* **11571**
American Congress on Surveying and
Mapping **11156**
American Conservatory Theater
Foundation **129**
American Correctional Association **2649**
American Correctional Food Service
Association **10234**
American Correctional Health Services
Association **5160**
American Council on Alcoholism **744**
American Council on Exercise **4351, 9835**
American Council of Life Insurers **256,
5747, 11514**

American Council on the Teaching of
Foreign Languages Convention **10589**
American Counseling Association **2791**
American Counseling Association World
Conference **740, 2788, 7113**
American Credit Union Mortgage
Association **2850**
American Crystallographic
Association **1689, 9031**
American Culinary Federation **1021, 1491**
American Dance Guild **2899**
American Dental Assistants
Association **2980**
American Dental Association **2981, 3042,
3085, 3163**
American Dental Association Annual Session
& Technical Exhibition **2976, 3034, 3151**
American Dental Education
Association **2982, 3043, 3086, 3164**
American Dental Hygienists'
Association **3044**
*American Dental Hygienists' Association
Access* **2940, 2996, 3055, 3099, 5126,
5359**
American Dental Hygienists' Association
Convention **3035**
American Dental Society of Anesthesiology
Scientific Meeting **3152**
American Design Drafting Association **3242,
3405**
American Dietetic Association **3304**
American Dietetic Association Annual
Meeting and Exhibition **3300**
*American Directory of Job and Labor Market
Information* **11986, 13605**
American Disc Jockey Association **3349**
American Economic Association **3449**
American Education Finance
Association **3485**
American Electrology Association Annual
Convention **2675, 6730**
*American Electronics Association-
Directory* **3650, 3726**
American Engineering Association **4520,
11290**
American Executive Management
Inc. **4199, 4657, 6990**
American Express Tax & Business
Services **2589, 4658**
American Family Physician **6456, 8644,
8715, 9879**
American Federation of Musicians of the
United States and Canada **7624**
American Federation of Police and
Concerned Citizens **6070**
American Federation of School
Administrators **3564**
American Federation of Teachers **362,
5921, 9233, 10600, 10919**
American Feed Industry Association Feed
Industries Show **545**
American Film Marketing Association **217**
American Financial Services
Association **1043, 2851, 4297**
American Fire Journal **3835, 4311**
American Fire Services **4318**
American Forests **4478**
American Gaming Association **4589**
American Gastroenterological
Association **8841**
American Geographical Society **4953**
American Geological Institute **4995**
American Geophysical Union **4971, 7126**
American Group Practice **5190**
*American Group Psychotherapy Association-
Membership Directory* **2742, 8866, 9388,
9944, 10709**
American Guild of Musical Artists **7625**
American Guild of Organists **7626**
*American Hardware Manufacturers
Association-Rep/Factory Contact Service
Directory* **6790**
American Harp Society National
Conference **7616**

American Health Care Association **5256,
5426, 6583, 7843, 7915, 8582, 9861,
10030, 10961**
American Health Care Association Annual
Convention and Exposition **5247**
American Health Information Management
Association **7301**
American Health Quality Association **8842**
American Heart Association Scientific
Sessions **8957**
American Heart Journal **3608, 8716**
American Highway Users Alliance **11368**
American Historical Association **5347**
American Historical Association Annual
Meeting **5339**
American Hockey Coaches
Association **11024**
*American Holistic Medical Association-
National Referral Directory* **8867**
American Hospital Association **5257, 6584,
7844, 8370, 8975, 9124, 10031**
American Hospital Association
Convention **5248**
American Hotel and Lodging
Association **5490**
American Hotel and Motel Association
Annual Conference and Leadership
Forum **5482**
American Human Resources Associates Ltd.
(AHRA) **1037, 4200, 9715**
American Humane Association Annual
Meeting and Training Conference/Animal
Protection **788, 11600**
American Humanics **5501**
American Hydrogen Association **4521**
American Incite **4659**
American Indian Science and Engineering
Society **389, 1179, 1522, 1774, 2259,
2446, 3718, 3946, 4012, 5555, 7170,
7333, 7433, 7652, 8241, 10804, 11307,
13397**
*American Industrial Hygiene Association-
Directory* **5686**
*American Industrial Hygiene Association
Journal* **5675**
American Institute of Aeronautics and
Astronautics **390**
American Institute of Aeronautics and
Astronautics Career Planning and
Placement Services **447, 12233**
American Institute of Architects **867**
American Institute of Architects, Minnesota
Annual Convention and Exhibition **901**
American Institute of Biological
Sciences **558, 1156, 10497**
American Institute of Biological Sciences
Annual Meeting **1145**
American Institute of Biological Sciences
Classifieds **1137, 12234**
American Institute of Certified
Planners **11544**
American Institute of Certified Public
Accountants **94**
American Institute of Chemical
Engineers **1523**
American Institute of Chemists **1602, 1690**
*American Institute of Chemists-Professional
Directory* **1529, 1648**
American Institute for Conservation of
Historic and Artistic Works **952, 5348**
American Institute for CPCU **5748, 11515**
American Institute of Engineers **4522,
11291**
American Institute of Graphic Arts **5076,
9269, 11452, 11719**
American Institute of Physics **9011**
American Institute of Professional
Geologists **4996**
American Institute of Ultrasound in
Medicine **9652**
American Intellectual Property Law
Association **6207**
American Jail Association Training
Conference & Jail Expo **2647**

Branches of Your State: Banks, Savings and Loans, Credit Unions, & Savings Banks **2820, 4160, 6612**
The Brand Company Inc. **4747, 5582**
Brandjes Associates **4214**
Brandywine Consulting Group **4748, 8339**
Brandywine Management Group **3972, 4749**
Branthover Associates **4750**
Brass Ring **12246**
Brault & Associated Ltd. **4751**
The Brazik Group LLC **4752, 5200**
Breakin' into the Music Business **3321, 7575**
Breaking into Advertising **6945**
Breaking into the Catering Business **1429**
Breaking into Commercials **173**
Breaking into Film **174, 8478**
Breaking into Television **175, 1325, 8479, 9602**
Breitner Clark & Hall Inc. **5201, 8920**
Brenner Executive Resources Inc. **2128, 4753**
The Brentwood Group Inc. **1674, 4754**
The Brentwood Group Ltd. **2129, 4755**
Brentwood International **423, 4756**
Briant Associates Inc. **1675, 4757**
Brick Show **1267**
Bridal Association of America **11787**
BridgeGate LLC **4758**
Bridgeport Regional Business Council **12848**
Brigham Hill Consultancy **2029**
BrillantPeople.com **13628**
The Brimeyer Group Inc. **4759**
Brindisi Search **8155**
Bristol Associates, Inc. **5481, 10219**
Britt Associates Inc. **9515, 11822**
Broadcast Education Association **9571, 10110**
Broadcast Foundation of College/University Students **1301, 9572, 10059**
Broadcast Technicians **1353**
Broadcasting & Cable **111, 1283, 8428, 9553, 10047**
Broadcasting & Cable Yearbook **139, 1307, 8454, 9581, 10065**
Brooke Chase Associates Inc. **1568, 4760**
Brookings Papers on Economic Activity **1028, 1366, 2808, 3407**
Brown Venture Associates Inc. **4761, 7201**
Brownson & Associates LP **4762**
Brownstone Sales & Marketing Group Inc. **10357**
Brownsville Chamber of Commerce **12849**
Bruce Edwards & Associates Inc. **4763, 10490**
Bruce Lowery & Associates **5634**
Brush Creek Partners **4215, 4764**
Bryant Bureau Sales Recruiters **10358**
BtoB Magazine **6744, 6864, 6895, 10665**
Budget Analyst **1373**
Budget and Management Analyst **1367, 6711**
Buffalo Niagara Partnership **12850**
Buffkin & Associates LLC **4765, 7002**
Build and Manage Your Music Career **3322, 7576**
Builder **855, 1251, 1385, 2517, 2686, 3174, 3380, 3792, 9041, 10301, 11143, 11527**
Building Blocks for Working with Exceptional Children & Youth: A Primer **10904**
Building and Managing a Career in Nursing: Strategies for Advancing Your Career **6517, 9961**
Building Officials and Code Administrators International **2535**
Building Owners and Managers Association International **9341**
Building Owners and Managers Association International Annual Convention and The Office Building Show **9336**
Building Professionals: Creating a Successful Portfolio **2542, 2584**

Building Supply Home Centers **6745, 10244**
Building Trades **1273, 1413, 3826, 5306, 9074, 10323**
Buildings **9300**
Buildings Show **2609**
Bulletin of Dental Education **2941, 2997, 3056, 3101**
Burbank Chamber of Commerce **12851**
Burglar Alarm Systems Wholesale Directory **10636**
Burke, O'Brien & Bishop Associates Inc. **4766**
Burkholder Group Inc. **5723**
The Burling Group Ltd. **4216, 4767**
Burrelle's New York Media Directory **1308, 8455, 9582, 10066, 11857**
Burton & Grove Inc. **4768, 9261**
Bus Ride **982**
Busch International **2130, 4769**
Business and Administration Support Occupations **312, 1855, 5750, 7981**
Business Awareness for Optometrists: A Primer **8055**
Business and Careers in Marine Sciences **1098**
The Business of Chiropractic: How to Prosper after Startup **1737**
Business Council of Alabama **12852**
Business Council of New York State, Inc. **12853**
Business Credit **1029, 2809, 4133**
Business Detail **12100**
Business Economics-Membership Directory Issue **3426**
The Business of Event Planning: Behind-the-Scenes Secrets of Successful Special Events **4094**
Business First of Buffalo **12787**
The Business of Getting More Gigs as a Professional Musician **7577**
Business Ideas Newsletter **6896**
Business Incubators of North America **13547**
Business Insurance **231, 1835, 3408, 4134, 5700, 8125, 11486**
Business Insurance-Agent/Broker Profiles Issue **5708, 11490**
Business Insurance-Third-Party Claims Administrators Issue **1839**
The Business Journal of Charlotte **12788**
Business and Legal Forms for Graphic Designers **3200**
Business Management Consultants Directory **6645**
Business Network International **13142**
Business and Professional Women's Foundation **13520**
Business & Technology Solutions Show **86**
Business: The Ultimate Resource **6646**
Business Times **12789**
Business Travel News **11394**
Business of Wedding Photography **8480, 11774**
The Business Writer's Companion **13746**
BusinessWoman Magazine **13492**
Butterfass, Pepe & MacCallan Inc. **2838, 4217**
Buxbaum/Rink Consulting L.L.C. **57, 4218**
Buyer's Guide & Membership Directory **3652, 3802**
Byron Leonard International **4770, 7003**

C

C. Berger Group Inc. **6377**
C Magazine **112, 915, 960, 2866, 11627**
CA Durakis Associates, Inc. **1897, 2131**
CAA Search **4771, 10359**
CAA Voice **13383**
Cabinet Makers Directory **1394**
Cabot Consultants **424, 4772**

Cadillac Engineering and Manufacturing Inc. **1569, 3973**
Cal-OSHA Reporter **5677, 7856**
The Caler Group **4773, 6827**
Caliber Associates **1117, 4774**
California Academy of Physician Assistants Convention **8694**
California Chamber of Commerce **12854**
California Dietetic Association Meeting **3301**
California Employer Advisor **12680**
California Employment Law Monitor **12681**
California Fuel Cell Partnership **4524**
California Job Journal **12743**
California Labor and Employment ALERT Newsletter **12682**
California Labor and Employment Law Quarterly **12683**
California Land Surveyors Association Conference **11155**
California Landscape Contractors Association-Roster **5963, 6005**
California Lawyer **6083, 6220**
California Society of Certified Public Accountants Classifieds **80, 12247**
California State Oriental Medical Association **280**
California Thoroughbred **760**
Callaghan International Inc. **2547, 4775**
Callan Associates Ltd. **4776, 6675**
Calland & Company **4777, 5202**
Cambridge Chamber of Commerce **12855**
Cameron Consulting Group **1213, 4778**
Campbell/Carlson LLC **3910, 4779**
Camping Magazine **9782**
Camps Directory **9802**
Canadian Environmental Directory **12358**
Canadian Special Events Society **4101**
Cancer Nursing **5363, 6459, 7747, 9884**
Cannellos-Smartt Associates **4219, 4780**
Canny, Bowen Inc. **4220, 7004**
Cantor Executive Search Solutions Inc. **4781, 7005**
CAP Today **1867, 5129**
Capital District Business Review **12790**
Capitol Search **1723, 3230, 11755**
Caplan Associates Inc. **5203, 8340**
The Caplan Taylor Group **1214, 5204**
Capodice & Associates **4782, 5205**
Caprio & Associates Inc. **4783, 5064**
Capstone Consulting Inc. **58, 4784**
Capstone Inc. **1570, 4785**
Cardiac Nuclear Medicine **7710, 8889**
Cardinal Mark Inc. **2929, 7006**
Cardwell Enterprises Inc. **7007**
Career After Cosmetology School: Step-by-Step Guide to a Lucrative Career and Salon Ownership **2665, 6724**
Career Bounce-Back!: The Professionals in Transition Guide to Recovery and Reemployment **12155**
Career Center, Inc. **304, 4051**
Career Choices for Veterinarians: Beyond Private Practice **11579**
Career Close-ups: School Teacher **5923, 10604**
Career Cluster Series **12101**
Career Consulting International **4786, 6676**
Career Counseling for African Americans **13362**
Career Counseling in Schools: Multicultural and Developmental Perspectives **2768**
Career Development: A Special Issue of the Journal of Management in Engineering **1791**
Career Development Services **2930, 10859, 11255, 11952**
Career Directions **12156**
Career Employment Opportunities Directory **12507, 13288**
Career Engine Network **12248**
Career Evaluation **12102**
Career Exploration: You're in the Driver's Seat **12103**
The Career Fitness Program: Exercising Your Options **11994**

I

Index to Information Sources

Megargee's Guide to Obtaining a Psychological Internship **9425, 13700**

Membership Directory and Roster of State and National Archives and Records Officials **932**

Membership and Peer Network Directory **9808**

Memphis Gift and Jewelry Show Spring **5823**

Memphis Regional Chamber of Commerce **13009**

MENC: The National Association for Music Education **7630**

Mental Health Directory **2757, 5505, 7791, 9406, 10713**

Mental Health Services Directory **2758, 5506, 7792, 9407, 10714**

Mental Help Net **2759, 7106, 9408, 10715**

Mental Measurements Yearbook **9409**

Mental Retardation **9370, 10695**

Mergent Bank and Finance Manual **240, 1844, 2826, 3427, 4165, 5714, 6615, 11495**

Merit Systems Protection Board **12409**

Merritt Hawkins & Associates **8931**

Mesa Chamber of Commerce **13010**

Mesquite Chamber of Commerce and CVB **13011**

Metal Architecture **862**

Metal Finishing **7321**

Metal Powder Industries Federation **7337**

METALFORM **7375, 11315**

Metalforming **7322**

Metallurgical, Ceramic, and Material Engineers **7386**

Meteorologists **7409**

Metro Augusta Chamber of Commerce **13012**

Metro Evansville Chamber of Commerce **13013**

Metro Hartford Chamber of Commerce **13014**

Metro Jackson Chamber of Commerce **13015**

Metro Magazine **10054, 11838**

Metro Milwaukee Association of Commerce **13016**

Metro New York JobBank **12061, 12769**

Metro Tulsa Chamber of Commerce **13017**

Metro Washington DC JobBank **12062, 12770**

Metrocrest Chamber of Commerce **13018**

Metropolitan Personnel Inc. **7976**

Mfg/Search, Inc. **5602, 7993, 11312**

MH Executive Search Group **10413**

MIACON - Miami International Construction Show/Expo **2614**

Miami Today **12802**

Michael Anthony Associates Inc. **2151, 4268**

Michigan Bar Journal **6096, 6232**

Michigan Chamber of Commerce **13019**

Michigan Consulting Group **5655**

Michigan Employment Law Letter **12715**

Michigan Florist-Membership Directory **4383**

Michigan Library Association Annual Conference **6392**

Michigan Plumbing and Mechanical Contractors Association Conference **9066**

Michigan Plumbing and Mechanical Contractors Association-Membership Directory **5287, 9054**

Microwave Journal **3704, 3935**

Mid-America Farm Show **548**

Mid-American Placement Service Inc. **10414**

Mid-Atlantic Archivist **918**

Mid-Atlantic Industrial Woodworking Expo **1407**

Mid-Atlantic Nursery Trade Show **6018**

Mid-Career Changes: Strategies for Success **12176**

Mid-Continent Dental Congress **3156**

Mid East States Regional Print Competition and Exhibition and Trade Show **8506**

Mid-South Farm and Gin Supply Exhibit **549**

Midcontinental Journal of Archaeology **832**

Midsouthwest Foodservice Convention and Exposition **1451, 10227**

Midwest Archives Conference-Membership Directory **933, 6359, 6428**

Midwest Beauty Show **2678, 6733**

The Midwest Clinic An International Band and Orchestra Conference **7618**

Midwest Farm Show **550**

Midwest Foodservice News **1420, 1466, 10170**

Midwest Roofing Contractors Association Convention and Trade Show **10317**

Midwest Travel Writers Association-Membership Directory **11874**

Migrant Education: A Reference Handbook **13373**

Mike Farr's Get a Job Workshop on CD-ROM **12150**

Military Career Guide Online **12317, 13337**

The Military Engineer **863, 1764**

The Military Engineer-Directory **881**

Military Medicine **6481, 8797, 9914, 13333**

Military Officers Association of America **13349**

Military Operations Research Society **7999**

Miller & Associates Inc. **485**

Miller Personnel Consultants Inc. **5656**

Millimeter Magazine **120, 1293**

Milling & Baking News **1009, 6769**

Milwaukee Boma Expo **9337**

Mind Your Own Business! **13570**

The Minerals, Metals & Materials Society Membership Directory **7346**

Mining Engineers **7468**

The Mining Record **7423**

Minneapolis Regional Chamber of Commerce **13020**

Minneapolis/St. Paul JobBank **12771**

Minnesota Employment Law Letter **12716**

The Minnesota History Interpreter **5320**

Minnesota Medicine **5146, 8652, 8798**

Minnesota P-H-C Contractor-Membership Directory Issue **5288, 9055**

Minority Business Information Center **13374**

Minority Business Information Resource Directory **13571**

Minority Executive Search Inc. **5231**

The Minority Executive's Handbook **13375**

Minority Health Today **3844, 5147, 5377, 7240, 8653, 8799, 10133, 11117**

Minority Nurse Newsletter **6482, 7764, 9915**

Minority Search Inc. **4269**

Minority Women In Science **562, 1160, 1696, 4485, 5005, 7410, 9036, 10499**

Miramar-Pembroke Pines Regional Chamber of Commerce **13021**

MIS Manager's Appraisal Guide: Practical Guidelines and Forms for Evaluating and Appraising Your MIS Staff **2114**

Mississippi Economic Council **13022**

Missoula Area Chamber of Commerce and Convention and Visitors' Bureau **13023**

Missouri Association of Insurance Agents Exhibition **5738**

Missouri Chamber of Commerce **13024**

Missouri Employment Law Letter **12717**

Missouri JobBank **12772**

MIT Computer Science and Artificial Intelligence Laboratory **609**

Mix **1294**

M.J. Curran & Associates Inc. **2301, 6843**

MJSA Expo Providence **5824**

MLA News **6327, 6411**

MLA Salary Survey **6371**

Mobile Air Conditioning Society Worldwide Convention and Trade Show **5299**

Mobile Area Chamber of Commerce **13025**

The Mobile DJ Handbook: How to Start and Run a Profitable Mobile Disc Jockey Service **3338**

Model & Talent Directory **4116, 11166**

Modeling Agencies Directory **4117, 11167**

The Model's Work Book: A Hollywood Agents 20-Step Guide to Launching Your Modeling Career **4123**

Modem Engineering Design Associates **7211**

Modern Casting Magazine **7323**

Modern Grocer **6770, 10252**

Modern Healthcare **5148, 5378, 6483, 7765, 9916, 10696**

Modern Language Association of America **2072, 10969**

Modern Language Association of America-Job Information List **1992**

Modern Metals **3936, 7324**

Modern Moonlighting: How to Earn Thousands Extra without Leaving Your Day Job **13572, 13701**

Modern Plastics **1511, 1624, 6771**

Modern Salon **2655, 6717**

Modernism Magazine **961, 5019, 11635**

Modesto Chamber of Commerce **13026**

Mompreneurs: A Mother's Step-by-Step Guide to Work-at-Home Success **13646**

Money Making Opportunities **6772, 10253, 10666**

Money Smart Secrets for the Self-Employed **13573**

Moneymaking Moms: How Work at Home Can Work for You **13647**

The Monster Board **12318**

Monster Healthcare **3141, 6565, 8951, 10008, 12319**

Monster Networking **13140**

Monsters and Angels: Surviving a Career in Music **7599**

MonsterTRAK **12142, 12320**

Montana Chamber of Commerce **13027**

Montgomery Area Chamber of Commerce **13028**

The Montgomery Group Inc. **486**

Monthly Energy Review **7424, 8231**

Monument Builders of North America Conference **4570**

More About This Business of Music **7600**

More Successful Less Stressful Interviewing for Women: A Guide to Improving Your Interviewing Skills While Reducing Stress **12616**

Morency Associates **10415**

The Morgan Horse **766, 11563**

Morgantown Area Chamber of Commerce **13029**

Mortgage Banking Magazine **4142, 6602**

Mosby's Assestest: A Practice Exam for RN Licensure **6532**

Mosby's Review Questions for NCLEX-RN **6533**

Mosby's Tour Guide to Nursing School: A Student's Road Survival Guide **6534, 9972**

Mothers on the Job: Maternity Policy in the U. S. Workplace **12666**

The Motion Systems Distributor **987**

Motor Service **988**

Moving up in the Music Business **3339, 7601**

Moving on in Your Career **12063**

MRA Blue Book Research Services Directory **6875**

MRI of Atlanta West **10416**

MRI of the Baltimore Washington Corridor **10417**

MRI of Dearborn **5657**

MRI of Houston **10418**

MRI of Milwaukee North **10419**

MRI of Morris County, NJ **10420**

MRI of Spencer **487**

MRI of Tucson **488**

MRI of Williamsburg **489**

Multi-Hospital Systems and Group Purchasing Organizations Report & Directory **9511**

Multi-Housing News **6773**

Summer Jobs **12337**
Summer Jobs Britain **12570, 13722**
Summer Theater Directory **156, 2886, 7572, 13723**
Summit Executive Search Consultants, Inc. **5693**
Summit Group Consultants Inc. **5667**
Sunbelt Foodservice **3278, 10177**
Sunny Bates Associates **2040, 4913**
Sunnyvale Chamber of Commerce **13086**
Super Job Search: The Complete Manual for Job-Seekers and Career-Changers **12081**
Supermarket Industry Convention and Educational Exposition **9523, 11826**
Supervising for Success: A Guide for Supervisors **7974**
Supervisors Legal Update **12733**
Supplier Diversity Information Resource Guide **13592**
Supply Chain Management Review **290, 4606, 5625, 6641, 7971, 10335**
Support Services Conference & Expo - Washington DC **10685**
Sure-Hire Resumes **13837**
Surfaces **5798**
Surgical Rounds **8826, 11120**
Surgical Technicians **11140**
Surgical Technologist **11131**
Survey of State Tourism Offices **11335, 11408**
Surveyors **11163**
Surveyors-Land Directory **11152**
Survival Guide for the First-Year Special Education Teacher **10915**
Survival Guide for School-Based Speech-Language Pathologists **10950**
Survival Jobs: 118 Ways to Make Money While Pursuing Your Dreams **13724**
Survive and Profit from a Mid-Career Change **12186**
SWE **385, 464, 1176, 1519, 1769, 3713, 3941, 4008, 4501, 5551, 7167, 7327, 7429, 7648, 8237, 10803, 11267**
SYMPHONY **7551**
Symposium of the New Orleans Academy of Ophthalmology **8022**
Synectics for Management Decisions Inc. **6300**
Systems Careers **6703**

T

T & D Magazine **6642, 8133**
Table Talk: The Savvy Girl's Alternative to Networking **13135**
Tacoma-Pierce County Chamber of Commerce **13087**
Take This Job and Love It: A Personal Guide to Career Empowerment **12187**
Taking Charge of Your Career Direction **12082, 12188**
Taking Charge of Your Job Search **12128**
Taking Flight: Education & Training for Aviation Careers **417, 634, 670, 698**
Taking the Leap: Building a Career as a Visual Artist **5062, 11709**
Talent Network.com **4129**
Tallahassee Chamber of Commerce **13088**
Tapping New Talent for Business Success **13193**
Tax Advisor **11180**
Tax Examiner **11185**
Tax Return Preparation & Filing Service Directory **30**
Taxes **11181**
Teacher Education and Special Education **10899**
Teacher Magazine **5849, 10520**
The Teaching Career **5911**
Teaching (Career Portraits) **356, 2025, 5912, 9227, 10585**
Teaching Children Mathematics **5850**

Teaching Exceptional Children **5851, 7880, 8539, 9377, 10521, 10703, 11209**
Teaching/K-8 **5852, 9214, 11210**
Teaching in the Middle and Secondary Schools **10586**
Teaching Persons with Severe Disabilities **10916**
Teaching & Related Occupations **373, 2082, 2805, 3584, 5947, 6403, 9237, 10626, 10927**
Team Placement Service, Inc. **1136, 1681, 2972, 3029, 3137, 3626, 6559, 7952, 8572, 8624, 8938, 9112, 10000**
Tech Comments **11844**
Tech Directions **332, 3479, 5853, 10522, 11211**
Technical & Related Occupations **705, 1363, 2388, 3097, 3406, 3993, 6314, 8035, 11164**
Technical Talent Locators Ltd. **2304, 2490, 3766, 8102, 10867, 11957**
Technical Writing for Technicians: How to Build a Career As a Hardware Technical Writer **11940**
Technology & Conservation of Art, Architecture & Antiquities **922**
Technology Review **386, 1177, 1520, 1770, 3714, 3942, 4009, 5552, 7168, 7328, 7430, 7649, 8238**
The Technology Teacher **1949, 10523**
Technology Trends **2103**
Techsearch Services, Inc. **2305, 2491**
Techtronix Technical Search **443, 499, 1230, 1589, 3767, 4065, 4512, 5605, 7214, 7681, 8276, 10868, 11285**
Tecnobanca Expo **4294**
Teen Guide to Getting Started in the Arts **13440**
Teen Missions International **7503**
A Teen's Guide to Finding a Job **13441**
Teens for Hire **13443**
Teknon Employment Resources Inc. **5668**
Telecommuting Jobs **12338, 13666**
TeleCon East **1350**
Teleflora Subscribers Directory **4386**
Telemarketing Services Directory **11242**
Television & Cable Factbook **1320, 8472, 9598**
Television Program Producers Directory **157**
Television/Radio Service & Repair Directory **3654**
Television Stations & Broadcasting Companies Directory **1321, 9599**
Temp by Choice **13456**
Temp: How to Survive and Thrive in the World of Temporary Employment **13457**
The Temp Track: Make One of the Hottest Job Trends of the 90s Work for You **13458**
The Temp Worker's Guide to Self-Fulfillment: How to Slack Off, Achieve Your Dreams, and Get Paid for It! **13459**
Tempe Chamber of Commerce **13089**
Tempo Personnel Services **10217**
10 Basics of Business Etiquette **12129**
Ten Commandments of Resumes **13854**
The 10 Hottest Consulting Practices: What They Are, How to Get into Them **5534, 6665**
Ten Insider Secrets Career Transition Workshop: Your Complete Guide to Discovering the Ideal Job! **12189**
Ten Ways to Get a Great Job: Back to the Basics **12130**
Tennessee Chamber of Commerce and Industry **13090**
Tennessee Employment Law Update **12734**
Tennessee JobBank **12780**
Tennessee Library Association Annual Convention **6395**
Teratology Society **1165**
TEST Engineering & Management **387, 6332**
Test & Measurement World **3715, 3943**

Texas Architect **866**
Texas Association of Business and Chamber of Commerce **13091**
Texas Association for Health, Physical Education, Recreation, and Dance Annual State Convention **2898**
Texas Bar Journal **6101**
Texas Employment Law Letter **12735**
Texas Funeral Directors Association Convention **4574**
Texas Ground Water Association Trade Show and Convention **4073**
Texas International Theatrical Arts Society **133, 2876, 7559**
Texas Library Association Conference **6396**
Texas Pharmacy Association Annual Meeting and Exhibit **8366**
Textbook for Dental Nurses **2968, 3025**
Theater Artist's Resource: The Watson-Guptill Guide to Workshops, Conferences & Artists' Colonies **205**
Theatrical Agencies Directory **158, 11170**
Theatrical Index **159**
Theken Associates Inc. **5235**
A Therapist's Guide to Art Therapy Assessments: Tools of the Trade **970**
Third Sector Search Associates **13175**
30-Minute Writer: How to Write & Sell Short Pieces **11941**
30 Steps to Becoming a Writer & Getting Published **11942**
33 Metal Producing **3944, 7329**
This Business of Music Marketing and Promotion **3347, 6979, 7614**
Thomas P. Hinman Dental Meeting & Exhibits **2978, 3038, 3159**
Thomas Register of American Manufacturers **6806, 12533**
Thomson Bank Directory **2830, 3432, 4170, 6619**
Thomson North American Financial Institutions Directory **2831, 3433, 4171, 6620**
Thoroughbred Racing Associations of North America-Directory and Record Book **4584**
Thorsen Associates Inc. **5669**
Thousand Oaks - Westlake Village Chamber of Commerce **13092**
306 Search Advisors Inc. **4279, 4914**
303 Off-the-Wall Ways to Get a Job **12083**
Three Rivers Dental Conference **3039, 3160**
Thriving and Surviving at Work: Disabled People's Employment Strategies **13186**
Thy Neighbor's Talent-Directory of Cottage Industry Show Dates **13653**
TIA Newsline **11396**
Timber Harvesting **6781**
Timothy D. Crowe Jr. **444, 2155**
Tips for Finding the Right Job **12084, 12629**
Tire Business **10260, 11809**
Tire Review **10261, 11810**
Tissue Engineering **11268, 11280**
Tissue Engineering: Engineering Principles for the Design of Replacement Organs and Tissues **11281**
Tissue Engineering: Principles and Applications in Engineering **11282**
The Tissue Engineering Society International **11303**
Tissue Engineering, Stem Cells, and Gene Therapies **11283**
TMS Annual Meeting and Exhibition **7377**
To Boldly Go: A Practical Career Guide for Scientists **538, 1110, 1669, 4991, 7144, 9026**
Toby Clark Associates Inc. **7058, 9493**
Today's Insurance Woman **5704**
Today's OEA **1950, 3480, 5854, 9215, 10524, 10900, 11212**
Todd Arro Inc. **7059, 10450**
Toledo Area Chamber of Commerce **13093**
Tom Allison Associates **500**